R
Inspiring everyor

Plant Finder 2020

Devised by Chris Philip and Realised by Tony Lord

Editor-in-Chief
Janet Cubey

RHS Editors
Richard Dee   Dawn Edwards   Kálmán Könyves
Neil Lancaster   Rosalyn Marshall   Mathew Rees

Compiler
Lindsay Durrant

RHS

Inspiring everyone to grow

Published and compiled by
Royal Horticultural Society
80 Vincent Square
London SW1P 2PE

Reg charity no: 222879/SC038262

First edition 1987
Thirty-fourth edition 2020

British Library Cataloguing Publication Data
A catalogue record for this book is available from the British Library

ISBN 9781911666066

RHS Publisher – Rae Spencer-Jones

RHS Art Editor – Mark Timothy

RHS Prepress Designer – Anthony Masi

RHS Head of Editorial – Chris Young

Designer – Peter Cooling

Printed and bound by CPI WILLIAM CLOWES, Copland Way, Ellough, Beccles, Suffolk NR34 7TL

The compiler and editors of the *RHS Plant Finder* have taken every care, in the time available, to check all the information supplied to them by the nurseries concerned. Nevertheless, in a work of this kind, containing as it does hundreds of thousands of separate computer encodings, errors and omissions will inevitably occur. The RHS, the Publisher and Editors, cannot accept responsibility for any consequences that may arise from such errors.

If you find any mistakes, we hope that you will let us know so that the matter can be corrected in the next edition.

Front cover photograph: *Dahlia* 'Kilburn Glow' (Anthony Masi)

Back cover photographs from top:
Prunus 'Beni-tamanishiki' AGM (RHS / Joanna Kossak)
Thick-legged flower beetle (*Oedemera nobilis*) on *Geranium sanguineum* (RHS / Carol Sheppard)
Echinacea 'Big Kahuna' (RHS / Joanna Kossak)
Syngonium 'Arrow' (RHS / Joanna Kossak)

The Royal Horticultural Society is the UK's leading gardening charity dedicated to advancing horticulture and promoting good gardening. Its charitable work includes providing expert advice and information, training the next generation of gardeners, creating hands-on opportunities for children to grow plants and conducting research into plants, pests and environmental issues affecting gardeners.

For more information visit www.rhs.org.uk or call 020 3176 5800.

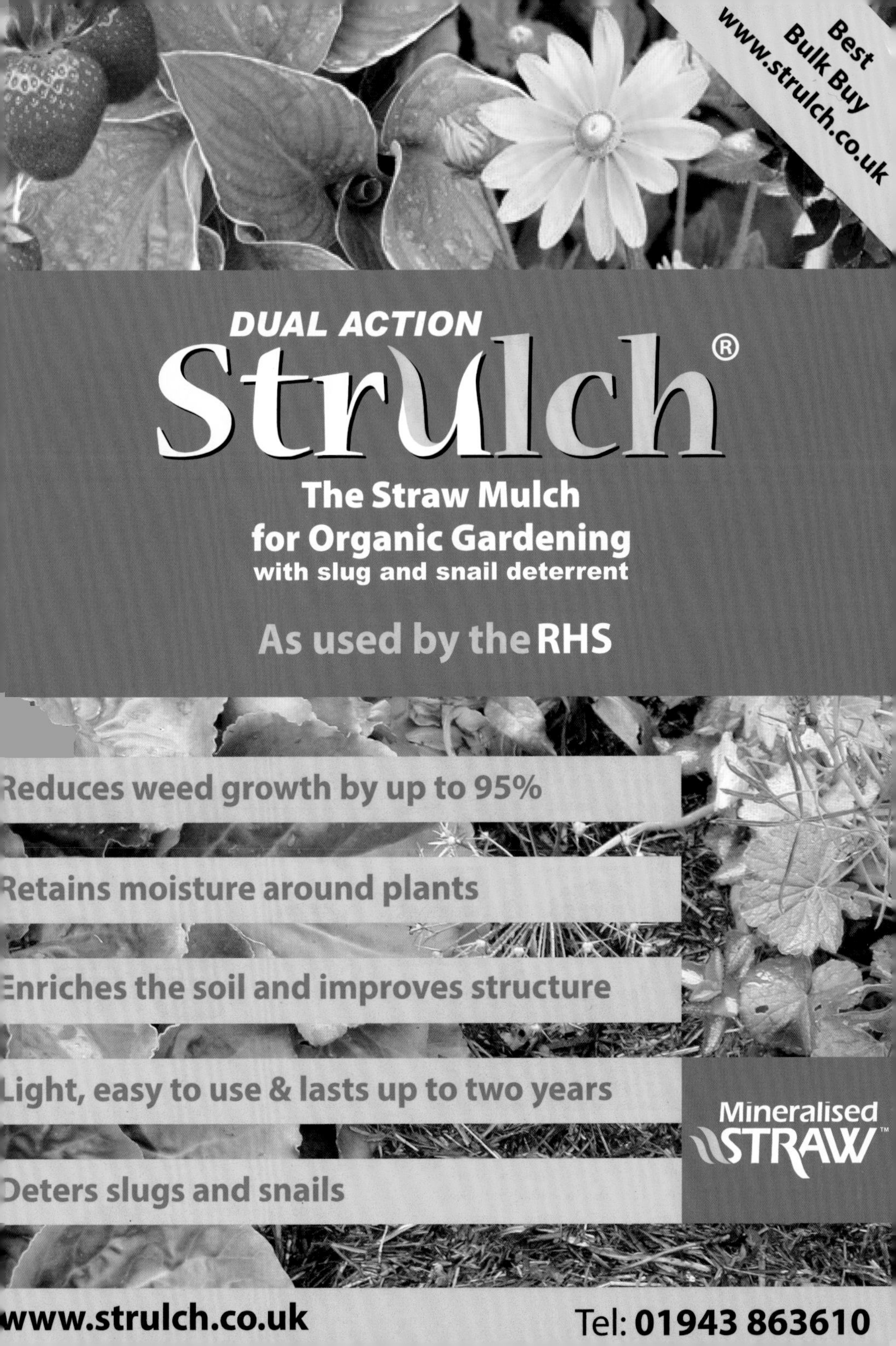
Best
Bulk Buy
www.strulch.co.uk
DUAL ACTION
Strulch®
The Straw Mulch
for Organic Gardening
with slug and snail deterrent
As used by the RHS
Reduces weed growth by up to 95%
Retains moisture around plants
Enriches the soil and improves structure
Light, easy to use & lasts up to two years
Deters slugs and snails
Mineralised
STRAW™
www.strulch.co.uk
Tel: 01943 863610

Contents

Take the RHS
home with you
Proud to champion the best of British nurseries, you'll find all your favourites, as well as more unusual cultivars in our RHS plant centres. Our 5 year hardy plant guarantee means you can buy in confidence, and with friendly staff on hand to answer your questions, your dream outdoor haven can become a reality.
Discover a world of gifts, accessories, homewares, foods and RHS exclusive collections in our gift shops, along with a vast selection of horticultural books for all levels of gardener. Visit today and take a piece of the RHS home with you.
Shop online at **rhsshop.co.uk** and **rhsplants.co.uk**
RHS
Inspiring everyone to grow
Your purchase supports our work as a charity
RHS Registered Charity No. 222879/SCO38262

New plant highlights

For this celebration of plants new to the *RHS Plant Finder*, I was spoilt for choice with more than 3,300 new entries for 2020, and it's fascinating to see which plants our Plant Finder nurseries put forward. It's also a joy to celebrate the addition of all cacti to the book, and an increase in the number and diversity of tender plants.

Author: **Janet Cubey,** Editor-in-Chief

RHS / SARAH CUTTLE

Acanthophyllum cerastioides Pretty Maid ('Yatgyp')

More familiar as *Gypsophila cerastioides*, this is now recognised as an *Acanthophyllum* (see *The Plant Review*, December 2019, and Nomenclatural Notes on page 49 for more information on name changes in this edition).

I first saw compact Pretty Maid at the 2019 RHS Chelsea Flower Show. The relatively large, spring flowers are white, fragrant and have a light pink veining. Bred in Cheshire by Fred Yates, this hardy perennial with a ground-covering, mounding to tumbling-trailing habit is equally at home in a border or container in a sunny situation and, once established, should cope well with dry spells.

Agastache 'Crazy Fortune'

Variegated plants are usually found by observation of a chance sport and it was Dutch gardener Harry ten Duis who spotted this mutation back in 2012. Gardeners who aren't usually keen on variegated plants might like 'Crazy Fortune' because the variegation isn't that bold; there are just delicate, irregular cream "stripes" variably within or around the dark green leaves, giving a delicacy and lightness to the foliage in summer. In addition to the dense, mauve-purple flower spikes, the young leaves also take on a temporary purple hue and it still has the anise scent typical of a hyssop.

Alchornea davidii

One of the many joys of growing plants is that you're always learning more. However, it's not every year that I come across a genus I've never heard of before. My first meeting with *Alchornea davidii* in 2018 filled me with delight as the young foliage was just at its most charming shrimp pink. The broad, toothed leaves with a long acuminate tip (tapering to a point) become green by summer, sometimes producing yellow and/or red tints in autumn.

A relatively recent introduction from China, it was added to the 2019 edition of the *Hillier Manual of Trees & Shrubs* and now I'm pleased to see it included in the *RHS Plant Finder 2020* as it becomes more readily available. It is a member of the *Euphorbia* family and the young foliage is susceptible to damage from late frosts and cold winds, so site with care.

If you like becoming acquainted with new species, then also take a look at this year's entries for *Araucaria* and see just how many you don't yet know...

ALAMY / WIERT NIEUMAN

GARDEN BEAUTY

Antirrhinum 'Oh That's Cute'

Many people will remember being introduced to snapdragons in their childhood, well this is a snapdragon with a difference. Cut it back once it has flowered and it will bloom again, and perhaps even again, through to September or October. 'Oh That's Cute' was bred by Peter Moore of Longstock Park Nursery, Hampshire, and it has lovely delicate flowers in two pastel tones: pink and yellow, the pink enhanced by slightly darker veins and edges.

It grows best in full sun, or light partial shade, in either a border or large pot.

LEE BETTS, EXOTIC EARTH PLANTS

***Brugmansia* hybrid (*B. sanguinea* × *B. vulcanicola* 'Zuñac 4')**

New this year from Exotic Earth Plants, this is one of the new plants in the book that hasn't yet been given a cultivar name and so is referred to by the hybrid formula of its parentage for the time being. It's known as a 'Vulsa', the "breeding history set" for hybrids with *Brugmansia vulcanicola* and *B. sanguinea* in their parentage. Both these parents are in *Brugmansia* section *Sphaerocarpium*, the "cold group", which are tolerant of cooler temperatures and potentially even a light frost. Exotic Earth Plants tell us that "the 20cm long funnel-shaped flowers are a beautiful red/orange/yellow combination. Although the flower is not scented (because its native pollinator is the hummingbird), it truly is a stunning specimen."

Carpinus betulus 'Orange Retz'

Selected by Jean Blondeau in France and first introduced by Minier Solutions Pro, 'Orange Retz' is a strikingly attractive hornbeam. I find the regular veining on the leaves of all hornbeams pleasing but with this cultivar you get the bonus that they turn a stunning bright orange in autumn.

The growth habit of this selection is more erect and the compact habit – it reaches between 2m and 3m tall – a third win. A popular future hedging plant, maybe?

I haven't found proof of this, but I assume it was named Retz after the former region of France (now part of Loire-Atlantique), rather than the small town in Austria of the same name.

HORTIVAL DIFFUSION

RICHARD HODSON

Clematis 'Long Tall Sally'

Bred by Richard Hodson of Hawthornes Nursery in Lancashire, holder of the National Plant Collections of *Clematis* Viticella, Texensis and Viorna Groups, 'Long Tall Sally' belongs to the Viorna Group. This cultivar "has masses of tubular bell-shaped flowers over a long period in summer, perfect through a shrub or obelisk in the mixed border". The lilac-purple bells have an attractive long-dipped, white, icing effect that spreads halfway up the flower from the tepal edge.

The nursery is also introducing 'Tutti Frutti', another Viorna Group cultivar, with lots of small, lilac-purple bells with a frilly, white edge.

Both these cultivars are hardy and should be pruned hard in spring.

JAN RAVENSBERG

Crinodendron hookerianum 'Alf Robbins'

I've always loved the red hanging lantern flowers, teamed with glossy, dark green foliage, of *Crinodendron hookerianum*.

I've read about, but not yet seen, 'Ashmount' with its dark pink hue to the deeply-coloured flowers and then there is 'Ada Hoffmann' with delicate pale pink flowers. Now, I've another to add to my future wishlist... 'Alf Robbins' has pure white flowers against the deep green incised leaves. Said to be slow-growing, it's been raised at Ravensberg Nurseries in Ireland, and is described as a "special selection from seedlings of 'Ada Hoffmann'".

Dicentra 'Sulphur Hearts'

This new *Dicentra*, from Compass Plants BV, has large sulphur-yellow, heart-shaped flowers with lilac tips and dark red stems up to 30cm tall. The delicate ferny foliage has a blue-grey hue, becoming bluer in more direct light.

It is said that both PBR and a US Plant Patent has been applied for this plant, but could not be confirmed at point of publication.

JPARKERS.CO.UK

Echeveria × *bombycina* AGM

As a corresponding member of the RHS Tender Ornamental Plant Committee, it's a joy to see more tender plants in this edition of *RHS Plant Finder*. Surprisingly, in the top 10 genera by number of new entries to the Plant Directory, *Echeveria* comes in this year at number 6 with more than 70 new listings (following *Narcissus* and ahead of *Salvia*).

Echeveria × *bombycina*, a hybrid of *E. pulvinata* and *E. setosa*, is a neat evergreen succulent with spoon-shaped, red-tipped, thick green leaves that are covered in white hairs giving them a grey hue. The flower stems, standing proud of the foliage rosette, hold red and yellow urn-shaped flowers in late summer and early autumn.

RHS/SARAH CUTTLE

RHS / TIM SANDALL

Echinocactus grusonii AGM

We are delighted to now be including all cacti in the *RHS Plant Finder*, regardless of their hardiness, so, even though this plant is a timeless classic, it is the first time it has appeared in the book.

If you asked me to pick my favourite cactus this would probably be it. It's just so instantly recognisable with its barrel shape, deep ribs and yellowish spines (though there is a spineless form too) and, when you are lucky to have a mature plant, yellow flowers.

The hardiness rating for this species is H1c (Heated greenhouse – warm temperate 5–10°C) but with plenty of light it can be grown as a houseplant as well as in a conservatory or greenhouse.

Epimedium 'Sparkler'

A new introduction this spring from Straight Mile Nursery Gardens, Essex, 'Sparkler' seems to sparkle for its long flowering season. If you love the distinctive starry flower form of an *Epimedium*, but bemoan the season being over too quickly, this might be the cultivar for you. Straight Mile Nursery Gardens reports: "Its main attribute is that it flowers from spring, as they all do, but continues to flower up to November".

'Sparkler' has substantial, long-spurred, pale yellow petals held under paler off-white inner sepals, both tinged with a rosy hue.

STRAIGHT MILE NURSERIES

RICHARD LOADER / FAIRWEATHERS

Lavandula × *cadevallii* Fairy Wings Series

Bred to be fragrant, compact and free-flowering by PGA InnovaBred in Australia, Fairy Wings cultivars are hybrids of *Lavandula pedunculata* and *L. stoechas*. They are also characterised by their short flowerheads with the bracts at their apex being extra long and ribbony. The three cultivars belonging to the collection have all entered *RHS Plant Finder* this year, after their release in the southern hemisphere in 2017. The names that are being used for their PBR applications are 'FW Radiance', 'FW Spellbound' and 'FW Whimsical', but you will also find them referred to as Fairy Wings Pink, Purple and Blush respectively.

A sunny location and well-drained soil are required but they can be planted in both containers and borders.

RICHARD LOADER / FAIRWEATHERS

Lilium 'Easy Vanilla'

It's not often that a lily enters *RHS Plant Finder* with four suppliers but 'Easy Vanilla' has achieved this.

It was selected, named and registered by Lily Company BV of the Netherlands, and it is said to be capable of flowering 90 days after planting. It's an Asiatic hybrid with outward-facing, pale but bright, citrus-yellow flowers that have very few brown spots toward their centre. Very hardy, it flowers in early season (May-June) on stems less than 1m high.

Perhaps most noticeable is the lack of pollen, so it is ideal as a cut flower and for gardeners who worry about lily pollen and their cats.

DIRECT BULBS

KNOLL GARDENS

Miscanthus sinensis 'Red Spear'

Knoll Gardens from Dorset is launching this new *Miscanthus* this summer. It is "named for its strongly upright habit and spear-like upward-facing buds, which open into bright red airy flowers held clear above the foliage".

Miscanthus like an open, sunny situation. This cultivar is one of the taller ones, growing to between 1.8m and 2.1m in height.

***Osteospermum* Purple Sun ('Kleoe19396')**

Bred by Selecta One in Germany, which has more than 20 years' experience of breeding *Osteospermum*, Purple Sun has an eye-catching flower colour. As with others in this genus, it prefers a warm, sheltered position in full sun. Regularly dead-heading this compact, well-branched cultivar encourages it to flower for a longer period of time.

Growing brightly-coloured flowers in full sun can, at times, lead to a problem with fading flower hues. However, this 2019 release is said to have fade-resistant flowers, so you'll keep the vibrancy of colour. The ray flowers are orange with an ever-strengthening purple zone at their base that collectively forms a ring around the central disc of the flowerhead.

Picea glauca 'Sun on the Sky'

Selected by Michał Kałuziński of Polish Roots nursery in Poland, this new cultivar of *Picea glauca* has the lovely tight, conical habit exhibited by some cultivars of this species. The young foliage is a bright pale yellow in spring, slowly changing to the typical blue-green of the species.

A slow-growing cultivar, it should reach about 1m in height after 10 years of growth. Planted in the garden or in a container it favours a sunny location.

If you're looking for other slow-growing conifers, particularly with a narrow upright habit, you might want to consider two new members of the extending 'Smaragd' family: *Thuja occidentalis* SUNNY SMARAGD ('Hoogi023') and TOTEM SMARAGD ('Thucavlo').

Rhododendron 'Alan Leslie'

The result of a *Rhododendron prunifolium* × *R. viscosum* f. *rhodanthum* cross made by the late Ted Millais of Millais Nurseries, Surrey, in 1999, this hardy, deciduous Viscosa azalea was named and registered by his son David in 2018.

David Millais notes its hardiness as H6 (Hardy – very cold winter -10 to -15°C) and describes this cultivar as having "small, tubular, bright rosy-pink flowers, scented and late flowering in July". A compact growth habit gives a neat appearance and a height of 125–150cm after 10 years. It was "named for the RHS botanist Dr Alan Leslie, who has recently retired as International Registrar for Rhododendrons".

MILLAIS NURSERIES

PHENO GENO ROSES / TREVOR WHITE ROSES

Rosa Pear ('Bozedib023')

This shrub rose, new to the UK, was created by the Serbian/Dutch company Pheno Geno Roses, which markets their roses as "unique, as they are bred by women for women". Aiming to remind people that roses are edible, Pear is one of four roses entering *RHS Plant Finder* this year, that is part of their Taste of Love collection. Best picked in the early morning, the flowers are said to have a "mild spicy fragrance and a taste like sweet and sour pears" and to be "excellent for salads and confectionary".

Growing to 60–70cm tall, it's quite a compact rose, but produces an abundance of repeat-flowering clusters of subtle, pale pink, double flowers. It's ideal for cultivation in both borders and containers.

BLACKMOOR NURSERIES

Rubus idaeus BonBonBerry Yummy ('Jdeboer19')

BonBonBerry Yummy raspberry was suggested by Blackmoor Nurseries of Hampshire. It is described as "a naturally compact new cultivar that is ideally suited for growing in patio containers. A primocane variety so it fruits on the new growth." They note that, in spite of its size, it gives heavy crops of juicy, sweet, red fruit and that the "canes are spine-free making them easy to pick" during their harvesting time of late June to early July.

So the name might be a bit of a mouthful but I do like the grow-anywhere compactness of this cultivar and I look forward to popping a fruit, or two, in my mouth.

Salvia 'Dad's Brown Trousers'

Four of our new-entry salvias were suggested by nurseries for inclusion in this selection; it was hard to choose just two. When I saw the name 'Dad's Brown Trousers' I smiled and instantly knew what colour this would be before I saw the photograph. Described by Ivy Hatch Plant Supplies, Kent, as having a "strongly branching habit, with charming, large, peachy-pink toned flowers that fade to light brown with age".

It was discovered in 2011 by Tom Hart Dyke at Lullingstone Castle in the Mexican section of his World Garden there. It has been named in memory of his father the late Guy Hart Dyke.

IVY HATCH PLANT SUPPLIES

MICHELLE COOPER / NORFOLK HERBS

Salvia JEMIMA'S GEM ('Jemco')

Vibrant flowers and vigour drew me to JEMIMA'S GEM. Developed by Norfolk Herbs manager Michelle Cooper, it has been tested at the nursery for 30 months prior to its launch in 2020. It is named for Michelle's young niece, who they hope will inherit her brother's love of gardening.

Norfolk Herbs describes this cultivar as "hardy through most winters in a sheltered, sunny spot with free-draining soil. Drought tolerant with large, glowing, ruby-red flowers fading to magenta and more flowers per plant than many other similar salvias. The foliage is healthy and strong. It really is a wonderful plant."

Growing to 80cm in height with dark green, glossy foliage it's said to be very floriferous throughout summer and autumn.

Sarracenia × *mitchelliana* 'Victoria Morley' AGM

This hybrid (*Sarracenia leucophylla* x *S. purpurea*), 'Victoria Morley', had its RHS Award of Garden Merit ratified in 2016, when it was described by the RHS Trial Forum as, "A robust grower. Even coloration. Lid is very pretty, extremely ruffled and well-spotted with pale windows".

Its hardiness is recorded as H3 (Half-hardy – unheated greenhouse/mild winter -5 to 1°C) but in a more recent trial in Hampshire, concluded in 2019, that tested pitcher plants for their hardiness, it performed well, even though plants were frozen solid at times.

This cultivar was raised in England in the 1980s and registered with the International Carnivorous Plant Society in 2005. It was named for the raiser's wife and is noted for a long season of pitcher production through the summer and autumn.

STEPHEN MORLEY / WACK'S WICKED PLANTS

Sedum takesimense Atlantis ('Nonsitnal')

Winner of RHS Chelsea Plant of the Year 2019, Atlantis is an eye-catching plant that stops you in your tracks. It was found growing as a sport by Dave MacKenzie at his nursery, Hortech, in Michigan. Following years of testing and multiplication, it is now launched to the world.

The serrated, fleshy leaves are tightly-packed into rosettes; each leaf has a broad cream margin that takes on a blush to pink hue when cooler weather arrives. Dense clusters of star-shaped yellow flowers top the foliage rosettes from midsummer onwards.

A low-spreading hardy perennial, it requires a sunny, well-drained position – it's even said to be drought tolerant once established – but could also be grown as a houseplant.

RHS / NEIL HEPWORTH

CROCUS.CO.UK

Tilia × *europaea* Golden Sunset ('Wiltil')

Another award-winner, Golden Sunset won Best in Category for Trees and Conifers and also the Visitor Vote at the HTA National Plant Show in 2019. It was entered by Frank P Matthews of The Tree Shop, Worcestershire.

It has striking bright coral buds and shoots in winter with bright golden foliage emerging in spring. As with many yellow-leaved plants, the foliage does fade from yellow to green by midsummer but that makes it a good backdrop for other plants during summer months. It is said to be slightly less vigorous than *Tilia cordata* 'Winter Orange' but particularly well-suited to both pleaching and pollarding.

ACCESS
Garden Products
MINI GREENHOUSES
AND GROWHOUSES
Ideal where space is limited
• Toughened Safety Glass
• Extra Strong Aluminium
• Adjustable Shelving
• Mist Watering
GUARANTEE 25 YEAR GUARANTEE
MADE IN BRITAIN
Call for a FREE
40 page brochure
0800 298 6284
Ref: RHP20 • Crick, Northampton NN6 7XS
www.garden-products.co.uk

DAVID AUSTIN®
Breeders of
exquisite
English Roses
since 1961
Shop online at
www.davidaustinroses.co.uk
Rosa 'WISLEY 2008' (Ausbreeze)

Bumblebee on *Salvia farinacea* 'Victoria'.

RHS / CAROL SHEPPARD

How gardens can help our wildlife

RHS research supported by the Wildlife Gardening Forum

It's often assumed that insects and other invertebrates living in the UK are best supported by native plants, but is this true? The four-year RHS Plants for Bugs research study has shed new light on the plantings British invertebrates prefer

Authors: **Helen Bostock,** RHS Senior Horticultural Advisor
and **Andrew Salisbury,** RHS Principal Entomologist

Encouraging good garden stewardship

Plants for Bugs has been one of the most significant and wide-reaching research studies ever undertaken at the RHS.

Over four years, this field experiment at RHS Garden Wisley, in Surrey, considered whether the geographic origin of garden plants affected the abundance and diversity of invertebrates they were able to support.

The results have promoted discussion about the role of native and non-native plants in the garden both in the UK and further afield, with findings prompting articles and discussion in publications in Germany and the USA. At an amenity level, beneficiaries of the advice developed on the basis of this research include BREEAM (Building Research Establishment Environmental Assessment Method), TDAG (Tree Design Action Group) and the Defra National Pollinator Strategy.

Reports of declining insect populations increasingly appear in the news. Now gardeners, landscapers and designers can benefit from the reliable information this research provides on how best to support invertebrates in gardens. With three peer-reviewed publications now translated into clear, practical advice on what gardeners can do, the future looks a little brighter for the UK's garden wildlife.

RHS / GEORGI MAREF

RHS / CAROL SHEPPARD

RHS / MARK BOLTON

Above: Caterpillar of the knotgrass moth (*Acronicta rumicis*).

Right: Choose plenty of native and near-native plants to support the greatest number of invertebrates.

Collecting invertebrates from foliage with a Vortis suction sampler.

What did we do?

It's often assumed that insects and other invertebrates that live in gardens are best supported by native plants. But is this true, especially in Britain, where the number of plants classed as 'native' are relatively few?

To make a comparison between British native and non-native garden plants and the invertebrates they support, two sites were chosen for a field experiment at RHS Garden Wisley. Each site was divided into eighteen 3 × 3m plots. Every plot contained 14 species of plants from one of three geographical regions (Britain; northern hemisphere excluding Britain, referred to here as 'near-native'; and southern hemisphere, referred to as 'exotic').

Invertebrates were recorded from all plots by several methods: ground-active invertebrates were recorded using pitfall traps, plant-inhabiting invertebrates with a Vortis suction sampler and flower visitors (pollinators) by visual observation. Findings from the study, supported throughout by the Wildlife Gardening Forum, have shed new light on the garden plantings British invertebrates prefer.

"The power of a garden lies in its very smallest inhabitants. Gardeners who look after them have the greatest positive impact for biodiversity, helping to forge a new generation of wildlife champions."

Dr Andrew Salisbury, RHS Principal Entomologist

What did we find?

Our first paper, published in 2015 in the *Journal of Applied Ecology*, looked at gardens as habitats for flower-visiting aerial insects (pollinators such as bees, wasps, butterflies and hoverflies). We concluded that, in a garden containing solely native flowering plants, the number of pollinators visiting these British natives wouldn't differ much from a garden consisting only of near-native plants, but would be almost double the number in a garden with only exotic plants (Fig. 1). However, exotic plants do help provide for some specific pollinators and extend the flowering season, benefiting pollinators that are active into autumn.

Paper 2, published in *Biodiversity and Conservation* in 2017, looked at plant-dwelling invertebrates such as caterpillars, ladybirds, earwigs and springtails. We concluded that if you were to choose plants from a specific region (as we did in this experiment), to obtain the same number of invertebrates as from a plot of British native plants, you would need about a fifth more vegetation from the northern hemisphere, and about a quarter more from the southern hemisphere (see Fig. 2).

Paper 3, also published in *Biodiversity and Conservation*, in 2019, looked at ground-active invertebrates such as wingless weevils and carnivorous ground beetles. We found that, overall, regardless of plant origin, the denser the vegetation, the higher the ground-active invertebrate abundance, although greater numbers of ground-active spiders – useful natural pollinators – were found in sparser plantings. However, planting schemes based on exotic plants may support more ground-active invertebrates in winter than British native or near-native planting schemes, perhaps because of the greater use of evergreens.

Fig. 1 Garden habitats showing the differing number of pollinators attracted to native, near-native and exotic plants

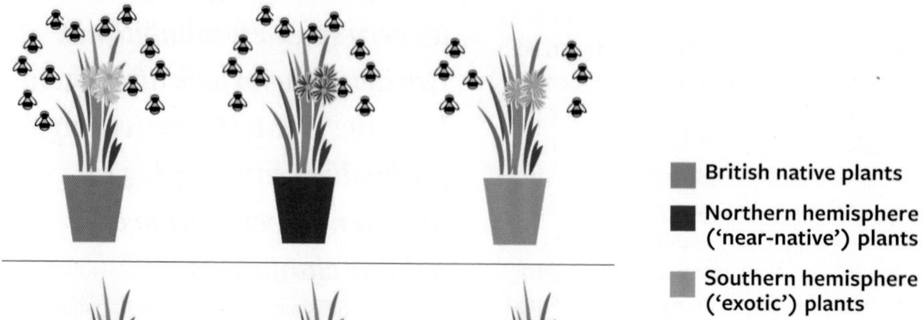

Fig. 2 Garden habitats showing the number of native, near-native and exotic plants required to support the same number of plant-dwelling invertebrates

How can I encourage pollinators?

Our findings on pollinators support what many UK gardeners are doing – predominantly planting with British native and northern hemisphere plants while including a few from the southern hemisphere. Gardens can be enhanced for pollinators through plant choice:

1 Consider the seasons, especially early and late when fewer plants are in flower for insects to forage, and try to have plants flowering every month.

2 Don't skimp on the flowers – pack them in wherever they will thrive. They usually do best in sun or part shade.

3 Choose a mixture of plants – gardens that are themed on plants from just one region may not be the optimum strategy for supporting our pollinating insects.

Thick-legged flower beetle (*Oedemera nobilis*) on *Geranium sanguineum*, RHS Garden Wisley.

IMAGES: RHS / CAROL SHEPPARD

Brimstone butterfly (*Gonepteryx rhamni*) on *Lythrum salicaria*.

Include a mixture of plants from different regions to support pollinators.

4 Observe the plants in your garden and other local gardens, and grow more of whatever is popular with pollinators in your neighbourhood.

5 Allotment holders can make a huge contribution to pollinator conservation by allowing some herbs and vegetables to flower, and by planting nectar-rich flowers for cutting on their plots.

6 If you need some help on where to start, choose RHS Plants for Pollinators (see **rhs.org.uk/plantsforpollinators** and lists on pp.873 to 879).

How can I encourage plant-dwelling and ground-active invertebrates?

ISTOCK / ALESSANDROZOCC

Ladybirds help keep aphids in check.

RHS / JOANNA KOSSAK

Leave some bare patches to help ground-active spiders and ground-nesting bees.

1 Think closer to home. Include plenty of British native plants to support maximum numbers of herbivores, predators, detritivores and omnivores.

2 Decide priorities. Choosing more exotics (especially flowering ones) in your planting scheme might mean it supports marginally fewer plant-dwelling and ground-active herbivores, but will mean potentially fewer nibbled plants and should help extend the season for pollinators.

3 Let it fill out. Whatever you decide to plant, allow plants to fill the space to maximise foliage density and cover.

4 Keep some areas sparser to help specific ground-active groups, notably spiders and ground-nesting bees, which make use of patches of bare ground.

5 Be relaxed. Tolerate some nibbled leaves, don't spray at the first sign of damage and allow some plant debris to accumulate if you want to support your garden's food chain.

6 Provide winter protection. Whatever the plant origin, try to include some evergreens in your garden to help shelter invertebrates.

"Any planting is better than none, and don't limit yourself to just a few different plants – our studies suggest that the greater the variety of plants in a garden, the greater the abundance and diversity of invertebrates it will support."

Helen Bostock, RHS Senior Horticultural Advisor

big plant
nursery
www.bigplantnursery.co.uk
AN OUTTA SPACE SELECTION OF:
HARDY EXOTICS
PALMS
BAMBOO
MAPLES
TREES
SHRUBS
FERNS
GRASSES
Hole Street, Ashington, West Sussex RH20 3DE
e: info@bigplantnursery.co.uk
t: 01903 891466

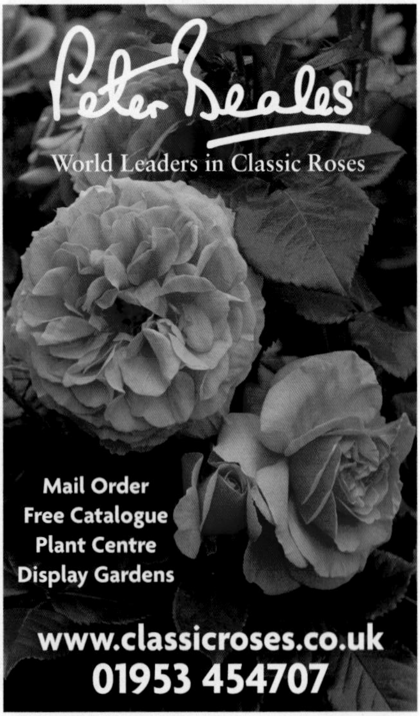
Peter Beales
World Leaders in Classic Roses
Mail Order
Free Catalogue
Plant Centre
Display Gardens
www.classicroses.co.uk
01953 454707

Pheasant Acre Plants
Award Winning Nursery with over 500 varieties of Dahlia available and over 150 varieties of Gladioli.
Gladioli Corms, Dahlia Tubers and Plants for Summer Flowering available from Februrary to June.
Also an Extensive Range of Spring Flowering Bulbs including: Alliums, Daffodils, Fritillaria, Hippeastrum and Tulips.
Catalogue Available on Request
Call us on: 01656 664086 or 07816 236462
RHS Shows - Gold Medal Winners
2010, 2011, 2012, 2013, 2014, 2015, 2016, 2017, 2018 & 2019
For an Exhibit of Gladioli, Dahlia & Other Bulbous Plants
www.pheasantacreplants.co.uk

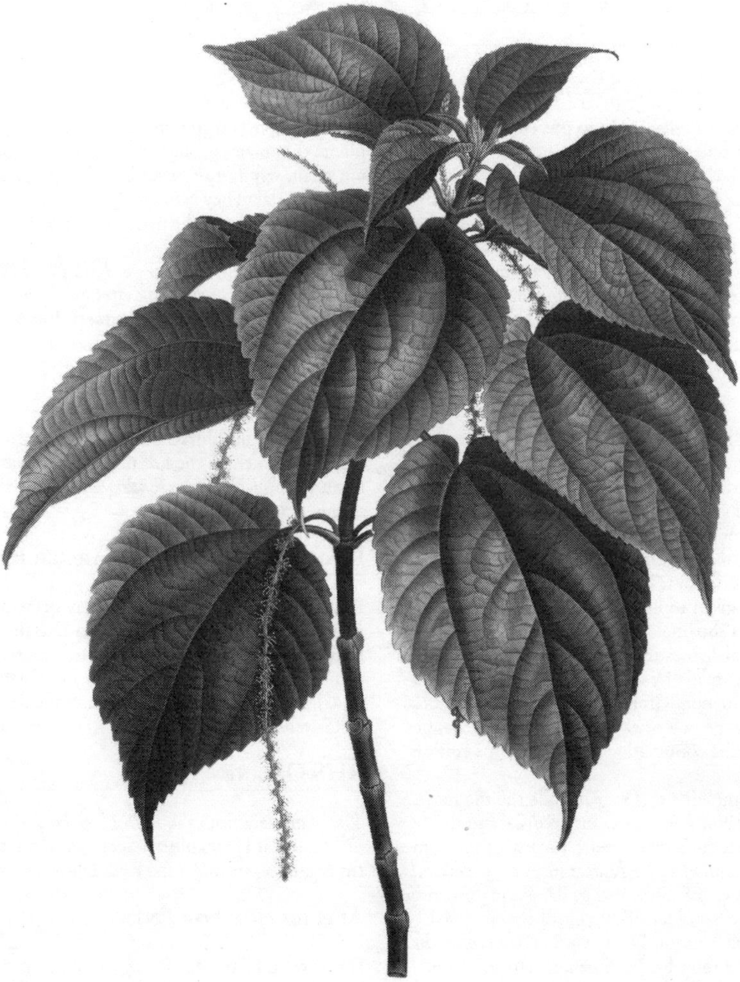

I
GENERAL INFORMATION

INTRODUCTION

The *RHS Plant Finder* exists to put enthusiastic gardeners in touch with suppliers of plants. It is comprehensively updated every year.

The book is divided into two related sections: **PLANTS** and **NURSERIES**.

PLANTS includes an A-Z Directory of around 81,000 plant names, against which are listed a series of nursery codes. These codes point the reader to the full nursery details contained in the **NURSERIES** section towards the back of the book.

It is important to remember when ordering plants that many of the nurseries listed in the book are small, family-run businesses that propagate their own material. They cannot, therefore, guarantee to hold large stocks of the plants they list. Some will, however, propagate to order.

Nurseries appearing in the *RHS Plant Finder* for the first time or re-entering after an absence are printed in bold type in the **Nursery Index by Name** (pp.981-985).

NEW IN THIS EDITION

For our fourth colour section we've an article on Plants for Bugs. Alongside this is the third Editor's choice of new plant highlights, illustrating 25 of the plants that are appearing in the book for the first time in this addition. These have been compiled from suggestions given to us by some of the nurseries appearing in the book this year.

The plant names used in the 2020 edition reflect the decisions made by the RHS Nomenclature and Taxonomy Advisory Group (NATAG). Nomenclatural Notes (p.49) gives a brief overview of these changes made since the compilation of the previous edition of the book.

Significant edits this year include the the move of *Perovskia* and *Rosmarinus* into *Salvia,* and the updates made to *Betula* to reflect many of the names used by Ashburner & McAllister in *The Genus Betula.* An explanation of some of the changes made can be found in the new Plant Bulletin feature, in *The Plant Review* (previously known as *The Plantsman*) in the last 12 months. For further changes made, please go to the Nomenclatural Notes on p.49.

LISTS OF NURSERIES FOR PLANTS WITH MORE THAN 30 SUPPLIERS

To prevent the book from becoming too big, we do not print nursery codes where more than 30 nurseries offer the same plant. The plant is then listed as being "widely available". See **How to Use the Plant Directory** (p.55).

A full list of all the nurseries held on file as current suppliers can be found by searching the RHS website RHS Find-a-plant facility or can be made available in printed form by post from the Compiler at the address below. For the latter, please ensure you include the full name of the plant (as given in the *RHS Plant Finder*) and enclose a stamped addressed envelope.

PLANTS LAST LISTED IN EARLIER EDITIONS

Plants cease to be listed for a variety of reasons. For more information, turn to **How to Use the Plant Directory** (p.55). A listing of more than 60,000 plants listed in earlier editions but for which we have no current suppliers will be made available on the RHS website.

RHS ONLINE

The plant data from the *RHS Plant Finder* is available on the Royal Horticultural Society's website at www.rhs.org.uk/plants under the RHS Find-a-plant section.

APPLICATION FOR ENTRY

If you would like your nursery to be considered for inclusion in the next edition of the *RHS Plant Finder*, please contact the Compiler. Entries to the book are free.

Contact details

Lindsay Durrant
Compiler, *RHS Plant Finder*
RHS Garden Wisley
Woking
Surrey
GU23 6QB
Ⓣ (01483) 226577
Ⓔ plantfinder@rhs.org.uk

ACKNOWLEDGEMENTS

This edition was compiled by Lindsay Durrant with Jane Rowlands, assisted by Sam Webster. Richard Sanford managed the editing of the plant names in the database and Julia Barclay and Rupert Wilson administered the RHS Horticultural Database using the BGBase™ Collection Management Software.

RHS botanists Dawn Edwards, Kálmán Könyves, Neil Lancaster, Rosalyn Marshall, and new members of the team, Richard Dee (Horticultural Taxonomist) and Mathew Rees (Botanist) undertook the task of editing the new plant names for this edition of the book. Extra thanks to Dawn Edwards for guiding them through their first season.

RHS Book Publisher Rae Spencer-Jones collated the colour section and we acknowledge the contribution of Louise Bowering, Louise Tee, Mark Timothy, Anthony Masi, Marina Jordan-Rugg, John David, Gerard Clover, Lisa Ward and Gill Skilton. We would also like to thank those who have kindly provided plant images, especially our nurseries featuring in the book this year.

Thanks also to Helen Bostock, Senior Horticultural Advisor, Andrew Salisbury, Principal Scientist, Entomology, and Richard Sanford, Horticultural Data Officer, for preparing the 'Plants for Bugs' article for the book this year.

We say farewell to Duncan Donald and thank him for all of his hard work for the RHS as Clematis Registrar since 2006 and Lily Registrar since 2010. Duncan has been instrumental in the work of the International Clematis Society in drawing up a new horticultural classification for Clematis, which we are looking to implement in the RHS Plant Finder within the next few years. We welcome Sarah Holme as our new International Clematis and Lilium Registrar.

As ever, we are grateful for the professional support of Kerry Walter and Mahir Akbalik of BG-Base (UK) Ltd and Max Phillips of Strange Software Ltd. Finally, we are greatly indebted to Peter Cooling for his skill in turning our data into a publishable form.

Our colleagues on the RHS Nomenclature and Taxonomy Advisory Group, along with the RHS International Cultivar Registrars, have all provided valuable guidance and information. Many nurseries have supplied useful details on new plants and have suggested corrections to existing entries. Some of these remain to be checked and will be entered in the next edition, although those that contravene the Codes of Nomenclature may have to be rejected. We appreciate your patience while these checks are made. We are also grateful to our regular correspondents and to all those readers who have made helpful comments.

Clematis	Sarah Holme, Int. Cultivar Registrar
Chrysanthemum	J. Barker
Conifers	S. McDonald, Int. Cultivar Registrar
Dahlia	S. McDonald, Int. Cultivar Registrar
Dianthus	S. MacDonald, Int. Cultivar Registrar
Delphinium	M.R. Underwood, Int. Cultivar Registrar
Ilex	S. Andrews
Lilium	Sarah Holme, Int. Cultivar Registrar
Narcissus	M.R. Underwood, Int. Cultivar Registrar
Nerine	Dr J.C. David
Orchids	J.M.H. Shaw, Int. Cultivar Registrar
Rhododendron	S. McDonald, Int. Cultivar Registrar
Sorbus	Dr H. McAllister
Thymus	M. Easter, Int. Cultivar Registrar

Janet Cubey
RHS Editor-in-Chief
February 2020

Symbols and Abbreviations

Symbols Appearing to the Left of the Name

*	Name not validated. Not listed in the appropriate International Registration Authority checklist nor in works cited in the Bibliography. For fuller discussion see p.37
I	Invalid name. See *International Code of Botanical Nomenclature 2018* and *International Code of Nomenclature for Cultivated Plants 2016*. For fuller discussion see p.37
§	Plant listed elsewhere in the Plant Directory under a synonym
×	Hybrid genus
+	Graft hybrid genus

Symbols Appearing to the Right of the Name

✿	Plant Heritage National Plant Collection® exists for all or part of this genus. Further details can be found by searching the National Plant Collections online or in the Plant Heritage Directory available from www.plantheritage.org.uk or by phone (01483) 447540.
🏆H4	The Royal Horticultural Society's Award of Garden Merit, see p.37
(d)	double-flowered
(F)	Fruit
(f)	female
(m)	male
(v)	variegated plant, see p.41
PBR	Plant Breeders' Rights see p.39
new	New plant entry in this edition

For abbreviations relating to individual genera see **Classification of Genera** p.50

For **Collectors' References** see p.45

For symbols used in the **Nurseries** section see p.885

Symbols and Abbreviations used as Part of the Name

×	hybrid species
aff.	affinis (akin to)
agg.	aggregate, a single name used to cover a group of very similar plants, regarded by some as separate species
ambig.	ambiguous, a name used by two authors for different plants and where it is unclear which is being offered
cf.	compare to
cl.	clone
f.	forma (botanical form)
gx	grex
sensu stricto	in the narrow sense
sp.	species
subsp.	subspecies
subvar.	subvarietas (botanical subvariety)
var.	varietas (botanical variety)

It is not within the remit of this book to check that nurseries are applying the right names to the right plants or to ensure nurseries selling plants with Plant Breeders' Rights are licensed to do so.

We recommend that you use the latest edition of the *RHS Plant Finder*

Extended Glossary

This glossary combines some of the helpful introductory sections from older editions in an alphabetical listing. A fuller, more discursive account of plant names, *Guide to Plant Names*, and a detailed guide to the typography of plant names, *Recommended Style for Printing Plant Names*, are both available as leaflets. To request a copy of either please send an A4 sae to The Compiler at the contact address given on page 34.

Advisory Committee on Nomenclature and Taxonomy

See **Nomenclature and Taxonomy Advisory Group**

Authorities

In order that plant names can be used with precision throughout the scientific world, the name of the person who coined the name of a plant species (its author, or authority) is added to the plant name. Usually this information is of little consequence to gardeners, except in cases where the same name has been given to two different plants or a name is commonly misapplied. Although only one usage is correct, both may be encountered in books, so indicating the author is the only way to be certain about which plant is being referred to. This can happen equally with cultivars. Authors' names, where it is appropriate to cite them, appear in a smaller typeface after the species or cultivar name to which they refer and are abbreviated following Brummitt and Powell's *Authors of Plant Names*.

♈ Award of Garden Merit

The Award of Garden Merit (AGM) is intended as a practical guide for the gardener and is therefore awarded only after a period of assessment by the RHS Standing and Joint Committees. The AGM is awarded only to plants that are:

- excellent for ordinary use in appropriate conditions
- available
- of good constitution
- essentially stable in form and colour
- reasonably resistant to pests and diseases

The AGM symbol is cited in conjunction with the **hardiness** rating. A full list of AGM plants may be found on the RHS website at www.rhs.org.uk/agmplants.

The AGM list was originally reviewed every ten years, to ensure that every plant still merited the award. The last review took place in 2012; since 2013, the list has been subject to a "rolling review", and AGMs may now be rescinded at any time.

Botanical Names

The aim of the botanical naming system is to provide each different plant with a single, unique, universal name. The basic unit of plant classification is the species. Species that share a number of significant characteristics are grouped together to form a genus (plural **genera**). The name of a species is made up of two elements; the name of the genus followed by the specific epithet, for example, *Narcissus romieuxii*.

Variation within a species can be recognised by division into subspecies (usually abbreviated to subsp.), varietas (or variety abbreviated to var.) and forma (or form abbreviated to f.). Whilst it is unusual for a plant to have all of these, it is possible, as in this example, *Narcissus romieuxii* subsp. *albidus* var. *zaianicus* f. *lutescens*.

The botanical elements are always given in italics, with only the genus taking an initial capital letter. The rank indications are never in italics. In instances where the rank is not known it is necessary to form an invalid construction by quoting a second epithet without a rank. This is an unsatisfactory situation, but requires considerable research to resolve.

In some genera, such as *Hosta*, we list the cultivar names alphabetically with the species or **hybrid** to which they are attributed afterwards in parentheses. For example, *Hosta* 'Reversed' (*sieboldiana*). In other situations where the aim is not to create a list alphabetically by cultivar name we would recommend styling this as *Hosta sieboldiana* 'Reversed'.

Classification of Genera

Genera that include a large number of species or with many cultivars are often subdivided into informal horticultural classifications or more formal Cultivar Groups, each based on a particular characteristic or combination of characteristics. Colour of flower or fruit and shape of flower are common examples and, with fruit, whether a cultivar is grown for culinary or dessert purposes. How such groups are named differs from genus to genus.

To help users of the *RHS Plant Finder* find the plants they want, the classifications used within cultivated genera are listed using codes and plants are marked with the appropriate code in brackets after its name in the Plant Directory. To find the explanation of each code, simply look it up under the genus concerned in the **Classification of Genera** starting on p.50. The codes relating to edible fruits are also listed here, but these apply across several genera.

Collectors' References

Abbreviations (usually with numbers) following a plant name refer to the collector(s) of the plant. These abbreviations are expanded, with a collector's name or expedition title, in the section **Collectors' References** starting on p.45.

A collector's reference may indicate a new, as yet unnamed range of variation within a species. The inclusion of collectors' references in the *RHS Plant Finder* supports the book's role in sourcing unusual plants.

The Convention on Biological Diversity calls for conservation of biodiversity, its sustainable use and the fair and equitable sharing of any derived benefits. Since its adoption in 1993, collectors are required to have prior informed consent from the country of origin for the acquisition and commercialisation of collected material.

Common Names

In a work such as this, it is necessary to refer to plants by their botanical names for the sake of universal comprehension and clarity. However, at the same time we recognise that with fruit and vegetables most people are more familiar with their common names than their botanical ones. Cross-references are therefore given from common to botanical names for fruit, vegetables and the commoner culinary herbs throughout the Plant Directory.

Cultivar

Literally meaning cultivated variety, cultivar names are given to denote variation within species and that generated by hybridisation, in cultivation. To make them easily distinguishable from botanical names, they are not printed in italics and are enclosed in single quotation marks. Cultivar names coined since 1959 should follow the rules of the International Code of Nomenclature for Cultivated Plants (**ICNCP**).

Descriptive Terms

Terms that appear after the main part of the plant name are shown in a smaller font to distinguish them. These descriptive elements give extra information about the plant and may include the **collector's reference**, **authority**, or what colour it is. For example, *Clematis henryi* B&SWJ 3402, *Penstemon* 'Sour Grapes' M. Fish, *Akebia quinata* cream-flowered.

Families

Genera are grouped into larger groups of related plants called families. Most family names, with the exception of eight familiar names, end with the same group of letters, *-aceae*. While it is still acceptable to use these eight exceptions, the modern trend adopted in the *RHS Plant Finder* is to use alternative names with *–aceae* endings. The families concerned are *Compositae* (*Asteraceae*), *Cruciferae* (*Brassicaceae*), *Gramineae* (*Poaceae*), *Guttiferae* (*Clusiaceae*), *Labiatae* (*Lamiaceae*), *Leguminosae* (*Fabaceae*), *Palmae* (*Arecaceae*) and *Umbelliferae* (*Apiaceae*).

Apart from these exceptions we now follow (from 2010) *Mabberley's Plant-book* (3rd edition).

Genus (plural – genera)

Genera used in the *RHS Plant Finder* were originally based on Brummitt's *Vascular Plant Families and Genera* but are now based on a range of sources. For spellings and genders of generic names, Greuter's *Names in Current Use for Extant Plant Genera* has also been consulted. See **Botanical Names**.

Grex

Within orchids, hybrids of the same parentage, regardless of how alike they are, are given a grex name. Individuals can be selected, given cultivar names and propagated vegetatively. For example, *Pleione* Versailles gx 'Bucklebury', where Versailles is the grex name and 'Bucklebury' is a selected **cultivar**.

Group

This is a collective name for a group of cultivars within a genus with similar characteristics. The word Group is always included and, where cited with a cultivar name, it is enclosed in brackets, for example, *Actaea simplex* (Atropurpurea Group) 'Brunette', where 'Brunette' is a distinct cultivar in a group of purple-leaved cultivars.

Another example of a Group is *Rhododendron concinnum*. In this case *Pseudoyanthinum* Group was a species that is now 'botanically sunk' within *Rhododendron pseudoyanthinum*, but it is still recognised horticulturally as a Group.

Group names are also used for swarms of hybrids with the same parentage, for example, *Rhododendron* Polar Bear Group. These were formerly treated as **grex** names, a term now used only for orchids. A

single clone from the Group may be given the same cultivar name, for example, *Rhododendron* 'Polar Bear'.

HARDINESS

Hardiness ratings are shown for **Award of Garden Merit** plants. To assist gardeners to determine more clearly which plants are hardy in their local area, the RHS introduced a new, enhanced, hardiness rating scheme in 2013, to coincide with the publication of the new **Award of Garden Merit** plant list. The categories now used are as follows:
Temperature ranges given are intended to be absolute minimum winter temperatures (°C).
H1a = Heated greenhouse – tropical >15
H1b = Heated greenhouse – subtropical 10 to 15
H1c = Heated greenhouse – warm temperate 5 to 10
H2 = Tender – cool or frost-free greenhouse 1 to 5
H3 = Half-hardy – unheated greenhouse/mild winter -5 to 1
H4 = Hardy – average winter -10 to -5
H5 = Hardy – cold winter -15 to -10
H6 = Hardy – very cold winter -20 to -15
H7 = Very hardy <-20

Further definition of these categories can be found on the RHS website, in the Feb 2013 edition of *The Garden* and in the *RHS Plant Finder 2013* essay.

HYBRIDS

Some species, when grown together, in the wild or in cultivation, are found to interbreed and form hybrids. In some instances a hybrid name is coined, for example hybrids between *Primula hirsuta* and *P. minima* are given the name *Primula* × *forsteri*, the multiplication sign indicating hybrid origin. Hybrid formulae that quote the parentage of the hybrid are used where a unique name has not been coined, for example *Eucryphia cordifolia* × *E. lucida*. In hybrid formulae you will find parents in alphabetical order, with the male (m) and female (f) parent indicated where known. Hybrids between different genera are also possible, for example × *Mahoberberis* is the name given to hybrids between *Mahonia* and *Berberis*.

There are also a few special-case hybrids called graft hybrids, where the tissues of two plants are physically rather than genetically mixed. These are indicated by an addition rather than a multiplication sign, so *Laburnum* + *Cytisus* becomes + *Laburnocytisus*.

ICNCP

The ICNCP is the International Code of Nomenclature for Cultivated Plants. First published in 1959, the 9th edition was published in 2016.

Cultivar names that do not conform to this Code, and for which there is no valid alternative, are flagged I (for invalid). This code states that the minimum requirement is for a cultivar name to be given in conjunction with the name of the genus. However, in the *RHS Plant Finder* we choose to give as full a name as possible to give the gardener and botanist more information about the plant, following the Recommendation in the Code.

NOMENCLATURE AND TAXONOMY ADVISORY GROUP

This Group advises the RHS on individual problems of nomenclature regarding plants in cultivation and, in particular, use of names in the *RHS Horticultural Database*, reflected in the annual publication of the *RHS Plant Finder*.

The aim is always to make the plant names in the *RHS Plant Finder* as consistent, reliable and stable as possible and acceptable to gardeners and botanists alike, not only in the British Isles but around the world. Recent proposals to change or correct names are examined with the aim of creating a balance between the stability of well-known names and botanical and taxonomic correctness. In some cases the conflicting views on the names of some groups of plants will not easily be resolved. The Group's policy is then to wait and review the situation once a more obvious consensus is reached, rather than rush to rename plants only to have to change them again when opinions have shifted.

As we start 2020, Dr. John David is Chairman of the Group. The Group also includes Susyn Andrews, James Armitage, Chris Brickell, Dr James Compton, Dr. Alastair Culham, Mark Griffiths, Dr John Grimshaw, Dr Stephen Jury, Dr Alan Leslie, Dr Tony Lord, Chris Sanders, with Björn Aldén, Dr Crinan Alexander, Dr Janet Cubey, Dr Marco Hoffman, Prof David Mabberley, Svengunnar Ryman and Julian Sutton (corresponding members) and Mike Grant and Julian Shaw (attending RHS staff) and Dr Dawn Edwards as Secretary.

NOTES ON NOMENCLATURE AND IDENTIFICATION

The **Notes on Nomenclature and Identification**, p.49, give further information for names that are complex or may be confusing. See also **Nomenclature and Taxonomy Advisory Group**.

PLANT BREEDERS' RIGHTS

Plants covered by an *active* grant of Plant Breeders' Rights (PBR) are indicated throughout the Plant Directory. Grants indicated are those awarded by both UK and EU Plant Variety Rights offices. Because grants can both come into force and lapse at any time, this book can only aim to represent the situation at one point in time, but it is hoped

that this will act as a useful guide to growers and gardeners. UK and EU grants represent the published position as of the end of December 2019. We do not give any indication where PBR grants may be pending. All EU and UK grants are effective in the UK for the whole of 2020.

To obtain PBR protection, a new plant must be registered and pass tests for distinctness, uniformity and stability under an approved name. This approved name, under the rules of the **ICNCP**, established by a legal process, has to be regarded as the cultivar name. Increasingly however, these approved names are a code or "nonsense" name and are therefore often unpronounceable and meaningless, so the plants are given other names designed to attract sales when they are released. These secondary names are often referred to as selling names but are officially termed **trade designations**. We do our best to link PBR names to their trade descriptions but if you spot any we've missed, do let us know.

On the odd occasion the name for a plant with Plant Breeders' Rights in the EU differs from the name by which it is known outside of the EU and indeed may be different to that given in the relevant International Cultivar Registration Authority (ICRA) register. As the *RHS Plant Finder* has to use the correct name for the plant within the EU, on these occasions this may not be the same name given as the accepted name in the relevant RHS Cultivar Register and Checklist which, being international provides the name that complies with the **ICNCP**.

For further information on UK PBR contact:
Plant Variety Rights Office,
Animal and Plant Health Agency,
Eastbrook,
Shaftesbury Road,
Cambridge CB2 8DR
Ⓣ (0208) 026 5993
Ⓔ pvs.helpdesk@apha.gsi.gov.uk
Ⓦ www.gov.uk/plant-breeders-rights

For details of plants covered by EU Community Rights contact:
Community Plant Variety Office (CPVO)
3 Boulevard Maréchal Foch, CS 10121
49101 Angers Cedex 2, France
Ⓣ 00 33 (02) 41 25 64 00
Ⓔ cpvo@cpvo.europa.eu
Ⓦ www.cpvo.europa.eu

The *RHS Plant Finder* takes no responsibility for ensuring that nurseries selling plants with PBR are licensed to do so.

Reverse Synonyms

It is likely that users of this book will come across names in certain genera that they did not expect to find. This may be because species have been transferred from another genus (or **genera**).

Selling Names

See **Trade Designations**

Series

With seed-raised plants and some popular vegetatively propagated plants, especially bedding plants and pot plants such as *Petunia* or *Glandularia*, Series have become increasingly popular. A Series contains a number of similar cultivars, but differs from a **Group** in that it is a marketing device, with cultivars added to create a range of flower colours in plants of similar habit. Individual colour elements within a Series may be represented by slightly different cultivars over the years.

The word Series is always included and, where cited with a cultivar name it is enclosed in brackets, for example *Aquilegia* 'Robin' (Songbird Series). The Series name usually follows the rest of the plant name, but sometimes in this book we list it before the cultivar name in order to group members of a Series together when they occur next to one another on the page.

Species

See under **Botanical Names**

Subspecies

See under **Botanical Names**

Synonyms

Although the ideal is for each species or cultivar to have only one name, anyone dealing with plants soon comes across a situation where one plant has received two or more names, or two plants have received the same name. In each case, only one name and application, for reasons of precision and stability, can be regarded as correct. Additional names are known as synonyms. Further information on synonyms and why plants change names is available in *Guide to Plant Names*. See the introduction to this glossary for details of how to request a copy.

See also **Reverse Synonyms**.

Trade Designations

A **trade designation** is the name used to market a plant when the cultivar name is considered unsuitable for selling purposes. It is distinguished typographically (see below) from a cultivar name, and is not enclosed in single quotation marks.

In the case of **Plant Breeders' Rights** it is a legal requirement for the cultivar name to appear with the trade designation on a label at the point of sale. Most plants are sold under only one trade designation, but some, especially roses, are sold under a number of names, particularly when cultivars are introduced from other countries. Usually, the correct cultivar name is the only way to ensure that the same plant is not bought unwittingly under two or more different trade designations. The *RHS Plant Finder* follows the recommendations of the **ICNCP** when dealing with trade designations and PBR. These are always to quote the cultivar name and trade designation together and to style the trade designation in small capitals, for example *Choisya* × *dewitteana* GOLDFINGERS ('Limo'PBR). Here GOLDFINGERS is the trade designation and 'Limo' is the cultivar name that has been granted **Plant Breeders' Rights**.

TRANSLATIONS

When a cultivar name is translated from the language of first publication, the translation is regarded as a **trade designation** and styled accordingly. We endeavour to recognise the original cultivar name in every case and to give an English translation where it is in general use.

VARIEGATED PLANTS

Following a suggestion from the Variegated Plant Group of the Hardy Plant Society, a (v) is cited after those plants which are "variegated". The dividing line between variegation and less distinct colour marking is necessarily arbitrary and plants with light veins, pale, silver or dark zones, or leaves flushed in paler colours, are not shown as being variegated unless there is an absolutely sharp distinction between paler and darker zones.

Further details of the Variegated Plant Group can be found at www.hardy-plant.org.uk.

VARIETY

See under **Botanical Names** and **Cultivar**

HORTAX

The Cultivated Plant Taxonomy Group

If you have an interest in the names of garden plants and wish to learn more or would like to make a comment about the International Code of Nomenclature for Cultivated Plants (ICNCP) visit the HORTAX website:

www.hortax.org.uk

Conservation and the Environment

Invasive Plants

As the *RHS Plant Finder* demonstrates, gardens in Britain have been greatly enriched by the diversity of plants introduced to cultivation from abroad. While the vast majority of those introduced have enhanced our gardens, a few have proved to be highly invasive and to threaten native habitats. Once such plants are established it is very difficult, costly and potentially damaging to native ecosystems to eradicate or control the invasive "alien" species. Gardeners can help by choosing not to buy or distribute non-native invasive plants and by taking steps to prevent them escaping into the wild and by disposing of them in a responsible way.

Invasive non-native species are controlled by two pieces of legislation in the UK. The list of species of Union concern is added to on a regular basis and the list below is up to date as of August 2019. No species on the list is included in the *RHS Plant Finder*.

Acacia saligna – Golden wreath wattle
Ailanthus altissima – Tree of heaven
Alternanthera philoxeroides – Alligator weed
Andropogon virginicus – Broomsedge
Asclepias syriaca – Milkweed
Baccharis halmifolia – Tree groundsel
Cabomba caroliniana – Carolina fanwort
Cardiospermum grandiflorum – Balloon vine
Cortaderia jubata – Purple pampas grass
Ehrharta calycina – Purple veldgrass
Eichhornia crassipes – Water hyacinth
Elodea nuttallii – Nuttall's water weed
Gunnera tinctoria – Chilean rhubarb
Gymnocoronis spilanthoides – Senegal tea
Heracleum mantegazzianum – Giant hogweed
Heracleum persicum – Giant hogweed (Tromso palm)
Heracleum sosnowskyi – Giant hogweed
Humulus scandens – Japanese hop
Hydrocotyle ranunculoides – Floating pennywort
Impatiens glandulifera – Himalayan balsam
Lagarosiphon major – Curly waterweed
Lespedeza cuneata – Chinese shrub clover
Ludwigia grandiflora – Water primrose
Ludwigia peploides – Water primrose
Lygodium japonicum – Climbing fern
Lysichiton americanus – American skunk cabbage
Microstegium vimineum – Japanese stiltgrass
Myriophyllum aquaticum – Parrot's feather
Myriophyllum heterophyllum – Broadleaf watermilfoil
Parthenium hysterophorus – Parthenium weed
Pennisetum setaceum – Crimson fountain grass
Persicaria perfoliata – Asiatic tearthumb
Prosopis juliflora – mesquite
Pueraria montana var. *lobata* – Kudzu
Salvinia molesta – Giant salvinia
Triadica sebifera – Chinese tallow tree

The EU Regulation is backed up in UK law by the Alien Invasive Species (Enforcement and Permitting) Order which came into force on 1st October 2019, and sets out the financial penalties and other enforcement measures for breaches of the Regulation.

Gardeners in possession of any of the listed species may dispose of the plants through composting, burning or in local authority green waste recycling as provided for in the Environment Agency's Regulatory Position Statement 178: https://www.gov.uk/government/publications/treatment-and-disposal-of-invasive-non-native-plants-rps-178/treatment-and-disposal-of-invasive-non-native-plants-rps-178

The second piece of legislation is the Wildlife and Countryside Act (1981). This legislation lists the species for which it is an offence to plant or cause to grow in the wild (Schedule 9). An amendment to the Act in 2014 brought in a ban of sale for the most serious aquatic invasive plants (indicated by a *). Those not covered by the EU Regulation are listed below. In addition we have also decided not to include two other plants on Schedule 9 as they are serious invasive species.

**Azolla filiculoides* – fairy fern
**Crassula helmsii* – New Zealand pygmy weed
Reynoutria japonica – Japanese knotweed
Impatiens glandulifera – Himalayan balsam

In Scotland the Wildlife and Natural Environment Act (2011) makes it an offence to release any non-native plant into the wild without a permit.

Species control provisions

The UK Government introduced new provisions in the Infrastructure Act (2015) to control invasive non-native species in England and Wales. There are two levels of control: a species control agreement and a species control order. In the former the owner of land where an invasive non-native species is present, when approached by the relevant environmental authority, agrees to take action to limit or remove the species. If the landowner fails to do so, or does not agree, or where it is not known who the landowner is, then the environment authority can take action to enforce the control of the species. This may involve entry of the property by the authority to carry out the control if the owner fails to comply. In the case of an emergency then a species control order may be issued without

going through the previous steps. Only those species listed on Schedule 9 of the Wildlife & Countryside Act can be subject to these control measures. For the purposes of the Act, Defra, Natural England, the Environment Agency and the Forestry Commission are defined as Environmental Authorities in England. For Wales it is Natural Resources Wales.

Bringing plants back from abroad

Travelling can be a great source of inspiration for gardeners and often provides an opportunity to encounter new and interesting plants. Anyone wishing to bring plants back into Britain from overseas must realise, however, that this is a complex matter. Various regulations are in force that apply to amateur gardeners as well as to commercial nurseries. The penalties for breaking these can be serious.

Most countries have regulations concerning the collection of plants from the wild, including seed. These regulations are likely to ban collection from certain protected places, such as national parks, ban the collection of rare or endangered species, and require permits to collect where special protection measures are not in place. In addition there is likely to be an additional permit to export any collected plant material. Travellers are frequently reminded of regulations in force at airports and other points of entry to a country. Anyone wishing to collect wild plants, for whatever purpose, will need to contact the country concerned well in advance of travel to seek the relevant permits. Breach of the regulations will result, as a minimum, in the confiscation of plant material if discovered. Any such material brought back to the UK is illegal.

The situation with plants in cultivation in another country is less clear and travellers are advised to check with the authorities in the country, particularly with regard to any Access and Benefit Sharing requirements (see Nagoya Protocol below), export permits or phytosanitary certificates that might be needed.

Plant Health Regulations. For private users within the EU, you can bring in most plants and plant products as long as they are grown in an EU country, are free from pests and diseases and are for your own use or consumption. However, some material intended for planting is prohibited, e.g. plants and seeds of *Castanea* (sweet chestnut) and plants of *Platanus* (plane).

Following the introduction of new plant health regulations on 14 December 2019 (Plant Health Regulation (EU) 2016/2031; https://www.gov.uk/government/publications/smarter-rules-for-safer-food-what-we-are-doing/smarter-rules-for-safer-food), there is no longer a passenger baggage concession for imports of plants and plant products from countries outside the EU. Almost all plants and plant products (including seeds) imported into the EU will need to be accompanied by a phytosanitary certificate; the only exemption being for tropical fruit of a few species (pineapple, coconut, durian, banana and dates). These requirements apply to domestic and commercial imports. Plants and plant products deemed "high risk" will be prohibited from entering the EU from all third countries until a risk assessment has been done. This list includes plants for planting of around 35 genera including *Malus*, *Prunus* and *Taxus*. These genera can continue to be traded within the EU in the meantime.

The Convention on International Trade in Endangered Species (CITES) affects the transport of animal and plant material across international boundaries. Its aim is to prevent exploitative trade and thereby to prevent harm and the ultimate extinction of wild populations. A tighter regime on trade in species of wild fauna and flora exists in the EU that requires export permits for any plants listed in Appendices A, B & C and import permits for Appendices A & B. There is a further Appendix D for non-CITES listed species that the EU consider to be endangered. A broad range of plants is covered in these Appendices, including *Cactaceae* and *Orchidaceae* and, although species are mentioned in the convention title, the restrictions cover all cultivars and hybrids of listed species too, except for specific exclusions, where there are annotations in the Appendices.

Ⓦ www.gov.uk/cites-imports-and-exports#cites-species

The Convention on Biological Diversity (**CBD** or the "Rio Convention") recognises the property rights of individual countries in relation to their own biodiversity. It exists to enable access to that biodiversity, but equally to ensure the sharing of any benefit derived from it. In principle it is possible to collect plant material from other countries that have asserted their rights under the CBD, by ensuring that you have obtained documentary evidence of prior informed consent on the basis of mutually agreed terms for any uses that the material will be put to in the future. In practice the legal requirements for collecting plant material vary from country to country and it is advisable to contact the National Focal Point for further information.

Ⓦ www.cbd.int

The **Nagoya Protocol**, is a supplementary agreement of the CBD which entered into force in 2015, and provides a framework for Access and Benefit Sharing. In the UK this is implemented by the European Union Regulation which is effective from 12 October 2014, and requires anyone utilising genetic resources from another country which is a signatory of the Nagoya Protocol, collected after 12 October 2014, to carry out due diligence to ensure that the material was collected in

accordance with the Protocol and the CBD. While the most likely examples of utilisation are the development of new products or medicines from plants, breeding programmes to raise new plants for horticulture would also be covered. Although the burden to prove legitimate use of the genetic resource lies with the person or organisation utilising the genetic resource, anyone providing the source of the genetic resource (such as wild collected plants) will need to be able to provide the relevant paperwork, such as a Material Transfer Agreement and Prior Informed Consent.
Ⓦ http://www.cbd.int/abs/about/

In March 2015 the UK Government put in place the scheme of penalties for failure to comply with the EU Regulation which includes a range of both civil and criminal penalties, with the ultimate sanction of a two-year prison sentence. This legislation also formally appointed Regulatory Delivery (formerly National Measurement and Regulation Office) as the authority to enforce compliance in the UK, effective from June 2015.
Ⓦ https://www.gov.uk/guidance/abs

European Habitats Directive. The full implementation of this Directive into UK law in 2007 extended protection to all of the European Protected Species (EPS) listed in the Appendices of that Directive (these are Appendices II(b) and IV(b) for plants) whether they are native to the UK or not. This requires a licence for material of any of these species collected in the wild after 1994. These are issued by Natural England (for England), Natural Resources Wales (in Wales) and Scottish Natural Heritage (for Scotland).
Ⓦ www.gov.uk/guidance/wild-plants-sell-them-legally

EU Exit ("Brexit"). As of 31st of January 2020 the UK left the European Union. The UK has translated the EU Regulations covered above into UK law which means that there is no change to the regulatory provisions on departure from the EU. The UK Government has stated that there will be an implementation period up to 31st December 2020 during which the UK will continue to follow EU Regulations and as a result existing arrangements for CITES will continue until that date.

Contact addresses

The UK authorities issue licences for UK plants. For other EU states a collector would need to contact the relevant national authorities.

Department for Environment, Food & Rural Affairs (Defra)
Nobel House
17 Smith Square
London
SW1P 3JR
For biodiversity queries:
Ⓔ biodiversity@defra.gsi.gov.uk

Plant Health
Room 11G02
Animal and Plant Health Agency
The National Agri-food Innovation Campus
Sand Hutton,
York
YO41 1LZ
Ⓣ 01904 405 138
Ⓔ planthealth.info@apha.gov.uk

CITES
Animal & Plant Health Agency (APHA)
Centre for International Trade – Bristol
1/17 Temple Quay House
2 The Square
Temple Quay
Bristol
BS1 6EB
Ⓣ 0117 372 8774
Ⓕ 0117 372 8206
Ⓔ wildlife.licensing@apha.gov.uk
Ⓦ www.gov.uk/plant-health-controls

Invasive Species
Natural England
Wildlife Management & Licensing
Horizon House
Deanery Road
Bristol
BS1 5AH
Ⓣ 020 8026 1089
Ⓔ wildlife@naturalengland.org.uk

Non-Native Species Secretariat
Animal and Plant Health Agency
Sand Hutton
York
YO41 1LZ
Ⓦ www.nonnativespecies.org

Nagoya Protocol
Office for Product Safety and Standards (OPSS)
Stanton Avenue
Teddington
TW110JZ
Ⓣ 020 8943 7272

The information provided on these pages is correct at the time of going to press, but current uncertainties over the nature of the UK's departure from the European Union mean that provisions concerning the movement of plants out of the UK into the EU, and from the EU into the UK, could be subject to significant change. Should this occur, the RHS will seek to provide relevant updates on our website.

Supplementary Keys to the Directory

Collectors' References

Abbreviations following a plant name, refer to the collector(s) of the plant. These abbreviations are expanded below, with a collector's name or expedition title. For a fuller explanation, see p.38.

A&JW	Watson, A. & J.
A&L	Ala, A. & Lancaster, Roy
AB&S	Archibald, James; Blanchard, John W. & Salmon, M.
AC	Clark, Alan J.
AC&H	Apold, J.; Cox, Peter & Hutchison, Peter
AC&W	Albury; Cheese, M. & Watson, J.M.
ACE	AGS Expedition to China (1994)
ACL	Leslie, Alan C.
AER	Robinson, Allan
AGS/ES	AGS Expedition to Sikkim (1983)
AGSJ	AGS Expedition to Japan (1988)
AH	Hoog, A.
AIM	Avent, Tony Mexico (1994)
Airth	Airth, Murray
Akagi	Akagi Botanical Garden
AL&JS	Sharman, Joseph L. & Leslie, Alan C.
APA	Cox, K.; Hootman, S.; Hudson, T.; et al, Expedition to Arunchal Pradesh (2005)
ARG	Argent, G.C.G.
ARGS	Alaska Rock Garden Society trip to China
ARJA	Ruksans, J. & Siesums, A.
B	Blanchard, John
B&F MA	Brown, Robert & Fisher, Rif & Middle Atlas (2007)
B L.	Beer, Len
B&L	Brickell, Christopher D. & Leslie, Alan C.
B&M & BM	Brickell, Christopher D. & Mathew, Brian
B&S	Bird P. & Salmon M.
B&SWJ	Wynn-Jones, Bleddyn & Susan
B&V	Burras, K. & Vosa, C.G.
BB	Bartholomew, B.
BBJMT	Boland, Brownless, Jamieson & McNamara
BC	Chudziak, W.
BC&W	Beckett; Cheese, M. & Watson, J.M.
Beavis	Beavis, Derek S.
Berry	Berry, P.
Berry & Brako	Berry, P. & Brako, Lois
BKBlount	Blount, B.K.
BKN	Bis, J., Kupčák, P. & Novak, H.
BL&M	University of Bangor Expedition to NE Nepal
BM	Mathew, Brian F.
BM&W	Binns, David L.; Mason, M. & Wright, A.
BO	Olsen, Bjornar
BOA	Boardman, P.
Breedlove	Breedlove, D.
BR	Rushbrooke, Ben
BS	Smith, Basil
BSBE	Bowles Scholarship Botanical Expedition (1963)
BSSS	Crûg Expedition, Jordan (1991)
Bu	Bubert, S.
Burtt	Burtt, Brian L.
BWJ	Wynn-Jones, Bleddyn
C	Cole, Desmond T.
C&C	Cox, P.A. & Cox, K.N.E.
C&Cu	Cox, K.N.E. & Cubey, J.
C&H	Cox, Peter & Hutchison, Peter
C&K	Chamberlain & Knott
C&R	Christian & Roderick
C&S	Clark, Alan & Sinclair, Ian W.J.
C&V	K.N.E. Cox & Vergera, S.
C&W	Cheese, M. & Watson, J.M.
CC	Chadwell, Christopher
CC&H	Chamberlain, David F.; Cox, Peter & Hutchison, P.
CC&McK	Chadwell, Christopher & McKelvie, A.
CC&MR	Chadwell, Christopher & Ramsay
CCH&H	Chamberlain, D.F.; Cox, P.; Hutchison, P. & Hootman, S.
CD&R	Compton, J.; D'Arcy, J. & Rix, E.M.
CDB	Brickell, Christopher D.
CDC	Coode, Mark J.E.; Dockrill, Alexander
CDC&C	Compton; D'Arcy; Christopher & Coke
CDPR	Compton; D'Arcy; Pope & Rix
CE&H	Christian, P.J.; Elliott & Hoog
CEE	Chengdu Edinburgh Expedition China (1991)

CGG	Glendoick Gardens Expedition to Guizou (2009)
CGV	Vosa, Canio
CGW	Grey-Wilson, Christopher
CH	Christian, P. & Hoog, A.
CH&M	Cox, P.; Hutchison, P. & Maxwell-MacDonald, D.
CHB	Boulanger, Charles
CHP&W	Kashmir Botanical Expedition
CL	Lovell, Chris
CLD	Chungtien, Lijiang & Dali Exped. China (1990)
CM&W	Cheese M.; Mitchel J. & Watson, J.
CN&W	Clark; Neilson & Wilson
CNDS	Nelson, C. & Sayers D.
COLA	Costin, J.J. & Lancaster, R., Japan (1990)
Cooper	Cooper, R.E.
Cox	Cox, Peter A.
CPC	Cobblewood Plant Collection
CPN	Compton, James
CS	Stapleton, Christopher
CSE	Cyclamen Society Expedition (1990)
CT	Teune, Carla
CW&T	Clark, A., Wilson, H. & Taggart, J., North Vietnam
CWJ	Colley, Finlay; Wynn-Jones, Bleddyn, Taiwan (2007)
Dahl	Dahl, Sally
DBG	Denver Botanic Garden, Colorado
DC	Cheshire, David
DF	Fox, D.
DG	Green, D.
DHTU	Hinkley, D., Turkey (2000)
DJF	Ferguson, Dave
DJH	Hinkley, Dan
DJHC	Hinkley D., China
DJHS	Hinkley, D., Sichuan
DJHT	Hinkley, Dan in Taipingshan, Taiwan
DJHV	Hinkley, D., Vietnam
DM	Millais, David
Doleshy	Doleshy, F.L.
DS&T	Drake, Sharman J. & Thompson
DWD	Rose, D.
DZ	Zummell, D.
ECN	Nelson, E. Charles
EDHCH	Hammond, Eric D.
EGM	Millais, T.
EKB	Balls, Edward K.
EM	East Malling Research Station
EMAK	Edinburgh Makalu Expedition (1991)
EMR	Rix, E.Martyn
EN	Needham, Edward F.
ENF	Fuller, E. Nigel
ETE	Edinburgh Taiwan Expedition (1993)
ETOT	Kirkham, T.S.; Flanagan, Mark
F	Forrest, G.
F&M	Fernandez & Mendoza, Mexico
F&W	Watson, J. & Flores, A.

Farrer	Farrer, Reginald
FK	Kinmonth, Fergus W.
FMB	Bailey, F.M.
FO	Otiery, Felix
FSYNI	Furse, Paul. & Synge, Patrick. 1700m in the Elburz Mountains, Iran October 1977
G	Gardner, Martin F.
G&K	Gardner, Martin F. & Knees, Sabina G.
G&P	Gardner, Martin F. & Page, Christopher N.
GDJ	Dumont, Gerard
GG	Gusman, G.
GS	Sherriff, George
Green	Green, D.
Guitt	Guittoneau, G.G.
Guiz	Guizhou Expedition (1985)
GWJ	Goddard, Sally; Wynne-Jones, Bleddyn & Susan
G-W&P	Grey-Wilson, Christopher & Phillips
H	Huggins, Paul
H&B	Hilliard, Olive M. & Burtt, Brian L.
H&D	Howick, C. & Darby
H&M	Howick, Charles & McNamara, William A.
H&W	Hedge, Ian C. & Wendelbo, Per W.
Harry Smith	Smith, K.A.Harry
Hartside	Hartside Nursery
HCM	Heronswood Expedition to Chile (1998)
HECC	Hutchison; Evans; Cox, P.; Cox, K.
HEHEHE	Zetterlund, H. et al, Gothenburg Botanic Gardens Expedition to northern China
Hird	Hird
HH&K	Hannay, S & S & Kingsbury, N.
HK	Kuenzler, Horst
HLMS	Springate, L.S.
HM&S	Halliwell, B.; Mason, D. & Smallcombe
HOA	Hoog, Anton
HOLUB	Holubec, V.
HRS	Hers, J.
Hummel	Hummel, D.
HW&E	Wendelbo, Per; Hedge, I. & Ekberg, L.
HWEL	Hirst, J.Michael; Webster, D.
HWJ	Crûg Heronswood Joint Expedition
HWJCM	Crûg Heronswood Expedition
HWJK	Crûg Heronswood Expedition, East Nepal (2002)
HZ	Zetterlund, Henrik
ICE	Instituto de Investigaciónes Ecológicas Chiloé & RBGE
IDS	International Dendrological Society
ISI	Int. Succulent Introductions
J&JA	Archibald, James & Jennifer
J. Jurasek	Jurasek, J.
JCA	Archibald, James
JE	Jack Elliott
JJ	Jackson, J.
JJ&JH	Halda, J. & Halda, J.
JJH	Halda, Joseph J.
JL	Lode, Joel

JLS	Sharman, J.L.
JMH	Hoog, J. & M.
JM-MK	Mahr, J.; Kammerlander, M.
JMT	Mann Taylor, J.
JN	Nielson, Jens
JR	Russell, J.
JRM	Marr, John
JW	Watson, J.M.
K	Kirkpatrick, George
K&LG	Gillanders, Kenneth & Gillanders, L.
K&Mc	Kirkpatrick, George & McBeath, Ronald J.D.
K&P	Josef Kopec & Milan Prasil
K&T	Kurashige, Y. & Tsukie, S.
KC	Cox, Kenneth
KEKE	Kew/Edinburgh Kanchenjunga Expedition (1989)
KGB	Kunming/Gothenburg Botanical Expedition (1993)
KM	Marsh, K.
KMR	Kupčák, M.
KR	Rushforth, K.D.
KRW	Wooster, K.R. (distributed after his death by Kath Dryden)
KW	Kingdon-Ward, F.
KWJ	Crûg-World of Ferns Joint Expedition, Vietnam (2007)
L	Lancaster, C. Roy
L&S	Ludlow, Francis & Sherriff, George
LA	Long Ashton Research Station clonal selection scheme
LB	Bercht, L. (*Cactaceae*)
LB	Bird P.; Salmon, M.
LEG	Lesotho Edinburgh/Gothenburg Expedition (1997)
Lismore	Lismore Nursery, Breeder's Number
LM&S	Leslie, Mattern & Sharman
LP	Palmer, W.J.L.
LS&E	Ludlow, Frank; Sherriff, George & Elliott, E. E.
LS&H	Ludlow, Frank; Sherriff, George & Hicks, J. H.
LS&T	Ludlow, Frank; Sherriff, George & Taylor, George
LZ	Lutz, Eberhard
M&PS	Mike & Polly Stone
M&T	Mathew & Tomlinson
Mac&W	McPhail & Watson
McB	McBeath, R.J.D.
McLaren	McLaren, H.D.
MDM	Myers, Michael D.
MECC	Scottish Rock Garden Club, Nepal (1997)
MESE	Alpine Garden Society Expedition, Greece (1999)
MF	Foster, Maurice
MH	Heasman, Matthew T.
MK	Kammerlander, Michael
MP	Pavelka, Mojmir
MPF	Frankis, M.P.
MS	Salmon, M.
MS&CL	Salmon, M. & Lovell, C.
MSF	Fillan, M.S.
MUG	Uhlig, M.
NAPE	Expedition to Naglaland and Arunachal Pradesh (2003)
NICE	North India Expedition (1997)
NJM	Macer, N.J.
NMWJ	Taiwan National Museum of Natural Science; Wynn-Jones, B. & S.
NN	Nielsen & Nielsen (2009)
NNS	Ratko, Ron
NS	Turland, Nick
NVD	Expedition to Vietnam
NVFDE	Northern Vietnam First Darwin Expedition
Og	Ogisu, Mikinori
ORO	Oron, Peri
OS	Sonderhousen, O.
P. Bon	Bonavia, P.
P&C	Paterson, David S. & Clarke, Sidney
P&W	Polastri & Watson, J. M.
PAB	Barney, P.A.
PB	Bird, Peter
PBR	Bruggeman, P.
PC&H	Pattison, G.; Catt, P. & Hickson, M.
PD	Davis, Peter H.
PDM	Purdom, William
PF	Furse, Paul
PG	Pichler, G.
PJC	Christian, Paul J.
PJC&AH	P.J. Christian & A. Hogg
PNMK	Nicholls, P.; Kammerlander, M.
Polunin	Polunin, Oleg
Pras	Prasil, M.
PS&W	Polunin, Oleg; Sykes, William & Williams, John
PW	Wharton, Peter
R	Rock, J.F.C.
RB	Brown, R.
RBS	Brown, Ray, Sakharin Island
RCB AM	Brown, Robert, Expedition to Armenia
RCB/Arg	Brown, Robert, Argentina, (2002)
RCB E	Brown, Robert, Expedition to Spain (Andalucia)
RCB/Eq	Brown, Robert, Ecuador, (1988)
RCB RA	Brown, Robert
RCB RL	Brown, Robert, Expedition to Lebanon
RCB/TQ	Brown, Robert, Turkey (2001)
RE	Evans, Ron
RH	Hancock, R.
RJN	Neilsen, R.
RKMP	Ruksans, J.; Krumins, A.; Kitts, M.; Paivel, A.
RM	Ruksans, J. & Kitts, M.
RMRP	Rocky Mountain Rare Plants, Denver, Colorado

RS	Suckow, Reinhart
RSC	Richard Somer Cocks
RV	Richard Valder
RWJ	Crûg Farm-Rickards Ferns Expedition to Taiwan (2003)
S&B	Blanchard, J.W. & Salmon, M.
S&F	Salmon, M. & Fillan, M.
S&L	Sinclair, Ian W.J. & Long, David G.
S&SH	Sheilah & Spencer Hannay
Sandham	Sandham, John
SB	Brack, Steven
SB&L	Salmon, Bird & Lovell
SBEC	Sino-British Expedition to Cangshan
SBEL	Sino-British Lijiang Expedition
SBQE	Sino-British Expedition to Quinghai
Sch	Schilling, Anthony D.
SD	Sashal Dayal
SDR	Rankin, Stella & David
SEH	Hootman, Steve
SEP	Swedish Expedition to Pakistan
SF	Forde, P.
SG	Salmon, M. & Guy, P.
SH	Hannay, Spencer
Sich	Simmons, Erskine, Howick & Mcnamara
SJ	Johansson, Stellan
SLIZE	Swedish-Latvian-Iranian Zagros Expedition to Iran (May 1988)
SOJA	Kew/Quarryhill Expedition to Southern Japan
SS&W	Stainton, J.D. Adam; Sykes, William & Williams, John
SSNY	Sino-Scottish Expedition to NW Yunnan (1992)
T	Taylor, Nigel P.
T&K	Taylor, Nigel P. & Knees, Sabina
TCM	Mitchell, Thomas Carly
TG	Thomas, H-P. & Gilmer, K.
TH	Hudson, T.
TJR	Roberts, Tim
TS&BC	Smythe, T. & Cherry, B.
TSS	Spring Smyth, T.L.M.
TW	Weston, Tony
USDAPI	US Department of Agriculture Plant Index Number
USDAPQ	US Dept. of Agriculture Plant Quarantine Number
USNA	United States National Arboretum
VdL	Van de Laar, Harry
VHH	Vernon H. Heywood
VV	Victor, David
W	Wilson, Ernest H.
W&B	Watkins, D. & Brown, R., Bulgaria (2012)
W&O	Wu, August & Olsen, Bjornar
WJC	Wynn-Jones, B. & S. & Colley, F.
WM	McLewin, William
Woods	Woods, Patrick J.B.
Wr	Wraight, David & Anke
WWJ	Wharton, Peter; Wynn-Jones, Bleddyn & Susan
Yu	Yu, Tse-tsun
ZE&S	Zetterlund, H., Eriksson, A-I. & Strid, A.

NOMENCLATURAL NOTES

The following changes have been made during 2019 to the names used in the *RHS Plant Finder* based upon decisions of the RHS Nomenclature and Taxonomy Advisory Group (NATAG). If you have any suggestions for other plant name changes within the *RHS Plant Finder*, then please write, stating your reasons in full to:

The Secretary
Dr Dawn Edwards
Nomenclature and Taxonomy Advisory Group
Royal Horticultural Society
RHS Garden Wisley
Woking
Surrey
GU23 6QB

- *Bulbocodium* and *Merendera* (and *Androcymbium*) moved into *Colchicum*
- *Betula* updated to reflect many of the names used by Ashburner & McAllister in *The Genus Betula*
- Some *Caesalpinia* moved to other genera: you'll find *Biancaea*, *Erythrostemon* and *Tara* in this edition
- *Callerya reticulata* transferred to *Wisteriopsis reticulata*
- *Catalpa fargesii* included within *C. bungei* with recognition of Fargesii Group and Duclouxii Group; acknowledging that most plants for sale in the British Isles as *C. bungei* are *C. ovata*
- *Corynabutilon* as distinct from *Abutilon*
- Identification of plants grown as *Delosperma* 'Ruby Coral' as *Ectotropis seanii-hoganii*
- *Fatsia japonica* 'Tsumugi-shibori' identified as the correct name for 'Spider's Web'
- *Gaura* moved into *Oenothera*; identifiable by the horticultural classification (G)
- *Halesia macgregorii* moved to *Perkinsiodendron macgregorii*
- *Lewisia tweedyi* transferred to *Lewisiopsis tweedyi*
- Some species of *Lithodora* moved into *Glandora*; some cultivars of *G. diffusa* identified as *G. prostrata* (others are still being investigated)
- Changes to the generic boundary of *Gypsophila*: incorporating *Vaccaria* but separating out others including *Acanthophyllum* and *Psammophiliella*
- *Nectaroscordum* included within *Allium*
- *Perovskia* and *Rosmarinus* moved into *Salvia*; distinguishable by the horticultural classification codes (Pe) and (Ro) respectively
- Identification of the correct names for some *Petrocosmea* in cultivation
- *Reynoutria* resurrected out of *Fallopia*
- Cultivars of apomictic *Sorbus* now synonymised with the clonal microspecies to which they are attributed
- Recognition that most of the plants grown under the names *Sorbus wilsoniana* and *S.* aff. *wilsoniana* belong to a new species, *S. splendens*
- Identification of plants grown under the invalid name *Thalictrum sphaerostachyum* as *T. flavum* subsp. *glaucum*
- *Zauschneria* incorporated within *Epilobium*; identifiable by the horticultural classification code (Z)

This is not intended to be an exhaustive list of the changes made to the RHS Horticultural Database, reflected in the *RHS Plant Finder*; many more changes are made during the year by the RHS botanical team. This list just highlights some of the NATAG changes.

You'll find some of these have had explanatory articles, or will have been mentioned in the new Plant Bulletin feature, in *The Plant Review* (previously *The Plantsman*) in the last 12 months. Watch out for articles in the coming year on future changes.

CLASSIFICATION OF GENERA

Genera including a large number of species, or with many cultivars, are often subdivided into informal horticultural classifications, or formal cultivar groups in the case of *Clematis* and *Tulipa*. The breeding of new cultivars is sometimes limited to hybrids between closely related species, thus for *Saxifraga* and *Primula*, the cultivars are allocated to the sections given in the infrageneric treatments cited. Please turn to p.37 for a fuller explanation.

ACER PALMATUM

(A) Amoenum Group
(D) Dissectum Group
(Dw) Dwarf Group
(L) Linearilobum Group
(M) Matsumurae Group
(P) Palmatum Group

ACTINIDIA

(s-p) Self-pollinating

BEGONIA

(C) Cane-like
(R) Rex Cultorum
(S) Semperflorens Cultorum
(T) × *tuberhybrida* (Tuberous)

BRUGMANSIA

(Breeding History Sets, from the International *Brugmansia* Register, for hybrid combinations with no corresponding hybrid binomial)

(AI) Aurinsi (*B. aurea* & *B. insignis*)
(AVS) Arbovulsa (B. arborea, *B. vulcanicola* & *B. sanguinea*)
(SA) Saurea (*B. suaveolens* & *B. aurea*)
(SI) Suavinsi (*B. suaveolens* & *B. insignis*)
(SIA) Suavinsaurea (*B. suaveolens*, *B. insignis* & *B. aurea*)
(SIVA) Siva (*B. suaveolens*, *B. insignis*, *B. versicolor* & *B. aurea*)
(SV) Suaver (*B. suaveolens* & *B. versicolor*)
(SVI) Suaverinsi (*B. suaveolens*, *B. versicolor* & *B. insignis*)
(VA) Vularbo (*B. vulcanicola* & *B. arborea*)
(VI) Verinsi (*B. versicolor* & *B. insignis*)
(VIA) Verinsaurea (*B. versicolor*, *B. insignis* & *B. aurea*)
(VS) Vulsa (*B. vulcanicola* & *B. sanguinea*)

CHRYSANTHEMUM

(By the National Chrysanthemum Society)

(1) Indoor Large (Exhibition)
(2) Indoor Medium (Exhibition)
(3a) Indoor Incurved: Large-flowered
(3b) Indoor Incurved: Medium-flowered
(3c) Indoor Incurved: Small-flowered
(4a) Indoor Reflexed: Large-flowered
(4b) Indoor Reflexed: Medium-flowered
(4c) Indoor Reflexed: Small-flowered
(5a) Indoor Intermediate: Large-flowered
(5b) Indoor Intermediate: Medium-flowered
(5c) Indoor Intermediate: Small-flowered
(6a) Indoor Anemone: Large-flowered
(6b) Indoor Anemone: Medium-flowered
(6c) Indoor Anemone: Small-flowered
(7a) Indoor Single: Large-flowered
(7b) Indoor Single: Medium-flowered
(7c) Indoor Single: Small-flowered
(8a) Indoor True Pompon
(8b) Indoor Semi-pompon
(9a) Indoor Spray: Anemone
(9b) Indoor Spray: Pompon
(9c) Indoor Spray: Reflexed
(9d) Indoor Spray: Single
(9e) Indoor Spray: Intermediate
(9f) Indoor Spray: Spider, Quill, Spoon or Any Other Type
(10a) Indoor, Spider
(10b) Indoor, Quill
(10c) Indoor, Spoon
(11) Any Other Indoor Type
(12a) Indoor, Charm
(12b) Indoor, Cascade
(13a) October-flowering Incurved: Large-flowered
(13b) October-flowering Incurved: Medium-flowered
(13c) October-flowering Incurved: Small-flowered
(14a) October-flowering Reflexed: Large-flowered
(14b) October-flowering Reflexed: Medium-flowered
(14c) October-flowering Reflexed: Small-flowered
(15a) October-flowering Intermediate: Large-flowered
(15b) October-flowering Intermediate: Medium-flowered
(15c) October-flowered Intermediate: Small-flowered
(16) October-flowering Large
(17a) October-flowering Single: Large-flowered
(17b) October-flowering Single: Medium-flowered
(17c) October-flowering Single: Small-flowered
(18a) October-flowering Pompon: True Pompon

(18b) October-flowering Pompon: Semi-pompon
(19a) October-flowering Spray: Anemone
(19b) October-flowering Spray: Pompon
(19c) October-flowering Spray: Reflexed
(19d) October-flowering Spray: Single
(19e) October-flowering Spray: Intermediate
(19f) October-flowering Spray: Spider, Quill, Spoon or Any Other Type
(20) Any Other October-flowering Type
(21a) Korean: Anemone
(21b) Korean: Pompon
(21c) Korean: Reflexed
(21d) Korean: Single
(21e) Korean: Intermediate
(21f) Korean: Spider, Quill, Spoon, or any other type
(22a) Charm: Anemone
(22b) Charm: Pompon
(22c) Charm: Reflexed
(22d) Charm: Single
(22e) Charm: Intermediate
(22f) Charm: Spider, Quill, Spoon or Any Other Type
(23a) Early-flowering Outdoor Incurved: Large-flowered
(23b) Early-flowering Outdoor Incurved: Medium-flowered
(23c) Early-flowering Outdoor Incurved: Small-flowered
(24a) Early-flowering Outdoor Reflexed: Large-flowered
(24b) Early-flowering Outdoor Reflexed: Medium-flowered
(24c) Early-flowering Outdoor Reflexed: Small-flowered
(25a) Early-flowering Outdoor Intermediate: Large-flowered
(25b) Early-flowering Outdoor Intermediate: Medium-flowered
(25c) Early-flowering Outdoor Intermediate: Small-flowered
(26a) Early-flowering Outdoor Anemone: Large-flowered
(26b) Early-flowering Outdoor Anemone: Medium-flowered
(27a) Early-flowering Outdoor Single: Large-flowered
(27b) Early-flowering Outdoor Single: Medium-flowered
(28a) Early-flowering Outdoor Pompon: True Pompon
(28b) Early-flowering Outdoor Pompon: Semi-pompon
(29a) Early-flowering Outdoor Spray: Anemone
(29b) Early-flowering Outdoor Spray: Pompon
(29c) Early-flowering Outdoor Spray: Reflexed
(29d) Early-flowering Outdoor Spray: Single
(29e) Early-flowering Outdoor Spray: Intermediate
(29f) Early-flowering Outdoor Spray: Spider, Quill, Spoon or Any Other Type
(29Rub) Early-flowering Outdoor Spray: Rubellum
(30) Any Other Early-flowering Outdoor Type

Clematis

(Cultivar Groups as per Matthews, V. (2002) *The International Clematis Register & Checklist 2002*, RHS, London.)

(A) Atragene Group
(Ar) Armandii Group
(C) Cirrhosa Group
(EL) Early Large-flowered Group
(F) Flammula Group
(Fo) Forsteri Group
(H) Heracleifolia Group
(I) Integrifolia Group
(LL) Late Large-flowered Group
(M) Montana Group
(T) Texensis Group
(Ta) Tangutica Group
(V) Viorna Group
(Vb) Vitalba Group
(Vt) Viticella Group

Dahlia

(Classification according to The International Dahlia Register (1969), 22nd Supp. (2012) formed through consultation with national dahlia societies.)

(Sin) 1 Single
(Anem) 2 Anemone-flowered
(Col) 3 Collerette
(WL) 4 Waterlily
(D) 5 Decorative
(Ba) 6 Ball
(Pom) 7 Pompon
(C) 8 Cactus
(S-c) 9 Semi-cactus
(Misc) 10 Miscellaneous
(Fim) 11 Fimbriated
(SinO) 12 Single Orchid (Star)
(DblO) 13 Double Orchid
(P) 14 Peony-flowered
(B) Botanical
(DwB) Dwarf Bedding
(Lil) Lilliput

Dianthus

(By the RHS)

(b) Carnation, border
(M) Carnation, Malmaison
(p) Pink
(p,a) Pink, annual
(pf) Carnation, perpetual-flowering
(pt) Carnation, pot

Epilobium

(Z) previously in the genus *Zauschneria*

Fruit

(B) Black (*Vitis*), Blackberry (*Rubus*), Blackcurrant (*Ribes*)
(Ball) Ballerina (*Malus*)
(C) Culinary (*Malus, Prunus, Pyrus, Ribes*)
(Cider) Cider (*Malus*)
(D) Dessert (*Malus, Prunus, Pyrus, Ribes*)
(F) Fruit
(G) Glasshouse (*Vitis*)
(O) Outdoor (*Vitis*)
(P) Pinkcurrant (*Ribes*)
(Perry) Perry (*Pyrus*)
(R) Red (*Vitis*), Redcurrant (*Ribes*)
(S) Seedless (*Citrus, Vitis*)
(s-p) Self-pollinating
(W) White (*Vitis*), Whitecurrant (*Ribes*)

Fuchsia

(E) Encliandra
(T) Variants and hybrids of *F. triphylla*

Gladiolus

(B) Butterfly
(E) Exotic
(G) Giant
(L) Large
(M) Medium
(Min) Miniature
(N) Nanus
(P) Primulinus
(S) Small
(Tub) Tubergenii

Hepatica nobilis

(Adapted from the International Hepatica Society classification for *Hepatica nobilis*)
(1) Hyoujun (normal)
(2) (degenerated anther)
(3) Otome (degenerated stamen)
(4) Henka (petal deformity)
(5/d) Herashibe (semi-double, primitive)
(5A/d) Choji (semi-double, primitive)
(6/d) Nidan (semi-double, advanced)
(7/d) Sandan (double, primitive)
(8/d) Karako (double, advanced)
(9/d) Sene-e (double, completed)

Hydrangea macrophylla

(H) Hortensia
(L) Lacecap

Impatiens

(NG) New Guinea Group

Iris

(Adapted from the American Iris Society Classification)
(AB) Arilbred
(BB) Border Bearded
(Cal-Sib) Series *Californicae* × Series *Sibiricae*
(CH) Californian Hybrid
(DB) Dwarf Bearded (not assigned)
(Dut) Dutch (can be assigned to *I.* × *hollandica*)
(IB) Intermediate Bearded
(J) Juno (subgenus *Scorpiris*)
(La) Louisiana Hybrid
(MDB) Miniature Dwarf Bearded
(MTB) Miniature Tall Bearded
(Rc) Regeliocyclus (Section *Regelia* × Section *Oncocyclus*)
(Reticulata)
(SDB) Standard Dwarf Bearded
(Sib) Siberian
(Sino-Sib) Series *Sibiricae*, chromosome number 2n=40
(SpH) Species Hybrid
(Spuria) Spuria
(TB) Tall Bearded

Lilium

(Classification according to *The International Lily Register* (ed. 4, 2007))
(I) Asiatic hybrids derived from *L. amabile, L. bulbiferum, L. callosum, L. cernuum, L. concolor, L. dauricum, L. davidii, L.* × *hollandicum, L. lancifolium, L. lankongense, L. leichtlinii, L.* × *maculatum* and *L. pumilum, L.* × *scottiae, L. wardii* and *L. wilsonii.*
(II) Martagon hybrids derived from *L. dalhansonii, L. hansonii, L. martagon, L. medeoloides and L. tsingtauense*
(III) Euro-Caucasian hybrids derived from *L. candidum, L. chalcedonicum, L. kesselringianum, L. monadelphum, L. pomponium, L. pyrenaicum* and *L.* × *testaceum.*
(IV) American hybrids derived from *L. bolanderi, L.* × *burbankii, L. canadense, L. columbianum, L. grayi, L. humboldtii, L. kelleyanum, L. kelloggii, L. maritimum, L. michauxii, L. michiganense, L. occidentale, L.* × *pardaboldtii, L. pardalinum, L. parryi, L. parvum, L. philadelphicum, L. pitkinense, L. superbum, L. vollmeri, L. washingtonianum* and *L. wigginsii.*
(V) Longiflorum lilies derived from *L. formosanum, L. longiflorum, L. philippinense and L. wallichianum.*
(VI) Trumpet and Aurelian hybrids derived from *L.* × *aurelianense, L. brownii, L.* × *centigale, L. henryi, L.* × *imperiale, L.* × *kewense, L. leucantheum, L. regale, L. rosthornii, L. sargentiae, L. sulphureum* and *L. sulphurgale* (but excluding hybrids

	of *L. henryi* with all species listed in Division VII).
(VII)	Oriental hybrids derived from *L. auratum*, *L. japonicum*, *L. nobilissimum*, *L.* × *parkmanii*, *L rubellum* and *L. speciosum* (but excl. all hybrids of these with *L. henryi*).
(VIII)	Other hybrids not covered by any of the previous divisions (I-VII)
(IX)	Species and cultivars of species
a/	upward-facing flowers
b/	outward-facing flowers
c/	downward-facing flowers
/a	trumpet-shaped flowers
/b	bowl-shaped flowers
/c	flat flowers (or with only tepal tips recurved)
/d	recurved flowers

MALUS *SEE* FRUIT

NARCISSUS

(By the RHS, revised 1998)

(1)	Trumpet
(2)	Large-cupped
(3)	Small-cupped
(4)	Double
(5)	Triandrus
(6)	Cyclamineus
(7)	Jonquilla and Apodanthus
(8)	Tazetta
(9)	Poeticus
(10)	Bulbocodium
(11a)	Split-corona: Collar
(11b)	Split-corona: Papillon
(12)	Miscellaneous
(13)	Species

NYMPHAEA

(H)	Hardy
(D)	Day-blooming
(N)	Night-blooming
(T)	Tropical

OENOTHERA

(G)	previously in the genus *Gaura*

PAEONIA

(S)	Shrubby

PELARGONIUM:

(Based on the International *Pelargonium* Register)

(A)	Angel
(B)	Bird's egg (in combination)
(C)	Coloured foliage (in combination)
(Ca)	Cactus (also known as Quilled) (in combination)
(Dec)	Decorative
(Dw)	Dwarf (in combination)
(Fr)	Frutetorum
(I)	Ivy-leaved
(Mic)	Micro-minature (in combination)
(Min)	Minature (in combination)
(R)	Regal
(Ros)	Rosebud (in combination)
(Sc)	Scented-leaved
(St)	Stellar (in combination)
(T)	Tulip (in combination)
(U)	Unique
(Z)	Zonal
(Za)	Zonartic

PRIMULA

(Classification by Section as per Richards. J. (2002) *Primula* (2nd edition). Batsford, London)

(Ag)	*Auganthus*
(Al)	*Aleuritia*
(Am)	*Amethystinae*
(Ar)	*Armerina*
(Au)	*Auricula*
(A)	Alpine Auricula
(B)	Border Auricula
(S)	Show Auricula
(St)	Striped Auricula
(Bu)	*Bullatae*
(Ca)	*Capitatae*
(Cf)	*Cordifoliae*
(Ch)	*Chartaceae*
(Co)	*Cortusoides*
(Cr)	*Carolinella*
(Cu)	*Cuneifoliae*
(Cy)	*Crystallophlomis*
(Da)	*Davidii*
(De)	*Denticulatae*
(Dr)	*Dryadifoliae*
(F)	*Fedtschenkoanae*
(G)	*Glabrae*
(Ma)	*Malvaceae*
(Mi)	*Minutissimae*
(Mo)	*Monocarpicae*
(Mu)	*Muscarioides*
(Ob)	*Obconicolisteri*
(Or)	*Oreophlomis*
(Pa)	*Parryi*
(Pe)	*Petiolares*
(Pf)	*Proliferae*
(Pi)	*Pinnatae*
(Pr)	*Primula*
(Poly)	Polyanthus (can be assigned to *P.* × *polyantha*)
(Prim)	Primrose
(Pu)	*Pulchellae*
(Py)	*Pycnoloba*
(R)	*Reinii*
(Si)	*Sikkimenses*
(So)	*Soldanelloides*
(Sp)	*Sphondylia*
(Sr)	*Sredinskya*

(Su) *Suffrutescentes*
(Y) *Yunnannenses*

PRUNUS *SEE* FRUIT

PYRUS *SEE* FRUIT

RHODODENDRON

(A) Azalea (deciduous, species or unclassified hybrid)
(Ad) Azaleodendron
(EA) Evergreen azalea
(G) Ghent azalea (deciduous)
(K) Knap Hill or Exbury azalea (deciduous)
(M) Mollis azalea (deciduous)
(O) Occidentalis azalea (deciduous)
(R) Rustica azalea (deciduous)
(V) Vireya rhododendron
(Vs) Viscosa azalea (deciduous)

RIBES *SEE* FRUIT

ROSA

(A) Alba
(Bb) Bourbon
(Bs) Boursault
(Ce) Centifolia
(Ch) China
(Cl) Climbing (in combination)
(D) Damask
(DPo) Damask Portland
(F) Floribunda or Cluster-flowered
(G) Gallica
(Ga) Garnette
(GC) Ground Cover
(HM) Hybrid Musk
(HP) Hybrid Perpetual
(HT) Hybrid Tea or Large-flowered
(Min) Miniature
(Mo) Moss (in combination)
(N) Noisette
(Patio) Patio, Miniature Floribunda or Dwarf Cluster-flowered
(Poly) Polyantha
(Ra) Rambler
(RH) Rubiginosa hybrid (Hybrid Sweet Briar)
(Ru) Rugosa
(S) Shrub
(SpH) Spinosissima Hybrid
(T) Tea

RUBUS *SEE* FRUIT

SALVIA

(Pe) previously in the genus *Perovskia*
(Ro) previously in the genus *Rosmarinus*

SAXIFRAGA

(Classification by Section from Gornall, R.J. (1987). *Botanical Journal of the Linnean Society,* 95(4): 273-292)
(1) *Ciliatae*
(2) *Cymbalaria*
(3) *Merkianae*
(4) *Micranthes*
(5) *Irregulares*
(6) *Heterisia*
(7) *Porphyrion*
(8) *Ligulatae*
(9) *Xanthizoon*
(10) *Trachyphyllum*
(11) *Gymnopera*
(12) *Cotylea*
(13) *Odontophyllae*
(14) *Mesogyne*
(15) *Saxifraga*

STREPTOCARPUS

(AV) African violets (previously in the genus *Saintpaulia*)

TULIPA

(Classification by Cultivar Group from *Classified List and International Register of Tulip Names* by Koninklijke Algemeene Vereniging voor Bloembollencultuur 1996)
(1) Single Early Group
(2) Double Early Group
(3) Triumph Group
(4) Darwin Hybrid Group
(5) Single Late Group (including Darwin Group and Cottage Group)
(6) Lily-flowered Group
(7) Fringed Group
(8) Viridiflora Group
(9) Rembrandt Group
(10) Parrot Group
(11) Double Late Group
(12) Kaufmanniana Group
(13) Fosteriana Group
(14) Greigii Group
(15) Miscellaneous

VIOLA

(C) Cornuta Hybrid
(dVt) Double Violet
(ExVa) Exhibition Viola
(FP) Fancy Pansy
(P) Pansy
(PVt) Parma Violet
(SP) Show Pansy
(T) Tricolor
(Va) Viola
(Vt) Violet
(Vtta) Violetta

VITIS *SEE* FRUIT

How to Use the Plant Directory

Nursery Codes

Look up the plant you require in the alphabetical Plant Directory. Against each plant you will find one or more four or five letter codes, for example WCru, each code represents one nursery offering that plant. The first letter of each code indicates the main area of the country in which the nursery is situated. For this geographical key, refer to the **Nursery Codes and Symbols** on p.884.

Turn to the **Nursery Details by Code** starting on p.888 where, in alphabetical order of codes, you will find details of each nursery which offers the plant in question. For a fuller explanation of how to use the nursery listings please turn to p.886. **Always check that the nursery you select has the plant in stock before you visit.**

Plants with more than 30 Suppliers

In some cases, against the plant name you will see the term 'Widely available' instead of a nursery code. If we were to include every plant listed by all nurseries, the *RHS Plant Finder* would become unmanageably bulky. We therefore ask nurseries to restrict their entries to those plants that are not already well represented. As a result, if more than 30 nurseries offer any plant the Directory gives no nursery codes and the plant is listed instead as being 'Widely available'.

You should not have difficulty in locating these in local nurseries or garden centres. If, however, you are unable to find such plants, a list of all the current suppliers we have on file is available by post or online. See the Introduction (p.34).

Finding Fruit, Vegetables and Herbs

You will need to search for these by their botanical names. Common names are cross-referenced to their botanical names in the Plant Directory.

If you have Difficulty Finding your Plant

If you cannot immediately find the plant you seek, look through the various species of the genus. You may be using an incomplete name. The problem is most likely to arise in very large genera such as *Phlox* where there are a number of possible species, each with a large number of cultivars. A search through the whole genus may well bring success. For space reasons, we are not able to list in the Plant Directory annuals, orchids or cacti (except hardy terrestrial orchids and hardy cacti), or non-ornamental vegetables. For fruit and vegetables with an RHS Award of Garden Merit please see the relevant sections on p.840 and p.854.

Cross-references

It may be that the plant name you seek is a synonym. Our intention is to list nursery codes only against the correct botanical name. Where you find a synonym you will be cross-referred to the correct name.

Plants Last Listed in Earlier Editions

It may be that the plant you are seeking has no known suppliers and is thus not listed.

The loss of a plant name from the Directory may arise for a number of reasons – the supplier may have gone out of business, or may not have responded to our latest questionnaire and has therefore been removed from the book. Such plants may well be available but we have no knowledge of current suppliers. Alternatively, some plants may have been misnamed by nurseries in previous editions and are now appearing under their correct name.

For further information on plants last listed in earlier editions please see the Introduction (p.34).

We recommend that you use the latest edition of the *RHS Plant Finder*

USING THE PLANT DIRECTORY

The purpose of the Plant Directory is to help the reader correctly identify the plant they seek and find stockists. Each nursery has a unique code which appears to the right of the plant name. **Nursery Details by Code** (p.888) gives details about each nursery. The first letter in each code denotes its geographical region. Turn to the **Nursery Codes and Symbols** (p.884) to find the correct code for an area.

The Plant Directory provides information about plants through symbols and notes. For example: if a plant has an alternative name; is new to the book; or has received the RHS Award of Garden Merit.

Rudbeckia (Asteraceae)

	AUTUMN SUN	see *R. laciniata* 'Herbstsonne'
	'Berlin'	EBee LRHS NRHS
	californica B&SWJ 14105	WCru
	deamii	see *R. fulgida* var. *deamii*
	fulgida	SWvt WFar
	- 'American Gold Rush' PBR **new**	LBar
	- 'City Garden'	GBin LRHS NLar SRms WFar
§	- var. ***deamii*** 🏆H6	Widely available
	- 'Early Bird Gold'	CWGN ECtt EHyd EPfP GBin GMaP LBar LCro LRHS MHol NGrs NLar NRHS SAko SCob WCAu WFar
	- 'Forever Gold'	NCth SEdd SMad
	- var. ***fulgida***	EBee EPfP LEdu SPoG
	- 'Little Goldstar' PBR	CBod CKno CRos ECtt EHyd ELan EPfP LBar LCro LOPS LRHS MACG MAsh MPri MTin NGrs NLar NRHS SCob SCoo SPoG SRms WFar WHil
§	- var. ***speciosa*** 🏆H6	CBod EBee ECha ECtt EHyd ELan ELon EPfP GAbr GBin LRHS MMuc NRHS SEND SHar SPlb SPtp SRms SWvt WFar WOld XLum
	- var. ***sullivantii***	CDoC EMor
	- - 'Goldsturm' 🏆H6	Widely available
	- - 'Pot of Gold'	NBPC NLar SCob
	- VIETTE'S LITTLE SUZY ('Blovi')	CBod EBlo EHyd EPfP LBar LRHS LSou WFar
	gloriosa	see *R. hirta*
§	***hirta***	NRHS SRms SIvy
	- AUTUMN COLORS (mixed)	CWnw EBee EHyd ELan EPfP LCro LRHS NRHS
	- (Big Smileyz Series) 'Big Kiss Smileyz' **new**	LBar
	- - 'Big Love Smileyz' **new**	LBar
	- - 'Big Smile Smileyz' **new**	LBar
	- 'Cappuccino'	EBee EHyd ELan EPfP LRHS NRHS
	- CHEROKEE SUNSET (mixed) (d)	CSpe
	- 'Cherry Brandy'	CSpe LRHS MNHC NLar SPhx
	- CHIM CHIMINEE (mixed)	SCoo
	- 'Goldilocks'	SVic
	- 'Indian Summer' 🏆H3	CRos EBee EHyd EPfP LRHS MNHC NRHS SPhx
	- 'Irish Eyes'	SPhx SVic
	- 'Marmalade'	EPfP SPhx SVic
	- 'Prairie Sun'	CRos EBee EHyd EPfP LRHS MBros MDon NGrs NRHS SPhx WHil WHlf
	- SAHARA (mixed) **new**	CWnw
	- (Smileyz Series) 'Garden Smileyz'	see *R. hirta* (Smileyz Series) 'Glowing Smileyz'
	- - 'Giggling Smileyz' PBR **new**	LBar

DESCRIPTIVE TERM
See p.38.

ABBREVIATIONS
To save space a dash indicates that the previous heading is repeated. If written out in full the name would be Rudbeckia hirta *'Sonora'.*

SYMBOLS TO THE LEFT OF THE NAME
Provides information about the name of the plant. See p.36 for the key.

TRADE DESIGNATION
See p.40.

SYMBOLS TO THE RIGHT OF THE NAME
Tells you more about the plant itself, e.g. (d) *indicates that the plant is double-flowered,* (F) = *fruit. See p.36 for the key.*

NEW
Plant new to this edition.

CROSS-REFERENCES
Directs you to the correct name of the plant and the nursery codes. See p.55.

🏆H6
This plant has received the RHS Award of Garden Merit. See p.37.

PBR
Plant Breeders' Rights. See p.39.

WIDELY AVAILABLE
Indicates that more than 30 Plant Finder nurseries supply the plant, and it may be available locally. See p.55.

NURSERY CODE
A unique code identifying each nursery. Turn to p.888 for details of the nurseries.

II
PLANTS

THE PLANT DIRECTORY

A

Abelia (*Caprifoliaceae*)

	chinensis misapplied	see *A.* × *grandiflora* 'Lake Maggiore'
§	***chinensis*** R. Br.	CBcs CExl CKel CMCN CMac EBee EHed ELan EPfP LRHS MGil MMuc SEND SPer SRms WLov
	'Edward Goucher' 🏆H5	Widely available
	engleriana	CExl CRos EPfP LRHS MAsh MBlu MGil NLar SBrt WLov
	floribunda	see *Vesalea floribunda*
§	× ***grandiflora***	see *A.* × *grandiflora* 'Lake Maggiore'
	- 'Aurea'	see *A.* × *grandiflora* 'Gold Spot'
	- 'Brockhill Allgold'	CKel EMil EPfP LRHS SPoG
	- common clone	see *A.* × *grandiflora* 'Lake Maggiore'
	- 'Compacta'	WFar
	- CONFETTI ('Conti'PBR) (v)	CBcs CDoC CEme CKel CMac CRos CSBt EHyd ELan EPfP ERom GMcL LPar LRHS LSRN MGos MPri MRav NLar SEle SGbt SGol SGsty SPer SPoG SWvt
	- dwarf	MSwo
§	- 'Francis Mason' (v)	Widely available
	- GOLD JEWEL ('Abhfgold') **new**	LSou MPri SGBe
§	- 'Gold Spot' (v)	CBod CCoa CDoC EPfP NLar SPer
	- 'Gold Strike'	see *A.* × *grandiflora* 'Gold Spot'
	- 'Goldsport'	see *A.* × *grandiflora* 'Gold Spot'
	- 'Hopleys'PBR (v) 🏆H4	CBcs CMac CRos CSBt CTri EHed EHyd ELan EPfP LRHS LSou MAsh MGos NLar SCoo SEND SGBe SGol SPoG SRms SWvt WHlf WHtc WLov
	- 'Kaleidoscope'PBR (v)	Widely available
	- LADY LIBERTY ('Keylib')	SGBe
§	- 'Lake Maggiore' 🏆H5	Widely available
	- LUCKY LOTS ('Wevo2') (v)	CKel EBee ERom NLar SEdd SGol WHtc
	- MAGIC DAYDREAM ('Opstal103')	CBod LCro LOPS MGos NEoE SCoo
	- MYSTIC DAYDREAM ('Opstal40')	EBee
	- 'Panache' (v)	WCot
	- 'Prostrate White'	GKev LPar NLar SPoG
	- 'Radiance' (v)	EBee MMrt NEoE SEdd SGBe WHtc WLov
	- 'Semperflorens'	CKel CWnw LRHS WFar WHtc
	- 'Sherwoodii'	EBee EHeP MGil MGos MRav
	- 'Sparkling Silver' (v)	CKel CWnw ELan EMil LRHS LSRN SEND SEdd SGBe SGsty
	- SUNNY CHARMS ('Mindu01'PBR)	CBcs
	- 'Sunrise' (v)	NLar
	- SUNSHINE DAYDREAM ('Abelops'PBR) (v)	CBod CEnd EBee LCro LOPS LSou MGos MMrt NLar SGBe SGbt SGol SPad SRms
	- 'Tanya'	WAvo
	- 'Variegata'	see *A.* × *grandiflora* 'Francis Mason'
§	'Lynn'PBR	MGos SPoG XSte
	mosanensis	CBcs CBod CMCN CRos EHyd ELan EPfP LRHS MBlu MGil NLar NQui SCoo SRHi WCot WGob WHlf WLov
	- BRIDAL BOUQUET ('Monia')	EHed SChF
	- 'Korean Spring' 🏆H6 **new**	WHlf
	parvifolia	CBcs CBod CEme CExl CKel CMCN CMac CSBt CTri EBee EHyd EPfP LRHS LSto MGil NLar SNig SPer SPoG SWvt WLov
	- 'Bumblebee'	CRos LCro MAsh MGos NLar SPoG SRms XSte
	PASTEL CHARM ('Minduo2')	LRHS
	PETITE GARDEN ('Minedward'PBR)	CDoC CEme CKel GKev
	PINKY BELLS	see *A.* 'Lynn'
	rupestris misapplied	see *A.* × *grandiflora*
	rupestris Lindl.	see *A. chinensis* R. Br.
	triflora	see *Zabelia triflora*
	umbellata	see *Zabelia umbellata*

Abeliophyllum (*Oleaceae*)

distichum	CBcs CEnd CRos CSde EBee EHed EHyd ELan ELon EPfP IDee LPar LRHS MAsh MBlu MSwo NRHS SGsty SPer SWvt WCFE WCot WFar WHlf
- Roseum Group	CBcs CBod CExl CRos EHyd ELan ELon EPfP EShb LCro LOPS LRHS MAsh MGil MHtn MMuc MRav NQui SPer SPoG WCot WHlf WLov

Abelmoschus (*Malvaceae*)

esculentus	SVic

Abies ✿ (*Pinaceae*)

alba	CAco CPer EPfP MMuc NWea
- 'Barabits' Star'	CAco
- 'Bystricka'	NLar
- 'Chmel W.B.'	CKen
- 'Fastigata'	CAco
- 'Green Spiral'	CAco
- 'Minaret' **new**	NLar
- 'Mirek' **new**	NLar
- 'Münsterland'	CKen
- 'Nana' misapplied	see *Picea glauca* 'Nana'
- 'Pendula'	CAco CKen
- 'Pyramidalis'	CAco
- 'Scarabantia'	CAco
- 'Schwarzwald'	CKen
amabilis	CAco LRHS NWea
- 'Spreading Star'	CAco SLim
arizonica	see *A. lasiocarpa* var. *arizonica*
× ***arnoldiana***	CAco
balsamea	CAco MMuc NWea
- 'Bruce's Variegated' (v)	NLar
- 'Cook's Blue'	CKen
- 'Eugene Gold'	NLar
- Hudsonia Group	CKen GArf LRHS
- - 'Hudsonia' 🏆H7	EPot NBwr

	- - 'Nana'	CAco CKen ELan LPar LRHS MGil NLar
	- 'Jamie'	CKen
	- 'Kiwi'	NLar
	- 'Le Feber'	CKen
	- var. ***phanerolepis*** 'Bear Swamp'	CKen NHol NLar
	- 'Piccolo'	CAco CKen LRHS LSta MGil NLar
	- 'Prostrata'	LSta
	- 'Renswoude'	CKen
	- 'Tyler Blue'	CKen
	- 'Verkade's Prostrate'	CKen NLar
	borisii-regis	CAco
*	- 'Pendula'	CAco CKen
	- 'Spring Delight'	CAco NLar
	brachyphylla dwarf	see *A. homolepis* 'Prostrata'
	bracteata	CAco
	cephalonica	CAco CMCN LRHS
	- 'Barabits' Gold'	CAco
	- 'Greg's Broom'	CKen NLar
§	- 'Meyer's Dwarf'	CAco SLim
	- 'Nana'	see *A. cephalonica* 'Meyer's Dwarf'
	cephalonica* × *nordmanniana	MHtn
	chensiensis	CAco LRHS
	cilicica	CAco
	- 'Spring Grove'	CKen
	concolor	CAco CBcs CBod IPap LMaj LPar MMuc NWea SEND SSha
	- 'Archer's Dwarf'	CAco CKen MAsh NLar SLim
	- 'Bedoń'	CAco
	- 'Birthday Broom'	CKen
	- 'Blue Cloak'	CKen
	- 'Blue Sapphire'	CKen
	- 'Clarence' **new**	NLar
§	- 'Compacta' ♀H7	CAco CKen MGos NHol NLar SLim WLea
	- 'Fagerhult'	CKen
	- 'Gable's Weeping'	CKen
	- 'Glauca'	see *A. concolor* (Violacea Group) 'Violacea'
	- 'Glauca Compacta'	see *A. concolor* 'Compacta'
	- 'Globosa'	CAco
	- 'Hillier Broom'	see *A. concolor* 'Hillier's Dwarf'
§	- 'Hillier's Dwarf'	CKen
	- 'Husky Pup'	CKen
	- 'La Veta'	CKen
	- Lowiana Group	CAco
	- - 'Creamy'	CKen NLar
	- 'Masonic Broom'	CKen
	- 'Mike Stearn'	CKen
	- 'Mora'	CKen
	- 'Piggelmee'	CKen MAsh
	- 'Pygmy'	CKen
	- 'Scooter'	CKen NLar
	- 'Sherwood's Blue'	CAco
	- Violacea Group	CKen LRHS
§	- - 'Violacea' ♀H7	CAco
	- - 'Violacea Prostrate' ♀H7	CAco NHol NLar
	- 'Wattez Prostrate'	SLim
	- 'Wattezii'	CKen
	- 'Wintergold'	CAco CKen MBlu NHol NLar SLim
	delavayi	CMCN EPfP LEdu WPGP
	- var. ***delavayi***	CExl
	- - Fabri Group	see *A. fabri*
	- 'Gold Splash'	LRHS
	- 'Green Giant' **new**	NLar
	- 'Major Neishe'	CKen
	- 'Midnight Blue'	CAco NLar
	- 'Nana Headfort'	see *A. fargesii* 'Headfort'
	durangensis var. ***coahuilensis***	CAco
§	***fabri***	CAco CKen LRHS
	fanjingshanensis	CAco
	fargesii	CKen
	- var. ***faxoniana***	CAco
§	- 'Headfort'	NLar
	firma	CAco
	forrestii	CAco CKen
	- var. ***ferreana***	CAco
	fraseri	CAco CBcs CPer EWhm LIns MMuc MPri NWea WTSh
	- 'Blue Bonnet'	CAco CKen NLar
	- 'Franklin'	NLar
	- 'Kline's Nest'	SLim
	- 'Palmeri'	NLar
§	- 'Raul's Dwarf'	CKen NLar
	- 'Rawles'	see *A. fraseri* 'Raul's Dwarf'
	grandis	CAco CMCN CMac CPer EPfP IPap MMuc NWea WMou WTSh
	- 'Compacta'	CKen
	- 'Van Dedem's Dwarf'	CKen NLar SLim
	guatemalensis	CAco
	holophylla	CAco
	homolepis	CAco CKen
	- 'F.R. Newman'	SLim
§	- 'Prostrata'	CKen
	- var. ***umbellata***	CAco
	× ***insignis***	CAco
	kawakamii	CAco
	koreana ♀H7	Widely available
	- 'Alpin Star'	CAco CKen MAsh NLar
	- 'Aurea'	see *A. koreana* 'Flava'
	- 'Blaue Zwo'	CKen
	- 'Blauer Eskimo' ♀H7	CAco CKen MAsh NLar SLim
	- 'Blauer Pfiff'	CAco CKen NLar
	- 'Blinsham Gold'	CKen
	- 'Blue Emperor'	CAco MBlu NLar
	- 'Blue Magic'	CAco CKen NLar
	- 'Blue 'n' Silver'	CAco
	- blue-leaved	CDoC
I	- 'Brevifolia'	NLar
	- 'Brilliant'	CAco CKen LRHS SCoo
	- 'Cis' ♀H7	CAco CKen MGil NHol NLar SLim
	- 'Compact Dwarf'	CAco LPar
	- CRYSTAL GLOBE	see *A. koreana* 'Kristallkugel'
	- 'Dark Hill'	CAco NLar
	- 'Discus'	CAco NLar
	- 'Doni-tajuso'	CKen NLar
	- 'Eisregen'	CKen NLar
	- 'Festival'	NHol NLar
§	- 'Flava'	CAco
	- 'Frosty'	CAco NLar SLim
	- 'Gait'	CAco CKen NLar
	- 'Golden Glow'	SLim
	- 'Goldener Traum'	CKen NLar
	- 'Green Carpet'	CAco CKen NLar SLim
	- 'Green 'n' Cream'	CAco LRHS
	- 'Grüne Spinne'	MBlu
	- 'Horstmann'	CKen
	- 'Inge'	NLar
	- 'Inverleith'	CKen
	- 'Kleiner Prinz'	NLar
	- 'Kohout'	CAco CKen
	- 'Kohout's Ice Breaker' PBR ♀H7	CAco CKen LRHS MAsh MGos NLar SAko SLim
§	- 'Kristallkugel'	CKen LRHS MAsh MBlu MGil NLar
	- 'Lippetal'	CKen
	- 'Luminetta'	CAco CKen NHol NLar
	- 'May'	CAco
	- 'Nadelkissen'	CKen NHol
	- 'Nisbet'	CAco LRHS NHol
	- 'Oberon'	CAco CKen MAsh MGil NHol NLar SLim
	- 'Piccolo'	CKen
	- 'Pinocchio'	CAco CKen MGil NHol

	- 'Prostrata'	see *A. koreana* 'Prostrate Beauty'
§	- 'Prostrate Beauty'	CKen
	- 'Ry'	MGil NLar
	- 'Schwedenkönig'	CAco SLim
	- 'Sherwood Compact'	CKen
	- 'Shorty'	CKen NLar
	- 'Silberkugel'	CKen LRHS SLim
	- 'Silberlocke' ♀H7	CAco CCVT MAsh MBlu MGos NLar NOrn SCoo SLim WMat
	- 'Silbermavers'	CAco CKen
	- 'Silberperl'	CKen LRHS NLar SLim
	- 'Silver Show'	CAco MGil NHol NLar SLim WLea
	- 'Super Bush' **new**	CAco
	- 'Threave'	CKen NHol
	- 'Tundra'	CAco NLar SLim
	- 'Verdener Dom'	NLar
	- 'Wellenseind'	CKen NLar
	- 'Winter Goldtip'	SLim
	koreana* × *lasiocarpa	CAco
	lasiocarpa	CAco NWea
	- 'Alpine Beauty'	CKen
§	- var. ***arizonica***	CAco
	- - 'Compacta' Beissn.	CAco
	- - 'Compacta' Hornibr. ♀H7	CAco CCVT CKel CKen LMaj LRHS MAsh MGos NHol NLar SLim SPoG WMat
	- - 'Kenwith Blue'	CAco CKen SLim
	- 'Beano Broom'	CKen NLar
	- 'Chikov'	CKen
	- 'Day Creek'	CKen
	- 'Duflon'	CKen
	- 'Elaine'	CKen
	- 'Glacier'	see *A. lasiocarpa* 'Logan Pass'
	- 'Green Globe'	CAco CKen NLar SLim
	- 'Hurricane Ridge'	CKen
	- 'Joe's Alpine'	CKen
	- 'Kyle's Alpine'	CKen
	- var. ***lasiocarpa***	CAco
§	- 'Logan Pass'	CKen NLar
	- 'Lopalpun'	CKen
	- 'Mikolaš'	CAco NLar
	- 'Mulligan's Dwarf'	CKen
	- 'Prickly Pete'	CKen NLar
	- 'Stevens Blue'	CKen
	- 'Toenisvorst'	CKen
	- 'Utah'	CKen
	magnifica	CAco IPap
	- 'Glauca'	CAco
	- 'Mount Si'	CKen
I	- 'Nana'	CKen
	- var. ***shastensis***	CAco
	- witches' broom	CKen
	marocana	see *A. pinsapo* var. *marocana*
	nebrodensis	CAco CKen
	- 'Sicilian Gold'	NLar
	nephrolepis	CAco
	nobilis	see *A. procera*
	nordmanniana	CAco CBcs CBod CBrac CCVT CKel CMCN CMac CPer CSBt ELan EWhm GMcL IPap LBuc LCro LMaj LPar MMuc MPri NBwr NLar NTrD NWea SGsty SPoG SWeb WHtc WMou WTSh
	- 'Ambrolauri' **new**	CAco
	- 'Barabits' Spreader'	CKen
	- subsp. ***equi-trojani***	CAco
	- - 'Archer'	CKen
	- - 'Franke'	NLar
	- 'Filip's Gold Heart'	NLar
	- 'Hasselt'	see *A. nordmanniana* subsp. *nordmanniana* 'Pévé Hasselt'
	- 'Kilian' **new**	CAco
	- subsp. ***nordmanniana*** 'Arne's Dwarf'	CKen

	- - 'Aurea'	LRHS
	- - 'Barabits' Compact'	CAco NLar
	- - 'Dobřichovice'	CAco NLar
	- - 'Golden Spreader' ♀H7	CAco CKen LRHS MAsh MBlu MGos NLar SCoo SLim
	- - 'Jakobsen'	CKen
	- - 'Midwinter Gold'	CAco NLar
	- - 'Münsterland'	CAco NLar
	- - 'Pendula'	CAco MBlu MGil SMad
§	- - 'Pévé Hasselt'	CKen NLar
	- - 'Saerling'	NLar
	- - 'Silberspitze'	CKen
	- 'Peli'	NLar
	numidica	CAco CKen
	- 'Delicado'	CAco
	- 'Glauca'	CAco CKen NLar
	pindrow	NWea
	- var. ***brevifolia***	CAco
	pinsapo	CAco EPfP LRHS WMou WThu
	- 'Atlas'	CKen
	- 'Aurea' ♀H6	CAco CCVT CKen ELan LMaj NHol NLar SLim
I	- 'Aurea Nana'	CKen
	- 'Fastigiata'	CAco NLar SAko
	- 'Fatima'	CKen
	- 'Glauca' ♀H6	CAco CCVT CKen ELan LMaj LRHS MBlu NLar SEND SLim
	- 'Hamondii'	CKen
I	- 'Horstmann'	CAco CKen NHol NLar SLim
	- 'Kelleriis'	NLar
§	- var. ***marocana***	CAco LRHS
	- 'Marokko'	CKen
	- 'Pendula'	CAco CKen
	- var. ***pinsapo***	CAco
	- 'Quicksilver'	CKen
	- 'San Pedro'	CKen
	- var. ***tazaotana***	CAco
§	***procera***	CAco CBcs CMCN EPfP IPap MGil NWea WTSh
	- 'Bizarro'	CAco NLar
	- 'Blaue Hexe'	CAco CKen SLim
	- 'Delbar Cascade'	CAco CKen
	- Glauca Group	EPfP GKin MBlu NHol
	- - 'Glauca' ♀H7	CAco ELan LMaj SAko SCoo
I	- - 'Glauca Pendula'	CAco
	- - 'Glauca Prostrata' ♀H7	CAco CKen LRHS MAsh SLim
	- 'Hupp's Dwarf'	CAco CKen NLar
	- 'Hupp's Single Snake'	CAco
	- 'Jeddeloh'	CKen
	- 'La Graciosa'	CAco NLar
	- 'Noble's Dwarf'	SLim
	- 'Rat Tail'	CAco NLar
	- 'Rick's Foxtail'	CAco
	- 'Seattle Mount'	CKen
	- 'Sherwoodii'	CKen NLar SLim
	recurvata	CAco
	Rosemoor hybrid	CKen
	sachalinensis	CAco CKen
	sibirica	CAco EPfP
	spectabilis	EPfP IDee
	veitchii	CAco NWea WTSh
	- 'Glauca'	CAco
	- 'Heddergott'	CKen NHol NLar SLim
	- 'Heine'	CKen LRHS
	- 'Kramer'	CAco CKen NLar
I	- 'Pendula'	CAco CKen
	- 'Rumburk'	CKen MAsh NLar SLim
	- 'Syców'	CKen
	vejarii	CAco
	× ***vilmorinii***	CAco

Abromeitiella see *Deuterocobnia*

Abutilon (*Malvaceae*)

'Apfelsine'	SPad
'Aphrodite'	EHed SPad WCot
'Ashford Red'	CBcs CCCN CHll CKel ELan LRHS WKif
Bella Series	CDoC
'Buttercup'	SPad
'Canary Bird' 🏆H2	CBcs CCCN CHll CSde WKif
'Cannington Carol' (v) 🏆H2	CCCN CEme CHll LSRN SEND
'Cannington Peter' (v) 🏆H2	CCCN
'Cloth of Gold'	CMac
'Color Sensation'	SPad
'Cynthia Pike' (v)	CRos EHyd LRHS NGrs NRHS
dark yellow-flowered **new**	CHll
'Estella's Little Bird' **new**	WPGP
'Fairy Tales'	SPad
'Feuerwerk'	SPad
'Flamenco'	CCCN CWGN
'Fool's Gold'	EHed SPad
'Gerdemann's Red' **new**	WPGP
'Giant Orange'	SPad
'Golden Terracotta'	SPad
'Himbeere'	SPad
'Hinton Seedling'	CCCN CHll CRHN LSRN SPad
indicum	EBtc
'Isabella'	SPad
'Jacqueline Morris'	LRHS
'John Thompson'	CBcs CCCN CKel CWGN
'Kentish Belle' 🏆H3	Widely available
'Kleine Schönheit'	SPad
'Lachskönigin'	SPad
'Leila Jackson'	EBee EHed EShb SPad
'Lilac Jewel'	SPad
'Lilac Wonder'	SPad
'Lilli'	SPad
'Lillian'	SPad
'Lisa Roja'	SVen
'Louis Marignac'	CHll
'Marion' 🏆H2	CCCN CRHN CRos EHyd LRHS LSRN NGrs NRHS SPlb WKif
'Master Michael'	CMac
megapotamicum 🏆H3	Widely available
- 'Big Bell'	CCCN ECre WFar WGob
- 'Ines'	CHll ELon SPad WPGP
- 'Pink Charm'	CCCN EHed ELon EShb SPad
- 'Variegatum' (v) 🏆H3	CBcs CBod CCCN CDoC CKel CMac ELon EPfP LRHS MGil SEle SMad SPer SPoG SWvt WGob
- 'Wisley Red'	CCCN CKel CRHN EHed ELon LRHS WGob WHlf
× ***milleri*** hort. 🏆H3	CCCN CMac CRHN EHed ELon SPad WCot WGob
- 'Variegatum' (v)	CCCN CKel CMac EBee LRHS WCot
- 'Ventnor Gold'	SVen
'Moonlight Shadow'	SPad
'Nabob' 🏆H2	CBcs CCCN CDow CExl CHll CKel CRHN CSde EBee ELan EPfP EShb NGrs SEND SIvy SPad WCot WFar
'Orange Hot Lava'	CBcs CExl EBee ECre WPGP
'Paddy's Nephew'	EBee WFar
'Patrick Synge'	CBcs CCCN CDow CHll EBee SChF SDix SPhx WPGP
pictum 'Thompsonii' (v) 🏆H2	CCCN CHll MGil SEND SPad
'Pink Lady'	CCCN
'Red Bells'	SVen
'Red Tiger'	CCCN LRHS SPad WKif XSte
RED TRUMPET ('Oostredtrump'PBR)	WCot
'Rose Glow'	WCot
'Rosela'	SPad
'Roter Vulkan'	SPad
'Russels Dwarf'	CCCN
'Schneeflocke'	SPad
'Silver Belle'	CCCN
'Simcox White'	CCCN
'Sonnenkind'	SPad
'Souvenir de Bonn' (v) 🏆H2	CCCN CHll WCot
'Sunny'	SPad
× ***suntense***	see *Corynabutilon* × *suntense*
'Tango'	CCCN CRos CWGN ELan LRHS SMad SPad WCot WGob
'Thomasii' **new**	CCCN
'Tinkerbell' **new**	CHll
'Versicolor'	CCCN SPad
'Victorian Lady' (d)	CCCN CHll SPad
'Victory'	CCCN CWGN
vitifolium	see *Corynabutilon vitifolium*
'Waltz'	CCCN CWGN EBee ELan EShb SIvy SPad WBor WCot WGob

Acacia (*Fabaceae*)

acinacea	SPlb
adunca	SPlb
angustissima	SPlb
axillaris	SPlb
baileyana 🏆H3	CBcs CBod CCCN CDoC CEme CMac CSBt EAri EDir ELan EPfP LSRN MGos SCoo SEdd SPlb SSha SWvt WFar
- var. ***aurea***	SPlb
- 'Purpurea' 🏆H3	Widely available
boormanii	CDoC CTsd EDir EGrI SEdd SPlb WCot WPGP
cognata 'Limelight'PBR	XSte
cultriformis	CTsd ESwi SPtp
dealbata 🏆H3	Widely available
- 'Gaulois Astier'	CDoC CKel CSBt EPfP IDee LRHS LSRN MAsh MGos NRHS SPoG SWeb SWvt WCot
'Exeter Hybrid'	CSBt
farnesiana	WJur
glaucoptera	SPlb
gregorii	SPlb
jibberdingensis	SPlb
julibrissin	see *Albizia julibrissin*
karroo	see *Vachellia karroo*
longifolia	CBcs CDTJ CDoC CMac ELan WLov XSte
macradenia	SPlb
mearnsii	EBee EDir SEdd
melanoxylon	CBcs CBod CDTJ CMCN SGBe SPlb SSha XSte
nanodealbata	EHed SPad
obliquinervia	XSte
pataczekii	CDTJ CSBt WPGP
pendula	SPlb
podalyriifolia	CDTJ SPlb
pravissima 🏆H3	CBcs CBod CChe CDoC CEme CExl CMac CTsd EAri EHed ELan EPfP GBin IDee LRHS LSRN SArc SEdd SGBe SPlb SSha SWvt
retinodes 🏆H2	CBcs CCCN CCht CDTJ CTsd EAri IDee SEND SEdd SPad SWvt XSte
- 'Lisette'	IDee WCot XSte
riceana	CTsd SVen
rubida	SPlb
sentis	see *A. victoriae*
spectabilis	SPlb
suaveolens	SPlb
truncata	SPlb

verticillata	CBcs CBod CDTJ CDoC ELan EPfP
- riverine form	CCCN EPfP LRHS SEND SEle
§ ***victoriae***	SPlb

Acaena (*Rosaceae*)

adscendens misapplied	see *A. affinis*, *A. saccaticupula* 'Blue Haze'
adscendens ambig. 'Glauca'	NBir
§ ***affinis***	EBee ECha
anserinifolia misapplied	see *A. novae-zelandiae*
buchananii	EBee GAbr GBin GKev NLar SRms XLum
caerulea hort.	see *A. caesiiglauca*
§ ***caesiiglauca***	CTri EPPr GAbr GMaP GQue
inermis	NWad SPlb
- 'Purpurea'	EBee ECha ELan EShb GAbr GArf GKev GMaP GQue MACG MMuc NDov NHol NHpl NLar NWad SLee SPlb WCav
magellanica	GKev XLum
microphylla	EBee GArf GQue MBel NLar SLee SPlb SRms XLum
- Copper Carpet	see *A. microphylla* 'Kupferteppich'
- 'Dichte Matte'	NLar
- 'Glauca'	see *A. caesiiglauca*
- 'Grüner Zwerg'	NLar
§ - 'Kupferteppich'	CKel ECtt ELan EPPr GAbr GKev GLog GMaP MRav NBir NBro NLar SEdd SLee SRms
minor var. ***antarctica***	GBin GQue
myriophylla	EBee
§ ***novae-zelandiae***	CTri EBee GAbr GKev SDix
'Pewter'	see *A. saccaticupula* 'Blue Haze'
'Purple Carpet'	see *A. microphylla* 'Kupferteppich'
'Purple Haze'	CSpe
saccaticupula	EBee GKev LShi MMuc
§ - 'Blue Haze'	CRos EBee ECha EHyd LRHS LShi MACG MRav NBir NFav NLar NRHS SPlb SRms
tesca	GBin GQue

Acalypha (*Euphorbiaceae*)

§ ***herzogiana***	CCCN
pendula misapplied	see *A. herzogiana*

Acanthocalyx see *Morina*

Acantholimon (*Plumbaginaceae*)

androsaceum	see *A. ulicinum*
§ ***ulicinum***	WAbe

Acanthopanax see *Eleutherococcus*

ricinifolius	see *Kalopanax septemlobus*

Acanthophyllum (*Caryophyllaceae*)

§ ***cerastioides***	CAby CRos CTri EBou ECtt EDAr EHyd EPfP EWoo GAbr ITim LShi MHol NBwr NFav NGdn NHpl NLar NRHS NSla SLee SPlb SRms SRot SWvt WAbe WFar WIce XLum
- 'Pixie Splash'	LRHS
- Pretty Maid ('Yatgyp') **new**	CBod LBar MACG WHlf
- 'Rosy Stripe'	GKev WAbe

Acanthus ✿ (*Acanthaceae*)

balcanicus misapplied	see *A. hungaricus*
caroli-alexandri	see *A. spinosus* L.
'Colin's Folly' **new**	ECha
dioscoridis	CDor LRHS SMHy
- var. ***perringii***	CDor EBee ECha MNrw NLar WCot WFar XLum
eminens	WCot XLum
hirsutus	CDor EPri WCot WHil
- JCA 106.700	WHil
- subsp. ***syriacus***	ECha LShi
'Hollande du Nort'	CRos EBee LRHS NRHS XLum
§ ***hungaricus***	CBod CDoC CDor CMac CRos EBee ELan EMor GQue ILea LCro LRHS NLar SDix SPer WCot WFar
- MESE 561	EPPr
- 'White Lips'	EBee LBar MNrw MThu NLar WCot WFar WHil WHlf XLum
longifolius Host	see *A. hungaricus*
mollis	Widely available
- 'Fielding Gold'	see *A. mollis* 'Hollard's Gold'
- free-flowering	ESwi MAvo SChr XLum
§ - 'Hollard's Gold'	Widely available
- 'Jefalba'	see *A. mollis* (Latifolius Group) 'Rue Ledan'
- Latifolius Group	CDor MRav SRms XLum
§ - - 'Rue Ledan' ♀H6	CBWd EBee ECtt EPPr EWTr LBar LCro LRHS LSto MAvo MNrw NGdn NLar NSti SMHy SPhx WCAu WCot WHil XLum
- 'Niger'	EBee
- 'Tasmanian Angel' (v)	CAbb CDor CGBo CWGN ECtt LBar LRHS NBPC NFav NHpl SPoG SRHi WCot WFar
'Morning's Candle'	CBod EBee ECha ECtt ELan LBar MAsh MNrw NGdn NLar WFar WHlf XLum
§ ***polystachius***	WHil XLum
pubescens	see *A. polystachius*
'Ruth's Gold' **new**	WFar
sennii	CWnw EBee ECha ESwi LRHS SMad SPeP SPhx WAvo WCot WHil WSHC XLum
'Snow Storm' **new**	MThu
spinosus misapplied	see *A. spinosus* Spinosissimus Group
§ ***spinosus*** L.	Widely available
- Ferguson's form	EBee WCot
- 'Lady Moore' (v)	CDor NBPC NLar
- 'Royal Haughty'	XLum
§ - Spinosissimus Group	CBWd CBct CDor EBee GBin LEdu MGos MRav NChi NLar WCot WFar WHil XLum
'Summer Beauty'	EBee ECtt EWes LRHS NLar WCot WFar WHil WHlf XLum
'Whitewater' (v)	CBcs CBct CDor CGBo CWGN EBee ECtt ELan EPfP GKin LBar LCro NLar NSti SCoo SPad SPeP SPer SPoG SRHi SRms WBor WCot WHil XLum XSte

Acca (*Myrtaceae*)

sellowiana (F)	Widely available
- 'Apollo' (F)	XVPe
- 'Coolidge' (F)	XSen XVPe
- 'Gemini' (F)	CBcs SGol XVPe
- 'Mammoth' (F)	CBcs CCCN XVPe
- 'Marian' (F)	XVPe
- 'Triumph' (F)	CBcs CCCN IDee LPar LShi XVPe
- 'Variegata' (F/v)	CCCN EBee

Acer ✿ (*Sapindaceae*)

acuminatum	CMCN
albopurpurascens NMWJ 14455	WCru
amoenum	WJur
- B&SWJ 10916	WCru
- B&SWJ 10977	WCru
- 'Firecracker'	see *A. palmatum* 'Firecracker'
'Ample Surprise'PBR	LIns MBlu

	argutum	WJur
	'Asian Queen'	CJun
	buergerianum	CAco CMen EBee IPap LPar MMuc NLar SBrt SGsty WJur WPGP
	- B&SWJ 12676 from South Korea	WCru
	- var. ***formosanum*** CWJ 12477	WCru
	- 'Integrifolium'	see *A. buergerianum* 'Subintegrum'
	- 'Naruto'	CMCN MPkF
§	- 'Subintegrum'	CMCN
	campbellii	GKev MBlu
	- subsp. ***campbellii***	WPGP
	- - GWJ 9360	WCru
	- - PAB 13.071	LEdu
	- 'Exuberance'	CJun
	campestre 🏆^{H6}	Widely available
	- 'Anny's Globe'	MBlu
	- 'Carnival' (v) 🏆^{H6}	CBod CEnd ELan MAsh MBlu MTrO NOra NOrn NPoe SPer SPoG SWvt
	- 'Elegant'	see *A. campestre* 'Huibers Elegant'
	- 'Elsrijk'	CAco CCVT CLnd CPer IPap LMaj LPar MNic NOrn NRog SCoo SGsty
	- 'Evelyn'	see *A. campestre* 'Queen Elizabeth'
	- 'Evenley Red'	EBee EPfP ESwi MBlu SMad WHtc WPGP
	- 'Green Column'	CAco LRHS
§	- 'Huibers Elegant'	CAco EHeP LMaj
	- 'Nanum'	CAco MBlu SGsty
	- 'Pendulum'	CEnd
	- 'Postelense'	ELan MBlu
	- 'Pulverulentum' (v)	EBee SMad
§	- 'Queen Elizabeth'	CAco MGos SGol
	- 'Red Shine'	CAco CCVT EBar LMaj MMuc SGol
	- 'Royal Ruby'	MGos
	- 'Ruby Glow' 🏆^{H6}	CEnd
	- 'Streetwise' **new**	EHeP
	- 'William Caldwell'	CAco CEnd LRHS MBlu
	capillipes	CAco CBcs CMCN EBee ELan LMaj LPar MMuc MTrO NBwr NOrn NRog SGbt SPlb WJur WMat WTSh
	- 'Antoine'	CJun LRHS MBlu
	- 'Candy Stripe'	see *A.* × *conspicuum* 'Candy Stripe'
	- 'Honey Dew'	SSta
	aff. ***capillipes***	NWea
	cappadocicum	CAco CCVT CMCN LPar WHtc WJur
	- 'Aureum' 🏆^{H6}	CAco CBcs CLnd CMCN EBee ELan EPfP GKin IArd LMaj LPar MAsh MBlu MRav MTrO NLar NOra NOrn NWea SGbt SGol SPer SWvt WFar WMat WMou WTSh
	- var. ***mono***	see *A. pictum*
	- 'Rubrum' 🏆^{H6}	CAco CArg CBcs CLnd CMCN EBee ELan EPfP GKin LMaj LPar MBlu MRav MTrO NOra NOrn SGol SPer WFar WMat
	- subsp. ***sinicum***	SPtp
	cappadocicum × (***conspicuum*** 'Phoenix')	MTrO
	carpinifolium	CAco CMCN EBee EPfP EWTr LRHS MBlu MMuc NLar WJur WPGP
	- B&SWJ 10955	WCru
	- B&SWJ 11124	WCru
§	***caudatifolium***	WPGP
	- CWJ 12403	WCru
	- NMWJ 14459	WCru
§	***caudatum*** GWJ 9279	WCru
	- GWJ 9317	WCru
	- HWJK 2240	WCru
	- HWJK 2338	WCru
	- subsp. ***ukurunduense***	MPkF
	- - B&SWJ 12602	WCru
	cinnamomifolium	see *A. coriaceifolium*
	circinatum	CAco CBcs CCVT CJun CMCN EGrI MBlu MMuc NLar SEND SPlb
	- B&SWJ 9565	WCru
	- 'Burgundy Jewel'	CJun LCro LRHS MPkF NLar
	- 'Monroe'	CJun CMCN
	- 'Pacific Fire'	CJun NLar
	- 'Whitney Broom'	NLar
	cissifolium	CMCN EPfP NLar
	- B&SWJ 10801	WCru
§	× ***conspicuum*** 'Candy Stripe'	CJun
	- 'Elephant's Ear'	CJun MBlu NLar
	- 'Phoenix'	CEnd CJun CMCN EBee EPfP GKin LRHS MBlu NLar NOra SPoG WPGP
	- 'Silver Ghost'	MPkF SWvt
§	- 'Silver Vein'	CAco CEnd CJun CMCN EPfP MTrO NLar SGol SSta SWvt WHtc
§	***coriaceifolium***	CMCN
	crataegifolium	CMCN SSta
	- B&SWJ 11036	WCru
	- 'Ittai-san-nishiki'	SSta
	- 'Meuri-no-ōfu' (v)	SSta
	- 'Veitchii' (v)	CMCN EBee EPfP LRHS MBlu SSta
	creticum misapplied	see *A. sempervirens*
	dasycarpum	see *A. saccharinum*
	davidii	CAco CBcs CExl CPer EGrI EHeP EHed IPap ITim LCro LMaj LOPS LPar MBlu MGos MMuc MRav NBwr NOrn NRog SGol SGsty SOrN SSta WHtc WLea WOut XSte
§	- 'Canton'	CJun SSta
	- 'Cantonspark'	see *A. davidii* 'Canton'
	- 'Cascade'	MBlu
	- 'George Forrest' 🏆^{H5}	CBcs CExl CMCN CMac EBee ELan EPfP IArd LRHS MGos MMuc NLar NOra NOrn SGbt SPoG SSta SWvt WHtc WMat
	- 'Hagelunie'	SSta
	- 'Hansu-suru' (v)	SSta
	- 'Karmen'	CJun EPfP SSta
	- 'Madeline Spitta'	CAco
	- 'Purple Bark'	CExl CJun SSta
	- 'Rosalie'	CJun EPfP MAsh MBlu SSta
	- 'Sekka'	SSta
	- 'Silver Vein'	see *A.* × *conspicuum* 'Silver Vein'
	- VIPER ('Mindavi')	CAco CKel CWnw EBee EPfP IArd LMaj LRHS MAsh MNic NOra NOrn SGsty SPer SPoG SRHi WLea WMat
	diabolicum	CMCN
	duplicatoserratum NMWJ 14599	WCru
	elegantulum	CExl CJun GBin WPGP
	erythranthum FMWJ 13157	WCru
	fabri WWJ 11614	WCru
	flabellatum	CJun
	- var. ***yunnanense***	CMCN MMuc SPtp
	forrestii	CMCN MMuc SPtp WPGP
	- BWJ 7515	WCru
	- 'Alice'	CEnd CJun SSta
	- 'Inoense'	SSta
	- 'Sirene'	SSta
	- 'Sparkling'	CJun
	× ***freemanii***	CMCN CPer LMaj LPar
	- 'Armstrong'	CAco EHeP LSRN
	- AUTUMN BLAZE ('Jeffersred') 🏆^{H6}	CAco CBTr CBcs CCVT CDoC CLnd CMCN EBee EHeP EPfP IArd IPap LMaj LPar LRHS MBlu MGos

		MMuc MTrO NBwr NOra NOrn SCob SCoo SGsty SPer SPoG WMat WMou
	- CELEBRATION ('Celzam')	CArg CCVT EBee EHeP IPap LMaj MGos
	- 'Indian Summer'	see *A.* × *freemanii* 'Morgan'
§	- 'Morgan'	LRHS MGos WHtc
	ginnala	see *A. tataricum* subsp. *ginnala*
	glabrum B&SWJ 14119	WCru
	globosum	see *A. platanoides* 'Globosum'
	grandidentatum	see *A. saccharum* subsp. *grandidentatum*
	griseum ♀H5	Widely available
	grosseri	CMCN CTri
	- var. ***hersii***	CBcs CDoC EBee EGrI ELan EPfP LSRN MMuc NOra NOrn NRog NWea SSta SWvt WHtc WMat
	- 'Leiden'	EPfP LRHS
	heldreichii	CMCN
	henryi	NLar
	heptaphlebium B&SWJ 11713	WCru
	- FMWJ 13369	WCru
	japonicum	CMCN SEWo SavN
	- B&SWJ 12847	WCru
	- CWJ 12840	WCru
§	- 'Aconitifolium' ♀H6	Widely available
	- 'Ao-jutan'	CJun
	- 'Attaryi'	CMen
	- 'Aureum'	see *A. shirasawanum* 'Aureum'
	- 'Emmit's Pumpkins'	CJun
	- 'Ezo-no-momiji'	see *A. shirasawanum* 'Ezo-no-momiji'
	- 'Filicifolium'	see *A. japonicum* 'Aconitifolium'
	- 'Green Cascade' ♀H6	CEnd CJun CMCN CMac CMen MGos MPkF NBPC NLar SJap
	- 'King's Copse'	CJun
	- 'Laciniatum'	see *A. japonicum* 'Aconitifolium'
	- f. ***microphyllum***	see *A. shirasawanum* 'Microphyllum'
	- 'Ogurayama'	see *A. shirasawanum* 'Ogurayama'
	- 'Ō-taki'	CJun
	- 'Ruby'	MPkF NLar WLea
	- 'Vitifolium' ♀H6	CAco CDoC CEnd CJun CMCN CMac EGrI ELan EPfP LMaj LPar LRHS MBlu MGos MPkF NLar SMil SPer SPoG SSta WFar WLea WLov WTSh
	kawakamii	see *A. caudatifolium*
	laevigatum	IArd
	- FMWJ 13378	WCru
	- FMWJ 13439	WCru
§	- var. ***reticulatum*** B&SWJ 11698	WCru
	laurinum FMWJ 13412	WCru
	laxiflorum	SSta
§	***longipes***	SPtp
	macrophyllum	CAco CBcs CMCN EPfP MBlu MMuc WJur
	- B&SWJ 13183	WCru
	mandshuricum	LRHS
§	***maximowiczianum***	CBcs MPkF WJur
	maximowiczii	MPkF
	micranthum ♀H6	EPfP LRHS MBlu WJur WPGP
	- CWJ 12843	WCru
	mono	see *A. pictum*
	monspessulanum	CAco CMCN LEdu SEND WJur WLea XSen
	morifolium B&SWJ 11473	WCru
	morrisonense Hayata	see *A. caudatifolium*
	negundo	CAco CMCN EBar GDam LPar NRog NWea SWvt
	- B&SWJ 14060	WCru

	- 'Auratum'	CMCN
	- 'Aureomarginatum' (v)	CAco CCVT LPar
§	- 'Elegans' (v)	CEnd CMCN SCoo
	- 'Elegantissimum'	see *A. negundo* 'Elegans'
	- 'Flamingo' (v)	CAco CCVT CEnd CMCN CMac EBar EDir ELan IPap LPar MAsh MDon NLar NOra NWea SCob SGol SGsty SPer SPoG SWvt WHtc WMat
	- 'Kelly's Gold'	CAco CBcs CCVT CEnd EDir ELan MDon MTrO NLar NWea SGol SPoG WMat
	- 'Sensation'	NLar
	- 'Variegatum' (v)	CAco LPar SCob
	- var. ***violaceum*** ♀H6	CEnd ELan EPfP SVen
	nikoense misapplied	see *A. maximowiczianum*
	nipponicum	SPtp WJur
	'Norwegian Sunset'	CBod CCVT
	oliverianum	MBlu
	- subsp. ***formosanum*** NMWJ 14460	WCru
	- - NMWJ 14514	WCru
	- - NMWJ 14521	WCru
	opalus	CAco CMCN LMaj SEND
	orientale misapplied	see *A. sempervirens*
	ORIENTALIA ('Minorient')	CAco EHed MGos MMrt
	orizabense	EBee
	PACIFIC SUNSET ('Warrenred')	CAco LMaj NLar SEWo
	palmatum	Widely available
	- (D)	CAco CBcs CCVT CEnd CJun CMac CTri LCro LMaj LOPS LRHS LSRN MAsh MGos MRav NHol NLar NRHS SCob SCoo SGol SSta SWvt WCFE WFar WLea WMat
	- 'Akane' (P)	CMen EBee LRHS MPkF NBPC NLar WFar
§	- 'Aka-shigitatsu-sawa' (M)	CAco CJun CMCN CMac CMen LRHS MGos MPkF NLar WFar
	- 'Akegarasu' (M)	CJun CMCN CMen NLar
	- 'Alpenweiss' (P)	CJun MPkF
	- 'Alpine Surprise'	SAko
	- 'Amagi-shigure' (M)	CJun LCro LOPS MPkF NLar
	- 'Amber Ghost' (M)	CJun MPkF
	- 'Anne Irene'PBR (P)	LRHS MPkF NLar
	- 'Aoba-jo' (Dw)	CJun CMen MPkF NBPC SMil WLea
	- 'Ao-kanzashi' (P/v)	MPkF
	- 'Ao-shidare' (D)	CJun
	- 'Aoshime-no-uchi'	see *A. palmatum* 'Shinobuga-oka'
	- 'Aoyagi' (P)	CAco CEnd CJun CMCN CMen EMac GKin LRHS MGos MPkF NBPC NLar NRHS SCoo SMil WFar WLea
	- 'Aoyagi-gawa'	CJun
§	- 'Arakawa' (P)	CAco CEnd CMCN CMen ESMi MGos MPkF NBPC NLar
	- 'Arakawa-ukon'	CJun
	- 'Aratama' (Dw)	CJun CMCN CMen EMac MPkF
	- 'Ariadne' (M/v) ♀H6	CEnd CJun EGrI MGos MPkF NBPC NLar SCoo SMil SPoG WLea
	- 'Ariake-nomura' (A)	CMen MPkF
	- 'Asahi-zuru' (P/v)	CAco CJun CMCN CMen LRHS MGos NBPC NLar SMil SPer WMat
	- 'Atrolineare' (L)	CAco CMen MPkF NLar SMil WFar WLea
	- 'Atropurpureum' (A)	Widely available
	- 'Attraction' (P)	CMac CMen NTrD
	- 'Aureum' (P)	CAco CMCN CMen ELan EPfP LMil LRHS MAsh MBlu MDon MGos MPkF NLar SPoG WFar
	- 'Autumn Fire' (D)	CJun
	- 'Autumn Glory' (M)	CEnd CJun CMen NBPC WFar
	- 'Autumn Red' (M)	CMen WLea

*	- 'Autumn Showers'	CEnd CJun
	- 'Azuma-murasaki' (M)	CJun CMen MPkF SMil
	- 'Baby Lace' (Dw)	CWGN SAko
	- 'Baldsmith' (D)	CAco CJun EMac MPkF
	- 'Barrie Bergman' (D)	CJun NLar
	- 'Beni-chidori' (P)	CMen
	- 'Beni-fushigi' (P)	MPkF
	- 'Beni-gasa' (M)	MPkF
	- 'Beni-hime' (Dw)	MPkF
	- 'Beni-hoshi' (Dw)	MPkF
	- 'Beni-kagami' (M)	CAco CEnd CJun CMCN IDee MPkF NLar
	- 'Beni-kawa' (P)	CJun CMCN CMen LRHS MPkF NOrn
	- 'Beni-komachi' (P)	CAco CDoC CEnd CMCN CMen EDir ELon EPfP MGos MPkF NBPC NOrn WHtc
	- 'Beni-kosode' (v)	MPkF NLar
	- 'Beni-maiko' (P) ♀H6	CAco CBod CDoC CEnd CJun CMCN CMen CRos EDir EGrI EPfP IDee LRHS MGos MPkF NBPC NLar NOrn NRHS SCoo SGsty SJap SMil SOrN SRms SWeb SWvt WHlf WLea WLov
	- 'Beni-otake' (L)	CBcs CJun CMen EPfP ESMi MGos MPkF NLar SAko SMil WFar WLea
	- 'Beni-otome'	MPkF
	- 'Beni-schichi-henge' (P/v)	CEnd CJun CMCN CMen CRos CWGN EDir EHed LRHS MAsh MGos MPkF NBPC NHol NLar NOra NOrn NRHS SAko SCoo SLau SSta WMat
	- 'Beni-shidare' (D)	LRHS
	- 'Beni-shidare Tricolor'	see *A. palmatum* 'Toyama-nishiki'
	- 'Beni-shidare Variegated'	see *A. palmatum* 'Toyama-nishiki'
	- 'Beni-shi-en' (P)	CJun MPkF
	- 'Beni-shigitatsu-sawa'	see *A. palmatum* 'Aka-shigitatsu-sawa'
	- 'Beni-tsukasa' (P/v) ♀H6	CAco CEnd CJun CMCN CMen ESMi LMaj NBPC SMil SSta
	- 'Beni-tsuru'	MPkF
	- 'Beni-yubi-gohon' (P)	CJun MPkF
	- 'Berrima Bridge' (D)	CJun MPkF
	- 'Berry Broom'	CAco MPkF NLar WLea
	- 'Berry Dwarf' (Dw)	CJun
	- 'Bewley's Red' (D)	CJun
	- 'Bi Hō' (P)	CAco CDoC CJun CRos ELan EPfP LCro LMil LOPS LRHS LSRN MAsh MPkF NLar SAko SGol WLea
	- 'Black Lace' (M)	CAco GKin LRHS MAsh MGos MPkF NLar NTrD WLea
	- 'Bloodgood' (A) ♀H6	Widely available
	- 'Bloodgood' seedling (A)	WHtc
	- 'Bonfire' (v)	LRHS
	- 'Bonfire' ambig.	CJun
	- 'Bonnie Bergman'	WFar
	- 'Boskoop Glory' (A)	GKin
	- 'Brandt's Dwarf' (Dw)	EHed
	- 'Brocade' (D)	CJun MPkF NLar WLov
	- 'Bronzewing' (D)	CJun
	- 'Bultinck' (M)	MPkF
	- 'Burgundy Lace' (M) ♀H6	CAco CBcs CEnd CJun CMCN CMen ELan EMac EPfP GKin LMil LRHS LSRN MAsh MGos MPkF NBPC SCoo SGol SOrN SPoG SSta WLea
	- 'Butterfly' (P/v)	Widely available
	- BUTTERSCOTCH ('Jww8'PBR) **new**	CAco NCth
	- 'Calico' (P)	CJun NLar WLea
	- 'Candy Kitchen'	see *A. palmatum* 'Kandy Kitchen'
	- 'Caperci Dwarf' (Dw)	MPkF
	- 'Carminium'	see *A. palmatum* 'Corallinum'
	- 'Caroline' (v)	NLar
	- 'Cascade'	LRHS NOrn
	- 'Cascade Gold' (P)	LRHS MPkF NLar
	- 'Chantilly Lace' (D)	CJun
	- 'Chikuma-no' (A)	CMen MPkF
	- 'Chirimen-nishiki' (P/v)	MPkF
	- 'Chishio' (P)	CAco CMCN CMen ESMi LMil MPkF NBPC NLar SMil
	- 'Chishio Improved' (P)	CDoC CEnd CJun CMCN CMac CMen EPfP LRHS MAsh MGos NHol NLar NOrn SWvt
	- 'Chitose-yama' (M) ♀H6	CJun CMCN CMen EGrI EPfP GKin LPar LRHS MAsh MGos MPkF NLar SGsty SSta WFar WLea
§	- 'Chiyo-hime' (Dw)	CAco EDir LCro LMaj LOPS LPar LRHS NBPC NTrD WFar WLea
	- 'Cobhay Glow' **new**	CJun
	- 'Coonara Pygmy' (Dw)	CJun CMCN CMac CMen EMac GKin MPkF SCoo
	- 'Coral Pink' (Dw)	CMen MPkF SSta
§	- 'Corallinum' (P) ♀H5	CAco CEnd CJun CMCN CMen EGrI EPfP LMil NBPC NLar SMil SPoG WLea
	- var. ***coreanum*** B&SWJ 8606	WCru
	- 'Crimson Carol' (M)	CJun NLar WLea
	- 'Crimson Prince'	CJun NLar SCoo
	- 'Crimson Princess' (D)	CBcs CDoC CRos EDir EPfP LRHS MPkF NBPC NOrn NRHS SWeb WMat
	- 'Crimson Queen' (D) ♀H6	Widely available
	- 'Crippsii' (D)	CBcs CMac CMen MPkF NBPC SCoo SLau XSte
§	- 'Crumple Leaf' (M)	CJun MPkF
	- 'Deshojō' (P)	CAco CMCN CMen ELon LMaj LPar MBlu MGos NBPC NLar NPoe SCoo SGsty SMil WLea WMat XSte
	- 'Diana' (Dw)	CJun CMen NTrD
	- 'Dissectum' (D)	CAco CDoC CEme CTri CWnw EDir EGrI EHeP ELon EWTr LBuc LCro LPar LRHS MDon MTrO NOra NOrn NWea SOrN WFar WJur WLea WTSh
	- 'Dissectum Atropurpureum' (D)	CAco CRos EGrI LMil MDon NWea SGsty SOrN
	- 'Dissectum Flavescens' (D)	CAco CBcs CEnd CJun CMac CMen EMac LPar MBlu MGos MPkF NBPC SGsty SJap WMat
§	- 'Dissectum Nigrum' (D)	CJun CMac CMen MAsh NOrn WFar WLea
	- 'Dissectum Palmatifidum' (D)	CAco CMen EMac MPkF SCoo SJap
	- 'Dissectum Rubrifolium' (D)	CAco MPkF
§	- 'Dissectum Variegatum' (Dw/v)	CJun MPkF
	- Dissectum Viride Group	Widely available
	- 'Doctor Tilt' (P)	CAco
	- 'Donzuru-bo'	CJun
	- 'Dormansland'	CEnd
	- 'Dr Seuss' (L)	MPkF NLar
	- 'Dragon's Fire'	CJun
	- 'Dwarf Shishi' (Dw)	NLar
	- 'Earthfire'	MPkF
I	- 'Ebbingei'	CMac
	- 'Eddisbury' (P) ♀H6	CAco CJun CMen CSBt MBlu NLar SSta
	- 'Edna Bergman' (M)	CJun
	- 'Effegi'	see *A. palmatum* 'Fireglow'
	- 'Eimini' (Dw)	MPkF NLar
§	- 'Elegans' (M) ♀H6	CAco CMen EPfP LRHS MAsh
	- 'Elizabeth' (Dw)	CJun
	- 'Ellen' (D)	CJun MPkF
	- 'Elmwood' (v)	WLea

	- 'Emerald Lace' (D) 🏆H6	Widely available
§	- 'Emperor 1' (A)	CAco CJun EMac LMaj LPar MAsh MPkF NLar SJap WMat XSte
	- 'Englishtown' (Dw)	MPkF NLar WFar
	- 'Enkan' (L)	CDoC CEnd CJun CMen CWGN EHed EPfP LMil LRHS MAsh MGos MPkF MTrO NLar NOra NTrD SPoG WFar WLea WLov WMat
	- 'Eono-momiji'	CMen
	- 'Ever Red'	see *A. palmatum* 'Dissectum Nigrum'
	- 'Fairy Hair' (L)	CJun
	- 'Fall's Fire' (P)	CJun
	- 'Fascination' (M)	CJun WLea
	- 'Felice' (D)	CJun MPkF WLea
	- 'Fenna' (L)	WLea
	- 'Festival'	EBee MPkF NLar SGsty
	- 'Filigree' (Dw/v)	CAco CJun CMCN CMen EPfP MAsh MGos MPkF NBPC NLar
	- 'Fior d'Arancio' (M)	CAco CJun MPkF NLar WLea
	- 'Fireball'	CJun
§	- 'Firecracker'[PBR] (D)	CAco CDoC CRos EBee EDir EHed GKin LRHS MAsh MPkF NLar NRHS NTrD SOrN SWeb
§	- 'Fireglow' (A)	Widely available
	- 'First Ghost' (M/v)	CJun
	- 'Frederici Guglielmi'	see *A. palmatum* 'Dissectum Variegatum'
	- 'Fujinami'	NLar
	- 'Fukaya' (M)	WLea
	- 'Gaki-no-sugi' (P/v)	WLea
	- 'Garnet' (D) 🏆H6	Widely available
	- 'Garnet Tower' (D)	EDir LRHS MPkF NLar
	- 'Garyū' (Dw)	MPkF
	- 'Geisha Gone Wild' (P/v)	CJun
	- 'Genji-yama'	WLea
	- 'Gentaku'	CJun
	- 'Germaine's Gyration' (D)	CJun
	- 'Gibbsii'	CMen
	- 'Glowing Embers' (P)	CJun
	- GOING GREEN ('Sonkootgre'[PBR])	CAco CRos EDir LCro LOPS LRHS MPkF NLar NRHS SCoo WLea
	- 'Going Red'	LRHS NLar
	- 'Golden Hornet'	NLar
	- 'Golden Pond' (A)	CJun
	- 'Goshiki-kotohime' (Dw/v)	CMCN NLar
	- 'Goshiki-shidare'	see *A. palmatum* 'Toyama-nishiki'
	- 'Grandma Ghost' (M)	CJun MPkF
	- 'Green Fingers' (D)	MPkF NLar
	- 'Green Flag'	CJun
	- 'Green Globe' (D)	CAco CJun
	- 'Green Hornet' (D)	CJun
	- 'Green Lace' (D)	CMen LMaj MPkF
	- 'Green Mist' (D)	CJun
	- 'Green Trompenburg' (M)	CAco CJun CMen GMcL MPkF WFar WLea
	- 'Green Ueno-Yama'	CAco CBcs CJun LMaj LPar MPkF SPer
§	- 'Hagoromo'	CMac CMen SCoo WLea
	- 'Hamaotome' (A)	WLea
	- 'Hana-matoi'[PBR] (v)	CMCN EHed MPkF
	- 'Hanami-nishiki' (Dw)	CMen MPkF SMil
	- 'Hanzel' (D)	NLar
	- 'Happy Corallinum' (A)	CJun
	- 'Haru-iro'	CJun
	- 'Harusame' (P/v)	MPkF NLar
	- 'Hazeroino' (v)	CMen
	- 'Heartbeat' (D)	CDoC CJun MPkF
	- 'Heffner's Red'	CJun
	- var. ***heptalobum***	CMCN
	- 'Heptalobum Elegans Purpureum'	see *A. palmatum* 'Hessei'
	- 'Herbstfeuer' (P)	CJun MAsh NLar WFar WLea
§	- 'Hessei' (M)	CEnd CMen MPkF WFar
	- 'Higasa-yama' (P/v)	CAco CEnd CJun CMCN CMen CWGN LRHS MPkF NBPC
	- 'Highland Sunset'	CEnd
	- 'Hime-shojo'	CAco MGos
	- 'Hino-tori-nishiki'	CMen WLea
	- 'Hi-no-tsukasa'	MPkF
	- 'Hiryu' (P)	CAco
	- 'Hōgyoku' (A)	CAco CJun CMCN CMen MPkF
	- 'Hoshi-kuzu' (Dw)	MPkF
	- 'Hupp's Dwarf' (Dw)	CJun MPkF
	- 'Hupp's Red Willow'	MPkF NLar WMat
	- 'Ibo-nishiki' (P)	CMen MPkF
	- 'Ichigyōji' (A)	CEnd CJun CMen MAsh WLea
	- 'Ightham Gold'	SSta
	- 'Iijima-sunago' (M)	CMen MPkF
	- 'Inaba-shidare' (D) 🏆H6	Widely available
	- 'Inazuma' (M)	CAco CJun CMCN CMen EGrI MPkF SCoo SLau
	- 'Irish Lace'	CJun
	- 'Irish Lace' × ***palmatum*** 'Yasemin'	CJun
	- 'Isobel'	NLar NTrD
	- 'Iso-chidori' (Dw)	MPkF
	- 'Issai-nishiki'	CMen MPkF
	- 'Jane'	CJun MPkF NTrD
	- 'Japanese Sunrise' (P)	CJun MPkF NLar NTrD WLea WMat
	- 'Jerre Schwartz' (Dw)	CAco CDoC CEnd CKel CRos CWnw EDir EPfP LCro LOPS LRHS MGos MPkF NBPC NLar NRHS SCoo SOrN SPoG WLea
	- 'Jingo-ji' (M)	WLea
	- 'Jirō-shidare' (P)	MPkF NLar SMil
	- 'JJ'	CJun
	- 'Johnnie's Pink' (P)	MPkF
	- 'Julia D.'	CJun
	- 'Jūnihitoe'	see *A. shirasawanum* 'Jūnihitoe'
	- 'Kaba' (Dw)	CMen MPkF SPoG
	- 'Kagero' (A/v)	MPkF
§	- 'Kagiri-nishiki' (P/v)	CJun CMCN CMac CMen CWGN MPkF NBPC SMil SPer
	- 'Kamagata' (Dw)	CAco CEnd CJun CMCN CMen ESMi LRHS MAsh MGos MPkF NBPC NLar SCoo SMil WLea XSte
§	- 'Kandy Kitchen' (Dw)	CMen MPkF WFar WLea XSte
	- 'Karaori-nishiki' (P/v)	CMen MPkF NLar
	- 'Karasu-gawa' (P/v)	CJun CMen CWGN MPkF
	- 'Kasagiyama' (M)	CEnd CJun CMen MPkF
	- 'Kasen-nishiki' (P)	CMen MPkF
	- 'Kashima' (Dw)	CEnd CJun CMCN CMen MBlu MPkF NBPC NLar SMil WLea
	- 'Katja'	CJun CMen
	- 'Katsura' (P) 🏆H6	Widely available
	- 'Katsura-nishiki'	MPkF
	- 'Kawahara Rose'	MPkF NLar
I	- 'Kawaii' (D)	CJun
	- 'Ki-hachijō' (M)	CAco CJun CMCN CMen GMcL LRHS MPkF SMil SWeb
	- 'Killarney' (M)	CJun
	- 'Kingsville Variegated' (P/v)	SMil
	- 'Kinky Krinkle' (P)	CJun LRHS NLar
	- 'Kinran' (M)	CAco CJun CMen MPkF WLea
	- 'Kinshi' (L) 🏆H6	CEnd CJun CMCN CMen EPfP LRHS MPkF MTrO NLar NOra NOrn SAko WLov WMat
	- 'Kiri-nishiki' (D)	CJun CMen MPkF NLar
	- 'Ki-shuzan' (M)	CJun WLea
	- 'Kiyohime' (Dw) 🏆H6	CAco CMCN CMen ESMi MPkF NBPC SMil WLea
	- 'Koba-shōjō' (M)	MPkF
	- 'Kogane-nishiki' (P)	CMen LPar NLar

- 'Kogane-sakae' (A)	CJun MPkF
- 'Kokobunji-nishiki' (v)	MPkF
- 'Komachi-hime' (Dw)	CJun CMen MPkF NBPC WLov
- 'Komon-nishiki' (P/v)	CJun CMen MPkF
- 'Komyo-ji' (A)	WLea
- 'Korean Gem' (M)	CJun CMen MPkF
- 'Koriba' (P)	CJun MPkF NLar
- 'Koshibori-nishiki' (P)	MPkF
- 'Kotohime' (Dw)	CAco CJun CMCN CMen CWnw LRHS MGos MPkF NLar SCoo SPoG
- 'Koto-ito-komachi' (Dw/L)	CJun CMen MAsh MPkF NBPC
- 'Koto-maru' (Dw)	CAco NLar
- 'Koto-no-ito' (L)	CAco CMCN ELan LBuc LRHS MAsh MBlu MGos MPkF NLar SAko SPoG WFar WLea
- 'Koya-san' (Dw)	CMen MPkF
- 'Kurabu-yama' (M)	CMen MPkF
- 'Kurenai-jishi' (Dw)	MPkF
- 'Kuro-hime' (Dw)	MPkF WFar
- 'Kurui-jishi' (Dw)	MPkF
- 'Kyōryū'	MPkF
- 'Kyra'	CMen MPkF
- 'Lace Lady' (D)	NOrn
- 'Limelight' (P)	CDoC NLar
§ - 'Linearilobum' (L)	CAco CBcs CDoC CMen EPfP MGos MPkF MTrO NLar NOra SCoo SLau SMil WLea WMat
* - 'Lionheart' (D)	CAco CJun CMen CWGN ESMi MGos MPkF NLar SCoo SMil
- 'Little Princess'	see *A. palmatum* 'Chiyo-hime'
- 'Little Red' (Dw) **new**	NLar
- 'Lozita' (P)	NLar
- 'Lutescens' (A)	CMen MPkF
- 'Lydia'	MPkF
- 'Maiko' (P)	CMen MPkF
- 'Mallet'	NLar
- 'Mama' (P)	CMen
- 'Manyō-no-sato' (P/v)	CAco LCro LRHS MPkF NLar
- 'Mapi-no-machi-hime' (Dw)	CEnd CJun CMCN CMen LRHS MPkF NHol SMil
- 'Marakumo' (P)	MPkF
- 'Marasaki-yama'	MPkF
- 'Mardi Gras'	CJun
- 'Margaret'	MPkF
- 'Margaret Bee' (A)	CJun NLar
- 'Marjan' (M)	CJun MPkF NLar WLea
- 'Marlo'[PBR] (D)	CRos LRHS MAsh MGos NLar
- 'Masamurasaki'	CMen MPkF
- 'Masukagami' (P/v)	CAco CEnd CJun MPkF NLar
- 'Matsu-ga-e' (P/v)	CMen MPkF
- 'Matsukaze'	CJun CMCN CMen LRHS
- var. ***matsumurae*** B&SWJ 11100	WCru
- - B&SWJ 11195	WCru
- 'Matsuyoi' (A)	CJun MPkF
- 'Meihō-nishiki' (A/v)	CJun
- 'Melanie'	CJun
- 'Mendip Fantasy'	CMen
- 'Meoto'	CJun
- METAMORPHOSA ('Arjos1'[PBR])	CBcs WFar
- 'Midori-no-teiboku' (Dw)	CJun MPkF
- 'Mika' (P)	LRHS MPkF
- 'Mikasayama'	see *A. sieboldianum* 'Mikasa-yama'
- 'Mikawa-yatsubusa' (Dw)	CAco CMCN CMac CMen EHed EMac MGos MPkF NLar SAko
- 'Mikazuki' (M/v)	CJun LRHS MPkF WLea
- 'Mila' (M)	MPkF
- 'Mimaye'	CJun
- 'Mini Mondo'	MPkF
- 'Mirte' (M)	CAco CJun CMen MPkF NLar
- 'Mischa'	MPkF

- 'Mizuho-beni' (P)	CJun CMen NLar
- 'Mizu-kuguri' (A)	CJun MPkF
- 'Momiji-gawa' (A)	MAsh WFar
- 'Momoiro-koya-san' (Dw)	CJun LRHS MPkF NLar
- 'Mon Papa' (M)	CJun CMen MPkF NLar
- 'Mono-zigawa'	WLea
- 'Monzukushi' (A)	CJun MPkF SMil
- 'Moonfire' (M)	CAco CBcs CJun CMCN EMac EPfP LRHS MAsh MPkF NLar WLea
- 'Moonglow'	CJun
- 'Moss Gold' (D)	MPkF WLea
- 'Murasaki-hime' (Dw)	MPkF
- 'Murasaki-kiyohime' (Dw)	CEnd CJun CMCN CMen MPkF WLea
- 'Murasaki-shikibu'	MPkF
- 'Mure-hibari' (M)	CJun CMen MPkF
- 'Murogawa' (A)	CJun CMen
- 'Musashino' (M)	CJun
- 'Mutsu-beni-shidare' (D)	NLar
- 'Mystic Jewel' (P)	MPkF
- 'Nakata'	NLar
- 'Nanase-gawa' (A)	MPkF NLar
- 'Nicholsonii' (M)	CAco CMen MPkF NLar WLea
- 'Nigrum' (A)	CMCN CTri NOra WLea
- 'Nishiki-gasane' (P/v)	CMen MPkF
§ - 'Nishiki-gawa' (P)	CJun CMen MPkF SMil WFar WLea
- 'Nishiki-momiji' (P)	CMen WLea
- 'Nomura'	CJun CMen
- 'Nomura-nishiki' (Dw/v)	CMen
- 'Nomurishidare' misapplied	see *A. palmatum* 'Shōjō-shidare'
- 'Nuresagi' (M)	CAco CEnd CJun MPkF
- 'Octopus' (D)	CJun MPkF NLar
- 'Ōgi-nagashi' (P/v)	MPkF NLar
- 'Ōgi-no-sen'	WLea
- 'Ōgon-sarasa' (A)	CJun MPkF
- 'Ojishi' (Dw)	CMen MPkF
- 'Ō-kagami' (P)	CAco CBcs CEnd CJun CMac CMen EGrI EPfP ESMi MAsh MGos MPkF NBPC NLar SCoo SJap SMil WFar WLea
- 'Okukuji-nishiki' (P)	CAco CJun
- 'Okushimo' (P)	CEnd CJun CMCN CMen EHed LRHS MPkF NBPC NLar WLea
- 'Omato' (A)	CJun MPkF WLea
- 'Omure-yama' (M)	CAco CEnd CJun CMCN CMen EPfP ESMi MGos MPkF NBPC SCoo SGol SJap SMil WLea
- 'Orange Dream' (P) 🏆H5	Widely available
- 'Orange Flame' (D)	NLar
- 'Orangeola' (D) 🏆H6	CAco CEnd CJun CMen CSBt CTri GKin LRHS MAsh MGos MPkF NBPC NHol NLar NOrn NRHS SCoo SJap SLau SPoG SRms SWeb WFar WLea WMat
- 'Oranges and Lemons' (M)	CJun
- 'Oregon Sunset' (M)	CJun MPkF WMat
- 'Oridono-nishiki' (P/v)	CAco CEnd CJun CMCN CMac CMen CWGN ELan EPfP ESMi IArd LPar MBlu MGos MPkF NBPC NLar SGsty SPoG SSta SWeb
- 'Oriental Mystery'	CJun
- 'Ornatum' (D) 🏆H6	CAco CMCN CMen GMcL LMaj LSRN MAsh MDon MGos MPkF MRav NBPC NLar NOrn NWea SCoo SJap WLea
- 'Ōsakazuki' (A) 🏆H6	Widely available
- 'Osakii'	LRHS
- 'Ōshio-beni' (A)	CJun CMen EGrI
- 'Ōshū-beni' (M)	CJun
- 'Ōshū-shidare' (M)	CJun CMen MPkF

	- 'Oto-hime' (Dw)	CJun CMen EGrI MPkF
	- 'Otome-zakura' (P)	CJun CMen MPkF NBPC SMil WLea
	- 'Otto's Dissectum' (D)	CJun
	- 'Patricia'	WLea
	- 'Peaches and Cream' (M/v)	CJun CMen ESMi MPkF NBPC NLar SMil
	- 'Pendulum Julian' (D)	CAco CMCN MPkF
	- 'Pévé Chameleon'	MPkF NLar
	- 'Pévé Dave'	CEnd CRos EBee ELan LRHS LSRN MAsh MPkF NLar NRHS WFar WLea
	- 'Pévé Multicolor'	CJun NLar
	- 'Pévé Ollie' [PBR]	MPkF NLar
	- 'Pévé Stanley'	MPkF NLar
	- 'Pévé Starfish'	NLar
	- 'Phoenix' (P)	CAco CJun EPfP IPap LMil LRHS MGos MPkF NBPC NLar NTrD SCoo WFar WHlf
	- 'Pine Bark Maple'	see *A. palmatum* 'Nishiki-gawa'
	- 'Pink Ballerina' (Dw/v)	CJun NLar
	- 'Pink Filigree' (D)	CAco CJun CMen
	- 'Pink Passion' (v)	CAco LPar LRHS LSRN
	- 'Pixie' (Dw)	CAco CMen CSBt ESMi LBuc LPar MGos MPkF MTrO NOra SAko SWeb WFar WLea WMat XSte
	- 'Princetown Gold'	CCVT
	- 'Pung-kil'	MPkF SAko WFar WLea
	- 'Purple Ghost' (M)	CJun
	- 'Rainbow' (M/v)	NLar
	- 'Raraflora' (D)	CJun
	- 'Red Autumn Lace' (D)	CJun LMaj
	- 'Red Baron' (A)	CJun
	- 'Red Cloud' (L)	CJun MPkF
	- 'Red Dragon' (D)	CAco CJun CMen CWGN MAsh MPkF NBPC SAko
	- RED EMPEROR	see *A. palmatum* 'Emperor 1'
	- 'Red Feather' (D)	CJun MPkF NLar
	- 'Red Filigree Lace' (D)	CEnd CJun CMCN CMen CWGN MPkF
	- 'Red Flame'	NLar
	- 'Red Flash' (A)	CJun CMen MPkF NLar
	- 'Red Jonas'	CAco MPkF NLar
	- 'Red Lane' (D)	WLea
	- 'Red Pygmy' (L) ♀H6	Widely available
	- 'Red Select' (D)	MPkF
	- 'Red Spider' (L)	CJun
	- 'Red Wood' (P)	CJun SGol SLau
	- 'Redwine' [PBR] (P)	CRos EPfP LRHS MAsh MPkF NLar NRHS WLea
	- 'Relish' (M/v)	MPkF
	- 'Renjaku-maru'	MPkF
	- 'Reticulatum'	see *A. palmatum* 'Shigi-tatsu-sawa'
	- 'Ribesifolium'	see *A. palmatum* 'Shishi-gashira'
	- 'Rilas Red' (D)	NLar
	- 'Rising Sun'	CJun
	- 'Roseomarginatum'	see *A. palmatum* 'Kagiri-nishiki'
	- 'Rough Bark Maple'	see *A. palmatum* 'Arakawa'
	- 'Rubrum' (A)	CMen WLea
I	- 'Rubrum Kaiser'	CJun
	- 'Ruby' (P)	MPkF
	- 'Ruby Ridge'	see *A. palmatum* 'Crumple Leaf'
	- 'Ruby Star'	CJun MPkF
	- 'Rufescens' (P)	MPkF
	- 'Ruslyn-in-the-Pink' (Dw)	MPkF NLar
	- 'Ryokū-ryū' (P)	CMen MPkF
	- 'Ryusen'	CAco LCro LRHS MBlu MPkF NLar SCoo SGsty SPoG WLea
	- 'Ryuzu' (Dw)	CJun MPkF NLar
	- 'Sagara-nishiki' (v)	CEnd CMen MPkF NBPC
	- 'Sai-ho'	MPkF
	- 'Samidare' (A)	CJun MPkF NLar
	- 'Sandra' (Dw)	CMen
§	- 'Sango-kaku' (P) ♀H6	Widely available

	- 'Sanguineum' (P)	NLar
	- 'Saoshika' (A)	CAco CJun CMen MPkF NLar
	- 'Sa-otome' (P)	CMen MPkF
	- 'Satsuki-beni' (M)	CJun CMen EGrI MPkF NBPC SMil WLea
	- 'Sawa-chidori' (M)	MPkF WLea
	- 'Sazanami' (M)	CEnd CJun CMen LRHS MPkF NBPC WLea
	- 'Scolopendriifolium'	see *A. palmatum* 'Linearilobum'
	- 'Seigen' (Dw)	CEnd CMCN CMen MBlu MPkF SMil
	- 'Seiryū' (D) ♀H6	Widely available
	- 'Seiun-kaku' (P)	CJun CMen LRHS WFar WLea
	- 'Sekimori' (D)	CJun NLar SMil
	- 'Sekka-yatsubusa' (P)	CMCN CMen MPkF NLar WLea
	- 'Senkaki'	see *A. palmatum* 'Sango-kaku'
	- 'Septemlobum Elegans'	see *A. palmatum* 'Elegans'
	- 'Septemlobum Purpureum'	see *A. palmatum* 'Hessei'
	- 'Sessilifolium' dwarf	see *A. palmatum* 'Hagoromo'
	- 'Shaina' (P)	Widely available
	- 'Sharp's Pygmy' (P)	CJun CMen MPkF NBPC SMil XSte
	- 'Sherwood Elfin' (Dw)	MPkF
	- 'Sherwood Flame' (M)	CAco CJun CMen EGrI MAsh MBlu MGos MPkF NLar SCoo SJap
	- 'Shichihenge' (P)	MTrO NLar
	- 'Shidava Gold' (Dw)	CBcs CJun EMac MPkF
	- 'Shigarami' (P)	CJun CMen MPkF
§	- 'Shigi-tatsu-sawa' (A/v)	CAco CEnd CJun CMCN CMac CMen LRHS MGos MPkF NBPC NLar NRHS SWeb WLea
	- 'Shigure-bato' (M)	CJun MPkF NLar
	- 'Shigurezome' (M)	MPkF WLea
	- 'Shikageori-nishiki' (P)	CJun CMen MPkF
	- 'Shime-no-uchi' (L)	CJun CMen
	- 'Shin nyo' [PBR]	CAco MBlu MPkF
	- 'Shin-chishio' (P)	CJun
	- 'Shin-deshōjō' (P) ♀H5	CAco CEnd CJun CMCN CMac CMen CRos CSBt CWGN EMac EPfP LMil LRHS LSRN MAsh MGos MPkF MPri NBPC NLar NOrn NRHS SCoo SJap SLau SMil SPer SPoG SSta
	- 'Shin-koto-hime' (M)	CBod
§	- 'Shinobuga-oka' (L)	CJun CMCN CMen MPkF NLar SLau SWeb
	- 'Shinonome' (M)	CAco CJun CMen MPkF
	- 'Shirazz' (P/v)	CAco CBcs CDoC CEnd CWGN EMac GKin LMil LPar LRHS LSRN MAsh MGos MPkF NBPC NLar NOra NRHS NTrD SJap SMil SPer SWvt WLea WMat XSte
§	- 'Shishi-gashira' (P) ♀H6	CAco CJun CMCN CMac CMen CWnw ESMi GMcL LMaj LPar LRHS MBlu MGos MPkF NBPC NLar SCoo SJap SWeb WFar WLea
	- 'Shishio-hime' (Dw)	MPkF
	- 'Shishi-yatsubusa'	CJun MPkF
	- 'Shōjō' (A)	CJun CMCN WLea
	- 'Shōjō-no-mai' (P)	CJun
	- 'Shōjō-nomura' (A)	CEnd CMen MPkF SWeb WLea
§	- 'Shōjō-shidare' (D)	CEnd CJun CMen MPkF NOra WLea WMat
	- 'Shu-shidare' (D)	CJun
	- 'Silhouette' [PBR]	LCro LRHS MPkF NLar WLov
	- 'Sister Ghost' (M)	CJun MPkF
	- 'Skeeter's Broom' (Dw)	CAco CBcs CBod CJun CKel CMen CSBt CWnw EBee EDir ELan EPfP IArd LMaj LRHS MAsh MGos MPkF NLar NRHS SCoo SJap SMil SPoG WFar WLea WLov
*	- 'Sode-nishiki' (P)	CJun MPkF
	- 'Spreading Star'	NOrn
	- 'Spring Delight' (D)	CJun MPkF SAko
	- 'Stanley's Jewel' (Dw)	MPkF NLar WLea

	- 'Starfish'[PBR]	CAco EBee LCro LRHS MPkF
	- 'Stella Rossa' (D)	CAco CEnd CJun LMaj MPkF NBPC NLar WLea
	- 'Suisei' (Dw/v)	MPkF
	- 'Sumi-nagashi' (M)	CAco CJun CMen CRos LRHS MAsh MGos MPkF MTrO NBPC NLar NOra NOrn NRHS SCoo SJap SMil WFar WLea WMat
	- 'Sumi-shidare' (D)	NLar
I	- 'Summer Gold' (P)	CAco CJun CRos CWnw LRHS MPkF NLar NRHS NTrD SGsty SJap SWvt WFar WLea
	- 'Sunset' (D)	CJun MPkF WLea
	- 'Sunshine' (D)	MPkF NTrD WLea
	- 'Super Ruby' (L)	NLar
	- 'Susan'	MPkF
	- 'Taimin' (A)	CAco
	- 'Taimin-nishiki' (M) new	CAco
	- 'Takao' (P)	CMen
	- 'Takatori' (A)	WLea
	- 'Tama-hime' (Dw)	CMen MPkF WLea
	- 'Tamukeyama' (D)	CAco CJun CMCN CMen IDee LBuc LMaj LRHS MAsh MGos MPkF MTrO NBPC NLar NOra NOrn SAko SCoo SJap SLau SMil WLea WMat XSte
	- 'Tana' (A)	CJun CMCN CMen MPkF
	- 'Tarō-yama' (Dw)	CJun MPkF WFar
	- 'Tatsuta'	CMen MPkF
	- 'Taylor'[PBR] (P/v)	CAco CEnd CRos CWGN EPfP LCro LPar LRHS LSRN MAsh MGos MPkF NLar NRHS SCoo SPoG
	- 'Tennyo-no-hoshi' (P)	CMen MPkF NBPC NLar SMil WLea
	- 'The Bishop' (A)	NLar
	- 'Tiger Rose' (M)	CJun MPkF
	- 'Tiny Tim'	CJun
	- 'Tobiosho' (P)	CJun
	- 'Tochi-no-hikari'	LRHS
§	- 'Toyama-nishiki' (Dw/v)	CAco CJun CMCN CMen CWGN MPkF NBPC
	- 'Trompenburg' (M) ♀H6	Widely available
	- 'Trompenson'	NLar
	- 'Tsuchigumo' (P)	CJun CMen MPkF NLar
	- 'Tsukubane' (A)	WLea
	- 'Tsukuma-no'	MPkF
	- 'Tsukushigata' (A)	MPkF
	- 'Tsuma-gaki' (A)	CAco CJun CMCN CMen LCro LRHS MGos MPkF NLar SJap WFar WLea
	- 'Tsuri-nishiki' (M)	CJun CMen MPkF WLea
	- 'Twombly's Red Sentinel'	CJun LCro LRHS MAsh MBlu MPkF NLar WFar
	- 'Ueno-homare' (P)	CMen NBPC
	- 'Uki-gumo' (P/v)	CAco CEnd CJun CMCN CMac CMen LCro LRHS MGos MPkF NBPC NHol SCoo SJap SPer SPoG SSta
	- 'Umegae' (A)	CJun
	- 'Uncle Ghost' (M)	CJun
	- 'Uncle Red' (P)	MPkF
	- 'Usu-midori'	CJun
	- 'Utsu-semi' (A)	CJun MPkF WLea
	- 'Van der Akker'	CJun
	- 'Versicolor' (P/v)	CMCN MPkF
	- 'Vic Pink' (D)	CJun
	- 'Villa Taranto' (L) ♀H6	CAco CBcs CEnd CJun CMCN CMen EPfP MAsh MBlu MGos MPkF MTrO NBPC NLar NOra SCoo SGol SJap WLea WMat XSte
	- 'Volubile' (P)	CMCN CMen MPkF
	- 'Wabito' (P)	CJun CMen MPkF
	- 'Waka-midori'	CMen
	- 'Waka-momiji' (P/v)	CJun
	- 'Wakehurst Pink' (M/v)	CMCN LRHS MPkF NOra NOrn
	- 'Waterfall' (D)	CJun CMCN
	- 'Watnong' (D)	CJun MPkF
	- 'Wendy' (P)	CJun CMen MPkF NLar
	- 'Werner's Pagoda' (P)	MPkF
	- 'Westonbirt Orange' (A)	LRHS NOrn WLea
	- 'Westonbirt Red' (M)	NOrn WFar
	- 'Wetumpka Red'	CJun NLar
	- 'White Butterfly' (P/v)	MPkF
	- 'Whitney Red' (A)	CMen
	- 'Wild Goose' (P)	MAsh MPkF WFar WLea
	- 'Will's Devine'	CJun MPkF
	- 'Wilson's Pink Dwarf' (Dw)	CAco CEnd CJun CMen CRos CWnw EDir LCro LRHS MAsh MGos MPkF NBPC NLar NRHS SCoo SPoG WFar
	- 'Winter Flame' (P)	CJun LRHS MPkF NHol NOrn WLea XSte
	- 'Wou-nishiki'	CMCN CMen MPkF NBPC
	- 'Yana-gawa'	CMen
	- 'Yasemin' (M)	CJun CMen CWGN LRHS MPkF NBPC NLar NOrn
	- 'Yashio'	MPkF
	- 'Yatsubusa' (Dw)	MPkF
	- 'Yezo-nishiki' (A/v)	CMen MBlu MPkF
	- 'Yūba-e' (M)	CAco MPkF NOra NOrn
	- 'Yū-fuji'	MPkF
	- 'Yūgure' (M)	LRHS MPkF
	- 'Zaaling' (D)	CMen
	- 'Zoë' (Dw)	MPkF NLar
	papilio	see *A. caudatum*
	pauciflorum 'Blaze Away'	CJun
	pectinatum	MMuc WPGP
	- GWJ 9354	WCru
	- 'Mozart'	CJun LPar LRHS MBlu NLar NWea SSta
	- subsp. ***pectinatum***	WPGP
	- - HWJ 569	WCru
	- - HWJ 944	WCru
	pensylvanicum	CAco CBcs CLnd CMCN EBee EPfP MGos MMuc MRav NRog SCob SPtp SSta WJur
	- 'Erythrocladum'	CEnd CJun CMCN MAsh NHol NLar NOrn
	pentaphyllum	CMCN WPGP
§	***pictum***	CMCN
	- B&SWJ 12737	WCru
	- subsp. ***macropterum***	WPGP
	- 'Mallet Court'	CMCN
	- subsp. ***okamotoanum***	CMCN
	- - B&SWJ 12623	WCru
	- 'Shufu-nishiki'	CMCN
	platanoides	Widely available
	- 'Cleveland'	CAco EBar LPar
	- 'Columnare'	CAco CMCN EBar EHeP LMaj LPar SCob SCoo
	- 'Crimson King' ♀H7	Widely available
	- 'Crimson Sentry'	CAco CArg CBod CCVT CEme CEnd CLnd CMac EBee EDir EHeP ELan LCro LMaj LPar LRHS LSRN MAsh MGos MNic MRav NOrn SGol SGsty SPer SWvt WHtc
	- 'Deborah'	CAco CLnd EBar LMaj LPar NBwr SCob SPer
	- 'Dissectum'	CAco IArd NRog
	- 'Drummondii' (v)	Widely available
	- 'Emerald Queen'	CAco EBar LMaj LPar SCob
	- 'Faassen's Black'	EHeP NWea
	- 'Farlake's Green' new	CAco
§	- 'Globosum'	CAco CMCN LMaj LPar MNic NLar SArc SCob SGsty SWvt

	- 'Laciniatum'	CMCN EBtc EPfP
	- 'Olmsted'	CAco
	- PRINCETON GOLD ('Prigo'[PBR]) ♀H7	Widely available
	- 'Royal Red'	CAco CLnd EBar EDir EPfP LMaj LPar MDon MRav NLar SCoo SEWo SGsty WFar WHtc
	- 'Schwedleri' ♀H7	CAco CMCN WTSh
	- SENSATION	see *A. platanoides* 'Ulmers Sensation'
	- subsp. ***turkestanicum***	CMCN SSta
§	- 'Ulmers Sensation'[PBR] (v)	SPoG
	pseudoplatanus	CBTr CBcs CBrac CCVT CLnd CMCN CPer CTri EDir GDam LPar MGos MTrO NBwr NRog NWea SCob SavN WMou WTSh
§	- 'Atropurpureum'	EHeP MMuc SCob SEND SEWo
	- 'Brilliantissimum' ♀H7	Widely available
	- f. ***erythrocarpum*** 'Erythrocarpum'	CMac
	- 'Gadsby'	CAco
	- 'Leopoldii' misapplied	see *A. pseudoplatanus* f. *variegatum*
	- 'Negenia'	EBar LPar
	- 'Prinz Handjéry'	CEnd CMCN CTri MGos MTrO NHol NLar NOra NOrn NWea WHtc WMat
	- f. ***purpureum***	NRog NWea
	- 'Spaethii' misapplied	see *A. pseudoplatanus* 'Atropurpureum'
§	- f. ***variegatum*** (v)	LPar MMuc NRog NWea
	- - 'Esk Sunset' (v)	EBee ELan LSRN MGos MTrO NLar NOra SPer SPoG WMat
	- - 'Leopoldii' ambig. (v)	CMCN MDon SEND SWvt
	- - 'Leopoldii' Vervaene (v)	WHtc
	- - 'Simon-Louis Frères' (v)	CBcs CCVT CLnd CMCN EDir LRHS MAsh MDon MGos MTrO NLar NOra NOrn NRog SWvt WHtc WMat
	- 'Worley'	CMCN CMac EHeP LMaj MMuc MRav NRog NWea SEND SLim
	pseudosieboldianum	CMCN LRHS MBlu MPkF
	- B&SWJ 8468	WCru
	- B&SWJ 8746	WCru
	- B&SWJ 8769	WCru
	- var. ***microsieboldianum*** B&SWJ 8766	WCru
	- subsp. ***takesimense***	MBlu
	- - B&SWJ 8500	WCru
	- - B&SWJ 8540	WCru
	'Red Flamingo' (v)	CAco CBcs CJun CMac CRos EPfP LCro LRHS MAsh MBlu MTrO NOra SGol SGsty SPoG WMat
	'Red Wings' (*A. palmatum* hybrid)	CJun
	reticulatum	see *A. laevigatum* var. *reticulatum*
	rubescens	WPGP
	- CWJ 12438	WCru
	- NMWJ 14525	WCru
	rubrum	CAco CAgr CBcs CBod CLnd CMCN CPer CSBt CTri EBee EGrI EPfP IPap LCro LMaj LOPS MGos MTrO NBwr NRog NWea SCoo SEWo SGol WCFE WHtc WMat WTSh
	- 'Autumn Flame'	CCVT WMat
	- 'Autumn Spire'	CJun
	- 'Brandywine'	CAco CEnd CJun CMac EPfP LMaj LRHS LSRN MAsh MBlu MTrO NLar NOra NOrn NWea SCoo SPoG WHtc WMat
	- 'Embers'	CJun
	- FAIRVIEW FLAME	see *A. rubrum* 'Pete's Fairview'
	- 'Firedance'	CJun

	- 'Florida Flame'	CMCN
	- 'Joseph'	NLar
	- 'Karpick' **new**	CAco
	- 'New World'	SCoo
	- 'Northwood'	LMaj
	- 'October Glory' ♀H6	Widely available
§	- 'Pete's Fairview'	CAco CJun NLar NOrn
	- 'Red King'	CJun
	- 'Red Rocket'	MTrO
	- RED SUNSET ('Franksred') ♀H6	CAco CBcs CEnd CMCN EBee EPfP EWTr LMaj LPar NLar SCoo SGol SLim SPer SPoG WMat
	- 'Scanlon'	CAco CBTr CBcs CEnd CJun CMCN EBee ELan EPfP LRHS MTrO NOra NWea SLim SPer WMat
	- 'Schlesingeri'	CEnd CJun CMac
I	- 'Sekka'	MBlu
	- 'Somerset'	CJun SCoo WHtc WMat
	- SUMMER RED ('Hosr')	CAco EBee LRHS SCoo SMad SRHi WMat
	- 'Sun Valley'	CAco CJun CMac MAsh MTrO NOra NOrn NWea WMat
	- 'Tilford'	CJun
§	***rufinerve***	CAco CBcs CLnd CMCN EBee EGrI EPfP LPar MMuc NLar NOra NOrn NWea SCob SCoo SGol SPtp SSta SWvt WHtc WLov WMat WTSh
	- 'Albolimbatum' (v)	CJun CMCN LRHS NLar
	- 'Erythrocladum'	CJun MBlu
	- 'Ko-fuji-nishiki'	SSta
I	- 'Sunshine'	SSta
	- 'Winter Gold'	CJun NLar SSta
	- 'Yellow Ribbon'	LRHS
§	***saccharinum***	CAco CBcs CCVT CMCN EBee EGrI EHeP EPfP LPar MGos MTrO NOra NRog NWea SCoo SPer WMat WTSh
	- 'Born's Gracious'	CAco
	- 'Fastigiatum'	see *A. saccharinum* 'Pyramidale'
	- f. ***laciniatum***	CAco EBee MBlu MMuc
	- - 'Laciniatum Wieri'	CAco CMCN IPap NLar SCob
§	- 'Pyramidale'	CAco CLnd EHeP IPap LMaj
	saccharum	CAco CAgr CBcs CLnd CMCN CPer EBee EPfP IPap LMaj MBlu MTrO NWea WTSh
§	- subsp. ***grandidentatum***	CMCN
§	***sempervirens***	EBee EPfP IArd SEND WJur
	'Sensu'	CJun MPkF NLar
	'Serendipity'	SSta
	'Serpentine'	CAco CBcs CJun CMCN EPfP IArd MAsh MBlu NLar NOrn SSta
	serrulatum CWJ 12437	WCru
	- hybrid NMWJ 14548	WCru
	shirasawanum	LRHS SavN
§	- 'Aureum' ♀H6	Widely available
	- 'Autumn Moon'	CAco CBcs CBrac CJun CMCN CMen CWGN EGrI EMac EPfP GKin IDee LPar MAsh MPkF MTrO NBPC NLar NOra SCoo SGol SMil SPoG WLea WMat XSte
§	- 'Ezo-no-momiji'	CMen
	- 'Gloria'	CJun
	- 'Green Snowflake'	MPkF NLar
	- 'Johin'	MPkF
	- 'Jordan'	Widely available
§	- 'Jūnihitoe'	WLea
	- 'Kakure-gasa'	CJun
	- 'Lovett'	CJun
§	- 'Microphyllum'	NLar
	- MOONRISE ('Munn 001'[PBR])	CBcs EBee EPfP LCro LOPS LRHS MPkF NLar SCoo SGsty
	- 'Mr Sun'	CJun

§	- 'Ogurayama'	CJun CMen
	- 'Palmatifolium'	CJun
	- 'Red Dawn'	CJun MPkF
	- 'Sonya Marie' (v)	MPkF
	- 'Susanne'	CJun CMen NLar
	- var. ***tenuifolium*** B&SWJ 11073	WCru
	sieboldianum 🏆 H6	CMCN CMen MAsh MBlu MMuc NOra SEND SGol
	- B&SWJ 10849	WCru
	- B&SWJ 11049	WCru
	- B&SWJ 11090	WCru
	- 'Katsura-gisan' **new**	CAco
§	- 'Mikasa-yama'	SMil
	- 'Miyama-nishiki'	SMil
	- 'Sode-no-uchi'	CJun CMen
	- var. ***tsushimense*** B&SWJ 10962	WCru
	sikkimense	GKev
	- B&SWJ 11689	WCru
	- B&SWJ 11703	WCru
	- FMWJ 13166 from northern Vietnam	WCru
	- WJC 13674 from Sikkim	WCru
	- WWJ 11601	WCru
	- WWJ 11613	WCru
	- WWJ 11853	WCru
	- subsp. ***sikkimense***	WLov
	'Silver Cardinal' (v)	CEnd CJun CMCN EPfP MBlu NLar SSta
	'Silver Vein'	see *A.* × *conspicuum* 'Silver Vein'
	sinense	CMCN
	- 'Rogou'	CJun
	spicatum	CMCN NLar WLov
§	***sterculiaceum***	EBee WJur
	- subsp. ***franchetii***	CMCN
	- subsp. ***sterculiaceum*** NJM 13.087	WPGP
	- subsp. ***franchetii***	WPGP
	tataricum	CMCN SPtp
§	- subsp. ***ginnala***	CAco CArg CBcs CMCN EBar EGrI EHeP IPap LPar MBlu MGos NLar NWea SGol WJur
	- - 'Flame'	CAco CCVT EBee EPfP MGos MMuc NWea SGbt SPoG WHtc
	- HOT WINGS ('Gar Ann')	EHed
	- subsp. ***semenovii***	SPtp WLov
	tegmentosum 🏆 H5	CJun CMCN EPfP MBlu
	- 'Cobhay Ghost'	CJun
	- subsp. ***glaucorufinerve***	see *A. rufinerve*
	- 'Joe Witt'	WHtc
	tonkinense subsp. ***liquidambarifolium*** DJHV 06173	WCru
	triflorum 🏆 H7	CAco CBcs CCVT CMCN EBee EPfP LMaj LRHS MBlu NLar NOra WMat
	truncatum 'Akikaze-nishiki' (v)	MPkF
	tschonoskii	GKin
	- subsp. ***koreanum***	MPkF
	- - B&SWJ 12596	WCru
	- - B&SWJ 12603	WCru
	turkestanicum from Kyrgyzstan	WPGP
	velutinum	CMCN
	villosum	see *A. sterculiaceum*
	wardii	WPGP
	'White Tigress'	CJun EBee EPfP NLar NWea SSta WMat
	× ***zoeschense***	MPkF
	- 'Annae'	CAco LPar MMuc

Aceriphyllum see *Mukdenia*

Achillea (*Asteraceae*)

	ageratifolia 🏆 H5	ELan SRms XSen
§	***ageratum***	CBod CCBP CLau ENfk EWhm GPoy GQue LEdu MHer MHoo SEdi SRms SVic WFar WGwG WJek WTre XSen
	'Alabaster'	EBee LRHS NRHS
	ANTHEA ('Anblo')	EBee ECtt ECul EShb GMaP LRHS MBriF MCot MRav NRHS SHar SRms SWvt WFar
§	'Apfelblüte' (Galaxy Series)	EBee ECha ECtt ECul ELan EPfP EShb EWTr LEdu LRHS LSRN MHer MMuc MRav NGdn NHol NRHS NSti SEND SPad SPer SRms WCAu WFar
	APPLEBLOSSOM	see *A.* 'Apfelblüte'
	'Apricot Beauty'	ECul
	'Apricot Seduction' (Seduction Series)	ECul NGrs WFar
	argentea misapplied	see *A. clavennae*, *A. umbellata*
	argentea Lamarck	see *Tanacetum argenteum*
	aurea	see *A. chrysocoma*
	'Bahama'	EPPr GQue
	biebersteinii	XLum
§	***chrysocoma***	XLum
	- 'Grandiflora'	ECha MBel NGdn WBrk WFar
§	***clavennae***	EDAr NBir SPlb SRms WAbe
	clypeolata Sm.	SPlb SRms
	coarctata	CKel NBir XSen
	Colorado Group	CBod ECul EHyd LRHS NRHS
	'Coronation Gold' 🏆 H7	CEme CRos EBee ECtt ECul ELan EPfP LRHS MAsh MRav NChi NDov NRHS SCob SGbt SOrN SPer SRms SWvt WCAu WCot WSpi XSen
	'Credo' 🏆 H7	Widely available
	crithmifolia	CKel XLum XSen
	decolorans	see *A. ageratum*
	(Desert Eve Series) DESERT EVE CREAM ('Deseve')	ECul
	- DESERT EVE DEEP ROSE ('Desderos')	ECul LRHS
	- DESERT EVE LIGHT YELLOW	ECul LRHS SRms
	- DESERT EVE RED ('Desred'[PBR])	CWnw ECul LRHS
	- DESERT EVE TERRACOTTA ('Dester')	NGrs
	- DESERT EVE YELLOW ('Desyel'[PBR])	LRHS
§	'Fanal'	CAby CBod CCBP CEme CKel CPla CRos CWCL EBee ECha ECtt ECul ELan EPfP EWoo LRHS MACG MAsh MRav NBPC NBir NHol NRHS SCoo SGBe SGbt SPer SWvt WCAu
	'Faust'	CDor ELon MACG
	'Feuerland'	EBee ECha ECtt ELon EPfP LRHS MRav NBir NDov NGdn NRHS SPoG WFar WSpi XSen
	filipendulina	XSen
	- 'Cloth of Gold' 🏆 H7	Widely available
	- 'Gold Plate' 🏆 H7	Widely available
	- 'Hymne'	EBee ECha XLum
	- 'Parker's Variety'	EBee GQue XLum
	'Fleur van Zonneveld'	NDov WGoo
	FLOWERS OF SULPHUR	see *A.* 'Schwefelblüte'
	(Forncett Series) 'Forncett Beauty'	SWvt
	- 'Forncett Bride'	EBee
	- 'Forncett Citrus'	ECtt WFar
	- 'Forncett Fletton'	ECtt ECul EPfP MACG MBel MCot MPie NGdn NHol WCAu WFar

	- 'Forncett Ivory'	MAvo
	'Gloria Jean'	SHar
	'Golden Fleece'	LRHS
	grandifolia misapplied	see *Tanacetum macrophyllum* (Waldst. & Kit.) Sch.Bip.
§	***grandifolia*** Friv.	GGro MArl MHol NBro WFar
	'Great Expectations'	see *A.* 'Hoffnung'
	'Hannelore Pahl'	XLum
	'Heidi' ♀H7	MRav XSen
	'Heinrich Vogeler'	XLum
	'Hella Glashoff' ♀H7	CRos EBee EBlo ETod LRHS MACG NDov NLar NRHS WGoo
§	'Hoffnung'	NLar NRHS
	× ***huteri***	EDAr LShi MMuc NBwr NHpl NRya SEND SRms SWvt WFar
	'Inca Gold'	CBcs ECha ECtt ECul EPPr LRHS MCot MRav NDov NHol NRHS SPer SRms SWvt WFar WHoo WSpi
	'Jacqueline'	NCth
	× ***kellereri***	XLum XSen
	'King Alfred'	NHpl SRms
	× ***kolbiana***	EWes SRms WFar XSen
§	'Lachsschönheit' (Galaxy Series) ♀H7	CAby CDor CEme CRos EBee ECha ECtt ELan EPfP GMaP LRHS MAsh MBNS MCot MRav NBir NDov NHol NLar NRHS NSti SCob SPer SRms WCAu
	× ***lewisii***	NBwr
	- 'King Edward' ♀H5	EBou EDAr ELan LShi NBir NBwr SLee SRms WAbe WFar WIce
	'Lucky Break' ♀H7	CWnw EBee ECha ECtt EWes MACG NBPC SMrm WCot
	macrophylla	MBNS
	'Marmalade'	CDor NDov SMrm
	'Martina' ♀H7	CAby ECtt EWoo LRHS MBNS MBel NGdn NHol NRHS WBrk WCAu WCot WHoo
	'McVities'	CWCL
	millefolium	CBod CCBP CHab ECul ENfk GPoy GQue LCro LOPS LShi MBow MHoo MNHC NAts NGrd NMir SRms SVic WHer WJek WSFF WSpi WWild
	- 'Angie' (Song Siren Series)	ECul
	- 'Apricot Delight' (Tutti Frutti Series)	EBee ECul ELan GBee LRHS NRHS SCoo WHlf
	- 'Bloodstone'	ECtt EWes MRav
	- 'Carla Hussey'	WFar
	- 'Cassis'	CBod CSpe CWal ECul EHyd EPfP GQue LDai LRHS MCot NChi NGBl NLar NRHS SBls WFar WWke
§	- 'Cerise Queen'	Widely available
	- 'Chamois'	MNrw
	- 'Cherry King'	NBir
	- 'Circus'	ECul XLum
	- 'Crème de la Crème' (Rainbow Series) <u>**new**</u>	MNrw
	- 'Dark Lilac Beauty'	ECul
	- KIRSCHKÖNIGIN	see *A. millefolium* 'Cerise Queen'
	- 'Lansdorferglut' ♀H7	CRos EBee EBlo ECha EPPr LRHS NDov NRHS
	- 'Laura' (Song Siren Series)	CWGN ECtt ECul EPfP MNrw NBPC NLar WFar
	- 'Lavender Beauty'	see *A. millefolium* 'Lilac Beauty'
	- 'Layla' (Song Siren Series) <u>**new**</u>	ECul
§	- 'Lilac Beauty'	Widely available
*	- 'Lilac Queen'	MArl
	- LITTLE MOONSHINE ('Acbz0002'PBR)	ECul
	- 'Little Susie' (Song Siren Series)	CWGN ECtt ECul NLar WFar
	- 'Lollypop'	LDai
	- MILLY ROCK ROSE ('Florachro1')	CBod
	- (New Vintage Series) NEW VINTAGE LILAC	see *A. millefolium* (New Vintage Series) NEW VINTAGE VIOLET
	- - NEW VINTAGE RED ('Balvinred')	CSBt ECul LBar LRHS SCob SCoo WNPC
	- - NEW VINTAGE ROSE ('Balvinrose')	ECul LBar LRHS NFav SCob SCoo
§	- - NEW VINTAGE VIOLET ('Balvinviolet')	ECul LBar LRHS MHol SCob SCoo WNPC
	- - NEW VINTAGE WHITE ('Balvinwite')	ECul LBar LRHS NFav SCob SMrm WNPC
	- 'Old Brocade'	EShb NDov
	- Pastel Shades	WFar
	- 'Peggy Sue'	CWGN ECtt EWes LRHS MDon WFar
	- 'Pineapple Mango' (Tutti Frutti Series) <u>**new**</u>	LBar
	- 'Pink Grapefruit' (Tutti Frutti Series)	CRos EBee ECul LBar LRHS MACG NLar NRHS SCoo WCAu
	- 'Pomegranate' (Tutti Frutti Series)	CAby CRos CWGN ECul EPfP EWTr IPot LBar LCro LDai LOPS LRHS MNrw NGrs NLar NRHS SHar WCot WHlf WTor XLum
	- 'Pretty Woman' (Song Siren Series)	CWGN EBee ECul
	- 'Raspberry Ripple'	ECul GBin
	- 'Red Beauty'	CWCL EBee EPfP MBNS SRms XLum
	- 'Red Velvet' ♀H7	Widely available
	- (Ritzy Series) RITZY ROSE ('Acbz0003'PBR)	ECul
	- - RITZY RUBY ('Acbz0004'PBR)	ECul
	- 'Rose Madder'	CWCL CWnw ECtt ECul EPfP EWTr GKev LRHS LSto LSun MNrw MPie NBPC NBir NCth NGdn NHol NLar NRHS SMHy SMrm SPer SPoG SWvt WCot WFar WGwG XLum
	- 'Ruby Port'	WFar
	- 'Salmon Queen'	NGrs NHol WFar
	- 'Sammetriese'	EBee ELon MNrw
	- (Sassy Summer Series) 'Sassy Summer Lemon' <u>**new**</u>	ECul
	- - 'Sassy Summer Sangria' <u>**new**</u>	ECul
	- - 'Sassy Summer Sunset' <u>**new**</u>	ECul
	- - 'Sassy Summer Taffy' <u>**new**</u>	ECul
	- 'Schneetaler'	ECul EWTr MNrw
	- 'Sue's Pink'	ECul
	- (Summer Fruits Series) 'Summer Fruits Carmine'	ECul ELan SCoo
	- - 'Summer Fruits Lemon'	ECul ELan LRHS NRHS WFar WSpi
	- - 'Summer Fruits Salmon'	ECul ELan LRHS SCoo SPoG WFar
	- 'Summertime'	WFar
	- 'White Beauty'	ECul NCth WCAu
	- 'Wonderful Wampee' (Tutti Frutti Series)	EBee ECul EHyd ELan EWes LBar LRHS MNrw NRHS SCob SCoo SPoG
	'Mondpagode' ♀H7	ECtt EPfP EWTr MBNS MRav NGdn SWvt
	MOON DUST ('Novaachdus')	CBod ECul LBar MDon
*	'Moonbeam'	SEND
	'Moonshine' ♀H7	Widely available
	'Moonwalker'	CBod ECul EPfP MACG SCoo WCot XLum
	nobilis	XSen

	- subsp. ***neilreichii***	ECha LRHS MBNS NSti SWvt WFar WGwG
*	***odilis***	EWTr
	'Paprika' (Galaxy Series)	Widely available
	'Petra'	EBee MMrt NLar XLum
	pindicola subsp. ***integrifolia***	EWes
	'Pretty Belinda'	CDor CRos EBee ECtt EHyd EPfP ETod EWhm LRHS LSRN MAvo MBel MCot MDon MSpe NBPC NLar NRHS SCob SPoG SRms WCAu WFar
	'Prospero'	WCot
	ptarmica	CBod CPud MHer NAts NMir SRms
*	- 'Ballerina'	NDov
	- 'Double Diamond' (d)	CWal LShi LSto
	- 'Nana Compacta'	CMac GBin MACG NBir SPlb SPoG
	- 'Noblessa'	MACG NLar
	- 'Perry's White' (d)	ECha MBNS MNrw WCot
	- 'Peter Cottontail' **new**	ECul LBar WNPC
	- 'Stephanie Cohen'	see *A. sibirica* 'Stephanie Cohen'
	- The Pearl Group seed-raised (d)	CTri ECul ELan MACG MMuc SBls SGbt SPlb WFar
	- - 'Boule de Neige' (clonal) (d)	ELan MRav NPer SHar SPer WFar WSpi XLum
	- - 'The Pearl' (clonal) (d)	Widely available
	pyrenaica	XLum
	'Rougham Salmon'	CDor
	'Ruby Wine'	SHar WFar
	'Safran'	EBee ECul NLar XLum
	salicifolia 'Silver Spray'	NLar SDix
	'Sally'	CKno ECha EPPr
	SALMON BEAUTY	see *A.* 'Lachsschönheit'
	'Sandra Wagg'	ECtt
	'Sandstone'	see *A.* 'Wesersandstein'
	'Saucy Seduction' (Seduction Series)	CWCL ECul ELan ELon EPfP LBar LRHS MACG NDov NLar SCob
	'Saucy Sensation'	ECul SCob
§	'Schwefelblüte'	MRav NBir
	'Schwellenburg'	ECha WCot WFar
	sibirica subsp. ***camschatica***	GGro
	- - 'Love Parade'	EBee GQue MNrw NLar SGbt SPer WFar WTor XLum
§	- 'Stephanie Cohen'	SMrm
	SUMMER BERRIES (mixed)	CBod CRos ECul EHyd LRHS NGrd NRHS WFar
	Summer Pastels Group	CBod EHyd EPfP LRHS NGrd NLar NRHS SRms WFar
	- (Seduction Series) 'Peachy Seduction'PBR	ECul LBar NLar WCAu
	- - 'Strawberry Seduction'	ECtt ECul EPfP LRHS NLar
	'Summerwine' ♀H7	Widely available
	'Sunbeam'	SHar
	'Sunny Seduction' (Seduction Series)	ECul ELon LBar LRHS NLar WTor
I	'Taygetea'	EBee ECul ELan LCro LOPS LPal SPoG SRkn WCAu WCot WFar WSpi
	'Terracotta'	Widely available
	'The Beacon'	see *A.* 'Fanal'
	'Tissington Old Rose'	MNrw
	tomentosa ♀H5	CKel CTri EBou ECha GPSL LCro XSen
§	- 'Aurea'	LPar LShi MTin NBro
	- 'Maynard's Gold'	see *A. tomentosa* 'Aurea'
	'Tri-colour'	EWTr MBNS NGdn
§	***umbellata***	LCro XSen
	'W.B. Childs'	MNrw MRav NDov SHar
	'Walther Funcke'	Widely available
§	'Wesersandstein'	CWCL GMaP MNrw NBir SGbt
	'Wilczekii'	SRms
	'Yellowstone'	LDai

× *Achimenantha* (*Gesneriaceae*)

'Cool Inferno'	WDib
'Golden Jubilee'	WDib
'Himalayan Sunrise'	SDir WDib
'Inferno' ♀H1b	WDib
'Pisces'	WDib
'Star of Stars'	WDib

Achimenes (*Gesneriaceae*)

admirabilis	WDib
'Aimee Saliba'	WDib
'Ambroise Verschaffelt' ♀H1c	LAma SDir WDib
'Apricot Glow'	WDib
'Aquamarine'	WDib
'Aurora Charm'	WDib
'Ballerina'	WDib
'Beautiful Fire'	WDib
'Big Weiss'	WDib
'Blue Sparks'	SDeJ
'Caligula'	WDib
'Cameo Rose'	WDib
'Candy Shop'	WDib
'Caprice'	WDib
'Cascade Fairy Pink'	WDib
'Cascade Fashionable Pink'	WDib
'Cascade Rose Red'	WDib
'Cattleya'	LAma SDir
cettoana	WDib
'Charm'	SDeJ WDib
'Claret'	WDib
'Crummock Water'	WDib
'Dale Martens'	WDib
'Dot'	WDib
'Double Picotee Rose' (d)	WDib
'Double Pink Rose' (d)	WDib
erecta	WDib
'Erlkönig'	WDib
'Escheriana'	LAma
'Extravaganza'	WDib
'Femme Fatale'	WDib
'Firefly'	WDib
'Flamenco'	WDib
'Forget Me Not'	WDib
'George Houche'	WDib
'Glory'	WDib
'Golden Butterfly'	WDib
'Golden Lady'	WDib
'Harry Williams'	LAma SDir WDib
'Hilda Michelssen' ♀H1c	WDib
'Himalayan Mandarin' (Himalayan Series)	LAma SDir WDib
'Hugues Aufray'	WDib
'Ice Tea'	WDib
'Imperial Light'	WDib
'Jay Dee Large White' (Jay Dee Series)	WDib
'Jennifer Goode'	WDib
'Johanna Michelssen'	WDib
'Just Divine'	WDib
'Kim Blue'	WDib
'Lady in Black'	WDib
'Lavender Fancy'	WDib
'Light Lilac'	WDib
'Little Beauty'	WDib
'Little Lulu'	WDib
longiflora var. ***alba*** 'Snow Queen'	LAma SDir
- 'Major'	WDib
'Madame Bovary'	WDib
'Magnificent'	WDib
'Mauve Delight'	WDib

'Melon Ice Cream'	WDib
mexicana	LAma SDeJ
misera	WDib
'Nocturne'	WDib
'Old Rose Pink'	WDib
'Opal'	WDib
'Orange Delight'	WDib
'Orange Orchard'	WDib
'Pally'	WDib
'Patens Major'	WDib
'Peach Blossom'	LAma SDeJ WDib
'Peach Cascade'	WDib
'Peach Glow'	WDib
pedunculata	WDib
'Petite Fadette'	WDib
'Poil de Carotte'	WDib
'Primadonna'	SDeJ WDib
'Pulcherrima'	LAma SDeJ
'Purple King'	WDib
'Queen of Queens'	WDib
'Rai'	WDib
'Rainbow'	WDib
'Rainbow Warrior'	WDib
'Rozi Roza'	WDib
'Santa Claus'	WDib
'Schneewittchen'	WDib
'Serge Saliba'	WDib
'Serge's Fantasy'	WDib
'Show-off'	WDib
'Shy Sun'	WDib
skinneri	WDib
'Snow Princess'	SDeJ
'Stan's Delight' (d) 🏆^{H1c}	WDib
'Sterntaler'	WDib
'Sugarland'	WDib
'Sun Dance'	WDib
'Sun Wind'	WDib
'Sweet and Sour'	WDib
'Tango'	WDib
'Tarantella'	WDib
(Tetra Series) 'Tetra Himalayan Purple'	LAma WDib
- 'Tetra Purple'	SDir
'Tiger Eye'	WDib
'Valse Bleu'	WDib
'Veronika Gotmanova'	WDib
'Violacea Semiplena' (d)	WDib
'Vivid'	LAma WDib
'Weinrot Elfe'	WDib
'Wetterlow's Triumph'	WDib
'Yellow Beauty'	WDib
'Yellow English Rose' (d)	WDib

Achimenes × *Smithiantha* see × *Achimenantha*

Achlys (*Berberidaceae*)

triphylla	EMor SBls WCru
- B&SWJ 13541	WCru

Achnatherum see *Stipa*

Acidanthera see *Gladiolus*

Aciphylla (*Apiaceae*)

aurea	GKev SPlb
glaucescens	CBrP SPlb
kirkii	GKev
lyallii	GKev
montana	CMen

Acis (*Amaryllidaceae*)

§ ***autumnalis*** 🏆^{H5}	Widely available
- var. ***autumnalis***	NRog
- var. ***oporantha***	CBor CMiW CWCL EPri GKev NRog
- - f. ***dispathacea***	GEdr GKev NRog
- var. ***pulchella***	CElw GKev NRog
- 'September Snow'	ELan EPri GKev LAma NLar NRog
ionica	CBor GKev NRog WMal
I - subsp. ***vlorensis***	GKev
nicaeensis	CTtf EHyd EPot GKev NWad WAbe WCot
§ ***rosea***	CBor CTtf NRog WAbe
§ ***tingitana***	CBro
§ ***trichophylla***	CBor
- pink-flowered	EPri
- f. ***purpurascens***	WCot
§ ***valentina***	CTtf NRog WCot

Acmella (*Asteraceae*)

§ ***oleracea***	CLau

Acmena (*Myrtaceae*)

smithii	WJur

Acnistus see *Iochroma*

australis	see *Eriolarynx australis*

Acoelorrhaphe (*Arecaceae*)

wrightii	EAri NPlm

Aconitum (*Ranunculaceae*)

ACE 1449	EPPr
'Album'	WWtn
altissimum	see *A. lycoctonum* subsp. *vulparia*
anglicum	see *A. napellus* subsp. *napellus* Anglicum Group
§ ***anthora***	EBee GKev SPeP WCot
anthora × ***carmichaelii*** Arendsii Group	NCth
arcuatum	see *A. fischeri* var. *arcuatum*
austroyunnanense	WSHC
- BWJ 7902	WCru
autumnale misapplied	see *A. carmichaelii* Wilsonii Group
autumnale Rchb.	see *A. fischeri* Rchb.
× ***bicolor***	see *A.* × *cammarum* 'Bicolor'
'Blue Lagoon'^{PBR}	CWGN EBee GMcL LBar NCth SCob WHil
'Blue Opal'	EBee EWes MAvo
'Blue Sceptre'	LDai NLar SRms
§ 'Blue Sparrow'	EBee EHed LBar LSou MHol WCAu
'Bressingham Spire' 🏆^{H7}	ECtt EHyd ELan EPfP GKin GMcL LRHS MAvo MCot NCth NGdn NPer NRHS SRms SSut WFar WSpi
bulbilliferum HWJK 2120	WSHC
× ***cammarum***	NChi
§ - 'Bicolor' 🏆^{H7}	Widely available
- 'Eleanora'	ECtt EMor EPfP EWld LBar MHol NLar SRms
- 'Grandiflorum Album'	EMor LPla MNrw WGoo
- 'Pink Sensation'^{PBR}	NLar
§ ***carmichaelii***	CBod EHyd ELan EPfP GKin LRHS MMuc MNrw NBro NChi NGdn NRHS SEND SMrm SRms WCot WFar WSpi
- B&SWJ 8809	ESwi
- Arendsii Group	CAby EBee ECtt GKev LEdu WCAu WCFE
- - 'Arendsii' 🏆^{H7}	Widely available
- - 'Cloudy'^{PBR}	CAby CWGN EBee ECtt EMor ITim LBar LEdu LPla MACG MAvo MBriF NGdn NLar NRHS NSti SPer WCot WFar WHlf WSpi
- 'Moody Blues'	EBee
- 'Redleaf'	see *A. carmichaelii* 'Royal Flush'

	- 'River Finn'	WCot
	- 'River Lugg'	WCot
	- 'River Medway'	WCot
	- 'River Nene'	WCot
	- 'River Ouse'	WCot
	- 'River Spey'	WCot
	- 'River Teifi'	WCot
	- 'River Trent'	WCot
	- 'River Welland'	WCot
§	- 'Royal Flush' PBR	CWGN EBee ECha ECtt LBar MBNS MCot MNrw NLar SPeP SPoG WCot
	- var. ***truppelianum***	WCot
§	- Wilsonii Group	CMac EBee EGrI LEdu MRav NDov WHoo
	- - 'Autumn Amethyst'	SMHy
	- - 'Barker's Variety'	CKno EBee ELon GKev NGdn NLar NSti SRms WCAu WCot WSpi
	- - 'Kelmscott' ♀H7	LCro MCot MRav SDix SMHy WCot WFar WSpi
	- - 'Spätlese'	CDor CWGN EBee ECtt GElm LRHS MCot NBir NGdn NLar SPer SPoG WCAu WCot XLum
§	***chasmanthum***	CRos EBee LRHS NRHS
	- GWJ 9393	WCru
	chiisanense B&SWJ 4446	ESwi WCru
	cilicicum	see *Eranthis hyemalis* Cilicica Group
§	***columbianum*** new	GKev
	compactum	see *A. napellus* subsp. *vulgare*
	confertiflorum	see *A. anthora*
	episcopale	EWld WCru
	excelsum	see *A. lycoctonum* subsp. *lycoctonum*
	ferox	EBee
	fischeri misapplied	see *A. carmichaelii*
§	***fischeri*** Rchb.	EBee NBid NLar WCot
	- B&SWJ 8809	WCru
§	- var. ***arcuatum***	EBee
	- - B&SWJ 774	WCru
	formosanum B&SWJ 3057	WCru
	fukutomei B&SWJ 337	WCru
	gmelinii	see *A. lycoctonum* subsp. *lycoctonum*
	grossedentatum	LPla NLar
	- subsp. ***paniculatum***	see *A. variegatum* subsp. *paniculatum*
§	***hemsleyanum***	CExl CRHN CWGN GElm GKev GLog NBid WCru
	- dark blue-flowered	WSpi
	- 'Red Wine'	CBcs CBod EMor LBar SMad
	hyemale	see *Eranthis hyemalis*
	'Ivorine'	CEme CRos EBee ECha EHyd EMor EPfP GMaP LRHS LShi MCot MHol NGdn NLar NRHS NSti SPer WFar WPnP
	jaluense B&SWJ 8741	WCru
	japonicum	EBee GQue NLar WCot WOut
	- var. ***hakonense***	CExl
	- var. ***montanum*** B&SWJ 5507	WCru
§	- subsp. ***napiforme***	EWes
	- - B&SWJ 943	EBee ELon WCru
§	- subsp. ***subcuneatum*** B&SWJ 6228	WCru
	kitadakense B&SWJ 11173	WCru
	lamarckii	see *A. lycoctonum* subsp. *neapolitanum*
	lasianthum	see *A. lycoctonum* subsp. *vulparia*
	loczyanum	WCot
	- B&SWJ 11529	WCru WSHC
	lycoctonum	GBin NGrd NLar NSti WSpi
	- 'Darkeyes'	WCot
§	- subsp. ***lycoctonum***	SRms
§	- subsp. ***moldavicum***	WCot
§	- subsp. ***neapolitanum***	EBee GMaP LBar MACG MMuc NLar SEND WHlf WSpi
	- 'Russian Yellow'	ESwi EWld
§	- subsp. ***vulparia***	GKev GPoy LEdu MHol MRav NGdn SRms
	mairei	see *A. vilmorinianum*
	moldavicum	see *A. lycoctonum* subsp. *moldavicum*
	nagarum	LEdu WCot
	- KR 7589	EBee
	napellus	CBod CCBP ECtt EPfP GAbr GKev GPoy MBel MBros MCot MHol MMuc MNHC NAts NGrd SMrm SPoG SRms WCot WFar WHlf WHoo WPnP WShi
	- 'Bergfürst'	LRHS
	- 'Gletschereis'	EBee WCAu
§	- subsp. ***napellus*** Anglicum Group	MHol MMuc SEND WCot
	- - - 'Spring Yellow'	WCot
	- 'Rubellum'	EMor GKev NBro NLar WFar WHlf
	- 'Schneewittchen'	EMor EWes LBar MCot SCob
§	- subsp. ***vulgare***	GKev
	- - 'Albidum'	CBcs CBod EGrI EHed EMor EPfP EWoo GMaP LEdu LPla MBel MHol NBid NHol NLar NRHS NSti SBls SPeP SPer SPoG
	- - 'Carneum'	EBee EPfP NGrd WHer
	- 'William Turner'	NGrd
	napiforme	see *A. japonicum* subsp. *napiforme*
	nasutum	WCot
	- white-flowered	WCot
	neapolitanum	see *A. lycoctonum* subsp. *neapolitanum*
	'Newry Blue'	CBcs CRos EBee ECtt ELan GMcL LRHS LSto MArl MBNS MHol MRav NBir NRHS NWad SBls SRms WSpi
	orientale misapplied	see *A. lycoctonum* subsp. *vulparia*
	paniculatum misapplied	see *A. variegatum* subsp. *paniculatum*
	piepunense	EBee GKev
	proliferum	WCot
	- B&SWJ 4107	WCru
	pseudolaeve var. ***erectum*** B&SWJ 8466	WCru
	pterocaule	GGro
	'Purple Sparrow'	see *A.* 'Blue Sparrow'
	pyramidale	see *A. napellus* subsp. *vulgare*
	pyrenaicum misapplied	see *A. lycoctonum* subsp. *neapolitanum*
	ranunculifolium	see *A. lycoctonum* subsp. *neapolitanum*
	sachalinense	WCot
	- subsp. ***yezoense***	EBee NLar WCot
	scaposum	GKev
	senanense var. ***incisum*** B&SWJ 11032	WCru
	- subsp. ***paludicola*** B&SWJ 10866	WCru
	seoulense	EBee
	- B&SWJ 694	SBls WCru
	- B&SWJ 864	WCru
	septentrionale	see *A. lycoctonum* subsp. *lycoctonum*
	'Spark's Variety' ♀H7	Widely available
	spicatum GWJ 9394	WCru
	'Stainless Steel' ♀H7	CBcs CExl EBee ECtt EMor EPfP EWoo GElm GMaP GQue LEdu LRHS LSto NBro NCth NDov NGdn NLar SAko SCob SPoG WCAu WCot WFar WPnP WSHC WSpi

subcuneatum	see *A. japonicum* subsp. *subcuneatum*
'Surprise'	WCot
tenue	see *A. columbianum*
× ***tubergenii***	see *Eranthis hyemalis* Tubergenii Group
uchiyamae B&SWJ 1005	WCru
- B&SWJ 1216	ECha SBls WCru
- B&SWJ 4446	NLar
variegatum	EBee
§ - subsp. ***paniculatum***	EBee LPla WCot
- - 'Roseum'	WFar
§ ***vilmorinianum*** BWJ 8055	WCru
violaceum var. ***robustum***	see *A. chasmanthum*
volubile misapplied	see *A. hemsleyanum*
vulparia	see *A. lycoctonum* subsp. *vulparia*
yamazakii	WCru
zigzag var. ***ryohakuense*** B&SWJ 8906	WCru

Aconogonon see *Persicaria*

Acorus ✿ (*Acoraceae*)

calamus	CBen CKno CLau CPud CWat GPoy LLWG LPfP MNHC NPer WMAq
- subsp. ***angustatus***	GPoy
- 'Argenteostriatus' (v)	CBen CWat ECha MMuc SEND SRms WMAq
* ***christophii***	ELon EPPr
gramineus	CKel GPoy NPer
- 'Golden Delight'	CBod LRHS SRms SSha
- 'Golden Edge' (v)	ELon LLWG NRHS NWad
- 'Hakuro-nishiki' (v)	GMcL NWad SRms SWvt WFar XLum
- 'Licorice'	LPla WBrk
- 'Masamune' (v)	EWes
- 'Oborozuki' misapplied	see *A. gramineus* 'Ōgon'
§ - 'Ōgon' (v)	Widely available
- var. ***pusillus***	NBro
- 'Variegatus' (v)	CBcs CBen CBod CEme CRos CWat ELan EMor GMaP GQue LPar LPfP LRHS LSun MGos MMuc MRav NBid NBro NFav NRHS SArc SCoo SEND SPoG SRms SSha SWvt
'Intermedius'	NPer

Acradenia (*Rutaceae*)

frankliniae	CBcs CCCN CMac EPfP IArd IDee MBlu MHtn SPlb WPGP

Actaea (*Ranunculaceae*)

alba misapplied	see *A. pachypoda*, *A. rubra* f. *neglecta*
arizonica	CRos EBee LPla LRHS NRHS WCru
asiatica B&SWJ 616	WCru
- B&SWJ 6351 from Japan	WCru
- B&SWJ 8694 from Korea	WCru
- BWJ 8174 from China	WCru
biternata B&SWJ 8917	NLar WCru
- B&SWJ 11190	WCru
'Chocoholic'	CBWd CWGN EBee ECtt EHed ELan ELon EMor GJos ILea IPot LBar LRHS LSou MAsh MHol MMrt MNrw MPri NCth NRHS SPVi
§ ***cimicifuga***	GPoy
aff. ***cimicifuga*** WJC 13720	WCru
§ ***cordifolia***	EBee GBin GMaP LPla LRHS MBros NLar SWvt
- 'Blickfang'	SPVi
dahurica	GBin LPla
- B&SWJ 8426	WCru
- B&SWJ 8573	WCru
- tall	NBid
'Dark Chocoholic'	IPot
erythrocarpa	see *A. rubra*
§ ***japonica***	ECha NLar
- B&SWJ 5828	WCru
- B&SWJ 11136	WCru
- B&SWJ 11526	WCru
- from Jejudo, South Korea	EBee MNrw
- var. ***acutiloba*** B&SWJ 6257	WCru
- 'Cheju-Do'	EMor GGro LBar LPla LRHS MHol MMrt NCth NLar SPVi
- compact B&SWJ 8758A	WCot WCru
- 'Silver Dance'	EMor NLar
mairei BWJ 7635	WCru
- BWJ 7939	WCru
§ ***matsumurae***	NLar
- B&SWJ 11187	WCru
- B&SWJ 11528	WCru
- 'Elstead Variety' ♀H7	CExl MRav
- 'White Pearl' ♀H7	CBcs CDor CExl CRos EBee ECha ECtt ELan EPfP GMaP GMcL GQue ILea LRHS MNrw MRav NBid NLar NRHS NSti SCob SPer SPoG SRms SWvt WPGP XLum
§ ***pachypoda***	CExl EBee EPfP GKev GLog GPoy LShi MBel NBid NLar WCru
- MISTY BLUE ('Lk05'PBR)	CAvo CBcs CBod CDor CWGN EBee ECha ECtt EHed ELan EMor ESwi GEdr LPla LRHS LSou MNrw NLar SEdd SMad SPeP SPoG WCot WHlf WNPC XSte
- 'Silver Leaf'	CSpe EMor GKev WSHC
§ ***podocarpa***	EBee LPla NLar SPlb SRms WCru
'Queen of Sheba'PBR	CWGN EBee EMor IPot MAvo MBel NDov NLar SPVi
racemosa ♀H7	CBod CMac EBee ELan EPfP GBin GPoy MHoo MNHC MPri NBid NGdn NLar NSti SEdd SPer SWvt WCAu WFar WHlf XLum
§ ***rubra***	EBee ECha ELan MBel MMrt NBid NWad SMad SPoG WCru
- B&SWJ 9555	WCru
- ***alba***	see *A. pachypoda*, *A. rubra* f. *neglecta*
§ - f. ***neglecta***	GLog WCot WCru
simplex	GLog WCot WHlf
- B&SWJ 8653	WCru
- B&SWJ 8664	WCru
- B&SWJ 10957	WCru
- B&SWJ 11133	WCru
§ - Atropurpurea Group	CBod EBee ECha EGrI ELan ELon EMor GMaP LCro LOPS LRHS MACG MGos MHoo MNHC MRav NBir NChi NGdn NLar SPeP SPer SRms SWvt WCAu WFar WPnP WSHC
- - 'Black Negligee'	Widely available
- - 'Brunette' ♀H7	Widely available
- - 'Carbonella'	CWGN EBee ECtt ELan EMor LBar MNrw NLar SPVi WFar WHil
- - 'Hillside Black Beauty' ♀H7	CDor CTtf EBee ECtt EMor EPfP GKin GMaP LBar LRHS NBir NLar WNPC
- - 'James Compton' ♀H7	CDor CExl CKel CPar EBee ECha EMor EWoo GBee GBin GMaP ILea IPot LRHS MAvo MBel MCot NDov NGBl NGdn NLar NRHS SWvt WCAu WCot WFar
- - 'Mountain Wave'	ECtt NDov SPVi
- 'Cally Dappled' (v)	MBriF
- 'Pink Spike'	Widely available
§ - 'Prichard's Giant'	CBWd ECha ELon EMor MBros MNrw MRav NDov NLar WFar

- ***ramosa***	see *A. simplex* 'Prichard's Giant'
- 'Silver Axe'	NLar
- variegated (v)	WCot
spicata	GBin GPoy WCru
taiwanensis B&SWJ 3413	WCru
- RWJ 9996	WCru
yesoensis	LPla NLar
- B&SWJ 6355	WCru
- B&SWJ 10860	ESwi WCru

Actinella see *Tetraneuris*

Actinidia (*Actinidiaceae*)

BWJ 8161 from China	WCru
arguta	CRHN EBee MGil WJur
- (f/F)	CAgr LRHS
- B&SWJ 4455 from Jejudo, South Korea	WCru
- B&SWJ 4823 from Japan	WCru
- B&SWJ 8529 from Ulleungdo, South Korea	WCru
- 'Ambrosia Grande' (f/F)	NLar
- 'Ananasnaya' (f/F)	CAgr WPGP
- 'Bayern' (f/F)	CAgr CCCN
- 'Geneva 2' (f/F)	CAgr
- 'Honigbeere' (m)	NLar
- 'Issai' (s-p/F)	CAgr CBcs CCCN CMac EPom LBuc LEdu MBlu SVic WHlf WJur WKor WPGP
- 'Jumbo' (f/F)	CAgr LEdu SNig SVic WHlf
- 'Ken's Red' (f/F)	CAgr CCCN CDoC EDir IDee LEdu SVic SWeb WHlf WPGP
- 'Kokuwa' (s-p/F)	CAgr
- 'Meader' (m)	CAgr
- var. ***purpurea*** 'Hardy Red' (f/F)	CAgr
- - 'Purpurna Sadowa' (f/F)	IDee NLar
- 'Rogow' (f/F)	CAgr
- SCARLET SEPTEMBER KIWI ('Mirzan') (f/F)	CAgr
- 'Shoko' (f/F)	WCru
- 'Unchae' (m)	WCru
- 'Weiki' (m)	CAgr CCCN IDee LEdu SVic WPGP
chinensis misapplied	see *A. deliciosa*
chinensis ambig.	LShi
chinensis Planch. var. ***setosa*** H.L. Li B&SWJ 3563	WCru
coriacea WWJ 11895	WCru
§ ***deliciosa***	CCCN MRav
- 'Atlas' (m)	NLar SVic
* - 'Boskoop' (s-p/F)	IDee
- 'Hayward' (f/F)	CBcs CCCN CKel EPfP ERom LSRN SCob SVic SWvt WFar
- 'Jenny' (s-p/F)	CAgr CBod CEnd CMac CRos CTri EBee EDir ELan EPfP EPom LBuc LCro LPar LRHS MBros MGos NLar NTrD SBmr SNig SPoG SPre SSFr SVic WFar
- 'Oriental Delight' (s-p/F)	CRHN
- SOLISSIMO ('Renact'PBR) (s-p/F)	CDoC CKel EBee EHyd IDee LRHS MCoo MTrO NRHS SBmr SSFr
- 'Solo' (s-p/F)	CCCN CKel CMac CRHN EDir EPfP LRHS LSRN NLar SBmr SPer SWvt
- 'Tomuri' (m)	CBcs CCCN EBee EPfP LSRN SWvt
hypoleuca B&SWJ 5942	WCru
'Kiwai Bee'	CCCN
kolomikta ♀H5	Widely available
- B&SWJ 4243	LSRN WCru
- (m)	CDoC CWnw MBlu
- 'Adam' (m)	EBee
- 'Doctor Szymanowski' (s-p/F)	CAgr
- 'Sentyabraskaya' (f/F)	NLar
- 'Tomoko' (f/F)	WCru
- 'Yazuaki' (m)	WCru
melanandra	SPlb
petelotii FMWJ 13137	WCru
- HWJ 628	WCru
pilosula misapplied	see *A. tetramera* var. *maloides*
pilosula (Finet & Gagnep.) Stapf ex Hand.-Mazz.	CDoC CKel CRos EHyd ELan IArd IDee LRHS MBNS NRHS SIvy SPoG SRms WKif
polygama	WJur
- B&SWJ 5444	WCru
- B&SWJ 8525 from Korea	WCru
- B&SWJ 8923 from Japan	WCru
- B&SWJ 12564 from Korea	WCru
rufa B&SWJ 3525	WCru
strigosa WJC 13662	WCru
- WJC 13807	WCru
aff. ***strigosa*** HWJK 2367	WCru
§ ***tetramera*** var. ***maloides*** ♀H5	CBcs CExl CKel CWGN EBee ELon EPfP LCro MGil NLar SBrt SCoo WBor WCru WPGP WSHC

Adansonia (*Malvaceae*)

digitata new	EAri NPlm
grandidieri	EAri NPlm SPlb
madagascariensis	SPlb
perrieri new	NPlm
rubrostipa	SPlb
za	SPlb

Adelocaryum see *Lindelofia*

Adenanthos (*Proteaceae*)

sericeus	SPlb

Adenium (*Apocynaceae*)

obesum ♀H1a	CCCN CDoC EAri NPlm
- 'Olivia'	LCro

Adenocarpus (*Fabaceae*)

decorticans	SPlb

Adenophora (*Campanulaceae*)

'Afterglow'	see *Campanula rapunculoides* 'Afterglow'
asiatica	see *Hanabusaya asiatica*
bulleyana	NBid NLar SBls SPlb WCot WFar
capillaris	NLar
subsp. ***leptosepala***	
- - BWJ 7986	WCru
coelestis	NBid
- B&SWJ 7998	WCru
confusa	LDai
* ***cymerae***	LDai
divaricata B&SWJ 11018	WCru
FAIRYBELLS	see *A.* 'Gaudi Violet'
§ 'Gaudi Violet'	EMor LBar LRHS MBriF MHol NCou NCth SCoo SPoG WCot
grandiflora B&SWJ 8555	NLar WCru
khasiana	GKev NLar XLum
kurilensis	GArf
lamarkii B&SWJ 8738	WCru
latifolia misapplied	see *A. pereskiifolia*
liliifolia	EBee EMor EPfP GJos GKev NPer WFar
maximowicziana B&SWJ 11008	WCru
morrisonensis RWJ 10008	MHol WCru
- subsp. ***uehatae***	GEdr XLum
- - B&SWJ 126	WCru

§ ***nikoensis***	GEdr GJos NBid WCot
- B&SWJ 11201	WCru
§ ***pereskiifolia***	SHar SPlb WCot
- 'Alba'	SRms
- 'White Blaze'	LCro
polyantha	GElm NLar SRms
polymorpha	see *A. nikoensis*
potaninii	CPla EBee MACG MMuc SEND WFar
remotiflora	EBee MHol
- B&SWJ 8714	WCru
- B&SWJ 11016	WCru
stricta subsp. ***confusa***	EBee
- subsp. ***sessilifolia***	EBee
takedae	EBee GArf
- B&SWJ 11424	WCru
taquetii	GEdr
tashiroi	CPla EBee GKev XLum
triphylla	GKev
- B&SWJ 10916	WCru
- var. ***japonica***	CBor LDai
- - B&SWJ 10933	WCru

Adenostyles (*Asteraceae*)

alpina	EMor

Adesmia (*Fabaceae*)

longipes	SPlb

Adiantum (*Pteridaceae*)

§ ***aleuticum*** 🏆H6	CAby CLAP CMiW LCro LOPS LPal NBro NLar SPlb WFib
- 'Imbricatum'	Widely available
- 'Miss Sharples'	CDTJ CElw CLAP GEdr LEdu LRHS NLar NRHS SRms
§ - 'Subpumilum' 🏆H5	CLAP NBro WCot WFib
- 'Tasselatum'	WCot
capillus-veneris	EBee ISha NBro WFib
- 'Mairisii'	see *A.* × *mairisii*
caudatum	CDoC EShb ISha LEdu
cuneatum	see *A. raddianum*
fulvum	CDoC EShb
hispidulum 🏆H4	CBdn CCCN CDoC EBee EPfP LEdu LRHS MAsh NRHS SPlb WPGP
- 'Bronze Venus'	CCCN CDoC CRos EShb ISha LRHS NRHS SRms
§ × ***mairisii*** 🏆H5	CBdn CLAP CRos EShb ISha LEdu LRHS MAsh NRHS WPGP
pedatum misapplied	see *A. aleuticum*
pedatum ambig.	CBdn CBod CTsd EMor SEdd
pedatum L.	CBcs CBct CDor CLAP EFer EHed ELan ELon GAbr GMaP ISha LEdu NBro NLar SPlb WCot WFar
- var. ***subpumilum***	see *A. aleuticum* 'Subpumilum'
poiretii	LEdu
§ ***raddianum***	CDoC
- 'Fragrans'	see *A. raddianum* 'Fragrantissimum'
§ - 'Fragrantissimum'	LCro LOPS
- 'Fritz Lüthi'	CDoC EShb
- 'Misty Cloud'	SMrm
reniforme	WCot
× ***tracyi***	ISha LEdu WPGP
venustum 🏆H7	Widely available
- 'Texas'	LEdu

Adlumia (*Papaveraceae*)

fungosa	CSpe

Adonis (*Ranunculaceae*)

aestivalis	CKel
amurensis misapplied	see *A.* 'Fukujukai'
amurensis ambig.	EBee GEdr LEdu
- 'Pleniflora'	see *A. multiflora* 'Sandanzaki'
- 'Ryokuho'	GEdr
annua	CKel SPhx
brevistyla	GEdr
'Chichibu-beni'	GEdr
§ 'Fukujukai'	GEdr
multiflora 'Beni-nadeshiko'	GEdr
- 'Hakuju'	GEdr
- 'Hanazono' (d)	GEdr
§ - 'Sandanzaki' (d)	GBin GEdr LEdu WHil
ramosa	GEdr
'Sado-no-maboroshi' (d)	GEdr
vernalis	GPoy SMad

Adoxa (*Adoxaceae*)

moschatellina	EBee EWld LEdu MNrw NGrd NRya WHer WShi WWtn

Adromischus (*Crassulaceae*)

alstonii **new**	EAri
caryophyllaceus **new**	EAri SPlb
cooperi 🏆H2	CDoC EAri SIvy
cristatus	EAri
filicaulis	EAri SIvy
- red **new**	EAri
inamoenus **new**	EAri
maculatus 🏆H2	CDoC
marianiae **new**	EAri
- var. ***hallii*** 'Red Coral' **new**	EAri
- var. ***immaculatus*** **new**	EAri
- 'Little Spheroid' **new**	EAri
- 'Tanqua' **new**	EAri
roaneanus **new**	EAri
schuldtianus	CDoC
triflorus **new**	EAri
trigynus **new**	SPlb
umbraticola	EAri
subsp. ***ramosus*** **new**	

Aechmea ✿ (*Bromeliaceae*)

abbreviata	NPic
'Blue Rain' PBR	NPic
blumenavii	NPic
bracteata	NPic
calyculata	NPic
caudata	NPic
coelestis	NPic
- var. ***albomarginata***	NPic
distichantha	NPic
drakeana **new**	NPic
fasciata	NPic WSFF
- 'Primera' PBR 🏆H1b	NPic
filicaulis	NCft NPic
'Foster's Favorite'	NPic
fulgens var. ***discolor***	NPic
gamosepala	NPic
kertesziae	NPic
lamarchei	NPic
lindenii 'Makoyana'	NPic
lueddemanniana	NPic
mariae-reginae	NPic
mexicana	NPic
miniata var. ***discolor***	NPic
'Nigre' ambig.	NCft
nudicaulis	NPic
- 'Manchas Negras' **new**	NPic
orlandiana	NPic
racinae	NPic
ramosa	NPic
recurvata	NCft NPic
- var. ***benrathii***	NCft NPic
- 'Paraguay'	NPic
'Red Bands'	NCft

Aegle (*Rutaceae*)

sepiaria	see *Citrus trifoliata*

Aegopodium (*Apiaceae*)

podagraria gold-margined (v)	EPPr
- 'Variegatum' (v)	CEme EBee ECha EPPr EShb GGro GKev GMaP GQue LRHS MHoo MRav NBid NRHS NSti SEND SPer WCot WFar WHil XLum

Aeonium ✿ (*Crassulaceae*)

appendiculatum	SIvy
arboreum	CDTJ CDoC CHll CKno CPla ELan EShb NCft SChr SEND SIvy SMrm WHlf
- 'Albovariegatum' (v)	SIvy
- var. ***arboreum***	SEdd
- 'Atropurpureum'	CAbb CCCN CDTJ CPla CSde ELan EShb NCft NPer SEND SIvy
- subsp. ***holochrysum***	CAbb NCft
I - 'Magnificum'	NCft SArc SEdd SIvy
- var. ***rubrolineatum***	SEdd
- 'Tip Top'	CSpe EAri ELan SEdd XSte
- 'Variegatum' (v)	CPla NPer SEdd
arboreum* × *spathulatum **new**	SChr
balsamiferum	CCCN CDTJ CDoC CPbh NCft SChr SEdd SIvy SSim WCot
'Black Cap'	CCCN
'Black Magic'	EAri SEdd
'Blush'	CKno
'Blushing Beauty' 🏆H1c	CAbb EGrl NCft SEdd SIvy SSim WCot
'Bronze Medal'	EAri SEdd WCot WOld
'Bronze Teacup'	WOld
* ***calderense*** **new**	SEdd
canariense	CCCN CDTJ CTsd SIvy SVen
- var. ***palmense***	SEdd SIvy SVen
§ - var. ***subplanum***	SEdd
- var. ***virgineum*** **new**	CDTJ SEdd SPlb
castello-paivae	EAri NCft SChr
ciliatum	SEdd SPlb WCot
'Copper Kettle'	CCCN WAvo
'Cornish Pixie' **new**	SEdd
'Cornish Tribute'	CCCN CPbh SEdd SIvy SSim WOld
'Cristata Sunburst'	CDTJ WCot
cuneatum	CDTJ CPbh CSde NCft SEND
- blue-leaved	SChr
'Cupcake' **new**	SEdd
'Cyclops'	CAbb CCCN CPbh EAri NCft WCot
davidbramwellii	NCft SEdd
decorum	SEdd
* - var. ***guarimiarense*** **new**	SEdd
* - 'Variegatum' (v)	WCot
'Dinner Plate'	CDTJ CPbh NCft WOld
diplocyclum	see *Greenovia diplocycla*
× ***domesticum***	see *Aichryson* × *aizoides* var. *domesticum*
'Du Rozzen'	CPbh
'Durango' **new**	SEdd
'Emerald Flame'	SEdd WOld
* ***escobarii***	SPlb
'Firecracker'	CAbb CCCN SEdd
'Garnet'	SEdd
glandulosum	SEdd SVen
'Goblin'	SEdd WOld
gomerense	CPla
goochiae	SIvy
- 'Ballerina' (v)	EAri NCft SEdd SGro SIvy SSim WCot
gorgonium	NCft SEdd
haworthii 🏆H1c	CDTJ CDoC NCft SEND SEdd SSim SVen
- 'Kiwi'	CCCN EAri EGrl NCft SEdd SIvy SSim WCot WOld
- 'Variegatum' (v) 🏆H1c	CDTJ CPbh CSBt EAri EShb MHer SIvy SVen
hierrense	CPbh SEdd SPlb
× ***hybridum***	SEdd
korneliuslemsii	SEdd
lancerottense	SEdd SIvy
'Lemon-Lime' (v)	WOld
leucoblepharum	EAri EShb NCft SEdd SIvy
- 'Spoonbill' **new**	CCCN
lindleyi	NCft SChr
- var. ***viscatum***	SEdd
× ***loartei***	SEdd
'Logan Rock'	CCCN CPbh SEdd WCot
'Mardi Gras' (v) **new**	WOld
'Marnier-Lapostolle'	NCft
× ***mascaense***	SEdd
'Maximus'	NCft SEdd
'Merry Maiden'	CPbh
* ***multiflorum*** 'Variegatum' (v)	CDTJ
nobile	EAri SChr SEdd
percarneum	SEdd
'Phoenix Flame'	SEdd WCot
'Plum Purdy'	CCCN
'Plum Thumb' **new**	SEdd
'Poldark'	CCCN CPbh
'Pomegranate'	CCCN SEdd
pseudourbicum **new**	SEdd
* ***puntallanense*** **new**	SEdd
I 'Pygmaeum'	SEdd
'Red Edge' **new**	CSBt SEdd
'Rose Bowl' **new**	CCCN
rubrolineatum	SEdd WCot
'Saturn' **new**	SEdd
saundersii **new**	SEdd
sedifolium	CPbh CPla NCft SEdd SIvy SSim WAbe
'Simply Misty'	SSim
'Simply Scarlet'	SSim
simsii	CDTJ CTsd NCft SEdd
- variegated (v)	EShb
simsii × 'Zwartkop'	CCCN CDoC CPbh CPla CSBt EAri ELan ETod MHer NCft SEdd WCot
spathulatum	CDTJ EDAr NCft SEdd WCot
subplanum	see *A. canariense* var. *subplanum*
'Sunburst' (v) 🏆H1c	CPbh EAri NCft SIvy WCot WOld
'Suncup'	SEdd
tabuliforme 🏆H1c	CCCN CDTJ CDoC CPbh NCft SBls SEND SMad SPlb SSim WCot
'Torchbearer'	CPbh WCot
'Trewidden'	WCot
undulatum	CDTJ SEdd SPlb
urbicum	EShb SIvy
valverdense	SEdd
'Velour'	CCCN CDTJ CDoC CPbh EAri EPfP NCft NPer SChr SEdd SIvy SSim
volkeri **new**	SEdd
'Voodoo'	CAbb EAri EGrl ELan NCft SIvy SSim WCot WOld
'Zwartkop' 🏆H1c	Widely available

Aeschynanthus ✿ (*Gesneriaceae*)

Black Pagoda Group	WDib
buxifolius	WAbe
'Fire Wheel'	WDib
'Hot Flash'	WDib
'Japhrolepis' **new**	LCro
'Little Tiger'	WDib
longicalyx	see *A. rhododendron*

§	***longicaulis*** ♀H1a	CDoC LCro WDib
	marmoratus	see *A. longicaulis*
	'Mona Lisa'	LCro
	radicans ♀H1a	WDib
§	***rhododendron***	WDib
	'Scooby Doo'	WDib
	speciosus ♀H1a	WDib
	'Twister'PBR	LCro

Aesculus ✿ (*Sapindaceae*)

	arguta	see *A. glabra* var. *arguta*
	assamica	WPGP
	- WWJ 11886	WCru
	'Autumn Splendor'	CAco
§	× ***bushii***	MBlu
	californica	CBcs CMCN EPfP SBrt WPGP
	- 'Canyon Pink'	CMCN
	× ***carnea***	CAco NRog SCob SGol
	- 'Briotii'	Widely available
*	- 'Variegata' (v)	CMCN
	chinensis	CBcs CMCN
	'Dallimorei' (graft-chimaera)	CAco
	flava ♀H5	CAco CMCN EBee EPfP IArd LMaj MMuc SEND
	- 'Burning Gold' **new**	MBlu
	- f. ***vestita***	EPfP MBlu
	georgiana	see *A. sylvatica*
	glabra	CMCN MMuc SEND WJur WPGP
	- 'April Wine' **new**	MBlu
§	- var. ***arguta***	NLar
	- 'October Red'	EPfP
	glaucescens	see *A.* × *neglecta*
	hippocastanum	CAco CBTr CBcs CBrac CCVT CMac CSBt CTri EBee EHeP ELan IPap LCro LPar LRHS MGos MMuc MSwo MTrO NBwr NLar NOra NRog NWea SCob SEWo SPer WFar WMat WTSh
	- 'Aureomarginata' (v)	CMac
§	- 'Baumannii' (d)	CAco CMCN ELan LPar MGos MSwo NRog SPer
	- 'Digitata'	CMCN IPap
	- 'Flore Pleno'	see *A. hippocastanum* 'Baumannii'
	- 'Globosa'	see *A. hippocastanum* 'Umbraculifera'
	- 'Hampton Court Gold'	CMCN CMac
	- f. ***laciniata***	CAco CMCN NLar
	- 'Pyramidalis'	LPar
§	- 'Umbraculifera'	CAco
	- 'Wisselink'	CMCN
	indica	CMCN ELan EPfP EWTr MMuc MTrO SEND SPtp WJur WMou WTSh
	- 'Sydney Pearce' ♀H5	CAco CBcs CEnd CMCN ELan EPfP MBlu MGos MTrO NLar NOra WMat
	× ***mississippiensis***	see *A.* × *bushii*
	× ***mutabilis*** 'Induta'	CAco CMCN EPfP MTrO NOra NOrn WMat
§	× ***neglecta***	CMCN
	- 'Autumn Fire'	CAco EPfP MTrO NLar NOrn WHtc WMat
	- 'Erythroblastos' ♀H5	CBcs CEnd CMCN EPfP MBlu SCoo WCot WMat
	parviflora ♀H5	CAco CBcs CMCN CTri ELan EPfP EWTr GKin IDee LMaj MBlu MGos MMuc MRav MTrO NLar NOra SEND SMad SPer SWvt WJur WMat
	pavia	CAco CBcs CMCN MMuc
	- 'Atrosanguinea'	CAco CEnd CMCN EPfP
	- var. ***discolor*** 'Koehnei'	CAco CMCN ELan EPfP MTrO NLar NOra SPoG WMat
	- northern	SBrt
	- 'Purple Spring'	EPfP
§	- Splendens Group	CMCN EPfP
	splendens	see *A. pavia* Splendens Group
§	***sylvatica***	CMCN
	turbinata	CAco CBcs MMuc WJur WMou
	wilsonii	CBcs CExl MBlu

Aethionema (*Brassicaceae*)

§	***grandiflorum*** ♀H5	EDAr EPot GJos GKev MACG MHol SRms
	- Pulchellum Group ♀H5	CSpe
*	***kotschyi*** hort.	EPot WAbe
	membranaceum	GJos
	pulchellum	see *A. grandiflorum*
	schistosum	SPlb
	'Warley Rose' ♀H5	CRos EHyd ELan EPot GKev LRHS MAsh MNrw NBir NRHS SRms WTor XSen
	'Warley Ruber'	EPot WAbe

Agapanthus ✿ (*Agapanthaceae*)

	'African Moon'	CPrp IBal MAvo
	'African Queen' **new**	CPrp SFai
	'African Skies' ♀H3	CAbb CPrp IBal LBuc LRHS NBwr SFai SGBe XSte
	africanus misapplied	see *A. praecox*
	africanus 'Albus' misapplied	see *A. praecox* 'Albiflorus'
*	- 'Albus'	CBod CKel CSde EAri EHeP LCro MDon NBwr SPer WPnP
	- hybrid	CBod CCht LBar MDon WPnP
	'Aimee'	CBro IBal
	'Alan Street' ♀H4	CAvo IBal MAvo
	'Albatross'	ECha
	'Albus' ambig.	GMaP MNHC
I	'Albus Nanus'	IBal
I	'Albus Roseus'	IBal
	'Alice Double' (d)	CPbh
	'Allisio'	IBal
	'Amsterdam'	EBee ELon IBal
	'Angela'	CKel CWnw ELon IBal MAvo
	'Ankara'	IBal
	'Anneke'	IBal
	'Antibe'	IBal
	'Aquamarine'	CAvo EPri IBal
	'Arctic Star' ♀H4	CAvo CBWd CBod CCCN CDoC CExl CKno CMac CPar CWCL CWnw EBee ELan ELon EPfP IBal LRHS LSRN LSou MAvo NHoy NLar SCoo SDys SFai SGBe SPoG WTor XSte
	'Ardernei'	IBal
	'Ardernei Hybrid'	CAvo CExl ECha ECtt EWes IBal WCot WGwG
§	'Argenteus Vittatus' (v)	WSHC
	'Ascona'	IBal
	'Aureovittatus' (v)	IBal
	'Autumn Mist'	IBal
§	'B in B'PBR	CBro CExl ECha ELan IBal ILea MBNS MRav NBid NLar SCob SMrm WCot WFar
	'Baby Blue'	see *A.* 'Blue Baby' Rom.
	'Baby Pete'PBR	EWoo IBal NHoy
	BACK IN BLACK	see *A.* 'B in B'
	'Ballerina' ♀H3	IBal
	'Balmoral'	CPrp
	'Barcelona' **new**	IBal
	'Barley Blue'	IBal
	'Barnfield Blue'	CPrp EBee IBal
	'Beatrice'	CPrp
	'Beeches Dwarf'	IBal
	'Ben Hope'	CBro IBal NBPC XLum
	'Berlin'	IBal

'Best Barn Blue'	CPrp
'Beth Chatto'	see *A. campanulatus* 'Albovittatus'
'Bethlehem Star'	CPrp EPri
'Bicton Bell'	IBal
'Bicton Bride'	IBal
'Big Ben'	IBal
'Big Blue'	CBod CCCN CChe CEnd CGBo CKel CMac CPrp CSde CWCL EBee SEND SRkn WSpi
'Big Dutch Blue'	IBal
BINGO BLUE	see *A.* EVER SAPPHIRE
BINGO WHITE	see *A.* EVER WHITE
'Black Beauty'	CPrp EBee EPfP IBal LSou WSpi
'Black Buddhist'	EBee ECtt EPfP EPri ESwi GKev GMcL IBal IPot LAma NGdn NHoy NSti SPer XSen
'Black Magic'	CAbb CAby CBdn CBod CPar CPrp CWCL EBee ELan ESwi IBal IPot LBar MNrw NHoy NSti SCob SFai SMad SPoG WFar WHlf WTor WTyc
'Black Pantha'[PBR]	Widely available
BLITZ PRESTIGE ('Allprestige'[PBR])	IBal IPot LRHS
'Blitzza'	IBal
'Bloemfontein'	IBal
§ 'Blue Baby' Rom.	CCCN EHyd ELan ELon IBal LRHS
'Blue Bird'	CPrp
§ 'Blue Brush'	CPrp SCoo
'Blue Companion'	CPrp
'Blue Dot'	CBod CPrp EPfP LSou SDys
'Blue Formality'	IBal
'Blue Giant'	CBro CCCN CChe CDor CPrp EBee EGrl ELan EPfP ETod IBal LRHS MGos WAvo WSpi
'Blue Globe'	EBee EPri GMaP IBal
'Blue Heaven'[PBR]	CWGN EWes EWoo IBal ILea NHoy
'Blue Horizons'[PBR] (v)	CCCN IBal
'Blue Ice' [H4]	CBdn CPrp EBee EWoo IBal NHoy SAko SEdd WTyc XSte
'Blue Imp'	CBro IBal NWad
'Blue Jay'	IBal
'Blue Magic' [H5]	EBee IBal IPot NHoy
'Blue Moon'	CBro CPrp EBee ECha ECtt EPri GAbr GMcL IBal MAvo MHol SEND WCot
'Blue Nile'	CBdn CPrp IBal
'Blue Pixie'	IBal
'Blue Prince'	CPrp ELon
'Blue Rinse'	IBal
'Blue Sparkler'	CBdn CPrp
'Blue Spear'	CRos
'Blue Steel'	CBdn IBal
BLUE STORM ('Atiblu'[PBR]) (Storm Series)	CPrp EHyd EPfP ERom IBal LBuc LRHS MAsh SArc SCoo SGBe
BLUE THUNDER ('Sdb002') **new**	IBal
'Blue Triumphator'	CDor EPfP GMaP IBal ILea MAvo NHoy SCob WSpi
'Blue Umbrella'	CDor CPrp GMcL SGsty WSpi
'Blue Velvet'	CBdn
blue-flowered	WAvo
'Bluety'[PBR]	IBal
'Boleyn Blue'	ECha
'Bray Valley' [H4]	CBdn CPrp
'Bressingham Blue'	CAbb CBro CDoC CPrp CTri EBee EBlo EPfP EWes IBal LRHS LSou MAvo MRav NHoy SFai SMHy
'Bressingham Bounty'	EBee EBlo IBal LRHS
'Bressingham White'	CDoC CPrp EPfP LRHS MRav
'Bridal Bouquet'	CBdn EBee EPfP IBal LBuc LRHS LSRN LSou NHoy SAko SFai SGBe
'Bright Blue'	IBal

BRILLIANT BLUE ('Aga0451')	CBdn CBod CCht CEnd CKno EBee EPfP IBal LRHS LSou MHol SCoo SFai WHoo XSte
'Bristol'	IBal
'Broadleigh Babe'	CBro
'Buckingham Palace'	CBro EBee ECha ELon EWes IBal NChi WCot
'Calimero'	IBal
'Cally Blue'	GAbr IBal
'Cally Large White'	GAbr
'Cally Pale Blue'	IBal
'Cambridge'	CWnw
'Camilla' **new**	CBdn
campanulatus	CBod CMac CPbh CPrp ELan ELon EOli EPfP EWTr GKin IBal MRav NChi SGbt WAvo WFar WKif WSpi
- var. ***albidus*** misapplied	see *A.* 'Franni'
- var. ***albidus***	CBod CPrp ECha ELan EPfP GKev GKin LRHS MCot MHer MMuc NBid NGdn NHoy SEND SPer WGwG WHoo WSHC WSpi
§ - 'Albovittatus' (v)	CTtf IBal
- bright blue-flowered	IBal
- 'Cobalt Blue'	CBod CPrp ECha EGrl ELan EPri GKin IBal LPal LSou MAsh MMuc NGdn SMrm WHoo
- dark blue-flowered	CPrp
- 'Oxford Blue'	GDam LRHS
- subsp. ***patens***	CEme GKev IBal LRHS MRav
- - deep blue-flowered	LRHS
- 'Profusion'	CBro ECha EPri IBal LRHS NHoy
- 'Ultramarine'	IBal
- variegated (v)	EBee ECha NPer
- 'Wedgwood Blue'	CPrp EBee IBal
- 'Wendy'	EBlo EPfP LRHS
- 'White Hope'	EBlo IBal LRHS
'Carefree'	CPrp
'Carnival Heaven'	CPrp
'Castle of Mey'	CAvo CBdn CBro CExl CPrp EBee ELon GAbr IBal LCro LOPS LRHS LSou MAvo NHoy SFai WCAu WSpi
'Catharina'	IBal
§ ***caulescens***	CBdn CPrp IBal LRHS SMHy
- subsp. ***angustifolius***	ELon IBal SEND
'Cedric Morris'	EPri IBal
'Celebration' [H4]	CBdn CPrp IBal LCro SFai XSte
'Chandra'	IBal
'Charlotte'[PBR]	CBdn CMac CRos EBee ELan EPfP IBal LBar LRHS LSou MAsh MHol MTin SCoo SEdd SFai SPoG WTor
'Cherbours'	IBal
'Cherry Holley'	ELon IBal
'Chika's Blue'	EBee IBal MAvo
'Clarence House'	CBro CPrp IBal
'Cloudy Days'	IBal
coddii	CPbh CPrp EPri IBal MHer WCot
'Columba'	CPrp EBee ELon IBal LAma LDai NBid XSen
comptonii	see *A. praecox* subsp. *minimus*
'Connie's Delight'	ETod
'Cool Blue'	CPrp
DANUBE	see *A.* 'Donau'
'Dart Valley'	CPrp IBal
'Dartmoor'	CBdn CPrp
'Dawn Star'	ECha
'Debbie'	IBal
'Delft'	IBal
'Delft Blue'	EPau GBee IBal NLar
'Dnjepr'	CBro EBee IBal
'Dokkum'	IBal
'Dokter Brouwer'	EWTr GKev ILea LAma MCot MPtr SDir

§	'Donau'	CBro EBee EPri EShb IBal MPtr NBir
	DOUBLE DIAMOND ('Rfdd'PBR) ♀H3	CBdn EBee EHyd EPfP EPri EWes IBal LRHS LSRN LSou NHoy NWad SCob SCoo SEdd SFai SGBe SPoG WSpi WTyc
	'Dublin'	IBal
	'Duivenbrugge Blue'	IBal
	'Durban'	IBal
	'Dutch Seaside'	IBal
	dwarf blue	EOli IBal NHoy
	dyeri	see *A. inapertus* subsp. *intermedius*
	'Early Blue'	EBee ELon EWoo IBal
	'Ed Carman' (v)	WCot
	'Eggesford Sky' ♀H4	CBdn CPrp EBee IBal
	'Elaine'	IBal
	'Elisa'	IBal
	'Elizabeth Salisbury'	CPrp IBal
	'Ellamae'	IBal
	'Elsie's Sunshine'	WFar
	'Enigma'	Widely available
	'Enigma Variations'	EBee
	'Ethel's Joy'	EPri IBal LBar
	'Evening Eclipse'	EPfP IBal LBar LRHS MACG MAsh
	'Evening Star'	CPrp ECha EPri
	EVER AMETHYST	see *A.* POPPIN' PURPLE
	EVER BLUE	see *A.* EVER SAPPHIRE
§	EVER SAPPHIRE ('Andbin')	CBdn IBal LRHS SFai SGBe
§	EVER WHITE ('Wp001') ♀H3	CBdn CBro IBal LRHS MHtn SFai SGBe
	'Exmoor' ♀H4	CBdn CPrp IBal MAvo
	'Findlay's Blue'	SMHy
	'Finnline' (v)	SRms
	'Fiona'	IBal
	FIREWORKS ('Mdb001') ♀H3	CBdn CBro CWnw IBal LCro MHtn NSti SFai SGBe WNPC XSte
	'First Love' **new**	IBal
	'Flore Pleno' (d)	CExl CMac CPrp ECha ECtt GKin IBal MAvo MHer MHol NGdn NHoy SMrm WCot WFar WSHC
	'Flower of Love' ♀H4	CAvo CBdn CBro CPrp EPfP IBal LCro LOPS LRHS LSou MAsh NLar SFai SPoG WHlf WNPC WTyc XSte
	'Fluor' **new**	IBal
I	'Forma'	IBal
	FRAGRANT BLUE	see *A.* 'Blue Brush'
	FRAGRANT GLEN	see *A.* 'Glen Avon'
	FRAGRANT SNOW	see *A.* 'Snow Cloud'
§	'Franni'	WCav
	'Full Moon' ♀H3	IBal SFai
	'Gail's Purple'	IBal
	'Galgery' **new**	IBal
	'Gayle's Lilac'	CBcs CBod CCCN CElw CExl CPrp ELan ELon EPfP EWTr EWoo GKin LSou MAsh MPie MRav NGdn WGwG WWke
	'Gem'	CPrp ELon MAvo
	'Genua'	IBal
	'Glacier'	IBal
	'Glacier Stream'	CBro CDor EPri IBal NLar XSen
§	'Glen Avon'	CAbb CExl EBee EPfP EWoo IBal LBar LRHS SCoo SFai WHlf
	'Gold Strike'PBR (v)	CBdn IBal LSou NHoy SFai SPoG WCot
	'Golden Drop'PBR (v)	CBcs EHyd EPfP ESwi IBal LBar LRHS LSou NHoy NSti SFai SPad SPeP SRms
	'Gothenburg'	IBal
	'Greenfield'	EBee IBal
	'Hamar'	IBal
	'Hanneke'	CBdn IBal SAko SFai
	'Hannover'	IBal
	'Happy Blue' ♀H4	IBal

	'Harvest Blue'	IBal
§	Headbourne hybrids	Widely available
	- dark blue-flowered	LRHS
	'Headbourne White'	EPri
	'Heavenly Blue'	CCCN
	'Helsinki'	IBal
	'His Majesty'	CBod IBal LBar
	'Hole Park Blue'	NHoy WMal
	'Hoyland Blue' ♀H3	CPrp IBal NCth NHoy WFar
	'Hoyland Chelsea Blue' ♀H3	NCth NHoy
	'Ice Blue Star' ♀H5	CBro CPrp IBal
	'Ice Lolly'	CBro IBal
	ICICLES ('Duivenbrugge White')	CKno IBal LSou MHol NSti SFai
	inapertus	CAvo CBro CKel CPbh CPrp CWnw EWes IBal WBrk WPGP WSHC
	- 'Avalanche' ♀H4	WSpi
	- 'Cascade Crystal'	IBal
	- 'Cascade Diamond'	IBal
	- 'Crystal Drop'	CAbb CBdn CExl CPrp EPri IBal LBar LSou SFai
	- subsp. ***hollandii***	IBal
	- - 'Sky' ♀H4	CAbb CBdn CBro CDor EBee EPri EWTr EWoo IBal LEdu LRHS NBid SRms
	- 'Ice Cascade'	EBee IBal
	- 'Icicle'	SPoG
	- subsp. ***inapertus*** 'White'	CPrp IBal
§	- subsp. ***intermedius***	CPrp IBal NHoy
*	- - 'August Bells'	CBro
	- - 'Long Tom'	CExl
	- 'Midnight Cascade'	CExl CPar CPrp CSpe EBee ECtt IPot LEdu NBid NHoy SEdd SRms WFar WTyc
	- 'Mood Indigo'	EBee EPri IBal NHoy
	- subsp. ***pendulus***	IBal
	- - 'Black Magic'	CBdn CWnw IBal SPeP WTyc XSte
	- - 'Graskop'	CBod CExl EBee EPfP EPri EWoo IBal LBar LLWG MNrw NHoy NSti SEdd SFai SMHy SRms WTyc
	- tall pale blue-flowered	WPGP
	- 'Tempest'	WPGP
	- 'White Cloud'	IBal
	'Indigo Dreams'	CBdn CKno CPar CPrp CWnw EBee IBal LPla LRHS MAvo MHol NHoy SFai WTyc
	INDIGO FROST	see *A.* TWISTER
	'Inkspots'	CMac CPrp EPfP IBal LSou NHoy SEdd SPoG
	'Intermedius' Leichtlin	IBal LEdu
I	'Intermedius' van Tubergen	IBal LAma MACG NBid
	'Isis'	CAvo CBro CPrp CSde ECha ELon EPfP EPri IBal LRHS MAvo
	'Jacaranda' ♀H3	CMac IBal LRHS LSou NHoy SCoo SEdd SFai SGBe
	'Jack's Blue'	CBro CDor EBee ECtt ELan ELon IBal LSRN MHol MNrw NGdn NHoy NLar SCoo WCot WFar WSpi
	'James'	CBdn CPrp
	'Jersey Giant'	CPrp
	'Jessica' ♀H4	CBdn IBal LSou SFai
	'Jodie'	CBdn CPrp ELon MAvo
	'Johanna'	CPrp IBal
	'Johannesburg'	IBal
	Johannesburg hybrids	ECha
	'Jolanda'	CPrp IBal LAma
	'Jonie' ♀H4	IBal
	'Jonny's White' ♀H4	IBal
	'Kalmthout Blue'	IBal
	'Kew White'	SMHy
	'Kilmurry Blue'	IBal
	'Kilmurry White'	IBal

	'Kingston Blue'	ECha NBid NHoy WSHC
	'Kobold'	CBro IBal WFar
	'Lady Moore'	SMHy
	L'AMOUR D'ÉTÉ BLEU ('Corag02bl'PBR)	IBal
§	'Lapis'	CBdn CBod CDoC CMac CPrp CSde EBee EPfP EPri EWoo IBal LRHS LSou MHol MPri NHoy NLar SCoo SEdd SFai SGBe WTyc XSte
	'Lapis Lazuli'	see *A.* 'Lapis'
	'Latent Blue'	CPrp
	'Lavender Haze'	CBdn CDoC CMac EBee EHyd EPfP IBal LRHS NHoy SCoo SEdd SFai SGBe
	'Leanne'	CBdn IBal
	'Leicester' 🏆H4	IBal
	'Liam's Lilac'	CAby CBdn CDoC CExl ELon IBal LCro LOPS LSou MAvo NHoy NLar SFai WFar
	'Lilac Bells'	CBdn
	'Lilac Flash'	CPbh IBal MACG
	'Lilac Lullaby'	IBal
	'Lilac Time'	CBdn CExl ELon IBal
	'Lilliput'	CBcs CBro CCCN CMac CPrp CSpe EBlo ECha ECtt ELan ELon EPfP GArf GKev GMaP IBal LRHS LSou MRav NGdn SPer SRms WCFE WFar WWke XSen
	'Lissabon'	IBal
	'Lisse'	IBal
	'Little Dutch Blue'	EWoo IBal MHol SMad WCot
	'Little Dutch White'PBR	IBal LEdu MHol SEdd WCot
	'Little Frank'	NHoy
	'Little Sebastian'	NHoy
	'Little White'	IBal
	'Littlecourt'	CBro IBal MAvo
	'Loch Hope' 🏆H5	CBro CPrp EBee EBlo ECtt ELon EPfP IBal LPla LRHS MAvo MHol MRav SDix WCot WSpi
	'Los Angeles'	IBal
	'Luly' 🏆H4	IBal MAvo MGos WFar
	'Luna'	IBal
	'Lydenburg'	EPri IBal LEdu WPGP
	'Lyn Valley'	CBdn CPrp IBal
	'Madurodam'	IBal
	'Magnifico'	CPrp
	'Malaga'	IBal
	'Malmo'	IBal
	'Marchants Midnight Blue'	SMHy
	'Marcus'	IBal LAma SDir
	'Margaret'	ELon IBal LSRN NHoy WFar
	'Maria'	CBdn
	'Marianne'	IBal
	'Mariètte'	CPrp
	'Marijke'	IBal
	'Marnie' 🏆H4	CBdn
	'Martine'	IBal
	'Maureen' 🏆H5	CBdn CPrp EBee IBal LSRN MAvo
	'Maurice'	IBal
	'May Snow' (v)	WCot
	'Medan'	IBal
	'Medusa'	IBal
	'Megan's Mauve' 🏆H3	CBdn CBro EBee ELon EPri IBal LCro LSRN MAvo NSti SFai XSte
	'Meibont' (v)	IBal WCot
	'Melbourne'	IBal
	'Messina'	IBal
	MI CASA ('Aaopr017')	CBdn IBal SPad
	'Michelle'	IBal
	mid blue	IBal
	'Middleburg'	IBal
	MIDKNIGHT BLUE ('Monmid')	EWes WSHC
	'Midnight'	EWes IBal
	'Midnight Blue' ambig.	CDoC ELan EPfP EWoo GKev IBal MCot NLar NWad SMHy WFar
	'Midnight Dream'	EBee ECtt EPot IBal LEdu NHoy WFar
	'Midnight Madness' **new**	IBal LCro SFai
§	'Midnight Star' 🏆H5	Widely available
	'Mini Blue'	IBal
	'Misty Dawn' (v)	CBcs CPrp CWGN EBee ECtt ELon EWhm IBal MHol SPeP WCot
	'Mole Valley'	IBal
	'Molly Howick'	EBee EBlo ELon LRHS
	'Monique' 🏆H4	IBal
	'Montreal'	IBal
	'Moody Blue'	IBal
	'Moonlight Star'	EBee IBal IPot LRHS MAsh MHol NHoy SFai SMad WFar
	'Moonshine'	IBal WFar
I	'Mooreanus' misapplied	EBee IBal NBid
	'Morning Star'	IBal
	'Mount Stewart'	IBal
	'Nancy'	IBal
	'Napoli'	IBal
	'Navy Blue'	see *A.* 'Midnight Star'
	'Newa'	EBee
	'Newcastle'	IBal
	'Night Sky'	CBdn IBal MHol SFai
	'Nikki'	IBal
	'Northern Light'	IBal
	'Northern Star'PBR 🏆H4	Widely available
	nutans	see *A. caulescens*
	'Odessa'	IBal
	'Oslo'	ELon IBal
I	'Ovatus'	ERom
	'Oxford'	IBal
	'Pacific Blue'PBR	CDoC IBal IPot
	Palmer's hybrids	see *A.* Headbourne hybrids
	'Patent Blue'	CPrp IBal
	'Pavlova'	EPfP IBal SFai
	'Penelope Palmer'	CPrp IBal
	'Peter Franklin' 🏆H3	IBal
	'Peter Pan' ambig.	Widely available
	'Peter Pan American'	NHoy
	'Phantom'	CBdn CPrp EBee IBal LBar MAvo MHtn NLar SAko SFai WCot WFar
	'Picton Blue'	WFar
	'Pino' 🏆H4	IBal MHtn SFai
	'Pinocchio'	GKev IBal SDeJ
	'Pirame'	IBal
	PITCHOUNE BLUE ('Scrarey09'PBR)	CKel IBal
	'Plas Merdyn Blue'	CPrp
	'Plas Merdyn White'	IBal
	'Podge Mill'	IBal
	'Polar Ice'	CKel CPrp EBee ELon EPfP EPri GKev IBal ILea LAma MBow MNrw MPtr NCth NHoy SDir WCAu WFar WSpi
	'Polar Star'	IBal LBar SCoo
§	POPPIN' PURPLE ('Mp003') **new**	LBar SFai
	'Porcelain'	IBal
§	***praecox***	CBcs CElw CEme CExl CKel CPrp CTsd EPfP ETod IBal ILea LCro LPal LPar LRHS MBros MNHC NHoy SArc SChr SCob SDeJ SVic WSHC XLum XSen
§	- 'Albiflorus'	CBcs CBod CBro CEme CExl CTri CTsd EPfP EPri ERom ETod IBal ILea LCro LPal LPar LRHS LSRN MBros MGos NHoy SCob SDeJ SEND SGsty SPeP SRms XLum XSen
	- 'Maximus Albus'	IBal
§	- subsp. ***minimus***	CElw IBal SEND
	- - 'Adelaide'	CPrp IBal

§ - subsp. ***orientalis***	CBro CCCN
- - 'Mount Thomas'	CPrp
- - 'Silver Star' (v)	IBal
- subsp. ***praecox*** 'Variegatus'	see *A.* 'Argenteus Vittatus'
- 'Storms River'	IBal
'Pretty Heidy'	LSou MHol SFai
'Pretty Wendy'	IBal
'Pride of Bicton'	CBdn
'Prince of the Night'	SMHy
'Princess Margaret'	CPrp IBal
§ 'Purple Cloud'	Widely available
'Purple Delight' ♀H3	CBdn CPar CPbh CPrp EBee EPfP IBal LCro LOPS LRHS SAko SCoo SFai SGBe WFar XSte
'Purple Emperor'	IBal MHol SFai
'Purple Fountain'	IBal SRms
'Purple Haze'	IBal
'Purple Heart'	CBdn SFai
'Purple Magic'	IBal
'Purple Ripple'	IBal
'Purple Star'	CCCN
'Queen Anne'	IBal
'Queen Mother'	CPrp IBal WSpi
QUEEN MUM ('Pmn06'[PBR])	Widely available
'Queen of the Ocean'	IBal
'Quink Drops'	SMHy
'Radiant Star'	IBal LRHS
'Regal Beauty'	CBdn CBro CSBt EWoo IBal LSRN NBid SAko SFai
'Rhapsody in Blue' ♀H4	CBdn
'Rhone'	CBro IBal
'Rob Cole' **new**	WCot
'Robin'	IBal
'Rosewarne'	CBcs CBod CCCN CDoC CExl IBal
'Rotterdam'	IBal XSen
'Roxanne'	IBal
'Royal Blue' ♀H5	CBro CPrp GMaP IBal WCot WSpi
'Royal Knight'	IBal
'Royal Purple'	CWnw
'Royal Velvet' ♀H4	CBdn CKno EPfP IBal LCro MAvo MHol SFai SGBe WFar XSte
'Ruan Vean'	CPrp
'Ruthie's Sunshine'	WFar
'Sabang'	IBal
'Sally Anne'	CBdn CPrp
'San Remo'	IBal
'Sandringham' ♀H5	CBcs CKel CPrp CWnw EBee ELon EPfP EPri EWes IBal LSRN NBid NHoy SEdd WFar
'Sandy'[PBR] ♀H4	CKno IBal IPot LSou MHol SFai
'Sapphire'	CPrp
'Sarah'[PBR]	CBdn EBee IBal MTin NLar SFai
'Saville Blue'	CPrp
'Sea Coral'	CBod CMac CPrp EBee ECtt EMor EPri IBal LPla MPie NCth NSti SCoo SMrm SPoG
'Sea Foam'	CMac XLum
'Sea Mist'	CPrp
'Sea Spray'	EBee EPri IBal WFar
'Sea Storm' (Storm Series)	CBod
'Second Chance' **new**	IBal
'Selma Bock'	CPbh
'Semarang'	IBal
'Senna'[PBR]	EPot GKev IBal SIvy
'Septemberhemel'	IBal
'Shades of Grey' **new**	CAvo
'Shooting Stars'	IBal
'Silberpfeil'	IBal MPtr
'Silver Anniversary'	IBal NHoy
'Silver Baby' ♀H3	CAbb CAvo CBcs CBdn CBod CBro CDoC CKno CPrp CWGN CWnw EBee EHyd ELon EPfP EPri ETod IBal LBar LEdu LRHS LSou MBros NHoy SCoo SFai SPoG SRms WNPC WTyc
'Silver Jubilee'	IBal
'Silver Lining'	CBod ECtt EMor IBal LBar LRHS SFai
'Silver Mist'	CDor IBal
SILVER MOON ('Notfred'[PBR]) (v) ♀H5	CAvo CBcs CBdn CBod CBro EBee EHyd ELan EPfP GKev IBal LBar LRHS LSou MCot MGos MHol NBPC NHoy NLar NSti SCob SEdd SFai SGsty SPoG WCot
'Silver Stream'	NHoy
'Silver Suzy'	IBal
'Sky Rocket'	CPrp IBal WMal
'Sky Star'	IBal
'Skyscraper'	IBal
§ 'Snow Cloud' ♀H4	CAbb CBcs CBdn CBro CExl EBee EHyd EPfP LCro LRHS NLar SAko SCoo SEND SEdd SFai SPoG WSpi
'Snow Crystal' ♀H3	CBro IBal LCro LRHS SCoo SFai SPoG XSte
'Snow Pixie'	CBdn CSpe EBee EBlo IBal LSou NHoy SFai WSpi
'Snow Princess'	ELon IBal
'Snow Shadows'	CBro IBal
'Snowball'	CExl
'Snowdrops'	EBee
'Snowstorm'[PBR] (Storm Series)	CCht EBee ERom IBal LRHS SArc SCoo
'Sofie'[PBR]	EBee IBal STPC
'Sorento'	IBal
'Sosua' **new**	IBal
'Southern Cross'	CPrp IBal NHoy SFai SGsty
'Southern Star'	CPrp IBal
'Star Quality'	IBal LRHS LSRN LSou MNrw SCoo SFai
'Starburst Blue'	CBod IBal LBar
'Starburst White'	IBal LBar
'Stardust'	EPfP IBal SCoo
'Stargazer'	IBal LRHS
'Stars and Stripes'	IBal
'Stellenbosch'	LEdu WPGP
'Stéphanie Charm'	IBal
'Stockholm'	IBal LAma SDir
'Storm Cloud' Reads	see *A.* 'Purple Cloud'
'Storm Cloud' (d)	CBro IBal
'Strawberry Ice'	CBdn CBro EBee EMil EPfP IBal LBar LCro SEdd SFai WSpi WTyc
'Streamline'	CBcs CBod CElw CEnd CKno CPla CPrp EAJP EBee ECtt EGrI EHyd ELon EPfP EShb EWoo GAbr GKin GMaP GMcL IBal LRHS MACG MRav NHoy SDys SEND WSHC
'Su Casa'	CBod IBal
'Summer Blue'	IBal
'Summer Clouds'	CPrp ELan
'Summer Days' ♀H4	CBdn CPrp IBal
'Summer Delight' ♀H4	CPrp IBal
'Summer Skies'	CPrp ELon IBal
'Summer Snow'	IBal
'Sunfield'	CDor EPfP IBal ILea LAma LRHS MNrw MPtr NLar NPer
'Super Star'	CBro CPrp IBal
'Susan Elizabeth'	CPrp
'Suzan'	IBal
'Sweet Surprise'	CBdn EPfP IBal LBuc LRHS SFai SGBe
'Sylvia'[PBR]	IBal
'Sylvine'	CKel CPrp CWnw IBal
'Tarka'	CBdn CExl CPrp ELon EPfP EPri EWoo IBal LSou NHoy SDys
'Taw Valley'	CKno CPrp ELon EPPr IBal LCro MGos NHoy SEdd

'Thorn'	IBal
'Three Times' **new**	IBal
'Thumbelina'	CBro CMac EBee IBal LSou NHoy
THUNDER STORM ('Dunaga02') (Storm Series) (v)	CWGN IBal SPeP
'Timaru'	CBro CElw CPrp EBee ECha ECtt ELan EPfP GMaP GMcL MHol NGdn WCot XSte
'Tinkerbell' (v)	CBcs CBdn CBor CBro CCCN CEme CTtf EBee EBlo ELan EPfP EPri IBal LRHS MGos MHol MRav NHoy NPer SPoG SRms SWvt
'Tiny White'	EPri
'Titch'	IBal
'Tom Thumb' PBR	CBod CDoC CExl CKel CPrp CSde CTsd ECtt EHyd EPfP IBal LRHS NHoy
'Top Slice' (v)	WCot
'Torbay'	CBod CElw CPrp CWCL ECtt ELon EPfP EShb GAbr GKev GKin IBal MNrw NCth NHol NLar SGbt WAvo WBrk WHoo
'Tornado'	CPrp EBee ECtt ETod IBal ILea LRHS NLar
'Triangle'	CPbh CPrp IBal
'Tripoli' **new**	IBal
'Tsolo'	IBal
'Twilight Zone'	EBee IBal LRHS SCoo
§ TWISTER ('Ambic001' PBR) ♀H4	Widely available
umbellatus Redouté	see *A. praecox* subsp. *orientalis*
'Underway'	EWes GKev IBal
'Vallée Blanche'	IBal
'Vallée de la Loire'	IBal
'Vallée de la Sarthe'	IBal
'Vallée de l'Authion'	IBal
Ventnor hybrid	SVen
'Volendam'	IBal
'Washington'	IBal
'Wavy Navy'	IBal
'Wedding Day'	EBee IBal
'Wembworthy'	CBdn CPrp EBee IBal
'White Baby'	IBal
'White Dwarf'	see *A.* white-flowered, dwarf
'White Giant'	CBod CSBt EGrI MBros WSpi
'White Heaven' PBR	EBee ECtt EPfP EWes EWoo GAbr IBal IPot LCro LEdu LRHS MAvo MHol NBPC NHoy NSti SCob SDix SEND SEdd SFai SMad WCot WSpi
'White Ice'	CPbh IBal
'White Pixie'	CBdn IBal SFai
'White Smile'	EPri
'White Superior'	CBod EBee EPfP GMaP IBal MNHC
'White Umbrella'	EHyd ELan GMcL LRHS MAsh
white-flowered	WAvo WCFE
§ - dwarf	CBro ECha EPfP EShb EWoo IBal MAsh NBir NGdn NHol SGbt
'Whitney' PBR	IBal
'Windlebrooke'	EAJP ECha EPot EPri IBal MAvo NLar SDeJ WCot WKif
'Windsor Castle'	CPrp
'Windsor Grey'	Widely available
'Winter Sky'	IBal
'Wolga'	CBro EBee IBal
'Wolkberg' Kirstenbosch	CPrp IBal
'Yellow Tips'	IBal
'Zachary'	CPrp EBee ELon EPri
'Zeal Thomas'	IBal
'Zigzag White' ♀H3	WCot

Agapetes (*Ericaceae*)

'Ludgvan Cross' ♀H2	CBcs CCCN CTsd LRHS MGil
serpens ♀H2	CBcs CCCN CTsd
- 'Scarlet Elf'	CCCN CTsd

Agastache (*Lamiaceae*)

'After Eight'	CDor CMiW ECha ECtt EWTr LBar LRHS NLar WHlf
anethiodora	see *A. foeniculum* (Pursh) Kuntze
anisata	see *A. foeniculum* (Pursh) Kuntze
'Arcado Pink' **new**	LBar
'Astello Indigo'	SPhx XLum
aurantiaca	SPhx SPlb
- 'Apricot Sprite'	CSpe LDai LShi MACG MHol MHoo NGdn NRHS SCoo SRkn
- 'Navajo Sunset'	WWke
- 'Sunset Yellow'	LBar
'Ayala'	EBee
'Blackadder'	Widely available
'Blaue Sangria'	NDov
'Blue Boa' PBR	CBod CDor CKno CWGN CWnw EBee ECha ECtt ETod LBar LCro LOPS LSRN MAvo MBel NCou NDov NLar NSti SGBe SIvy SMad SPoG SRms WCAu WHlf WHoo WSpi WTor
* 'Blue Bonnet'	CSpe
'Blue Fortune' ♀H6	CBcs CRos ECha EHyd EPfP EWoo GBee GKev LCro LOPS LPla LRHS MCot MRav NDov NLar NRHS SCob SCoo SEdd SMad SMrm SPhx SRms SWvt WCAu WHlf WNPC WSpi XSen
'Bolero'	LRHS MHoo SPhx
§ ***cana***	LDai SPhx
- 'Heatwave' PBR	EBee WNPC
'Cotton Candy' PBR	EBee LCro LOPS
'Crazy Fortune' (v) **new**	LBar WHil
'Firebird'	CWGN EBee ECtt ELan LBar LRHS MAsh SRms SWvt WGwG
'Fleur'	ECtt SEdd WGoo
foeniculum misapplied	see *A. rugosa*
§ ***foeniculum*** (Pursh) Kuntze	CBee CCBP CLau ELan ENfk GPoy LRHS MHer MHoo MNHC SPhx SRms SVic WJek WTre
- 'Alabaster'	CBcs EBee EWes GMaP LCro LOPS MAsh NLar WHlf
'Globetrotter'	EAJP MNrw SPhx
'Kolibri'	ECtt ILea NDov NLar WGoo
(Kudos Series) 'Kudos Ambrosia' PBR	ELan LRHS NRHS SGBe SPoG WCot
- 'Kudos Coral' PBR	CKno CPla EBee ELan EPfP LBar LRHS MHol NLar NRHS SGBe SOrN SRkn WNPC
- 'Kudos Gold' PBR	CKno EBee ELan EPfP MHol NLar NSti SCoo SGBe SPoG WNPC
- 'Kudos Mandarin' PBR	ELan EPfP LRHS NCth NLar NRHS SGBe SPoG
- 'Kudos Red'	LBar NLar
- 'Kudos Silver Blue'	EBee ECtt ELan EPfP LRHS NLar NRHS
- 'Kudos Yellow' PBR	ELan EPfP LBar LRHS
'Linda'	CWGN WCot WMal
§ ***mexicana***	LDai MNHC NWad
- 'Red Fortune' PBR	CBcs CWGN EBee ECtt EHyd ELan EPfP LBar LCro LOPS LRHS MHol MPie NRHS SEdd SPad SPoG WCot WMal WNPC
- 'Rosea'	see *A. cana*
- 'Sangria'	CWGN MHoo NGdn SBut SPhx SRms XLum XSen
'Morello'	ECtt LBar SPad SPeP
nepetoides	CBWd EPPr
ORANGE NECTAR (Nectar Series)	EBee MPie WCot

'Painted Lady'	ECtt
pallidiflora	SPlb
var. ***neomexicana***	
- - 'Rose Mint'	CDor CSpe NWad
- var. ***pallidiflora***	GElm
'Pink Pop'	MHoo
POQUITO DARK BLUE ('Tnagapdb'PBR) (Poquito Series) **new**	LBar
'Purple Haze'	CDoC EAJP EBee EBlo LRHS MAvo MPri NDov NRHS
'Raspberry Summer'PBR	CWGN EBee ECtt EPfP LRHS MHtn NRHS
'Rosie Posie'PBR **new**	LBar NCth
§ ***rugosa***	CAby CBod ECha GPoy MHoo MNHC SPhx SPlb SRms WJek
- f. ***albiflora***	WCAu
- - 'Alabaster'	CDor LBar NDov WGwG
- - 'Liquorice White'	CBod ELan EPfP LRHS MArl MBel MHoo SBls SGbt SMrm SPer SPlb SPoG SRms
- BEELICIOUS PURPLE ('Agapd')	CBod ECtt GElm LCro LRHS LSou MMrt NCth WNPC
- 'Golden Jubilee'	CBod CRos CSpe EBee EBlo EBou ECha ELan EMor EPfP LBar LDai LRHS MAvo MHol NGdn NLar NRHS NSti SBls SGbt SRms SWvt WCav WJek WPnP
- 'Heronswood Mist'	EBee
- 'Korean Zest'	WCru
- 'Liquorice Blue'	CBod CDor EGrI ELan EPfP GKev LRHS MBel NGdn SBls SGbt SMrm SPer SPoG SRms SSut SWvt WHoo
- 'Little Adder'	CBcs CBod ECtt LBar LRHS MHol MTin NCth NDov SPad WGwG WHoo WNPC
rupestris	CSpe MHoo SPhx XSen
- 'Apache Sunset'	SPlb XSen
'Serpentine'	EBee EWes NLar WGoo
'Spicy'	NDov
'Summer Glow'	CWGN ECtt EPfP LBar LRHS NDov NLar NRHS SDys SEdd SPoG WCot
'Summer Love'PBR	NLar
'Summer Sunset'PBR	CDor CWGN LBar LCro LOPS LRHS NRHS
'Tangerine Dreams'	ECtt EPfP LRHS MPie NRHS SCoo
'Tango'	CAby GElm MHoo SBls
'Tutti-frutti'	ECtt
'Violet Vision'PBR	CWGN ECtt EPfP LCro LOPS

Agathaea see *Felicia*

Agathis (*Araucariaceae*)

australis	SMad

Agathosma (*Rutaceae*)

capensis	LRHS
ovata	CCCN
- 'Glentana'	LRHS
serpyllacea	CCCN

Agave ✿ (*Asparagaceae*)

albomarginata	CDTJ
americana ♀H2	CAbb CBcs CBen CDow CPbh CPla EPfP EShb LPal LPar LSun NPlm SArc SChr SCob SEND SEdd SGsty SPlb SPre SSim SVen SWeb SWvt WCot
- var. ***expansa***	EOli
- 'Marginata' (v) ♀H2	CAco CBrP CDTJ GMcL NQui SEND SVen WCot WSFF
- 'Mediopicta' misapplied	see *A. americana* 'Mediopicta Alba'
- 'Mediopicta' (v) ♀H2	CDTJ EAri SArc
§ - 'Mediopicta Alba' (v) ♀H2	CAbb CBrP CCCN CDTJ CJun CPbh ELan EOli NCft NPlm SPlb WBor WCot
- 'Mediopicta Aurea' (v)	CTtf NPlm WCot
- subsp. ***protamericana***	CDTJ EOli NCft
- - blue	SPlb
- 'Striata' (v)	CDTJ EShb WCot
- 'Variegata' (v) ♀H2	CAbb CBcs CBen CBod CDow CEme CKel CPbh CSde CWal ELan EOli EPfP EShb LPal LSun NCft NPer NPlm SArc SChr SCob SGsty SPlb SSim SWeb SWvt WBor
angustifolia	see *A. vivipara* var. *vivipara*
- var. ***marginata*** hort.	NPlm SSim WCot
applanata	CJun SPlb
asperrima	CDTJ
§ - subsp. ***maderensis***	SPlb
atrovirens	WCot
- var. ***mirabilis***	CDTJ
attenuata	CDTJ CPbh EOli SPlb
beauleriana	EOli
'Bloodspot'	EOli WCot
'Blue Brian'	NPlm SArc
§ 'Blue Glow'	LCro
boldinghiana	WCot
bovicornuta	WCot
bracteosa	CAco CDTJ NPlm WCot XVPe
celsii	see *A. mitis* var. *mitis*
cerulata subsp. ***nelsonii***	CDTJ
chiapensis	EOli
chrysantha	CAco CDTJ WCot
- 'Black Canyon'	WCot
chrysoglossa	CDTJ
colimana	see *A. ortgiesiana*
colorata	CDTJ CJun NPlm WCot
'Confederate Rose' **new**	EAri
'Cornelius'	WCot
cupreata	CDTJ
decipiens	SPlb
de-meesteriana	EOli
- variegated (v) **new**	NPlm
deserti	CAco CDTJ CJun WCot
- var. ***simplex***	WCot
difformis	CDTJ
durangensis	SPlb
elongata	see *A. vivipara* var. *vivipara*
ensifera	CJun
'Falling Waters' **new**	NPlm
ferdinandi-regis	see *A. victoriae-reginae*
ferox	see *A. salmiana* var. *ferox*
filifera ♀H2	CDTJ CDoC CJun CPbh NCft SChr SPlb SSim WCot
I - 'Variegata' (v)	EOli
flexispina	SPlb
garciae-mendozae	CDTJ
geminiflora	CBcs CDTJ CJun CPbh EShb NPlm XSte
gentryi	CDTJ LPal NPlm SPlb WCot
ghiesbreghtii	CPbh EAri
gigantea	see *Furcraea foetida*
guadalajarana	CDTJ CPbh NPlm
guttata	WCot
havardiana	CDTJ CPbh NPlm XSen XVPe
horrida	CDTJ CJun
- subsp. ***horrida***	SPlb
- 'Perotensis'	CDTJ EShb
impressa	WCot
isthmensis	SPlb
kerchovei	WCot
lechuguilla	CDTJ WCot XSen
lophantha	see *A. univittata*
- var. ***caerulescens***	see *A. univittata*

	'Macha Mocha'	WCot
	macroacantha 🏆H1c	CDTJ
	maculosa	WCot
	marmorata	CJun
	maximilliana	SPlb
	mckelveyana	WCot
	- DJF 1575 from Bagdad, Arizona	WCot
*	***minuata*** **new**	SPlb
	mitis	CDoC
	- var. ***albidior***	NPlm
§	- var. ***mitis***	CDTJ SPlb SSim
	- var. ***mitis* × *variegata***	EOli WCot
	montana	CDTJ CPbh EAri EOli LPal SArc SPlb SPtp XSen
	'Moonglow' **new**	NPlm
	multifilifera	XSen
§	***obscura***	CDTJ WCot
§	***ortgiesiana***	WCot
	ovatifolia	CDTJ CJun EAri EOli NPlm SPlb WCot XSen XVPe
	palmeri	CDTJ EOli SPlb WCot XSen
	panamana	see *A. vivipara* var. *vivipara*
	parrasana 🏆H2	CDTJ SSim WCot
	parryi 🏆H2	CBod CDTJ CPbh LPal SPlb SPtp SSim WCot XSen
	- var. ***couesii***	CDTJ EAri
	- 'Cream Spike' (v)	CBcs NCft SEdd SMad SMrm SPad WCot
	- var. ***huachucensis***	CDTJ WCot
	- subsp. ***neomexicana***	CCCN CDTJ NPlm SPlb WCot
	- - SB 948 from W of Artesia, New Mexico	WCot
	- 'Ohi-kissho-ten-nishiki' (v)	WCot
	- subsp. ***parryi***	CDTJ WCot WPGP
	- var. ***truncata***	CDTJ EOli NPlm SEdd SPlb
	- - variegated (v)	WCot
	parviflora 🏆H2	WCot
	polyacantha var. ***xalapensis***	see *A. obscura*
	potatorum 🏆H2	WCot
	- 'Gary Fisher'	WCot
	- var. ***verschaffeltii***	NPlm
	'Red Edge' **new**	NPlm
	'Royal Spine' **new**	NPlm
	salmiana	CDTJ SPlb
	- subsp. ***crassispina***	SPlb
§	- var. ***ferox***	CDTJ EOli SArc SChr SPlb
	scabra	WCot
	- subsp. ***maderensis***	see *A. asperrima* subsp. *maderensis*
	schidigera	LPal NPlm WCot
	- 'Shira-ito-no-ohi' (v)	WCot
	schottii	CDTJ WCot
	'Shaka Zulu'	see *A.* 'Blue Glow'
	'Sharkskin Shoes'	NPlm WCot
	shrevei subsp. ***magna***	SPlb
	sileri	WCot
	sisalana	CDTJ
	stictata	WCot
	striata	SEdd
	- subsp. ***falcata***	WCot
*	- 'Rubra'	CDTJ SPlb WCot
	stricta 🏆H2	CCCN CDTJ NCft NPlm WCot
	- 'Nana'	CDTJ NCft SMad
	- 'Rubra'	WCot
	tenuifolia	CPla
	titanota 🏆H1c	SPlb WCot
	toumeyana 🏆H2	CPbh SPlb WCot
	- var. ***bella***	CDTJ
	triangularis	CDTJ
	undulata	WCot
	- 'Chocolate Chips'	WCot
§	***univittata***	CDTJ CJun LPal WCot
	- 'Quadricolor' (v) 🏆H2	CDTJ CPbh NCft SMad SPlb SSim WCot
I	- 'Splendida' (v)	NCft
	utahensis 🏆H3	CDTJ EOli SEND SPlb WCot XSen
	- DJF 1521 from Peach Springs, Arizona	WCot
	- var. ***eborispina***	EAri WCot
	- subsp. ***kaibabensis***	WCot
	- var. ***nevadensis***	EAri
	variegata	WCot
	- B&SWJ 10234	WCru
§	***victoriae-reginae*** 🏆H2	CCCN CDTJ CJun CPbh EAri EOli LPal NCft NHrt SPlb SSim WCot XSen
	- dwarf	WCot
	- 'Golden Princess' (v) **new**	EAri
	- variegated (v)	CTtf
	vilmoriniana	NPlm
	virginica	WCot
§	***vivipara*** var. ***vivipara***	WCot
	'Whale Tale' **new**	NPlm
	× ***winteriana***	EOli
	wocomahi	WCot
	xylonacantha	CDTJ SChr SPlb WCot
	- blue-leaved	EAri

Ageratina (*Asteraceae*)

§	***altissima***	CMac SMrm
	- 'Braunlaub'	EBee NBir NLar WCAu
	- 'Chocolate'	Widely available
	- LUCKY MELODY ('Allmelody'PBR)	IPot LBar LRHS
§	***aromatica***	SBut
§	***ligustrina***	CBcs CBod CCht CCoa CDoC CExl CKel CMCN CRHN CTri EBee ECha ELan LRHS MBlu MNHC NAts SDix SEND SPer SPoG SRkn SRms WLov WMal WSFF

Ageratum (*Asteraceae*)

	'Blue Champion'	MPri SCob
	corymbosum	CHll CSpe EShb WFar
	houstonianum 'Blue Danube' 🏆H2	LCro
	- 'High Tide Blue'	MPri
	petiolatum	LRHS SGBe SHar WFar

Aglaonema (*Araceae*)

	'Crete' **new**	LCro NHrt
	'Cutlass' **new**	LCro
	'Freedman' **new**	NHrt
	'Jubilee Compacta'PBR	LCro LOPS
	'Maria' **new**	NHrt
	'Silver Queen' 🏆H1b	NHrt
	'Silver Queen Compact' **new**	NHrt

Agrimonia (*Rosaceae*)

	eupatoria	CBod CHab EMor ENfk GPoy MHer MHoo NAts NMir SRms WHer WOut WWild
*	- var. ***alba***	EMor MHoo NLar
	- 'Cambridge Lace' (v)	WCot
	odorata misapplied	see *A. procera*
§	***procera***	SPhx

Agropyron (*Poaceae*)

	glaucum	see *Elymus hispidus*
	magellanicum	see *Elymus magellanicus*
	pubiflorum	see *Elymus magellanicus*

Agrostemma (*Caryophyllaceae*)

	coronaria	see *Lychnis coronaria*
	githago	CBod CHab ELan LCro LOPS MBow MNHC NBir SRms

- 'Ocean Pearl'	CSpe SPhx
- 'Purple Queen'	CSpe

Agrostis (*Poaceae*)

calamagrostis	see *Stipa calamagrostis*
capillaris	CHab SPhx
nebulosa	SPhx WCot
stolonifera	WCot
'Julia Ann' (v)	

Aichryson (*Crassulaceae*)

§ × ***aizoides***	SEdd
var. ***domesticum***	
- - 'Variegatum' (v) 🏆H1c	CDTJ CPbh EAri SIvy SSim WCot
tortuosum subsp. ***bethencourtianum*** new	EAri
- - variegated (v)	EAri SEdd

Ainsliaea (*Asteraceae*)

apiculata	MAsh
chapaensis B&SWJ 11732	WCru
latifolia FMWJ 13426	WCru
nervosa B&SWJ 11344	WCru
petelotii FMWJ 13427	WCru
tonkinensis B&SWJ 11819	WCru

Ajania see *Chrysanthemum*

Ajuga (*Lamiaceae*)

genevensis	GEdr LRHS SPhx
incisa	EWld
- 'Bikun' (v)	NEoE SPoG WCot
- 'Blue Enigma'	CExl NLar WFar
- 'Blue Ensign'	EHed LDai WSHC
'Little Court Pink'	see *A. reptans* 'Purple Torch'
lupulina	GEdr
- BO 15-009	GGro
metallica hort.	see *A. pyramidalis*
'Pink Lightning' (v)	ELan LRHS NHpl NRHS SRms WCot WFar WHil
'Pink Spires'	WFar
§ ***pyramidalis***	EGrl
- 'Metallica Crispa'	EBee ELan EWes GBin GJos GKev NBir NEoE NHol NHpl NLar SRms SWvt WCav WFar XLum
reptans	CBod CHab ECtt EHeP ENfk GDam GKev GPoy LCro LOPS MBel MHer MHoo MNHC NAts NMir SRms
- f. ***albiflora***	CDor WFar
- - 'Alba'	CBod EBee EGrl ELon LBar MBel MRav NBro SRms WCAu WFar
- 'Arctic Fox' (v)	GEdr NBro NHpl SWvt
- 'Argentea'	see *A. reptans* 'Variegata'
§ - 'Atropurpurea'	CTri ECha EGrl EHeP ELan EPfP LCro LOPS MGos MMuc NFav NWad SEND SGol SPlb SRms SWvt WBrk XLum
- BLACK SCALLOP ('Binblasca'PBR)	Widely available
- 'Blueberry Muffin'	ECtt EWTr LCro LOPS
- 'Braunherz'	Widely available
- 'Burgundy Glow' (v)	Widely available
§ - 'Catlin's Giant' 🏆H7	Widely available
- 'Choc Ice'	EWTr
- 'Chocolate Chip'	see *A. tenorei* 'Valfredda'
- 'Dixie Chip'	see *A. tenorei* 'Dixie Chip'
- 'Evening Glow'	EBee GJos LRHS WIce
- 'Gold Chang' new	CBod LBar SPad SPeP
- 'Golden Beauty' (v)	LPar MDon SRms WFar
- 'Golden Glow' (v)	ELan EMor LBar LRHS NRHS WFar WIce
- 'Harlequin' (v)	SWvt
- 'John Pierpoint'	SHar
- 'Macrophylla'	see *A. reptans* 'Catlin's Giant'
- 'Mahogany'	NLar SRms
§ - 'Multicolor' (v)	CEme ELan LLWG LRHS MAsh MPri NRHS SCob SPer SPlb SPoG SRms SWvt WFar
- 'Pink Elf'	CDor GQue MRav NBro
- 'Pink Surprise'	MHer NRya WFar
- 'Purple Brocade'	NLar
§ - 'Purple Torch'	ELon MPie NLar SHar SRms SWvt
- 'Purpurea'	see *A. reptans* 'Atropurpurea'
- 'Rainbow'	see *A. reptans* 'Multicolor'
- 'Rosea'	CBod ELon MBel SBut WCAu WFar XLum
- 'Rowden Amethyst'	EBtc WHil
- 'Rowden Royal Purple'	WBrk
- 'Tricolor'	see *A. reptans* 'Multicolor'
§ - 'Variegata' (v)	CGBo ECtt LRHS LShi NHpl SPer SPoG SRms WFar WTor
'Rose Glow'	NHpl
'Sparkler' (v)	NHpl
SUGAR PLUM ('Binsugplu'PBR) (v)	ECul ELan EMor LBar MCot NGdn
§ ***tenorei*** 'Dixie Chip'	WFar
- PRINCESS NADIA ('Piotrek01') (v)	LBar LCro NLar WNPC
§ - 'Valfredda'	EHyd EPfP EShb EWoo GQue LLWG LRHS NLar NRHS NWad SEdd SRms SWvt WBrk WFar XLum

Akebia (*Lardizabalaceae*)

longeracemosa	CBcs CRHN EBee LRHS MGil SBrt SChF SMDa
- B&SWJ 3606	CBod CExl LEdu WCot WCru WPGP
× ***pentaphylla***	CBcs CKel EBee EHyd ELan EPfP LRHS MAsh MGil MRav NChi SPer
quinata	Widely available
- B&SWJ 4425	WCru
- 'Amethyst Glow'	CDoC CKel CRos CWCL EHyd ELan ELon EPfP LRHS MHtn NLar SEle SMad SMrm SPer SPoG SSha WLov
- cream-flowered	CBod CCCN CKel CRHN CWCL EBee EHyd EPfP LCro LOPS LPar LRHS MGil MGos MHtn MRav SCob SGsty SMrm SPer SRms SSha SWvt WBor WLov WPGP
- 'Shirobana'	CBcs CWGN EAri MBlu MGil NLar WCru WHtc XSen
- 'Silver Bells'	EBee
- 'White Chocolate' 🏆H6	ELon ESwi NLar WCru WSHC
trifoliata	CBcs CRHN EBee EHyd ELan EPfP LRHS MGil MGos
- B&SWJ 5063	WCru
- B&SWJ 14570	WCru
- 'Big Fruit' new	NLar

Alangium (*Cornaceae*)

platanifolium	CBcs WPGP
- var. ***macrophyllum***	CCCN EPfP MGil WBor

Albizia (*Fabaceae*)

chinensis	EPfP
distachya	see *Paraserianthes lophantha*
§ ***julibrissin***	CAco CDTJ CTsd EAri EBee EGrl EHed EPfP IDee IPap LPar LRHS MGil MVil WJur WLov WOut
- NJM 13.018	WPGP
- CHOCOLATE FOUNTAIN ('Ncaj1')	CAco ELan LCro LPar LRHS MTrO NOra WMat
- 'Evy's Pride'	CAco MTrO WMat
- 'Evy's Purple'	ELan

	- LEONIDAS	see *A. julibrissin* 'Summer Chocolate'
	- OMBRELLA ('Boubri'^{PBR})	CAco ELan LCro MTrO NOra WMat WPGP
	- f. ***rosea*** 🏆^{H4}	CAco CBcs CEme CKel CMCN CWGN EAri EBee ELan EPfP MGil SArc SEND SEle SIvy SLim SMad SPad SPlb SPoG WHtc WLov WPGP
I	- 'Rouge Selection'	CKel EPfP SPoG
	- 'Shidare'	ELan LRHS MTrO NOra WMat
§	- 'Summer Chocolate'^{PBR} 🏆^{H4}	CAco CRos CWGN EHed EHyd ELan EPfP IDee LRHS LSRN MAsh MTrO NOra NRHS SCoo SPoG WMat
	- TROPICAL DREAM ('Pos 1')	CAco
	kalkora	SPlb
	lophantha	see *Paraserianthes lophantha*

Albuca ✿ (*Asparagaceae*)

	'Ausgrabies Hills'	WHil
	canadensis (L.) F.M. Leight.	EPri NFav
	glauca	EBee MPie
	humilis	CExl CPla EDAr ELan EPot MHer WHil
	humilis × ***shawii*** new	GEdr
	longifolia	WHil
	nelsonii	CAvo CPrp EBee LAma MPie
	polyphylla	WHil
	setosa	CTca
	shawii	CBor CBro CPrp EAJP EBee EPfP EPri EWld GBin GEdr LAlb LBar LRHS MACG MHer MHol MPie NBPC NSla SChr SCoo SMrm SPoG SRms WAvo WGwG WHil WKif
	spiralis	GKev WCot
	- 'Frizzle Sizzle'	CDoC MHer

× *Alcalthaea* (*Malvaceae*)

	suffrutescens 'Freedom'	WFar
	- 'Parkallee' (d)	CDor EBee ECha ECtt ELan GMaP LDai LPla LRHS MAvo MHol MNrw MPie NLar SPhx WCot WMal XLum
	- 'Parkfrieden' (d)	ECha ECtt MAvo MNrw NLar XLum
	- 'Parkrondell' (d)	CDor ECha ECtt ELan LRHS MAvo MNrw MPie SHar WCot XLum
	- 'Poetry'	ECtt ELan LRHS

Alcea (*Malvaceae*)

	ficifolia	LShi MHer WFar WSpi
	- pink-flowered	LShi
	- yellow-flowered	LShi
	froloviana	GGro
	'Las Vegas'	WFar
	nudiflora	GGro
	pallida	XSen
§	***rosea***	EPfP WFar
	- 'Blacknight' (Spotlight Series)	EDAr ELan EPfP LRHS MHer NLar SCoo SGBe
	- Chater's Double Group (d)	EHeP EPfP GMcL SCob SPoG SRms SVic WFar
	- - chamois (d)	EPfP
	- - chestnut-brown-flowered (d)	EPfP
	- - maroon-flowered (d)	EPfP LRHS MPri SPoG
	- - pink-flowered (d)	ELan EPfP
	- - red-flowered (d)	ELan GMcL SCob SPoG
	- - rose-pink-flowered (d)	LRHS MPri
	- - salmon-pink-flowered (d)	EPfP
	- - scarlet-flowered (d)	EPfP LRHS MPri SPoG
	- - violet-flowered (d)	EPfP
§	- - white-flowered (d)	ELan EPfP GMcL LCro LOPS LRHS LShi MPri SPoG
	- - yellow-flowered (d)	EPfP GMcL LRHS MPri SPoG SRms
	- 'Crème de Cassis'	ELan EPfP
	- double scarlet-flowered (d)	LRHS
	- Halo Series	WFar
	- - 'Halo Apricot'	CRos EHyd EPfP LRHS LSto NRHS SPoG WHoo
	- - 'Halo Blush'	CRos EHyd EPfP LRHS NRHS SPoG
	- - 'Halo Cerise'	CRos EHyd EPfP LRHS NRHS SPoG WHil
	- - 'Halo Cream'	CRos EHyd EPfP LRHS NRHS SPoG
	- - 'Halo Red'	EPfP LRHS NRHS SCoo SPoG
	- - 'Halo White'	EHyd EPfP LRHS NRHS SPoG
	- 'Mars Magic' (Spotlight Series)	EBee EDAr ELan EPfP LRHS MHer NLar SCoo SGBe WHil
	- 'Nigra'	CKel CSpe ELan EPfP EWoo GMcL LCro LOPS LPal LRHS LSRN LShi LSto NFav NGdn SCob SHar SRms WCAu WPnP
	- 'Polarstar' (Spotlight Series)	EBee ELan EPfP LRHS NLar SCoo SGBe
	- 'Radiant Rose' (Spotlight Series)	ELan EPfP LRHS MHer SCoo SGBe WHil
	- single-flowered	MMuc SRms
	- - pink-flowered	EWoo
	- (Spring Celebrities Series) 'Spring Celebrities Lemon' (d)	NRHS
	- - 'Spring Celebrities White' (d)	NRHS
	- Summer Carnival Group	SRms
	- 'Sunshine' (Spotlight Series)	EBee EPfP LRHS NLar SGBe
	- 'The Watchman'	WHil
§	***rugosa***	EBee ECha LEdu SHar XSen
	THE BRIDE	see *A. rosea* Chater's Double Group white-flowered

Alcea × *Althaea* see × *Alcalthaea*

Alchemilla ✿ (*Rosaceae*)

	alpina misapplied	see *A. conjuncta*, *A. plicatula*
	alpina ambig.	EGrI MCot
	alpina L.	EBee ELan EPfP GMaP GPoy GQue LEdu LRHS MAvo MBel MMuc MRav NBir NChi NLar SEND SRms WFar WPGP WSHC
	caucasica	EMor
§	***conjuncta***	CDor CKel CMac CSpe EBee ECha EGrI ELan EMor EPfP GAbr GKev GLog GMaP GMcL LEdu MHer MRav NBid NGrd NRya NSti SPer SPlb SRms SRot WCAu WHoo
	ellenbeckii	EGrI NChi WTor
	epipsila	EBee ELan EMor EPfP EShb LRHS NLar SHar SHor SPhx
	erythropoda 🏆^{H7}	Widely available
	- from Turkey	ECha
	- 'Alba'	LRHS
	- (Cepa Group) 'Alma'	EMor LSun
	faeroensis	EGrI XLum
	- var. ***pumila***	EBee WAbe
	glabra	EBee
	hoppeana misapplied	see *A. plicatula*
	iniquiformis	EGrI
	'Irish Silk'	CBod LBar
	lapeyrousei	EBee
	mollis 🏆^{H7}	Widely available
I	- 'Auslese'	SWvt

- 'Robustica'	CWal GQue LBar LSun MMuc SEND SPlb WFar
- 'Thriller'	CBod EHyd EPfP LRHS MDon NRHS WFar
'Mr Poland's Variety'	see *A. venosa*
pectinata new	CBcs
pedata	NChi
peristerica	EBee
§ ***plicatula***	NLar
saxatilis	CBod EBou EMor MACG NLar SHar
sericata 'Gold Strike'	EBee ECtt ELan EPfP GLog LBar LRHS NRHS SCoo SHar SWvt
straminea	EBee MRav
valdehirsuta	EBee
§ ***venosa***	EBee SMHy
vetteri	EBee NFav WHrl
vulgaris misapplied	see *A. xanthochlora*
vulgaris L. agg.	GQue
§ ***xanthochlora***	EMor GPoy MHoo NLar SRms

Alchornea (*Euphorbiaceae*)

davidii new	NCth SBrt

alecost see *Tanacetum balsamita*

Alectryon (*Sapindaceae*)

excelsus	CBcs

Alisma (*Alismataceae*)

lanceolatum	LLWG
plantago-aquatica	CBen CHab CPud CWat LPfP MWts NPer WMAq WWtn
- var. ***parviflorum***	CBen LLWG LPfP SPlb WWtn

Allagoptera (*Arecaceae*)

arenaria	NPlm

Allamanda (*Apocynaceae*)

cathartica	CCCN

Alliaria (*Brassicaceae*)

petiolata	CCBP GPoy SPhx WHer WSFF

Allium ✿ (*Alliaceae*)

RCB AM 21	WCot
SSSE 250	GEdr
§ ***acuminatum***	NRog
acutiflorum	GKev LAma LHWs NRog
aflatunense misapplied	see *A. hollandicum*
aflatunense ambig.	ECha EGrI GMcL LRHS LSRN NRog SCob SDeJ
akaka	NRog
albidum	see *A. denudatum*
albopilosum	see *A. cristophii*
alexeianum	NRog
altissimum	LAma NRog
- 'Album'	GKev LAma
- 'Goliath'	GKev LRHS NRHS NRog WCot
amabile	see *A. mairei* var. *amabile*
'Ambassador' ♀H5	CAvo CRos ECul ELan ERCP GKev LAma LCro LHWs LOPS LRHS MPtr NRHS NRog SDir SDix SPer WCot WFar WPhe
amethystinum	NRog
- 'Red Mohican' PBR	EBee ERCP GKev LAma LEdu LHWs MBNS MBriF MNrw MPtr SDeJ WCot WHoo WPhe
ampeloprasum	ECha GKev LAma SDix SPlb WHer WShi
- var. ***babingtonii***	CAgr GKev GPoy LEdu NRog SRms WHer WKor WPGP WShi
- - 'Green Drops'	GKev LHWs
§ - 'Elephant'	LCro LEdu LOPS WCot
- 'Hairy Friend'	LHWs
- 'Pink Lady'	GKev LHWs
- 'Purple Mystery'	GKev LHWs WCot
- 'Rose Picture'	LHWs
- 'White Cloud'	ELan ERCP LHWs
amphibolum	GKev NRog
amplectens	NRog
- 'Graceful Beauty'	ELan EPot ERCP ETay GKev LAma LCro LOPS MBow NLar SDeJ SDir SPer WHlf
§ ***angulosum***	CAvo CMiW GKev LAma LEdu MHol MPtr NHpl NRog SDix WCot WMal XSen
aschersonianum	SDeJ WCot
atropurpureum	EBee ECha ECul ELan ERCP ETay EWoo GBin GKev LAma LCro LHWs LOPS LRHS NRHS NRog SDeJ SDir SPhx WCot WHlf
atropurpureum × ***schubertii***	SGBe
atroviolaceum	WCot
W&B BG A-5	
austroiranicum	NRog
azureum	see *A. caeruleum*
backhousianum	NRog
- 'Green Craze'	GKev LAma LHWs
barsczewskii 'Aman Kutan'	NRog
'Beau Regard' ♀H7	CWCL EBee ELan ERCP GKev LCro LOPS LRHS NLar NRog SDir
beesianum misapplied	see *A. cyaneum*
beesianum W.W. Sm.	CMiW CTtf EBee GRum LEdu NBir NHpl
- from Sichuan, China	CMiW
bisceptrum	NRog
blandum	see *A. carolinianum*
bodeanum	see *A. cristophii*
bolanderi var. ***mirabile***	NRog
'Bolero'	NRog
brevicaule	GKev
bucharicum	ETay
bulgaricum	see *A. siculum* subsp. *dioscoridis*
§ ***caeruleum***	CAvo CBod CBor EBee EGrI EPfP EPot ERCP ETay EWoo GKev LAma LCro LHWs LOPS LRHS MGos MNrw NBir NLar NPer NRHS NRog NRya SDeJ SDir SDix WHlf
- ***azureum***	see *A. caeruleum*
caesium ♀H5	ERCP GKev NRog WCot
- AQUAMARINE	see *A. caesium* 'Pskem's Beauty'
§ - 'Pskem's Beauty'	NRog WCot
- 'Summer Sky'	GKev
- 'Wine'	GKev
- 'Zaamin'	NRog
callimischon subsp. ***callimischon***	GKev NRog
- subsp. ***haemostictum***	NRog WCot
'Caméléon'	CCBP ERCP GKev IPot LAma LCro LHWs LOPS LRHS NRHS NRog WCot WHlf
campanulatum	NRog
canadense	CAvo SHar WKor
candolleanum	GKev LAma NRog
§ ***carinatum***	LAma WHer
§ - subsp. ***pulchellum*** ♀H5	CSpe CTtf ECha EGrI EPot GKev LAma MHer MMuc MNrw NBir NRog SDeJ SPhx WThu
- - f. ***album*** ♀H5	CSpe CTtf ECha EGrI GKev LAma LEdu MNrw NBir SPhx
§ ***carolinianum***	WCav
caspium new	GKev
- subsp. ***baissunense***	NRog
cepa	CBod LAma SVic

	- Aggregatum Group	CLau GPoy SRms
	- 'Kew White'	WCot
	- 'Perutile'	GPoy GQue LEdu MHer WKor
	- Proliferum Group	CAgr CLau EWhm GPoy GQue LEdu MHer MHoo MNHC SRms WHer WJek WKor
	- var. ***viviparum***	GKev LHWs
	cernuum	Widely available
§	- 'Hidcote' ♀H6	EBee EDAr MHoo WKif XSen
	- 'Major'	see *A. cernuum* 'Hidcote'
	- pink-flowered	CLau
I	- 'Purple King'	GKev
	- 'White Dwarf'	CBor CTtf ELan EPot GKev LAma LHWs
	- 'White Master'	GKev LEdu LHWs
	- 'White Max'	LHWs
	chinense	CAgr GPoy LEdu WFar
	- 'October Mist'	LEdu
	circinnatum **new**	GKev
	cirrhosum	see *A. carinatum* subsp. *pulchellum*
	colchicifolium	NRog
	convallarioides	NRog
	cowanii	see *A. neapolitanum* Cowanii Group
	crenulatum	NRog
	crispum	NRog
§	***cristophii*** ♀H5	Widely available
	cupanii	GKev NRog
	cupuliferum	GKev NRog
	curtum RCB RL 13	WCot
§	***cyaneum*** ♀H5	CBor CMiW CTtf EPot GArf GEdr GKev LAma LBee MHer NHpl NRog NRya WCot WFar
	cyathophorum	CBor LAma
§	- var. ***farreri***	CBro CMiW CTtf EPPr EPot GKev LAma LEdu LHWs MHer MNrw NHpl NRya WCot WSHC WThu
	darwasicum	WCot
	- 'Darwas Wonder'	NRog
	decipiens	GKev
	- subsp. ***decipiens***	NRog
	- subsp. ***quercetorum***	NRog
§	***denudatum***	GKev
	diabaloense	NRog
	douglasii	NRog
§	***drummondii***	LRHS NRHS
	'Dutchman'	GKev LAma
	egorovae	NRog
	elatum	see *A. macleanii*
	elburzense	NRog
	'Emir'	GKev
	ericetorum	GKev WCot
	- PAB 1009	LEdu
	'Eros'	CBor CTtf ERCP GKev LAma LCro LOPS SDir
	falcifolium	GKev LAma LHWs NRog WCot
	farreri	see *A. cyathophorum* var. *farreri*
	fetisowii	NRog
	fimbriatum	NRog
	'Firmament'	CBor ECha ERCP GKev LAma SDeJ WCot
	fistulosum	CAgr CBod CHby CLau ENfk EWhm GKev GPoy GQue LCro LHWs LOPS MHer MHoo MNHC MPri NRog SRms SVic WCot WGwG WJek
	- red-flowered	WHil
	fistulosum* × *pskemense	GKev LHWs
	flavum ♀H5	CBor CTtf ECha EPPr EPot ERCP EShb LAma NHpl SDeJ SPhx WThu XSen
	- subsp. ***flavum***	GKev NRog
	- - var. ***minus***	MMuc NRog
	- subsp. ***tauricum***	GKev WCot
	'Forelock'	EBee ERCP GKev LAma LHWs MNrw NRog WCot
	forrestii	WCot
	geyeri	EBee
	giganteum	Widely available
	- 'Twinkling Stars'	ERCP
	- white-flowered **new**	NBwr
	'Gimli'	NRog
	'Gladiator' ♀H6	CAvo CRos CWCL EBee EPfP ERCP EWoo GKev GMaP ILea LAma LCro LHWs LOPS LRHS MACG MPtr NBwr NLar NRHS NRog SDeJ SDir SGBe WPhe
	glaucum	see *A. senescens* subsp. *glaucum*
	'Globemaster' ♀H6	Widely available
	'Globus'	EBee GKev NRog
	grande	NRog
	guttatum	GKev
	subsp. ***dalmaticum***	
	- subsp. ***sardoum***	GKev
	gypsaceum	NRog
	haemanthoides	WCot
	'Hair'	see *A. vineale* 'Hair'
	heldreichii	NRog
*	***hirtifolium*** var. ***album***	EBee GKev LAma NRog
§	***hollandicum***	CArg CAvo ECha EPfP GKev LCro LOPS NRog SCob SPlb WFar XLum
	- 'Purple Sensation' ♀H6	Widely available
	- 'Purple Surprise'	NBir WCot
	hookeri	LEdu
	- ACE 2430	GGro LEdu WCot
	- var. ***muliense***	EDAr GEdr LEdu
	- 'Zorami'	CAgr ELan LEdu WMal WPGP
	howellii var. ***clokeyi***	GKev
	huber-morathii	CBor
	humile	GEdr
	hyalinum	CAvo GKev LHWs
	- pink-flowered	WCot
	'In Orbit'	LBar LPla LSou SGBe WNPC
§	***insubricum*** ♀H5	EDAr GBin GEdr LRHS MNrw NBir NHpl NRHS NRya
	'Jackpot'	CWCL EBee ERCP GKev LAma MPtr NRog
	jajlae	see *A. rotundum* subsp. *jajlae*
	jesdianum	GKev
	- 'Akbulak' ♀H5	EBee GKev LAma LHWs NRog
	- 'Early Emperor' ♀H5	CAvo CWCL EBee ERCP GKev LAma LRHS NRHS NRog
	- 'Michael Hoog'	see *A. rosenorum* 'Michael H. Hoog'
	- 'Pendjikent'	NRog
	- 'Per Wendelbo'	GKev NRog
	- 'Purple King'	GKev LRHS NRHS NRog
	- 'Shing'	GKev LAma
	- 'White Empress' PBR	EBee
	- white-flowered	NRog
	jodanthum	NRog
	'Judith'	WCot
	'Judith's Findling'	WCot
	kansuense	see *A. sikkimense*
	karataviense	CAby EBee ECha ELan EPot EWoo GAbr GKev LAma LCro LRHS MBow NBir NBwr NHpl NLar NRHS NRog SCob SDeJ SWvt WCAu
	- subsp. ***henrikii***	LAma NRog
	- 'Ivory Queen'	CAvo EBee ECha ERCP GKev LAma LCro LOPS LRHS LSRN NHpl NLar NRHS NRog SDeJ SDir SMrm SPlb WHlf XSte
	- 'Red Giant'	LAma NRog
	kharputense	NRog
	kokanicum	GRum
	komarovianum	see *A. thunbergii*
	komarovii	NRog

	kwakense	NRog
	lacunosum var. ***davisiae***	NRog
	ledebourianum	GKev LAma
	lemmonii	GKev NRog
	lenkoranicum	CAvo GKev WCot
	lipskyanum	NRog
	litvinovii	EBee NRog WCot WFar
	longifolium	GKev
	loratum	EBee
	'Lucy Ball'	ERCP LAma LRHS NBir NLar NRHS NRog SDeJ
§	***lusitanicum***	CBWd CBor CBro CCBP CLau CSpe ECha ERCP EShb GKev GMaP LAma LBar LEdu LHWs MBros MHol NDov SDix SMHy SRms WGoo WHoo XLum XSen XSte
	- 'Lisa Blue'	GKev LEdu LHWs
	- 'Lisa Green'	LEdu LPla
	luteolum	GKev
§	***macleanii***	GKev LRHS NRHS NRog
	- 'His Excellency'	CAvo EBee ERCP GKev LAma LRHS NLar NRog
	macranthum	CSpe EBee GKev LAma NHpl NRog SBrt
	- S&L 5369	GGro
	mairei	EHyd LRHS MMuc NRHS NRya
§	- var. ***amabile***	GEdr LEdu NRya
	- - dark-flowered	CBor
	maximowiczii	GKev LAma LHWs NHpl NRog
	- white-flowered	GKev
	'Mercurius'[PBR]	EBee GKev LAma LCro LRHS NRHS NRog SDeJ WCot
	'Metallic Shine'	GKev LAma SDir SPhx
	meteoricum	CTtf GKev LAma WCot
	'Miami'	CRos EBee ERCP GKev LAma LHWs LRHS NRHS NRog SDeJ SPhx
	'Millennium'	CKno CMiW EPfP GKev GMaP LBar LCro LOPS LPla LRHS LSou MAsh MHol NDov NSti SMHy WCot WGoo WHoo WMal WNPC WTor XSen
	minutiflorum	NRog
	moly	CAgr CBod CWCL EWld GKev GQue LAma LCro LOPS MRav NBwr NRya SDeJ SRms WCav XLum
	- 'Jeannine' 🏆H6	EBee EPot GKev LAma LBar LRHS NRHS NRog SDix
	'Mont Blanc'	CBod CRos EBee ELan ERCP GKev ILea LAma LRHS MACG NLar NRHS NRog SDir
	monticola	NRog
	moschatum	GKev
	multibulbosum	see *A. nigrum*
	murrayanum misapplied	see *A. unifolium*
	murrayanum Regel	see *A. acuminatum*
	myrianthum	EBee
	narcissiflorum misapplied	see *A. insubricum*
§	***narcissiflorum*** Vill.	CBor CSpe LEdu MNrw NSla WMal
	neapolitanum	CAgr GKev LAma LRHS NRHS NRog SRms WHlf WKor XLum
§	- Cowanii Group	GKev LAma LCro LOPS LRHS NRHS NRog SDeJ WCot
§	***neriniflorum***	NSla
	'Nevsar'	NRog
	nevskianum	EPot GKev LHWs NRog
§	***nigrum***	CArg CAvo CBro CKel ECha EPfP EPot ERCP EWoo GKev LAma LCro LHWs LOPS LRHS MCot MPtr NBir NPer NRHS NRog SDeJ SDir WCot WHlf WPhe
	- pink-flowered **new**	LAma
	- f. ***roseum***	CBro

	nutans	EWhm GKev LAma LEdu LHWs MHer MHoo SRms WJek
	- 'Caroline'	EMul GKev LEdu LHWs WGoo
	- 'Esmee'	GKev LEdu LHWs
	- 'Isabelle'	LEdu
	nuttallii	see *A. drummondii*
§	***obliquum***	CAvo CBor CBro CSpe ECha EGrI EPri ERCP GEdr GKev LAma LCro LPla MBriF MMuc NRog SDeJ SPhx WCot WHlf WMal
	ochotense	GKev LPla WCot
	odorum L.	see *A. ramosum* L.
	oleraceum	WHer
	opacum	GKev
§	***oreophilum***	CRos ECha GJos GKev LAma LCro LOPS LRHS NRHS NRog SRms WHlf
	- 'Agalik Giant'	NRog
	- 'Kusavli Curl'	NRog
	- 'Purple Gem'	NRog
	- 'Samur'	WCot
	- 'Sulev's Dwarf'	NRog
	- 'Zwanenburg' 🏆H6	EPot
	orientale	GKev
	'Ostara'	ERCP GKev LAma MPtr
	ostrowskianum	see *A. oreophilum*
	ovalifolium var. ***leuconeurum***	GEdr
	pallens	NBir
§	***paniculatum***	GKev LAma NRog WCot
*	- var. ***minor***	GKev
	paradoxum	LEdu NBir
	- var. ***normale*** 🏆H5	CBro CTtf EPot EWld GKev NBir WCot
	parciflorum	GKev
	parvum	NRog
	pedemontanum	see *A. narcissiflorum* Vill.
	pendulinum	GKev
	'Pinball Wizard'	CAvo EBee EHyd EPfP ERCP GKev LAma LCro LHWs LRHS MPtr NBwr NLar NRHS NRog
	'Ping Pong'	GKev LAma MPtr NLar
	'Pink Jewel'	CAvo ERCP GKev SDeJ WCot
	'Pink Planet' **new**	GKev
	platycaule	WCot
	plummerae	EBee GKev
	polyphyllum	see *A. carolinianum*
	'Powder Puff' 🏆H5	CAvo ELan GKev LAma MMrt
	prattii	EBee WCot
	protensum	NRog
	przewalskianum	EBee SGro
	pseudowinklerianum	NRog
	pskemense	GKev LAma LEdu NLar WCot
	pulchellum	see *A. carinatum* subsp. *pulchellum*
	'Purple Rain' 🏆H5	CAby CAvo CBro ECha ELan ERCP GKev LAma LCro LHWs LOPS LRHS MPtr NRHS NRog SDeJ SGBe SPhx WCot WPhe
	'Purple Suze'	GKev LHWs
	pyrenaicum misapplied	see *A. angulosum*
	pyrenaicum Costa & Vayr.	XSen
	ramosum Jacq.	see *A. obliquum*
§	***ramosum*** L.	GKev LEdu MHoo
	'Red Eye'	LCro LOPS
	'Rien Poortvliet'	GKev
	roborowskianum	GKev
	robustum	NRog
	rosenbachianum misapplied	see *A. stipitatum*
	rosenbachianum Regel	CBro LRHS NRHS NRog
	- 'Album'	CRos GKev NRHS WCot
	- 'Michael Hoog'	see *A. rosenorum* 'Michael H. Hoog'
§	***rosenorum*** 'Michael H. Hoog' 🏆H5	EPot LAma NRog

	roseum	CBod CRos EAJP EWoo GKev LAma LCro LOPS LRHS NRHS NRog SDeJ WHlf XLum
	- ***albiflorum***	GMcL
	rotundum	GKev
§	- subsp. ***jajlae***	NRog
	'Round 'n' Purple' ♀H5	EBee ERCP GKev LAma LCro LOPS NRog
	rupestre	GKev
	saralicum	NRog
	sarawschanicum	NRog
	- 'Chinoro'	NRog
	sativum	ENfk LOPS MPri SPoG SRms
	- 'Elephant'	see *A. ampeloprasum* 'Elephant'
	- var. ***ophioscorodon***	ERCP GKev GPoy LAma SPlb WKor
	saxatile	GKev WCot
	scabriflorum	NRog
	schmitzii	LEdu WPGP
	schoenoprasum	Widely available
	- f. ***albiflorum***	CCBP CLau EWhm GKev LEdu LHWs MHer NBir SRms XLum
	- 'Black Isle Blush'	GPoy LEdu LPla MBriF MHer WGoo
	- 'Cha Cha'	MBriF WHil WJek
	- 'Colesbourne Giant'	EBee
	- 'Corsican White'	EBee LEdu XSen
	- 'Curly Mauve' **new**	LBar
	- dwarf, white-flowered	SRms
	- 'Elbe'	LEdu
	- 'Evergreen'	CLau
	- fine-leaved	CLau
	- 'Forescate'	ECha EWhm GKev LAma LEdu LHWs LRHS LSou MRav NBir NRHS SRms WJek XLum
	- 'Glowing Amethyst'	GKev
	- 'Grande'	CLau
	- medium-leaved	CLau MPri
	- 'Pink Bere'	LEdu WPGP
	- 'Pink Perfection'	GPoy LEdu MHer
	- 'Polar Bere'	LEdu WPGP
	- 'Polyvert'	CLau
	- 'Rising Star'	XSen
	- 'Shining Silver'	LEdu
	- var. ***sibiricum***	SDix WShi
	- 'Silver Chimes'	CBor EPPr EWhm MHoo
	- 'Staro'	CLau
	- thick-leaved	CLau SRms
	schubertii	CAvo CSpe EGrI EHyd ELan EPfP EPot ERCP EShb ETay GKev GMcL LAma LCro LHWs LOPS LRHS MPtr NBwr NRHS NRog SCoo SDeJ SPer WCot WFar WHlf WPhe
	- 'Magic'	LAma
	scorodoprasum 'Art'	CRos ERCP GKev LAma LRHS NRHS
	- subsp. ***jajlae***	see *A. rotundum* subsp. *jajlae*
	- 'Passion'	CRos LRHS NRHS NRog
	- 'Purple Caila'	GKev
	- subsp. ***scorodoprasum***	NRog
	scorzonerifolium **new**	WCot
	senescens ♀H6	CBro CTca CTri EBee EPot LAma LEdu LHWs LRHS MBel MHoo MRav NRHS SPtp SRms WBrk WCAu XSen
§	- subsp. ***glaucum***	CAvo CMiW CSpe EAJP EBlo ECha EDAr EPfP EShb EWTr GKev LEdu LPla LRHS MACG MHer MHol NBPC NDov NGdn NLar NRya SEND SGro SMHy SOrN WCot WHoo XSen
	- subsp. ***senescens***	EGrI GKev LEdu WPGP
	shelkovnikovii	NRog
	sibthorpianum	see *A. paniculatum*
	siculum	CArg CAvo CBod CBro CSpe ELan EPfP ERCP EWoo GKev LCro LEdu LHWs LOPS LRHS LSto NBir NChi NSti SCob SDeJ SDir SDix SHor SPer SPoG
	- subsp. ***bulgaricum***	see *A. siculum* subsp. *dioscoridis*
§	- subsp. ***dioscoridis***	CKel CRos EBee ECha EGrI EHyd EPot GKev LAma LRHS MNrw NRHS NRog SPhx WBrk WCot XLum
	- subsp. ***dioscoridis*** × ***tripedale***	LAma NRog
§	***sikkimense***	CBor ECha EDAr EWTr GArf GEdr GKev GQue MHer MMuc NHpl NSla WCot WFar
	'Silver Spring'	EPot ERCP ETay GKev LAma LCro LOPS SDeJ WHlf
	siskiyouense	NRog
	sivasicum	NRog
	sphaerocephalon ♀H6	Widely available
	- subsp. ***arvense***	NRog WCot
	'Spider'	CBor EPot ERCP GKev LAma NRog SMrm WCot
I	***splendens*** var. ***kurilense***	GEdr
	stamineum	GKev
	- W&B BGF-2	WCot
	staticiforme	GKev
	'Statos'	EBee GKev LAma LRHS MPtr NRHS NRog WCot WPhe
	stellatum	LRHS NRHS WGwG WHer
	stellerianum var. ***kurilense***	NRya WThu
	'Stipineva'	NRog
§	***stipitatum***	GKev LAma NRog WCot WHlf
	- 'Album'	NRog
	- 'Glory of Pamir'	NRog
	- 'Mars'	EBee GKev GMcL LAma LRHS NRHS NRog SDix WHlf
	- 'Mount Everest' ♀H5	Widely available
	- 'Pink Ball'	NRog
	- 'Pink Globe'	NRog
	- 'Titan'	NRog
	- 'Violet Beauty' ♀H5	CAvo CRos CWCL EPfP GKev LAma LCro LHWs LOPS LRHS MHtn MMrt NLar NRHS WCot WPhe
	- 'White Giant'	CRos CWCL GKev LAma LEdu LHWs LRHS MPtr NLar NRHS NRog SArc SDir WHlf
	stracheyi	WCot
	strictum Schrad.	ITim
	struzlianum	NRog
	suaveolens	MMuc
	'Sugar Melt'	GKev LAma
	'Summer Beauty'	see *A. lusitanicum*
	'Summer Drummer'	ECha EPfP ERCP GKev LAma LHWs LRHS MBros NRog SDeJ SDir WCot WHlf
	'Sweet Discovery'	NRog
	taquetii	see *A. thunbergii*
	tardans	GKev
	tauricola	GKev
§	***thunbergii*** ♀H5	CTtf NBir NRya WAbe
	- PAB 3821	LEdu
	- 'Album'	LEdu NRya WAbe
	- 'Ozawa'	GEdr SMHy SRms WCot WFar
	tibeticum	see *A. sikkimense*
	tolmiei var. ***platyphyllum***	GKev NRog
	trifoliatum	GKev
	tripedale	CAvo CBro EPot ERCP GKev LAma
	triquetrum	ELan EPot GKev GPoy GQue LAma LEdu MHoo NBir SEND WCot WHer
*	***tschikatschevii***	NRog
	tschimganicum	EBee
	tuberosum	Widely available

- B&SWJ 8881	WCru
- purple/mauve-flowered	CHby CLau
- 'White Dwarf'	SPhx WCot
tuncelianum	GKev LHWs NRog WCot
'Turkish Delight'	NRog
ubipetrense	NRog
§ ***unifolium*** ♀H5	CAvo CWCL EPot ERCP ETay EWoo GKev LAma LCro LOPS NBir NPer NQui NRog SDeJ SRms WCot WGwG
ursinum	CBod CHab CHby CLau CTtf ENfk EWhm GKev GPoy LAma LCro LEdu LOPS MHer MHoo MNHC MPri NAts NPoe NRog SPlb SRms SVic WFar WKor WSFF WShi XLum
- 'Golden Fleece'	CTtf WCot
validum NNS 06-41	WCot
victorialis	GKev NRog
- 'Cantabria'	EBee GKev
vineale	GQue WHer WJek
- 'Dready'	ERCP GKev LAma
§ - 'Hair'	CAby CBor CRos ELan ERCP GKev LAma LRHS NBir NPer NRHS NRog SDeJ
violaceum	see *A. carinatum*
virgunculae	EDAr GEdr WAbe
- f. ***albiflorum***	GEdr
wallichii	CBor CSpe EWes GArf GKev GMaP LEdu NBir NChi WCot
- CLD 1500	GGro LEdu NBid
- PAB 2976	LEdu WPGP
- PAB 9191	LEdu
- dark-flowered	CTtf WCot WFar
'White Cloud'	see *A. ampeloprasum* 'White Cloud', *A. cepa* (Cepa Group) 'White Cloud'
winklerianum	GKev
woronowii	NRog
zaprjagajevii	WCot
zebdanense	GKev NRog

Alluaudia (*Didiereaceae*)

dumosa new	EAri
procera new	EAri NPlm

almond see *Prunus dulcis*

Alniphyllum (*Styracaceae*)

eberhardtii FMWJ 13121	WCru
fortunei FMWJ 13013	WCru

Alnus ✿ (*Betulaceae*)

cordata ♀H6	Widely available
cremastogyne	EBtc
firma	CSto
glutinosa	Widely available
- 'Aurea'	CEnd MGos MTrO NLar WCot
- 'Imperialis' ♀H7	CCVT CDoC CEnd CLnd CMac CPer EBee ELan EPfP EWTr IDee IPap LRHS MBlu MMuc MTrO NBwr NOra NOrn NWea SCob SEND SMad WHtc WMat WMou WTSh
- 'Laciniata'	CCVT EHeP IPap LMaj MGos NBwr NLar NWea SCob WHtc
- 'Pyramidalis'	MBlu
incana	CAco CBTr CBcs CBod CCVT CLnd CMCN EBar EHeP LBuc LMaj LPar MGos NBwr NRog NWea SCob WMat WTSh
- 'Aurea' ♀H7	CCVT CEnd CMac EBee EHeP ELan EPfP IArd IPap LMaj LPar LRHS MBlu MGos MRav NBwr NLar NOra NOrn NPoe NRog NWea SCob SEWo SPer SPoG WHtc WMat
- 'Laciniata'	LPar NOrn NWea SCoo SEND WMou
- 'Pendula'	WMou
japonica	MBlu
maximowiczii	CSto GKev MVil
- from Ulleungdo, South Korea	WCru
nitida	EBtc
oregana	see *A. rubra*
pendula B&SWJ 10895	WCru
rhombifolia	EBtc
§ ***rubra***	CMCN ELan MCoo NWea WHtc WMat WTSh
- f. ***pinnatisecta***	CMCN MBlu NRog
serrulata	CMCN GKev
sieboldiana	LRHS MVil WCru
× ***spaethii***	EBar IArd LMaj LPar MBlu
subcordata NJM 13.009	EBee WPGP
viridis	CAgr CSto MCoo NWea WTSh
- subsp. ***sinuata***	CAgr

Alocasia (*Araceae*)

× ***amazonica*** 'Bambino'	NHrt
- BAMBINO ARROW ('Ruhe 1'PBR)	CDoC NHrt
- 'Polly'	CDoC LCro LOPS LWaG NHrt
- 'Polly Bambino'	NHrt
'Calidora'	CDTJ
cucullata	EAri NHrt
'Dragon Scale'	LCro
gageana	EAri
lauterbachiana	LCro LOPS
macrorrhizos	CDTJ CTsd EAri
odora	EAri LAma
'Portodora'	EAri NHrt
'Stingray'	LWaG NHrt
wentii	EAri
zebrina	LWaG NHrt NPlm

Aloe ✿ (*Asphodelaceae*)

arborescens	CDTJ CDoC CPbh EAri EOli EShb LCro LWaG NCft NPlm SEND SIvy SPlb SSim
- blue-leaved	SEND
- 'Variegata' (v) ♀H1c	CPbh EShb SRms
aristata ♀H3	CBcs CBen CBod CCht CSde EAri EWoo LWaG NCft SArc SBls SChr SEND SEdd SIvy SPad SPlb SSim XLum
- COSMO ('Green Pearl'PBR)	EPfP LCro NHrt SMad SPad
bakeri ♀H1b new	LCro SRms
barbadensis	see *A. vera*
barberae	CPbh
'Bedford's Beau'	NCft
'Blizzard' (v) new	SPlb
'Brass Hat'	NCft
brevifolia ♀H2	EAri EShb LWaG SArc SIvy SSim
broomii	SPlb
burgersfortensis new	CPbh
camperi 'Maculata'	SEND
castanea	CPbh
'Christmas Carol' new	SPad
ciliaris	CHll EShb SChr
'Cleopatra'	EAri SEdd WCot
commixta new	SEND
cooperi	CCCN NCft
* ***delaetii***	SEND
deltoideodonta	NCft
dichotoma	CAbb SPlb
ecklonis	CCCN SPlb
ferox	CAbb CBod CCCN CPbh CTrC SCoo SPoG
globuligemma	CPbh

greatheadii var. ***davyana***	SChr SPlb WHil
haworthioides ♀H1c	SIvy
humilis	CDoC EAri NCft SChr
jucunda	NCft
juvenna	SEND SRms
marlothii	CAbb SPlb
'Midnight Exchange'	NCft
mitriformis	LCro NCft NGBl SChr
mutabilis	SEND
× ***nobilis*** **new**	SEND
- variegated (v) **new**	SPlb
peglerae	NCft SRms
petricola	CAbb
polyphylla ♀H3	CDTJ CPbh SArc WPGP XVPe
rauhii ♀H1b	CPbh SIvy SRms SSim
reitzii	CAbb CPbh NCft SPlb
'Snowflake'	EShb
somaliensis ♀H1b	NCft
× ***spinosissima***	CWnw EAri
squarrosa	CDoC NCft
striata	CBcs CCCN CPbh EAri EShb SPlb SSim
striatula ♀H3	CBrP CDTJ CSde CTca CTrC EOli ETod IKel LEdu LWaG SArc SChr SCoo SEND SPlb SPoG SVen WCot WMal XVPe
- var. ***caesia***	WPGP
succotrina	CAbb
tenuior	EShb
variegata (v) ♀H1c	CBen EAri EShb LSun MPri SSim
§ ***vera*** ♀H1c	Widely available
wickensii	SPlb
yavellana	SPlb
zebrina 'Dannyz' **new**	LCro

Aloe × *Haworthia* see × *Alworthia*

Aloinopsis (*Aizoaceae*)

lueckhoffii	SSim
orpenii **new**	EAri
rosulata	SSim
spathulata	GEdr SPlb

Alonsoa (*Scrophulariaceae*)

acutifolia var. ***candida***	LBar
'Bright Spark'	CSpe LBar
incisifolia	CCCN CSpe
meridionalis	CCCN LBar
- 'Rebel'	LBar SCoo SRkn
- 'Shell Pink'	LBar
warscewiczii	CCCN
- 'Peachy-keen'	CSpe

Alopecurus (*Poaceae*)

pratensis	CHab
- 'Aureovariegatus' (v)	CTri GMaP GMcL NBid SPer SRms
- 'Aureus'	NBro SPlb

Alophia (*Iridaceae*)

lahue	see *Herbertia lahue*

Aloysia (*Verbenaceae*)

chamaedryfolia	EPfP
§ ***citrodora*** ♀H3	Widely available
- 'Spilsbury Mint'	CRos ELan EPfP LRHS MHer
gratissima	WJek
triphylla	see *A. citrodora*

Alpinia (*Zingiberaceae*)

galanga	XVPe
japonica	CExl LEdu XSte XVPe
- B&SWJ 8889	ESwi WCru
- PAB 6441	LEdu
roxburghii **new**	EAri
zerumbet 'Variegata' (v)	XVPe

Alsobia (*Gesneriaceae*)

§ ***dianthiflora***	WDib
§ 'San Miguel'	WDib

Alstroemeria ✿ (*Alstroemeriaceae*)

'Adonis' PBR	SAlS WViv
'Aimi'	CTtf EGrI MNrw SAlS SWvt WViv
'Alexis' PBR	SAlS WViv
'Amarillo'	SAlS
'Andez Rose'	CDor
'Andez Vanilla'	CDor
'Angelina'	SWvt
'Anne' (Midi Series)	WHlf
'Apollo' ♀H4	ELan MNrw NBir NRHS SAlS SWvt WViv
'Arthur' (Maxi Series)	SAlS
'Athena'	SAlS WViv
'Aubance' (Garden Series)	WHlf
aurantiaca	see *A. aurea*
§ ***aurea***	MRav SRms XLum
- 'Lutea'	MACG NLar SDeJ SPlb
- 'Orange King'	EGrI ELan MACG NLar SDeJ
'Authion' (Garden Series)	SAlS
'Avanti'	EHyd ELan ELon LRHS NRHS SAlS WViv
'Avrillé' (Garden Series)	SAlS
'Baugé' (Garden Series)	SAlS WHlf
'Béatrice' (Midi Series)	SAlS
'Blushing Bride'	SAlS SWvt WViv
'Bodega' PBR	SAlS WViv
'Bolero'	SAlS WViv
'Bonanza'	SAlS WViv
brasiliensis	WCot WSHC WViv XLum
- 'Cally Star' (v)	EBee EPPr NLar
'Brézé' (Garden Series)	WHlf
'Briançon' (Garden Series)	SAlS
'Brissac' (Garden Series)	WHlf
'Cahors' (Planet Series) ♀H4	LCro LOPS
'Camille' (Mini Series)	WHlf
'Candy'	SAlS WViv
'Caroline' (Midi Series)	EGrI
'Carousel' **new**	SAlS
'Catherine' (Little Miss Series)	WViv
'Charles' (Maxi Series)	SAlS
'Charlotte' (Mini Series)	EGrI
'Charm'	SAlS SWvt WViv
'Chinon' (Garden Series)	SAlS
§ 'Christina' PBR (Little Miss Series)	CWnw EGrI ELan LRHS MPri NRHS SAlS SWvt WViv
'Christine' (Midi Series)	SAlS
'Christine Marsh'	WViv
CINDERELLA ('Stapula') **new**	MAsh
'Cindy'	WViv
'Dana' **new**	SAlS
'Dandy Candy'	CWnw EHyd MACG MHol NGdn NLar WCot
'Davina' PBR (Little Miss Series)	EHyd LRHS MPri NRHS SAlS WViv
'Dayspring Delight' (v)	MNrw
§ DIANA, PRINCESS OF WALES ('Stablaco')	CBcs EHyd LRHS NRHS
'Diane' (Midi Series)	SAlS
Doctor Salter's hybrids	SRms
Duchesses d'Anjou Series	see *A.* Midi Series
Ducs d'Anjou Series	see *A.* Maxi Series
'Eleanor' (Little Miss Series)	EHyd LRHS NRHS SAlS WViv
ELIZABETH ('Stamutro')	EGrI
'Elvira'	SAlS WViv
'Emily' PBR (Little Miss Series)	LRHS SAlS WViv

'Etna'^{PBR}	SAlS WViv
'Evening Song'	SAlS SMHy SWvt
exserens	WCot
'Flaming Star'	LSvl SAlS WViv
'Flirt'	LOPS
'Fougeré' (Garden Series)	CTtf SAlS
'Frances' (v)	CAvo CBro
'François' (Maxi Series)	SAlS
'Freedom'	CWGN CWnw ECtt ELon EWoo MHol NBir NLar NSti SCob SCoo SPoG WCot WFar
'Friendship' ♀^{H5}	EHyd ELan LRHS NRHS SAlS SWvt WMal WViv
'Gaspard' (Mini Series)	SAlS
'Georges' (Maxi Series)	SAlS
'Gina'^{PBR} (Little Miss Series)	EGrI LRHS NRHS SAlS WViv
'Gloria'	ELan LRHS NRHS SAlS SWvt WViv
'Glory of the Andes' (v)	CWGN NLar
'Golden Delight'	EHyd ELan LRHS NRHS SAlS WViv
§ H.R.H. Princess Alice ('Staverpi')	LRHS NRHS
'Hawera'	GBin
'Henri' (Maxi Series)	CBod LBar MHol SAlS WHlf
§ Holiday Valley ('Tessumholid') (Summer Paradise Series)	LHWs LRHS SAlS
hookeri	WFar
(Inca Series) Inca Adore ('Koadore')	MThu WViv
- Inca Avanti ('Koncavanti'^{PBR})	CWGN
- Inca Azure ('Konazur'^{PBR})	WViv
- Inca Bandit ('Koncaband')	SAlS SGBe WViv
- Inca Battle	SAlS SGBe
- Inca Blue Heaven	WViv
- Inca Classic ('Konclassic')	WViv
- Inca Coral ('Konocoral')	WViv
- Inca Devotion ('Konevotio'^{PBR})	NLar
- Inca Dream ('Kodream')	WViv
- Inca Exotica ('Koexotica')	SAlS
- Inca Fire	SCoo SPoG WViv
- Inca Flamingo	WViv
- Inca Glow ('Koglow')	CWGN EGrI ELon MHol NLar SDeJ SRms
- Inca Goal ('Koncagoal')	CBod LBar SCoo WViv
- Inca Husky ('Koncahusky'^{PBR})	CBod CWGN CWnw ELon LBar LHWs LRHS MHol SCoo SEdd SPad WViv
- Inca Ice ('Koice')	CWGN NLar WViv
- Inca Lake ('Koncalake')	CWGN WViv
- Inca Lolly ('Koncalolly'^{PBR})	WViv
- Inca Lucky ('Koncalucky'^{PBR})	LHWs SAlS
- Inca Mambo ('Koncamambo'^{PBR})	WViv
- Inca Milk ('Koncamilk')	WViv
- Inca Mystic ('Koncamystic'^{PBR})	SAlS
- Inca Noble ('Koncanoble')	WViv
- Inca Pretty	WViv
- Inca Pulse ('Konpulse'^{PBR})	CWGN ELon NLar SDeJ SMad WViv
- Inca Rio	WViv
- Inca Serin ('Koserin'^{PBR})	CWGN WViv
- Inca Smile ('Koncasmile'^{PBR})	CWGN
- Inca Sundance ('Koncasuna')	CBod CPla CWnw ELon LBar LHWs SCoo SEdd SGBe SPad
- Inca Sweety ('Koncasweet'^{PBR})	CPla LBar LHWs SGBe WViv
- Inca Toto ('Koncatoto'^{PBR})	WViv
- Inca Tropic ('Kotrop')	CWGN
- Inca Vito ('Koncavito'^{PBR})	CBod CPla CWGN CWnw ELon LBar LHWs MHol NLar SCoo SEdd SPad SPoG WTyc
- Inca Yuko ('Koncayuko'^{PBR})	CBod CWGN ELon LBar MHol WSpi WViv
Indian Summer ('Tesronto'^{PBR}) (Summer Paradise Series)	Widely available
(Inticancha Series)	WViv
Inticancha Antarctica ('Tesantarc')	
- Inticancha Bryce ('Tesbryce'^{PBR})	CBod LHWs LRHS LSou MDon MHol NLar SAlS SCob SCoo WFar WHlf WViv
- Inticancha Cabana ('Tescaban')	CBod CRos EHyd LHWs LRHS LSou MHol NRHS SAlS SCob SCoo SPoG
- Inticancha Creamy Dark Pink ('Tescreda')	SDeJ WViv
- Inticancha Dark Purple ('Tesdarklin'^{PBR})	CRos LHWs LRHS MSCN NRHS SAlS WFar WViv
- Inticancha Doba ('Tesdoba'^{PBR})	LHWs
- Inticancha Indigo ('Tesindig'^{PBR})	CBod LHWs MDon SAlS SCoo WHil
- Inticancha Kanika ('Tesikani')	SAlS
- Inticancha Machu ('Tesmach'^{PBR})	SAlS WFar WViv
- Inticancha Magic White ('Tesmaghwi'^{PBR})	CBod LHWs LSou MHol SAlS SCoo
- Inticancha Maya ('Tesmaya'^{PBR})	CRos CWGN ECtt EHyd LHWs LRHS MDon NRHS SAlS SCob SCoo WFar WHil WViv
- Inticancha Moonlight ('Tesmoonli'^{PBR})	LHWs SAlS
- Inticancha Navayo ('Tesnava'^{PBR})	ECtt LHWs LRHS LSou MDon MHol SAlS SCoo WFar
- Inticancha Passion ('Tespassion'^{PBR})	ECtt LHWs LSou SAlS SCoo WHlf WViv
- Inticancha Purple ('Tespurplin'^{PBR})	CWGN WFar WViv
- Inticancha Red ('Tesrobin'^{PBR})	CBod CRos CWGN LRHS MHol NRHS SAlS SCoo WFar WHlf WViv
- Inticancha Sunday ('Tessunday'^{PBR})	SAlS
- Inticancha Sunlight ('Tessunlight'^{PBR})	ECtt NLar WFar WViv
- Inticancha Sunshine ('Tesshine'^{PBR})	CBod LHWs LRHS LSou MDon MHol SAlS WHlf
- Inticancha Valentino ('Tesvalen'^{PBR})	LRHS
- Inticancha White Pink Blush ('Tesblushin'^{PBR})	EHyd LRHS NRHS WFar WViv
- Inticancha White Pink Heart ('Teshearti n')	NLar SAlS SCoo
'Isabel' (Little Miss Series)	LRHS SAlS WFar WViv
Isabella ('Stalis')	LSRN
§ ***isabellana***	SBrt WCru WMal
'Isabelle' (Midi Series)	SAlS
'Jazze Purple Rose' (Jazze Series)	GMcL
'Jessica'^{PBR} (Little Miss Series)	LRHS SAlS WViv
'Joséphine' (Midi Series)	SAlS
'Junon' (Planet Series)	LCro LOPS
'Jupiter' (Planet Series) **new**	LCro
'Laguna'	SAlS WViv

	LAURA ('Stalauli'PBR)	ECtt
	'Layon' (Garden Series)	SAlS WHlf
	'Léo' (Mini Series)	SAlS
	'Leonie'	SAlS
	ligtu hybrids	CAvo ECha EPfP GKev LCro LOPS MACG MNrw NPer SDeJ SRms SWvt WBrk
	'Lilac Bush' (Garden Jewels Series)	LHWs WViv
	'Liré' (Garden Series)	CTtf MHol SAlS WHlf
	'Little Miss Natalie'	see *A.* 'Natalie'
	'Little Miss Vanessa' (Little Miss Series)	EGrI LRHS MPri SAlS
	'Louis' (Maxi Series)	CBod LBar SAlS
	'Louise' (Midi Series)	LSRN SAlS
	'Lucas' (Mini Series)	SAlS
	'Lucca'	SAlS WViv
	LUCIANA ('Stalluc') **new**	SAlS
	'Lucinda'	SAlS SWvt WViv
	'Lucy' (Little Miss Series)	SAlS WViv
	'Maestro'PBR	SAlS WViv
	Majestic Series	see *A.* Garden Series
	'Marcé' (Garden Series)	SAlS WHlf
	'Marguerite' (Midi Series)	SAlS WHlf
	'Marie' (Midi Series)	SAlS
	'Mars' (Planet Series)	CTsd CWnw EHyd LRHS MThu SMHy
	'Mathilde' (Midi Series)	NLar SAlS
	'Matilda' (Little Miss Series)	SAlS WViv
	'Mauve Majesty'	ELon LRHS MACG NLar SPoG WCot WHoo
§	Maxi Series	WHlf
	'Mazé' (Garden Series)	SAlS WHlf
§	Midi Series	WHlf
	'Miranda' (Little Miss Series)	LRHS SAlS WViv
	'Montsoreau' (Garden Series)	SAlS WHlf
	'Moulin Rouge'	SAlS WViv
§	'Natalie'PBR (Little Miss Series)	EHyd LRHS NRHS SAlS WViv
	'Neptune'	LCro LOPS
	'Nicolas' (Maxi Series)	SAlS
	'Nina'	SAlS
	'Noah' (Mini Series)	SAlS
	'Océane' (Mini Series)	SAlS
	'Orange Flame' **new**	SAlS
	'Orange Glory' ♀H4	ELon MNrw SAlS SWvt WViv
	'Orange Supreme'	EHyd LRHS NRHS SAlS WViv
	'Oriana' ♀H4	SAlS SWvt
	pallida	SPlb
	'Pandora'PBR	LRHS NRHS SAlS WViv
	'Peaches' (Garden Jewels Series)	LHWs WViv
	'Perfect Orange'	WViv
	'Phoenix' (v) ♀H4	ELon SAlS SWvt WViv
	'Pink' (Garden Jewels Series)	LHWs WViv
	'Pink Lady'	SAlS WViv
	'Pink Perfection'	NLar
	'Pink Sensation'	LRHS NRHS SAlS WViv
	Pitchounes Series	see *A.* Mini Series
	Planet Series	EGrI
	'Polka'	SAlS WViv
	presliana RB 94103	WCot
	(Princess Series) PRINCESS ALICE	see *A.* H.R.H. PRINCESS ALICE
	- PRINCESS AMINA ('Zapriamin'PBR)	CBcs SPoG WViv
	- PRINCESS ANOUSKA ('Zaprinous'PBR)	NLar WViv
	- PRINCESS ARIANE ('Zapriari'PBR)	WViv
	- PRINCESS BEATRIX ('Stadoran')	SChr
	- PRINCESS CAMILLA ('Stapricamil')	SPoG

	- PRINCESS CLAIRE ('Zapriclair'PBR)	CBcs CRos CWGN EHyd EPfP LHWs LRHS NRHS SAlS
	- PRINCESS DANIELA ('Stapridani')	SCoo
	- PRINCESS DIANA	see *A.* DIANA, PRINCESS OF WALES ('Stablaco'), *A.* PRINCESS DIANA ('Zapridapal')
§	- PRINCESS DIANA ('Zapridapal'PBR)	CWGN EPfP LHWs SCoo SPoG WViv
	- PRINCESS ELIANE LIGHT PINK ('Zaprieliali') **new**	CSBt
	- PRINCESS ELIANE ORANGE ('Zapriliarange'PBR) **new**	CSBt LHWs
	- PRINCESS ELIANE ('Zaprielia'PBR)	CBcs CRos EHyd LRHS NRHS SAlS WViv
	- PRINCESS FABIANA ('Zaprifabi'PBR)	CBcs CRos CWGN EHyd LRHS LSou NRHS SAlS SPoG WViv
	- PRINCESS ISABELLA ('Zapribel'PBR)	LSRN SAlS WViv
	- PRINCESS IVANA ('Staprivane'PBR)	SPoG
	- PRINCESS JULIETA ('Zaprijul'PBR)	NLar
	- PRINCESS KATE ('Zaprikate'PBR)	CBcs CRos CWGN EHyd EPfP LHWs LRHS NRHS SAlS
	- PRINCESS KATIANA ('Zaprikatia') **new**	LSou
	- PRINCESS LAUREN	LRHS SAlS
	- PRINCESS LETIZIA ('Zaprilet')	EPfP SPoG
	- PRINCESS LILIAN ('Zaprilian'PBR)	CRos EHyd EPfP LRHS NRHS SAlS WViv
	- PRINCESS LISA ('Zaprilisa'PBR)	CBcs CWGN LHWs LRHS SAlS
	- PRINCESS LOUISE ('Zaprilou'PBR)	CBcs LSRN WViv
	- PRINCESS MARGARET ('Staprimar')	NLar
	- PRINCESS MARY ('Zaprimary'PBR)	NLar
	- PRINCESS MATHILDE ('Zaprimat'PBR)	WViv
	- PRINCESS PAOLA ('Stapripal'PBR)	CRos CWGN EHyd LHWs LRHS NRHS SCoo SPoG WViv
	- PRINCESS SARA ('Staprisara'PBR)	CRos EHyd EPfP LRHS NRHS SAlS SPoG
	- PRINCESS SUSANA ('Staprisusa')	SCoo
	- PRINCESS TAMARA ('Zapritama'PBR)	CBcs CWGN LHWs LRHS SCoo SPoG
	- PRINCESS THERESA ('Zapriteres'PBR)	NLar SAlS
	- PRINCESS VICTORIA	see *A.* 'Victoria'
	- PRINCESS ZAVINA ('Staprivina'PBR)	NLar SPoG
	pseudospathulata	WCot
§	***psittacina***	CBro ECha EPPr EPfP GBin MCot MHer SHar SRms WAvo WFar WViv
	- 'Mona Lisa'	CBod EShb XLum
	- 'Royal Star' (v)	CBod CBro CExl CWCL EHyd EPPr EPfP EPri EWTr EWoo LBar LDai LRHS LSto MHol NRHS SBea SHar SMrm SPoG SRms WCot WFar WGwG WHoo WSHC WSpi XLum
	pulchella Sims	see *A. psittacina*
	'Purple Rain'	ELon SAlS SWvt WViv
	'Querré' (Garden Series)	SAlS
	'Rachel' **new**	WViv
	'Red Beauty' (v)	see *A.* 'Spitfire'
	'Red Beauty'	EHyd ELan GMaP LRHS NRHS SAlS SWvt WViv
	'Red Elf' ♀H4	SAlS SMHy SWvt WViv
	'Regina'	see *A.* 'Victoria'

'Rhubarb and Custard'	ELan
ROCK 'N' ROLL ('Alsdun01'[PBR]) (v)	CDor CTtf EBee ELan LBar LCro LOPS LSou MHol MHtn MNrw NHpl SGBe SMad SPoG SRms WCot WFar WViv
'Rosanna' (Little Miss Series)	SAlS WViv
§ 'Roselind' (Little Miss Series)	EGrI ELan LRHS MPri NRHS SAlS SWvt WViv
'Rosie' (Mini Series)	SAlS
'Roxane' (Mini Series)	CBod LBar
'Saturne' (Planet Series)	CDor LCro LOPS
'Segré' (Garden Series)	SAlS
'Selina'	MNrw SAlS WViv
'Serenade'	SAlS WViv
'Sirius' (Planet Series) ♀H4	LCro LOPS
'Sonata' ♀H4	SAlS WViv
§ 'Sophie'[PBR] (Little Miss Series)	ELan LRHS MPri SAlS SWvt WViv
§ 'Spitfire' (v) ♀H4	LCro LOPS SAlS SWvt WCot WViv
Summer Paradise Series	MHol
- SUMMER BREAK ('Tessumbreak')	CBod ECtt EPfP LHWs LRHS LSou MAsh MHol SAlS SCoo SGBe WViv
- SUMMER BREEZE ('Teshunte'[PBR])	CBod CRos ECtt EHyd LHWs LRHS NRHS SAlS SCoo SGBe SPoG SRms WFar WHlf WViv
- SUMMER HOLIDAY	see *A.* HOLIDAY VALLEY
- SUMMER PARTY ('Tessumpar')	CRos ECtt EHyd LRHS NRHS WFar
- SUMMER RED ('Tessumred')	LHWs LSou MDon
- SUMMER RELIEVE ('Gasumrelie')	LHWs LRHS MHol
- SUMMER SAINT ('Tessumsaint')	CBod ECtt EPfP LHWs LRHS LSou MHol SCoo SGBe WViv
- SUMMER SKY ('Tessumsky')	CBod CWGN EPfP LHWs LRHS MHol MHtn SAlS SCoo SGBe WViv
- SUMMER SNOW ('Gasumsnow')	LHWs LSou SAlS SCoo
'Summertime'	LRHS NRHS WViv
'Sunstar'	GMaP
'Sweet Laura'[PBR]	CBod ECtt ELan ELon EWoo LRHS LSRN MHol MNrw NGdn NLar NSti SPoG WCot
'Tangerine Tango'	WViv
'Tanya'	MNrw SAlS WViv
§ 'Tara'[PBR] (Little Miss Series)	CWnw ELan LRHS NLar NRHS SAlS SWvt WViv
'Tessa' ♀H4	SAlS WViv
'Thorigné' (Garden Series)	SAlS
'Tiercé' (Garden Series)	SAlS
TIME VALLEY (Summer Paradise Series)	LHWs
'Uranus'	LCro LOPS
'Valley Girl'	LHWs
'Ventura'	SAlS WViv
'Venus' (Planet Series)	LCro LOPS WViv
'Veronica' (Little Miss Series)	WViv
§ 'Victoria'	EGrI
'William' (Maxi Series)	SAlS WHlf
'Yellow' (Garden Jewels Series)	LHWs WViv
'Yellow Friendship' ♀H4	MNrw NLar SWvt WViv
'Zoé' (Mini Series)	WHlf

Althaea (*Malvaceae*)

armeniaca	EPPr MAvo WCot
cannabina	CAby CCBP CDor CSpe CTtf ECha ELan EPPr EPri GGro MAvo MBel MHer MNrw NGBl SBls SBut SHar SMHy SPhx SPtp WCot WKif WOld WSHC WTor
officinalis	CBee CBod CCBP CHab CPud CTsd ELan ENfk EPPr GPoy GQue MAvo MBow MHer MHoo MMuc MNHC NAts NLar SRms SVic WHer WJek WSpi XSen
§ - 'Romney Marsh'	MAvo MRav WMal
rosea	see *Alcea rosea*
rugosostellulata	see *Alcea rugosa*

Altingia see *Liquidambar*

× *Alworthia* (*Asphodelaceae*)

'Black Gem'	EBee EShb NCft SIvy SRms SSim WCot

Alyogyne (*Malvaceae*)

§ ***huegelii***	CCCN EAri EShb SEND SEle SIvy SPlb
- 'Santa Cruz'	CCCN CHll
MAGIC MOMENTS ('Hutwow')	CCCN ELan SMad SPad SPoG

Alyssoides (*Brassicaceae*)

utriculata	CFis

Alyssum (*Brassicaceae*)

cuneifolium	GJos
montanum	ECha MAsh SPlb SRms
§ - 'Berggold'	EBou ECha ELan EPfP LRHS WIce
- 'Luna'	CBod LBar
- MOUNTAIN GOLD	see *A. montanum* 'Berggold'
- subsp. ***pluscanescens***	WCot
oxycarpum	EPot SLee WAbe
saxatile	see *Aurinia saxatilis*
- 'Summit'	EDAr EPfP GJos LRHS SRms
spinosum	see *Hormathophylla spinosa*
tortuosum	SEND
'Variegatum' (v)	CBod LBar
wulfenianum	WIce

Amaranthus (*Amaranthaceae*)

'Autumn Palette'	CSpe
caudatus	LCro LOPS
cruentus	CLau
- 'Velvet Curtains' ♀H2	LCro LOPS
hypochondriacus 'Pygmy Torch' ♀H2	CSpe
tricolor	CLau SRms

× *Amarcrinum* (*Amaryllidaceae*)

'Dorothy Hannibal'	WCot
memoria-corsii	CBor EPri GKev LAma LEdu MPie
'Howardii'	NRog SDeJ WCot

× *Amarine* (*Amaryllidaceae*)

tubergenii Belladiva Series	CBro CSpe EBee ELan ERCP GKev LAma LCro LOPS LRHS NHoy SDir
- - 'Anastasia'[PBR]	CAvo CBro ELan ERCP GKev LAma LBar NHoy SEdd SHar SMad
- - 'Aphrodite'[PBR]	CBro GKev LAma LBar NHoy SDir SMad WFar
- - 'Elvi'	LAma NHoy
- - 'Emanuelle'[PBR]	CAvo CBro ELan ERCP GKev LAma LBar NHoy
- - 'Paris'	CBro
- - 'Smilla'	CBro GKev LAma NHoy SEdd
- - 'Tomoka'[PBR]	CBro
- 'Fletcheri'	WCot
- 'Zwanenburg'	GKev LAma MPie NRog WCot

× *Amarygia* (*Amaryllidaceae*)

§ ***bidwillii*** 'Alba'	CAvo CBro
- 'Rosea'	WCot

Amaryllis (*Amaryllidaceae*)

§ ***belladonna*** ♀H4	CBcs CBor CBro CPbh CPrp CTca CTri EBee EGrI EPfP ERCP EShb

	GKev LAma LCro LOPS MPie NRog SDeJ SDir SEND SEdd SPeP WCot
- 'Hathor'	CBro
- 'Johannesburg'	CBro WCot
- 'Major'	SChr
- 'Parkeri Alba'	see × *Amarygia bidwillii* 'Alba'
- 'Purpurea'	WCot
- white-flowered	NRog SDeJ

Amaryllis × *Brunsvigia* see × *Amarygia*

Amaryllis × *Crinum* see × *Amarcrinum*

Amaryllis × *Nerine* see × *Amarine*

Ambrosina (*Araceae*)

bassii	WCot

Amelanchier ✿ (*Rosaceae*)

alnifolia	MGil MPri NGrd SBmr WKor
- 'Forestburg'	MBlu NLar
- 'Honeywood' (F)	CAgr MBlu MCoo NLar NOra
- 'Jb30' (F)	CAgr MCoo NOra
- 'Martin' (F)	CAgr NOra
- 'Northline' (F)	CAgr EBee LCro LOPS LRHS MCoo NLar NOra SBmr
- 'Obelisk'PBR	Widely available
§ - var. ***pumila***	WCot
- 'Regent' (F)	CAgr
- 'Smokey' (F)	CAco CAgr MBlu MCoo NLar NOra SPoG WKor
- 'Thiessen'	MCoo NLar NOra SBmr
* ***alpina***	SSta
bartramiana	SSta
- 'Eskimo'	NLar
canadensis K. Koch	see *A. lamarckii*
canadensis ambig.	CAco CBod CDoC CKel CPer EGrI EHeP ERom GMcL ILea IPap LMaj LShi MACG MDon MMuc MPri NOra NWea SCgs SEND SEWo SPoG SRHi WFar WKor WLov
canadensis (L.) Medik.	CAgr CLnd CMac CSBt CTri EBee ELan EPfP LEdu LRHS MGos MRav MSwo SArc SPer WMat
§ - 'Glenn Form'	CAco CCVT CEnd EBee EHeP EPfP LMaj LPar LRHS MGos MTrO NLar NOra SEWo SGol SLim SPer SPoG WTSh
- 'October Flame' **new**	CWnw SRHi
- 'Prince William'	CAgr MBlu MCoo SGol
- RAINBOW PILLAR	see *A. canadensis* 'Glenn Form'
× ***grandiflora***	EHeP SCob
- 'Autumn Brilliance'	CEnd EPfP MBlu NHol NLar NOrn NRHS SGol WHtc
- 'Ballerina'	Widely available
- 'Cole's Select'	EBee LRHS SWvt
- 'Princess Diana' ♀H7	SSta
§ - 'Robin Hill' ♀H7	Widely available
- 'Rubescens'	CEnd EBee SSta SWvt
'La Paloma' ♀H6	CPer EBee EPfP LRHS LSRN MAsh MGos MTrO NOra NOrn SCoo SLim SSta WHtc WMat
laevis	CBcs CTri EPfP
- 'Prince Charles'	NLar
- 'R.J. Hilton' ♀H7	CDoC EBee EPfP LRHS MAsh MTrO NOra SCoo SSta WMat WMou
- 'Snow Cloud'	CCVT MPri SSta
- 'Snowflakes'	CAco CBTr CBod CDoC CDow CEnd CSBt EBee EPfP LCro LPar LRHS LSRN MAsh MNic MTrO NLar NOra NOrn SCob SEWo SLim SOrN SPer SPoG SSta SWvt WMat
§ ***lamarckii*** ♀H7	Widely available
- 'Snowberry'	SBmr
obovalis 'Jennybelle' (F) **new**	SSta
ovalis misapplied	see *A. spicata* (Lam.) K. Koch
ovalis Medik.	SPlb
- 'Edelweiss'	CAco EPfP LRHS MGos MRav MTrO NLar SCoo
- 'Helvetia'	MAsh NLar
pumila	see *A. alnifolia* var. *pumila*
rotundifolia ambig.	CAgr MCoo
sanguinea 'Chimney Rock'	NLar
§ ***spicata*** (Lam.) K. Koch	CAgr MCoo
stolonifera	CTri

Amelanchier × *Sorbus* see × *Amelasorbus*

× *Amelasorbus* (*Rosaceae*)

raciborskiana	MBlu NLar

Amellus (*Asteraceae*)

asteroides	MAsh

Amentotaxus (*Taxaceae*)

argotaenia	WPGP
var. ***argotaenia*** **new**	

Amicia (*Fabaceae*)

zygomeris	CBcs CDTJ CDow CHll CMCN CSde CSpe EBee EPfP EWes IPot LEdu LRHS MGil SChF SDix SEle SHor SMad SMrm SPoG WCot WPGP WSHC XSte
- 'John's Big Splash' (v)	WCot

Ammi (*Apiaceae*)

majus ♀H6	CKel CSpe EPfP EWoo LCro LEdu LOPS LRHS LSto MAvo MNHC SDix SHor SPhx WHlf WJek
- 'Graceland' ♀H6	LCro WWke
visnaga	see *Visnaga daucoides*

Ammobium (*Asteraceae*)

alatum	SPlb

Ammocharis (*Amaryllidaceae*)

coranica	WCot

Ammophila (*Poaceae*)

arenaria	CKno EBee XLum XSen
breviligulata	EBee XLum

Amomum (*Zingiberaceae*)

sp.	SDir
subulatum	SDir SPre

Amomyrtus (*Myrtaceae*)

§ ***luma***	CBcs CTri CTsd EBee ELon IDee LEdu MMuc SEND SPoG WJek WPGP WPav
meli	WPGP

Amorpha (*Fabaceae*)

canescens	CBWd CSpe SBls SPlb
fruticosa	EPPr LAlb MBlu MGil MMuc SEND SPlb WJur

Amorphophallus ✿ (*Araceae*)

albus	CDTJ LEdu SPlb WCot
bulbifer	CDTJ ESwi LAma LCro SDeJ SDir SPlb
dunnii	CDTJ LEdu
henryi	WCot
kerrii	CExl WCot

kiusianus B&SWJ 4845	WCru
konjac	CBor CDTJ CExl LEdu MVil NGKo SChr SDeJ SPlb WCot
- 'Tattered Umbrella'	SPlb
napalensis	LAma SDir WCot XLum
ongsakulii	WCot
paeoniifolius	LAma
stipitatus	LEdu WCot
yuloensis	WCot

Ampelodesmos (*Poaceae*)

mauritanicus ♀H3	CKno ECha EShb EWes MAvo SDix SEND SPlb SPtp WCot

Ampelopsis (*Vitaceae*)

aconitifolia	NLar WCru WJur
- 'Chinese Lace'	EBee EShb ESwi EWTr MRav NLar WBor WCot
arborea	WCru
brevipedunculata	ELan LShi MGil SCoo SPer WAvo
- 'Elegans' (v)	CBcs CBod CDoC CKel CMac EBee ELan ELon EPfP EShb LCro LRHS MGil MGos MHtn MRav SPer SPoG SWvt WAvo WCot WHtc WLov
delavayana	EShb MGil MMuc
glandulosa var. ***hancei*** B&SWJ 1793	WCru
- var. ***heterophylla***	WJur
henryana	see *Parthenocissus henryana*
megalophylla	NLar
sempervirens hort. ex Veitch	see *Cissus striata*
tricuspidata 'Veitchii'	see *Parthenocissus tricuspidata* 'Veitchii'

Amphicome see *Incarvillea*

Amsonia (*Apocynaceae*)

'Blue Ice'	Widely available
ciliata	EMor EWld LEdu MCot MMrt NLar SHar WPGP XLum
§ ***elliptica***	EBee EMor EPPr WFar
'Ernst Pagels'	EBee ECha EMor EPPr EShb EWld LEdu MAvo SHar SMHy WCot WGoo
hubrichtii	Widely available
illustris	CSpe EBee EBlo EMor EPPr LEdu LRHS NLar NRHS SBls SBut SHar SMHy SPhx WPGP
§ ***orientalis***	CPla CSpe CTri EBee ECha EGrI ELan EMor GBin LEdu LPla LRHS LShi MAvo MCot MRav NDov NLar NRHS SBut SPhx SVen SWvt WCot WFar WKif XLum
- from Turkey	LEdu SMHy
- 'Cally Dark Stem'	LPla
sinensis	see *A. elliptica*
tabernaemontana	Widely available
* - ***galacticifolia***	EGrI
- 'Montana'	SWvt
- var. ***salicifolia***	CBWd EBee EBlo EMor LCro LEdu LOPS LPla LRHS MACG NRHS SCob SHor WCAu WPGP
- 'Stella Azul'	EBee EMor LBar MNrw
- 'Storm Cloud'	EMor IPot LBar LCro SMad

Amygdalus see *Prunus*

nana	see *Prunus tenella*

Anacampseros (*Portulacaceae*)

rufescens new	EAri
- 'Sunrise' new	SEdd
telephiastrum	CPla
- 'Sunrise'	see *A. telephiastrum* 'Variegata'
- 'Variegata' new	WOld

Anacamptis (*Orchidaceae*)

§ ***laxiflora***	NLAp
§ ***morio***	LAma NLAp
pyramidalis	CHab NLAp

Anacyclus (*Asteraceae*)

pyrethrum	GPoy
- var. ***depressus*** ♀H4	EBee EBou ELan EPfP GKev MAsh MMuc NSla SPlb SRot
- - 'Garden Gnome'	CTri MACG SRms
- - 'Silberkissen'	CGBo CPla EDAr

Anagallis (*Primulaceae*)

arvensis	SPhx
monellii 'Gentian Blue' ♀H3	LCro LOPS
- subsp. ***linifolia*** 'Blue Light'	CSpe
- 'Skylover'	CCCN LCro LOPS WHlf
tenella	CWat LLWG LPfP
- 'Studland'	EPot WAbe

Ananas (*Bromeliaceae*)

comosus (F)	CCCN NTrD SPre
- 'Champaca' (F) ♀H1a	CCCN LCro SPre
- CORONA ('Duranas2'PBR) (F) new	LCro

Anaphalis (*Asteraceae*)

margaritacea	CBcs ECha EWTr GMaP NBid NLar SRms WCAu WFar
§ - 'Neuschnee'	EBee GJos LPla MACG NLar SBls WFar
- NEW SNOW	see *A. margaritacea* 'Neuschnee'
- var. ***yedoensis***	CTri SDix
§ ***nepalensis*** var. ***monocephala***	EBee NSti SRms
nubigena	see *A. nepalensis* var. *monocephala*
transnokoensis	EWes MACG
triplinervis ♀H7	EBee ELan EPfP EShb EWld EWoo GAbr GDam GMaP LPal LRHS MCot MRav NBid NLar NRHS SBls SBut SCob SMrm SPer WCAu WFar WHlf XLum
- CC 1620	NBir
- 'Silberregen'	SAko
- 'Silver Wave' new	NLar
§ - 'Sommerschnee' ♀H7	CBod CMac CTtf ECha ECtt EPfP GMcL LRHS MCot MHol MRav NLar NRHS NWad SCob SGbt SPer WGwG WHoo WTre WWtn
- SUMMER SNOW	see *A. triplinervis* 'Sommerschnee'

Anaphaloides (*Asteraceae*)

§ ***bellidioides***	CTri ECha

Anchusa (*Boraginaceae*)

§ ***azurea***	CBod NLar WHlf
- 'Dropmore'	CDor EBee EBou EPfP LCro LOPS LRHS MRav NLar SAng SCob SRms
- 'Feltham Pride'	EBee ELan LRHS NRHS SRms SWvt WHoo
- 'Little John'	SRms
- 'Loddon Royalist'	Widely available
- 'Opal'	CBod CFis ECtt LRHS NRHS SMrm WCAu WGwG
capensis 'Blue Angel'	SWvt WFar
cespitosa	EWes WAbe WIce
italica	see *A. azurea*
laxiflora	see *Borago pygmaea*
myosotidiflora	see *Brunnera macrophylla*

officinalis	MNHC SRms
sempervirens	see *Pentaglottis sempervirens*

Ancylostemon see *Orecharis*

Andrachne (*Phyllanthaceae*)

colchica	see *Leptopus chinensis*

Androcymbium see *Colchicum*

Andromeda (*Ericaceae*)

polifolia	LPar SavN SPlb
- 'Alba'	EHyd LRHS MAsh SWvt
- 'Alisa'	GKev
- 'Blue Ice'	CDoC EHyd ELan EPot GArf GBin IDee LRHS LSRN MAsh NBir NLar SPer SPoG WAbe WFar XSte
- 'Blue Lagoon'	CDoC LCro MAsh NLar
- 'Compacta' 🏆H6	CDoC EHyd ELan EPot LCro LRHS LSRN MAsh NLar NWad SWvt WFar
- 'Grandiflora'	GKev
- 'Kirigamine'	GArf LRHS
- 'Macrophylla' 🏆H6	EPot WThu
- 'Nikko'	CMac NLar
- 'Shibutsu'	GArf

Andropogon (*Poaceae*)

gerardii	GQue XLum
- 'Prairie Sommer'	NDov
- 'Red Arrow'	IPot
- 'Red October'	LPla MACG
- 'Weinheim Burgundy'	IPot MNrw NDov
hallii 'JS Purple Konza' PBR	IPot MNrw
ischaemum	see *Bothriochloa ischaemum*
scoparius	see *Schizachyrium scoparium*

Androsace (*Primulaceae*)

sp.	MAsh
alpina	EPot WAbe
bulleyana	GEdr WAbe
cantabrica	EPot
carnea	GEdr
- subsp. ***brigantiaca***	GKev NHar NHpl NSla
- var. ***halleri***	see *A. carnea* subsp. *rosea*
- subsp. ***laggeri*** 🏆H5	EDAr NBwr NHar NSla WAbe
- - 'Andorra'	GArf
§ - subsp. ***rosea***	NHpl NSla
carnea* × *pyrenaica	ELan EPot WAbe WIce
ciliata	EPot WAbe
cylindrica	CRos EPot LRHS NRHS WAbe
cylindrica* × *hirtella	CRos EHyd EPot LRHS NRHS
delavayi	WAbe
- ACE 1786	WAbe
geraniifolia	CPla EBee ECha GKev SRms
globifera	EPot WAbe
halleri	see *A. carnea* subsp. *rosea*
hedraeantha	NSla WAbe
himalaica	EPot GEdr WAbe
hirtella	WAbe
idahoensis	WAbe
idahoensis* × *laevigata	WAbe
jacquemontii	see *A. villosa* var. *jacquemontii*
kosopoljanskii	EPot
lactea	WAbe
laevigata	CPla GArf
- 'Gothenburg'	WFar
lanuginosa 🏆H5	CSpe EDAr EPot GBin GKev NHol NHpl SBut SGro SLee SRms SRot WIce
laxa new	GKev
limprichtii	see *A. sarmentosa* var. *watkinsii*
× ***marpensis***	EPot WAbe
mathildae	WAbe
microphylla	see *A. mucronifolia* G.Watt
montana	WAbe
mucronifolia misapplied	see *A. sempervivoides*
§ ***mucronifolia*** G.Watt	EPot WAbe
mucronifolia G.Watt × ***sempervivoides***	EPot WAbe
muscoidea	WAbe
- 'Dolpo Lilac'	WAbe
- 'Millennium Dome' new	WAbe
- Schacht's form	WAbe
nivalis	SPlb
ochotensis	WAbe
primuloides	see *A. studiosorum*
pubescens	CRos EHyd EPot LRHS NRHS
pyrenaica	CRos EHyd EPot ITim LRHS NRHS SPlb WAbe
robusta subsp. ***purpurea***	WAbe
- - 'Dolpo Dwarf'	EPot WAbe
rotundifolia	CTtf GArf
sarmentosa misapplied	see *A. studiosorum*
sarmentosa ambig.	NHpl SPlb
sarmentosa Wall.	EBou SRms WHoo
- from Namche, Nepal	EPot WAbe
- Galmont's form	see *A. studiosorum* 'Salmon's Variety'
- 'Sherriffii'	MMuc SRms WIce
§ - var. ***watkinsii***	EPot
- var. ***yunnanensis*** misapplied	see *A. studiosorum*
selago	WAbe
- 'Red Eye'	WAbe
§ ***sempervivoides***	CRos EBou EDAr EHyd ELan EPot GArf GBin GKev GMaP LRHS MAsh NFav NHol NRHS NSla SGro SLee SPlb SRms WIce
- 'Susan Joan'	CBor EPot GKev NHar NWad WAbe
septentrionalis	CSpe
- 'Stardust'	EDAr ELan LRHS
strigillosa	GKev NHpl
§ ***studiosorum*** 🏆H5	EPot GAbr WAbe
- 'Chumbyi'	CBor EPot NHpl SRms WIce
- 'Conwy Gem'	WAbe
- 'Conwy Jewel'	WAbe
- 'Doksa' 🏆H5	EPot WAbe
§ - 'Salmon's Variety'	CTri EDAr
vandellii	ITim NSla WAbe
villosa	GArf WAbe
§ - var. ***jacquemontii***	CTtf WThu
- - lilac-flowered	EPot
- - pink-flowered	EPot WAbe
vitaliana	see *Vitaliana primuliflora*
watkinsii	see *A. sarmentosa* var. *watkinsii*

Andryala (*Asteraceae*)

agardhii	WAbe
glandulosa	WCot
lanata	see *Hieracium lanatum*

Anemanthele (*Poaceae*)

§ ***lessoniana*** 🏆H4	Widely available
- 'Buffalo Gold'	LRHS LSun SGBe
- 'Gold Hue'	ELon
- 'Sirocco'	EMor LRHS MACG MAvo WCot WFar

Anemarrhena (*Asparagaceae*)

asphodeloides	SBrt WCot

Anemone ✿ (*Ranunculaceae*)

aconitifolia Michx.	see *A. narcissiflora*
altaica	EMor EWes NLar SRms
'Annerose'	ECha NLar

apennina 🏆^{H6}	CAvo GEdr LEdu WShi
- var. ***albiflora***	ECha EPot LAma SPlb
- double-flowered (d)	CTtf ECha
- 'Petrovac'	CBor EPot GKev LAma LEdu NRog
baldensis	EMor GKev SRms
barbulata	CExl EBee EMor EWes GKev GPSL LEdu
blanda 🏆^{H6}	CAby CRos EPfP ETay LAma LCro LOPS LRHS MACG MAsh MBow NBwr NLar NRHS NRog SEND SRms WCav WFar WShi
I - 'Alba'	CRos EHyd LRHS NRHS
- blue-flowered	CAvo CRos CTri CTtf EHyd ELan EPfP EPot ERCP EShb GAbr GKev GMaP LAma LCro LOPS LRHS MPie NRHS NRog SCob SDeJ SDir SPer SPoG SRms WCot WHlf
- 'Charmer'	EPot GKev LAma NHpl NLar NRog SDeJ WCot
- 'Ingramii'	EPot GKev WCot
- pink-flowered	EShb
- var. ***rosea***	CRos EHyd LRHS NRHS NRog SDeJ SPoG
- - 'Pink Star'	CAvo EShb GKev LAma NBir NRog
- - 'Radar'	CBor EPot GKev LAma MNrw NBir NHpl NRog SDeJ
- 'Violet Star'	GKev LAma NRog SDeJ SHar WHil
- 'White Splendour' 🏆^{H6}	CAby CAvo CBor CTri CTtf ECha ELan EPot ERCP EShb ETay GAbr GKev LAma LCro LEdu LOPS NBir NRog SDeJ SDir SPhx SPoG SRms WCot WHil
- white-flowered	CRos LRHS NRHS WHlf
'Bowles's Mauve'	GEdr
caerulea	LEdu
canadensis	EMor EPPr GEdr LEdu SBrt WCot
caroliniana	EMor GKev
chapaensis HWJ 631	WCru
coelestina var. ***linearis***	GKev
coronaria	SVic WHlf
- De Caen Group	CBod CCBP CRos EHyd EPfP GKev LAma LOPS LRHS MACG NRHS SPoG
- - 'Bicolor'	GKev LAma SDeJ WCot
- - blue-flowered	CRos LRHS NRHS
- - 'Bordeaux'	ETay LAma LCro LOPS WCot
§ - - 'Die Braut'	CCBP ERCP GKev LAma LCro LOPS NBir SDeJ
- - 'His Excellency'	see *A. coronaria* (De Caen Group) 'Hollandia'
§ - - 'Hollandia'	EGrI GKev LAma SDeJ
- - 'Mister Fokker'	EGrI ERCP GBin GKev LAma LCro LOPS SDeJ
- - pink-flowered	CRos LRHS NRHS
- - red-flowered	CRos LRHS NRHS
- - THE BRIDE	see *A. coronaria* (De Caen Group) 'Die Braut'
- - 'The Governor'	ERCP GKev SDeJ
- (Harmony Series) 'Harmony Blue'	LRHS
- - 'Harmony Orchid'	EHyd EPfP LRHS NRHS
- - 'Harmony Pearl'	EHyd EPfP LRHS NRHS
- - 'Harmony Scarlet'	CRos EHyd EPfP LRHS NRHS
- - 'Harmony White'	LRHS
- Saint Bridgid Group (d)	EHyd GKev LRHS NRHS
- - 'Lord Lieutenant' (d)	ERCP GKev LAma NBir SDeJ
- - 'Mount Everest' (d)	ERCP GKev LAma NBir SDeJ
- - 'The Admiral' (d)	GKev LAma NBir SDeJ
- 'Sylphide' (Mona Lisa Series)	EGrI ERCP ETay GKev LAma LCro LOPS NBir SDeJ
cylindrica	CElw EMor GEdr
DAINTY SWAN ('Macane005'^{PBR})	CAvo CWGN EBee EHed EMor EPfP GEdr LBar MNrw NLar WTor
'Danish White'	MNrw WCot

decapetala	MHer
demissa	GEdr
- var. ***major***	EBee
DREAMING SWAN ('Macane004'^{PBR})	CMiW CPar CWGN EBee ELan EMor EPfP GBin GEdr GElm GMaP LBar LRHS LSou MBNS MBel MNrw NCth NLar NSti SCoo SEdd SHar SPoG SWvt WFar WHlf WNPC
drummondii	CWCL GKev
ELFIN SWAN ('Macane017'^{PBR})	CAvo CPar CWGN EHed EMor EPfP GEdr LRHS MBel MHol MNrw MPri NCth NLar NRHS SPoG WCot
FALL IN LOVE	see *A.* 'Sweetly'
fasciculata	see *A. narcissiflora*
filisecta	CBod EBee EMor MHol WCot
flaccida	CBor CBro CMiW EHyd EPPr GEdr LEdu LRHS MAvo MNrw NRHS SHar WCot WSHC
- 'Futabazuru' (d)	GEdr WFar
- 'Ginpai' (d)	GEdr WFar
'Frilly Knickers' (d) **new**	SHar
× ***fulgens*** 'Multipetala'	XLum
globosa	see *A. multifida* Poir.
'Guernica'	EWes
'Hatakeyama Double' (d)	LPla WSHC
'Hatakeyama Single'	LPla
hepatica L.	see *Hepatica nobilis*
§ ***hortensis***	EBee
§ ***hupehensis***	CExl CWal EBou GDam GMaP LSun XLum
- BWJ 1583 **new**	WCru
- BWJ 8190	WCru
- f. ***alba***	CExl CSpe
- BELLE ('Ifanfb'^{PBR}) (Fantasy Series) **new**	GEdr LBar
§ - 'Bowles's Pink' 🏆^{H7}	CDor CExl EBee LCro NLar
- 'Cinderella'^{PBR} (Fantasy Series)	EHyd LRHS NLar SCoo SEdd
- 'Crispa'	see *A.* × *hybrida* 'Lady Gilmour' Wolley-Dod
- 'Eugenie'	ECtt EPfP NBir
- 'Hadspen Abundance' 🏆^{H7}	Widely available
- var. ***hupehensis***	WFar
§ - var. ***japonica***	SRms
- - B&SWJ 4886	WCru
- - 'Bodnant Burgundy'	EBee LRHS SWvt
§ - - 'Bressingham Glow'	CExl CMac EBee ECtt ELan EPfP EPot EShb GKev GKin NBir NLar SPer WBrk WCAu WFar WHil
§ - - 'Pamina' 🏆^{H7}	Widely available
- - 'Pink Saucer'	CBod EBee GMcL MACG WBrk WFar WHil
- - PRINCE HENRY	see *A. hupehensis* var. *japonica* 'Prinz Heinrich'
§ - - 'Prinz Heinrich'	Widely available
§ - - 'Rotkäppchen' 🏆^{H7}	CDor ECtt EShb GKin LSun NHol NLar NSti SPad SWvt WCot
- - 'Splendens'	CKel CRos EHyd ELan EPfP GDam LCro LRHS NGrs NLar NRHS SCob SCoo SPoG SRms SWvt WSpi XLum
- - 'Tiki Sensation'^{PBR}	CWGN ECtt LBar LCro
- JASMINE ('Ifanfj') (Fantasy Series) **new**	LBar WFar
- 'Little Princess'^{PBR}	ECtt EShb MACG MNrw NLar WHil
- LITTLE SUMMER BREEZE ('Anem081'^{PBR}) **new**	WHil
- 'Ouvertüre'	ECtt
- 'Pocahontas'^{PBR} (Fantasy Series)	CNor ECtt EHyd EPfP GEdr LBar LRHS MAsh MNrw NLar NRHS SCoo SEdd
- 'Praecox'	CBod CRos EPfP LRHS LSto MBNS MBros NBir NRHS SGbt SMrm SRms SWvt WCAu WGwG WHoo

- 'Red Riding Hood' (Fantasy Series)	GEdr LRHS NRHS SEdd
- 'September Charm'	see *A.* × *hybrida* 'September Charm'
- SNOW ANGEL ('Ifansa') (Fantasy Series) **new**	LBar
- SUMMER BREEZE ('Anem080'PBR) **new**	WHil
- 'Superba'	WSpi
§ × ***hybrida***	CWal NChi
- 'Alba' misapplied (UK)	see *A.* × *hybrida* 'Honorine Jobert'
- 'Alba Dura'	see *A. tomentosa* 'Albadura'
- 'Albert Schweitzer'	see *A.* × *hybrida* 'Elegans'
- 'Andrea Atkinson'	CCBP CDor EBee EBou ECtt ELan EMor EPfP GAbr GElm LRHS LSRN LSun MNHC MPie NBid NGdn NLar NRHS NSti SGbt SPad SPoG SRms SWvt WCot WHoo WSpi XLum
- 'Bowles's Pink'	see *A. hupehensis* 'Bowles's Pink'
- 'Bressingham Glow'	see *A. hupehensis* var. *japonica* 'Bressingham Glow'
- 'Carmen'	LPla LSou MHol MNrw NLar
- 'Cloudy Abundance'	MNrw
- 'Coupe d'Argent'	EBee ECtt LBar NLar SHar XLum
§ - 'Elegans' 🏆H7	ECtt GMaP LCro LOPS LRHS MMuc NBir NLar SEND SWvt WFar
- 'Frau Marie Maushardt'	WBrk
§ - 'Honorine Jobert' 🏆H7	Widely available
- 'Josephine'	WFar
§ - 'Königin Charlotte' 🏆H7	Widely available
- 'Kriemhilde'	EBee
- 'Lady Gilmour' misapplied	see *A.* × *hybrida* 'Montrose'
- 'Lady Gilmour' ambig.	EBou GMcL SGbt XLum
§ - 'Lady Gilmour' Wolley-Dod	EBee ECtt EPfP LRHS MRav NBir NChi NRHS SRms WSpi
- 'Leather and Lace' **new**	LBar WHil
- 'Loreley'	CBWd CDor EPfP GPSL LPla MBNS MCot MPri NLar SWvt WCot
- 'Märchenfee'	MNrw
§ - 'Margarete' Kayser & Seibert	CExl ECtt ELan EPfP SHar WHil
- 'Max Vogel'	see *A.* × *hybrida* 'Elegans'
- 'Monterosa'	see *A.* × *hybrida* 'Montrose'
§ - 'Montrose'	EBee ECha ELan EPfP EWes GMaP LCro LPla NBir NLar SPeP SRms WCAu
- 'Pamina'	see *A. hupehensis* var. *japonica* 'Pamina'
§ - PINK CLOUD ('Pkan'PBR)	EMor LPla WHil
- PINK KISS	see *A.* × *hybrida* PINK CLOUD
- Pretty Lady Series	NCth SCob
- - 'Pretty Lady Diana'PBR	EBee ECtt LCro LRHS NCth NLar SCob SCoo SGBe SWvt WTyc
- - 'Pretty Lady Emily'PBR	CBod EPfP GEdr LRHS NCth NLar SCob SCoo SGBe SWvt WHil
- - 'Pretty Lady Julia'PBR	EBee GEdr NCth NLar WHil
- - 'Pretty Lady Maria'	EBee GEdr LRHS NCth NLar SCob SCoo SGBe WHil
- - 'Pretty Lady Susan'	CWGN EBee GEdr LCro LRHS NCth NLar SGBe SWvt
- PRINCE HENRY	see *A. hupehensis* var. *japonica* 'Prinz Heinrich'
- 'Profusion'	CTri LBuc
- QUEEN CHARLOTTE	see *A.* × *hybrida* 'Königin Charlotte'
- 'Richard Ahrens'	CRos ECtt EPfP EShb EWoo GBee GMaP LRHS LSRN LSto MGos NGdn NLar NRHS SCoo SWvt WGwG
§ - 'Robustissima'	CBWd CBod CRos EBee EMor EPfP GMaP LBar LRHS LSRN MCot MHol MMuc MNHC MNrw NBir NGdn NLar NRHS NSti SEND SPer SRms SWvt WAvo WCAu WFar
- 'Rosea'	LRHS
- 'Rosenschale'	EWes LRHS MNrw NLar NRHS SHar
- 'Rotkäppchen'	see *A. hupehensis* var. *japonica* 'Rotkäppchen'
§ - 'September Charm' 🏆H7	Widely available
- 'Serenade'	ECtt ELan EPfP GMcL LBar LRHS LSRN MRav NBir NLar NRHS SPoG WCAu XLum
- TOURBILLON	see *A.* × *hybrida* 'Whirlwind'
§ - 'Whirlwind'	Widely available
- WIRBELWIND	see *A.* × *hybrida* 'Whirlwind'
japonica	see *A. hupehensis*, *A. hupehensis* var. *japonica*, *A.* × *hybrida*
- 'Crustata'	CMac
§ × ***lesseri***	ECha GEdr GKev LBar MBel SRms
leveillei	Widely available
- BWJ 7919	WCru
§ × ***lipsiensis***	CBro CTtf EBee ECtt EMor GAbr GEdr GKev GMaP LEdu MBel MNrw NHpl NLar NRog WCru WFar WHoo WSHC WSpi
- 'Pallida' 🏆H5	CBor CElw CMiW CSpe ELon GEdr GKev LEdu NLar NRog WCot WFar WIce WShi
- 'Schwefelfeuer'	LEdu MAvo NDry
- 'Sioux'	EPPr
- 'Stiby'	NDry
- 'Vindobonensis'	GEdr MAvo WCot
lithophila	EDAr GEdr
lyallii	GKev
magellanica hort. ex Wehrh.	see *A. multifida* Poir.
'Margarette'	see *A.* × *hybrida* 'Margarete' Kayser & Seibert
matsudae B&SWJ 1452	WCru
- NMWJ 14517	WCru
multifida misapplied, red-flowered	see *A.* × *lesseri*
§ ***multifida*** Poir.	CTsd ECha EDAr EGrl EHyd EPPr EPfP GKev LRHS LSun NBir NRHS NSti SGBe WFar WHoo
- Annabella Series	GKev
- 'Major'	CSpe EPfP WIce
- 'Rubra'	ECtt EDAr EHed EPPr EPfP GBin GEdr GKev LRHS MPie MSCN NBir NFav NLar NRHS SPoG WFar WGwG
- white-flowered	EHed
- yellow-flowered	GArf GEdr
§ ***narcissiflora***	EBee EDAr EMor LPla NBir NChi
nemorosa	Widely available
- 'Alba'	CCBP CMiW EGrl WFar
- 'Alba Plena' (d)	ECha ECtt EPPr EPfP GKev MAvo NBPC NGdn NLar NRog WFar WSHC
- 'Allenii' 🏆H5	CBor CBro CElw CMiW CRos ELon EPPr EPfP EPot GEdr GKev GMaP ITim LRHS MAvo MBel MRav NRHS NRog NRya WFar WShi
- 'Apuseni'	LEdu
- 'Atley'	EBee GEdr MAvo NRog WCot WFar
- 'Atrocaerulea'	GArf NLar
- 'Atrorosea'	EPPr
- 'Axel'	EPPr
- 'Behemoth Blue'	LEdu
- 'Big Blush'	SPVi
- 'Bill Baker's Pink'	CLAP LEdu
- 'Birka'	SPVi
- 'Blue Beauty'	CMiW EBee ELon GMaP MAvo
- 'Blue Bonnet'	EPot ITim LEdu MAvo
- 'Blue Eyes' (d)	CAvo CBor CElw CLAP EMor EPPr GBin GEdr GKev GMaP IPot ITim LAma LEdu LShi MAvo NBir NHpl

		NLar SMHy SPVi WFar WHlf WHoo WPnP WSHC WTyc
	- 'Blue Queen'	ELon NRog
	- blue-backed double (d)	CBro
	- 'Blush'	LEdu
	- 'Bowles's Purple'	CBor CMiW EBee EMor EPot GEdr GMaP LRHS MAvo NBid NHar NHpl NRog NRya WCot WFar WSHC
	- 'Bracteata'	CBro CMiW CTca GEdr GKev LAma MMrt NRog NSla SDir SPVi
	- 'Bracteata Pleniflora' (d)	CLAP CMiW CTtf EBee EPot GKev GMaP LEdu LShi MAvo MNrw NBir NLar SDeJ WCot WShi
	- 'Buckland'	EPfP EPot SPVi
	- 'Caerulea'	EPot ITim
	- 'Cedric's Pink'	CMiW ECha EPPr MAvo WFar
	- 'Celestial'	EPPr MAvo
	- 'Dark Leaf'	MAvo
	- 'Dee Day'	EPPr LEdu MAvo
	- 'Dell Garden'	EPPr
	- 'Evelyn Meadows'	MAvo WSHC
	- 'Explosion' (d)	NDry
	- 'Flash'	NDry
	- 'Flore Pleno' (d)	CBor CPla EBee LShi NBir WFar
	- 'Flushing'	GEdr MAvo WFar
	- 'Frenzy'	WCot
	- 'Frühlingsfee'	EPPr MAvo NLar
	- 'Gerda Ramusen'	CBro ELan ELon EPot EShb EWes LEdu WHoo
I	- 'Gigantea Rubra'	WCot
	- 'Glyncoch Gold'	WCot
	- 'Green Dream'	WSHC
	- 'Green Fingers'	EPPr GEdr GKev GMaP MMrt NHar NLar NRog WSHC
	- 'Hakumane Senjuizaki'	WCot
	- 'Hall Farm Blue'	MAvo
	- 'Hannah Gubbay'	EPot
	- 'Helsinki'	MAvo
	- 'Hilda'	EBee ECtt GEdr GKev IPot LAma LBar LEdu NBir NLar NRog NRya SPeP WPnP
	- 'Ice and Fire'	EPot GKev LEdu
	- 'Isabell' **new**	MAvo
	- 'Jack Brownless'	LEdu
	- 'Kentish Pink'	GBin GMaP SPVi
	- 'Knightshayes Vestal' (d)	CExl CLAP CMiW MRav WSHC
	- 'La Rochanne'	MAvo MNrw
	- 'Lady Doneraile'	EPot LEdu NBir WFar WSHC
	- 'Lapis'	NDry
	- 'Latvian Pink'	EPot GEdr LEdu MAvo WFar
	- 'Leeds' Variety'	CMiW EPot GAbr GKev GMaP LEdu SPVi
	- 'Lionel Bacon'	LEdu MAvo
	- 'Lismore Blue'	EBee EPPr EPot MAvo
	- 'Lismore Pink'	GEdr
	- 'Lucia'	EPot GEdr GKev LEdu MAvo WCot WFar
	- 'Lychette'	CAvo CBor ECha EPPr EPot ERCP GAbr GEdr GKev LAma MAvo NRog SHar WSHC
	- 'Maret' (d)	NDry
	- 'Marie Rose'	EPot WFar
	- 'Mart's Blue'	CBor EPfP GKev WCot WFar
	- 'Monstrosa'	EPot GKev MAvo NRog WHlf
	- 'Multiplicity'	EPPr MAvo
	- 'New Pink'	MAvo
	- 'Parlez Vous'	CExl EPPr GEdr GKev LEdu MNrw NHpl NRog WFar WPnP WSHC
	- 'Pentre Pink'	EPot
	- 'Pink Carpet'	GEdr LEdu
	- 'Pink Delight'	LEdu
	- 'Ploeger de Bilt'	MAvo
	- 'Ploeger's Plena' (d)	ECha

	- 'Robinsoniana' ♀H5	Widely available
	- 'Rosea'	CBor LEdu NLar
I	- 'Rotkäppchen'	SPVi
	- 'Royal Blue'	CBor CBro CMiW CTca EBee ECtt EMor EPPr GAbr GEdr GKev GMaP IPot LAma LBar LEdu MAvo NCth NHpl NLar NRog SDir WCot WFar WHoo WPnP
	- 'Rubra'	CBor
	- 'Salt and Pepper'	LEdu MAvo NDry
	- 'Slack Top Pink'	MAvo
	- 'Slenaken'	MAvo
§	- 'Stammerberg' (d)	EPPr MAvo
	- 'Stammheim'	see *A. nemorosa* 'Stammerberg'
	- 'Tage Lundell' (d)	SPVi
	- 'Tilo'	MAvo
	- 'Tinney's Blush'	CLAP
	- 'Tomas'	CLAP ELon EPot GEdr LEdu MAvo NHpl NRya WFar
	- 'Tups'	LEdu NDry
	- 'Vestal' (d) ♀H5	Widely available
	- 'Virescens' ♀H5	CAvo CMiW CTtf CWCL EBee EGrI ELon EMor EPPr GEdr GKev GMaP LEdu LShi MAvo NBir NHar NRog WShi
	- 'Viridiflora'	CExl CLAP EPfP GAbr GBin MNrw NBir WCot WSHC
	- 'Westwell Pink'	CToG EPPr MAvo MNrw SPVi WBor WCot WFar WSHC WShi
	- white-flowered	CRos LRHS NRHS
	- 'Wilks' Giant'	MAvo NRog
	- 'Wilks' White'	ELon EPPr GEdr MAvo
	- 'Wisley Pink'	EPot LEdu MAvo WFar
I	- 'Wisley White Form'	MAvo NLar
	- 'Wyatt's Pink'	ELon EPot GKev LEdu MAvo SPVi WHoo
	- 'Yerda Ramusem'	EMor EPPr LEdu MAvo MNrw WSHC
	nemorosa* × *ranunculoides	see *A.* × *lipsiensis*
	obtusiloba	EMor GBin GEdr NHar NHpl WAbe
	- CLD 1549	GEdr
	- 'Alba'	EMor GEdr WAbe
	- Harperley selection	NHpl
	- 'Large Blue'	EPot GEdr LEdu NSla WAbe
	- 'Pradesh'	GEdr NHar NHpl WFar
I	- 'Sulphurea'	GEdr WAbe
	palmata	EDAr EMor GEdr LDai LEdu WKif
	parviflora	GKev
	patens	see *Pulsatilla patens*
	pavonina	CAby CMiW CSpe ECha MHol SMHy SPoG WFar
	polyanthes	CRos EBee EHed EPfP LRHS NRHS
	prattii	CExl GEdr LEdu NHpl
	pseudoaltaica	LEdu
	- double pink-flowered (d) **new**	GEdr
	- pink-flowered	WFar
	- 'Yuki-no-sei' (d)	GEdr WFar
	pulsatilla	see *Pulsatilla vulgaris*
	raddeana	NRog
*	- f. ***rosea***	GEdr
	ranunculoides ♀H6	Widely available
	- 'Anne' (d)	NDry
	- 'Ants' (d)	NDry
	- 'Aureus' (d)	NDry
	- 'Bill Baker'	LEdu MAvo
	- 'Crazy Vienna'	EPPr WCot
	- 'Dagerort' (d)	NDry
	- 'Dagö' (d)	NDry
	- 'Ellen' (d)	NDry
	- 'Ferguson's Fancy'	EPPr
	- 'Frank Waley'	MAvo WCot

- 'Fuchsis Traum'	LEdu MAvo WCot WSHC
- 'Golden Dream' (d)	NDry
- 'Grandiflora'	MAvo
- 'Hiiumaa' (d)	NDry
- 'Kahar' (d)	NDry
- 'Kreet' (d)	NDry
* - ***laciniata***	MAvo WCot
- 'Leena' (d)	NDry
- 'Leida' (d)	NDry
- 'Linda' (d)	NDry
I - 'Linearis'	NDry
- 'Orjaku' (d)	NDry
- 'Papa' (d)	NDry
- 'Pleniflora' (d) ♀H6	CBor ECha EPPr GKev LRHS MAvo NBPC NLar NRHS NRog WFar
- subsp. ***ranunculoides***	GKev
- 'Sääre' (d)	NDry
- 'Semi-Plena'	CTtf GEdr LEdu NRog
- 'Siil' (d)	NDry
- 'Sirje' (d)	NDry
- 'Star 1' (d)	NDry
- 'Tafka' (d)	NDry
- 'Tapio' (d)	NDry
- 'Virve' (d)	NDry
- 'Vulkaan' (d)	NDry
- subsp. ***wockeana***	LEdu MAvo
reflexa	GKev
rivularis	CPar CSde CSpe CTsd CTtf EBee EBlo ECha EMor GArf GEdr GKev GPoy ILea IPot ITim LEdu LRHS MBriF MNrw NBir NLar NRHS SRms WCru WFar WKif WSpi
- B&SWJ 13944	WCru
- BWJ 7611	WCru
- CC 4588	CExl
- 'Glacier'	EBee EMor EWoo ILea MHol SBls SBut WHil
aff. ***rivularis***	WSpi
RUFFLED SWAN ('Macane007'[PBR])	CBod CWGN EBee EHed EMor EPfP GBin GPSL LBar LRHS LSou MBNS MNHC MNrw MPri NCth NLar NRHS NSti SCoo SEdd SHar SPoG WNPC WTyc
rupestris new	EMor
rupicola	EMor GEdr NBir WCot
× ***seemannii***	see *A.* × *lipsiensis*
stellata Lam.	see *A. hortensis*
stolonifera double-flowered (d)	EBee LShi WCot WSHC
sulphurea misapplied	see *Pulsatilla alpina* subsp. *apiifolia*
sumatrana B&SWJ 11265	WCru
§ 'Sweetly' new	LBar
sylvestris	Widely available
- 'Elise Fellmann' (d)	EBee
- 'Madonna'	LSun
tenuifolia	NHpl
tetrasepala	WCot
§ ***tomentosa***	LRHS NRHS SDix SRms
§ - 'Albadura'	EBee GKev
- 'Robustissima'	see *A.* × *hybrida* 'Robustissima'
- 'September Glanz'	EBee
trifolia L.	CMiW EPPr GEdr LEdu NBid NLar WCot
trullifolia	GArf GBin GEdr NHar NQui WAbe
- 'Alba'	GEdr
- var. ***linearis***	GEdr WAbe
udensis	GEdr WCot
vernalis	see *Pulsatilla vernalis*
virginiana	EBee EMor LDai LEdu LPla MNrw WHrl
vitifolia misapplied	see *A. tomentosa*
vitifolia Buch.-Ham. ex DC.	LEdu WPGP
WILD SWAN ('Macane001'[PBR])	Widely available

Anemonella (*Ranunculaceae*)

thalictroides	CBor CElw CTtf ECha EMor GEdr GKev LAma MBel NHpl NLar NRya NSla SPVi SPlb WAbe WFar WPnP WSHC WSpi WTyc XLum
- 'Alba Plena' (d)	WSHC
- 'Amelia'	CElw GEdr NBro NHpl
- 'Babe'	WCot
- 'Betty Blake' (d)	CBor CElw EBee EMor GEdr LAma MMrt NBro NHpl NRya NSla SDir SPVi WCot WFar
- 'Blushing Bride' (d)	GEdr NBro WAbe WCot
- 'Cameo'	CBor GEdr LAma MNrw NHpl SDir WCot WFar
- 'Charlotte'	GEdr WFar
- 'Dark Pink'	EBee EMor GBin MAvo NHpl
- 'Diamante'	CElw LPla MAvo WCot
- 'Double Diamante' (d)	WCot
- 'Full Double White' (d)	NHpl
- 'Green Hurricane' (d)	CBor EMor GEdr LAma SDir SPVi WCot WFar
- 'Hakikomi-fu' (v)	GEdr
- 'Kikuzaki Pink' (d)	CBor GEdr LAma WFar
- 'Kikuzaki White' (d)	CBor GEdr LAma WFar
- 'Pink Fairy'	SMHy
- 'Pink Flash' (d)	SPVi
- f. ***rosea***	CElw ELan EMor NLar WAbe WPnP WTyc
- - 'Oscar Schoaf' (d)	CElw ECha EMor GArf GEdr LAma NHpl SPVi WCot WFar
- - 'Rosea Plena' (d)	CBor EMor GArf
- - semi-double pink-flowered (d)	CElw MAvo
- semi-double white-flowered (d)	CElw
- 'Shiozaki' (d)	GEdr
- 'Spring Nymph'	LAma SMHy
- 'Spring Symphony' (d) new	SDir
- 'Tairin'	CBor GEdr LAma NHpl WCot WFar

Anemonopsis (*Ranunculaceae*)

macrophylla	CBWd CDor CExl CMiW CSpe EBee EHed EMor EPfP EWes EWld GArf GEdr GKev LEdu LRHS MNrw MRav NFav NHpl NLar WCru WFar WPGP WSHC
- 'Alba'	GKev
- double-flowered (d)	GEdr WSHC
- 'White Swan'	CMiW GEdr WSHC

Anemopsis (*Saururaceae*)

californica	CPud CToG EWat LCro LLWG LOPS LPfP MWts SBrt WCot

Anethum (*Apiaceae*)

graveolens	CArg CBod ENfk GPoy LCro LOPS MHer MHoo MNHC MPri SPhx SRms SVic
- 'Dukat'	LCro LOPS MHoo
- fern-leaved	MHoo

angelica see *Angelica archangelica*

Angelica (*Apiaceae*)

acutiloba	SDix WFar
- var. ***iwatensis*** B&SWJ 11197	WCru
anomala B&SWJ 10886	ESwi WCru WFar
archangelica	Widely available

- subsp. ***decurrens***	LEdu WPGP
- - from Kazakhstan **new**	GGro
arguta B&SWJ 14115	WCru
- B&SWJ 14162	WCru
atropurpurea	EPfP LRHS MHoo MNrw MRav SWvt
brevicaulis	GGro LEdu
breweri B&SWJ 14083	WCru
cartilaginomarginata B&SWJ 12663	WCru
cyclocarpa WJC 13658	WCru
dahurica	EWTr GGro LRHS MHoo SPhx WFar WHil WOut
decursiva B&SWJ 5746	WCru
edulis	WHer
- B&SWJ 10968	WCru
genuflexa B&SWJ 14109	WCru
gigas	Widely available
- B&SWJ 4170	WCru
hendersoni	SPhx WPGP
hispanica	see *A. pachycarpa*
japonica B&SWJ 11480	WCru
montana	see *A. sylvestris*
morii RWJ 9802	WCru
nubigena WJC 13763	WCru
§ ***pachycarpa***	CBod CRos EBee EPPr GBin GGro GMaP LBar LRHS MHer MHoo MRav NBir NGBl NLar NRHS SPhx WCot WFar WHlf WOut WSHC
pubescens	NDov
- B&SWJ 5593	LEdu WCru
sachalinensis	GBin GGro
sinensis	GGro LEdu MHoo
'Summer Delight'	see *Ligusticum scoticum*
§ ***sylvestris***	CHab LLWG NAts SArc WOut
- B&SWJ 15332	WCru
- 'Burgundy'	NGBl
- 'Ebony' 🏆H5	CBod CCBP CKel CPla CTtf CWCL CWnw ECha ECtt GAbr GJos LBar LEdu LRHS MBNS MHer MHol MHoo NLar NSti SPad SPoG WCot
- 'Purple Giant'	EBee
* - 'Purpurea'	CDor EWes MAsh
- 'Vicar's Mead'	EBee ECha ELan GGro GJos LRHS NBir NLar SCoo SPhx SWvt WCAu WHlf
taiwaniana	CDTJ EBee ELan ESwi GGro LEdu MMuc SPVi WCot WOut
triquinata B&SWJ 15429	WCru
ursina	EBee WCru

Angelonia (*Plantaginaceae*)

ADESSA BLUE BICOLOR	LSou WHlf
ADESSA PINK **new**	WHlf
(Angelface Series) ANGELFACE PINK IMPROVED ('Anpinkim'[PBR])	MHol
- ANGELFACE WEDGWOOD BLUE ('Anwedg')	MHol
ARCHANGEL DEEP ROSE ('Balarcrose')	CRos EHyd LRHS NRHS

Anigozanthos (*Haemodoraceae*)

'Bush Ranger' (Bush Gems Series)	CCCN
flavidus	SPlb
- 'Ember'	CCCN
- 'Illusion'	CCCN
- 'Opal'	CCCN
- 'Pearl'	CCCN
- 'Splendour'	CCCN
- 'Yellow Gem'	CCCN
manglesii	SPlb
rufus	SEle

anise see *Pimpinella anisum*

Anisodontea (*Malvaceae*)

§ ***capensis*** 🏆H2	CBod CCCN ELan EPri SChF SEle SPlb SRkn SRms SSha SVen SWvt WHil WLov
- 'Elegans Princess'	CCCN WCot WHil
'Crystal Rose'	EPfP MGos
'El Rayo'	Widely available
huegelii	see *Alyogyne huegelii*
× ***hypomadara*** misapplied	see *A. capensis*
§ × ***hypomadara*** (Sprague) D.M. Bates	MAvo SMad WCot
julii	SVen
LADY IN PINK ('Nuanilaninp')	LBar MBNS MBros MHol NCou SEdd SHar WHil WHlf
'Large Magenta'	EBee ELon EPfP LBar LRHS SEdd SGBe SWvt
malvastroides	XSen

Anisodus (*Solanaceae*)

carnioliciodes BWJ 7501	WCru

Anisotome (*Apiaceae*)

imbricata var. ***imbricata***	WAbe
lyallii	IKel

Annona (*Annonaceae*)

cherimola (F)	CCCN WJur
squamosa (F)	SPlb

Anoda (*Malvaceae*)

cristata 'Candy Cups'	CSpe

Anoiganthus see *Cyrtanthus*

Anomalesia see *Gladiolus*

Anomatheca (*Iridaceae*)

cruenta	see *Freesia laxa*

Anredera (*Basellaceae*)

§ ***cordifolia***	CRHN EShb GKev LEdu

Antennaria (*Asteraceae*)

aprica	see *A. parvifolia*
dioica	CTri ECtt GAbr GBin GPoy MACG SPlb SRms WAbe XLum
- 'Alba'	GQue MCot
- 'Alex Duguid'	GPSL NWad
- 'Aprica'	see *A. parvifolia*
- 'Bright Rose'	LRHS
- 'Minima'	GMaP NBro NBwr NSla WAbe
- 'Nyewoods Variety'	SRms
- var. ***rosea***	see *A. rosea*
- 'Rotes Wunder'	ECha NSla WAbe WHoo
- 'Rubra'	ECha ECtt EDAr NBir SRms WCav WIce XLum
'Joy'	WAbe
§ ***parvifolia***	CTri SRms
§ ***rosea*** 🏆H5	CRos EDAr EHyd EPfP GArf GKev GMaP LRHS MAsh NRHS SPlb SRms WIce

Antenoron see *Persicaria*

Anthemis ✿ (*Asteraceae*)

from Turkey	ECtt EWes
arvensis	CHab MBow MNHC SRms
- subsp. ***sphacelata***	WCot
§ 'Beauty of Grallagh'	WSpi

'Cally Cream'	ELon LPla LRHS SDix SMrm SPhx WMal
'Cally White'	GAbr GBin LPla WBrk
carpatica	NBro
- 'Karpatenschnee'	EHyd EPfP LRHS NRHS SAko SRms
cretica subsp. ***leucanthemoides***	EPot WAbe
- subsp. ***tenuiloba***	EWes
frutescens Voss	see *Argyranthemum frutescens*
'Grallagh Gold' misapplied, orange-yellow	see *A.* 'Beauty of Grallagh'
'Grallagh Gold'	ECha ECtt LDai NPer SPhx WFar
§ ***marschalliana***	CBor EBou LRHS NHpl NRHS SMrm SPlb SRms WAbe WCot WKif
nobilis	see *Chamaemelum nobile*
'Orange Dream'	CBcs
punctata subsp. ***cupaniana*** ♀H4	Widely available
- - 'Nana'	NBir NPer SHar WCot
rudolphiana	see *A. marschalliana*
sancti-johannis	EPfP LDai LRHS MACG NPer NRHS SMrm SRms WMal
SUSANNA MITCHELL ('Blomit')	CBod CDor CRos CTtf EBee ECtt ELon GAbr GElm GMaP LBar LRHS MAvo MHol MNrw NDov NLar NRHS SMrm SWvt WMal WSHC XLum
'Tetworth'	ECha ELan EPfP LRHS SAko
tinctoria	CBod CHby CMac CWal ENfk GPoy MHer MHoo MNHC MRav NAts NPer SRms SVic SWvt WSFF
- 'Alba'	EBee LRHS NRHS WFar
- 'Charme'[PBR]	LRHS NLar SMad SPoG SRms SWvt
- 'Compacta'	EWes XLum
- dwarf	NLar
- 'E.C. Buxton' ♀H6	Widely available
- 'Eva'	NDov NFav
- 'Hall Farm Frilly'	ECtt ELon
- 'Kelwayi'	CRos EBee EBou EPfP GLog GMcL GQue LRHS MACG NLar NPer NRHS SPer SRms WFar
- 'Lemon Ice'	EBee GBin LBar MBel NCth NLar SMad
- 'Lemon Maid'	ECtt ELon SMrm WHoo
- 'Mieke' **new**	EWes
- 'Pom Pom' **new**	EWes
- 'Sauce Hollandaise'	Widely available
- subsp. ***tinctoria***	SMrm
- 'Top Gold' **new**	EWes
- 'Wargrave Variety'	CBod CElw CMac ECha ECtt ELan EPfP GBin LBar LRHS MAvo MHol NBir NGdn NLar NRHS SDix SPhx SWvt WCAu WFar
'Tinpenny Sparkle'	EBee ECtt EWes EWhm GMcL MHol NLar WFar WHoo
triumfettii	EBee NDov NPer
tuberculata	NChi

Anthericum (*Asparagaceae*)

algeriense	see *A. liliago*
* ***bovei***	CBro
§ ***liliago***	CSpe ELan ESwi EWTr EWoo GKev GMaP MCot MRav NLar SPer XSen
- 'Major' ♀H5	CAvo CBro ECha MHol SPhx
plumosum	see *Trichopetalum plumosum*
ramosum	CAby CCBP CSpe EBee ECha EPPr EPfP EPot EPri EWes GKev LEdu LRHS LSun MBrN NBid NBir NLar NSla SMHy SPhx WCot WSHC XSen

Antholyza (*Iridaceae*)

coccinea	see *Crocosmia paniculata*
paniculata	see *Crocosmia paniculata*

Anthoxanthum (*Poaceae*)

odoratum	CHab GPoy GQue SPhx

Anthriscus (*Apiaceae*)

cerefolium	CBod CHby CLau ENfk GPoy LCro MHer MHoo MNHC SEdi SPhx SRms WSFF
nemorosa	LEdu
sylvestris	CBod CHab GQue LCro LOPS LRHS SPhx WFar WSFF
- 'Going for Gold'	CTtf EPPr EWes MAvo MHol MNrw NChi WCot WMal WOut
- 'Golden Fleece'	ECha ELan GGro LShi SPad SPtp
- 'Kabir'	LRHS
- 'Ravenswing'	Widely available
- yellow-leaved	GBin

Anthurium (*Araceae*)

andraeanum ♀H1a	CWal
CORAL CHAMPION ('Anthdotfan'[PBR]) **new**	LCro
JUNGLE BUSH ('Antingo')	LPal
PINK CHAMPION ('Antinkeles'[PBR])	LCro LOPS
RED CHAMPION ('Anthbnena'[PBR])	LCro LOPS
VANILLA ('Anthlepam'[PBR]) **new**	LCro

Anthyllis (*Fabaceae*)

hermanniae 'Compacta'	see *A. hermanniae* 'Minor'
§ - 'Minor'	ELan EPot ITim WAbe
montana	XSen
- subsp. ***atropurpurea***	LRHS NRHS
- 'Rubra' ♀H5	CSpe EDAr EPot GAbr LShi SPhx
vulneraria	CHab GEdr GJos NAts NMir NRya SPhx WSFF
- subsp. ***alpestris*** **new**	WOut
- var. ***coccinea***	CBor CKel EAJP EDAr ELan EWld GJos GKev LCro MACG MBel NAts NSla SPhx WIce
- dark red-flowered	CSpe SPhx

Antirrhinum (*Plantaginaceae*)

(Antirinca Series) ANTIRINCA BRONZE APRICOT **new**	WHlf
- ANTIRINCA PEACHY **new**	WHlf
- ANTIRINCA ROSE **new**	WHlf
asarina	see *Asarina procumbens*
barrelieri	SEND
braun-blanquetii	WCot
- 'Lemon Sherbet' **new**	SVic
CANDELABRA RED **new**	WWke
'Eva Grey'	CKel LRHS
glutinosum	see *A. hispanicum* subsp. *hispanicum*
hispanicum 'Avalanche'	ECtt
§ - subsp. ***hispanicum***	CSpe
majus 'Admiral White'	LCro LOPS
- APPEAL BICOLOUR MIX	LOPS SCob
- 'Black Prince'	CSpe ECtt ELan LPla
- 'Night and Day'	CSpe EWTr LCro
- 'Rocket White' (Rocket Series)	CSpe
- Sonnet Series	WWke
- - formula mixed	MBros MPri
molle	CSpe EBee GKev MCot NPer SChF
- pink-flowered	MCot SBut
- white-flowered	EBee SBut SEND
'Oh That's Cute' **new**	LBar SGBe WHlf
PRETTY IN PINK ('Pmoore07'[PBR])	CKel CSBt ECtt IPot LBar LCro LOPS LRHS LSou MBros MHol SGBe SPeP SRHi WHil WHlf WNPC

pulverulentum GKev
sempervirens CFis WAbe XLum
siculum EBee

añu see *Tropaeolum tuberosum*

Aphyllanthes (*Asparagaceae*)

monspeliensis XLum XSen

Apios (*Fabaceae*)

§ ***americana*** EWes LEdu NBir SBrt WCot WCru WKor WPGP WSHC
- 'Nutty' CAgr
tuberosa see *A. americana*

Apium (*Apiaceae*)

graveolens CBod CHab CLau CTsd ENfk GPoy MHer MHoo MNHC SRms SVic WJek
- var. ***dulce*** 'Aurora' LOPS
- - 'Brydon's Prize Red' SVic
- - 'Celebrity' 𝕐[H2] LRHS MCtn NRHS
- - 'Golden Self-blanching' LCro LOPS SVic
- - 'Victoria' 𝕐[H2] EDel EKin MBros
- 'Giant Pink' - Mammoth Pink 𝕐[H4] NRob
- var. ***rapaceum*** 'Prinz' 𝕐[H4] CHby EDel EKin LCro MCtn SVic
§ - (Secalinum Group) 'Par-cel' MHer SRms
- - 'Zwolsche Krul' MBow
nodiflorum see *Helosciadium nodiflorum*

Apium × *Petroselinum* (*Apiaceae*)

hybrid, misapplied see *A. graveolens* Secalinum Group

Apocynum (*Apocynaceae*)

cannabinum GPoy

Apodasmia (*Restionaceae*)

similis SPlb XSte

Aponogeton (*Aponogetonaceae*)

desertorum EWat LLWG
distachyos CBen CPud CWat EWat LCro LLWG LOPS LPfP MWts NPer SVic WMAq XLum

Aporocactus see *Disocactus*

apple see *Malus domestica*; see also AGM Fruit Section

apricot see *Prunus armeniaca*

Aptenia (*Aizoaceae*)

cordifolia CCCN NPer SChr SPlb SVen
- 'Variegata' (v) CCCN

Aquilegia (*Ranunculaceae*)

akitensis misapplied see *A. flabellata* var. *pumila*
'Alaska' (State Series) EBee NRHS
alpina EBee EBou ECha EPfP GMcL LCro LPal LRHS MAsh MNHC NBir NGdn SCob SPer SRms WHoo WSpi XLum
amaliae see *A. ottonis* subsp. *amaliae*
aragonensis see *A. pyrenaica*
§ ***atrata*** CKel EBee EMor GKev GQue LRHS
atrovinosa from Kazakhstan GGro
barnebyi GKev
bertolonii 𝕐[H5] CBor GEdr LRHS NRHS NSla SRms WAbe
Biedermeier Group CRos EPfP GJos LRHS NGdn NLar NRHS WHil
'Blackberry Ice' EMor
'Blue Star' (Star Series) EAJP ELan EPfP GMaP LRHS NRHS SBls SCoo SGbt SPtp
'Bluebird' (Songbird Series) LBuc NBir NPer SCoo SGBe WFar
buergeriana GKev
- 'Calimero' GKev NLar WHlf
- var. ***oxysepala*** see *A. oxysepala*
'Bunting' (Songbird Series) SGbt
canadensis CBor CSpe EBou ELan EMor GAbr GKev GLog NBir NBro SBls SRms WFar WSpi
- 'Corbett' EMor EWTr SBls WAbe
- 'Little Lanterns' EAJP EDAr EMor NHpl NLar
- 'Pink Lanterns' EMor
'Cardinal' (Songbird Series) LBuc SCoo SGBe
chaplinei GKev NBir
chrysantha ECha GJos GKev MCot SRms SWvt WKif XSen
- 'Denver Gold' CSpe WHil
- 'Yellow Queen' CAby CExl CKel CWCL ECha EMor EPPr EPfP EWoo GBin GMaP LCro LOPS LPal LRHS MBel NGdn SGbt SPeP SPtp SWvt WCFE WTor
clematiflora see *A. vulgaris* var. *stellata*
Clementine Series LRHS
coerulea GKev SRms
'Colorado' (State Series) EMor NRHS
'Crimson Star' CRos ELan EMor EPfP GMcL LRHS MBel NRHS SCoo SMrm SPoG
desertorum GKev
discolor GAbr WThu
'Dove' (Songbird Series) LBuc MHer SGBe SGbt SHar SMrm
I 'Dragonfly' CRos ELan EPfP LRHS NRHS SPoG
ecalcarata see *Semiaquilegia ecalcarata*
elegantula GKev
flabellata Cameo Series MHer SRot
- - 'Cameo Blue and White' EDAr GMcL SRms
- - 'Cameo Pink and White' EDAr GMcL
- - 'Cameo Pink' EWTr
- - 'Cameo Red and White' EDAr GMcL
- - 'Cameo Rose and White' MHer
- - 'Cameo White' GMcL
- 'Georgia' (State Series) LRHS NRHS
- 'Ministar' EDAr
- 'Nana Alba' see *A. flabellata* var. *pumila* f. *alba*
§ - var. ***pumila*** 𝕐[H5] EBou ECha EDAr EPfP GEdr GKev LRHS NGdn NRHS SRms
§ - - f. ***alba*** ECha LRHS NRHS
- - 'Atlantis' CBod EPot GMcL LRHS
I - - f. ***kurilensis*** 'Rosea' EMor EWTr WAbe
- 'Vermont' (State Series) EBee
flavescens EMor
'Florida' (State Series) LRHS MSCN NRHS WHil
formosa GQue NChi
§ ***fragrans*** EBee GArf GKev
'Fruit and Nut Chocolate' EBee WCot
glauca see *A. fragrans*
'Goldfinch' (Songbird Series) LBuc NBir SCoo SGBe SGbt WHil
grahamii WAbe
'Heavenly Blue' CDor EBee
'Hensol Harebell' ELan MBriF SHar SPtp SRms WSpi
hybrida 'Double Pleat Blackberry' (d) CGBo
japonica see *A. flabellata* var. *pumila*
jonesii GEdr GKev SPlb
jonesii × ***saximontana*** GKev
'Kansas' (State Series) LRHS
karelinii GKev
'Koralle' CDor EMor SBls WHil
'Kristall' EShb EWTr LEdu MBel
* ***kuhistanica*** CBor EBee GGro
'Leprechaun Gold' (v) EMor EPfP NGdn SBls

	'Lime Sorbet'	LRHS SRms
	'Little Plum'	EBee
	longissima	CPla GKev GQue LEdu MHer SHar WCav WHil WHoo WPGP
	'Louisiana' (State Series)	EMor LRHS NRHS
	'Magpie'	see *A. vulgaris* 'William Guiness'
	× ***maruyamana***	EBee
	McKana Group	CTri CWCL EHeP ELan EPfP GAbr GJos GMcL MGos NGdn NHol NLar SCob SPer SPlb SPoG SRms SVic SWvt WCav WFar
	'Montana' (State Series)	EMor EPot LRHS
	Mrs Scott-Elliot hybrids	CBod EPfP SCoo
	Music Series	SRms
	'Nightingale' (Songbird Series)	SGbt
	nigricans	see *A. atrata*
	olympica	GKev LSun
	'Oregon' (State Series)	EMor LRHS
§	***ottonis*** subsp. ***amaliae***	WAbe
§	***oxysepala***	CExl EMor GGro GLog
	- var. ***kansuensis***	GKev
	Perfumed Garden Group	GAbr WFar
§	***pyrenaica***	GKev
	- dwarf	WAbe
	'Red Hobbit'	CSpe CWCL ELan EPfP EPot GEdr GMcL LRHS MBros NChi NGdn NHpl NLar SCoo WFar
	'Red Star' (Star Series)	EAJP EPfP LRHS SGbt SPoG WHil
	'Robin' (Songbird Series)	SGbt WHil
	rockii	EPPr GKev
	'Rose Queen'	CDor EPfP SPtp
	'Roundway Chocolate'	SBls
	saximontana	CBor GKev NSla
§	'Schneekönigin'	LRHS NLar NRHS WCFE
	scopulorum subsp. ***perplexans***	GKev
	sibirica	EBee EMor GKev
	'Silver Queen'	EMor EWoo
	skinneri	CExl GLog
	- 'Tequila Sunrise'	CSpe ELan EMor EPfP LRHS MACG MHer MPnt NRHS
	SNOW QUEEN	see *A.* 'Schneekönigin'
	Spring Magic Series	MPri WCav
	- SPRING MAGIC BLUE AND WHITE	LRHS MPri SCob
	- SPRING MAGIC LIGHT RED AND YELLOW **new**	WHil
	- SPRING MAGIC NAVY AND WHITE	MPri
	- SPRING MAGIC PINK AND WHITE	WHil
	- SPRING MAGIC ROSE AND IVORY	MPri
	- SPRING MAGIC ROSE AND WHITE	GMcL LRHS MPri SMrm
	- SPRING MAGIC WHITE	GMcL MPri NRHS SCob
	- SPRING MAGIC YELLOW	GMcL LRHS
	stellata	see *A. vulgaris* var. *stellata*
	'Sunburst Ruby'	CWCL
	'Sunshine'	CGBo
	Swan Series	MDon WWke
	- 'Swan Lavender'	SCob WFar
	- 'Swan Pink and Yellow'	CBod LBar SCob
	- 'Swan Red and White'	CBod CGBo LBar SCob WFar WHil
	- 'Swan Violet and White'	SCob WFar
	'Virginia' (State Series)	EMor LRHS NRHS
	viridiflora	CBor EAJP EMor GElm GGro GKev LRHS WAbe WCot
	- 'Chocolate Soldier'	CAby CSpe EMor GQue SBls SPeP
	'Volcano!' (mixed)	GQue
	vulgaris	CBod CHab EPfP GPoy GQue LCro LOPS MBow MHer MNHC NBro NGdn NGrd SCob SPlb WCAu WShi XSen
	- 'Adelaide Addison'	ECha
	- var. ***alba***	EPfP LRHS MMuc NRHS SCob SEdd WCAu WHoo
	- 'Aureovariegata'	see *A. vulgaris* Vervaeneana Group
	- 'Blackbird' (Songbird Series) (d)	CWCL
	- ***clematiflora***	see *A. vulgaris* var. *stellata*
	- (Clementine Series) 'Clementine Blue' (d)	CRos ECha EPfP NRHS SPoG WCot
	- - 'Clementine Dark Purple' (d)	CRos EPfP NRHS SPoG
	- - 'Clementine Red' (d)	LRHS NRHS
	- - 'Clementine Rose' (d)	CRos GQue LRHS NRHS SPoG
	- - 'Clementine Salmon Rose' (d)	CRos EPfP LRHS NRHS SPoG
	- - 'Clementine White' (d)	CRos EPfP LRHS NRHS SPoG WSpi
	- 'Crystal Star'	EPfP LRHS NRHS
	- 'Eyecatcher'	WCot
	- var. ***flore-pleno*** black-flowered (d)	MMuc SEND WCot
	- - 'Dorothy Rose' (Dorothy Series) (d)	SPtp
	- - purple-flowered (d)	WSpi
	- 'Heidi'	EWTr WSpi XSen
	- 'Mellow Yellow'	EPfP GPSL
	- MUNSTEAD WHITE	see *A. vulgaris* 'Nivea'
§	- 'Nivea'	CDor CSpe EBee ECha ELan EPfP EWoo LCro LOPS NChi SEND SPoG WCot WSpi
	- 'Pom Pom Crimson' (Pom Pom Series)	WCot
§	- var. ***stellata***	CDor GAbr LBar NBir NBro
	- - (Barlow Series) 'Black Barlow' (d)	Widely available
	- - - 'Blue Barlow' (d)	CDor CRos CSpe EBee ECtt EMor EPfP GMaP LCro LOPS LRHS LSRN NRHS SCob SCoo SEdd SPer STPC SWvt WCot WSpi
	- - - 'Bordeaux Barlow' (d)	EPfP LRHS NRHS STPC
	- - - 'Christa Barlow' (d)	CRos EBee EPfP LRHS NLar NRHS SHar
	- - - 'Nora Barlow' (d)	Widely available
	- - - 'Rose Barlow' (d)	EPfP LRHS LSRN NRHS SCob WSpi
	- - - 'White Barlow' (d)	CDor CRos ECha EPfP GMaP LCro LOPS LRHS MBel MPri NLar NRHS SCob SPer STPC SWvt WHlf
	- - blue-flowered	MMuc NBir SEND
	- - 'Greenapples' (d)	CDor CWCL EMor EPfP EWhm GQue LRHS MBros MCot MSpe SCob WHoo
	- - 'Royal Purple' (d)	NBro
	- - 'Ruby Port' (d)	CAby CBcs CDor ECha ELan EMor EPfP EWoo GMaP LCro LOPS LRHS LSRN MNrw NChi NGdn NLar NRHS SBls SCob SEdd SGbt SPer WCAu WTyc
	- - white-flowered	MPnt NBir NBro
	- variegated foliage	see *A. vulgaris* Vervaeneana Group
§	- Vervaeneana Group (v)	CDor CSpe EPfP GAbr LRHS MBow NBir NPer SPlb SRms WHoo
	- - 'Woodside White' (v)	NBir WBrk
§	- 'William Guiness'	Widely available
	- 'Winky Double Dark-Blue-White' (Winky Series) (d)	GDam
	'White Star' (Star Series)	CDor EBee ELan EPfP GMaP LRHS SCoo SGbt SPoG WHil
	'White Swan'	WFar
	Winky Series	GJos GQue LRHS SWvt WFar

- 'Winky Blue-White'	CRos LRHS NLar NRHS SCoo SPoG
- 'Winky Purple-White'	LRHS NRHS
- 'Winky Red-White'	LRHS NRHS SWvt
- 'Winky Rose-Rose'	CRos LRHS NRHS
yabeana	EBee LRHS
'Yellow Star' (Star Series)	CBcs CDor CWCL ECtt EPfP LRHS MHol NRHS SGbt

Aquilegia × *Semiaquilegia* (*Ranunculaceae*)

hybrid, blue-flowered	NGdn

Arabis (*Brassicaceae*)

albida	see *A. alpina* subsp. *caucasica*
allionii	EDAr
alpina	SPlb
§ - subsp. ***caucasica***	GDam
- - 'Arctic Joy' (v)	NWad WCot WHoo
- - 'Douler Angevine' (v)	CBod ECtt LBar NHpl SPoG SRms WIce
- - 'Flore Pleno' (d) ♀H6	CElw CTri ECtt ELan EPfP EWld GAbr GMaP SGro SRms WBrk XLum
- - LITTLE TREASURE DEEP ROSE ('Ararosa')	LRHS
- - LITTLE TREASURE WHITE ('Aralba')	LCro LRHS
- - 'Lotti Deep Rose'	CBod LBar MACG
- - 'Lotti White'	CBod LBar
- - 'Pink Pearl'	WFar
- - 'Pinkie'	LPal
- - 'Pixie Cream'	ECtt EPfP NGdn SRms
- - 'Rosea'	EPfP GJos NBir SRms
§ - - 'Schneehaube' ♀H6	CTri EPfP GMaP NBir NGdn SPoG SRms WCav
- - SNOWCAP	see *A. alpina* subsp. *caucasica* 'Schneehaube'
- - 'Snowdrop'	WFar
- - 'Variegata' (v)	ELan SPoG SRms
androsacea	GKev SRms
× ***arendsii*** 'Compinkie'	GJos SPlb SRms
blepharophylla	MPri
§ - 'Frühlingszauber' ♀H5	CTri EAJP ELan EPfP GJos MAsh NBir NGdn SPoG SRms WHlf
- 'Rose Delight'	EPfP GJos LRHS NRHS
- 'Rote Sensation'	ELan NGdn
- SPRING CHARM	see *A. blepharophylla* 'Frühlingszauber'
carduchorum	XLum
caucasica	see *A. alpina* subsp. *caucasica*
§ ***collina*** subsp. ***rosea***	GJos NFav
cypria	GJos
ferdinandi-coburgi	NBwr NHol SRms WCav
- 'Aureovariegata' (v)	CTri ECtt ELan SWvt
- 'Old Gold' (v)	EBou ECha EPfP GQue LRHS LShi MAsh MHer NBir NBwr NFav NHol NRya SLee SPoG SRms SRot SWvt WCFE WCav WFar WJam WWke XLum
- 'Variegata'	see *A. procurrens* 'Variegata'
procurrens	WCot XSen
§ - 'Variegata' (v) ♀H6	CTri ECha ECtt ELan EWes GPSL LRHS MAsh MBrN SLee SPlb SRms WCot WFar XLum
purpurea	GJos
rosea	see *A. collina* subsp. *rosea*
SNOW CAP	see *A. alpina* subsp. *caucasica* 'Schneehaube'
× ***suendermannii***	XLum

Arachniodes (*Dryopteridaceae*)

aristata	CTsd SAko
davalliaeformis	CLAP EBee LRHS MAsh NRHS SPlb WCot WPGP
miqueliana	LEdu WPGP
simplicior	CBod CCCN CLAP EBee EHed EPfP ESwi LBuc LEdu LLWG LRHS MAsh MSCN NRHS SPad SPlb WCot WPGP
standishii	CLAP CRos EBee EHed LEdu LRHS MAsh SPlb WCot WPGP

Araiostegia (*Davalliaceae*)

faberiana	CExl
hymenophylloides	WCot
parvipinnata	see *A. perdurans*
§ ***perdurans***	LEdu WCot WPGP
- B&SWJ 1608	WCru
pulchra HWJ 1007	ESwi WCru

Aralia ✿ (*Araliaceae*)

apioides EDHCH 9720	WCru
armata B&SWJ 6916	WCru
bipinnata Blanco	WPGP
- CWJ 12407	WCru
- RWJ 10101	WCru
cachemirica	CDTJ ESwi EWld NBid SDix SMad SPlb WCru
californica	ESwi GPoy NLar WCru
castanopsidicola CWJ 12411	WCru
chapaensis B&SWJ 11812	WCru
- HWJ 1013	WCru
chinensis misapplied	see *A. elata*
chinensis L. BWJ 8102	WCru
continentalis	LEdu NLar
- pink-flowered B&SWJ 8437	WCru
§ ***cordata*** Thunb.	CAgr GPoy LEdu MBlu
- B&SWJ 5596	WCru
- B&SWJ 8524 from Ulleungdo, South Korea	WCru
- var. ***sachalinensis*** B&SWJ 4773	WCru
- 'Sun King'	CBod CKel EBee ECtt EPfP LAlb LBar LCro LOPS LRHS LSou MGil MHol MNrw NBid NEoE SDix SGBe SPad SPeP SPoG SWvt WBor WFar WHil WLov
dasyphylla	LEdu
decaisneana	WPGP
- NMWJ 14531	WCru
- NMWJ 14542	WCru
- RWJ 9910	WCru
§ ***elata***	CBcs CDoC CMac EBee EHeP ELan EPfP IPap LMaj LPal LPar LRHS MBlu MGos MHtn MMuc SArc SGol SPoG SWvt WFar WJur WSpi
- B&SWJ 5480	WCru
- 'Albomarginata'	see *A. elata* 'Variegata'
- 'Aureo-marginata' (v)	WSpi
- 'Aureovariegata' (v) ♀H5	CBcs ELan NLar
- 'Golden Umbrella' (v)	NLar
- 'Silver Umbrella' (v)	NLar
§ - 'Variegata' (v) ♀H5	CBcs ELan NLar SWvt
foliolosa	MBlu
- B&SWJ 8360	WCru
- NJM 13.033	WPGP
- NJM 13.061	WPGP
kansuensis B&SWJ 9515	ESwi
- BWJ 7650	WCru
leschenaultii B&SWJ 9515	WCru
- B&SWJ 11789	WCru
nudicaulis Blume	see *A. cordata* Thunb.
nudicaulis L.	GPoy
papyrifera	see *Tetrapanax papyrifer*

racemosa	GPoy LEdu SBls SRms WJek
- B&SWJ 9570	WCru
searelliana B&SWJ 11736	WCru
sieboldii de Vriese	see *Fatsia japonica*
spinosa L.	MBlu NChi SPlb
subcordata HWJK 2385	WCru
verticillata B&SWJ 11797	WCru
vietnamensis B&SWJ 12349E	WCru

Araucaria (*Araucariaceae*)

sp.	GDam MAsh
angustifolia	CAco CDTJ IKel WPGP XVPe
angustifolia* × *araucana	GMcL
§ ***araucana***	Widely available
bernieri new	CAco
bidwillii	CAco MMuc
biramulata new	CAco
columnaris	CAco
cunninghamii	CAco
excelsa misapplied	see *A. heterophylla*
§ ***heterophylla*** 🏆H2	CAco CCCN CDoC ERom LCro LPal SArc SEND
imbricata	see *A. araucana*
laubenfelsii	CAco
luxurians	CAco
montana new	CAco
muelleri new	CAco
nemorosa new	CAco
rulei new	CAco

Araujia (*Apocynaceae*)

sericifera	CBcs CHll CRHN ECha SVen WJur WSHC

Arbutus ✿ (*Ericaceae*)

andrachne	CBcs CDow CKel LRHS XSte
× ***andrachnoides*** 🏆H4	CBrP CPer CRos ELan EPfP LRHS LSRN MAsh MRav NRHS SArc SPoG SRHi WPGP WSpi
× ***androsterilis***	WPGP
menziesii	CBcs CMCN MBlu MGil MHid WFar WHtc
× ***reyorum*** 'Marina'	CJun EBee ELan EPfP LRHS MAsh MBlu MPkF SMad SPoG WPGP
× ***thuretiana***	WPGP
unedo	Widely available
- 'Atlantic' 🏆H5	CCCN CDoC CJun EBee EPfP IDee LAlb LRHS LSRN MAsh MGos MPkF NLar SCob SGbt SGol SSha SWvt XSte
- 'Compacta'	CBcs CCCN CRos EBee ELan EPfP LRHS MAsh NLar SCob SGol SRHi SWvt WFar WTyc
- 'Elfin King'	ELan EPfP LRHS MAsh SPoG SWvt
- 'Quercifolia'	CCCN CJun EBee ELan LEdu LRHS MAsh NLar SMad WKif
- 'Red Grange' new	WPGP
- ROSELILY ('Minlily'[PBR])	CDoC CKel CWnw EBee EHed ELan LRHS LSRN MPkF SGsty XSte
- f. ***rubra*** 🏆H5	Widely available
xalapensis	SPlb

Archontophoenix (*Arecaceae*)

alexandrae	LPal NPlm
cunninghamiana	EAri NPlm

Arctanthemum (*Asteraceae*)

§ ***arcticum***	EWTr NLar XLum
- 'Polarstern'	EBee MNrw WFar
- 'Roseum'	EBee ELon WFar
- 'Schwefelglanz'	WFar

Arcterica see *Pieris*

Arctium (*Asteraceae*)

lappa	GPoy SEdi SRms SVic WHer WSFF
minus	GQue NMir
nidulans new	GKev

Arctostaphylos (*Ericaceae*)

uva-ursi	GArf GMcL GQue LCro NLar SPlb
- 'Snowcap'	MAsh
- 'Vancouver Jade'	CRos ELan GArf GKin LRHS LSRN MAsh SCoo SPer SPoG SSta SWvt

Arctotheca (*Asteraceae*)

calendula	EBee WMal WSHC

Arctotis (*Asteraceae*)

'Heidi'	CCht MBNS
'Holly'	CCht CPla MHol
'Hope'	CCht
× ***hybrida*** hort. 'Apricot'	CCCN ECtt
- 'Flame' 🏆H2	CCCN CCht ECtt SCoo SMrm SRkn
- 'Red Devil'	CCCN CCht EWoo MBNS SCoo SMrm
- 'Wine'	CCCN CCht SCoo SGBe SMrm SRkn
(Opera Series) OPERA FIRE ('Kleat12611')	LRHS
- OPERA ORANGE ('Kleat12609')	LRHS
- OPERA ROSE ('Kleat12610'[PBR])	LRHS
(The Ravers Series) BUMBLEBEE ('Arc406')	LRHS
- CHERRY FROST ('Arc245')	LRHS
§ - HANNAH ('Archnah'[PBR])	CCht ECtt LRHS MBNS SGBe
§ - HAYLEY ('Archley'[PBR])	CCht ECtt MBNS SGBe
- 'Pink Sugar'	LRHS
- PUMPKIN PIE	see *A.* (The Ravers Series) HANNAH
- SUNSPOT	see *A.* (The Ravers Series) HAYLEY

Ardisia (*Primulaceae*)

crenata BOSPREMIUM RED	see *A. crenata* 'Queen Star'
§ - 'Queen Star'[PBR]	LCro LOPS
japonica	WCot
- B&SWJ 1032	WCru
- var. ***angusta***	WCot
- 'Houkan' (v)	CDTJ EBee SMad WPGP
- 'Ito-fukurin' (v)	CBct CDTJ EBee WPGP
- var. ***minor***	GEdr
- - B&SWJ 1841	WCru
- - B&SWJ 3809	WCru
- variegated (v)	CBct

Arecastrum see *Syagrus*

Arenaria (*Caryophyllaceae*)

§ ***alfacarensis***	EPot NLar SPlb WAbe XLum
balearica	EWes LLWG MAsh NAts NBwr NSla SPlb SRms WFar WIce XLum
capillaris	CTri
festucoides	GKev
hookeri subsp. ***desertorum***	WAbe
ledebouriana	EDAr MACG SBrt
montana 🏆H5	CTri ECha EPfP EWoo LCro LOPS LRHS MGos NBir NRHS NSla SPlb SRms SRot WAbe WCav WFar WHoo WIce WKif
- 'Avalanche'	CBod ECtt LBar LSun MACG

- 'Lemon Ice'	LBar
pulvinata	see *A. alfacarensis*
purpurascens	EWes NBwr SRms WAbe WHlf
tetraquetra	EDAr
- subsp. ***amabilis***	EPot

Arenga (*Arecaceae*)

engleri	LPal NPlm

Argania (*Sapotaceae*)

spinosa	WPGP

Argemone (*Papaveraceae*)

grandiflora	CSpe EPPr WHil
mexicana	ELan LRHS
platyceras	CSpe WFar

Argyranthemum ✿ (*Asteraceae*)

canariense hort.	see *A. frutescens* subsp. *canariae*
CHERRY LOVE ('Supacher') (Daisy Crazy Series) (d) ♀H2	CCCN
Citronelle ('Supa511'PBR)	CBcs
'Cornish Gold' ♀H2	CBcs CCCN ECtt EShb
'Donington Hero' ♀H2	ECtt
double pink-flowered (d)	SVen
'Everest'	NRHS SPoG
'Flamingo'	see *Rhodanthemum gayanum*
foeniculaceum misapplied pink-flowered	see *A.* 'Petite Pink'
§ ***foeniculaceum*** (Willd.) Webb & Sch.Bip.	MCot
- 'Royal Haze' ♀H2	CCCN NPer
§ ***frutescens***	LCro LOPS MBros WKif XLum
§ - subsp. ***canariae*** ♀H2	CCCN
'Gill's Pink'	ECtt
gracile 'Chelsea Girl' ♀H2	CCCN CSpe MBNS MCot WKif
Grandaisy Series	see × *Argyrimelia* Grandaisy Series
- GRANDAISY YELLOW	see × *Glebianthemum* GRANDAISY YELLOW
GYPSY ROSE ('M9/18d')	CCCN
'Jamaica Primrose' ♀H2	CSpe CTri SDix
aff. 'Jamaica Primrose'	CDow
LARITA BANANA SPLIT ('Kleaf10067') (LaRita Series) ♀H2	NRHS SPoG
'Levada Cream' ♀H2	CSpe
'Lolly'	MBNS WHil
(Madeira Series) MADEIRA CRESTED HOT PINK ('Bonmad 11277')	LSou
- MADEIRA CRESTED IVORY ('Bonmadcivy') (d)	SPoG
- MADEIRA CRESTED MERLOT ('Bonmadmerlo'PBR) (d)	LSou
- MADEIRA CRESTED PINK ('Bonmadcink'PBR)	SPoG
- MADEIRA CRESTED YELLOW ('Bonmadcrel'PBR)	SPoG
- MADEIRA RED ('Bonmadre'PBR)	SPoG
- MADEIRA WHITE IMPROVED ('Bonmadwitim'PBR)	SPoG
'Mary Wootton' (d)	ECtt
mawii	see *Rhodanthemum gayanum*
METEOR RED ('Supa742') (Daisy Crazy Series)	CBcs CWGN MBNS WHil
MOLIMBA XL PASTEL YELLOW ('Argyrayesi'PBR) (Molimba Series)	SPoG
PACIFIC GOLD ('Pacargone'PBR) (d)	CWGN
§ 'Petite Pink' ♀H2	CCCN
PING-PONG ('Innping'PBR) (d)	CCCN
'Pink Delight'	see *A.* 'Petite Pink'
POLLY ('Innpolly')	CBcs
'Powder Puff' (d)	ECtt
'Raspberry Ruffles' (d)	CBcs CPla MCot WHil
'Sugar and Ice' (d)	CCCN
'Sugar Baby' (d)	CCCN
'Summer Melody' (d)	CCCN
'Vancouver' (d) ♀H2	CCCN ECtt
'Vera'	CCCN
'White Spider'	CCCN

Argyranthemum × *Glebionis* see × *Glebianthemum*

Argyranthemum × *Ismelia* see × *Argyrimelia*

× *Argyrimelia* (*Asteraceae*)

(Aramis Series) 'Aramis Apricot'	ECtt LRHS LSou
- 'Aramis Deep Rose'	LSou
- 'Aramis Double Primrose' (d)	LRHS
- 'Aramis Ice'	LRHS
- 'Aramis Lemon'	LSou
- 'Aramis Pink Eye'	LRHS
- 'Aramis Rose'	LRHS LSou
- 'Aramis Wine Red'	LRHS
- 'Aramis Yellow'	LRHS
§ Grandaisy Series	SCob WHlf
- GRANDAISY DEEP RED ('Bonmax 14143') <u>**new**</u>	WHlf
- GRANDAISY PINK HALO ('Bonmax 9163'PBR) ♀H3	MBros SCob
- GRANDAISY RED ('Bonmax 1472')	MBros SCob
- GRANDAISY YELLOW	see × *Glebianthemum* GRANDAISY YELLOW

Argyrocytisus (*Fabaceae*)

§ ***battandieri***	Widely available
- 'Yellow Tail' ♀H5	ELan EPfP LAlb LRHS MGos MTrO NLar NOrn SPoG SSta WAvo WMat XSte

Arisaema (*Araceae*)

amurense	CBor CElw EPfP WThu
§ - subsp. ***robustum***	GKev
angustatum var. ***peninsulae*** B&SWJ 8639	WCru
brachyspathum	see *A. heterophyllum*
candidissimum ♀H4	CAvo CBor CDor ECha ELon EPPr EPot GEdr GKev LAma LRHS MRav NLar NRHS NSla SDeJ SDir SMHy WAbe WCot WPnP
- pink-flowered	NGKo
- white-flowered	GEdr
ciliatum ♀H4	CPla CWCL EPot GEdr LAma NLar WTyc
- var. ***liubaense***	GKev ITim WCot
- - CT 369	GEdr SDys WSHC
aff. ***ciliatum***	SDir
concinnum	GKev LAma LPal NGKo SDir WPnP XLum
consanguineum	CBcs CMiW EBee EPfP GBin GEdr GKev LAma SMrm SPtp WCot WFar WMal WPnP WTyc XLum

	- subsp. ***kelung-insulare*** B&SWJ 256	WCru
	- 'The Perfect Wave'	WCot
	- variegated (v)	GKev WCot
	cf. ***consanguineum***	SDir
	costatum	CCCN EBee EPfP EPot GKev LAma LPal NGKo WCot WFar WPGP XLum
	dracontium	ISha
	exappendiculatum	WPnP WTyc
	fargesii	CExl EPot GKev
	flavum	CMiW CWCL EBee EPfP ESwi GArf GBin GKev ISha LAma NGKo SDir SPlb SPtp WTyc
	- CC 6303	ITim
	- subsp. ***abbreviatum***	MBel
	- - CC 6300	ITim
	galeatum	LAma WCot
§	***griffithii***	EMor GKev LAma NBid NLar SDeJ SDir
	- var. ***pradhanii***	CAby GKev LAma
	- - WJC 13660	WCru
	aff. ***griffithii***	SDir
	helleborifolium	see *A. tortuosum*
§	***heterophyllum***	ITim LAma
	intermedium	EBee LAma MNrw SDir XLum
	jacquemontii	GKev
	- CC 5184	ITim
	japonicum Blume	see *A. serratum* var. *mayebarae*
	japonicum Komarov	see *A. serratum*
	kishidae	GEdr
	kiushianum	GKev LAma SDir WCot
	- 'Kikkou-fu'	WCot
§	***nepenthoides***	CAby EGrl EPot GKev LAma SDir WPnP WTyc
	ochraceum	see *A. nepenthoides*
	propinquum	EBee GKev LAma
	quinatum	GKev
	ringens misapplied	see *A. amurense* subsp. *robustum*
	ringens ambig.	CDTJ EBee EPfP GEdr GKev
	- green-flowered	GKev SDir
	aff. ***ringens***	LAma NHpl
	robustum	see *A. amurense* subsp. *robustum*
	sazensoo	GEdr
§	***serratum***	GKev LAma
	- B&SWJ 14607	WCru
§	- var. ***mayebarae***	GEdr GKev
	sikokianum	CMiW EWld GEdr GKev ISha LAma LRHS NHpl NLar SDir WPnP WTyc
	- variegated (v)	GEdr NHpl
	speciosum	EGrl GEdr GKev ISha LAma LCro LPal NGKo SDeJ SDir SPlb WCot WPnP XLum
*	- var. ***magnificum***	CAby CBcs GKev LAma NLar XLum
	- var. ***mirabile***	GKev LAma
	taiwanense	GEdr GKev
	- B&SWJ 269	WCru
	- NMWJ 14541	WCru
	- f. ***cinereum***	WMal
	- - NMWJ 14530	WCru
	- silver-leaved	WFar
	thunbergii	GEdr
	- subsp. ***urashima***	GKev LAma WTyc
	- - red-flowered **new**	LAma
§	***tortuosum***	CBor ECha EPfP GKev LAma LEdu NGKo NLar SDir WFar WPnP WTyc XLum
	- var. ***helleborifolium***	NBid XLum
	tosaense	LAma
	triphyllum	CElw EMor GPoy SPlb
§	***utile***	EPot GKev LAma
	verrucosum	see *A. griffithii*
	- var. ***utile***	see *A. utile*

Arisarum (*Araceae*)

	proboscideum	Widely available
	vulgare	ESwi GKev

Aristea (*Iridaceae*)

§	***capitata***	CDoC CPla
	ecklonii	CBcs CBod CExl CPbh CTsd EAri EBee EPri EShb EWld GBin LRHS MHol
	- GWJ 9469	CDoC MHol WCru
	thyrsiflora	see *A. capitata*

Aristolochia (*Aristolochiaceae*)

	baetica	SBrt WCru
	- B&SWJ 15071	WCru
	californica	LEdu
	chilensis	CCCN SPlb
	clematitis	GPoy LEdu MHer
	contorta	EBee EPfP WPGP
	cucurbitifolia B&SWJ 7043	WCru
	durior	see *A. macrophylla*
	fimbriata	CPla SBrt
	- B&SWJ 13612	WCru
	gigantea ♀H1b	CCCN
	grandiflora	CCCN CHll
	griffithii B&SWJ 2118	WCru
	kaempferi	CCCN CHll
	- B&SWJ 14674	WCru
	- NMWJ 14565	WCru
	× ***kewensis***	CCCN
§	***macrophylla***	CBcs CCCN EAri LPar MRav WPGP WSpi
	manshuriensis	EBee
	- B&SWJ 12557	WCru
	- B&SWJ 16071 **new**	WCru
	sempervirens	CBcs CPla GGro LEdu WCru
	- B&SWJ 13600	ESwi WCru
	- from Carqueiranne, Toulon	SBrt
	sipho	see *A. macrophylla*

Aristotelia (*Elaeocarpaceae*)

§	***chilensis***	LEdu MGil WJur WKor WPav
	- 'Variegata' (v)	CCCN CMCN
	macqui	see *A. chilensis*
	serrata	CTsd ESwi MGil SVen

Armeria (*Plumbaginaceae*)

	'Abbey Deep Rose' (Abbey Series)	CBod
	alliacea f. ***leucantha***	SRms
	Bees' hybrids	SBut
	'Brutus'	MHCG
	caespitosa	see *A. juniperifolia*
	- 'Bevan's Variety'	see *A. juniperifolia* 'Bevan's Variety'
§	***curvifolia***	GKev
	euscadiensis	EWld
	(Joystick Series) 'Joystick Lilac Shades'	EBee ELan EPfP NRHS SPoG
	- 'Joystick Red'	ELan EPfP NRHS SPoG
	- 'Joystick White'	ELan EPfP NRHS SPoG
§	***juniperifolia*** ♀H5	EGrl ELan EPfP GArf GJos GKev LRHS MAsh MHer NRHS NSla SGro SLee SPlb SRms WAbe WIce XLum
	- 'Alba'	ELan EPfP EPot GBin GJos MHer NBwr NHpl SLee SRms SRot WAbe WHoo
	- 'Babi Lom'	NLar
§	- 'Bevan's Variety' ♀H5	CBod CSBt EBou ECha EGrl ELan EPfP EPot GEdr GMaP MHer MMuc NLar NRya SHar SIvy SPoG SRms SRot WCav WHoo
	- dark-flowered	WAbe

- 'New Zealand Form'	see *A. juniperifolia* 'Sugar Baby'
§ - 'Sugar Baby'	NLar SRms
juniperifolia* × *maritima	SRms
§ ***maritima***	CBod CHab CSde ECtt ELan EPfP GJos GKev LRHS MBel NAts NRHS SRot SWvt WBrk WWild
§ - 'A Little in the Red'	WFar
- 'Alba'	CBcs CKel CTri ECha ELan EPfP EWoo GJos LRHS LSun MAsh MBel MCot MMuc NBwr NHpl NRHS NRya SEND SLee SPlb SPoG SRms WBrk WCFE WCav WIce WJam
- subsp. ***andina***	see *A. curvifolia*
- (Armada Series) 'Armada Deep Rose'	LRHS
- - 'Armada Rose'	EPfP LRHS NBwr NRHS SRms
- - 'Armada White'	LRHS
- 'Bloodstone'	CTri ELan
- 'Corsica'	CBor CTri NBir NRya WIce
- DÜSSELDORF PRIDE	see *A. maritima* 'Düsseldorfer Stolz'
§ - 'Düsseldorfer Stolz'	CBod CElw CPbh CSBt CSde EBou ECha ECtt ELan EPfP EPot GKev GMaP LCro LRHS MACG MBros NLar NRHS SPoG SWvt WIce XLum
§ - 'In the Red'	CAby CBod CBor CSde ECha ELon GEdr LRHS MAvo MBel MHer MMuc NBwr NHol NHpl NLar NRya SEND SEdd SLee SPad SRms SRot SSut SWvt WFar WHoo WIce
- 'Laucheana'	WCav WHoo
- 'Morning Star Deep Rose'	LSun NFav
- 'Morning Star White'	CBod CPbh CPla EDAr
- 'Nifty Thrifty' (v)	CBor CTri ECtt ELan LCro MHer SPoG SRms WFar
- 'Rubrifolia'	see *A. maritima* 'In the Red'
- 'Rubrifolia Compacta'	see *A. maritima* 'A Little in the Red'
- 'Ruby Glow'	CTri
- 'Splendens'	CBcs CKel CTri EDAr EHeP EPfP EWoo LCro LRHS LShi MAsh MBros MMuc NGrs NHpl NMir NRHS NRya SGBe SLee SPoG SSut
- 'Splendens Alba'	NGrs
pseudarmeria	EPfP WMal
- (Ballerina Series) 'Ballerina'	NBir
- - 'Ballerina Lilac'	CBod CRos EPfP LRHS MACG NRHS SLee SPeP WBrk WFar WTor
- - 'Ballerina Pink'	CRos LRHS
- - 'Ballerina Red'	CBod CRos EPfP EShb LRHS LShi MACG NFav NRHS SLee SPeP SRms WFar WTor
- - 'Ballerina White'	CRos EPfP LRHS LShi MACG NRHS WBrk WFar WTor
splendens 'Perfecta'	NRHS
tweedyi	GKev
'Vesuvius'	XLum
vulgaris	see *A. maritima*

Armoracia (*Brassicaceae*)

§ ***rusticana***	CBod CCBP CHby CLau CTri ELan ENfk GAbr GJos GPoy GQue LCro MHer MHoo MNHC NPer SPoG SRms SVic WHer WHrl WSpi XLum
- 'Horwood'	LCro
- 'Variegata' (v)	ELan LEdu MHoo NSti SRms WHer

Arnebia (*Boraginaceae*)

echioides	see *A. pulchra*
longiflora	see *A. pulchra*
§ ***pulchra***	EDAr

Arnica (*Asteraceae*)

angustifolia subsp. ***iljinii***	NBir
chamissonis Less.	CBod CCBP CHby ENfk MNHC NLar SRms
lessingii	GArf
montana	CPla GPoy MHer MHoo MNHC SRms

Aronia (*Rosaceae*)

arbutifolia	EDir EPfP LSRN MBlu SPlb
- 'Erecta'	CBod CCVT CKel EBee ELan EPfP LRHS MBlu MGil MMuc SPoG SRms SWvt WCFE
melanocarpa	CCVT CMCN CPla CRos CSpe EDir EGrI ELan EPfP EWld GKin LRHS MAsh NRHS NWea WHtc WKor
- 'Hugin'	CAgr GKin LEdu LPar MCoo MMuc MPkF NLar SVic WPGP XSte
* - 'Red Viking'	NOra
× ***prunifolia***	IDee WJur WKor
- 'Aron' (F)	CAgr MCoo WPGP
- 'Autumn Magic'	CBcs EBee ELan MAsh
- 'Brilliant'	CBcs CDoC CKel EBee EHed ELan EPfP IDee MGil NLar SGol SPer WMat
- 'Karhumäki' (F)	NLar
- 'Nero' (F)	CAgr CBcs CBod ELan GBin LEdu MCoo MGil NLar SVic WMat WPGP
- 'Viking' (F)	CAgr CCVT CDoC CKel EBee EDir EPfP EPom GBin IDee LAlb LBuc LCro LEdu LOPS LRHS MBlu MMuc MTrO NLar SGol SVic WFar WPGP

Aronia × *Sorbus* see × *Sorbaronia*

Arrhenatherum (*Poaceae*)

elatius	CHab
- var. ***bulbosum***	GMcL
- - 'Variegatum' (v)	ELan EPPr GKev GMaP MMuc NBid NWad SEND

Artemisia ✿ (*Asteraceae*)

from Taiwan	WHer
§ ***abrotanum***	Widely available
- 'Courson'	ECha XSen
absinthium	CBod CEls CHab CLau ELan ENfk GJos GPoy GQue LShi MGil MHer MHoo MNHC NLar SRms SVic WHer WJek XSen
- 'Lambrook Mist'	CEls CFis CKel CMac ECtt ELan EPfP GQue LRHS MRav SCob SMrm WCAu
- 'Lambrook Silver'	CCBP CDor CEls EBee ECha ELan EPfP EWoo GMaP LSRN MHer MRav NBro NLar SCob SPer SRms SWvt
- 'Persian Lace'	CEls
- 'Silver Ghost'	CEls
afra	CEls XSen
§ ***alba***	CBod CEls GPoy SRms WJek XSen
§ - 'Canescens' ♀H5	CEls EBee ECha EGrI EPfP GMaP LShi MAsh MHer MRav NLar SMrm XLum XSen
annua	CEls
anomala	CEls
§ ***arborescens*** ♀H4	CEls CKel GAbr GMcL SPer SRms
- 'Brass Band'	see *A.* 'Powis Castle'
- 'Faith Raven' ♀H3	CEls GBin MBNS NLar WLov
- 'Porquerolles'	XSen
arbuscula	CEls
argentea misapplied	see *A. arborescens*
argentea L'Hér.	CEls
argyi	CEls
§ ***armeniaca***	CEls WHer

	assoana	see *A. caucasica*
	atrata	CEls
	barrelieri	CEls
	caerulescens subsp. ***cretacea***	CEls WCot
	- subsp. ***gallica***	CEls
	californica	CEls WHer
	- 'Canyon Gray'	CEls
	- 'Montara'	CEls
	campestris	XSen
	- subsp. ***borealis***	CEls
	- subsp. ***campestris***	CEls
	- subsp. ***maritima***	CEls XLum
	- - from Wales	CEls
	camphorata	see *A. alba*
	cana	CEls
	canariensis	see *A. thuscula*
	canescens misapplied	see *A. alba* 'Canescens'
	canescens Willd.	see *A. armeniaca*
	capillaris	CEls XLum
	carruthii	CEls
§	***caucasica*** ♀H7	CEls CKel EWes MHer SRms
	chamaemelifolia	CBod CEls SRms SSut XLum XSen
	cretacea	see *A. nutans*
	discolor Dougl. ex Besser	see *A. michauxiana*
	douglasiana	CEls
	- 'Valerie Finnis'	see *A. ludoviciana* 'Valerie Finnis'
	dracunculus	CKel ECha EWTr GQue LCro MNHC MRav SDix SPhx SPlb SRms SVic WBrk XSen
	- French	CBod CCBP CEls CLau CTsd EBou ENfk EWhm GJos GPoy LCro LEdu MBow MBros MHer MHoo MPri NGrd SEND WCav WFar WGwG WJek
	- Russian	CEls EBou ENfk LCro SVic
	ferganensis	CEls
	filifolia	CEls
	fragrans	CEls
	frigida	CEls
	genipi	CEls
	glacialis	CEls
	gmelinii	CEls
	gnaphalodes	see *A. ludoviciana*
	gorgonum	CEls SEND
	herba-alba	CEls XSen
	indica var. ***momiyamae***	CEls ECha WCot
	japonica	CEls
	kitadakensis 'Guizhou'	see *A. lactiflora* Guizhou Group
	laciniata	CEls
	lactiflora ♀H7	CEls CElw EBee ECha GMaP MHoo MRav NDov NGdn SBls SDix SMrm SPer SRms WTre WWtn
	- NJM 11.010	CEls
	- 'Elfenbein'	CEls EPPr LPla MNrw MRav NDov SMHy
§	- Guizhou Group	Widely available
	- - 'Dark Delight'	CEls EBee ECha ECtt EWes WMal
	- 'Jim Russell'	CDor CEls CElw EBee EWes LEdu
	- ***purpurea***	see *A. lactiflora* Guizhou Group
	- 'Weisse Dame'	CEls MNrw
	- 'Weisses Wunder'	CEls EBee
	lanata Willd.	see *A. caucasica*
	lanata Lam.	XSen
	laxa	see *A. umbelliformis*
	'Little Mice'	CEls LBar NLar
§	***ludoviciana***	CEls GBee NLar NPer SBls SRms WFar XLum
	- subsp. ***ludoviciana*** var. ***incompta***	CEls
	- - var. ***latiloba***	CEls NBro SWvt
	- subsp. ***mexicana*** var. ***albula***	CEls

	- 'Silver Queen'	Widely available
§	- 'Valerie Finnis' ♀H6	Widely available
	maritima	XSen
	- 'Coca-Cola'	CEls EBee LCro SRms
	- var. ***maritima***	CEls
	mauiensis	CEls
§	***michauxiana***	CEls EBee
	molinieri	CEls XLum XSen
	mutellina	see *A. umbelliformis*
	nova	CEls
§	***nutans***	CEls MRav
	ORIENTAL LIMELIGHT ('Janlim') (v)	CBod CEls CEme GMcL MHoo MPri NLar SDix SWvt WHrl
	palmeri hort.	see *A. ludoviciana*
	aff. ***parviflora*** CLD 1531	CEls
	pedemontana	see *A. caucasica*
	pontica	CEls EBee ECha EGrI GMaP GPoy GQue LShi MMuc MRav NBro NLar NSti SRms WFar WHoo WPGP
§	'Powis Castle' ♀H3	Widely available
	princeps	CEls EBee GPoy
	procera Willd.	see *A. abrotanum*
	purshiana	see *A. ludoviciana*
	pycnocephala	CEls
	- 'David's Choice'	CEls
	'Rosenschleier'	CEls EPPr GQue SHar WWtn
	schmidtiana ♀H5	CEls ECha SDix SRms
	- 'Nana' ♀H5	Widely available
	- 'Nana Attraction'	GJos MBNS SRot
	selengensis	CEls
	somai var. ***batakensis*** NMWJ 14559	WCru
	splendens misapplied	see *A. alba* 'Canescens'
	stelleriana	CEls CTri ECha GKev LShi MACG MHol NBro SRms
	- RBS 0207	CEls
	- from Alaska	WCot
§	- 'Boughton Silver'	CBcs CBod CDor CEls CRos EBee ECtt EPfP EWoo GMaP LBar LDai LRHS MAsh MAvo MHer NLar NRHS NSti SCob SPer SRms SWvt
	- 'Mori'	see *A. stelleriana* 'Boughton Silver'
	- 'Nana'	CEls SWvt
	- 'Prostrata'	see *A. stelleriana* 'Boughton Silver'
	- 'Shemya'	CEls
	- 'Silver Brocade'	see *A. stelleriana* 'Boughton Silver'
	suksdorfii	CEls
	taurica	CEls
§	***thuscula***	CEls
	tridentata	WHer
	- subsp. ***tridentata***	CEls
	- subsp. ***wyomingensis***	CEls
§	***umbelliformis***	CEls EWes
	vallesiaca	CEls
	verlotiorum	CEls
	vulgaris	CBod CEls GJos GPoy MGil MNHC WHer
	- 'Variegata' (v)	ELan SRms
	× ***wurzellii***	CEls

Arthropodium (*Asparagaceae*)

candidum 'Little Lilia' (v)	CBct CCht SMad WCot
- 'Maculatum'	MPie NHpl SPlb
- 'Purpureum'	CTtf ECha GEdr NWsh
cirratum	CTsd EAri ESwi EWld MHer MPie SVen WCFE WFar
- bronze	CPla
- 'Matapouri Bay'	CBcs LRHS SEND
milleflorum	SBrt

artichoke, globe see *Cynara cardunculus* Scolymus Group

artichoke, Jerusalem see *Helianthus tuberosus*

Artocarpus (*Moraceae*)

heterophyllus	WJur

Arum (*Araceae*)

byzantinum	GKev
'Chameleon' ♀H7	CDor EPri GRum LEdu MAvo MCor NBir NLar SEND SMad SPer WBrk WCot
§ ***concinnatum***	GKev
- 'Mount Ida'	ESwi
cornutum	see *Sauromatum venosum*
creticum	CBro CMiW EBee EPot GKev LAma MNrw MRav
- 'Karpathos'	CExl GKev WAbe WCot
- 'Marmaris White'	EBee WCot
- white-spotted	EWes
cyrenaicum	GKev
dioscoridis	CBor EBee GKev NRog
- var. ***syriacum***	GKev
dracunculus	see *Dracunculus vulgaris*
gratum	GKev
hygrophilum	CBor LEdu
- B&SWJ 15277	WCru
italicum	CTri LAma LCro LPal MHol NRog SDeJ WCot WShi
- 'Angelique'	WCot
- 'Edward Dougal'	WCot WFar
- 'Green Marble'	WFar
- 'Indubitable' **new**	WCot
- subsp. ***italicum***	GKev MHer WBrk
§ - - 'Marmoratum' ♀H6	Widely available
- - 'Spotted Jack'	WCot
- - 'Tiny'	SWvt
- - 'Uniquity'	WCot
§ - - 'White Winter' ♀H6	LEdu WBrk WCot
- 'Nancy Lindsay'	WCot
- subsp. ***neglectum***	SChr
- - 'Miss Janay Hall' (v)	ESwi MAvo WCot
- 'Pictum'	see *A. italicum* subsp. *italicum* 'Marmoratum'
- 'Sandy McNabb'	WCot
- 'Tresahor Beauty'	MAvo
- 'Yarnells'	LEdu WCot
aff. ***italicum***	CMiW SDir
italicum* × *maculatum	CBor ISha WHer
korolkowii	WCot
maculatum	EPot GKev GPoy MBow MRav NLar NRog WHer WShi
- 'Painted Lady' (v)	WCot
- 'Pleddel'	MRav
- Tar Spot Group	SEND
megobrebi	GKev
§ 'Monksilver'	WCot
nickelii	see *A. concinnatum*
§ ***nigrum***	GKev LEdu
orientale subsp. ***orientale***	GKev
petteri misapplied	see *A. nigrum*
pictum	CExl CMac EWes GKev LEdu
- B&SWJ 15276	WCru
- 'Taff's Form'	see *A. italicum* subsp. *italicum* 'White Winter'
purpureospathum	CBor EPPr LEdu
rupicola var. ***rupicola***	GKev
- var. ***virescens***	LEdu
'Streaked Spectre'	LEdu
'The Patch'	see *A.* 'Monksilver'

Aruncus ✿ (*Rosaceae*)

aethusifolius ♀H7	Widely available
- 'Filigran'	EBee GBin
- 'Little Gem'	WCru
- 'Porzellan'	EBee
asiaticus B&SWJ 8624	WCru
dioicus	Widely available
- (f)	LBar
§ - (m) ♀H6	CBar CBen CMac ELan MBNS MRav MWts NBro NSti SPer SRms
- var. ***astilboides*** **new**	LEdu
- CHILD OF TWO WORLDS	see *A. dioicus* 'Zweiweltenkind'
- 'Glasnevin'	ECha ECtt MRav NHol WFar
- var. ***kamtschaticus***	CPla EMor EWes LSun NLar NWad WHrl
- - RBS 0208	NGdn
- 'Kneiffii'	Widely available
- 'Whirlwind'	EMor EWhm LPla MPie
§ - 'Zweiweltenkind'	EWTr GElm LPla LRHS NLar SBls SMad WCot
'Guinea Fowl'	CKel ECtt ELon EMor GQue LLWG MCot MHol NBid NBir NGdn NLar WCAu
'Horatio'	Widely available
'Johannifest'	EBee ECtt EMor MACG MAvo MCot WCot
'Misty Lace'	CKel CWnw EBee ECtt ELan EMor LBar NBPC NCth NGdn NLar SAko SMrm
'Noble Spirit'	GMcL LSun MPie NGdn NLar
plumosus	see *A. dioicus*
* ***sinensis***	EMor
'Sparkles'	ELan ILea
sylvestris	see *A. dioicus*
- 'Sommeranfang'	ECha
'Ulf'	MAvo
'Woldemar Meier'	GQue ILea MAvo MCot NLar WCot

Arundinaria (*Poaceae*)

anceps	see *Yushania anceps*
auricoma	see *Pleioblastus viridistriatus*
disticha	see *Pleioblastus pygmaeus* 'Distichus'
falconeri	see *Himalayacalamus falconeri*
fargesii	see *Bashania fargesii*
fastuosa	see *Semiarundinaria fastuosa*
fortunei	see *Pleioblastus variegatus*
hookeriana Munro	see *Himalayacalamus hookerianus*
japonica	see *Pseudosasa japonica*
jaunsarensis	see *Yushania anceps*
marmorea	see *Chimonobambusa marmorea*
murielae	see *Fargesia murielae*
nitida	see *Fargesia nitida*
oedogonata	see *Oligostachyum oedogonatum*
palmata	see *Sasa palmata*
pumila	see *Pleioblastus argenteostriatus* f. *pumilus*
pygmaea	see *Pleioblastus pygmaeus*
quadrangularis	see *Chimonobambusa quadrangularis*
simonii	see *Pleioblastus simonii*
tessellata	see *Bergbambos tessellata*
vagans	see *Sasaella ramosa*
variegata	see *Pleioblastus variegatus*
veitchii	see *Sasa veitchii*
viridistriata	see *Pleioblastus viridistriatus*

Arundo (*Poaceae*)

donax	CAbb CKno EAri EBee EBlo ELan ELon EWes LPfP LRHS MAvo MBlu MNrw MRav SArc SCob SDix SEND SMad SPlb SPoG SSut
- 'Golden Chain' (v)	CKno EPPr EWes SMad
- 'Macrophylla'	CKno EBlo EPPr EWes LEdu WPGP
- 'Variegata'	see *A. donax* var. *versicolor*

§	- var. ***versicolor*** (v)	CBcs CBen CEme CKel CKno CPla EAri EBee EBlo ELan ELon EWes GBin LRHS MRav NRHS NWsh SArc SCob SDix SEND SIvy SMad SPeP SPer SPlb SPoG SSta XLum
I	- - 'Aureovariegata' (v)	CBcs CDTJ SEND
	formosana	CKno EPPr
	- 'Golden Showers'	ESwi

Asarina (*Plantaginaceae*)

	barclayana	see *Maurandya barclayana*
	erubescens	see *Lophospermum erubescens*
	lophantha	see *Lophospermum scandens*
	lophospermum	see *Lophospermum scandens*
§	***procumbens***	CTri EBou GAbr GElm GKev NBir NRya SBut SLee SPhx SRms WBrk WKif

Asarum (*Aristolochiaceae*)

Chen Yi 5	ESwi
arifolium	EBee EPPr MBriF
- 'The Giant'	EBee EMor NLar XSte
- white-flowered	EBee
canadense	CDor EMor GEdr GKev GPoy LEdu MBriF
caudatum	EBee ECha ELan EMor ESwi GEdr GKev LEdu LPla MBriF NBro NLar SMad SRms WCot WSpi
- 'Little Murphy'	WCot
- white-flowered	GGro
caulescens	EPPr GGro
- green-flowered	WFar
- near-white-flowered	GGro
delavayi	WCot
- giant	EBee
epigynum	CDTJ CDor EBee EMor ESwi GKev MNrw NCth NLar SMad WCot XLum
- 'Silver Web'	ELan GGro NSti WCot
europaeum ♀H6	Widely available
- PAB 4377	LEdu WPGP
- Pontic	WPGP
fauriei	GGro
'Koton'	EMor LBar SMad
longirhizomatosum	GEdr WCru
maculatum	GKev
- B&SWJ 1114	WCru
maximum	CBor GKev ISha
- 'Green Panda'	CDTJ EMor
- 'Ling Ling'	EMor LAma NCth SMad
- 'Silver Panda'	CBct CDTJ ELan EMor ESwi LBar MNrw NGBl SMad SMrm WCot
pulchellum	CBor ESwi
sieboldii green-flowered	GGro WFar
splendens	CBct CBor CBro CDTJ EBee ELan EMor EPfP GKev ISha LAma LEdu LPal MBriF MHol MNrw NGKo NLar NSti SDir SDix SPlb SPoG WCot WFar XLum
taipingshanianum 'Elfin Yellow'	ESwi

Asclepias ✿ (*Apocynaceae*)

'Cinderella'	EShb
curassavica	CCCN CSpe EAri EShb SRkn
- 'Silky Gold'	EShb
exaltata	SBrt
fruticosa	see *Gomphocarpus fruticosus*
incarnata	CPla CSpe ECha EWld MRav SBrt SPeP SPlb WTre XLum
- 'Ice Ballet'	CBWd CBod EBee LBar MACG NLar SPer WHlf
- 'Soulmate'	CBor EBee EPfP GQue LBar MHol SBls SMad SPer
physocarpa	see *Gomphocarpus physocarpus*
speciosa	GGro MMuc SBea SBls SBrt SBut
tuberosa	CBWd CBcs CBod CBor CSpe EBee EShb GJos GPoy LBar LRHS MAsh MBel MHer MNHC MPie NRHS SMad SPeP SPoG SRms WGwG WHil XLum XSen
- Gay Butterflies Group	LBar
- subsp. ***interior***	EPPr MHol SBls

Asimina (*Annonaceae*)

triloba (F)	CBcs CCCN CDTJ LPar MBlu NLar SGol SPlb WHlf WJur WKor
- 'Davis' (F)	XVPe
- 'Kentucky Champion' (F) **new**	XVPe
- 'Ksu-Atwood' (F) **new**	XVPe
- 'Ksu-Benson' (F) **new**	XVPe
- 'Ksu-Chappell' (F) **new**	XVPe
- 'Nc-1' (F)	XVPe
- 'Overleese' (F)	XVPe
- 'Potomac' (F) **new**	XVPe
- 'Prima 1216'PBR (F) **new**	XVPe
- 'Prolific' (F)	XVPe
- 'Rappahannock' (F) **new**	XVPe
- 'Sunflower' (F)	CCCN IDee SAko XVPe
- 'Susquehanna' (F) **new**	XVPe
- 'Wabash' (F) **new**	XVPe

asparagus see also AGM Vegetables Section

Asparagus (*Asparagaceae*)

	acutifolius	XSen
	albus **new**	XSen
	asparagoides ♀H3	EShb
	densiflorus	WCot
	- 'Mazeppa'	EShb
	- 'Myersii' ♀H1c	EShb LCro LOPS SEND
	- 'Myriocladus'	EShb
	- Sprengeri Group ♀H1c	EShb LCro LOPS NGBl NHrt SEND
	falcatus	CDoC EShb NHrt SEND
	filicinus NJM 12.024	WPGP
	- var. ***giraldii***	WCot
	aff. ***meioclados*** B&SWJ 8309	WCot WCru WFar
	plumosus	see *A. setaceus*
	pseudoscaber 'Spitzenschleier'	EBee SDix WCot
	retrofractus	WCot
	scandens	EShb WCot
	schoberioides	LEdu
	- B&SWJ 8814	WCru
§	***setaceus*** ♀H2	CDoC EShb LCro LOPS NHrt SPlb WCot
	- 'Pyramidalis' ♀H1c	CDoC
	tenuifolius	WPGP
	virgatus	EBee EShb LEdu SMad SPlb WPGP

Asperula (*Rubiaceae*)

§	***arcadiensis*** ♀H3	EPot SPlb WAbe
	aristata subsp. ***scabra***	ECha MMuc WCot
	- subsp. ***thessala***	see *A. sintenisii*
	boissieri	EPot SPlb WAbe
	daphneola	ELan EPot EWes
	gussonei	ELan EPot WAbe WHoo
	hexaphylla	EDAr
	lilaciflora var. ***caespitosa***	see *A. lilaciflora* subsp. *lilaciflora*
§	- subsp. ***lilaciflora***	EBou ELan
	nitida	ELan EPot WIce
	- subsp. ***puberula***	see *A. sintenisii*
	odorata	see *Galium odoratum*
§	***sintenisii***	EPot WAbe WHoo

suberosa misapplied	see *A. arcadiensis*
taurina	EBee
- subsp. ***caucasica***	NLar WBor
tinctoria	GPoy GQue MHer SRms

Asphodeline (*Asphodelaceae*)

liburnica	CBro CFis CPla EAri ECha EPri LCro MMuc SEND XSen
§ ***lutea***	Widely available
§ - 'Gelbkerze'	SBls WAvo
- YELLOW CANDLE	see *A. lutea* 'Gelbkerze'
taurica	SBrt XSen

Asphodelus (*Asphodelaceae*)

acaulis	WCot
§ ***aestivus***	CKel EBee EWes MBel WCot
albus	CBro CKel EAri EBee ECha EGrI EPPr EPfP GAbr GBin NBid NGBl SBls SPlb SRms XLum XSen
cerasiferus	see *A. ramosus*
fistulosus	CBro CKel EBee LEdu SVen XSen
lusitanicus	see *A. ramosus*
luteus	see *Asphodeline lutea*
microcarpus	see *A. aestivus*
§ ***ramosus***	CPar MCot WCot

Aspidistra ✿ (*Asparagaceae*)

B&SWJ 6645 from Thailand	WCru
Chen Yi 135	ESwi WCot
attenuata B&SWJ 377	WCru
- B&SWJ 2001	WCru
- B&SWJ 3727	WCru
- 'Dungpu Dazzler'	ESwi WCru
- 'Small 'n' Smart'	WCru
- 'Xitou Starlet'	WCru
caespitosa 'Jade Ribbons'	see *A. hainanensis* 'Jade Ribbons'
daibuensis B&SWJ 312b	WCru
- B&SWJ 1949	WCru
- B&SWJ 3236	WCru
- B&SWJ 6863	WCru
- B&SWJ 6866	WCru
- 'Taiwan Stars'	ESwi WCru
- 'Tidy Trim'	ESwi WCru
- 'Totally Dotty' (v)	ESwi WCru
- 'Yuli Yummy'	ESwi WCru
elatior ♀H3	CBct CDTJ CTsd EBee EShb ESwi LCro LEdu LOPS MHtn MRav SEND SMad SPlb WCot XLum
- 'Akebono' (v)	WCot
- 'Asahi' (v)	ESwi WCot
- 'Hoshi-zora' (v)	WCot
- 'Lennon's Song' (v)	ESwi SEND WCot
- 'Milky Way' (v)	EBee EShb ESwi SEND XLum
- 'Okame' (v)	WCot
- 'Variegata' (v) ♀H3	CPla EShb
aff. ***elatior*** 'Mystery Man'	WCru
fasciaria	WCru
fungilliformis 'China Star' (v)	ESwi SMad WCot WCru
aff. ***geastrum*** 'Opium Hit'	WCru
§ ***hainanensis*** 'Jade Ribbons'	EShb ESwi WCot WCru
linearifolia	WCru
- 'Leopard' (v)	ESwi WCot WCru
- 'Skinny Dippin''	WCru
lurida	EShb LAma
- 'Ginga'	see *A. sichuanensis* 'Ginga'
- 'Ginga Giant' (v)	ESwi WCot WCru
minutiflora	ESwi WCot
- 'Spangled Ribbons'	WCru
mushaensis B&SWJ 315	WCru
- B&SWJ 1953	WCru
- 'Purple Picket'	WCru
- 'Wushe Wacky'	WCru
aff. ***mushaensis*** 'Spotty Dotty' (v)	ESwi WCru
omeiensis	WCot
punctata	WCru
retusa 'Nanjing Green'	WCru
saxicola 'Uan Fat Lady'	see *A. zongbayi* 'Uan Fat Lady'
sichuanensis	WCru
- 'Beauty Spot'	WCru
§ - 'Ginga' (v)	ESwi WCot
- 'Misty Spot'	WCru
- 'Rarely Spotted'	WCru
- 'Spotty'	WCru
- 'Well Spotted'	WCru
subrotata B&SWJ 5252	WCru
sutepensis B&SWJ 5216	WCru
- B&SWJ 6645	WCru
- 'Chiang-dao Chace'	WCru
- 'Pha-Hom Pok-adot'	WCru
tonkinensis	ESwi WCot WCru
typica 'China Sun'	ESwi GGro WCot
vietnamensis	WCru
zongbayi	WCot
§ - 'Uan Fat Lady'	EBee ESwi WCot WCru

Asplenium ✿ (*Aspleniaceae*)

antiquum ♀H3	EShb LCro NHrt
- HURRICANE ('Vitasphur'PBR) **new**	NHrt
- 'Leslie' ♀H3 **new**	LCro
- 'Osaka'	LCro NHrt
bulbiferum misapplied	see *A.* × *lucrosum*
bulbiferum ambig. 'Suze'	IKel
bulbiferum Forst.f.	EShb ESwi SPlb
§ ***ceterach***	CLAP ISha NHar NLar SMad WCot WHer WHoo
cuneifolium **new**	WCot
daucifolium	NWad WCot
difforme × ***dimorphum***	EShb
× ***ebenoides*** ♀H4	EMor GEdr ISha NBro NHar SPlb
§ × ***lucrosum*** ♀H2	ESwi LPal LWaG
'Maori Princess' ♀H2	WFib
nidus ♀H1b	IKel LCro LOPS LWaG NHrt
- 'Campio'PBR **new**	LCro
- 'Crispy Wave'PBR	CDoC LCro LOPS NHrt
- 'Osaka' **new**	NHrt
nitidum	SPlb
'Parvati'	CDoC NHrt
§ ***scolopendrium*** ♀H6	Widely available
- 'Angustatum' ♀H6	Widely available
- Crispum Group ♀H6	CLAP EFer ELan EMor NBid SRms WAbe WFar WFib
- - 'Crispum Bolton's Nobile'	WFib
- - 'Golden Queen'	CDor
- Crispum Cristatum Group	EMor SCob SMrm
- Crispum Fimbriatum Group	CLAP
- Cristatum Group	CAby CBod CDor CKel CLAP CRos CWnw EBee ECtt ELan ELon EMor EPfP ISha LRHS MGos MRav NBro NLar NRHS SPer SRms SRot WFib WHlf
- 'Fimbriatum Cristatum'	CLAP
- 'Furcatum'	CDTJ EBee EHed ELan EMor MHtn NLar SPad
- 'Kaye's Lacerated' ♀H5	EFer WFib
- Marginatum Group	EFer
- 'Muricatum'	ELan MRav NBid WFib
- 'Sagittatocristatum'	CLAP
- 'Sagittatoprojectum Sclater'	WFib
- Undulatum Group	CDTJ CRos EBee ECha EPfP GBin LPal LRHS LSto MAsh NBir NLar

	NRHS SRms WCot WFar WGwG XLum
- Undulatum Cristatum Group	EMor
trichomanes ♀H6	Widely available
- Cristatum Group	CLAP CRos ISha LRHS NLar NRHS
- Incisum Group ♀H6	EFer WAbe

Astelia (*Asteliaceae*)

banksii	CBcs CBct CBod CCht CPbh CPla CRos CTrC EPfP IBal LRHS LSRN MCot MGos NCou NLar NRHS SCoo SEdd SGBe SPeP
§ ***chathamica*** ♀H3	CAbb CBcs CCCN CCht CTrC CTsd ELan EPfP GAbr GDam LPal LPar LRHS LSRN MGos MHol MPri SArc SCob SCoo SPlb SPoG SWvt WCot WSpi
- 'Silver Spear'	see *A. chathamica*
fragrans	LEdu
grandis	LEdu WPGP
nervosa	SArc
- 'Westland'	CBcs CBod CCCN CCht CPla CRos CTrC CTsd GBin ILea LCro LPar LRHS LSRN MGos NRHS SCob SGBe SWvt
'Red Devil'	CBcs CBod CPla CTrC LCro MGos MHol NLar SCob SEdd SGBe SMrm SPoG WHer WPav
'Red Shadow'	CBcs XSte
'Silver Shadow'PBR	CBcs CRos EPfP LCro LOPS LRHS NRHS SCob SGBe SMad SPad SWvt WFar WSpi XSte

Aster ✿ (*Asteraceae*)

acris	see *Galatella sedifolia*
'Afternoon Delight'	EBee
ageratoides	WCot
- 'Adustus Nanus' **new**	NDov
- 'Ashvi'	CKno CMil ECtt ELon EShb EWoo GBin GElm MBel MHol MMuc NDov NSti SDix SPoG WCAu WCot WFar WOld WSHC
- 'Asmo' **new**	SEdd
- 'Asran'	ECtt ELon EPPr EWes EWhm LEdu MACG MHer MHol MMuc MPie NLar SEND SEdd WBrk WCAu WCot WFar WOld XLum
- 'Ezo Murasaki'	CDor CSpe ECha ELon GBin LEdu LPla MAsh MAvo MNrw NDov SAko SMHy SPoG WCot WOld XLum
- var. ***firmus***	WPGP
- 'Harry Smith'	GAbr ILea MAsh NSti SAko SEdd SMHy SPoG WCot WFar WOld
- 'Stardust'	WHoo
- 'Starshine'PBR	CBcs CBod CKno CWGN EBee ECtt EPfP EWTr EWoo MAvo WCot
alpigenus	see *Oreostemma alpigenum*
alpinus ♀H5	EBou EPfP GArf GKev LCro LOPS MAsh MHol SRms WFar
- var. ***albus***	ELan EPfP GKev LRHS WCot XLum XSen
- 'Antje'	MNrw
- DARK BEAUTY	see *A. alpinus* 'Dunkle Schöne'
- var. ***dolomiticus***	GKev
§ - 'Dunkle Schöne'	CCBP EBou GPSL LDai MACG SRms WFar XLum XSen
- 'Goliath'	EBee ELan EPfP GPSL LBar SPlb WFar
- 'Happy End'	CRos EPfP GMcL LRHS NRHS SRms WCAu XLum XSen
- 'Pinkie'	EBee EBou ELan EPfP ITim MACG
- 'Trimix'	NBir NFav SRms
- violet-flowered	GMcL LRHS
- 'White Beauty'	MACG
amelloides	see *Felicia amelloides*
amellus	ELon
- 'Blue King'	EWes IPot NLar SMrm SWvt WFar WSpi
- 'Breslau'	ELon MAvo
- 'Brilliant'	CBod ECtt ELon EPPr GElm LPla LRHS LSou LSto MBNS MRav NBir NLar NRHS NSti NWsh SAko SGbt SOrN SPer SPhx SRms WCAu WHoo WOld WSpi
- 'Butzemann'	ELon WCot WFar
- 'Danzig'	NDov NLar
- 'Doktor Otto Petschek'	ELon NLar WCot
- EMPRESS	see *A. amellus* 'Glücksfund'
- 'Forncett Flourish' ♀H7	ECtt MAvo MHCG SMHy WCot WHoo WMal WOld
- 'Framfieldii' ♀H7	SMHy WCot WFar WOld
§ - 'Glücksfund'	SAko XSen
- 'Gründer'	MAvo MHCG SMHy WCot WOld
- 'Jacqueline Genebrier' ♀H7	MHCG WOld
- 'King George' ♀H7	Widely available
- 'Kobold' ♀H7	LPla
- 'Lac de Genève'	LPla WCot XLum
- 'Lady Hindlip'	ELon WCot WMal
- 'Louise'	MBrN MHCG
- 'Mira'	ELon GBin SAko
- 'Moerheim Gem'	ECtt WCot WOld
- 'Mrs Ralph Woods'	WOld
- 'Nocturne'	ELon MAvo WCot WOld
- PINK ZENITH	see *A. amellus* 'Rosa Erfüllung'
§ - 'Rosa Erfüllung' ♀H7	CBod CDor CMac EBee ECtt ELan EPPr EPfP EWes GMaP LPla LRHS LSto MACG MAvo MNrw MRav NLar NRHS NWsh SAko SCob SGbt SPhx SPoG SWvt WCAu WOld WSpi
- 'Rotfeuer'	ELon WSpi
- 'Rudolph Goethe'	CBod EBee ECtt EHeP ELan ELon EMil EPfP LRHS MACG NLar NRHS SCob WCAu WOld WSpi
- 'September Glow'	SAko SHar WOld
- 'Silbersee' ♀H7	ELon SAko
- 'Sonia'	ECha ECtt ELon LRHS NRHS SWvt
- 'Sonora' ♀H7	LPla MAsh MNrw SHar SPhx WKif WOld WTor
- 'Sternkugel'	ELon MAvo WOld
- 'Ultramarine'	WOld
- 'Vanity'	MAvo WOld
§ - 'Veilchenkönigin' ♀H7	Widely available
- VIOLET QUEEN	see *A. amellus* 'Veilchenkönigin'
× ***amethystinus***	see *Symphyotrichum* × *amethystinum*
asperulus misapplied	see *A. peduncularis*
batangensis W&O 7057	GGro
'Betel Nut'	ECha SDix
capensis 'Variegatus'	see *Felicia amelloides* variegated
'Carmen'	XLum
'Cassandra'	NCth
'Cheavers'	LRHS NRHS
'Chilly Fingers'	MAvo MNrw SMHy
ciliolatus	see *Symphyotrichum ciliolatum*
'Climax' misapplied	see *Symphyotrichum laeve* 'Arcturus', *S. laeve* 'Calliope'
coelestis	see *Felicia amelloides*
coloradoensis	see *Xanthisma coloradoense*
'Connecticut Snow Flurry'	see *Symphyotrichum ericoides* var. *prostratum* 'Snow Flurry'
cordifolius	see *Symphyotrichum cordifolium*
corymbosus	see *Eurybia divaricata*
'Cotswold Gem'	LRHS MHCG MNrw SMHy WCot WOld

diffusus see *Symphyotrichum lateriflorum*
diplostephioides EWhm GArf GEdr GKev GLog MMrt SPlb
divaricatus see *Eurybia divaricata*
'Dwarf Barbados' LRHS NRHS
'Dwarf Blue' LRHS
'Eleven Purple'PBR MNrw NDov SEdd
ericoides see *Symphyotrichum ericoides*
falcatus see *Symphyotrichum falcatum*
'Fanny's Fall' see *Symphyotrichum oblongifolium* 'Fanny's'
'Fingers and Thumbs' MAvo
foliaceus see *Symphyotrichum foliaceum*
× ***frikartii*** CBod CMac EBee EPfP EWTr LRHS MRav SGbt SWvt WSHC
- 'Eiger' WOld
- 'Flora's Delight' CRos EBlo ELon EMor EPfP LRHS MRav NLar NRHS SEdd SPoG SRms WCAu WHoo WSpi
- 'Jungfrau' CFis CWGN EBee ELan EPPr GBee GMaP LRHS MNHC MRav NLar NRHS SPhx SRms WCAu WOld WSHC
- 'Mönch' ♀H7 Widely available
- WONDER OF STAFA see *A.* × *frikartii* 'Wunder von Stäfa'
§ - 'Wunder von Stäfa' ♀H7 CEnd CKno EBee ECtt ELon EPPr EPfP GBin GElm GMaP LCro LRHS LSto MBNS MBel MCot NBir NGdn NLar SRGP SWvt WCAu WCot WFar WHoo WOld WSpi
furcatus see *Eurybia furcata*
glehnii WCAu
- 'Aglenii' MNrw NDov SAko
greatae see *Symphyotrichum greatae*
× ***herveyi*** see *Eurybia* × *herveyi*
himalaicus GArf NSla WFar
hybridus luteus see *Solidago* × *luteus*
'Ice Cool Pink' ECha IPot SMHy
'Ivy House' ECtt
'JS El Macho' MNrw
* ***kotarimus*** MHol MMrt XLum
laevis see *Symphyotrichum laeve*
lateriflorus see *Symphyotrichum lateriflorum*
laterifolius 'Snow Flurry' see *Symphyotrichum ericoides* var. *prostratum* 'Snow Flurry'
linosyris see *Galatella linosyris*
macrophyllus see *Eurybia macrophylla*
mongolicus see *Kalimeris mongolica*
'Moody Blue' MAvo
'Mrs Dean' ECtt
natalensis see *Felicia rosulata*
novae-angliae see *Symphyotrichum novae-angliae*
novi-belgii see *Symphyotrichum novi-belgii*
oblongifolius see *Symphyotrichum oblongifolium*
OCTOBERLIGHT see *Symphyotrichum* 'Oktoberlicht'
oolentangiensis see *Symphyotrichum oolentangiense*
pappei see *Felicia amoena*
§ ***peduncularis*** EBee EBlo ECha EMor EShb GBee LBar MAsh MHol NCou NSti SHar SMad WCot WFar WHil WMal WOld
petiolatus see *Felicia petiolata*
pilosus see *Symphyotrichum pilosum*
ptarmicoides see *Solidago ptarmicoides*
puniceus see *Symphyotrichum puniceum*
pyrenaeus 'Lutetia' CBWd CBod CKno ECha EPPr EPfP EShb EWTr GMaP LRHS LSto MAvo MBow MNrw NLar NRHS SBut SEdd SPhx SRGP SRms WCAu WCot WFar WKif WOld XLum
radula see *Eurybia radula*
rotundifolius 'Variegatus' see *Felicia amelloides* variegated
rugulosus 'Asrugo' CKno
savatieri new SHar
§ ***scaber*** WCot
- 'Ki Hakikomi-fu' GGro
schreberi see *Eurybia schreberi*
sedifolius see *Galatella sedifolia*
sericeus see *Symphyotrichum sericeum*
sibiricus see *Eurybia sibirica*
'Small-Ness' EBlo EShb GBin LRHS MAvo NWad
'Snow Flurry' see *Symphyotrichum ericoides* var. *prostratum* 'Snow Flurry'
souliei EBee GArf
spathulifolius WCot XLum
spectabilis see *Eurybia spectabilis*
subcaeruleus see *A. tongolensis*
tataricus 'Jindai' CBWd EBee SPeP WCAu
thomsonii CBod GBin IPot SHar SMHy WCot WOld WSpi
- 'Nanus' EBee GBin GMaP LRHS SPoG WOld WSpi
§ ***tongolensis*** NHpl
- 'Berggarten' LDai LRHS MHol MNrw NRHS
- 'Wartburgstern' EMor EPfP LRHS SGbt XLum
tradescantii misapplied see *Symphyotrichum pilosum* var. *pringlei*
tradescantii L. see *Symphyotrichum tradescantii*
trinervius var. ***harae*** WFar WOld
tripolium see *Tripolium pannonicum*
'Triumph' WCot
turbinellus see *Symphyotrichum turbinellum*
vimineus Lam. see *Symphyotrichum lateriflorum*
- 'Ptarmicoides' see *Solidago ptarmicoides*

Asteranthera (*Gesneriaceae*)

ovata CExl GGGa WAbe WPGP

Asteriscus (*Asteraceae*)

'Gold Coin' see *Pallenis maritima*
maritimus see *Pallenis maritima*

Asteromoea (*Asteraceae*)

mongolica see *Kalimeris mongolica*
pinnatifida see *Kalimeris pinnatifida*

Asteropyrum (*Ranunculaceae*)

cavaleriei GEdr
peltatum GEdr

Asterotrichion (*Malvaceae*)

discolor CTsd EBee SPlb SVen

Astilbe ✿ (*Saxifragaceae*)

'Alive and Kicking' LRHS LSou
'Amerika' (× *arendsii*) CMHG CSBt NBPC SRms
'Amethyst' (× *arendsii*) CMHG CMac LBuc MBel MRav NBPC NBir NHol SPer WFar
'Angel Wings' (× *arendsii*) CMHG NEoE
'Anita Pfeifer' (× *arendsii*) CMHG NLar XLum
'Aphrodite' (*simplicifolia* hybrid) CBcs GMcL XLum
× ***arendsii*** LBuc XLum
(Astary Series) 'Astary Pink' (× *arendsii*) LRHS NRHS
- 'Astary Red' (× *arendsii*) LRHS NRHS
- 'Astary White' (× *arendsii*) LRHS NRHS
astilboides SWvt
'Avalanche' NEoE NHol SPad WBor WBrk WSpi
'Bakker's Beauty' (× *arendsii*) new CMHG
§ 'Beauty of Ernst' (× *arendsii*) CBod CMHG EBee ELon EMor EPfP LRHS MNrw SRms XSte
§ 'Beauty of Lisse' (× *arendsii*) ELon EMor MNrw

	'Bergkristall' (× *arendsii*)	CMHG
	'Betsy Cuperus' (*thunbergii* hybrid)	CMHG WCAu
	'Bonn' (*japonica* hybrid)	CMHG CWCL CWat NLar SCoo SRms
§	'Brautschleier' (× *arendsii*) ♀H7	CBod CMHG CMac ECtt GBin GKev LCro LOPS LRHS LSRN NGdn NLar NQui NRHS WPnP XLum
	'Bremen' (*japonica* hybrid)	CMHG
	'Bressingham Beauty' (× *arendsii*) ♀H7	CRos CWCL EBee EBlo ECtt EHeP ELan EPfP EWoo GBin GKev GMaP LCro LLWG LOPS LRHS MRav NEoE NHol NRHS SEdd SRms SWvt WFar
	BRIDAL VEIL (× *arendsii*)	see *A.* 'Brautschleier'
§	'Bronce Elegans' (*simplicifolia* hybrid) ♀H7	ECha EMor GLog GMaP GMcL MBow NHol NLar SRms WFar WSpi
	'Bronze Sprite' (*simplicifolia* hybrid)	WFar
	'Bronzelaub' (× *arendsii*)	CMHG
*	***bumalda*** 'Bronze Pygmy'	NHol
	'Bumalda' (× *arendsii*)	CSBt EGrl EMor GBin GLog GMaP NBid NChi NGdn NRHS SPlb WFar WWtn
	'Bunter Zauber' (× *arendsii*)	XLum
	'Burgunderrot' (× *arendsii*)	MNrw NLar SRms
	'Cappuccino' (× *arendsii*)	CBcs CBod EMor ILea LRHS MAsh MBel MBros WWtn
	'Catherine Deneuve'	see *A.* 'Federsee'
	'Cattleya' (× *arendsii*)	CMHG GMcL LRHS NLar NRHS SAko WSpi XLum
	'Cattleya Dunkel' (× *arendsii*)	CMHG
	'Ceres' (× *arendsii*)	CMHG
	'Cherry Ripe'	see *A.* 'Feuer'
	chinensis	EPfP MBros WSHC
	- B&SWJ 8178	WCru
	- 'Black Pearls' **new**	LBar
	- 'Brokat'	CMHG GBin
	- var. ***davidii***	GBin XLum
	- - B&SWJ 8583	WCru
	- - B&SWJ 8645	WCru
	- 'Diamonds and Pearls'[PBR]	CWGN ECtt EMor LRHS LSou WFar
	- 'Finale'	GKev NHol
	- 'Glitter and Glamour' **new**	LBar LLWG
	- 'Intermezzo'	GBin GMaP NLar
	- 'Little Vision in Pink'[PBR]	EPfP WFar
	- 'Milk and Honey'[PBR]	CWGN ECtt EMor EWTr LRHS NBPC WFar WSpi
§	- var. ***pumila*** ♀H7	Widely available
	- - 'Serenade'	CMHG CMac NGdn
I	- - 'Tiny Form'	GRum
	- 'Spätsommer'	CMHG
	- var. ***taquetii***	CMac ELan NSti SRms XLum
	- - PURPLE LANCE	see *A. chinensis* var. *taquetii* 'Purpurlanze'
§	- - 'Purpurlanze' ♀H7	CBWd CKno EBee ECha ECtt EMor EShb GBin GMaP LSRN MCot MRav NBir NBro NChi NDov NGdn NHol NLar SCob SPoG SWvt WBor WCAu WFar WHoo WSpi WWtn
§	- - 'Superba' ♀H7	CMac ECha GMcL LRHS NBro NWad SDix SEdd SRms WFar
	- 'Troll'	GBin
	- 'Veronika Klose'	CMHG GBin LRHS NLar WHoo
	- 'Vision in Pink'[PBR]	CMHG CWCL ELan EPfP MBNS MNrw NBPC SCob WFar
	- 'Vision in Red'[PBR]	CMHG CWCL CWat ECtt EGrl ELan EMor EPfP LRHS MBNS MNrw NBPC NLar SCob SGbt SPoG SRkn WCAu WFar WWke
	- 'Vision in White'	EPfP LCro LOPS MBros NBPC NEoE SAko SCob SPoG WFar
	- 'Visions'	CMac ELan EPfP LRHS MBNS NBro NEoE NGdn NRHS SCob SCoo SPoG

	- 'White Cloud'	NQui
	'Chocolate Cherry'[PBR] (Mighty Series)	EMor GJos ILea LBar LCro LOPS MAsh SEdd SPeP
	'Chocolate Shogun'	CBcs CMil CSpe CWGN EBee EMor LPla LRHS LSou LSun MBNS MHol MNrw MThu NCou NSti SMad SPad SPoG WCot WFar WTor XSte
	COLOGNE	see *A.* 'Köln'
	COLOR FLASH	see *A.* 'Beauty of Ernst'
	COLOR FLASH LIME	see *A.* 'Beauty of Lisse'
	'Country and Western'[PBR] (× *arendsii*)	NEoE
	'Cream of Marwood' (× *arendsii*) **new**	CMHG
	'Crimson Feather'	see *A.* 'Gloria Purpurea'
	× ***crispa***	SMad
	- 'Lilliput'	ECtt NBir NEoE NLar NRya
§	- 'Perkeo' ♀H5	CBcs ECtt GMaP LRHS NBir NEoE NHpl NLar NRHS SRms WFar
	- 'Peter Pan'	see *A.* × *crispa* 'Perkeo'
	- 'Red Rog'	NEoE
	- 'Snow Queen'	NBir NEoE
	'Darwin's Dream'	CMHG MBros MNrw NEoE NLar WFar
	'Darwin's Favourite' (× *arendsii*)	CWCL
	'Delft Lace'	CAbb CMHG EBee EMor EWoo LBuc LRHS MBel MMrt NRHS SRms
	'Deutschland' (*japonica* hybrid) ♀H7	Widely available
§	'Diamant' (× *arendsii*)	CMHG LSRN MMuc MNrw NBir NFav NGdn NHol WFar
	DIAMOND	see *A.* 'Diamant'
	'Donna' (× *arendsii*) **new**	CMHG
	'Drayton Glory' (× *arendsii*)	see *A.* × *rosea* 'Peach Blossom'
	'Drum and Bass'[PBR]	LSou NLar
	'Dusseldorf' (*japonica* hybrid)	CMHG CWCL EBee LRHS NRHS
	'Eden's Odysseus'	NHol NWad
	'Elegans' (*simplicifolia* hybrid)	CMac
	'Elisabeth' van Veen (× *arendsii*)	CBod CMHG
	ELIZABETH BLOOM ('Eliblo'[PBR]) (× *arendsii*)	EBlo EMor LLWG LRHS MRav NGdn NHol NRHS
	'Ellie' (× *arendsii*)	CMHG CMac CWCL ECtt ELan EPfP GBee GQue LBar LLWG MBNS MBel NCth NGdn NHol NLar SGBe SPoG WFar
	'Else Schluck' (× *arendsii*)	ECha
	'Erica' (× *arendsii*)	CAby CMHG CTri EGrl EMor EWTr GBin GLog GQue NEoE NLar WBrk WFar
	'Etna' (*japonica* hybrid)	CBcs CMHG CPud ECtt LRHS NBPC NGdn NLar SRms WFar WHoo
	'Europa' (*japonica* hybrid)	CMHG CMac ECtt EMor GBin GMcL LRHS MGos NGdn NLar NRHS SCoo SPoG SRms WCAu WFar WHlf
	'Fanal' (× *arendsii*) ♀H7	Widely available
	'Fata Morgana' (× *arendsii* hybrid)	CMHG
§	'Federsee' (× *arendsii*)	CBcs CMHG CWCL EBee ECha ECtt LRHS MBNS NBro NEoE NGdn NRHS WFar WWtn XLum
§	'Feuer' (× *arendsii*)	CMHG CMac ECtt NEoE NGdn NHol NLar WFar
	FIRE	see *A.* 'Feuer'
	'Fireberry'[PBR] (Short 'n' Sweet Series)	LBar NCth NLar
	'Flamingo'[PBR] (*simplicifolia* hybrid)	CMHG ECtt MBNS MBel NLar
§	***formosa*** B&SWJ 10946	WCru

	'Gertrud Brix' (× *arendsii*)	CMHG CWat MMuc NBir NGdn XLum
§	***glaberrima***	NBid
§	- var. ***saxatilis*** ♀H5	GArf GBin GEdr NFav WAbe WFar
	- - 'Candy Floss'	NEoE
	- saxosa	see *A. glaberrima* var. *saxatilis*
	'Gladstone' (× *arendsii*)	see *A.* 'W.E. Gladstone'
§	'Gloria Purpurea' (× *arendsii*)	CMHG NQui
	'Gloria' (× *arendsii*)	CMHG CMac CTri ECtt LRHS
	GLOW	see *A.* 'Glut'
§	'Glut' (× *arendsii*)	CAby CMHG CWCL EBee ECtt LLWG MMuc NGdn NHol SGbt SRms WFar
	'Granat' (× *arendsii*)	CMHG CMac MAsh NBir NGdn NHol NLar
	grandis	WHer
	- BWJ 8076A	NLar
	'Grete Püngel' (× *arendsii*)	ECha GBin SRms WFar
	'Happy Day' **new**	LLWG
	'Happy Spirit'	EPfP LLWG MHol NLar
	'Harmony' (× *arendsii*)	CMHG
	'Heart and Soul'PBR	CWGN EPfP LRHS LSou WWke
	'Hennie Graafland' (*simplicifolia* hybrid)	CBcs CBod CMHG CWCL EMor NBPC NLar SHar WFar
	'Holden Clough' (*japonica* hybrid)	NHol
	HYACINTH	see *A.* 'Hyazinth'
§	'Hyazinth' (× *arendsii*)	CMHG CRos EBee GBin GMaP LRHS MACG NBir NHol NRHS
	'Icecream' (× *arendsii*)	CBod CMHG
	'Inshriach Pink' (*simplicifolia* hybrid)	CMHG GBee LRHS NBir NHol NLar NRHS SGro SRms
	'Irrlicht' (× *arendsii*)	CMHG CMac EBee EShb MHol NWad SRms WHoo WPnP WWtn
*	***japonica*** 'Catherine Gladstone'	LRHS
*	- 'Pumila'	NBir NGdn
	- var. ***terrestris***	see *A. glaberrima*
	'Jo Ophorst' (*davidii* hybrid)	NGdn NLar
	'Jump and Jive'PBR	WFar
	'Juno'	XLum
	'Koblenz' (*japonica* hybrid)	CMHG
§	'Köln' (*japonica* hybrid)	CMHG CRos CWat LRHS NRHS
	koreana	WCot
	- B&SWJ 8611	WCru
	- B&SWJ 8680	WCru
	'Kvële' (× *arendsii*)	CMHG CRos LRHS NRHS WFar
	'Lara' (× *arendsii*) **new**	CMHG
	'Lilli Goos' (× *arendsii*)	CMHG GBin
	'Little Vision in Purple'PBR	GKev
	'Lollipop'	CMHG ECtt LBar MBNS NEoE SRms
	longicarpa B&SWJ 6711	WCru
	'Look at Me'PBR (× *arendsii*)	CWGN ECtt EPfP LCro LOPS LSou MNrw NBPC SPoG
	'Lovely Day' **new**	LLWG
	'Maggie Daley' (× *arendsii*)	CBod CKel CMHG CWnw NBro NEoE SRms
	'Mainz' (*japonica* hybrid)	CMHG EBee ECtt LRHS NRHS
	'Mars' (× *arendsii*)	CMHG
	microphylla	CMHG
	- B&SWJ 11085	WCru
	'Midnight Arrow' (*davidii* hybrid)	CMHG
	(Mighty Series) 'Mighty Pip' (× *arendsii*)	CBod LBar SPeP
	- 'Mighty Plonie' **new**	LBar
	'Moerheim Glory' (× *arendsii*)	GBin NGdn NLar
	'Moerheimii' (*thunbergii* hybrid)	CMHG
	'Mont Blanc' (× *arendsii*)	CMHG
	'Montgomery' (*japonica* hybrid) ♀H7	CRos CWCL EMor EPfP GAbr GMcL LRHS LSRN LSou MAsh MBNS MBel MCot MNrw NCth NGdn NHol NLar NRHS SPoG
	'Moulin Rouge'PBR **new**	LBar
	'Nemo'	CMHG
	'New Wave'	LLWG
	'Nikki'	CMHG NEoE NLar
§	***okuyamae*** B&SWJ 10975	WCru
	'Opal' (× *arendsii*)	CMHG
	OSTRICH PLUME	see *A.* 'Straussenfeder'
	'Peaches and Cream'	EMor NBro NLar
	'Peter Barrow' (*glaberrima* hybrid)	SRms
	'Pink Lightning'PBR (*simplicifolia* hybrid)	CBod EShb LBar LLWG MBNS NLar WFar
	PINK PEARL (× *arendsii*)	see *A.* 'Rosa Perle'
	'Poschka'	NEoE
	'Professor van der Wielen' (*thunbergii* hybrid)	CMHG ECha GBin MACG NHol NLar NWad SRms WSpi
	pumila	see *A. chinensis* var. *pumila*
	'Purple Rain'PBR (× *arendsii*)	ILea
	'Queen of Holland' (*japonica* hybrid)	CMHG
	'Radius' (× *arendsii*)	CMHG EGrI ELon NGdn NLar WPnP
	'Raspberry' (Short 'n' Sweet Series)	CBod EPfP LBar
	'Red Baron'	NEoE WBor WBrk
	RED LIGHT	see *A.* 'Rotlicht'
	'Red Quin'PBR (Mighty Series)	LBar
	'Red Sentinel' (*japonica* hybrid)	CBcs CPud CWCL CWat EMor EPfP EWoo GMaP MBros MHol NBro NEoE NGdn NHol NLar NWad WFar
	'Rheinland' (*japonica* hybrid) ♀H7	CBcs CMHG CPud CWCL EMor GMcL LRHS MAsh NBPC NGdn NLar NRHS SCob SEND WPnP
	'Rhythm and Blues'PBR	ECtt NLar
	rivularis	SDix WCot
	- CC 5201	GKev
	- GWJ 9366	WCru
	- PAB 9763	LEdu
I	- 'Grandiflora'	GBin
§	- var. ***myriantha***	EBee WPGP
	- - BWJ 8076a	WCru
	- - SICH 757	CExl
	'Robinson's Pink'	NGdn
	'Rock and Roll'PBR	WBor
§	'Rosa Perle' (× *arendsii*)	CMHG NHol
§	× ***rosea*** 'Peach Blossom'	CBcs CBod CMHG EHeP EMor EWTr LLWG NBir NEoE NGdn SBls SCob SCoo SPoG SWvt WFar WHoo WWtn
	- 'Queen Alexandra'	CMHG XLum
	'Rosea' (*simplicifolia* hybrid)	NHol
§	'Rotlicht' (× *arendsii*)	CMHG CMac CRos GBin GKev LRHS NEoE NGdn NHol NLar NRHS
	'Salmonea' (*simplicifolia* hybrid)	CMHG
	'Saxosa'	see *A. glaberrima* var. *saxatilis*
	'Sheila Haxton' (*chinensis*)	CMHG EBlo
	Showstar Group (× *arendsii*)	CSBt SRms WWtn
	simplicifolia ♀H5	GArf WFar
	- BRONZE ELEGANCE	see *A.* 'Bronce Elegans'
	- 'Darwin's Snow Sprite'	CMac NHol NLar SCob WFar
	- 'Isa Hall'	CMHG NEoE NFav NWad
	- 'Jacqueline'	CMHG NHol
*	- 'Nana Alba'	NEoE
	- 'Praecox Alba'	CMHG
	- 'Rose of Cimarron'	CMHG NEoE NWad
	- 'White Sensation'PBR	ELan LRHS MACG NLar NRHS

	'Snowdrift' (× *arendsii*)	CPud CRos CWat GMaP LLWG LRHS MAsh MBNS MMuc NBir NEoE NRHS
	'Solferino' (× *arendsii*)	CMHG
	'Spartan' (× *arendsii*)	see *A.* 'Rotlicht'
	'Spinell' (× *arendsii*)	GMcL MACG WFar WPnP
	'Spotlight'PBR	GBin LBar LRHS NCth
	'Sprite' (*simplicifolia* hybrid) 𝕐H7	Widely available
§	'Straussenfeder' (*thunbergii* hybrid) 𝕐H7	CBod CMac EBlo ECtt EPfP GBin GMaP GQue LRHS MACG NBir NBro NGdn NHol NLar NRHS SPoG SRms WCAu WHlf
	'Sugar Plum' (*simplicifolia* hybrid)	NGdn
	'Sugarberry'PBR (Short 'n' Sweet Series)	NLar
	'Sunny Day' **new**	LLWG
	'Superba'	see *A. chinensis* var. *taquetii* 'Superba'
	thunbergii	LRHS NRHS
	- var. ***congesta*** B&SWJ 10961	WCru
	- var. ***formosa***	see *A. formosa*
	- var. ***hachijoensis*** B&SWJ 5622	WCru
	- var. ***okuyamae***	see *A. okuyamae*
	- var. ***sikokumontanum*** B&SWJ 11164	WCru
	- - B&SWJ 11534	WCru
	- var. ***terrestris*** B&SWJ 6125	WCru
	'Thunder and Lightning' (*chinensis* hybrid)	NEoE
	'To Have and To Hold'	MNrw
	'Venus' (× *arendsii*)	ECha ECtt GMaP MBNS MMuc NGdn NHol SEND WFar
	'Vesuvius' (*japonica* hybrid)	CBcs CKel CWnw ECtt EMor NBro NLar
	virescens	see *A. rivularis* var. *myriantha*
§	'W.E. Gladstone' (*japonica* hybrid)	EMor EWoo WHlf
	'Walküre' (× *arendsii*)	CMHG
	'Walter Bitner'	CAby GBin NHol NRHS
	'Washington' (*japonica* hybrid)	CAby EMor LRHS NGdn WPnP
§	'Weisse Gloria' (× *arendsii*)	CAby CMHG CMac ECha EMor GBin GMcL LLWG LRHS NBro NHol SCoo SEdd SGbt WCAu WFar WWtn
	'Weisse Perle' (× *arendsii*)	CMHG
	'White Diamond' (× *arendsii*)	WFar
	WHITE GLORIA	see *A.* 'Weisse Gloria'
	'White Wings'PBR (*simplicifolia* hybrid)	CMHG NLar
	'Whiteberry'PBR (Short 'n' Sweet Series)	CBod LBar LLWG MBros NLar
	'William Reeves' (× *arendsii*)	CMHG NHol NWad
	'Willie Buchanan' (*simplicifolia* hybrid)	CBcs CMHG CRos CToG GAbr GBin GKev GMaP LRHS NHol NHpl NRHS NWad SLee SRms WAbe WCFE WFar
	'Wonderful Day' **new**	LBar
	(Younique Series) YOUNIQUE CARMINE ('Verscarmine'PBR)	CWat ILea LLWG LRHS LSou
	- YOUNIQUE CERISE ('Verscerise'PBR)	CWat ILea LRHS
	- YOUNIQUE LILAC ('Verslilac'PBR)	EGrI ILea LRHS
	- YOUNIQUE PINK ('Verspink'PBR)	CWat LRHS
	- YOUNIQUE RASPBERRY ('Versraspberry')	LRHS
§	- YOUNIQUE RED ('Versred'PBR)	ILea LRHS
	- YOUNIQUE RUBY RED	see *A.* (Younique Series) YOUNIQUE RED
	- YOUNIQUE SALMON ('Verssalmon'PBR)	ILea LBar LRHS
	- YOUNIQUE SILVERY PINK ('Versilverypink'PBR)	EWTr LRHS WFar
	- YOUNIQUE WHITE ('Verswhite'PBR)	ILea LRHS
	'Zuster Theresa' (× *arendsii*)	CMHG LRHS MBNS MNrw NLar NRHS

Astilboides (*Saxifragaceae*)

§	***tabularis***	Widely available

Astragalus (*Fabaceae*)

	canadensis	LRHS NRHS
	glycyphyllos	GJos NAts SPhx WCot
	macrocarpus	SPhx
	sinicus	GJos

Astrantia ✿ (*Apiaceae*)

	'Atomic Sunburst'	GQue
	bavarica	GKev WFar
	'Berendien Stam'	CElw MNrw NLar WFar
	'Bloody Mary'	EBee GAbr GLet LEdu MAvo MNrw NGdn NLar
	'Bright and Breezy'	MAvo
	'Buckland' 𝕐H7	Widely available
	'Bullseye' **new**	MNrw
	'Burgundy Manor'	CBod CWCL ELon EMor GLet LBar MAvo MHol NLar SHar SHor
	'Bury Court'	NDov
	carniolica major	see *A. major*
	- 'Rubra'	CBcs GMaP WSpi
	- 'Variegata'	see *A. major* 'Sunningdale Variegated'
	'Censation Milano'	CWGN EMor LRHS NLar WFar
	'Dark Shiny Eyes'	CExl ECtt EMor GLet LPal MAvo NLar NSti SWvt
	'Good Pink'	MAvo
	'Hadspen Blood'	Widely available
	'Harvington Adrian's Choice Pink'	NRHS
	'Harvington Selected Red'	NRHS
	'Helen'	NLar WFar
	helleborifolia	see *A. maxima*
	'Keisby' (v) **new**	MNrw
	'Larch Cottage Clear Pink'	NLar WFar
	'Larch Cottage Magic'	MAvo WFar
	'Madeleine'	see *A. major* 'Madeleine van Bennekom'
§	***major***	Widely available
	- 'Abbey Road'PBR	CEme CExl ECtt EMor EPfP EWoo LBar LRHS LSou MAsh MBel MHol MPnt MidI NLar NRHS SRms
I	- 'Alba'	CBcs EMor GKev GLet LPal LRHS MRav NBir NGdn NPer SCob SPer WFar WPnP WSpi
	- 'April Love'	GLet IPot LBar NCth
	- 'Berdien'	EBee EMor
	- subsp. ***biebersteinii***	NBir WFar
	- 'Bo-Ann'	CWCL NLar WFar
	- 'Can Candy'	GLet MAvo MNrw
	- 'Capri' **new**	GLet
	- 'Celtic Star'	SWvt
	- 'Claret'	Widely available
	- 'Côte d'Azur'	WSpi
	- 'Cottage Herbery'	MNrw WFar

- 'Dark Desire'	GLet NDov WGoo
- 'Elaine's Pink'	WHoo
- 'Elmblut'	MAvo WFar
- 'Florence' PBR	CAvo CBWd CBod CBor CKno CRos CWCL CWGN EBee ECha ECtt EMor EPfP GLet LBar LRHS MHol MNrw MPri MIdl NCth NDov NLar NRHS SOrN SPeP SPoG SWvt WFar WSpi
- Gill Richardson Group	Widely available
- 'Gracilis'	EBee EPfP MNrw WFar
- 'Green Tapestry' (v)	WCot
- 'Gwaun Valley'	WFar
- subsp. ***involucrata***	CElw WGoo
- - 'Barrister'	NLar
- - 'Canneman'	MNrw NLar SMHy WCot
- - 'Jumble Hole'	IPot MAvo NDov WFar WGoo WHoo
- - 'Margery Fish'	see *A. major* subsp. *involucrata* 'Shaggy'
- - 'Moira Reid'	CExl ECtt GLet GMaP MAvo MRav WGoo
- - 'Orlando'	MNrw WFar
§ - - 'Shaggy'	Widely available
- - 'Snape Cottage'	MAvo WFar
- 'Jade Lady'	WFar
- 'Jitse'	WFar
- 'Large White'	LCro LOPS SRms
- 'Lars'	EMor EWTr GMcL LRHS MNrw NGdn NLar SPer SPoG SRms SWvt WCAu WFar
- 'Little Snowstar'	CWCL
- 'Lola'	CDor EBee GLet NLar
§ - 'Madeleine van Bennekom'	ECtt GLet WFar
- 'Midnight Owl'	ECtt EMor MNrw NBPC NSti WFar
- 'Penny's Pink'	EBee EWhm EWoo LCro LOPS LRHS MNrw MIdl NCth WFar WHlf WSpi
- 'Pink Crush'	CRos EBlo EPfP LRHS NRHS
- 'Pink Joyce' **new**	LBar LLWG MNrw
- 'Pink Pride'	GLet GMcL MIdl SHar WCAu WFar
- 'Pink Sensation'	EBee GLet GMcL LBar NCth
- 'Pink Surprise'	GMcL MNrw NLar WFar
- 'Pisa' **new**	GLet
- 'Primadonna'	CRos EBee EBlo EBou EMor EPfP EPri GMaP LRHS NLar NRHS SBls SPlb SRms WHlf
- 'Princesse Sturdza'	WFar
- 'Purple Joyce' **new**	LLWG MNrw
- 'Red Joyce'	EBee LBar MNrw NCth NLar WCAu
- 'Reverse Sunningdale Variegated' (v)	WFar
- 'Rosa Lee'	CElw NLar WGoo
- var. ***rosea***	CRos CWCL EMor EPfP GLet LRHS MRav NGdn NRHS WCAu WFar XLum
- - George's form	EPPr NCth WFar
- 'Rosensinfonie'	EBee EHed GJos GMaP NBro SBls WPnP
§ - 'Rubra'	CRos CWCL EMor EPfP GKev GKin GMcL LCro LOPS LRHS MGos NBir NChi NPer NRHS SRms WBor WCAu
- 'Ruby Cloud'	ECtt EHed EMor EPfP EPri GLet LSou NBro NGdn NLar NRHS SPad WFar WSpi
- 'Ruby Giant'	EBee GKin LBar SMad
- 'Ruby Wedding'	Widely available
- 'Silver Glow'	EBee ECtt
- Sparkling Stars Series	CWCL MBros
- - 'Sparkling Stars Pink'	CBod GLet LBar MHol MNrw NBPC NCth
- - SPARKLING STARS RED ('Westarr')	GLet LBar NCth
- - SPARKLING STARS WHITE ('Westarwit') **new**	GLet LBar
- 'Star of Beauty' PBR (Sparkling Stars Series)	CKno CRos CWCL ECtt ELan EMor EPfP GLet LBar LEdu LRHS MNrw MPri NDov NLar NRHS NSti SCob SCoo SGBe SPoG SRkn SRms SWvt WFar WSpi
- 'Star of Billion' PBR	EBee ECtt ELan EMor EPfP GElm GLet LRHS LSun MBros MHol MNrw MIdl NBPC NLar NRHS SCob SCoo SEdd SOrN SPoG SWvt WCAu WCot WFar
- 'Star of Fire' PBR	CWGN ECtt GLet LRHS MAsh MBros MNrw NBPC NLar SCob SEdd WFar
- 'Star of Love'	CKno EMor EPfP GLet LBar LRHS LSou MHol NDov SCoo SOrN SPoG WSpi
- 'Star of Magic' PBR (v)	GLet MNrw NCth SPoG WCAu WCot
- 'Star of Royals' PBR	CWCL ECtt EShb GLet LBar LRHS MIdl NCth NRHS SPoG WFar
- 'Star of Summer'	EBee
- 'Starburst'	MNrw WFar
- 'Stardust'	GLet
- 'Sue Barnes' (v)	MNrw NLar WFar
§ - 'Sunningdale Variegated' (v) ♀H7	Widely available
- 'Titoki Point'	WCot
- 'Venice' PBR	Widely available
§ ***maxima*** ♀H7	Widely available
- 'Mark Fenwick'	MNrw NBir
I - 'Rosea'	CDor ECtt MNrw NBir NGdn
'Millwood Crimson'	CMiW
minor	EMor LRHS
'Moulin Rouge' PBR	Widely available
§ 'Mrs MacGregor'	MAvo MNrw MPie WFar
'Old Warwickshire Pink'	see *A.* 'Mrs MacGregor'
'Orion'	EMor
'Queen's Children'	CDor
'Rainbow'	NLar WFar
'Roma' PBR ♀H7	Widely available
rubra	see *A. major* 'Rubra'
'Ruby Star' PBR	Widely available
'Sheila's Red'	MNrw
'Snow Star' PBR	CRos CWCL EBee ELan EMor EPfP EWoo GLet LBar LRHS MACG MBNS MMrt MNrw NLar NRHS
'Star of Flame' **new**	LBar
'Star of Heaven'	NLar
'Star of Passion' PBR	EBee ECtt ELan EPfP GLet LBar LRHS NRHS SCob
'Star of Treasure' PBR	EBee ELan EMor EPfP GLet LRHS NLar NRHS
'Superstar' PBR	CAvo CDor CWCL EBee ECtt ELan ELon EPfP EWTr GLet LBar LRHS MAvo MBel MHol MNrw MRav NBPC NDov NLar NSti SCoo SEdd SMad SWvt WCot WFar WHlf WSpi WTor
'Warren Hills'	EBee GMaP MNrw MPie NLar WFar
'Washfield'	EGrI LBar NCth NDov NLar WFar
'White Angel'	CKno CWGN LBar NCth

Astrodaucus (*Apiaceae*)

littoralis	SPhx WPGP

Astrolepis (*Pteridaceae*)

sinuata	SPlb WCot

Astrophytum (*Cactaceae*)

capricorne ♀H2 **new**	EAri
- var. ***aureum*** **new**	NMen

- 'Crassispinoides' **new**	NMen
myriostigma 🏆H2	EAri SPad
- subsp. ***quadricostatum*** **new**	NMen
myriostigma × ***ornatum*** **new**	NMen
ornatum 🏆H2 **new**	EAri
- var. ***mirbelii*** **new**	NMen

Asyneuma (*Campanulaceae*)

campanuloides	GKev SGro
§ ***prenanthoides***	SMrm
pulvinatum	EPot SPlb WAbe

Asystasia (*Acanthaceae*)

bella	see *Mackaya bella*

Athamanta (*Apiaceae*)

cretensis	SPhx SPtp
macedonica	SPhx
turbith	CSpe
- subsp. ***haynaldii***	CMiW MACG SPhx
vestina	LRHS SPhx

Athanasia (*Asteraceae*)

§ ***parviflora***	SPlb

Athrotaxis (*Cupressaceae*)

cupressoides	CBcs LRHS
laxifolia	SMad
selaginoides	CAco WJur

Athyrium ✿ (*Woodsiaceae*)

auriculatum	CBdn
'Branford Beauty'	CLAP CRos EMor ISha LEdu LPal LRHS NRHS
'Branford Rambler'	CLAP EBee EMor ISha LEdu NBro
filix-femina	Widely available
§ - subsp. ***angustum*** 🏆H6	EMor LRHS MRav NGdn NRHS
- - f. ***rubellum*** 'Lady in Red' 🏆H6	Widely available
- 'Clarissimum Jones'	WCot WFib
- 'Crispum Grandiceps Kaye'	NGdn
- Cristatum Group	CLAP EFer ELan LSRN NGdn SMHy WCot WFib
- 'Dre's Dagger'	CBod CLAP CMiW EMor LCro LEdu NBro NFav SPoG WPGP
- 'Fieldii'	CLAP EFer
- 'Frizelliae' 🏆H6	Widely available
- 'Frizelliae Capitatum'	CLAP WFib
- 'Frizelliae Cristatum'	CLAP
- 'Howardii'	NBro
- 'Lady-in-Lace' 🏆H6	EBee
- 'Minutissimum'	EBee ELan EMor LRHS NRHS WCot
- Plumosum Group	MRav WFib XLum
- 'Plumosum Axminster'	CLAP EFer WCot WFar
- 'Plumosum Cristatum Drueryi'	WCot
- 'Plumosum Percristatum'	WCot
- RED STEM	see *A. filix-femina* 'Rotstiel'
§ - 'Rotstiel'	CLAP LPal NBro NLar WCot
- 'Setigerum Cristatum'	WFar
- 'Vernoniae' 🏆H6	CLAP MRav
- 'Vernoniae Cristatum'	CLAP WFib
- 'Victoriae'	CAby CDor CRos CWCL EBee ECtt EFer ELan EMor EPfP GMaP LEdu LLWG LRHS MHtn NBid NLar NRHS SPad WFar WPGP WSpi XLum
- aff. 'Victoriae'	CBod CLAP CSta ISha MACG MAsh WFar
- Victoriae Group	see *A. filix-femina* subsp. *angustum*
'Ghost' 🏆H5	CLAP CRos EBee EHed EMor ESwi LEdu LRHS MAsh MAvo MGos NBro NLar NRHS NSti SPlb SPoG WCot
goeringianum 'Pictum'	see *A. niponicum* var. *pictum*
minimum	CLAP EMor LEdu NBro NLar WCot WPGP
niponicum	CLAP CPud
- 'Godzilla'	CLAP EBee EHed LEdu NBro WPGP
- f. ***metallicum***	see *A. niponicum* var. *pictum*
§ - var. ***pictum*** 🏆H5	Widely available
- - 'Apple Court'	CBdn CLAP CRos EBee EHed EMor ESwi ISha LEdu LRHS MAsh NBro NRHS WPGP
- - 'Burgundy Lace'	CAby CLAP CMiW EBee ECtt EGrI EHed EMor ESwi LPal LSun MPnt NBro NLar SEdd WCot
* - - 'Cristatoflabellatum'	EBlo
- - 'Pearly White'	CLAP ISha LEdu MAsh NBro
- - 'Pewter Lace'	CLAP CMiW EBee ECtt EMor ISha LEdu MACG MCot NBro NLar SMad SPad SPeP WHlf WSpi
- - 'Red Beauty'	Widely available
- - 'Regal Red'	CLAP EBee ISha LRHS MAsh NRHS
- - 'Silver Falls' 🏆H5	CBcs CLAP CRos CSde EBee EMor EShb ESwi ISha LEdu LRHS LSun MAsh NBro NLar NRHS SCoo SMrm SPoG WCot WHlf
- - 'Ursula's Red'	CBod CLAP CMiW CSta EBee EGrI ELan ELon EMor EShb LCro LLWG LOPS LPal LRHS LSun MHol NBPC NBid NHpl NLar SCob SMad SPoG WCAu WCot WFar WHlf WPGP
'Ocean's Fury'	CLAP EBee ECtt EMor EShb ESwi LPla SPoG WCot
otophorum 🏆H4	MRav NBid WPGP
- var. ***okanum*** 🏆H4	Widely available
vidalii	CBdn CBod CLAP CRos EGrI EHed EMor GKev LEdu LRHS NBro NLar NRHS SCob WFar WFib XLum

Atragene see *Clematis*

Atriplex (*Amaranthaceae*)

canescens	CAgr EPPr
halimus	CAgr CBcs CCoa CLau CWal CWnw EBee ECha EPPr NLar SPer SPlb WCot XSen
- 'Cascais'	WCot
- 'Limelight' (v)	ECha EPPr
hortensis	ENfk
- var. ***rubra***	CKel CSpe ELan MNHC SMrm SRms
portulacoides	see *Halimione portulacoides*

Atropa (*Solanaceae*)

belladonna	GPoy SEND
mandragora	see *Mandragora officinarum*

aubergine see AGM Vegetables Section

Aubrieta (*Brassicaceae*)

'Agnetta'	ECtt
'Alba'	see *A.* 'Fiona'
albomarginata	see *A.* 'Argenteovariegata'
§ 'Argenteovariegata' (v) 🏆H6	CRos EPfP LRHS NRHS
(Audrey Series) 'Audrey Blue'	GDam
- 'Audrey Light Blue'	LCro
- 'Audrey Purple Shades' **new**	LCro
- 'Audrey Red'	LCro
- 'Audrey Sky Blue' **new**	LCro

§	'Aureovariegata' (v) 🏆H6	NPer XLum
	(Axcent Series) AXCENT BURGUNDY	EPfP LCro LRHS
	- AXCENT DARK RED ('Audeldare')	WIce
	- AXCENT DEEP PURPLE ('Audelpur'PBR)	LCro
	- AXCENT DEEP RED ('Abrz0001'PBR)	SRms
	- AXCENT LIGHT BLUE ('Abrz0002'PBR)	CRos EPfP LCro LRHS NRHS
	- AXCENT LILAC ('Audelip'PBR)	CRos EPfP LCro LRHS NRHS SCoo SPoG
	BLAUE SCHÖNHEIT	see *A.* 'Blue Beauty'
	'Blaumeise'	EBou MHol XSen
§	'Blue Beauty'	CBod EBou ECtt EPfP GBin GMaP NHpl NLar
	'Blue Emperor'	ECtt
	'Blue Whale'	ECtt GAbr LBuc NLar NSla SRms SWvt
§	'Bob Saunders' (d)	ECtt
	'Boundary Haze'	EBou
	'Boundary Purple'	EBou
	'Bressingham Pink' (d) 🏆H6	ECtt SRms
	'Bressingham Red'	ECtt EPfP GMaP GRum SRms
	Cascade Series	MAsh SPoG
	- 'Blue Cascade'	CTri EGrI EPfP GMaP SPlb SPoG SRms
	- 'Lilac Cascade'	SPoG SRms
	- 'Purple Cascade'	CTri LCro LOPS LSRN SPlb SPoG SRms
	- 'Red Cascade' 🏆H6	CTri EBou ECtt EGrI ELan EPfP LSRN SPlb SPoG
	× ***cultorum***	CKel LSun SVic XSen
	deltoidea Variegata Group (v)	CBod MAsh MHol WFar
	- - 'Nana Variegata' (v)	GRum
	'Doctor Mules' 🏆H6	ECtt SRms WCav
	'Doctor Mules Variegata' (v)	ECtt ELan EPfP GDam GMaP LRHS MHer NLar SCoo SPoG SRot SWvt WIce
	double pink-flowered (d)	CBod ELan GMaP MBros MHol
	'Elsa Lancaster'	EPot NHpl
§	'Fiona'	EWes
	'Florado Rose Red'	EPfP LRHS
	glabrescens	EPot NHpl WAbe
	'Gloria'	CBod ECtt NHpl NLar WIce
	'Golden King'	see *A.* 'Aureovariegata'
	gracilis 'Kitte'	EBou ECtt ELan EPfP MHer NLar SPoG SRms
	- 'Kitte Blue'	CBod CRos ELan EPfP LBuc LRHS MPri NRHS SPoG SRms WIce
	- 'Kitte Blue Blush Bicolour'	ELan
	- 'Kitte Purple'	ELan EPfP SPoG
	- 'Kitte Red Shades' **new**	CBod
	- 'Kitte Rose'	CRos EPfP LBuc LRHS NRHS SCoo SPoG
	- 'Kitte Rose Blush Bicolour'	ELan
	- 'Kitte Rose Red'	ELan
	- 'Kitte White'	CRos EPfP LRHS MHer NRHS
	'Greencourt Purple' 🏆H6	ECtt MHer
	'Hamburger Stadtpark'	CWCL ECtt ELan EPfP GMaP SRms XLum
	'Hemswell Purity'	see *A.* 'Snow Maiden'
	'Hürth'	GBin
	'Ida'	ECtt WIce
	JUST SPRING BLUE ('Yataub43') **new**	LSou
	JUST SPRING RED ('Yataub17') **new**	LSou
	'Kati'	GMaP MACG
	'Lime Variegated' (v)	NHpl WCav
	pinardii	GKev
	'Pixie Pearls'	LRHS NSla
	'Purple Charm'	SRms
	'Red Carpet'	MAsh MHer SRms
	'Rose Queen'	ECtt
	Royal Series 🏆H6	LCro
	- 'Royal Blue'	CKel CTri ELan EPfP EPot MBros NLar SRms WFar
	- 'Royal Lilac'	CTri WFar
	- 'Royal Red'	CTri ELan EPfP GBin SRms WCav
	- 'Royal Violet'	ELan EPfP WFar
	'Schofield's Double'	see *A.* 'Bob Saunders'
	'Silberrand' (v)	ECha LBuc
§	'Snow Maiden'PBR	NHpl SCoo SPoG
	'Somerfield Silver'	ELan EPfP
	'Somerford Lime' (v)	ELan SRms WIce
	'Swan Red' (v)	EBou ECtt NHpl NSla WTor
	'Valerie' (v)	EWes GRum
	'Westacre Gold' (v)	CBod ECtt EWes MDon MHol
	'Whitewell Gem'	CWal

Aucuba ✿ (*Garryaceae*)

	chlorascens B&SWJ 11815	WCru
	himalaica	CDTJ GBin SBrt
	var. ***dolichophylla***	
	- - Og 95038	WCru
	japonica	CCVT CDoC CEme EHeP GMcL LPar MDon NBwr NLar SEWo WCru WFar
	- B&SWJ 14602	WCru
	- var. ***borealis*** (f) CWJ 12898	WCru
	- 'Clent Wortley Hall' (m)	WCFE
	- 'Crassifolia' (m)	EPfP SArc
	- 'Crotonifolia' (f/v) 🏆H5	Widely available
	- 'Crotonifolia' (m/v)	CMac MAsh SDix SGsty SRms
	- 'Dentata' (f)	SRms WAvo WCru WHtc
	- 'February Star' (f/v)	ESwi SDix
	- 'Golden Girl' (v)	CBod CBrac CEnd LRHS MAsh NRHS WHtc
	- 'Golden King' (m/v) 🏆H5	CAco CBod CDoC CEme CKel CMac CSBt CWnw EBee ELan ELon EPfP LRHS LSto MAsh MGos NLar NRHS SCob SGsty SLim SMad WFar
	- 'Golden Spangles' (f/v)	CBcs CKel EMil EPfP LRHS SWvt
	- 'Leucocarpa' (f)	SPer
	- f. ***longifolia***	CMac EHeP EPfP SArc SDix WCru
	- - 'Salicifolia' (f) 🏆H5	CEme EBee EHeP ESwi MRav WCru WFar WHtc WPGP
	- 'Maculata' misapplied	see *A. japonica* 'Variegata'
	- 'Marmorata' (v)	CBod CGBo LRHS MAsh NRHS
	- 'Mr Goldstrike' (m/v)	CBod CEnd CGBo CKel CRos EPfP LRHS MAsh SCoo SGBe SGbt WFar
	- 'Nana Rotundifolia' (f)	WHtc
	- PEPPER POT ('Shilpot') (m/v) 🏆H5	CRos EPfP LRHS MAsh WCFE
	- 'Picturata' (m/v)	CBod CEme CMac ELan ELon ESwi LCro MAsh NBwr NLar SEND SMad WFar
	- 'Rozannie' (f) 🏆H5	Widely available
	- 'Sulphurea Marginata' (f/v)	CBod CKel CMCN CMac CTri ESwi LRHS NLar NRHS SPer WFar
§	- 'Variegata' (f/v)	CBrac CCVT CChe CEme CMac CRos CSBt CTri EBee EHeP ELan ELon EPfP LBuc LRHS MAsh MGos NHol NRHS NWea SCob SGbt SLim SPer SRms SSha SWeb WAvo WHtc
	- 'Variegata' white-flowered (m/v)	SGbt
	omeiensis	CBcs CDTJ CExl CMCN IDee
	- B&SWJ 2864	ESwi WCru
	- BWJ 8048	WCru
	- L 614	WPGP
	robusta B&SWJ 11826 **new**	WCru

Aulax (*Proteaceae*)

cancellata	CCCN SPlb

Aurinia (*Brassicaceae*)

§ ***saxatilis*** ♀H5	ELan EPfP MMuc SLee SPlb WFar XSen
- 'Citrina' ♀H5	ECha EGrI SRms
- 'Compacta'	GJos WIce
- 'Dudley Nevill'	WFar
- 'Dudley Nevill Variegated' (v)	ECha EWes
- GOLD BALL	see *A. saxatilis* 'Goldkugel'
- 'Gold Cushion'	LRHS
- 'Gold Dust'	GJos SRms
§ - 'Goldkugel'	CBod GJos NBwr NFav SPoG SRms WFar
- 'Variegata' (v)	SPoG SRms WHoo

Austrocedrus (*Cupressaceae*)

§ ***chilensis***	CAco CKen SLim

Austrocylindropuntia (*Cactaceae*)

subulata **new**	EAri SEND
§ ***verschaffeltii*** **new**	NPlm
vestita 'Cristata' **new**	EAri

Avena (*Poaceae*)

candida	see *Helictotrichon sempervirens*

Avenula see *Helictotrichon*

Averrhoa (*Oxalidaceae*)

carambola (F)	CCCN SVic

avocado see *Persea americana*

Azalea see *Rhododendron*

Azara ✿ (*Salicaceae*)

dentata	CBcs CMac CTrC WFar WPav
- 'Variegata'	see *A. integrifolia* 'Variegata'
integrifolia	CCCN IDee MGil WPav
- 'Uarie'	CCCN
§ - 'Variegata' (v)	CCCN CKel
lanceolata	CBcs CTri CTsd NSti SPer SSha WPav
microphylla ♀H4	CBcs CCCN CDoC CEme CKel CMac CTri EBee ELan ELon EPfP LRHS LSRN MAsh MGil MHtn MMuc NQui SArc SEND SPer SPlb SRHi SSha WFar WPGP WPav WSpi
* - 'Albovariegata' (v)	CTri WPav
- 'Gold Edge' (v)	CEme WFar WPav
- 'Variegata' (v)	CBcs CKel CMac EBee ELan EPfP GMcL LRHS LSto MAsh MGil NFav NLar SEND SPer SPoG SSha WAvo WFar WPav
* ***patagonica***	MBlu WPav
petiolaris	CTri MGil WPav
serrata ♀H4	CBcs CBrac CCCN CEnd CKel CMCN CTsd ELan EPfP GBin LRHS LSto MGil MHtn MMuc NLar SDix SEND SPer SPoG SRms SSha SVen WBor WFar WKif WPav WSpi
- 'Maurice Mason'	EBee
uruguayensis	CCCN CTsd GBin IDee SEND WPav

Azorella (*Apiaceae*)

filamentosa	GEdr WAbe
glebaria misapplied	see *A. trifurcata*
glebaria A. Gray	see *Bolax gummifer*
gummifer	see *Bolax gummifer*
lycopodioides	SPlb WAbe
patagonica	SPlb
§ ***trifurcata***	CPar CSpe CTri EDAr GAbr GKev MMuc NBir NBwr NFav SPlb WAbe
- 'Nana'	CBor GArf GEdr GMaP XLum

Azorina (*Campanulaceae*)

§ ***vidalii***	EShb SPlb WFar

B

Babiana (*Iridaceae*)

angustifolia	NRog
disticha	see *B. fragrans*
§ ***fragrans***	CPbh NRog
nana	MBros
- 'Claudia'	GKev
- subsp. ***maculata***	NRog
- 'Tender of Heart' **new**	GKev
- 'The Bride'	GKev
- white-flowered **new**	GKev
odorata	CPla NRog
patersoniae	NRog SPlb
plicata	see *B. fragrans*
pygmaea	NRog
rubrocyanea	CPla
sambucina	NRog
stricta ♀H2	CCCN GKev NRog SDeJ
- Kew hybrids	GKev NRog
- 'Purple Star'	CBor CExl NRog
thunbergii	CPbh
tubulosa	NRog
vanzyliae	NRog
villosa	NRog
villosula	NRog
'Zwanenburg's Glory'	CPrp

Baccharis (*Asteraceae*)

genistelloides	CKel CWnw MPkF XSte
patagonica	EHyd MMuc SArc SVen

Backhousia (*Myrtaceae*)

citriodora	GPoy MHer

Bacopa (*Plantaginaceae*)

'Snowflake'	see *Chaenostoma cordatum* 'Snowflake'

Baeckea (*Myrtaceae*)

gunniana	CExl
linifolia	SPlb
virgata	SPlb

Baeometra (*Colchicaceae*)

uniflora	CPla

Balbisia (*Ledocarpaceae*)

peduncularis	CCCN

Baldellia (*Alismataceae*)

ranunculoides	CPud EWat LPfP WMAq
- f. ***repens***	LLWG

Ballota (*Lamiaceae*)

acetabulosa	ECha EWes WCot WHtc XSen
'All Hallow's Green'	see *Marrubium bourgaei* var. *bourgaei* 'All Hallows Green'
hirsuta	XSen

nigra	GPoy MHoo NMir SRms
§ – 'Archer's Variegated' (v)	LDai
– 'Variegata'	see *B. nigra* 'Archer's Variegated'
pseudodictamnus 𝕐H4	CBcs CBod CCBP CKel CMac CTtf CWal EBee ECha EHyd ELan EPfP EWld EWoo GMaP IDee LRHS LSRN MPie MRav NPer SCob SDix SEND SMrm SPer WGwG WSHC XLum XSen
– B&M 8119	WCot WPGP
– from Crete	ECha
– 'Candia'	LShi SHar
– compact	MAvo SPer XSen
rupestris 'Frogswell Carolyn' (v)	XSen

Baloskion (*Restionaceae*)

§ ***tetraphyllum*** 𝕐H3	CPbh LRHS SPlb SPoG XSte
§ – 'Cornish Gold' (v)	CPbh

Balsamita see *Tanacetum*

Balsamorhiza (*Asteraceae*)

rosea	GEdr

Bambusa (*Poaceae*)

pubescens	see *Dendrocalamus strictus*

banana see *Ensete*, *Musa*

Banksia ✿ (*Proteaceae*)

ashbyi	CPbh
benthamiana new	CCCN
blechnifolia	CPbh
caleyi	CPbh
canei	SPlb
ericifolia	CPbh
– var. ***ericifolia***	CCCN CTsd
– var. ***macrantha***	SPlb
formosa	CPbh SPlb
'Giant Candles'	CPbh CTrC LRHS XSte
grandis	CCCN CPbh
§ ***heliantha***	SPlb
integrifolia	CBcs CCCN CDTJ CPbh CTrC CTsd IArd IDee LRHS SPlb XSte
marginata	CTrC CTsd SPlb
media	CPbh SPlb
meisneri new	CCCN
menziesii	CPbh CTsd
– shrubby	CCCN
oblongifolia	SPlb
occidentalis	CTsd
paludosa	CTrC SPlb
praemorsa	CCCN CPbh CTsd XSte
– yellow-flowered	CCCN CTsd
prionotes	CCCN
pulchella new	CCCN
repens new	CPbh
robur	CCCN SPlb
sceptrum new	CCCN
serrata	CCCN SPlb XSte
solandri new	CCCN
speciosa	SPlb
spinulosa	CPbh CTrC LRHS
– 'Birthday Candles'	CPbh
– var. ***collina***	SPlb
– var. ***spinulosa***	CCCN
violacea	SPlb

Baptisia (*Fabaceae*)

§ ***alba***	EMor EWTr LPla MBel MNrw NSti SBls SCob SPhx WHil
– var. ***alba***	WCAu
§ – var. ***macrophylla***	CBor EHyd EWes LRHS NRHS SPhx
australis 𝕐H7	Widely available
– 'Blueberry Sundae'	CSpe CWGN EBee EMor EWTr ILea IPot LBar LEdu MSCN NCth NDov SMrm WHil
– 'Caspian Blue'	CExl ECha IPot LEdu SBls
– 'Exaltata' 𝕐H7	EBee ECtt GElm LPla LSun MBNS MSCN NBPC NLar WCot
– var. ***minor***	CSpe EMor MMrt SPhx
– 'Nelson's Navy'	SMHy
× ***bicolor*** 'Starlite' (Prairieblues Series)	MNrw SMHy
'Blue Towers' new	NCth
'Brownie Points' new	WHil
'Carolina Moonlight'	CBcs EBee ECtt EWes GBin LRHS MNrw NSti SCob SHar XLum
'Cherries Jubilee'	CWGN EBee EMor GKev ILea LCro LOPS LRHS MSCN WCot WHil WHlf
'Chocolate Chip'	MCot NCth SHar
'Dutch Chocolate' (Decadence Series)	CBcs CWGN EBee ECtt ELan EMor EWes ILea IPot LBar LCro LEdu LOPS MACG MNHC MNrw NDov NSti SHar SPad SPoG WCot WPGP WTyc
'Grape Taffy'	EWTr LCro LOPS MSCN WHil
'Indigo Spires'	EBee ILea MBel
lactea	see *B. alba* var. *macrophylla*
'Lavender Stardust' new	LBar
'Lemon Meringue'	CBod CWGN EBee ECha ELan EMor EWTr LBar LCro LEdu LOPS MNrw NCth NDov SMrm SPoG WCot WHlf WMal
leucantha	see *B. alba* var. *macrophylla*
'Nachthemel' new	SMHy
pendula	see *B. alba*
'Pink Lemonade'	EMor EWTr LBar LCro LOPS SMad WHil WHlf
'Pink Truffles' (Decadence Series)	EBee EMor IPot LCro LOPS NSti SHar WCot WHil WHlf
'Purple Smoke'	CBcs CExl CSpe EBee ECtt GKev LCro LEdu LOPS LRHS MAvo MBel MNrw SMHy SPhx WHlf WPGP WSHC XSte
'Solar Flare' (Prairieblues Series)	ILea LBar MBel NCth SHar
'Sparkling Sapphires' (Decadence Series)	IPot WHil
sphaerocarpa	LPla SPlb
'Vanilla Cream'	EMor IPot LBar LCro LEdu LOPS LRHS NDov NSti SHar WCot WHlf
× ***variicolor*** 'Twilite' (Prairieblues Series)	CPla EBee GMaP ILea LBar LRHS MNrw SCob WCAu WMal WTyc

Barbarea (*Brassicaceae*)

praecox	see *B. verna*
rupicola 'Sunnyola'	CBor NBwr
§ ***verna***	CBod GPoy MHer SRms SVic
vulgaris	CBod
– 'Variegata' (v)	CBod CCBP LDai NBro
– 'Variegated Winter Cream' (v)	EPfP

Barleria (*Acanthaceae*)

obtusa	EShb
oenotheroides	CCCN
suberecta	see *Dicliptera sericea*

Barnardia (*Asparagaceae*)

japonica white-flowered	NRog

Barosma see *Agathosma*

Bartlettina (*Asteraceae*)

§	***sordida***	CCCN

Basella (*Basellaceae*)

	rubra	CLau SPre SVic

Bashania (*Poaceae*)

§	***fargesii***	MMuc MRav MWht SEND
I	***qingchengshanensis***	MWht

basil see *Ocimum basilicum*

Bauhinia (*Fabaceae*)

	alba hort.	see *B. variegata*
*	***lutea***	CCCN
	natalensis	SPlb
	purpurea L.	CCCN SPlb
	tomentosa	CCCN
§	***variegata***	CAco
	'White Lady'	CCCN
	yunnanensis	EAri SBrt SPlb

Baumea see *Machaerina*

bay see *Laurus nobilis*

beans see AGM Vegetables Section

Beaucarnea (*Asparagaceae*)

	recurvata ♀H1c	CDoC LCro LOPS LPal NCft NHrt SPad SPlb

Beaufortia (*Myrtaceae*)

	sparsa	CTrC
	squarrosa	SPlb

Bedfordia (*Asteraceae*)

	linearis	SPlb

Beesia (*Ranunculaceae*)

§	***calthifolia***	CBct CDTJ CDor EBee EPfP ESwi EWes EWld GEdr LEdu SChF SMad WCot WCru WPGP WSHC
	- DJHC 98447	CExl
	deltophylla misapplied	see *B. calthifolia*

beetroot see AGM Vegetables Section

Begonia ✿ (*Begoniaceae*)

	from China, sp. 168 **new**	GGro
	from Sikkim, India	GGro
	from Siam	GGro
	from Taiwan	GGro
	'Abel Carrière' (R)	WDib
	aconitifolia (C)	EShb
	albopicta 'Rosea' (C)	EShb WDib WFar
	AMOUR ('Yamour') (Million Kisses Series)	MBros
	'Angela Jane' (T)	WFib
	aff. ***angularis***	SPlb
§	***annulata*** ♀H1b	LEdu
	- HWJK 2424	ESwi GGro WCru WFar
	- 'Karma Khonoma'	WPGP
	'Apricot Delight' (Fragrant Falls Improved Series) (T)	WFib
	'Apricot Nectar' (Fragrant Falls Improved Series) (T)	NRHS
	'Apricot Shades'	WHlf
I	'Apricot Shades Improved'	SDeJ
	'Argenteo-guttata'	EShb
	'Aya' (C)	WDib
	balansana	CBct
	baviensis BWJ 15651 **new**	WCru
	'Beatrice Haddrell'	CBct WFar
	'Benitochiba' (R) ♀H1b	CAbb CBcs CBct CDTJ CExl CSpe ECtt ESwi GGro SPoG WCot WDib
	'Beryl Rhodes' (T)	WFib
	'Bethlehem Star'	NWad WDib
	'Betulia Double Red' (d) **new**	LAma
	'Billy Langdon' (T)	WFib
	'Black Fang' ♀H1b	WDib
	'Black Knight' (R)	WDib
	'Blackberry Swirl' (R)	WDib
	'Blazing Star' (T)	LCro LOPS
	'Blue Sky Appleblossom'	MBros
	'Blushing Star' (T)	LCro LOPS
	'Bokit' × ***imperialis***	WDib
	boliviensis (T)	ESwi
	- 'Firecracker'	WDib
	BONFIRE ('Nzcone'PBR) ♀H1b	SPoG
	'Bouton de Rose' (T)	LAma SDeJ
	'Buffey'PBR (T)	MPri
	burkillii	GGro
	'Buttermilk' (T)	WFib
	'Can-can' (T)	WFib
	'Candy Floss'	see *B. labordei* 'Candy Floss'
	carolineifolia ♀H1b	WDib WFar
	× ***carrierei***	see *B.* Semperflorens Cultorum Group
	'Cascade Florence'	SDeJ
	'Cascade Sunray'	SDeJ
	'Casey Corwin' (R)	WDib
	cathayana	EBee
	- B&SWJ 8315	WCru
	'Champagne'	LCro LOPS
	'Chantilly Lace'	NWad
I	***chapaensis*** HWJ 642	WCru
	'China Curl' (R) ♀H1b	WDib
	chitoensis	GGro WFar
	- B&SWJ 1954	WCru
	'Christmas Candy'	WFar
	× ***chungii*** DJHT 99168	GGro WFar
	chuyunshanensis PB 07-1111	GGro WFar
	'Cleopatra' ♀H1b	WDib WFar
	coccinea (C)	WFar WPav
	'Comte de Lesseps' (C)	WDib
	conchifolia f. ***rubrimacula***	WFar
	'Connee Boswell' ♀H1b	WDib WFar
	'Crestabruchii'	WCot
	cucullata var. ***arenosicola*** (S)	ECtt ESwi LRHS SEND
	'Curly Fireflush' (R) ♀H1b	WDib
	'Daisy Trinder' (T)	WFib
	'Dark Eyes' (C) **new**	WDib
	'David Blais' (R) ♀H1b	WDib
	'Dawnal Meyer' (C)	WDib
I	'De Elegans'	WDib
	Devil Series (S)	MDon SCob
	- 'Devil White' (S)	SCob
	- DEVIL'S DELIGHT (mixed) (S)	LCro LOPS SCob
	'Dewdrop' (R) ♀H1b	WDib
	'Dibleys Pink Showers' ♀H1b	WDib
	discolor	see *B. grandis* subsp. *evansiana*
	'Doublet White' (Doublet Series) (S/d)	LAma
	'Doublonia Rose' (Doublonia Series) (S/d)	LAma
	'Down Home' (C)	WDib
	DRAGON WING RED ('Bepared'PBR) ♀H1b	EShb MBros
§	***dregei*** (T) ♀H1b	CSpe EShb WFar
	- var. ***dregei*** (T)	EAri

- 'Glasgow' (T)	WFar
ELEGANCE ('Yagance'PBR) (Million Kisses Series) ♀H1b	MBros
emeiensis	CAbb CBct EBee EPPr GGro WFar WPGP
- DJHC 98473 **new**	EWld
'Emerald Giant' (R)	WDib
'Erythrophylla' ♀H1b	EShb
'Escargot' (R) ♀H1b	WDib
fagifolia **new**	NWad
'Fairy Lights' (T)	WFib
'Fay Lindsey' **new**	WFib
Fimbriata Group (T)	SDeJ
'Fireworks' (R) ♀H1b	WDib
'Flo'Belle Moseley' (C)	WDib
§ ***foliosa*** var. ***miniata*** ♀H1b	CTsd EShb MArl SDix SIvy WCot WDib WFar
- - pink-flowered	CCCN SIvy
formosana f. ***albo-maculata*** B&SWJ 6881	WCru
Fortune Series (T) **new**	MDon
Fragrant Falls Improved Series (T)	MPri SCob SPoG
fuchsioides	see *B. foliosa* var. *miniata*
'Funky Pink' (Funky Series) (T/d)	SCob
fusca	ESwi WMal WPGP
'Garden Angel Blush' (Garden Angel Series)	CBct WCot
'Gay Gordon' (T)	WFib
'George McCormick' (T)	WFib
glaucophylla	see *B. radicans* Vell.
'Glowing Embers' ♀H1b	CRos ECtt LBuc MBros NWad SCob SPoG
grandis (T)	IDee
- PB 03-718 **new**	WFar
§ - subsp. ***evansiana*** ♀H2	CAby CBct CKel CMiW CTsd CWal EAri ELan EPPr EPfP EShb EWld LEdu LRHS LWaG SDix SEND SPlb WCot WCru WFar WOld XLum
- - B&SWJ 11188	WCru
- - var. ***alba*** hort. ♀H2	CAby CMiW EBee EPPr EShb ESwi EWld LEdu SDix SGro WCot WPGP XLum
- - 'Claret Jug'	CExl EBee ECtt EPPr ESwi MSCN
- - pink-flowered	WFar
- - 'Pink Parasol'	ESwi
- - 'Simsii'	EBee WFar
- - 'Sublime'	LEdu WFar
- 'Heron's Pirouette'	EPPr ESwi WFar
- subsp. ***holostyla*** 'Nanjiang Silver'	EPPr GGro WFar
- 'Sapporo'	EPPr ESwi GGro SChr WCru WFar
§ - subsp. ***sinensis*** (T)	NWad WFar
- - BWJ 8011A	GGro WFar
I - - 'Red Undies'(T)	ESwi GGro WCru WFar
- - 'Snowpop'(T)	ESwi GGro WFar WPGP
- aff. subsp. ***sinensis*** BWJ 8133 (T)	GGro WCru WFar
'Green Gecko' (C) **new**	WDib
'Green Gold' (R) ♀H1b	WDib WFar
'Green Sparkles' (R)	WDib
'Green Valleyleaf'	NWad
griffithii	see *B. annulata*
'Gryphon'	CBct CCht LWaG
§ ***guaniana*** 'Pink Lady'	GGro WCru WFar
haageana hort. ex W. Watson	see *B. scharffii*
(Hanging Basket Series) 'Hanging Basket Orange' (T)	SDir
- 'Hanging Basket Pink' (T)	SDir
- 'Hanging Basket Red' (T)	SDir
- 'Hanging Basket Salmon' (T)	SDir
- 'Hanging Basket White' (T)	SDir
hatacoa	LEdu
- 'Silver'	GGro WDib
HEAVEN DELIGHT (mixed) (S)	LCro LOPS
Heaven Series (S)	MDon SCob
- 'Heaven Red' (S)	SCob
- 'Heaven White' (S)	MBros
'Helen Teupel' (R)	WDib
'Helena Hall' (T)	WFib
§ ***heracleifolia***	WFar
- var. ***longipila***	see *B. heracleifolia*
- var. ***nigricans***	see *B. heracleifolia*
'Hilo Holiday' (R) ♀H1b	WDib
homonyma	see *B. dregei*
HONEYMOON ('Yamoon'PBR) (Million Kisses Series)	MBros
Illumination Series (T/d)	LCro LOPS MBros MDon MPri
- 'Illumination Apricot' (T/d)	SCoo
- 'Illumination Rose' (T/d)	SCoo
- 'Illumination Salmon Pink' (T/d) ♀H2	SCoo
- 'Illumination White' (T/d)	SCoo
'Immense' **new**	WFar
INCA NIGHT ('Krbelin02'PBR) (Beleaf Series) (R)	SCob
incarnata 'Metallica'	see *B. metallica*
× ***intermedia*** 'Bertinii' (T)	LCro LOPS SDeJ
'Jennifer Wilson' (T)	WFib
'Jessie Cruickshank' (T)	WFib
'John Smith' (T)	WFib
'Jolly Noel'	WDib
josephii (T)	WFar
'Joyful Blaze' (R)	WDib
* ***koelzii***	CDTJ EShb ESwi LEdu
- NJM 12.077	GGro WFar WPGP
'La Paloma' (C)	WDib WFar
§ ***labordei*** 'Candy Floss'	WCru WFar
aff. ***labordei*** sp. 71 **new**	GGro
Large-flowered Double Group (T/d)	SDeJ
'Lianne' (T)	WFib
'Lime Green'	GGro
'Limeade' ♀H1b	WDib
limmingheana	see *B. radicans* Vell.
'Linda Jackson' (T)	WFib
listada ♀H1b	WDib WFar
'Little Brother Montgomery' ♀H1b	NWad WDib WFar
'Lois Burks' (C)	WDib
'Lucerna' (C)	ELan EShb WDib WFar
luxurians ♀H1b	CAbb CBct CDTJ CHll CSpe EBee ECtt ELan ESwi LWaG SDix SIvy SMad SPlb WCot WFar
maculata (C)	LCro LWaG
- 'Wightii' (C)	CSpe WDib
'Madame Butterfly' (C)	NWad
(Majestic Series) 'Majestic Pink' (T)	SCob
- 'Majestic Red' (T)	SCob
- 'Majestic Sunburst' (T)	MBros SCob WHlf
- 'Majestic Yellow' (T)	SCob
'Majesty' (T)	WFib
Marginata Group (T)	SDeJ
* 'Marginata Crispa White'	SDeJ
'Marmaduke' ♀H1b	WDib
'Marmorata' (T)	SDeJ
'Martin Johnson' (R) ♀H1b	WDib
masoniana ♀H1b	ESwi GGro WDib WSFF
I 'Matador' (T)	WFib

	'Matisse' (Impressionist Series)	NRHS
	'Melissa' (T)	WFib
	'Merry Christmas' (R)	WDib
	'Metallic Mist'^{PBR}	ESwi
§	***metallica*** 🏆^{H1b}	EShb WFar
	'Midnight Magic' (R) 🏆^{H1b}	WDib
	Million Kisses Series	MPri
	'Mishmi Silver'	CBct GGro LEdu WFar WPGP
	'Monet' (Impressionist Series)	NRHS
	'Mother's Day' (T)	LCro LOPS
	'Mrs E. McLaughlan' (T)	WFib
	'Mrs Peters' (T)	WFib
	'Munchkin' 🏆^{H1b}	WDib
	'My Best Friend'	WDib
	'Namur' (R) 🏆^{H1b}	WDib
	nantoensis NMWJ 14461 **new**	WCru
	natalensis	see *B. dregei*
	'Nick Woodfield'	WFib
	Nonstop Series (T/d)	MBros SCob SDeJ
	- 'Nonstop Pink' (T/d)	SDeJ
	- 'Nonstop Red' (T/d)	MBros SDeJ
	- 'Nonstop Rose Petticoat' (T/d)	MBros
	- 'Nonstop Salmon' (T/d)	SDeJ
	- 'Nonstop White' (T/d)	MBros SCob SDeJ
	- 'Nonstop Yellow' (T/d)	MBros SCob SDeJ
	- 'Northern Lights' (R)	MBros SCob
	(Northern Lights Series) 'Northern Lights Pink' (T)	MBros SCob
	- 'Northern Lights Scarlet Burst' (T)	SCob
	'Odorosa'	SDeJ
	'Ollykey' (T)	WFib
	'Orange Rubra' (C)	WDib WHlf
	'Orangeade' (C)	NWad
	'Organdy' (mixed)	MBros MDon
	palmata	CBct CDTJ GGro WFar
	- CMBTW 1566 **new**	GGro
	- 'Dark Star'	GGro WFar
	- 'Snow Splash'	CBct GGro
	panchtharensis	SPlb WFar
	- B&SWJ 2692	GGro WCot WCru WFar
	partita	see *B. dregei*
	'Peardrop'^{PBR}	MBros MPri
	pedatifida	CBct GGro WFar
	- DJHC 98473	ESwi EWld WCru WFar
	- 'Apalala'	WFar WPGP
	Pendula Group (T)	LAma SDeJ
	- 'Pink Giant' (T)	LCro LOPS
	- 'Red Giant' (T)	LCro LOPS
	- 'White Giant' (T)	LCro LOPS
	'Picasso' (Impressionist Series)	NRHS
	'Picotee' (T)	SDeJ
	picta Sm. (T) **new**	WFar
	'Pink Cascade'	SDeJ
	'Pink Champagne' (R) 🏆^{H1b}	WDib
	'Pink Flamingo' (T)	LCro LOPS
	'Pink Gin' (R)	WDib
	'Pink Spirit' (R)	WDib
	'Pink Twist'	WDib
	'Pollux' 🏆^{H1b}	WDib
	'Powder Puff' (T)	WFib
	'Président Carnot' (C) 🏆^{H1b}	NWad
	'Preston Guild' (T)	WFib
	'Princess Alice' (T)	WFib
	'Princess of Hanover' (R) 🏆^{H1b}	WDib
	procumbens	see *B. radicans* Vell.
	putii B&SWJ 7245	WCru
	'Queen Olympus'	WDib
§	***radicans*** Vell. 🏆^{H1b}	WFar
	'Raspberry Swirl' (R)	WDib
	ravenii (T)	CDTJ WFar
	'Ray Peters'	WFib
	'Red Admiral' (T)	WFib
	'Red Glory' (T)	LCro LOPS
	'Red Robin' (R) 🏆^{H1b}	WDib
	'Red Tempest'	WDib
	'Red Undies' (*grandis*)	see *B. grandis* subsp. *sinensis* 'Red Undies'
	'Regal Minuet' (R) 🏆^{H1b}	WDib
	'Renoir' (Impressionist Series)	NRHS
	rex (R)	CWal WCot
	'Richmondensis' (S)	EShb WFar
	'Ricinifolia'	WFar
	'Rocheart' (R) 🏆^{H1b}	WDib
	'Rosebud Tutu' **new**	LCro
	'Rosy Jewel' (R)	WDib
	'Roy Hartley' (T/d)	WFib
	'Ruby Celebration' (C) **new**	WDib
	'Sal's Comet' (R) 🏆^{H1b}	WDib
	'Sandra Haynes' (T)	WFib
	'Satin Starburst' (R)	WDib
	'Sceptre' (T)	WFib
	'Sceptre Cross' (T)	WFib
§	***scharffii***	SDix
	'Scherzo'	WDib
	schmidtiana (S) **new**	WOld
	'Sea Urchin'	WDib WFar
	semperflorens hort.	see *B.* Semperflorens Cultorum Group
§	Semperflorens Cultorum Group (S)	SCob
	'Senator White' (Senator Series)	MBros
	serratipetala 🏆^{H1b}	WDib
	'Shamus'	WDib
*	***shepherdii***	EShb WDib WFar
	sikkimensis	ESwi GGro WFar
	- var. ***kamengensis***	GGro WFar
	aff. ***sikkimensis*** U614	GGro WFar
	silletensis	WCot
	- subsp. ***mengyangensis***	WCot WFar
	'Silver Cloud' (R) 🏆^{H1b}	WDib
	'Silver Jewell' 🏆^{H1b}	WDib
	'Silver Lace'	WDib WFar
	'Silver Spirit' (R)	WDib
	'Silver Splendor'	CSpe ECtt ESwi WFar
	sinensis	see *B. grandis* subsp. *sinensis*
	sizemoreae	GGro WDib WFar WMal
	'Smooch' **new**	WFar
	'Snow Storm'	WDib
I	'Snowcap' (C) 🏆^{H1b}	EShb WDib
	solananthera A. DC. 🏆^{H1b}	WDib WFar
	'Solid Silver' (R)	WDib
	soli-mutata 🏆^{H1b}	WDib WFar
	'Splendide Ballerina' (T) **new**	LCro
	'Stained Glass'	WDib
	'Star Bright'	WDib
	'Star Light'	WDib
	STARSHINE MIXED	LSou
	'Sugar Candy' (T/d)	WFib
	'Sugar Plum'	MAsh
	SUMMERWINGS DARK ELEGANCE ('Insumdaele'^{PBR}) (Summerwings Series)	CRos SPoG
	'Sunset Yellow Champagne'	LCro LOPS
	'Susan' (T)	WFib
	sutherlandii (T) 🏆^{H2}	CAvo CCCN CWCL EBee EShb ESwi EWld LWaG NPer SAdn SDix SGro SIvy WCot WDib WMal WPGP

- 'Papaya' (T) CSpe
'Sweet Dreams' (T/d) WFib
(Sweet Spice Series) LSou MBros MPri SCob
SWEET SPICE CITRUS ('Kerbespicit') (T/d)
- SWEET SPICE ENGLISH ROSE ('Kerbespiros'PBR) (T/d) MBros MPri SCob
'Switzerland' (T) SDeJ
'Tahiti' (T) WFib
taliensis EDHCH 042 GGro WCot WCru WFar
- W&O 8043 **new** GGro
tapatia (T) F&M 337 WPGP
'Tapestry' NWad
tengchiana WFar
- PB 07-1110 GGro WFar
'Tessa Robinson' (T) WFib
'Thurstonii' ♀H1b EShb WFar
'Tiger Paws' ♀H1b EShb
'Tiny Gem' WDib WFar
'Torsa' GGro WFar
* ***tripartita*** (T) WDib WFar
'Truffle Cream' MBros
'Two Face' WDib
'Tye Dye' CBct GGro WFar
undulata (C) WFar
'Van Gogh' (Impressionist Series) NRHS
'Vera Coates' (T) WFib
versicolor BWJ 15726 **new** WCru
'Vesuvius' (R) WDib
'Vibrant Star' (T) LCro LOPS
'Wavy Green' CBct EBee ESwi GGro WFar
'Whispers' (T) WFib
'Wild Swan' GGro WCru WFar
wynn-jonesiae 'Pink Lady' see *B. guaniana* 'Pink Lady'
xanthina **new** WFar
'Ziggy' (T) WFib

Belamcanda see *Iris*

chinensis see *Iris domestica*

Bellevalia (*Asparagaceae*)

sp. GArf
'Cream Pearl' WCot
cyanopoda GKev
desertorum JCA 0.227.690 WCot
dubia GKev NRog WCot WSHC
forniculata WCot
hyacinthoides WCot
longistyla GKev
§ ***paradoxa*** CAby CBor ERCP GBin GKev LAma MNrw NRog SDeJ WCot
pycnantha misapplied see *B. paradoxa*
pycnantha ambig. SDeJ
pycnantha (K. Koch) Losinsk. 'Green Pearl' CBor ERCP GKev LAma SDeJ
romana ERCP GKev NRog SDeJ WCot
sarmatica GKev
tabriziana WCot
trifoliata GKev

Bellis (*Asteraceae*)

§ ***caerulescens*** CMiW ECtt GAbr
perennis SPhx WWild
- 'Alba Plena' (d) LShi
- 'Alice' ECtt
- Bellissima Series LCro LOPS MBros
- 'Big Bob' (d) ECtt WCot
- 'Dresden China' LShi
- HEN AND CHICKENS see *B. perennis* 'Prolifera' single-flowered
- 'Miss Mason' CMiW WCot
- old strain WCot
- 'Prolifera' double-flowered (d) WCot
§ - 'Prolifera' single-flowered ECtt
- 'Rob Roy' (d) LShi
- Rusher Series LRHS
- 'Single Blue' see *B. caerulescens*
- 'The Pearl' LShi WCot
rotundifolia 'Caerulescens' see *B. caerulescens*

Belloa (*Asteraceae*)

chilensis SPlb

Beloperone see *Justicia*

Benthamiella (*Solanaceae*)

patagonica EPot SPlb WAbe
- F&W 9345 WAbe
- white-flowered WAbe
- yellow-flowered WAbe

Berberidopsis (*Berberidopsidaceae*)

beckleri CBcs
corallina CBcs CDoC CMac CRHN CRos EBee EGrI ELan EPfP IArd LRHS MGil MGos MRav NLar SCob SLim SPoG SWvt

Berberis (*Berberidaceae*)

CC 7810 CMCN
aggregata GKev NBir SRms WKor
amurensis var. ***latifolia*** B&SWJ 8539 WCru
aquifolium see *Mahonia aquifolium*
- 'Fascicularis' see *Mahonia × wagneri* 'Pinnacle'
aristata misapplied see *B. glaucocarpa*
asiatica WPGP
bealei see *Mahonia bealei*
buxifolia 'Nana' misapplied see *B. microphylla* 'Pygmaea'
calliantha SBrt WFar
candidula C.K. Schneid. LRHS MMuc MSwo NLar SEND
- 'Jytte' see *B.* 'Jytte'
× ***carminea*** 'Buccaneer' WSpi
- 'Pirate King' CSBt EBee EHyd EPfP LRHS SPer SPoG SWvt WAvo
chilensis WPav
darwinii ♀H5 Widely available
I - 'Compacta' CBod CDoC CEme CMac CPla CRos CSBt EBee EFPl ELan EPfP GMcL LBuc LRHS MAsh MGos NLar SCob SLim SNig SPad SPoG SWvt WCot WFar WPav
densa B&SWJ 14873 WCru
aff. ***densa*** B&SWJ 14880 WCru
dictyophylla ELan EPfP LRHS MMuc NLar WSpi
dulcis 'Nana' see *B. microphylla* 'Pygmaea'
empetrifolia LEdu WPav WSpi
'Fireball' SRHi
× ***frikartii*** 'Amstelveen' ♀H5 CCVT CDoC CEme CEnd EHeP EPfP LPar MBNS MMuc NBwr SCob
- 'Telstar' SCob
gagnepainii misapplied see *B. gagnepainii* var. *lanceifolia*
gagnepainii C.K. Schneid. CMac NWea
§ - var. ***lanceifolia*** EHeP MMuc NLar SEND WHtc
- - 'Fernspray' EBee EPfP MRav SRms
- 'Purpurea' see *B. × interposita* 'Wallich's Purple'
'Georgei' ♀H6 EPfP LRHS SPtp
§ ***glaucocarpa*** SPtp
'Goldilocks' CKel EBee EPfP MBlu MMuc SPoG
goudotii B&SWJ 10769 WCru
- B&SWJ 14721 WCru

	- B&SWJ 14892	WCru
	hamiltoniana H&M 1919	EBee GKev
	hypokerina	CMac SPtp WPGP
	insignis	IDee WFar
	- subsp. ***insignis*** var. ***insignis*** B&SWJ 2432	WCru
§	× ***interposita*** 'Wallich's Purple'	CCVT EHeP EPfP LRHS MSwo WFar
	jamesiana	SPtp
	julianae	CArg CBcs CBrac CEme CEnd CMac EHeP ELan EPfP GMcL MGos MMuc MSwo NWea SCob SEND SGsty SPer SRms SWvt WFar WHtc WSpi
§	'Jytte'	CKel CWnw
	koehneana	SPtp
	koreana	NLar
	linearifolia 'Orange King'	see *B. trigona* 'Orange King'
	'Little Favourite'	see *B. thunbergii* f. *atropurpurea* 'Atropurpurea Nana'
	× ***lologensis*** 'Apricot Queen' ♀H5	CBcs CMac CRos EPfP LRHS MAsh MGos NLar SPer SPoG SWvt
	- 'Mystery Fire'	IArd MGos NLar SWvt
	- 'Stapehill'	CBrac CMac CRos EHyd ELan EPfP LRHS MAsh SPoG
	malipoensis	GRum
	× ***media*** PARK JEWEL	see *B.* × *media* 'Parkjuweel'
§	- 'Parkjuweel'	SRms
	- 'Red Jewel' ♀H5	CDoC CMac EPfP GMcL LRHS MAsh MGos MMuc SPoG WCFE WFar
	microphylla	GKev WCFE
§	- 'Pygmaea'	CBod EBee EHeP EHyd EPfP GMcL LRHS MRav SPer WPav
	× ***ottawensis*** 'Auricoma'	SWvt
	- f. ***purpurea***	CCVT CMac
§	- - 'Silver Miles' (v)	MRav WFar WLov
§	- - 'Superba'	Widely available
	panlanensis 'Cally Rose'	see *B. triacanthophora* 'Cally Rose'
	polyantha var. ***polyantha***	CTri
	'Red Tears'	MRav WFar
	× ***rubrostilla*** 'Cherry Ripe'	CMac
	- 'Wisley'	EHyd
	sibirica	GBin
	sieboldii	LEdu MRav WLov WPav WSpi
§	***soulieana***	CEme MDon NWea
	stenophylla Hance	see *B. soulieana*
	× ***stenophylla*** Lindl. ♀H5	CBod CCVT CMac CSBt CTri EPfP GBin GMcL LBuc MMuc MRav SPer SRms
	- 'Claret Cascade'	EBee ELan MRav SPoG
	- 'Corallina Compacta' ♀H5	CMac CRos EDAr EHyd ELan EPfP EPot GKev LRHS MAsh MHer SPoG SRms WCot
	- 'Cornish Cream'	see *B.* × *stenophylla* 'Lemon Queen'
	- 'Crawley Gem'	GAbr NWea
	- 'Cream Showers'	see *B.* × *stenophylla* 'Lemon Queen'
	- 'Etna'	EHyd ELan LRHS MAsh SCoo SPoG
	- 'Irwinii'	CKel CMac LRHS
§	- 'Lemon Queen'	WSpi
	- 'Nana'	EHyd
	subacuminata FMWJ 13290	WCru
	sublevis PAB 8943	LEdu
	temolaica ♀H5	EPfP EWes IDee NLar WAvo WSpi
	thunbergii	CArg CBcs CEnd CKel CMac EHeP GMcL LBuc LPar LSto NBwr NWea SCob SPer SWvt WFar
	- f. ***atropurpurea***	CBTr CBcs CBod CBrac CCVT CDoC CMac CSBt CTri EBee ELan GMcL LBuc LCro LIns LOPS MGos MPri MRav MSwo NBwr NLar NWea SCob SGol SPer SPlb SRms WAvo WTSh
	- - 'Admiration'[PBR] ♀H7	Widely available
§	- - 'Atropurpurea Nana' ♀H7	Widely available
	- - 'Bagatelle'	CDoC CEme CRos EDir EGrI ELan EPfP GMcL IArd LRHS LSRN MAsh MGos MRav NBwr NLar SCob SPer SWvt WLov
	- - 'Chocolate Summer'[PBR] **new**	CBod
	- - 'Concorde' ♀H7	CRos EHyd ELan EPfP LPar LRHS MAsh NRHS SCob
	- - 'Dart's Red Lady' ♀H7	CDoC CRos CSBt EDir EHyd ELan EPfP GMcL LRHS MAsh NBwr NLar NRHS SCob SPer SWvt WAvo WFar
	- - 'Golden Ring' (v) ♀H7	CBcs CDoC CEme CMac CRos EHyd ELan EPfP GMcL LRHS MAsh MGos MRav NRHS SGbt SPer SPoG SWvt WAvo WFar WHtc
	- - 'Harlequin' (v) ♀H7	CBod CBrac CChe CDoC CEme CEnd CKel CRos CWnw EDir EHyd ELan EPfP GMcL LCro LOPS LPar LRHS LSRN MAsh MGos NBwr NRHS SGol SPer SPoG SRHi SRms SWvt WFar
	- - 'Helmond Pillar'	Widely available
	- - 'Pink Queen' (v)	CKel EDir EHeP ELan EPfP LRHS MAsh WFar WHtc
	- - 'Red Chief'	CBcs CBod CMac EDir EHeP ELan EPfP GMcL LPar LRHS MAsh MGos NRHS SGol SPoG SRms SWvt WFar
	- - 'Red Pillar'	CBod CChe CDoC CMac EDir ELan EPfP MAsh MGos SGbt SWvt WFar WLov
	- - 'Red Rocket'	EBee EDir EFPl EGrI ERom GMcL LPar LRHS NLar NRHS SCob SCoo
	- - 'Rose Glow' (v) ♀H7	Widely available
	- - 'Rosea' **new**	EHeP
	- - 'Rosy Rocket'[PBR] (v)	CBod CBrac CKel CWGN EBee ELan EPfP LRHS MRav NHol NLar SPer SPoG WFar
	- 'Atropurpurea Superba'	see *B.* × *ottawensis* f. *purpurea* 'Superba'
	- 'Aurea'	CBcs CBrac CDoC CMac EDir EGrI EHeP EHyd ELan EPfP GMcL LRHS LSRN MBlu MGos MRav NBwr NLar NRHS SCob SGbt SPlb SRms SWvt WHlf
	- BONANZA GOLD ('Bogozam'[PBR])	CRos EHeP EHyd ELan LRHS MAsh NLar
	- 'Crimson Pygmy'	see *B. thunbergii* f. *atropurpurea* 'Atropurpurea Nana'
	- 'Diabolic'	CBod EGrI MAsh NHol NRHS SPer SPoG
	- 'Erecta'	CMac EPfP MRav SPer WCFE
	- 'Fireball'[PBR] ♀H7	CRos EHyd EPfP LRHS MAsh
	- 'Florence'[PBR] **new**	CBod
	- 'Golden Dream'[PBR]	MGos
	- GOLDEN HORIZON ('Hoho 2'[PBR])	CBod
	- 'Golden Rocket'[PBR]	CBod CRos EBee EHyd ELan EPfP GArf LRHS MAsh MGos MRav NLar NRHS SCoo SPoG WFar WHtc WLov
	- GOLDEN RUBY ('Goruzam') (v)	LCro
	- 'Golden Torch'	CDoC CSBt EHeP EHyd ELan EPfP LPar LRHS MAsh MRav NHol NRHS SWvt WHtc WLov
	- 'Green Carpet'	CBod CMac EDir EGrI EHeP LRHS MBlu SPoG SWvt
	- 'Green Mantle'	see *B. thunbergii* 'Kelleriis'
	- 'Green Marble'	see *B. thunbergii* 'Kelleriis'
	- 'Green Ornament'	NHol

§	- 'Kelleriis' (v)	EHyd GMcL LRHS MRav
	- 'Kobold'	CMac EPfP MGos NLar WFar
	- 'Lutin Rouge'PBR	CSBt LCro LOPS WLov
	- 'Maria'PBR ♀H7	CWGN EGrI EHyd ELon EPfP GMcL LCro LRHS LSou MGos MRav NLar NRHS SCob SGBe SGol SPad SPoG WLov
	- 'Natasza'PBR	LRHS
	- 'Orange Dream'PBR	CDoC EBee LPar MGos SCoo
	- 'Orange Ice'PBR	LRHS XSte
	- 'Orange Rocket'PBR	CBTr CDoC CKel CRos EBee EGrI EHyd ELan EPfP GMcL LCro LOPS LPar LRHS MAsh MGos MRav NHol NRHS SCob SCoo SPoG SRHi WFar WLov
	- 'Orange Sunrise'PBR (v)	CBod CWnw LCro LOPS LRHS MAsh SPad
	- 'Orange Torch'	LRHS SCoo
	- 'Pow-wow'	EDir EHyd ELan LPar MGos NLar NRHS SCoo SPoG SWvt WLov
	- 'Redtorch'PBR	CRos EHyd LRHS NRHS
	- 'Ruby Star'PBR	LRHS
	- 'Silver Beauty' (v)	EDir
	- 'Silver Mile'	see *B.* × *ottawensis* f. *purpurea* 'Silver Miles'
	- 'Silver Pillar'PBR	NLar
	- 'Smaragd'	WFar
	- 'Somerset'	CMac GMcL
	- 'Starburst'PBR (v)	CBod CSBt EBee EHyd EPfP LRHS MAsh MGos NEoE NHol NRHS SCoo SGBe SRms SWvt WHtc
	- 'Summer Sunset'PBR new	CBod WLov
	- 'Tiny Gold'PBR	EHyd ELan GKev LCro LOPS LRHS MAsh SLim SOrN SWvt WFar WLov
*	- 'Tricolor' (v)	CMac MRav WFar
§	***triacanthophora*** 'Cally Rose'	EPfP GBin WPGP
§	***trigona*** 'Orange King'	CBcs CMac ELan EPfP GBin LRHS MAsh MGos NLar SPer SPoG SRHi
	valdiviana ♀H5	CBcs CJun EPfP GBin IArd IKel MBlu MMuc SChF WPGP
	verruculosa ♀H5	CBcs CBrac CDoC EHeP GMcL LRHS LSto MBlu MGos NBwr SRms SWvt WFar
	aff. ***verticillata*** B&SWJ 10672	WCru
	virescens B&SWJ 2646D	WCru
	vulgaris	CAgr GPoy MCoo NWea WKor XSen
	- 'Atropurpurea'	NWea
	wallichiana DC.	GArf
	wilsoniae	CBcs CBod CMac CTri ELan ELon EPfP GLog GMcL NWea SPer SRms WAvo WFar WHtc WSpi
	- blue-leaved	WFar
	- var. ***guhtzunica***	EWes
	aff. ***wilsoniae***	CBrac
	yingjingensis new	WPGP

Berberis × *Mahonia* see × *Mahoberberis*

Berchemia (*Rhamnaceae*)

	racemosa	NLar

bergamot see *Citrus* × *limon* Bergamot Group

Bergbambos (*Poaceae*)

§	***tessellata***	MMuc SEND

Bergenia ✿ (*Saxifragaceae*)

	'Abendglocken'	CMac ECha ECtt EGrI EPfP NSti WCot WFar
§	'Abendglut'	Widely available
	'Admiral'	CBct CMac ECha EGrI EPri WCot
	afghanica	XLum
*	***agavifolia***	CBct XLum
	'Andrea'	WCot
	'Angel Kiss' (Dragonfly Series)	CMil CWCL ECtt ELan GBin LCro LOPS LRHS MNrw NLar SCob SWvt WCot WTor
	'Apple Blossom'	CRos EHyd EPfP LRHS MAsh NRHS WCAu
	'Apple Court White'	CBct
	'Autumn Magic'	CBct CBod CKel EGrI ELon EPfP LRHS MBow NCou SCoo WFar
	'Baby Doll'	Widely available
	'Bach'	CBct CDor CRos ECtt EHyd EPfP GAbr LPla LRHS LSto LSun MBel MMuc NGBl NLar NRHS NSti SCob SGbt SRms SWvt WCAu WCot WFar WMal
§	'Ballawley' clonal	CRos EBlo ECha EHyd LRHS MRav NRHS WCot XLum
	'Ballawley' seed-raised	see *B.* Ballawley hybrids
	'Ballawley Guardsman'	CBct
§	Ballawley hybrids	CMac SWvt WSpi
	'Bartók'	CBct ECtt NRHS SRms WCAu WCot
	beesiana	see *B. purpurascens*
	'Beethoven'	CBct ECha EGrI GBin NBir WCAu WCot
	'Biedermeier' ♀H7	ECha
	'Bizet'	CBct XLum
	'Borodin'	CBct WCAu
	'Brahms'	CBct
	'Bressingham Beauty'	GKev
	'Bressingham Bountiful'	CBct
	'Bressingham Ruby'	CBct CRos CWCL EBee EBlo ECha ECtt ELon EPfP LPal LRHS LSRN MGos MRav NBir NLar NRHS SOrN SPer SWvt WCAu WCot WHoo WSpi
	'Bressingham Salmon'	CBct EBee ECha ECtt ELon GMaP LBar MRav NLar SRms WCAu WCot
	'Bressingham White' ♀H6	Widely available
	'Britten' ♀H7	CBct CMac GBin
	ciliata	CBct CDor CMac ECha EGrI EMor EPri EShb GMaP LEdu LRHS MBriF MRav NHol NLar WAvo WFar WPGP WSHC WSpi XLum
	- 'Dumbo'	CBct GBin IBal LEdu NLar SMrm WCAu
	- f. ***ligulata***	see *B. pacumbis*
	- 'Wilton'	CBct ETod EWld LEdu MAvo SHar WCot WPGP WSHC
	ciliata × ***crassifolia***	see *B.* × *schmidtii*
	'Claire Maxine' ♀H7	CBct ECtt EPPr GBin GQue LBar LRHS MPie NFav NLar SRms WCAu WCot WSHC
	cordifolia	CBar CKel CMac CSBt CTri EBee EHeP EHyd ELan EPfP GDam GMaP GMcL LPal LRHS LWaG MBel MBros MGos MMuc MSwo NGrd NLar NRHS SCob SEND SPlb SRms SWvt XSen
	- 'Flore Pleno' (d)	CBct
	- 'Jelle'	CBct CBod CKel EBee ECtt NCth NLar WCAu
	- 'Lunar Glow'	ECtt EPfP SRms WFar
	- 'Purpurea'	CBcs CMac CRos CWCL EBee ECha EGrI EHeP EHyd ELan EPfP GBin GKev GMcL GQue LBuc LCro LOPS LRHS NBir NRHS SCob SMrm SPer SRms SWvt WFar XLum
	- 'Rosa Schwester'	CBct ECha
	- 'Rosa Zeiten' ♀H7	CBct GBin
	- 'Tubby Andrews' (v)	CBct CMac CTtf ECha EShb LEdu LRHS MAvo NEoE NLar SRms WHrl

	- 'Vinterglöd'	CBod EBou ELon EPfP GMaP LSun MBel MGos MPri NLar SBls SRms SWvt WPnP XLum
	crassifolia	EPfP SRms XLum
	- DF 90028	CBct GBin
	- 'Autumn Red'	CBct ECha
	- 'Orbicularis'	see *B.* × *schmidtii*
	'Croesus'	GBin
*	***cyanea***	WCot
	'Dark Damsel'	CBct IBal LBar
	'David'	EBee ECha
	'Delbees'	see *B.* 'Ballawley' clonal
	'Diamond Drops'	IBal LBar NEoE NSti SMrm WWke
	'Eden's Dark Margin'	CBct CBod ECtt EHed ELan ELon GBin LDai MHol MNrw NLar WCot
	'Eden's Magic Giant' ♀H7	CBct CToG ECtt ELan ELon EPfP EShb GBin GQue LRHS MHol MMrt MPie NLar SDix SRms WCot WFar XSen
	emeiensis	CBct CDor EMor EPfP LEdu LSun SBrt WCot WSHC
	- 'Snow Chimes' **new**	EMor
	'Eric Smith' ♀H7	ECha EGrI SWvt WCAu
	'Eroica' ♀H7	Widely available
	'Evening Glow'	see *B.* 'Abendglut'
	'Fire and Ice' **new**	CBcs LBar SMrm
	'Flirt'[PBR]	LBar LRHS NCth SPad
	'Godfrey Owen'	EBee WSHC
	'Harzkristall'	CBct CBod CChe CDor CKel CMac CPla CRos CWnw EHyd ELan EPfP GBin GKev LRHS MAsh NCou NRHS SCob SCoo SHar SPoG SWvt WPnP WSpi
	'Helen Dillon'	see *B. purpurascens* 'Irish Crimson'
	'Herbstblute'	EBee GBin WCAu
	'Ice Queen'	EBee ELan EWoo GBin LCro LOPS LRHS NLar SWvt WCAu WCot
	'Jo Watanabe'	CBct ECha MRav
	'Kashmir'	XLum
	'Kerstin'	ECtt
	'Lambrook'	see *B.* 'Margery Fish'
	'Little Pine'	WCot
§	'Margery Fish'	CBct ECha
	'Memelinks Pride'	NLar WCAu
	milesii	see *B. stracheyi*
§	'Morgenröte' ♀H6	CBcs CBct CBod CMac CRos EBlo ECha EGrI ELon EPfP EWoo GMaP LRHS LSRN MRav NHol NLar NSti SPer SRms SWvt WCAu WCot WHlf XSen
	MORNING RED	see *B.* 'Morgenröte'
	'Mrs Crawford'	ECha
	'Oeschberg'	CBct EPPr GBin
	'Opal'	CBct EBee
	'Overture'	Widely available
§	***pacumbis***	EBee ECha GBin NBid NSti XLum
	- B&SWJ 2693	WCru
	- CC	GGro
	- CC 1793	SGro WCot
	- CC 3616	CBct WSHC
	- 'Bouncing Babe' **new**	WCot
	'Pink Dragonfly'	CBct CMac CRos ECtt EHyd ELon EPfP EWes GKev LPla LRHS NLar NRHS SCob SWvt WCAu WCot WFar
	'Pink Ice'	CDor WSHC
	'Pinneberg'	CBct
	'Pugsley's Pink' ♀H7	CBct ECha MAvo
§	***purpurascens*** ♀H5	CEme CMac EBee EPfP GMaP LWaG SCoo SPer WPGP WSpi
	- SDR 4548	GKev
	- var. ***delavayi*** ♀H5	EBee EHyd LRHS NRHS SRms
§	- 'Irish Crimson' ♀H7	ECha EGrI GBin WCot
	aff. ***purpurascens***	NGdn
	'Purpurglocken'	ECtt WCAu
	'Rietheim'	CBct GBin
	'Rosenkristall'	CRos EHyd EPfP LRHS MAsh NRHS WHlf
	'Rosi Klose'	CBct CDor CRos ECha ECtt EGrI ELon EPfP EWes GMcL LRHS MAsh MHol NGdn NRHS SCoo WCot WFar WHoo
	'Rosi Ruffles'	EBee
	'Rotblum'	ELon EPfP GMaP LBuc NBir NGdn NGrd NRHS SGBe SRkn SRms WPnP
	'Sakura' (Dragonfly Series)	CWCL GBin LBar LSou MNrw SCob
§	× ***schmidtii***	CBct CMac GBin MRav NBir NLar
	'Schneekissen'	CBct CMac ECtt EPri WCAu WGwG
§	'Schneekoenigin'	CBct ECha EGrI SWvt WCot
§	'Silberlicht' ♀H6	Widely available
	SILVERLIGHT	see *B.* 'Silberlicht'
	'Simply Sweet'	WCot
	SNOW QUEEN	see *B.* 'Schneekoenigin'
	'Spring Fling'[PBR] (Dragonfly Series)	GBin LRHS
§	***stracheyi***	ECha GBin NBid NLar WCot
	- Alba Group	ECha EGrI SMHy
	'Sunningdale' ♀H7	CBcs CMac CToG ECha ECtt EHyd EPfP GMaP LRHS MRav NBir NGdn NRHS SWvt WCAu
	'Walter Kienli'	GBin
	WINTER FAIRY TALES	see *B.* 'Wintermärchen'
§	'Wintermärchen' ♀H7	CBct CChe CRos ECha EGrI ELan ELon EPfP EPri EShb LRHS MMuc MRav NHol NRHS SEND SPoG SRms SWvt WCot
	'XXL'	WCot WMal

Bergenia × *Mukdenia* see × *Mukgenia*

Bergera (*Rutaceae*)

§	***koenigii***	EOHP GPoy SCit SPre SVen WJek WSFF

Bergeranthus (*Aizoaceae*)

sp.	SCoo SPoG
multiceps	EAri
scapiger	SRot
vespertinus	XLum

Berkheya (*Asteraceae*)

cirsiifolia	EBee GGro NFav SPhx
macrocephala	SPlb
multijuga	GGro SPlb
purpurea	CAby CBcs CBod CDor CRos CSpe CWnw EBlo ECha EDAr EHyd ELon EPfP GGro LRHS NRHS SBls SPhx SPlb SRms WCot WKif
- 'Silver Spike'	EGrI EPfP NGdn
- 'Zulu Warrior'	CMac EGrI LShi MHer SMrm
radula	EBee GGro WCot

Berlandiera (*Asteraceae*)

lyrata	GEdr

Berula (*Apiaceae*)

erecta	CAco NPer

Berzelia (*Bruniaceae*)

galpinii	SPlb
intermedia	LRHS

Beschorneria (*Asparagaceae*)

albiflora	LRHS WCot XSte
calcicola	CBcs CCht CDTJ SMrm WCot

'Red Bells'	WCot
rigida	WCot
septentrionalis	CBcs CCht CDTJ EAri EBee GBin LRHS MBNS MHol NGBl SEdd SPad SPeP WCot WLov XSte
- variegated (v)	WCot
tubiflora	CDTJ
wrightii	WCot
yuccoides ♀H3	CAbb CCht CHll CPla EBee NPlm SChr SEND SPlb
- FLAMINGO GLOW ('Besys'PBR) (v)	CBcs CBod CCht CDTJ EAri MBNS SPad XVPe
- 'Quicksilver'	CCCN CEnd EPfP LRHS MHtn SPoG WPav

Bessera (*Asparagaceae*)

elegans	CBor CPla EPot GKev LAma SDeJ WCot

Besseya (*Plantaginaceae*)

alpina	GEdr
wyomingensis	EBee

Beta (*Amaranthaceae*)

vulgaris	WHer
- subsp. ***maritima***	CAgr

Betonica (*Lamiaceae*)

§ ***macrantha***	CAby CDor CMac CTri EBee ECha EGrI EHyd GJos GKev LBar LEdu LRHS NBir NChi NFav NLar NRHS NSti SPhx SRms WCAu WCFE WCot WKif WWke
* - 'Alba'	CBWd EBee ECha MSpe WCAu
- 'Ben' (v)	LEdu MAvo
- 'Morning Blush'	EMor LBar SPhx WCot WFar
* - 'Nivea'	EBee
- 'Robusta' ♀H7	ELan ELon GAbr LEdu MAvo MMuc NBro NGdn WCot WJam
- 'Rosea'	CElw EHyd ELan GBee GMaP LRHS MAvo NRHS SPlb WCAu
- 'Superba' ♀H7	CSpe EBee ECtt EPfP GKev GMaP LBar LEdu MAvo MHol MRav NLar SAng SCob SMad SPer SRms SWvt WBor WCAu WCot WFar XLum
- 'Violacea' ♀H7	EBee GKev NChi WCot
§ ***nivea***	EWes LRHS NLar SWvt WCAu WCot
§ - subsp. ***ossetica***	GEdr
- parsley-leaved **new**	WCot
§ ***officinalis***	CBee CCBP CHab EGrI EMor GJos GKev GPoy GQue ILea LWaG MBow MHer MHoo MNHC NAts NGrd NMir NRya SRms WCot WHer WShi WTre WWild
- 'Alba'	LEdu MArl MAvo NBro SMHy WCAu
- 'Cally Bicolor'	GBin
- dwarf	NDov
- - white-flowered	GRum NFav
§ - 'Hummelo' ♀H7	Widely available
- 'Marchant's Pink'	SMHy
- 'Pink Cotton Candy'	SCob SPhx
- 'Rosea'	EAJP EGrI MAvo NBro WFar
- 'Rosea Superba'	CTtf ECha WCot
- 'Saharan Pink'	EBee LSRN MHol NLar
- 'Spitzenberg'	LPla
- 'Ukkie'	NLar WHlf
- 'Wisley White'	CRos ECtt EHyd GKev LEdu LRHS MHol NGrd NHpl NRHS SCob SRms WCot WFar
'Summer Crush' **new**	CAby LBar
'Summer Romance' **new**	LBar

Betula ✿ (*Betulaceae*)

alba	see *B. pendula*, *B. pubescens*
albosinensis	see *B. utilis* subsp. *albosinensis*
- var. ***septentrionalis***	see *B. utilis* subsp. *albosinensis*
§ ***alleghaniensis***	CBcs CMCN CSto EPfP GKev MMuc NLar WCru
ashburneri	CAco WPGP
bomiensis	GKev
'Charlotte' **new**	CJun
chichibuensis	GKev MMrt MVil
chinensis	GKev MVil
'Rhinegold'	MBlu
'Cobhay Cream Spire'	CJun
'Cobhay Snow Spire'	CJun
'Conyngham'	CJun MBlu SLau
cordifolia 'Clarenville'	CJun
costata misapplied	see *B. ermanii* 'Grayswood Hill'
costata ambig.	CAco CMCN LMaj SGol
costata Trautv.	MSwo
- 'Daleside'	see *B. ermanii* 'Daleside'
- 'Fincham Cream'	see *B. ermanii* 'Fincham Cream'
'Crimson Frost'	see *B. pendula* 'Crimson Frost'
cylindrostachya	WPGP
dauurica	CBrP MVil
- 'Maurice Foster'	CSto EBee MBlu WPGP
- 'Stone Farm'	CJun
'Edinburgh'	CJun CLnd LRHS MBlu MTrO NLar NOra WMat
ermanii	CAco CBcs CCVT CMCN CMac CSto EBar EGrI ELan GBin IPap LMaj LPar MBlu MDon MGos MMuc MRav NOrn NRog NWea SGol WHtc
- B&SWJ 8801 from South Korea	WCru
- B&SWJ 10852 from Aomori, Japan	WCru
- B&SWJ 12600 from South Korea	WCru
- from Hokkaido, Japan	CAco
- 'Blush'	CJun EPfP MBlu SCoo WHtc
§ - 'Daleside'	EBee MTrO NDal NOra WMat
§ - 'Fincham Cream'	CJun
§ - 'Grayswood Hill' ♀H7	CEnd CJun CLnd CMCN CSBt EBee EPfP LRHS MBlu SCob SCoo SWvt WPGP
- 'Hakkoda Orange'	CJun CSto EBee SCoo WPGP
- 'Kwanak Weeping' ♀H7	CJun EDir MBlu
- 'Mount Zao'	CJun CSto EBee EPfP NOrn WMou WPGP
fargesii **new**	MVil
'Fascination' ♀H6	Widely available
'Fetisowii'	CJun MBlu MTrO NOra NWea WHtc WMat
§ ***fruticosa***	MVil
globispica	CJun MVil
§ ***gmelinii*** 'Mount Apoi' ♀H7	CJun LRHS MGos MTrO WMat
'Hergest'	CJun EBee EPfP MGos MTrO NOra WHCr WHtc WMat
'Holland'	IArd LMaj
'Hoseri' **new**	CAco
insignis	see *B. kweichowensis*
jacquemontii	see *B. utilis* subsp. *jacquemontii*
'Kerscott Charm'	CSto
kweichowensis	CJun WPGP
- subsp. ***fansipanensis***	IArd IDee MVil SAko
- - B&SWJ 11751	WCru
- - FMWJ 13149	WCru
- subsp. ***kweichowensis***	GKev
lenta	CMCN IDee MBlu MMuc
'Long Trunk'	EBee EHeP MBlu NOrn SGol SLim
luminifera	EBee IArd WPGP
lutea	see *B. alleghaniensis*

	maximowicziana	CMCN GKev IArd MBlu NLar SGol WSpi
	medwediewii	CAco CMCN CSto EBee EPfP GKev MVil NLar WPGP
	- 'Gold Bark'	CJun CMCN EPfP MBlu
	megrelica	CSto GKev MVil
	michauxii	MVil NLar WCru
	microphylla **new**	MVil
	'Mount Apoi'	see *B. gmelinii* 'Mount Apoi'
	nana	CAco NWea
	- 'Glengarry'	EPot GEdr MVil
	nigra	CAco CBcs CCVT CEnd CLnd CMCN CPer EBee ELan IPap LMaj LPar NLar NRog NWea SArc SCob SEWo SGol SGsty WHtc WTSh
	- 'Black Star'	CBTr EBee NOra NOrn WMat
§	- 'Cully'	CMCN EBee LMaj LRHS MBlu MTrO NOra NOrn NWea SGol
	- HERITAGE	see *B. nigra* 'Cully'
	- 'Little King'	CMCN
	- 'Peter Collinson'	CJun
	- 'Shiloh Splash'	CAco LPar SSta
	- 'Summer Cascade'^{PBR}	CAco EBee LPar LSRN NOra NOrn WHtc WMat WMou
	- 'Wakehurst'	EPfP SPoG WPGP WSpi
	ovalifolia	see *B. fruticosa*
	papyrifera	CAco CBcs CCVT CMCN CMac CSto EBar EBee EHeP ELan GKev IPap LBuc LMaj LPar MGos MMuc MSwo MTrO NBwr NOra NRog NWea SGol WMat WTSh
	- 'Belle Vue'	EBee
	- 'Saint George'	CAco EBee WHtc WMat
	pendula	Widely available
§	- 'Crimson Frost'	CDoC EBee
§	- subsp. ***mandshurica***	CSto
	- - DAKOTA PINNACLE ('Fargo')	NOra SCoo
	- subsp. ***pendula*** 'Dalecarlica' misapplied	see *B. pendula* subsp. *pendula* 'Laciniata'
	- - 'Dalecarlica' ambig.	CAco EHeP LMaj LRHS MDon MRav NBwr NOra SWvt WFar WMat WTSh
	- - 'Dark Prince'	NOrn
	- - 'Fastigiata'	CAco CCVT CLnd CSBt EBee EHeP ELan IArd IPap LMaj LPar LRHS MGos NOrn NWea SCoo SGol SPer
	- - FASTIGIATA JOES ('Jolep 1'^{PBR})	EBee ELan LCro LPar MAsh MGos MNic MTrO NOra NOrn SEWo SPoG WMat
§	- - 'Globe'^{PBR} **new**	CAco
	- - 'Golden Beauty'	CEnd CMac MAsh MGos MTrO NBwr NOra NOrn NRog NTrD NWea SGol SLim SPer WMat
§	- - 'Golden Cloud'	see *B. pendula* subsp. *pendula* 'Schneverdinger Goldbirke'
	- - 'Golden Fountain'	MTrO WHtc WMat
	- - 'Golden Obelisk'	NOrn
	- - 'Karaca'^{PBR} **new**	CAco MGos
§	- - 'Laciniata' ♀^{H7}	CAco CBcs CMCN CMac EBee ELan EWTr LMaj LPar MBlu MGos MSwo MTrO NOra NOrn NRog NWea SCob SCoo SGol SPer WMou WTSh
	- - MAGICAL GLOBE	see *B. pendula* subsp. *pendula* 'Globe'
	- - 'Obelisk'	LMaj
	- - 'Purpurea'	CAco CCVT CMCN CMac CSBt EHeP ELan IDee IPap LPar LSRN MGos MSwo NBwr NOrn NRog NWea SCoo SEdd SGol SPer WFar WTSh

§	- - 'Schneverdinger Goldbirke'	CAco
	- - 'Silver Grace'	CJun MBlu
§	- - 'Spider Alley'^{PBR}	CAco EBee ELan GBin LPar LRHS MTrO NOra WMat
	- - SWISS GLORY	see *B. pendula* subsp. *pendula* 'Zwitsers Glorie'
	- - 'Tristis' ♀^{H7}	Widely available
	- - 'Youngii'	Widely available
§	- - 'Zwitsers Glorie'	CAco LMaj
	- subsp. ***pendula*** × ***utilis***	LPar
	- subsp. ***szechuanica*** 'Liuba White'	CJun MBlu
	platyphylla	see *B. pendula* subsp. *mandshurica*
	× ***plettkei*** 'Golden Treasure'^{PBR}	CAco GKev NLar
	'Polar Bear'	CJun CLnd EBee EPfP MBlu MTrO NOrn SCoo WHtc WMat
	populifolia	EBtc MVil
	potaninii	GKev MVil
§	***pubescens***	CAco CCVT CHab CPer CTri EBee EHeP GDam IPap LMaj LPar MDon MMuc NBwr NRog NWea SCob WHtc WTSh
	- 'Armenian Gold'	NRog
	pumila	CSto MVil
	× ***purpusii***	MVil
	raddeana	EBtc GKev
	'Royal Frost'	CAco CBcs EBee EWTr LCro LMaj LRHS LSRN MBlu MTrO NLar NOra NWea SGol WHtc WMat WMou
	'Silver Trestles'	see *B. pendula* subsp. *pendula* 'Spider Alley'
	szechuanica	see *B. pendula* subsp. *szechuanica*
	tianschanica	WPGP
	utilis	CMCN LMaj LRHS NWea SSta
	- GWJ 9259	WCru
	- HWJK 2250	WCru
	- HWJK 2345	WCru
	- Sch 2168	EBee
	- S&L from Nepal	CAco
§	- subsp. ***albosinensis***	CAco CBrP CCVT CEnd CLnd CMac CMCN EBee ELan ELon EPfP GBin IPap MBlu MGos MMuc MRav MSwo NOrn NRog SCob SGol SLim SPer WPGP WSpi
	- - PDM 752	WPGP
	- - 'Bowling Green' ♀^{H7}	CJun EBee MBlu WPGP
§	- - 'China Rose'	CBcs CJun CSto EBee EPfP MTrO WMat WPGP
	- - 'China Ruby' K. Ashburner	see *B. utilis* subsp. *albosinensis* 'China Rose'
	- - 'China Ruby' ambig.	CJun CLnd EPfP MTrO NOra
	- - 'China Ruby' B. Humphrey ♀^{H7}	MTrO
	- - 'Chinese Garden'	CJun CSto MBlu WPGP
	- - 'Chris Lane'	CJun WPGP
	- - 'Chris Sanders'	WPGP
	- - clone F	see *B. utilis* subsp. *albosinensis* 'Ness'
§	- - 'Jim Russell'	WPGP
	- - 'Joseph Rock'	CJun
	- - 'K. Ashburner'	CAco CJun CPer
	- - 'Kansu' ♀^{H7}	CJun CLnd EBee MAsh MBlu MTrO NOra NWea WHtc WMat
§	- - 'Ness'	CJun
	- - 'Pink Champagne'	CBcs CJun CSto EPfP LCro LRHS MBlu MGos MTrO WHtc WMat WPGP
	- - 'Purdom'	CJun
	- - 'Red Panda' ♀^{H7}	CAco CJun CSto EBee LCro LRHS MTrO WHtc WMat WPGP
	- - 'Rhinegold'	see *B. chinensis* 'Rhinegold'

* - 'Fastigiata'	CJun NOrn SSta
§ - subsp. ***jacquemontii***	Widely available
- - Polunin	WPGP
§ - - 'Doorenbos' ♀H7	Widely available
- - 'Grayswood Ghost' ♀H7	Widely available
- - 'Inverleith'	CJun CSto SCoo WPGP
- - 'Jermyns' ♀H7	CBcs CEnd CJun CLnd EBee EPfP LRHS LSRN MBlu MTrO NOra NOrn SCob SCoo SPer SSta SWvt WMat WPGP
- - 'Knightshayes'	CJun CPer CSto EBee WPGP
§ - - 'Kyelang'	CJun
- - 'McBeath'	MGos MTrO
- - 'Moonbeam'	CJun CSBt EBee EHyd LRHS MAsh MTrO NOrn NWea SCoo SEWo SLim SPer SPoG SWeb WMat
§ - - 'Ramdana River'	CJun MBlu WPGP
- - 'Sacred Scroll' **new**	CSto
- - 'Silver Shadow' ♀H7	CEnd CJun CLnd CMCN EBee ELan EPfP LRHS LSRN MAsh MBlu MTrO NOra NOrn NRHS NRog NWea SCob SCoo SGbt SLau SLim SPer SPoG SSta WHtc WMat WSpi
- - 'Snow Leopard'	CJun CSto EBee WPGP
- - 'Snow Queen'	see *B. utilis* subsp. *jacquemontii* 'Doorenbos'
- - 'Trinity College'	CJun EBee ELan LRHS MAsh MGos MTrO NOrn SCoo WLov WMat WPGP
- subsp. ***occidentalis***	WPGP
- - 'Kyelang'	see *B. utilis* subsp. *jacquemontii* 'Kyelang'
- var. ***prattii***	see *B. utilis* subsp. *utilis*
- 'Silver Queen'	CTri EWTr MPri WSpi
§ - subsp. ***utilis***	CJun MBlu MVil
- - 'Bhutan Sienna'	CJun CSto EBee WPGP
§ - - 'Buddha' ♀H7	CJun EBee MBlu WPGP
- - 'China Bronze'	EBee MBlu WPGP
- - 'Cobhay Amber'	CJun
- - 'Cobhay Sentinel'	CJun
- - 'Dark-Ness'	CJun MBlu MTrO NOra WHtc WMat WPGP
- - 'Forest Blush' ♀H7	CJun CSto EBee EPfP WPGP
- - 'Himalayan Pink'	see *B. utilis* subsp. *utilis* 'Nepalese Orange'
- - 'Jim Russell'	see *B. utilis* subsp. *albosinensis* 'Jim Russell'
- - 'Mount Luoji'	CJun CSto EBee EPfP WPGP
- - 'Nepalese Orange'	CBcs CJun CSto EBee ELan EPfP MTrO NOrn SGol WHtc WMat WMou WPGP WSpi
- - 'Park Wood'	CAco CJun EPfP WPGP
§ - - 'Ramdana River'	see *B. utilis* subsp. *jacquemontii* 'Ramdana River'
- - 'Schilling'	see *B. utilis* subsp. *utilis* 'Buddha'
- - 'Sichuan Red'	CJun
- - 'Wakehurst Place Chocolate' ♀H7	CBcs CJun CSBt GBin MBlu MGos MTrO NLar NOra NWea SCoo SGbt SLim WHtc WMat WSpi
- - 'White-Ness'	EBee MBlu MTrO WMat
cf. ***utilis***	SGol WHtc
verrucosa	see *B. pendula* subsp. *pendula*

Biancaea (*Fabaceae*)

§ ***decapetala***	WJur

Biarum (*Araceae*)

S&L 604	WCot
SB&L 597	WCot
carratracense from Spain	WCot
davisii	EPot GKev WCot
ditschianum from Turkey	WCot
marmarisense	NRog WCot
rhopalospadix	GKev
tenuifolium	WCot
- LB 295	WCot
- PB 357	WCot
- S&L 174	WCot
- subsp. ***abbreviatum***	GKev SBrt
- - MS 974	WCot
- subsp. ***arundanum***	GKev WCot
- - from Spain	NRog
- subsp. ***galianii*** PB 435	WCot
- subsp. ***zelebori***	WCot
- - CRL 502	WCot
- - LB 300	WCot

Bidens (*Asteraceae*)

atrosanguinea	see *Cosmos atrosanguineus*
§ ***aurea***	CCBP ECtt EPPr EWes LEdu MAsh MCot MHol MRav MSpe NPer SBut SIvy SMrm WBor WFar WMal WPGP XLum
- cream-flowered	MNrw SPeP WMal
- 'Hannay's Lemon Drop'	CKno CTtf ECtt ELan ELon EPPr EPfP EWTr LEdu LShi MAsh MHol MSpe SDix SGbt SPeP SPoG SPtp SRms WBor WFar WMal WPGP
* - 'Lemon Queen'	SBls
- 'Mellow Yellow'	WCot
- 'Rising Sun'	ECtt EWes
- 'Super Nova'	EPPr
- white-flowered	EBee ELon EMor EPPr GMaP GPSL NSti WFar
'Compact Bicolour Star' (Hawaiian Flare Series)	LSou
ferulifolia	NPer
- 'Bee Alive' (Bee Series)	MBros
- BEEDANCE PAINTED RED ('Sunbidevb 2'[PBR])	SPoG
- BEEDANCE PAINTED YELLOW ('Sunbidevb4'[PBR])	SPoG
- BLAZING FIRE **new**	LSou WWke
- 'Golden Empire' **new**	MPri
- 'Golden Eye'	MBros SPoG WWke
- 'Golden Glory'	MBros
- SUN DROP ('Danbid7346')	LSou
'Giant Yellow Red Tip' (Hawaiian Flare Series)	LSou
heterophylla Ortega	see *B. aurea*
'Moonlight' **new**	WWke
'Rockstar'	CPla
triplinervia 'Sunny Days'	WCru
'Yellow Red Star' (Hawaiian Flare Series)	LSou

Bigelowia (*Asteraceae*)

nuttallii	CSpe

Bignonia (*Bignoniaceae*)

capreolata	CCCN CRHN XSen
- 'Dragon Lady'	CRHN
lindleyana	see *Clytostoma calystegioides*
tweedieana	see *Dolichandra unguis-cati*
unguis-cati	see *Dolichandra unguis-cati*

Bijlia (*Aizoaceae*)

tugwelliae	SSim

Bilderdykia see *Fallopia*

Billardiera (*Pittosporaceae*)

longiflora	CBcs CHll CKel CRos CSBt EBee EHyd EPfP LRHS MAsh MGil MGos

MRav SCob SCoo SEdd SNig SPoG SWvt
- 'Cherry Berry' CBcs CRos EHyd EPfP LRHS SPoG SRms SWvt
- 'Fructu-albo' CBcs EHyd EPfP LRHS NLar SPoG SWvt

Billbergia ✿ (*Bromeliaceae*)

buchholtzii NPic
chlorosticta hort. Saunders NPic
distachya NPic
elegans NPic
euphemiae NPic
- var. ***purpurea*** NPic
'Hallelujah' NPic
horrida NPic
- var. ***tigrina*** hort. ex Baker NPic
magnifica NPic
nutans CCCN CHll EAri EShb LEdu NGBl NPic SChr SEND SPlb WSFF
- var. ***schimperiana*** EShb
* - 'Variegata' (v) CCCN CHll CPla EAri ELan EShb NCft SChr WCot
pyramidalis NPic
rosea hort. ex Beer NPic
'Santa Barbara' (v) NPic SChr
vittata NPic
× ***windii*** 🏆H1b EAri NCft NPic
aff. × ***windii*** **new** SRms
zebrina NPic

Biophytum (*Oxalidaceae*)

sensitivum CDoC WSFF

Biscutella (*Brassicaceae*)

laevigata MACG

Biserrula (*Fabaceae*)

pelecinus LShi

Bismarckia (*Arecaceae*)

nobilis CCCN LPal NPlm

Bistorta see *Persicaria*

Bituminaria (*Fabaceae*)

bituminosa CKel WCot

blackberry see *Rubus fruticosus*; see also AGM Fruit Section

blackcurrant see *Ribes nigrum*; see also AGM Fruit Section

Blechnum (*Blechnaceae*)

alpinum see *B. penna-marina* subsp. *alpinum*
brasiliense 🏆H1a ESwi IKel SPlb WCot
- 'Volcano' CBcs CBct CBdn CBrP CMiW CTsd LBuc LCro LOPS LRHS LWaG MSCN SMrm SPad SPoG
cartilagineum CDTJ
§ ***chilense*** 🏆H4 CDTJ CKel CLAP CTsd EBee ECha EHyd ELan EPfP EWes GAbr GBin IBal IKel LEdu LPal LRHS MWht NBro NRHS SArc SMad SPlb SRms WCru XSte
cycadifolium CDTJ CTsd IKel LEdu WPGP
discolor IKel XSte
- 'Silver Lady' CDoC
fluviatile CDTJ IKel
gibbum 🏆H1a CDoC CKel IKel LPal LRHS SPlb
- 'Silver Lady' EShb ISha
longicauda IKel
magellanicum misapplied see *B. chilense*
magellanicum (Desv.) Mett. IKel LEdu SPlb
minus IKel LEdu
montanum IKel LEdu
§ ***niponicum*** GEdr WCot
novae-zelandiae CTrC CTsd IKel XSte
nudum CBdn CDTJ IKel LEdu LPal
palmiforme IKel LEdu WPGP
penna-marina Widely available
§ - subsp. ***alpinum*** EBee ECha EPfP GEdr NWad SHar WAbe
- - BR 68 GEdr
- 'Cristatum' CLAP GAbr GEdr NBro NHar NWad
spicant 🏆H6 Widely available
tabulare misapplied see *B. chilense*
tabulare (Thunb.) Kuhn CBcs CBdn CDTJ CKel CTsd IKel LEdu WCot
vulcanicum CPla
wattsii LEdu

Blepharocalyx (*Myrtaceae*)

§ ***cruckshanksii*** CBcs CCCN CMCN CSde CTsd MGil MHtn MMuc MVil SVen WLov WPGP
- 'Heaven Scent' see *B. cruckshanksii*

Blephilia (*Lamiaceae*)

ciliata SPhx

Bletilla (*Orchidaceae*)

sp. NDav
Brigantes gx NLAp
Coritani gx NLAp
formosana NLAp
hyacinthina see *B. striata*
ochracea LAma NLAp SDir
Penway Dragon gx NLAp
§ ***striata*** 🏆H4 CBct CBor CDoC CTri CTsd EBee EMor EPot EWoo GAbr GKev LAma LCro LEdu LOPS LRHS MHer MNHC MNrw NBPC NRHS SDeJ SDir SIvy SPer SPlb WCot WFar XLum
- ***alba*** see *B. striata* f. *gebina*
- 'Albostriata' CBct EHed ELan EMor ESwi SEdd WCot WSHC XLum
- BLUE DRAGON see *B. striata* 'Soryu'
- blue-flowered NLAp
§ - f. ***gebina*** CBod CTri EBee ELan GKev LAma LCro LEdu LOPS LRHS MACG NLAp NRHS SDeJ SDir SIvy SPeP SPer WCot XLum
- - variegated (v) EBee GKev LAma LEdu
- 'Kuchi-beni' EBee GKev LAma LRHS NLAp SDir SEdd
- 'Lips' GKev LAma NLAp SDir
- pink-flowered **new** LAma
- 'Shi-ran' EBee LRHS
§ - 'Soryu' CBor EHed GKev LAma LRHS MHol SDir SPeP WTyc WWke
- variegated (v) CTtf EMor GKev
- yellow-flowered GKev
Yokohama gx 'Sweet Lips' GKev

Bloomeria (*Asparagaceae*)

crocea var. ***aurea*** NRog
humilis NRog

blueberry see *Vaccinium corymbosum*; see also AGM Fruit Section

Blumea (*Asteraceae*)

balsamifera CHab

Bocconia (Papaveraceae)

cordata see *Macleaya cordata* (Willd.) R. Br.
frutescens B&SWJ 10654 WCru
microcarpa see *Macleaya microcarpa*

Boehmeria (Urticaceae)

CMBJP 1941 **new** GGro
holosericea GGro
CMBJP 2095 **new**
japonica var. ***tenera*** GGro
'Chantilly' (v) **new**
aff. ***japonica*** GGro
CMBJP 1943 **new**
nipononivea GGro
'Kogane-mushi' (v)
aff. ***nipononivea*** GGro
CMBJP 1924 **new**
nivea LEdu LPla WCot WPGP
platanifolia EWld MNrw
aff. ***platanifolia*** GGro
- CMBJP 1909 **new** GGro
sieboldiana EBee EMor EPPr GGro LPla SBrt SDix WFar
splitgerbera **new** GGro
tricuspis EPPr
- PB 96.976 WPGP
- var. ***unicuspis*** EWld GGro
- - CMBJP 1907 **new** GGro
virgata var. ***rotundifolia*** WPGP
PB 02.530

Boenninghausenia (Rutaceae)

albiflora B&SWJ 1479 WCru

Bolax (Apiaceae)

glebaria see *B. gummifer*
§ ***gummifer*** GEdr SPlb WAbe WFar

Bolboschoenus (Cyperaceae)

§ ***maritimus*** LPfP

Boltonia (Asteraceae)

asteroides GQue NGrd NWsh SMrm SPer XLum
- var. ***latisquama*** GMaP MACG MHol MRav NCth NLar SHar XLum
- - JIM CROCKETT ('Masbolimket'[PBR]) EBee
- - 'Nana' EWTr MACG
- - 'Snowbank' CAby ELan MSpe WCAu WGoo
decurrens EMor EPPr
incisa see *Kalimeris incisa*

Bomarea (Alstroemeriaceae)

acuminata see *B. andreana*
acutifolia EAri EBee WCot
- B&SWJ 14291 WCru
- F&M 104 WPGP
§ ***andreana*** B&SWJ 14310 WCru
- B&SWJ 14376 WCru
aff. ***andreana*** B&SWJ 10617 WCru
boliviensis misapplied see *Alstroemeria isabellana*
boliviensis Baker EAri
aff. ***bredemeyerana*** WCru
B&SWJ 14706
- B&SWJ 14725 WCru
caldasii see *B. multiflora*
costaricensis EAri EBee
- B&SWJ 10467 WCru
§ ***edulis*** ♀H3 CPla CRHN EWld MGil WAvo WCot WPav
- B&SWJ 9017 WCru
'Fiesta' WCot
frondea see *B. multiflora*
hirsuta CPla EAri
- B&SWJ 14442 WCru
- B&SWJ 14902 WCru
hirtella see *B. edulis*
§ ***multiflora*** ♀H2 CCCN CTsd EBee SBrt WCot WCru WFar WPGP WSHC
- B&SWJ 14347 WCru
- B&SWJ 14354 WCru
- B&SWJ 14406 WCru
- B&SWJ 14419 EAri WCru
- B&SWJ 14847 WCru
aff. ***multiflora*** B&SWJ 14730 WCru
- B&SWJ 14946 WCru
ovallei CCCN
patacocensis JCA 13987 WCot
patinii B&SWJ 14213 WCru
- B&SWJ 14310 WCru
- B&SWJ 14895 WCru
puracensis B&SWJ 14705 WCru
- B&SWJ 14729 WCru
salsilla ♀H3 CAvo CCCN
setacea B&SWJ 10681 WCru
- B&SWJ 14875 WCru

Bombax (Malvaceae)

ceiba SPlb

Bongardia (Berberidaceae)

chrysogonum CAvo EHyd EPot GKev NRHS

Bonia (Poaceae)

§ ***solida*** MMuc MWht SEND

Boquila (Lardizabalaceae)

trifoliolata CBcs WCru

borage see *Borago officinalis*

Borago (Boraginaceae)

laxiflora see *B. pygmaea*
officinalis CBod CCBP CHby CLau ENfk EPfP GPoy LCro LOPS MBow MHer MHoo MNHC MPri NBir SEdi SPhx SRms SVic
- 'Alba' CBod ENfk LCro LOPS LRHS MBow MHoo SEdi SPhx SRms WJek
§ ***pygmaea*** CAby CSpe EWld MHer MHoo MNrw NBir NChi NSti SBut SRms WHer WJek

borecole see AGM Vegetables Section

Borinda (Poaceae)

KR 5287 MWht
KR 5600 MWht
KR 6438 MWht
KR 6439 MWht
KR 7346 MWht
KR 7613 MWht
KR 7662 MWht
albocerea ♀H4 EPfP MWht
- Yunnan 2 CDTJ
- Yunnan 3a CDTJ
angustissima CDTJ EPfP LPar MMuc MWht NLar XSte
boliana SSut
frigida CDTJ
- KR 4059 MWht
grossa CDTJ
- KR 5931 MWht
'Harlequin' WCot

lushuiensis	WCot
§ - Yunnan 4	CDTJ MWht
macclureana	WCot
- KR 5051	MWht
- KR 5177 from Gyala, Nepal	MWht
aff. ***macclureana*** KR 6900	MWht
nujiangensis	CDTJ WPGP
papyrifera	MWht WCot WPGP XSte
- CS 1046	CBdn CJun MWht
- KR 3968	MWht
perlonga Yunnan 6	MWht
Yunnan 4	see *B. lushuiensis* Yunnan 4

Boronia (*Rutaceae*)

anemonifolia 'Pink Star'	LCro
crenulata	CBcs CCCN
heterophylla	CAbb CBcs CBod CCCN CKel CSde CTsd ECre EGrI EPfP MPkF SEle SIvy WCot XSte
- 'Ice Charlotte'	CBod CCCN CTsd SEle

Bossiaea (*Fabaceae*)

riparia	SPlb
scolopendria	SPlb

Bothriochloa (*Poaceae*)

§ ***bladhii***	CKno EBee EPPr SMHy SRms
caucasica	see *B. bladhii*
§ ***ischaemum***	EPPr

Bougainvillea (*Nyctaginaceae*)

'Alexandra'	CCCN SPre SWeb
§ × ***buttiana*** 'Poulton's Special' ♀H2	CHll
glabra ♀H2	SPre
§ - 'Sanderiana'	SWeb
'Poultonii Special'	see *B.* × *buttiana* 'Poulton's Special'
'Sanderiana'	see *B. glabra* 'Sanderiana'
'Sentimento'	CCCN
Vera Series	CCCN

Boussingaultia (*Basellaceae*)

baselloides Hook.	see *Anredera cordifolia*

Bouteloua (*Poaceae*)

curtipendula	LPla
§ ***gracilis***	CBWd CBod SBls

Bouvardia (*Rubiaceae*)

ternifolia	EBee ESwi WCot WSHC

Bowiea (*Asparagaceae*)

volubilis	GKev LAma SPlb

Bowkeria (*Stilbaceae*)

sp.	CCCN
cymosa	SPlb SVen

Boykinia (*Saxifragaceae*)

aconitifolia	CElw CMac GEdr GLog MACG NRya WCru
elata	see *B. occidentalis*
heucheriformis	see *B. jamesii*
§ ***jamesii***	CPla
lycoctonifolia	LEdu NLar
§ ***occidentalis***	MBriF WCru
rotundifolia	EPPr NBir WCru
tellimoides	see *Peltoboykinia tellimoides*

boysenberry see *Rubus* 'Boysenberry'

Brachychilum see *Hedychium*

Brachychiton (*Malvaceae*)

acerifolius	EAri SPlb WJur
bidwillii	EShb
discolor	WJur
populneus	EAri SPlb WJur
§ ***rupestris***	EAri EShb

Brachyglottis (*Asteraceae*)

§ ***bidwillii***	CBcs EBee WCot WPGP
- 'Basil Fox'	WAbe
§ ***compacta***	EHyd LRHS MAsh SPer
Dunedin Group	CWal
- 'Drysdale'	CRos EHyd ELan EPfP LRHS NRHS SCoo SGBe SGsty SWvt
§ - 'Sunshine' ♀H4	Widely available
greyi misapplied	see *B.* (Dunedin Group) 'Sunshine'
greyi ambig.	CBod NBwr
§ ***greyi*** (Hook. f.) B. Nord.	CMac
greyi × ***repanda***	GDam
huntii	SVen
laxifolia misapplied	see *B.* (Dunedin Group) 'Sunshine'
§ ***monroi***	CBcs CMac CSBt CWal EHyd ELan EPfP LRHS MAsh MRav SVen WFar
§ ***rotundifolia***	CCCN EBee ELan WCot
'Silver Waves'	CBod CKel
I 'Sunshine Improved'	CBcs CBrac MAsh MPri SGbt
WALBERTON'S SILVER DORMOUSE ('Walbrach'PBR) ♀H4	CBcs CBod CEme CRos CSBt EBee EHyd ELan EPfP GBin LRHS MGos MRav MTin NCou NLar NRHS NSti SCob SCoo SPoG SWvt WNPC

Brachypodium (*Poaceae*)

pinnatum	EPPr
sylvaticum	CHab MMuc SEND

Brachyscome (*Asteraceae*)

angustifolia 'Billabong Mauve Delight'PBR	LSou
- BRASCO VIOLET ('Dbrasc9'PBR) (Brasco Series) **new**	WHil
'Magenta Delight'	LSou MDon WHil
'Royal Blue'	WHil

Bracteantha see *Xerochrysum*

Brahea (*Arecaceae*)

armata ♀H1c	CBrP CDTJ CPHo CTsd LPal NPlm SArc SPlb
calcarea	NPlm
decumbens	NPlm
edulis	CCCN CPHo LPal NPlm SChr
'Super Silver'	CPHo NPlm

Brainea (*Blechnaceae*)

insignis	WPGP

Brasiliopuntia (*Cactaceae*)

§ ***brasiliensis*** **new**	EAri

Brassaia see *Schefflera*

Brassaiopsis (*Araliaceae*)

dumicola KWJ 12217 **new**	WCru

Brassica (*Brassicaceae*)

japonica	see *B. juncea* var. *crispifolia*
juncea	SVic
§ - var. ***crispifolia***	MNHC
- f. ***juncea***	MBros
oleracea	CAgr CLau SVic WHer
- var. ***ramosa***	LEdu NGrd

- - 'Cotswold Cream' (v)	WCot
- - 'D'Aubenton Panaché' (v)	WCot
- - 'Luigi Leopold' (v) **new**	WCot
rapa	SVic
- subsp. ***nipposinica*** var. ***laciniata***	LCro SVic

× *Brigandra* see *Oreocharis*

Briggsia (*Gesneriaceae*)

Briggsia × *Opithandra* see *Oreocharis*

Brighamia (*Campanulaceae*)

insignis	CCCN LCro SPad

Brillantaisia (*Acanthaceae*)

kirungae	CCCN EShb

Brimeura (*Asparagaceae*)

§ ***amethystina*** ♀H5	EGrI EPri GBin LEdu SDeJ WPGP WThu
- 'Alba'	EGrI SDeJ

Briza (*Poaceae*)

maxima	CTtf NGdn NWad SPhx
media	Widely available
- 'Golden Bee'	CBWd CKno CRos EHyd EPPr EPfP EWes LEdu LRHS MMrt NRHS SMad SPhx WMal
- 'Limouzi'	CAby CBod CElw CKel CKno CWCL ELon EPPr GBee GBin LEdu LRHS MACG MAvo NLar NSti SMHy SMad SPoG WPnP XLum
- 'Romany Silver'	LEdu
- 'Russells'PBR	CBod CDor CTtf EBee ELan ELon EPfP LEdu MACG MGos NLar NRHS NWsh SCob SPer SPoG SRms SWvt XLum
subaristata	EPPr LPal
triloba	EAJP ECha NWsh SPhx

broccoli see AGM Vegetables Section

Brodiaea (*Asparagaceae*)

§ ***californica***	CSpe EBee ERCP WCot
- NNS 00-109	WCot
- 'Babylon'	EAri ERCP GKev
- lavender-flowered	NRog
- var. ***leptandra***	NRog
- violet-flowered	NRog
'Corrina'	see *Triteleia* 'Corrina'
elegans	NRog
filifolia	NRog
ida-maia	see *Dichelostemma ida-maia*
jolonensis	NRog
kinkiensis	NRog
laxa	see *Triteleia laxa*
§ ***minor***	NRog
pallida	NRog
peduncularis	see *Triteleia peduncularis*
purdyi	see *B. minor*
stellaris	NRog

Bromus (*Poaceae*)

erectus	CHab
- W&B BG B-5	WCot
inermis 'Skinner's Gold' (v)	EPPr WCot

Broussonetia (*Moraceae*)

papyrifera	CMCN ELan ESwi LMaj MGil WAvo WBor WCot WHtc WJur WKor WLov
- 'Golden Shadow'	LRHS XSte

Browallia (*Solanaceae*)

americana	SPhx

Bruckenthalia see *Erica*

Brugmansia (*Solanaceae*)

'Angels Long John' × orange-flowered **new**	CExo
'Angels Long John' × 'Rosalla' **new**	CExo
'Angels Magic Moments' (d) **new**	CExo
'Angels New Fascination' (d) **new**	CExo
§ ***arborea*** ♀H1c	CBcs CDTJ CExo NGKo
* - 'Rosea' variegated (v)	ELan
- variegated (v)	ELan
arborea × ***sanguinea***	see *B.* × *rubella*
aurea	CCCN SAdn
- 'Goldenes Kornett'	CExo
aurea × ***versicolor***	see *B.* × *candida*
aurea × ***suaveolens***	SAdn
§ × ***candida***	CCCN
- 'Alicia' **new**	CExo
- 'Angels Daydream' (d)	CExo
- 'Angels Flight' (d)	CExo
- 'Angels Honeymoon' (d)	CExo
- 'Angels Phänomena' (d)	NGKo
- 'Angels Shredded Dress' (d)	CExo
- 'Angels Sunbeam' (d) ♀H1c	CExo ELan
- 'Creamsickle' (d) ♀H1c	NGKo
- 'Dorthea' **new**	CExo
- 'Double White' (d)	CExo CHll
- double-flowered (d)	SAdn
- 'Eisprinzessin' (d) **new**	CExo
- 'Esmeraldas' **new**	CExo
§ - 'Grand Marnier' ♀H1c	CExo CHll NGKo
- 'Joli' **new**	CExo
§ - 'Knightii' (d) ♀H1c	CDTJ CDow
- 'Kurpark Bad Salzschlirf'	CExo
- 'Maya' (v)	CExo
- 'Pink Perfektion' (d)	CExo NGKo
- 'Plena'	see *B.* × *candida* 'Knightii'
- 'Salmon Perfektion' (d)	CExo
- 'Schloss Burg' (d)	CExo
- 'Super Spot'	CExo
§ - 'Variegata' (v)	CCCN CDTJ CExo NGKo
- 'Wuppergold' (d)	CExo
'Chartreuse'	CDow
cream-flowered **new**	CHll
× ***cubensis*** 'Angels Endless Summer' (d) ♀H1c	CExo
- 'Anja' (d)	CExo
- 'Baby Doll' (d)	CExo CHll
- 'Canarybird'	CExo
- 'Charles Grimaldi'	CExo NGKo
- ('Costa Rican Lady' × 'Sarah-Sophie') **new**	CExo
- 'Fandango' (d)	CExo
- 'Georgia Peach' **new**	CExo
- 'Jamie' (v)	NGKo
- 'Jericho' **new**	CExo
- 'Madame Foster'	NGKo
- ('Miss Edith Winnette' × 'Painted Lady') **new**	CExo
- 'Pink Smitty' (d)	CExo
- yellow-flowered **new**	CExo
'Dalen's Pink Amour' (d)	CDow
double orange-flowered (d)	CHll

	'Frosty Pink'	CExo
	insignis	CExo
	'Lilac 1'	CExo
	'Miner's Claim' (v)	NGKo
	'Pink Delight'	CExo
	'Poison' (SA) **new**	CExo
	rosei	see *B. sanguinea*
§	× ***rubella***	CExo
	- 'Gelber Engel' **new**	CExo
	- 'Mobisu'	CExo NGKo
	- ('Mobisu' × 'Wildfire') **new**	CExo
§	***sanguinea*** 🏆H1c	CCCN CDow CExo SAdn SPlb
	sanguinea × ***vulcanicola*** 'Zuñac 4' (VS) **new**	CExo
§	***suaveolens*** 🏆H1c	CBcs
	- 'Variegata' (v)	EShb
	- yellow-flowered	EShb
	'Triple A' (d) **new**	CExo
	'USA Rosa'	NGKo
	'Variegata Sunset'	see *B.* × *candida* 'Variegata'
	versicolor misapplied	see *B. arborea*
§	***versicolor*** Lagerh.	CCCN SAdn
	- 'Apricotqueen'	NGKo
	- 'Ecuador Pink'	CExo
	- 'Ecuador Pink' × 'Versicolor Peach' **new**	CExo
	vulcanicola	CExo
	- 'Zuñac 4' **new**	CExo
	Vulsa, red-flowered (VS)	NGKo
*	'Yellow Trumpet'	ELan

Brunfelsia (*Solanaceae*)

	americana	CCCN WFib
	australis	WFib
	calycina	see *B. pauciflora*
	lactea	CCCN
§	***pauciflora*** 🏆H1c	CCCN EShb

Brunia (*Bruniaceae*)

	albiflora	SPlb

Brunnera ✿ (*Boraginaceae*)

§	***macrophylla***	Widely available
	- 'Alba'	see *B. macrophylla* 'Betty Bowring'
	- ALCHEMY SILVER ('Tnbruas') (Alchemy Series) **new**	IPot
	- 'Alexanders Great'PBR	Widely available
§	- 'Betty Bowring'	Widely available
	- 'Blaukuppel'	CBod EWes NBir
	- 'Dawson's White' (v)	Widely available
	- 'Diane's Gold'PBR	CBcs EBee ECha ECtt EMor LBar MGos MHol MNrw MPri NBid NLar SHeu SPeP
	- 'Emerald Mist'PBR (v)	EBee ECtt EMor LPla MBel MGos MTin NCth NLar SWvt WSpi
	- 'Golden Jack Frost'	CBcs CBct CBod MPnt
	- 'Gordano Gold' (v)	WCot
	- 'Green Gold' (v)	EMor NLar WFar
	- 'Hadspen Cream' (v) 🏆H6	Widely available
	- 'Henry's Eyes'	EBee EPfP
	- 'Jack Frost'PBR 🏆H6	Widely available
	- 'Jack's Gold'PBR	EMor GKev LBar MSCN NCth NSti
	- 'Jennifer'	EMor LBar MBel NLar NSti WCAu
	- 'Joanna'	NSum
	- 'King's Ransom'PBR (v)	CWGN EMor GPSL NLar NSti SCob WFar
	- 'Langtrees'	CBct CMac EBee ECha MCot MMuc NBir NGdn SEND SPer WSpi
	- 'Little Jack' (v)	CRos EBee EHyd EMor EPfP LRHS LSou NRHS SPoG
	- 'Looking Glass'PBR 🏆H6	Widely available
	- 'Marley's White'	EMor
§	- 'Mister Morse'PBR (v) 🏆H6	CDor CExl CWGN ECtt EHed EMor GDam GMaP GMcL LEdu MACG MAvo MBel MCot MNrw MPnt MPri NBir NGdn NLar NSti SCob SWvt WCAu WCot WFar WSpi
	- 'Queen of Hearts' **new**	LBar
	- 'Sea Heart'PBR	CSpe EBee ECha ECtt EMor EPfP IPot LCro LEdu LRHS LSou MAvo MBel NGdn NLar NSti SCob SHeu WCAu WPnP
	- 'Silver Heart'PBR	CCht CDor CWGN ECtt EHed EMor LRHS LSou MCot MSCN NCth SCob SCoo SGBe SHeu SPad WBor
	- 'Silver Lining' **new**	EMor
	- 'Silver Spear'	CDor EBee GAbr GElm LRHS LSun MGos NGBl NLar SCoo SPoG WCAu WCav WCot WHoo
	- 'Silver Wings'	CElw EBee ECtt EPfP GKev MBel MGos NBir NGdn NLar NSti WCAu WFar
	- 'Spring Yellow'	WCAu
	- 'Starry Eyes'	MCot
	- 'Sterling Silver'	IPot LBuc MPri NCth WTor
	'Mrs Morse'	see *B. macrophylla* 'Mister Morse'
	sibirica	EBee EPPr EWes NBid NLar WCAu

Brunsvigia (*Amaryllidaceae*)

	bosmaniae	WCot
	elandsmontana	WCot
	josephinae	WCot
	- LAV 30394	WCot
	marginata	WCot
	multiflora	see *B. orientalis*
§	***orientalis***	WCot
	pulchra	WCot
	radulosa	WCot
	rosea 'Minor'	see *Amaryllis belladonna*

Brussels sprouts see AGM Vegetables Section

Bryonia (*Cucurbitaceae*)

	dioica	GGro GPoy

Bryophyllum see *Kalanchoe*

Buddleja ✿ (*Scrophulariaceae*)

	W&O 7061	GGro
	agathosma	CExl WCFE WLav WPGP WSHC
	albiflora	WLav
	- BO 15-041	GGro
	alternifolia 🏆H6	Widely available
	- 'Argentea'	CBcs CDoC EHyd ELan EPfP EShb LRHS MBNS MRav NLar SPer SPoG SWvt WCot WLav XSen
	asiatica 🏆H3	EShb WLav
	- B&SWJ 11278	WCru
	asiatica × ***lindleyana***	WSpi
	auriculata	CBcs CExl CMCN CSde CTrC ELan EPPr EPfP IArd IDee LAlb MGil NSti SDix SPlb SVen WGwG WLav
	'Bel Argent'	EBee WPGP
	BERRIES AND CREAM ('Pmoore14'PBR)	CDoC CSBt LCro SGBe
	'Blue Chip Junior' (Lo and Behold Series)	SPoG
	'Blue Chip'PBR (Lo and Behold Series)	EPfP LBuc LPar LSou MAsh MGos NLar SGol SRms SWvt WCot WFar WLav
*	'Blue Trerice'	CExl
	caryopteridifolia	EBtc MGil SEND
	colvilei	CBcs CCCN CKel ELan EPfP GBin GKin IArd IDee LRHS SSha SWvt WBor WSpi

- B&SWJ 2121	WCru
- GWJ 9399	WCru
- WJC 13760	WCru
- 'Kewensis'	CExl CRHN ELan EPfP EWes LAlb MGil NLar SMad SVen WCFE WLav WLov WSHC
- large-leaved	SBrt
- pink-flowered	EHed EPPr EShb GBin MGil NLar WSpi
- 'Tregye'	WPGP
cordata	LRHS SVen
- B&SWJ 10433	WCru
§ ***crispa***	CBcs CDoC CDow CExl CKel EBee ECha EHyd ELan EPfP LRHS SPer SVen SWvt WFar WKif WPGP WSHC WSpi
- var. ***farreri***	MGil SPoG
- - Farrer 44 **new**	WPGP
- 'Stone House Cottage'	CKel WSHC
davidii	CCVT CDoC NPol NWea WTSh
- B&SWJ 8083	WCru
- ADONIS BLUE ('Adokeep'PBR)	CBcs CSBt MAsh SCob SPoG WLav
- 'African Queen'	CRos EPfP WLav
- var. ***alba***	LShi
- 'Apollonaria'	WLav
§ - 'Autumn Beauty'	WLav
- 'Beijing'	see *B. davidii* 'Autumn Beauty'
- 'Billy's Blue'	WLav
- 'Black Knight' ♀H6	Widely available
- 'Blue Eyes'	WLav
- 'Blue Horizon' ♀H6	ELon LRHS NLar SRGP WCot WLav
- 'Border Beauty'	CRos LRHS NBwr WLav
- 'Butterfly Heaven'PBR	WLav
- BUTTERFLY TOWER ('Tobud1305') **new**	CBod WNPC
- Buzz Series	LBuc MDon NHol SOrN
- - BUZZ CANDY PINK ('Tobudsopin')	CBod CDoC CPla CRos EHyd ELan GJos LRHS LSou NRHS SPad SPoG WFar WLav
- - BUZZ HOT RASPBERRY	CSBt ELan GJos LRHS MPri NPer SCoo SGBe WFar WLav
- - BUZZ INDIGO	CBod CDoC CRos CSBt EHyd ELan EPfP LRHS LSRN LSou MACG MPri NRHS SGBe WLav
- - BUZZ IVORY ('Tobudivory'PBR)	CBod CEnd CMac CRos EHyd ELan EPfP GMcL LRHS LSRN MGos NHol NLar NRHS SCob SPer SPoG SSha WCot WLav WSpi
- - BUZZ LILAC	ELan MGos NHol
- - BUZZ MAGENTA IMPROVED ('Tobudmagen')	CNor MBros MPri
- - BUZZ MAGENTA ('Tobudpipur'PBR)	CBod CChe CDoC CEnd CGBo CKel CMac CSBt EHyd ELan GMcL LRHS LSRN MGos NHol NLar NRHS SCob SCoo SGBe SPoG SRms SSha SWvt WFar WLav WSpi
- - BUZZ SKY BLUE ('Tobudskybl'PBR)	CDoC CGBo CKel CMac CRos EGrI EHyd EPfP GJos GMcL LRHS MBros MGos MPri NHol NLar NRHS SCoo SGBe SPer SPoG SRms WFar WLav
- - BUZZ VELVET ('Tobudvelve'PBR)	CRos EGrI ELan EPfP LRHS NRHS SPer WCav
- - BUZZ VIOLET ('Tobudviole')	CBod CDoC CGBo CKel CSBt EGrI EHyd ELan EPfP GDam GJos GMcL LRHS MGos NHol NLar NRHS SCob SPer SPoG SWvt WHtc WLav
- CAMBERWELL BEAUTY ('Camkeep') (English Butterfly Series) ♀H6	MAsh WLav
- 'Castle Blue'	CRos LRHS
- 'Castle School'	WLav
- 'Clive Farrell'	see *B. davidii* 'Autumn Beauty'
- 'Corinne Tremaine'	WHer
- 'Cotswold Blue'	WLav
- 'Cotswold Twilight'	WLav
- 'Dartmoor' ♀H6	Widely available
- 'Dart's Ornamental White'	MRav WLav
- 'Dart's Papillon Blue'	LRHS WLav
- 'Dart's Purple Rain'	LRHS WLav
- 'Dubonnet'	WLav
- 'Ecolonia'	WLav
- 'Empire Blue'	CBcs CDoC CSBt ECtt EHyd EPfP GKin LRHS LSRN MAsh MGos NBir NPer NRHS NWea SCoo SGBe SPer SPlb SPoG SRHi SRms SWvt WHtc XSen
- 'Fair Lady'	WLav
- 'Fascinating'	MRav NBir WLav
- 'Flaming Violet'	WLav
- FLORENCE ('Watflor')	NLar SCob WFar
- 'Foxtail'	WLav
- 'Glasnevin Hybrid'	EPfP LRHS NLar WLav
- 'Golden Sunset'	EDir
- 'Gonglepod'	CRos LRHS WLav
- 'Greenway's River Dart'	LRHS
- 'Grey Dawn'	WLav
- 'Griffin Blue'	WLav
- 'Gulliver'PBR	CBod EHyd LRHS NLar NRHS SCob SGol WFar WLav
- 'Harlequin' (v)	CBcs CMac CTsd EHed ELan EPfP GMcL LRHS MAsh MGos MSwo NBwr NLar NRHS NWea SEND SGBe SGol SPer SPlb SPoG SRms SWvt WFar WHtc WLov XSen
- 'Île de France'	LPar NLar NWea SRms WLav
- 'Leela Kapila'	LRHS
- 'Les Kneale'	WLav
- 'Lilac Moon'	WLav
- 'Loganberry Jam'	WLav
- 'Longstock Autumn Delight'	LRHS
- MARBLED WHITE ('Markeep') (English Butterfly Series)	CBod EShb NEoE WLav
- MASQUERADE ('Notbud') (v)	MRav
- MOONSHINE ('Buddma'PBR)	NEoE WFar
§ - NANHO BLUE ('Mongo')	CBcs CMac CRos CSBt EDir EPfP GKev GKin GMcL LPar LRHS MAsh MGos MRav MSwo NBir NLar NRHS SCoo SGol WSpi XSen
- 'Nanho Petite Indigo'	see *B. davidii* NANHO BLUE
- 'Nanho Petite Plum'	see *B. davidii* NANHO PURPLE
- 'Nanho Petite Purple'	see *B. davidii* NANHO PURPLE
§ - NANHO PURPLE ('Monum') ♀H6	CBcs CMac CRos CTri EPfP LRHS LSRN MGos MRav NLar NRHS SGol SPer SPlb SRms XSen
- NANHO WHITE ('Monite') ♀H6	CMac CRos EPfP GKev LRHS SGol SRms XSen
- var. ***nanhoensis***	SGol WFar WLav
- - BO 15043 **new**	GGro
- - blue-flowered	EPfP NWad
- 'Orchid Beauty'	LRHS WLav
- 'Orpheus'	CRos EPfP LRHS WLav
- 'Panache'	CRos EHyd EPfP LRHS MAsh NRHS WLav
- 'Peace'	CMac CTri LSRN NLar SPoG WLav
- PEACOCK ('Peakeep'PBR) (English Butterfly Series)	CSBt GMcL MAsh SCob WLav
- 'Persephone'	WLav
- 'Petite Indigo'	see *B. davidii* NANHO BLUE

- 'Pink Beauty'	LSRN MBlu SRGP WFar
- 'Pink Pearl'	WLav
- 'Pink Spreader'	LRHS WLav
- 'Pixie Blue'	GMcL LBuc MAsh NLar WLav
- 'Pixie Red'	GMcL LBuc MAsh NLar WLav
- 'Pixie White'	LBuc MAsh NLar SCob SGol WLav
- PURPLE EMPEROR ('Pyrkeep') (English Butterfly Series)	NBir WLav
- 'Purple Friend'	LRHS WLav
- 'Purple Prince'	NBwr
- RÊVE DE PAPILLON BLUE ('Minpap3')	WLav
- RÊVE DE PAPILLON ('Minpap')	CRos EHyd LRHS MAsh NRHS SCoo WLav
- 'Royal Purple'	SWvt
- 'Royal Red' 🏆H6	Widely available
- 'Saith Ffynnon Early'	WSFF
- 'Santana' (v)	CMac EHyd ELon EPfP EWes GMcL LRHS MAsh MGos NBwr NHol NLar NRHS NWad SCob SGol SPoG SRms SWvt WAvo WHlf WSpi XSen
- 'Shire Blue'	WLav
- 'Son of Orpheus'	WLav
- 'Sophie'PBR	EBee NLar
- 'Southcombe Splendour'	CRos LRHS
- 'Summer Beauty'	MBlu WLav
- 'Summerhouse Blue'	EMil SGBe WLav
- 'Twotones'	WLav
- 'Variegata' (v)	MAsh SWvt WLav
- 'White Ball'	ELan NLar WLav
- 'White Bouquet'	CBod CCVT CSBt EPfP GKin MSwo NLar NWea SPer SRGP SWvt WLav XSen
- 'White Cloud'	EPfP LRHS SRms WGwG
- 'White Harlequin' (v)	WCFE
- 'White Profusion' 🏆H6	Widely available
- 'White Wings'	CRos LRHS WLav
- 'Wisteria Lane'	CBod LCro LOPS NLar SPad WHlf WNPC
davidii* × *fallowiana	WSpi
§ ***delavayi***	CExl ECre GBin SEND WCru
DREAMING LAVENDER ('Hinebud1'PBR)	CBod WNPC
DREAMING PURPLE ('Hinebud4'PBR)	LSou NLar WNPC
DREAMING WHITE ('Hinebud3'PBR)	LSou NLar WNPC
'Ellen's Blue'	CRos ELon EPfP LRHS NLar WLav
fallowiana misapplied	see *B.* 'West Hill'
fallowiana Balf.f. & W.W.Sm.	CRos LRHS WLav
- ACE 2481	LRHS
- BWJ 7803	WCru
- var. ***alba*** 🏆H5	CMac CRos EHyd ELan EPPr EPfP LRHS MBNS MRav NLar NRHS SDix WLov
- 'Bishop's Violet'	CTsd
'Flower Power'	see *B.* × *weyeriana* 'Bicolor'
(Flutterby Series) FLUTTERBY PINK ('Podaras 9'PBR)	EMil
(Flutterby Flow Series) FLUTTERBY FLOW LAVENDER ('Podaras 12')	LCro LOPS
(Flutterby Petite Series) FLUTTERBY PETITE BLUE HEAVEN ('Podaras 8'PBR)	CBod LCro LOPS MThu NLar
- FLUTTERBY PETITE DARK PINK ('Podaras 10'PBR)	CBod LCro LOPS NLar
- FLUTTERBY PETITE PINK ('Podaras 16') **new**	EBee
- FLUTTERBY PETITE SNOW WHITE ('Podaras 15'PBR)	CBod LCro LOPS LSto NLar
- FLUTTERBY PETITE TUTTI FRUITTI PINK ('Podaras 13'PBR)	CBod CSBt LAlb LCro LOPS SRms
forrestii	WCru
- BWJ 8020	EBee WCru
globosa 🏆H5	Widely available
- RCB/Arg C-11	WCot
- 'Cally Orange'	GBin WGwG
- 'Cannington Gold'	CWal
- cream-flowered HCM 98.017	WPGP
- 'Lemon Ball'	LRHS MBlu NPer WLav
glomerata	EShb LAlb MGil SPlb SSha
- 'Silver Service'	CDow CKel CPla EPfP LRHS SMad
heliophila	see *B. delavayi*
indica	WLav
INSPIRED PINK	see *B.* × *weyeriana* 'Pink Pagoda'
japonica B&SWJ 8912	WCru
'Lilac Chip' (Lo and Behold Series)	CDoC LPar NLar SGol
limitanea	SPtp
- from Cangshan, Yunnan, China	SBrt
lindleyana	Widely available
- 'Little Treasure'	NEoE
- 'Miss Vicie'	LRHS
aff. ***lindleyana***	EShb WLov WSpi
- B&SWJ 11478	WCru
'Lochinch' 🏆H5	Widely available
longifolia	WPGP
'Longstock Gem'	SGBe
'Longstock Silver'	LRHS
loricata	CExl CMCN EHyd EPPr EPfP GBin LRHS LShi MGil SBrt SPlb WCFE WLav WSpi XSen
macrostachya	WCot WPGP
- HWJ 602	WCru
- PAB 4198 **new**	WCot
- WWJ 12016	WCru
§ ***madagascariensis*** 🏆H2	CRHN EShb NLar SPlb SVen
marrubiifolia × ***saligna*** **new**	WPGP
megalocephala B&SWJ 9106	WCru WPGP
'Miss Ruby'PBR 🏆H5	CDoC EBee LBuc LPar LRHS LSRN MAsh NRHS WLav
§ 'Morning Mist'PBR	CBcs CDoC CExl CKel CMac CSBt CWGN EPfP GBin LAlb LCro LOPS LPar LRHS LSRN NHol NRHS SGBe SRms SSha SWvt WCot WFar WHlf XSte
myriantha	CExl WPGP
nicodemia	see *B. madagascariensis*
nivea	CExl MGil WLav WSpi XSen
- B&SWJ 2679	WCru
aff. ***nivea***	WSpi
officinalis 🏆H3	CExl WLav
paniculata	WPGP
- GWJ 9286 from Sikkim	WCru
parvifolia MPF 148	WLav
× ***pikei*** 'Hever'	SRms XSen
- UNIQUE ('Pmoore12'PBR)	CBod CDoC CMac LCro LOPS NLar SGBe SPad SPoG SRkn WCot WHlf XSte
'Pink Delight' 🏆H5	Widely available
'Pink Micro Chip' (Lo and Behold Series)	SPoG
'Pink Perfection'	WFar
'Pride of Hever'	SDys
'Pride of Longstock'	LAlb SPoG
pterocaulis	EBee
'Purple Chip' (Lo and Behold Series)	LPar

'Purple Splendour'	GJos
'Red Chip' (Lo and Behold Series)	SGol
saligna	WPGP
'Salmon Spheres'	WLav
salviifolia	CBcs CBct CCCN CExl CMac CSde CTrC CTsd EBee IDee LRHS MBlu MGil NLar SBrt SEND SPlb SVen WAvo WCFE WGwG WKif WLav WLov WPGP
- white-flowered	EBee WPGP
SILVER ANNIVERSARY	see *B.* 'Morning Mist'
speciosissima	WPGP
stachyoides	WLav WPGP
stenostachya	CBcs CExl
sterniana	see *B. crispa*
SUGAR PLUM ('Lonplum'^{PBR})	CBrac CKel CSBt EGrl EHyd EMil EPfP LBuc LCro LOPS LRHS MAsh NRHS SGBe SPoG WNPC
SUMMER BIRD COMPACT PURPLE (Summer Bird Series) **new**	CGBo
tibetica	see *B. crispa*
TRUE BLUE ('Bostulu'^{PBR})	EBee MMrt NLar WHlf
tubiflora	WLav
venenifera B&SWJ 895	EBee
- B&SWJ 6036	WCru
× ***wardii*** KR 4881	WPGP
§ 'West Hill' ♀^{H5}	CRos EHyd EPfP LRHS NRHS WLav
× ***weyeriana***	CMac ECtt EPPr EWTr GJos MBNS MGil MNrw MSwo NBir SIvy SPlb SSha SWvt WAvo WBor WHtc
§ - 'Bicolor'	CBod CWal EBee EHed ELon EPPr EPfP LCro LOPS LSRN MNrw NLar NQui SCob SCoo SRms WHlf WLav WMal XSen XSte
- 'Boy Blue'	WLav
- 'Golden Glow'	GBin LRHS SWvt WLav WSFF XSen
- 'Honeycomb'	CBod EHed EShb MGos NLar SPad
- 'Lady de Ramsey'	NLar SEND
- 'Moonlight'	CDoC CExl ELan EMil EPPr GBin LRHS SPer WCot WLav WMal WSpi XSen
§ - 'Pink Pagoda'^{PBR}	CEme CSBt EPfP LAlb NLar SGBe SPoG
- pink-flowered	XSen
- 'Sungold' ♀^{H6}	Widely available
'White Chip' (Lo and Behold Series)	LPar LSou SGol
yunnanensis	CBcs GGro NLar SBrt
- B&SWJ 8146	WCru

Buglossoides (*Boraginaceae*)

§ ***purpurocaerulea***	ECha EPfP EWld LPla MNrw NBid WCot WFar WKif

Bukiniczia (*Plumbaginaceae*)

cabulica	EDAr

Bulbine (*Asphodelaceae*)

annua misapplied	see *B. semibarbata*
bulbosa misapplied	see *B. semibarbata*
caulescens	see *B. frutescens*
§ ***frutescens***	CBod EDAr LRHS MHer NChi SRms SVen SVic WHlf WJek XLum
- 'Hallmark'	CCCN CKel LRHS
latifolia	CCCN
narcissifolia **new**	WCot
§ ***semibarbata***	CBod CCCN

Bulbinella (*Asphodelaceae*)

angustifolia	GKev MHer WSHC
hookeri	CExl EBee EWld GBee GBin GEdr GKev ITim SMad SRms WCot
latifolia subsp. ***latifolia***	CBor
nutans	EBee

Bulbinopsis see *Bulbine*

Bulbocodium see *Colchicum*

vernum	see *C. bulbocodium*

bullace see *Prunus insititia*

Bunias (*Brassicaceae*)

orientalis	CAgr LEdu

Bunium (*Apiaceae*)

bulbocastanum	CAgr LEdu LRHS SDix SPhx WPGP XLum
ferulaceum	MACG MHol MPie NSti SMad
- W&B BG B-10	WCot

Buphthalmum (*Asteraceae*)

salicifolium	EBee ELan EPfP MMuc NBro NGdn SPer SRms WCot WFar WHil
- 'Alpengold'	ECha GMaP NLar
- 'Dora'	ECtt WCot WFar
- 'Sunwheel'	SRms
speciosum	see *Telekia speciosa*

Bupleurum (*Apiaceae*)

angulosum	NBir
- copper-leaved	see *B. longifolium*
candollei	LEdu SAng WPGP WSHC
falcatum	ECha GMaP LRHS NDov SDix SPhx WCot WKif
- tall	CSpe
fruticescens	XSen
fruticosum	CBcs CBod CCCN CKel CSpe EBee ECre EHyd ELan EPfP EShb EWes GKev LAlb LRHS MNrw NRHS SCob SDix SEND SMad SPer SPoG SPtp WCot WLov WMal WSHC XLum XSen
gibraltaricum	XSen
griffithii 'Decor'	CSpe
§ ***longifolium***	CElw CSpe EBee ECre EWes LEdu MNrw NAts NBPC NBir WFar WPGP
- subsp. ***aureum***	LPla LRHS SPhx
- 'Bronze Beauty'	CPla ELan EMor GEdr MBriF MMrt SPtp
- lime-green-flowered **new**	WPGP
- subsp. ***longifolium***	WPGP
ranunculoides	CSpe LPla LShi SPhx XLum
rotundifolium	CSpe LEdu SAng SPhx WCot
- 'Copper'	NDov

Bursaria (*Pittosporaceae*)

spinosa	CCCN

Butia (*Arecaceae*)

archeri **new**	NPlm
capitata ♀^{H1c}	CCCN CDTJ CPHo ETod LPal LPar NPlm SArc
§ - var. ***odorata***	SArc SPlb
eriospatha	CPHo NPlm
odorata	see *B. capitata* var. *odorata*
paraguayensis **new**	NPlm
yatay	LPal NPlm

Butomus (*Butomaceae*)

umbellatus	CBen CPud CSpe CWat ECha EWat GBin LPfP MNrw MRav MWts NBir NPer SBls WHlf WMAq WWtn

	- f. ***albiflorus***	ECha
	- 'Rosenrot'	EWat LLWG
	- 'Schneeweisschen'	EWat LLWG MWts

butternut see *Juglans cinerea*

butternut squash see AGM Vegetables Section

Buxus ✿ (*Buxaceae*)

	aurea 'Marginata'	see *B. sempervirens* 'Marginata'
	balearica	CJun EBtc WSpi
	bodinieri	LTop
	'Green Gem'	NWad
	'Green Mountain'	CBod
	'Green Velvet'	NWad
	harlandii misapplied	CMen SRiv
	japonica 'Nana'	see *B. microphylla*
	macowanii	LTop
	macrophylla	NWea WSpi
§	***microphylla***	NWad SGol
	- 'Asiatic Winter'	see *B. microphylla* var. *japonica* 'Winter Gem'
	- 'Badsey Kingsville'	WCot
§	- 'Compacta'	CMen MHer WCot
	- 'Faulkner' ♀H6	CBod LBuc LIns MGos SCob SGol SGsty SRiv SRms SSha SWeb WHtc WSpi
	- 'Golden Triumph'PBR (v)	NLar
	- 'Green Pillow'	MHer SRiv WSpi
	- 'Herrenhausen'	WSpi
	- var. ***insularis***	see *B. sinica* var. *insularis*
	- var. ***japonica***	SGol
	- - 'National'	WSpi
§	- - 'Winter Gem'	MRav
	- 'John Baldwin'	SRiv
	- var. ***sinica***	LTop WSpi
	sempervirens	Widely available
§	- 'Angustifolia'	MRav NWad SMad
	- 'Arborescens'	LIns LMaj NBwr
	- 'Argenteo-variegata' (v)	SGol WFar
	- 'Aurea'	see *B. sempervirens* 'Aureovariegata'
	- 'Aurea Maculata'	see *B. sempervirens* 'Aureovariegata'
	- 'Aurea Marginata'	see *B. sempervirens* 'Marginata'
§	- 'Aureovariegata' (v)	EPfP EShb LTop MGos MRav NLar NWad SRiv SRms WHtc
	- 'Bentley Blue'	LTop NWea
	- 'Blauer Heinz'	GQue LTop MRav NWea SRiv SSha WAvo WSpi
	- 'Bowles's Blue'	WCFE
	- 'Bullata'	LMaj
	- clipped ball	CEme CWnw EDir EPfP GDam LSRN LTop MGos NLar SRiv SRms
	- clipped bird	LTop SRiv
	- clipped cone	CEme CWnw EDir GDam LSRN LTop SRiv SRms
	- clipped pyramid	EDir EPfP LSRN LTop MGos NLar SRiv SRms
	- clipped spiral	EDir LSRN LTop NLar SRiv SRms
	- dwarf **new**	WSFF
	- 'Elegans'	LTop
§	- 'Elegantissima' (v) ♀H6	Widely available
	- 'Fiesta'	SRms
	- 'Gold Tip'	see *B. sempervirens* 'Notata'
§	- 'Graham Blandy' ♀H6	MHer SAko SGol SRiv WSpi
	- 'Green Balloon'	LBuc
	- 'Greenpeace'	see *B. sempervirens* 'Graham Blandy'
	- 'Handsworthensis'	LTop NWea SEND SRms WCFE WSpi
	- 'Ickworth Giant'	WSpi
	- 'Japonica Aurea'	see *B. sempervirens* 'Latifolia Maculata'
	- 'Kensington Gardens'	WSpi
	- 'King Midas'	SAko
	- 'Kingsville'	see *B. microphylla* 'Compacta'
	- 'Kingsville Dwarf'	see *B. microphylla* 'Compacta'
	- 'Latifolia'	WMou
§	- 'Latifolia Maculata' (v) ♀H6	CBod EPfP LTop MMuc NPer SEND SPoG SRiv WSpi
	- 'Longifolia'	see *B. sempervirens* 'Angustifolia'
§	- 'Marginata' (v)	LTop NBwr WHtc WSpi
	- 'Memorial'	LTop NWad SRiv WSpi
	- 'Myosotidifolia'	SRiv WCot WSpi
	- 'Myrtifolia'	WSpi
§	- 'Notata' (v)	NBwr WSpi
	- 'Pendula'	WSpi
	- 'Prostrata'	NWad WSpi
	- 'Pylewell'	WSpi
	- 'Raket'	NWea SGsty
	- 'Rosmarinifolia'	MRav
	- 'Rotundifolia'	ELan LIns LTop MMuc SEND WSpi
	- 'Silver Beauty' (v)	CBod
	- 'Silver Variegated'	see *B. sempervirens* 'Elegantissima'
	- 'Suffruticosa'	CArg CBrac CKel CSBt EHeP ELan EShb GPoy LSRN LTop MGos MHed MRav MSwo NHol NLar NWea SCob SEND SGol SRiv SRms SWvt WCFE WSpi
	- 'Suffruticosa Variegata' (v)	SRms SWvt
	- 'Twisty'	WFar
	- 'Vardar Valley'	NWad SRiv WSpi
	- 'Variegata' (v)	CBrac CPla CWal MSwo SArc WHtc
	- 'Wisley Blue'	CBod LTop WSpi
§	***sinica*** var. ***insularis***	LTop
	- - 'Filigree'	NWad WSpi
	- - 'Justin Brouwers'	LPla SRiv SSha WSpi
	- - 'Tide Hill'	LTop SRiv WFar WSpi
	wallichiana	LTop

Bystropogon (*Lamiaceae*)

canariensis **new**	WCot

C

cabbages see AGM Vegetables Section

Cacalia (*Asteraceae*)

suaveolens	see *Hasteola suaveolens*

Cachrys (*Apiaceae*)

alpina	LEdu SBrt SPhx WHil

Caesalpinia (*Fabaceae*)

decapetala	see *Biancaea decapetala*
gilliesii	see *Erythrostemon gilliesii*
pulcherrima ♀H3	CCCN EAri
spinosa	see *Tara spinosa*

Caiophora (*Loasaceae*)

coronata	GEdr

calabrese see AGM Vegetables Section

Caladium (*Araceae*)

'Aaron' (v)	SDir
'Candidum' (v)	SDeJ SDir
'Carolyn Whorton'	SDeJ
'Florida Cardinal' (v)	SDeJ
'Frieda Hempel'	SDeJ SDir
'White Christmas' (v)	SDeJ

Calamagrostis (*Poaceae*)

× ***acutiflora***	XLum
- 'Avalanche'	Widely available
- 'Eldorado' (v)	CKno ECha EPPr LRHS MAvo MMuc WCot
- 'England' (v)	ECha EPPr GBin MNrw WFar
- 'Karl Foerster' ♀H6	Widely available
- 'Overdam' (v)	Widely available
- 'Stricta'	EPPr
- 'Waldenbuch'	CKno ECha EPPr SMHy
argentea	see *Stipa calamagrostis*
arundinacea	CMac SPlb XSen
§ ***brachytricha*** ♀H6	Widely available
- 'Mona'	NDov
emodensis	CElw EAJP EPPr ESwi EWoo GElm LEdu LRHS MBel NBid SBls WChS
epigejos	EMor WPGP
'Glenorchy Fireworks'	EPPr
'Kyrgyz Giant'	WPGP
ophitidis	SPlb
splendens misapplied	see *Stipa calamagrostis*
splendens Trin.	LPla
varia	CKno ELon GBin LPla SMrm

Calamintha (*Lamiaceae*)

alpina	see *Clinopodium alpinum*
§ ***ascendens***	EBee
clinopodium	see *Clinopodium vulgare*
cretica	SPhx
§ ***grandiflora***	CBod CCBP ECha EGrI GJos LShi MHer MNHC MRav NBir NLar NPer SPhx SPlb SRms WCAu XSen
- 'Elfin Purple'	SBut
- 'Variegata' (v)	EBee ELon ENfk MHoo SRms WCAu
'Harrogate'	WGoo
§ ***nepeta***	Widely available
- subsp. ***glandulosa***	SBut
- - ACL 1050/90	WHoo
- - 'White Cloud'	CAby ECtt ELan EPfP LSto MBel MBriF MPie MRav NBir SBut SRms WCAu XSen
- 'Gottfried Kuehn'	MRav
- 'Lila Riese'	NDov
- 'Marvelette Blue'	NLar
§ - subsp. ***nepeta***	CAby CBWd ELan ELon EPfP GMaP MHer MMuc MRav NDov SPer WFar XLum
- - 'Blue Cloud'	CCBP CSpe EBee EBou ECha ECtt EMor EPfP EPri GElm GMaP MBel MBriF MRav NBir NDov SPhx SPoG SRms WCAu WFar XSen
- 'Triumphator'	WGoo XSen
- 'Weisse Riese'	EBee NDov
- white-flowered **new**	ECha
nepetoides	see *C. nepeta* subsp. *nepeta*
officinalis misapplied	see *C. ascendens*
sylvatica	see *Clinopodium menthifolium*
I - 'Menthe'	LRHS SHor WHil
vulgaris	see *Clinopodium vulgare*

calamondin see *Citrus* × *microcarpa*

Calandrinia (*Portulacaceae*)

caespitosa	EDAr
grandiflora	EDAr
sibirica	see *Claytonia sibirica*
umbellata	CBor EDAr WIce

Calanthe (*Orchidaceae*)

aristulifera	WFar
bicolor	see *C. striata*
Chiseki gx	NLAp
discolor	CBor EBee GKev LAma NLAp SDir
- var. ***flava***	see *C. striata*
discolor × ***hancockii***	NLAp
Fuji gx	NLAp
hancockii × **Kozu gx** red-flowered	NLAp
hancockii × ***striata***	NLAp
Higo gx	NLAp
Kazusa gx	NLAp
Kozu gx	GKev LEdu NLAp WPGP
light green-flowered	NLAp
reflexa	GKev LAma NLAp
sieboldii	see *C. striata*
§ ***striata***	LAma NLAp
striata × ***yueana***	NLAp
Takane gx × ***yueana***	NLAp
tricarinata	NLAp SDir WFar

Calathea (*Marantaceae*)

crocata	see *Goeppertia crocata*
lancifolia	see *Goeppertia insignis*
makoyana	see *Goeppertia makoyana*
orbiculata	see *Goeppertia truncata*
ornata	see *Goeppertia ornata*
roseopicta	see *Goeppertia roseopicta*
rufibarba	see *Goeppertia rufibarba*
stromata	see *Ctenanthe burle-marxii*
zebrina	see *Goeppertia zebrina*

Calceolaria (*Calceolariaceae*)

acutifolia	see *C. polyrhiza* Cav.
andina	EDAr
arachnoidea	EDAr GEdr SPlb
- 'Darcies Velvet' **new**	EDAr
§ ***biflora***	EDAr EWes LShi
- 'Goldcap'	GEdr
- 'Goldcrest Amber'	SPlb
'Camden Hero'	CBcs EPPr EShb
cavanillesii	SPlb
corymbosa	CTsd EBee
'Darcies Gold' **new**	EDAr
filicaulis	EBee
fothergillii	EDAr WAbe
(Fruticohybrida Group) 'Kentish Hero'	EDAr ELan LShi MGil MHer NHpl SDys WAbe WMal
§ ***integrifolia*** ♀H2	CAbb CBcs CDTJ CFis CTri EAri ECtt ELan MGil MSCN SAdn SPoG SRms
- bronze-flowered	MSCN
- 'Gaines' Yellow'	EPPr
paralia 'Lemon Drops' **new**	EDAr
pavonii	MGil
aff. ***pavonii***	CRHN
perfoliata B&SWJ 14722	WCru
plantaginea	see *C. biflora*
§ ***polyrhiza*** Cav.	EDAr EPot
rugosa	see *C. integrifolia*
Sunset Series	EDAr
tenella	EPot WAbe
thyrsiflora	LShi
trilobata var. ***trilobata*** B&SWJ 14896	WCru
uniflora var. ***darwinii***	GKev NHpl WAbe
'Walter Shrimpton'	WAbe

Caldcluvia (*Cunoniaceae*)

paniculata	IArd

Calendula ✿ (*Asteraceae*)

arvensis	CCCN
'Bronze Beauty'	CSpe

officinalis	CBod CCBP CLau ENfk GPoy LCro LOPS MHer MHoo MNHC SRms SVic SWvt WSFF
- 'Apricot Twist'	LSou
- Fiesta Gitana Group ♀H5	LCro LOPS SCob
- 'Indian Prince' (Prince Series)	LCro LOPS SPhx
- 'Lemon Twist' (d)	LCro
- OOPSY DAISY (mixed) **new**	MHoo
- 'Snow Princess' **new**	LCro
PowerDaisy Series	LRHS
- POWERDAISY TANGO ('Kercaltan')	MHol
'Tarifa'	SEND
(Winter Wonders Series) WINTER WONDERS AMBER ARCTIC ('212372D')	LCro
- WINTER WONDERS BANANA BLIZZARD ('2012357d'PBR)	LCro
- WINTER WONDERS GOLDEN GLAZE ('2012329d')	LCro
- WINTER WONDERS PEACH POLAR ('2012391D'PBR)	LCro

Calibrachoa (*Solanaceae*)

Cabaret Series	MDon SCob
- CABARET BRIGHT RED ('Balcabrite'PBR) ♀H2	LSou MBros
- CABARET DEEP BLUE ('Balcabdebu'PBR)	LSou MBros SCob
- CABARET DEEP YELLOW ('Balcabdepy'PBR)	LSou MBros
- CABARET HOT PINK ('Balcabhopi')	LSou MBros
- CABARET LEMON YELLOW ('Balcablemy')	LSou
- CABARET PURPLE ('Balcabpurp')	LSou
- CABARET WHITE ('Balcabwit')	MBros
(Can-can Series) CAN-CAN BLACK CHERRY	MBros
- CAN-CAN CORAL REEF ('Balcanoree')	LSou MBros
- CAN-CAN DOUBLE BLUE (d)	MBros WHlf
- CAN-CAN DOUBLE DARK YELLOW (d)	MBros
- CAN-CAN DOUBLE PINK (d)	WHlf
- CAN-CAN DOUBLE PROVENCE BLUE (d)	LSou WHlf
- CAN-CAN NEON PINK ('Balcaneoni')	LSou
- CAN-CAN SUNLIGHT	LSou WWke
- CAN-CAN SUNRISE **new**	LSou
CELEBRATION ORIENT (Celebration Series) (mixed) **new**	WHlf
(Chameleon Series) CHAMELEON DOUBLE PINK YELLOW ('Wescachadpiyecheba') (d) **new**	WHlf
- CHAMELEON PINK PASSION ('Wescachapipa') **new**	WHlf
Kabloom Series	MBros
- KABLOOM DEEP PINK ('Pas1020305')	MBros
- KABLOOM DENIM ('Pas1122759') **new**	LCro
- KABLOOM WHITE ('Pas1020307')	MBros
MINIFAMOUS DOUBLE PINKTASTIC ('Kleca18085') (MiniFamous Series) (d) ♀H2 **new**	LSou
(Superbells Series) SUPERBELLS BANANA CHOCOLATE ('Uscal12202'PBR)	WWke
- SUPERBELLS STRAWBERRY PUNCH ('Uscal58205')	MBros
TRIXI EARLY SODA (mixed)	MDon
TRIXI EARLY SUNSET (mixed)	MDon
TRIXI EARLY TRICOLORE (mixed)	MDon
TRIXI HOT PETTICOAT (mixed) (d)	MDon MPri
TRIXI LOLLIPOP (mixed)	MDon

Calibrachoa × *Petunia* see × *Petchoa*

Calla (*Araceae*)

aethiopica	see *Zantedeschia aethiopica*
palustris	CPud CWat EWat LLWG LPfP NPer SRms WMAq

Callerya (*Fabaceae*)

reticulata	see *Wisteriopsis reticulata*

Calliandra (*Fabaceae*)

'Dixie Pink'	CCCN
portoricensis	CCCN
surinamensis	CBcs CCCN SMad
tweediei ♀H1b	CCCN

Callianthemum (*Ranunculaceae*)

alatavicum	GKev
anemonoides	EDAr GEdr WAbe WCot
coriandrifolium	GEdr
kernerianum	GEdr WAbe

Callicarpa (*Lamiaceae*)

CW&T 6228	CMCN
americana var. ***lactea***	CMCN
bodinieri	CChe EGrl EHeP ILea SavN
- var. ***giraldii***	CBrac MRav NLar
- - 'Profusion' ♀H6	Widely available
- 'Imperial Pearl'	EPfP LRHS WHlf
'Cardinal'	CJun
cathayana	NLar
dichotoma	CBcs NLar WJur
- f. ***albifructa***	NLar WHlf WJur
- 'Issai'	CBod CKel EBee EPfP ILea MBlu NLar
formosana NMWJ 14553	WCru
japonica	CMen NLar SBrt
- B&SWJ 12621	WCru
- f. ***albibacca***	NLar
- 'Heavy Berry'	CBod NLar
- 'Koshima-no-homate'	NLar
- 'Leucocarpa'	CBcs CBod CMac EBee ELan EPfP NLar SPoG WGob WHtc WLov
- var. ***luxurians*** B&SWJ 8521	WCru
kwangtungensis	CBcs NLar
psilocalyx NJM 13.057	WPGP

shikokiana	NLar
× ***shirasawana***	NLar
aff. ***tikusikensis*** B&SWJ 7127	WCru
Van den Broek selection	NLar
yunnanensis	NLar

Callirhoe (*Malvaceae*)

bushii	WSHC
digitata	SBrt
involucrata	CTsd SBrt SBut XLum
- var. ***tenuissima***	EBee

Callisia (*Commelinaceae*)

elegans	EShb
fragrans	EOHP EShb
- 'Melnickoff' (v)	EShb
§ ***navicularis***	SSim
repens	EShb LWaG
'Turtle'	CDoC

Callistemon (*Myrtaceae*)

acuminatus	CCCN
'Amorette' **new**	CBod
brachyandrus	SVen
citrinus	CTri EDir EGrI EPfP SEle SGBe SPlb
- 'Albus'	see *C. citrinus* 'White Anzac'
- 'Amarette' **new**	SPad
- 'Firebrand'	LRHS
- 'Splendens' 🏆H3	CBcs CBrac CCCN CDoC CEme CKel CMac CRos CSBt CSde CWnw EGrI EHyd ELan EPfP IArd ILea LCro LRHS MAsh MGos NRHS SAko SEND SGbt SIvy SPoG SVen SWeb SWvt
§ - 'White Anzac'	CBod CBrac CCCN CDoC CKel CMac CSBt CSde ELan ELon EMil EPfP LRHS MMrt SEND SIvy SPoG
comboynensis	CCCN
* 'Country Park'	CTrC
glaucus	see *C. speciosus*
'Honey Maker'	CTsd
INFERNO ('Yanferno')	CTrC EGrI SPad
laevis hort.	see *C. rugulosus*
linearifolius	LSRN
linearis 🏆H2	CBrac CKel CMac CSde CTrC CTri ELan EPfP LRHS LSRN MGos SCob SEND SIvy SPlb SWvt
macropunctatus	SPlb SVen
'Masotti'^{PBR}	EGrI SPoG
'Mauve Mist'	CAbb CBod CCCN CDoC CSde ELan ELon EPfP EWTr LRHS SAko SEND SGBe SIvy SPad SPoG SVen
pallidus	CBcs CBrac CCCN CDoC CKel CMac CTrC CTsd EGrI EHyd ELan EPfP LRHS MRav NRHS SEND SEle SGBe SIvy SPlb SVen WBor
paludosus	see *C. sieberi* DC.
pearsonii 'Rocky Rambler'	CTrC
'Perth Pink'	CAbb CBcs CCCN CDoC CKel CSBt CSde EGrI ELan EPfP LRHS SEND SEle SGBe SIvy SPad SSha SVen XSte
pinifolius	SPlb SVen
§ ***pityoides***	CCCN CTsd EGrI ELan EWTr NLar SEle SGBe SIvy SVen
'Red Clusters'	CBcs CBod CBrac CCCN CDoC CKel CMac CSde CTrC ELan EPfP LRHS MAsh MMrt SCoo SGBe SSha SWvt WFar
'Red Rocket' **new**	SRHi
rigidus	CBcs CBod CChe CDoC CRos CTri CTsd EDir EHeP EHyd ELan EPfP GMcL LRHS LSRN MDon MGos MMuc MRav NLar NRHS SCoo SPer SSha SSut SVen SWvt XSen
§ ***rugulosus***	CBrac CCCN CKel EDir GMcL IDee LPar MPri SGbt SVen SWvt
salignus 🏆H2	CBcs CBod CCCN CEme CMac CTrC CTri EPfP LPal MRav NLar SEle SIvy SVen
sieberi misapplied	see *C. pityoides*
§ ***sieberi*** DC.	CBcs CDoC CKel CMCN CTsd EBee EPfP LRHS MGil MMuc NLar SPlb
§ ***speciosus***	NLar SEND SPlb
subulatus	SArc SPlb
- 'Crimson Tail'	CTrC MGil MMuc SPtp
viminalis	CCCN LPal SPlb
- 'Captain Cook'	CMac SVen SWvt WFar
- 'Endeavour'	CCCN
- 'Hannah Ray'	WFar
- HOT PINK ('Kkho1'^{PBR})	CKel CTrC CWnw EDir EGrI IDee LRHS MGos SCob SCoo WHlf
- 'Little John'	CBcs CBod CBrac CSde IArd SEND SGBe SSha SWvt
'Violaceus'	CBod NLar SPlb SVen
viridiflorus	CTrC CTsd SEND SPlb SPtp WGwG
'White Anzac'	see *C. citrinus* 'White Anzac'

Callistephus (*Asteraceae*)

chinensis	SVic

Callitriche (*Plantaginaceae*)

sp.	WSFF
brutia subsp. ***hamulata***	LLWG
§ ***palustris***	CBen CPud
stagnalis	EWat LPfP WMAq
verna	see *C. palustris*

Callitris (*Cupressaceae*)

endlicheri	CBrP

Callitropsis see *Chamaecyparis*

× ***leylandii***	see × *Cuprocyparis leylandii*
nootkatensis	see *Xanthocyparis nootkatensis*

Calluna ✿ (*Ericaceae*)

vulgaris	LSto
- 'Alba Elongata'	see *C. vulgaris* 'Mair's Variety'
§ - 'Alba Plena' (d)	GPer
§ - 'Alba Rigida'	CFst GPer
- 'Alex Warwick'	GPer
- 'Alexandra'^{PBR} (Garden Girls Series)	SCoo SPoG
- 'Alicia'^{PBR} (Garden Girls Series) 🏆H7	SCoo SPoG
- 'Allegro'	GPer SCoo
- 'Alportii'	GPer
- 'Amethyst'^{PBR} (Garden Girls Series)	SPoG
- 'Amilto'	CFst
- 'Anette'^{PBR} (Garden Girls Series)	SCoo
- 'Angie' (Garden Girls Series)	CFst
- 'Annemarie' (d) 🏆H7	GPer SCoo SPlb
- 'Anne's Goldzwerg'	CFst
- 'Anne's Zwerg'	CFst
- 'Arina'	GPer SCoo
- 'Athene'^{PBR} (Garden Girls Series)	CFst
- 'August Beauty'	GPer
- 'Baby Ben'	CFst
- 'Beoley Crimson'	GPer SCoo
- 'Beoley Gold' 🏆H7	CTri GPer MAsh NHol SCoo

- 'Beoley Silver'	SCoo
- 'Blazeaway'	CTri GPer MAsh SCoo
- 'Bonfire Brilliance'	GPer NHol
- 'Boskoop'	GPer MAsh NHol
- 'C.W. Nix'	GPer
- 'Caerketton White'	GPer
- 'Colette'	LBar
- 'Con Brio'	GPer SCoo
- 'Corrie's White'	GJos GPer
- 'Cottswood Gold'	GJos GPer SCoo
- 'County Wicklow' (d) ♀H7	CTri ELan GPer NHol SCoo WTyc
- 'Cramond' (d)	GPer
- 'Cuprea'	SCoo
- 'Dark Beauty' PBR (d) ♀H7	CBcs CFst ELan GPer LCro LOPS MAsh NHol SCoo WTyc
- 'Dark Star' (d) ♀H7	GJos GPer MAsh NHol SCoo
- 'Darkness' ♀H7	CBcs CFst CTri GPer SCoo WTyc
- 'David Hagenaars'	CFst
- 'Disco Queen'	GPer
- 'Drum-ra'	GPer
- 'Dunnet Lime'	SPlb
- 'Easter-bonfire'	SCoo
- 'Elsie Purnell' (d) ♀H7	CFst ELan GPer NHol SCoo SPlb
- 'Feuerwerk'	SCoo
- 'Firefly' ♀H7	CFst GPer NHol SCoo SPer
- 'Flamingo'	GPer SCoo
- 'Forest Fire'	CFst
- 'Foxii Nana'	NHol
- 'Fred J. Chapple'	GPer
- 'Galaxy' PBR	CFst
- 'Glenfiddich'	GPer
- 'Gold Flame'	GPer
- 'Gold Haze'	CTri MAsh NHol SCoo
- 'Gold Knight'	SCoo
- 'Golden Angie' (Garden Girls Series)	CFst
- 'Golden Carpet'	GJos GPer MAsh NHol
- 'Guinea Gold'	GPer
§ - 'H.E. Beale' (d)	CTri GPer MAsh NHol SCoo
- 'Hammondii Aureifolia'	GPer SPlb
- 'Hannover'	CFst
- 'Highland Rose'	SPlb
- 'Hilda' PBR (Garden Girls Series)	CFst
§ - 'Hugh Nicholson'	GPer
- 'J.H. Hamilton' (d)	CTri GPer MAsh NHol SCoo
- 'Jan Dekker'	GPer
- 'Jana' (d)	CFst
- 'Johnson's Variety'	SCoo
- 'Joy Vanstone'	GJos GPer
- 'Kerstin' ♀H7	CFst GPer NHol SCoo SPlb
- 'Kinlochruel' (d) ♀H7	CBcs CFst CTri GPer MAsh NHol SPlb WTyc
- 'Kirby White'	MAsh SPlb
- 'Klaudine' PBR (Garden Girls Series)	CFst
- 'Leslie Slinger'	SCoo
- 'Loch Turret'	GPer
§ - 'Mair's Variety'	GPer SCoo
- 'Melanie' (Garden Girls Series)	NHol SCoo
- 'Mrs Pat'	CFst MAsh
- 'Multicolor'	MAsh NHol
§ - 'My Dream' (d)	SCoo
- 'Nana Compacta'	GPer
- 'Orange Max'	GPer
- 'Pepper and Salt'	see *C. vulgaris* 'Hugh Nicholson'
- 'Peter Sparkes' (d) ♀H7	CBcs CFst GPer MAsh NHol SCoo
- 'Pink Beale'	see *C. vulgaris* 'H.E. Beale'
- 'Purple Passion'	SCoo
- 'Radnor' (d)	GJos GPer
- 'Ralph Purnell'	ELan SCoo
- 'Red Beauty'	CBcs CFst
- 'Red Favorit' (d)	CFst GJos GPer
- 'Red Fred'	SCoo
- 'Red Haze'	GPer NHol SCoo
- 'Red Pimpernel'	SCoo
- 'Red Star' (d)	NHol
- 'Rigida Prostrata'	see *C. vulgaris* 'Alba Rigida'
- 'Robert Chapman' ♀H7	CFst CTri MAsh NHol
- 'Rosalind, Underwood's'	NHol
- 'Rosita' PBR (Garden Girls Series)	CFst
- 'Ruby Slinger'	NHol
- 'Ruth Sparkes' (d)	NHol
- 'Salmon Leap'	GPer
- 'Sandy' PBR (Garden Girls Series)	SPoG
- 'Silvana' PBR (Garden Girls Series)	CFst
- 'Silver Fox'	CBcs CFst
- 'Silver Knight'	ELan GJos GPer MAsh NHol SCoo SPlb
- 'Silver Queen' ♀H7	CFst GPer MAsh NHol
- 'Sir John Charrington'	GPer NHol
- 'Sister Anne' ♀H7	GPer SCoo
- 'Snowball'	see *C. vulgaris* 'My Dream'
- 'Spitfire'	GPer
- 'Spring Cream' ♀H7	CBcs GPer MAsh NHol SCoo
- 'Spring Torch'	CBcs GPer MAsh NHol SCoo
- 'Stefanie'	MNHC
- 'Strawberry Delight' (d)	SCoo
- 'Summer Orange'	GJos GPer
- 'Sun Sprinkles'	CFst
- 'Sunset'	GJos GPer
- 'Tib' (d) ♀H7	CFst GPer MAsh WTyc
- 'Tricolorifolia'	SCoo
- 'Velvet Fascination' ♀H7	GPer SCoo
- 'White Bouquet'	see *C. vulgaris* 'Alba Plena'
- 'White Coral' (d) ♀H7	ELan SCoo
- 'White Lawn'	GPer NHol
- 'Wickwar Flame' ♀H7	CBcs CFst ELan GPer MAsh NHol SCoo SPlb
- 'Winter Chocolate'	MAsh NHol SCoo
- 'Yellow Beauty' PBR	CFst
- 'Yvette's Gold'	CFst
- 'Zoe' PBR (Garden Girls Series) **new**	CFst

Calocedrus (*Cupressaceae*)

§ ***decurrens*** ♀H7	CAco CBcs EPfP IPap LPar MBlu MGil NWea SPtp SSha WJur WTSh
- 'Aureovariegata' (v) ♀H7	CAco LPar NPlm
- 'Berrima Gold' ♀H7	CAco NLar
- 'Columnaris'	CAco
§ - 'Depressa'	CKen
- 'Maupin Glow' (v)	CAco NLar
- 'Nana'	see *C. decurrens* 'Depressa'
- 'Pillar'	CKen NLar

Calocephalus (*Asteraceae*)

sp.	MBros
brownii	see *Leucophyta brownii*

Calochortus (*Liliaceae*)

'Cupido' PBR	EPot GKev NRog SDeJ
luteus 'Golden Orb' PBR	NRog SDeJ
splendens 'Violet Queen'	NRog SDeJ
superbus	NRog SDeJ
'Symphony' PBR	SDeJ
venustus	NRog SDeJ
- 'Burgundy'	SDeJ

Calomeria (*Asteraceae*)

§ ***amaranthoides***	WJek

Calonyction see *Ipomoea*

Calopogon (*Orchidaceae*)

tuberosus	NLAp
- f. ***albiflorus***	NLAp

Caloscordum see *Allium*

Calothamnus (*Myrtaceae*)

quadrifidus	SEle XSte
validus	SPlb
villosus	SPlb

Calpurnia (*Fabaceae*)

aurea	SPlb

Caltha (*Ranunculaceae*)

howellii	see *C. leptosepala* subsp. *howellii*
laeta	see *C. palustris* var. *palustris*
leptosepala	EBee ELon GArf GEdr GKev GMaP LLWG LPfP NLar
§ - subsp. ***howellii*** NNS 07-87	GKev
natans	LLWG
palustris	Widely available
- var. ***alba***	Widely available
- 'Auengold'	LLWG
- 'Auenwald'	LLWG
- var. ***barthei***	GEdr
- 'Bronze Age'	CDor
- 'Flore Pleno' (d) ♀H7	CBen CEme CMac CTtf EBee ECha ELan ELon EWat GAbr GKin GMaP MMuc MRav NBir NChi NFav NGdn NHol NLar NPer NRya SEND SPlb SRms WFar WPnP XLum
- 'Himalayan Snow'	EBee LLWG WFar
- 'Honeydew'	CDor ELon LLWG MNrw WCot WSHC
- var. ***laeta***	LLWG
- 'Marilyn'	LLWG
- 'Multiplex' (d)	CDor EMor
- Newlake hybrid	LLWG
§ - var. ***palustris***	CBen CToG ECha LLWG NCth WWtn
- - 'Plena' (d)	CBod CPud CRos CWat EHeP EHyd EWat LPfP LRHS MTin NRHS WHil
- var. ***radicans***	EWat GEdr
- - 'Flore Pleno' (d)	WWtn
- 'Stagnalis'	MWts
polypetala Hochst. ex Lorent	CDor CPud CWat LPfP MSCN NPer SMad WMAq
sagittata	GEdr WSHC

Calycanthus (*Calycanthaceae*)

'Aphrodite'	CBcs CJun CMCN EHed ELan EPfP GKin LPar LRHS MGos MTrO NLar SHor SRHi WMat
chinensis	CBcs CCCN CMCN EBee EGrI EHed EHyd EPfP LRHS MBlu MGil NLar SPtp
floridus	CAgr CBcs CDoC CEme CMCN CTsd EAri EBee EPfP IArd IDee LEdu MBNS MBlu MGil NLar SGsty SIvy SPad SPer SPlb SPoG SSha SWvt SavN WCFE WFar WHlf WLov
- 'Athens'	NLar WPGP
- 'Burgundy Spice' **new**	EDir
- 'Foxy Lady' **new**	NLar
- var. ***glaucus*** 'Purpureus'	CJun EGrI MBlu NLar
- 'Michael Lindsay'	NLar WPGP
mohrii	NLar
occidentalis	CMCN CPla MAsh MBlu MGil MMuc SBrt
× ***raulstonii*** 'Hartlage Wine' ♀H5	Widely available
'Venus'	CBcs CJun CMCN EHed ELan ELon EPfP LCro LOPS LPar LRHS MAsh MBlu MPkF NLar SHor SRHi SavN XSte
'White Dress'	NLar

Calystegia (*Convolvulaceae*)

§ ***hederacea*** 'Flore Pleno' (d)	SMad
japonica 'Flore Pleno'	see *C. hederacea* 'Flore Pleno'
soldanella	CPla

Calytrix (*Myrtaceae*)

tetragona	SPlb

Camassia ✿ (*Asparagaceae*)

'Blue Candle'	EPfP EPot LAma NHsp
'Blue Heaven'	CAvo CRos ELan EPfP ERCP ETay GKev GMaP LAma LHWs LRHS LSun MAvo NHsp NLar NRHS NRog SDeJ
Broadleigh Belle Group	CBro
cusickii	Widely available
- 'Crystal Star'	NHsp NRog
- 'Zwanenburg'	CRos EHyd ERCP GKev IPot LAma LHWs LRHS NHpl NHsp NRHS NRog WCot
esculenta Lindl.	see *C. quamash*
'John Treasure' (d)	CBro
'Lavender Mist'	MAvo
leichtlinii misapplied	see *C. leichtlinii* subsp. *suksdorfii*
leichtlinii 'Alba' misapplied	see *C. leichtlinii* subsp. *leichtlinii*
* - 'Alba Plena'	LAma LHWs LSun MHol MNrw MPtr NBir NHpl
- Avon's Stellar Group	CAvo
- BLUE DANUBE	see *C. leichtlinii* subsp. *suksdorfii* 'Blauwe Donau'
- 'Blue Wave'	NHsp NWad
- 'Harlequin' (v)	NHsp
§ - subsp. ***leichtlinii***	Widely available
- 'Pink Star'	GKev IPot NHsp
- 'Plena' (d)	ECha MBow
- 'Sacajawea' (v)	CAvo CBor CRos CTtf ECha EHyd EPfP ERCP GKev GPSL LAma LHWs LRHS MAvo NHsp NLar NRHS NRog SDeJ SMrm WCot WFar WTor
- 'Semiplena' (d)	CAvo CBro CRos CTtf EBee ECtt EHyd EPfP EPot ERCP ETay GKev IPot LAma LHWs LRHS MBriF MNrw NHsp NRHS NRog NSti WBor WCot WHlf WPnP WShi
§ - subsp. ***suksdorfii***	EGrI LCro LHWs LOPS MBriF NPoe SMrm WCot
- - 'Alba'	CAvo CBod CRos EGrI EHyd EPot EWoo GBin GMaP LCro LHWs LOPS LRHS LSto NRHS NSti SCob SEdd WBor
§ - - 'Blauwe Donau'	ILea NHsp
- - Caerulea Group	Widely available
- - - 'Maybelle'	CAvo ERCP LRHS MBriF MPri NHsp
- - 'Electra'	CBro ECha MAvo NHsp SMrm WCot
- - 'Lady Eve Price'	CBro MAvo WCot
§ ***quamash***	Widely available
- 'Blue Melody' (v)	CRos EBee EHyd EPot ERCP GKev GMaP LAma LEdu LRHS NHsp NRHS NRog SDeJ
- 'Orion'	CRos CTtf EBee EHyd ERCP GKev LAma LEdu LRHS NHsp NRHS NRog WCot
- var. ***quamash***	CBcs LPfP MHol

Camellia ✿ (*Theaceae*)

	'Admiral Spry'	CSgt
	'Adorable' (*pitardii* hybrid)	LRHS XSte
	'April Blush'	WFar
	'Auburn White'	see *C. japonica* 'Mrs Bertha A. Harms'
	'Autumn Jewel'	XSte
	azalea	SavN
	'Baby Bear'	XSte
	'Barbara Clark' (*reticulata* × *saluenensis*)	CSgt MAsh NRHS SRot
	'Bertha Harms Blush'	see *C. japonica* 'Mrs Bertha A. Harms'
	'Black Lace' ♀H5	CDoC CSgt CTrh CTri EGrI ELan EPfP LCro LMaj LMil LOPS LPar LRHS LSRN MAsh MPri NRHS SArc SGol SGsty SRot SWeb SWvt XSte
	'Blissful Dawn'	CTrh
	'Bonnie Marie'	CBcs SCam
	'Canterbury'	EGrI LRHS SCam XSte
*	'Chatsworth Belle'	SCam
	'Christmas Daffodil' (*japonica* hybrid)	CBcs LRHS XSte
	'Cinnamon Cindy'	CBcs LRHS SCam SRot XSte
	'Cinnamon Scentsation'	LRHS XSte
	'Congratulations'	CSBt
	'Contessa Lavinia Maggi'	see *C. japonica* 'Lavinia Maggi'
	'Cornish Snow' (*cuspidata* × *saluenensis*) ♀H4	CBod CDoC CEnd CMac CTri CTsd SRot SSha SWvt WFar
	'Cornish Spring' (*cuspidata* × *japonica*) ♀H4	CBcs CBod CCCN CSBt CSgt CTrh EGrI MAsh NRHS SCam
	'Crimson Candles' ♀H5	LRHS XSte
	cuspidata	CMac
	'Debut' (*japonica* × *reticulata*)	XSte
	'Delia Williams'	see *C.* × *williamsii* 'Citation'
	'Den Burton' (*japonica* × *reticulata*)	XSte
	'Doctor Clifford Parks' (*japonica* × *reticulata*) ♀H4	XSte
	'Donckelaeri'	see *C. japonica* 'Masayoshi'
	edithae	XSte
	'Extravaganza' (*japonica* hybrid) ♀H5	CBcs CTrh IArd SCoo
	'Fairy Blush'	LRHS MGos NLar XSte
	'Fairy Wand'	LRHS XSte
	'Fascination'	SWvt
	'Faustina Lechi'	see *C. japonica* 'Faustina'
	'Felice Harris' (*reticulata* × *sasanqua*)	SCoo
	'Fiesta Grande'	XSte
	forrestii	GKev WPGP
	'Forty-niner' (*japonica* × *reticulata*)	CSgt LRHS NRHS
	'Fragrant Pink'	CBcs SCam
	'Francie L' ♀H4	CMac XSte
	fraterna	CBcs
	'Frau Minna Seidel'	see *C. japonica* subsp. *rusticana* 'Otome'
	'Free Spirit'	CTrh
	'Freedom Bell' ♀H5	CDoC CSgt CTrh EGrI EPfP GKin LMil MGos MPri NRHS SCam SCob SGol XSte
	'Frosted Star'	LRHS XSte
	'Gay Baby'	LRHS XSte
	'Golden Anniversary'	see *C. japonica* 'Dahlohnega'
	grijsii	CBcs CTrh XSte
	'Happy Anniversary'	CSBt SWvt
§	***hiemalis*** 'Bonanza'	CTrh LRHS XSte
	- 'Chansonette'	CDoC CSgt LRHS SCam
§	- 'Dazzler'	NRHS SCam SRot
	- 'Elfin Rose'	LRHS
	- 'Kanjirō'	CKel CWnw MHtn SCam SRot SWeb
I	- 'Maiden's Blush'	SRot
	- 'Shishigashira'	CTrh
	- 'Shōwa-no-sakae'	LRHS MHtn XSte
	'High Fragrance'	LRHS WHlf XSte
	'Hooker'	CSgt NRHS
	'Imbricata Rubra'	see *C. japonica* 'Imbricata'
	'Innovation'	CDoC CSgt LRHS
	'Inspiration' (*reticulata* × *saluenensis*) ♀H5	CBcs CDoC CMac CSgt CTrh EPfP LRHS MGos SCam XSte
	japonica	LMaj SEWo SPre WJur
	- 'Aaron's Ruby'	ELon NRHS SCam
	- 'Ace of Hearts'	CAco CKel CWnw SCoo
	- 'ACS Jubilee'	LRHS XSte
	- 'Ada Pieper'	CTrh
	- 'Adelina Patti' ♀H5	CBcs CTrh SCam
	- 'Adeyaka'	CSgt LRHS NRHS SGol
	- 'Adolphe Audusson' ♀H5	Widely available
§	- 'Akashigata' ♀H5	CBcs ELon EPfP LSRN NRHS SCam
	- 'Alba Plena' (d) ♀H5	CAco CBod CTrh EDir LRHS SCob SWvt WFar XSte
	- 'Alba Simplex'	CMac CTrh EPfP GMcL LMaj MPri SSta
§	- 'Albertii'	XSte
	- 'Alexander Hunter' ♀H5	NRHS
§	- 'Althaeiflora'	ELon NRHS SCam
	- 'Anemoniflora'	EPfP NRHS
	- 'Angel'	SCam
	- 'Angela Cocchi'	LPar
	- 'Angello'	NRHS
	- 'Annie Wylam' ♀H5	CBcs CTrh LRHS SCoo
	- 'Apollo' ambig.	CBcs GMcL LRHS MAsh NRHS
§	- 'Apollo' Paul, 1911	MSwo SCam
§	- 'Apple Blossom'	CBcs CSgt NRHS
	- 'April Blush'	CSgt
	- 'April Kiss'	CSgt
	- 'April Remembered'	CSgt WFar
	- 'April Rose'	CSgt WFar
	- 'April Tryst'	EGrI
	- 'Arajishi' misapplied	see *C. japonica* subsp. *rusticana* 'Beni-arajishi'
	- 'Augustine Supreme'	CMac
	- 'Australis' ♀H5	LPar
	- 'Ave Maria' ♀H5	CTrh MGos NRHS XSte
	- 'Baby Pearl'	SCam
	- 'Baby Sis'	NRHS
	- 'Baby Sis Pink'	XSte
	- 'Ballet Dancer' ♀H5	SCam
	- 'Baron Gomer'	see *C. japonica* 'Comte de Gomer'
	- 'Baronne Leguay'	SCam
	- 'Beau Harp'	NRHS
	- 'Bella Lambertii'	CKel CWnw
	- 'Bella Romana'	SCam
	- 'Berenice Boddy' ♀H5	CTrh LRHS NRHS
	- 'Betty Foy Sanders'	CTrh LRHS
	- 'Betty Robinson'	NRHS
	- 'Betty Sheffield'	LRHS MAsh NRHS
	- 'Betty Sheffield Pink'	LMil NRHS SCam
	- 'Betty Sheffield Supreme'	CBcs
	- 'Betty's Beauty'	XSte
	- 'Billie McCaskill'	SCam
	- 'Binda'	CSgt
	- 'Black Magic'	CDoC CSgt CTrh LRHS MAsh NRHS
	- 'Black Tie'	CEnd CTrh ELon LRHS MGos NRHS SCam WFar
	- 'Blackburnia'	see *C. japonica* 'Althaeiflora'
§	- 'Blood of China'	CAco CBcs CKel CSBt CWnw EDir LRHS LSRN MGos NLar NRHS SCam SCoo SEdd SGol SWvt
	- 'Blush Tinsie'	NRHS
	- 'Bob Hope' ♀H5	CAco CBcs CDoC CKel CTrh CTri CWnw NRHS SCam
	- 'Bob's Tinsie' ♀H5	CSBt ELon EPfP MGos NRHS SPoG XSte

§	– 'Bokuhan' 🏆H5	SCam XSte
	– 'Bonomiana'	CAco EDir EGrI LCro LRHS SGol SGsty WFar
	– 'Bright Buoy'	NRHS
	– 'Brushfield's Yellow'	CAco CBcs CBod CDoC CKel CSBt CSgt CTrh CTsd CWnw EDir EGrI ELan ELon EPfP IArd LCro LRHS LSRN MAsh MGos NGrs NLar NRHS SCam SCoo SGol SPer SRot SSta
	– 'Bush Hill Beauty'	see *C. japonica* 'Lady de Saumarez'
§	– 'C.M. Hovey' 🏆H5	CMac CSgt NRHS
	– 'C.M. Wilson'	CMac
	– 'Campari'	XSte
	– 'Campsii Alba'	CAco EGrI SCam SCoo
	– 'Can Can'	ELon
	– 'Cara Mia'	NRHS SCoo
	– 'Carolyn Tuttle'	CSgt MAsh NRHS
	– 'Carter's Sunburst' 🏆H5	CBcs ELon
	– 'Cereixa de Tollo' **new**	EDir
	– 'Chandleri Elegans'	see *C. japonica* 'Elegans'
	– 'Charlotte de Rothschild'	CTrh CTri
	– 'Cinderella'	NRHS
	– CLASSIQUE ('Kerguelen'[PBR]) (v)	LRHS SRot WFar XSte
	– 'Colonel Firey'	see *C. japonica* 'C.M. Hovey'
	– 'Colonial Dame'	CAco
	– 'Commander Mulroy' 🏆H5	CBcs SCoo
	– 'Compacta Alba'	LPar
§	– 'Comte de Gomer'	ELon EPfP LPar MPri NRHS SGol
	– 'Conspicua'	CBcs
§	– 'Coquettii' 🏆H5	CAco CSgt LRHS MAsh NRHS XSte
	– 'Curly Lady'[PBR]	CAco MPri WFar
§	– 'Dahlohnega'	CBcs CBod CSBt CTrh EFPl EPfP LMil LRHS LSRN MAsh MGos NRHS SEdd SGol WFar XSte
	– 'Daitairin'	see *C. japonica* 'Dewatairin'
	– 'Daphne du Maurier'	CSgt NRHS
	– 'Dark of the Moon'	NRHS
	– 'Dear Jenny'	CSgt
	– 'Debutante'	CBcs CMac ELon SCam SGsty
	– 'Desire' 🏆H5	CBcs CBod CEnd CSBt CSgt CTrh EPfP GMcL LCro LMil LOPS LRHS LSRN MAsh MGos NRHS SCam SGol SPoG SRot WFar XSte
	– 'Devonia'	CBcs
§	– 'Dewatairin' (Higo)	CBcs SCam XSte
	– 'Diddy's Pink Organdie'	NRHS
	– 'Dixie Knight'	NRHS SCam
	– 'Dobreei'	CMac
	– 'Doctor Burnside'	CBcs CTrh LPar SCam SGsty SWeb
	– 'Doctor King'	CAco CDoC CEnd CKel CSgt CWnw EDir EPfP LCro LMil LRHS MAsh MPri NGrs NRHS SCob SCoo SGol SPoG WFar
	– 'Doctor Tinsley' 🏆H5	CDoC CSgt EPfP LRHS MAsh MPri NRHS SCam SWeb
	– 'Dona Herzilia de Freitas Magalhães'	CBcs
	– 'Donckelaeri'	see *C. japonica* 'Masayoshi'
	– 'Donnan's Dream'	CTrh
	– 'Drama Girl' 🏆H5	CBcs NRHS SCam
	– 'Duchesse Decazes'	CBcs SCam
	– 'Edelweiss'	SCam
	– 'Effendee'	see *C. sasanqua* 'Rosea Plena'
§	– 'Elegans'	CBcs CPla CSgt EGrI EPfP GMcL LCro LMil LPar LRHS MGos NRHS SCam SGol SLim SPoG SRot SWvt
	– 'Elegans Champagne'	CSgt
	– 'Elegans Supreme'	CSgt
	– 'Elisabeth'	LRHS NRHS
	– 'Elizabeth Cooper'	CTrh
	– 'Elizabeth Hawkins'	CSgt CTrh LRHS NRHS
	– 'Elizabeth Weaver'	CTrh
	– 'Emmett Pfingstl'	SCam
	– 'Emperor of Russia'	CBcs NRHS
	– 'Eric Baker'	SCam
	– 'Eugène Lizé'	SCam
	– 'Eximia'	NRHS
	– 'Faith'	CSgt
§	– 'Faustina'	NRHS
	– 'Filla de Tollo' **new**	EDir
	– 'Fimbriata'	XSte
	– 'Finlandia Variegated' (v)	ELon SCam
	– 'Fire Dance'	EDir
	– 'Firebird'	CBcs CTsd
	– 'Flashlight'	ELon NRHS
§	– 'Fleur Dipater'	CBcs LRHS NRHS SCam XSte
	– 'Flowerwood'	SGsty
	– 'Forest Green'	SRot
	– 'Fred Sander'	NRHS
§	– 'Général Lamoricière'	EDir
	– 'Giardino Santarelli'	CAco
§	– 'Gigantea'	ELon NRHS
	– 'Giuditta Rosani'	NRHS
	– 'Giuseppe Traverso' **new**	CWnw
	– 'Glen 40'	see *C. japonica* 'Coquettii'
	– 'Gloire de Nantes' 🏆H5	CTrh EGrI XSte
	– 'Gold Tone'	SCam
	– 'Golden Wedding' (v)	NTrD WHlf
	– 'Goshozakura'	XSte
	– 'Grace Albritton' (d)	XSte
	– 'Grace Bunton'	CBcs ELon
	– 'Grand Prix' 🏆H5	ELon NLar SWeb
	– 'Grand Slam' 🏆H5	SCam
	– 'Guest of Honor'	EGrI NRHS
	– 'Guilio Nuccio' 🏆H5	CAco CBcs CTri ELon LSRN MAsh MPri NRHS SCam SLim SWeb
	– 'Gus Menard'	SCam
	– 'Gwenneth Morey'	CBcs
	– 'H.A. Downing'	SCam
§	– 'Hagoromo' 🏆H5	CBcs CSBt CTrh LPar MMuc NRHS SWeb XSte
§	– 'Hakurakuten' 🏆H5	CTrh CTri SCam SCoo SRot
	– 'Hanafūki'	NRHS SCam
	– 'Happy Birthday'	EGrI LSRN
	– 'Happy Higo'	SCam
	– 'Haru-no-utena'	CTrh
	– 'Hatsuzakura'	see *C. japonica* 'Dewatairin'
	– 'Hawaii'	CBcs CMac CSBt CTrh ELon NRHS SCam
	– HERME	see *C. japonica* 'Hikarugenji'
	– 'High Hat'	CBcs
§	– 'Hikarugenji'	NRHS
	– 'Hinomaru'	CMac
	– 'Holly Bright'	CTrh LRHS XSte
§	– 'Imbricata'	CTrh LRHS MAsh NRHS SGol
	– 'In the Pink'	CSgt
	– 'Italiana Vera'	CDoC CSgt LRHS MAsh NRHS
	– 'J.J. Whitfield'	CMac
	– 'Janet Waterhouse'	CBcs LRHS XSte
§	– 'Japonica Variegata' (v)	NRHS
	– 'Jingle Bells'	CBcs
	– 'Joseph Pfingstl' 🏆H5	CSgt CTri EPfP LRHS MAsh NLar NRHS SCam
	– 'Jovey Carlyon'	CBcs CDoC CSgt MAsh NRHS
	– 'Joy Sander'	see *C. japonica* 'Apple Blossom'
	– 'Juno'	NRHS
	– 'Jupiter' Paul, 1904 🏆H5	CMac CSgt CTri EGrI LRHS LSRN SCam
	– 'Kellingtoniana'	see *C. japonica* 'Gigantea'
	– 'Kenny'	CBcs
	– 'Kentucky'	LRHS NRHS
	– 'Kick-off'	CSgt CTrh LRHS SCam
	– 'Kimberley'	CBcs CTsd EGrI SCam SGol SRot
	– 'King's Ransom'	CMac CSgt LRHS MAsh NRHS
	– 'Kingyoba-shiro-wabisuke'	SCam

	- 'Kingyo-tsubaki'	ELon LPar SCam SSta
	- 'Kitty Berry'	CTrh
	- 'Kokinran'	SCam
§	- 'Konronkoku' 🏆H5	CSgt LRHS MAsh NRHS
	- 'Kouron-jura'	see *C. japonica* 'Konronkoku'
	- 'Kramer's Beauty'	CBcs
	- 'Kramer's Supreme' 🏆H5	CAco CBcs CCCN CDoC CSgt ELon GMcL LSRN MAsh MGos NRHS SCam SCob SCoo SGol XSte
§	- 'Kumasaka'	CSgt CTri LRHS NRHS
	- 'L.T. Dees' (d)	XSte
	- 'La Graciola'	see *C. japonica* 'Odoratissima'
	- 'La Pace Rubra'	SCam
	- 'Lady Campbell'	CAco CBod CKel CTri EDir EGrI EPfP GMcL LPar LRHS MPri SCam SCoo SGol WFar
	- 'Lady Clare'	see *C. japonica* 'Akashigata'
§	- 'Lady de Saumarez'	CBcs CMac CSgt CTsd
	- 'Lady Loch'	CTrh
	- 'Lady Marion'	see *C. japonica* 'Kumasaka'
	- 'Lady McCulloch'	NRHS
	- 'Lady Vansittart'	CBod CDoC CSBt CSgt CTrh EPfP LCro LMil LOPS LRHS LSRN MAsh MGos NRHS SCam SCob SGol SLim SPoG SSta XSte
§	- 'Lady Vansittart Pink'	CMac
	- 'Lady Vansittart Red'	see *C. japonica* 'Lady Vansittart Pink'
	- 'Lady Vansittart Shell'	see *C. japonica* 'Yours Truly'
	- 'Latifolia'	SCam
	- 'Laurie Bray'	CAco CKel EDir SCoo SGsty SRot SWeb
§	- 'Lavinia Maggi' 🏆H5	CAco CBcs CSgt CTri EDir EPfP GMcL LRHS LSRN MGos MPri NRHS SCam SCob SCoo SGol SPoG SRms SSta XSte
	- 'Lavinia Maggi Rosea'	LMaj XSte
	- 'Lemon Drop'	CBcs CTrh
	- 'Lily Pons'	CTrh
	- 'Lipstick'	LRHS XSte
	- 'Little Bit'	ELon SSta
	- 'Little Man'	NRHS
	- 'Lovelight' 🏆H5	CTrh NRHS
	- 'Ludgvan Red'	NRHS
	- 'Lulu Belle'	CBcs
	- 'Mabel Blackwell'	SCam
	- 'Madame de Strekaloff'	CMac CSBt SCam
	- 'Madame Lourmand'	XSte
	- 'Madge Miller'	NRHS
	- 'Magnoliiflora'	see *C. japonica* 'Hagoromo'
	- 'Maiden's Blush'	CMac
	- 'Manuroa Road'	XSte
	- 'Margaret Davis' 🏆H5	CBod CCCN CDoC CPla CSBt CSgt CTrh ELan ELon EPfP LCro LOPS LRHS LSRN MAsh MGos NRHS SCam SCoo SGol WFar XSte
	- 'Margaret Davis Picotee'	CBcs
	- 'Margaret Rose'	SCam
	- 'Margherita Coleoni'	CAco XSte
	- 'Marian Mitchell'	SCam
	- 'Mariana'	ELon
	- 'Marie Bracey'	SGol
	- 'Marie-Galante' **new**	XSte
	- 'Marinka'	CBcs
	- 'Mariottii Rubra'	CMac
	- 'Marjorie Magnificent'	CSgt MAsh
	- 'Mark Alan'	LSRN
	- 'Maroon and Gold'	NRHS
	- 'Mars' 🏆H5	SCam
	- 'Marshmallow'	LRHS XSte
	- 'Mary Costa'	CTrh SCam
§	- 'Masayoshi' 🏆H5	CSBt CSgt NRHS XSte
	- 'Mathotiana Alba'	CAco CBcs CMac CTri EPfP GMcL LSRN MGos SCam WSpi
§	- 'Mathotiana Rosea'	CBcs CMac NLar
	- 'Mathotiana Supreme'	SCam
	- 'Matilija Poppy'	SCam
	- 'Matterhorn'	CTrh
	- 'Mercury' 🏆H5	CMac
	- 'Mermaid'	NRHS
	- 'Midnight'	CBcs CSgt CTsd EGrI LRHS NRHS
	- 'Midnight Magic'	CBcs CSgt CTrh CTri LRHS NRHS
	- 'Midnight Serenade'	NRHS
	- 'Midnight Variegated' (v)	LRHS XSte
§	- 'Mikenjaku'	CAco CSgt EPfP LRHS NRHS SGol SRot
	- 'Mikuni-no-homare' (Higo)	XSte
	- 'Miriam Stevenson'	SCam
	- 'Miss Charleston'	CBcs
	- 'Miss Lyla'	CAco
	- 'Monstruosa Rubra'	see *C. japonica* 'Gigantea'
	- 'Monte Carlo'	SCam
	- 'Montironi'	XSte
	- 'Moshe Dayan'	CDoC CSgt CTsd LMil LRHS MAsh NRHS
§	- 'Mrs Bertha A. Harms'	NRHS
	- 'Mrs D.W. Davis'	EPfP
	- 'Mrs Tingley' (d)	CKel CWnw SGol
	- 'Mrs William Thompson'	NRHS SCam
	- 'Nagasaki'	see *C. japonica* 'Mikenjaku'
	- 'Nancy Bird'	SCam
	- 'Nigra'	see *C. japonica* 'Konronkoku'
	- 'Nina Avery'	SCam
	- 'Nobilissima' 🏆H5	CAco CBcs CBod CMac CSgt CTrh CTri LCro LMil LOPS MBlu SCam SCob SGol SPer SPoG SRot WFar XSte
	- 'Nuccio's Cameo' 🏆H5	CBcs CDoC CSgt CTrh ELan EPfP GMcL LCro LRHS MAsh MPri NLar NRHS SCob
	- 'Nuccio's Gem' 🏆H5	CDoC CSgt LCro LOPS LPar LRHS NLar NRHS SGol SGsty SWeb XSte
	- 'Nuccio's Jewel' 🏆H5	CBcs CDoC CSBt CSgt EPfP LMil LPar LRHS LSRN MAsh NRHS SCam SGol SWeb XSte
	- 'Nuccio's Pearl' 🏆H5	CAco CEnd ELon EPfP LPar LRHS LSRN MPri NRHS SArc SRot SWeb XSte
	- 'Nuccio's Pink Lace'	CBcs CDoC CSgt CTri LRHS NRHS
§	- 'Odoratissima'	SGol
	- 'Okan' (Higo)	XSte
	- 'Oki-no-nami'	LPar
	- 'Onetia Holland'	LSRN SCam SRot WFar
	- 'Oo-La-La'	CTrh LRHS
	- 'Optima'	ELon NRHS SCam
	- 'Orandakō'	CAco SCob
	- 'Paulette Goddard'	SCam
	- 'Paul's Apollo'	see *C. japonica* 'Apollo' Paul, 1911
	- 'Peachblossom'	see *C. japonica* 'Fleur Dipater'
	- 'Pearl Harbor'	SCam
	- 'Pearl Maxwell'	EGrI
	- 'Pink Chiffon'	NRHS
	- 'Pink Clouds'	CBcs
	- 'Pink Perfection'	see *C. japonica* subsp. *rusticana* 'Otome'
	- 'Pope John Paul XXIII'	SCam
	- 'Powder Puff'	CAco LRHS
	- 'Preston Rose'	CBcs
	- 'Primavera'	CTrh LRHS SCam
	- 'Prince Albert'	see *C. japonica* 'Albertii'
	- 'Prince Murat'	NRHS
	- 'Princess Baciocchi'	CAco SCam
	- 'Princess du Mahe'	CMac
	- 'R.L. Wheeler' 🏆H5	CBcs CDoC CSBt CSgt CTri EPfP GMcL LCro LMil LPar LRHS MAsh MGos MPri NRHS SCam SCoo SGol SRot

– 'Red Dandy' SCam
– 'Red Red Rose' NRHS XSte
– 'Robert Lasson' XSte
– 'Roger Hall' CBcs CDoC CSgt CTrh LRHS LSRN NRHS SGol SPoG
– 'Rōgetsu' CBcs
– 'Rosularis' ELon
– 'Royal Velvet' CTrh
– 'Rubescens Major' CBcs
– 'Ruddigore' CTrh
– subsp. ***rusticana*** 'Arajishi' misapplied see *C. japonica* subsp. *rusticana* 'Beni-arajishi'
– – 'Arajishi' Ko'emon SCam
§ – – 'Beni-arajishi' CBcs CSgt NRHS
– – 'Botanyuki' XSte
§ – – 'Otome' SCam SGsty
– 'Sabiniana' NRHS XSte
– 'Sacco Nova' LPar XSte
– 'Saint André' CMac CSgt LRHS MAsh NRHS
– 'San Dimas' ♀H5 CTrh NRHS SCam SWeb XSte
– 'Sanpei-tsubaki' XSte
– 'Sarah Frost' LPar
– 'Satsuma' XSte
– 'Saturnia' CDoC CSgt ELon LMil LRHS MAsh NRHS
– 'Scentsation' ♀H5 CTri LRHS NRHS
– 'Sea Foam' NRHS SCam
– 'Sea Gull' SCam
– 'Sensation' **new** EDir
– 'Shikibu' CTrh XSte
– 'Shiro Chan' ELon SCam
– 'Shirobotan' ELon NRHS SCam
– 'Shūgetsu' LRHS
– 'Silver Anniversary' ♀H5 Widely available
– 'Silver Chalice' CSgt
– 'Silver Mayer' **new** CWnw
– 'Silver Ruffles' CTrh ELon NRHS SCam
– 'Silver Waves' XSte
– 'Snow White' (d) CAco
– 'Snowball' SGsty
– 'Something Beautiful' SCam
– 'Souvenir de Bahuaud-Litou' ♀H5 CBcs CSgt SCam
– 'Splendens Carlyon' CSgt LRHS MAsh NRHS
– 'Spring Fever' SCam
– 'Spring Fling' CTrh LRHS SPoG XSte
– 'Spring Formal' CTrh LRHS XSte
– 'Spring Frill' SCam
– 'Stacy Susan' XSte
– 'Strawberry Parfait' CBcs
– 'Sugar Babe' NRHS SCam
– 'Sundae' CBcs
– 'Sunny Side' XSte
– 'Sweet Dreams' XSte
– 'Sylvia' CMac
– 'Takanini' CTrh SCam XSte
– 'Tammia' ELon LRHS NRHS
– 'Teresa Ragland' SCam
– 'The Mikado' NRHS
– 'Tiffany' CAco EDir EGrI ELon NRHS SCam
– 'Tiki' SCoo
– 'Tinker Bell' ELon
– 'Tom Pouce' XSte
– 'Tom Thumb' ♀H5 CTrh ELon NRHS SRms
– 'Tomorrow' EGrI SCam
– 'Tomorrow's Dawn' SCam
– 'Trewithen White' NRHS
§ – 'Tricolor' ♀H5 CBcs CMac CSBt CTrh ELon MGos NRHS SCam SRot
– 'Tricolor Red' see *C. japonica* 'Lady de Saumarez'
– 'Triphosa' LPar SWeb
– 'Triumphans' XSte
– 'Valtevareda' XSte
– 'Variegata' **new** ELon
– 'Vergine di Collebeato' XSte
– 'Victor Emmanuel' see *C. japonica* 'Blood of China'
– 'Ville de Nantes' CSgt NRHS XSte
– 'Ville du Havre' XSte
– 'Virginia Carlyon' CBcs CSgt
– 'Virginia Robinson' SCam XSte
– 'Visconti Nova' NRHS
– 'Vittorio Emanuele II' CSgt CTrh LRHS MAsh NRHS
– 'Volcano' XSte
– 'Volunteer' LCro LOPS LRHS MGos XSte
– 'Wheel of Fortune' NRHS
– 'White Nun' LPar
– 'White Swan' CDoC CMac CSBt CSgt LRHS NRHS
– 'Wildfire' NRHS
– 'William Bartlett' CAco CBcs CKel CTrh CWnw SCoo
– 'William Honey' CTrh
– 'Winter Perfume Pearl' **new** NLar
– 'Winter Perfume Pink' **new** NLar
– 'Wisley White' see *C. japonica* 'Hakurakuten'
– 'Witman Yellow' CTrh
§ – 'Yours Truly' CMac CSgt CTrh CTsd ELon LSRN MAsh NRHS
– 'Yukimi-guruma' LPar
japonica* × *saluenensis see *C.* × *williamsii*
'Jury's Yellow' see *C.* × *williamsii* 'Jury's Yellow'
'Koto-no-kaori' (*lutchuensis* hybrid) LRHS XSte
'Larry Piet' (*reticulata* hybrid) XSte
'Lasca Beauty' (*japonica* × *reticulata*) XSte
'Lavender Queen' see *C. sasanqua* 'Lavender Queen'
'Leonard Messel' (*reticulata* × (× *williamsii*)) ♀H5 CDoC CMac CTrh CTri EPfP MGos NLar NRHS SCam SPer
'Lila Naff' (*reticulata* hybrid) XSte
'Lovely Lady' XSte
'Magic Mum' LSRN
'Marguérite Gouillon' misapplied see *C. japonica* 'Général Lamoricière'
'Maud Messel' (*reticulata* × (× *williamsii*)) SCam
'Mimosa Jury' LRHS XSte
'Nicky Crisp' (*japonica* × *pitardii*) CTrh LMil LRHS NRHS SPoG XSte
oleifera CTrh
'Paddy's Perfumed' XSte
'Paolina Guichardini' XSte
'Paper Dolls' EGrI
'Pink Goddess' (*hiemalis* hybrid) LRHS XSte
'Pink Icicle' (*oleifera* hybrid) CBcs SCam SGol
'Pink Spangles' see *C. japonica* 'Mathotiana Rosea'
pitardii WWJ 11925 from Vietnam WCru
'Portuense' see *C. japonica* 'Japonica Variegata'
'Quintessence' (*japonica* × *lutchuensis*) LRHS XSte
reticulata 'Arch of Triumph' XSte
– 'Captain Rawes' XSte
– 'Jean Morel' XSte
– 'Kerdalo' XSte
– 'Les Jury' MMuc
– 'Mary Williams' CAco EDir EGrI LCro LRHS SCob SGol SPoG
– 'Miss Tulare' XSte
– 'Nuccio's Ruby' XSte
rosthorniana CUPIDO see *C. rosthorniana* 'Elina'
§ – 'Elina' PBR ELan EPfP LCro LMaj LOPS LRHS MGos NRHS SPoG XSte

	sasanqua Thunb.	MHid
I	- 'Alba'	CMac CSgt CTri LMil
	- 'Baronesa de Soutelinho'	CSgt ELon
	- 'Ben'	CSgt
	- 'Bonanza'	see *C. hiemalis* 'Bonanza'
	- 'Cleopatra'	CSgt EGrI EPfP LPar MAsh SCob SEWo SGsty
	- 'Crimson King' 🏆H4	CSgt CTrh EGrI MAsh NRHS
	- 'Dazzler'	see *C. hiemalis* 'Dazzler'
	- 'Dwarf Shishi'	CTrh
	- 'Early Pearly'	LRHS SCam XSte
I	- 'Fanny'	MHtn
	- 'Fragrans'	ELon
	- 'Fuji-no-mine'	SCam
	- 'Fuji-no-yuki'	XSte
	- 'Gay Border'	CBcs
	- 'Gay Sue'	CTrh EGrI SCam WHlf
	- 'Hinode-gumo'	SEWo SGsty
	- 'Hiryū'	EGrI LRHS MHtn NRHS SCam SEWo WHlf XSte
	- 'Hugh Evans' 🏆H4	CBcs CSgt CTrh EGrI ELan EPfP LMil LRHS NRHS SCam SRot SSta
	- 'Jean May' 🏆H4	ELon EPfP NRHS WCot
	- 'Jennifer Susan'	CTrh CTri LPar
	- 'Kenkyō'	ELon SCam SSta
§	- 'Lavender Queen'	SCam
	- 'Maiden's Blush'	CSgt EGrI NRHS SCam WCot
	- 'Mignonne'	CSgt CTrh
	- 'Mine-no-yuki'	CTrh
I	- 'Narcissiflora' **new**	CWnw
	- 'Narumigata' 🏆H4	CBcs CBod CKel CMac CTrh CTsd CWnw EGrI ELon EPfP LCro LOPS LRHS MBlu MGos NRHS SCam SPoG SSta XSte
	- 'Navajo'	CTrh
	- 'New Dawn'	SRot
	- 'Nyewoods'	CMac
	- 'Papaver'	SCam
	- 'Paradise Audrey'	LMil LSRN SPoG
	- 'Paradise Belinda'	EPfP LMil SPoG
	- 'Paradise Blush'	CBcs CBod LMil SWvt
	- 'Paradise Glow'	CBcs
	- 'Paradise Helen'	LMil LSRN
	- 'Paradise Hilda'	CBcs
	- 'Paradise Pearl'	CBcs EPfP LMil
	- 'Paradise Venessa'	EPfP LMil SCam
	- 'Peach Blossom'	EGrI
	- 'Plantation Pink'	CSgt CTrh EGrI LCro LMil LOPS LRHS MAsh NRHS SCob SPer SRkn SWvt WCot
	- 'Rainbow'	CBcs CDoC CKel CSgt CTrh CWnw EGrI ELan ELon EPfP LCro LRHS MAsh NRHS SCoo SPer SRot SSta WHlf
	- 'Rosea'	CMac CSgt ELon NRHS SCam
§	- 'Rosea Plena' (d)	CBcs
	- 'Sasanqua Rubra'	CMac SCam
	- 'Sasanqua Variegata' (v)	CTrh SCam
	- 'Sekiyō'	LRHS XSte
	- 'Snowflake'	SCam WHlf
	- 'Sparkling Burgundy'	see *C.* 'Sparkling Burgundy'
	- 'Tanya'	CTrh SCam
	- 'Versicolor'	CSgt LCro LOPS LRHS NRHS XSte
	- 'Winter's Joy'	CBcs SCam
	- 'Winter's Snowman'	CBcs LCro LRHS NLar NRHS SGol
	'Satan's Robe' (*reticulata* hybrid)	CBcs
	'Scented Sun'	CTrh
	'Show Girl' (*reticulata* × *sasanqua*) 🏆H4	CBcs SCam
§	***sinensis***	CBcs CCCN CTrh CTsd GPoy LSto MHtn NLar NRHS NTrD SPlb SPre SWeb SWvt WPGP XSte
	- var. ***assamica***	CCCN SPre
	- var. ***sinensis***	CCCN CSgt LCro LOPS
	'Snow Flurry'	CBcs CTrh NRHS SGol
§	'Sparkling Burgundy' 🏆H4	LCro MGos NRHS SRot
	'Spring Daze'	XSte
	'Spring Festival' (*cuspidata* hybrid) 🏆H4	CAco CBcs CEnd CTrh EGrI ELan EPfP LCro LMil LOPS LRHS MGos NLar NRHS SCam SGol XSte
	'Sugar Dream'	CTrh SCam
	'Superscent'	CTrh
	'Survivor'	LRHS
	'Swan Lake'	EPfP LMil MGos MPri NRHS SGol
	'Sweet Emily Kate' (*japonica* × *lutchuensis*)	LRHS XSte
	'Sweet Jane'	LRHS SCam
	'Sweet Olive' (d)	XSte
	'Tamzin Coull' (d)	XSte
	'Tarōkaja' (wabisuke)	SCam
	thea	see *C. sinensis*
	'Tinsie'	see *C. japonica* 'Bokuhan'
	'Tom Knudsen' (*japonica* × *reticulata*) 🏆H4	NRHS SCam WHlf XSte
	transnokoensis 🏆H4	CTrh LRHS WAbe XSte
	'Transtasman'	LRHS
	'Tricolor Sieboldii'	see *C. japonica* 'Tricolor'
	'Tristrem Carlyon' (*reticulata* hybrid)	CBcs CDoC CSgt CTri CTsd EPfP LRHS MAsh MPri NRHS
	tsaii	IDee XSte
	'Usu-ōtome'	see *C. japonica* subsp. *rusticana* 'Otome'
	'Valley Knudsen' (*reticulata* × *saluenensis*)	XSte
	× ***vernalis*** 'Yuletide'	CBcs CDoC CSgt CTrh EGrI LCro LMil LOPS LRHS LSRN MGos NRHS NTrD SCob SWeb WHlf XSte
	'Volcano'	LRHS
	'White Retic' (*japonica* × *reticulata*)	XSte
§	× ***williamsii***	SWeb
	- 'Angel Wings'	NRHS
	- 'Anticipation' 🏆H5	Widely available
	- 'Anticipation Variegated' (v)	CBcs NRHS
	- 'Ballet Queen'	CBcs CSBt SCam
	- 'Ballet Queen Variegated' (v)	ELon
	- 'Bartley Number Five'	CMac
	- 'Beatrice Michael'	CBcs CMac
	- 'Blue Danube'	CBcs SCoo
	- 'Bow Bells'	CTri
	- 'Bowen Bryant' 🏆H5	CSgt CTrh EPfP GMcL LRHS NRHS SGol
	- 'Brigadoon' 🏆H5	CBcs CSgt CTrh CTri EPfP GGGa NRHS SCam XSte
	- 'Burncoose'	CBcs
	- 'Buttons 'n' Bows'	XSte
	- 'C.F. Coates'	SCam
	- 'Caerhays'	CBcs
	- 'Carolyn Williams'	CBcs SCam
	- 'Celebration'	CBcs CSBt LSRN
	- 'Charles Michael'	CBcs
	- 'China Clay' 🏆H5	CDoC CSgt LSRN NRHS
§	- 'Citation'	CBcs CMac
	- 'Contribution'	CTrh LRHS MAsh
	- 'Crinkles'	SCam
	- 'Daintiness' 🏆H5	XSte
	- 'Debbie' 🏆H5	Widely available
	- 'Debbie's Carnation'	NRHS
	- 'Donation' 🏆H5	Widely available
	- 'Dream Boat'	LRHS XSte
	- 'E.G. Waterhouse'	CAco CBod CKel CSBt CSgt CTrh CTri CWnw EDir EGrI ELan ELon

	EPfP GKin GMcL LRHS MGos NRHS SCam SGol SSta WFar XSte
- 'E.G. Waterhouse' variegated (v)	XSte
- 'E.T.R. Carlyon' ♀H5	CBcs CDoC CSgt CTrh CTri EPfP LMil LRHS MAsh MGos NLar NRHS SGol SLim SRot XSte
- 'Edward Carlyon'	CSgt
- 'Elegant Beauty' ♀H5	CBcs CDoC CSgt CTrh ELon LMaj LRHS MAsh NLar NRHS SCam SRot
- 'Elizabeth Anderson'	CTrh
- 'Elsie Jury' ♀H5	CBcs CDoC CMac CSgt CTri ELon GKin LRHS MAsh MGos NLar NRHS SCam SGol
- 'Exaltation'	SCam
- 'Francis Hanger'	CTrh NRHS SRot
- 'Galaxie'	SCam
- 'Gay Time'	CSgt LRHS NRHS
- 'George Blandford' ♀H5	CMac
- 'Glenn's Orbit' ♀H5	NLar SCam
- 'Golden Spangles' (v)	CMac ELon EPfP MGos MMuc NRHS SPoG
- 'Grand Jury'	ELon NRHS
- 'Gwavas'	CBcs CCCN CSgt CTrh LRHS MAsh NRHS SCam
- 'Hilo'	SCam
- 'J.C. Williams' ♀H5	CBcs CMac CTri MMuc SRot
- 'Jamie'	LRHS XSte
- 'Jennifer Trehane'	CTrh
- 'Jill Totty'	CTrh
- 'Julia Hamiter' ♀H5	CBcs CSgt LRHS MAsh NRHS
§ - 'Jury's Yellow' ♀H5	CBcs CBod CCCN CDoC CPla CSBt CSgt CTrh CTri EGrl EPfP GGGa LCro LMil LRHS LSRN MAsh MGos MPri SCam SCob SGol SLim SPoG SRot SSta SWvt XSte
- 'Laura Boscawen'	CBcs CTrh SCam
- 'Les Jury' ♀H5	CBcs CBod CDoC CSBt CTrh LMil LSRN MGos MMuc NRHS SGol SLim SPer SRot WFar XSte
- 'Lucky Star' (d)	XSte
- 'Margaret Waterhouse'	CDoC CSgt SCam
- 'Marjorie Waldegrave'	CSgt NRHS
- 'Mary Jobson'	CBcs
- 'Mary Larcom'	CBcs
- 'Mary Phoebe Taylor' ♀H5	CBcs NLar SCam SLim
- 'Mildred Veitch'	CSBt
- 'Mirage'	CTrh
- 'Monica Dance'	CBcs
- 'Muskoka' ♀H5	CBcs EPfP
- 'New Venture'	CBcs
- 'Night Rider'	WPGP XSte
- 'November Pink'	CBcs SCam
- 'Philippa Forward'	CBcs CMac
- 'Pink Wave'	CSgt NRHS
- 'Red Dahlia'	CBcs
- 'Rendezvous'	CSgt CTrh SCam
- 'Rose Parade'	CSgt
- 'Rose Quartz'	CSgt LRHS
- 'Rosemary Williams'	CMac
- 'Ruby Wedding' (d) ♀H5	CBcs CBod CDoC CEme CKel CPla CSBt CSgt CTrh EGrl EPfP LCro LMil LRHS LSRN MAsh MGos MHtn MPri NRHS NTrD SCam SCoo SLim SPoG SWvt WFar WHlf
- 'Saint Ewe' ♀H5	CBcs CSBt CSgt CTrh CTri EPfP MGos NRHS SCam XSte
- 'Saint Michael'	CBcs
- 'Señorita' ♀H5	CSgt EGrl ELon GMcL LRHS NLar NRHS SCam SGol SRot
- 'Shocking Pink'	CSgt NRHS
- 'The Duchess of Cornwall'	CSgt LRHS NRHS
- 'Tiptoe'	CTrh SCoo
- 'Toni Finlay's Fragrant'	CTrh
- 'Tulip Time'	XSte
- 'Twinkle Star'	CSgt NRHS
- 'Water Lily' ♀H5	CBcs CSgt CTri ELon LRHS NLar NRHS SCam SRot
- 'Wilber Foss'	CBcs CSgt LRHS NRHS SCam
- 'William Carlyon'	CSgt NRHS
- 'Winter Gem'	LRHS XSte
'Winter's Charm'	CBcs CDoC CSgt LRHS NRHS
'Winter's Dream'	CBcs
'Winter's Interlude'	CBcs CDoC CSgt LRHS MAsh NRHS
'Winter's Star'	SGol
'Winter's Toughie'	CBcs CSgt MAsh NRHS SCam
'Winton' (*cuspidata* × *saluenensis*)	CBcs
'Yoimachi' (*fraterna* × *sasanqua*)	CTrh LRHS XSte
'Yume'	LRHS XSte
yunnanensis	IDee

Camissonia (*Onagraceae*)

bistorta 'Sunflakes'	CSpe

Campanula (*Campanulaceae*)

RCB AM 13	WCot
abietina	see *C. patula* subsp. *abietina*
alata	CCBP GJos
'Albert Kirkham'	EBee WCot
§ ***alliariifolia***	Widely available
- DHTU 0126	WCru
alliariifolia* × *makaschvilii new	GElm
- 'Ivory Bells'	see *C. alliariifolia*
- 'Ivory Towers'	EBee
- 'Minor'	GKev
allionii	see *C. alpestris*
§ ***alpestris***	ITim NSla
americana	WFar
armena	GJos
arvatica	EACa EHyd EPot LRHS NRHS SRms WAbe WFar
aucheri	see *C. bellidifolia* subsp. *aucheri*
'Barbara Valentine'	EBee EWTr LBar WCAu WHil
barbata	EACa EBee EMor GKev
bayerniana	GJos
'Belinda'	EPot SGro
bellidifolia	NSla
§ - subsp. ***aucheri***	EPot GEdr
§ - subsp. ***besenginica***	GEdr
- subsp. ***saxifraga***	GEdr
besenginica	see *C. bellidifolia* subsp. *besenginica*
§ ***betulifolia*** ♀H5	GEdr NSla WCot WFar
biebersteiniana	GEdr ITim NSla
'Birch Hybrid'	EACa EHyd ELan EPot LRHS NRHS SAko SRms WFar
'Blue Moon'	LRHS
BLUE OCTOPUS ('Jls0504m'PBR)	CWGN ELon LBar LSou NCth SRms WSpi
'Blue Pearl'	WAbe
bononiensis	SRms
'Burghaltii'	MACG NLar SHar
calaminthifolia	ITim
* ***campanulata***	MCot
'Cantata'	WAbe
carpatica ♀H5	EPfP GQue LRHS LShi NGdn SPlb SRms WFar
- f. ***alba***	EHyd LRHS NGdn NRHS SPlb
§ - - 'Weisse Clips'	CKel EHyd EPfP GDam GJos GMaP LCro LOPS LRHS MAsh NGdn NHol NRHS SPer SPoG SRms SWvt WFar

§	- 'Blaue Clips'	CBcs CKel ECtt EHyd EPfP GDam GJos GMaP LCro LPar LRHS MAsh MGos NFav NGdn NGrs NRHS SPer SPoG SRms SRot SWvt WFar
	- BLUE CLIPS	see *C. carpatica* 'Blaue Clips'
	- 'Blue Moonlight'	EACa EHyd LRHS NRHS
	- 'Blue Uniform'	LRHS
	- 'Chewton Joy'	EACa EHyd LRHS NRHS
	- 'Kathy'	EPot
	- 'Pearl Deep Blue'	MTin
	- 'Rapido Blue'	CBod LBar MACG MHol
	- 'Rapido White'	LBar MACG
	- var. ***turbinata***	SRms
	- - 'Foerster'	EHyd NRHS
	- - 'Isabel'	EHyd NRHS
	- - 'Jewel'	EHyd LRHS NRHS
	- WHITE CLIPS	see *C. carpatica* f. *alba* 'Weisse Clips'
	- white-flowered	LRHS
§	***cashmeriana***	WAbe
	cephallenica	see *C. garganica* subsp. *cephallenica*
§	***chamissonis***	EPot GArf GEdr NWad
	- 'Alba'	WFar
	- 'Major'	EWes
§	- 'Superba' ♀H5	CBor EACa EDAr NHpl WAbe WIce
	'Chloe'	CMiW EBee EWTr WFar
	choruhensis	EWes GEdr SPlb
	ciliata	GEdr
	portenschlagiana Clockwise Series	LRHS SRot
§	***cochlearifolia*** ♀H5	EBee EBou EHyd ELan EPfP GAbr GJos GMaP LRHS MAsh MMuc NHpl NRHS NWad SPoG WFar WHoo
	- var. ***alba***	EBou ELan LShi NHpl NRya SRms WAbe WFar WHoo
	- - 'Advance White'	WFar
	- - double white-flowered (d)	WFar
	- - 'White Baby' (Baby Series)	EACa EHyd EPfP EPot NRHS NWad SPoG SRms WFar
	- 'Bavaria Blue'	LSun NHol
	- 'Blue Baby' (Baby Series)	EPfP LRHS NHpl SPoG SRms SRot
	- 'Blue Wonder'	ECtt
	- 'Elizabeth Oliver' (d) ♀H5	EACa ECtt EDAr EHyd ELan GArf GEdr LRHS MBros MHer NBir NBwr NHar NHpl NRHS SEdd SPeP SPlb SRms WAbe WFar WHoo WIce WSHC
	- 'Flore Pleno' (d)	WFar
	- 'R.B. Loder' (d)	EHyd LRHS MHer NRHS
	- 'Silver Bells'	ECha LSou
	- 'Tubby'	ELan EPot MHer SGro SRms
	collina	EACa EHyd EMor GEdr LRHS NRHS
	'Constellation'	EACa
	'Covadonga'	EACa EHyd LRHS NRHS WAbe WThu
	'Cremewit'	EPot
	'Crystal'	ECtt MAvo MCot MHol NLar WCot WFar
	dasyantha	see *C. chamissonis*
	dolomitica	GJos
	'E.K. Toogood'	EACa EBou ECtt EPot SRms WFar
	erinus	MHol
	'Faichem Lilac'	WCot
	fenestrellata	EACa EPot SGro SLee
	finitima	see *C. betulifolia*
	fragilis subsp. ***cavolinii***	GArf
	garganica ♀H5	EACa EBou EHyd EPfP GMaP MAsh MRav NFav NRHS SRms SVic SWvt WFar
	- 'Alba' **new**	WFar
	- 'Aurea'	see *C. garganica* 'Dickson's Gold'
	- 'Blue Diamond'	EBou NLar
§	- subsp. ***cephallenica***	EACa
§	- 'Dickson's Gold'	Widely available
	- 'Erinus Major'	EACa
	- 'Filigree'	MNHC NBwr WBrk WCot WFar
	- 'Major'	SPoG WFar
	- 'Mrs Resholt'	CTri ECtt EWoo NBir NBwr NLar SEdd SRms SWvt WBrk WFar WIce
	- 'W.H. Paine' ♀H5	EACa ECtt NFav NLar NSla WAbe WBrk WFar WHoo
	'Glandore'	EACa SAko XLum
	glomerata	CBee EMor GAbr GEdr LSRN LShi MHer NAts NBir NGrd NGrs NMir WFar
	- var. ***acaulis*** hort.	EPfP GMcL NGrd NLar SCob SRms WFar
	- var. ***alba***	CBcs CDor CNor CRos CSpe EACa ECha ECtt EHyd ELan EMor EPfP GMaP LBar LRHS MBel NRHS SCob SGbt SPlb SPoG WCAu WGwG
§	- - 'Schneekrone'	LCro LOPS NBir WFar
	- (Bellefleur Series) BELLEFLEUR BLUE	GMcL
	- - BELLEFLEUR WHITE	EWTr
	- 'Caroline' ♀H7	Widely available
	- CROWN OF SNOW	see *C. glomerata* var. *alba* 'Schneekrone'
	- var. ***dahurica***	CSpe EBee NLar SHar
	- 'Emerald'	EBee EHyd EMor EPfP LBar LRHS MAsh MHer MNrw NCth NLar NRHS SCob SPad SRms WFar XSen
	- 'Freya'[PBR] ♀H7	EACa EBee ECtt EPfP LBar LPla MNrw NCth SPad WCot WFar WHil
	- (Genti Series) GENTI BLUE ('Allgentibl'[PBR])	LRHS MPri WFar
	- - GENTI TWISTERBELL ('Allgentitwist'[PBR])	CBod EMor GElm MHol NEoE SCob
	- - GENTI WHITE ('Allgentiw'[PBR])	CWGN EPfP LRHS MPri SCoo WFar
	- 'Joan Elliott'	EBee ECha ECtt EPfP LBar LEdu LRHS MHol SGbt WGwG XSen
	- 'Purple Pixie'	SRms
	- 'Stevie's Wonder'	LRHS
	- 'Superba' ♀H7	Widely available
	grossekii	EBee GJos
	'Hannah'	EHyd EPot NRHS
	× ***haylodgensis*** misapplied	see *C.* × *haylodgensis* 'Plena'
§	× ***haylodgensis*** W. Brockbank 'Marion Fisher' (d)	WAbe WFar
§	- 'Plena' (d)	EACa ECtt EHyd EPot LRHS NRHS SRms WAbe WFar
	- 'Yvonne'	ECtt ELan LBar NHpl WFar
	hercegovina 'Nana'	WAbe
	'Hilltop Snow'	EPot WAbe
	hofmannii	GJos GKev NWad
	hypopolia	WAbe
	incanescens **new**	GKev
§	***incurva***	CSpe EACa EDAr GArf GEdr GJos GKev NSti
	- 'Blue Ice'	GArf
	IRIDESCENT BELLS ('Iribella'[PBR])	CAby CWGN EACa EBee EMor EWTr LBar LCro LSou MBel MHol MNrw NCth NSti SCob SPer WCAu WHil WPnP WTyc
	isophylla ♀H2	CPla EPot
	JENNY ('Harjen')	CWGN SHar
	'Joan Beeston'	WAbe
	'Joe Elliott'	WAbe
	kemulariae	GJos WCot XLum
	'Kent Belle' ♀H7	Widely available
	kirpicznikovii	EBee GEdr GKev
	komarovii	WCot
	lactiflora	CAby CElw CMac CSpe CWal EACa EBee ECha EHyd EPfP GJos LCro

	LRHS LSto MCot MNrw NRHS SPer WCAu WFar WSpi
- ***alba***	see *C. lactiflora* white-flowered
- 'Alba' ♀H7	EBee ECha ELan EPfP GBin GMaP LBar MAvo MBel MMuc SEND WBrk WCAu WCot WSpi
- 'Assendon Pearl' ♀H7	ELon LBar LPla LRHS MHol SHar SPhx WCot
- AVALANCHE ('Camblo')	EACa EBee ECtt LCro
- 'Border Blues'	ECha ECtt EPfP MACG MHol MNrw NDov NLar WFar
- 'Dixter Presence'	LPla SMHy
- dwarf pink-flowered	NLar SMHy WFar
- 'Favourite' ♀H7	ECtt EWoo NGdn SHar
- 'Loddon Anna' ♀H7	Widely available
- 'Marchants Nimbus'	GBin SMHy
- 'Monica's Dream'	EACa ECtt MAsh MBel NLar SMHy WGwG
- 'Platinum' ♀H7	LPla
- 'Pouffe'	CRos EACa EBee ECtt EHyd EPfP GMaP LRHS MNrw NGdn NRHS SGbt SPer SWvt
- 'Prichard's Variety' ♀H7	Widely available
- 'Superba' ♀H7	EACa ECtt ELon
- 'Violet'	EPfP WSpi
- 'White Pouffe'	EACa ECtt EHyd EPfP GDam GMaP GMcL LRHS NChi NDov NLar NRHS NSti SCob SGbt SPer SPoG WFar
§ - white-flowered	CWal EHeP NBir SEdd SPer WCAu WCav
lasiocarpa	EPot
latifolia	EACa ECha EPfP GJos GQue LShi MCot NBid NChi NMir SPer SRms WCAu WSpi
- var. ***alba***	CRos EBee EHyd EMor EPfP EWTr GJos LRHS MBel NRHS SPer SRms WSpi WTor
* - 'Amethyst'	SBls WSpi
- blue-flowered	SEND
- 'Brantwood'	EPfP WSpi
- 'Gloaming'	EBee ECtt WSpi
- var. ***macrantha***	EBee EHyd EMor EPfP GMaP LRHS NFav NRHS NSti SWvt
- - 'Alba'	ECha ELan EMor GLog GMaP MRav NFav NLar NWad WCAu
latiloba	WCot WKif
§ - 'Alba'	EBee MCot MNrw NLar WBrk
- 'Hidcote Amethyst'	CDor CWGN ECtt EHyd ELan ELon GAbr LBar LRHS MBriF NBid NBir NGdn NLar SPer WCAu WCot WKif WSpi
- 'Highcliffe Variety' ♀H7	EACa EBee ECtt EHyd EPfP GElm LBar LRHS MACG MBriF MPie NLar NRHS SPer SPoG WCAu WCot WGwG WSpi
- 'Percy Piper' ♀H7	CKel CRos EACa EBee EHyd LBar LRHS MAsh MPie MRav NLar NRHS WCAu WSpi
- 'Splash'	MNrw
'Linda'	IPot
'Lynchmere'	EPot WAbe
makaschvilii	CPla CWal ELan EMor EWhm GArf GElm GKev SPtp WHil
makaschvilii* × *trachelium	WCot
'Margaret Brine'	WAbe
'Marion Fisher'	see *C.* × *baylodgensis* W. Brockbank 'Marion Fisher'
massalskyi	GKev
medium	GQue
§ - var. ***calycanthema*** hort.	WSpi
- 'Cup and Saucer'	see *C. medium* var. *calycanthema* hort.
'Mevr.V.Vollenhove'	EBee LBar MAvo MHol
'Misty Dawn' ♀H7	NLar WCot
moesiaca	GKev
muralis	see *C. portenschlagiana*
myrtifolia	WAbe
- 'Helmi'	WAbe
nitida	see *C. persicifolia* var. *planiflora*
'Norman Grove'	EPot
ochroleuca	EPPr GBin WCot XLum
odontosepala	EBee NWad WFar
- from Iran	EMor EPPr NLar
olympica misapplied	see *C. rotundifolia* 'Olympica'
ossetica	ECtt WBor
pallida subsp. ***tibetica***	see *C. cashmeriana*
parviflora Lam.	see *C. sibirica*
patula	CSpe EACa WKif
§ - subsp. ***abietina***	CSpe
'Paul Furse'	ECtt NSti WCot
'Pearlescent Pink'	EWes LSou
'Pearlescent White'	EWes LSou
pelia	CPla
pendula	EPfP LBar LRHS SBls SGBe
persicifolia	Widely available
- var. ***alba***	Widely available
§ - 'Alba Coronata' (d)	GAbr LShi SRms XLum
- 'Alba Flore-Pleno' (d)	SGbt
- 'Alba Plena'	see *C. persicifolia* 'Alba Coronata'
- 'Azure Beauty'	ECtt NLar WCot WSpi XSen
- 'Beau Belle'	EWld NLar
- blue and white-flowered	SRms
- 'Blue Bell'	MACG WPnP
- 'Blue Bloomers' (d)	CDor CGBo EACa EPri EWes MRav NQui SRms WCFE WCot XLum
- 'Blue-eyed Blonde' PBR (v)	NLar
- blue-flowered	CSBt EWoo GMcL MBow SPlb SRms
- 'Boule de Neige' (d)	CDor WSpi
§ - 'Chettle Charm'	CDor CWCL ECtt EHyd EPfP EShb GAbr LRHS MBriF MRav NBPC NBir NLar NRHS SCob SRms SWvt WBor WCot WFar
- 'Cornish Mist'	CDor EBee EPfP MPie NLar WCAu WSpi
- double silver-blue-flowered (d) **new**	LShi
- 'Fleur de Neige' (d)	MRav
- 'Frances' (d)	WCot
- 'Gawen'	CMac ECtt SGbt WCAu
- 'George Chiswell'	see *C. persicifolia* 'Chettle Charm'
- 'Grandiflora'	CDor EAJP
- 'Grandiflora Alba'	EAJP NLar SDix
- 'Hampstead White' (d)	WSpi
- 'Kelly's Gold'	SRms
- 'La Belle' (d)	EBee MNrw NLar
- 'La Bello' PBR	LBar MNrw NLar
- 'La Bonne Amie' (d)	EBee EPfP LBar MNrw NLar SPoG
- 'Moerheimii' (d)	WSpi
- 'Perry's Boy Blue'	NPer
§ - var. ***planiflora***	WAbe
- - f. ***alba***	NHpl WAbe
- 'Powder Puff' (d)	EPfP GBin GMcL NLar
- 'Pride of Exmouth' (d) ♀H7	CDor CMiW MHer MRav WSpi
- subsp. ***sessiliflora*** 'Alba'	see *C. latiloba* 'Alba'
- 'Snowdrift'	SRms
- (Takion Series) 'Takion Blue'	EHyd ELan LBar LRHS LSou MPri NGrs NRHS SCoo SPoG SRms
- - 'Takion White'	CSpe EHyd ELan EPfP GQue LBar LRHS LSou MPri NGrs NRHS SCoo SPoG SRms
- 'Telham Beauty' ambig.	CSBt EHeP EWTr LBar MACG SCob SGbt SMrm SWvt WSpi WWke XLum
- 'Telham Beauty' misapplied	EBee EHyd EPfP LRHS MRav NRHS SPer SRms SWvt

	- 'Telham Beauty' D.Thurston	MBow NFav NLar
	- 'Tinpenny Blue'	WCot
	- 'White Bell'	MACG WPnP
	- 'Wortham Belle' ambig.	EWoo MHol MRav SGbt WCAu
	- 'Wortham Belle' Blooms	CFis ECtt EHyd LRHS NRHS WGwG
	petrophila	WAbe
	pilosa	see *C. chamissonis*
	- 'Superba'	see *C. chamissonis* 'Superba'
	'Pink Octopus'^{PBR}	Widely available
	planiflora	see *C. persicifolia* var. *planiflora*
§	***portenschlagiana*** ♀^{H5}	Widely available
	- 'Alba'	WFar
	- AMBELLA INTENS PURPLE ('Ptdb141301'^{PBR}) **new**	LCro
	- 'Blue Magic' **new**	LBar
	- 'Blue Sky'	LRHS
	- 'Catharina'	EACa ECtt EHyd EShb LRHS NRHS SPoG SRms WFar
	- CLOCKWISE DEEP BLUE (Clockwise Series)	NBir
	- 'Lieselotte'	EACa ECtt SAko WAbe WFar
	- 'Major'	CBod GJos NCou
	- 'Resholdt's Variety'	CBar CKel CTri EACa EAJP EBou ECtt EHyd ELan EPfP GJos GKev LRHS MBel MRav NRHS SAko SLee SRms WAbe WCot XLum XSen
	- 'Sago'	CBod LBar MDon MHol
	poscharskyana	Widely available
	- 'Blauranke'	EACa EWes SAko WFar
	- 'Blue Gown'	EACa ECtt NCth SAko
	- 'Blue Rivulet'^{PBR}	ECtt
	- BLUE WATERFALL ('Camgood')	CWGN EACa ECtt EPfP LRHS MBNS NCth NDov SPoG WBrk WCot
	- 'E.H. Frost'	CElw EACa ECha ECtt ELan EPPr EPfP EShb EWTr GKev GMaP LBar MACG MCot MMuc NLar NRya SAko SEND SLee SPer SRms SWvt WBrk WFar WSpi
	- 'Erich G. Arends'	SAko
I	- 'Freya'	EACa SAko
	- 'Frühlingszauber'	WCot
	- 'Garden Star'	CBod MHol
	- 'Hirsch Blue'	LRHS SRms SRot
	- 'Lilacina'	EACa EPPr
	- 'Lisduggan Variety'	CElw EACa ECtt EPPr EWes GMaP MACG MHer NLar SAko SLee SRms WBrk WFar WIce WJam XSen
	- 'Nana Alba'	EACa EPPr MACG SAko WBrk
	- 'Pinkins'^{PBR}	CBod EACa ECtt
	- 'Schneeranke'	XSen
	- 'Silberregen'	SAko
	- 'Stella' ♀^{H5}	EACa ECha ECtt EGrI EHyd ELan EPfP GMaP IPot LRHS LSRN MAvo MRav NRHS SAko SPer SWvt WBrk WCav WCot WHoo WJam XLum
	- 'Trollkind'	EACa EPPr SAko WFar
	- variegated (v)	EBee EPPr
	- 'Weissranke'	WFar
	- white-flowered	CTri WFar
	prenanthoides	see *Asyneuma prenanthoides*
	× ***pseudoraineri*** hort.	EHyd EWes NRHS
	pulla	EACa EBou ECtt EHyd ELan EPot GEdr LRHS NBwr NHpl NRHS NSla SCob SPoG SRms WIce
	- 'Alba'	EACa EHyd LRHS NRHS NSla WAbe WIce
	- 'Blue Drops' **new**	LBar
	× ***pulloides*** hort. 'G.F. Wilson' ♀^{H5}	EACa ECtt GEdr GMaP IPot NLar SRkn WFar
	- 'Jelly Bells'^{PBR}	NLar
	punctata	GAbr GArf GJos MCot NBro NSti SMrm WCAu WFar
	- f. ***albiflora***	WFar
	- 'Alina's Double' (d)	NLar
	- dwarf	WAbe
	- 'Folies Bergère'	CBor
	- var. ***hondoensis***	GKev
	- 'Hot Lips'	CMac
*	- var. ***howozana***	GKev
	- 'Kurokawa'	WFar
	- var. ***microdonta*** B&SWJ 5553	WCru
	- 'Milky Way'	EMor LBar LSou NEoE WNPC WPnP
*	- 'Nana'	WFar
	- 'Pantaloons' (d)	CBor CDor CMac CWGN EMor EWes NLar SCob SRms
	- 'Pink Chimes'	CBod CDor EMor LBar NLar SEle SMrm WPnP WWke
	- 'Plum Wine'	NWad
	- purple-flowered	EHyd EPfP LRHS
	- f. ***rubriflora***	CBod CDor CRos CSde CSpe EBee EBou ECtt EGrI EHyd ELan EMor EPfP GElm LRHS MBel MCot MNrw NRHS SBls SCob SPer SRms WCAu WPnP
	- - 'Beetroot'	CWCL EBee EMor GKev MHer MHol NLar WFar
	- - 'Bowl of Cherries'	NLar SRms
	- - 'Cherry Bells'	EHyd EMor EPfP LRHS LSRN NRHS
	- - 'Vienna Festival'	CSBt
	- - 'Wine 'n' Rubies'	EBee EMor
I	- 'Silver Bells'	EMor EPfP LBar NCth NLar NSti SRms WFar WHil WWke
	- 'Wedding Bells'	CDor CKel EACa EBou EHyd EMor EPfP EPri LBar LDai LRHS LSRN MBriF MBros MSpe NLar NRHS SCob SMrm SRms WCAu WHil WWke
I	- 'White Bells'	MHol
	- white hose-in-hose (d)	XLum
	'Purple Sensation'^{PBR}	CWGN EBee EPfP LSou MNrw MSCN NLar WCot
	pusilla	see *C. cochlearifolia*
	pyramidalis	CCBP CSpe CWal EACa EBee EGrI ELan EPfP GJos GMcL LBar MMuc NGBl SDix SPlb
	- 'Alba'	CSpe EACa ELan EPfP GJos LBar NGBl SCoo SDix SPlb
	- lavender blue-flowered	GMcL
	- variegated (v)	LRHS
	raddeana	EACa SBrt WBrk
	raineri	EPot NSla WAbe
*	- 'Alba'	WAbe
	- 'Nettleton Gold'	EACa EHyd LRHS NRHS
§	***rapunculoides***	SBut SRms WCFE
§	- 'Afterglow'	MAvo WFar
	- 'Alba'	WFar
	- 'Campbell Blue'	WBrk
	rapunculus	MNHC
	recurva	see *C. incurva*
	rhomboidalis Gorter	see *C. rapunculoides*
	rhomboidalis L.	GKev WCot
	rigidipila	GJos WHer
	(Ringsabell Series) 'Ringsabell Indigo Blue'	ELan EMor EPfP LBar SPoG
	- 'Ringsabell Mulberry Rose'	ELan EMor EPfP LBar SRms WBrk WCAu
	- 'Ringsabell Opal White'	ELan EMor
	rotundifolia	CBod CMac EACa EBou EHyd ELan EPfP GAbr GJos GLog MBow MHer MNHC NAts NMir SPhx SPlb SRms WBrk WWild
	- var. ***albiflora***	CElw EWes
	- 'Jotunheimen'	EACa WAbe

§	– 'Olympica'	EACa EBee LBar WHoo
	– 'White Gem'	EACa EHyd ELan EPfP GKev LBar LRHS NRHS WHoo
	'Royal Wave'	IPot LBar NCth NLar
	'Samantha'	EACa ECtt GAbr GEdr GKev LRHS LSRN MACG NHpl SEdd SGBe SHar SMrm WFar
	'Sarastro'	Widely available
	sarmatica	EACa EPfP GElm SGro SRms WFar
	– 'Hemelstraling'	EShb GElm MCot MHol
	– subsp. ***woronowii***	ITim
	sartorii	GEdr WAbe
	scheuchzeri	WAbe
	'Senior'	EACa ECtt ELon EPPr WCot WGoo
§	***sibirica***	GJos
	– 'Royal Wedding'	IPot
	'Snow Dune'	LBar NCth WCAu
	'Stansfieldii'	EHyd EPot LRHS NRHS
	stevenii	see *C. stevenii* subsp. *beauverdiana*
§	– subsp. ***beauverdiana***	SBrt
	subramulosa	see *C. cochlearifolia*
	'Summer Pearl'	ECtt LBar LLWG SGBe
	'Summertime Blues'PBR	EBee EHyd ELan GElm LBar LRHS MHol NCth NLar NRHS WCot
§	'Swannables'	EShb MAvo MRav NCth WCAu WFar
	takesimana	CBod CSpe CTtf ECha ECtt EHyd ELan EPfP GKin GQue LEdu LRHS NGrd NLar NRHS SRms SWvt
I	– 'Alba'	EMor WFar XLum
	– 'Beautiful Trust'	CDor LBar MHol
	– 'Bellringers'	SBls
	– 'Elizabeth'	Widely available
	– 'Elizabeth II' (d)	EMor EPPr SHar WFar
	– 'Feenrock JP'	XLum
	– 'White Giant'	SHar
	thyrsoides	CSpe GJos GKev LBar SBls
	'Timsbury Chimes'	WAbe
	'Timsbury Perfection'	WAbe
	tommasiniana 🏆H6	EPot SBrt WAbe
	trachelium	EACa EBee ELon EMor GJos GKev LBar MBow MHer MNHC MRav NAts NGrd NMir WCot WFar WHer WShi WSpi
	– f. ***alba***	EBee ELan EMor GJos NLar SGbt WCot WFar
	– – 'Alba Flore Pleno' (d)	LEdu LPla
	– 'Bernice' (d)	CDor EACa EBee ELan EMor EPfP EWTr GMaP LBar LRHS MAvo MCot MHol MNrw MPie NLar NSti SCob SPer WCAu WCot WFar WSpi XSen
	– 'Purple Break'	MHol WCot
	– 'Snowball'	CMac
	'Van-Houttei'	CDor NLar WCot
	versicolor	CDoC SRms
	vidalii	see *Azorina vidalii*
	'Viking'PBR	LBar SPad SRms WHil
	waldsteiniana	GKev WAbe
	wanneri	CPla EDAr GJos LBar
	'White Octopus'	ECtt EMor LSou SEle
	× ***wockei*** 'Puck'	EACa ECtt EDAr EHyd EPot LRHS NRHS WAbe
	zangezura	CAby EACa EBou ELan EPfP GJos GKev LBar SGbt
	zoysii	WAbe

Campanula × Symphyandra see *Campanula*

Campanumoea see *Codonopsis*

Campsis (*Bignoniaceae*)

	'Fire Light' **new**	LCro
	grandiflora	CBcs CKel CWGN EHyd ELan EPfP LRHS LSRN SPer SWvt WCFE
	radicans	CBcs CBod CMac CRHN CWCL EGrI EHyd ELan EPfP LPar LRHS MGil MHtn MSwo NRHS SCoo SNig SPer SPlb WJur
	– 'Atrosanguinea'	SVen
	– 'Flamenco'	CBcs CBrac CDoC CKel CMac CWCL EBee EDir EHyd ELan EPfP EWTr LRHS LSRN MGil MMrt SAdn SCob SCoo SNig SPoG SVen SWvt WLov
§	– f. ***flava*** 🏆H4	CBcs CKel CMac CRos CTri CWCL EBee EDir EHyd ELan EPfP EWTr LRHS MBlu MGil MGos NRHS SCob SCoo SGbt SPer SPoG SSha SVen SWvt
	– 'Stromboli'	EHed EPfP SGsty
	– 'Yellow Trumpet'	see *C. radicans* f. *flava*
	× ***tagliabuana*** DANCING FLAME ('Huidan'PBR)	CWCL CWGN EHyd EPfP LRHS
	– INDIAN SUMMER ('Kudian'PBR)	CBcs CDoC CKel CRos CWCL CWGN CWnw EHyd ELon EPfP LCro LRHS LSRN MGil MGos NRHS SCoo SNig SPeP
	– 'Madame Galen' 🏆H4	Widely available
	– ORANGEADE ('Tracamp') **new**	EHed MMrt
	– (Summer Jazz Series) 'Takarazuka Yellow'PBR	EHyd LRHS NRHS
	– – 'Takarazuka Zujin'PBR	EHyd LRHS NRHS

Camptosorus see *Asplenium*

Campylandra see *Tupistra*

Campylotropis (*Fabaceae*)

macrocarpa	WSHC

Canarina (*Campanulaceae*)

canariensis 🏆H2	CCCN CMCN CTsd EAri SBrt
– from Los Silos, Tenerife	WCot

Candollea see *Hibbertia*

Canna ✿ (*Cannaceae*)

	'Alberich'	SHaC
	altensteinii	CDTJ SHaC SPlb
	'Ambassador'	SDeJ
	'Ambassadour'	SHaC
	'Angelique' **new**	SEdd
	'Angie Summers'	CSBt
	'Annaeei' 🏆H3	EAri ETod SHaC SPlb
	'Anthony and Cleopatra' (v)	WCot
I	'Aphrodite' van Klaveren	MBros
	'Argentina'	SHaC
	'Assaut'	SHaC
	'Australia'	CDTJ EAri ETod SHaC
	'Baron Seguier'	XLum
	'Bird of Paradise'	ETod SHaC
	'Black Knight'	ETod LAma LPal LSvl SCob SDeJ SHaC
	'Bonfire'	CDTJ CTsd EAri
	brasiliensis	CPla EShb EWld SHaC
	'Brillant'	CWnw SDeJ SHaC
	'Burbank'	CDTJ
	'Caballero'	SHaC XLum
	'Caliméro'	SHaC
	'Carnaval'	SHaC
	'Centenaire de Rozain-Boucharlat'	SDeJ SHaC XLum
	'Champion'	SHaC
	'Chocolate Sunrise'	LCro LOPS
	'Chouchou'	SHaC

§	'City of Portland'	SDeJ SHaC
§	'Cleopatra'	CCCN SDeJ SHaC
	coccinea	SArc
	compacta	EAri SHaC
	'Corail'	SHaC
	'Corsica' (Island Series)	SHaC
	'Durban' Hiley, orange-flowered	see *C.* 'Phasion'
	'Durban' ambig.	CBen CChe CWGN ETod LPal SArc SEdd SHaC
	'E. Neubert'	ELan ETod SHaC
	edulis	CDTJ XLum XSte
§	× ***ehemanii*** ♀H3	CAvo CDTJ SBrt SHaC
	'Emblème'	SHaC
	'En Avant'	SHaC SPlb
	'Endeavour'	SHaC
	'Erebus' ♀H3	EAri SHaC
	'Ermine'	SHaC
	'Extase'	SHaC
	'Fatamorgana'	SHaC
	'Feuerzauber'	SHaC
	'Fiesta'	SHaC
	FIREBIRD	see *C.* 'Oiseau de Feu'
	'Firebird'	EAri SHaC
	flaccida	EAri SHaC
	'General Eisenhower' ♀H3	ETod SHaC
	× ***generalis*** Cannova Series	SHaC
	- - CANNOVA BRONZE ORANGE ('Fcaa33')	CCht SHaC
	- - CANNOVA BRONZE SCARLET ('Fcaa35') ♀H2	CCht ETod SHaC
	- - CANNOVA LEMON	SHaC WHlf
	- - CANNOVA ORANGE SHADES ('Fcaa17')	SHaC WHlf
	- - CANNOVA MANGO ('Fcaa10')	CCht SHaC
	- - CANNOVA RED SHADES ('Fcaa23') ♀H2	CCht SHaC
	- - CANNOVA ROSE ('Fcaa05') ♀H2	SHaC
	- - CANNOVA YELLOW ('Fcaa02') ♀H2	CCht SHaC
	× ***generalis*** × ***indica***	SHaC
	glauca	SHaC
	'Gnom'	SDeJ
	'Golden Girl'	MBros
	'Golden Lucifer'	SDeJ
	'Golden Orb'	ETod SHaC
	'Grand Duc'	SHaC
	'Grande'	EShb ESwi SHaC SPlb
	'Grandiose'	SHaC
	'Happy Carmen' (CannaSol Series)	ELan ETod SHaC
	'Happy Cleo' (CannaSol Series)	ETod SHaC
	'Happy Emily' (CannaSol Series)	ETod MSCN NLar SHaC
	'Happy Isabel' (CannaSol Series)	ETod SHaC
	'Happy Julia' (CannaSol Series)	ETod SHaC SPad
	'Happy Wilma' (CannaSol Series)	NLar SArc SHaC
	Henlade hybrids	CDTJ
	'Herman'	SHaC
	'Hossegor'	XLum
	'Indiana'	EAri SHaC
	indica	CAbb CDTJ CPla CTsd EAri EWld NGKo SArc SHaC SPlb
	- 'Kreta' (Island Series)	ETod
	- 'Purpurea'	CDTJ SHaC SIvy SPlb
	- 'Red King Rupert'	CCCN
	- 'Russian Red' ♀H3	EAri ETod SHaC
	- TROPICANNA GOLD ('Mactro'[PBR])	CBcs CCCN CCht CKel CRos CSBt EAri LCro LOPS LRHS MPie MSCN SPeP WCot
	'Intrigue'	EAri SHaC
	iridiflora misapplied	see *C.* × ***ehemanii***
	iridiflora Ruiz & Pav.	CDTJ SArc
	'Italia'	CDTJ
	jacobiniflora	SHaC
	jaegeriana	ETod SHaC
	'Jivago'	SHaC
I	'King Humbert' (blood-red)	CBcs CDTJ SDeJ
	KING HUMBERT (orange-red)	see *C.* 'Roi Humbert'
	'King Midas'	see *C.* 'Richard Wallace'
§	'Königin Charlotte'	SDeJ SHaC
	'La Bohème' (Grand Opera Series)	LAma
	latifolia	SHaC
I	'Leopoldii'	SHaC
	'Lesotho Lil'	SHaC
	'Libération'	XLum
	'Liberté'	see *C.* 'Wyoming'
	'Lion Rouge'	XLum
	'Lolita'	SHaC
	'Louis Cayeux' ♀H3	SHaC
	'Louis Cottin'	CCCN CWnw LAma NBPC
	'Lucifer'	CCCN LAma MBros NBPC NPer SDeJ XLum
	'Lucy Steele'	SHaC
	lutea	SHaC
	'Madame Angèle Martin'	SEdd
	'Madame Paul Casaneuve'	SHaC
	'Madeira' (Island Series)	ETod SHaC
	'Malawiensis Variegata'	see *C.* 'Striata'
	'Marlena'	SHaC
	'Marshmallow'	SHaC
	'Montaigne'	SHaC
	'Moonshine'	CCCN LCro LOPS
	'Mrs Oklahoma'	SDeJ
	'Musifolia' ♀H3	CDTJ EAri ESwi ETod NGKo SHaC SIvy
	'Mystique' ♀H3	SHaC
§	'Oiseau de Feu'	XLum
	'Oiseau d'Or'	SHaC
	'Orange Beauty'	ETod
	'Orange Chocolate'	CCht EAri SHaC
	'Orange Punch'	EAri SHaC
	'Orchid'	see *C.* 'City of Portland'
	'Panache'	CDTJ EAri ETod SHaC
	'Panama'	SHaC
	paniculata	SHaC
	'Perkeo'	SHaC
§	'Pfitzer's Salmon Pink'	CWnw
§	'Phasion' (v) ♀H3	CAbb CBod CCCN EAri ECtt ELan LCro LOPS LPal LRHS NPer SHaC SPeP SPoG WCot XLum
	'Picasso' ♀H3	CBcs CCCN LAma SHaC
	'Pink Futurity' (Futurity Series)	CBod CCCN
	'Pink Perfection'	SHaC
	'President'	ETod SDeJ SHaC XLum
	'Pretoria'	see *C.* 'Striata'
	'Pretoria Variegata'	see *C.* 'Striata'
	'Prince Charmant'	SHaC
	'Professor Lorentz'	see *C.* 'Wyoming'
	'Purpurea Floribunda'	EAri
	'Queen Charlotte'	see *C.* 'Königin Charlotte'
	'Ra' ♀H3	SHaC
	'Red Cherry'	SDeJ
	'Red Giant'	CWnw
§	'Richard Wallace'	CBod SDeJ SHaC SPlb
	'Robert Kemp'	SHaC
§	'Roi Humbert'	ETod SHaC

'Roi Soleil' SHaC
'Roma' SHaC
'Rosa Fuerta' SHaC
'Rosemond Coles' SDeJ SHaC
'Saladin' SHaC
'Salmon Pink' see *C.* 'Pfitzer's Salmon Pink'
'Salsa' SHaC
'Sémaphore' SHaC WCot
'Shenandoah' ♀H3 SHaC
'Singapore Girl' SHaC
'Society Belle' ♀H3 SHaC
'Soudan' CCht
'South Pacific' EAri SHaC
'South Pacific Ivory' SHaC
speciosa SPlb
'Strasbourg' NPer XLum
'Striata' misapplied see *C.* 'Stuttgart'
§ 'Striata' (v) ♀H3 CBcs CBen CCCN CDTJ CTsd CWGN EAri ETod LPal SEND SHaC SIvy WCot XLum
'Striped Beauty' (v) CCCN CDTJ CTsd EAri SHaC
§ 'Stuttgart' (v) CBod CDTJ ESwi EWes SHaC
'Sunset' WCot
'Tali' ETod SHaC
'Talisman' LAma
'Taney' SHaC
'Taroudant' SHaC
'Tenerife' (Island Series) ETod
'Triomphe' SHaC
(Tropical Series) 'Tropical Bronze Scarlet' SHaC
- 'Tropical Red' SHaC
- 'Tropical Rose' SHaC
- 'Tropical Salmon' SHaC
- 'Tropical White' SHaC
- 'Tropical Yellow' SHaC
TROPICANNA see *C.* 'Phasion'
TROPICANNA BLACK ('Lon01'PBR) CAbb CBcs CCht CKel CPla CRos CSBt EAri ECtt ELan EPfP ETod LCro LOPS LRHS MBros MPie SIvy SPeP SPoG WCot WTyc
tuerckheimii EAri ETod SHaC
'Valentine' WCot
'Vanilla Cream' SDeJ
'Velvet Red' ETod
'Verdi' ♀H3 LAma SHaC
warscewiczii CDTJ EAri EShb SHaC
'Whithelm Pride' ♀H3 SDeJ SHaC
'Wilma' ETod
'Wintzer's Colossal' SHaC
§ 'Wyoming' ♀H3 CBcs CBod CCCN CDTJ CWnw LAma LCro LOPS LPal NBPC SCob SDeJ SEND SHaC
'Yara' SDeJ SHaC
'Yellow Humbert' misapplied see *C.* 'Cleopatra', *C.* 'Richard Wallace'
'Yellow Humbert' SDeJ

Cannomois (*Restionaceae*)

grandis ♀H4 CPbh LRHS SPlb

Cantua (*Polemoniaceae*)

buxifolia ♀H3 CBcs CCCN CCoa CTsd EAri ECre MGil SIvy
- 'Alba' CBcs CCCN EAri EShb
- 'Dancing Oaks' SVen

Cape gooseberry see *Physalis peruviana*

Capeochloa (*Poaceae*)

§ ***cincta*** WCot

Capnoides see *Corydalis*

Capparis (*Capparaceae*)

spinosa CCCN WJek
- subsp. ***rupestris*** SPlb

Capsicum (*Solanaceae*)

annuum CCCN SVic
- 'Ancho' SVic
- var. ***annuum*** 'Blondy' LRHS NRHS
- - (Cerasiforme Group) 'Piccante Calabresé' SVic
- - (Conioides Group) 'Super Chili' ♀H1c SPre SVic
- - 'Demetra' EKin
- - (Grossum Group) 'Almapaprika' SVic
- - - 'Bell Boy' LCro LRHS NRHS
- - - 'Bendigo' MBros
- - - 'Corno di Toro Rosso' ♀H1c CHby LCro MCtn
- - - 'Friggitello' ♀H1c MCtn
- - - 'Mini Bell Red' SVic
- - - 'Mini Bell Yellow' SVic
- - - 'Mohawk' ♀H1c CRos EHyd EKin LRHS MBros NRHS
- - - 'Redskin' ♀H1c CRos EHyd EKin LCro LRHS NRHS
- - - 'Thor' LRHS
- - - 'Topepo Rosso' ♀H1c MCtn
- - (Longum Group) 'Bolivian Rainbow' ♀H1c SVic
- - - 'Filius Blue' ♀H1c NRob
- - - 'Fish' SVic
- - - 'Golden Cayenne' SVic
- - - cayenne CCCN LCro
- - - jalapeño EHyd LCro LOPS LRHS NRHS SVic
- - - 'Hot Thai' ♀H1c CRos EHyd LRHS NRHS
- - - 'Joe's Long Cayenne' SVic
- - - 'Loco' ♀H1c CRos EHyd LRHS NRHS
- - - 'Piccante Di Cayenna' LCro LOPS
- - - 'Ring of Fire' SEdi SVic
- - - 'Serrano' SVic
- - - 'Tokyo Hot' SVic
- - 'Marconi Rosso' LOPS SVic
- - 'Prairie Fire' ♀H1c CCCN CRos EHyd LCro LRHS NRHS NRob SVic
- - 'Purple Mavros' LRHS NRHS
- - 'Red King' EKin
- - SWEETONIA MIX EKin
- 'Apache' ♀H1c CCCN CRos EHyd EKin LRHS MBros MPri NRHS NRob SPre
- 'Apple Crisp' **new** SVic
- 'Basket of Fire' ♀H1c CRos EDel EHyd EKin NRHS SPre SVic
- 'Britney' LRHS
- 'Bulgarian Carrot' SVic
- 'Cayenne Purple' SVic
- 'Cayenne Red' SEdi SPre SVic
- 'Cayenne Sweet' SVic
- 'Cheyenne' CRos EHyd LRHS NRHS
- 'Cow Horn' SVic
- 'Cozumel' SVic
- 'Demon Red' ♀H1c CRos EHyd EKin LRHS MCtn NRHS SPre SVic
- 'Etna' ♀H1c CRos EHyd LRHS MCtn NRHS
- 'Explosive Ember' SVic
- 'Fat Bird' SVic
- 'Fresno' ♀H1c LRHS NRHS
- var. ***glabriusculum*** SVic
- 'Holy Mole' SVic
- 'Hungarian Hot Wax' ♀H1c CHby EKin LCro LOPS MCtn NRob SVic
- 'Hungarian Yellow Wax' SVic

- 'Jalapeño Farmer's Market Potato'	SVic
- 'Jalapeño Fooled You'	SVic
- 'Jericho'	CRos EHyd LRHS NRHS
- 'Jigsaw'	SVic
- Kashmiri chilli **new**	SVic
- 'Krakatoa' ♀H1c	CRos EHyd LRHS NRHS
- 'Las Cruces Cayenne'	SVic
- 'Masquerade'	CRos EHyd LRHS NRHS
- 'Medina'	LRHS
- 'Medusa'	CRos EHyd LRHS NRHS
- 'Nosferatu'	SVic
- 'Numex April Fools' Day'	SVic
- 'Numex Centennial' **new**	SVic
- 'Numex Cinco de Mayo' **new**	SVic
- 'Numex Garnet'	SVic
- 'Numex Heritage Big Jim'	SVic
- 'Numex Lemon Spice'	SVic
- 'Numex Orange Spice'	SVic
- 'Numex Piñata'	SVic
- 'Numex Primavera'	SVic
- 'Numex Sweet'	SVic
- 'Numex Trick or Treat' **new**	SVic
- 'Numex Twilight'	CRos EHyd LRHS NRHS SPre SVic
- 'Padron'	LCro LOPS SVic
- 'Paper Lantern'	CRos EHyd LRHS NRHS
- 'Pasilla Bajio'	SVic
- 'Peter Pepper'	SVic
- 'Pinocchio's Nose'	SVic
- 'Pot Black' ♀H1c	EDel SVic
- 'Razzamatazz'	CRos EHyd NRHS
- 'Red Cherry Small'	SEdi
- 'Serrano Purple'	SVic
- 'Spaghetti' **new**	SVic
- 'Treasure's Red' ♀H1c	LRHS
- 'Tricolor Variegatum' (v)	NRob
- 'Trinidad Perfume'	LRHS
- 'Uchu Cream Red' (v) **new**	SVic
- 'Vampire'	SVic
baccatum 'Aji Limon'	SVic
- 'Aji Omnicolor'	SVic
- 'Brazilian Starfish'	SVic
- 'Christmas Bell'	SVic
chinense 'Aribibi Gusano' **new**	SVic
- 'Bhut Jolokia'	LRHS SVic
- 'Carolina Reaper'	SVic
- 'Cheiro Roxa'	SVic
- Habanero Group	EKin NRob
- - 'Habanero Caribbean Red'	SVic
- - 'Habenero Mustard'	SVic
- - 'Naga Morrich'	SVic
- - 'Turtle Claw' **new**	SVic
- - 'Caribbean Antillais' ♀H1c	SVic
- 'Hot Paper Lantern'	SVic
- 'Machu Pichu' **new**	EKin
- 'Numex Suave Orange'	SVic
- 'Numex Suave Red'	SVic
- 'Peito de Moca'	SVic
- 'Scotch Bonnet'	CRos EHyd LRHS MBros NRHS SPre
- 'Seven Pod Brain Strain Yellow'	SVic
- 'Shabu Shabu'	SVic
- 'Trinidad Moruga Scorpion'	EKin LRHS SVic
frutescens 'Adorno'	LCro
- Tabasco Group	LRHS SVic
'Goan Button' **new**	SVic
'Goan Hot Sweet' **new**	SVic
'Rodeo'	SVic

Caputia (*Asteraceae*)

§ ***tomentosa*** ♀H1c	LCro SEdd SIvy SMrm

Caragana (*Fabaceae*)

arborescens	CAgr CMCN ELan EPfP NLar NWea SPer SPlb
- PAB 13.376	LEdu
- 'Lorbergii'	MBlu NLar SPer
- 'Pendula'	CMac ELan MBlu NLar SCoo SPer WSpi
- 'Walker'	ELan LPar MAsh MBlu MGos NHol NLar NWea SCoo SPer
aurantiaca	NLar SBrt
halodendron	CBcs LPar MBlu SPer

carambola see *Averrhoa carambola*

caraway see *Carum carvi*

Cardamine (*Brassicaceae*)

asarifolia misapplied	see *Pachyphragma macrophyllum*
bipinnata	WCot
bulbifera	CCBP EBee ELon EPPr ESwi GBin GEdr GGro GQue LEdu NAts NRya WCru
californica	EBee EPPr LEdu LShi MAvo NRya WCot WCru
concatenata	WCru
digitata	EBee
diphylla	EBee WCot WCru
- 'American Sweetheart'	CExl CMiW
- 'Eco Cut Leaf'	CExl CMiW EBee ECha LEdu MAvo WCru
- 'Eco Moonlight'	WCru
enneaphylla	NBid NLar
glanduligera	CElw CTtf EBee ECha ELon EMor EPPr EPri GEdr LEdu MAvo MNrw NLar NSla SBrt WCot WCru WFar
§ ***heptaphylla***	CMiW ECha ELon EMor GEdr GKev ILea LEdu MBel WCru WSHC
- from the Pyrenees	NLar
- 'Big White'	EBee EPPr GBin MAvo MNrw NCth NLar WFar
- Guincho form	EPPr GEdr LEdu MAvo WCot
- 'Helen Myers'	GEdr
§ ***kitaibelii***	CMiW EMor EPPr EWld LEdu MNrw NLar SBrt WCot WCru WFar
latifolia Vahl	see *C. raphanifolia*
macrophylla	CTtf EBee EWld GEdr LEdu WCot WSHC
- 'Bright and Bronzy'	CExl EPPr MAvo WCru
maxima	WCru
microphylla	GKev
pentaphylla ♀H5	CBor CSpe EBee ECha EMor EPPr EWld GBin GKev GMaP LEdu MCot NHpl NLar SPhx WCru WSHC
* - 'Alba'	EPPr
pratensis	CBcs CBod CDor CPud CTtf CWat EMor GJos LCro LOPS LPfP LRHS MACG MBow MHer MNHC NAts NMir SPhx SRms WHer WSFF WShi
- 'Flore Pleno' (d)	CDor CTtf ECha GArf GQue LEdu MHer NBid NBir NBro NLar NRya
- 'Flore Pleno' white-flowered (d)	LEdu
- white-flowered	CDor
- 'William' (d)	LEdu
quinquefolia	CAby CElw CMiW CTtf ECha EHed ELon EMor EPfP ILea LEdu MAvo MBel MNrw MPie NLar

	SDix SDys SMrm WBrk WCot WCru WFar
- PAB 9992	LEdu
§ ***raphanifolia***	CExl EAJP EBee ECha GAbr LLWG NBid NBro NRya WBor WFar
- PAB 204	LEdu
trifolia	CAby CElw CMac EBee ELon EMor EPPr EWld GBin GEdr GMaP ILea LEdu MAvo MNrw NBir NBro NLar NRya WCot WCru WFar
waldsteinii	CElw CExl EBee EPPr GArf GEdr ILea LEdu NBro NLar SMHy WCru WFar WSHC
yezoensis	GBin
- B&SWJ 4659	EBee EPPr ESwi WCru

cardamon see *Elettaria cardamomum*

Cardiandra (*Hydrangeaceae*)

alternifolia B&SWJ 5719	WCru
- B&SWJ 5845	WCru
- B&SWJ 6177	WCru
- B&SWJ 6354	WCru
- subsp. ***moellendorffii***	CExl WPGP
- 'Pink Geisha'	WCru
amamiohshimensis	WCru
formosana	CExl IDee WPGP
- B&SWJ 2005	WCru
- 'Crûg's Abundant'	WCru
- 'Hsitou'	WCru
- 'Hsitou Splendour'	WCru

Cardiocrinum ✿ (*Liliaceae*)

cordatum B&SWJ 2812	WCru
- B&SWJ 4841	WCru
- B&SWJ 5427	WCru
- B&SWJ 6336	WCru
- B&SWJ 11069	WCru
- var. ***glehnii***	CCCN GEdr GKev LAma
- - B&SWJ 10827	WCru
- - B&SWJ 10843	WCru
giganteum	CBcs CBor CCCN EBee EHyd GAbr GEdr GKev LAma LRHS MNrw NBid NHpl NLar NRHS SBea SDir SMad WCru WPnP WTyc
- B&SWJ 2419	WCru
- GWJ 9219 from Sikkim	WCru
- HWJK 2158 from Nepal	WCru
- WJC 13661 from Sikkim	WCru
- WJC 13698 from Sikkim	WCru
- 'Big and Pink'	WCru
- var. ***giganteum***	CSpe
- var. ***yunnanense***	CBct EPfP GEdr GKev IKel ITim NBid WCru WPGP
- - PAB 8347	LEdu
- - NJM 11.023 from Guizhou	WPGP
aff. ***giganteum*** from Nagaland, India	NCth

cardoon see *Cynara cardunculus*

Carduus (*Asteraceae*)

nutans	GGro SPhx

Carex (*Cyperaceae*)

from Kyoto, Japan	EPPr GGro
acuta	CHab CPud LPfP
- 'Variegata' (v)	CBen CMac CWat GMaP LLWG NBro
acutiformis	MMuc NMir
alba	WCot
'Amazon Mist'	EPfP LRHS MACG NLar NRHS SCob SRms SSha SWvt WFar
arenaria	CKno
§ ***atrata*** subsp. ***pullata*** KEKE 494	EBee
aurea	CBod WChS
baccans	SBrt
berggrenii	NFav SPlb
brunnea	CMac
- 'Jenneke' (v)	EBee EMor SGBe SMad SWvt
- 'Jubilo'[PBR]	EBee
- 'Lady Sunshine'	CKno EMor NLar
- 'Variegata' (v)	WHoo WSpi
buchananii	Widely available
- 'Firefox'	CEme LRHS
- 'Green Twist'	EHyd EShb LRHS NLar NRHS
- 'Red Rooster'	CBod EBee EPfP EWoo LBuc LSun MACG NLar NWsh SCob
- 'Viridis'	XLum
chathamica	LRHS SVen
ciliatomarginata 'Treasure Island' (v)	EBee EMor NLar
comans	EPfP NBro
- 'Bronco' **new**	EShb
- bronze-leaved	CBod CDoC CPla CRos CSBt EHeP EHyd ELan EPfP GArf GDam GMcL LRHS LSto MAsh MDon NBir NRHS NSti NWsh SCob SCoo SPer SRms SSha SWvt WCAu XLum
- 'Bronzita'	EShb LRHS WFar
- 'Dancing Flame'	CWCL
- 'Frosted Curls'	Widely available
- 'Phoenix Green'	MDon NWsh
- red-leaved	NLar SRms
- 'Small Red'	see *C. comans* 'Taranaki'
§ - 'Taranaki'	SCoo
conica 'Hime-kan-suge'	see *C. conica* 'Snowline'
- 'Kiku-sakura' (v)	EPPr
§ - 'Snowline' (v)	CMac ELan GGro GMaP LEdu NBro NLar NWsh SWvt XLum
davalliana	EBee
dioica	LLWG
dipsacea	CKno CMac CRos CWCL EBlo EHyd GMaP GQue LRHS NLar NRHS NWad
- 'Dark Horse'	MMuc
divulsa	CKno
- subsp. ***leersii***	EPPr
§ ***dolichostachya*** 'Kaga-nishiki' (v)	CSBt EPPr GKev LRHS NLar SGBe
duthiei	see *C. atrata* subsp. *pullata*
§ ***elata*** 'Aurea' [H6]	Widely available
- 'Bowles's Golden'	see *C. elata* 'Aurea'
- 'Knightshayes'	CKno WCot WFar
elongata	CHab
'Evergold'	see *C. oshimensis* 'Evergold'
'Feather Falls' (v)	SMad WHlf
firma 'Green Dragon'	GEdr
- 'Variegata' (v)	EDAr GEdr
flacca	CBod CHab CKno EPPr
- 'Blue Zinger'	CAby CBod CKno CSpe ELan EPfP NCth NLar SCoo SPad SPeP WFar XSen
§ - subsp. ***flacca***	EBee NSti
flagellifera	CBod CMac CRos CSpe CTri CWCL EAJP EBee EBlo EHeP EHyd ELan ELon EPPr EPfP GMaP LRHS MMuc NBir NRHS SCob SDix SEND SPlb SPoG
- 'Auburn Cascade'	MDon NWsh
- 'Kiwi'	EHyd NRHS
folliculata	EPPr
glauca Scop.	see *C. flacca* subsp. *flacca*
'Gold Fountains'	see *C. dolichostachya* 'Kaga-nishiki'

	grayi	EHyd LEdu LPfP LRHS LShi MACG MBlu MSCN NLar NRHS SBls SPlb WHoo WSHC
	'Ice Dance' (v)	Widely available
	laxiculmis 'Bunny Blue'[PBR]	CBod CKno NLar XLum
	limosa	LLWG
	maorica	EPPr
	MILK CHOCOLATE ('Milchoc'[PBR]) (v)	CBod ECtt ELan EPfP LRHS LSou MAsh NGdn SGbt SRms
	morrowii misapplied	see *C. oshimensis*
	morrowii Boott 'Everglow'[PBR] (EverColor Series) (v)	CKno LCro XSte
I	- 'Fisher's Form' (v)	CBrac CTri EPPr MRav SSha SWvt WBrk WOld
	- 'Gilt' (v)	EPPr NWad
	- 'Gold Band'	EFPl EMor GMcL
	- 'Irish Green'	CBod WFar
	- 'Nana Variegata' (v)	CTri
	- 'Pinkie'	CDoC
	- VANILLA ICE ('Vanice'[PBR]) (v)	CKno EMor SCoo
	- 'Variegata' (v)	CBod EHeP ELan EPPr EWoo GMaP LRHS MMuc NBir NSti SRms SSha WAvo XLum
*	***multifida***	EGrI
	muskingumensis	CKel CKno CWCL ELan EPPr EPfP EShb GBin LEdu LLWG LPfP LRHS MACG NBro NLar SCob SDix WChS WPnP
	- 'Little Midge'	CKno CMac LPla NLar
	- 'Oehme' (v)	CKno CWCL LLWG NBid NHol NWad SSut
	- 'Silberstreif' (v)	CKno EShb GBin LEdu MMuc XLum
	nigra (L.) Reichard	WAvo
§	- 'On-line' (v)	EPPr
	- 'Variegata'	see *C. nigra* 'On-line'
	No 4, Nanking (Greg's thin leaf)	EPPr
	obnupta	CKno
	ornithopoda 'Aurea'	see *C. ornithopoda* 'Variegata'
§	- 'Variegata' (v)	NHol NWsh
§	***oshimensis***	EPPr WCot
	- (EverColor Series) 'Everillo'[PBR]	CBcs CBct CBod CKel CKno EBee ELon EMor EPfP LBuc LCro LRHS MAsh NGBl NLar NWad NWsh SCob SCoo SGBe SPeP SPoG SRms WCot
	- - 'Everlime'[PBR]	CBct CKel CKno LRHS LSou MAsh MDon SCoo SGBe XSte
	- - 'Everlite' (v)	LCro LOPS LRHS
	- - 'Everoro' (v)	CKno LRHS LSun MHol SGBe WCot
	- - 'Eversheen'[PBR] (v)	LRHS MDon SCoo SGBe XSte
	- EVERCREAM ('Ficre'[PBR]) (v)	CKno SCoo SPoG XSte
	- EVEREST ('Fiwhite'[PBR]) (v)	Widely available
§	- 'Evergold' (v) ♀H7	Widely available
	- 'Evergreen'	SCob SGBe
	otrubae	CHab CPud
	panicea	CPud CWCL CWat EBee EPPr LLWG LPfP XLum
	pendula	CHab CKno CPud CTri ECha EHeP ELan EPfP GMaP GMcL LPfP LRHS MMuc NBro NBwr NLar NMir NSti SCob SEND SMad XLum XSen
	- 'Cool Jazz' (v)	EPPr
	- 'Moonraker' (v)	ESwi WCot
	petriei	EBee ECha
	phyllocephala 'Spark Plug'[PBR] (v)	EMor SPad
	- 'Sparkler' (v)	CKel GMcL LRHS SCob SPoG SSha SWvt
	plantaginea	EPPr GBin LEdu WPGP WSHC XLum
	praegracilis	CKno
	pseudocyperus	CPud LPfP NPer NWsh WPnP
	remota	CKno EPPr LPla
	RIBBON FALLS ('Et Crx02'[PBR])	CBod
	riparia	CHab CPud LPfP MWts NPer
	- 'Bowles's Golden'	see *C. elata* 'Aurea'
	rostrata	MMuc
	sabynensis	see *C. umbrosa* subsp. *sabynensis*
	scaposa	ESwi WCot
	- KWJ 12304	ESwi LEdu WCru
	secta	CKno CRos EHyd EPPr EPfP GMaP LPla LRHS NRHS SRms
	- from Dunedin, New Zealand	EPPr
	siderosticta	WSHC
	- 'Banana Boat'	see *C. siderosticta* 'Golden Falls'
§	- 'Golden Falls' (v)	EMor MNrw SMad
	- 'Kisokaido' (v)	EShb
	- 'Variegata' (v)	CPla CTri CTsd ELan EShb GGro GMcL LEdu MACG NBir NLar NSti NWsh
	'Silver Sceptre' (v)	CBod CBrac EBlo EFPl EHyd EMor GKev GMaP LPar LRHS MBNS MBel MGos NRHS NSti NWad NWsh SIvy SPlb SSha SWvt WFar XLum
	solandri	CKno
	spicata	CHab
	spissa	MNrw
	stricta Gooden. 'Bowles's Golden'	see *C. elata* 'Aurea'
	stricta Lam.	MMuc SEND
	strictissima new	SPlb
	sylvatica	CHab CKel
	tenuiculmis	CWCL EHyd LRHS NRHS NSti NWad WCot
	testacea	Widely available
	- LIMESHINE ('Wilshine')	SSha WFar
	- 'Old Gold'	SPlb
	- 'Prairie Fire'	CBar CBod CSpe EPfP GMaP LBuc LCro LOPS LRHS LWaG MACG NLar NRHS SBls SCob SCoo SGBe SPtp SRms SSha XLum
	texensis	EPPr
	'The Beatles'	LRHS MHtn NBir NGdn
	trifida	EPPr MACG
	- 'Chatham Blue'	MMuc SEND
	- 'Rekohu Sunrise'[PBR] (v)	CKel ELon EMor EPfP GMcL LRHS LSun MMuc NSti SCoo SEND SPoG WCot
§	***umbrosa*** subsp. ***sabynensis*** 'Thinny Thin' (v)	EShb

Carica (*Caricaceae*)

	sp.	EAri
	papaya (F)	EAri SPre SVic
	- 'Babaco'	CCCN
	pubescens	see *Vasconcellea pubescens*

Carissa (*Apocynaceae*)

	grandiflora	see *C. macrocarpa*
§	***macrocarpa*** (F)	CCCN EShb SVic WKor

Carlina (*Asteraceae*)

	acaulis	SPlb
	- bronze-leaved	LDai
	- var. ***caulescens***	see *C. acaulis* subsp. *simplex*
§	- subsp. ***simplex***	ECha EHyd LRHS NRHS

	- - bronze-leaved	GGro SPhx
	vulgaris	GPoy
	- 'Silver Star'	SPhx

Carmichaelia (*Fabaceae*)

	stevensonii	CBcs CCCN EBee IArd MBlu NLar WPGP
	williamsii	CTsd

× *Carmispartium* see *Carmichaelia*

Carnegiea (*Cactaceae*)

	gigantea new	NPlm

Carpenteria (*Hydrangeaceae*)

	californica	CCCN CEme CKel CTri EBee EHyd ELan EPfP GBin IDee LCro LOPS LRHS MGil MGos NLar NRHS SCob SPer SWvt WFar WHtc WSpi XSte
	- 'Bodnant' ♀H4	CBcs CCCN EBee EHed EHyd ELan LRHS LSRN MAsh MGos NLar NRHS SGBe SSha SWvt WFar WPGP WSpi XVPe
	- 'Elizabeth' ♀H4	CSBt CWGN EPfP LSRN MAsh MGil NLar SPoG
	- 'Eskimo'	CCCN CDoC CKel SWvt WSpi
	- 'Ladhams' Variety'	CBcs CKel CMac EPfP LRHS MRav SGBe SSha SWvt WKif WSpi

Carpinus ✿ (*Betulaceae*)

	betulus ♀H7	Widely available
*	- 'A. Beeckman'	CLnd LMaj
	- 'Columnaris'	CAco CLnd EBee
*	- 'Columnaris Nana'	MPkF WLov
§	- 'Fastigiata' ♀H7	Widely available
I	- 'Folis Argenteovariegatis Pendula' (v)	MBlu NLar
	- 'Frans Fontaine'	Widely available
	- 'Globus'	MBlu
	- 'Lucas'	CCVT LIns LMaj LPar MBlu MNic MTrO NOra SGol WHtc WMat
	- 'Monument'	MPkF
I	- 'Monumentalis'	CAco LMaj NLar
	- 'Orange Retz' PBR new	CKel CWnw EHed WMou
	- 'Pendula'	CAco CEnd EBee LPar MBlu SWvt WHtc
	- 'Purpurea'	CAco CEnd CLnd MBlu
	- 'Pyramidalis'	see *C. betulus* 'Fastigiata'
	- ROCKHAMPTON RED ('Lochglow')	CPer LRHS MBlu MNic MSwo MTrO NOra NOrn SGol WMat WMou
	- 'Rockingham Red'	WReH
	- 'Stegemanns Primus' PBR	EBee LSRN
	caroliniana	CAco CLnd CMCN EPfP LMaj
	- from Mexico	WPGP
	- 'Red Fall'	EPfP LRHS MBlu
	- 'Sentinel Dries'	LRHS MBlu WMou
	cordata	MBlu SSta
	coreana	LMaj
	fangiana	CBcs CEnd CJun EBee EPfP MBlu WPGP
	fargesiana	EBee MBlu WPGP
	- KR 8780	WPGP
	fargesii	see *C. viminea*
	henryana	CMen EBtc
	- var. ***simplicidentata***	CMCN MBlu
	japonica ♀H6	CAco CBcs CEnd CLnd CMCN CMen EPfP IPap LMaj LPar MBlu NOra SCoo SEWo SSta WMat
	- B&SWJ 10803	WCru
	- B&SWJ 11072	WCru
	- 'Chinese Lantern'	MTrO WMat
	kawakamii	CBcs CMCN
	- CWJ 12412	WCru
	- CWJ 12449	WCru
	laxiflora	CMen
	- B&SWJ 10809	WCru
	- B&SWJ 11035	WCru
	- var. ***longispica*** B&SWJ 8772	WCru
	- var. ***macrostachya***	see *C. viminea*
	omeiensis	EBee MBlu NLar
	- KR 280	WPGP
	orientalis	CMCN
	- 'Perdika'	LRHS
	polyneura	CMCN EBee MBlu SSta WPGP
	pubescens	EBee WPGP
	rankanensis	SSta
	- NMWJ 14544	WCru
	- RWJ 9839	WCru
	× ***schuschaensis***	EBtc LRHS
	shensiensis	EBee NLar WPGP
	tschonoskii	EPfP
	- B&SWJ 10800	WCru
	- BBJMT 297	WPGP
	turczaninowii	CBcs CMCN CMen IPap MBlu NLar SSta
	- var. ***turczaninowii***	WPGP
	- - Farrer 331 new	WPGP
§	***viminea***	CEnd SSta WCot

Carpobrotus (*Aizoaceae*)

	acinaciformis	EAri SVen
§	***edulis***	CCCN CDTJ CSde CWal SArc SEND SVen XLum
	- 'Gugh Dawn' (v)	SVen
	- var. ***rubescens***	CCCN
	- white-flowered	CCCN
	muirii	CCCN SVen
	sauerae	CCCN

Carpoxylon (*Arecaceae*)

	macrospermum new	NPlm

Carrierea (*Salicaceae*)

	calycina	IArd WPGP

carrot see *Daucus carota* for species; also AGM Vegetables Section for cultivars

Carthamus (*Asteraceae*)

	dianius	SBrt
	mitissimus	EDAr GEdr
	tinctorius	MNHC SRms SVen
	- 'Kinko'	CSpe

Carum (*Apiaceae*)

	carvi	CBod ENfk GPoy MHer MHoo MNHC SRms SVic WJek
	petroselinum	see *Petroselinum crispum*

Carya ✿ (*Juglandaceae*)

	cordiformis	CMCN MBlu WJur
	illinoinensis (F)	CAgr CBcs CLnd MBlu MVil WJur
	- 'Carlson No 3' seedling (F)	CAgr
	- 'Colby' seedling (F)	CAgr
	- 'Cornfield' (F)	CAgr
	- 'Lucas' (F)	CAgr
	laciniosa (F)	EPfP
	- 'Henry' (F)	CAgr
	- 'Keystone' seedling (F)	CAgr
	ovata (F)	CAgr EPfP MBlu WPGP
	- 'Grainger' seedling (F)	CAgr
	- 'Neilson' seedling (F)	CAgr
	- 'Weschcke' seedling (F)	CAgr
	- 'Yoder No 1' seedling (F)	CAgr
	tomentosa	WPGP

Caryophyllus see *Syzygium*

Caryopteris (*Lamiaceae*)

× ***clandonensis***	CMac ECtt EHeP MGil NBir
- 'Arthur Simmonds' ♀H4	ECha
- BLUE BALLOON ('Korball')	NLar WHlf
- BLUE EMPIRE ('Elst33'PBR)	CTsd EBee
- 'Dark Knight'	Widely available
- 'Ferndown'	NLar SEND SRms
- aff. 'Ferndown'	CBrac
- 'First Choice' ♀H4	CBrac CRos EHyd EPfP LRHS LSRN MAsh MGil NRHS SPer SRkn SSha SWvt
- 'Gold Giant'	CRos EHyd EPfP LRHS MAsh NRHS
- GRAND BLEU ('Inoveris'PBR)	CMac EBee EFPl EHyd ELan EPfP LCro LRHS LSRN MGil MGos MHtn NLar SGbt SGsty SWvt SavN WLov
- 'Heavenly Baby' ♀H4	CRos EHyd EPfP EWTr LRHS MAsh
- 'Heavenly Blue'	Widely available
- 'Hint of Blue'	SGol
- HINT OF GOLD ('Lisaura'PBR) ♀H4	CRos CSBt EHyd ELan EPfP LCro LOPS LRHS MAsh MPri NLar NRHS SCob SGBe SRHi WTor
- 'Kew Blue'	CBcs CRos CSBt EBee EHyd ELan EPfP EShb LRHS MAsh MGos MHer MSwo NLar SCoo SGBe SGbt SGol SPer SRms SSta SWvt XSen
- 'Longwood Blue'	CRos ECha EPfP LRHS
- 'Pershore'	WAvo
- PETIT BLEU ('Minbleu'PBR)	LRHS
- PINK PERFECTION ('Lisspin'PBR)	CRos CSBt EHyd ELan LCro LRHS MAsh NEoE NRHS SEle SMad SPoG WHil WHlf
- STEPHI ('Lissteph'PBR)	CBcs CRos CSBt EHed EHyd ELan EPfP LRHS MAsh NRHS SPoG WHtc WNPC
- STERLING SILVER ('Lissilv'PBR) ♀H4	CKel CMac CRos EBee EHyd EPfP GMcL LCro LPar LRHS LSRN MAsh NEoE NRHS SCob SPer SPoG SRkn SRms SSta
- 'Summer Gold'	CMac MAsh
- 'Summer Sorbet'PBR (v) ♀H4	CEme CMac CRos CWGN EBee EFPl ELan EPfP EWes GMcL LRHS MAsh MGos NLar SCob SCoo SGbt SGol SNig SPer SRms SWvt WCot WFar
- weeping	ELan EPPr WFar
- 'White Surprise'PBR (v)	CEme CMac CWGN EHed EHyd EPfP LCro LRHS MAsh NRHS SCob SGol SGsty SPer SPoG SRHi WFar WHil WHlf
- 'Worcester Gold' ♀H4	CBcs CMac CSBt CTri ECha EDir EHeP EHyd ELan EPfP GMcL LRHS LSto MAsh MGos MHer MRav MSwo NBwr NRHS SEND SGol SNig SPer SPlb SRms SWvt WAvo WFar WHtc
divaricata	CMCN LPla SBrt WFar
- 'Electrum'	MHer WCot WFar WSHC
- 'Jade Shades'	WSHC
- pink-flowered	WFar
- 'Snow Fairy' (v)	MGil
§ ***incana***	SPer
- 'Blue Cascade'	CKel ELan EPfP LRHS MRav NLar SRms WAvo WHtc
- 'Delft Blue'	CKel EBee EPfP
§ - 'Jason'PBR	CBcs CBrac EGrI MGos NLar SPoG WFar
- SUNSHINE BLUE	see *C. incana* 'Jason'
mastacanthus	see *C. incana*

Caryota (*Arecaceae*)

maxima new	EAri
mitis	CCCN
- 'Himalaya'	EAri LPal NPlm

Cassandra see *Chamaedaphne*

Cassia (*Fabaceae*)

corymbosa Lam.	see *Senna corymbosa*
fistula	CDow
marilandica	see *Senna marilandica*
nemophila	SPlb

Cassinia (*Asteraceae*)

fulvida	SVen
leptophylla	CBcs
vauvilliersii	SVen
'Ward Silver'	CWal XSte

Cassinia × *Helichrysum* (*Asteraceae*)

hybrid	WKif

Cassiope ✿ (*Ericaceae*)

'Askival Snowbird'	EPot
'Askival Snow-wreath'	see *C.* Snow-wreath Group
'Edinburgh'	EPot ITim WThu
lycopodioides	ITim
- 'Beatrice Lilley' ♀H6	EPot GArf GRum ITim WThu
- 'Jim Lever'	WAbe
- 'Rokujō'	ITim
mertensiana	GArf
- 'California Pink'	GKev
- subsp. ***californica***	ITim WAbe
- var. ***gracilis***	GArf ITim WThu
'Muirhead'	WAbe WThu
'Randle Cooke'	EPot
selaginoides	GArf
- LS&E 13284	EPot WAbe WThu
§ Snow-wreath Group	EPot
'Suzuki' new	EPot
wardii	EPot

Castanea ✿ (*Fagaceae*)

'Bouche de Bétizac' (F)	CAgr
crenata	CAgr
henryi	CMCN
- CBS 0755.04	WPGP
'Maraval' (F)	CAgr WMat
'Maridonne' (F)	CAgr
'Marigoule' (F)	CAgr EPom NRog WMat
'Marsol' (F)	CAgr NRog WMat
'Précoce Migoule' (F)	CAgr
sativa	Widely available
§ - 'Albomarginata' (v) ♀H6	CEnd EPfP NOra SPoG WMat
- 'Argenteovariegata'	see *C. sativa* 'Albomarginata'
- 'Aureomarginata'	see *C. sativa* 'Variegata'
- 'Belle Epine' (F)	CAgr
- 'Bournette' (F)	CAgr
* - 'Doré de Lyon'	CAgr
- 'Marlhac' (F)	CAgr CHab NOra NRog WMat
- 'Marron Comballe' (F)	CAgr
- 'Marron de Goujounac' (F)	CAgr
- 'Marron de Lyon' (F)	CAgr CEnd CHab EPfP EPom NRog NWea
- 'Regal' (F)	EPom
§ - 'Variegata' (v)	CAco CMCN ELan SCob
seguinii	WPGP

Castilleja (*Orobanchaceae*)

integra	SPlb
miniata	LShi SPlb WAbe
sessiliflora	SPlb

Casuarina (*Casuarinaceae*)

cunninghamiana	CAco EBtc SPlb
glauca	SVen

Catalpa ✿ (*Bignoniaceae*)

bignonioides ♀H6	Widely available
- B&SWJ 15090	WCru
- 'Aurea' ♀H6	Widely available
* - 'Aurea Nana'	LPar
- 'Nana'	ELan ERom LPal MNic SGsty WLov
- 'Purpurea'	see *C.* × *erubescens* 'Purpurea'
- 'Variegata' (v)	EBee EPfP WLov
bungei misapplied	see *C. ovata*
bungei ambig.	CAco CCVT CMCN CPer MBlu SArc
§ ***bungei*** C.A. Mey. Duclouxii Group ♀H6	CAco CBcs CEnd CLnd EBee EPfP MBlu SAko WLov WPGP
§ × ***erubescens*** 'Purpurea' ♀H6	Widely available
fargesii f. ***duclouxii***	see *C. bungei* Duclouxii Group
§ ***ovata***	CMCN EGrI EHed WJur
speciosa ♀H6	CAco CMCN SVen
- 'Frederik'	NLar
- 'Pulverulenta' (v)	CAco EBee EHed MBlu SMad WLov

Catalpa × *Chilopsis* see × *Chitalpa*

Catananche (*Asteraceae*)

caerulea	Widely available
- 'Alba'	CBod CRos CSpe EAJP EBee ECha EHyd ELan EPfP EShb EWoo LRHS MBel MNrw NRHS SCob SEdd SGbt SPoG SWvt WCAu WGwG WSHC XLum XSen
- 'Amor Blue'	CFis CRos EBee EHyd EPfP LRHS MACG NRHS SPoG
- 'Amor White'	SPeP
- 'Major' ♀H5	CRos EHyd LCro LDai LOPS LRHS NRHS SEdd SRms

Catha (*Celastraceae*)

edulis	GPoy

Catharanthus (*Apocynaceae*)

roseus ♀H1c	GPoy
- (Roseus Group) 'Mediterranean Lilac'	LShi

Cathaya (*Pinaceae*)

argyrophylla	CAco

Cathcartia (*Papaveraceae*)

§ ***chelidoniifolia***	NBid

Catopsis (*Bromeliaceae*)

morreniana	NCft NPic

cauliflower see AGM Vegetables Section

Caulokaempferia (*Zingiberaceae*)

petelotii B&SWJ 11818	WCru
- HWJ 541	WCru

Caulophyllum (*Berberidaceae*)

thalictroides	EBee EMor EPPr GKev LEdu WCru WHil WPGP WPnP WSHC
- subsp. ***robustum***	EBee WCru

Cautleya ✿ (*Zingiberaceae*)

cathcartii	LEdu
- 'Tenzing's Gold'	EBee ESwi EWld LEdu WCru WPGP WSHC
§ ***gracilis***	CDTJ CSpe EBee GKev LAma
- BWJ 7843	WCru
- from Manipur, India	WPGP
- 'Crûg Gold'	WCru WPGP
- 'Dzoukou'	LEdu
- 'Purple Splendour' **new**	WPGP
lutea	see *C. gracilis*
spicata	CCCN CDTJ CSpe EAri ELon GKev LAma MHid NGKo XLum
- 'Arun Flame'	CBct ESwi LEdu MNrw WCru WPGP
- 'Bleddyn's Beacon'	ESwi WCru WSHC
- 'Crûg Canary'	LEdu MHid WCru WPGP
- 'Crûg Compact'	WCru
* - var. ***lutea***	CDTJ LEdu MHid WPGP
- 'Robusta'	CAvo CBcs EAri EBee EBlo ELan EPPr EPfP LEdu LRHS MNrw SMad WCot WPGP XSte

Cayratia (*Vitaceae*)

japonica B&SWJ 6636	WCru
§ ***thomsonii*** BWJ 8123	EPPr

Ceanothus ✿ (*Rhamnaceae*)

'A.T. Johnson'	EDir EHeP EPfP MDon SGol SPer SRms WHtc
arboreus	SArc
- 'Trewithen Blue' ♀H4	Widely available
'Autumnal Blue' ♀H4	Widely available
'Blue Cushion'	CTri EPfP LRHS MDon MGos NLar NRHS SWvt
'Blue Diamond'PBR	LSRN
'Blue Jeans'	MMuc NLar
'Blue Mound' ♀H4	Widely available
'Blue Sapphire'PBR	CCCN CWGN EDir EPfP GMcL LRHS LSRN MAsh SPoG SRms SWvt WTyc
'Blue Sensation'	NLar
'Burkwoodii' ♀H4	CBcs CBrac CEnd CKel CRos CSBt ELan EPfP LRHS MAsh MDon MGos MRav SCob SCoo SPer SRHi SRms SWvt
'Cascade' ♀H4	CBcs EDir LPar SPlb WAvo
'Concha' ♀H4	Widely available
'Cynthia Postan'	CBod CCCN CKel EMil EPfP MAsh MHer NLar SNig WHtc
'Dark Star' ♀H4	CBcs CCCN CChe CRos CSBt CTri CWGN EHyd ELan EPfP GMcL LRHS LSRN MAsh NHol NRHS SEND SNig SPoG SSta SWvt
'Delight'	CBcs EDir MDon
× ***delileanus*** 'Gloire de Versailles' ♀H4	CBcs CKel ELan EPfP EWTr GMcL ILea LSto MGos MRav MSwo NLar SCoo SGol SPer SPoG SRHi SWvt WKif WSpi
- 'Henri Desfossé'	CKel ELan EPfP LSRN MHtn MRav MSwo NLar SPer SPoG WKif WSpi
- 'Topaze' ♀H4	CKel CTsd ELan EPfP GMcL LRHS MRav NLar WKif WSpi
dentatus misapplied	see *C.* × ***lobbianus***
dentatus Torr. & A. Gray	SPlb
- var. ***floribundus***	EHeP
'Diamond Heights'	see *C. griseus* var. ***horizontalis*** 'Diamond Heights'
'Edinburgh'	EHeP
EL DORADO ('Perado') (v)	CKel CSBt ELan NBwr SGol WAvo WHtc
gloriosus 'Emily Brown'	CBcs CBrac MRav NLar
§ ***griseus*** var. ***horizontalis*** 'Diamond Heights' (v)	LRHS MAsh NLar SCob SPer
- - 'Silver Surprise'PBR (v)	LBuc LCro NLar SRms
- - 'Yankee Point'	CBcs CBod CBrac CDoC CMac CRos CSBt EDir EHyd EPfP EShb GDam LPar LRHS LSRN MDon MGos MPri

		MRav MSwo NLar NRHS SCob SCoo SGsty SPlb SPoG SWvt WCFE WHtc
	impressus	CTri MDon MPri SPer SWvt WFar
	'Italian Skies'	Widely available
	'Julia Phelps'	CBod NLar WAvo
	'Lemon and Lime'[PBR]	CKel LBuc LCro MAsh SCoo
§	× ***lobbianus***	EDir EHeP
	'Madagascar'	SCoo SPoG
	MARIE-ROSE ('Minmarose')	CKel EPfP WHtc WKif
	× ***pallidus*** 'Marie Simon'	EDir EGrl EHyd ELan EPfP GMcL LPar LSRN MAsh MGos SPer SPoG SRms SWvt WCFE WKif WSpi
	- 'Perle de Jade'	ILea
	- 'Perle Rose' ♀H4	CBcs EPfP MGos MHtn NBwr NLar SPer WKif WSpi
	papillosus	IArd SBrt WPav
§	'Pershore Zanzibar'[PBR] (v)	CEme CMac CRos CTri EDir EHyd GMcL LRHS MGos MRav MSwo NRHS SCoo SGbt SPer SPoG SRms WAvo
	'Pin Cushion'	CCCN CDoC EHyd EPfP LRHS
	'Point Millerton'	see *C. thyrsiflorus* 'Millerton Point'
	'Popcorn'	LRHS
	'Puget Blue' ♀H4	Widely available
	'Puget Blue' × ***thyrsiflorus*** var. ***repens***	LOPS LPar
	'Ray Hartman'	NLar
	repens	see *C. thyrsiflorus* var. *repens*
	'Skylark' ♀H4	Widely available
	'Snow Flurries'	see *C. thyrsiflorus* 'Snow Flurry'
	'Snow Showers'	CBcs
	'Southmead' ♀H4	CCCN CRos CTri EHeP EHyd ELan EPfP GMcL LRHS MAsh MGos MSwo NBwr NRHS WHtc
	thyrsiflorus	CTri SRms SWvt
	- 'Cool Blue'	CBod EPfP LSto NLar SGBe
§	- 'Millerton Point'	CBod CCCN ELan EPfP NLar SGol WHtc
	- 'Mystery Blue' ♀H4	EHyd LRHS NRHS SWvt
§	- var. ***repens*** ♀H4	Widely available
§	- 'Snow Flurry'	CBod CCCN EDir ELan MSwo NBwr NFav SCob SRHi SSha
	- 'Variegata' (v) **new**	NBwr
	'Tilden Park'	CRos EHyd LRHS
	'Tuxedo'[PBR]	EDir MRav NLar SCob
	× ***veitchianus***	CSBt EPfP MDon SPer
	'Victoria'	CEnd EBee EDir LPar LRHS LSRN MSwo NBwr NLar SEdd SGsty SRms
	'Zanzibar'	see *C.* 'Pershore Zanzibar'

Cedrela (*Meliaceae*)

	sinensis	see *Toona sinensis*

Cedronella (*Lamiaceae*)

§	***canariensis***	CBod CCBP ENfk EShb GPoy MNHC SRms WJek
	mexicana	see *Agastache mexicana*
	triphylla	see *C. canariensis*

Cedrus (*Pinaceae*)

	atlantica	CAco CBod ERom LMaj LRHS NWea SCob SSha WMat WTSh
	- 'Aurea' ♀H6	CAco NLar SLim
	- 'Fastigiata'	CAco LMaj LRHS NLar SLim
	- Glauca Group	CCVT CMac CMen CPer EDir ELan EPfP ERom EWTr GMcL IPap MBlu MGos MNic NLar SCob SEWo SGol SPlb SPoG SWeb WMat WMou
	- - 'Glauca' ♀H6	CAco CLnd LMaj LPar MAsh MMuc MTrO NOra NOrn NWea SAko SGsty WHtc WTSh
	- - 'Glauca Pendula' ♀H6	CAco CCVT CLnd ERom LPar LRHS MBlu MGos NLar NOra NWea SGol SGsty SLim WHtc WMat
	- - 'Silberspitz'	CAco CKen NLar
	- 'La Fontaine' **new**	CAco
	- 'Pendula'	NOra NOrn
	- 'Sapphire Nymph'	CAco CKen MAsh SLim
	brevifolia	CAco EBtc LMaj LRHS
	- 'Epstein'	CAco
	- 'Hillier Compact'	CKen NLar
	- 'Jade Medusa'	CAco NLar
	- 'Kenwith'	CAco CKen NLar
	deodara ♀H6	Widely available
	- 'Albospica' (v)	SWvt
	- 'Aurea' ♀H6	CAco CCVT CKen EPfP LMaj LPar MGos NHol NOra NOrn SGol SGsty WFar WMat
I	- 'Aurea Pendula'	CAco EBtc
	- 'Blue Dwarf'	CKen
	- 'Blue Globe' **new**	CAco
*	- 'Blue Mountain Broom'	CKen
	- 'Blue Snake'	CKen
	- 'Blue Surprise'	CAco SLim
	- 'Bush's Electra'	CAco MBlu NLar
	- 'Cream Puff'	CAco
	- 'Deep Cove'	SLim
	- 'Devinely Blue'	CKen
	- 'Eisregen'	CAco
	- 'Feelin' Blue' ♀H6	CAco CKen ELan LMaj LRHS MAsh MMuc MTrO NLar NPlm SGsty SLim SWeb SWvt WFar WMat
	- 'Gold Cascade'	SLim
	- 'Golden Horizon'	CAco CKen CMen ELan MAsh MTrO NLar SCob SLim SPoG WFar WMat
	- 'Karl Fuchs'	CAco LMaj LRHS NLar
	- 'Kelly Gold'	EBee
	- 'Klondyke'	CAco MAsh
	- 'Lime Glow'	CAco CKen SLim
	- 'Mr Blue'	CAco SPoG
	- 'Nana'	CKen
	- 'Pendula' ♀H6	CAco CKen LRHS NWea SLim
	- 'Polar Winter'	CAco
	- 'Pygmy'	CKen
	- 'Robusta'	CAco WPGP
	- 'Roman Candle'	CAco EBtc
	- 'Scott'	CKen
	- 'Silver Mist'	CKen
	- 'Silver Spring'	CAco
	libani ♀H6	Widely available
	- 'Blue Angel'	SLim
	- 'Blue Fountain'	CAco EBtc NLar
	- 'Comte de Dijon'	NLar
	- 'Fontaine'	NLar
	- 'Glauca'	CAco EHeP
	- 'Golden Dwarf'	CKen
	- 'Hedgehog'	CKen
	- 'Home Park'	CKen NLar
	- 'Italie'	CAco NLar
	- 'May'	CAco LRHS NLar SLim
	- 'Minitaur'	CAco NLar
	- Nana Group	CAco CKen ELan
	- 'Pendula'	CAco CKen
	- 'Sargentii'	CAco MBlu NLar
	- 'Taurus'	CAco

Ceiba (*Malvaceae*)

	pentandra	EAri SPlb

Celastrus (*Celastraceae*)

	angulatus	WJur
	dependens CWJ 12478	WCru
	- NMWJ 14556	WCru
	flagellaris B&SWJ 8572	WCru

glaucophyllus new	WJur
hookeri B&SWJ 11667	WCru
kusanoi CWJ 12445	WCru
orbiculatus	CBcs MRav WHer WJur
- Hermaphrodite Group ♀H6	LAlb MGil SDix
- var. ***papillosus*** B&SWJ 591	WCru
- var. ***punctatus*** CWJ 12439	WCru
scandens	CMac SPhx SPlb
stephanotiifolius B&SWJ 4727	WCru
stylosus WJC 13746	WCru

celeriac see AGM Vegetables Section

celery see AGM Vegetables Section

Celmisia (*Asteraceae*)

allanii	GArf GKev WAbe
alpina	WAbe
argentea	EPot GArf NHar WAbe
bellidioides	GAbr GArf GKev NSla WAbe
coriacea misapplied	see *C. semicordata*
coriacea Raoul	see *C. mackaui*
'Eggleston Silver'	NBir
gracilenta	GKev WAbe
haastii* × *viscosa	NSla
hectorii	GArf WAbe
§ ***mackaui***	GArf
ramulosa	ITim NHar WAbe
- var. ***tuberculata***	NSla
§ ***semicordata***	GKev ITim NHar NHpl
sessiliflora	EPot GArf WAbe
spectabilis subsp. ***magnifica***	ITim
I 'Wooley Hybrid'	EPot

Celosia (*Amaranthaceae*)

argentea var. ***cristata*** (Plumosa Group) 'Dragon's Breath' ♀H2	LSou
- - - Kimono Series	MBros SPoG
- - 'First Flame Orange' (First Flame Series) new	MPri

Celsia see *Verbascum*

× *Celsioverbascum* see *Verbascum*

Celtica see *Stipa*

Celtis (*Cannabaceae*)

australis	CMCN EBee IPap LEdu LPar MBlu WKor
- var. ***eriocarpa***	MVil
biondii	NLar
choseniana B&SWJ 12774	WCru
occidentalis	EBtc IPap WKor
tetrandra	IArd

Cenolophium (*Apiaceae*)

denudatum ♀H6	Widely available

Centaurea ✿ (*Asteraceae*)

HH&K 271	NBid
alba	LDai
alpestris	NLar SPhx
'Amethyst on Ice'	EMor LBuc SRms WCav
§ ***atropurpurea***	CAby CSpe EBee EGrl ELan EPPr EWTr EWes GQue LDai LRHS MBNS MBel MHol MMuc NBid NGBl NLar NSti SBls SMad SPhx SPlb WCot
babylonica RCB/TQ 18	WCot
bella	CBod EBee ECtt EHyd ELon EWoo LRHS MRav MSpe MTin NBro NGrd NRHS NSti SBut SMHy SPhx WFar WKif WMal XLum XSen
benoistii misapplied	see *C. atropurpurea*
benoistii ambig.	MRav
benoistii ambig. × ***orientalis***	SPhx
cana	see *C. triumfettii* subsp. *cana*
candidissima misapplied	see *C. cineraria*
candidissima Lam.	see *C. rutifolia*
'Caramia'	CBcs CBod EBee ECtt EHyd ELan EPfP LBar LEdu LRHS MHol MNrw MSpe NBPC NBid NHpl NLar NRHS WCAu
carniolica	SHar
- SDR 5443	EBee
cheiranthifolia	CAby EPPr MHol MNrw MSpe NBid NBir NLar SBut SHar SPhx
§ ***cineraria***	ECre LDai WSpi
- subsp. ***cineraria*** ♀H3	SEND WCot WMal
clementei	XSen
I 'Copper Hybrid'	CPla
cyanoides	LRHS
cyanus	CBod CHab CSpe GArf LCro LOPS MBow MHer MHoo MNHC SVic WWke
- 'Black Ball'	CSpe LCro LOPS LRHS MHoo MNHC SPhx WWke
- 'Blue Ball'	CSpe
- (Classic Series) CLASSIC MAGIC (mixed) new	MHoo
- - CLASSIC ROMANTIC (mixed) new	MHoo
- 'Florence Blue' (d)	LRHS
- 'Mauve Ball'	CSpe
- 'Pinkie' (d)	MNHC
- 'Red Ball' new	WWke
- 'Snowman'	LRHS
cynaroides Link	see *Rhaponticum centaureoides*
dealbata	CBod CMac CWal EAJP EBee EHyd EPfP GMcL LRHS MBel MHol MMuc NBro NGrd NLar NMir NRHS SCob SEND SRms WOut
- 'Steenbergii'	CMac LBar LRHS NBid NBir NGdn NPer NSti SPer SPoG WCAu WCot
- 'Steenbergii' variegated (v)	LDai
declinata RCB UA 18	WCot
gigantea	WHer
glastifolia	EBee
gymnocarpa	see *C. cineraria*
jacea	ELon GAbr MMuc NBid NLar SBut SDix SPhx WCot WOut WPGP XLum
- PAB 8821	LEdu
- var. ***nemoralis***	LDai
'John Coutts'	CRos EBee ECha ECtt EHyd ELan EPfP GLog GMaP LBar LEdu LRHS MAvo MBel MMuc MRav NBPC NBid NBir NLar NRHS NSti SEND SGbt SPoG SRms WCAu WHoo
'Jordy'	Widely available
karabaghensis	EBee MSpe
macrocephala	CAby CWal ECha ECtt EHyd ELan ELon EPPr EPfP EShb EWTr GAbr GQue LEdu LRHS MBel NBid NBro NChi NGBl NLar NRHS SBls SDix SPoG SRms WCAu
marschalliana W&B BBG1 new	WCot

	mollis	NBid
	montana	Widely available
	- 'Alba'	Widely available
	- 'Amethyst Dream'PBR	CBod CRos EAJP EBee EHed EHyd ELan EPfP LBar LRHS MNrw NLar NRHS SCoo SPoG WCAu
	- 'Amethyst in Snow'	CElw CRos EAJP EBee ECtt EHyd ELan EPfP LBar LEdu LRHS MAvo MBNS MHol MNHC NBPC NHol NLar NRHS NWad SCob SPoG WBor WCAu WPGP WTor
	- 'Black Sprite'	CBod CSpe CWGN EAJP EBee ECtt EHyd ELan ELon EMor EPfP GMaP LBar LRHS MBNS MPnt NBPC NFav NLar NRHS NSti SPoG WBor WFar WHil
	- 'Blewit'	NLar WCAu
§	- 'Carnea'	CElw ELon EPPr GMaP LBar LRHS MBel MSpe NBir NChi NLar SHar SPhx WBrk WCAu WFar
	- 'Elworthy Glacier'	CElw WMal
	- 'Gold Bullion'	CSpe CWGN ECtt EHyd EWes LDai LRHS MAvo MRav NBid NRHS SMad SMrm WSHC
	- 'Grandiflora'	CCBP EBee ELon MPie
	- 'Joyce'	CElw LDai NBid NLar SCob SHar WCAu WSHC
	- 'Lady Flora Hastings'	CElw CSpe EPPr LDai NBid WBrk
	- 'Lavender Mist'	NRHS
	- lilac-flowered	NBid NLar
	- 'Ochroleuca'	CElw LDai NBid
	- 'Parham'	CBod CRos ECtt EHyd GAbr GKev GQue LBar LRHS MNrw MRav NBPC NLar NRHS NSti SPer SPlb WSHC
	- 'Purple Heart'	Widely available
	- 'Purple Prose'	CElw EPPr LPla
	- 'Purpurea'	CElw
	- 'Rosea'	see *C. montana* 'Carnea'
I	- 'Violacea'	NBid
	- 'Violetta'	CElw EBee ELon LCro MAvo MBel MSpe NBid NBir WBrk WCAu
	nervosa	NBid NBro
	nigra	CBod CDor CHab EBee ELan ELon EPfP EWTr GJos GQue LCro LOPS MNHC NLar NMir SPhx SRms WHlf WSFF WWild
	- var. ***alba***	NBid
	- subsp. ***rivularis***	LDai MMuc NBid
	- 'Waterfall White'	MAvo MHol MSpe
	orientalis	CSpe EHyd EWes LBar LRHS LSou MHol MSpe NGBl SGbt SPhx SRms WHoo
	pannonica	EPPr
	- subsp. ***pannonica*** HH&K 259	NBid
	Phoenix hybrids	LRHS
	phrygia	CBod GGro NLar SPhx WCot
	- subsp. ***abbreviata*** new	GKev
	pulcherrima	EDAr MNrw WPnP
	'Pulchra Major'	see *Rhaponticum centaureoides*
	rigidifolia	EBee
	rupestris	EBee SPhx
	ruthenica	CAby CFis EWTr SPhx SPlb WGoo
§	***rutifolia***	WMal
	salicifolia	NBir
	scabiosa	CBod CCBP CDor CHab GQue LCro LOPS MHer MNHC MSpe NBid NBir NGrd NMir SPhx SRms WShi
	- subsp. ***adpressa*** new	GGro
	'Silver Feather'	CBcs LBar LRHS MHol NLar NRHS NSti SGBe SPoG SRms WNPC
	simplicicaulis	EBee MAsh NBir NChi NHpl SHar SRms WCav WHoo XLum XSen
	stoebe new	SPhx
	thracica	WCot
	triumfettii 'Blue Dreams'	LDai
§	- subsp. ***cana***	NBid
	- 'Hoar Frost'	MSpe NDov
	- subsp. ***stricta***	LPla SHar
	woronowii	MAvo

Centaurium (*Gentianaceae*)

	erythraea	GKev GPoy MHoo
	scilloides	NSla WAbe

Centella (*Apiaceae*)

§	***asiatica***	GPoy LCro LEdu SPre WJek

Centradenia (*Melastomataceae*)

	inaequilateralis	CCCN
	- 'Cascade' ♀H2	MBros

Centranthus (*Caprifoliaceae*)

§	***lecoqii***	ECha ECtt EPPr EWes LRHS SHor SPhx WCot WGoo
	macrosiphon	CMac
§	***ruber***	Widely available
§	- 'Albus'	Widely available
	- 'Atrococcineus'	ECha MMuc SGbt
	- var. ***coccineus***	CBcs CRos EAJP EBee EHeP EHyd ELan EPfP EWoo GAbr GBin GKin GMaP GMcL LRHS MRav NRHS SBut SCob SEND SOrN SPer SPhx SSut WCot WFar XLum XSen
	- mauve-flowered misapplied	see *C. lecoqii*
	- mauve-flowered	XSen
	- 'Roseus'	EPfP
	- 'Ruby Red'	LSun
	- 'Snowcloud'	EBee ECtt EHyd ENfk EPfP MBow MNHC NFav SBut SRms

Centratherum (*Asteraceae*)

	punctatum	CSpe

Centropogon (*Campanulaceae*)

	ferrugineus B&SWJ 10665	WCru

Cephalanthus (*Rubiaceae*)

	'Magical Moonlight'	LCro LOPS LRHS NLar
	occidentalis	CBod EBee MAsh MBlu NLar NQui SPhx SPoG WHlf
	- FIBER OPTICS ('Bailoptics') new	MPkF
	- SUGAR SHACK ('Smcoss')	LRHS

Cephalaria (*Caprifoliaceae*)

§	***alpina***	EHyd ELan EPPr EPfP LRHS MAsh MNrw MSpe NRHS SDix SHar SPhx SPtp SRms WBrk WFar XLum
	caucasica	see *C. gigantea*
	dipsacoides	CDor CSpe LRHS MSpe SHor SPhx SRms WGoo
	galpiniana	SPlb
§	***gigantea***	Widely available
	leucantha	CAby MMuc NLar SEND SPhx WBrk
	litvinovii	SPhx
	radiata	EAJP NDov SPhx
	tatarica hort.	see *C. gigantea*
	tchihatchewii	ILea NLar WCot
	transsylvanica	SPhx
	- W&B BGJ-1	CSpe WCot

Cephalaria × *Scabiosa* (*Caprifoliaceae*)

	hybrid new	MAsh

Cephalophyllum (*Aizoaceae*)

alstonii	EAri
pillansii **new**	EAri

Cephalotaxus (*Taxaceae*)

fortunei	CAco LEdu WCru WJur
- var. ***fortunei***	CAco
harringtonia	CAco CMCN LEdu WJur
- var. ***drupacea***	CAco
- 'Fastigiata'	CAco CWnw ERom IArd IDee LPar LRHS MAsh MGil MGos NWea SLim SPoG
- 'Gimborn's Pillow'	CAco
- 'Korean Gold'	CAco LRHS SLim
sinensis	CAco WJur

Cephalotus (*Cephalotaceae*)

follicularis ♀H2	CHew NWac SHmp

Cerastium (*Caryophyllaceae*)

alpinum	SRms
- var. ***lanatum***	EWes
biebersteinii	XLum
candidissimum	EWes
fontanum	CHab
tomentosum	CBar CBod CKel CSBt CTri CWCL EBee ELan EPfP EWTr GKev LRHS MACG MHol MMuc NBir SEND SEdd SLee SPer SPlb SPoG WFar WWke
- var. ***columnae***	ECha EWes GMaP WIce XLum XSen

Ceratonia (*Fabaceae*)

siliqua	SEND SPlb SVic WJur

Ceratophyllum (*Ceratophyllaceae*)

demersum	CBen CPud CWat EWat LCro LOPS LPfP MWts WMAq WSFF
submersum	LLWG

Ceratostigma (*Plumbaginaceae*)

abyssinicum	CBcs EGrI ELan ESwi EWTr SIvy
asperrimum B&SWJ 7260	WCru
capensis	CMac
griffithii	Widely available
- 'Tiny Dragon' **new**	NLar
§ ***plumbaginoides*** ♀H5	Widely available
'Summer Skies'	WHlf
willmottianum ♀H4	Widely available
- BWJ 8140	WCru
- DESERT SKIES ('Palmgold'PBR)	CMac EPfP NLar SCob SWvt
- FOREST BLUE ('Lice'PBR) ♀H4	CBrac CDoC CEnd CKel CMac CRos CSBt EHyd ELan EPfP LCro LOPS LRHS LSRN MAsh MGos MPri MRav NRHS SAko SCoo SEdd SGBe SPer SPoG SSta SWvt XSte
- SAPPHIRE RING ('Lissbrill'PBR)	CBcs CCCN CDoC CKel CPla CRos EBee EHyd ELan EPfP LRHS LSRN MAsh MGos NRHS SCoo SPoG WFar WHil WHlf

Cercidiphyllum ✿ (*Cercidiphyllaceae*)

japonicum ♀H5	Widely available
- 'Boyd's Dwarf'	CJun CRos EHyd ELan EPfP LRHS MBlu NLar SPoG SSta
- 'Chameleon' (v)	MBlu NLar
- GLOWBALL ('Jww4'PBR)	CAco MBlu SMad
- 'Herkenrode Dwarf'	MBlu NLar
- 'Heronswood Globe' ♀H5	CAco CJun CMCN EPfP MBlu NLar SSta
- 'Kreukenberg Dwarf'	CJun NLar SSta
- 'Morioka Weeping'	CJun CPer EBee MPkF NLar SChF SSta WPGP
- 'Peach'	CJun NLar
§ - f. ***pendulum*** ♀H5	Widely available
- - 'Amazing Grace'	MBlu SGbt SSta
- RA ('Jww3'PBR)	CAco NLar
- 'Raspberry'	CJun MBlu NLar
- RED FOX	see *C. japonicum* 'Rotfuchs'
§ - 'Rotfuchs'	CAco CBcs CEme CEnd CJun CLnd CMCN CMac CPer CRos EHyd ELan EPfP GMcL LRHS MAsh MBlu MGos NLar SAko SChF SGol SGsty SPoG SSta WFar WMat
- 'Ruby'	CJun MBlu
- 'Strawberry'	CBcs CJun MBlu NLar SSta
- 'Tidal Wave'	CJun LRHS MBlu NLar SSta
- 'Titania'	NLar SSta
magnificum	CEnd CMCN EBee MBlu MMrt NLar
- f. ***pendulum***	see *C. japonicum* f. *pendulum*

Cercis ✿ (*Fabaceae*)

canadensis	CAco CAgr CBcs CMCN CPer CTsd CWGN LPar MGil MGos MTrO NLar NWea SCob SavN WHlf WLov XSen
- f. ***alba***	CMCN LSRN
- - 'Royal White'	CAco CKel CWnw EPfP EWTr MBlu SPer
- 'Alley Cat' (v)	CAco LCro MTrO WMat XVPe
- 'Appalachian Red'	MBlu MGos WMou
- CAROLINA SWEETHEART ('Nccc1')	IArd LRHS MTrO WMat XVPe
- 'Cascading Hearts'	EHyd NRHS
- 'Flame'	SSta
- 'Forest Pansy' ♀H5	Widely available
- 'Hearts of Gold'PBR	CAco CMac CWGN EBee ELan LPar LRHS MGos MTrO NLar NOra NOrn SPoG WMat XSte XVPe
- LAVENDER TWIST ('Covey')	CAco CBTr CMac EBee ELan EPfP LCro LMaj LOPS LPar LRHS LSRN MBlu MGos MTrO NLar NOra NOrn NRHS SPoG SRms WMat XVPe
- LITTLE WOODY ('Litwo'PBR)	NLar
- 'Melon Beauty'	MBlu NLar
- 'Merlot'	CAco IArd MGos NLar NOrn SGsty WMat
- var. ***mexicana*** NJM 09.024 **new**	WPGP
- 'Pauline Lily'	NLar
- 'Pink Pom Poms'	CAco EBee MAsh MTrO NLar NOrn WMat
- RED FORCE ('Minrouge3'PBR)	CBod CDoC CKel CLnd CWnw EHed LRHS LSRN NLar SGsty WCot XSte
- 'Ruby Falls'PBR ♀H5	CAco CBcs CKel CMac CTri CWnw EBee ELan EPfP EWTr LCro LMaj LOPS LPar LRHS LSRN MAsh MGos MTrO NOra NOrn NRHS SMad SPoG WMat XVPe
- 'Rubye Atkinson'	NLar
- var. ***texensis*** 'Oklahoma'	CAco EBee ELan EPfP MGos MTrO WMat WPGP
- - 'Texas White'	CAco CEnd CMac EBee ELan EPfP LRHS MTrO NLar NOrn WMat
- - 'Traveller'	CAco LPar SGol
- THE RISING SUN ('Jn2')	CAco CWGN IArd LPar WHlf XVPe
- 'Vanilla Twist'PBR	CAco CMac EBee IArd LPar MTrO NLar SPoG WMat
chinensis	CAco EGrI EWTr GKev IDee LMaj MACG NLar SavN WMou
- B&SWJ 12665	WCru

- 'Avondale' 🏆H5	CAco CBcs CEnd CJun CMac CPer EGrI EHed EHyd ELan EPfP EWes LCro LMaj LOPS LPar LRHS LSRN MAsh MBlu MGos MTrO NLar NOra NOrn SCoo SPoG SWvt WMat WMou
- 'Diane'	SSta
- 'Don Egolf' 🏆H5	CJun MBlu MGos NLar
- 'Shirobana'	CAco LMaj LPar WMat
chingii	WPGP
gigantea	CAco
griffithii	CMCN LEdu NLar SSta WPGP
occidentalis	SSta
racemosa	WPGP XSen
siliquastrum	Widely available
- f. ***albida***	EHyd ELan EPfP
- 'Bodnant' 🏆H5	CMac CPer EPfP LRHS LSRN MBlu MGos NLar NOra SSta WMat

Cereus (*Cactaceae*)

azureus **new**	NHrt
jamacaru **new**	EAri
repandus	NPlm
'Monstruosus' **new**	
'Spiralis' **new**	CDoC LCro NHrt

Cerinthe (*Boraginaceae*)

major	SWvt
- 'Purpurascens'	CSpe CWCL EBee ELan EPfP LCro LOPS LSto MNHC SMrm SPhx SPoG WCav WHlf WKif WTor
retorta	LDai

Ceropegia (*Apocynaceae*)

ampliata	EAri
§ ***linearis*** subsp. ***woodii*** 🏆H1c	CDoC EAri EShb LCro NHrt
§ - - 'Lady Heart' (v)	EAri
- - 'Variegata'	see *C. linearis* subsp. *woodii* 'Lady Heart'
nilotica **new**	EAri
radicans	EAri
sandersonii 🏆H1c	CCCN CDoC EShb SPre
woodii	see *C. linearis* subsp. *woodii*

Ceroxylon (*Arecaceae*)

parvifrons **new**	NPlm

Cestrum (*Solanaceae*)

aurantiacum	SEND WHlf
buxifolium B&SWJ 14395	WCru
× ***cultum*** 'Cretan Pink'	CCCN
- 'Cretan Purple'	CBcs CCCN CHll EAri EBee EGrI EHyd ELan ELon EPfP EShb IDee LRHS MGil SWvt WKif WSHC
§ ***elegans***	CBod CDow CEme CHll CKel CSde CTsd EAri ELon EPfP EWTr EWld IDee LAlb LRHS MGil SEND SIvy SPad SWvt WCFE WHlf
fasciculatum	SDix
'Newellii' 🏆H3	CBcs CCCN CKel EBee EGrI EHyd ELan ELon EPfP LRHS SIvy SPlb SVen SWvt WKif
nocturnum	CBcs CCCN CDow CHll EAri EShb SPre WCFE WHlf
parqui 🏆H3	CBcs CBod CCCN CEme CHll CKel CMCN CTsd EAri EBee EGrI ELan EPfP IDee MGil SDix SEND SIvy SMad SWvt WKif WSHC
- purple-tinged	SBrt
purpureum misapplied	see *Iochroma cyaneum* 'Trebah'
purpureum (Lindl.) Standl.	see *C. elegans*
roseum B&SWJ 10255 from Oaxaca State, Mexico	WCru
- 'Ilnacullin'	CCCN CSde EBee
violaceum misapplied	see *Iochroma cyaneum* 'Trebah'

Ceterach see *Asplenium*

officinarum	see *Asplenium ceterach*

Chaenomeles ✿ (*Rosaceae*)

cathayensis	CAgr EPfP EWTr LEdu LSto NLar WCru WFar WHer WJur WKor WPGP
§ ***japonica***	CAco CCCN EHeP LSto MMuc NWea SCob SEND SPre WJur WKor
- 'Chojubai'	CMen
- 'Cido'	CAco CAgr LEdu MCoo
- 'Orange Beauty'	NHol SCob
- 'Rising Sun'	NLar
- 'Sargentii'	CAco LPar MBlu NLar SGol
MADAME BUTTERFLY ('Whitice')	CBod CKel EBee EHyd ELan EPfP LRHS LSRN MAsh MRav NRHS SCob SGol SPoG SRms
maulei	see *C. japonica*
'Orange Star'	CEme CEnd SGol WHlf
sinensis	see *Pseudocydonia sinensis*
speciosa 'Apple Blossom'	see *C. speciosa* 'Moerloosei'
- 'Contorta'	WFar
I - 'Contorta Rosea'	WFar
- 'Eximia'	LRHS NLar SGsty
- 'Falconnet Charlet' (d)	EHyd LRHS MRav NRHS SGol SRms
- 'Flocon Rose'	SGol
- 'Friesdorfer'	LRHS SGsty
- 'Geisha Girl' (d) 🏆H6	Widely available
- 'Grayshott Salmon'	WSpi
- HOT FIRE ('Minvesu')	CDoC CRos EHed EPfP LRHS SGsty WCot WSpi
- 'Kinshiden'	CEme CKel EMil EPfP LRHS LSRN NLar SGol SGsty WSpi
- MANGO STORM ('Mincha01'PBR)	CAco CKel CRos CWnw EBee ELan EPfP LRHS MAsh NLar SGol SGsty
§ - 'Moerloosei' 🏆H6	Widely available
- 'Nivalis'	Widely available
- 'Orange Storm'PBR	CAco CRos EBee ELan LCro LRHS LSRN NLar SGol
- 'Pink Storm'PBR	CAco CRos EBee ELan EPfP LCro LRHS NLar SGol WHlf
- RED KIMONO ('Ainoomoi'PBR)	CAco LRHS NLar SGol
- 'Rubra Grandiflora'	CAco SGsty WSpi
- 'Scarlet Storm'PBR	CAco CRos EBee EPfP LRHS NLar SGol WHlf
- 'Simonii' (d)	MRav NWea WSpi
- 'Snow'	MSwo SRms
- 'Umbilicata'	MBlu SRms
- 'Yukigotan' (d)	CDoC LEdu MMrt NLar SGol SWvt WFar WSpi
× ***superba*** 'Boule de Feu'	CTri
- 'Cameo' (d)	CAco CBrac CEnd ELon EPfP LEdu LPar LRHS MBNS MMrt MRav NLar SCob SGbt SGol SPer SRms WCot WFar WHtc
- 'Clementine'	CAco
- 'Coquelicot'	NLar
- 'Crimson and Gold' 🏆H6	Widely available
- 'Elly Mossel'	CAco CMac EHeP SGol SRms WFar
- 'Etna'	CAco GDam GMcL WFar
- 'Fascination'	WFar
- 'Fire Dance'	CAco CTsd MSwo SGol WCot WLov WSpi
- 'Fusion'	CAgr
- 'Hollandia'	CAco SRms
- 'Issai White'	MRav
- 'Jet Trail'	CAco CBcs CKel CMac CRos CSBt EHeP EHyd ELan EPfP GDam GMcL LPar LRHS MGos MRav MSwo NLar

	NRHS SCob SGbt SGol SRms SWvt WFar
- 'Knap Hill Scarlet'	CRos EBee EHyd ELan EPfP LRHS MGos MMuc SCob SCoo SPer SPoG SRms SWvt WCot
- 'Lemon and Lime'	CBcs CBod CEme CMac ELan LRHS MGos MRav NLar SPer SRms WLov WSpi
- 'Nicoline' ♀H6	CAco CBcs CKel EPfP LPar LRHS MGos SPer
- 'Orange Trail'	CAco GDam
- 'Pink Lady' ♀H6	Widely available
- PINK TRAIL ('Interpitra')	CAco NLar SGbt SRms
- 'Red Joy'	CKel EPfP LRHS MRav NLar SRms
- 'Red Trail'	CKel MRav
- 'Rowallane' ♀H6	MRav
- 'Salmon Horizon'	CAco IArd NLar SGol
- 'Texas Scarlet'	CAco CKel MMrt SRms WMou
- 'Tortuosa'	CBod CKel MBNS NLar WCot
'Toyo-nishiki'	MBlu WFar

Chaenorhinum (*Plantaginaceae*)

'Bon Bini'	LRHS
glareosum	NBwr NHpl
§ ***origanifolium***	GArf GKev SPlb SRot
- 'Blue Dream'	CSpe EBou ELan EPfP EWTr GKev LBar LRHS LShi MAsh SBls SBut SMad SPoG SWvt WFar WIce

Chaenostoma (*Scrophulariaceae*)

cordatum (Abunda Series) ABUNDA COLOSSAL BLUE ('Balabolue')	LSou MBros WHlf
- - ABUNDA COLOSSAL PINK	MBros WWke
- - ABUNDA COLOSSAL WHITE ('Balabowite'PBR)	LSou MPri WHlf
- 'Olympic Gold' (v)	SCoo
§ - Scopia Series	WHlf
- - SCOPIA DOUBLE BALLERINA SNOWBALL (d)	LSou
- - SCOPIA GOLDEN LEAVES WHITE ('Dancop15')	MBros
§ - 'Snowflake'	MBow MBros NPer SCoo SPoG SWvt

Chaerophyllum (*Apiaceae*)

aromaticum	LEdu
aureum	NAts
azoricum	ELan LEdu LPla LShi MAvo WCot WOut
coloratum	SPtp
creticum	ELan
hirsutum 'Roseum'	Widely available

Chaetanthera (*Asteraceae*)

villosa	SPlb

Chamaecrista (*Fabaceae*)

fasciculata	SPhx

Chamaecyparis ✿ (*Cupressaceae*)

funebris	see *Cupressus funebris*
lawsoniana	CAco CBrac GDam IPap LMaj NWea SCob WTSh
- 'Allumii Aurea'	see *C. lawsoniana* 'Alumigold'
§ - 'Alumigold'	CAco LPar LRHS NOrn
- 'Alumii'	CAco CBrac NOrn
- 'Aurea'	CBrac
- 'Aurea Densa' ♀H6	CKen CSBt MGos
- 'Aurea Nana'	see *C. lawsoniana* 'Aurea Densa', *C. lawsoniana* 'Minima Aurea'
- 'Bleu Nantais' ♀H6	CKen LBee LRHS MGos NBwr SCoo SPoG SSha WCFE
- 'Blom'	CKen
- 'Blue Surprise'	CBod CKen
- 'Brégéon'	CAco CKen NLar
- 'Broomhill Gold' ♀H6	CSBt GMcL LBee MGos NOrn SCoo SPoG SVic
- 'Caudata'	CKen
§ - 'Chilworth Silver' ♀H6	CBod CBrac CSBt LBee MAsh SSha
- 'Columnaris'	CAco EPfP LBee LPar SCoo SPoG WFar
- 'Columnaris Aurea'	see *C. lawsoniana* 'Golden Spire'
- 'Columnaris Glauca'	CBrac CMac EDir GMcL MGos NBwr NOrn NWea SCob SCoo SGsty SPer
- 'Cream Glow'	CKen CSBt LRHS
- 'Dik's Weeping' ♀H6	CAco ESwi NLar NWea
- 'Drooping Solo'	CAco CKen NLar
- 'Dutch Gold'	MAsh
- 'Dwarf Blue'	see *C. lawsoniana* 'Pick's Dwarf Blue'
- 'Eclipse'	CKen
- 'Elegantissima' ambig.	CMac
- 'Ellwoodii' ♀H6	CAco CBod CBrac CMac CSBt CTri EDir ELan GMcL LPar LRHS MAsh MGil MGos NBwr NLar NWea SCob SCoo SGsty SLim SPer SSha
- 'Ellwood's Empire'	CAco EDir
- 'Ellwood's Gold' ♀H6	CAco CBcs CBod CBrac CEme CMac CSBt EDir ELan EPfP GMcL LBee LPar LRHS MAsh MGos NBwr NOrn NWea SCob SGsty SLim SPer SPlb SPoG SSha SVic
- 'Ellwood's Gold Pillar' ♀H6	GMcL LBee LRHS MAsh NHol NLar SLim WHtc
§ - 'Ellwood's Nymph'	CKen
- ELLWOOD'S PILLAR ('Flolar') ♀H6	CMac GMcL LBee LCro LRHS MAsh MGos NLar NOrn SCoo SLim WHtc
- 'Ellwood's Pygmy'	CMac
- 'Ellwood's Silver Threads'	CMac LBee
- 'Ellwood's Variegata'	see *C. lawsoniana* 'Ellwood's White'
§ - 'Ellwood's White' (v)	CMac GMcL SPoG
- 'Erecta Aurea'	CAco
- 'Erecta Viridis'	CAco CBrac CMac GMcL NBwr
- 'Filip's Golden Tears'	CAco ELan NLar
- 'Fleckellwood'	MAsh NBwr
- 'Fletcheri' ♀H6	CBrac CMac EDir NWea
- 'Fletcheri Aurea'	see *C. lawsoniana* 'Yellow Transparent'
- 'Fletcher's White'	NBwr
- 'Forsteckensis'	CBrac NWea
- 'Gimbornii' ♀H6	NBwr NLar
- 'Glauca Pendula'	CAco
- 'Globosa'	CAco GMcL
- 'Gnome'	CKen CMac NHol SCoo SPoG
- 'Golden King'	NWea
§ - 'Golden Pot'	CBod CSBt GMcL LBee LSto
§ - 'Golden Spire'	CAco
- 'Golden Wonder' ♀H6	NBwr NWea SCoo
- 'Grayswood Feather' ♀H6	GMcL LBee MAsh SCob
- 'Grayswood Gold'	GMcL
- 'Green Globe' ♀H6	CKen CMen CSBt LBee LSta MAsh MGil
§ - 'Green Hedger'	CSBt
§ - 'Green Pillar'	EPfP GMcL LBee NWea SSha
- 'Green Spire'	see *C. lawsoniana* 'Green Pillar'
- 'Ilona'	CAco
- 'Imbricata Pendula' ♀H6	CAco CKen IDee MBlu NLar SLim SMad WPGP

	- 'Intertexta'	SLim
	- 'Ivonne' ♀H6	CAco EBtc EPfP GDam GMcL LCro LPar MAsh MGos NLar NWea SCoo SLim SPoG
	- 'Jackman's Green Hedger'	see *C. lawsoniana* 'Green Hedger'
	- 'Jackman's Variety'	see *C. lawsoniana* 'Green Pillar'
	- 'Jeanette'	CKen
	- 'Karaca'	CAco NLar
	- 'Kilmacurragh' ♀H6	CAco
	- 'Kilworth Column'	LRHS NLar NWea
	- 'Knowefieldensis'	CMac
	- 'Lane' misapplied	see *C. lawsoniana* 'Lanei Aurea'
	- 'Lane' den Ouden	CBrac LMaj NBwr
§	- 'Lanei Aurea' ♀H6	NWea
	- 'Lemon Queen'	SSha
	- 'Little Spire' ♀H6	CAco LRHS NLar SSha WLea
	- 'Lutea'	NBwr
§	- 'Lutea Nana'	CBrac CMac
	- 'Luteocompacta'	LBee
	- 'Mason's Pillar'	CKen
	- 'Minima Argentea'	see *C. lawsoniana* 'Nana Argentea'
	- 'Minima Aurea' ♀H6	CAco CBrac CKen CMac CSBt EPfP GMcL LBee MAsh MGil MGos NBwr NWea SCoo SLim SPer SPoG SSha WHtc
	- 'Minima Glauca' ♀H6	CAco CBrac CMac GMcL LCro NBwr NWea SCoo SLim WFar WHtc
	- 'Moonsprite' ♀H6	CKen MAsh NLar SCoo SLim SPoG SSha
	- 'Naberi'	NBwr
	- 'Nana'	CBrac
	- 'Nana Albospica' (v)	LBee
§	- 'Nana Argentea'	CKen EPfP SPoG
	- 'Nana Lutea'	see *C. lawsoniana* 'Lutea Nana'
	- 'Nicole'	MAsh NWea SCoo
	- 'Nyewoods'	see *C. lawsoniana* 'Chilworth Silver'
	- 'Nymph'	see *C. lawsoniana* 'Ellwood's Nymph'
	- PEARLY SWIRLS ('Spicwirl') (v)	NLar SCoo SPoG
§	- 'Pelt's Blue'	CAco CBrac CSBt NLar SSha
	- 'Pembury Blue' ♀H6	CBod CBrac EPfP GMcL LBee LCro LSto MGos NBwr NLar NOrn SCob SCoo SLim SPoG
§	- 'Pick's Dwarf Blue'	CBrac SSha
	- 'Pina Colada'PBR	LRHS
	- 'Pitt Lane'	CKen
	- POT OF GOLD	see *C. lawsoniana* 'Golden Pot'
	- 'Pottenii'	CBrac GMcL LBee NBwr NLar NOrn NWea
	- 'Pygmaea Argentea' (v) ♀H6	CBrac CEme CKen CMac CSBt ELan MAsh MGos NBwr SCoo SLim SPoG WCFE
	- 'Pygmy'	CMen NWea
	- 'Rijnhof'	LBee
	- 'Rimpelaar'	CKen MGil NWad
	- 'Robusta Glauca' **new**	CAco
	- 'Romana'	NLar
	- 'Royal Gold'	NBwr
	- 'Silver Queen' (v)	CKen
	- 'Silver Threads' (v)	LBee SCoo SPoG
	- 'Silver Tip' (v)	LRHS
	- 'Snow Flurry' (v)	CKen
	- 'Snow White' (v) ♀H6	CAco GMcL LBee LCro LRHS MAsh MGos NBwr NHol SCoo SLim SPoG SVic
	- 'Somerset'	CMac
	- 'Springtime'PBR	CBod CSBt LBee SSha
	- 'Stardust' ♀H6	CAco CBcs CSBt EDir ELan GMcL MAsh MGos NLar NOrn SCob
	- 'Stewartii'	NBwr NWea
	- 'Sulphur Spire'PBR	LRHS
	- 'Summer Snow' (v) ♀H6	GMcL NHol SCoo
	- 'Sunkist'	CAco SLim
	- 'Sunny Smile'PBR	SCoo
	- 'Tharandtensis Caesia'	CAco NLar
	- 'Treasure' (v)	MAsh
	- 'Uschi's Curtain' **new**	CAco
	- 'Van Pelt'	see *C. lawsoniana* 'Pelt's Blue'
	- 'Waterfall'	CAco
	- 'White Spot' (v)	CAco GMcL NBwr
	- 'Winston Churchill'	CMac NOrn NWea
	- 'Wisselii' ♀H6	CAco CKel CKen CWnw LRHS MGos NLar NWea SCoo SLim
	- 'Wisselii Nana'	CKen
	- 'Wissel's Saguaro' ♀H6	CAco CKen LRHS NLar SLim
	- 'Yellow Spire'	SLim
§	- 'Yellow Transparent'	CMac
	× ***leylandii***	see × *Cuprocyparis leylandii*
	nootkatensis	see *Xanthocyparis nootkatensis*
	obtusa 'Albovariegata' (v)	CKen
	- 'Arneson's Compact'	CKen
	- 'Aurea'	CAco
	- 'Aurora' ♀H7	CAco CKen ELan LRHS SCoo SLim SPoG
	- 'Bambi'	CKen CMen WAbe
	- 'Barkenny'	CKen NLar
	- 'Bartley'	CKen
	- 'Bassett'	CKen
	- 'Bess'	CKen
	- 'Birgit' **new**	CAco
	- 'Blizzard' (v)	NLar
	- 'Brigitt'	CAco CKen SCoo SPoG
	- 'Butterball'	CKen CMen LRHS
	- 'Caespitosa'	WAbe
	- 'Chabo-yadori'	CAco NBwr NLar
	- 'Chilworth'	CKen NWad
	- 'Chima-anihiba'	CKen
	- 'Chirimen'	CAco CKen CMen MGil NLar
	- 'Clarke's Seedling'	CKen
	- 'Confucius'	LRHS LSRN
	- 'Contorta'	MGil
§	- 'Coralliformis'	CBod CMac NLar
§	- 'Crippsii' ♀H7	CMac
	- 'Crippsii Aurea'	see *C. obtusa* 'Crippsii'
	- 'Dainty Doll'	CKen NHol NWad
	- 'Densa'	see *C. obtusa* 'Nana Densa'
	- 'Draht'	CAco LRHS
	- 'Draht Hexe'	CKen
	- 'Elf'	CKen NLar
	- 'Ellie B'	CKen CMen
	- 'Ericoides'	CKen
	- 'Erika'	NBwr
	- 'Fernspray Gold' ♀H7	CAco CCVT EPfP GMcL LRHS MGos MMrt NLar SCoo SPoG WLea
	- 'Filiformis Aurea'	CAco
	- 'Flabelliformis'	CKen NWad
	- 'Gitte'	CAco SLim
	- 'Gnome'	CKen CMen
	- 'Gold Fern'	CKen
	- 'Golden Fairy'	CKen
	- 'Golden Filament' (v)	CKen
	- 'Golden Nymph'	CKen
	- 'Golden Sprite'	CKen WAbe
	- 'Gracilis'	CAco CKel SSha
	- 'Gracilis Aurea'	CMen
	- 'Green Cushion'	CKen
	- 'Green Diamond'	CKen
	- 'Hage'	CKen
	- 'Hannah'	NLar
	- 'Hypnoides Nana'	CKen
	- 'Intermedia'	CKen WAbe
	- 'Junior'	CKen
	- 'Juniperoides'	CKen LRHS
	- 'Juniperoides Compacta'	WAbe

	- 'Kamarachiba' 𝕐H7	CAco CKen CSBt GMcL LBee LSRN MAsh NLar SCoo SLim SPoG
	- 'Kerdalo'	CAco LRHS NLar
	- 'Kojolcohiba' **new**	SAko
	- 'Konijn'	GMcL
	- 'Kosteri' 𝕐H7	CAco CKen CMac ELan LBee NHol SCoo
	- 'Leprechaun'	WAbe
	- 'Limerick'	CKen
	- 'Little Markey'	CKen CMen
	- 'Lucas'[PBR]	CAco LRHS
	- 'Lutea Nova'	CAco
	- 'Lycopodioides'	CAco CKel CWnw
	- 'Lycopodioides Aurea'	CAco NLar
	- 'Marian'	CKen
§	- 'Mariesii' (v)	CKen
	- 'Maureen' **new**	CAco
	- 'Melody'	CAco CKen NLar
	- 'Meroke'	CAco MGil
	- 'Minima'	CKen
	- 'Nana' 𝕐H7	CKen CMac CMen LBee LPar NHol NWad
	- 'Nana Aurea' 𝕐H7	CAco CBrac CKel CMac CSBt CWnw EPfP MAsh NBwr NHol
§	- 'Nana Densa'	CKen CMac
	- 'Nana Gracilis' 𝕐H7	CAco CBrac CKen CMen CSBt CWnw ELan EPfP GMcL LCro LRHS MAsh MGil MGos NBwr NWea SCob SCoo SLim SPoG WHtc WLea
I	- 'Nana Gracilis Aurea'	CMen
I	- 'Nana Lutea' 𝕐H7	CAco CKen CMen ELan GMcL LBee LRHS MAsh MGos NHol NWea SLim SSha
	- 'Nana Rigida'	see *C. obtusa* 'Rigid Dwarf'
	- 'Nana Variegata'	see *C. obtusa* 'Mariesii'
	- 'Oregon Crested'	LRHS MGil NLar
	- 'Pagoda'	CAco
	- 'Petite Minorette'	CAco
	- 'Pygmaea'	CBrac CSBt SCoo SLim
	- 'Rashahiba'	LRHS
	- 'Rezek'	see *C. obtusa* 'Rezek Dwarf'
§	- 'Rezek Dwarf'	CKen CMen
§	- 'Rigid Dwarf'	CKen LBee LRHS
	- 'Saffron Spray'	CAco LRHS NLar SLim
	- 'Snowflake' (v)	CKen
	- 'Snowkist' (v)	CKen
	- 'Sparkles'	NLar
	- 'Spiralis'	CKen
	- 'Spirited'	CAco NLar
	- 'Stoneham'	CKen CMen
	- 'Strangman'	CKen
	- 'Suiroya-hiba'	SLim
	- 'Teddy Bear'	CAco
	- 'Tempelhof'	CAco CKen SCoo SLim
	- 'Tetragona Aurea'	CAco CMac NWad
	- 'Timothy'	CMac
	- 'Tonia' (v)	CKen SLim
	- 'Torulosa'	see *C. obtusa* 'Coralliformis'
	- 'Tsatsumi Gold' 𝕐H7	CAco CKen CMen ELan EPfP LRHS SCoo SLim SPoG
	- 'Verdon'	NLar
	- 'Villa Marie'	LRHS NLar
	- 'Wiels Baby'	NLar
	- 'Wyckoff'	CKen
	- 'Yellowtip' (v)	CKen MAsh
	pisifera	CAco
	- 'Baby Blue'	CKel CKen CWnw ELan EPfP LRHS SCoo SPoG
	- 'Blue Bun'	CKen
	- 'Blue Globe'	CKen
	- 'Blue Moon'[PBR]	LCro LOPS LRHS MGos
	- 'Boulevard' 𝕐H7	CBcs CBod CBrac CEme CMac CSBt ELan EPfP GMcL LBee LPar LRHS MAsh MGos MMuc NBwr SCob SCoo SLim SPer SSha
	- 'Compacta'	LRHS
	- 'Curly Top' 𝕐H7	EPfP LRHS MAsh NHol SCoo SLim SPoG SSha
	- 'Filifera'	CMac CSBt MMuc
	- 'Filifera Aurea' 𝕐H7	CEme CKel CKen CMac CWnw ELan EPfP LBee LPar MAsh MGos NHol NWea SCob SCoo SSha WCFE
	- 'Filifera Nana'	EPfP LCro LRHS SLim
	- 'Filifera Nana Aurea'	see *C. pisifera* 'Golden Mop'
	- 'Filifera Sungold'	see *C. pisifera* 'Sungold'
	- 'Fuiri-tsukomo'	CKen
	- 'Gold Cushion'	CKen
	- 'Gold Dust'	see *C. pisifera* 'Plumosa Aurea'
	- 'Gold Spangle'	CBrac CKen
§	- 'Golden Mop'	CBrac CKen
	- 'Green Pincushion'	CKen CMen
	- 'Hime-himuro'	CKen
	- 'Hime-sawara'	CKen CMen
	- 'Lime Pie'	CKen
	- 'Nana'	CBrac CKen CMen GMcL LRHS NHol
	- 'Nana Aureovariegata' (v)	CSBt LBee
	- 'Nana Aurescens'	LRHS
I	- 'Nana Compacta'	CMac
	- 'Nana Variegata' (v)	CMac LBee
I	- 'Parslorii'	CKen
	- 'Pici'	CKen
	- 'Plumosa'	NPlm
§	- 'Plumosa Aurea'	CKen LPar MAsh
	- 'Plumosa Aurea Compacta'	CKen NWad
	- 'Plumosa Aurea Nana'	MAsh
I	- 'Plumosa Aurea Nana Compacta'	CMac
	- 'Plumosa Aurescens'	CMac
§	- 'Plumosa Compressa' 𝕐H7	CBrac CKen NWad SSha
	- 'Plumosa Densa'	see *C. pisifera* 'Plumosa Compressa'
I	- 'Plumosa Juniperoides'	CKen
§	- 'Plumosa Rogersii'	GMcL NBwr
	- 'Pygmy'	see *C. pisifera* 'Tsukumo'
	- 'Rogersii'	see *C. pisifera* 'Plumosa Rogersii'
	- 'Silver Lode' (v)	CKen
	- 'Silver Surprise'	LRHS
	- 'Snow' (v)	CKen LRHS
	- 'Snowflake'	CKen
	- 'Spaan's Cannon Ball'	CKen CMen
	- 'Squarrosa Dumosa'	CKen
I	- 'Squarrosa Lombarts'	CMac CSBt SSha
	- 'Squarrosa Lutea'	CKen
	- 'Squarrosa Sulphurea'	CSBt LRHS NBwr SCoo
§	- 'Sungold' 𝕐H7	CBod CKel CKen CSBt CWnw EPfP LRHS MAsh MGos NBwr NWea SCoo SLim SPoG SRms
	- 'Tama-himuro'	CKen
	- 'True Blue'	CKen EPfP LRHS MAsh
§	- 'Tsukumo'	CKen
	thyoides 'Andelyensis'	CMac CSBt NBwr
	- 'Blue Rock'	SLim
	- 'Conica'	MAsh
	- 'Ericoides'	LBee SPlb
	- 'Little Jamie'	CKen
	- 'Red Star'	see *C. thyoides* 'Rubicon'
§	- 'Rubicon'	CBod CEme CMac CSBt EPfP LBee MAsh SCoo SPoG SSha
	- 'Top Point'	LBee MAsh SCoo SLim SPoG

Chamaecytisus see *Cytisus*

Chamaedaphne (*Ericaceae*)

calyculata	CBcs

Chamaedorea (*Arecaceae*)

elegans 🏆H1a	LCro LPal LWaG NHrt
erumpens	see *C. seifrizii*
metallica misapplied	see *C. microspadix*
§ ***microspadix*** 🏆H1a	CPHo EAri LPal NPlm
radicalis	CBrP CPHo NPlm SArc
§ ***seifrizii***	EAri LPal NPlm

Chamaelobivia see *Echinopsis*

Chamaemelum (*Asteraceae*)

§ ***nobile***	CBod CCBP CHby CLau CTri EBou ENfk EPfP GPoy LCro LOPS LRHS MBow MHer MHoo MNHC MPri NGdn SPlb SRms SVic WSpi WTre
- dwarf	SMor SVic
- - double-flowered (d)	LEdu
- 'Flore Pleno' (d)	CElw CLau CTri ECha ENfk EPfP GElm MHer MHoo MNHC MRav NBro NGdn NGrd SGro SRms WFar WJek WTre
- 'Treneague'	CBod EBou ECha EHyd ELan ENfk EPfP EWhm GAbr GPoy GQue LRHS MBow MCot MHer MHoo MNHC NRHS SMad SMor SPer SPlb SRms WFar WJek WTre

Chamaenerion (*Onagraceae*)

§ ***angustifolium***	WSFF
§ - 'Album'	Widely available
- 'Isobel'	CTtf MRav WCot
- 'Stahl Rose'	EBee EWes LBar LEdu LRHS MBel MBriF NSti SGbt SMad SMrm SPhx WCot WHrl
§ ***dodonaei***	EWes LBar MHer SBut SPhx WCot

Chamaepericlymenum see *Cornus*

Chamaerops (*Arecaceae*)

excelsa misapplied	see *Trachycarpus fortunei*
excelsa Thunb.	see *Rhapis excelsa*
humilis 🏆H4	CAbb CAco CBcs CBod CBrP CDoC ELan EPfP ETod LPal LPar MDon MGos MPri NHrt SArc SChr SEND SGsty SIvy SPlb SPoG SWeb WLov
§ - var. ***argentea***	CBrP CDTJ CPHo EOli LPal LPar MGos NPlm SChr SPlb SWeb WCot WPGP
- var. ***cerifera***	see *C. humilis* var. *argentea*
- var. ***humilis***	EOli ERom NPlm
- 'Vulcano'	CDTJ LPal LPar NPlm SArc SChr SGsty WLea

Chamaespartium see *Genista*

Chamaesphacos (*Lamiaceae*)

ilicifolius misapplied	see *Siphocranion macranthum*

Chambeyronia (*Arecaceae*)

macrocarpa	NPlm

Chamelaucium (*Myrtaceae*)

uncinatum	CCCN
- 'Snowflake'	CCCN

Chamerion see *Chamaenerion*

chard see AGM Vegetables Section

Charybdis (*Asparagaceae*)

§ ***maritima***	CBod GKev LAma MHol NRog WCot WHlf

Chasmanthe (*Iridaceae*)

aethiopica	CPbh EPri SBrt SChr
bicolor	CTca EAri EPri EWld
floribunda	CCht EPri GKev SDeJ XSte
- var. ***duckittii***	GKev LAma SDeJ SPeP
- 'Saturnus'	EAri EGrI GKev LAma SDir SPeP

Chasmanthium (*Poaceae*)

§ ***latifolium***	Widely available
- 'Little Tickler'	EMor SBls
- 'River Mist' (v)	ELan EMor SPoG XLum
- 'Variegatum' (v)	EMor

Chasmatophyllum (*Aizoaceae*)

sp.	EDAr

Cheilanthes (*Pteridaceae*)

distans	WCot
eckloniana	WCot
farinosa	LEdu
grisea	WCot
lanosa	CBdn CBod CCCN CCht CDoC CMiW CSpe CTsd EBee EHyd EWes LBuc LRHS NRHS SPlb SPoG SRot XLum XSte
lindheimeri	WCot
myriophylla	WCot
tomentosa	CAby CBct CBdn CBod CCCN CRos CTsd EHyd LEdu LPal LRHS MAsh NRHS SMrm WHlf
wootonii	WCot

Cheiranthus see *Erysimum*

Cheiridopsis (*Aizoaceae*)

pillansii new	EAri

Cheirolophus (*Asteraceae*)

benoistii misapplied	see *Centaurea atropurpurea*
benoistii (Humb.) Holub	MRav
sempervirens B&SWJ 15321	WCru

Chelidonium (*Papaveraceae*)

hylomeconoides	GEdr
japonicum	see *Hylomecon japonica*
majus	GPoy NBir NMir WHer WSFF
- 'Flore Pleno' (d)	GJos NBid NBir NBro
- var. ***grandiflorum*** W&O 7061	GGro
- var. ***laciniatum***	LShi WCot

Chelone (*Plantaginaceae*)

sp.	MAsh
barbata	see *Penstemon barbatus*
§ ***glabra***	CBod CMac EBee ECha ELan EMor GMaP LRHS MHol MMuc MPie NBid NBro NGdn NHol NLar SBls SPeP SPlb SRms WFar WNPC WPnP WSHC WWtn
lyonii	EBee NLar WShi
- 'Hot Lips'	WPnP
- 'Pink Temptation'	EBee GEdr SBls
- TINY TORTUGA ('Armitpp02')	SPad
obliqua	Widely available
- var. ***alba***	see *C. glabra*
- 'Pink Sensation'	WFar
- PINK TURTLE ('Arturtle'PBR)	MBros MHol

Chelonopsis (*Lamiaceae*)

moschata	EBee EGrI EWld LEdu SPlb

- white-flowered EWld GGro WFar
yagiharana WFar WTre

Chengiopanax (*Araliaceae*)

sciadophylloides WCru

Chenopodium (*Amaranthaceae*)

ambrosioides SEdi SVic
bonus-henricus CAgr CHab CHby ENfk EWhm GPoy GQue MCoo MHer MNHC SRms SVic WHer WJek WKor
capitatum CSpe MHoo SVic
giganteum CBod CLau MNHC SRms WJek

cherimoya see *Annona cherimola*

cherry, Duke see *Prunus × gondouinii*

cherry, sour or morello see *Prunus cerasus*; see also AGM Fruit Section

cherry, sweet see *Prunus avium*; see also AGM Fruit Section

chervil see *Anthriscus cerefolium*

chestnut, sweet see *Castanea sativa*

Chiastophyllum see *Umbilicus*

simplicifolium see *Umbilicus oppositifolius*

chicory see *Cichorium intybus*; also AGM Vegetables Section

Chiliotrichum (*Asteraceae*)

diffusum CCCN GAbr GArf MMuc
- 'Siska' GBin

chilli pepper see *Capsicum*; also AGM Vegetables Section

Chimonanthus ✿ (*Calycanthaceae*)

fragrans see *C. praecox*
nitens CMCN NLar
§ ***praecox*** Widely available
- 'Brockhill Goldleaf' NLar
- 'Cobhay Sunshine' **new** CJun
- 'Diane' EPfP MAsh
- 'Grandiflorus' ♀H5 CJun CKel CRos CWnw EHed EHyd ELan EPfP LRHS MAsh MPkF SPoG WCot
- 'Luteus' ♀H5 CJun CRos EHyd ELan EPfP LEdu LRHS MAsh MGos NLar SPoG WCot
- 'Moonlight' EPfP MAsh
- 'Red Heart' NLar
- 'Winter Sunshine' **new** EPfP
yunnanensis W.W.Sm. NLar

Chimonobambusa (*Poaceae*)

KR 7592 MWht
§ ***marmorea*** CDTJ LPar MMuc
- 'Variegata' (v) CDTJ ESwi
§ ***quadrangularis*** CBcs CDTJ EPfP ESwi MWht
- 'Suow' (v) CDTJ
tumidissinoda CBcs CDTJ ESwi MWht WCot WFar

Chinese cabbage see AGM Vegetables Section

Chinese chives see *Allium tuberosum*

Chiogenes see *Gaultheria*

Chionanthus (*Oleaceae*)

retusus CBcs CCCN CEme EHed EHyd EPfP EWTr LAlb LMaj NLar SBrt WJur
virginicus CBcs CCCN CMCN EHyd ELan EPfP EWTr LPar MBlu MGil MMuc MRav NLar SPer SPlb WHtc WSpi XVPe

Chionochloa (*Poaceae*)

conspicua CAby CElw EBee EPfP GAbr GBee GKev NBid NBir NFav WPGP
- subsp. ***conspicua*** WCot
- 'Rubra' see *C. rubra*
flavescens EBee EPfP MAvo WPGP
flavicans CAby CSpe EBee EPfP
§ ***rubra*** ♀H7 CElw CSpe EBee ELan EPfP EWes GBin GQue MRav NWsh SMHy WCot WHoo WPGP
- PAB 67 LEdu
- subsp. ***cuprea*** SBls SMHy

Chionodoxa see *Scilla*

gigantea see *Scilla luciliae* Gigantea Group

Chionographis (*Melanthiaceae*)

japonica GEdr

Chionohebe (*Plantaginaceae*)

§ ***densifolia*** GArf
pulvinaris WAbe
'Vera Cox' WAbe

Chionophila (*Plantaginaceae*)

jamesii GEdr

× *Chionoscilla* see *Scilla*

Chiranthodendron (*Malvaceae*)

pentadactylon SPlb

Chirita see *Primulina*

sinensis see *Primulina dryas*
speciosa see *Henckelia speciosa*
tamiana see *Deinostigma tamiana*

Chironia (*Gentianaceae*)

baccifera SPlb

× *Chitalpa* (*Bignoniaceae*)

tashkentensis CBcs CEnd EPfP ESwi SBrt
- 'Morning Cloud' MBlu
- 'Pink Dawn' CBcs ESwi IPap MBlu SMad
- SUMMER BELLS ('Minsum') CCCN CDoC EBee EHed ELan EWTr LAlb LPar MHtn SIvy WCot WLov WMal

chives see *Allium schoenoprasum*

Chlidanthus (*Amaryllidaceae*)

fragrans CBor CCCN GKev SDeJ

Chloranthus (*Chloranthaceae*)

fortunei CMiW ESwi WCot
glaber see *Sarcandra glabra*
henryi GEdr SIvy WCot
japonicus ESwi GEdr GGro WCru
oldhamii EWld WPGP
- B&SWJ 2019 ESwi GEdr LEdu WCru
serratus GEdr GGro WCru
sessilifolius 'Domino' ESwi LEdu WCot

Chloris (*Poaceae*)

distichophylla see *Eustachys distichophylla*

Chlorogalum (*Asparagaceae*)

pomeridianum 'Berkeley Hills'	SBrt
- tall, from Siskiyou Mountains, Oregon	SBrt

Chlorophytum (*Asparagaceae*)

chinense	SBrt
comosum	CWal EShb LWaG SEND SVic
- 'Aureomarginata' (v)	SEND
- 'Bonnie'[PBR] (v)	CDoC EShb NHrt
- 'Lemon' **new**	LCro
- 'Ocean'[PBR] **new**	LCro NHrt
- 'Variegatum' (v) 🏆H2	EShb LCro LOPS NGBl NHrt SEND SPre WSFF
- 'Vittatum' (v) 🏆H2	CDoC EShb NGBl NHrt
graminifolium	EBee
krookianum	CPbh WCot
macrophyllum	EShb
nepalense	WPGP
- B&SWJ 2528	WCru
- PAB 13.034	LEdu
orchidastrum	EShb NHrt
- 'Green Orange'	NHrt
saundersiae	CPbh EPPr
- 'Starlight'[PBR] (v)	LCro LOPS SMad

Choisya (*Rutaceae*)

× ***dewitteana*** APPLE BLOSSOM ('Pmoore09'[PBR])	CBcs CEnd CSBt EGrI EMil LCro LOPS LRHS MAsh MDon NCth SPoG WHtc XSte
- 'Aztec Gold'[PBR]	CBcs CDoC CKel CRos CWnw EBee EFPl EGrI EHyd EPfP LCro LPar LRHS MAsh MGos NLar NRHS SCob SCoo SRms XSte
- 'Aztec Pearl' 🏆H4	Widely available
- GOLDEN GIFT ('Lismarty'[PBR])	MAsh
- GOLDFINGERS ('Limo'[PBR])	Widely available
- SNOW FLURRIES ('Lisflurry'[PBR])	CRos EHyd ELan EPfP ILea LRHS MAsh MRav NRHS SPoG SRHi XSte
- WHITE DAZZLER ('Londaz'[PBR]) 🏆H4	Widely available
dumosa var. ***arizonica*** 'Whetstone'	WPGP
GREENFINGERS ('Lissfing') **new**	ELan MAsh NLar
ROYAL LACE ('Pmoore06'[PBR])	LBuc LRHS MPri SGBe
ternata 🏆H4	Widely available
- MOONSHINE ('Walcho'[PBR])	CBcs NLar
- MOONSLEEPER	see *C. ternata* SUNDANCE
- SCENTED GEM ('Lissbrid') **new**	CBcs
§ - SUNDANCE ('Lich') 🏆H4	Widely available

Chondrosum (*Poaceae*)

gracile	see *Bouteloua gracilis*

Chordospartium see *Carmichaelia*

Chorisia (*Malvaceae*)

speciosa	CCCN EAri SPlb

Chorizema (*Fabaceae*)

cordatum 🏆H2	SVen
dicksonii	SPlb
ilicifolium	LRHS

Chromolaena (*Asteraceae*)

arnottiana RCB RA 2	EBee

Chronanthus see *Cytisus*

Chrysalidocarpus see *Dypsis*

Chrysanthemopsis see *Rhodanthemum*

Chrysanthemum ✿ (*Asteraceae*)

E.H.Wilson s.n.	ECre EPPr EWes EWoo LShi MHCG MNrw NWad WCot WHoo WMal
'Action Yellow' (22) 🏆H3	WFar
'Agnes Ann' (21d)	MNrw NWad
'Ahlemer Rote' (21)	LDai MHCG MNrw NWad SAko
'Alan Brown' (25a)	MCms
'Alan Foxall Yellow' (3b)	MCms
'Alex Young' (25b)	MCms
'Alfredo Mauve' (12)	MCms
'Alfredo Orange' (12)	MCms
'Alice Jones' (24b)	MCms
'Aline' (21)	MHCG
'Alison' (29c)	ECtt EWoo MNrw WFar
'Alison's Dad'	MNrw NWad
'Allouise' (25b) 🏆H3	NHal
'Allouise Orange' (25b)	MCms NHal
'Allouise Pink' (25b)	MCms
'Allyson Peace' (14a)	MCms NHal
'Amber Matlock' (24b)	MCms
'Amelia Rose' (7a) **new**	MCms
'American Beauty Lemon' (5b)	MCms
'American Beauty Snowball' (5b)	MCms
'American Beauty White' (5b)	MCms
'Anastasia' ambig.	SAko WBor
'Anastasia' (21c)	CRos EBlo EHyd ELon EWoo LDai LRHS MCms MNrw MRav NRHS SRms
'Anderton' (6b)	MCms
'Angela Blundell' (19b)	ECtt MACG MHCG MNrw WCot WFar
'Angelic' (21b) 🏆H4	EWoo
'Ann Dickson' (25b)	MCms
'Anne Jones' (24a)	NHal
'Anne Ratsey' (21)	EWoo MNrw NWsh WBrk WFar
'Anne, Lady Brocket' (21d)	ECtt MNrw
'Anthony Peace' (25b)	MCms
'Antigua'[PBR]	MCms
'Apollo' H. Shoesmith	MNrw
'Apollo' (21)	ECtt LDai MCms MHCG WFar
'Apricot'	see *C.* 'Cottage Apricot'
'Apricot Chessington' (25a)	MCms
'Apricot Courtier' (24a)	MCms NHal
'Apricot Enbee Wedding'	see *C.* 'Bronze Enbee Wedding'
'Apricot Mundial' (6b)	MCms
'Arctic Beauty' (4b)	MCms
arcticum L.	see *Arctanthemum arcticum*
argenteum	see *Tanacetum argenteum*
'Arthur Ellis' (15b)	MCms
'Astro' (25b)	MCms NHal
'Aunt Millicent' (21d) 🏆H4	ECre EPPr EWoo MHCG NHal WCot
'Balcombe Perfection' (5a)	MCms NHal
balsamita	see *Tanacetum balsamita*
BARBARA ('Yobarbara') (22) 🏆H3	NHal
'Barbara Dakin' (25b)	MCms NHal
'Beacon' (5a) 🏆H2	MCms NHal
'Beechcroft' (29Rub)	MHCG MNrw WFar
'Belle' (21d)	MHCG MNrw NWad WMal
'Beppie Bronze' (29e)	MCms
'Beppie Purple' (29e)	MCms

'Beppie Red' (29e)	MCms
'Beppie Rose' (29e)	MCms
'Beppie Yellow' (29e)	MCms
'Betty Wiggins' (25b)	MCms
'Bienchen'	SAko WFar
'Bill Holden' (14a)	MCms NHal
'Bill Wade' (25a)	MCms NHal
'Billy Bell' (15a)	MCms NHal
'Blanche Poitevene' (12c)	EMal MCms
'Bob Green' (13b)	MCms
'Boulou Pink' (12)	MCms
'Boulou White' (12)	MCms
'Boulou Yellow' (12)	MCms
BRAVO ('Yobra') (22c)	NHal
* 'Breitner's Supreme'	ECtt MHCG MNrw WFar
'Brennpunkt'	EPPr MNrw NWad
'Bretforton Road'	ECtt EPPr MCms MHCG MNrw WBrk WCot WFar WHoo WMal WOld
'Brightness' (21)	MNrw
'Bronze Cassandra' (5b) ♀^{H2}	MCms NHal
'Bronze Dee Gem' (29c)	MCms NHal
§ 'Bronze Elegance' (21b) ♀^{H4}	CDor CRos CTri EBlo ECtt EHyd ELan EPPr EShb LDai LRHS MNrw NBir NGdn NRHS NWsh SHar SRms
§ 'Bronze Enbee Wedding' (29d) ♀^{H3}	MCms NHal
'Bronze Fleece' (12b) **new**	MCms
'Bronze Matlock' (24b)	MCms NHal
'Bronze Max Riley' (23b) ♀^{H3}	MCms NHal
'Bronze Mayford Perfection' (5a) ♀^{H2}	MCms
'Bronze Mei-kyō'	see *C.* 'Bronze Elegance'
'Bronze Talbot Parade' (29c) ♀^{H3}	MCms
'Bronze William Florentine' (15a)	MCms
'Brooke Farm Red'	NWsh
'Brown Eyes' (21b) ♀^{H4}	MNrw
'Bryony Wade' (13b)	MCms NHal
'Bryony Wade White' (13b)	MCms
'Buff William Florentine' (15a)	MCms
burnt orange-flowered	CDor CFis EWoo MNrw WCot WFar WMal
'Burntwood Belle' (3b)	MCms
'Buxton Ruby'	EWoo LShi MNrw NWad
'Candy John Wingfield' (14b)	MCms
'Capel Manor'	EBee LShi MHCG MNrw WCot
'Capella' (10a)	MCms
'Carlene Welby' (25b)	MCms
'Carmine Blush' (21d) ♀^{H4}	CDor ELan LShi MHCG MNrw WBrk WCot WFar
'Casablanca' (25a)	MCms NHal
'Cassandra' (5b) ♀^{H2}	MCms NHal
'Cawthorne' (29d)	WFar
'Ceres' (6b) **new**	MCms
'Cerisa' (29d)	MCms NHal
'Charles Tandy' (5a)	MCms
'Charles Tandy Primrose' (15a)	MCms
'Charles Tandy Yellow' (15b)	MCms
'Charlie' (24b)	MCms
'Chatsworth' (29c)	NHal
'Chelsea Physic Garden'	EBee ELon EPPr EPfP EWoo GAbr LShi MACG MHCG MNrw MPie SPhx WCot WFar WMal
'Cherry Chessington' (25a)	MCms
'Cherry Tracey Waller' (24b)	MCms
CHESAPEAKE ('Yochesapeake'^{PBR}) (10a)	MCms NHal
'Chesapeake Primrose' (10a)	MCms
'Chessington' (25a)	MCms
'Chessington Oyster' (25a)	MCms
'Chestnut Talbot Maid' (29c)	MCms
'Chestnut Talbot Parade' (29c) ♀^{H3}	MCms WFar
'Chloe Ball' (13b)	MCms
'Christmas'	MNrw NWad WFar
'Christopher Lawson' (24b)	MCms NHal
cinerariifolium	see *Tanacetum cinerariifolium*
'Citronella'	MNrw
'Clapham Delight' (23a)	MCms NHal
'Clara Curtis' (21d)	Widely available
'Clare Louise' (24b)	MCms
'Clarksdale' (15b)	MCms NHal
coccineum	see *Tanacetum coccineum*
'Colsterworth'	MHCG MNrw NWad WFar
'Connie Mayhew' (5a) **new**	MCms
'Coral Reef' (10b)	MCms NHal
'Corinna' (21d)	CDoC ELan GBin MNrw
'Cornetto' (25b)	MCms NHal
'Corsair' (9d)	MCms
corymbosum	see *Tanacetum corymbosum*
§ 'Cottage Apricot' (21)	CDor CRos EBee ECtt EHyd ELan EPfP LDai LRHS MBNS MRav NRHS SMHy SRms WFar
'Cottage Bronze'	MNrw NWad
'Cottage Lemon'	EShb MHCG MNrw NWad WFar WHoo
'Cottage Pink'	see *C.* 'Emperor of China'
'Courtier' (24a)	MCms NHal
'Cousin Joan' (21d) ♀^{H4}	CDor ECtt ELan ELon LDai MCms MHCG MNrw WBor WCot WFar WMal
'Cream Dorridge Crystal' (24a)	MCms
'Cream John Hughes' (3b)	MCms
'Cream Talbot Maid' (29c)	MCms
'Cream Talbot Parade' (29c) ♀^{H3}	MCms
'Cream West Bromwich' (14a)	MCms
'Cricket' (25b)	MCms
'Crimson Purple Glow' (5a)	MCms
DANA ('Yodana') (25b)	NHal
DANCE ('Fidance'^{PBR}) (9f)	MCms
'Dance Red' (9f)	MCms
DANCE SALMON ('Fidancesal') (9f)	MCms
'Dance Sunny' (9f)	MCms
'Dance White' (9f)	MCms
'Daniel Cooper' (21d) ♀^{H4}	ECtt ELan MNrw SGro WFar
'Daphne Davis' (29d)	NHal
'Darren Pugh' (3b)	MCms NHal
'Darren Pugh Primrose' (3b)	MCms
'David Shoesmith' (25a)	MCms
'Dawn Charlton' (14a)	MCms
'Dee Gem' (29c) ♀^{H3}	MCms NHal WFar
'Denise Oatridge' (5a)	MCms
'Dernier Soleil'	MNrw XLum
'Disco Club'	MCms
'Dixter Orange'	EBee EPPr EWes LShi MHCG MNrw MSpe SDys SMad SPhx WMal
§ 'Doctor Tom Parr' (21c)	EWoo MCms MNrw
'Domingo' (14b)	MCms
'Doreen Hall' (15a)	NHal
'Doreen Statham' (14b)	MCms NHal
'Doris Ozols' (25a)	MCms

'Dorothy Stone' (25b)	NHal
'Dorridge Crystal' (24a)	MCms NHal
'Dorridge King' (4b)	MCms
'Downpour' (10a)	MCms
'Duchess of Edinburgh' (21d)	CBod CDor EBee ECtt EHyd ELan ELon EPfP EWoo LRHS LShi MHer MNrw NLar NRHS WCAu WFar WMal XLum
'Dulwich Pink' (21d) ♀H4	MHCG MNrw NWad WCot WFar
'Early Yellow'	EBee ELan ELon EWoo MNrw WCot WFar
'Edelweiss' (21)	EShb MNrw NWad
'Edina' (29d)	NHal
'Edmund Brown'	EPPr GAbr MNrw WCot WFar WMal
'Egret' (23b)	MCms NHal
'Elaine's Hardy White'	MHCG MNrw WCot WFar WHoo WMal
'Eliška'	MNrw
'Elizabeth Lawson' (5b)	NHal
'Elspeth' (6b) **new**	LShi
§ 'Emperor of China' (21)	CDor ECha ECtt EWoo LShi MHer MNrw MRav NHal SMHy SMad SRms WBor WFar XLum
'Enbee Wedding' (29d) ♀H3	MCms NHal
'Energy'[PBR] (9)	MCms
'Erntekranz'	MNrw WMal
'Esther' (21d)	EShb EWTr LEdu MHCG MHer MNrw NCth SMad WFar
'Etta Dakin' (15b)	MCms NHal
'Eugen's Messingknopf' **new**	SAko
'Eugen's Neue Halbhohe' **new**	SAko
'Fairweather' (3b)	MCms
'Fairweather Cream' (3b)	MCms
'Fairweather Peach' (3b)	MCms
'Fanfare Claret'	ELan
'Fanfare Flame'	ELan
'Feeling Green Dark'[PBR]	MCms
'Feeling Sunny'[PBR]	MCms
'Fellbacher Wein' (21)	XLum
'Finn Lyttle' (29d)	NHal
'Fleur de Lis' (10a)	MCms
foeniculaceum (Willd.) Desf.	see *Argyranthemum foeniculaceum* (Willd.) Webb & Sch.Bip.
'Folk Song' (4b)	MNrw
'Fred's Yellow'	NWad
'French Rose'	WFar
'Frizbee' (29d)	NHal
'Froggy'[PBR] (9)	MCms
frutescens	see *Argyranthemum frutescens*
'Gambit' (24a)	MCms
'Geoff Amos' (3b)	MCms
'Geoff Brady' (5a)	MCms NHal
'George Griffiths' (24b)	MCms NHal
'George Simmonds'	WHoo
'Gerlinde' **new**	SAko
'Gillette' (23b)	MCms
'Ginger Nut' (25b)	MCms
'Ginger Nut Yellow' (25b)	MCms
I 'Gladys' (12a)	NHal
'Gladys Emerson' (3b)	MCms NHal
'Gold Enbee Wedding' (29d) ♀H3	MCms
'Gold Hoagy' (29d)	NHal
'Gold Mundial' (6b) ♀H2	MCms
'Golden Cassandra' (5b) ♀H2	MCms NHal
'Golden Chalice' (12a)	NHal
'Golden Courtier' (24a)	MCms NHal
'Golden Masons' (7b)	MCms
'Golden Mayford Perfection' (5a) ♀H2	MCms
'Golden Rain' (10a) ♀H2	MCms NHal

'Golden Shoesmith Salmon' (4a)	MCms
'Golden Splendour' (10a)	MCms NHal
'Golden William Florentine' (15a)	MCms
'Goldengreenheart' (21d) ♀H4	EBee ECtt ELon EShb MHCG MNrw SPhx SRms WFar WHoo
'Goldmarianne' (21)	GBin WFar XLum
'Goodlife Sombrero' (29a) ♀H3	MCms
'Gordon Dowson' (25b) **new**	MCms
'Goshu Penta' (10a)	MCms
'Grandchild' (21c) ♀H4	MNrw NHal WMal
'Green Goddess' (2)	MCms
'Hana-no-yume' (12b) **new**	MCms
'Hanenburg' (25b)	MCms NHal
haradjanii	see *Tanacetum haradjanii*
'Hardwick Lemon' (29c)	MHCG
'Harold Lawson' (5a)	NHal
* 'Harry Lawson'	MCms
'Harry Woolman' (13b)	MCms
'Hatsuhikari' (12b) **new**	MCms
'Heather James' (3b)	MCms NHal
'Hebe' (21d)	MNrw
'Heda'	MNrw
'Heide' (29c) ♀H3	NHal
'Helen Harrison'	MAvo MHCG
'Helen Louise' (25b)	MCms NHal
'Helen Ward'	MNrw
'Herbie McCauley' (24b)	NHal
'Herbstbrokat'	GBin WFar XLum
'Herbstfeuer' (21)	MNrw NWad
'Hillfield Apricot'	EShb
'Hillside Apricot'	ECtt
'Hoagy' (29d)	MCms NHal
HOLLY ('Yoholly') (22b)	NHal
'Honey Enbee Wedding' (29d)	MCms NHal
'Horningsea Pink' (19d)	WBor
hosmariense	see *Rhodanthemum hosmariense*
indicum	SVic
'Innocence' (21d) ♀H4	CDor CFis ECtt ELan ELon GBee LShi MBNS MCms MNrw MRav NCth NGdn SHar WFar WHoo
'Jan Jones' (29d) **new**	NHal
'Janet South'	MNrw
'Jante Wells' (21b) ♀H4	EWoo MCms MNrw WBor
'Jasoda Dark Orange'[PBR]	LCro LOPS
'Jasoda Mauve'[PBR]	LCro LOPS
'Jasoda Pink'[PBR]	LCro LOPS
'Jasoda White'[PBR]	LCro LOPS
'Jasoda Yellow'[PBR]	LCro LOPS
'Jennie Atkinson' (7b) **new**	MCms
'Jenny Wren' (12a)	NHal
'Jessie Cooper' misapplied	see *C.* 'Mrs Jessie Cooper' (21d)
'Jill Anderton' (6b) **new**	MCms
'Jimmy Tranter' (14b)	NHal
'John Hughes' (3b)	MCms NHal
'John Riley' (14a)	NHal
'John Wingfield' (14b)	MCms NHal
'John Wingfield Honey' (14b)	MCms
'John Wingfield Pearl' (14b)	MCms
'Jolie Rose'	WCot WFar WOld
'Joyce Fountain' (24a)	MCms
'Joyce Frieda' (13b)	MCms NHal
'Judy Dakin' (25b)	NHal
JULIA ('Yojulia')	NLar
'Julia' (28)	MNrw
'Julia Arnold'	WHoo
'Julia Peterson'	MHCG MHer MNrw SRms WCot WFar

	'Julie Lagravère' (28)	ECtt MHCG MNrw WFar
	'June Peace' (25b) **new**	MCms
	'Karen Taylor' (29c) ♀H3	NHal
	'Kay Woolman' (13b)	MCms NHal
	'Kay Woolman Cream' (13b)	MCms
	'Kay Woolman Primrose' (13b)	MCms
	'Kay Woolman Yellow' (13b)	MCms
	'Killerton Tangerine'	MHCG MNrw NWad WFar WMal
	'Kimberley Marie' (15b)	MCms NHal
	'Kiyomi-no-meisui'	MCms NHal
	'Kleiner Bernstein'	MNrw
	'Kurume' (12b)	MCms
	'La Damoiselle'	WCot
§	'Lady in Pink' (21)	LDai MNrw MPie NWad SDix
	'Lakelanders' (3b)	MCms NHal
	'Laura Jayne' (25a)	MCms
	'Lava' (10a)	MCms
	'Leo' (21b) ♀H4	EWoo
	leucanthemum	see *Leucanthemum vulgare*
	'Lexy'PBR (9)	MCms
	'Lexy Red'PBR (9)	MCms
	'Lighthouse'	NHal
	'Lilac Chessington' (25a)	MCms
	'Lilly Emily' (25b)	NHal
	'Lily Anderton' (6b) **new**	MCms
	LINDA ('Lindayo') (22c) ♀H3	NHal
	'Liverpool Festival' (23b)	MCms
	'Lollipop'PBR (9e)	MCms
	LOLLIPOP PURPLE ('Filollipop Purple'PBR) (9e)	MCms
	'Long Island Beauty' (6b)	MCms
	'Lorna Wood' (13b)	MCms NHal
	'Lucy' (29a)	MCms NHal
	'Lucy Simpson' (21d)	EWoo
	LYNN ('Yolynn') (22c) ♀H3	NHal
	'Lynn Johnson' (15a)	MCms
	macrophyllum	see *Tanacetum macrophyllum* (Waldst. & Kit.) Sch.Bip.
	'Malcolm Perkins' (25a)	NHal
	'Mancetta Symbol' (5a)	MCms
	'Mandarin' (5b)	SAko
I	'Mandarin'	MNrw
	'Manito'	MNrw
	maresii	see *Rhodanthemum hosmariense*
	'Margery Fish'	EShb MNrw WFar
	'Marion' (25a)	LDai MNrw WCot WFar WHoo
	'Marion Couchman' (25b)	NHal
	'Martin Bell' (29d)	WFar
	MARTINA ('Dlfmart12'PBR)	MCms
	'Mary' (21f)	LDai MHCG NHal
	'Mary Aldred' (29d)	MCms
	'Mary Stoker' (21d)	CDor CTri EBee ECtt EHyd ELan EPPr EShb EWoo LRHS LShi MAvo MNrw MPie MRav NHal NLar NRHS NWsh WCAu
	'Mason's Bronze' (7b)	MCms
	'Matlock' (24b)	NHal
	'Mauve Gem' (21f) ♀H3	NHal
	'Mavis' (21)	MHCG MNrw
	'Mavis Smith'	EWoo LShi MNrw
	mawii	see *Rhodanthemum gayanum*
	'Max Riley' (23b) ♀H3	MCms NHal
	maximum misapplied	see *Leucanthemum × superbum*
	maximum Ramond	see *Leucanthemum maximum* (Ramond) DC.
	'Maxine Charlton' (24b)	NHal
	'Maxine Johnson' (25b)	MCms
	'May Shoesmith' (5a) ♀H2	MCms
	'Mayford Perfection' (5a) ♀H2	MCms

	'Megumi' (12b)	MCms
	'Mei-Kyō' (28b) ♀H4	CDor CTri EBee EBlo ECre ECtt EHyd ELan EPPr EPfP EShb EWoo LRHS LShi MCms MHCG MNrw MPie MSpe NRHS SMHy SRms WCAu WFar WHil XLum
	'Membury' (24b)	NHal
	'Mezzo Bronze Red' (Poppins Series) ♀H3	MCms
	'Mezzo Gold' (Poppins Series)	MCms
	'Mezzo Magenta' (Poppins Series) ♀H3	MCms
	'Mezzo Pink' (Poppins Series)	MCms
	'Migdale' (24b)	MCms NHal
	'Milkshake'	MNrw
	'Millennium' (25b) ♀H3	MCms NHal
	'Misty Cream' (25b)	MCms
	'Misty Golden' (25b)	MCms
	'Misty Lemon' (25b)	MCms
	'Moonlight' (29d/K)	MNrw MRav NWad
	'Morning Star' (12a)	NHal
	'Mount Fuji' (10b)	MCms
	'Mr Mappie' (21c)	MNrw WCot
§	'Mrs Jessie Cooper' (21d) ♀H4	EBee ECtt ELan ELon EShb EWTr EWoo GQue LDai MACG MCms MNrw NWad NWsh SDys SGro SMrm SRms WCot WFar WHoo
	'Mrs Jessie Cooper No 2'	EPPr MNrw
	'Mundial' (6)	MCms
	'Mundial Peach' (6b/9a)	MCms
	'Mundial Rose' (6b)	MCms
	'Mundial Ruby' (6b)	MCms
	'Music' (23b)	MCms NHal
	'Myss Debbie' (29e)	NHal
	'Myss Dorothy' (29c)	MCms NHal
	'Myss Eliza' (29c)	MCms
	'Myss Goldie' (29c)	MCms
	'Myss Rihanna' (29c)	MCms NHal
	'Myss Saffron' (29c) ♀H3	MCms NHal
	'Nancy Perry' (21d)	MRav XLum
	'Nantyderry Sunshine' (28b) ♀H4	CDor CRos EBee EBlo ECre EHyd ELon EPPr EWld EWoo GAbr LRHS LShi MHCG MNrw MPie NRHS NWsh SRms WCot WFar WOld
	'Natalie Sarah' (29d) ♀H3	NHal
	'Nell Gwynn' (21d)	MNrw NHal
	NICOLE ('Yonicole') (22c)	NHal
	nipponicum	see *Nipponanthemum nipponicum*
	'Norwell Gold' **new**	MNrw
	'Nutcracker' (23b)	MCms
	'Old Norwell'	WMal WOld
	'Orange Enbee Wedding' (29d)	NHal
	'Orchid Helen'	MNrw
	'Pacific Lady' (29d)	NHal
	pacificum	CBor WFar
	parthenium	see *Tanacetum parthenium*
	'Pat Bahn' (29c)	NHal
	'Patricia Millar' (14b)	MCms
	'Patricia Millar Cerise' (14b)	MCms
	'Patricia Millar Coral' (14b)	MCms
	'Patricia Millar Orange' (14b)	MCms
	'Patricia Millar Yellow' (14b)	MCms
	'Paul Boissier' (30)	CDor CFis ECtt EWoo LDai MCms MNrw SPhx WFar XLum
	'Pauline White' (15a)	MCms
	'Peach Courtier' (24a)	NHal
	'Peach Enbee Wedding' (29d) ♀H3	MCms NHal

'Peach John Wingfield' (14b)	MCms NHal
'Peach Patricia Millar' (14b)	MCms
'Peach Southway Sheeba' (29d)	NHal
'Pearl Celebration' (24a)	MCms
'Pearl Dorridge Crystal' (24a)	MCms
'Pearl Enbee Wedding' (29d)	MCms
'Peggy' (28a)	MCms MHCG
'Pennine Bullion'	NHal
'Pennine Gambol' (29a)	MCms
'Pennine Jude' (29a)	MCms
'Pennine Oriel' (29a) ♀H3	MCms NHal
'Pennine Point' (19c)	NHal
'Pennine Polo' (29d)	NHal
'Pennine Punch' (29a)	MCms
'Pennine Swan' (29c)	MCms
'Penny's Yellow'	MCms MNrw WBrk
'Percy Salter' (24b)	MCms NHal
'Perry's Peach' (21d) ♀H4	ELan ELon LDai MCms MHCG MNrw NHal NPer SPhx
'Peter Jolley' (25b)	MCms
'Peter Rowe' (23b)	MCms NHal
'Peterkin'	CMac EBee ECtt ELon EPPr XLum
'Picasso'	EShb LShi MHCG MNrw WCot WFar
'Pink John Wingfield' (14b)	NHal
'Pink Progression'	see *C.* 'Lady in Pink'
'Pocahontas' (10a)	MCms
'Poesie'	ECtt MHer MNrw NWsh SAko WCot WFar WMal
'Polar Gem' (3a)	MCms NHal
'Pomander' (25b)	MCms
'Pomegranate' **new**	MNrw
'Pot Black' (14b)	MCms
'Prelude Apricot' (Poppins Series)	MCms
'Prelude Autumn Bronze' (Poppins Series)	MCms
'Prelude Popcorn' (Poppins Series)	MCms
'Prelude Rose Pink' (Poppins Series)	MCms
'Prelude White' (Poppins Series)	MCms
'President Osaka'	MNrw NWad
'Primrose Allouise' (24b) ♀H3	MCms NHal
'Primrose Chessington' (25a)	MCms
'Primrose Courtier'	see *C.* 'Yellow Courtier'
'Primrose Cricket' (25b)	MCms
'Primrose Dorridge Crystal' (24a)	MCms
'Primrose Egret' (23b)	MCms
'Primrose Enbee Wedding' (29d) ♀H3	MCms NHal
'Primrose Fairweather' (3b)	MCms
'Primrose John Hughes' (3b)	MCms
'Primrose Mayford Perfection' (5a) ♀H2	MCms
'Primrose Pauline White' (15a)	MCms
'Primrose Pennine Oriel' (29a)	MCms
'Primrose West Bromwich' (14a)	MCms
'Princess' (21d)	MNrw
'Princess Anne' (4b)	MCms
'Promise' (25a)	MCms NHal
'Purleigh White' (28b)	ELon EPPr LDai LShi MNrw NWsh WFar
'Purple Dee Gem' (29c)	NHal
'Purple Glow' (5a)	MCms
'Raquel' (21)	MNrw
'Ray's Red'	EPPr MHCG MNrw
'Rebecca Read' (7b) **new**	MCms
'Red Balcombe Perfection' (5a)	MCms NHal
'Red Goodlife Sombrero' (29a)	MCms
'Red Mayford Perfection' (5a)	MCms
'Red Regal Mist' (25b)	MCms NHal
'Red Shirley Model' (3a)	MCms NHal
'Redbreast' (12a)	NHal
'Regal Mist' (25b)	NHal
'Regal Mist Purple' (25b)	MCms
'Regent' (5b)	MCms
'Rehauge' **new**	SAko
I 'Rhumba'	MNrw WCot
'Richard's Yellow' **new**	NWad
'Riley's Dynasty' (14a)	MCms
'Ringdove' (12a)	NHal
'Rita Fox' (15b)	MCms NHal
'Rita McMahon' (29d) ♀H3	NHal
ROBIN ('Yorobi') (22c)	NHal
'Roen Sarah' (29c)	NHal
'Romantica'	EWoo MNrw NWad WOld
'Rose Enbee Wedding' (29d)	MCms NHal
'Rose Madder'	EWoo GAbr MNrw WCot WFar
'Rose Mayford Perfection' (5a) ♀H2	MCms
'Rose Patricia Millar' (14b)	MCms
'Rose Talbot Parade' (29c)	MCms
'Rosedew' (25b)	MCms
'Rosetta'	MHCG MNrw
roseum	see *Tanacetum coccineum*
'Rosie Lyttle' (29c)	NHal
'Roter Spray'	MNrw NWad WHoo WMal
'Rotes Julchen' **new**	SAko
'Roy Bevan' (29d)	MCms
'Royal Command' (21a)	EPPr MHCG MNrw WCot WHoo
'Royal Sport'	MNrw
rubellum	see *C. zawadzkii*
'Ruby Enbee Wedding' (29d) ♀H3	MCms WFar
'Ruby Mound' (21c) ♀H3	CDor EWoo LShi MCms MHCG MNrw NHal SAko SDys SHar SPhx WBrk WCot WFar WMal WOld
'Ruby Raynor' (21c) ♀H4	MNrw NHal NWsh WFar
'Rumpelstilzchen' (21d)	CFis ECtt MHer MNrw WMal
'Rusty Margaret' (29c)	MNrw
'Salhouse Dream' (10a)	MCms
'Salhouse Joy' (10a)	MCms NHal
'Salmon Allouise' (25b)	MCms NHal
'Salmon Enbee Wedding' (29d) ♀H3	NHal
'Salmon Fairweather' (3b)	MCms
'Salmon John Wingfield' (24b)	MCms
'Salmon Patricia Millar' (14b)	MCms
'Salmon Pauline White' (15a)	MCms
'Salmon Talbot Maid' (29c)	MCms
'Salmon Talbot Parade' (29c) ♀H3	MCms WFar
'Salmon Tracey Waller' (24b)	MCms
'Salmon Venice' (24b)	MCms
'Sam Vinter' (5a)	NHal
'Samba'	WCot WFar
'Samson'	MCms

'Samson Orange'	MCms
'Samson Purple'	MCms
'Sarah Louise' (25b)	NHal
'Satomi Orange' (12b) **new**	MCms
'Savanna Charlton' (25a)	NHal
'Schaffhausen'	WFar
'Schweizerland'	WFar
'Sea Urchin' (21f) 𝕐^{H3}	NHal
'Seaton's Galaxy' (10a)	MCms
'Seizan' (12b) **new**	MCms
'Senkyo Karyu' (10a)	MCms
'Senkyo Kenshin' (10a)	MCms NHal
'Shamrock' (10b)	MCms
'Sheffield'	XLum
'Sheila Coles' (7b)	MCms
'Sheila Harris' (3b)	MCms
'Shining Light' (21f)	WCot WFar
'Shoesmith Salmon' (4a)	MCms
'Shoesmith Salmon Bright Bronze' (4a)	MCms
'Shoesmith Salmon Crimson' (4b)	MCms
'Shoesmith Salmon Purple' (4a)	MCms
'Skomer' (9f)	MCms
'Skomer Pink' (9f)	MCms
'Skomer Yellow' (9f)	MCms
'Soir d'Orient'	WFar
'Sonya' (21)	MNrw
'Sound' (9d)	MCms
'Southway Sheba' (29d) 𝕐^{H3}	MCms NHal
'Southway Sheba Apricot' (29d)	MCms
'Southway Sheba Bronze' (29d)	MCms
'Southway Sheba Chestnut' (29d)	MCms
'Southway Sheba Salmon' (29d)	MCms
'Southway Shimmer' (29d)	MCms NHal WFar
'Southway Shiraz' (29d)	MCms WFar
'Southway Sloe' (29d)	NHal
'Southway Spectacular' (29d)	MCms
'Southway Strontium' (29d)	MCms NHal
'Spartan Canary' (21d) 𝕐^{H4}	EWoo LShi
'Spartan Display'	ECre EWes MNrw
'Spartan Seagull' (21d)	MNrw
'Stallion' (9)	MCms
'Stallion Yellow'	MCms
'Starlet' (21f) 𝕐^{H4}	EWoo LShi MHCG NHal
'Steve Packham' (23b)	NHal
'Stockton' (3b)	MCms
'Stratford Pink' (21d)	MNrw NWad
'Suffolk Pink'	ECtt EShb EWoo MNrw NWsh
'Sunny John Wingfield' (14b)	MCms NHal
'Super-Bronze Shoesmith Salmon' (4a)	MCms
SWAN ('Fiswan'^{PBR}) (9)	MCms
'Swan Cream'	MCms
'Swan Sunny'	MCms
'Sweetheart Pink'	MHCG MNrw WMal
'Syllabub' (21f) 𝕐^{H3}	ECtt MHer MNrw
'Symphony' (10a)	MCms NHal
'Talbot Maid' (29c)	MCms
'Talbot Parade' (29c) 𝕐^{H3}	MCms
'Talbot Parade Pink' (29c)	MCms
'Tapestry Rose' (21d)	LDai MNrw NCth NWsh SRms WBrk WFar WHoo WOld
'Thomas Russell' (7b) **new**	MCms
'Thoroughbred' (24a)	NHal
'Tickle Pink' (29f/K)	MNrw NWad
'Tom Parr'	see *C.* 'Doctor Tom Parr'
'Tom Snowball' (3b)	MCms
'Tonto' (29d)	NHal
'Topsy' (21d) 𝕐^{H4}	EWoo MHCG
'Tracey Waller' (24b)	MCms
trilobatum	GKev
TRIUMPH ('Yotri') (22)	NHal
uliginosum	see *Leucanthemella serotina*
'Uri'	CFis EBee ELon MHCG MNrw SAko WFar
'Vagabond Prince'	ECtt ELon EWoo MHCG MNrw SRms WFar WHoo
'Venice' (24b)	MCms NHal
'Venice Peach' (24b)	MCms
'Venice Rose' (24b)	MCms
'Venus' (21)	WCot WMal
'Venus One'	ECtt LDai MNrw NHal
'Vysočina'	MNrw
'Wedding Day' (29k)	MNrw NWad
'Wedding Sunshine' (21)	LDai MNrw NWad WFar
welwitschii	see *Glebionis segetum*
'Wembley' (24b)	MCms
'Wendy Tench' (21d)	EBee MCms MNrw NWsh
'West Bromwich' (14b)	MCms
weyrichii	CBor CTri CTsd EBou EHyd EPfP EPot GGro GPSL LEdu LShi MHol MNrw NFav NHpl SGro SRms WFar WIce
'White Allouise' (25b) 𝕐^{H3}	MCms NHal
'White Beppie' (29e)	MCms WFar
'White Bouquet' (28)	WFar
'White Cassandra' (5b)	MCms NHal
'White Enbee Wedding' (29d)	MCms NHal
'White Fairweather' (3b)	MCms
'White Gem' (21f)	MHCG NHal
'White Gloss' (21e)	MNrw
'White Pearl Celebration' (24a)	MCms
'White Tower' (27)	MNrw MPie
'Wilder Charms'	MNrw NWad
'William Florentine' (15a)	MCms NHal
'Wills Wonderful' (21d) 𝕐^{H4}	MHCG MNrw WMal
'Wind Dancer' (10a)	MCms
'Winning's Red' (21)	ECtt MHCG NCth SMad WCot WFar
'Winter Queen' (5b)	MCms
'Winter Queen Yellow' (5b)	MCms
'Woolley Globe' (15b)	MCms
'Woolman's Glory' (7a)	MCms
'Woolman's Glory Red' (7a)	MCms
'Woolman's Star' (3a)	MCms NHal
'Woolman's Venture' (14b)	NHal
'Woolman's Venture Red' (14b)	MCms
'Xiang'	NWad
'Yellow Allouise' (25b)	MCms
'Yellow American Beauty' (5b) 𝕐^{H2}	MCms
'Yellow Billy Bell' (15a)	NHal
'Yellow Chessington' (25a)	MCms
'Yellow Clapham Delight' (23a)	MCms NHal
§ 'Yellow Courtier' (24a)	MCms NHal
'Yellow Egret' (23b)	MCms
'Yellow Enbee Wedding' (29d)	MCms NHal
'Yellow Goodlife Sombrero' (29a)	MCms
'Yellow Heide' (29c) 𝕐^{H3}	NHal
'Yellow Jewel' (Poppins Series) 𝕐^{H3}	MCms
'Yellow John Hughes' (3b) 𝕐^{H2}	MCms NHal

'Yellow John Wingfield' (14b)	MCms
'Yellow Mayford Perfection' (5a) 🏆H2	MCms
'Yellow Pennine Oriel' (29a) 🏆H4	MCms NHal
'Yellow Percy Salter' (24b)	MCms
'Yellow Spray' (12b)	SCob
'Yellow Talbot Parade' (29c)	MCms
'Yellow Woolman's Glory' (7a)	MCms
yezoense	CDor MNrw SRms
- B&SWJ 10872	WCru
- 'Roseum'	ECtt
aff. ***yezoense***	MHol
'Yvonne's Rot-Goldene'	SAko
§ ***zawadzkii***	CMac SRms WFar
'Zoe Russell' (7a) **new**	MCms

Chrysogonum (*Asteraceae*)

virginianum	EBee EWes SavN WFar
- var. ***australe***	SBrt
- - 'Andre Viette'	CBod ECha

Chrysopogon (*Poaceae*)

gryllus	EBee NDov WPGP

Chrysosplenium (*Saxifragaceae*)

alternifolium	EBee GEdr
davidianum	EBee GJos GKev NBid WCru WFar WSHC
- SBEC 233	CExl
aff. ***hebetatum*** B&SWJ 9835	NWad
lanuginosum var. ***formosanum***	GEdr
- - B&SWJ 6979	ESwi WCru
macrophyllum	CExl EBee ECha EGrl EPPr EPfP EWld GKev GMaP LEdu MAvo MNrw NBid SDix SHar WBor WCot WCru WFar WSHC
- green-flowered	GGro WFar
oppositifolium	CTtf ECha WSFF WShi

Chusquea (*Poaceae*)

breviglumis misapplied	see *C. gigantea*
culeou 🏆H4	CBcs EPfP LEdu LPal LPar MAvo MGos MWht SPlb SSta WCot WPGP
- 'Purple Splendour'	WPGP
§ ***gigantea*** 🏆H3	CDTJ EPfP MAvo
montana	CDTJ

Cicerbita (*Asteraceae*)

BO 16-085	GGro
§ ***alpina***	GAbr NBid SPlb
bourgaei	MHol MMuc
macrophylla (Willd.) Wallr.	MBow
- subsp. ***macrophylla***	CTtf
plumieri	GAbr WCot WSHC
- 'Blott' (v)	WCot

Cichorium (*Asteraceae*)

endivia 'Pancalieri' 🏆H3	CHby EKin MCtn
intybus	CBod CHby CLau CSpe CTtf ELan ENfk EWoo GPoy GQue LShi LSun MHer MHoo MNHC NCth NGBl NMir SBut SPer SPhx SPlb SPoG SRms WFar WHrl WSHC WWild
- f. ***album***	CTtf ECha ECtt EHyd EPPr LRHS LSto MBel MHoo NBPC NGBl NRHS SBut SPer
- 'Brussels Witloof'	SVic
- 'Halico a Costa Rossa' **new**	CBod
- 'Indigo'	LRHS
- 'Palla Rossa' 🏆H5	CHby MCtn SRms
- 'Pan di Zucchero' 🏆H5	CHby
- 'Red Rib'	SRms
- 'Roseum'	CTtf ECha ECtt EHyd ELan EPPr LEdu LRHS LSto MBel MHoo NBPC NRHS SBut SPer SPoG WGwG WHrl

Cimicifuga see *Actaea*

acerina	see *Actaea japonica*
americana	see *Actaea podocarpa*
cordifolia (DC.) Torrey & A.Gray	see *Actaea cordifolia*
cordifolia Pursh	see *Actaea podocarpa*
foetida	see *Actaea cimicifuga*
racemosa var. ***cordifolia***	see *Actaea cordifolia*
- 'Purpurea'	see *Actaea simplex* Atropurpurea Group
ramosa	see *Actaea simplex* 'Prichard's Giant'
rubifolia	see *Actaea cordifolia*
simplex var. ***matsumurae***	see *Actaea matsumurae*

Cineraria (*Asteraceae*)

× ***hybrida***	see *Pericallis × hybrida*
maritima	see *Jacobaea maritima*

Cinnamomum (*Lauraceae*)

camphora	CBcs CKel WJur WPGP
japonicum B&SWJ 14627	WCru

Circaea (*Onagraceae*)

lutetiana	WHer
- 'Caveat Emptor' (v)	NBid WCot

Cirsium (*Asteraceae*)

altissimum	SPhx
aomorense **new**	GGro
arvense	WSFF
canum	CSpe GGro GQue MHol
diacantha	see *Ptilostemon diacantha*
eriophoroides	GEdr
eriophorum	GGro LDai
helenioides	see *C. heterophyllum*
§ ***heterophyllum***	CDor GGro LDai MHol NAts NChi NLar SHar SPhx
- PAB 067	LEdu WMal
- 'Pink Blush'	CBcs CTtf EMor LBar LCro LOPS MHol NSti WHlf WNPC
japonicum	GGro
- 'Early Pink Beauty'	LDai
- 'Pink Beauty'	LRHS SBls
- 'Rose Beauty'	WSpi
'Mount Etna'	CBod CSpe EBee EHyd ELan EPfP GDam GGro GKin LBar LRHS MBNS MBriF MMuc MSpe NBPC NDov NFav NGdn NRHS SEND SGbt WCAu WWke
occidentale **new**	WHil
oleraceum	GGro LEdu NBid NLar SBrt WKor
rivulare 'Atropurpureum' 🏆H7	Widely available
- FROSTED MAGIC ('Lowcir'[PBR])	Widely available
- 'Trevor's Blue Wonder'	see *C. rivulare* 'Trevor's Felley Find'
§ - 'Trevor's Felley Find'[PBR]	Widely available
setidens **new**	GGro
tuberosum	ECha GGro LEdu LRHS SDix SPhx WCot
vulgare	WSFF

Cissus (*Vitaceae*)

amazonica **new**	EShb LCro
antarctica 🏆H1c	CCCN EShb SEND

	hamaderohensis new	EAri
	nodosa	EShb
	quadrangularis	EAri
	rhombifolia 🏆H1c	EOHP EShb
	- 'Ellen Danica' 🏆H1c	EShb
	rotundifolia	EShb
§	***striata***	CBcs CDoC CKel CMac CWCL EBee EDir EHyd EPfP EShb LCro LRHS MGil MRav NChi SBrt SEND SPtp SWvt
	trifoliata 'Guadalupe' new	WPGP

Cistus ✿ (*Cistaceae*)

	acutifolius misapplied	see *C.* × *pulverulentus*
	× ***aguilarii***	CTri MRav WMal WSHC
	- 'Maculatus' 🏆H4	CBcs CBod CDoC CGBo CKel CRos CSBt EGrI ELan EPfP LRHS LSRN MAsh NLar SEle SPer SPoG SWvt WKif WMal WPGP WSpi
	albidus	CWal XSen
	algarvensis	see *Halimium ocymoides*
	'Ann Baker'	WMal
	'Anne Palmer'	see *C.* × *fernandesiae* 'Anne Palmer'
	× ***argenteus*** 'Blushing Peggy Sammons'	EHyd ELan LRHS NLar NRHS SWvt
	- 'Paper Moon'	CGBo NLar SEdd
§	- 'Peggy Sammons'	CBrac CGBo ECha EFPl EHeP ELan EPfP LRHS MAsh MGos NLar SAko SCob SGbt SPer SWvt WSHC XSen
	- 'Silver Ghost'	CDoC CKel LRHS SWvt
	- 'Silver Pink' misapplied	see *C.* × *lenis* 'Grayswood Pink'
	- 'Silver Pink' ambig.	Widely available
	- 'Silver Pink' Hillier	NBwr
	atriplicifolius	see *Halimium atriplicifolium*
	'Blanche'	see *C. ladanifer* 'Blanche'
	× ***bornetianus*** 'Jester' 🏆H4	CBod CBrac CKel CSBt EHyd ELan EPfP EWTr LRHS NLar SEND SWvt WLov
	× ***canescens***	WMal
	- f. ***albus***	XSen
	'Christopher Gable'	WMal
	clusii subsp. ***multiflorus***	XSen
	× ***corbariensis***	see *C.* × *hybridus*
	creticus	CBcs CDoC CKel CRos CWal EHyd GPoy LCro LRHS MAsh MGos SNig SPoG SRms SWvt WSpi
	- subsp. ***corsicus***	XSen
§	- subsp. ***creticus***	EBee ELan EPfP MRav SCoo SPer
	- subsp. ***eriocephalus***	CBod
§	- subsp. ***incanus***	SGBe WCot
§	× ***crispatus*** 'Warley Rose'	GMaP WKif
	crispus misapplied	see *C.* × *pulverulentus*, *C.* × *purpureus*
§	***crispus*** L.	ELan SEND XSen
	- 'Prostratus'	see *C. crispus* L.
	- 'Sunset'	see *C.* × *pulverulentus* 'Sunset'
§	× ***cyprius*** 🏆H4	CBrac EBee EHyd ELan EPfP LRHS NRHS SDix SRms SWvt WKif WSpi
§	- var. ***ellipticus*** 'Elma' 🏆H4	CRos EHyd ELan EPfP LRHS MAsh MHtn NLar NRHS SPer WAvo WCot WLov
§	× ***dansereaui***	CKel CMac CSBt LRHS SWvt WSpi XSen
	- 'Decumbens' 🏆H4	Widely available
	- 'Jenkyn Place' 🏆H4	CDoC EBee ELan GMaP LRHS LSRN MBNS MMuc NLar SEdd SPer SPoG WKif
	'Elma'	see *C.* × *cyprius* var. *ellipticus* 'Elma'
	× ***escartianus***	WMal
§	× ***fernandesiae*** 'Anne Palmer'	CDoC CKel EBee MAsh NLar SEdd SGBe WSpi
	× ***florentinus*** misapplied	see × *Halimiocistus* 'Ingwersenii'
	florentinus ambig.	WSpi XLum
§	***florentinus*** Lam.	GMaP XSen
*	- 'Tramontane'	XSen
	'Gordon Cooper' 🏆H4	CBod ELan LSRN MMrt MMuc NLar SPoG WMal WSpi
	halimifolius	see *Halimium halimifolium* Willk.
	× ***heterocalyx*** 'Chelsea Bonnet'	CBod EWTr GMaP MACG NLar SCoo SPoG
	'Highlights'	MAsh
§	× ***hybridus***	Widely available
	- 'Coral Tears'	CKel LRHS
	- 'Gold Prize' (v)	CBod CWGN ECha LCro NBwr NLar SCob SWvt
	- LITTLE MISS SUNSHINE ('Dunnecis'PBR) (v)	MAsh MGos NHol NLar SRms SWvt
	- ROSPICO ('Rencis'PBR) (v)	NLar
	incanus	see *C. creticus* subsp. *incanus*
	ingwerseniana	see × *Halimiocistus* 'Ingwersenii'
	'Jessamy Beauty'	WAvo
	'Jessamy Charm'	SPhx
	ladanifer misapplied	see *C.* × *cyprius*
	ladanifer ambig.	CMac ECha SPer WKif
	ladanifer L.	CBcs CSBt CSde CTri ELan EPfP GPoy LRHS MAsh MRav MSwo SCob SWvt WSpi XSen
	- B&SWJ 15064	WCru
§	- 'Blanche'	EPfP LSRN MMuc NLar SWvt WKif WSpi
§	- 'Paladin'	SArc
	- Palhinhae Group	see *C. ladanifer* var. *sulcatus*
	- 'Pat'	CDoC CRos EHyd EPfP LRHS LSRN MAsh NLar NRHS SPoG SWvt WKif
	- var. ***petiolatus*** 'Bennett's White'	WAvo WMal
§	- var. ***sulcatus***	ELan MNHC
	lasianthus	see *Halimium lasianthum*
	laurifolius	CBod EPfP LRHS MGos SWvt WMal WSpi XSen
	- subsp. ***atlanticus***	XSen
	× ***laxus*** 'Snow White' 🏆H4	CBrac CWGN EBee EPfP GMcL MAsh MNHC NLar NPer WLov
§	× ***lenis*** 'Grayswood Pink' 🏆H4	Widely available
	× ***loretii*** misapplied	see *C.* × *dansereaui*
	× ***loretii*** Rouy & Foucaud	see *C.* × *stenophyllus*
	× ***lusitanicus*** Maund	see *C.* × *dansereaui*
	'Merrist Wood Cream'	see × *Halimiocistus wintonensis* 'Merrist Wood Cream'
	monspeliensis	CMac CRos EPfP GMcL LRHS MAsh SPer SPoG WLov XLum XSen
	- 'Vicar's Mead'	CCCN EHyd LRHS WMal
	monspeliensis × ***salviifolius***	see *C.* × *florentinus* Lam.
	× ***oblongifolius***	SWvt XSen
	× ***obtusifolius*** ambig.	CKel ELan EPfP LRHS WSpi
	obtusifolius Sweet	WPGP
§	- 'Thrive' 🏆H4	CRos EHyd EPfP LRHS MGos SCoo
	ocymoides	see *Halimium ocymoides*
	× ***pagei***	WMal
	'Paladin'	see *C. ladanifer* 'Paladin'
	palhinhae	see *C. ladanifer* var. *sulcatus*
	parviflorus misapplied	see *C.* × *lenis* 'Grayswood Pink'
	parviflorus Lam.	ECha
	aff. ***parviflorus***	GMaP
	'Peggy Sammons'	see *C.* × *argenteus* 'Peggy Sammons'
	× ***platysepalus***	SDix SPhx
	populifolius	CEme CMac ECha EHyd EPfP NLar SPer SWvt
	- var. ***lasiocalyx***	see *C. populifolius* subsp. *major*
§	- subsp. ***major***	LRHS LSRN WLov WPGP WSpi

§ × ***pulverulentus***	CTri ECha WSHC XLum XSen
- (Delilei Group) 'Fiona'	WMal
§ - 'Sunset' ♀H4	Widely available
- 'Warley Rose'	see *C.* × *crispatus* 'Warley Rose'
§ × ***purpureus*** ♀H4	Widely available
- 'Alan Fradd'	Widely available
- 'Betty Taudevin'	see *C.* × *purpureus*
- f. ***stictus***	WAvo
× ***rodiaei*** 'Jessabel'	EPfP MAsh MRav NLar SWvt WPGP
'Ruby Cluster'	CCCN CDoC CGBo
sahucii	see × *Halimiocistus sahucii*
salviifolius	CCCN CWal WMal XLum XSen
- B&SWJ 15066	WCru
- 'Avalanche'	WAbe
- 'Gold Star'	CDoC NLar
- 'May Snow'	MAsh SGBe
- 'Prostratus'	CDoC CKel CSde ELan EPfP LRHS SWvt WSpi
× ***skanbergii***	CDoC CEme CEnd CMac CTri ECha ELan EPfP MGos MRav NBir NLar SCob SDix SEND WCFE WSpi XLum XSen
'Snow Fire' ♀H4	CBrac CCCN CKel CRos EBee EFPl ELan EPfP LRHS MAsh MMuc NLar SCoo SWvt WAvo
§ × ***stenophyllus***	CMac
'Thrive'	see *C.* × *obtusifolius* 'Thrive'
tomentosus	see *Helianthemum nummularium* subsp. *tomentosum*
× ***verguinii***	XSen
villosus	see *C. creticus* subsp. *creticus*
wintonensis	see × *Halimiocistus wintonensis*

Cistus × *Halimium* see × *Halimiocistus*

Citharexylum (*Verbenaceae*)

quadrangulare Jacq.	see *C. spinosum*
spicatum	CCCN
§ ***spinosum***	CBcs EBee

citrandarin see *Citrus reticulata* × *C. trifoliata*

citrange see *Citrus* × *insitorum*

citrangequat see *Citrus* × *georgiana*

× *Citrofortunella* see *Citrus*

mitis	see *Citrus* × *microcarpa*

citron see *Citrus medica*

Citronella (*Icacinaceae*)

§ ***gongonha***	IArd SVen
mucronata	see *C. gongonha*

Citrullus (*Cucurbitaceae*)

lanatus 'Charleston Gray'	SVic
- 'Little Darling' **new**	EKin

Citrus (*Rutaceae*)

§ × ***aurantiifolia*** (F)	CCCN EPfP SCit SPre
- key lime	see *C.* × *aurantiifolia*
§ × ***aurantium*** (F)	SCit
- 'Aber's Narrowleaf' (F)	SCit
- subsp. ***bergamia***	see *C.* × *limon*
- 'Bergamot de Versailles' (F)	EPfP
- 'Bouquet de Fleurs'	see *C.* × *aurantium* (Sour Orange Group) 'Bouquet'
- 'Gou-tou Cheng' (F)	SCit
§ - Grapefruit Group (F)	CCCN NTrD SPre SWeb
- - 'Foster' (F)	SCit
- - 'Golden Special' (F)	SCit
- - 'Marsh' (F)	SCit
- - 'Oroblanco' (F)	SCit
- - 'Red Blush' (F/S)	SCit
- - 'Star Ruby' (F/S)	CCCN EDir SCit SPre SVic
- - 'Wheeny'	see *C. maxima* 'Wheeny'
- var. ***myrtifolia***	see *C.* × *aurantium*
- 'Pursha' (F)	SPre
- 'Robinson' (F)	SCit
§ - (Sour Orange Group) 'Bouquet' (F)	SCit
- - 'Bouquetier de Nice' (F)	SCit
- - 'Chinotto' (F)	NTrD SCit SPre SWeb
- - 'Seville' (F)	LSRN SCit SPre
- - 'Smooth Flat Seville' (F)	SCit
§ - Sweet Orange Group (F)	CCCN EDir ETod NTrD SCit SGsty SPre SVic SWeb
§ - - 'Baia' (F/S)	SCit SPre
- - 'Embiguo' (F)	SCit
- - 'Fukumoto' (F)	CCCN
- - 'Jaffa'	see *C.* × *aurantium* (Sweet Orange Group) 'Shamouti'
- - 'Lane Late' (F)	CCCN SCit SPre
§ - - 'Malta Blood' (F)	SCit
- - 'Maltaise Sanguine'	see *C.* × *aurantium* (Sweet Orange Group) 'Malta Blood'
- - 'Navelate' (F)	SCit
- - 'Navelina' (F/S)	CCCN LCro SCit SPre
- - 'Newhall' (F/S)	NLar SCit
- - 'Salustiana' (F/S)	SCit
§ - - 'Sanguinelli' (F)	CCCN NPlm SCit SPre SVic
§ - - 'Shamouti' (F)	SCit
- - 'Spanish Sanguinelli'	see *C.* × *aurantium* (Sweet Orange Group) 'Sanguinelli'
- - 'Succari' (F)	SCit
- - 'Tarocco' (F)	SCit
- - 'Valencia' (F)	CCCN EDir SCit SPre
- - 'Washington'	see *C.* × *aurantium* (Sweet Orange Group) 'Baia'
- - 'Washington Navel'	see *C.* × *aurantium* (Sweet Orange Group) 'Baia'
§ - (Tangelo Group) 'Minneola' (F)	SCit
§ - - 'Nova' (F/S)	CCCN SCit SVic
- - 'Orlando' (F)	SCit
- - 'Seminole' (F)	SCit
- - 'Ugli' misapplied	see *C.* × *aurantium* 'Minneola'
- - 'Ugli' (F)	SCit
- (Tangor Group) 'Dweet' (F)	SCit
- - 'Ellendale' (F)	SCit
- - 'Murcott' (F)	SCit
australasica (F)	NPlm SCit SPre SVic
bergamia	see *C.* × *limon*
- bergamot	see *C.* × *limon* Bergamot Group
'Buddha's Hand'	see *C. medica* 'Fingered'
calamondin	see *C.* × *microcarpa*
§ ***cavaleriei*** (F)	WPGP
citrandarin	see *C. reticulata* × *trifoliata*
deliciosa	see *C. reticulata* 'Willowleaf'
§ × ***floridana***	NTrD SWeb
- 'Eustis' (F)	SCit SPre
- 'Lakeland' (F)	SCit SPre
× ***georgiana*** 'Thomasville' (F)	SCit
§ ***hystrix***	CCCN CDoC ELan LSRN NLar NPlm NTrD SCit SPre SWeb
Ichang lemon	see *C. cavaleriei*
ichangensis	see *C. cavaleriei*
× ***insitorum*** 'C-35' (F)	SCit
- 'Carrizo' (F)	SCit
- 'Citromon' (F)	SCit
- 'Curafora' (F)	SCit
- 'Swingle' (F)	SCit

	- 'Us119' (F)	SCit
	- 'Venasca' (F)	SCit
	jambhiri	see *C.* × *taitensis*
§	***japonica*** (F) ♀H1c	CBcs ELan EPfP LCro NTrD SCit SPre SVic
	japonica* × *limon (F)	ERom
	- Hong Kong kumquat (F)	SCit
	- 'Nagami' (F)	SPre SWeb
	- 'Reale'[PBR] (F)	SPre
§	× ***junos***	SCit SPre SVic XVPe
	kinokuni	see *C. japonica*
	kotokan	see *C.* × *aurantium*
	'Kucle' (F)	SCit SPre
	'Kulci' (F)	CCCN
	kumquat	see *C. japonica*
	'La Valette' (F)	CCCN SPre
	× ***latifolia*** (F/S)	CCCN ELan EPfP ETod NPlm SCit SPre SWeb
	- 'Bearss' (F)	LCro SCit SVic
	- variegated (F/v)	SPre
	latipes Hook. f. & Thomson ex Hook. f.	see *C. hystrix*
	limetta (F)	CCCN CHll SPre SVic SWeb
	limettioides (F)	SCit SPre
§	× ***limon*** (F)	LSRN NPlm SCit SPre SVic WKor
§	- Bergamot Group (F)	SPre
	- - 'Fantastico' (F)	SCit
	- 'Eureka'	see *C.* × *limon* 'Garey's Eureka'
	- 'Eureka Variegated' (F/v)	SCit
	- 'Fino' (F)	CCCN SCit
	- 'Four Seasons'	see *C.* × *limon* 'Garey's Eureka'
§	- 'Garey's Eureka' (F)	CCCN ELan EPfP LCro LOPS NLar SCit SPre
	- 'Imperial' (F)	SCit SPre
	- 'Improved Meyer'	see *C.* × *limon* 'Meyer'
	- 'Lemonade' (F)	SCit
	- 'Lisbon' (F)	SCit
	- 'Lunario' (F)	SCit SPre
§	- 'Meyer' (F)	CBcs CCCN CDoC CEme ELan EPfP LSRN NLar SCit SCoo SPre SWeb XVPe
	- 'Ponderosa' (F)	SCit
	- 'Quatre Saisons'	see *C.* × *limon* 'Garey's Eureka'
	- 'Rangpur' (F)	SCit SPre
	- 'Romana' (F)	SCit
	- 'Sfusato d'Amalfi' (F)	SCit
	- 'Siracusano' (F)	SCit
	- 'Variegata' (F/v) ♀H2	CCCN ELan NPlm SCit SPre
	- 'Verna' (F)	CCCN SCit
	- 'Villa Franca' (F)	SCit
	- 'Yen Ben' (F)	SCit
	- 'Zagara Bianco' (F)	SCit
	× ***limonia***	see *C.* × *limon*
	'Lipo' (F)	CCCN SCit SPre
	macrophylla (F)	SCit
	madurensis	see *C. japonica*
	maxima (F)	SWeb
§	- 'Wheeny' (F)	SCit
§	***medica*** (F)	CHll SWeb
	- 'Cedra' (F)	SPre
	- 'Cidro Digitado'	see *C. medica* 'Fingered'
	- var. ***digitata***	see *C. medica* 'Fingered'
	- 'Ethrog' (F)	SCit SPre
§	- 'Fingered' (F)	CHll NPlm NTrD SCit SPre SWeb XVPe
*	- 'Rubra'	SPre
	- var. ***sarcodactylis***	see *C. medica* 'Fingered'
	× ***meyeri***	see *C.* × *limon*
§	× ***microcarpa*** (F) ♀H3	CCCN LWaG NLar NPlm NTrD SCit SPre SWeb
	- Philippine lime	see *C.* × *microcarpa*
§	- 'Tiger' (F/v)	SCit SPre SVic
	- 'Variegata'	see *C.* × *microcarpa* 'Tiger'
	× ***mitis***	see *C.* × *microcarpa*
	natsudaidai	see *C.* × *aurantium*
	'Nippon'	SCit
	× ***nobilis*** Lour.	see *C. reticulata* 'Willowleaf'
	- var. ***inermis***	see *C. japonica*
	- Ortanique Group	see *C.* × *aurantium* Sweet Orange Group
	× ***obovata*** (F)	SPre
	- 'Fukushu' (F)	CCCN SCit
	× ***paradisi***	see *C.* × *aurantium* Grapefruit Group
	- 'Wheeny'	see *C. maxima* 'Wheeny'
	'Pursta' (F)	CCCN
	reshni	see *C.* × *aurantium*
§	***reticulata*** (F)	CCCN CHll NTrD SCit SPre SWeb
	- 'Clausellina' (F/S)	SCit XVPe
	- var. ***deliciosa***	see *C. reticulata* 'Willowleaf'
	- 'Fina' (F/S)	SCit
	- 'Hashimoto' (F/S)	SCit
	- 'Hernandina' (F)	CCCN
	- Mandarin Group (F)	EDir EPfP NPlm NTrD SPre SWeb
	- - 'Clementine' (F)	EPfP SPre SWeb
	- - 'Encore' (F)	SCit
	- - 'Esbal' (F)	CCCN
	- - 'Fortune' (F)	SCit
	- - 'Fremont' (F)	SCit
	- - 'Nules' (F/S)	CCCN SCit SPre
	- 'Marisol' (F/S)	SCit
	- 'Miyagawa' (F)	CCCN SCit XVPe
	- 'Nour' (F)	SCit
	- 'Nova'	see *C.* × *aurantium* (Tangelo Group) 'Nova'
	- 'Okitsu' (F/S)	CCCN SCit
	- 'Owari' (F/S)	SCit
	- Satsuma Group	see *C. reticulata*
	- (Tangerine Group) 'Dancy' (F)	SCit
§	- 'Willowleaf' (F)	SCit
§	***reticulata* × *trifoliata***	SCit
	sinensis	see *C.* × *aurantium* Sweet Orange Group
	- 'Jaffa'	see *C.* × *aurantium* (Sweet Orange Group) 'Shamouti'
	- 'Washington'	see *C.* × *aurantium* (Sweet Orange Group) 'Baia'
	sudachi	see *C. medica*
§	× ***taitensis*** (F)	SCit SPre
	- 'Otaheite' (F)	CCCN SCit SPre
§	- rough lemon (F)	SCit
	- Schaub rough lemon	see *C.* × *taitensis* rough lemon
§	***trifoliata***	CAgr CBcs CBod CCCN CMCN EBee EHyd ELan ELon EPfP IDee MBlu MGil MMuc MRav SCit SMad SPer SPlb SVic WFar WHlf WJur WKor
	- 'Flying Dragon'	SCit WJur
	unshiu	see *C. reticulata*
	volkameriana	see *C.* × *limon*
	wilsonii	see *C.* × *junos*

Cladrastis (*Fabaceae*)

§	***kentukea***	CBcs CEme CLnd CMCN EBee ELan EPfP ESwi EWTr IPap LEdu MBlu MTrO MVil NLar SChF SMad WJur WMat WPGP
§	- 'Perkins Pink'	MBlu
	- 'Rosea'	see *C. kentukea* 'Perkins Pink'
	lutea	see *C. kentukea*
	sinensis	EBee EPfP MBlu WPGP
	wilsonii	WPGP

Clarkia (*Onagraceae*)

	CROWN DOUBLE MIXED (d)	SVic

Claytonia (*Portulacaceae*)

alsinoides	see *C. sibirica*
§ ***perfoliata***	CBod GPoy MNHC WHer
§ ***sibirica***	CAgr CCBP CTtf WKor XLum
- f. ***albiflora***	EWld MPie SPlb WCot
virginica	CBor EBee GKev LAma WFar

Cleistocactus (*Cactaceae*)

neoroezlii **new**	EAri
strausii ♀H2 **new**	EAri NPlm
tominensis **new**	EAri

Clematis ✿ (*Ranunculaceae*)

BWJ 7630 from China	WCru
'Abigail' (Vt)	NHaw
ABILENE ('Evipo027'PBR) (EL)	CRos CWCL EHyd ELan EPfP LRHS MAsh NRHS NTay SCoo SPoG
'Abundance' (Vt) ♀H6	CArg CBcs CKel CRHN CWCL ELan EPfP ETho GMcL LCro LRHS LSRN MAsh NHol NTay SNig SPer WFar WSpi
ACROPOLIS ('Evipo078'PBR) (Boulevard Series)	CBod CWGN ELan EPfP ETho LRHS LSou NTay SCoo SNig
addisonii	NHaw
'Advent Bells' (C)	CWGN ETho LCro LOPS NTay WSpi
'Akaishi' (EL)	ETho SNig
akebioides	GKev
ALABAST ('Poulala'PBR) (EL) ♀H6	ETho LRHS SCoo WSpi
ALAINA ('Evipo056'PBR) (EL)	CRos EHyd ETho LRHS NRHS NTay SCoo SNig SPoG
'Alba Luxurians' (Vt)	CBcs CDoC CKel CRHN CWCL EHyd ELan EPfP ETho LCro LOPS LRHS LSRN MGos NHol NRHS NTay SCob SPer SPoG
'Albiflora' (A)	NTay
'Albina Plena' (A/d)	ETho SNig
'Alice Fisk' (EL)	EBee ETho LSRN MSwo
'Alionushka' (I) ♀H6	CBar CKel CRHN CWCL EHyd ELan EPfP ETho LCro LRHS LSRN NTay SNig
ALITA ('Evipo070'PBR) (Vt)	CRos CWCL EPfP LRHS NTay SCoo
'Allanah' (LL)	ETho IPot LRHS LSRN NTay SCoo WSpi
alpina	EHeP GDam GKev GLog LCro LOPS LRHS LSRN MAsh MCot MDon MRav NPer NTay SEWo SOrN SPlb SPre SWvt WFar
- 'Albiflora'	see *C. sibirica*
- 'Columbine White'	see *C.* 'White Columbine'
§ - 'Pamela Jackman' (A) ♀H6	CMac CRos EHyd ELan ETho LRHS LSRN MAsh MMuc NRHS SCob SCoo SPer SPoG SRkn SWvt WFar
- pink-flowered (A)	GKev
- 'Stolwijk Gold' (A)	CWGN EBee MBlu NTay SMDa SRms
alternata	CWGN EBee ETho GGro NHaw
'Amethyst Beauty' (A)	EHyd EPfP LRHS MGos SCoo
AMETHYST BEAUTY ('Evipo043'PBR) (LL)	CRos ETho MAsh NLar NTay SPoG
'Andante' (I)	CWGN WSpi
'Andromeda' (EL)	CDoC CRos EHyd EPfP ETho IPot LCro LRHS MGos NLar NRHS NTay SCoo SNig
ANETA ('Evipo055'PBR) (Vt)	CWGN
ANGELA ('Zoang'PBR) (EL)	LSRN NTay
ANGELIQUE ('Evipo017') (EL)	CRos CWGN EHyd ELan EPfP ETho LRHS MAsh MGos NRHS SCoo SPer
'Anissa' (V)	NHaw
'Anita' (Ta)	EPfP ETho IPot LSRN MAsh NHaw NTay
ANNA LOUISE ('Evithree'PBR) (EL) ♀H6	CKel CRos CWCL EHyd EPfP ETho LRHS LSRN MGos NTay SCoo
'Annabel' (EL)	LSRN MAsh
ANNABELLA ('Zo08169') (V)	CWGN ETho IPot NTay
'Anniseed' (M)	NHaw
ANNIVERSARY ('Pynot') (EL)	LSRN SCoo
ANSLEY ('Evipo103') (EL) **new**	MGos
'Aotearoa' (LL)	ETho NHaw
'Aphrodite' (I)	MAsh
'Aphrodite Elegafumina' (I)	CWGN
apiifolia	NHaw WSpi
- 'Hakikomi Fu' **new**	GGro
'Apollonia'	CWGN
'Apple Blossom' (Ar) ♀H4	Widely available
'Arabella' (I) ♀H6	CBar CKel CRHN CRos CWCL CWGN EHyd ELan EPfP ETho LCro LRHS LSRN MAsh MGos NLar NRHS NTay SCoo SNig SPer SRkn SWvt WFar WSpi
'Archie' (EL) **new**	ETho
§ ARCTIC QUEEN ('Evitwo'PBR) (EL) ♀H6	CRos EHyd EPfP ETho LRHS LSRN MAsh NRHS SCoo SPoG
armandi	Widely available
- 'Enham Star' (Ar)	CRos EDir EHyd EPfP LRHS MGos NRHS
§ - 'Little White Charm' (Ar)	CRos EBee EHyd ELan EPfP LRHS NLar NRHS SCoo
- 'Meyeniana'	see *C. armandi* 'Little White Charm'
§ - 'Snowdrift' (Ar)	CBcs CBod CEme CKel CRos CWCL EBee EDir EHyd ELan EPfP ETho GDam GMcL LCro LOPS LRHS LSRN MAsh MGos MSwo NLar NRHS NTay SCoo SPer SPoG SRms WFar WHlf
× ***aromatica***	CWGN EBee EHyd ELan EPfP ETho IPot LCro LRHS MMrt NHaw NTay SCoo WCot WSpi
'Asao' (EL)	CArg CRos EHyd EPfP ETho LRHS NTay SCoo SPoG
'Ascotiensis' (LL) ♀H6	EBee EHyd EPfP ETho LRHS SCoo
'Ashva' (LL)	CWGN NTay SNig
ASTRA NOVA ('Zo09085'PBR) (Vt)	CWGN IPot NTay WSpi
'Aureolin' (Ta)	CDoC NLar
AVANT-GARDE ('Evipo033'PBR) (Vt)	CDoC CRos CWCL CWGN EHyd ELan EPfP ETho LCro LRHS NTay
AZTEK	see *C.* 'Helios'
BABY DOLL ('Zobadol') (EL)	NLar WSpi
'Baby Pink' (I)	NHaw
BABY STAR ('Zobast'PBR) (EL)	ETho NTay
§ 'Bagatelle' (LL)	EBee ETho GMcL NHaw
'Bal Maiden' (Vt)	CRHN NHaw
'Barbara' (LL)	LSRN NTay SNig
'Barbara Dibley' (EL)	CTri CWCL ETho MAsh SCoo SNig
'Barbara Harrington'PBR (LL)	EHyd LRHS LSRN
'Barbara Jackman' (EL)	CArg CWCL EHyd ETho LRHS LSRN MAsh MGos NTay SCob SCoo SPer
'Beata' (LL)	CWCL NHaw SNig
'Beautiful Bride'PBR (EL)	ETho LCro LOPS NTay SNig
'Beauty of Worcester' (EL)	CDoC CWCL ELan EPfP ETho IPot LRHS LSRN MAsh NTay SCoo SNig SOrN SPer
'Bees' Jubilee' (EL)	CArg CBcs CMac CRos CWCL EBee EHeP EHyd ELan EPfP ETho LCro LOPS LRHS LSRN LSto MAsh MGos NLar NTay SCoo SNig SPer SPoG SWvt
'Belle Nantaise' (EL)	EHyd LRHS NRHS SRms
'Belle of Woking' (EL)	EHyd LRHS LSRN SCoo SNig SWvt

	BELLISSIMA ('Zo10075') (EL) **new**	IPot LCro
	'Benikomachi'	SNig
	BERNADINE ('Evipo 061'PBR) (EL)	CBod CPla CRos CWGN EHyd ETho LRHS NRHS NTay SCoo SNig
	'Best Wishes'	CRos CWCL EHyd ETho LRHS LSRN NRHS NTay WSpi
§	'Beth Currie' (EL)	EHyd EPfP LRHS SCoo SNig
	'Betty Corning' (Vt)	CKel CRHN CWCL CWGN EBee EHyd ELan EPfP ETho IPot LRHS LSRN MGos NLar NRHS NTay SCoo SNig SPoG SRms SWvt
	bigelovii	SBrt
	BIJOU	see *C.* THUMBELINA
	'Bill MacKenzie' (Ta) ♀H6	Widely available
	'Black Prince' (Vt)	CRHN CRos CWGN EHyd ELan EPfP ETho IPot LCro LRHS LSRN NLar NRHS NTay SPer SPoG SRms
	'Black Tea' (LL)	CKel CRos EHyd EPfP LRHS NRHS
§	'Błękitny Anioł' (LL) ♀H6	CKel CRHN CWCL CWGN EBee EDir EHyd EPfP ETho LCro LOPS LRHS MAsh MCot NLar NRHS NTay SCoo SNig SOrN SPoG WBor
	BLUE ANGEL	see *C.* 'Błękitny Anioł'
	'Blue Belle' (Vt)	CRHN LRHS NLar WFar
	'Blue Bird' (A/d)	CArg CBcs CWCL EBee ELan GDam GMcL LRHS MAsh SRms
	BLUE BLOOD	see *C.* 'Königskind'
	'Blue Boy' (EL)	see *C.* 'Elsa Späth'
	'Blue Boy' (I)	see *C.* × *diversifolia* 'Blue Boy' (I)
	'Blue Carillon' (I) **new**	NHaw
	'Blue Dancer' (A)	CBcs CDoC CKel CRos EHyd EPfP ETho LRHS MGos NLar NTay SCoo SNig SPer
	'Blue Eclipse' (A)	CWGN EHyd ETho NHol NLar NRHS NTay SPoG
	'Blue Explosion' (EL)	SNig
	'Blue Eyes' (EL)	ETho LSRN NLar
§	'Blue Light'PBR (EL/d)	CWGN ELan ETho IPot NLar NTay
	BLUE MOON ('Evirin'PBR) (EL)	CRos CWCL EHyd EPfP ETho LRHS LSRN SCoo SNig
	BLUE OCEAN ('Zo09045'PBR) (I)	EBee
	BLUE PIROUETTE ('Zobluepi'PBR) (I)	ELan ETho NTay
	BLUE RAIN	see *C.* 'Sinii Dozhd'
	'Blue Ravine' (EL)	EPfP SCoo
	'Blue Ribbon'	SBut SGBe
	BLUE RIVER ('Zoblueriver'PBR) (I)	CWCL CWGN ELan ETho NTay
	'Blue Tapers' (A)	ETho MGos
	'Bolam Belle' (Vt)	CRHN NHaw
	BONANZA ('Evipo031'PBR) (Vt)	CRos EHyd EPfP LRHS NLar SCoo SPoG
	× ***bonstedtii*** 'Crépuscule' (H)	ECtt MCot WSpi
	BOURBON ('Evipo018'PBR) (EL)	CRos CWCL EHyd ELan EPfP ETho LCro LRHS MPri NTay SCoo SNig
	'Brianna' (Vt)	NHaw
	'Brocade' (Vt)	CRHN NHaw
	'Broughton Bride' (A)	CBcs CDoC CWCL CWGN EHyd EPfP ETho LRHS NHol NRHS NTay SRms
	'Broughton Star' (M/d) ♀H5	Widely available
	'Brunette' (A)	ELan EPfP ETho NTay
	buchananiana Finet & Gagnep.	see *C. rehderiana*
	'Buckland Beauty' (V)	CWGN NHaw
	'Buckland Pixie' (Vt)	NHaw
	'Burford Bell' (V)	NHaw WSHC
	'Burford Princess' (Vt)	CRHN NHaw
	'Burma Star' (EL)	CWGN EPfP ETho NTay
	BURNING LOVE ('Vitiwester'PBR) (Vt)	ETho
	CADDICK'S CASCADE	see *C.* 'Semu'
	calycina	see *C. cirrhosa* var. *balearica*
§	***campaniflora***	CRHN ETho GGro NHaw NTay
	'Candy Stripe'	LRHS SCoo SPoG
	'Capitaine Thuilleaux'	see *C.* 'Souvenir du Capitaine Thuilleaux'
	'Cardinal Wyszynski'	see *C.* 'Kardynał Wyszyński'
	'Carlien' (Vt)	CRHN
	'Carlotta' (Vt)	NHaw
	'Carmencita' (Vt)	CRHN EBee LRHS LSRN NHaw NTay SCoo
	'Carnaby' (EL)	CArg CWCL EHyd ELan EPfP ETho LRHS LSRN MAsh NTay SCoo SNig SWvt WSpi
	'Carol Klein' (I)	NHaw NTay
	'Carol Leeds' (Vt)	NHaw
	'Caroline' (LL)	CWGN LSRN NTay SNig
	× ***cartmanii*** 'Avalanche'PBR (Fo/m)	CBod CRos EHyd ELan EPfP ETho LPar LRHS MGos NLar NRHS NTay SCob SCoo SPoG SWvt
	- 'Joe' (Fo/m) ♀H4	CBcs CBod CDoC CRos CWCL EHyd ELan EPfP ETho EWes ITim LCro LOPS LRHS LSRN NRHS NTay SCob SCoo SPoG SWvt WIce
	- 'Joe' × ***cirrhosa***	CWCL
	- 'Joe' × 'Sharon' (Fo)	LSRN
	- MICHIKO ('Evipo044'PBR) (Fo)	CRos EHyd EPfP ETho LRHS NRHS NTay SPoG
	- 'White Abundance'PBR (Fo/f)	LRHS NLar
	CASSIS ('Evipo020'PBR)	ETho LSRN NTay SCoo SPer
	'Catherine Clanwilliam' (T)	CWGN NHaw
	'Catherine Penny' (VT)	NHaw
	'Celebration'PBR Godfrey (EL)	ETho
	CÉZANNE ('Evipo023'PBR) (EL)	CDoC CRos CWCL EHyd ELan EPfP ETho LRHS MAsh MGos NLar NRHS NTay SCoo SNig
	'Chacewater' (Vt)	CRHN
	'Change of Heart' (EL)	EBee SNig
	CHANTILLY ('Evipo021'PBR) (EL)	CRos EHyd ELan EPfP ETho LRHS LSRN NRHS NTay SCoo
	'Charissima' (EL)	CWGN SCoo
	'Charlie Brown' (LL)	CRHN NHaw
	CHARMAINE ('Evipo022'PBR) (EL)	CRos CWGN EHyd EPfP ETho LCro LRHS MGos NLar NRHS NTay SCoo SNig SPoG
	'Chatsworth' (Vt)	CRHN CWGN NHaw NTay
	CHELSEA ('Evipo100'PBR)	CDoC CRos EHyd EPfP ETho LRHS NRHS NTay SCoo SNig
	CHEROKEE	see *C.* OOH LA LA
	CHEVALIER ('Evipo040'PBR) (EL)	CRos CWCL EHyd EPfP ETho LRHS MAsh MGos NLar NRHS NTay SCoo SNig SPoG
	chinensis misapplied	see *C. terniflora*
	CHINOOK ('Evipo013'PBR)	SRms
	'Chris' (H)	SMDa
	chrysantha	see *C. tangutica*
	chrysocoma misapplied	see *C. spooneri*, *C.* × *vedrariensis*
	chrysocoma Franch.	WSpi
	'Cicciolina' (Vt)	CRHN NHaw
	cirrhosa	CHll CTri EHyd LRHS MAsh
§	- var. ***balearica***	CBcs CDoC CMac CRos CTri EHyd ELan EPfP ETho LCro LOPS LRHS LSRN MAsh MGos MRav MSwo NTay SCob SCoo SEND SPoG SWvt
	- 'Jingle Bells' (C)	CDoC CKel CMac CRos CWCL EBee EHyd ELan EPfP ETho LCro LOPS LRHS LSRN MAsh MGos NLar NRHS NTay SCoo SRms WHlf

- 'Ourika Valley' (C)	CWCL CWGN EBee ETho LRHS MAsh NLar NTay
- var. ***purpurascens*** 'Freckles' (C) 🏆H4	Widely available
- - 'Lansdowne Gem' (C)	CMac CWGN EHyd ETho LRHS NLar NTay SCoo SPoG SWvt WSpi
- 'Winter Parasol' (C)	EBee
- 'Wisley Cream' (C) 🏆H4	CBcs CDoC CMac CRos CWCL EBee EHyd ELan EPfP ETho LCro LOPS LRHS LSRN MAsh MSwo NLar NRHS NTay SCoo SNig SPer SPoG SRms SWvt WHlf
cirrhosa × 'Early Sensation'	CWCL MDon
clarkeana misapplied	see *C. urophylla* 'Winter Beauty'
'Cloudburst' (LL)	EBee ETho
coactilis	NHaw SBrt
columbiana	GKev
- var. ***tenuiloba*** 'Ylva' (A)	WAbe
'Columbine' (A)	EBee EPfP NTay SCoo
'Columella' (A)	CWGN EBee
'Comtesse de Bouchaud' (LL) 🏆H6	CArg CKel CRos CTri CWCL EBee EHyd ELan EPfP ETho LCro LOPS LRHS LSRN MAsh MGos MRav NRHS NTay SCob SCoo SPer SPoG
CONFETTI ('Evipo036'PBR) (Vt)	EPfP LSRN
'Congratulations' (EL)	EHyd LRHS NRHS NTay SPoG
connata W&O 7066	GGro
aff. ***connata*** HWJK 2176 from Nepal	WCru
'Consort' (LL)	CWGN
'Constance' (A) 🏆H6	CArg CKel CWCL EBee EHyd EPfP ETho GMcL LRHS LSRN NLar NRHS NTay SCoo SNig SPre SRms WFar
'Continuity' (M)	CWGN NTay
'Cora' (I)	CWGN
'Coralie' (T)	NHaw
CORINNE ('Evipo063'PBR) (EL)	CRos EHyd ETho LCro LRHS MAsh NLar NRHS NTay SCoo SNig SPoG
'Cornish Spirit' (Vt)	CRHN
'Corona' (EL)	EPfP LRHS SCoo
'Côte d'Azur' (H)	CKel ELan LRHS MNrw NTay
'Countess of Lovelace' (EL)	CBcs EPfP ETho LRHS LSRN NTay SCoo SNig
COUNTRY ROSE ('Zocoro'PBR) (A)	NTay WSpi
'Cragside' (A)	NRHS SCoo
§ 'Crimson King' (LL)	ETho
'Crinkle'PBR (M)	CCCN
§ ***crispa***	CWGN NHaw SBrt
'Crispa Angel' (V) **new**	NHaw
'Crispa Niccy' (V) **new**	NHaw
§ CRYSTAL FOUNTAIN ('Evipo038'PBR) (EL)	CDoC CRos CWCL CWGN EHyd ELan EPfP ETho LBuc LCro LOPS LRHS LSRN MGos NTay SCoo SNig SPer SPoG SRms
'Danae' (Vt)	CRHN NHaw
DANCING QUEEN ('Zodaque'PBR) (EL)	NTay WSpi
DANCING SMILE ('Zodasmi'PBR) (EL)	NTay
'Daniel Deronda' (EL) 🏆H6	CArg CDoC CKel CRos CWGN EBee ELan EPfP ETho LRHS LSRN MAsh NRHS NTay SCob SCoo SNig SPer SPoG
'Darius' (EL)	SNig
'Dark Eyes' (Vt)	CBar CKel CRHN CWGN ETho IPot LCro LOPS LRHS NTay SCoo SNig WTyc
'Dark Secret' (A)	NHol NLar
dasyandra NJM 11.075	WPGP
'Dawn' (EL)	CCCN CWCL EHyd ETho LRHS LSRN NTay SCoo WSpi

'Dazzle' (EL)	ETho LCro NTay
'De Vijfhoeven' (Vt)	NHaw
'Débutante' (EL)	NHaw
'Dedication' (V)	NHaw
'Denny's Double' (EL/d)	CWGN NTay
DIAMANTINA ('Evipo039'PBR) (EL)	CDoC CRos CWCL EHyd EPfP ETho LRHS NLar NRHS NTay SCoo SNig
'Diamond Anniversary' (A)	CWCL EPfP ETho LCro NTay
'Diana' (LL)	LSRN NHaw NTay
DIANA'S DELIGHT ('Evipo026'PBR) (EL)	CRos CWCL EHyd EPfP ETho LCro LRHS LSRN MAsh NRHS NTay SPoG
dioscoreifolia	see *C. terniflora*
§ × ***diversifolia***	CRHN LRHS NHaw SWvt WCot
- 'Benedikt' (I)	CWGN WSpi
§ - 'Blue Boy' (I)	CRHN NHaw WSpi
- 'Heather Herschell' (I)	CRHN CTsd
§ - 'Hendersonii' (I)	CBod CKel EGrI EHyd LRHS LSRN MRav MSCN NTay SPer SWvt WCot
§ - 'Olgae' (I)	NHaw
'Doctor Mary' (V)	NHaw
'Doctor Ruppel' (EL)	CArg CDoC CKel CMac CRos CWCL EHeP EHyd EPfP ETho GDam GMcL LCro LOPS LRHS LSRN MAsh MDon NRHS NTay SCob SCoo SNig SPer
'Dominika' (LL)	NHaw
'Dorath'	CWGN EPfP LRHS
'Dorothy Tolver' (EL)	ETho IPot
'Dorothy Walton'	see *C.* 'Bagatelle'
DOUBLE DELIGHT ('Doudeli'PBR) (M)	CWGN
'Duchess of Albany' (1897) (T)	CArg CDoC CTri CWCL EHyd ELan EPfP ETho LRHS LSRN MGos NHol SPer SRkn
'Duchess of Edinburgh' (EL)	CBcs CDoC CKel CMac CWCL EHyd ELan EPfP ETho LRHS LSRN MAsh MGos MSwo NHol NRHS NTay SCob SCoo SNig SPer SPoG SWvt
× ***durandii*** 🏆H6	CBcs CRHN CRos CSpe EHyd ELan EPfP ETho IPot LRHS LSRN MAsh MGos MRav NRHS NTay SCob SCoo SNig SPoG SWvt WSpi
'Dutch Sky' (LL)	CWGN ETho
'Dzieci Warszawy' (EL)	SNig
'Early Sensation' (Fo/f)	CBcs CBod CDoC CKel CRos CWCL EHyd ELan EPfP ETho GMcL LCro LOPS LPar LRHS LSRN MAsh NRHS NTay SCoo SGsty SPoG SPre SWvt WHlf
EAST RIVER ('Zoeastri'PBR) (I)	NTay
'Eclipse' (H)	NTay
EDDA ('Evipo074'PBR) (Boulevard Series) (EL)	CRos EHyd EPfP ETho LRHS MAsh NRHS NTay SCoo SNig
'Edith' (EL) 🏆H6	ETho LSRN NHaw NTay
'Édouard Desfossé' (EL)	ETho LRHS
'Edward Prichard'	CKel EPfP ETho NTay
'Eetika' (LL)	CRHN NHaw
'Ekstra' (LL)	NHaw
'Eleanor' (Fo/f)	GEdr NFav
'Elf' (Vt)	CWGN NHaw
'Elgar'	see *C.* 'Sir Edward Elgar'
'Elizabeth' (M) 🏆H5	Widely available
'Elly Elisabeth' (I)	NHaw
ELODI ('Evipo115') **new**	LCro NTay
§ 'Elsa Späth' (EL)	CArg CMac CRos CTri EHyd ELan EPfP ETho LRHS LSRN MAsh NLar NRHS NTay SCoo SNig SPer SPoG SWvt
'Elvan' (Vt)	CRHN NHaw

'Ember' (I)	CWGN NHaw
'Emerald Dream'PBR (Fo)	EPfP LCro LRHS NTay
'Emilia Plater' (Vt)	CRHN CWGN EPfP ETho NHaw NTay
EMPRESS ('Evipo011'PBR) (EL)	ELan EPfP ETho LRHS NLar SNig
'Empress Amy Lai'	CWCL
ENDELLION ('Evipo076'PBR) (EL)	CRos EHyd ETho LRHS NRHS NTay SNig
'Entel' (Vt)	CRHN EBee NHaw
× ***eriostemon***	see *C.* × *diversifolia*
'Ernest Markham' (LL) 🏆H6	CBcs CDoC CKel CMac CRos CWCL EHyd ELan EPfP ETho LRHS LSRN MAsh MGos MSwo NLar NRHS NTay NWea SCoo SNig SPer SPoG SWvt WSpi
ESME ('Evipo048'PBR)	CRos CWGN EPfP ETho LRHS NLar NTay SNig
ESTHER ('Zo09143'PBR) (EL)	IPot NTay SNig
ETOILE NACRÉE	see *C.* 'Sakurahime'
'Étoile Rose' (Vt)	CMac CRHN CTri CWCL EBee EHyd ELan EPfP ETho IPot LRHS LSRN NHaw NHol NTay SCoo
'Étoile Violette' (Vt) 🏆H6	Widely available
'Everett' (V)	NHaw WSHC
'Fair Rosamond' (EL)	ETho NTay
FAIRY BLUE	see *C.* CRYSTAL FOUNTAIN
'Fairydust' (Vt)	NHaw
× ***fargesioides***	see *C.* 'Paul Farges'
fasciculiflora L 657	WCru WPGP
'Fascination'PBR (I)	CWCL CWGN LRHS MGos NTay WCot WSpi
FAUN ('Evipo108') **new**	ETho
'Fay' (Vt)	NHaw
'Fenna' (EL)	CWGN
FILIGREE ('Evipo029'PBR) (EL)	CRos EHyd ETho LBuc LRHS MAsh MGos NLar NRHS NTay SCoo SNig
'Filomae' (Vt)	NHaw
finetiana misapplied	see *C. paniculata* J.G. Gmel.
'Fireworks' (EL)	CArg CWGN EHyd EPfP ETho LRHS LSRN MAsh MRav NLar NTay SPoG
'First Love' (EL)	SNig
FLAMENCO DANCER ('Bfccfla'PBR)	LCro LOPS
flammula	CArg CDoC EHyd ELan EPfP LCro LOPS LRHS LSRN MAsh MBlu MRav NBid NLar NRHS NTay SPoG SRms SWvt WSpi XSen
- B&SWJ 15041	WCru
- 'Rubra Marginata'	see *C.* × *triternata* 'Rubromarginata'
FLEURI ('Evipo042'PBR) (Boulevard Series) (EL)	CRos CWCL EHyd EPfP ETho LRHS LSRN NRHS NTay SCoo SNig SPoG WSpi
florida	CWGN SWvt
- 'Bicolor'	see *C. florida* var. *florida* 'Sieboldiana'
- var. ***flore-pleno*** 'Plena' (d)	CCCN CRos CWCL EHyd EPfP ETho LRHS LSRN MAsh NRHS NTay SCoo SNig SPoG
§ - var. ***florida*** 'Sieboldiana' (d)	CBcs CKel CRos CWCL CWGN EHyd ELan EPfP ETho LCro LOPS LRHS LSRN MAsh NRHS NTay SCob SCoo SNig SPoG SWvt WHlf
- var. ***normalis*** PISTACHIO ('Evirida'PBR) (LL)	CCCN CKel CWCL CWGN EHyd ELan EPfP LRHS MAsh MGos NTay SPoG
'Floris V' (I)	CWCL EGrI NHaw NLar
'Fluffy Duck' (Vt/d)	NHaw
'Fond Memories' (EL)	CWCL CWGN EPfP ETho IPot LCro LOPS LSRN MAsh NHaw NLar NRHS NTay
FOREVER FRIENDS ('Zofofri'PBR) (LL)	CWGN EHyd EPfP ETho LCro LRHS NRHS NTay
'Forget-me-not NLP1'	ETho LSRN NLar
forrestii	see *C. napaulensis*
§ ***forsteri***	WSHC
'Foxtrot' (Vt)	CRHN
'Foxy' (A) 🏆H6	ETho LRHS NTay
FRAGRANT OBERON ('Hutbron'PBR) (Fo)	ETho LCro LOPS NTay SWvt
'Fragrant Spring' (M)	CBod CDoC CKel CSBt CWGN EBee EDir EPfP ETho GMcL NLar NTay SCoo WFar
'Frances Rivis' (A) 🏆H6	CArg CBcs CDoC CRos CWCL EHyd ELan EPfP ETho GBin LCro LOPS LRHS LSRN MAsh MBlu MRav NLar NTay NWea SCob SPoG SRms
'Francesca' (A)	LSRN
'Frankie' (A) 🏆H6	EHyd ELan EPfP ETho LCro LOPS LRHS LSRN MAsh MGos MHer NTay SCoo SNig
FRANZISKA MARIA ('Evipo008') (EL)	CRos EHyd EPfP LRHS MAsh MGos NTay SCoo
'Frau Susanne' (EL)	EBee
'Freda' (M) 🏆H6	CRHN CRos CTri CWGN EDir ELan EPfP ETho LCro LOPS LRHS LSRN MAsh MBlu MRav NHol NTay SCoo SPer SPoG SRms
FREEDOM ('Zo06128'PBR) (EL)	NTay
fremontii	NHaw SBrt
'Fryderyk Chopin' (EL)	SNig
'Fudō' (V)	NHaw
'Fujimusume' (EL) 🏆H6	CRos CWGN EHyd EPfP ETho IPot LRHS MAsh NHaw NRHS NTay SNig SPoG
'Fukuzono' (I)	EHyd LRHS LSRN NHaw NRHS
fusca misapplied	see *C. japonica*
fusca Turcz.	NHaw
- dwarf	CWGN
- large-flowered B&SWJ 8431	WCru
GALORE	see *C.* VESUVIUS
GAZELLE ('Evipo014'PBR) (I)	MAsh SRms
'Generał Sikorski' (EL)	CBcs CDoC CKel CRos CWCL EHyd ELan EPfP ETho LCro LRHS LSRN MAsh MGos NRHS NTay SCoo SNig SPer SWvt WSpi
'Geoffrey Tolver' (LL)	CWGN
GIANT STAR ('Gistar'PBR) (M)	EDir EHyd EPfP GDam GMcL LRHS NLar NPer NRHS SPoG
'Gillian Blades' (EL) 🏆H6	CKel CRos EBee EHyd ELan EPfP ETho LBuc LRHS LSRN MAsh MGos NRHS NTay SCoo SNig SPoG SWvt
GINA ('Evipo092'PBR) (Garland Series) (LL)	CWGN
'Ginny' (V)	NHaw
§ 'Gipsy Queen' (LL) 🏆H6	CArg CBcs CKel CRos CWCL EHyd ELan EPfP ETho LRHS LSRN MAsh MGos NTay SCoo SPer SPoG SWvt
GISELLE ('Evipo051'PBR)	CRos CWCL EHyd EPfP ETho LRHS NLar NRHS NTay SCoo SNig SPoG
'Gladys Picard' (EL)	NHaw
glauca ambig.	SBrt
glaucophylla	NHaw SBrt
'Gojōgawa' (EL)	ETho
'Golden Harvest' (Ta)	EPfP ETho LSRN NLar
GOLDEN TIARA ('Kugotia'PBR) (Ta) 🏆H6	CWGN ETho IPot LSRN NTay SRms WCot
'Gothenburg' (M)	ETho
'Grace' (Ta)	EPfP IPot NHaw
gracilifolia BWJ 8002	WCru
I 'Grandiflora' (F)	CDoC ETho WFar
'Grandiflora Sanguinea' (Vt)	NHaw

	grata misapplied	see *C.* × *jouiniana*
	'Gravetye Beauty' (T)	CDoC CKel CRHN CWCL EBee EHyd ELan EPfP ETho LRHS LSRN MGos NHol NTay SCoo SNig SPoG SRms SWvt
§	'Grażyna' (LL)	NTay
	GREEN PASSION ('Zo11050'^{PBR}) (EL/d)	CWGN ETho LCro LOPS LRHS NTay
	GREFVE ERIK RUUTH ('Kbk02'^{PBR}) (EL)	CWGN
	'Guernsey Cream' (EL)	CDoC CKel CRos CWCL EDir EHyd EPfP ETho LCro LOPS LRHS LSRN MAsh MCot MGos MSwo NLar NTay SCoo SNig SOrN SRkn WHlf
	GUIDING PROMISE ('Evipo053'^{PBR})	NTay SCoo SNig
	'Guiding Star' (EL)	IPot
	'H.F.Young' (EL)	CRos EHyd ELan EPfP ETho LRHS LSRN MGos NLar NTay SCob SCoo SNig SPer SWvt
	'Hågelby Blue' (Vt)	NHaw
	'Hågelby Pink' (Vt) Υ^{H6}	CRHN CWGN ELan NHaw
	'Hågelby White' (Vt)	CRHN CWGN ELan NHaw
	'Hagley Hybrid' (LL)	CArg CBcs CKel CMac CRos CWCL EBee EHyd ELan EPfP ETho GMcL LRHS LSRN MAsh MGos MRav NLar NRHS NTay NWea SCob SCoo SGsty SNig SOrN SPer SPoG SRms SWvt
	'Hakuōkan' (EL)	EPfP LSRN SCoo WSpi
	'Hanaguruma' (EL)	ETho LSRN SNig
	'Happy Anniversary' (EL)	ETho LBuc LCro LOPS LSRN NLar NTay
§	HAPPY BIRTHDAY ('Zohapbi'^{PBR}) (LL) Υ^{H6}	CWCL LCro LOPS LSRN NTay SNig WSpi
	'Happy Diana' (T)	NHaw
	HARLOW CARR ('Evipo004'^{PBR})	CRos EHyd EPfP LRHS NRHS NTay SCoo SRms
	'Haru Ichiban' (EL)	ETho
	'Hayate'	CWGN
§	'Helios' (Ta)	CRos ETho NTay
	'Helsingborg' (A) Υ^{H6}	CDoC CKel CRos EHyd ELan EPfP ETho LRHS MAsh NLar NTay SCoo SPoG SRms
	aff. 'Helsingborg' (A)	NTay
I	'Hendersonii' (I)	GElm LRHS LSRN LSto MCot
	hendersonii Koch	see *C.* × *diversifolia* 'Hendersonii'
	hendersonii Stand.	see *C.* × *diversifolia*
I	'Hendersonii Rubra' (Ar)	EDir LRHS SCoo
	'Hendryetta'^{PBR} (I)	CWGN NTay SWvt
	henryi	CKel LSRN MAsh NTay SNig
	- B&SWJ 3402	WCru
	- var. ***morii*** B&SWJ 1668	WCru
	'Henryi' (EL)	CDoC CMac CRos CTri EBee ELan EPfP LCro LOPS LRHS LSRN MRav MSwo NRHS SPer SPoG
	heracleifolia	CBod CMac CSBt ECtt ELan GLog SBls WHlf
	- 'Blue Dwarf' (H)	CWGN
	- 'Cassandra' (H) Υ^{H5}	CRos CSpe CWGN ECtt EHyd ELan ELon EPfP ETho EWld GLog LBar LRHS LSRN MCot MHer MHol NRHS NTay SMDa SRms WCot WTre
	- 'China Purple' (H)	CBod ECtt GBin LBar LRHS MHol
	- var. ***davidiana***	see *C. tubulosa*
	- 'Pink Dwarf' (H)	CWGN NHaw NTay
	- 'Roundway Blue Bird' (H)	SMDa
	hexapetala Forster	see *C. forsteri*
	hexasepala	see *C. forsteri*
	hirsutissima	SBrt
	- var. ***scottii***	EBee SBrt
	'Honora' (LL)	CRos CWGN EHyd LRHS MAsh NRHS NTay SCoo SNig
	'Hope' (A)	LRHS
	'Horn of Plenty' (EL)	EHyd ETho LRHS
	'Hoshi-no-flamenco' (T)	CWGN
	huchouensis	NHaw
	HUDSON RIVER ('Zo06137'^{PBR}) (I)	NTay
	'Huldine' (LL) Υ^{H6}	CBcs CKel CRHN CWCL ELan EPfP ETho LRHS LSRN MRav NTay SCoo SNig SPer SWvt
	'Huvi' (LL)	CWGN NHaw
	'Hybrida Sieboldii' (EL)	SCoo
	HYDE HALL ('Evipo009'^{PBR}) (EL)	CKel CMac CRos CWCL CWGN EHyd ELan EPfP LRHS MAsh MGos NRHS NTay SCoo SNig SRms
	'Hythe Egret' (Fo)	WIce
	I AM A LITTLE BEAUTY ('Zolibe') (Vt)	CRHN EBee NHaw NTay SNig
	I AM HAPPY ('Zoiamha') (Vt)	CWGN ELan NTay
	I AM LADY J ('Zoiamlj') (Vt)	ELan NHaw
	I AM LADY Q ('Zoiamladyq'^{PBR}) (Vt)	CWGN EBee ETho NHaw NTay
	I AM RED ROBIN ('Zorero'^{PBR}) (A)	CWGN NTay
	ianthina var. ***kuripoensis***	EBtc SBrt
	- - B&SWJ 700	WCru
	'Ibi' (EL)	CWGN WSpi
	ICE BLUE ('Evipo003'^{PBR}) (Prairie Series) (EL)	CRos CWCL EHyd ELan EPfP ETho LRHS MAsh NLar NTay SCoo
	'Ice Queen' (EL)	MAsh
	indivisa Willd.	see *C. paniculata* J.G.Gmel.
	INES ('Evipo059'^{PBR}) (Boulevard Series)	CRos EHyd ETho LRHS NRHS NTay SNig
	'Ingrid Biedenkopf' (Vt)	NHaw
	'Innocent Blush'^{PBR} (EL)	EBee EPfP ETho SNig
	'Innocent Glance'^{PBR} (EL)	EBee ETho SNig
	INSPIRATION ('Zoin'^{PBR}) (I)	NLar NTay SCoo
	integrifolia (I)	CCBP ELan EPfP ETho GArf GKev GQue LRHS MBriF NChi NHaw NLar NPer NTay SRms WHlf WHoo WMal
I	- 'Alba' (I)	CRos CWCL ECtt EPfP ETho GKev LRHS LSRN NHaw NLar NTay SCoo SRms
	- 'Baby Blue' (I)	NHaw
	- 'Baby Rose' (I) **new**	NHaw
	- 'Baby White' (I) **new**	NHaw
	- 'Blue Ribbons' (I)	CSpe NCth NLar SBls WFar
	- dark blue-flowered (I)	GKev
	- 'Gletschereis' (I)	CWCL
	- 'Hendersonii' Koch	see *C.* × *diversifolia* 'Hendersonii'
	- MONGOLIAN BELLS ('Psharlan') (I)	CSpe CWCL NCth NHaw
	- 'Olgae'	see *C.* × *diversifolia* 'Olgae'
	- 'Ozawa's Blue' (I)	CWGN MBNS NTay WAvo
	- violet-flowered (I)	GKev
	- white-flowered	see *C. integrifolia* 'Alba'
	intricata 'Harry Smith' (Ta)	NHaw WSpi
	ISABELLA ('Zo12220') (EL)	IPot LRHS NTay
	ispahanica	NHaw SBrt
	'Iubileinyi-70' (LL)	NHaw
	'Ivan Olsson' (EL)	CWCL ETho LCro SNig
	'Jackmanii' (LL) Υ^{H6}	CArg CBcs CMac CRos CTri EBee EHyd EPfP ETho GDam GMcL LCro LOPS LRHS LSRN MAsh MCot MGos NTay NWea SCob SCoo SPoG SWvt
	'Jackmanii Alba' (EL)	CRos EHyd ELan EPfP ETho LRHS LSRN MAsh NTay SCoo SPoG
	JACKMANII PURPUREA ('Zojapur'^{PBR}) (LL)	ETho LCro NTay
	'Jackmanii Rubra' (EL)	NTay
	'Jackmanii Superba' misapplied	see *C.* 'Gipsy Queen'

	'Jackmanii Superba' ambig. (LL)	CDoC CKel CRos CWCL EHyd ELan EPfP ETho LCro LOPS LRHS MAsh MGos MRav MSwo NPer NTay NWea SCob SNig SPer SPoG
	'Jacqueline du Pré' (A) 🏆^{H6}	CBcs CDoC EBee ELan EPfP LRHS NTay
	'James Mason' (EL)	ETho
	'Jan Fopma'^{PBR} (I)	CWGN NTay
	'Jan Lindmark' (A/d)	CDoC CKel CRos EHyd EPfP ETho LRHS MAsh NLar NRHS NTay SCoo SNig SPoG SPre
§	'Jan Paweł II' (EL)	EHyd ELan ETho LRHS SCoo SNig SPer
	'Jane Ashdown' (M)	NHaw
§	***japonica***	NHaw WFar
	'Jean Caldwell' (Vt)	NHaw
	'Jean Cumpston' (C)	NHaw
	'Jeanne's Pink' (EL)	ETho NTay
I	'Jenny' (Cedergren) (LL)	ETho NHaw
	'Jenny' (M/d)	LRHS LSRN SPoG WSpi
	'Jenny Caddick' (Vt)	NHaw
	JEWEL OF MERK	see *C.* HAPPY BIRTHDAY
	'Joan Baker' (Vt)	CRHN
	'John Gould Veitch' (EL)	EBtc
	JOHN HOWELLS ('Zojohnhowells'^{PBR}) (Vt)	CWCL CWGN LSRN NTay WSpi
	'John Huxtable' (LL)	EHyd ETho LRHS NTay SNig WSpi
	JOHN PAUL II	see *C.* 'Jan Paweł II'
	'John Treasure' (Vt)	CRHN NHaw
	'John Warren' (EL)	EHyd LRHS MAsh NRHS SCoo
	JOSEPHINE ('Evijohill'^{PBR}) (EL)	CDoC CKel CRos CWCL CWGN EHyd EPfP ETho LCro LOPS LRHS LSRN MAsh MGos NLar NRHS NTay SCoo SNig SPer SPoG SWvt WSpi
	'Josie's Midnight Blue' (V)	NHaw
§	× ***jouiniana***	MRav NHaw SEND SHar SWvt WSHC
	- 'Chance' (H)	NTay
	JULIANE ('Evipo049'^{PBR})	ETho NTay SNig
	'Julka' (EL)	CDoC CWCL EPfP ETho MGos NHaw SNig WSpi
	'Justa' (Vt)	ETho MGos NHaw NLar
	'Juuli' (I)	LSRN NHaw
	'Kaaru' (LL)	CRHN NHaw
	'Kacper' (EL)	NHaw
	'Kaiser'^{PBR}	ETho SNig
	'Kaiu' (V)	CWGN IPot NHaw NTay
§	'Kakio' (EL)	CWCL EHyd EPfP ETho LRHS LSRN MAsh MGos NTay SCoo SNig SPer
I	'Kamilla' (EL)	CWGN
§	'Kardynał Wyszyński' (EL)	SNig
§	'Kasmu' (Vt)	NHaw
	'Kathleen Dunford' (EL)	LSRN NTay SCoo
	'Kathryn Chapman' (Vt)	CRHN CWGN NHaw
	'Kaunitar' (LL)	NHaw
	'Ken Donson' (EL) 🏆^{H6}	LRHS SCoo
	'Kermesina' (Vt) 🏆^{H6}	CDoC CKel CRHN EBee EHyd ELan EPfP ETho LCro LOPS LRHS MAsh NTay SCoo SPer SPoG SRms WBor
	'Kiev' (Vt)	CRHN NHaw
	'Killifreth' (Vt)	CRHN NHaw
	KIMIKO ('Evipo066'^{PBR}) (Boulevard Series) (Fo)	CKel CRos EHyd LRHS NRHS NTay SNig SPoG
	'King Edward VII' (EL)	LRHS
	KINGFISHER ('Evipo037'^{PBR}) (EL)	CRos CWCL EHyd ELan EPfP ETho LCro LRHS NTay SCoo SPoG
	'Kinju Atarashi' (LL)	CWCL NTay
	'Kiri Te Kanawa' (EL)	CWCL EPfP LRHS NLar NTay SNig WSpi
	kirilowii	NHaw
	KITTY ('Evipo097') (EL)	CRos EHyd ETho LRHS NRHS NTay SCoo SNig SPoG WSpi

	'Kokonoe' (d) **new**	CWGN IPot LCro WHlf
	'Kommerei' (LL)	NHaw
	KÖNIGIN MAXIMA ('Wellmax'^{PBR}) (T)	CWGN IPot NHaw
§	'Königskind' (EL)	ETho NLar
	'Korean Beauty' (Ta)	WHil
	koreana	MAsh WCru
	- AMBER ('Wit141205'^{PBR}) (A)	CWGN EHyd ELan ETho IPot LCro LOPS LRHS NRHS NTay WHlf
	- var. ***carunculosa***	WSHC
	- - B&SWJ 12725	WCru
	- - 'Lemon Bells' (A)	CRos EHyd EPfP LRHS SCoo SPoG
	- - 'Love Child' (A)	NTay
	'Krakowiak'^{PBR} (Vt)	EBee NHaw SNig
	ladakhiana	NHaw
	- CC 7135 **new**	GGro
	'Lady Betty Balfour' (LL)	CMac EHyd ETho LRHS NTay SCoo SWvt
	'Lady Bird Johnson' (T)	CWCL EHyd LRHS LSRN SCoo
	'Lady Caroline Nevill' (EL)	LRHS NRHS
	'Lady Kyoko' (d)	LCro
	'Lady Londesborough' (EL)	NHaw
	'Lady Northcliffe' (EL)	CTri EPfP ETho MAsh NTay
	'Lambton Park' (Ta) 🏆^{H6}	CRHN ETho NHaw NLar NTay
	lasiandra	NHaw
	'Last Dance' (Ta)	CRHN EBee
	LASTING LOVE	see *C.* 'Grażyna'
	'Lasurstern' (EL) 🏆^{H6}	CArg CBcs CMac CRos CTri EBee EHyd ELan EPfP ETho LCro LOPS LRHS LSRN MAsh NTay SCob SPer SPoG SWvt WFar
	'Laura Denny' (EL)	ETho
	'Lavender Twirl' (Vt)	CRHN
	'Lawsoniana' (EL)	LRHS
	'Lech Wałęsa' (EL)	ETho
	'Lemon Beauty' (A)	ETho SNig
	'Lemon Chiffon' (EL)	EHyd LRHS
	'Lemon Dream'^{PBR} (A)	ETho LRHS SNig
	LIBERATION ('Evifive'^{PBR}) (EL)	NLar SCoo SNig WSpi
	LIBERTY ('Zo08095'^{PBR}) (EL)	ETho IPot NTay
	ligusticifolia	NHaw
	'Lilac Wine' (I)	NHaw
	'Lilacina Floribunda' (EL)	SNig
	'Lily the Pink' (Vt)	NHaw
	'Lincoln Star' (EL)	CArg CMac EHyd LRHS MAsh SWvt
	'Lisboa' (Vt)	CRHN NHaw
	'Little Bas' (Vt)	CDoC CRHN CWGN ELan ETho NHaw NTay
	'Little Butterfly' (Vt)	CRHN NHaw
	LITTLE LEMONS ('Zo14100') (Ta) **new**	CWGN LCro NTay
	'Little Mermaid' (EL)	EPfP LCro LOPS NTay
	'Little Nell' (Vt)	CCCN CRHN EBee ELan EPfP ETho LRHS LSRN MAsh NLar NTay SCoo
	'Liviana' (V)	NHaw
	'Long Tall Sally' (V) **new**	NHaw
	'Lord Herschell'	CWCL CWGN ETho
	'Lord Nevill' (EL)	EPfP LRHS
	'Louise Rowe' (EL)	CWCL EHyd ELan ETho LRHS LSRN NTay
	'Love Jewelry' (EL)	SNig
	LUCKY CHARM ('Zo09067'^{PBR}) (LL)	CWGN NTay
	LULA ('Evipo057'^{PBR}) (Boulevard Series)	CWGN NTay SNig
	'Lunar Lass' (Fo/f)	GArf NRHS NTay WAbe
	'Luxuriant Blue' (Vt)	CRHN MAsh NHaw NTay
	'M. Koster' (Vt)	CDoC CRHN ETho LRHS NHaw NTay SRms
	macropetala (d)	CDoC CEme CKel CRos EHeP EHyd ELan EPfP ETho GGro GMcL LRHS

		MAsh MGos MMuc MRav NRHS SCoo SNig SPer
	- 'Blue Lagoon'	see *C. macropetala* 'Lagoon' Jackman 1959
	- 'Lagoon' Jackman 1956	see *C. macropetala* 'Maidwell Hall' Jackman
§	- 'Lagoon' Jackman 1959 (A/d) ♀H6	EHyd ETho LCro LOPS LRHS LSRN MAsh MSwo NHol NRHS NTay SCoo
	- 'Maidwell Hall' ambig.	CKel
§	- 'Maidwell Hall' Jackman (A/d)	CTri EPfP LSRN MAsh NTay
	- 'Maidwell Hall' O.E.P.Wyatt (A)	CBcs SCob
	- 'Wesselton' (A/d) ♀H6	CBcs CDoC CRos CTri EHyd EPfP ETho LCro LOPS LRHS MAsh NLar NRHS NTay SPoG SPre SRms
	- 'White Moth'	see *C.* 'White Moth'
	'Madame Baron-Veillard' (LL)	EHyd ETho LRHS SCoo
	'Madame Édouard André' (LL)	CRos CWCL EHyd EPfP ETho LRHS MAsh NRHS NTay SCoo
	'Madame Grangé' (LL)	EHyd LRHS NHaw SCoo
	'Madame Julia Correvon' (Vt) ♀H6	CDoC CKel CRHN CTri CWCL EBee EHyd ELan EPfP ETho LCro LOPS LRHS LSRN MAsh MCot MGos MPri NLar NRHS NTay SCob SCoo SNig SPer SPoG SSta SWvt
	'Madame le Coultre'	see *C.* 'Mevrouw Le Coultre'
	'Majojo' (Fo)	GEdr
	MANDY ('Zo12153') **new**	NTay
	MANON ('Evipo054'PBR) (Boulevard Series) (EL)	CRos EHyd EPfP LRHS NRHS NTay SNig
	marata	WThu
	'Margaret Hunt' (LL)	ETho LSRN NHaw NTay
	'Mari' (LL)	NHaw
	'Maria' Kivistik (LL)	NHaw
	'Maria Băsescu'	NTay
	'Maria Cornelia'PBR (Vt)	CWGN ETho IPot LCro NTay
	'Maria Louise Jensen' (EL)	IPot
	'Maria Skłodowska-Curie'PBR (EL)	SNig
	'Marie Boisselot' (EL) ♀H6	CArg CBcs CKel CMac CTri CWCL EHyd ELan EPfP ETho LCro LRHS LSRN MAsh MGos MPri MSwo NLar NTay SCob SCoo SNig SPoG SWvt
	'Marinka'	CWGN
	'Marjorie' (M/d)	Widely available
	'Markham's Pink' (A/d) ♀H6	CArg CBcs CDoC CKel CTri CWCL EHyd ELan EPfP GMcL LCro LOPS LRHS LSRN MAsh MGos MRav MSwo NHol NLar NRHS NTay SCob SPer SPoG SRms SWvt WFar
	marmoraria	CRos EHyd EPot LRHS NRHS SPlb SRms WAbe
	marmoraria × petriei	EPot
	'Marmori' (LL)	CWGN NHaw
	MARTA ('Evipo071'PBR) (Garland Series)	SNig
	'Mary Habberley' (Vt)	NHaw
	'Mary Rose'	see *C. viticella* 'Flore Pleno'
	MASA ('Evipo089'PBR) (Garland Series)	CWGN ETho
	maximowicziana	see *C. terniflora*
	'Mayleen' (M) ♀H5	CBod CKel CTri EDir EPfP ETho LRHS MAsh MMuc MRav NRHS NTay SCoo SNig SPer SPoG SRms SWvt WFar
	'Meghan' (EL) **new**	LCro NTay
I	'Melodie' (Vt)	NHaw
§	'Mevrouw Le Coultre' (EL)	GMcL NTay WHlf
	'Mia' (EL/d)	CWGN
	MIENIE BELLE ('Zomibel'PBR) (T)	CWGN NHaw
	'Mikelite' (Vt)	LRHS NHaw
	'Miniseelik' (LL)	NHaw
	'Minuet' (Vt) ♀H6	CDoC CKel CRHN EBee EHyd EPfP LCro LOPS LRHS MAsh MGos NTay SCoo SNig SPer SPoG SWvt
	MIRABELLE ('Evipo072'PBR) (Boulevard Series)	NTay SNig
	MIRANDA ('Floclemi'PBR) (I)	CWGN NHaw
	'Miss Bateman' (EL)	CDoC CKel CMac CRos CTri CWCL EBee EHyd ELan EPfP ETho GDam GMcL LCro LOPS LRHS LSRN MAsh MGos NRHS NTay SCob SCoo SNig SOrN SPer SPoG WBor
	'Miss Christine' (M)	CDoC ELan ETho LCro LOPS LSRN NTay SPoG SWvt
	MISSISSIPPI RIVER ('Zomisri') (I)	LRHS
	'Mister Hans Horn' (Vt)	NHaw
	MON AMOUR ('Zomoa'PBR) (EL)	CWGN NTay
	MON CHERRY ('Zomonch') (EL)	CWGN
	montana	CPla EHeP GDam MAsh SCob SEWo SGbt WJur
	- W&O 7064	GGro
	- W&O 7065	GGro
	- WJC 13713 from the Himalaya	WCru
	- var. ***alba***	see *C. montana* var. *montana*
	- 'Alexander' (M)	CRos EHyd EPfP LRHS NRHS SPoG
	- 'Da Yun' (M)	CWGN
	- var. ***grandiflora*** (M) ♀H5	Widely available
I	- 'Lilacina' (M)	NLar
§	- var. ***montana***	CBar CBcs CBod CSBt EDir ETho GDam GMcL LCro LOPS LRHS NWea SNig SPer SPoG WFar
	- var. ***rubens*** misapplied	see *C. montana* var. *montana*
	- var. ***rubens*** Buch.-Ham. ex DC.	CDoC CRos CSBt CTri EHyd ELan GMcL LRHS NHol NRHS SPlb
I	- - 'Odorata' (M)	EPfP ETho GKin MRav NTay SCoo
	- - 'Pink Perfection' (M)	CDoC CKel CMac CRHN CRos EDir EHyd ELan EPfP ETho GKin LCro LOPS LRHS LSRN MAsh NRHS NTay SCoo SNig SOrN SPer SPoG SWvt WFar
I	- - 'Rubens Superba' (M)	CTri ECtt ETho GKin LPar NTay SRms WFar
	- - 'Tetrarose' (M) ♀H5	Widely available
	- var. ***sericea***	see *C. spooneri*
	- var. ***wilsonii***	CBod CKel CWCL ECtt EDir EHyd ELan EPfP ETho GKin GLog LRHS LSRN MMuc MRav MSwo NTay SPer SPoG SRms SWvt
	'Monte Cassino' (EL)	CWGN SNig
	'Moonbeam' (Fo)	EPot GEdr ITim WIce
	'Moonglow' (EL)	CWCL ETho LCro NTay SNig
§	'Moonlight' (EL)	LRHS MAsh
	MORNING CLOUD	see *C.* 'Yukikomachi'
	'Morning Heaven' (Vt)	CRHN NHaw NTay
	MORNING STAR ('Zoklako'PBR) (EL)	CWGN
	MORNING YELLOW ('Cadmy'PBR) (M)	CCCN EDir GMcL LRHS SCoo
	'Mrs Cholmondeley' (EL) ♀H6	CKel CWCL EHyd ELan EPfP ETho LRHS LSRN MAsh MDon MGos MPri MSwo NLar NTay SCob SCoo SNig SPer SPoG WHlf
	'Mrs George Jackman' (EL) ♀H6	CWCL EBee EHyd ETho LRHS NLar NTay SCoo SNig WSpi
	'Mrs James Mason' (EL)	EBee

	'Mrs N.Thompson' (EL)	CArg CDoC CKel CMac CTri CWCL EBee EHyd ELan ETho LCro LRHS LSRN LSto MAsh MGos NHol NPer NTay SNig SPer SSut
	'Mrs P.B.Truax' (EL)	EPfP ETho
	'Mrs Robert Brydon' (H)	CWCL NTay SRms
	'Mrs T. Lundell' (Vt)	CRHN EPfP LRHS NHaw
	'Multi Blue' (EL)	CArg CBcs CKel CRos CWCL EDir EHyd ELan EPfP GMcL LRHS LSRN MAsh MGos NLar NTay SCoo SNig SPer SPoG SRkn SRms WSpi
	MULTI PINK ('St17333') (d) **new**	CWGN LCro
	'My Angel'PBR (Ta)	ELan ETho IPot LCro LOPS LRHS NTay WSpi
	'My Darling' (EL)	SNig
	'Myōjō' (EL)	LRHS
	MYOSOTIS ('Zo08159') (EL)	LRHS NTay
§	***napaulensis***	CWCL ELan EPfP ETho LCro LOPS MNrw NHaw SPtp WCru WHlf WSpi
I	'Natacha' (EL)	EBee NHaw NLar NTay SCoo
	'Natascha' (EL)	CWCL ETho LSRN SWvt
	'Negritianka' (LL)	NHaw
	'Negus' (LL)	NHaw
	'Nelly Moser' (EL) ♀H6	Widely available
	'Nelly Moser Neu' (EL)	GMcL
	NEVA ('Evipo050'PBR) (Boulevard Series) (EL)	EHyd LRHS NLar NRHS NTay SNig
	'New Love'PBR (H)	CWGN ETho LCro LOPS LSRN NCth NTay SPoG WHil
	'Night Veil' (Vt)	CDoC MGos NHaw
	NINON ('Evipo052'PBR) (Boulevard Series)	CBod CWGN EPfP LRHS NTay SCoo SNig
	'Niobe' (EL) ♀H6	Widely available
	'North Star' (EL)	ETho
	NUBIA ('Evipo079'PBR) (Boulevard Series) (LL)	CBod CRos CWCL CWGN EPfP ETho LCro LRHS LSou NLar NTay WTyc
	'Nunn's Gift' (Fo)	NTay
	nutans var. ***thyrsoidea***	see *C. rehderiana*, *C. veitchiana*
	'Oberek' (Vt)	CRHN NHaw
	'Ocean Pearl' (A)	LSRN NTay
	ochotensis	GKev
	ochroleuca	NHaw
	OCTOPUS ('Zooct'PBR) (A)	CWGN NTay
	'Odoriba' (V)	CRHN CWGN NHaw
	OLYMPIA ('Evipo099'PBR) (Boulevard Series)	ETho LRHS MGos NTay SNig
	'Omoshiro' (EL)	CWCL CWGN ETho IPot LRHS NHaw NTay
§	OOH LA LA ('Evipo041'PBR) (Boulevard Series) (EL)	CRos CWCL EHyd EPfP ETho LRHS MAsh MGos NRHS NTay SCoo SNig SPer SPoG WSpi
	orientalis misapplied	see *C. tibetana* subsp. *vernayi*
	orientalis ambig.	SRms
	orientalis L.	EBee EPfP GGro SCoo SWvt
	- PAB 13.731	LEdu
	- from Kyrgyzstan	WPGP
	- 'Orange Peel'	see *C. tibetana* subsp. *vernayi* var. *vernayi* 'Orange Peel'
	- var. ***orientalis***	ETho
	- 'Sherriffii'	see *C.* 'Sherriffii'
	orientalis* × *tangutica	SWvt
	'Oshikiri' (V)	NHaw
	otophora	NHaw
	'Ovation'PBR (Fo)	LCro LOPS NTay
	'Pagoda' (Vt)	CRHN EBee EPfP LRHS SCoo SRms
	'Pamela' (F)	NHaw NTay
	'Pamela Jackman' (A)	see *C. alpina* 'Pamela Jackman'
	'Pamiat Serdtsa' (I)	ELon NHaw
	'Pamina' (EL)	ETho MGos NLar
	'Pangbourne Pink' (I) ♀H6	EHyd EPfP LRHS NHaw NRHS SCoo
	paniculata Thunb.	see *C. terniflora*
§	***paniculata*** J.G. Gmel.	MNrw
	- var. ***lobata***	WSpi
	'Paradise Queen' (EL)	ETho NTay
	PARADISO ('Zo11154') (EL)	LCro LOPS LRHS NTay
	PARISIENNE ('Evipo019'PBR) (Boulevard Series) (EL)	CDoC CRos CWCL CWGN EHyd EPfP ETho LRHS MAsh NLar NRHS NTay SCoo SPoG
	parviflora DC.	see *C. campaniflora*
	parviloba var. ***bartlettii*** B&SWJ 6788	WCru
	'Pastel Pink' (I)	NHaw
	'Pastel Princess' (EL)	ETho
	'Pat Coleman' (EL)	CWCL ETho
	patens 'Korean Moon' (EL)	WCru
§	- 'Manshuu Ki' (EL)	CKel EHyd ETho LRHS SNig
	- 'Yukiokoshi' (EL)	EBee ETho
	PATRICIA ANN FRETWELL ('Pafar') (EL)	NTay SNig
§	'Paul Farges' (Vb) ♀H6	CArg CDoC CKel CWGN EPfP EShb ETho GLog IPot MNrw NHaw NLar NTay SMDa
	PAULIE ('Evipo058'PBR) (EL) **new**	SNig
	'Pauline' (A/d) ♀H6	EHyd ETho LRHS LSRN NTay SCoo
	'Peggy West' (LL)	NHaw
	'Pendragon' (Vt)	CRHN NHaw
	'Pennell's Purity' (LL)	NTay
	PEPPERMINT ('Evipo005'PBR) (d)	EHyd ELan EPfP NTay SCoo
	'Perida' (LL)	CWGN
	'Perle d'Azur' (LL) ♀H6	CBcs CDoC CRHN CTri CWCL EBee EHyd ELan EPfP ETho LCro LOPS LRHS LSRN MAsh MGos MSwo NTay SCob SCoo SPoG SRms WFar WSpi
	PERNILLE ('Zo09113'PBR) (Vt)	CWGN ETho LCro LRHS NTay SGsty
	'Perrin's Pride' (Vt)	CRos EBee EHyd LRHS MGos NHaw NTay SCoo
	PETIT FAUCON ('Evisix'PBR) (I) ♀H6	CKel CWCL EHyd EPfP ETho LRHS LSRN MGos MMrt NLar NTay SCoo SPer SRms SWvt
	petriei	WThu
	'Peveril Pristine' (Vt)	CWGN NHaw
	'Peveril Profusion' (T)	NHaw
	PICARDY ('Evipo024'PBR) (EL)	CRos CWCL EHyd EPfP ETho LRHS MAsh NRHS NTay SCoo SNig SPoG WSpi
	PICOTEE ('Zo09124'PBR) (EL)	CWGN ETho LRHS NTay WSpi
I	'Picton's Variety' (M)	ETho MGos
	'Piilu' (EL)	CArg CDoC CRos CWCL CWGN EBee EHyd ELan EPfP ETho GMcL LCro LRHS LSRN MAsh MBNS NLar NTay SCoo SGsty SNig SRkn
	PINK CHAMPAGNE	see *C.* 'Kakio'
	'Pink Fantasy' (LL)	CTri ETho MAsh NLar NTay SCoo SNig SRkn WHlf
	'Pink Flamingo' (A) ♀H6	CRos CWCL EHyd ELan EPfP ETho LRHS LSto MGos NRHS NTay SCoo SNig SPoG
	'Pink Swing' (A)	ETho
	'Pirko' (Vt)	NHaw
§	***pitcheri***	CWGN NHaw NTay SBrt
	- from Illinois	SBrt
	'Pixie' (Fo/m)	CBod CDoC ELan EPfP ETho GMcL LCro LOPS LRHS MGos NBwr NLar NTay SCoo SPoG
I	'Pleniflora' (M/d)	NTay
	pogonandra	NHaw
	POLAR BEAR	see *C.* ARCTIC QUEEN

'Poldice' (Vt) ♀H6	CRHN
'Polish Spirit' (LL) ♀H6	Widely available
'Polonez' (Vt)	NHaw
potaninii 'Summer Snow'	see *C.* 'Paul Farges'
'Praecox' (H) ♀H6	CDoC CKel CRHN CWCL EBee EHyd EPfP ETho LRHS LSto MCot NQui NTay SAdn SMrm SPer WCot WGwG
'Prairie River' (A)	WSpi
PRETTY IN BLUE ('Zopre'PBR) (F)	ETho SWvt
'Primrose Star'	see *C.* 'Star'
'Prince Charles' (LL) ♀H6	CDoC CKel CRHN CTri CWCL ELan EPfP ETho IPot LCro LOPS LRHS LSRN MCot NHaw NLar NTay SCoo SNig SPer SWvt
'Prince George' (LL)	CDoC CWCL EPfP ETho LCro LOPS LSRN MGos NLar NTay WHlf
'Prince Louis' (EL) **new**	LCro
'Prince Philip' (EL)	ETho LCro LOPS
PRINCE WILLIAM ('Zo08171') (EL)	CWGN IPot LCro LOPS NTay
'Princess Charlotte' (EL)	ETho LCro LOPS NTay
§ 'Princess Diana' (T) ♀H5	CBcs CKel CRHN CSBt CTri CWGN EBee EGrI EHyd ELan EPfP ETho IPot LBuc LCro LOPS LRHS LSRN MBlu MCot MSwo NHol NTay SCoo SNig SOrN SPer SPoG SRms SWvt
PRINCESS KATE ('Zoprika'PBR) (T)	CKel CWGN EBee EHyd EPfP ETho LCro LOPS LPar LRHS MBlu MGos MPri NRHS NTay SCoo SPoG WBor WCot WSpi
§ 'Princess of Wales' (1875) (EL)	CDoC CWCL LSRN NLar SWvt
'Princess Red' (V) **new**	NHaw
'Propertius' (A)	CArg CDoC CWCL CWGN EHyd EPfP ETho LRHS MGos NLar NTay SNig SPoG WSpi
'Prosperity' (M)	CRHN ETho
'Proteus' (EL)	CKel EHyd ELan EPfP ETho LRHS MAsh MGos NLar NTay SCoo SNig
psilandra CWJ 12377	WCru
'Purple Dream'PBR (A)	ETho SNig
'Purple Haze' (Vt)	CRHN NHaw
'Purple Princess' (H)	CDoC LRHS SCoo SPoG
'Purple Rain' (A)	CDoC NLar
'Purple Spider' (A/d)	EPfP ETho LRHS MAsh MBlu NTay SCoo
'Purpurea Plena Elegans' (Vt/d) ♀H6	CBcs CDoC CKel CMac CRHN CRos CTri CWCL EBee EHyd ELan EPfP ETho LCro LOPS LRHS LSRN MAsh MSwo NHol NRHS NTay SCob SCoo SNig SPer SPoG SWvt WBor
QUEEN MOTHER ('Zoqum') (Vt)	CWGN EBee EPfP ETho LRHS NTay SCoo
'Radar Love' (Ta)	LSto
'Radiance'	CWGN NHaw NLar
'Ramona' (LL)	EHyd LRHS LSRN
ranunculoides	NHaw
- W&O 7069	GGro
'Rapture' (T)	NHaw
'Raspberry Ripple' (V)	NHaw
'Rasputin' (LL)	CWGN ETho
REBECCA ('Evipo016'PBR) (EL)	CDoC CRos CWCL CWGN EHyd ELan EPfP ETho LCro LOPS LRHS LSRN MAsh MGos NRHS NTay SCoo SPer SPoG WSpi
recta	ECtt GAbr MNrw NHaw NLar WOld
- PAB 9005	LEdu
- 'Purpurea' (F)	CDor EHyd ELan EMor EPfP ETho GKev LRHS MAvo MBriF MCot MHol MNrw NChi NTay NWea SEND SPtp WHlf
- 'Velvet Night' (F)	CBod ECtt LRHS NLar NSti WCot
'Red 5' (T)	NHaw
'Red Ballon' (Ta)	IPot
'Red Cooler'	see *C.* 'Crimson King'
RED PASSION ('Zo11056'PBR) (EL/d) **new**	CWGN
'Red Pearl' (EL)	CKel CWCL LSRN
I 'Red Star' (d)	EBee
REFLECTIONS ('Evipo035') (LL)	CRos EHyd EPfP LRHS MAsh NTay
§ ***rehderiana*** ♀H5	CDoC CRHN EBee ELan EPfP ETho IDee LRHS MBlu NHaw NLar NTay SNig SWvt WCot WFar WSHC
aff. ***rehderiana*** BO 16-026	GGro
REIKO ('Evipo088'PBR) (Garland Series)	CWGN WHtc
'Reiman' (LL)	NHaw
REMBRANDT ('Zo16356') (M) **new**	CWGN
'Remembrance' (LL) ♀H6	ETho LSRN NHaw
reticulata	NHaw
'Retrousse' (V)	NHaw
'Reverie' (T)	NHaw
'Rhapsody' ambig.	CDoC EPfP LBuc MAsh MGos SCoo
'Rhapsody' B. Fretwell (EL)	CRos EHyd ETho LCro LRHS LSRN NHaw NTay
'Ribble Red' (V)	NHaw
'Richard Pennell' (EL) ♀H6	CDoC EHyd ETho LRHS
'Richard's Picotee' (Vt)	CRHN NHaw
'Rising Star'	NHaw
'Ristimägi' (LL)	NHaw
'Rituaal' (LL)	NHaw
'Roelie' (Vt)	NHaw
'Roko' (LL)	CWGN
'Roko-Kolla' (LL) ♀H6	ETho NHaw SNig
'Romance' (Vt)	NTay
'Romantika' (LL)	CRos EHyd ELan EPfP ETho LCro LRHS LSRN MAsh NHaw NRHS NTay SCoo SGsty
'Rooguchi' (I)	CDoC CWCL CWGN ETho NHaw NTay SCoo
'Rooran' (EL)	CWCL
'Rosa Königskind' (EL)	ETho NLar
ROSALYN ('Zo09087'PBR) (Vt)	CWGN ETho IPot NTay
'Rosamunde' (LL)	SNig
I 'Rosea' Westphal. (Vt)	CRHN NHaw
I 'Rosea' (I)	EPfP ETho LSRN NTay WHoo
ROSEBUD ('Robud'PBR) (M/d)	NPer
ROSEMOOR ('Evipo002'PBR) (EL)	CKel CRos CWCL CWGN EHyd EPfP LRHS MAsh NRHS NTay SCoo SNig SWvt
'Rosy O'Grady' (A) ♀H6	MAsh NLar SRms
'Rosy Pagoda' (A)	ELan ETho NLar NTay
'Rouge Cardinal' (LL)	CArg CBcs CDoC CKel CRos EBee EDir EHyd ELan EPfP ETho GMcL LRHS LSRN LSto MAsh MGos NRHS NTay SCob SCoo SNig SPer SPoG SRms
'Royal Velours' (Vt)	CKel CRHN CRos CTri ELan EPfP ETho LCro LOPS LRHS LSRN MAsh MGos NHol NLar NRHS NTay SCob SCoo SNig SPer SPoG WSpi
ROYAL VELVET ('Evifour'PBR) (EL)	EHyd LRHS LSRN SCoo
'Royal Wedding' (EL) **new**	LCro
'Royalty' (EL)	CDoC EHyd ELan EPfP ETho LCro LRHS LSRN MAsh SCoo WSpi

	'Rubens Superba'	see *C. montana* var. *rubens* 'Rubens Superba'
	'Rubra' (Vt)	NTay
	'Ruby' (A)	ELan EPfP ETho LRHS LSRN MAsh NTay SCoo SPer SRms
	'Ruby Celebration' (A)	CDoC
	'Ruby Glow' (EL)	EHyd EPfP LRHS LSRN SCoo
	'Ruby Tuesday' (V)	NHaw
	'Ruby Wedding' New Leaf Plants (EL)	see *C.* 'Ruby Wedding NLP2'
	'Ruby Wedding' Fretwell (T)	CWGN NHaw SWvt WSpi
§	'Ruby Wedding NLP2' (EL)	CWCL EPfP ETho LBuc LCro LSRN MGos NLar NTay
	'Rüütel' (EL)	CWCL ETho MAsh NHaw NTay SCoo SNig
	'Saalomon' (LL)	NHaw
	SABINE ('Bfccsab'PBR) (LL)	CWGN
	SACHA ('Evipo060') (EL)	CRos EHyd EPfP ETho LRHS NLar NRHS NTay SCoo SNig SPoG
	'Sakala' (EL)	WSpi
§	'Sakurahime' (EL)	IPot
	SALLY ('Evipo077'PBR) (EL)	CRos EHyd ELan EPfP ETho LRHS MAsh NLar NRHS NTay SCoo SNig SPoG
	SAMARITAN JO ('Evipo075')	CRos CWGN EHyd EPfP ETho LCro LRHS MAsh NLar NRHS NTay SCoo SNig SPoG
	'Sander' (H)	SMDa
	SAPHYRA DOUBLE ROSE ('Cleminov29'PBR) (LL) **new**	NHaw
	SAPHYRA INDIGO ('Cleminov 51'PBR) (I)	NHaw
	SARAH ELIZABETH ('Evipo098')	CRos ELan LCro LRHS MGos NLar NTay SCoo
	SAVANNAH ('Evipo015'PBR) (Vt)	MAsh
	'Scartho Gem' (EL)	LRHS SCoo SNig
§	'Scented Clem'PBR (Vt)	ETho LCro
	SEA BREEZE ('Zo09063'PBR) (Vt)	CWGN ETho LCro LOPS NTay WSpi
§	'Semu' (LL)	CWGN ETho NHaw NLar
	serratifolia	CBcs CTsd ECtt GKev GLog SBrt SPlb
	- B&SWJ 8458 from Korea	WCru
I	'Sherriffii' (Ta)	NLar SWvt
	'Shikoo' (EL)	CWCL EPfP ETho LSRN NLar NTay
	SHIMMER ('Evipo028'PBR) (LL)	CRos EHyd EPfP LRHS MAsh NRHS NTay SNig
§	***sibirica***	EHyd GDam NRHS
	- from Kazakhstan	GGro
	'Signe' (Vt)	see *C.* 'Kasmu'
	'Siirus' (EL)	NHaw
	'Silver Moon' (EL)	ETho LRHS NLar SCoo WSpi
	simsii Small	see *C. pitcheri*
	simsii Sweet	see *C. crispa*
§	'Sinii Dozhd' (I)	NHaw
§	'Sir Edward Elgar' (A)	LRHS NLar NRHS
	'Sir Eric Savill' (M)	CWGN ETho
	'Sir Trevor Lawrence' (T)	NHaw
	'Skyfall' (LL)	ETho SNig
	smilacifolia	WPGP
	'Snow Queen' (EL)	CDoC CKel CWCL EHyd EPfP ETho LRHS NTay SNig SOrN SRms
	'Snowbird' (A/d)	EHyd LRHS NTay SPoG
	'Snowdrift'	see *C. armandi* 'Snowdrift'
	SO MANY RED FLOWERS ('Zo06178'PBR) (EL)	NTay
	socialis	NHaw
	'Södertälje' (Vt)	CRHN ETho NHaw SCoo
	'Sokojiro' (EL)	ETho LRHS
	'Solina' (Vt)	NHaw
	songarica	GKev NHaw SBrt
	'Sonnette' (V)	CRHN CWGN IPot NHaw
	'Sophie' (V)	NHaw
	SORBET ('Zosor'PBR) (A)	NTay
§	'Souvenir du Capitaine Thuilleaux' (EL)	EDir ETho SNig
	'Special Occasion' (EL)	CWGN EHyd EPfP ETho LCro LRHS LSRN NLar NTay SCoo
	SPIKY ('Zospi'PBR) (A/d)	NTay
§	***spooneri***	CTsd EPfP ETho IDee LRHS NTay SCoo SGsty SWvt WSpi
	SPOTLIGHT ('Zo08160') (EL) **new**	IPot NTay
	SPRING JOY ('Zo12053'PBR) (M)	NTay SCoo SPoG
	'Sputnik' (I)	NHaw
	stans	CDoC ETho GGro
	- B&SWJ 5073	WCru
	- B&SWJ 6345	WCru
§	'Star'PBR (M/d)	CDoC EPfP LCro MGos NLar NTay
	'Star of India' (LL)	EHyd ELan EPfP ETho LRHS MGos NTay SCoo
	STAR OF PAKISTAN ('Zostapa') (LL)	CWGN
	STAR RIVER ('Zostarri'PBR) (I)	ELan NTay
I	'Starfish' (EL)	NHaw
	'Starlight' (M)	CWCL NTay SNig
	'Stasik' (LL)	NHaw
	'Stefan Franczak' (EL)	ETho
	STILL WATERS ('Zostiwa'PBR) (EL)	ETho
	'Strawberry Kiss' (V)	NHaw
	'Strawberry Splash' (V)	NHaw
	'Sue Reade' (V)	NHaw
	SUGAR CANDY ('Evione'PBR) (EL)	LRHS MAsh NTay SCoo
	SUGAR SWEET	see *C.* 'Scented Clem'
	SUMMER SNOW	see *C.* 'Paul Farges'
	SUMMERDREAM ('Zosumdre') (EL)	NTay
	'Sundance' (Ta)	NHaw
	SUNNY SKY ('Zosusk'PBR) (Vt)	NHaw NTay SGsty SNig
	'Sunrise' (M/d)	CDoC EBee EPfP ETho MSwo NLar NTay
	'Sunset' (EL) ♀H6	CArg CWCL EHyd EPfP ETho LRHS LSRN MGos NLar NTay SCoo SNig
	SUPER CUTE ('Zo09122') (Vt)	CWGN LCro NTay
	SUPER NIGHT ('Zo11112') (Vt)	CWGN IPot NTay
	SUPER NOVA ('Zo09088'PBR) (Vt)	ELan ETho NTay
	'Suzy Mac' (EL)	NTay
	'Swedish Bells' (I)	CWGN ETho
	'Sweet Scentsation' (F)	CDoC EPfP ETho LCro MGos NHaw NTay WSpi
	'Sweet Summer Love'PBR (F)	CDoC CWGN EPfP ETho LCro LOPS NHaw NTay
	SWEETHEART ('Witswe'PBR) (I)	ELan NTay
	'Sylvia Denny' (EL)	CArg EPfP ETho LRHS MAsh WSpi
	'Sylviorna' (v)	NHaw
	szuyuanensis CWJ 12455	WCru
	'Tae'	see *C.* 'Toltae'
	TAI YANG ('Evipo045'PBR) (Fo)	NTay
	'Taiga'PBR (d)	CBcs CRos CWGN ELan ETho IPot LCro LOPS LRHS NTay SCoo WHlf
	'Tamakazura' (V)	CWGN NHaw
	'Tango' (Vt)	CRHN NHaw
§	***tangutica***	Widely available
	'Tapestry' (I)	NHaw

	'Tartu' (EL)	NHaw
	tashiroi 'Yellow Peril'	WCru
	TEKLA ('Evipo069'[PBR]) (LL)	CRos CWCL EHyd ETho LCro LRHS NRHS NTay SCoo SNig SPoG WSpi
	'Teksa' (LL)	NHaw
	TEMPTATION ('Zotemp'[PBR]) (EL)	ETho MGos
	'Tentel' (LL)	NHaw
§	***terniflora***	EPfP ETho LRHS NHaw NTay
	- B&SWJ 5751	WCru
	- var. ***mandshurica***	ETho NHaw WSpi
	- - dwarf	CWGN
	texensis	NHaw WSHC
	- 'The Princess of Wales'	see *C.* 'Princess Diana'
	'The Bride' (EL)	CWCL CWGN ETho LSRN NTay
	THE COUNTESS OF WESSEX ('Evipo073') (EL)	CRos CWCL EHyd EPfP ETho LRHS NRHS NTay SCoo SNig SPoG
	'The First Lady' (EL)	CWCL ETho LCro
	'The President' (EL) ♀H6	CArg CDoC CKel CMac CTri CWCL EHeP EHyd ELan EPfP ETho GDam GMcL LCro LOPS LRHS LSRN MGos MSwo NLar NRHS NTay SCob SCoo SNig SPer SPoG SRms WFar WSpi
	'The Princess of Wales' (EL)	see *C.* 'Princess of Wales' (1875) (EL)
	'The Princess of Wales' (T)	see *C.* 'Princess Diana' (T)
	'The Vagabond' (EL)	CWCL CWGN ELan EPfP ETho LSRN MAsh NLar NTay SCoo SNig WSpi
§	THUMBELINA ('Evipo030'[PBR]) (EL)	CKel CRos CWCL EHyd EPfP ETho GMcL LRHS NRHS NTay SCoo SNig SPoG
	thunbergii misapplied	see *C. terniflora*
	'Thyrislund' (EL)	SNig
	tibetana	NHaw
	- 'Black Tibet' (Ta)	CWGN NHaw
§	- subsp. ***vernayi***	SCob
	- - 'Glasnevin Dusk' (Ta)	IArd IDee SMDa WSHC
	- - 'Lorcan O'Brien' (Ta)	IArd IDee
§	- - var. ***vernayi*** 'Orange Peel' LS&E 13342 (Ta)	ETho LRHS
	'Tie Dye' (LL)	CDoC CWGN ELan EPfP ETho LRHS NTay SCoo SNig SPoG SRms WHlf
	'Tim's Passion' (Vt)	CRHN
	'Titipu' (V)	NHaw
	'Toki' (EL)	CWGN ETho SCoo
§	'Toltae'[PBR] (EL)	CDoC CWGN EHyd LRHS NRHS
	tongluensis	WPGP
	TRANQUILITÉ ('Evipo111')	CDoC CRos EPfP LRHS MGos NTay SCoo
	'Tranquility'	CWGN
	'Triinu' (Vt)	NHaw
	'Trikatrei' (LL)	LRHS
§	× ***triternata*** 'Rubromarginata'	CDoC CKel CMac CRHN CRos CWCL CWGN EHyd ELan EPfP ETho GArf LCro LOPS LRHS LSRN MAsh MGos MRav NLar NRHS NTay SCob SCoo SPer SPoG SRms
	TRY ME ('Zotrym'[PBR]) (A/d)	NTay
	TSUKIKO ('Evipo110'[PBR]) (Garland Series)	CWGN ETho LCro
§	***tubulosa***	SMDa
	- 'Wyevale' (H)	CMac CRHN CRos EBee EHyd ELan EPfP ETho LRHS MCot MRav NRHS NTay SCoo SPer
	'Tuchka' (EL)	CWGN
	'Tudor' (EL)	WHlf
	'Tutti Frutti' (V) **new**	NHaw
	'Twilight' (EL)	CRos EHyd EPfP ETho LRHS MAsh
	TWINKLE ('Zotwi') (I)	CWGN ETho LRHS NTay
	TWINKLE BELL ('Wer01')	NTay
	uncinata	CBcs
	'Uno Kivistik'[PBR] (LL)	NHaw
§	***urophylla*** 'Winter Beauty'	CDoC CKel CWCL EBee ELan EPfP ETho LCro LOPS LRHS LSRN MAsh MGos NTay SCoo SPoG WHlf WSHC WSpi
	urticifolia	GGro
	- B&SWJ 8651	WCru
	- B&SWJ 8852	WCru
	'Utopia' (EL)	CWGN
	'Valge Daam' (LL)	CWGN NHaw
	'Valour' (Vt)	ETho LCro NHaw
	'Van Gogh' (M)	CWGN ETho SMDa
	'Vanessa' (LL)	CRHN NHaw
	'Vanso'	see *C.* 'Blue Light'
	'Varenne' (EL)	EBee ETho
§	× ***vedrariensis***	WSpi
§	***veitchiana***	NHaw
	'Venosa Violacea' (Vt) ♀H6	CDoC CKel CRHN CRos EHyd ELan EPfP ETho LRHS LSRN MAsh NHaw NHol NTay SCob SCoo SPer SPoG SRms
	'Vera' (M)	EPfP ETho LRHS LSRN NTay SCoo
	vernayi	see *C. tibetana* subsp. *vernayi*
	'Veronica's Choice' (EL)	CWCL ELan ETho NTay SNig
	VERSAILLES ('Evipo025'[PBR]) (EL)	EPfP NTay
§	VESUVIUS ('Evipo032'[PBR]) (Vt)	SCoo
	VICKI ('Evipo114') (EL) **new**	LCro MGos NTay
	'Vicky' (A/d)	CRos LRHS
	VICTOR HUGO ('Evipo007'[PBR]) (LL)	CRos EHyd LRHS NLar SCoo
	'Victoria' (LL)	EHyd LRHS LSRN NHaw NTay
	VIENNETTA ('Evipo006'[PBR]) (d)	CRos CWCL CWGN EHyd EPfP ETho LRHS MGos NTay SCoo SNig SRms
	'Ville de Lyon' (LL)	CBcs CDoC CKel CRHN CWCL EDir EHyd ELan EPfP ETho GMcL LPar LRHS LSRN MAsh MGos NBwr NRHS NTay SCob SCoo SNig SPer SPoG
	vinacea	NHaw
	'Vince Denny' (Ta)	EBee NHaw SMDa
	VINO ('Poulvo'[PBR]) (EL)	NTay SCoo
	'Viola' (LL)	ETho LRHS LSRN NHaw NTay
	viorna	CWGN GKev NHaw
	virginiana misapplied	see *C. vitalba*
§	***vitalba***	CBod GKev GQue NHaw NTay NWea SCob WHer WSpi
	viticella	CRHN EHeP NHaw NTay SCob SNig WHlf
	- subsp. ***campaniflora***	see *C. campaniflora*
§	- 'Flore Pleno' (Vt/d)	CRHN CRos CWCL EHyd ELan EPfP ETho LCro LOPS LRHS LSRN NHaw NLar NRHS NTay SNig SPoG WHlf
	- 'Hanna' (Vt)	CRHN IPot LSRN NHaw SNig
	- 'Mary Rose'	see *C. viticella* 'Flore Pleno'
	'Vivienne'	see *C.* 'Beth Currie'
	VOLCANO ('Mazowsze') (LL)	SNig
	'Voluceau' (Vt)	CWCL EHyd ELan EPfP LRHS LSRN SCoo SRms
	VOLUNTEER ('Evipo080'[PBR]) (EL)	CRos EHyd ETho LRHS NRHS NTay SNig
	'Vostok' (LL)	NHaw
	'Vyvyan Pennell' (EL)	CArg CBcs CDoC CKel CMac CRos CTri CWCL EHyd ELan EPfP ETho LCro LRHS LSRN MAsh NLar NTay SCob SCoo SNig SPer SPoG SWvt WFar WHlf WSpi
	'W.E. Gladstone' (EL)	EHyd LRHS
	WADA'S PRIMROSE	see *C. patens* 'Manshuu Ki'
	'Walenburg' (Vt) ♀H6	CRHN CWGN ETho LRHS NHaw NTay
	'Walter Pennell' (EL)	SCoo

'Warsaw' (Ta)	NLar
'Warszawska Nike' (EL) ♀^{H6}	CKel CRHN CWCL EHyd ELan EPfP ETho GMcL LCro LOPS LPar LRHS MAsh MGos NTay SCob SCoo SNig SPoG
'Warwickshire Rose' (M)	CDoC CMac CRHN CTri CWGN EBee EDir EHyd ELan EPfP ETho LRHS LSRN MAsh NTay SCoo SNig SPoG
'Wedding Day' (EL)	EPfP ETho LCro LOPS LSRN NLar NTay
'Wee Willie Winkie' (M)	GMcL SRms
'Westerplatte' (EL)	CKel CWCL CWGN EHyd EPfP ETho LRHS MGos NHaw NTay SCoo SNig SPoG WSpi
WHITE ARABELLA ('Zo14089') **new**	CWGN LCro
§ 'White Columbine' (A) ♀^{H6}	CKel ELan LRHS NTay SCoo SPer
'White Heart' (Vt)	CRHN NHaw
'White Magic'^{PBR} (Vt)	NTay
§ 'White Moth' (A/d)	LSRN MAsh NHol NTay
WHITE PEARL ('Zo08080') (EL)	NTay
'White Prince Charles' (LL)	CWGN NHaw SNig
'White Satin' (A)	EHyd EPfP LRHS NTay SRms
'White Swan' (A/d)	ETho MAsh NHol NTay SCoo
'Wildfire' (EL) **new**	SNig
'Will Goodwin' (EL) ♀^{H6}	CWCL EHyd ELan EPfP LRHS SRms
'William Kennett' (EL)	CWCL ETho LRHS
williamsii	SMDa
'Willy' (A)	CArg CKel CRos EHyd ELan EPfP ETho LRHS MAsh MGos NLar NRHS NTay SCoo SRms
WISLEY ('Evipo001'^{PBR}) (Vt) ♀^{H6}	EPfP MGos NLar SNig
WONDERFUL ('Zo09073'^{PBR}) (Vt)	CWGN LCro LOPS NTay SNig
'Xerxes' misapplied	see *C.* 'Elsa Späth'
XIU ('Evipo065'^{PBR}) (Boulevard Series) (Fo)	LRHS NTay SNig
'Yellow Queen' Holland	see *C. patens* 'Manshuu Ki'
'Yellow Queen' Lundell/ Treasures	see *C.* 'Moonlight'
YUAN ('Evipo082'^{PBR}) (Boulevard Series)	LSou SNig
§ 'Yukikomachi' (EL)	NHaw SNig WSpi
'Yvette Houry' (EL)	EBee
ZARA ('Evipo062'^{PBR}) (EL)	ETho NTay
'Zephyr' (Vt)	NHaw

Clematopsis see *Clematis*

Clementsia see *Rhodiola*

Cleome (*Cleomaceae*)

hassleriana 'Helen Campbell' ♀^{H2}	CSpe LCro LOPS
- 'Violet Queen'	LCro LOPS
SEÑORITA ROSALITA ('Inncleosr'^{PBR})	MHol MPri

Clerodendrum (*Lamiaceae*)

CW&T 6506	CMCN
bungei	Widely available
- 'Pink Diamond' (v)	CCCN CKel CMac CWGN ELan ELon EPfP EWes LAlb LRHS LSRN MGos NLar SGbt SPer SPoG SWvt
§ ***chinense*** var. ***chinense*** (d) ♀^{H1b}	CCCN
- 'Pleniflorum'	see *C. chinense* var. *chinense*
colebrookianum B&SWJ 6651	WCru
- PAB 7794	LEdu
fragrans var. ***pleniflorum***	see *C. chinense* var. *chinense*
laevifolium 'Prospero'	CDoC LCro
myricoides	see *Rotheca myricoides*
paniculatum 'Starshine'	CCCN
philippinum	see *C. chinense* var. *chinense*
× ***speciosum***	CHII
aff. ***subscaposum*** WWJ 11735	WCru
thomsoniae ♀^{H1b}	WSFF
trichotomum	CBcs CKel CMCN CTri EGrI EPfP IArd LRHS MAsh MTrO NLar SCob SPer WBor WHtc WJur WMat WMou
- var. ***fargesii*** ♀^{H5}	Widely available
- - 'Carnival' (v) ♀^{H5}	CCCN CDoC CKel CMac EBee EHed EHyd ELan EPfP EWes LMil LRHS NLar SEle SMad SNig SPer SPoG SWvt WAvo WCot WHlf
- 'Purple Blaze'	CJun EBee LAlb LPar
- 'Purple Haze'	NLar
- 'Shiro'	LAlb SMad WCru

Clethra (*Clethraceae*)

CW&T 6497	CMCN
acuminata	NLar
alnifolia	CBcs EBee SRHi SRms WFar
- 'Anne Bidwell'	MBlu NLar
- 'Creel's Calico' (v)	NLar
- 'Fern Valley Pink'	CCCN CDoC CKel CMac ELon EPfP LRHS NLar SRms WFar
- 'Hokie Pink'	ELon NLar
- 'Hummingbird' ♀^{H5}	CCCN CDoC CEme CEnd CKel CMac CRos EDir ELan ELon EPfP GKin LAlb LRHS MAsh MBlu NLar SCoo SEle SPad SPoG SSha SWvt WFar XSte
- 'Paniculata'	CBod CKel EHed ELon LRHS MGil
- 'Pink Spice'	CRos
- 'Pink Spires'	CBcs CBod EDir EGrI GKin LAlb LEdu MMuc MPri MRav NLar SCoo SEle SNig SPer SRHi WBor WLov
- 'Rosea'	CTri GKin
- 'Ruby Spice' ♀^{H5}	Widely available
- 'September Beauty'	NLar
- 'Sixteen Candles'	GGGa GKin IDee LAlb LRHS NLar WHtc XSte
- VANILLA SPICE ('Caleb')	NLar
arborea	ECre IKel MGil
barbinervis ♀^{H5}	CBcs CExl CKel EPfP GGGa LRHS MBlu MGil NLar WPGP
- B&SWJ 11562	WCru
- GREAT STAR ('Minbarb')	EHed EPfP LRHS WPGP XSte
- 'White Star'	CJun CKel CMac EBee EPfP LRHS MACG NLar
delavayi Franch.	CBcs CCCN CDoC CMCN EBee EGrI EPfP GGGa IDee IKel MGil NLar WPGP
- SBEC 1513	CExl
fabri B&SWJ 11702	WCru
- FMWJ 13037	WCru
fargesii	CExl EBee EPfP IDee MBlu NLar SPtp WPGP
kaipoensis NJM 11.020	WPGP
- NJM 11.058	WPGP
- PAB 8571	LEdu
monostachya	CExl EBee MGil WPGP
pachyphylla	WPGP
petelotii FMWJ 13401	WCru
pringlei	CBcs EBee IArd IDee NLar
tomentosa 'Cottondale'	CBcs CJun IDee NLar

Cleyera (*Pentaphylacaceae*)

	fortunei	see *C. japonica* 'Fortunei'
	– 'Variegata'	see *C. japonica* 'Fortunei'
§	***japonica*** 'Fortunei' (v)	CCCN CMac EBee SSta
	– var. ***japonica***	EBee WPGP
	– 'Tricolor' (v)	IDee
	pachyphylla new	WPGP

Clianthus ✿ (*Fabaceae*)

	maximus	CTsd
	– 'Kaka King'	EWes LRHS MPkF XSte
*	***pauciflorus***	CCCN
§	***puniceus*** ♀H3	CAbb CBcs CCCN CCht CKel CSpe CTsd EAri EPfP MGil MHtn SChF SEdd SEle SGbt SPer SPlb SPoG SWvt
§	– 'Albus' ♀H3	CBcs CCCN CKel CSpe CTsd EAri EPfP LRHS SPer SPoG SWvt XSte
	– 'Flamingo'	see *C. puniceus* 'Roseus'
	– 'Red Admiral'	see *C. puniceus*
	– 'Red Cardinal'	see *C. puniceus*
§	– 'Roseus' ♀H3	CBcs CCCN CKel CPla EAri EHyd EPfP LRHS NRHS SMad SPer SPoG XSte
	– 'White Heron'	see *C. puniceus* 'Albus'

Clinanthus (*Amaryllidaceae*)

	incarnatus apricot-flowered	WMal

Clinopodium (*Lamiaceae*)

	acinos	SPhx
§	***alpinum***	EBou GJos SRms WJek
	ascendens	see *Calamintha ascendens*
	calamintha	see *Calamintha nepeta*
	chinense var. ***parviflorum*** new	GGro
§	***corsicum***	WHoo WKif
	grandiflorum	see *Calamintha grandiflora*
§	***menthifolium***	NLar
§	***vulgare***	CBod CHab EBee ECha GPSL LShi MBow MHer MHol MNHC NAts NMir SBut SRms WOut WWild
	– PAB 7562	LEdu

Clintonia (*Liliaceae*)

	andrewsiana	GBin

Clivia ✿ (*Amaryllidaceae*)

	caulescens	NHoy WCot
	– pink-flowered	NHoy WCot
	× ***cyrtanthiflora***	NHoy
	gardenii	LAma NHoy WCot
	miniata ♀H1c	CAbb CBcs CCCN CDoC CTca CTsd LAma LCro LOPS NHoy SAdn SEND SPlb WCot
	– 'Anshan Variegated' (v)	WCot
	– 'Arturo's Yellow'	NHoy WCot
	– 'Aurea'	CSpe
	– Belgian hybrids	NHoy WCot
	– – (improved strain)	NHoy
	– 'Beverley's Delight'	NHoy WCot
	– broad-leaved, variegated (v)	NHoy WCot
	– 'Chubb's Peach' × 'Vico Yellow'	NHoy
	– var. ***citrina*** ♀H1c	CTca LAma NHoy SDir
	– – variegated (v)	LAma NHoy WCot
	– 'Connemara Flame'	NHoy
	– 'Dancing Sisters' × 'Terracotta Green Throat'	NHoy WCot
	– Daruma Group	WCot
	– 'Florid White Lips'	NHoy
	– fragrant yellow-flowered	NHoy
	– green-centred	NHoy WCot
	– – orange-flowered	NHoy
	– historical clone	NHoy
	– 'Hot Number One'	NHoy
	– large strawberry orange-flowered	NHoy
	– 'Light of Buddha' (v)	NHoy WCot
	– 'Mitsuhashi Multipetal'	WCot
	– 'Mrs P. Lofus'	NHoy
	– Nakamura yellow-flowered	NHoy
	– 'Pale Majesty'	NHoy
	– pale yellow-flowered	NHoy
	– pastel shades	NHoy WCot
	– 'Pink Perfection'	NHoy WCot
	– 'Queen of the Strawberries'	NHoy
	– 'Strawberry Giant'	NHoy
	– 'Striata' (v)	NHoy WCot
	– 'Terracotta Treasure' (v)	NHoy WCot
	– 'Vico Shima'	WCot
	– 'Wide Leaf Monk'	WCot
	nobilis ♀H1c	NHoy SPlb WCot
	robusta	NHoy WCot
	'San Marcos Yellow' × 'Solomone Yellow'	WCot
	'Sweet Undress'	NHoy WCot

Clusia (*Clusiaceae*)

	rosea	CCCN NHrt
	– 'Green Magic' new	LCro
	– 'Princess'PBR new	LCro

Clytostoma (*Bignoniaceae*)

§	***calystegioides***	CCCN CRHN

Cnidium (*Apiaceae*)

	officinale	GPoy LEdu
	silaifolium	LEdu SPhx

Cobaea (*Polemoniaceae*)

	pringlei	CRHN WPGP
	– CD&R 1323	SBrt WCot
	scandens ♀H2	CCCN CDTJ CSpe EShb LWaG SPhx WHlf
	– f. ***alba***	CSpe ELan EShb LCro LOPS

cobnut see *Corylus avellana*; see also AGM Fruit Section

Coccothrinax (*Arecaceae*)

	borhidiana new	NPlm
	proctorii new	NPlm

Cocculus (*Menispermaceae*)

	laurifolius	IArd SBrt
§	***orbiculatus*** B&SWJ 535	WCru
	trilobus	see *C. orbiculatus*

Cochlearia (*Brassicaceae*)

	armoracia	see *Armoracia rusticana*
	danica	CAgr
	glastifolia	CAgr
	officinalis	CAgr SPhx WHer

Cochliasanthus (*Fabaceae*)

§	***caracalla***	CCCN EShb

Cocos (*Arecaceae*)

	plumosa	see *Syagrus romanzoffiana*
	weddelliana	see *Lytocaryum weddellianum*

Codiaeum ✿ (*Euphorbiaceae*)

variegatum var. ***pictum*** 'Excellent' (v)	LCro LOPS
- - 'Mammi' (v) **new**	LCro
- - 'Mrs Iceton' (v)	NHrt
- - 'Petra' (v)	NHrt

Codonanthe (*Gesneriaceae*)

gracilis	WDib
'Paula'	WDib

Codonanthe × *Nematanthus* see × *Codonatanthus*

× *Codonatanthus* (*Gesneriaceae*)

'Golden Tambourine'	WDib
'Sunset'	WDib
'Tambourine'	WDib

Codonopsis ✿ (*Campanulaceae*)

HWJK 2105 from Nepal	WCru
affinis	EBee
- HWJCM 70	WCru
- HWJK 2151	WCru
benthamii GWJ 9352	WCru
canescens **new**	SBrt
cardiophylla	EPPr EWld GArf WSHC
aff. ***celebica*** BWJ 15623	WCru
clematidea	CDor CSpe EBee ECha EPfP EWld GAbr MNrw NLar SPlb SWvt WKif
convolvulacea misapplied	see *C. grey-wilsonii*
- 'Alba'	see *C. grey-wilsonii* 'Himal Snow'
- Forrest's form	see *C. forrestii* Diels
'Dangshen'	see *C. pilosula*
aff. ***deltoidea*** SSSE 86	EBee EWld
forrestii misapplied	see *C. grey-wilsonii*
§ ***forrestii*** Diels	EWld GKev
- BWJ 7847	WCru
§ ***grey-wilsonii*** 🏆H5	CBro EWld GEdr GKev
- B&SWJ 7532	WCru
§ - 'Himal Snow'	EWld GEdr GKev WCru WHil
inflata GWJ 9442	WCru
kawakamii	EBee EWld
- B&SWJ 1592	WCru
- RWJ 10007	WCru
§ ***lanceolata***	CPla EPPr EWld SBrt
- B&SWJ 562	WCru
nepalensis Grey-Wilson	see *C. grey-wilsonii*
obtusa	EBee EWld
ovata	GKev NBro
§ ***pilosula***	CDor EBee EWld GKev GPoy SBrt
- var. ***modesta***	EBee GArf
rotundifolia	EBee SBrt WSHC
var. ***grandiflora***	
silvestris	see *C. pilosula*
subscaposa	GArf MVil SBrt
tangshen Oliv.	WSHC
ussuriensis	see *C. lanceolata*
vinciflora	EWld
viridis CC 7454	SBrt

Coffea (*Rubiaceae*)

arabica	CCCN SPre

coffee see *Coffea*

Colchicum ✿ (*Colchicaceae*)

× ***agrippinum*** 🏆H4	CWCL ECha EPot GKev LAma NBir NRog WAbe WCot WHoo WThu
'Antares'	ECha NRog
asteranthum	NRog
atticum	NRog
'Autumn Herald'	LAma NRog
'Autumn Queen' 🏆H5	NRog
§ ***autumnale***	CAvo CHab EPot GKev GPoy LAma NRya SDeJ WShi
- 'Alboplenum'	ELan ERCP GKev LAma NBir NRog SDeJ
- 'Album' 🏆H5	CAvo ELan EPfP EPot LAma LCro LOPS NBir NRog SPeP WShi
- 'Atropurpureum'	NRog
- 'Karin Persson'	GKev
- var. ***major*** hort.	see *C.* × *byzantinum* Ker Gawl.
- var. ***minor*** hort.	see *C. autumnale*
§ - 'Nancy Lindsay' 🏆H5	CBro EPot LAma NRog WShi
- 'Pannonicum'	see *C. autumnale* 'Nancy Lindsay'
§ - 'Pleniflorum' (d)	EGrI LAma NBir
- 'Roseum Plenum'	see *C. autumnale* 'Pleniflorum'
baytopiorum	NRog WThu
'Beaconsfield'	NRog
§ ***bivonae***	EPot
- 'Apollo'	NRog
- 'Petrovac'	GKev
§ ***boissieri***	EPot NRog
bornmuelleri misapplied	see *C. speciosum* var. *bornmuelleri* hort.
bornmuelleri Freyn	EGrI NBir NRog
- 'Artur Klark'	NRog
bowlesianum	see *C. bivonae*
§ ***bulbocodium***	EPot GKev LAma NRog SDeJ
× ***byzantinum*** ambig.	GKev LAma
§ × ***byzantinum*** Ker Gawl.	ELan NBwr NRog SDeJ WShi
- ***album***	see *C.* × *byzantinum* 'Innocence'
§ - 'Innocence' 🏆H5	CAvo LAma NRog WCot
cilicicum	EGrI NBir NRog
- 'Purpureum' 🏆H5	EPot LAma NRog
'Conquest'	see *C.* 'Glory of Heemstede'
corsicum	WThu
cupanii AH 9707	GKev
- var. ***pulverulentum***	GKev
'Daendels'	NRog
davisii	GKev NRog
'Dick Trotter'	EPfP EPot LAma SDeJ WFar
'Disraeli'	EPot NRog
'Faberge's Silver'	NRog
falcifolium	NRog
filifolium	NRog
'Flamenco Dance'	NRog
§ ***giganteum***	LAma NRog
§ 'Glory of Heemstede'	NRog
'Gothic Style'	NRog
'Gracia'	NRog
graecum	NRog
'Hannibal'	GKev
'Harlekijn'	EPot LAma NRog
hungaricum	EPot LAma
- 'Valentine'	ERCP GKev NRog
- 'Velebit Star'	EPot ERCP GKev LAma NRog
'Huxley'	LAma
illyricum	see *C. giganteum*
'Jarka'	LAma NRog
'Jaroslavna'	NRog
'Jochem Hof'	NRog
kesselringii	NRog
- 'My Choice'	NRog
- 'Purple Star'	NRog
kotschyi	NRog
laetum misapplied	see *C. parnassicum*
laetum Stev.	NRog
'Larisa'	NRog
'Lilac Bedder'	LAma NRog
'Lilac Wonder'	EGrI ELan LAma LCro LOPS MRav NBir NRog SDeJ WCot WHoo
longifolium	see *C. neapolitanum*
luteum	NRog

	- from Chimgan, Uzbekistan	NRog
	- 'Golden Baby'	NRog
	- 'Vahsh'	NRog
	'Lysimachus'	GKev
	macrophyllum	GKev LAma NRog WCot WMal
	minutum	NRog
	montanum 'Norman Barrett'	NRog
	munzurense	NRog
§	***neapolitanum***	NRog
	'Neptun'	NRog
	'Oktoberfest'	EPot
	parlatoris	GKev NRog
§	***parnassicum***	ECha NRog
	'Poseidon'	NRog
	'Prinses Astrid'	NRog
	procurrens	see *C. boissieri*
§	***robustum***	NRog
	'Rosy Dawn' 🏆H5	CBro ECha LAma NRog
	sanguicolle	NRog
	sibthorpii	see *C. bivonae*
	'Snow of Highland'	NRog
	soboliferum	NRog WCot
	'Spartacus'	GKev
	speciosum	CAvo ELan EPot GAbr GBin LAma NBir NRog WShi
	- 'Album' 🏆H5	CAvo CWCL ECha EPot ERCP GAbr LAma LEdu NBir NRog SDeJ WHlf
	- 'Atrorubens' 🏆H5	ECha EPot LAma
I	- var. ***bornmuelleri*** hort.	NRog WHoo
	- 'Dombai'	NRog
	- var. ***illyricum*** hort.	see *C. giganteum*
	- 'Ordu'	NRog
	szovitsii Fisch. & B. Mey.	NRog
	- white-flowered	NRog
	× ***tenorei*** 🏆H4	EPot ERCP NBir NRog WHlf
	'The Giant'	ECha EPfP EPot LAma LCro LOPS NBwr NRog SDeJ WFar
§	***trigynum***	NRog
	triphyllum	NRog
	variegatum	NRog
	'Violet Queen'	ERCP LAma NRog SDeJ
	'Waterlily' (d) 🏆H5	CAvo EGrI ELan EPot ERCP GAbr GKev GMcL LAma LCro LOPS MBow NBir NPoe NRog SDeJ SPeP WCot WFar WHlf WShi
	'William Dykes'	NRog
	'World Champion's Cup'	NRog
	'Yeti'	NRog
	zahnii from southern Greece	NRog
	'Zephyr'	NRog

Coleonema (*Rutaceae*)

§	***pulchellum***	CCCN CSde CSpe SVen
	- 'Breath of Gold'	CCCN
§	- 'Pink Fountain'	CAbb CCCN CTsd ECre EHyd ELan EPfP LRHS SEle SPoG WCot XSte
	pulchrum misapplied	see *C. pulchellum*
§	'Sunset Gold'	CAbb CBod CCCN CCht CDoC CKel CPbh CSBt CSde EBee EHyd ELan EPfP LRHS SCoo SEle SNig SPlb SPoG WHlf XSte

Coleus see *Solenostemon*

Colignonia (*Nyctaginaceae*)

	ovalifolia B&SWJ 10644	WCru

Colletia (*Rhamnaceae*)

	armata	see *C. hystrix*
	cruciata	see *C. paradoxa*
§	***hystrix***	CBcs CMCN CMac CTri CTsd EAri ELon EPfP MGil WPav
	- RCB RA S3	WCot
	- 'Rosea'	CMac MBlu SArc WPav
§	***paradoxa***	CBcs CCCN ELan EPfP SArc SPlb SPoG WFar WPav
	spinosissima	WPav
	ulicina	SVen

Collinsonia (*Lamiaceae*)

	canadensis	LEdu WPGP

Collomia ✿ (*Polemoniaceae*)

	grandiflora	WCot

Colocasia (*Araceae*)

	affinis var. ***jeningsii***	CAbb
	antiquorum	see *C. esculenta*
§	***esculenta*** 🏆H1b	CAbb CDTJ EAri LAma LCro LOPS SDir SPlb
	- B&SWJ 6909	ESwi WCru
	- 'Bikini-tini' **new**	XVPe
	- 'Black Magic'	CHll LAma LPfP SDir SGBe
	- 'Black Sapphire Gecko'	XSte
	- burgundy-stemmed	CAbb CDTJ CTsd LAma
	- 'Emerald'	CBct LAma SDir
	- 'Fontanesii'	CBct CDTJ
	- 'Illustris'	CAbb CDTJ
	- 'Jack's Giant'	CDTJ
	- 'Mammoth'	CDTJ
	- 'Pink China'	CAbb CBct CBod EAri SPlb XSte XVPe
	- (Royal Hawaiian Series) 'Black Coral'	CAbb EAri LRHS SPad WHlf
	- - 'Blue Hawaii'	CBod CDTJ CPla EAri SGBe SPad XSte
	- - 'Hawaiian Punch'	CAbb CDTJ SMrm
	- - 'Kona Coffee' **new**	XSte
	- - 'Maui Gold'	CBct CBod SMrm
	- 'Sangria'	XVPe
	gaoligongensis	CBct CDTJ CPHo SPlb
	gigantea 'Thailand Giant'	EAri
	'Madeira'	XVPe

Colquhounia (*Lamiaceae*)

	coccinea	CCCN CHll CSde EShb LEdu MBlu MGil MRav NQui SBrt SIvy SPoG WLov
	- Sch 2458	EBee EPfP WPGP
§	- var. ***mollis*** B&SWJ 7222	WCru
	- var. ***vestita*** misapplied	see *C. coccinea* var. *mollis*
	- var. ***vestita*** ambig.	CBcs CKel CTsd EBee EPfP LRHS MBNS SEND

Columnea (*Gesneriaceae*)

	'Aladdin's Lamp'	WDib
	× ***banksii*** 🏆H1c	WDib
§	'Broget Stavanger' (v) 🏆H1c	WDib
	'Chanticleer' 🏆H1a	WDib
I	'Firedragon'	WDib
	'Gavin Brown'	WDib
	'Inferno'	WDib
	'Katsura'	WDib
	'Merkur'	WDib
I	'Midnight Lantern'	WDib
	'Rising Sun'	WDib
	schiedeana	WDib
	'Sherbert'	WDib
	'Stavanger' 🏆H1a	WDib
	'Stavanger Variegated'	see *C.* 'Broget Stavanger'

Colutea (*Fabaceae*)

	arborescens	CAgr CBcs EHyd ELan ESwi EWTr ILea MBlu MGil MGos NWea SPlb
	× ***media*** 'Copper Beauty'	CBcs ELan MMrt MPie NLar
	orientalis	CCCN EBee

Colvillea (*Fabaceae*)

racemosa	SPlb

Colysis (*Polypodiaceae*)

elliptica	WCot

Comarum see *Potentilla*

Combretum (*Combretaceae*)

fruticosum	CCCN
indicum	CCCN

Commelina (*Commelinaceae*)

coelestis	see *C. tuberosa* Coelestis Group
dianthifolia	EBee EDAr EPPr GEdr LEdu LShi NHpl SBrt SBut WWke
- 'Electric Blue'	ELan SVic
robusta	WCot WFar
tuberosa	GKev MGil WWke
- B&SWJ 10353	SBrt WCru
- blue-flowered	SDeJ
§ - Coelestis Group	CAby CCBP CTtf ECha EGrI EWld LShi SDys SPtp WKif WSHC
- - 'Alba' **new**	LShi
- - 'Hopleys Variegated' (v)	WFar
- - 'Rhapsody'	WFar

Comptonia (*Myricaceae*)

peregrina	EBee WPGP

Conandron (*Gesneriaceae*)

ramondoides B&SWJ 8929	WCru

Conicosia (*Aizoaceae*)

pugioniformis	SVen

Coniogramme (*Pteridaceae*)

emeiensis	CBod CBrP CCht CTsd LCro LEdu SPad SPlb WCot
intermedia	LEdu WPGP
japonica	LEdu WCot WFib WPGP
- 'Flavomaculata'	CCht EBee GGro LEdu MSCN SPlb WCot WFar WPGP

Conoclinium (*Asteraceae*)

§ ***coelestinum***	EBee EHyd EShb LRHS SBrt SPeP

Conophytum ✿ (*Aizoaceae*)

× ***cupreiflorum*** **new**	EAri
meyeri **new**	EAri
§ ***minimum*** ♀H2 **new**	EAri
minutum ♀H2 **new**	EAri
scitulum	see *C. minimum*
wettsteinii ♀H2 **new**	EAri

Conopodium (*Apiaceae*)

majus	CEls SPhx WShi

Consolea (*Cactaceae*)

macracantha **new**	EAri

Consolida (*Ranunculaceae*)

§ ***ajacis***	CSpe
- Giant Imperial Series	SVic
ambigua	see *C. ajacis*

Convallaria ✿ (*Asparagaceae*)

japonica	see *Ophiopogon jaburan*
keiskei	EMor EPPr MAvo WFar
I - 'Marginata' (v)	WCot
- 'Shiro-shima-fu' (v)	GEdr GGro WFar
majalis ♀H7	Widely available
- from Tatra Mountains	EPPr
- 'Albostriata' (v)	CBct CTtf EBee EBlo EHyd EMor EPPr EPri ESwi GKev GMaP LEdu LPal LRHS MAvo MHer MHol MNrw NBPC NBir NRHS WCot WFar WHer WHoo WPnP WTyc
- 'Aurea'	WFar
- 'Berlin Giant'	EPPr EPri NRya SDeJ WFar
- 'Blush'	WFar
- 'Bordeaux'	CBro CDor CExl CWCL ELan EMor EPPr EPri ESwi GPSL MAvo NLar SEdd WCot WHlf WPnP WTyc
- 'Bridal Choice'	EBee EPot GBin GKev MCot NLar WFar
- 'Cream da Mint' (v)	WFar
- 'Dorien'	EMor EPPr LBar MAvo WFar
- 'Fernwood's Golden Slippers'	CAvo GEdr MAvo WCot WFar
- 'Flore Pleno' (d)	EMor GEdr MBel MMrt WFar
- 'Géant de Fortin' ♀H7	CAvo CBro CEme CExl EPot GEdr MRav NBir NLar WCot WFar
- 'Gérard Debureaux'	see *C. majalis* 'Green Tapestry'
- 'Gold Leaf'	EMor
- 'Golden Jubilee'	CBct EPPr EPri ESwi LEdu MNrw WCot WFar
- 'Grandiflora'	WFar
§ - 'Green Tapestry' (v)	EPPr WCot WFar
- 'Haldon Grange' (v)	CMiW EPPr MAvo WFar
- 'Hardwick Hall' (v)	CAvo CBct CDor CExl CTtf CWCL EBee EBlo ECha EMor EPri ESwi GEdr GKev LBar LEdu MAvo NSti SPeP WCot WFar
- 'Heitmann'	WFar
- 'Hitscherberger Riesenperle'	WFar XLum
- 'Hofheim' (v)	CAvo CBct CMiW ELon ESwi GEdr GKev LEdu WCot WFar
- 'Landgraaf' (v)	MAvo WFar
- 'Lineata' (v)	WFar
- 'Marcel' (v)	WFar
- 'Mary Brooks'	EBlo WFar
- POLISH BEAUTY	see *C. majalis* 'Polska Piękność'
§ - 'Polska Piękność' (v)	WFar
- 'Prolificans'	CBct CBod CDor EBee ECtt EMor EPPr EPfP ESwi GEdr GKev LAma LBar LCro LOPS MACG MAvo MRav NBPC NBir NLar NSti WCot WFar WPnP
- var. ***rosea***	Widely available
- 'Rosea Plena' (d)	EGrI LAma NBPC SPeP WHlf
- 'Silberconfolis' (v)	EPri WCot WFar
- 'Variegata' (v)	CPla EMor SMad WFar WThu
- 'Vic Pawlowski's Gold' (v)	CBct CBro CDor CExl CMac CMiW EMor EPPr GEdr WFar WPGP WSHC
- 'Vierländer Glockenspiel'	WFar
- 'Viktor'	WFar
* - 'Viridistriatus'	WFar
transcaucasica	GKev

Convolvulus (*Convolvulaceae*)

althaeoides	CFis ELan SBut
§ - subsp. ***tenuissimus***	EWes WCot
§ ***boissieri***	WAbe
cantabrica	SBut SPhx WSHC
chilensis	CCCN
cneorum ♀H4	Widely available
- 'Snow Angel'	LRHS SWvt
elegantissimus	see *C. althaeoides* subsp. *tenuissimus*
holosericeus	GKev
lineatus	EWes
mauritanicus	see *C. sabatius*
nitidus	see *C. boissieri*

§	***sabatius*** 🏆H3	CBod CCCN CCht CKel CTri EBee EBou ECtt ELan EPfP EPot EShb LRHS MCot MNHC SEND SGBe SMrm SPer SPhx SPlb SPoG SVen SWvt WCFE WSHC XLum
	- dark-flowered	CCCN LSou
	- 'Moroccan Beauty'PBR	ECtt
	- white-flowered	CCCN
	tricolor 'Blue Ensign' 🏆H3	CSpe LCro LOPS

× *Cooperanthes* see *Zephyranthes*

Cooperia see *Zephyranthes*

Copernicia (*Arecaceae*)

alba	NPlm
hospita **new**	NPlm

Copiapoa ✿ (*Cactaceae*)

humilis **new**	EAri
hypogaea	SPlb
subsp. ***laui*** **new**	

Coprosma (*Rubiaceae*)

	acerosa 'Hawera'	CTrC
	- 'Red Rocks'	CTrC
	baueri misapplied	see *C. repens*
	'Beatson's Gold' (f/v)	CBcs CTrC ELan EShb LRHS SEND SEle SWvt
	'Black Cloud'	CTrC ELon SEND
	brunnea	SEle SSha
	- (f)	WThu
	- (m)	WThu
	'Cappuccino'	EShb
	'Clearwater Gold'	SIvy
	× ***cunninghamii*** **new**	SSha
	× ***cunninghamii*** × ***macrocarpa*** (f)	CTrC
	× ***cunninghamii*** × ***macrocarpa*** (m)	CCoa
	'Evening Glow'PBR (f/v)	CCCN CCht CDTJ CEnd CSBt EHyd LRHS MGos SEle SIvy SRHi SRms WNPC
	'Fire Burst'PBR (f/v)	CAbb CBcs CBct CBod CCCN SEle SRHi SRms WNPC
	'Inferno'PBR (f/v)	CAbb CBcs CBod CCht CDoC CKel LCro SEle SPad
	'Karo Red'PBR (v)	SRms
	× ***kirkii*** 'Variegata' (f/v)	CKel CTsd CWnw ELan EShb LRHS
	'Lemon and Lime'PBR (v)	CBod CKel EHyd LCro LRHS NRHS SCoo SEle SGBe SGbt SIvy SPoG SRms SSha
	macrocarpa	CTrC
	'Mini Mac' **new**	CBod
	petriei	GArf
	- 'White Pearls'	WThu
	propinqua	GKev SSha
	'Rainbow Surprise'PBR (v)	CCCN CDoC CSBt MGos SRms WFar WNPC
§	***repens***	EShb SPlb SVen
	- 'County Park Plum' (v)	SVen
	- 'Inferno' (v)	CEnd CMCN
	- 'Marble Queen' (m/v) 🏆H3	EShb
	- 'Midnight Martini' (v)	EHyd LRHS SCoo WFar WNPC
	- 'Pacific Dawn'	CCht CEnd CSBt LCro SEle SRHi WNPC
	- PACIFIC NIGHT ('Hutpac'PBR) (m)	CBod CDoC CKel CSBt EBee EHyd LRHS MGos SCoo SGBe SGbt WFar WNPC
	- PACIFIC SUNSET ('Jwncopps') (m/v)	CBod CCCN CDoC CSBt ELan LCro LOPS LSRN SEle SGbt
	- 'Painter's Palette' (m)	SVen
	- 'Pina Colada'PBR (v)	CAbb CCht CDoC CSBt EHyd LRHS NRHS SCoo SEdd SEle SGBe SGbt SPoG WFar
	- 'Tequila Sunrise'	CAbb CBcs CCht CDoC CSBt EHyd LRHS LSRN NRHS SEdd SEle SRHi
	robusta	CTrC
	'Roy's Red' (m)	LSRN SSha
	'Scarlet O'Hara'	CCht SEle SGBe SPoG
	'Walter Brockie'	CSde CTrC

Coptis (*Ranunculaceae*)

chinensis B&SWJ 12865	WCru
japonica	GPoy WCru
- var. ***dissecta***	GEdr WCru
- var. ***major***	GEdr WCru WSHC
laciniata B&SWJ 12863	WCru
omeiensis	WCru
quinquefolia	GEdr
- B&SWJ 1677	WCru
ramosa B&SWJ 6000	WCru
- B&SWJ 6030	WCru
trifolia	WCru

Corallospartium see *Carmichaelia*

Cordyline ✿ (*Asparagaceae*)

	australis 🏆H3	Widely available
	- 'Albertii' (v) 🏆H3	CCCN SArc
	- 'Atlantic Green'	CBrac SavN
	- 'Atropurpurea'	CBrac CCCN WHtc
	- 'Black Night'	CCCN LRHS XSte
	- CHARLIE BOY ('Ric01'PBR) (v)	CTsd LCro SGBe SPad XSte
	- 'Coral' **new**	CBod
	- 'Karo Kiri'	CCCN
	- 'Olive Fountain'	CCCN
	- 'Peko'PBR	CCCN CDoC
	- PINK STAR ('Tus019'PBR) (v) **new**	LCro
	- 'Purple Heart'	CCCN MSwo
	- Purpurea Group	CBcs CDTJ CDoC ELan MGos SCob SEND SPlb SWeb WFar
	- 'Red Sensation'	CCCN SWvt
	- 'Sparkler' (v)	CCCN EPfP SEND
	- 'Torbay Dazzler' (v) 🏆H3	Widely available
	- 'Torbay Sunset'	CCCN
	- 'Variegata' (v)	CDoC LPar XSte
	'Autumn'	CCCN
	banksii	CCCN CCht
	- ELECTRIC FLASH ('Sprilecflash'PBR)	CKel CWnw XSte
	- ELECTRIC PINK ('Sprilecpink')	ELan
	- ELECTRIC STAR ('Sprilecstar'PBR) **new**	CWnw
	'Can Can'PBR (v)	CDoC CKel LBuc NPlm SCob WHlf
	'Cha Cha'PBR (v)	CCCN CEnd CKel EBee SEND WAvo WCot WHlf
	'Cherry Sensation' (v)	EHyd LRHS NRHS WFar XSte
	'Coffee Cream'	CCCN
§	***congesta***	SPlb
	'Dark Star'	CCCN CDTJ
	'Eurostar' (v)	CCCN
	FIRECRACKER ('Norfire'PBR)	CCCN
§	***fruticosa*** **new**	NHrt
	- 'Conga' (v) **new**	LCro
	- 'Kiwi'	EHyd LCro
§	***indivisa***	CCCN CDTJ CPbh CTsd MDon SArc SWeb
	'Jive'PBR (v)	CKel EBee LBuc LCro SEND
	kaspar	CCCN
	obtecta	CCCN
§	- 'Albatross' **new**	LCro

'Pacific Coral'	MDon
'Pacific Sunrise'PBR (v) **new**	SGBe
'Pacific Sunset'PBR	WFar
'Pink Champagne' (v)	CCCN MSwo XSte
PINK PASSION ('Seipin'PBR)	CCCN CPla ELan EPfP LBuc LRHS NPlm SCoo SGBe SGsty SPoG WHlf
'Pink Stripe' (v)	CCCN LSRN SWvt
'Purple Sensation'	CCCN
'Purple Tower' 🏆H3	LRHS NPlm
'Red Heart'	CCCN
'Red Star'	Widely available
'Rumba' **new**	NHrt
'Salsa'PBR	CKel WHlf XSte
'Southern Splendour' (v)	CBcs CCCN CDoC CEme CKel CPla EHyd ELan EPfP LRHS MACG MBros MDon NRHS SCoo SGBe SPoG
'Sundance' 🏆H3	CBcs MGos MSwo NPer SPoG SRms SWvt WFar
'Sunrise' (v)	CPla EHyd LRHS XSte
SUPERSTAR	see *C. obtecta* 'Albatross'
terminalis	see *C. fruticosa*
'Torbay Red' 🏆H3	CBrac CCCN CEme CMac CPla EHyd EPfP LRHS LSRN MAsh MPri SCob SGBe SPeP SPoG SWvt

Corema (*Empetraceae*)

album **new**	WJur

Coreopsis (*Asteraceae*)

'Astolat'	CBod LRHS SGbt SMrm
auriculata CUTTING GOLD	see *C.* 'Schnittgold'
- 'Elfin Gold'	EBou EHyd ELan EPfP XLum
- 'Zamphir'	CDor EPfP WCot
'Baby Gold'	see *C. lanceolata* 'Sonnenkind' (unblotched)
BABY SUN	see *C.* 'Sonnenkind' (red-blotched)
BLOOMSATION CHAMELEON ('Uribl02'PBR) **new**	LBar LCro WHlf
BLOOMSATION DRAGON ('Uribl01') **new**	LCro SEdd
'Buttermilk'PBR	CDor
'Calypso' (v)	SPoG
'Center Stage'	CWnw ELan LSou MACG
'Citrine'PBR (Hardy Jewel Series)	CWGN
'Cosmic Evolution' (Big Bang Series)	EBee EHyd ELan LRHS SPoG
'Cosmic Eye' (Big Bang Series)	EBee EHyd ELan LRHS NRHS SPoG WFar
'Cranberry Ice'	LRHS NRHS
'Daybreak' (Li'l Bang Series)	EHyd LRHS NRHS
'Enchanted Eve'PBR (Li'l Bang Series)	EHyd EPfP LBar LRHS NRHS WFar
'Fool's Gold'	EBee
'Full Moon'PBR (Big Bang Series)	EBee EHyd ELan LBar LRHS NLar NRHS SPoG WFar XLum
'Galaxy' (Big Bang Series)	EBee EHyd ELan LBar LRHS NRHS WFar
'Garnet'PBR (Hardy Jewel Series)	LRHS
gigantea	SPlb
grandiflora	GQue LRHS SBls
- 'Badengold'	CPla
- 'Bernwode' (v)	CMac SWvt
- COREY SINGLE GOLD ('Csgz0002'PBR)	NBir
- 'Domino'	EBee EHyd
- 'Double the Sun'	LBar MHol WHil
- 'Early Sunrise' 🏆H5	CBod CRos CSBt EAJP EBee EHyd EPfP LCro LDai LOPS LRHS MBow MPri NBir NPer NRHS SCoo SGbt SPoG SWvt WFar WPnP XLum
- FLYING SAUCERS ('Walcoreop'PBR)	CRos EHyd EPfP LRHS NRHS SCoo SPoG
- 'Heliot'	MPie
- 'Mayfield Giant'	EBee EHeP ELan EPfP EShb LRHS MAsh SGbt SRms SWvt
- 'Presto' (d)	CBod ELan NGBl NLar WFar
- 'Rising Sun'	EHyd ELan EPfP
- Solena Series	LRHS
- 'Sunburst'	EHeP ELan EPfP XLum
- 'Sunfire'	CRos EHyd LRHS MBros NRHS SBls SCob WFar
- SUNKISS ('M8867p'PBR)	CBod LRHS MACG MSCN
- 'Sunray'	CBcs CChe CRos CSBt ECtt EHyd EPfP GDam GMcL LRHS NGdn NRHS SGbt SHar SOrN SPlb SPoG SRms SWvt XLum
'Highland Blast'	LRHS
'Imperial Sun'PBR	ECtt ELan LSou
'Ladybird'	NCth
lanceolata	CWal LPal
- 'Goldfink'	MRav SRms
- 'Goldteppich'	CRos EHyd EPfP LRHS NRHS
- 'Grandiflora' **new**	CWal
§ - 'Sonnenkind' (unblotched)	EPfP GMaP XLum
- 'Walter'	EBee LRHS LSou SPoG WFar XLum XSen
'Limerock Passion'PBR	EHyd LRHS NRHS SCob
'Limerock Ruby'PBR	EHyd EWoo LRHS MHol NRHS SCob SPoG SWvt WFar XLum
'Limoncello' **new**	LBar SGBe
major	CBod EBee WFar
MANGO PUNCH ('Rp5') (Punch Series)	CAby EBee SGBe
maximiliani	see *Helianthus maximiliani*
'Mercury Rising'PBR (Big Bang Series)	EBee EHyd EPfP LEdu LRHS LSou NRHS SHar
'Moonlight'PBR	LRHS
palmata	SPhx
'Pink Lady'PBR	SGBe WCav
pubescens 'Sunshine Superman'	EHyd ELan
'Red Elf'PBR (Li'l Bang Series)	EHyd LBar LRHS NRHS
'Red Satin' (Permathread Series)	LRHS WTor
'Redshift'	EBee EHyd EMor LRHS NLar NRHS SCoo SPoG
rosea 'American Dream'	CBod CRos CSBt EHyd ELan EPfP GMaP LRHS MAsh MHol NBir NBro NGdn NLar NRHS SBut SGbt SMrm SPer SPlb SRms SWvt WCav WFar WGwG
- 'Heaven's Gate'PBR	EGrI EHyd LBar MHol NCth WFar WPnP
- 'Nana'	XLum
'Route 66'PBR	WCAu WFar
'Ruby Frost' (Hardy Jewel Series)	CBcs EBee LRHS NCth SEdd SGBe SMad SPoG WWke
'Rum Punch'PBR (Punch Series)	CAby
§ 'Schnittgold'	EHyd LRHS NRHS SHar
'Show Stopper'PBR	ELan LSou
'Sienna Sunset'	EHyd ELan LRHS NRHS
'Snowberry'	LRHS MBNS NCth NRHS
SOLANNA GOLDEN SPHERE ('Dcoreo16'PBR)	EPfP SPoG
'Solar Dance'	CWGN NLar SMad WHlf
I 'Sonnenkind' (red-blotched)	EHyd LRHS NRHS
'Star Cluster' (Big Bang Series)	CWGN EHyd ELan EMor EPfP LEdu LRHS LSou NRHS SMad SPoG WFar
'Starbright'PBR (Li'l Bang Series)	LRHS
'Starlight' (Li'l Bang Series)	EBee EHyd LBar LRHS NRHS WFar

'Starstruck'PBR (Li'l Bang Series)	LRHS
'Sterntaler'	CAby EBee EBlo EHyd ELon EPfP EWoo GBee LRHS LSou NCou NRHS SGBe SWvt XLum
SUN CHILD	see *C.* 'Sonnenkind' (red-blotched)
'Sun Splash' (Big Bang Series)	LBar LRHS
SUNNY DAY ('Balcorsunay')	WFar
'Sweet Marmalade'PBR	EPfP LRHS
tinctoria	MNHC SHar SRms
– 'Amulet'	CSpe
– 'Mahogany Midget' **new**	MNHC
tripteris	ELan EPPr EPfP MHol SPhx XLum
– 'Mostenveld'	EBee
– 'Red November'	MNrw
(UpTick Series) UPTICK CREAM & RED ('Balupteamed'PBR)	LBar LRHS LSou MACG MBros MDon
– UPTICK CREAM ('Balupteam'PBR)	LBar MDon MSCN
– UPTICK GOLD AND BRONZE ('Baluptgonz'PBR)	LRHS LSou MDon
– UPTICK YELLOW AND RED ('Baluptowed'PBR) ♀H3	LBar
verticillata	CMac CTri ECha EGrI MBel MBrN MHer NLar NPer SCob SRms WCAu
– 'Bengal Tiger'PBR	CWnw ELan LSou MACG NCth
– 'Crazy Cayenne' (Sizzle and Spice Series)	LRHS
– CRÈME BRÛLÉE ('Crembru'PBR)	ELan MACG NCth NLar SCoo SWvt
– 'Curry Up' (Sizzle and Spice Series)	EPfP LBuc LRHS
I – 'Golden Gain'	ECtt EPfP EShb MAsh NGdn WFar
– 'Golden Shower'	see *C. verticillata* 'Grandiflora'
§ – 'Grandiflora' ♀H5	CBcs EHyd ELan ELon EMor EPfP GMaP LRHS LSto MArl MRav NGdn NHol NRHS NWad SHar SPer WCAu WFar XLum
– 'Hot Paprika' (Sizzle and Spice Series)	EBee EPfP LRHS SEdd
– 'Limerock Dream'PBR	EBee EHyd LRHS NRHS WHlf
– 'Moonbeam'	Widely available
– 'Old Timer'	SDix
– 'Ruby Red'	CRos EHyd LRHS NRHS
– 'Sunbeam'	ELon
– 'Tweety'PBR	WFar
– 'Zagreb' ♀H5	Widely available

coriander see *Coriandrum sativum*

Coriandrum (*Apiaceae*)

sativum	CArg CBod CLau ENfk EWhm GPoy LCro LOPS LRHS MBros MHer MHoo MNHC MPri SPoG SRms
– 'Calypso'PBR ♀H2	EKin MCtn
– 'Confetti' ♀H2	EKin LCro MCtn MHoo
– 'Cruiser'PBR ♀H2	EDel
– 'Leisure'	LCro LOPS SVic
– 'Santo'	CBod
– 'Slobolt'	SPhx

Coriaria ✿ (*Coriariaceae*)

arborea	ESwi
intermedia B&SWJ 019	WCru
japonica	CTsd ESwi NLar SVen WCru
– B&SWJ 2833	WCru
– subsp. ***intermedia*** B&SWJ 3877	WCru
kingiana	WCru
§ ***microphylla***	WCru
– B&SWJ 8999	WCru
– B&SWJ 14702	WCru
myrtifolia	WCru
– B&SWJ 14003	WCru
nepalensis	NLar
pteridoides	WCru
ruscifolia	WCru
– HCM 98178	WCru
terminalis f. ***fructu-rubro***	WCru
– var. ***xanthocarpa***	WCru
– – GWJ 9204	WCru
– – HWJK 2112c	WCru
thymifolia	see *C. microphylla*

Cornus ✿ (*Cornaceae*)

NJM 12.048	WPGP
alba L.	CArg CBTr CCVT CLnd GArf MNic MRav NBwr NWea SEWo SRms WMou WTSh
– 'Alleman's Compact'	LRHS
– 'Argenteovariegata'	see *C. alba* 'Variegata'
– 'Aurea' ♀H7	Widely available
– BATON ROUGE ('Minbat'PBR)	CDoC CGBo CKel CRos CWnw EBee EHyd ELan ELon EPfP LRHS LSRN MAsh MRav NRHS SGsty SPoG SRHi SWvt WFar WLov
– 'Cream Cracker'PBR (v)	MRav
– 'Elegantissima' (v) ♀H7	Widely available
– 'Gouchaultii' (v)	CEnd CKel CMac EPfP GKin LPar LRHS LSto MGos MRav NBwr NLar NRHS SCob SCoo SGsty SPer SRms SWeb WFar
– 'Hessei' misapplied	see *C. sanguinea* 'Compressa'
– IVORY HALO ('Bailhalo'PBR)	CKel EMil EPfP LRHS LSRN MAsh MRav NLar NWea SPer WLov
– 'Kesselringii'	Widely available
– RED GNOME ('Regnzam')	ELon EPfP
– 'Siberian Pearls'	CBcs CRos EHyd ELan GKin LRHS MBlu NCth NLar NRHS SPoG
§ – 'Sibirica' ♀H7	Widely available
– 'Sibirica Ruby'	SavN
– 'Sibirica Variegata' (v) ♀H7	CBcs CEme CKel CMac CRos EBee EHeP EHyd ELon EPfP GKin GMcL LRHS LSRN MAsh MBlu MGos NRHS SCob SPer SWvt WHlf
– 'Spaethii' (v) ♀H7	Widely available
§ – 'Variegata' (v)	WFar
– 'Westonbirt'	see *C. alba* 'Sibirica'
alternifolia	CCVT GArf LMaj SSta WHtc
§ – 'Argentea' (v) ♀H6	Widely available
– 'Brunette'	CJun MBlu
– GOLDEN SHADOWS ('Wstackman'PBR) (v)	CKel CWGN EHed LRHS NLar SGsty
– 'Golden Surprise'	CJun
– 'Goldfinch' (v)	CJun MBlu
– 'Illusion' (v)	CJun
– 'Moonlight' (v)	CJun
– PINKY SPOT ('Minpinky')	EHed LAlb MPkF NLar XSte
– 'Silver Giant' (v)	CJun NLar WSpi
– 'Variegata'	see *C. alternifolia* 'Argentea'
amomum	EBtc NLar
– 'Blue Cloud'	CBcs CBod CRos EHed LRHS MBlu
– 'Lady Jane'	NLar
'Ascona'	CBcs CEnd CJun CLnd NLar SGol WGob
'Blooming Merry Tetra' **new**	NLar
'Blooming Pink Tetra' **new**	NLar
'Blooming White Tetra' **new**	NLar
canadensis	Widely available
candidissima Marshall	see *C. foemina* Mill.
capitata	CBcs CBod CEme CJun CMac CPla CRos CTsd EBee EGrI EHyd EPfP

	ESwi EWTr GKev IArd IDee MGil MGos SAko SEND SPoG WCru WFar WJur WKor WPGP
- subsp. ***emeiensis***	CJun
- 'Foreness Fog' (v)	SEND
- 'Kilmacurragh Rose'	IArd IDee
aff. ***capitata***	SRHi
'Celestial Shadow'	see *C.* × *rutgersensis* 'Michael Steinhardt'
chinensis	SSta SWvt
controversa	CAco CBcs CCVT CMCN CSBt EBar EPfP IPap LCro LIns LMaj LOPS LPar MBlu MGil NBwr NLar NWea SEND SEWo SGol SSta SWvt
I - 'Aurea'	MAsh
- 'Candlelight'	MBlu NLar SSta
§ - 'Frans Type' (v)	CJun
- 'Green Carpet'	LMaj NLar SSta
- 'Laska'	CJun LMaj MBlu NLar
- 'Lucia'	CJun NLar
I - 'Marginata Nord'	NLar
- 'Pagoda'	CJun LPar MBlu NLar
- 'Variegata' (v) $\mathbb{Y}^{H5}$	Widely available
- 'Variegata' Frans type	see *C. controversa* 'Frans Type'
'Dorothy'	CJun
'Eddie's White Wonder' $\mathbb{Y}^{H5}$	Widely available
elliptica	WPGP
- EMPRESS OF CHINA ('Elsbry')	CBcs EHed NCth NLar SMad SRHi
- 'First Choice'	CJun
- 'Full Moon'	CJun
× ***elwinortonii*** VENUS ('Kn30 8'^{PBR}) (Jersey Star Series)	CWGN EBee ELan EPfP LCro LPar LRHS MAsh MBlu SEWo SGsty SMad WPGP
excelsa F&M 57	WPGP
florida	CBcs CMCN EGrI ESwi IPap LCro MMuc MThu MTrO NOra NOrn NWea SCob SGsty SPer SSta WHlf WHtc WJur WMat WTSh
- 'Autumn Gold'	SSta
- CHEROKEE BRAVE ('Comco No 1')	EHyd LMil LRHS MAsh NRHS SPoG SSta WGob
- 'Cherokee Chief'	CBcs CEnd CJun CTri EGrI EHyd GDam LMaj LPar LRHS LSRN MThu NLar NRHS WSpi XSte
- 'Cherokee Daybreak'	see *C. florida* 'Daybreak'
- 'Cherokee Princess'	EHyd EWTr GDam LMil LRHS MAsh MTrO NLar NOra NOrn SSta WMat
- 'Cherokee Sunset'	see *C. florida* 'Sunset'
- 'Clear Moon'	LPar
- 'Cloud Nine'	CBcs CEme EGrI EHed ERom EWTr GKin LPar MTrO NLar NOrn SGsty
- 'Comanche Chief'	LRHS
§ - 'Daybreak' (v) $\mathbb{Y}^{H5}$	CBcs CEme EHyd LMaj LRHS LSRN MAsh MTrO NOra NOrn NRHS SGol SPer SPoG WMat
- 'Fragrant Cloud'	SWvt
- 'Granary Gold'	SSta
- 'Junior Miss'	CEnd
- 'Pink Flame' (v)	SSta
- 'Rainbow' (v) $\mathbb{Y}^{H5}$	CBcs EHyd LMil LPar LRHS MAsh MTrO NOra NOrn NRHS NWea SGol SPer SPoG WMat
- f. ***rubra***	CBcs EGrI ELan GKin LCro LMaj LOPS LPar MGil MRav NOrn SGsty SPoG WMat
- - 'Red Giant'	CBcs EWTr
- - 'Spring Song'	CMac EGrI WGob
- 'Spring Day'	CMac
- 'Stoke's Pink'	CEnd
§ - 'Sunset' (v)	CEme CEnd EHyd ELan LCro LMaj LMil LPar LRHS MAsh MTrO NLar NOrn NRHS SSta SWvt WMat
- 'Sweetwater'	SAko WGob
- subsp. ***urbiniana***	EBee LRHS WPGP
- 'Variegata' (v)	GKin
- 'White Cloud'	ERom LPar NOra WMat
§ ***foemina*** Mill.	SBrt
'Gloria Birkett'	CJun EHyd LMil LRHS MAsh WGob
hessei misapplied	see *C. sanguinea* 'Compressa'
hongkongensis	CBcs EHed LRHS MMrt MPkF NLar SRHi WPGP XSte
- HWJ 1033	EPfP
'Jerry Mundy'	CMac
'Kelsey Dwarf'	see *C. sericea* 'Kelseyi'
'Kenwyn Clapp'	CJun
kousa	CBcs CCVT CDoC CMCN CMac CPer EGrI EPau EPfP GArf GKev GKin GMcL LMaj LPar NGrs NLar SCob SGol SGsty SOrN SPer SPlb WJur WKor WLov
- B&SWJ 12610 from Korea	WCru
- B&SWJ 14620 from Japan	WCru
- 'Akabana'	CJun
- 'Akatsuki' (v)	MAsh NLar SSta
- 'All Summer'	CJun
- 'Autumn Rose'	CJun NLar SMad
- 'Beni-fuji'	CLnd EHed EHyd EWTr LRHS MAsh MBlu MPkF MThu NCth NLar NRHS
- 'Big Apple'	CJun CRos EHyd EPfP LMil LRHS MThu NLar SRHi WGob
- 'Blue Shadow'	CBcs CJun EPfP MBlu SRHi SSta
- 'Bonfire' (v)	CDoC NLar
- 'Bultinck's Beauty'	MAsh MPkF
- 'Bultinck's Giant'	CDoC CLnd EWTr LRHS MBlu MPkF NLar WGob
- 'Cappuccino'	CDoC CJun EWTr LPar LRHS MAsh MThu NLar NOrn NRHS SHor WTSh
- 'Cherokee'	CJun NLar
- 'China Dawn' (v)	CJun SSta
- var. ***chinensis***	Widely available
- - 'Barmstedt'	SAko
- - 'Bodnant Form'	CEnd CJun CPer EGrI EPfP LRHS NLar SSta WGob
- - 'China Girl' $\mathbb{Y}^{H5}$	Widely available
- - 'Claudia'	EPfP IArd NCth NLar SSta
- - 'Great Star'	CKel EHed EPfP LSRN MAsh SGsty
- - 'Greta's Gold' (v)	CJun SSta
- - 'Ikone'	SAko
- - 'PVG'	CJun
- - 'Snowflake'	CJun
- - 'Spinners'	CJun MAsh
- - 'Summer Stars'	CJun
- - 'Tri-Splendor'	EHed NLar
- - 'White Dusted' (v)	MBlu NLar SMad
- - 'White Fountain'	EPfP LSRN MGos MPkF MPnt NLar NOra NOrn WMat
- - 'Wieting's Select'	CJun EHed EWTr MBlu MPkF MThu NLar SAko
- - 'Wisley Queen' $\mathbb{Y}^{H5}$	CJun CRos EHyd EPfP LMil LRHS MAsh SChF SPoG SRHi SSta WPGP
- 'Claudine'	CJun
- 'Copacabana'	CKel EHed LRHS MBlu
- 'Couronne' **new**	SMad
- 'Daybreak'	SGol
- 'Doctor Bump'	NLar
- 'Doubloon'	CJun
- 'Dwarf Pink'	CJun MAsh MThu NLar
- 'Ed Mezitt'	CDoC CJun LRHS MAsh MThu NLar
- 'Elizabeth Lustgarten'	CJun MBlu SSta
- 'Eurostar'	MBlu
- 'Fanfare'	CJun MAsh
- 'Fernie's Favourite'	CJun
- GALILEAN ('Galzam')	CDoC EHed LMil MThu WGob
- 'Gay Head'	CJun

	- giant-flowered	MPkF
I	- 'Girard's Nana'	CJun MPkF NLar
	- 'Gold Cup' (v)	CJun MAsh SSta
	- 'Gold Star' (v)	CBcs CEnd CJun CMCN EHed ELan EPfP LMil MAsh MBlu NLar SChF SPoG SSta WGob
	- 'Greensleeves'	CJun EHyd EPfP LMil LRHS MAsh SRHi SSta WGob
	- HEART THROB ('Schmred')	MAsh NLar SCoo SGol
	- 'Highland'	CJun NLar
	- 'John Slocock' 🏆H5	CJun IArd NLar
	- 'Kim'	MAsh NLar
	- 'Koree'	NLar
	- 'Kreuzdame'	CJun MBlu
	- 'Laura'	CWGN MAsh MBlu NLar SMad
	- 'Little Beauty'	CJun
	- 'Lizzie P'	NLar
	- 'Lustgarten Weeping'	CJun
	- 'Madame Butterfly'	CJun CRos LRHS MBlu MThu NLar SPoG
	- 'Marwood Cream' **new**	SChF
	- 'Marwood Dawn'	SChF WPGP
	- 'Marwood Twilight'	EBee SChF
	- 'Milky Way'	CBod CDoC CJun CLnd CMCN EHed EPfP ERom EWTr GMcL IPap LPar LRHS LSRN MAsh MBlu MGos MPkF MRav MThu MTrO NCth NLar SGol SGsty WGob WMat WSpi
	- 'Milky Way Select'	CBcs CJun EHyd LRHS NRHS
	- 'Miss Petty'	CJun
	- 'Miss Satomi' 🏆H5	Widely available
	- 'Moonbeam'	CDoC CJun EWTr NLar SMad
	- 'Mount Fuji'	CJun MBlu SSta
	- 'National'	CDoC CJun EGrI EHed LMil LRHS MAsh NLar SSta WGob
	- 'Nicole'	EHed MAsh MPkF NLar WGob
	- 'Ohkan'	CJun MPkF
	- 'Pévé Foggy'	CDoC MAsh MThu NLar
	- 'Pévé Limbo' (v)	CJun
	- 'Pévé Sammy' (v) **new**	NLar
	- 'Pévé Satomi Compact'	EHed NLar
	- 'Pink Lips'	MAsh NLar
	- 'Polywood'	CJun MAsh NLar
	- RADIANT ROSE ('Hanros')	EPfP MAsh NLar SSta WGob WPGP
	- 'Rasen'	CJun MAsh NLar
	- 'Rel Whirlwind'	CJun
*	- 'Robert'	NLar
	- 'Rosea'	CJun
	- 'Rosemoor Pink'	CJun
	- 'Rosy Teacups'[PBR]	MTrO WMat
	- SAMARITAN ('Samzam') (v)	CBcs CDoC CEnd LPar LSRN MAsh MPkF MThu
	- SCARLET FIRE ('H 3 Dr 11 P21'[PBR])	LRHS
	- 'Schmetterling'	CJun EPfP EWTr LPar MBlu MPkF MThu NLar
	- 'Sluis Slim'	EHed MBlu
	- 'Snowbird'	CJun LRHS
	- 'Snowboy' (v)	CEnd MBlu
	- 'Snowflurries'	CJun SRHi
	- 'Southern Cross'	CJun WGob
	- 'Square Dance'	CJun MAsh NLar
	- 'Steeple'	CJun
	- 'Summer Fun' 🏆H5	CJun CRos EHyd LMil LRHS MAsh MPkF SPoG SSta
	- 'Summer Gold' (v)	MAsh
	- 'Summer Majesty'	CJun MAsh
	- 'Sunsplash' (v)	CJun LRHS SPoG SSta
	- 'Temple Jewel' (v)	CJun
	- 'Teresa' (v)	MAsh NLar
	- 'Teutonia' 🏆H5	CJun ELan EWTr IArd MAsh MGos MTrO NLar SAko SSta WGob WMat

	- 'Trinity Star'	CJun MAsh
	- 'Tsukubanomine'	CJun CLnd MAsh
	- 'Weaver's Weeping'	CJun EHed MPkF
	- 'Weisse Fontäne'	CJun MAsh MBlu MPkF MThu NLar
	- 'White Dream'	CJun EHed MPkF NLar
	- 'White Giant'	CJun
	- 'Willy Boy'	MAsh
	- 'Wolf Eyes' (v) 🏆H5	CJun EHed ELan EPfP LMil LRHS MAsh MBlu MPkF MThu NLar SPoG SSta
	macrophylla Wall.	EBee EGrI IDee MBlu SPtp WCru WPGP
	- MSF 821	WPGP
	- var. ***macrophylla***	SSta
	mas	Widely available
	- 'Aurea' (v) 🏆H6	EPfP LMil LPar LRHS MAsh MBlu MRav NLar SSta WCot WLov
§	- 'Aureoelegantissima' (v)	CMac NLar WCot WLov
	- 'Elegant' (F)	CAgr CJun
	- 'Elegantissima'	see *C. mas* 'Aureoelegantissima'
	- 'Elena'	NLar
	- 'Golden Glory' 🏆H6	CJun CLnd LRHS NLar
	- 'Gourmet' (F)	CAgr
	- 'Happy Face'	NLar
	- 'Hillier's Upright'	CJun
	- 'Jolico' (F) 🏆H6	CAgr CJun LEdu MBlu MTrO NLar WMat
	- 'Kasanlaker' (F)	CAgr NLar
	- 'Nikolka' (F)	NLar
	- 'Pancharevo' (F)	CAgr
	- 'Pioneer' (F)	CJun
	- 'Redstone' (F)	CJun
	- 'Shan' (F)	CAgr
	- 'Shumen' (F)	CAgr NLar
	- 'Spring Glow'	CJun NLar
	- 'Variegata' (v) 🏆H6	CAco CBcs CJun CMCN EPfP MAsh MBlu MGos NLar
	- 'Vraća Kaštel' (F)	CAgr
	- 'Xanthocarpa' (F)	CAgr CJun
	mas × officinalis	CJun
	'Norman Hadden' 🏆H5	Widely available
	nuttallii	CLnd EPfP EWTr LPar MGil SPer SWeb SWvt
	- 'Colrigo Giant'	CJun
	- 'Monarch'	CJun EHed EWTr LPar SPer
	- 'North Star'	CJun NLar
	- 'Osmunda'	CEnd
	- 'Portlemouth'	CEnd CJun
	- 'Zurico'	CJun
	oblonga	CExl EBee WPGP
	officinalis	CAgr CJun CKel CMCN CMac CWnw EBee EPfP LRHS MBlu NLar NOra SWvt WJur WSpi
	- 'Kintoki' 🏆H6	NLar WLov
	- 'Robin's Pride'	LMaj NLar
	'Ormonde' 🏆H5	CJun EBee EGrI EPfP NLar WGob WPGP
	'Pink Blush'	CJun
	'Porlock' 🏆H5	CJun CMCN EHyd EPfP LRHS NCth NLar NRHS SWvt WGob
	pumila	NLar
	racemosa	EBtc NLar
	rugosa	EBtc
	× ***rutgersensis***	LRHS
	- CELESTIAL SHADOW	see *C.* × *rutgersensis* 'Michael Steinhardt'
§	- 'Michael Steinhardt' (v)	SGol
	- (Stellar Series) AURORA ('Rutban')	CJun EHed MBlu SGol
§	- - CELESTIAL ('Rutdan')	CJun EHyd LMil LRHS MAsh NRHS SGol WGob
	- - CONSTELLATION ('Rutcan')	CJun LMil SGol

- - GALAXY — see *C.* × *rutgersensis* (Stellar Series) CELESTIAL
- - RUTH ELLEN ('Rutlan') — EWTr LMaj LMil LRHS
- - STARDUST ('Rutfan') — EHed SGol
- - STELLAR PINK ('Rutgan') — CBcs CJun CLnd EHed EHyd EWTr LRHS MGos NLar NRHS SAko SChF SCob SGol WGob WPGP

sanguinea — CBTr CBcs CBod CBrac CCVT CHab CLnd CMac CPer CTri EHeP EPfP LBuc LIns MNic MRav MSwo NWea SCob SEWo SPer SVic WMat WMou WTSh
§ - 'Anny' — GDam MBlu
- 'Anny's Winter Orange' ♀H5 — CBod CMac CRos EHyd ELan ELon EPfP EShb LPar LRHS LSRN LSvl MAsh MSwo NCth NRHS SPoG WAvo WBrk WCot WHtc
§ - 'Compressa' — GKev MBlu MGil MRav NLar
- 'Magic Flame' ♀H5 — CBod CDoC CKel CRos CWnw EHyd ELon EPfP LPar LRHS MAsh MPri NLar NRHS SPoG SRHi SWvt WCot WLov
- 'Midwinter Fire' — Widely available
- 'Winter Beauty' — CSBt EBee EPfP LPar LSto MAsh MBlu NLar NWea SCob SWvt WAvo
- WINTER FLAME — see *C. sanguinea* 'Anny'

sericea 'Bud's Yellow' — EHyd ELon EPfP LRHS MBlu NLar NRHS
- 'Cardinal' — CDoC CRos EBee EHyd ELon EPfP LRHS MAsh MGos NLar NRHS
- 'Flaviramea' ♀H7 — Widely available
- 'Hedgerows Gold' (v) ♀H7 — CKel CRos EBee EHyd ELan ELon EMil EPfP LRHS MAsh MGos NEoE NRHS SCoo SPoG WFar WHtc WLov
§ - 'Kelseyi' — CBod CMac EBee EPfP GMcL ILea MRav NLar SBrt SCob SPoG WLov
- KELSEY'S GOLD ('Rosco') — CMac CRos ELon LMil LRHS MAsh NRHS SPoG WLov
- subsp. ***occidentalis*** 'Sunshine' — EPfP NEoE NLar
§ - 'White Gold' (v) — CGBo CKel EBee ELon EPfP LSRN MRav NLar SPer SPoG SRms WFar
- 'White Spot' — see *C. sericea* 'White Gold'

stricta — see *C. foemina* Mill.
suecica — NHar
× ***unalaschkensis*** — GKev NHar
walteri — EBtc
wilsoniana — CJun MBlu WPGP
'Winter Orange' — CDoC NLar

Corokia ✿ (*Argophyllaceae*)

buddlejoides — CBcs CBod CCoa CSde CTrC CTsd ELan GBin NLar SEND WFar
cotoneaster — Widely available
'Geenty's Ghost' — CTrC
* ***parviflora*** — CTrC
× ***virgata*** — CChe CEnd CTrC CTri ELan EPfP NLar SArc SPlb SSut SWvt WKif
- 'Banana Royal' — CBct CDoC LRHS SIvy
- 'Bronze King' — CBrac CTrC ELan LPal SPer SPlb SVen
- 'Coppershine' — CCCN CCoa
- 'Frosted Chocolate' — CBod CCht CCoa CDoC CKel CSde CTrC CTsd CWnw ELan EPfP LRHS LSto MHtn SArc SEND SEdd SIvy SPoG SSta SSut SVen SWvt WFar WHtc WLov
- 'Geenty's Green' — CCoa CRos CTrC
- 'Limey' — CBod CCht LRHS
- 'Mangatangi' — CTrC
- 'Pink Delight' — CBod ELan EPfP MRav SSha
- 'Red Wonder' — CEnd CKel CMac CTrC EHyd ELan EPfP GAbr LRHS LSto SEND SEdd SPoG SVen WAvo WHtc WLov
- 'Sunsplash' (v) — CBcs CBod CBrac CCCN CCht CCoa CDoC CEme CKel CMac CTrC CTsd ELan EPfP LRHS MMrt NLar SEND SEle SPoG SSta SWvt WFar WLov
- 'Welsh Whiskey' — CBod CDoC LRHS SEle
- 'Yellow Wonder' — CBcs CKel CTrC ELan EPfP GAbr LRHS NLar SPlb SWvt

Coronilla (*Fabaceae*)

cappadocica — see *C. orientalis*
comosa — see *Hippocrepis comosa*
emerus — see *Hippocrepis emerus*
glauca — see *C. valentina* subsp. *glauca*
minima — WAbe
§ ***orientalis*** — EPPr WAbe
valentina — CRHN GMcL MGil
- 'Cotswold Cream' (v) — MPie SEdd SPoG WCot WMal
§ - subsp. ***glauca*** ♀H4 — CBod CCCN CDoC CKel CMac CSBt CSde CTri CWal EBee ELan EPfP LEdu LRHS LSRN SDix SEND SIvy SNig SPer SRms SVen SWvt XLum XSen
- - 'Brockhill Blue' — CKel EPfP LRHS SAko WCot WNPC
- - 'Citrina' ♀H4 — Widely available
- - 'Lauren Stevenson' — ELon MHol SHar SMrm WCot
* - - 'Pygmaea' — LRHS SEle SRms WAbe WCot
- - 'Variegata' (v) — CBcs CDoC CKel CMac CRos CTri EBee ELan EPfP LRHS MAsh MGil MHtn MNHC MRav SCoo SEle SMrm SNig SPer SPoG SRms SSha SVen WCot
- - 'XXS' — WCot

varia — see *Securigera varia*

Correa ✿ (*Rutaceae*)

alba — CCCN CTrC EPfP
- 'Pinkie' ♀H3 — CCCN CExl CSde CTrC CTsd WAbe
alba* × *backhouseana — CCCN SEle
backhouseana ♀H3 — CAbb CBcs CBod CCCN CGBo CKel CSBt CSde CTri CTsd EBee EHed EHyd ELan EPfP IDee LRHS NLar SBrt SEle SRkn SSha SVen WAbe
- 'Peaches and Cream' — CCCN SEle SRkn
decumbens — CTrC
'Dusky Bells' ♀H3 — CAbb CBcs CBod CCCN CKel CSde CTrC CTri CTsd EHyd ELan EPfP LRHS MAsh MGil SEle SPlb SPoG SRkn SSha SVen WLea
'Dusky Maid' — CCCN
'Federation Belle' — CCCN SVen
glabra — CTrC SEle
- var. ***glabra*** — SPlb
- green-flowered **new** — SSha
'Harrisii' — see *C.* 'Mannii'
lawrenceana — CTsd SEND SEle WPGP
- var. ***grampiana*** — SVen
§ 'Mannii' ♀H3 — CCCN MGil
'Marian's Marvel' ♀H3 — CBcs CBod CCCN CKel CSde CTrC CTsd ELan EPfP IArd IDee MAsh SEND SEle SMad SRkn SSha SVen WAbe WLea
'Peachy Cream' — CAbb CCCN CSBt
'Poorinda Mary' — CCCN CKel CTrC LRHS MHtn SEle
pulchella ♀H3 — CMac CTri IDee SEle
- orange-flowered — WAbe
- 'Pink Mist' — CTrC EPot WAbe
reflexa — CTsd MAsh MGil WAbe WCot
var. ***nummulariifolia*** — WPGP

	- var. ***reflexa***	WCot
	schlechtendalii	CCCN MGil SEle SVen

Cortaderia ✿ (*Poaceae*)

	araucana	ELan
	argentea	see *C. selloana*
	fulvida misapplied	see *C. richardii* (Endl.) Zotov
§	***fulvida*** (Buchanan) Zotov ♀H5	IArd IDee WCot
	richardii misapplied	see *C. fulvida* (Buchanan) Zotov
	richardii ambig.	CBod MMuc NBir NLar SGBe SPtp SWvt WSpi
§	***richardii*** (Endl.) Zotov ♀H5	CAby CBcs CDoC CKno ESwi EWes LRHS SArc SDix SRms WPGP
	- Brown's strain	WCot
	rudiuscula	EBee
§	***selloana***	CBcs CBod CEme CTsd EBee EHeP MDon MGos NBir NGrd SEdd SGsty SPlb SRHi
§	- 'Albolineata' (v)	CBcs ELon MWht SWvt
§	- 'Aureolineata' (v) ♀H6	CBcs CEme CKel CMac CSde EHyd ELan EPfP GMaP LRHS MWht NRHS SEND SPer SPoG SWvt
	- 'Esperanta' (v) **new**	NWsh
	- 'Evita'PBR ♀H6	CChe ECtt ELan LPar SPoG SWvt WCot
	- 'Gold Band'	see *C. selloana* 'Aureolineata'
	- 'Icalma'	CSde EPPr
	- 'Monstrosa' ♀H6	SEND SMad
	- 'Patagonia' ♀H6	EBlo EPPr
	- 'Pink Feather'	EDir EHyd EPfP GMcL NLar SCoo SEND SPer WFar
	- 'Pointe du Raz'	CKel EBee SWvt
	- 'Pumila' ♀H6	Widely available
	- 'Rendatleri'	CBcs SCoo SWvt
	- 'Rosea'	CBod EHeP EPfP LPar MDon NLar SBls SCob WFar
	- 'Senior'	NLar
	- 'Silver Comet'	ECtt
	- SILVER FEATHER ('Notcort') (v) ♀H6	SCob
	- 'Silver Fountain' (v)	EHyd ELan EPfP LRHS MAsh NRHS SPer SPoG
	- 'Silver Stripe'	see *C. selloana* 'Albolineata'
	- 'Splendid Star'PBR (v)	CRos EHyd LBuc LRHS MAsh MGos NRHS SCob SPoG SWvt
	- 'Sunningdale Silver' ♀H6	CBcs CBod CKel CMac ECha ELan ELon EPfP GMcL LSRN MGos SCob SCoo SEND SMad SPer SPoG SWvt
*	- 'White Feather'	CBod EHyd GMcL NLar SCoo SPer WFar
	Toe Toe	see *C. richardii* (Endl.) Zotov

Cortusa (*Primulaceae*)

	altaica	CBor
*	***caucasica*** 'Alba'	EBee
§	***matthioli***	CKel CPla EMor EWld GGro GPSL NHpl WFar WHil
	- var. ***congesta***	GKev GRum
	- subsp. ***matthioli***	GKev
	- subsp. ***pekinensis***	EBee GKev NBid WSHC WTyc
	- - var. ***sachalinensis***	GKev
	turkestanica	NWad

Corydalis ✿ (*Papaveraceae*)

	'Ambigua'	GKev
	angustifolia	WCot
	anthriscifolia	EWes EWld
	'Blackberry Wine'	EBee LCro MSCN NSti SPoG
	BLUE LINE ('Couriblue')	CBor CWGN GBin LRHS LSou NCth NHar SCob SPoG XLum
	'Blue Panda'	see *C. flexuosa* 'Blue Panda'
	bulbosa misapplied	see *C. cava*
	bulbosa (L.) DC.	see *C. solida*
	buschii	EBee NHar NRya
	calycosa	GBin IPot MAvo
	'Canary Feathers'PBR	CRos EHed EHyd LBar LRHS NHpl NRHS
	caseana subsp. ***brandegeei***	CSpe
	cashmeriana	EHyd GArf LRHS NBid NRHS WAbe
	- 'Kailash'	EBee
	cashmeriana × ***flexuosa***	WAbe
	caucasica var. ***alba*** misapplied	see *C. malkensis*
§	***cava***	EBee EMor GKev LAma NHpl NRog WShi
	- 'Albiflora'	NRog
	chaerophylla	EWld
	cheilanthifolia	CElw ECha EGrl EPot EWld GGro LEdu SRms
	'Craigton Blue'	CDor EMor EPPr EWld GBin GEdr GKev GMaP GQue MNrw NHar NLar NSti WAbe WFar WSHC
	'Craigton Purple'	EMor NHar
	curviflora	GKev WAbe
	- subsp. ***rosthornii*** 'Blue Heron'	CAby CBod CSpe CWCL CWGN ECtt EHyd EMor EPot GEdr LRHS MBNS NCth NHar NLar NRHS SPad SRHi SRkn WFar WPnP WSHC
	decipiens Schott, Nyman & Kotschy	see *C. solida* subsp. *incisa*
	decipiens misapplied	EPot LAma
	'Dzukou Mousse'	WPGP
	elata	CBod CTtf CWCL EHyd EWes GAbr GArf LRHS MArl MBel MBriF MCot MNrw NBid NBir NChi NRHS SPoG SPtp WSHC
	- 'Blue Summit'	EPPr WFar WPGP
	elata × ***flexuosa*** clone 1	GEdr
	erdelii	NRog
	flexuosa	EPfP GKev GMcL MNrw WBor WSHC
	- 'Blue Dragon'	see *C. flexuosa* 'Purple Leaf'
§	- 'Blue Panda' ♀H5	EPPr GMaP
	- 'Blue Panther'	LEdu
	- 'Blue Summit'	EMor LEdu
	- 'China Blue'	CAby CAvo CBcs CRos CWCL ECha ECtt EHyd ELan EMor EPau EPfP EWes GKev GMaP GMcL LCro LEdu LRHS MACG MCot NBir NLar NRHS SPoG SRkn SRms SWvt WFar
	- 'Golden Panda' (v)	NHpl
	- 'Hale Cat'	EMor EPPr
	- 'Nightshade'	WCot
I	- 'Norman's Seedling'	EPPr
	- 'Père David'	CDor CMac CSBt CSpe EBee ECha EHyd ELan EMor EPPr EPfP LEdu MHer NBir NCth SPlb SPoG SRms SWvt WIce XLum
§	- 'Purple Leaf' ♀H5	Widely available
	glauca	see *C. sempervirens*
	glaucescens 'Early Beauty'	NRog
	'Heavenly Blue'	GKev
	heterocarpa	GGro
	- var. ***japonica***	EBee
	'Kingfisher'	CBor CDor NBir NLar NSla WAbe WSHC
	'Korn's Purple'	ECha EMor EPPr EWes IPot LEdu NHar
	ledebouriana	CTtf NRog
	leucanthema DJHC 752	CExl
	- 'Silver Spectre' (v)	CExl ECha
	linstowiana CD&R 605	CExl
§	***lutea***	EPfP MMuc NBir NPer NSti SEND SRms WCot XLum

§ ***malkensis*** ♀H5	CBor CTtf EBee EMor EPot GKev MAvo NRya
microflora	GKev
moorcroftiana	CExl
mucronipetala	GKev
nobilis	GKev SPhx
§ ***ochroleuca***	CElw CMac CSpe EPot XLum
omeiana ♀H5	EPPr NLar SPtp WCot WFar XLum
ophiocarpa	ELan EMor GGro
pachycentra	CExl WAbe
paczoskii	EHyd GKev NRHS NRog
petrophila	GGro
'Porcelain Blue'	EMor GEdr LBar LRHS MPnt NHar NLar
pseudofumaria alba	see *C. ochroleuca*
pumila	GKev
'Rainier Blue'	WFar
'Rukšāns Red'	CWCL EMor
'Sapphire'	NHar
scandens	see *Dactylicapnos scandens*
schusteriana	GGro
BO 16003 **new**	
§ ***sempervirens***	EMor
shimienensis 'Berry Exciting' PBR	CAby CBod CPla EMor LBar MBNS NPer SPoG WPnP
siamensis B&SWJ 7200	WCru
§ ***solida***	CElw ECtt EHyd EMor EPot GKev LAma LEdu LRHS MRav NLar NRHS NRog NRya SDeJ SPhx WBrk WCot WShi
- 'Advocet'	GEdr
- 'Bird of Paradise'	GKev
- 'Coscoroba'	CBor GKev NRog
- 'Evening Shade'	GEdr
- 'Fire Bird'	GEdr
- 'Firecracker'	CBor EHyd GKev LRHS NRHS
- 'Galah'	GKev
- 'Gaviota'	GEdr GKev
§ - subsp. ***incisa*** ♀H5	EPot NRog SDeJ
- 'Linnet'	GKev
- 'Paloma'	NRog
- 'Piggelmee' **new**	GKev
- 'Pinkeltje' **new**	GKev
- 'Purple Beauty'	CBor CWCL
- 'Purple Bird'	CBor CWCL EPot ERCP GKev LAma SDeJ WFar
- 'Pussy'	CWCL EMor
- RAINBOW (mixed)	GKev
- 'Red Bird' **new**	GKev
- 'Robin'	GKev
- 'Snowy Owl'	EPot GKev
§ - subsp. ***solida***	EPot NBir NRya WCot
- - 'Alba'	NSla
- - 'Beth Evans'	CBro CTtf CWCL ECha ECtt EMor EPot ERCP GEdr GKev LAma LEdu LRHS MAvo MNrw NBir NHpl NLar NRog SDeJ SGro SPhx WBrk WFar WOld WShi
- - 'Blushing Girl'	GEdr WFar
- - 'Dieter Schacht'	GEdr
- - 'Evening Shade'	GEdr
- - 'George Baker'	Widely available
- - 'Nettleton Pink'	GKev
- - Prasil Group	CBor GEdr NHpl
- - 'White Knight'	GKev LAma NHpl NLar WCot
- f. ***transsylvanica***	see *C. solida* subsp. *solida*
- 'Turaco'	NRog
- 'White King'	WCot
- 'White Swallow'	CBor EMor EPot GEdr GKev SDeJ
- 'Zwanenberg'	GKev
'Spinners'	CDor CElw CFis EBee ECtt EPPr GKev GLog GPSL LEdu NQui WFar WPnP WSHC WTyc XLum
stipulata B&SWJ 2951	WCru
taliensis	CExl
tauricola	GEdr
temulifolia	WFar
- 'Chocolate Stars'	CBcs CMiW CSpe CWCL CWGN EBee ECtt EHed EMor ESwi EWld GKev MBNS MHol NCth SGBe SPoG WCot WSHC WTre
tomentella	GKev
'Tory MP'	CDor CExl CMiW CRos EBee EHyd EMor EPPr EPfP GEdr LEdu LRHS MNrw MPie NChi NCth NRHS WFar WPGP WSHC
transsylvanica hort.	see *C. solida* subsp. *solida*
vittae	GKev
vivipara	EPPr
wendelboi subsp. ***congesta***	GKev
'Wildside Blue'	CMil EPPr EWld NHar WSHC
wilsonii	CExl GKev

Corylopsis (*Hamamelidaceae*)

glabrescens	CBcs CJun EGrl EHyd EPfP LMil LRHS NLar WJur
- B&SWJ 14636	WCru
- var. ***gotoana***	CJun EHyd EPfP GKev LRHS MAsh NLar
- - 'Chollipo'	CJun EHyd NLar SSta
- 'Lemon Drop'	CJun NLar WPGP
glandulifera	CJun
pauciflora ♀H5	CBcs CBod CDoC CEnd CJun CRos EBee EPfP GDam GMcL IDee LCro LOPS LPar LRHS LSRN MAsh MGil MRav NLar SCob SGol SPer SPoG SRHi WCFE WPGP WSpi
platypetala	see *C. sinensis* var. *calvescens*
- var. ***laevis***	see *C. sinensis* var. *calvescens*
sinensis	CBcs EBee EPfP GKev WJur
§ - var. ***calvescens***	CBcs CJun EPfP NLar
§ - - f. ***veitchiana*** ♀H5	CJun EHyd EPfP LRHS MAsh
§ - var. ***sinensis*** ♀H5	CCCN CDoC CJun CMCN EBee EPfP LRHS MAsh NLar SGol WSpi
- - 'Spring Purple'	CBcs CEnd CJun CMac EBee EPfP EWes GMcL IDee LRHS MGos NLar NRHS SPoG WHtc WPGP WSpi XSte
- 'Veitch's Purple'	CJun NLar
spicata	CBcs CJun CMCN EGrl IDee LRHS MBlu MGil MMuc MRav NLar SGbt SGol
- 'Red Eye'	CJun NLar
veitchiana	see *C. sinensis* var. *calvescens* f. *veitchiana*
willmottiae	see *C. sinensis* var. *sinensis*

Corylus ✿ (*Betulaceae*)

avellana (F)	Widely available
- 'Anaconda'	MBlu
- 'Anny's Purple Dream' PBR	MBlu
- 'Anny's Red Dwarf'	NLar
- 'Aurea'	CBcs CEnd EBee EHeP ELan EPfP LMaj LPar MAsh MBlu MGos NLar NWea SLim SPoG SSta SWvt WBor WFar WLov
- 'Bollwylle'	see *C. maxima* 'Halle'sche Riesennuss'
§ - 'Butler' (F)	CAgr CBod CEnd CMac CTri LCro MTrO NRog SRms
- 'Casina' (F)	CAgr
- 'Clark' (F)	MCoo
- 'Contorta' ♀H6	Widely available
- 'Corabel' (F)	CAgr NLar NOra SRms WMat
- 'Cosford' (F)	CAgr CCVT CEnd CMac CSBt CTri EPom IArd LBuc MBlu MTrO NLar NOra NOrn NRog NWea SBdl SEWo SGol SPer SRms SWvt WHtc WMat

- Emoa Series	WMat
§ - 'Ennis' (F)	CAgr MTrO NLar NOra NRog
- 'Feriale' (F)	CAgr
- 'Fuscorubra' misapplied	see *C. avellana* 'Rotblättrige Zellernuss'
- 'Gustav's Zeller' (F)	MTrO NOra WMat
§ - 'Heterophylla'	CEnd EBee NLar SSta WLov
- 'Laciniata'	see *C. avellana* 'Heterophylla'
§ - 'Lang Tidlig Zeller' (F)	CAgr MCoo MTrO NLar NOra NWea WMat
- 'Lewis' (F)	CAgr
- 'Lombardii' (F) **new**	CLnd
- 'Merveille de Bollwyller'	see *C. maxima* 'Halle'sche Riesennuss'
- 'Nottingham Prolific'	see *C. avellana* 'Pearson's Prolific'
- 'Pauetet' (F)	CAgr
§ - 'Pearson's Prolific' (F)	CAgr CSBt IArd LBuc NLar SBdl SGol SSFr
- 'Pendula'	LMaj MBlu NOra SCoo SRms WCot
- 'Red Dragon' **new**	MBlu
- 'Red Majestic' PBR ♀H6	Widely available
§ - 'Rotblättrige Zellernuss' (F) ♀H6	CEnd CHab EDir EPfP EPom EShb GDam LMaj LPar MBlu MRav MTrO NLar NOrn NOra NRog SBmr SCoo SGol SGsty SKee SLim SRms SPoG SSFT SSta SWvt WCot WLov
- 'Rouge de Zeller'	see *C. avellana* 'Rotblättrige Zellernuss'
- 'Scooter'	MPkF NLar SGsty WHtc XSte
- 'Tonda di Giffoni' (F)	NOra WMat
- 'Twister'	CDoC LRHS MAsh
- 'Webb's Prize Cob' (F)	CAco CAgr CBod CDoC CTri EBee ELan GDam IArd LPar MBlu MCoo NLar NRog NWea SBmr SGol SKee SSFr SVic
chinensis	MBlu WPGP
colurna ♀H6	Widely available
× ***colurnoides*** 'Chinoka' (F)	CAgr NRog
- 'Freeoka' (F)	CAgr NRog
- 'Laroka' (F)	NRog
cornuta	WMou
EARLY LONG ZELLER	see *C. avellana* 'Lang Tidlig Zeller'
fargesii	WPGP
ferox	CJun
heterophylla **new**	GKev
maxima (F)	CLnd CTri EPom MSwo NWea
- 'Butler'	see *C. avellana* 'Butler'
- 'Ennis'	see *C. avellana* 'Ennis'
- 'Fertile de Coutard'	see *C. maxima* 'White Filbert'
- 'Frizzled Filbert' (F)	SBdl
- 'Frühe van Frauendorf'	see *C. maxima* 'Rotblättrige Zellernuss'
- 'Garibaldi' (F)	SBdl
- 'Grote Lambertsnoot'	see *C. maxima* 'Kentish Cob'
- 'Gunslebert' (F) ♀H6	CCVT CMac CTri MTrO NOra SBdl SPoG SRms SSFr WMat
- HALLE GIANT	see *C. maxima* 'Halle'sche Riesennuss'
§ - 'Halle'sche Riesennuss' (F)	CAgr CMac ELan IArd LMaj NLar NOra SKee SSFr WMat
§ - 'Kentish Cob' (F) ♀H6	Widely available
- 'Lambert's Filbert'	see *C. maxima* 'Kentish Cob'
- 'Longue d'Espagne'	see *C. maxima* 'Kentish Cob'
- 'Monsieur de Bouweller'	see *C. maxima* 'Halle'sche Riesennuss'
- 'Nottingham Cobnut' (F)	CDoC MCoo SBmr SKee SVic
- 'Purple Filbert'	see *C. maxima* 'Purpurea'
§ - 'Purpurea' (F)	Widely available
- 'Red Filbert' misapplied	see *C. avellana* 'Rotblättrige Zellernuss'
- 'Red Zellernut'	see *C. avellana* 'Rotblättrige Zellernuss'
- 'Spanish White'	see *C. maxima* 'White Filbert'
§ - 'White Filbert' (F)	CHab MCoo NRog SBdl
- 'White Spanish Filbert'	see *C. maxima* 'White Filbert'
- 'Witpit Lambertsnoot'	see *C. maxima* 'White Filbert'
'Nottingham Early' (F)	NLar
sieboldiana B&SWJ 11056	WCru
- var. ***mandshurica***	MBlu
'Te Terra Red'	CMCN EBee ELan EPfP MAsh MBlu SRms WMat
tibetica	LEdu WPGP
× ***vilmorinii***	GDam WPGP

Corymbia (*Myrtaceae*)

§ ***citriodora***	CBod CWCL MHer SKin SPlb WGrf
§ ***eximia***	SPlb
- 'Nana'	SPlb
§ ***ficifolia***	WGrf

Corynabutilon (*Malvaceae*)

§ × ***suntense***	CBcs CCCN CHll CSBt EHyd ELan GAbr LRHS LShi MSCN NPer NRHS
- 'Gorer's White'	LRHS
- 'Jermyns' ♀H4	CExl LSRN MGos SPoG SWvt
- 'Violetta'	WSpi
- white-flowered	ELan
§ ***vitifolium***	CCCN CDTJ LShi MGil SPad SPoG WCot WFar WKif WSpi
- 'Album'	CBcs CCCN CExl LShi WSpi
- 'Buckland'	CCCN
- 'Tennant's White' ♀H4	CCCN CExl CRos EHyd EPfP LRHS WCot
- 'Veronica Tennant' ♀H4	CExl EBee EPfP SChF

Corynephorus (*Poaceae*)

canescens	NBir

Corynopuntia (*Cactaceae*)

§ ***invicta*** **new**	SPlb

Coryphantha (*Cactaceae*)

§ ***elephantidens*** **new**	NMen
pycnacantha **new**	EAri
sulcolanata	see *C. elephantidens*

Cosmos (*Asteraceae*)

§ ***atrosanguineus***	CBcs CKel CSBt CSpe CWGN ECtt ELan EPfP EShb EWoo GElm LAma LCro LOPS LPal LRHS LSRN MRav NLar SCob SDeJ SDir SPoG SWvt WHlf WHoo
- 'Black Magic'	EDAr LBar SBls
- CHOCAMOCHA ('Thomocha' PBR)	CBcs CBod CCCN CPla CRos CSpe CWGN EBee ECtt EHyd EPfP GMaP LCro LOPS LRHS LSou MBros MGos NLar NRHS SGbt SPeP SPer SPoG WWke
- DARK SECRET ('3013/01')	LRHS
- ECLIPSE ('Hamcoec' PBR)	LRHS
- SPELLBOUND ('Hamcosp')	ECtt LBar
bipinnatus 'Antiquity'	MBros SBut SPhx
- (Apollo Series) 'Apollo Carmine' ♀H3	LSou MPri
- - 'Apollo Pink' ♀H3	LSou MPri
- - 'Apollo White' ♀H3	LSou MPri
- 'Apricot Lemonade' **new**	CSpe
- (Casanova Series) 'Casanova Pink'	SCob SPoG
- - 'Casanova Red'	SCob SPoG
- - 'Casanova Violet'	SCob SPoG
- - 'Casanova White'	SCob SPoG
- COSMIX (mixed) **new**	WHlf

- (Cupcakes Series) 'Cupcakes Blush' **new**	CSpe
- - 'Cupcakes White'	CSpe
- 'Daydream'	CArg
- 'Dazzler'	CArg LCro LOPS SPhx
- (Double Click Series) 'Double Click Cranberries' (d)	CArg CSpe SPhx
- - 'Double Click Rose Bonbon' (d)	CArg CSpe
- - 'Double Click Snow Puff' (d)	CArg CSpe SPhx
- 'Fizzy Rose Picotee' (Fizzy Series)	CArg
- 'Psyche White'	CSpe
- 'Purity'	CArg CSpe LCro LOPS SBut SMrm SPhx WHlf
- Razzmatazz Series	LCro LOPS MBros WWke
- 'Rubenza' ♀H3	CSpe LCro LOPS SPhx WHlf
- SEA SHELLS (mixed)	SMrm
- Sensation Series	SBut
- - 'Sensation Picotee'	LCro LOPS
- - 'Sensation Pinkie' ♀H3	CArg LCro LOPS
- Sonata Series	MBros SCob
- - SONATA CARMINE ('Pas1786')	CArg MPri
- - SONATA PINK ('Pas1787')	CArg MPri SCob WHlf
- - SONATA WHITE ('Pas1789')	CArg CSpe MBros MPri SCob
- 'Sweet Sixteen'	SPhx WHlf
- 'Velouette' ♀H3 **new**	WHlf
- 'Xanthos'	CRos CSpe LCro LOPS MBros WHlf
peucedanifolius	CSpe WSHC
- 'Flamingo'	LAma SDeJ
SONATA PURPLE SHADES ('Pas1248700') (Sonata Series)	LSou
sulphureus LADYBIRD (mixed)	SVic
- 'Sunset Orange' **new**	CSpe
- 'Tango' ♀H3 **new**	WHlf
'Yellow Garden'	SPhx

Cosmos × Dahlia (*Asteraceae*)

'Mexican Black'	see *Dahlia* 'Mexican Black'

costmary see *Tanacetum balsamita*

Costus (*Costaceae*)

barbatus	NGKo

Cotinus ✿ (*Anacardiaceae*)

americanus	see *C. obovatus*
'Candy Floss'	CRos EHyd LCro LRHS MBNS NRHS
§ ***coggygria***	CBcs CBrac CEme CMCN CMac EGrI EHeP ELan EPfP GDam LPal MRav MSwo NLar NWea SCob SEND SGbt SGsty SPer SRms SWvt SavN WFar XSen
- FLAMISSIMO ('Mincofla20') **new**	CWnw EHed
- GOLDEN LADY ('Mincojau3'PBR)	EPfP LRHS MMrt SGsty
- GOLDEN SPIRIT ('Ancot'PBR) ♀H5	Widely available
- GREEN FOUNTAIN ('Kolcot'PBR)	EBee LRHS
- 'Kanari'	NLar
- 'Lilla'PBR	CBcs CKel CWnw EMil EPfP LRHS MAsh MBlu MPkF NLar NRHS SCoo SGsty XSte
- 'Notcutt's Variety'	EGrI MRav
- 'Old Fashioned'PBR	CBcs CBod EBee EPfP LAlb MPkF NEoE NLar WLov WMou XSte
- 'Pink Champagne'	NLar SSta
- Purpureus Group	SRms
- 'Red Beauty'	NLar
- RED SPIRIT ('Firstpur')	NLar
- 'Royal Purple' ♀H5	Widely available
- Rubrifolius Group	CBcs EPfP SEND SWvt
- SMOKEY JOE ('Lisjo'PBR)	CBcs CRos EHyd EPfP LRHS MAsh MPkF SPoG SRHi SSta SWvt XSte
- 'Velvet Cloak'	MGos NLar SWvt
- 'Well Spotted'	EMil
- 'Westonbirt Orange'	NLar
- 'Young Lady'PBR ♀H5	Widely available
DUSKY MAIDEN ('Londus'PBR)	CEme CSBt CTsd EHyd ELan EPfP IArd IDee LRHS MAsh MGos NEoE NLar WFar WHlf WMou
'Flame' ♀H5	CBcs CBod CDoC CKel CRos EBee EGrI EHyd ELan EPfP EWTr LRHS MAsh MGos MRav NRHS NWea SEdd SGbt SGsty SPoG SRHi SWvt WAvo WFar WHtc XSte
'Grace'	Widely available
§ ***obovatus***	CMCN EGrI EPfP IArd LRHS MBlu MPkF MRav SSta WPGP
'Ruby Glow'	CRos EHyd EPfP LCro LOPS LRHS MBNS MGos NRHS

Cotoneaster ✿ (*Rosaceae*)

acuminatus	NLar SRms
acutifolius var. ***laetevirens***	see *C. laetevirens*
§ ***adpressus*** 'Little Gem'	NHar NLar
- var. ***praecox***	see *C. nanshan*
- 'Tom Thumb'	see *C. adpressus* 'Little Gem'
affinis	SPtp SRms
albokermesinus	SPtp SRms
ambiguus Rehder & E.H.Wilson	NLar
amoenus	NLar SRms
- ACE 1028	SPtp
§ ***apiculatus***	NLar SRms
§ ***ascendens***	SRms
assamensis	SRms
§ ***astrophoros***	CMac GRum MBlu NLar
atropurpureus	NLar SRms
§ - 'Variegatus' (v) ♀H6	CBcs CDoC CEme CKel CMac CRos EHeP EHyd ELan ELon EPfP LRHS MAsh MGos NGrs NLar NPer NRHS SCob SCoo SDix SPer SPoG SRms SWvt WAvo WFar WHtc
atuntzensis	SPtp
aurantiacus	NLar SPtp
beimashanensis	ELan NLar SPtp
boisianus	NLar SPtp SRms
bradyi	EBee GBin NLar SRms
brickellii	NLar SPtp
§ ***bullatus***	CTri EHeP EPfP NLar SPtp SRms WHtc WJur
- 'Firebird'	see *C. ignescens*
- f. ***floribundus***	see *C. bullatus*
- var. ***macrophyllus***	see *C. rehderi*
bumthangensis	NLar SRms
buxifolius blue-leaved	see *C. lidjiangensis*
- 'Brno'	see *C. marginatus* 'Brno'
- f. ***vellaeus***	see *C. astrophoros*
camilli-schneideri	SRms
canescens	NLar SRms
chadwelli	NLar
chuanus	NLar
- L 624	SPtp
chungtiensis	NLar

	cinerascens	SPtp
	- CLD 1440	SPtp
	cinnabarinus	SRms
§	***cochleatus***	EHeP NHar SPtp SRms
§	***congestus***	CSBt EHeP ELan MSwo NFav NLar SPer SPlb SRms XLum
	- 'Nanus'	CBor GEdr
	conspicuus	CBcs EHeP EWTr SPtp SRms
	- 'Decorus' ♀H6	CBod CBrac CDoC CEme CSBt EPfP GMcL LRHS LSto MGos MMuc MSwo NBwr NWea SCob SPer SPlb SPoG SWvt
	- 'Leicester Gem'	SRms
	- 'Red Glory'	CMac
	cooperi	SRms
	- 'Nicolette'	NLar
	cordifolius	MBlu NLar SRms
	- KW 13363	SPtp
	cornifolius	SRms
	- Og 93330	SPtp
§	'Cornubia' ♀H6	Widely available
	crispii	NLar SPtp
	cuspidatus	MBlu NLar SPtp
§	***dammeri***	Widely available
§	- 'Major'	EHeP LBuc SCob
§	- 'Mooncreeper'	CDoC CKel
	- 'Oakwood'	see *C. radicans*
	- var. ***radicans*** misapplied	see *C. dammeri* 'Major'
	- var. ***radicans*** (Dammer ex C.K. Schneid.) C.K. Schneid.	see *C. radicans*
	dammeri* × *microphyllus	CBrac NBwr
	dielsianus	NLar NWea SRms
	distichus	see *C. rotundifolius* Wall. ex Lindl.
	divaricatus	NLar SPer SRms
	duthieanus	NLar SPtp
	- 'Boer'	see *C. apiculatus*
	elatus	NLar SRms
	elegans	SPtp SRms
	emeiensis	NLar SRms
	encavei	NLar
	- KEKE 1239	SPtp
	'Erlinda'	see *C.* × *suecicus* 'Erlinda'
	'Exburiensis'	CBcs CBod CBrac CCVT CEme EBee EPfP MAsh MGos MMuc MRav MTrO NLar NOrn SCob SEND SPer WFar WMat
	falconeri	SRms
	fastigiatus	SRms
	flinckii	NLar SRms
	floccosus	GMcL IArd SEND SPtp
	floridus	SRms
	forrestii	GKev MVil NLar SRms
	franchetii	Widely available
	cf. ***franchetii***	CKel
	frigidus	CBee CMCN MDon SPtp SRms
§	- 'Pershore Coral'	WAvo
	froebelii	SPtp
	fulvidus	NLar
	gamblei	SRms
	- KR 1576	SPtp
	ganghobaensis	CMCN GKev NLar SPtp SRms
	- B&L 12234	SPtp WCru
	glabratus	SRms
	- KR 232	SPtp
	glacialis	LShi SRms
	glaucophyllus	IArd SRms
§	***glomerulatus***	NLar SRms
	gonggashanensis	SPtp
	gracilis	SRms
	granatensis	SRms
	'Green Fan'	SPtp
	harrovianus	SPtp SRms
	harrysmithii	NLar
	hebephyllus	NLar
	hedegaardii	SPtp
I	- 'Fructu Luteo'	SPtp SRms
	- 'Halliwell's Yellow'	SPtp
	- yellow-fruited	SPtp
	henryanus	SRms
	- 'Corina'	SRms
	'Herbstfeuer'	see *C. salicifolius* 'Herbstfeuer'
	'Highlight'	see *C. pluriflorus*
	hillieri	NLar SPtp
§	***hjelmqvistii***	LBuc NLar SPtp SRms
	- 'Robustus'	see *C. hjelmqvistii*
	- 'Rotundifolius'	see *C. hjelmqvistii*
	hodjingensis	SRms
	horizontalis	Widely available
	- 'Variegatus'	see *C. atropurpureus* 'Variegatus'
	- var. ***wilsonii***	see *C. ascendens*
	huahongdongensis	ELan
	hualiensis	NLar SRms
	- B&SWJ 3143	WCru
	humifusus	see *C. dammeri*
	hummelii	SRms
	hupehensis	NLar
§	'Hybridus Pendulus'	Widely available
§	***hylmoei***	ELan NLar SPtp SRms
	hypocarpus	SPtp SRms
	ignavus	SRms
§	***ignescens***	NLar SPtp SRms
	- CLD 612	SPtp
	ignotus	SRms
	incanus	NLar
	induratus	SRms
	insculptus	SPtp SRms
	insolitus	NLar SPtp
	integerrimus	SRms
§	***integrifolius***	ELan EPfP NLar SPtp SRms
	kangdingensis	SRms
	kingdonii	NLar
	kitaibelii	NLar SPtp
	kongboensis	SPtp
	konishii	NLar
	kuanensis SICH 56A	SPtp
	kweitschoviensis	NLar
	lacteus ♀H6	Widely available
	- F 10419	ELan GDam SPtp
	- 'Milkmaid' (v)	NLar
§	***laetevirens***	NLar
	lancasteri	NLar SRms
	- Og 94303	SPtp
	langei	SRms
	laxiflorus	SRms
§	***lidjiangensis***	NLar SPtp SRms
	- JFYU 137 **new**	SPtp
	lucidus	LPar SRms
	ludlowii	SPtp SRms
	magnificus	SRms
§	***mairei***	NLar SPtp SRms
	marginatus Lindl. ex Loudon	SRms
§	- 'Blazovice'	NLar SRms
§	- 'Brno'	SRms
	marquandii	NLar SRms
§	***meiophyllus***	MBlu NLar SPtp
	melanocarpus	NLar
	melanotrichus misapplied	see *C. cochleatus*
	melanotrichus (Franch.) G. Klotz	SPtp
	meuselii	NLar SRms
	- TSS 13864	SPtp
	microphyllus misapplied	see *C. purpurascens*
	microphyllus ambig.	CBcs CKel CSBt EBee GBin GMcL LSto NBwr NSla NWea SCob

microphyllus Wall. ex Lindl.	CTri LRHS SPer
- NICE 004	WCFE
- var. ***cochleatus*** (Franch.) Rehder & E.H. Wilson	see *C. cochleatus*
- var. ***cochleatus*** ambig.	EPot NSla
- 'Donard Gem'	see *C. astrophoros*
- 'Teulon Porter'	see *C. astrophoros*
- var. ***thymifolius*** (Lindl.) Koehne	see *C. integrifolius*
- var. ***thymifolius*** ambig.	EHyd LRHS NLar
milkedandaensis	SPtp SRms
miniatus	SPtp SRms
mirabilis	NLar SRms
monopyrenus	SPtp SRms
- F 11422	GKev
'Mooncreeper'	see *C. dammeri* 'Mooncreeper'
morrisonensis	NLar SRms
moupinensis	SRms
- BWJ 8167	WCru
mucronatus	NLar SPtp SRms
'My Pet'	GAbr
§ ***nanshan***	NWea SRms WAvo WHtc
- 'Boer'	see *C. apiculatus*
naoujanensis	NLar SPtp
- 'Berried Treasure'	CRos EHyd LCro LRHS MGos SPtp
nepalensis	NLar
newryensis	NLar SRms
nitens	NLar SRms
nitidifolius	see *C. glomerulatus*
nohelii	NLar SRms
notabilis	SRms
nummularioides	SRms
nummularius Fisch. & C.A. Mey.	SRms
obscurus	SPtp SRms
obtusus Wall. ex Lindl.	NLar SRms
ogisui	GBin LEdu SPtp
- Og 95101	SPtp
- Og 95105	EBee GKev WPGP
omissus	NLar SPtp
pangiensis	SRms
pannosus	SRms
paradoxus	SRms
parkeri	NLar SRms
parneyi	SPtp
pekinensis	SRms
permutatus	see *C. pluriflorus*
perpusillus	SRms
'Pershore Coral'	see *C. frigidus* 'Pershore Coral'
§ ***pluriflorus***	GKev SRms
- LS&E 13310	SPtp
poluninii	NLar SPtp SRms
polycarpus	SPtp SRms
praecox 'Boer'	see *C. apiculatus*
procumbens	SRms
- 'Needham'	NLar
- 'Queen of Carpets' ♀H6	CBod CBrac CDoC CEme CKel CRos EHyd ELan EPfP LRHS LSRN LSto MAsh MGos MRav NLar NRHS SCoo SLim SPoG SRms SWvt
- 'Streib's Findling'	see *C.* 'Streib's Findling'
prostratus	SRms
- 'Arnold-Forster'	ELan SPtp
przewalskii	SRms
pseudo-obscurus	SRms
* ***psikangensis***	NLar
§ ***purpurascens***	CSBt EHyd LRHS NRHS
pyrenaicus misapplied	see *C. congestus*
qungbixiensis	NLar SRms
raboutensis	NLar
racemiflorus	SRms
§ ***radicans***	CMCN
§ ***rehderi***	NLar SPtp SRms
reticulatus	NLar SPtp
rhytidophyllus	ELan GKev SPtp
- Og 95102	SPtp
rokujodaisanensis	NLar
roseus	NLar SRms
'Rothschildianus' ♀H6	Widely available
§ ***rotundifolius*** Wall. ex Lindl.	SPtp
rubens W.W. Sm.	NLar
rugosus E. Pritz. ex Diels	NLar SPtp SRms
'Saint Andrews Blaze'	ELan SPtp
'Saint Monica'	EPfP MBlu
salicifolius	CTri GDam MSwo NLar NWea SCob SPtp SRms WFar
- AUTUMN FIRE	see *C. salicifolius* 'Herbstfeuer'
§ - 'Avonbank'	CEnd NLar WAvo
- 'Brno Orangeade'	SRms
- 'Fructuluteo'	SPtp
- 'Gnom' ♀H6	CChe CDoC CEme CKel CMac CRos EHeP EHyd ELan EPfP GMcL LRHS MAsh MGos NBir SCob SPer SPoG SPtp SRms WAvo WHtc
§ - 'Herbstfeuer'	MRav MSwo SPtp SRms
- 'Pendulus'	see *C.* 'Hybridus Pendulus'
- 'Pink Champagne' ♀H6	CMac EPfP
- 'Repens'	CBod CBrac CKel EHeP EPfP MTrO NBwr NWea SCob SPer SPoG SRms WMat
- var. ***rugosus***	see *C. hylmoei*
salwinensis	NLar SPtp SRms
sandakphuensis	SRms
scandinavicus	SRms
schantungensis	NLar SRms
schlechtendalii 'Blazovice'	see *C. marginatus* 'Blazovice'
- 'Brno'	see *C. marginatus* 'Brno'
schubertii	SRms
'Seattle'	NLar
* ***sengorensis***	NLar
serotinus misapplied	see *C. meiophyllus*
serotinus Hutch.	SPtp SRms
shannanensis	ELan SPtp SRms
shansiensis	NLar SPtp SRms
sherriffii	NLar SRms
sikangensis	GBin SPtp SRms
simonsii	CBod CCVT CEnd CLnd CMac EBee EHeP ELan GKev GMcL LBuc LRHS LSto MGos MMuc NBwr NHol NLar NWea SCob SPer SRms WFar WHtc
- MF 904	SPtp
soczavianus	NLar
§ ***splendens***	ELan SPtp SRms
- 'Sabrina'	see *C. splendens*
spongbergii	SRms
staintonii	SRms
sternianus ♀H6	SPtp SRms
- ACE 2200	MSwo
aff. ***sternianus***	SPtp
- SICH 770	SPtp
- Yu 15716	SPtp
§ 'Streib's Findling'	EHyd GKev LPar LRHS MAsh NBwr NLar SGol SPtp
suavis	SRms
subacutus	SRms
subadpressus	SRms
submultiflorus	NLar
× ***suecicus*** 'Coral Beauty' ♀H6	Widely available
§ - 'Erlinda' (v)	CEnd MDon SPoG SRms
- 'Ifor'	SRms
- 'Juliette' (v) ♀H6	CMac CRos EHyd GMcL LRHS LSRN MAsh MDon MMrt MRav MTrO NBwr NLar NOrn NRHS SCoo SPer SPoG WHtc WMat

- 'Skogholm'	CBcs CRos EHeP EPfP LRHS MGos NBwr SCob SPer SRms
svenhedinii	NLar
taoensis	SPtp SRms
taofuensis	SPtp
- Sich 1878	SPtp
tardiflorus	NLar SPtp SRms
tauricus	SRms
teijiashanensis	NLar SPtp SRms
tengyuehensis	SPtp SRms
thimphuensis	NLar SRms
tomentellus	WCFE
tomentosus	SRms
transcaucasicus	NLar
turbinatus	NLar SPtp SRms
'Valkenburg'	SRms
vandelaarii	ELan NLar SPtp SRms
veitchii	NLar SRms
verruculosus	SRms
vestitus	NLar
villosulus	SRms
vilmorinianus	SPtp SRms
- F 5543	SPtp
wardii misapplied	see *C. mairei*
wardii W.W.Sm.	SRms
× ***watereri***	CBod CCVT ELon EPfP GDam LRHS MDon MSwo NBwr NWea WHtc
- 'Avonbank'	see *C. salicifolius* 'Avonbank'
- 'Cornubia'	see *C.* 'Cornubia'
- 'John Waterer'	EPfP SPer SPoG
- 'Pendulus'	see *C.* 'Hybridus Pendulus'
wilsonii	SRms
yalungensis	SRms
yinchangensis	SRms
zabelii	SPtp SRms

Cotula (*Asteraceae*)

coronopifolia	CBen CWat LPfP NPer
fallax	CKel
hispida ambig.	CPla EBou ECha EPfP EPot GKev MACG SLee SRot
§ ***hispida*** (DC.) Harv.	CTri EDAr GMaP MAsh MHer NPer NRya SPoG SRms XLum
pectinata	see *Leptinella pectinata*
perpusilla	see *Leptinella pusilla*
'Platt's Black'	see *Leptinella squalida* 'Platt's Black'
potentilloides	see *Leptinella potentillina*
pyrethrifolia	see *Leptinella pyrethrifolia*
squalida	see *Leptinella squalida*
'Tiffindell Gold' **new**	EWes

Cotyledon (*Crassulaceae*)

chrysantha	see *Rosularia chrysantha*
gibbiflora var. ***metallica***	see *Echeveria gibbiflora* 'Metallica'
oppositifolia	see *Umbilicus oppositifolius*
orbiculata	CPbh EShb ETod SPlb WCot
- 'Cedric Morris'	EMal SChr
- var. ***oblonga***	CDoC EShb LCro WCot
- 'Silver Waves'	MCot
- 'Snowline'	WThu
pendens	EShb
simplicifolia	see *Umbilicus oppositifolius*
tomentosa subsp. ***ladismithensis*** 🏆H1c	EShb

courgette see AGM Vegetables Section

Crambe (*Brassicaceae*)

sp.	MAsh
abyssinica	SPhx
cordifolia 🏆H5	Widely available
- 'Morning's Snow'	ESwi NLar
- variegated (v) **new**	WCot
hispanica	LRHS
maritima	Widely available
- 'Lilywhite'	CAgr ESwi LEdu SVic
orientalis	ESwi NLar
tatarica	SPhx

cranberry see *Vaccinium macrocarpon*, *V. oxycoccos*

Craspedia (*Asteraceae*)

* ***hispidula***	GArf

Crassula ✿ (*Crassulaceae*)

alba **new**	CPbh
anomala	see *C. atropurpurea* var. *anomala*
arborescens	CPbh EAri EShb SChr SPlb SSim
- subsp. ***undulatifolia***	CDoC EWoo NCft
argentea	see *C. ovata*
arta	EAri
§ ***atropurpurea*** var. ***anomala***	SChr
- subsp. ***arborescens*** 'Blue Mist'	SEND
- 'Tresco Seaspray' **new**	EWoo SCoo SPoG WOld
'Baby's Necklace' **new**	CSBt LCro LWaG NMen
barklyi 🏆H2 **new**	WOld
'Blue Waves'	SIvy
'Buddha's Temple'	EAri LCro NCft SSim WOld
capitella 'Campfire' **new**	SEdd
coccinea	CPbh EAri EShb SPlb WCot
columnaris	SSim
* ***coralloides***	SPlb
'Estagnol'	SSim
lycopodioides variegata	see *C. muscosa* 'Variegata'
marginata	see *C. pellucida* subsp. *marginalis*
'Morgan's Beauty' 🏆H2 **new**	EAri
multicava	SChr SEdd
muscosa	CBen EShb EWoo NCft SChr SEdd SIvy SPlb
- var. ***muscosa*** **new**	SEdd
§ - 'Variegata' (v)	SEdd SSim
§ ***ovata*** 🏆H2	CBen CHll CWal EWoo LCro LOPS NCft NGBl NHrt NPer NPlm SChr SEND SIvy SPlb SPre SSim SVen WThu
- 'Gollum' 🏆H2	EShb LCro NCft NHrt SEND SIvy
- 'Horn Tree'	NHrt
- 'Hummel's Sunset' (v) 🏆H2	EShb NCft NHrt NMen SSim WOld
- 'Minima'	NCft SIvy SSim
- 'Red Horn Tree' **new**	WOld
- 'Undulata'	NHrt WCot
- 'Variegata' (v)	EShb SIvy WCot
§ ***pellucida*** subsp. ***marginalis***	CDoC EWoo NMen SCoo SPoG
- - f. ***rubra***	CDoC EShb SEdd
§ - - 'Variegata' (v)	SSim WFar WOld
perfoliata **new**	WOld
- var. ***falcata*** 🏆H2	EShb WCot
perforata 🏆H2	CDoC CSBt EAri NCft NPlm SEdd SIvy
- 'Variegata' (v)	CDoC LLWG NCft NWad SEdd SSim WCot
portulacea	see *C. ovata*
pubescens **new**	SEdd
- subsp. ***rattrayi*** **new**	SEdd
pyramidalis **new**	NCft WOld
rupestris 🏆H2	CDoC EAri SSim
- subsp. ***marnieriana***	CDoC NCft SIvy
§ ***sarcocaulis*** 🏆H3	Widely available
I - 'Alba'	NHpl
schmidtii	SSim
- dark-flowered	SSim

- white-flowered SSim
sedifolia see *C. setulosa* 'Milfordiae'
sediformis see *C. setulosa* 'Milfordiae'
setulosa SPlb
§ - 'Milfordiae' CTri EPot NHpl NRya SLee WAbe
socialis EAri ELan WAbe
streyi new SBrt
tecta new EAri
tetragona CSBt SEND SEdd
'Tom Thumb' new SEdd
* ***tomentosa*** 'Variegata' (v) EShb

+ *Crataegomespilus* (*Rosaceae*)

'Jules d'Asnières' NLar

× *Crataegosorbus* (*Rosaceae*)

§ 'Granatnaja' CAgr

Crataegus (*Rosaceae*)

anomala 'Zbigniew' CAgr
arnoldiana CAgr CBod CLnd CTri EBee MCoo MTrO NLar NWea SPoG WHtc WMat
'Autumn Glory' CEnd
azarolus LEdu SGsty
- 'Geraki' (F) IArd
§ ***coccinea*** L. CAgr CLnd LIns LMaj NWea WMat
cordata see *C. phaenopyrum*
crus-galli misapplied see *C. persimilis* 'Prunifolia'
crus-galli L. CCVT CLnd EHeP EPfP MAsh NLar NRog NWea WHtc
douglasii EBtc
× ***durobrivensis*** CAgr CLnd EBee MBlu
ellwangeriana CAgr WCot
- 'Fire Ball' EWTr MBlu
eriocarpa CLnd
gemmosa CAgr
× ***grignonensis*** ♀H7 CLnd EHeP ELan LPar MBlu MMuc NLar
harbisonii IArd
jonesiae EPfP
laciniata misapplied see *C. orientalis*
§ ***laevigata*** GDam NWea SCob
- 'Coccinea Plena' see *C. laevigata* 'Paul's Scarlet'
§ - 'Crimson Cloud' ♀H7 Widely available
- 'Gireoudii' CBod GDam WLov
- 'Mutabilis' CTri SGol
§ - 'Paul's Scarlet' (d) ♀H7 Widely available
- 'Pink Corkscrew' EPfP MBlu WLov
- 'Plena' (d) Widely available
- 'Punicea' misapplied see *C. laevigata* 'Crimson Cloud'
- 'Rosea' GKin
- 'Rosea Flore Pleno' (d) ♀H7 Widely available
× ***lavalleei*** CBod CCVT CLnd CMCN CTri EBar MRav MSwo NOrn NWea SCoo WHtc WTSh
- 'Aurora' NLar
- 'Carrierei' ♀H7 CMac EPfP EWTr LMaj LSRN MMuc MTrO NLar NRog NWea SCob SCoo SEND SEWo SGsty SPoG WHtc WMat WMou
§ ***mexicana*** CPer EPfP
mollis CAgr EPfP IArd WSpi
monogyna Widely available
§ - 'Biflora' CEnd CLnd CPer CTri EBee MCoo MGos MLod NWea SLim WMat WSpi
- 'Compacta' LPar MBlu WCot WLov
- 'Praecox' see *C. monogyna* 'Biflora'
- 'Stricta' CCVT CLnd CSBt EBar EHeP EPfP LPar SCob
- 'Variegata' (v) SWeb
× ***mordenensis*** 'Toba' (d) CLnd EWTr LRHS SGsty
§ ***orientalis*** ♀H6 CBod CCVT CDoC CEnd CMCN ELan EPfP IArd MAsh MGos NOrn SCoo SLim WHtc WJas WMat WMou WSpi
oxyacantha misapplied see *C. laevigata*
pedicellata see *C. coccinea* L.
persimilis LIns LMaj LPar
§ - 'Prunifolia' ♀H7 Widely available
- 'Prunifolia Splendens' CAgr CCVT CPer EBar EBee EWTr LBuc LCro LMaj LPar MTrO NOra NOrn WMat
§ ***phaenopyrum*** CLnd CMCN EBee EPfP SPtp
pinnatifida var. ***major*** CEnd EPfP NOrn NWea WHtc
- - 'Big Golden Star' CAgr EBee EPfP MBlu MCoo MTrO NOra NWea WHtc WMat WMou
pojarkovae CAgr
pontica 'Poltzi' CAgr
'Praecox' see *C. monogyna* 'Biflora'
prunifolia see *C. persimilis* 'Prunifolia'
pubescens f. ***stipulacea*** see *C. mexicana*
punctata f. ***aurea*** EPfP MBlu
schraderiana CAgr CLnd EBee EPfP MBlu WHtc WMat
submollis CLnd
succulenta CAgr
- 'Jubilee' PBR EWTr LMaj MTrO NLar NOra WMat
- 'Long Thorn' MBlu
- var. ***macracantha*** CMCN
tanacetifolia CAgr EPfP MBlu
viridis 'Winter King' CAgr EPfP EWTr
wattiana CLnd ELan

Crataegus + *Mespilus* see + *Crataegomespilus*

Crataegus × *Mespilus* see × *Crataemespilus*

Crataegus × *Sorbus* see × *Crataegosorbus*

× *Crataemespilus* (*Rosaceae*)

gillotii NLar
grandiflora CLnd

Cremanthodium (*Asteraceae*)

delavayi GBin

Cremastra (*Orchidaceae*)

variabilis WCot

Cremnophila (*Crassulaceae*)

Cremnophila × *Sedum* see × *Cremnosedum*

× *Cremnosedum* (*Crassulaceae*)

§ 'Little Gem' SSim

Crenularia see *Aethionema*

Crepis (*Asteraceae*)

aurea LShi
incana ♀H5 CBor EWld GBin MNrw NSla SPhx SRms WAbe WMal
rubra CSpe

Crinitaria see *Aster*

Crinodendron (*Elaeocarpaceae*)

hookerianum ♀H4 Widely available
- 'Ada Hoffmann' CBcs CBod CBrac CCCN CEnd CMac CPla CSde EHyd EPfP GDam GEdr GKin GMcL LRHS MBlu MGil MGos NLar SEle SGol SSha SWvt WHlf WPav

	- 'Alf Robbins' **new**	CBod SPad
	- 'Ashmount'	IArd
	patagua	CBcs CCCN CMac EBee EHed ELan EPfP ESwi GBin MGil MVil NLar SEND SEle SPlb SSha SVen WPav

Crinum (*Amaryllidaceae*)

	amoenum	CCCN GKev LAma
	'Carolina Beauty'	WCot
	'Cintho Alpha'	GKev SDeJ
	'Elizabeth Traub'	WCot
	'Ellen Bosanquet'	CCCN ELan GBin GKev LAma SDir WCot
	'Emma Jones'	WCot
	'Hanibal's Dwarf'	WPGP
	moorei	CBro SChr
	- f. ***album***	CAvo CCCN EPri GKev LAma
	- hybrid	WCot WMal
	'Ollene'	WCot
§	× ***powellii***	CBcs CBro CKel CPrp CTsd ECha EHyd ELan ELon EPfP EWoo GKev LAma LCro LEdu LRHS MACG MNrw MRav NRHS NWad SDeJ SDir SEND SPer SRms WCot
	- 'Album'	CBro CPrp CTri EBee EBlo ECha EHyd ELan EPfP EWTr EWes GKev LAma LEdu LRHS MRav NRHS SDeJ SDir SEND SRms WAvo WCot WFar WPGP WSHC
	- 'Bak-madder'	EBee
	- 'Harlemense'	EBee
	- 'Krelagei'	EBee WMal
	- 'Roseum'	see *C.* × *powellii*
	'Sangria'	WCot
	'Summer Nocturne'	WCot
	'White Queen'	WCot
	yemense misapplied	GKev

Criogenes see *Cypripedium*

Crithmum (*Apiaceae*)

	maritimum	CBod CCBP CEls GPoy MNHC NFav SBrt SPhx SPlb SRms WHil WJek XSen

Crocosmia (*Iridaceae*)

	'Abundant Joy'	EBee ECrc IBal LBar SMad
	'African Beauty'	ECrc ECtt IBal NBwr
	'Anna Marie'	CBro ECtt ELan GAbr GKev LAma LRHS MAvo SDir WCot WFar
	'Antique Gold' **new**	SHar
	'Apricot'	IBal
	'Apricot Surprise'	ECtt IBal NBwr
	aurea misapplied	see *C.* × *crocosmiiflora* 'George Davison' Davison
	aurea ambig.	CPrp
	aurea (Pappe ex Hook.f.) Planch.	IBal LEdu
	- from Swaziland	IBal WOut
	- subsp. ***aurea***	CTca ECrc
	- 'Golden Ballerina'[PBR]	EBee ECtt IBal LRHS MBNS NCth SGBe SPoG
	'Auricorn'	IBal LEdu WPGP
	'Aurora'	NGdn
	'Ballyrogan Sundown'	CTca
	'Beth Chatto'	CTca ECrc IBal
	'Big Top'	IBal LBar
	'Blaze'	IBal
	'Bowland Blaze'	IBal
	BRESSINGHAM BEACON ('Blos')	MSpe
	'Bressingham Blaze'	CPrp CRos CTca EBee EBlo EHyd IBal LRHS NGdn NHol NRHS
	Bridgemere hybrid	ECrc
	BRIGHT EYES ('Walbreyes'[PBR])	EHyd EPfP LRHS NRHS
	'Buttercups'	ELan LBar MACG SWvt WCAu
	'Cadenza'	IBal NWad
	'Caistor Sunset'	IBal
	'Cascade'	IBal
	'Chinatown'	IBal
	'Chrome Spray'	CTca
	'Citronella' misapplied	see *C.* × *crocosmiiflora* 'Honey Angels'
	'Comet' Knutty	CTca EHyd EPPr IBal LRHS MAvo NRHS
	'Cornish Copper'	CTca
	× ***crocosmiiflora***	CTca CTri EHeP LCro SPlb SRms WBrk WShi XLum
	- 'A.J. Hogan'	IBal NHol
	- 'African Glow'	ECrc IBal NBwr
	- 'Amberglow'	IBal NHol NPer WFar
	- 'Apricot Queen'	NHol
	- 'Baby Barnaby'	WFar
	- 'Babylon' ♀H4	Widely available
	- 'Best of British'	ECtt
	- 'Bicolor'	CTca
	- 'Burford Bronze'	IBal NHol
	- 'Burnt Umber'	IBal
	- 'Buttercup'	CAby CDor CRos CTca EBlo ECrc ECtt EHyd EPfP IBal LAlb LRHS MMrt NHol NRHS SGBe WFar WSpi
	- 'Canary Bird'	CBro ECrc ECtt IBal NGdn NHol WBrk WSpi
§	- 'Carmin Brillant'	Widely available
	- 'Challa'	ECrc ECtt IBal
	- 'Citrina'	WSpi
	- 'Citronella' J.E. Fitt	CAby EBee ECrc EHyd EPfP EWoo GMaP LBar LRHS MBel NGdn NHol NRHS SDix
§	- 'Coleton Fishacre'	CTca CWCL ECha ECrc ECtt EHeP EPfP EPri EShb GMaP IBal LBar LEdu LRHS LSto MMuc MNrw NBid NChi NHol SEND SEdd WCot WFar WHoo WOld WSpi
§	- 'Columbus'	CAvo CBor CBro CPrp CTca EBlo ECrc EHyd EPfP EPri EWhm IBal ILea LAma LBar LRHS NHol NRHS SDir SPer SRms WFar XLum
	- 'Colwall'	IBal NWad WSHC
	- 'Comet'	EBee IBal
	- 'Constance'	CBro CDor CTca EBlo ECtt EHyd EPri GAbr IBal LAma LRHS NBid NGdn NHol NRHS WBrk WFar
	- 'Corona'	CPrp IBal MAvo NHol
§	- 'Croesus'	IBal
	- 'Custard Cream'	CPrp ECrc NHol
	- 'David Fitt'	IBal MAvo WFar
	- 'Debutante'	CPrp CTca ECrc EPri IBal NHol SHar WHoo WSHC
§	- 'Diadème'	CWCL IBal
	- 'Dusky Maiden'	CMac EBlo ECtt GKin GMaP IBal MSwo NHol SRms SWvt
	- 'Dwarf Gold'	IBal
§	- 'E.A. Bowles'	ECrc
	- 'Eastern Promise'	IBal MAvo
	- 'Elegans'	ECrc IBal
§	- 'Emily McKenzie'	Widely available
	- 'Fantasie'	ECrc IBal
	- 'Fire Jumper'	CTca EPfP IBal LBar MSpe WHoo
	- 'Fireglow'[PBR]	CRos ECtt EHyd IBal LRHS NRHS
	- 'George Davison' misapplied	see *C.* × *crocosmiiflora* 'Golden Glory', *C.* 'Sulphurea'
§	- 'George Davison' Davison	Widely available
	- 'Gillian'	IBal
	- 'Gloria'	ECrc IBal MAvo MSpe
	- 'Golden Glory' misapplied	see *C.* × *crocosmiiflora* 'Diadème'

§	- 'Golden Glory' ambig.	CBod CDor EHeP ELan ELon EShb GKev IBal LAma MSwo NBir SGbt SRms
	- 'Goldfinch'	EBee ECrc ELon
	- 'Goldie'	WFar
	- 'Hades'	IBal
	- 'Harlequin'	CAby CBcs CElw CKel CPrp CTca ECrc EPfP IBal ILea LBar LRHS MACG MAsh MBriF MHol NBPC SCoo SPoG SWvt WCAu WFar WSpi WTor WWke
	- 'His Majesty'	CBro IBal NHol WFar
	- 'Hoey Joey'	ECrc MAvo
§	- 'Honey Angels'	Widely available
	- 'Honey Bells'	ECrc WBrk WJam
	- 'Irish Dawn'	ECrc IBal NHol NWad
§	- 'Jackanapes'	CBor CRos CWCL ECtt ELon EPfP GKev IBal LBar LRHS MHtn MNrw SCob SCoo SRms WKif WSpi
	- 'Jackanapes VI'	IBal
	- 'James Coey' misapplied	see *C.* × *crocosmiiflora* 'Carmin Brillant'
	- 'James Coey' J.E. Fitt	CPrp ECha EPfP EShb EWoo GKev GKin IBal LBar LRHS MHer NLar SPoG
§	- 'Jessie'	CElw
	- 'Judith'	IBal
	- 'Kiautschou'	CPrp IBal NHol
	- 'Lady Hamilton'	CDor ECtt EHyd EPPr IBal LRHS NHol
	- 'Lady McKenzie'	see *C.* × *crocosmiiflora* 'Emily McKenzie'
	- 'Lady Oxford'	IBal NHol
	- 'Lady Wilson'	CRos EHyd GBin LRHS NRHS
	- 'Lambrook Gold'	CAvo CFis ECrc IBal
	- 'Lord Nelson'	IBal NHol
	- 'Loweswater'	ECrc IBal
	- 'Lutea'	ECrc IBal LRHS
	- 'Marjorie'	IBal
	- 'Mars'	ECrc EWes IBal LBar MAvo NGdn
	- 'Mephistopheles'	CBor CPrp CTca MSpe NHol WFar
	- 'Merryman'	ECrc IBal
	- 'Météore'	ECtt EHyd LRHS NRHS WFar
	- 'Morgenlicht'	ECrc IBal NHol WFar
	- 'Mount Usher'	CPrp ECrc EPPr IBal MNrw NHol
§	- 'Mrs Geoffrey Howard'	GBin IBal NCth NHol SRms WCru
	- 'Mrs Morrison'	see *C.* × *crocosmiiflora* 'Mrs Geoffrey Howard'
	- 'Newry Seedling'	see *C.* × *crocosmiiflora* 'Prometheus'
	- 'Nimbus'	IBal
§	- 'Norwich Canary'	ECha ECtt EGrI EHyd EPfP EPri GKev IBal LAma LBar LRHS MPie MRav NBir NGdn NHol NRHS SPer WSpi
	- 'Olympic Fire'	NHol
	- 'Plaisir'	IBal NBid NHol
	- 'Polo'	CPrp CWCL ECrc ECtt IBal
	- 'Princess'	see *C. pottsii* 'Princess'
	- 'Prolificans'	ECrc IBal
§	- 'Prometheus'	IBal MSpe NHol
§	- 'Queen Alexandra' J.E. Fitt	CPrp ECha EWes
	- 'Queen Charlotte'	IBal
	- 'Queen Mary II'	see *C.* × *crocosmiiflora* 'Columbus'
	- 'Queen of Spain'	ELon IBal
	- 'Rayon d'Or'	ECrc IBal
	- 'Red David'	WFar
	- 'Red King'	CBro CDor CEme EHyd EPfP GKev IBal LAma LRHS NLar NRHS SGBe WBrk WFar WPnP XLum
	- 'Red Knight'	IBal
	- 'Rheingold' misapplied	see *C.* × *crocosmiiflora* 'Diadème'
	- 'Saint Clements'	IBal NHol
	- 'Saracen' ♀H4	CBro CMac CTca CWCL EBee ECtt EWhm GKin IBal IPot LBar LEdu LRHS MAvo MHol MNrw NLar NSti SEdd SPoG SPtp WCot WFar
	- 'Sir Mathew Wilson'	IBal
	- 'Solfatare'	CBcs CBor CEme CMac CWCL ECha ECtt EGrI EHyd ELan EPfP GKin IBal LRHS MBel MHer MSpe NBid NGrd NHol SRms SWvt WCAu WFar WGwG WSHC WSpi
	- 'Solfatare Coleton Fishacre'	see *C.* × *crocosmiiflora* 'Coleton Fishacre'
	- 'Star of the East' ♀H4	Widely available
	- 'Sultan'	WFar
	- 'Sunglow'	CPla CTtf ECtt EPfP GKev IBal LAma LBar MNrw SBls WHil WSpi
	- 'Twilight Fairy Gold'	CPrp EBee ECha ECtt IBal MACG MBNS MNrw NHpl SMad WCot WFar WMal WSpi
	- 'Venus'	CDor ECtt IBal MAvo MHer MSpe NHol WSpi
	- 'Vesuvius'	ECrc IBal WSHC
	- 'Vic's Yellow'	IBal
	- 'Voyager'	ECtt IBal LAma NBir NHol NLar SDeJ SDir
	- Wasdale strain	ECrc IBal
	- 'Zeal Tan'	CBro EBee ECtt ELan ELon EPfP EPri EWhm IBal LEdu LRHS MNrw MPie NLar NRHS NSti SDix SEdd SGbt SPoG WCAu WCot WFar WGwG WHoo
	× ***crocosmioides*** 'Castle Ward Late'	CBro CPrp ECha ECtt EHyd EPfP EShb IBal LBar LEdu LRHS LSto NHol NLar NRHS SPtp SRms WCAu WCot WFar WSpi
	'Darkleaf Apricot'	see *C.* × *crocosmiiflora* 'Coleton Fishacre'
	'Doctor Marion Wood'	IBal
	'Eldorado'	see *C.* × *crocosmiiflora* 'E.A. Bowles'
	'Ellenbank Canary'	ECha GBin IBal MAvo
	'Ellenbank Firecrest' ♀H4	CPrp CTca EBee ECrc IBal IPot MAvo MHCG NCth
	'Ellenbank Goldcrest'	IBal WSHC
	'Ellenbank Skylark'	IBal
	'Emberglow'	Widely available
	'Fandango'	IBal NHol
	'Fernhill'	IBal
	'Fire King' misapplied	see *C.* × *crocosmiiflora* 'Jackanapes'
	'Fire King' ambig.	IBal LAma LBar LRHS NLar NRHS NSti SWvt
	'Firebird'	CRos EBlo ECtt EHyd ELon IBal LRHS MHol NHol NRHS SRms WCot
	'Firefly'	CPrp CRos ECtt EHyd EPfP GJos LAma LRHS NBwr NRHS
	'Firestarter' (Firestars Series)	SHar
	'Fleuve Jaune'	IBal
	'Forest Fire'	IBal
	fucata	CTca
	- 'Jupiter'	see *C.* 'Jupiter'
	fucata* × *paniculata	IBal
	'Fugue'	CTca IBal SMad
	'Golden Dew'	ECtt IBal MBNS NCth WCot WFar
	GOLDEN FLEECE *sensu* Lemoine	see *C.* × *crocosmiiflora* 'Coleton Fishacre'
	'Harmonia'	CTca EPri
	'Hellfire' ♀H5	Widely available
	'Highlight'	ECrc IBal MAvo NHol NWad
	'Hot Spot' (Firestars Series)	ECrc SHar
	'Jennine'	IBal
	JENNY BLOOM ('Blacro'PBR)	EBee EBlo IBal
	'John Boots'	ECtt ELon IBal LAma LRHS MCot NBid NLar SGBe SRms
§	'Jupiter'	CTca CWCL IBal LRHS NBir NChi NHol NLar

'Karin'	CTca ECrc EHyd GKev LAma LBar LRHS MACG NRHS SDir WFar WHil
'Kathleen'	ECrc
'Krakatoa'	ECrc IBal MHer SWvt WFar
'Lady Ann'	CBro ECrc LAma LBar MAsh SDir
'Lady Jane'	CRos CTca EBee ECrc EHyd EPfP LAma LBar LRHS MAsh NRHS
'Lady Wilson' misapplied	see *C.* × *crocosmiiflora* 'Norwich Canary'
'Lana de Savary'	ECtt EPPr EWes IBal MNrw NBid NHol NWad WCot
'Late Cornish'	see *C.* × *crocosmiiflora* 'Queen Alexandra' J.E. Fitt
'Late Lucifer'	CTri IBal MNrw
'Late Yellow'	IBal
'Lemon Spray'	CTca IBal
'Limpopo'	Widely available
'Lincolnshire Gold'	ECrc
'Lucifer' 🏆H5	Widely available
LUCIFER'S CHILDREN	ELan
'Marcotijn'	IBal
masoniorum 🏆H4	Widely available
- from Satan's Nek, South Africa	IBal
- 'African Dawn'	CElw CTca ECrc ECtt
- 'Dixter Flame'	ECha SDix SMHy
- 'Golden Swan'	SRms
- hybrid	ECrc
- 'Moira Reid'	IBal
- 'Rowallane Orange'	GBin IBal
- 'Rowallane Yellow'	CTca EBee EPPr EPri GBin IBal MNrw NHol WBor WMal WPGP WSHC
- 'Sherbert Orange'	IBal MAvo
- Slieve Donard selection	IBal
mathewsiana	CTca
aff. ***mathewsiana***	IBal
'Mex'	ECha IBal LEdu MAvo WPGP
'Ministar'	CBod CBro CRos EBee ECrc EHyd LBar LLWG LRHS NRHS WFar
'Minotaur'	IBal
'Miss Scarlet'	EHyd EPfP LRHS NRHS SAko
'Mistral'	CCCN CRos CTca ECtt EHyd EPfP GAbr GKev IBal LAma LRHS NHol NLar NRHS SCob SEdd WFar
'Moorland Sunset'	IBal
'Mount Stewart'	see *C.* × *crocosmiiflora* 'Jessie'
'Mr Bedford'	see *C.* × *crocosmiiflora* 'Croesus'
'Okavango'	CBcs CBor CBro CMac CTca ECtt ELon EPfP EPri EShb IBal IPot LBar LPla LRHS MAvo MBNS MCot MHol MNrw NLar NSti SDix WBor WCAu WCot WFar WSpi
OLD HAT	see *C.* 'Walberton Red'
'Orange Devil'	ECtt EHyd EPfP EShb EWes GKin IBal LBar LRHS MBNS NRHS SGbt WGoo
ORANGE PEKOE ('Pek Or'PBR)	GBin IBal LBar LCro LOPS NCth NSti SMad WHlf
'Orange River'	ECha WCot WFar
'Orangeade'	IBal NHol SRms
'Pageant'	IBal
§ ***paniculata***	CDor CMac GAbr LEdu NBid WBrk WOut WPGP
- 'Cally Greyleaf'	EBee EPPr GBin IBal MAvo MNrw WCot WMal
- 'Cally Sword'	CSpe EPPr IBal MAvo
- 'Major'	CTri
- 'Natal'	CTca IBal NHol
- red-flowered	IBal SWvt
'Paul's Best Yellow' 🏆H4	Widely available
'Peach Spray'	CTca
'Peach Sunrise'	IBal LBar
'Phillipa Browne'	CSde ECtt IBal MNrw NLar WCot
'Ping Pong'	CTca
'Plancheon'	IBal
pottsii	CRos CTca EHyd GMcL LEdu LRHS NRHS WOut
- 'Culzean Pink'	CElw CTca EBee EPPr EWhm GBin IBal LPla MNrw MSpe NBid NBir NHol NHpl WFar
- 'Grandiflora'	IBal
§ - 'Princess'	EBlo ECtt EHyd GBee GKev IBal LAma LRHS NRHS
- tall	IBal
'Pride of Plantion'	CBro CTca ECrc ILea
'Prince of Orange'	CBro CRos EBee EBlo EHyd EPfP ERCP GKev LAma LBar LRHS MSCN NRHS SDeJ WCAu WFar
'Queen Alexandria'	CRos EHyd LRHS NRHS WFar
'R.W. Wallace'	IBal
'Red Star'	IBal
rosea	see *Tritonia disticha* subsp. *rubrolucens*
'Rowden Bronze'	see *C.* × *crocosmiiflora* 'Coleton Fishacre'
'Rowden Chrome'	see *C.* × *crocosmiiflora* 'George Davison' Davison
'Sampford Yellow'	IBal
'Saturn'	see *C.* 'Jupiter'
'Scarlatti'	EBee ECtt IBal NHol NWad
'Scorchio' (Firestars Series)	ECrc SHar
'Severn Sunrise' 🏆H5	CBor CElw CMac CRos CTca EBlo ECha ECtt EGrI EHyd EPfP EWhm GKin GMaP IBal LRHS MHer NBir NGdn NHol NRHS SRms SWvt WBrk WCAu WFar WSHC WSpi
'Shocking'	IBal
'Sonate'	ECrc
'Spitfire'	CPrp CTca EBlo ECtt ELan IBal LRHS MArl MAvo MRav NHol SWvt WFar
§ 'Sulphurea'	ECtt EPfP IBal LRHS MSpe NHol
'Sun Flare'	CTca
'Sunzest'	ECtt MAvo WHoo
'Suzanna'	CPrp CTca ECrc ECtt LAma SDir
'Tai Pan'	IBal LBar SMad
'Tamar Double Red'	CTca
'Tamar Glow'	CTca WOld
'Tamar Gold'	CTca
'Tamar Golden Ring'	CTca
'Tamar New Dawn'	CTca
'Tangerine Queen'	GAbr IBal NHol NWad
'Tanllyd'	WCot
'Tiger'	CElw MSpe
'Twilight Fairy Crimson'	CWGN ECrc ECtt GBin LEdu LLWG NHpl NLar SPad WFar WSpi
I 'Vulcan' A. Bloom	CTca EBlo IBal LRHS MAvo
§ 'Walberton Red'	CTca EBee IBal LRHS MAvo NCth NWad SMad
WALBERTON YELLOW ('Walcroy'PBR)	EHyd EPfP LRHS NRHS SMad
'Zambesi'	CBro CMac ECtt ELon GBin IBal IPot MBNS MNrw SMad WCAu WCot XLum
'Zeal Giant' 🏆H4	CTca EBlo ECtt EPfP IBal LRHS MAvo NHol SChr WMal
'Zeal Unnamed'	CBro CTca ECrc IBal NHol

Crocus ✿ (*Iridaceae*)

'Advance'	GKev LAma LCro LOPS NRog SDeJ SDir
ancyrensis	EPot GKev NRog SDeJ
- 'Golden Bunch'	EHyd LAma LRHS NRHS SDeJ SDir WShi
§ ***angustifolius*** 🏆H6	EPot GKev LAma SDeJ WShi
- 'Berlin Gold'	GKev
- 'Minor'	EPot ERCP

	antalyensis	GKev
	- yellow-flowered	GKev
	'Ard Schenk'	CAvo CRos EHyd EPfP ETay GKev LAma LRHS NRHS NRog SDir
	asturicus	see *C. serotinus* subsp. *salzmannii*
	asumaniae	EPot GKev NRog
	'Aubade'	EPot NRog
	aureus	see *C. flavus* subsp. *flavus*
	autranii	NRog
	banaticus 🏆H6	EPot GArf GKev NDry NHar NHpl NRog
	- 'First Snow'	NRog
	- 'Snowdrift'	NHar NRog
	biflorus subsp. ***biflorus***	GKev
§	- - 'Parkinsonii'	GKev
	- 'Blue Pearl' 🏆H6	CAvo EPfP EPot ERCP ETay GKev LAma LCro LOPS LRHS NBir NRog SDeJ SDir SPer SPhx WCot WShi
	- subsp. ***isauricus***	NRog
	- subsp. ***melantherus***	GKev NDry NRog
	- 'Miss Vain'	EPot ERCP GKev LAma NRog SPer
	- subsp. ***nubigena***	NDry
	- var. ***parkinsonii***	see *C. biflorus* subsp. *biflorus* 'Parkinsonii'
	- subsp. ***stridii***	EPot GKev
	- subsp. ***tauri***	EPot NRog
	- subsp. ***weldenii*** 'Albus'	EPot GKev LAma NRog
	- - 'Fairy'	GKev LAma NRog SDir
	'Blue Bird'	EPot
	blue-flowered	EHyd LRHS NRHS
	boryi	CAvo EHyd GKev NRHS NRog
	cancellatus	NRog SDeJ
§	- subsp. ***cancellatus***	EPot LAma
	- var. ***cilicicus***	see *C. cancellatus* subsp. *cancellatus*
	- subsp. ***damascenus***	NRog
	- subsp. ***lycius***	EPot NRog
	- subsp. ***mazziaricus***	NRog
	- subsp. ***pamphylicus***	NRog
	candidus 'Lune'	GKev
	- var. ***subflavus***	see *C. olivieri* subsp. *olivieri*
	cartwrightianus 🏆H6	EHyd NRHS NRog WShi
	- from Crete	NRog
	- 'Albus' misapplied	see *C. hadriaticus*
	- 'Albus' Tubergen	EPot GKev SDeJ
	- 'Anaïs' **new**	GKev
	- 'Marcel'	NRog
	- 'Michel'	GKev NRog
	'Celia'	GKev
	chrysanthus	CHab
	- 'Blue Peter'	EPot
	- 'Buttercup' **new**	LAma
	- 'Constellation'	EPot
	- 'Cream Beauty' 🏆H6	CAvo EHyd EPfP EPot ERCP ETay GKev LAma LCro LOPS LRHS MBros NBir NRHS NRog SDeJ SDir WShi
	- var. ***fuscotinctus***	EPot GKev LAma LCro LOPS NRog SDeJ
	- 'Goldene Sonne'	EPot
	- 'Milea'	GKev NRog
	- 'White Beauty'	CWCL
	- 'Zwanenburg Bronze' 🏆H6	SDeJ
	'Cloth of Gold'	see *C. angustifolius*
	corsicus 🏆H6	EPot GKev LAma NRog
	dalmaticus	EPot
	- 'Petrovac'	GKev NRog
	danfordiae	GKev
	'Dorothy'	CAvo EPot GKev LAma NRog SDir WShi
	'Dutch Yellow'	see *C.* × *luteus* 'Golden Yellow'
	etruscus	NRog
	- 'Rosalind'	GKev NRog
	- 'Zwanenburg'	EHyd EPot GKev LAma LRHS NRHS NRog SDeJ SDir
	'Fantasy'	WShi
§	***flavus*** subsp. ***flavus*** 🏆H6	EPot GKev WShi
	fleischeri	EPot GKev LAma NRog
	'Florane'	GKev
	'Flower Record'	CArg CAvo GKev LAma LRHS NBir NRog SDeJ SDir
	gargaricus	GKev
	'Gipsy Girl'	EPot ERCP GKev LAma LCro LOPS NRog SDir SPer
	'Golden Mammoth'	see *C.* × *luteus* 'Golden Yellow'
	'Goldilocks' 🏆H6	ETay GKev LAma NRog SDeJ
	goulimyi 🏆H6	CAvo EHyd EPot LRHS NRHS NRog SDeJ WCot
	- subsp. ***leucanthus***	GKev NRog
	'Grand Maître'	ETay GKev LAma LCro NRog SDeJ SDir
§	***hadriaticus***	EHyd GKev LAma NDry NRHS NRog WShi
	- 'Annabelle'	GKev
	- var. ***chrysobelonicus***	see *C. hadriaticus*
	- subsp. ***hadriaticus*** f. ***lilacinus***	GKev
	- 'Jumbo'	NRog
	- 'Purple Eye' **new**	GKev
	'Herald'	ETay GKev LAma NRog SDeJ
§	***heuffelianus***	GKev LAma WShi
	- 'Drina Marvel'	GKev NRog
	- 'Graecus'	GKev
	- 'Krasno Polje'	NRog
	- 'Michael's Purple'	GKev
	- 'Shock Wave'	CBor CWCL
	- 'Snow Princess'	NDry
	- Uklin strain	GKev NRog
	imperati subsp. ***suaveolens***	CWCL EPot
	- - 'De Jager'	CAvo ERCP GKev LAma NRog SDeJ
	'Jeanne d'Arc'	CAby CArg CAvo EPot ETay GKev LAma LCro LOPS LRHS NBir NRog SDeJ SDir WShi
	'Jeannine'	NRog SDeJ
	× ***jessoppiae***	GKev
	karduchorum	EPot GKev LAma
	'King of the Striped'	GKev LAma LCro NRog SDeJ SPer WHlf
	korolkowii	CBor GKev LAma LHWs NRog WIce
	- 'Golden Nugget'	GKev
	- 'January Gold'	CAvo
	- 'Kiss of Spring'	EPot GKev LAma NRog
	- 'Mountain Glory'	NDry
	kosaninii	GKev
	- 'April View'	LAma
	kotschyanus 🏆H6	EGrI GKev LAma MBros NBir SDeJ
	- 'Albus'	GKev NRog SDeJ
	- subsp. ***cappadocicus***	NRog
§	- subsp. ***kotschyanus***	EPot GKev NRog SDeJ SDir
	- - var. ***leucopharynx***	NRog
	- 'Reliance'	GKev NRog
	'Ladykiller'	EPot GKev LAma NRog SDir WShi
	laevigatus 🏆H4	GKev LAma NDry NRog WIce
	- CE&H 612	EPot
	- 'Fontenayi'	EPot ERCP GKev LAma NRog
	'Large Yellow'	see *C.* × *luteus* 'Golden Yellow'
	large-flowered blue	SDir
	× ***leonidii*** 'Early Gold'	GKev LAma SDir
§	***ligusticus*** 🏆H6	CAvo EPot GKev NRog
	'Little Amber'	GKev
	longiflorus 🏆H6	EHyd EPot GKev NRHS NRog
§	× ***luteus*** 'Golden Yellow' 🏆H6	CArg CAvo EPot ETay GKev LAma LCro LOPS LRHS NRog SDeJ SDir WShi
§	- 'Stellaris'	EPot
	malyi 🏆H6	CWCL GKev NRog
	- 'Ballerina'	GKev

- 'Sveti Roc'	GKev LAma
mathewii	EPot GKev NDry NHpl NRog
- 'Dream Dancer'	EPot GKev NDry
medius	see *C. ligusticus*
minimus	EPot ERCP GKev LAma NRog
- 'Spring Beauty'	CAvo ERCP GKev LAma LCro LOPS SDeJ
'Negro Boy'	EPot
nevadensis	GKev
niveus	CBor EHyd EPot GKev NRHS NRog
- white-flowered	GKev
nudiflorus	EPot GKev NRog
ochroleucus	EPot GKev LAma SDeJ
olivieri AH 0156	GKev
- subsp. ***balansae***	NRog
§ - - 'Orange Monarch'	ERCP ETay GKev LAma LHWs SDir WIce
- - 'Zwanenburg'	EPot GKev LAma
§ - subsp. ***olivieri***	LAma NRog
'Orange Monarch'	see *C. olivieri* subsp. *balansae* 'Orange Monarch'
oreocreticus	NRog
pallasii VV KR.75	GKev
- subsp. ***dispathaceus***	NRog
- subsp. ***pallasii***	NRog
- subsp. ***turcicus***	GKev
paschei	GKev
pestalozzae	GKev NRog
'Pickwick'	CAby CArg CAvo ETay GKev LAma LCro LOPS LRHS NBir NRog SDeJ WHlf WShi
'Prins Claus'	CAvo CRos EHyd EPot ERCP GKev LAma LCro LOPS LRHS MBros NBir NRHS NRog SDeJ SDir
pulchellus 🏆H6	GKev LAma NRog SDeJ WCot
- 'Albus'	EPot LAma NRog
- 'Inspiration'	GKev NRog
- 'Michael Hoog'	GKev NRog
'Purple Heart'	GKev NDry NRog
'Purpureus'	see *C.* 'Purpureus Grandiflorus'
§ 'Purpureus Grandiflorus'	SDeJ
'Queen of the Blues'	CAvo EPot NRog SDeJ
'Remembrance'	CAby CArg CAvo EPot ETay GKev LAma LCro LOPS LRHS NBir NRog SDeJ WHlf WShi
robertianus	NRog
'Romance'	EHyd EPot GKev LAma LCro LOPS LRHS NBir NRHS NRog SDeJ
'Ruby Giant'	CAvo CRos EHyd EMor EPfP EPot ERCP ETay GKev LAma LCro LOPS LRHS NBir NRHS NRog SDeJ SPer WHlf WShi
rujanensis	GKev
salzmannii	see *C. serotinus* subsp. *salzmannii*
sativus	CAvo CBod CBor ELan EPot ERCP GKev GPoy ILea LAma LCro LOPS MBow NBir NRog SDeJ SDir SVic
'Saturnus'	EPot
scepusiensis	see *C. heuffelianus*
serotinus subsp. ***clusii*** 'Poseidon'	GKev NRog
§ - subsp. ***salzmannii***	GKev LAma NRog
- - 'Atropurpureus'	WCot
- - 'Erectophyllus'	NRog
sibiricus	see *C. sieberi*
§ ***sieberi***	EPot WShi
- 'Albus'	see *C. sieberi* 'Bowles's White'
- subsp. ***atticus***	NRog
- - 'Amfiklia'	NRog
- - 'Firefly'	EHyd EPot ERCP GKev LAma LRHS NRHS NRog SDeJ
§ - 'Bowles's White' 🏆H6	EPot GKev NRog SDeJ
- 'Hubert Edelsten' 🏆H6	EPot GKev NRog
'Snow Bunting' 🏆H6	CAvo ELan EPot GKev LAma LCro LOPS NBir NRog SDeJ SDir WShi
speciosus 🏆H6	CAvo LAma LCro LOPS NBir SDeJ WShi
- 'Aino'	GKev
- 'Aitchisonii'	EHyd GKev NRHS
- 'Albus' 🏆H6	CAvo EGrI EPot ERCP GKev LAma LCro LOPS NRog SDeJ WShi
- 'Artabir'	EHyd GKev LRHS NRHS NRog SDeJ
- 'Cassiope'	EHyd GKev LAma NRHS SDeJ
- 'Conqueror'	EHyd ELan ERCP GKev LAma LCro LOPS LRHS NBir NRHS NRog SDeJ
- 'Oxonian'	EHyd ELan EPot GKev LAma LRHS MCot NRHS NRog
- subsp. ***speciosus***	EPot GKev NBir NRog SDeJ
- subsp. ***xantholaimos***	NRog
aff. ***speciosus***	SDir
× ***stellaris***	see *C.* × *luteus* 'Stellaris'
striped	SDir
sublimis 'Tricolor' 🏆H6	CArg EHyd EPfP EPot ETay GKev LAma LCro LOPS LRHS NBir NRHS NRog SDeJ
susianus	see *C. angustifolius*
suterianus	see *C. olivieri* subsp. *olivieri*
thomasii	NRog
tommasinianus 🏆H6	CArg CHab ELan EPot GKev LAma LCro LOPS LSto NBir NRog SDeJ SDir SRms WShi
- 'Albus'	EPot GKev LAma NRog WShi
- 'Barr's Purple'	CAby EHyd EPot ETay GKev LAma LCro LOPS LRHS NBir NRHS NRog SDeJ SDir
- 'Bobbo'	EHyd NDry
- 'Claret'	CBor NDry
- 'Eric Smith'	EPot GKev NDry
- 'Lilac Beauty'	EPot GKev LAma NRog
- 'Pictus'	EPot NDry NRog WShi
- 'Roseus'	EPot GKev LAma NRog SDeJ SDir WCot WShi
- 'Whitewell Purple'	CAvo EHyd EPot ERCP ETay GKev LAma LCro LOPS LRHS NBir NRHS NRog SDeJ WCot WShi
tournefortii 🏆H4	CAvo EHyd EPot GKev NRHS NRog
'Twinborn'	EPot
vallicola	EPot
'Vanguard' 🏆H6	EPot GKev LAma LCro LOPS NRog SDeJ SDir WCot
veluchensis	GKev NRog
§ ***vernus***	NRog WShi
- subsp. ***albiflorus***	see *C. vernus*
- 'Lavender Symphony'	GKev
- subsp. ***vernus*** 'Grandiflorus'	see *C.* 'Purpureus Grandiflorus'
versicolor 'Picturatus'	EPot GKev LAma NRog SDeJ WShi
vitellinus	EPot GKev NRog
yalovensis	GKev
'Yalta'	CAvo GKev LAma WCot
'Yellow Mammoth'	see *C.* × *luteus* 'Golden Yellow'
'Zenith'	EPot GKev
'Zephyr' 🏆H6	GKev LAma SDeJ SPhx
zonatus	see *C. kotschyanus* subsp. *kotschyanus*

Croomia (*Stemonaceae*)

heterosepala	WCru

Crossyne (*Amaryllidaceae*)

flava	WCot

Crotalaria (*Fabaceae*)

laburnifolia 🏆H2	CCCN

Crucianella (*Rubiaceae*)

stylosa — see *Phuopsis stylosa*

Cruciata (*Rubiaceae*)

§ ***laevipes*** — NAts

Crusea (*Rubiaceae*)

coccinea — GEdr SBrt WCot
- 'Crûg Crimson' — WSHC

Cryosophila (*Arecaceae*)

williamsii **new** — NPlm

Cryptanthus (*Bromeliaceae*)

bivittatus ♀H1a — NCft NPic
- 'Pink Starlite' (v) ♀H1a — NCft
- 'Red Star' — NCft

lacerdae 'Menescal' — NCft
'Strawberries Flambé' — NCft

Cryptanthus × *Billbergia* see × *Cryptbergia*

× *Cryptbergia* (*Bromeliaceae*)

'Rubra' — SChr

Cryptocarya (*Lauraceae*)

alba — GBin SVen

Cryptogramma (*Pteridaceae*)

crispa — WHer

Cryptomeria ✿ (*Cupressaceae*)

fortunei — see *C. japonica*
§ ***japonica*** — CAco CBod CJun CMen CPer EPfP IPap LPar MBlu MMuc NWea SCob SEND SSha SWvt SavN WJur WMou WTSh
- Araucarioides Group — CAco SLim
- 'Atawai' — NLar
- 'Bandai-sugi' ♀H6 — CAco CKen CMac CMen IArd MGos NHol NLar SRms
- 'Barabits Gold' — CAco LRHS SavN
- 'Bicton Broom' — SLim
- 'Birodo' — CKen
- 'Black Dragon' — SLim
- 'Carmel' — MBlu
- 'Compressa' — CAco CKen EPfP LBee MAsh NLar SLim SRms
§ - 'Cristata' — CAco CMac ELan LRHS MGos SLim SRms SSha SavN
- 'Dacrydioides' — CAco MGil NLar
- 'Dinger' — CAco CKen LRHS NLar
- Elegans Group — CBcs CEme CMac CSBt ELan EPfP LRHS MGos NLar NWea SCoo SEND SPer SPoG SRms SSha WFar WMat
- - 'Elegans' ♀H6 — CBrac MGil NOrn SGsty SLim
- 'Elegans Aurea' — CBod CCVT CEme ELan LRHS LSta SPoG SSha SWvt WFar
- 'Elegans Compacta' ♀H6 — CEme CMac CSBt ELan GMcL LBee LRHS LSta MAsh MGil MMuc NBwr NLar NWea SCob SCoo SEND SLim SPad SRms SSha SWvt
- 'Elegans Nana' — MGil NBwr SRms
- 'Elegans Viridis' ♀H6 — CAco LPar MGil SGsty SLim WMat
I - 'Elegantissima' — CCVT
- 'Globosa Nana' ♀H6 — CAco EPfP ERom GMcL LBee LPal MGos NHol NPoe SArc SCob SCoo SGsty SPoG SWeb
- 'Golden Promise' ♀H6 — CAco CBcs CBod CKel LSto MAsh NHol NWad SLim SWvt
- Gracilis Group — CAco
- 'Green Pearl' **new** — CAco
- 'Hanoa' **new** — CKen
- 'HB Bandai' — MBlu
- 'Jindai-sugi' — CAco LRHS NLar WLea
- 'Kilmacurragh' — CKen NWea
- 'Kitayama-dai' **new** — CAco
- 'Kohui-yatsubusa' — CKen
- 'Koshyi' — CKen
- 'Little Champion' — CAco LRHS NLar SGsty SLim
- 'Little Diamond' — CKen
- 'Little Sonja' — CAco CKen SLim
- 'Little Yoko' — CKen NLar
- 'Lobbii' — LRHS
- 'Lobbii Nana' hort. — see *C. japonica* 'Nana'
§ - 'Mankichi-sugi' — CAco
- 'Midare' — CAco NLar
- 'Monstrosa' — LRHS NLar
- 'Monstrosa Nana' — see *C. japonica* 'Mankichi-sugi'
- 'Mushroom' — NLar SLim
§ - 'Nana' — SRms
- 'Osaka-tama' — CKen
- 'Pipo' — CAco CKen MBlu
- 'Pygmaea' — CAco LRHS MGil NHol NLar SRms
- 'Rasen-sugi' — CAco IDee LRHS MGil NFav NLar
- 'Rein's Dense Jade' — SLim
- 'Sekkan-sugi' ♀H6 — CAco CBcs CBod CBrac CCVT CEme CMac ELan EPfP ESwi GKin IArd LBee LCro LRHS MAsh MGos MTrO NLar NOrn NPoe SCoo SLim SPoG SWvt WBor WLea WMat
- 'Sekka-sugi' — see *C. japonica* 'Cristata'
- SERAMA ('Fm5') **new** — CAco
§ - 'Spiralis' ♀H6 — CAco CBod ELan EPfP GDam LBee LRHS MAsh MGil MGos NHol NLar NWea SAko SCoo SLim SPoG SRms SSha SWvt
§ - 'Spiraliter Falcata' — CAco NBwr NLar
§ - 'Tansu' — CAco CKen MGil
- 'Tenzan-sugi' ♀H6 — CAco CKen NHol NLar
- 'Tenzan-yatsubusa' — CMen
- 'Tilford Gold' — EPot GMcL LRHS LSRN NBwr NHol SCoo SLim
- 'Toda' — CKen
- 'Tsukomo' — NLar
- 'Twinkle Toes' — CAco CKen
- 'Vilmorin Gold' — CAco LRHS NHol
- 'Vilmoriniana' ♀H6 — CAco CEme CKel CKen CWnw ELan EPfP GKin GMcL LCro LSRN MAsh MGil MGos NHol NLar SCoo SLim SPoG SSha SWvt
- 'Winter Bronze' — CKen
- 'Yatsubusa' — see *C. japonica* 'Tansu', 'Yokohama'
- 'Yellow Twig' — NLar
- 'Yokohama' — CAco NFav
- 'Yore-sugi' — see *C. japonica* 'Spiralis', 'Spiraliter Falcata'
- 'Yoshino' — CKen SLim

sinensis — see *C. japonica*

Cryptostegia (*Apocynaceae*)

grandiflora — CCCN

Cryptotaenia (*Apiaceae*)

canadensis — GGro
japonica — CAgr CHby CLau GPoy MHoo MNHC SRms WHer WJek
- f. ***atropurpurea*** — CDor CSpe EBee ECha EWhm GGro LEdu MNrw WBor XLum

Ctenanthe (*Marantaceae*)

§ ***amabilis*** ♀H1b — NHrt
§ ***burle-marxii*** — CDoC NHrt
oppenheimiana — NGBl
- 'Amagris'PBR **new** — NHrt

Cucubalus (*Caryophyllaceae*)

	baccifer	GGro NLar

cucumber see AGM Vegetables Section

Cucumis (*Cucurbitaceae*)

	melo 'Alvaro' 🏆^{H1c}	EDel SCgs
	- 'Charentais'	SVic

Cudrania see *Maclura*

cumin see *Cuminum cyminum*

Cuminum (*Apiaceae*)

	cyminum	CBod SRms SVic

Cumulopuntia (*Cactaceae*)

§	***boliviana*** subsp. ***boliviana*** **new**	SPlb
§	***sphaerica*** **new**	SPlb

Cunninghamia (*Cupressaceae*)

	konishii	SMad
§	***lanceolata***	CAco CMCN CMac EPfP IDee LRHS MGil SSta WPGP
	- 'Glauca'	CAco CJun IDee
	- 'Samurai'	CAco
	sinensis	see *C. lanceolata*
	unicaniculata	see *C. lanceolata*

Cuphea (*Lythraceae*)

	caeciliae	WMal
	cyanea	CSpe LSvl SDix
	hyssopifolia 🏆^{H2}	CTsd EShb SWvt
	- 'Alba'	CCCN EShb SWvt
	- pink-flowered	CCCN
	- red-flowered	CCCN
	- 'Rosea'	SWvt
§	***ignea*** 🏆^{H2}	CTsd ELan
	- 'Matchless'	SVic
	- 'Roxy'	EPPr
	'Lilac Belle'	CSpe
§	***llavea*** 'Georgia Scarlet'	CCCN WHlf
	- 'Tiny Mice'	see *C. llavea* 'Georgia Scarlet'
I	***macrophylla*** hort.	CHll
	maculata	CCCN CHll
	platycentra	see *C. ignea*
	'Torpedo'	LCro MBros
	viscosissima	CSpe ELan MCot

× *Cupressocyparis* see × *Cuprocyparis*

Cupressus (*Cupressaceae*)

	arizonica	CAco CBod LPal LPar NPlm SArc SWeb
I	- 'Fastigiata Aurea'	LPar NPlm SGsty SWeb
§	- var. ***glabra***	CAco EBtc
	- - 'Angaston'	SLim
	- - 'Aurea'	CAco CEme MAsh SLim
	- - 'Blue Ice'	CAco CMac MAsh SLim SWvt
	- - 'Compacta'	CKen
I	- - 'Fastigiata'	CCVT SCob SGsty
	- - 'Glauca'	CAco
	- var. ***nevadensis***	CAco
	- 'Pyramidalis' 🏆^{H5}	SEND
	- 'Réka'	CAco
	- var. ***stephensonii***	CAco
I	- 'Sulfurea'	CAco
	austrotibetica KR 5528E **new**	WPGP
	bakeri	CAco
	cashmeriana 🏆^{H3}	CAco EBtc SPtp
	- KR 8688A	WPGP
	chengiana	CAco
	duclouxiana	CAco
	dupreziana var. ***atlantica***	CAco SLim SPtp WPGP WPav
§	***funebris***	CAco SMad
	gigantea	CAco
	glabra	see *C. arizonica* var. *glabra*
	goveniana	CAco
	- var. ***abramsiana***	CAco
	guadalupensis	CAco
	- var. ***forbesii***	CAco
	- var. ***guadalupensis***	CAco
	× ***leylandii***	see × *Cuprocyparis leylandii*
	lusitanica	CAco
	- var. ***benthamii***	CAco
	- 'Brice's Weeping'	CAco CKen SLim
	- 'Pygmy'	CKen
	macnabiana	CAco
	macrocarpa	CAco CBcs CBod CCVT IPap SEND
	- 'Compacta'	CKen
	- 'Gold Spread'	SLim
	- 'Goldcrest' 🏆^{H4}	CAco CBcs CCVT CEme CMac EDir ELan GMcL LPar LRHS MDon MGos MPri NBir SCob SEWo SGsty SLim SWeb SWvt WHtc
	- 'Golden Cone'	EBtc
	- 'Golden Pillar'	SWvt
	- 'Lohbrunner'	CKen
I	- 'Pendula'	SLim
	- 'Pygmaea'	CKen
	- 'Sulphur Cushion'	CKen
	- 'Wilma' 🏆^{H4}	CEme CSBt ELan EPfP EShb LBee LCro MAsh MDon MGos NBwr SCoo SLim SPer SPoG SWeb SWvt
	- 'Woking'	CKen
	nootkatensis	see *Xanthocyparis nootkatensis*
	sargentii	CAco
	sempervirens	CEme EDir ERom LPal LPar LWaG MGil MPri SPlb SWeb
	- 'Agrimed'	CCVT LPar
	- 'Bolgheri'	LSRN
	- 'Garda'	CKel CWnw
	- 'Green Pencil'	CKen
	- 'Karaca Fastigiata Aurea'	CAco
	- 'Pyramidalis'	see *C. sempervirens* Stricta Group
	- var. ***sempervirens***	see *C. sempervirens* Stricta Group
§	- Stricta Group	CBcs CBrac CCVT CPer EPfP LMaj LPal LRHS NBwr NLar NOrn SArc SCob SEND SEWo SGsty WSpi
	- 'Stricta Blue'	CAco LRHS
	- 'Swane's Gold'	CKen EBtc MAsh
	- 'Totem Pole'	CAco CBod CCVT CKen CSBt ELan EPfP IPap LBee LPal LRHS MAsh MGos NPlm SCoo SGsty SLim SPad SPoG SSha SWeb SWvt
	torulosa	CAco SPtp

Cupressus × *Xanthocyparis* see × *Cuprocyparis*

× *Cuprocyparis* ✿ (*Cupressaceae*)

§	***leylandii***	Widely available
I	- '2001'	CBod CCVT NBwr SGol
	- 'Blue Jeans'PBR	LPar SEND
§	- 'Castlewellan'	Widely available
	- EXCALIBUR GOLD ('Drabb'PBR)	SCob
	- 'Ferngold'	MAsh
	- 'Galway Gold'	see × *C. leylandii* 'Castlewellan'
	- 'Gold Rider' 🏆^{H6}	CBod CCVT CMac ELan MAsh NWea SCoo SEND SGsty SLim SMad SPer SPoG SWeb SWvt

- 'Green Ornament'	SMad
- 'Haggerston Grey'	SEND
§ - 'Harlequin' (v)	CMac SEND SGsty SWvt
- 'Leighton Green'	WTSh
- 'Naylor's Blue'	CMac SEND
- 'Olive's Green'	CBod SWvt
- 'Robinson's Gold'	CMac SGol
- 'Silver Dust' (v)	WAvo
- 'Variegata'	see × *C. leylandii* 'Harlequin'

Curculigo (*Hypoxidaceae*)

crassifolia B&SWJ 2318	WCru
- NJM 10.123	WPGP

Curcuma ✿ (*Zingiberaceae*)

alismatifolia	SDeJ
longa	GPoy SPlb SPre
roscoeana	SDeJ
zedoaria 'Bicolor Wonder'	CCCN
- 'Pink Wonder'	CCCN LAma
- 'White Wonder'	CCCN LAma SDeJ

Curio (*Asteraceae*)

§ ***articulatus***	EAri EShb
- f. ***variegatus*** new	EAri
§ ***citriformis*** new	EAri
§ ***ficoides***	EShb NGBl
- 'Mount Everest'PBR	EShb
radicans	SIvy
§ ***repens***	CDoC CKel CWal EAri EShb SArc SEdd SIvy SSim
§ ***rowleyanus***	CDoC EShb LCro LOPS LWaG NCft SEdd SIvy SSim WOld
talinoides 'Himalayan Blue'	WCot
§ - subsp. ***cylindricus***	CWal
§ - subsp. ***mandraliscae***	EAri
- - 'Blue Finger'	SEdd WCot

Curtonus see *Crocosmia*

Cussonia (*Araliaceae*)

paniculata	CDTJ CWGN SPlb
sphaerocephala	SPlb
spicata	CDTJ SPlb
transvaalensis	CDTJ

custard apple see *Annona cherimola*

Cyananthus (*Campanulaceae*)

incanus	GEdr GKev
integer misapplied	see *C. microphyllus*
lobatus ♀H5	EPot WAbe
- 'Albus'	NHar WAbe
- giant	GEdr NHar
lobatus × ***microphyllus***	GEdr WAbe
macrocalyx	NHar
§ ***microphyllus*** ♀H5	EPot GEdr GKev NHar NSla WAbe
microphyllus × 'Sherriff's Variety'	NHar
sherriffii	WAbe
spathulifolius	EPot

Cyanastrum (*Tecophilaeaceae*)

cordifolium	GKev

Cyanella (*Tecophilaeaceae*)

lutea	NRog

Cyanotis (*Commelinaceae*)

beddomei 'Coeruleus' new	WCot
somaliensis ♀H1b	EShb
speciosa new	WHil

Cyathea (*Cyatheaceae*)

atrox	CKel
australis	CAby CBdn CDTJ CKel CTrC CTsd EHed ESwi ETod IKel SPlb
brownii	CKel ETod
cooperi ♀H3	CAbb CBcs CBct CBdn CBrP CDTJ CKel CTrC CTsd ESwi ETod IKel LRHS NBro NPlm WFib XSte
- 'Brentwood'	EHed ESwi ISha
cunninghamii	CKel
dealbata	CBdn CDTJ CKel ETod IKel WPGP XSte
dregei	SPlb
medullaris	CBdn CKel ETod IKel WPGP XSte
robusta	CKel
smithii	CKel ETod IKel
tomentosissima	CDTJ CKel IKel ISha NPlm

Cyathodes (*Ericaceae*)

colensoi	see *Leucopogon colensoi*
fraseri	see *Leucopogon fraseri*

Cycas (*Cycadaceae*)

sp.	WLea
circinalis	NPlm
media	LPal
panzhihuaensis	CBrP LPal NPlm SPlb
revoluta ♀H3	CAbb CBcs CBrP CCCN CDoC CTsd EAri EDir EOli EPfP EShb LCro LOPS LPal LPar LWaG NHrt NPlm SArc SChr SEND SGsty SPlb SWeb
revoluta × ***taitungensis***	CBrP
§ ***rumphii***	CBrP LPal
taitungensis	CBrP
thouarsii	see *C. rumphii*

Cyclamen ✿ (*Primulaceae*)

abchasicum	see *C. coum* subsp. *caucasicum*
africanum	CBro EHyd GKev LRHS MAsh NRHS
africanum × ***hederifolium***	NCth
§ ***alpinum***	CRos EHyd EPot LAma LRHS MAsh NRHS NRog SDeJ
- 'Nettleton White'	MAsh
balearicum	EHyd EPot LAma NRHS NRog
cilicium ♀H3	CBro EGrl EHyd EPPr EPot ETay GKev GMcL GRum LAma LCro LOPS LRHS MAsh NBwr NHpl NRHS NRog NSla WHoo WShi
- f. ***album***	EGrl EHyd EPPr EPot GKev LAma LRHS MAsh NRHS
colchicum	MAsh
§ ***coum*** ♀H5	Widely available
- var. ***abchasicum***	see *C. coum* subsp. *caucasicum*
§ - subsp. ***caucasicum***	MAsh
- subsp. ***coum***	CBro
- - f. ***albissimum***	GKev
- - - 'George Bisson'	MAsh
- - - 'Golan Heights'	MAsh
- - - 'Lake Effect'	MAsh
- - f. ***coum*** Nymans Group	GRum
- - - Pewter Group ♀H5	CTtf GEdr GKev NRog WCot
- - - - 'Maurice Dryden'	CBro EHyd EPot LAma LEdu LRHS MAsh NRHS NRog WHoo
- - - - 'Tilebarn Elizabeth'	GRum MAsh NBir WHoo
- - - 'Roseum'	CAvo
- - - Silver Group	CBro EHyd EPot LAma LRHS MAvo NRHS NRya WHoo
- - - - red-flowered	WHoo
- - magenta-flowered	WHoo
- - f. ***pallidum*** 'Album'	CAvo CWCL EGrl EMor EWhm EWoo GEdr GKev GMaP LAma

		LCro LOPS LPal MAvo NRog SDeJ SEdd SPeP SPer WHoo WPnP WShi
	- dark pink-flowered	CAvo WHoo
	- hybrid	ERCP
	- marble-leaved	SBea WHoo
	- 'Marianne'	SAko
	- 'Meaden's Crimson'	GRum
	- red-flowered	EGrI
I	- 'Rubrum'	EWoo GKev LCro LOPS MAvo
	- 'Ruby Star' **new**	GEdr
	- silver speckled leaf	CAvo
	cyprium	EHyd EPot GKev GRum LRHS MAsh NRHS
	- 'E.S.'	WThu
	- 'Galaxy'	MAsh
	elegans	MAsh
	europaeum	see *C. purpurascens*
	graecum	EHyd EPot GKev LAma LRHS MHer NRHS WAbe WHoo WThu
	- subsp. ***candicum***	WThu
	- subsp. ***graecum*** f. ***album***	EHyd GKev LAma MAsh NRHS
	- - f. ***graecum*** 'Glyfada'	GKev LAma
§	***hederifolium*** ♀H5	Widely available
	- S&L 175/1	WCot XLum
	- (Amazeme Series) 'Amazeme'	WCot
	- - 'Amazeme Pink'	LRHS
	- subsp. ***crassifolium***	MAsh
	- var. ***hederifolium*** f. ***albiflorum*** ♀H5	CAby CAvo CBro CTsd EBee ECha EGrI EMor EWoo GKev LAma LCro LEdu LOPS MCot NGrs NRog NWad SBea SDeJ SEND SEdd SPeP WHoo WPnP XLum
	- - - 'Album'	CWCL SDeJ WShi
	- - - Bowles's Apollo Group	NWad
	- - - 'Discovery'	WCot
	- - - 'Nettleton Silver'	see *C. hederifolium* var. *hederifolium* f. *albiflorum* 'White Cloud'
	- - - 'Perlenteppich'	GMaP
	- - - silver-leaved	SDys
§	- - - 'White Cloud' ♀H5	GRum MAsh NHpl WHoo
	- - f. ***hederifolium*** 'Fairy Rings'	MAsh
	- - - 'Rosenteppich'	CMiW CTsd
	- - - 'Ruby Glow'	EHyd LRHS MAsh MHer NBir NRHS WThu
	- - - Silver Cloud Group ♀H5	CAby CBro GRum MAsh NBir WHoo
	- - - 'Silver Shield'	MAsh
	- - - 'Stargazer'	MAsh
	- island scented strain	WCot
	- 'Lysander'	GKev MAsh
	- 'Pewter Mist'	SPeP
	- 'Red Sky'	CAvo CBro GRum LAma MAsh WPGP
	- 'Rosy Pink'	EGrI
	- Silver-leaved Group	CAvo CTtf ECha EHyd EPot GAbr GEdr GKev LAma LRHS NRHS NSla
	- - 'Silver Leaf Pink'	GMaP
	- - 'Silver Leaf White'	GMaP NWad
	- 'Silverme Pink'	EPPr
	ibericum	see *C. coum* subsp. *caucasicum*
	'Indiaka Violet'	CRos
	intaminatum	EHyd EPot GKev GRum LAma LRHS MAsh NRHS WHoo
	- plain-leaved	WThu
	latifolium	see *C. persicum*
	libanoticum	EHyd EPot GKev LAma LRHS MAsh NRHS WThu
	mirabile ♀H4	EGrI EHyd EPot GKev GRum LAma LRHS MAsh NHpl NRHS NSla SDeJ
	- 'Alba'	EGrI GKev LAma SDeJ
	- f. ***mirabile*** 'Tilebarn Anne'	MAsh
	- - 'Tilebarn Nicholas'	MAsh
	- f. ***niveum***	SDeJ
	- - 'Tilebarn Jan'	MAsh
	neapolitanum	see *C. hederifolium*
	orbiculatum	see *C. coum*
§	***persicum***	EHyd GKev LRHS LWaG MAsh NRHS NRog WCot
	- Ashwood silver-leaved	MAsh
	- Metis Series	SCob
	- (Super Verano Series) VERANO NEON PINK	LCro LOPS
	- - VERANO RED	LCro LOPS
	- WINFALL WHITE ('Synwinfwhi') (Winfall Series)	LCro LOPS
	pseudibericum ♀H4	CBro EHyd EPot GKev GRum LRHS MAsh NRHS SDeJ WCot
	- AC&W 664	NWad
	- f. ***roseum***	ITim MAsh
§	***purpurascens***	GKev GRum LAma MAsh NHpl NRog NSla WHoo WThu
	- 'Lake Garda'	MAsh
	'Rainier Scarlet' (Rainier Series) **new**	LCro
	repandum	CAvo CBro CTtf EHyd EPot LAma LRHS MAsh NRHS NRog WHer
	rohlfsianum	EHyd LAma MAsh NRHS
	× ***schwarzii***	MAsh
	'Trena'	SDeJ
	trochopteranthum	see *C. alpinum*

Cyclosorus (*Thelypteridaceae*)

falcilobus **new**	LEdu
tottoides	LEdu WPGP

Cydonia ✿ (*Rosaceae*)

	japonica	see *Chaenomeles japonica*
	oblonga (F)	SGsty SPre WJur
	- 'Agvambari' (F)	SKee
	- 'Aromatnaya' (F)	CBod MCoo MTrO NOra SKee WMat
	- 'Bereczcki'	see *C. oblonga* 'Bereczki'
§	- 'Bereczki' (F)	MTrO
	- 'Champion' (F)	CAgr CHab EBee EDir ELan EPom LBuc LPar MCoo MTrO NOra NRog SEdi SGsty SKee SVic WFar WMat
	- 'Cydora Robusta'^PBR (F)	LPar
	- 'Early Prolific' (F)	SEND SEdi
	- 'Ekmek' (F)	SKee
	- 'Gamboa' (F)	SKee
	- 'Iranian' (F)	CAgr SKee
	- 'Isfahan' (F)	MTrO SKee WMat
	- 'Krymsk' (F)	CAgr WWct
	- 'Leskovac' (F)	CAgr EDir EPom LPar NOra SBmr WWct
	- 'Ludovic' (F)	LPar NRog
§	- 'Lusitanica' (F)	CAgr CHab ELan EPom LPar LRHS MLod MTrO NRog SKee SPer SSFr WMat
	- 'Meech's Prolific' (F)	CAgr CHab CLnd CTri EBee ELan EPfP EPom EWTr LCro LRHS MGos MMuc MRav MTrO NLar NOra NRog NWea SBmr SEdi SKee SPer SSFT SSFr WMat WWct
	- pear-shaped (F)	CHab NRog SPer
	- PORTUGAL	see *C. oblonga* 'Lusitanica'

- 'Rea's Mammoth' (F)	CHab LPar NLar NRog
- 'Seibosa' (F)	SKee
- 'Serbian Gold' (F) ♀H5	CMac CPer EBee ELan EPom LRHS MTrO NLar NOra NRog SKee SSFT WMat
- 'Shams' (F)	NRog SKee
- 'Smyrna' (F)	NLar NOra NRog SKee WMat
- 'Sobu' (F)	SKee
- 'Vranja' misapplied	see *C. oblonga* 'Bereczki'
- 'Vranja' ambig. (F)	CBcs CBod CDoC EDir IPap LMaj LPar MAsh MDon MLod MTrO NRog NWea SBdl SBmr SCoo SEdi SPoG
- 'Vranja' Nenadovic (F)	Widely available

Cylindropuntia (*Cactaceae*)

bigelovii new	EAri
§ ***fulgida*** new	NPlm
imbricata	EAri SPlb XSen XVPe
leptocaulis	XSen
§ ***spinosior***	XLum
versicolor	XSen

Cymbalaria (*Plantaginaceae*)

aequitriloba 'Alba'	GAbr NRya
§ ***hepaticifolia***	SBrt SPlb
§ ***muralis***	CGBo ECtt GAbr GJos LLWG MHer NRya WHer WHlf WIce
- 'Albiflora'	see *C. muralis* 'Pallidior'
- 'Kenilworth White'	GJos WCot
- 'Nana Alba'	ECtt EPfP WAbe
§ - 'Pallidior'	SPhx
- 'Snow Wave'	WCot WFar
§ ***pallida***	EPfP GQue MAsh MMuc SEND SGro SLee SPlb WAbe WCav WFar
- 'Alba'	EPfP WFar
§ ***pilosa***	ECtt NLar

Cymbopogon (*Poaceae*)

citratus	CBod CCCN ENfk GPoy LCro MHoo MNHC SEdi SPlb SPre SRms SVic
flexuosus	CCCN MHer SRms WJek
nardus	GPoy

Cynanchum (*Apocynaceae*)

ascyrifolium	EBee SBrt
atratum	GEdr
bosseri new	EAri
decorsei new	EAri
'Maradirmali Coimbrata' new	EAri
marnierianum new	EAri
oresbium new	EAri
stoloniferum new	EAri
vanlessenii new	EAri
viminale	EAri
subsp. ***mulanjense*** new	
- subsp. ***stipitaceum*** new	EAri

Cynara (*Asteraceae*)

§ ***baetica*** subsp. ***maroccana***	LDai
cardunculus ♀H5	Widely available
- 'Bianco Avorio'	SVic
I - 'Cardy'	EWoo
- dwarf	SDix
- subsp. ***flavescens***	SBrt
I - 'Florist Cardy'	NLar
- 'Gobbo di Nizza'	SRms
- 'Porto Spineless'	CAgr LShi
§ - Scolymus Group	CBcs EGrI EHyd EPfP EWes GPoy LCro LRHS LSRN MNHC MRav NRHS SCob SGBe SPhx SPoG WHer
- - 'Bere'	LEdu
- - 'Gros Camus de Bretagne'	MAvo WCot
- - 'Gros Vert de Lâon' ♀H5	CBcs CLau ELan LRHS SPtp WCot
- - 'Monica Lynden-Bell'	WCot
- - 'Purple Globe'	CBod LEdu SRms
- - 'Romanesco'	CLau LCro SRms SVic
- - 'Rouge d'Alger'	CAgr
- - 'Tavor'	CLau SVic
- - 'Vert Globe'	CBod CLau CSBt CTsd ENfk LCro LEdu MBros NLar NPer SRms SVic SWvt
- - 'Violet de Provence'	CSBt MHer SRms
- - 'Violetto di Chioggia' ♀H4	CLau
cornigera	SBrt SPhx
* ***gomerensis***	WCot
hystrix misapplied	see *C. baetica* subsp. *maroccana*
scolymus	see *C. cardunculus* Scolymus Group
syriaca	SPhx

Cynodon (*Poaceae*)

aethiopicus	EBee EPPr NWsh

Cynoglossum (*Boraginaceae*)

amabile ♀H5	CSpe GGro LCro LOPS LSto
nervosum	CAby CBWd CBod EBee EPPr GGro MBel MHol MMuc SEND SPer WCAu WCot WTyc
officinale	GGro

Cynosurus (*Poaceae*)

cristatus	CHab NMir SPhx WWild

Cypella (*Iridaceae*)

aquatilis	EWat

Cyperus (*Cyperaceae*)

§ ***albostriatus***	CCCN EShb
alternifolius misapplied	see *C. involucratus*
alternifolius L.	CBen CCCN EPfP LPal LPfP SArc WMAq
- 'Compactus'	see *C. involucratus* 'Nanus'
'Chira'	NWsh
diffusus misapplied	see *C. albostriatus*
§ ***eragrostis***	EPPr MWts NSti SDix SPlb WMAq
esculentus	CAgr EShb
glaber	EHyd LDai
haspan L.	WCot
§ ***involucratus*** ♀H1c	CWal EShb EWat MWts SEND XLum
§ - 'Nanus'	EShb
longus	CAgr CBen CPud CWat EWat LPfP MMuc MWts NPer NSti SEND SMad SPlb WMAq WWtn
papyrus ♀H1c	CCCN CDTJ CDow CTsd EShb LCro LOPS LPal LPfP LSun LWaG SArc SIvy SPlb
- 'Perkamentus' PBR	CCCN EShb LPfP
prolifer	EShb
vegetus	see *C. eragrostis*
'Zumila'	EShb

Cyphomandra see *Solanum*

Cyphostemma (*Vitaceae*)

mappia	SPlb

Cypripedium (*Orchidaceae*)

Achim gx	XFro
Aki gx	NLAp XFro
- 'Pastel'	XFro
Ann Elizabeth gx	NLAp
Anna gx	NLAp XFro

× ***barbeyi***	see *C.* × *ventricosum*
Barry Phillips gx	GKev LAma NLAp
Bernd gx	NLAp
- white-flowered	NLAp
Birgit gx pastel-flowered	XFro
calceolus	CBor GKev SDir SPVi
calceolus × ***macranthos*** f. ***albiflorum***	LAma
Chauncey gx	XFro
Christian gx	XFro
Cleo Pinkepank gx	NLAp XFro
corrugatum	see *C. tibeticum*
Dietrich gx 🏆H5	XFro
Emil gx	NLAp XFro
Eurasia gx	NLAp XFro
fasciolatum	LAma
flavum	NLAp WHlf
formosanum 🏆H3	CBor GKev LAma NLAp SDir
Francis gx	NLAp
Gabriela gx 🏆H5	NLAp
- 'Kentucky Maxi'	GKev NHpl
Gisela gx	CAvo SPVi XFro
GPH Quiet Waters gx	NLAp
guttatum	NLAp
Hank Small gx 🏆H5	XFro
Hans Erni gx	XFro
Henric gx	NLAp
henryi	NLAp
Inge gx	NLAp XFro
Ingrid gx	XFro
Ivory gx	LAma NLAp
Jimmy gx	NLAp
Karl Heinz gx	XFro
kentuckiense 🏆H5	CCCN GKev LAma NHpl NLAp SDir
'Kentucky Pink'	see *C.* Philipp gx 'Kentucky Pink'
Kristi Lyn gx	NLAp XFro
Lady Dorine gx	NLAp SPVi
Lucy Pinkepank gx	NLAp XFro
- 'Kentucky Pink Blush'	LAma NHpl
macranthos	CBor GKev WHlf
- 'Album'	CBor GKev
- John Hagger Group	XFro
- var. ***speciosum*** × ***tibeticum***	NLAp
Maria gx	XFro
Memoriam Shawna Austin gx	NLAp
§ **Michael gx** 🏆H5	NLAp SPVi XFro
Monto gx	XFro
Mops gx	XFro
Otto gx	NLAp
parviflorum	GKev SDir
- var. ***parviflorum***	LAma
§ - var. ***pubescens***	CBor GKev LAma NHpl NLAp SPVi WHlf
'Parville'	NHpl SDir
Paul gx	XFro
Peter gx	XFro
Philipp gx 🏆H5	NLAp SPVi XFro
§ - 'Kentucky Pink'	GKev LAma NHpl SDir
- pink-flowered **new**	LAma
- white-flowered **new**	LAma
Pluto gx	NLAp XFro
pubescens	see *C. parviflorum* var. *pubescens*
Rascal gx	XFro
reginae 🏆H5	CCCN GKev LAma NHpl NLAp SDir WCot WHlf
- f. ***albolabium***	NHpl
- f. ***album***	GKev LAma LRHS NLAp SDir
Renate gx pastel-flowered	XFro
Sabine gx 🏆H5	NLAp SPVi XFro
- pastel-flowered	NLAp XFro
Sebastian gx	XFro
- 'Frosch's Mountain King'	XFro
- 'Multiflower White'	NHpl
Sunny gx	XFro
§ ***tibeticum***	NLAp
Tilman gx	NLAp XFro
Ulla Silkens gx 🏆H5	NLAp WHlf XFro
Ursel gx	NLAp XFro
§ × ***ventricosum***	CBor GKev NLAp XFro
- 'Frosch's Queen of the Mist'	XFro
- 'Pastel'	NLAp XFro
- pink-flowered **new**	LAma
- white-flowered	GKev LAma
Victoria gx	NLAp XFro
Vintri gx	see *C.* × *ventricosum*
Wim gx	NLAp

Cyrilla (*Cyrillaceae*)

racemiflora	CMac

Cyrtanthus (*Amaryllidaceae*)

§ ***brachyscyphus***	EGrI EShb
breviflorus	CPbh WCot WPGP
'Edwina'	CCCN
§ ***elatus*** 🏆H2	CTsd GKev NSti SPtp WCot
elatus × ***montanus*** **new**	WCot
'Elizabeth'	CCCN
epiphyticus	WCot
falcatus 🏆H2	GKev SBrt WCot
mackenii	EShb WPGP
- cream-white-flowered	CCCN EShb GKev
- 'Himalayan Pink'	CCCN EShb GKev
- red-flowered	CCCN EShb GKev
montanus	WCot
parviflorus	see *C. brachyscyphus*
purpureus	see *C. elatus*
sanguineus	WCot
speciosus	see *C. elatus*

Cyrtomium (*Dryopteridaceae*)

§ ***caryotideum***	CBdn CLAP LEdu
devexiscapulae	CLAP CTsd LEdu LLWG NLar WPGP
§ ***falcatum*** 🏆H3	Widely available
- 'Rochfordianum'	CCCN CRos EHyd ISha LEdu LRHS MRav NRHS WFib
§ ***fortunei*** 🏆H3	CBct CBdn CBod CKel CLAP CRos EFer EHyd EMor EPfP LCro LOPS LPal LRHS MGos MRav NBid NBro NLar NRHS SCob SPer SPoG SRms SRot WFib WPnP XLum
- var. ***clivicola***	CAby CBdn EBee EHed EHyd EPfP EShb GKev ISha LEdu LPal LRHS MGos MRav NBro NGrd NLar NRHS SBea SCoo SEdd WBrk WCot XLum
macrophyllum	CLAP CRos EBee EHyd LPal LRHS NRHS WPGP
tukusicola	EBee

Cystopteris ✿ (*Woodsiaceae*)

bulbifera	WCot
dickieana	WFib
fragilis	EFer GKev LEdu WFib
moupinensis B&SWJ 6767	WCot WCru

Cytisus (*Fabaceae*)

'Andreanus'	see *C. scoparius* f. *andreanus*
battandieri	see *Argyrocytisus battandieri*
× ***beanii*** 🏆H5	CRos EHyd ELan EPfP LRHS MAsh NLar
'Boskoop Glory'	NLar
× ***boskoopii*** 'Apricot Gem'	CBod CSBt ELan ELon MAsh NBwr NLar

– 'Boskoop Ruby' ♀H5	CBcs CBod CBrac CDoC CEme CMac CRos CSBt CWnw EHyd ELan EPfP GDam GKin GMcL LCro LOPS LRHS LSRN MAsh NHol NRHS SCob SGbt SPer SWvt
– 'Dukaat'	NLar
– 'Hollandia' ♀H5	CBcs CSBt ELan EPfP GKin MAsh MRav NLar SPer
– 'La Coquette'	CBod CDoC EPfP SPlb
– 'Windlesham Ruby'	EHeP ELan EPfP LSRN NLar WFar
– 'Zeelandia' ♀H5	CMac ELan EPfP NHol NLar SCob SGsty SPer
'Burkwoodii' ♀H5	CBcs EHeP ELan ELon EPfP GMcL LSRN MSwo SCob SPoG WFar
canariensis	see *Genista canariensis*
§ ***decumbens***	GArf GKev
demissus ♀H5	WAbe
'Dorothy Walpole'	ELon
'Eastern Queen'	ELon
'Golden Cascade'	CBcs CBod EHyd ELan LRHS MAsh NRHS
'Goldfinch'	CBrac CRos EHyd ELan GMcL LRHS MSwo NHol NLar NRHS SNig WFar
§ ***hirsutus***	SBrt
× ***kewensis*** ♀H5	EHyd EPfP LRHS MAsh MGos NLar NRHS SRms
– 'Niki'	CEme EPfP GMcL MAsh NLar SPer
'Killiney Salmon'	CKel EMil GKin LSRN MRav
'Lena' ♀H5	CBod CEme CKel CMac CRos CSBt EHeP EHyd ELan EPfP GDam GKin GMcL LCro LRHS LSRN MAsh MGos NBir NHol NLar SCob SGbt SPoG WFar
'Luna'	ELon EPfP GMcL LRHS SCob
maderensis	see *Genista maderensis*
'Maria Burkwood'	WHlf
'Minstead'	SPer
'Moyclare Pink'	LCro LOPS WHlf
'Newry Seedling'	CMac
nigricans 'Cyni' ♀H5	CRos EHed EHyd ELan LRHS MAsh SPer SPoG
'Palette'	SCob
'Porlock'	see *Genista* 'Porlock'
× ***praecox***	CMac CRos EHeP EHyd ELon EPfP LRHS MAsh NBwr NRHS NWea SCob SPlb SPoG WFar
– 'Albus'	CBcs CBrac CDoC CMac CRos EHeP EHyd ELan EPfP GMcL LCro LPar LRHS LSRN MAsh MGos MMuc MRav NHol NRHS SCob SPer WFar
– 'Allgold' ♀H5	Widely available
– 'Frisia'	WFar
– 'Lilac Lady'	CRos EHyd EPfP LRHS MAsh
– 'Warminster' ♀H5	CBrac GKin MMuc MRav SPer SRms
procumbens	EHeP
purpureus	EPfP GMcL MMrt MRav WSHC
– 'Atropurpureus'	EPfP
racemosus	see *Genista* × *spachiana*
'Red Wings'	CBrac
scoparius	CPer EHeP NWea SCob WTSh
§ – f. ***andreanus***	CTri EPfP
– – 'Splendens'	SPer
– 'Cornish Cream'	CSBt ELan EPfP NWea
– 'Firefly'	CBcs CMac
– 'Fulgens'	EPfP
– 'Golden Sunlight'	CSBt GMcL MSwo
§ – subsp. ***maritimus***	CMac
– var. ***prostratus***	see *C. scoparius* subsp. *maritimus*
– 'Tiltstone Moonglow'	GBin
× ***spachianus***	see *Genista* × *spachiana*
supinus	see *C. hirsutus*
'White Lion'	CMac WHlf

D

Daboecia ✿ (*Ericaceae*)

§ ***cantabrica*** f. ***alba***	MAsh
– – 'Alba Globosa'	GPer
– – 'Alberta White'	CFst
– 'Andrea'	CFst
– 'Angelina'PBR	CFst
– f. ***blumii*** 'Pinky Perky'	CFst
– – 'Purple Blum'	CFst
– – 'White Blum'	CFst
§ – 'Donard Pink'	GJos GPer
– 'Glamour'	CFst
– 'Heather Yates'	CFst
– 'Lilac Osmond'	CFst
– 'Pink'	see *D. cantabrica* 'Donard Pink'
– 'Romantic Muxoll' (d)	CFst
– 'Rosella'PBR	CFst
– 'Stardust Muxoll'	CFst
– 'Sun Seeker'	CFst
– 'Vanessa'PBR	CFst
– subsp. ***scotica***	see *D.* × *scotica*
× ***scotica*** 'Goscote'	MGos
– 'Jack Drake'	CFst
– 'Katherine's Choice'	CBcs CFst
– 'Silverwells' ♀H5	CBcs MAsh
– 'William Buchanan' ♀H5	GAbr GJos GPer MAsh SCoo

Dacrycarpus (*Podocarpaceae*)

§ ***dacrydioides***	CBrP CTsd

Dacrydium (*Podocarpaceae*)

colensoi	see *Lepidothamnus colensoi*
cupressinum	SMad SPlb
franklinii	see *Lagarostrobos franklinii*

Dactylicapnos (*Papaveraceae*)

§ 'Golden Tears' **new**	GEdr
macrocapnos	CSpe LRHS MGil SHar WBor WCru
platycarpa	WPGP
§ ***scandens***	CRHN CSpe GEdr IRos SBrt WAvo WHil XLum
– GWJ 9438	WCru
– WJC 13793	WCru
§ ***ventii*** GWJ 9376	WCru
– WJC 13786	WCru

Dactylis (*Poaceae*)

glomerata	CHab SVic WSFF
– 'Variegata' (v)	MMuc NBid

Dactylorhiza (*Orchidaceae*)

Foliorella gx	NLAp
§ ***foliosa*** ♀H4	CCCN ECha MAvo NChi NLAp WSHC
§ ***fuchsii***	CCCN CHab CMil EPot EWat LEdu MNrw NBir NLAp WHer WHlf WSFF
– 'Eleanor'	MPhe
× ***grandis***	NLAp
– Blackthorn hybrid	CJun
iberica	NLAp
incarnata	NBid
§ ***maculata***	EDAr NLAp WHlf
– subsp. ***ericetorum***	NLAp
maderensis	see *D. foliosa*
§ ***majalis***	LAma NLAp WHlf WSFF
mascula	see *Orchis mascula*
praetermissa	CCCN CHab NLAp
purpurella	CHab CMiW GAbr GJos NFav NLAp NRya

Dahlia ✿ (*Asteraceae*)

	'A la Mode' (D)	CWGr
	'Abbie' (D)	NHal
I	'Abigail' (Fim)	LHWs
	'Abingdon Ace' (D)	SGbt
	'AC Abby' (C)	WPhe
	'Ace Summer Emotions' (D)	SDeJ
	'Ace Summer Sunset' (D)	LAma
	'Addison June' (Ba)	ERCP LCro LHWs
	'Admiral Rawlings' (D)	CWGr
	'Advance US' (D) **new**	EBee LAma SDir
	'After Dusk' (D)	WPhe
	'Aggie White' (D)	NHal
	'Aimie' (D)	CWGr
	'Aitara Caress' (C)	SGbt
	'Aitara Diadem' (D)	LSou
	'Akita' (Misc)	CWGr ELan LAma LCro LOPS MBros SDir SGbt
	'Aladdin's Lamp' (WL)	NJRG
	'Alauna Clair-Obscur' (Fim)	ERCP LCro LHWs LOPS SDir
	'Albert Schweitzer' (S-c)	CWGr SGbt
	'Alden Regal' (C)	CWGr
	'Alfred Grille' (S-c)	CWGr LCro LOPS SDeJ SGbt
	'Alf's Mascot' (D)	NJRG WPhe
	'All Directions' (D) **new**	LCro
	'All Triumph' (S-c)	CWGr
	'Allan Sparkes' (WL) 🏆H3	CWGr MCot
	'Alloway Candy' (Misc)	ERCP
	'Alloway Cottage' (D)	CWGr NHal SGbt WPhe
	'Alltami Apollo' (S-c)	CWGr
	'Alltami Ruby' (S-c)	CWGr
	'Almand's Climax' (D) 🏆H3	CWGr SGbt
	'Alpen Pauline' (D)	LHWs
	'Alstergruss' (Col)	CWGr SDeJ
	'Alva's Doris' (S-c) 🏆H3	CWGr LAyl
	'Alva's Lilac' (D)	CWGr
	'Alva's Supreme' (D) 🏆H3	CWGr LAyl NHal WPhe
	'Amanda Jarvis' (C)	CWGr
	'Amante' (D)	LCro LOPS
	'Amaran Guard' (D)	CWGr
	'Amaran Relish' (D)	SGbt
I	'Amazone' (Sin/DwB)	CRos SPoG
	'Amber Banker' (C)	CWGr SGbt
	'Amberglow' (Ba)	CWGr
	'Ambition' (S-c)	CWGr ERCP LCro LHWs LOPS
	'Amelia's Surprise' (D)	CWGr
	'American Dawn' (D)	ERCP LCro LHWs LOPS WPhe
	'American Moon' (D)	LOPS
	AMERICAN PIE ('Vdtg26'^{PBR}) (Dark Angel Series) (Sin)	SDeJ
	'American Sun' (D)	ERCP
	'Amgard Coronet' (D)	CWGr
	'Amgard Delicate' (D)	CWGr SGbt
	'Amy Cave' (Ba)	NHal NJRG WPhe
	'Amy Madison' (S-c)	CWGr
I	'Andrea' (D) **new**	LCro
	'Andrea Clark' (D)	NHal WPhe
	'Andrea Lawson' (Ba)	WPhe
	'Andrew Mitchell' (S-c)	CWGr NHal
	'Andries' Amber' (S-c)	CWGr
	'Andries' Orange' (C)	LRHS
	'Andy Murray' (Sin)	CWGr
	'Angora' (Fim)	SGbt
	'Ann Breckenfelder' (Col) 🏆H3	CWGr ECtt NHal NJRG SMrm WPhe
I	'Anna' (Sin)	WPhe
	'Anne Cornelia' (D)	LHWs WPhe
	'Annika' (Sin)	SDeJ
	'Another Pet'	see *D.* 'Mystic Enchantment'
	'Antique'^{PBR} (Sin)	EHyd LRHS
	'Apache' (Fim)	CWGr ERCP SDeJ SGbt SPer
	'Apopa Sky' (Sin)	NJRG
	'Apple Blossom' (C)	SGbt
	'Apricot Desire' (WL)	ERCP
I	'Apricot Parfait' (Fim)	CWGr
	'April Heather' (Col) 🏆H3	NHal WPhe
	'Arabian Night' (D)	CAby CBcs CWCL CWGr EBee ECtt ELan EPfP ERCP ETod EWoo LAma LAyl LCro LOPS LRHS LSRN NLar SDeJ SDir SEND SGbt WCot WPhe WSpi
	'Arbatax' (D)	ERCP LAma SDir
	'Arc de Triomphe' (D)	CWGr
	'Ariko Zsaza' (D)	LHWs
	'Arlequin' (D)	SGbt
	'Arnhem' (D)	CWGr
	'Asahi Chohje' (Anem) 🏆H3	CWGr
	'Ashpire Fancy' (Col) **new**	NJRG
	'Ashpire Girl' (Col)	NJRG
	'Ashpire Julie' (Col)	NHal NJRG
	'Ashpire Lady' (Col)	NJRG
	'Ashpire Ruby' (Col) **new**	NJRG
	'Ashpire Sunglow' (Col) **new**	NJRG
	'Askwith Edna' (D)	NHal WPhe
	'Askwith Josephine' (D)	NHal WPhe
	'Askwith Minnie' (D)	LHWs NHal WPhe
	'Askwith Rodger' (D)	WPhe
	'Aspen' (S-c)	LHWs
	'Athalie' (C)	CWGr
	'Athelstan John' (C)	CWGr
I	'Atlanta' (D)	SGbt
	'Audacity' (D)	LAyl SGbt
	'Aurora's Kiss' (Ba)	ERCP NHal SGbt
	'Aurwen's Violet' (Pom)	CWGr NHal WPhe
	australis	CSpe EBee
	- B&SWJ 10389	WCru
I	'Autumn Fairy' (S-c)	SCob SDeJ
	'Avignon' (D)	SDeJ
	'Avoca Amanda' (D)	NHal WPhe
	'Avoca Cree' (S-c)	CWGr
	'B.J. Beauty' (D)	CWGr NHal NJRG WPhe
	'Babette' (S-c)	CWGr
	'Baby Royal' (D)	CWGr
	'Babylon' (D)	LRHS SGbt
§	'Babylon Brons' (D)	ERCP LHWs SGbt
	'Babylon Bronze'	see *D.* 'Babylon Brons'
	'Babylon Lila' (D)	LHWs SGbt
§	'Babylon Paars' (D)	ECtt LHWs LRHS SDeJ SGbt
	'Babylon Purple'	see *D.* 'Babylon Paars'
	'Babylon Rose' (D)	LRHS SGbt
	'Bacardi' (D)	CAvo ERCP LHWs
	'Badger Twinkle' (S-c)	WPhe
	'Baeten' (D) **new**	NHal
	'Balham' (Sin)	WCot
	'Ballego's Glory' (D)	CWGr SGbt
	'Balthasar' (D)	ERCP
	'Bantling' (Pom)	CWGr EBee ERCP LAma LHWs SDir SGbt
	'Barbara's Pastelle' (S-c)	NJRG SGbt
	'Barbara's Yellow' (S-c)	NJRG
	'Barbarry Aleks' (D)	WPhe
	'Barbarry Ball' (Ba)	CWGr
	'Barbarry Banker' (D)	LAyl
	'Barbarry Bluebird' (D)	SGbt
	'Barbarry d'Amour' (D)	NHal
	'Barbarry Drum' (D)	NHal
	'Barbarry Gem' (Ba)	CWGr
	'Barbarry Maverick' (D)	LHWs WPhe
	'Barbarry Monitor' (Ba)	SGbt
	'Barbarry Olympic' (Ba)	CWGr
	'Barbarry Patriot' (Ba)	NHal
	'Barbarry Pip' (D)	NHal WPhe
	'Barbarry Primrose Hall' (D)	NHal WPhe
	'Barbarry Rover' (D)	WPhe
	'Barbarry Vulcan' (D)	NHal WPhe

'Baret Joy' (S-c)	CWGr WPhe
'Bargaly Blush' (D)	NHal
'Barry Williams' (D)	SGbt
'Bayamo' (D)	LHWs
'Bayou'^{PBR} (Anem)	ERCP LAyl LCro LOPS LSou NHal NJRG SGbt WPhe
'Bednall Beauty' (Misc/DwB) 🏆^{H3}	ECtt ELan LRHS NJRG WSpi
'Belfloor' (D) **new**	ERCP LCro
'Bell Boy' (Ba)	SGbt
'Belle Moore' (D)	CWGr
'Belle of Barmera' (D)	ERCP
'Bell's Delight' (S-c)	CWGr
'Berger's Rekord' (S-c)	CWGr
'Berwick Wood' (D)	NHal SGbt WPhe
'Best Bett'	see *D.* MYSTIC SPIRIT
'Beth's Chaplet' (Sin)	WCot
'Betty Ann' (Pom)	CWGr
'Biddenham Strawberry' (D)	CWGr SGbt
'Bilbao'^{PBR} (D)	ETod SDeJ
'Bill Holmberg' (D)	CWGr SGbt WPhe
I 'Bingo' (D)	SGbt
'Birkenshaw Garden Friends' (Col)	NJRG
'Bishop of Auckland'^{PBR} (Misc)	CAby CCBP CKel CRos CWCL CWGN CWGr ECtt EHyd ELan EPfP ERCP ETod LAma LCro LOPS LRHS MGos NJRG NRHS SDeJ SDir SGbt WCot WHil
'Bishop of Cambridge' (Sin)	SDir
'Bishop of Canterbury'^{PBR} (P)	CKel CRos CWGr ECtt EHyd ELan EPfP ERCP EWoo LAma LCro LOPS LRHS LSou MGos NHal NRHS SDeJ SDir SGbt SPoG WPhe
'Bishop of Dover' (Sin)	CWGr ELan EPfP LAma LCro LOPS LRHS SDeJ SDir SGbt WPhe
'Bishop of Lancaster' (Misc)	NLar SDir
'Bishop of Leicester' (Misc)	CKel CWGr EHyd ELan EPfP EWoo GDam LAma LCro LOPS LRHS NLar NRHS SDeJ SDir SGbt SHar WPhe
'Bishop of Llandaff' (P) 🏆^{H3}	Widely available
'Bishop of Oxford' (Misc)	CAby CCht CKel CRos CWGr CWnw EPfP ERCP EWoo LAma LCro LOPS LRHS MGos NJRG NRHS SCoo SDeJ SDir SGbt SPoG WHoo WPhe
'Bishop of Salisbury' (D)	CWGr
'Bishop of York' (Misc)	CAby CKel CRos CWGr ECtt EHyd ELan EPfP EWoo LAma LAyl LCro LOPS LRHS LSou MBow MGos MSCN NGdn NLar NRHS SDeJ SGBe SGbt SPoG WHil WPhe
'Bishop Peter Price' (Sin)	CWGr
'Bishop's Children' (Sin)	WFar
'Black Beauty' (Sin)	CSpe
'Black Fire' (D)	CWGr ECtt
'Black Jack' (D)	ERCP ETod NHal NJRG WBor WPhe
'Black Monarch' (D)	CWGr NHal SGbt
'Black Narcissus' (C)	CWGr ERCP SGbt
I 'Black R. Jack' (Misc)	NJRG
'Black Spider' (S-c)	CWGr
'Black Touch' (Fim)	CWGr ERCP
'Blackberry Ripple' (S-c)	CWGr LAma SDir
'Blaze' (D)	CWGr
'Blithe Spirit' (D)	CWGr
'Bloodstone' (D)	CWGr SGbt
'Bloody Mary' (D)	ERCP
'Bloom's Graham' (S-c)	CWGr
'Bloom's Kenn' (D)	SGbt
'Blue Bell' (D)	CBod
'Blue Boy' (D)	ELan ERCP LCro LOPS LSou
'Blue Wish' (WL)	ERCP LCro LOPS NJRG
'Blueberry Hill' (Col)	LAyl

'Blues Bird' (D)	ERCP
'Bluesette' (D)	CWGr NBwr WPhe
'Bluetiful' (D)	ERCP
'Blyton Everest' (D)	NHal
'Blyton Golden Girl' (D)	LHWs NHal WPhe
'Blyton Lady in Red' (D)	LAyl NHal WPhe
'Blyton Romance' (D)	NHal
'Blyton Shiraz' (D)	WPhe
'Blyton Softer Gleam' (D) 🏆^{H3}	CWGr LAyl NHal NJRG SGbt WPhe
'Blyton Stella' (D)	NHal
'Bob Fitzjohn' (S-c)	CWGr
'Bob's Bonaventure' (D)	NHal WPhe
'Bohemian Spartacus' (D)	ERCP LCro LHWs
'Bonesta' (D)	CWGr
'Boogie Woogie' (Anem)	CWGr SDeJ WPhe
'Boom Boom Red' (Ba)	LHWs
'Boom Boom White' (Ba)	CWGr ERCP LCro
'Boom Boom Yellow' (Ba)	ERCP SDeJ
'Bora Bora' (S-c)	CWGr
'Border Princess' (C/DwB)	SGbt
'Boy Scout' (Ba)	CWGr
'Bracken Lorelei' (WL)	NJRG
'Brackenridge Ballerina' (WL)	CWGr NHal NJRG SGbt WPhe
'Brandaris' (S-c)	CWGr SGbt
'Brandon James' (D)	SDeJ
'Brandysnap' (D)	SGbt
'Brasilia' (Dalina Series) (D)	CWGr
BRAVEHEART ('Vdtg67'^{PBR}) (Dark Angel Series) (Sin)	LCro LOPS SDeJ
'Brian's Dream' (D)	LAyl NHal
'Bride's Bouquet' (Col)	ERCP LRHS
'Bridge View Aloha' (S-c) 🏆^{H3}	MBros SGbt
'Bright Diamond' (D)	SDeJ
'Bright Eyes' (Sin)	ERCP
'Brindisii' (Anem)	SDeJ
'Bristol Stripe' (D)	CWGr LAma
I 'Bronze Queen' (Ba)	LHWs
'Brookfield Rachel' (Ba)	CWGr
'Brookside Cheri' (C)	CWGr
'Brookside Snowball' (Ba)	CWGr
'Brown Sugar' (Ba)	LHWs WPhe
'Bryce B. Morrison' (D)	CWGr
'Bryn Terfel' (D)	NHal SGbt WPhe
'Bull's Pride' (D)	CWGr
'Buran' (D)	LHWs
'Burlesca' (Ba)	ERCP LCro LHWs
'Butch' (D)	CWGr
'Butterball' (D/DwB)	SDeJ
'Cabana Banana' (S-c) **new**	LHWs SDir
'Café au Lait' (D)	CAby CWGr ELan EPfP ERCP EWTr LAma LAyl LCro LHWs LOPS LRHS MBros MSCN NHal NJRG SDeJ SDir SGbt WPhe WSpi
'Cafe au Lait Rosé' (D)	ERCP LHWs
'Café au Lait Royal' (D) **new**	ERCP
'Caitlin's Joy' (Ba)	WPhe
'Calima' (D)	LHWs
'Calin' (WL)	CWGr
'Camano Passion' (S-c)	CWGr
'Cambridge' (D)	LHWs
I 'Cameo' (WL)	CWGr ELan LAyl NHal NJRG SGbt WPhe
campanulata	CWGr EShb WFar
'Canary Fubuki' (Fim)	CWGr ERCP SDeJ SGbt
'Cancun' (D)	LRHS
'Candy Cane CZ' (D)	CWGr
CANDY EYES	see *D.* 'Zone Ten'
'Caproz Pizzazz' (D)	LHWs
'Captain Bruce Bairnsfather' (C)	CWGr

	'Caribbean Fantasy' (D)	LHWs
	'Carlien' (WL)	WPhe
	'Carol Klein' (Sin/DwB)	CWGr
	'Carole Chamberlain' (Col)	NJRG
	'Carolina Moon' (D)	CWGr NHal SGbt
	'Carol's Spanish Dancer' (C)	NJRG WPhe
	'Carstone Firebox' (Col)	LAyl WPhe
	'Carstone Ruby' (D)	NHal
	'Carstone Suntan' (C)	CWGr
	'Carstone Valiant' (Ba)	NHal WPhe
	'Cartouche' (D)	CWGr ERCP
	'Catherine Deneuve' (Misc)	CWGN CWGr NJRG SGbt
	'Cha Cha' (S-c)	CWGr MBros SGbt
	'Charles Dickens' (Ba)	CWGr
	'Charlie Dimmock' (WL) ♀H3	CWGr NJRG SGbt WPhe
	'Charlie Kenwood' (D)	CWGr
	'Charlie Two' (D)	NHal WPhe
I	'Charlotte' (Sin)	CWGr
	'Charlotte Bateson' (Ba)	CWGr
	'Chat Noir' (S-c) ♀H3	CWGr ERCP LAma LAyl LCro LOPS LRHS SDir SGbt SHar WPhe WTre
	'Chatsworth Splendour' (Sin/DwB)	CWGr
	'Checkers' (D)	CAvo CWGr WPhe
	'Chee' (WL)	CWGr
	'Cheerio' (S-c)	ECtt EHyd LRHS NRHS
	'Cherish' (Misc)	LHWs
	'Cherokee Beauty' (D)	CWGr
	'Cherwell Goldcrest' (S-c)	CWGr NHal SGbt WPhe
	'Cherwell Linnet' (Ba)	NHal WPhe
	'Chilson's Pride' (D)	CWGr SGbt
	'Chiltern Herald' (S-c)	CWGr
	'Chiltern Sylvia' (S-c)	CWGr
	'Chimacum Davi' (Ba)	LHWs
	'Chimacum Topaz' (S-c)	CWGr
	'Chimborazo' (Col)	CWGr EWes LAyl SGbt
	'Chloe's Keene' (S-c)	CWGr
	'Christine' (D)	CWGr EPfP SGbt
	'Christmas Carol' (Col)	CWGr ECtt NJRG WPhe
	'Christmas Star' (Col)	CWGr
	'Christopher Nickerson' (S-c)	CWGr SGbt
	'Christopher Taylor' (WL)	NHal SGbt SHar WPhe
	'City of Alkmaar' (C)	LRHS
	'City of Leiden' (S-c)	LCro LOPS
	'Clair de Lune' (Col) ♀H3	ECtt LRHS NHal NJRG SGbt WCot WPhe WSpi
	'Claire Louise Downting' (D)	WPhe
I	'Clarence' (WL) **new**	NJRG
	'Clarion' (S-c)	NRHS
I	'Clarion' (Sin)	CWGr WPhe
	'Classic A.1' (C)	CWGr
	'Classic Rosamunde'^{PBR} (Misc) ♀H3	NHal
§	'Classic Swanlake'^{PBR} (Misc)	CWGr ERCP LCro NJRG
	'Clayt's Candy' (S-c)	WPhe
	'Clearview Audrey' (S-c)	NHal WPhe
	'Clearview Cameron' (C) **new**	NHal
	'Clearview Daniel' (Ba) ♀H3	NHal
	'Clearview Debby' (D)	WPhe
	'Clearview Dorothy' (S-c)	WPhe
	'Clearview Edie' (DblO)	NHal WPhe
	'Clearview Louise' (S-c)	NHal WPhe
	'Clearview Sundance' (C)	NHal WPhe
	'Clearview Tammy' (S-c)	NHal WPhe
	'Cleo Laine' (S-c)	CWGr NHal
	coccinea	CSpe EShb MCot SGbt SHar SMHy WPGP
	- NJM 05.072	WPGP
	- hybrids	WHil
	- var. ***palmeri***	CAvo CSpe WPGP
	'Cocktail' (S-c)	CWGr
	'Color Spectacle' (S-c)	CWGr
	'Contessa' (D)	SDeJ
	'Contraste' (Misc)	ERCP
	'Coral Jupiter' (S-c)	CWGr NHal WPhe
	'Coral Strand' (D)	CWGr
	'Cornel' (Ba)	CWGr ERCP NHal NJRG SGbt WPhe
	'Cornel Brons' (Ba)	ERCP WPhe
	'Cornish Ruby' (Sin)	CWnw EBee EPfP
I	'Corona' (S-c/DwB)	SDeJ
	'Coronella' (D)	SGbt
	'Corson George' (S-c)	NHal
	'Corson Gold' (S-c)	NHal
	'Cortez Silver' (D)	CWGr
	'Country Boy' (S-c)	CWGr
	'Coupe de Soleil' (D)	CWGr
	'Craigowan' (S-c)	WPhe
	'Crazy Legs' (DblO)	SGbt
	'Crazy Love' (D)	CWGr LCro LOPS MBros
	'Cream Diane' (D)	NHal
	'Cream Elegans' (S-c)	CWGr
	'Cream Klankstad' (C)	CWGr
	'Cream Linda' (D)	CWGr
	'Cream Moonlight' (S-c)	NHal NJRG SGbt
	'Cream Ruskin Diane' (D)	WPhe
	'Crème de Cassis' (D)	CAvo CWGr EPfP ERCP ETod LCro LHWs LOPS NHal WPhe
	'Crème de Cognac' (D)	ERCP LHWs
	'Crève Coeur' (D)	LHWs
	'Crichton Cherry' (D)	CWGr
	'Crossfield Anne' (D)	CWGr
	'Croydon Superior' (D)	SGbt
	'Cryfield Harmony' (Ba)	WPhe
	'Cryfield Keene' (S-c)	CWGr
	'Crystal Ann' (S-c)	CWGr
	'Culdrose' (D)	SGbt
	'Curiosity' (Col)	NJRG
	'Currant Cream' (Ba)	SGbt
	cuspidata	EBee
	'Czar Willo' (Pom)	CWGr
	(Dahlegria Series) DAHLEGRIA BICOLORE ('Dahlgr128'^{PBR}) (Sin) **new**	ERCP
	- DAHLEGRIA WHITE ('Dahlgr95'^{PBR}) (Sin)	ERCP
	DAHLIETTA ISABELLE	see *D.* 'Isabella'
	DAHLIETTA JENNY	see *D.* 'Jenny'
	'Daisy Duke' (D)	ERCP LHWs
	DALAYA DEVI ('Kledh13037')	WHlf
	DALAYA SHIVA ('Kledh13033'^{PBR})	WHlf
	'Daleko Jupiter' (S-c)	CWGr NHal WPhe
	'Daleko Tangerine' (D)	CWGr
	DALINA COZUMEL (Dalina Maxi Series) (D/DwB)	LRHS
	'Dame Deidre' (S-c)	CWGr
	'Dana Dream' (S-c)	CWGr
	'Dana Iris' (S-c)	CWGr
	'Dana Sunset' (C)	CWGr
	'Dana US' (D)	LHWs
I	'Dandy' (Col)	SVic
	'Daniel's Favourite' (S-c) **new**	LAma
	'Danjo Doc' (D)	SGbt
	'Dannevirke' (Sin)	CWGr
	'Danum Hero' (D)	CWGr
	'Danum Meteor' (S-c)	CWGr
	'Danum Rebel' (S-c)	CWGr
	'Danum Rhoda' (D)	CWGr

	'Danum Torch' (Col)	CWGr ECtt SGbt
	'Dao Stan' (Sin)	CWGr
	'Dark Butterfly' (D)	CWCL CWGr ERCP ETod LCro LOPS
	'Dark Desire' (Sin/DwB)	ERCP SGBe
	'Dark Fubuki' (Fim)	ERCP LHWs
§	'Dark Side of the Sun'[PBR] (Sin)	CRos EHyd EPfP LRHS LSou NRHS SCoo SOrN SPoG WPhe
	'Dark Spirit' (D)	ECtt ERCP LAma LHWs LRHS SDeJ SGbt WPhe
	'Darkarin' (Misc)	ERCP
	'Dave's Choice' (Ba)	WPhe
	'David Digweed' (D)	SGbt
	'David Howard' (D) ♀H3	CAby CKel CWGr CWnw EAri ECtt EHyd ELan EPfP ERCP ETod EWoo LAyl LCro LOPS LRHS LSou NHal NJRG NRHS SCob SGbt SMrm SOrN SPer SWvt WCot WFar WPhe WSpi
	'David Wright' (S-c)	CWGr
	'David's Choice' (D)	CWGr
	'Dawn Sky' (D)	LAyl
	'Dazzling Magic' (D) **new**	EBee LAma
	'Dazzling Sun' (D)	LRHS
	'Debora Renae' (WL)	ERCP
	'Deborah's Kiwi' (C)	NHal SGbt
	'Debra Anne Craven' (S-c)	NHal WPhe
	'Decorette' (D/DwB)	SGbt
	'Deepest Yellow' (Ba)	SDeJ SGbt
	'De-la-Haye' (S-c)	NHal
	'Destiny's Teachers' (SinO) **new**	ERCP
	'Deuil du Roi Albert' (D)	CWGr
	'Devon Elegance' (S-c)	CWGr
	DIABLO MIXED (Misc/DwB)	MBros
	'Diamond Wedding' (D)	SGbt
	'Diamond Years' (D)	SGbt
	'Diana Gregory' (Pom)	CWGr SGbt
	'Diana's Memory' (D)	LCro LHWs LOPS
	'Dikara Jodie' (D)	NHal WPhe
	'Dikara Superb' (D)	LAyl NHal NJRG
	'Dilys Ayling' (Col)	NHal NJRG WPhe
	'Dionne' (Misc)	WPhe
I	'Disneyland' (Col)	SGbt
	dissecta	EBee
	'Diva US' (D)	ERCP SDeJ
	'Doctor Arnett' (S-c)	CWGr
	'Doctor Caroline Rabbit' (D)	SGbt
	'Doctor John Grainger' (D)	LRHS
	'Doctor P.H. Riedl' (D)	LHWs
	'Don Hill' (Col) ♀H3	NJRG WPhe
	'Doris Day' (C)	CWGr NHal SGbt
	'Doris Muldoon' (WL)	CWGr
	'Doris Rollins' (C)	CWGr
	'Dorothy Rose' (D)	WPhe
	'Dottie D.' (Ba)	CWGr
	'Double Dream Fantasy' (Dreamy Series) (Misc)	EHyd EPfP LRHS NRHS
	'Double Shine' (D)	ERCP LHWs
	'Downham Royal' (Ba)	CWGr ERCP LCro LOPS
	DRAGON BALL ('Vdtg31'[PBR]) (Dark Angel Series) (Sin)	SDeJ
	'Dream Seeker' (Col)	WPhe
	(Dreamy Series) DREAMY EYES (Misc)	CWGr LRHS
	- DREAMY FANTASY (Misc)	CWGr ELan LRHS SGBe
	- DREAMY KISS (P)	EHyd LRHS NRHS SGBe
	- DREAMY LIPS (P)	LRHS
	- DREAMY MOONLIGHT (Sin)	EHyd LRHS
	- DREAMY NIGHTS (Misc)	EHyd LRHS MBNS NRHS SGBe
	'Duet' (D)	CWGr ELan SGbt
	'Dusky Harmony' (WL)	SGbt
	'Dutch Carnaval' (D)	CWGr
	'Dutch Explosion' (S-c)	ELan
	'Dynamite' (D)	LHWs
	'Early Harvest' (D)	SGbt
	'East Anglian' (D)	CWGr
	'Eastwood Moonlight' (S-c)	CWGr NHal SGbt WPhe
	'Edge of Joy' (D)	CWnw LAma LCro LOPS SDir SRms
	'Edinburgh' (D)	CDoC CWGr EBee ERCP LAma NHal SDeJ SDir SGbt WPhe
	'Edith Jones' (Col)	CWGr NHal NJRG
	'Edith Mueller' (Pom)	CWGr
	'Edmund' (Sin)	WCot
	'Edna C.' (D)	CWGr
	'Edwin's Sunset' (WL) ♀H3	WPhe
	'Eileen Denny' (S-c)	CWGr
	'El Paso' (D)	CWGr LHWs MBros SDeJ
	'Elaine Beedle' (D)	CWGr
	'Electric Flash' (S-c) **new**	LAma
	'Elga-Bergerhoff' (C)	ERCP
	'Elgico Leanne' (C)	CWGr SGbt
	'Elizabeth Macnamara' (D)	CWGr
	'Ella Britton' (D)	EHyd LRHS NRHS WGwG
	'Ellen Huston' (Misc/DwB) ♀H3	CKel ECtt ERCP SGbt
I	'Elly' (WL)	WPhe
	'Elma E.' (D)	CWGr LHWs NHal WPhe
	'Elmbrook Rebel' (S-c)	CWGr
I	'Elsi' (D)	LHWs
I	'Embrace' (C)	WPhe
	'Emma's Coronet' (D)	WPhe
	'Emmas Ippenburg' (D) **new**	ERCP
	'Emmaus' (Fim)	CWGr
	'Emmie Lou' (D)	CWGr
	'Emory Paul' (D)	CWGr ERCP
I	'Encore' (Fim)	CWGr ERCP
	'Engelhardts Matador' (D)	CWnw ECtt ERCP LHWs LRHS NJRG SGbt WCot
I	'Esther' (Col)	SDeJ
	'Esther Chamberlain' (Col)	NJRG
	'Etheral' (Sin)	CWGr
	'Eunice Arrigo' (S-c)	CWGr
I	'Eurydice' (Fim)	CWGr
	'Evanah' (D)	ERCP
	'Eveline' (D)	CAby ERCP LCro LOPS SDeJ SGbt
	'Evelyn Rumbold' (D)	CWGr SGbt
	'Evelyn Taylor' (S-c)	NJRG
I	'Evita' (Anem)	NJRG
	excelsa (B)	CHll NJRG
	- B&SWJ 10238	ESwi
	- 'Penelope Sky' (Sin)	ESwi WCru
	'Excentrique' (Misc)	CWGr ERCP LHWs NJRG
	'Exotic Dwarf' (Sin/Lil) ♀H3	NJRG
	'Explosion' (S-c)	CWGr LRHS
	'Eye Candy' (Sin)	LRHS NJRG NRHS
	'Fabula' (Col)	LCro
	'Fairway Pilot' (D)	CWGr NHal WPhe
	'Fairway Spur' (D)	CWGr LHWs NHal WPhe
	'Fairy Queen' (C)	CWGr SGbt
§	'Famoso' (Col)	ERCP LCro
	'Fantastico' (Col)	CAvo LCro SDir
	'Fascination' (P) ♀H3	CAby CCht CWGr ECtt EHyd ERCP LAyl LRHS LSRN MCot MSCN NLar NRHS SCob SCoo SDeJ SGbt SOrN WHoo WSpi
	'Fashion Monger' (Col)	CAby ECtt ERCP LCro NHal NJRG SDir SGbt WPhe
	'Fata Morgana' (Anem)	NJRG SGbt
	'Fatima' (Pom)	LHWs
	'Feline Yvonne' (D) **new**	LCro LHWs
	'Ferncliff Illusion' (D)	CWGr ERCP SGbt
	'Ferncliff Inspiration' (D)	LHWs

	'Festivo' (Col)	CWGr
	'Fidalgo Blacky' (D)	CWGr
	'Fidalgo Climax' (Fim)	CWGr
	'Fidalgo Supreme' (D)	LAyl
I	'Fiesta' (Pom)	SDeJ
	Figaro Series (Misc/DwB)	MBros SCob
	'Figurine' (WL) 🏆H3	NJRG SHar
	'Fille du Diable' (S-c)	SGbt
	'Finchcocks' (WL) 🏆H3	CWGr LAyl
	'Fire and Ice' (Misc)	CWGr SDeJ
	'Fire Mountain' (D)	LAyl NHal NJRG WPhe
	'Firebird' (S-c)	see *D.* 'Vuurvogel'
	'Firebrand' ambig. (S-c)	SGbt
	'Firepot' (D)	ERCP LAma LRHS SGbt
	'First Lady' (D)	CWGr
	'Fleur'	see *D.* 'Fleurel'
§	'Fleurel' PBR (Fim)	ERCP EWTr LRHS MSCN SDeJ
	'Floorinoor' (Anem)	ERCP LCro LOPS SGbt WPhe
	'Fontmell Kaz' (Col)	NJRG SGbt
	'Formby Art' (D)	LAyl WPhe
	'Formby Supreme' (D)	SGbt
	'Forrestal' (S-c)	CWGr
I	'Forty Niner' (WL)	WPhe
	'Frank Heritage' (S-c)	CWGr
	'Frank Lovell' (S-c)	CWGr
	'Franz Kafka' (Pom)	CWGr ERCP LAma MBros NHal NJRG SDeJ SDir WPhe
	'Fred Wallace' (C)	CWGr
	'Freelancer' (C)	SGbt
§	'Freya's Paso Doble' (Anem) 🏆H3	CWGr EPfP LAyl SGbt WPhe
	'Freya's Thalia' (Sin/Lil)	CWGr
I	'Friendship' (C)	CWGr
	'Frigoulet' (C)	CWGr SGbt
	'Fringed Star' (S-c)	CWGr
	'Fusion' (D) 🏆H3	SGbt SHar WCot
	'Fuzzy Wuzzy' (D)	LAma LCro LHWs
	'G.H. Lammerse' (D)	ERCP
	'G.I. Joe' (D)	SGbt
	(Gallery Series) 'Gallery Art Deco' PBR (D) 🏆H3	CRos CWGr ERCP LRHS NHal NRHS SGbt WPhe
	- 'Gallery Art Fair' PBR (D) 🏆H3	ERCP LCro LOPS NLar SDeJ
	- 'Gallery Art Nouveau' PBR (D) 🏆H3	CWGr ERCP LRHS MBNS NHal NRHS SDeJ WFar WPhe
	- 'Gallery Bellini' PBR (D)	CRos EHyd LRHS NRHS SDeJ
	- 'Gallery Cézanne' PBR (D)	CWGr SDeJ SGbt
	- 'Gallery La Tour' PBR (D) 🏆H3	SDeJ
	- 'Gallery Leonardo' PBR (D) 🏆H3	CWGr LCro LOPS SDeJ
	- 'Gallery Pablo' PBR (D) 🏆H3	CWGr LSou SGbt
	- 'Gallery Pinto' PBR (D)	CRos CWGr EHyd LRHS MBNS NRHS
	- 'Gallery Rembrandt' PBR (D) 🏆H3	LCro LOPS
	- 'Gallery Renoir' PBR (D) 🏆H3	CWGr
	- 'Gallery Rivera' PBR (D)	LRHS MBNS NLar NRHS SDeJ
	- 'Gallery Salvador' PBR (D)	SGbt
	- 'Gallery Singer' PBR (D)	SDeJ
	- 'Gallery Valentin' PBR (D)	CRos EHyd LRHS MBNS NRHS WFar
	- 'Gallery Vermeer' PBR (D)	SGbt
	- 'Gallery Vincent' PBR (D) 🏆H3	CWGr EShb
	'Gardaia' (Anem)	CWGr
	'Garden Miracle' (D)	NJRG
	'Garden Princess' (C/DwB)	SGbt
	'Garden Time' (WL) **new**	ERCP
	'Garden Wonder' (D)	SDeJ
	'Gargantuan' (S-c)	CWGr
	GATESHEAD FESTIVAL	see *D.* 'Peach Melba'
	'Gay Triumph' (S-c)	CWGr
	'Geerlings Camelea' (Pom)	WPhe
	'Geerlings Cupido' (WL)	SGbt
	'Geerlings Daydream' (D)	NJRG WPhe
	'Geerlings Indian Summer' (S-c)	NHal
§	'Geerlings Sorbet' (S-c)	CAby MBros NHal SGbt WPhe
	'Gelber Vulkan' (S-c)	SGbt
	'Gemma Darling' (D)	CWGr
	'Genova' (Ba)	ERCP LHWs LRHS SDeJ SGbt WPhe
	'Gerald Grace' (S-c)	CWGr
	'Geri Scott' (S-c)	ERCP LHWs WPhe
I	'Geronimo' (S-c)	CWGr
	'Gerrie Hoek' (WL)	CWGr EHyd ERCP LRHS NJRG NRHS SDeJ SGbt WGwG WPhe WSpi
	'Gilwood Terry G' (C)	WPhe
	'Ginger Snap' (WL)	LHWs
	'Gipsy Night' (Ba)	ERCP LCro SDeJ
	'Giraffe' (DblO)	SGbt
	'Gitts Attention' (Fim)	LHWs
	'Gitty Up' (Anem)	WPhe
	'Glen Gharry' (Col)	CWGr
	'Glorie van Heemstede' (WL) 🏆H3	CWGr ERCP LAyl LCro LOPS NHal NJRG SDeJ SGbt WPhe
	'Glorie van Naardwijk' (D)	CWGr
	'Glorie van Noordwijk' (S-c)	ERCP LCro SDeJ SDir SGbt
	'Glow Orange' (Ba)	CWGr
	'Go American' (D)	CWGr NHal WPhe
	'Gold Crown' (S-c)	SDeJ
	GOLDALIA ROSE ('Goalia Rossa' PBR) (Col)	CRos
	GOLDALIA SCARLET ('Goalia Scarl' PBR) (Col)	CRos
	'Golden Charmer' (S-c)	CWGr
I	'Golden Emblem' (D)	ECtt SDeJ
	'Golden Scepter' (D)	CWGr MBros SDeJ SGbt SPer
	'Golden Symbol' (S-c)	CWGr
	'Goldener Vulkan' (S-c)	WPhe
	'Goldie Gull' (Anem)	NJRG
	'Good Earth' (C)	CWGr SDeJ
	'Gor Blimey' (Col)	CWGr
I	'Grace Wood' (S-c) **new**	NHal
	'Gracie S' (C)	NJRG
	'Grand Finale' (S-c)	SDeJ
	'Grand Prix' (D)	CWGr LAma SDeJ SGbt
	'Great Hercules' (D)	ERCP LCro LHWs
	'Great Silence' (D)	ERCP LHWs WBor
	'Greenway Zoe' (S-c)	NHal
	'Grenadier' (D) 🏆H3	CWGr ECtt ERCP LRHS NJRG SGbt WCot
	'Grenidor Pastelle' (S-c)	CWGr NHal NJRG WPhe
	'Groovy' (D)	WPhe
	'Gryson's Yellow Spider' (C) 🏆H3	WPhe
	'Gun Yuu' (D)	CWGr
	'Gurtla Twilight' (Pom)	NHal NJRG WPhe
	'Gwyneth' (WL)	NHal NJRG WPhe
	'Gypsy Girl' (D)	SGbt
	'Hadrian's Delight' (S-c) **new**	NHal
	'Hadrian's Glowing Embers' (Sin/DwB) **new**	NHal
	'Hadrian's Midnight' (Sin)	LAyl NHal WPhe
	'Hadrian's Sunlight' (Sin) 🏆H3	NHal
	'Hadrian's Sunset' (Sin)	NHal
	'Hallmark' (Pom)	NHal NJRG
	'Hamari Accord' (S-c) 🏆H3	LAyl
	'Hamari Bride' (S-c) 🏆H3	CWGr
	'Hamari Girl' (D)	CWGr SGbt
	'Hamari Gold' (D) 🏆H3	NHal SGbt WPhe
	'Hamari Rosé' (Ba) 🏆H3	CWGr NHal SGbt SHar

	'Hamari Sunshine' (D)	SGbt
	'Hamilton Lillian' (D) ♀H3	CWGr
	'Hanny' (WL)	WPhe
	'Hapet Blue Eyes' (D)	LHWs WPhe
	'Hapet Champagne' (Fim) **new**	NHal
	'Hapet Charmant' (WL)	NJRG
	'Hapet Daydream' (Ba) **new**	ERCP
	'Hapet Duo' (D)	WPhe
	'Hapet P' (Fim)	WPhe
	'Hapet Pearl' (Ba)	WPhe
	'Hapet Skyline' (S-c)	WPhe
	'Hapet Vinete' (Pom)	WPhe
	'Happy Butterfly' (D)	LHWs
	HAPPY DAYS BICO ('Hdbic34'PBR) (Sin) **new**	MBros
	HAPPY DAYS CREAM ('Hdw79'PBR) (Sin)	LRHS
	HAPPY DAYS LEMON ('Hdle105'PBR) (Sin)	ERCP
	HAPPY DAYS NEON ('Hdne33'PBR) (Sin)	LRHS
	HAPPY DAYS PINK ('Hdpi117'PBR) (Sin) ♀H3	LRHS WFar
	HAPPY DAYS PURPLE ('Hdpu165'PBR) (Sin) ♀H3	LRHS MPri WTyc
	'Happy Go Lucky' (D)	SDeJ
	'Happy Halloween' (D)	CWGr ERCP
	(Happy Single Series) HAPPY SINGLE DATE ('HS Date'PBR) (Sin)	CAvo CWGr ERCP SDeJ WHil
	- HAPPY SINGLE FIRST LOVE ('HS First Love'PBR) (Sin)	ERCP SDeJ
	- HAPPY SINGLE FLAME ('HS Flame'PBR) (Sin) ♀H3	CAvo CWGr ERCP LAma LRHS NJRG WHil
	- HAPPY SINGLE JULIET ('HS Juliet'PBR) (Sin)	CWGr ERCP SDeJ
	- HAPPY SINGLE PARTY ('HS Party'PBR) (Sin)	CWGr SDeJ
	- HAPPY SINGLE PRINCESS ('HS Princess'PBR) (Sin) ♀H3	CWGr ERCP LRHS SDeJ
	- HAPPY SINGLE ROMEO ('HS Romeo'PBR) (Sin)	CWGr LRHS SDeJ WFar WPhe
	- HAPPY SINGLE WINK ('HS Wink'PBR) (Sin) ♀H3	CAvo CWGr ERCP LAma LCro LOPS SDeJ SDir WPhe
	'Haresbrook' (Sin)	SHar WSpi
	'Harriet G' (WL)	NJRG
	'Hartenaas' (Col/DwB)	LHWs SDeJ
	'Harvest' (Fim)	CWGr
§	'Harvest Samantha' (Sin/Lil) ♀H3	NHal
	'Hawaiian Dreams'PBR (Sin)	EHyd EPfP LRHS WPhe
	'Hayley Jayne' (C)	CWGr LSou NJRG SGbt
	'Heather Huston' (D)	CWGr
	'Heather Linford' (Fim)	CWGr
I	'Henriette' (S-c)	CWGr WPhe
	'Herbert Smith' (S-c)	CWGr
	'Hexton Copper' (Ba)	CWGr SGbt
	'Higherfield Champion' (S-c)	CWGr
	'Hildepuppe' (Pom)	CWGr
	'Hillcrest Amour' (D)	CWGr SGbt
	'Hillcrest Aura' (D)	WPhe
	'Hillcrest Camelot' (S-c)	CWGr
	'Hillcrest Candy' (S-c) ♀H3	CWGr NHal SGbt WPhe
	'Hillcrest Contessa' (Ba)	CWGr
	'Hillcrest Delight' (D)	NHal SGbt
	'Hillcrest Duncan Edwards' (S-c)	WPhe
	'Hillcrest Fiesta' (S-c)	CWGr
	'Hillcrest Firecrest' (D)	LAyl NHal
	'Hillcrest Jake' (S-c)	WPhe
	'Hillcrest Jersie' (S-c)	NHal NJRG WPhe
	'Hillcrest Jessica J' (C)	WPhe
	'Hillcrest Jonathan' (D)	NHal
	'Hillcrest Kismet' (D)	NHal NJRG
	'Hillcrest Matt' (D)	WPhe
	'Hillcrest Regal' (Col) ♀H3	SGbt
	'Hillcrest Royal' (C) ♀H3	ELan LAyl NHal SGbt WPhe
	'Hillcrest Suffusion' (D)	NJRG WPhe
	'Holland Festival' (D)	CWGr LAma LHWs SGbt
	'Hollyhill Big Pink' (S-c)	SGbt
	'Hollyhill Calico' (Ba)	LAma LHWs
	'Hollyhill Lemon Ice' (P)	EPfP LHWs
	'Hollyhill Spiderwoman' (Misc)	CAby CWGr EPfP ERCP ETod
	'Homey' (D) **new**	ERCP
	'Honey' (Anem/DwB)	CWGr SDeJ
	'Honeypot' (Ba)	SGbt
	'Honka' (SinO) ♀H3	CWGr ECtt EWoo LAyl LCro LOPS LRHS NHal NJRG SDeJ WCot WHil WPhe
	'Honka Black' (SinO)	LAma SDir
	'Honka Fragile' (SinO)	CAby CSpe CWnw ERCP EWoo LCro LOPS SDeJ
	'Honka Orange' (SinO)	ERCP NJRG
	'Honka Pink' (SinO)	EWoo WPhe
	'Honka Pink Edge' (SinO)	NJRG
	'Honka Red' (SinO)	CAby EWoo LCro LOPS SDeJ WHil
	'Honka Rose' (SinO)	ERCP NJRG SDeJ WPhe
	'Honka Surprise' (SinO)	CAby EBee ECtt ERCP LCro NJRG SDeJ WCot
	'Honor Francis' (Misc)	WCot
	'Hootenanny - Swan Island' (Col) ♀H3	WPhe
	'Hot Chocolate' (D)	SGbt
	'Hy Clown' (D)	CWGr
	'Hy Trio' (S-c) **new**	CAvo
	'Ian Hislop' (Sin)	CWGr
	'Ice Crystal' (Fim)	LCro LSou
	'Ice Cube' (D)	SDeJ
	'Ice Queen' (WL)	CWGr
	'Icoon'PBR (D)	LRHS
	'Ida Gayer' (D)	CWGr
I	'Idylle' (S-c)	CWGr
	'Ieda' (Sin)	NJRG
	'I-lyke-it' (S-c)	CWGr
	imperialis (B)	CDTJ CHll CWGr EAri ERCP ESwi EWes EWoo LEdu LRHS NJRG SChr SDir SGbt WFar
	- B&SWJ 8997	WCru
	- B&SWJ 14341	WCru
	- 'Alba' (B)	CWGr EAri SDir
	- white-flowered (B)	ERCP
	aff. ***imperialis***	CWGr LHWs XLum
	'Impression Famosa'	see *D.* 'Famoso'
	'Inca' (Anem)	SDeJ
	'Inca Dambuster' (S-c)	SGbt WPhe
	'Independence' (D)	SGbt
	'Inglebrook Jill' (Col)	CWGr
	'Inland Dynasty' (S-c)	CWGr
	'Innocent Silence' (D) **new**	EWoo
	'Inn's Gerrie Hoek' (D)	CWGr
	'Irish Glow' (Pom)	LAyl WPhe
	'Irish Pinwheel' (Misc)	ERCP LHWs
§	'Isabella' (Dahlietta Surprise Series) (DwB)	LHWs
	'Isadora' (D)	WPhe
	'Islander' (D)	CWGr ERCP LHWs
	'Ivanetti' (Ba)	CWGr NHal SGbt WPhe

	'Ivor's Rhonda' (Pom)	NHal
	'J.R.G.' (Misc) ♀H3	NJRG
	'Jack Hood' (D)	SGbt
	'Jaldec Jerry' (S-c)	CWGr
	'Jamaica' (Dalina Series) (D)	CWGr SGbt
	'Jan van Schaffelaar' (Pom)	CAvo SDeJ
	'Janal Amy' (S-c)	CWGr NHal SGbt WPhe
	'Jane Horton' (Col)	CWGr SGbt
	'Javier G' (WL)	LHWs
	'Jazzy' (Col)	CWGr
	'Jean Ellen' (Fim)	WPhe
	'Jean Fairs' (WL) ♀H3	CWGr SGbt
	'Jean Melville' (D)	CWGr
	'Jean Shaw' (D)	NHal
I	'Jennie' (Fim)	CWGr
§	'Jenny' (Dahlietta Select Series) (Misc)	SGbt
	'Jescot Julie' (DblO)	ERCP LAyl LCro LOPS NJRG
	'Jescot Lingold' (D)	SGbt
	'Jescot Redun' (D)	CWGr
I	'Jessica' (S-c)	WPhe
	'Jessie G' (Ba)	CWGr ERCP
	'Jet' (S-c)	CWGr
	'Jill Doc' (D)	CWGr
	'Jim Branigan' (S-c)	NHal
	'Jive' (Anem)	ELan LCro SDeJ
	'Joan Walker' (D)	WPhe
	'Jocondo' (D)	CWGr ERCP NHal SGbt WPhe
	'Jodie Wilkinson' (Ba) ♀H3	NHal WPhe
	'Joe Swift' (Sin)	CWGr
	'John Friend' (D)	CWGr
	'John Hill' (D)	NHal
	'John Street' (WL)	WSpi
	'Johnnie Ellis' (S-c)	CWGr
	'Jolly Good' (Sin)	WPhe
	'Jomanda' (Ba) ♀H3	CWGr ERCP NHal NJRG SGbt WPhe
	'José Maria'	WPhe
	'Josie Gott' (Ba) ♀H3	NJRG SGbt WPhe
	'Josudi Andromeda' (C)	NHal
	'Josudi Aurora' (C)	NHal
	'Josudi Hercules' (S-c)	NHal WPhe
	'Josudi Neptune' (S-c)	NHal
	'Josudi Pluto' (S-c) **new**	NHal
	'Josudi Polaris' (C)	NHal
	'Jowey Arenda' (Ba)	LHWs
	'Jowey Chantal' (D)	LHWs
	'Jowey Frambo' (Ba)	ERCP LHWs
	'Jowey Joshua' (Ba)	LHWs
	'Jowey Linda' (Ba)	ERCP
	'Jowey Marilyn' (Misc)	LHWs
	'Jowey Mirella' (Ba)	ERCP LCro LHWs
	'Jowey Nicky' (D) **new**	ERCP
	'Jowey Winnie' (Ba)	ERCP LCro
	'Joy Donaldson' (C)	CWGr
	'Joyce Green' (S-c)	SGbt
	'Joyful Investment' (Col)	WPhe
	'JS Dorothy Rose' (D)	NHal
	'Jubilee Boy' (S-c) **new**	NHal
	'Jules Dyson' (Misc)	SDys
	'Julie One' (DblO)	CWGr ECtt SGbt
	'Julie's Delight' (S-c)	CWGr
	'Jura' (S-c)	CWGr
	'Kaga-komachi' (D)	LRHS NRHS
	'Karen G' (Col)	NJRG
	'Karenglen' (D) ♀H3	NHal SGbt
	'Kari Quill' (C)	CWGr
	'Karma Amanda'PBR (D)	CWGr
	'Karma Amora'PBR (D)	LAma LHWs LRHS
	'Karma Bon Bini'PBR (C)	CAby LRHS LSou SGbt
	'Karma Choc'PBR (D) ♀H3	CAby CAvo CBod CSpe CWGr CWnw EBee EHyd EPfP ERCP EWes EWoo LCro LHWs LOPS LRHS NRHS SDir SEND SGbt SOrN SPer WBor WCot WFar WHoo WPhe
	'Karma Corona'PBR (C)	CWGr ETod LHWs SGbt
	'Karma Fuchsiana' (D)	CWGr ERCP ETod LCro LOPS SGbt WPhe
	'Karma Gold'PBR (D)	CBod LHWs SOrN
	'Karma Irene'PBR (D)	CWGr ERCP LHWs
	'Karma Lagoon'PBR (D)	CWGr ERCP LHWs LRHS SGbt WPhe
	'Karma Maarten Zwaan'PBR (WL)	CAvo CWGr ERCP
	'Karma Naomi'PBR (D)	CAvo ERCP LHWs SGbt
	'Karma Pink Corona'PBR (C)	LCro LOPS
	'Karma Prospero'PBR (D)	CBod ERCP LCro LOPS NJRG SOrN
	'Karma Red Corona'PBR (C)	LRHS SDeJ SGbt
	'Karma Sangria'PBR (C)	CWGr LCro LHWs LOPS SDeJ SGbt
	'Karma Serena'PBR (D)	LHWs LRHS SDeJ
	'Karma Yin Yang' (D)	CWGr LRHS SGbt
	'Karras 150' (S-c)	CWGr
	'Kasasagi' (Pom)	ERCP
	'Kate Mountjoy' (Col)	SGbt
	'Kate's Dream' (D)	WPhe
	'Kayleigh Spiller' (Col)	SGbt
	'Keith's Choice' (D)	SGbt WPhe
	'Kelsey Annie Joy' (Col)	ERCP NJRG SDir WPhe
	'Kelvin Floodlight' (D)	SDeJ SDir SGbt
	'Kennemerland' (S-c)	CWGr LCro SDeJ SGbt
	'Kenora Challenger' (S-c)	CWGr NHal NJRG SGbt WPhe
	'Kenora Jubilee' (S-c)	SGbt WPhe
	'Kenora Lisa' (D)	CWGr
	'Kenora Macop-B' (Fim)	CWGr ECtt ERCP LAyl NHal WPhe
	'Kenora Ontario' (S-c)	CWGr
	'Kenora Sunset' (S-c) ♀H3	CWGr NHal SGbt
	'Kenora Superb' (S-c)	SGbt
	'Kenora Valentine' (D) ♀H3	CWGr LAyl NHal SGbt WPhe
	'Kenora Wow' (S-c)	NHal WPhe
	'Ken's Flame' (WL)	CWGr SGbt
	'Ken's Rarity' (WL)	LAyl NHal NJRG SGbt
	'Kerry Mitchell' (Col)	NJRG
	'Kick Off' (D)	LHWs
§	'Kidd's Climax' (D) ♀H3	CWGr ERCP WPhe
	'Kiev' (D)	LCro
	'Kikoski' (C)	SGbt
	'Kilburn Fiesta' (S-c)	NHal WPhe
	'Kilburn Glow' (WL)	LAyl LHWs NHal NJRG WPhe
	'Kilburn Rose' (WL) ♀H3	NJRG WPhe
	'Kilmorie' (S-c)	NHal WPhe
	'Kingston' (D)	CWGr SGbt
	'Kirsty G' (Col)	NJRG WPhe
	'Kiwi Gloria' (C)	CWGr NHal NJRG WPhe
	'Klondike' (S-c)	WPhe
	'Knockout' (S-c)	CRos LSou
I	'Knockout'PBR (Sin) ♀H3	CBcs CWGr ERCP LRHS LSRN NRHS SDys SPoG
	'Kordessa' (D)	EBee LAma
	'Kym Willo' (Pom)	CWGr
I	'Kyoto' (WL)	CWGr SGbt
	'L.A.T.E.' (Ba)	CWGr LAyl SGbt
	'La Gioconda' (Col)	CWGr
	'La Recoleta' (D)	CWGr ERCP
	'Labyrinth' (D)	ERCP WPhe
	'Lady Darlene' (D)	ERCP LSou
	'Lady Kate' (D)	LCro LHWs LOPS
	'Lady Liberty' (D)	ERCP
	'Lady Linda' (D)	SGbt
	'Lake Carey' (D)	LCro LOPS LRHS
	'Lake Ontario' (D)	CWGr
	'Lakeland Polly' (Pom)	NJRG WPhe
	'Lambada' (Anem)	ELan
	'L'Ancresse' (Ba)	LAyl LHWs NHal NJRG
	'Lavender Freestyle' (C)	CWGr
	'Lavender Leycett' (D)	CWGr
	'Lavender Perfection' (D)	CWGr SDeJ

	'Lavender Ruffles' (D)	CWGr
	'Le Baron' (D)	ERCP MCot
	'Le Castel' (WL) ♀H3	CWGr SDeJ
	'Le Feu du Soleil' (Fim)	NHal
	'Le Patineur' (D)	CWGr
	'Le Vonné Splinter' (S-c)	CWGr
	'Lee Marshall' (C)	CWGr
	'Lemon Crest' (S-c)	WPhe
	'Lemon Elegans' (S-c) ♀H3	CWGr NHal
	'Lemon Meringue' (D)	CWGr ECtt SGbt
	'Lemon Zing' (Ba)	SGbt
	'Leopold Chloe' (D)	WPhe
	'Leopold Sophie' (D)	WPhe
	'Leslie Skinner' (Col)	CWGr
	'Life Force' (D)	CWGr SGbt
	'Lilac Athalie' (C)	CWGr
	'Lilac Bull' (D)	ERCP LHWs LRHS
	'Lilac Marston' (D) ♀H3	NHal
	'Lilac Pathfinder' (Sin)	NJRG
I	'Lilac Time' (D)	CWGr ERCP SDeJ SGbt
	lilac-flowered B&SWJ 14942 from Colombia	WCru
	'Lilianna W' (Sin/DwB)	NJRG
	'Linda's Baby' (Ba)	ERCP SPer
	'Linda's Polly' (Pom)	NJRG
	'Lindsay Michelle' (Fim) **new**	LAma SDir
	'Linz' (D)	WPhe
	'Lisa' (Misc)	CWGr
	'Lismore Carol' (Pom)	NHal WPhe
	'Lismore Moonlight' (Pom)	NHal WPhe
	'Lismore Robin' (D)	NHal
	'Lismore Sunset' (Pom)	SGbt
	'Lisonette' (C)	WPhe
I	'Little Darling' (S-c)	WPhe
	'Little Dorrit' (Sin/Lil)	NJRG
	'Little Fawn' (S-c)	CWGr
	'Little Glenfern' (C)	CWGr
	'Little Matthew' (Pom)	SGbt
	'Little Robert' (D)	ERCP LAma SDir SGbt
	'Little Sally' (Pom)	CWGr SGbt
	'Little Scottie' (Pom)	CWGr
	'Little Snowdrop' (Pom)	SGbt
	'Little Sun' (WL)	WPhe
	'Little Willem' (Pom)	SDeJ SGbt
	'Liz' (S-c)	CWGr
	'Long Island Lil' (D)	CWGr
	'Loraine Mitchell' (WL)	NJRG
	'Lorona Dawn' (SinO)	WPhe
	'Loud Applause' (C)	CWGr
	'Louie Meggos' (D)	NHal
	'Louis V' (Fim)	SGbt
	'Louis White' (D) **new**	NHal
	LUBEGA BURGUNDY (D)	LRHS
	LUBEGA POWER BRONZE BICOLOR (D)	LRHS
	LUBEGA POWER BURGUNDY (D/DwB)	CRos LRHS
	LUBEGA POWER SCARLET-WHITE (D)	LRHS
	LUBEGA POWER TRICOLOR ('Voldah5612')	LRHS
	LUBEGA SCARLET (D)	LRHS
	LUBEGA WHITE (D)	LRHS
	LUBEGA YELLOW (D)	LRHS
	LUBEGA YELLOW ORANGE (D)	LRHS
	'Ludwig Helfert' (S-c)	ERCP
	'Luka Johanna' (WL)	LHWs
	'Mabel Ann' (D)	CWGr LAyl WPhe
	'Madame Simone Stappers' (P)	ECtt EHyd LAyl LRHS NRHS WSpi
	'Madame Vera' (D)	CWGr
	'Magenta Magenta' (D)	LAyl SGbt
	'Magenta Magic' (Sin/DwB)	NHal
	'Magenta Star' (Sin) ♀H3	CWGr ERCP SGbt WPhe
	'Maggie Pickering' (Sin)	CWGr
	'Maiko Girl' (DblO) ♀H3	LAyl
	'Maisha' (D)	CWGr
	'Malvern Spring' (Sin)	CWGr
	'Mambo NL' (Anem)	ERCP SDeJ
	'Manhattan Island' (D)	CWGr MSCN SDeJ
	'Manuel' (D)	CWGr
	'Marble Ball' (D)	EPfP SDeJ SGbt
	'Marie Schnugg' (SinO) ♀H3	NJRG SGbt
	'Mark Hardwick' (D)	WPhe
	'Marlene Joy' (Fim)	CWGr SGbt
	'Maroon Fox'PBR (Ba)	ERCP
I	'Mars' (Col)	SGbt
	'Marston George' (Ba)	NHal NJRG WPhe
	'Marston Karen' (D)	WPhe
	'Marston Suzanne' (D)	NHal WPhe
	'Martina' (D)	WPhe
	'Martin's Yellow' (Pom)	NHal
I	'Mary Eveline' (Col)	ECtt NHal
	'Mary Evelyn' (C)	SDir SGbt
	'Mary Hammett' (D)	WSpi
	'Mary Margaret Row' (D)	NHal
	'Mary Pitt' (D)	SGbt
	'Mary's Jomanda' (Ba) ♀H3	NHal NJRG SGbt WPhe
	'Mas Sixty' (D)	CWGr
	'Mascot Maya' (D)	NJRG
	'Matador' (D)	WPhe
	'Match' (S-c)	WPhe
	'Matilda Huston' (S-c)	CWGr NHal
	'Matt Armour' (Sin)	CWGr
	'Maureen Hardwick' (D)	CWGr SGbt
	'Maureen Jones' (Col)	NJRG
	'Maxi Romero' (Maxi Series) (D)	LRHS
	'Maxi Salinas' (Dalina Maxi Series) (D) **new**	MBros
	'Maxime' (D)	ERCP LAma LHWs SDir WPhe
	'Maxine Bailey' (D)	CWGr
	'Mayan Pearl' (DblO) ♀H3	CWGr LAyl NHal SGbt WPhe
	'Mayan Swan' (S-c)	SGbt
	'Mayan Warrior' (S-c)	NJRG
	'Maya's Rhonda' (Pom) **new**	NHal
	'Megan Dean' (Ba)	NHal WPhe
	'Meiro' (D)	CWGr
	'Melanie Jane' (S-c)	CWGr
	'Melody Allegro'PBR (D)	ERCP LHWs LRHS NRHS WFar
	'Melody Bolero'PBR (D)	ERCP LRHS SDeJ WFar WHil
	'Melody Dixie'PBR (D)	WFar
	'Melody Dora'PBR (D)	LCro LOPS LRHS
	'Melody Fanfare'PBR (D)	ERCP LHWs SDeJ
	'Melody Gipsy'PBR (S-c)	CWGr LHWs LRHS
	'Melody Harmony'PBR (D) ♀H3	LAma LRHS
	'Melody Latin'PBR (D)	CWGr LRHS
	'Melody Lizza'PBR (D)	NRHS WPhe
	'Melody Mambo'PBR (D)	LHWs LRHS
	'Melody Pink Allegro' (D)	ERCP
	'Melody Swing'PBR (D)	LRHS
	'Mel's Orange Marmalade' (Fim)	ERCP ETod LCro LOPS WPhe
	'Menorca' (D)	LCro LRHS
	'Mercator' (S-c)	SPer
	merckii	CSpe CTtf ECha EHyd EPPr EShb EWes LCro LRHS MCot MNrw MRav NRHS SBut SHar SIvy SMHy SMrm WFar WSHC
	- 'Alba' (B)	CSpe WFar
	- compact	WPGP
	- dark-flowered	WPGP
	'Mevrouw Clement Andries' (Fim)	ERCP

§	'Mexican Black' (Misc)	CWGr EBee ECtt ERCP EWoo NJRG SIvy WPGP
	'Mexican Star' (Sin)	CAvo EAri ERCP LRHS
	'Mexico Mogul' (D)	SGbt
	'Miami' (D)	CWGr
	'Michael Haynes' (D)	CWGr
	'Michigan' (D)	CWGr
	'Mick's American Dream' (S-c)	WPhe
	'Mick's Peppermint' (S-c)	CAby CWGr SGbt WPhe
	'Midas' (S-c)	CWGr
	'Midnight' (Pom)	SGbt
	'Midnight Star' (SinO)	NHal NJRG
	'Milena F' (D) **new**	ERCP LCro
	'Milk Shake' (D)	CWGr NRHS
I	'Milly' (D) **new**	NHal
	'Mingus Gregory' (S-c)	CWGr SDeJ
*	'Mingus Max'	ERCP
	'Mingus Randy' (S-c)	CWGr LRHS
	'Minley Carol' (Pom)	NHal NJRG WPhe
	'Minnesota Migrant' (S-c)	CWGr
	'Minouche' (S-c)	CWGr
	'Miss Delilah' (D) **new**	CAvo
	'Miss Rose Fletcher' (S-c)	CWGr
	'Mister Frans' (D)	ERCP LRHS NJRG
	'Mister Optimist' (D)	CAvo
	'Mister Sandman' (Fim)	MSCN
	'Misterton' (D)	SGbt
	'Mom's Special' (D)	CWGr
	'Monet Mystique' (WL)	SGbt
	'Monet Sunlight' (WL)	SGbt
	'Monrovia' (Ba)	CWGr
	'Moonfire' (Sin) ♀[H3]	CAby CAvo CBcs CCht CRos CWGN CWGr CWnw ECtt EHyd ELan EPfP ERCP LAyl LCro LRHS NHal NJRG NLar NRHS SCoo SGbt WCot WGwG WHlf WHoo WPhe WSpi
	'Moonlady' (D)	ERCP
	'Moor Place' (Pom)	CWGr NHal NJRG SGbt WPhe
	'Moret' (S-c)	CWGr
	'Motto' (D)	CWGr
	'Mrs Eileen' (D)	SDeJ SGbt
	'Mrs H. Brown' (Col)	SGbt
	'Mrs McDonald Quill' (D)	SGbt
	'Ms Kennedy' (Ba)	LAyl NHal WPhe
	'München' (D)	SDeJ SGbt
	'Murdoch' ambig. (D)	ECtt LRHS WCot WSpi
	'Murillo' ambig. (Sin)	LAyl
	'Musette' (D)	CWGr SGbt
	'Musson's Silverback' (Fim)	CWGr
	'My Irene' (WL)	NJRG
	'My Love' (S-c)	CWGr ECtt ERCP EWoo LCro LOPS SDir SEND SGbt SPer
	'My Neddy' (D)	SGbt
	'Myama Fubuki' (Fim)	ELan ERCP
	'Myrtle's Folly' (Fim)	ERCP SDeJ WPhe
	'Mystère' (Anem)	CWGr
	'Mystery Day' (D)	LAma SDir
	MYSTIC DESIRE	see *D.* 'Scarlet Fern'
	MYSTIC DREAMER	see *D.* 'Zone Ten'
§	'Mystic Enchantment'[PBR] (Sin)	CRos EHyd ELan EPfP LRHS LSou NRHS SDys SGBe SOrN SPoG
	'Mystic Haze'	see *D.* 'Dark Side of the Sun'
	MYSTIC ILLUSION	see *D.* 'Knockout' (Sin)
	MYSTIC MARS	see *D.* 'Scarlet Fern'
§	MYSTIC SPIRIT ('Hamspirit'[PBR]) (Sin)	CRos EHyd ELan EPfP LRHS LSou NRHS WPhe
	'Mystic Wonder' (Sin)	EHyd ELan LRHS NRHS WPhe
	'Nadia Ruth' (Fim)	LRHS
	'Nagano' (D)	SDeJ
	'Nargold' (Fim)	CWGr LAyl
	'Narrow's Tricia' (S-c)	NJRG WPhe
	'Natal' (Ba)	CAvo ECtt ELan LRHS MBros SDeJ
	'Natalie G' (D)	ERCP NJRG
	'Neal Gillson' (D)	CWGr
	'Nenekazi' (Fim)	LAyl LHWs WPhe
	'Néo' (D)	CWGr LHWs
	'Nepos' (WL)	CWGr NJRG SGbt WPhe
	'Nescio' (Pom)	CWGr LSou MBros SDeJ SDir
I	'New Baby' (Ba)	CWGr ERCP LCro LOPS MBros SGbt
	'New Dimension' (S-c)	CWGr
	'Newquay' (Sin)	CWGr
	'Nicholas' (D)	CWCL ERCP LHWs
	'Nick Sr' (D)	WPhe
	'Nienke' (D)	NJRG
	'Night Butterfly' (Col)	CAby ERCP WBor
I	'Night Queen' (Ba)	MBros
I	'Nina' (D)	WPhe
	'Nippon' (Sin)	EHyd LRHS
	'Nonette' (WL)	CWGr EBee ECtt SGbt WCot
	'Norbeck Dusky' (S-c)	CWGr
	'Noreen' (Pom)	NJRG WPhe
	'Norman Lockwood' (Pom)	CWGr
	'Normandie Delight' (Fim) **new**	NHal
	'Normandie Frills' (Fim)	NHal
	'Normandie Memories' (S-c) **new**	NHal
	'Normandie Wedding Day' (Fim)	NHal WPhe
§	'Nuit d'Eté' (S-c)	CWGr ELan ERCP EWoo LCro LOPS LRHS SDeJ SGbt WPhe
	'Nuland's Josephine' (Ba)	NHal NJRG WPhe
	'Oakwood Belle' (C)	CWGr
	'Oakwood Christina' (Ba)	CWGr
	'Oakwood Dazzle' (D)	CWGr
	'Oakwood Diamond' (Ba)	CWGr
	'Oakwood Fire' (S-c)	CWGr WPhe
	'Oakwood Goldcrest' (S-c)	CWGr NHal WPhe
	'Oakwood Heather' (Ba)	CWGr
	'Oakwood Katie' (S-c)	CWGr
	'Oakwood Lyndon S' (S-c)	CWGr
	'Oakwood Naranga' (D) ♀[H3]	CWGr
	'Oakwood Natasha' (Pom)	CWGr
	'Oakwood Vivian S' (S-c)	CWGr
	'Offshore Dream' (D)	LCro
	'Okapi's Sunset' (S-c)	LHWs
I	'Old Gold' (D)	SGbt
I	'Olivia' (Col)	NJRG WPhe
	'Olivia Mari' (WL)	NHal WPhe
	'Omega' (Fim)	LHWs
	'Omo' (Sin/Lil) ♀[H3]	NJRG
	'Onesta' (D)	CWGr ERCP ETod SDeJ
	'Optic Illusion' (D)	CWGr SOrN
	'Opus' (D)	SGbt
	'Orange Cushion' (D)	CWGr
	'Orange Explosion' (Misc)	SGbt
	'Orange Fire' (S-c)	CWGr
	'Orange Fubuki' (D)	ERCP LCro LHWs
	'Orange Girl' (D) **new**	LCro
	'Orange Keith's Choice' (D)	WPhe
	'Orange Kiss' (Col)	NJRG WPhe
	'Orange Nugget' (Ba)	SDeJ
	'Orange Pekoe' (D)	LHWs
	'Orange Pygmy' (S-c)	LRHS
I	'Orange Queen' (C)	CWGr SGbt
	'Orange Sun' (D)	CWGr
	'Orel' (Col)	SGbt
	'Oreti Bliss' (C)	LAyl NHal
	'Oreti Classic' (D)	NHal
	'Orfeo' (C)	LCro LOPS LRHS MNrw SDeJ SGbt
	'Ornamental Rays' (C)	CWGr
	'Ossie Latham' (Sin)	CWGr SGbt

	'Othello' (S-c)	CWGr
	'Otto's Thrill' (D) ♀H3	ERCP LRHS MSCN
	'Pacific Ocean' (WL)	ERCP
	'Paint It Black' (D)	LHWs
	'Painted Girl' (D)	ERCP LAma LSou
	'Palmares' (D)	LSou
	'Pam Howden' (WL)	NHal NJRG SGbt
	'Pari Taha Sunrise' (S-c)	CWGr
	'Park Princess' (C/DwB)	CWGr LAyl NBwr NHal NRHS SDeJ SGbt SOrN
	'Park Record' (S-c)	LCro LOPS NBwr
	'Parkland Glory' (D)	LSou
	'Parkland Rave' (S-c)	CWGr NHal
	'Paso Doble' misapplied	see *D.* 'Freya's Paso Doble'
	'Passion' (D)	CWGr
	'Pat Knight' (Col)	NJRG WPhe
	'Pat Mark' (S-c)	CWGr
	'Pat 'n' Perc' (Col)	NHal NJRG SGbt WPhe
	'Paul Chester' (C)	CWGr
	'Paul Critchley' (C)	CWGr
	'Peach Delight' (S-c)	SGbt
§	'Peach Melba' (D)	WPhe
	'Peaches and Cream'PBR (D)	CWGr ECtt LHWs MBros
	'Peachette' (Misc/Lil)	CWGr
	'Pearl of Heemstede' (D) ♀H3	LAyl NHal NJRG
	'Pearl Sharowean' (S-c)	CWGr
	'Pearson's Ben' (S-c)	CWGr NJRG
	'Pembroke Levenna' (Ba)	LAyl
	'Penhill Autumn Shade' (S-c)	NJRG SGbt
	'Penhill Dark Monarch' (D)	ERCP LHWs
	'Penhill Watermelon' (D)	ERCP ETod SDeJ
	'Penny Lane' (D)	LAma MBros SDir SPer
	'Peppermint Splash' (D)	WPhe
	'Peter' (D)	SGbt
	'Petite Harvest' (Misc/DwB)	NJRG
	'Petite Lilliput' (Sin/Lil)	WPhe
	'Petite Sunrise' (Sin)	NJRG
	'Petite Sunset' (Misc/Lil)	NJRG
	'Petra's Wedding' (D)	CWGr ERCP
	'Philadelphia' (D)	CWGr
	'Phyllis Farmer' (WL)	CWGr
	'Pianella' (S-c)	CWGr SGbt
	'Pinelands Pam' (Fim)	CWGr
	'Pinelands Princess' (Fim)	SGbt
	'Pink Carol' (Pom)	NJRG
	'Pink Giraffe' (DblO) ♀H3	LRHS SGbt
	'Pink Isa'PBR (D)	CAvo
	'Pink Jean Fairs' (WL)	CWGr
	'Pink Jupiter' (S-c)	CWGr NHal SGbt WPhe
	'Pink Katisha' (D)	CWGr
	'Pink Magic'PBR (D)	LRHS
	'Pink Pastelle' (S-c) ♀H3	SGbt
	'Pink Pat and Perc' (Col)	NHal NJRG WPhe
	'Pink Perception' (WL)	ERCP
	'Pink Preference' (S-c)	CWGr
	'Pink Sensation' (C)	CWGr
	'Pink Silk' (D)	ERCP
	'Pink Skin' (D)	ECtt LRHS SDeJ
	'Pink Spur' (D)	NHal
	'Pink Suffusion' (D)	WPhe
	'Pinkie Swear' (D)	LAma
	pinnata B&SWJ 10240	WCru
	- B&SWJ 14901 from Colombia	WCru
	'Piperoo' (C)	SGbt
	'Piper's Pink' (S-c/DwB)	ECtt EHyd LRHS NRHS SGbt WGwG
	'Platinum Blonde' (Anem)	ERCP WPhe
	'Playa Blanca' (C/DwB)	ELan SGbt SOrN
	'Polar Ice' (D)	CWGr
	'Polka NL' (Anem)	LHWs NJRG SDeJ SGbt WPhe
	'Polventon Kristobel' (D)	NHal WPhe
	'Polventon Supreme' (Ba)	WPhe
	'Pontiac' (C)	CWGr SGbt
	'Pooh' (Col)	see *D.* 'Pooh - Swan Island'
§	'Pooh - Swan Island' (Col) ♀H3	CAby CWGr CWnw EBee ECtt ERCP ESwi LAyl NHal NJRG WBor WCot WPhe
	'Poppyscotland' (Sin)	CWGr
	'Porcelain' (WL)	WPhe WSpi
	'Preference' (C)	CWGr ERCP SDeJ SGbt
	'Preston Park' (Sin/DwB) ♀H3	LAyl NHal
	PRETTY WOMAN ('Vdtg43'PBR) (Dark Angel Series) (Sin) ♀H3	LCro LOPS
	'Priceless Pink' (Misc)	ERCP
	PRIDE OF BERLIN	see *D.* 'Stolz von Berlin'
	'Primrose Diane' (D)	WPhe
	'Prince Valiant' (D)	CWGr
I	'Princess' (Col)	SDeJ
	'Princess Amalia' (D)	WPhe
	'Princess Marie José' (Sin)	CWGr
	'Procyon' (D)	CWGr SGbt
	'Profundo' (D)	LHWs
	'Promise' (Fim)	CWGr ECtt SDeJ
	PULP FICTION ('Vdtg61'PBR) (Dark Angel Series) (Sin)	CWGr
	'Purbeck Lydia' (S-c)	CWGr
	'Purple Duncan Edwards' (S-c)	NHal
	'Purple Flame'PBR (D)	ERCP ETod LCro
	'Purple Fox'PBR (Ba)	ERCP
	'Purple Gem' (S-c)	CWGr ERCP LAma LCro LOPS MSCN SDeJ SGbt
	'Purple Haze' (Misc)	ERCP LCro LOPS LSRN
	'Purple Pearl' (D)	NHal WPhe
	'Purple Petite' (Sin)	NJRG
	'Purple Planet' (D)	LHWs
	'Purple Puff' (Anem)	NHal NJRG WPhe
	'Purple Sensation' (S-c)	CWGr
	aff. ***purpusii*** B&SWJ 10321	WCru
	'Quel Diable' (S-c)	CWGr
	'Quinty' (D)	WPhe
	'R Mona' (WL)	WPhe
	'Rachel de Thame' (Sin)	CWGr
	'Rachel's Place' (Pom)	CWGr
I	'Radjah' (Pom)	NRHS
	'Ragged Robin' (Misc)	CSpe ECtt ERCP EWoo LRHS
	'Rainbow Silence' (S-c)	LHWs
	'Raisa' (D)	WPhe
	'Raiser's Pride' (C)	WPhe
	'Rancho' (WL)	WPhe
	'Raspberry Valiant' (B)	NHal
*	'Raymond Guernsey'	ECtt
	'Rebecca's World' (D)	CWGr ECtt ERCP LCro LOPS
	'Red and White' (D)	CWGr SGbt
	'Red Cap' (D)	CWGr
	'Red Carol' (Pom)	CWGr
	'Red Diamond' (D)	NHal
	'Red Fox'PBR (Ba)	CWGr LCro LOPS
	'Red Fubuki' (D)	SDeJ
	'Red Majorette' (S-c)	SDeJ
	'Red Pathfinder' (Sin)	NJRG
	'Red Pimpernel' (D)	WPhe
	'Red Pygmy' (S-c)	CWGr SDeJ
	'Red Sun' (D)	CWGr
	'Red Symphony' (Ba)	LHWs
	'Red Velvet' (WL)	CWGr
	'Rees' Dream' (D)	CWGr
	'Reginald Keene' (S-c)	CWGr NHal WPhe
	'Rejman's Firecracker' (Fim) **new**	LAma
	'Renato Tosio' (D)	WPhe

	'Reputation' (S-c)	CWGr SGbt
	'Requiem' (D)	ECtt ERCP NJRG
	'Reverend P. Holian' (S-c)	SGbt
	'Revive' (Misc)	CWGr
	'Rhonda' (Pom)	NHal WPhe
	'Rhubarb and Custard' (Sweet Candy Series) (Col)	WPhe
	'Richards Fortune' (Anem) **new**	ERCP
	'Rip City' (S-c)	CWGr ERCP ETod LCro LOPS LRHS MCot
	'Rising Sun' (S-c)	CWGr WPhe
	'Robann Regal' (D)	CWGr
	'Robert Too' (D)	CWGr
	'Rocco' (Pom)	ERCP LCro LOPS LSou SGbt WBor
	'Rockcliffe Billy' (S-c)	NJRG
	'Roger Turrell' (D)	NHal
	'Rokewood Opal' (C)	CWGr
	'Rose Jupiter' (S-c)	CWGr NHal WPhe
	'Rose Tendre' (S-c)	CWGr
	'Rosella' (D)	CWGr SDeJ SGbt
	'Rosemary Dawn' (Ba)	NHal
	'Rosemary Webb' (D)	SGbt
	'Rossendale Heidi' (D)	WPhe
	'Rossendale Jojo' (D)	NHal
	'Rossendale Mollie' (D)	WPhe
	'Rossendale Natasha' (Ba)	NHal SGbt
	'Rossendale Parky' (D)	NHal
	'Rossendale Roxy' (D)	NHal WPhe
	'Rothesay Reveller' (D)	CWGr
I	'Roxy' (Sin/DwB)	CAby CBcs CRos CWGr CWnw EBee ECtt EHyd ELan EPfP LAyl LRHS LSRN NJRG NRHS SGbt SOrN WCot WGwG WPhe WSpi
	'Royal Blood' (Misc)	LAyl
	'Royal Mail' (D)	SGbt
	'Royal Visit' (D)	SGbt
	'Ruby Wedding' (D)	SGbt
	rudis	EBee WPGP
	'Ruskin Andrea' (S-c)	NHal WPhe
	'Ruskin Avenger' (S-c)	NJRG WPhe
	'Ruskin Belle' (S-c)	CWGr
	'Ruskin Buttercup' (D)	SGbt
	'Ruskin Charlotte' (S-c)	CWGr
	'Ruskin Diane' (D)	NHal NJRG WPhe
	'Ruskin Harmony' (Ba)	WPhe
	'Ruskin Limelight' (C)	NHal
	'Ruskin Marigold' (S-c)	NHal
	'Ruskin Michelle' (S-c)	NHal WPhe
	'Ruskin Myra' (S-c)	WPhe
	'Ruskin Respectable' (S-c)	NJRG
	'Ruskin Tangerine' (Ba)	NHal SGbt WPhe
	'Rustig' (D)	CWGr
I	'Ruth Ann' (Ba)	LAyl NHal
	'Ryecroft Bella' (Ba)	NHal
	'Ryecroft Blackberry' (Pom)	NHal
	'Ryecroft Brenda T' (D)	NHal NJRG
	'Ryecroft Helen' (S-c)	NHal
	'Ryecroft Huntsman' (D)	NHal
	'Ryecroft Ice' (D)	SGbt
	'Ryecroft Jan' (Ba) ♀H3	NHal WPhe
	'Ryecroft Jim' (Anem)	LAyl WPhe
	'Ryecroft Laura' (Ba)	LAyl NHal
	'Ryecroft Misty' (D)	NHal
	'Ryecroft Pixie' (C)	NHal
	'Ryecroft Rebel' (D)	WPhe
	'Ryecroft Sparkler' (C)	SGbt
	'Ryecroft Zoe' (S-c)	NHal
	'Ryedale Pinky' (D)	CWGr
	'Sabrina' (D)	WPhe
	'Saint-Saëns' (S-c)	SDeJ
	'Salmon Runner' (D)	CAvo EBee ERCP

	'Salvation' (Ba)	LHWs
	'Sam Hopkins' (D)	ERCP LAyl NHal WPhe
	'Sam Huston' (D)	CWGr SGbt
	'Samantha'	see *D.* 'Harvest Samantha'
	'Sandia Serenity' (WL)	NJRG
	'Sandra' (D)	ERCP LCro LOPS
	'Sans Souci' (C)	CWGr
	'Santa Claus US' (D)	LHWs SGbt WPhe
	'Sarah' (S-c)	ECtt EHyd LRHS NRHS WGwG
I	'Sarah Elisabeth' (WC)	WPhe
	'Sascha' (WL) ♀H3	NHal
	'Sassy' (D)	SGbt
	'Scarborough Ace' (D)	CWGr
§	'Scarlet Fern' (Sin)	CWGr
	'Scarlet O'Hara' (D)	NJRG
	'Scarlet Rotterdam' (S-c)	CWGr
	'Scarlet Star' (S-c)	CWGr
	'Scaur Sunrise' (D)	NJRG
	'Scaur Swinton' (D)	SGbt
	'Scaur Topper' (Ba)	WPhe
	'Schneeflocke' (Ba)	CWGr
	'Seattle' (D)	CWGr LAma
	'Seduction' (D)	CAvo ERCP LHWs
	'Seirō' (S-c)	SGbt
	'Seniors Darkness' (D) **new**	LCro
	'Seniors Hope' (Misc)	ERCP
	'Seniors Love' (Misc)	LHWs
	'Shandy' (S-c)	CWGr LAyl SHar
I	'Sheila' (Ba)	WPhe
	'Shep's Memory' (WL) ♀H3	NJRG
	'Sheval Megan' (D)	NHal WPhe
	'Shiloh Noelle' (D)	ERCP
	'Shining Star' (C)	CWGr
	'Shirley Pillman' (Misc)	CWGr
	'Shirley Westwell' (D)	CWGr
	'Shirwell Greta' (D)	NHal WPhe
	'Shooting Star' (S-c)	CWGr
	'Show 'n' Tell' (Fim)	CWGr ERCP SGbt WPhe
	'Shy Princess' (C)	CWGr
	'Siberia'^{PBR} (D)	LAma
	'Sights of Summer' (D)	LAma
	'Silver City' (D)	NHal SGbt WPhe
	'Silver Slipper' (S-c)	CWGr
	'Silver Years' (D)	CWGr LHWs
	'Silvie's Queen' (D)	SDeJ
	SINCERITY ('Dahsc266'^{PBR}) (D)	LRHS
	'Sir Alf Ramsey' (D)	CWGr LAma LAyl LHWs NHal SDir SGbt WPhe
	'Small World' (Pom) ♀H3	CWGr LAyl NHal WPhe
	'Smiling Don' (D)	LHWs
	'Smokey' (D)	CWGr
	'Sneezy' (Sin/DwB)	CWGr
	'Snoho Sonia' (Ba)	WPhe
	'Snow Cap' (S-c)	SDeJ
	'Snowbound' (D)	SGbt
I	'Snowflake' (Pom)	ERCP SDeJ
I	'Snowstorm' (D)	LRHS SGbt
	'So Dainty' (S-c) ♀H3	CWGr
	'Sonia Henie' (Ba)	CWGr
	'Sophie Taylor' (SinO)	NJRG
	'Sorbet' (DwB)	LAyl
	'Sorbet' (S-c)	see *D.* 'Geerlings Sorbet' (S-c)
	sorensenii	CWGr
	'Soulman' (Anem)	ERCP SGbt WPhe
	'Sourire de Crozon' (D)	CWGr
	'Souvenir d'Eté' (Pom)	EPfP LRHS SDeJ
	'Spanish Conquest' (D)	NHal SGbt
	'Spartacus' Berbee (D) **new**	LAyl
	'Spartacus' Senior (D)	CWGr ERCP LAyl LCro NHal
	'Spassmacher' (S-c)	CWGr
	'Spectacular' (D)	SGbt
I	'Spike' (S-c)	SGbt

	'Spikey Symbol' (S-c)	CWGr
	'Staleen Condesa' (S-c)	SGbt WPhe
	'Stan's Nirvana' (WL)	CWGr
	'Star Elite' (C)	CWGr
	'Star Surprise' (C)	SDeJ
	STAR WARS ('Vdtg14'PBR) (Dark Angel Series) (Sin)	LCro LOPS SDeJ
	'Starry Night' (S-c)	CWGr
	'Star's Favourite' (C)	SDeJ
	'Steffan' (WL) **new**	NJRG WPhe
	'Stella J' (WL)	CWGr
	'Steve Bradley' (Sin)	CWGr
	'Steve Meggos' (D)	WPhe
	'Stevie D' (D) ♀H3	CWGr SGbt
§	'Stolz von Berlin' (Ba)	CWGr ELan ERCP LRHS MBros SDeJ SGbt
	'Storm Warning' (D)	CWGr
	'Storrs Julie' (Pom)	NJRG WPhe
	'Stratos' (D) **new**	ERCP
	STRAWBERRY ICE	see *D.* 'Kidd's Climax'
	'Striped Vulcan' (S-c)	CAby WPhe
	'Sue Mountjoy' (Col)	CWGr
	'Suffolk Punch' (D)	ELan
	'Suitzus Julie' (Misc)	CWGr NJRG WPhe
	'Summer Festival' (D)	SGbt
	'Summer Flame' (D) **new**	LCro
	'Summer Night' (S-c)	see *D.* 'Nuit d'Eté'
	'Summer Nights' (Misc)	NJRG
	'Sunlady' (D)	LSou
	'Sunny Boy' (Ba)	MBros SDeJ
	'Sunshine Girl' (Col)	NHal NJRG
	'Super Rays' (C)	CWGr
	'Superfine' (C)	CWGr
	'Surprise' ambig. (S-c)	WHlf
	'Susan Gilbert' (Col) ♀H3	NHal NJRG WPhe
	'Susan Gilliott' (S-c)	NHal
I	'Suzanne' (Col)	NJRG
	'Suzette' (D/DwB)	SGbt
	'Swan Lake'	see *D.* 'Classic Swanlake'
	'Swanvale' (D)	SGbt
	'Sweet Content' (D)	CWGr SGbt
	'Sweet Love' (D)	ERCP
I	'Sweet Sixteen' (WL)	CWGr
	'Sweet Surprise' (D)	LCro
	'Sweet Tiamo' (D)	ERCP
	'Sweetheart' (D)	CWGr NJRG SDeJ
I	'Sylvia' (Ba)	CWGr ERCP LCro
I	'Sympathy' (WL)	CWGr
	'Table Dancer' (Fim)	LAma MBros SDir
	'Tahiti Sunrise' (S-c)	LRHS LSou MBros SOrN
	'Tahoma Moonshot' (SinO)	CWnw
	'Take Off' (Anem)	ERCP LCro SDeJ WBor
	'Tally Ho' (Sin) ♀H3	ECtt EHyd EPfP LRHS NJRG NRHS SDys WCot
	tamaulipana	WPGP
	– F&M 312 **new**	
	'Tamburo' (S-c)	ERCP SPer
	'Tanjoh' (S-c)	SPer
I	'Tapestry' (Sin)	CWGr SGbt
	'Taratahi Ruby' (WL) ♀H3	CWGr ERCP NHal NJRG WPhe
	'Tartan' (D)	CWGr ERCP ETod EWTr LSou WPhe
	'Tartarus' (P)	CWGr
	'Teesbrooke Audrey' (Col)	CAby CWGr ECtt LCro LOPS NHal NJRG WPhe
	'Teesbrooke Red Eye' (Col)	NJRG SGbt WPhe
	'Temple of Beauty' (Misc) **new**	LCro
	tenuicaulis	CDTJ
	'Terracotta' (Misc/DwB)	NJRG
	'Terrie Bandey' (Fim)	LAyl WPhe
	'Thaïs' (Col)	NJRG
	'The Big Wow' (D)	CWGr
	'The Phantom' (Anem)	NJRG SDeJ
I	'The Queen' (S-c)	CWGr
	'Thomas A. Edison' (D)	CWGr ERCP LAma LCro LOPS MBros MSCN SDeJ SGbt
	'Tiffany Lynn' (SinO)	CWGr
I	'Tiger' (Sin/DwB)	CWGr
	'Tiger Eye' (D)	SGbt
	'Tioga Spice' (Fim)	CWGr
	'Tohsuikyoh' (Misc)	CWGr SGbt
	'Tomo' (D)	ELan LAyl
	'Tom's August Bride' (S-c)	CWGr
I	'Topaz Puff' (Anem)	CWGr
	'Topmix' (Sin/DwB)	SDeJ
	'Topmix Apricot' (Sin)	ERCP
	'Topmix Mama' (Sin)	NJRG
	'Topmix Orange' (Sin)	NJRG SDeJ
	'Topmix Pink' (Sin/DwB)	CWGr SDeJ
	'Topmix Purple' (Sin)	NJRG
	'Topmix Red' (Sin/DwB)	NJRG SDeJ
	'Topmix Reddy' (Sin)	NJRG
I	'Topmix Rose' (Sin)	NJRG
	'Topmix Salmon' (Sin)	ERCP
	'Topmix White' (Sin/DwB)	ERCP SDeJ
	'Topmix Yellow' (Sin/DwB)	SDeJ
	'Totally Tangerine' (Anem)	CWGr EPfP ERCP LCro WPhe
	'Toto' (Anem)	SDeJ
	'Tour du Monde' (WL)	CWGr
	'Trebbiano' (S-c)	MBros
	'Trelissick Purple'	CWGr
	'Trelyn Amber' (Col)	WPhe
	'Trelyn Crimson' (Col) ♀H3	WPhe
	'Trelyn Daisy' (Col) ♀H3	CWGr
	'Trelyn Kiwi' (S-c) ♀H3	NHal NJRG SGbt WPhe
	'Trelyn Kristia' (Col)	WPhe
	'Trelyn Rebecca' (Col)	WPhe
	'Trelyn Red Dragon' (SinO)	NJRG WPhe
	'Trelyn Rhiannon' (C) ♀H3	WPhe
	'Trelyn Seren' (SinO)	LAyl WPhe
	'Trengrove Autumn' (D)	CWGr SGbt
	'Trengrove Millennium' (D)	NJRG SGbt WPhe
I	'Trevor' (Col)	ECtt SGbt
	'Tricolor' ambig.	LSou MSCN
	'Trooper Dan' (S-c)	WPhe
	'Troy Dyson' (Misc)	SDys
	'Truly Scrumptious' (S-c)	SGbt
	'Tsuki-yori-no-shisha' (Fim)	LCro LHWs LOPS
	'Tui Avis' (C)	NJRG
	'Tui Orange' (S-c)	CWGr
	'Tu-tu' (S-c)	CWGr SGbt
	'Twiggy' (WL)	SGbt
	'Twilight Time' (D)	SDeJ WPhe
	'Twilite' (Anem)	CWGr
*	'Twinkle Stars'	SDeJ
	'Twyning's After Eight' (Sin) ♀H3	CAby CRos CSpe CWGN CWGr CWnw ECtt EHyd EPfP ERCP EWoo LAyl LCro LOPS LRHS NHal NJRG NRHS SDys SGbt WCot WGwG WHlf WHoo WPhe XSte
	'Twyning's Aniseed' (Sin)	CWGr
	'Twyning's Black Cherry' (D)	ECtt
	'Twyning's Candy' (Sin)	CWGr
	'Twyning's Chocolate' (Sin)	CWGr
	'Twyning's Peppermint' (Sin)	CWGr
	'Twyning's Pink Fish' (Col)	CWGr
	'Twyning's Revel' (Sin) ♀H3	CWGr WMal
	'Twyning's Smartie' (Sin)	EBee ECtt LCro LOPS LRHS SPer WPhe
	'Twyning's Velvet' (Sin)	CWGr
	'Twyning's White Chocolate' (Sin)	ERCP
	'Union Jack' (Sin)	CWGr

	'Uniquity' (Sin)	WCot
	'Urchin' (C)	CWGr
	'Val Saint Lambert' (Fim)	CWGr
I	'Valentino' (WL/DwB)	CWGr
	'Valerie Moody' (D)	CWGr
	'Val's Candy' (S-c)	NHal WPhe
	'Vancouver' (Misc)	ECtt LCro LOPS SDeJ WFar
I	'Vanessa' **new**	SOrN
	'Vassio Meggos' (D)	CWGr ERCP LHWs NHal WPhe
	'Veritable' (S-c)	LCro LOPS
	'Verrone's Obsidian' (SinO)	CAby CSpe CWGr EPfP ERCP EWoo LAma LCro LOPS LRHS SHor WPhe
	'Victoria Ann' (D) **new**	EWTr
I	'Viking' (Pom)	CWGr
	'Vino' (Pom)	WPhe
	'Violet Davies' (S-c)	CWGr
	'Vivian Russell' (WL)	NHal NJRG WPhe
	'Vossens Discovery' (Sin)	CWGr
	'Vulcan' (S-c)	CWGr SGbt WPhe
§	'Vuurvogel' (S-c)	SDeJ
	'Waltzing Mathilda' (Misc) ♀H3	ERCP EWoo LCro WPhe
	'Wanborough Gem' (Ba)	CWGr
	'Wandy' (Pom)	CWGr
	'War of the Roses' (D)	EWes SIvy WHer
	'Warkton Willo' (Pom)	CWGr
I	'Waterlily' (Sin)	EHyd NRHS
I	'Welcome Guest' (S-c)	CWGr
	'Westerton Ella Grace' (D)	NHal NJRG
	'Westerton Folly' (Ba) ♀H3	NHal WPhe
	'Westerton Harry' (D)	NHal
	'Westerton J.W.H.' (D)	NHal WPhe
	'Westerton Lilian' (D)	NHal WPhe
	'Westerton Pearl' (B) **new**	NHal
	'Westerton Southside' (D)	NHal
	'Westerton Sunset' (D) **new**	NHal
	'Weston Corsair' (C)	NJRG WPhe
	'Weston Miss' (S-c)	NJRG WPhe
	'Weston Nugget' (C)	CWGr
	'Weston Pirate' (C) ♀H3	CWGr LAyl NHal NJRG WPhe
	'Weston Spanish Dancer' (C) ♀H3	CWGr NHal NJRG SGbt WPhe
	'Weston Stardust' (C) ♀H3	NJRG WPhe
	'Weston Tea-time' (C)	CWGr
	'Weston Torero' (C)	CWGr
	'Whale's Rhonda' (Pom)	NHal
	'Wheels' (Col)	CWGr NJRG
	'White Alva's' (D) ♀H3	LAyl NHal SGbt WPhe
	'White Aster' (Pom)	CWGr ERCP SDir
	'White Ballerina' (WL)	NHal SGbt
	'White Ballet' (D) ♀H3	CWGr LAyl SGbt
	'White Charlie Two' (D)	NHal
	'White Hamari Katrina' (S-c)	WPhe
	'White Isa' (D) **new**	LCro
	'White Lace' (Fim)	WPhe
	'White Moonlight' (S-c)	CWGr NHal WPhe
	'White Nettie' (Ba)	SGbt
	'White Onesta' (D)	ERCP SDeJ
	'White Pastelle' (S-c)	WPhe
	'White Perfection' (D)	CWGr ECtt LAma SDeJ SDir WSpi
	white seedling (Sin)	CWGr
	'White Star' (S-c)	CWGr LCro LOPS LRHS SDeJ
	'White Swallow' (S-c)	LAyl NHal
	white-flowered B&SWJ 14340 from Colombia	WCru
	'Wicky Woo' (D)	CWGr
	'Wildwood Marie' (WL)	NJRG
	'William John' (Pom)	CWGr
	'Williamsburg' (S-c)	CWGr
	'Willo's Borealis' (Pom)	NHal
	'Willo's Night' (Pom)	CWGr
	'Willo's Surprise' (Pom)	SGbt
	'Willo's Violet' (Pom)	NHal NJRG SGbt WPhe
	'Will's Ringwood Rosie' (Pom)	CWGr
	'Wine & Roses' (WL)	SGbt
	'Wine Eyed Jill' (D)	ERCP
	'Winholme Diane' (D)	NHal WPhe
	'Winkie Colonel' (D)	CWGr
	'Winkie Lambrusco' (Pom)	NHal NJRG WPhe
	'Winston Churchill' (WL)	WSpi
	'Wishes n Dreams' (Sin)	ERCP NJRG
	'Wittem' (D)	EBee LAma SDir
	'Witteman's Best' (S-c)	CWGr MCot SGbt
	'Witteman's Superba' (S-c) ♀H3	NHal
	'Wizard of Oz' (Ba)	CWGr CWnw ERCP LCro LHWs LOPS
	'Woodbridge' (Sin)	SGbt
	'Woodside Finale' (D)	NHal
	'Wootton Impact' (S-c) ♀H3	WPhe
	'Wootton Tempest' (S-c)	CWGr
	'Wootton Windmill' (Col)	CWGr
	'Worton Blue Streak' (S-c)	CWGr SGbt
	'X Factor' (D)	CWGr LHWs SDir
	'Yamabiraki' (D)	CWGr
	'Yellow Galator' (C)	SGbt
	'Yellow Hammer' (Sin/DwB) ♀H3	NHal NJRG SGbt
	'Yellow Jill' (D) **new**	LCro
	'Yellow Perception' (WL)	ERCP SDeJ
	'Yellow Pet' (D)	CWGr
	'Yellow Sneezy' (Sin/Lil)	SDeJ
	'Yellow Star' (S-c)	CWGr ERCP SDeJ
	'Yelno Enchantment' (WL)	CWGr
	'Yelno Petite Glory' (D)	CWGr
	'York and Lancaster' (D)	CWGr EBee SGbt WAvo
	'Yvonne Geerlings' (WL)	WPhe
	'Zingaro' (D)	LCro LOPS
	'Zippity Do Da' (Pom)	ERCP
	'Zirconia' (D)	ERCP LHWs
	'Zoey Rey' (D)	WPhe
§	'Zone Ten' PBR (Sin/DwB)	CRos CWnw EHyd EPfP LRHS LSou NRHS SCoo SDys SOrN SPoG WBor WPhe
	'Zorro' (D) ♀H3	ERCP NHal SGbt
	'Zundert Mystery Fox' PBR (Ba)	ERCP LCro
	'Zurich' (S-c)	CWGr

Dais (*Thymelaeaceae*)

	cotinifolia	EShb

Daiswa see *Paris*

Dalea (*Fabaceae*)

	candida	EBee SPhx
	purpurea	EBee SBut SPhx
	- 'Stephanie'	CSpe EMor LRHS
	villosa **new**	SPhx

damson see *Prunus insititia*

Danae (*Asparagaceae*)

§	***racemosa*** ♀H5	CBcs CEme CMac CTri EBee EPfP EWes LEdu LPar LRHS MGil MGos MRav NFav SAko SEND SRms SWvt WCot WCru WJur WPGP WSpi

Daphne (*Thymelaeaceae*)

	acutiloba	GKev WSpi
	- 'Fragrant Cloud'	CExl CJun CTrC EWes SChF WPGP
	albowiana	CBcs CCCN CJun EPfP GKev LRHS NLar WSpi
	alpina	GKev

	altaica	CJun
	aurantiaca	IArd IDee
	- 'Gang-ho-ba'	CJun
	aurantiaca* × *gemmata new	SChF
	bholua	CBct CCCN CJun EHed EPfP ESwi GKev LAlb LEdu LRHS NLar SChF SavN WSpi
	- B&SWJ 8275 from Fansipan, Vietnam	WCru
	- GWJ 9436 from India	WCru
	- NJM 13.115	WPGP
I	- 'Alba'	GKev SSta WPGP WSpi
	- 'Cobhay Coral'	CJun
	- 'Cobhay Debut'	CJun
	- 'Cobhay Snow'	CJun
	- 'Darjeeling'	CBod CCCN CExl CJun EBee EPfP LRHS SEdd WPGP WSpi
	- 'Garden House Enchantress'	WPGP
	- 'Garden House Ghost'	EBee SChF WPGP
	- 'Garden House Red Stem'	WPGP
	- 'Garden House Sentinel'	WPGP
	- var. ***glacialis*** 'Gurkha' ♀H4	CExl CJun SChF WPGP
	- 'Jacqueline Postill' ♀H4	Widely available
	- 'Limpsfield'	CBcs CJun EBee LRHS SChF SSta WPGP
	- 'Mary Rose' new	CBcs SChF WPGP
	- 'Penwood'	CJun
	- 'Peter Smithers'	CExl CJun EBee SSta WPGP
	blagayana	GKev SRms
	- 'Brenda Anderson'	CJun EPot SChF WAbe
	'Bramdean'	see *D.* × *napolitana* 'Bramdean'
	× ***burkwoodii*** 'Albert Burkwood'	CJun
	- 'Astrid' (v)	ELon LPar LRHS MGil SGol
	- 'G.K. Argles' (v)	CJun
I	- 'Gold Sport'	CJun
	- 'Golden Treasure'	CCCN CJun LRHS NLar
	- 'Lavenirii'	CJun
	- 'Marjolein' PBR	LRHS NLar
	- 'Moonlight Sonata'	NLar
	- 'Somerset' ♀H4	CCCN CJun ELan LCro LOPS LRHS MGil MSwo NWea
§	- 'Somerset Gold Edge' (v)	CJun
§	- 'Somerset Variegated' (v)	SChF
	- 'Variegata' broad cream edge	see *D.* × *burkwoodii* 'Somerset Variegated'
	- 'Variegata' broad gold edge	see *D.* × *burkwoodii* 'Somerset Gold Edge'
	caucasica	CJun
	cneorum	CBcs EWes NBir NLar
	- 'Benaco'	EPot
	- 'Eximia' ♀H5	WAbe
	- 'Major'	EPot
	- 'Variegata' (v)	EWes GEdr
	- var. ***verlotii***	EPot SChF
	'Cobhay Pink Delight'	CJun
	collina	see *D. sericea* Collina Group
§	***gemmata***	CBcs IArd NLar
	- 'Royal Crown'	CCCN LAlb LCro LRHS NLar WSpi XSte
	genkwa	CJun LRHS
	gnidium PAB 8371	LEdu
	× ***hendersonii*** 'Apple Blossom'	EPot
	- 'Bonnie Glen'	EPot
	- 'Ernst Hauser'	CJun WIce WThu
	- 'Fritz Kummert'	WAbe
	- 'Jeanette Brickell'	WThu
	- 'Kath Dryden'	EPot GEdr
	- 'Marion White'	EPot
	- 'Rosebud'	EPot WThu
	'Hinton'	CJun
	× ***houtteana***	CJun
	japonica 'Striata'	see *D. odora* 'Aureomarginata'
	jezoensis	SSta
	'Kilmeston Beauty'	CJun
	× ***latymeri*** 'Spring Sonnet'	SChF
	laureola	CJun EBee EPfP GKev GPoy MMrt NBid NBir NLar NPer WSpi
	- 'Margaret Mathew'	NLar SChF
	- subsp. ***philippi***	CBcs CCCN CJun CMac EBee EGrI EPfP EWes IDee LCro LOPS LSto MBlu MGil NLar WCot WPGP WSpi
	longilobata	EBee GEdr GKev
	× ***mantensiana*** 'Manten'	CJun
	× ***mauerbachii*** 'Perfume of Spring'	CJun
	'Meon'	see *D.* × *napolitana* 'Meon'
	mezereum	CBod GDam GKev GPoy LPar LRHS NWea SChF SCob SWvt WCot WFar
	- f. ***alba***	GAbr GBin GKev GLog SRms SWvt WSpi
I	- var. ***alpina*** hort.	GKev
	- 'Rosea'	SRms
	- var. ***rubra***	CBcs CCCN CDoC ELan GDam GKin LRHS MGil MSwo SPer WFar WHlf WSpi
	modesta	WAbe
	× ***napolitana*** ♀H4	CJun
§	- 'Bramdean'	CJun SChF
§	- 'Meon'	CJun EPot SChF WThu
	odora	CBcs CCCN CJun CSBt EPfP GKev LCro LOPS LPar LRHS MSwo NRHS SCob SEle SGbt SGol SavN WFar WHlf WPGP WSpi
§	- f. ***alba***	CCCN LAlb LRHS NLar
	- - 'Sakiwaka'	CCCN CExl WLov
§	- 'Aureomarginata' (v)	Widely available
I	- 'Aureomarginata Alba' (v)	WSpi
	- 'Cameo'	CCCN CSBt LAlb LRHS NLar
	- 'Double Cream' (v)	CJun
	- 'Geisha Girl' (v)	CCCN LRHS
	- var. ***leucantha***	see *D. odora* f. *alba*
	- 'Mae-jima' (v)	CBcs CExl GMcL LRHS SMDa WSpi
	- 'Marginata'	see *D. odora* 'Aureomarginata'
	- MARIANNI ('Rogbret') (v)	CBcs CCCN CEnd CTrC EBee EHed IArd IDee LRHS MMrt MRav NCth NLar SEdd SGol SWvt WHlf
	- REBECCA ('Hewreb') (v)	CRos EBee ECre EHyd ELan EPfP LCro LOPS LRHS MAsh MBNS MGos NRHS SPoG WHlf WSpi
	- var. ***rubra***	CCCN CMac LRHS SGol
	- 'Sweet Amethyst' PBR	CCCN LCro LOPS NLar
	- 'Walberton' (v)	EHyd EPfP LRHS NRHS
	oleoides	EPot
	papyracea	CExl WPGP
	PERFUME PRINCESS ('Dapjur01')	Widely available
	petraea	WAbe
	pontica	CBcs CCCN CJun CMac EPfP GBin LRHS LSto MAsh NLar NRHS SChF SPoG SavN WPGP WSpi
	retusa	see *D. tangutica* Retusa Group
	× ***rollsdorfii*** 'Arnold Cihlarz'	CJun SChF WAbe
	- 'Wilhelm Schacht' ♀H5	CJun EPot MAsh SChF WThu
	'Rosy Wave'	CJun SChF
	× ***schlyteri*** 'July Glow'	EPot GEdr SChF WAbe
	- 'Lovisa Maria'	EPot GEdr
	sericea	CJun
§	- Collina Group	SChF WIce
	'Spring Beauty'	CBct CBod CCCN CEnd CJun CRos EPfP IArd IDee LRHS LSRN

	MAsh NLar SChF SHor WPGP WSpi XSte
'Spring Herald'	CCCN CJun EPfP LRHS MAsh NLar SChF SHor WPGP WSpi
'Stasek' (v)	CJun
× ***suendermannii*** 'Franz Suendermann'	EPot MMrt
sureil	LEdu WPGP
× ***susannae*** 'Anton Fahndrich'	NLar
- 'Cheriton' 🏆H5	CJun EPot LRHS SChF WThu
- 'Tichborne'	EPot GEdr SChF WAbe WIce
tangutica 🏆H5	CBcs CBor CExl CJun CRos CSpe CTri EPfP GArf GKev IArd LCro LOPS LRHS LSRN MAsh MGos NHol NLar SEdd SHor SMDa SRkn SRms WHlf WKif WPGP WSpi
- 'Golden Thread' (v)	LRHS
§ - Retusa Group 🏆H5	CExl CJun EPot EWes GBin GEdr GKev LRHS SRms WMal WSpi
× ***transatlantica*** 'Beulah Cross' (v)	CJun
- ETERNAL FRAGRANCE ('Blafra'[PBR]) 🏆H5	Widely available
§ - PINK FRAGRANCE ('Blapink'[PBR])	CBcs CDoC CEnd CRos EBee ECul EHyd ELan ELon EPfP GBin IDee ILea LCro LOPS LRHS MAsh MGos MMrt MRav NCth NLar NRHS SCoo SEdd SGol SHor SPoG WSpi XSte
- SPRING PINK ETERNAL FRAGRANCE	see *D.* × *transatlantica* PINK FRAGRANCE
- 'Summer Ice' (v)	CBod CKel CWnw EHed IDee NCth WHlf
'Valerie Hillier'	WCot
velenovskyi 'Weber's Findling'	SChF
'White Queen'	CCCN LCro LOPS LRHS NLar SHor SavN WSpi
× ***whiteorum*** 'Beauworth'	EPot LRHS WAbe
wolongensis	GKev
- 'Guardsman'	CCCN CJun GBin GKev LRHS SHor
- 'Kevock Star'	CExl GKev

Daphniphyllum (*Daphniphyllaceae*)

aff. ***angustifolium*** B&SWJ 11804	WCru
- WWJ 12020	WCru
chartaceum KWJ 12244	WCru
- KWJ 12313	WCru
glaucescens	WCru
subsp. ***oldhamii*** var. ***kengii*** B&SWJ 7119	
- - - CWJ 12351	WCru
humile	see *D. macropodum* var. *humile*
aff. ***longeracemosum*** B&SWJ 11788	WCru
macropodum	CBcs CBct CCCN CEme CSpe EBee ELan EPfP LAlb LEdu LRHS NLar SArc SPer SVen WCru WPGP XSte
- B&SWJ 581	WCru
- B&SWJ 2898	WCru
- B&SWJ 6809 from Taiwan	WCru
- B&SWJ 8507 from Ulleungdo, South Korea	WCru
- B&SWJ 8763 from Jejudo, South Korea	WCru
- B&SWJ 11489 from Yakushima, Japan	WCru
- B&SWJ 12691	WCru
- dwarf	WCru
§ - var. ***humile*** B&SWJ 11232	WCru
majus B&SWJ 11744	WCru
paxianum B&SWJ 9755	WCru
pentandrum B&SWJ 6888	WCru
- B&SWJ 7056	WCru
- CWJ 12393	WCru
- RWJ 9836	WCru
teysmannii B&SWJ 11112	WCru
- B&SWJ 14626 from Japan	WCru
aff. ***teysmannii*** CWJ 12350 from Taiwan	WCru

Darlingtonia (*Sarraceniaceae*)

californica 🏆H3	CHew NWac SHmp SPlb WSSs WTyc

Darmera (*Saxifragaceae*)

peltata 🏆H6	Widely available
- 'Nana'	EBee ECha LBar MBel NBid NHol NLar WFar

Dasylirion (*Asparagaceae*)

§ ***acrotrichum***	CDTJ CExl EShb SArc
berlandieri	CExl EAri
cedrosanum	CDTJ CJun EAri SPlb
durangense	EAri
glaucophyllum	CCht CJun EAri NPlm
gracile Planchon	see *D. acrotrichum*
leiophyllum	LRHS SPlb
longissimum	CCCN EAri EOli EShb LPal NPlm XSen
lucidum	EAri
miquihuanense	CCht CTsd
- F&M 321	EBee
quadrangulatum	EAri LPal SPlb
serratifolium	EAri EOli ERom LPal LPar NPlm
wheeleri 🏆H2	CBrP EOli LPal NPlm SPlb XSen

Dasyphyllum (*Asteraceae*)

diacanthoides	WPGP

date see *Phoenix dactylifera*

Datisca (*Datiscaceae*)

cannabina	CDTJ CSpe ECha IPot LEdu LRHS LShi MHoo SBls SMHy SMad WHer

Datura (*Solanaceae*)

arborea	see *Brugmansia arborea*
chlorantha	see *D. metel*
cornigera	see *Brugmansia arborea*
§ ***metel***	SAdn
- 'Double Purple' (d)	LSou
rosei	see *Brugmansia sanguinea*
sanguinea	see *Brugmansia sanguinea*
stramonium	EBtc
suaveolens	see *Brugmansia suaveolens*
versicolor	see *Brugmansia versicolor* Lagerh.
- 'Grand Marnier'	see *Brugmansia* × *candida* 'Grand Marnier'

Daubenya (*Asparagaceae*)

aurea	CBor
marginata	CBor

Daucus (*Apiaceae*)

carota	CBod CHab GQue LShi LSto SPhx SRms SVic WHer WSFF WWild
- subsp. ***maximus***	SPhx WHil

Davallia (*Davalliaceae*)

sp.	EFPl
canariensis 🏆H1c	LEdu

trichomanoides	CLAP
- f. ***barbata***	CMen

Davidia (*Nyssaceae*)

involucrata 🏆H5	Widely available
- 'Crimson Spring'	CAco NLar
- 'Kylee's Columnar' **new**	CAco NLar
- 'Lady Dahlia' (v)	NLar
- 'Sonoma'	CAco CBcs LAlb LRHS MBlu MPkF NLar SWeb XVPe
- var. ***vilmoriniana*** 🏆H5	CAco EHyd ELan EPfP LRHS MBlu NOrn SLim SPtp XSte

Daviesia (*Fabaceae*)

cordata	SPlb
pectinata	SPlb

Debregeasia (*Urticaceae*)

longifolia	SVen
- WWJ 11686	ESwi WCru

Decaisnea (*Lardizabalaceae*)

fargesii	Widely available

Decumaria (*Hydrangeaceae*)

barbara	CMac NLar WCru
- 'Vicki'	NBro NLar
sinensis	CKel CRos EBee EHyd EPfP LRHS NRHS SPoG SSha WCru

Degenia (*Brassicaceae*)

velebitica	GKev WAbe

Deinanthe (*Hydrangeaceae*)

bifida	CExl CMiW EBee EMor EPfP EWes EWld GEdr GKev MMrt WCru WPGP
- B&SWJ 5436	WCru
- B&SWJ 5551	WCru
- B&SWJ 5655	LEdu NLar
- 'Pink-Kii'	WCru
- 'Pink-Shi'	EWld IPot WCru WSHC
bifida* × *caerulea	WCru
'Blue Blush'	WCru
caerulea	CMiW EWes GEdr LEdu LRHS NLar WCru WSHC
- 'Blue Wonder'	CExl CTtf

Deinostigma (*Gesneriaceae*)

§ ***tamiana***	WDib

Delairea (*Asteraceae*)

§ ***odorata***	CExl EWld WPGP

Delonix (*Fabaceae*)

decaryi	SPlb
* ***grandiflora***	SPlb
regia	EAri SPlb

Delosperma (*Aizoaceae*)

from Graaf Reinet, South Africa	EPot NSla XLum XSen
§ ***aberdeenense*** 🏆H3	EWes SLee SSim XLum XSen
alpinum	see *Ectotropis alpina*
ashtonii	CCCN EPot EWes NSla SLee WThu XLum
basuticum	MAsh NHpl NSla
'Beaufort West'	EDAr EHyd EWes NRHS NSla
congestum misapplied	see *Malotigena frantiskae-niederlovae*
congestum ambig.	CTsd EDAr EPfP EPot GEdr SLee SMad WIce WJur XLum
cooperi	CCCN CRos CTri CWal EAri ECtt EHyd ELan EPfP EPot EWTr GArf GKev ITim LRHS MHer NFav NHpl NRHS SEdd SIvy SPlb SRms SSim SVen WIce WJur XLum XSen
- (Jewel of Desert Series) JEWEL OF DESERT AMETHYST ('Dsam131'PBR)	LBar WIce
- - 'Jewel of Desert Garnet'PBR	CCCN EAri ECtt EHyd GEdr LBar LCro LOPS LRHS NHpl NRHS SEdd SPad SPoG WHlf
- - JEWEL OF DESERT GRENADE ('Dsaa131'PBR)	CPla LCro SEdd
- - 'Jewel of Desert Moon Stone'PBR	CCCN EAri ECtt EHyd EPfP LBar LRHS NHpl NRHS WHlf WIce
- - JEWEL OF DESERT OPAL ('Dsab131'PBR) **new**	GEdr WIce
- - 'Jewel of Desert Peridott'PBR	CBod CCCN CWGN ECtt EHyd EPfP GEdr LBar LRHS NHpl NRHS SCoo SPad SPoG WHlf WIce
- - JEWEL OF DESERT ROSEQUARTZ ('12Rosk1'PBR)	CBod CCCN EHyd LRHS NRHS SEdd SPoG WHlf
- - 'Jewel of Desert Ruby'PBR	CCCN CWGN NHpl SEdd WIce
- - JEWEL OF DESERT SUNSTONE ('18sun52'PBR) **new**	SEdd
- - 'Jewel of Desert Topaz'PBR	CCCN CWGN EAri ECtt EHyd EPfP LBar LRHS NHpl NRHS SPoG WHlf WIce
- (Wheels of Wonder Series) FIRE WONDER ('Wowdry2'PBR)	CPla LBar
- - GOLDEN WONDER ('Wowd20111'PBR)	CCCN LBar LCro LOPS SPoG
- - HOT PINK WONDER ('Wowdry1'PBR)	CPla LBar LCro LOPS
- - ORANGE WONDER ('Wowdoy3'PBR)	CCCN SPoG
- - VIOLET WONDER ('Wowdrw5'PBR)	CCCN SPoG
- - WHITE WONDER ('Wowdw7'PBR)	CCCN SPoG
dyeri RED MOUNTAIN ('Psdold')	CRos EDAr EHyd EPot LRHS NBwr NRHS NSla WIce XLum
ecklonis	GKev
'Emotion de Feu'	LRHS
FIRE SPINNER ('P001s')	EDAr WIce XLum
floribundum 'Starburst'	EPfP SSim
- 'Stardust'	EWes
§ 'John Proffitt'	CCCN EDAr GKev SPlb SRot WMal XSen
lavisiae 🏆H6	ELon EWes SPlb XSen
- 'Letseng'	LRHS
'Lesotho Pink'	EWes
'Lilac Queen'	SRot
lineare	XLum
MESA VERDE ('Kelaidis')	ECtt SPer XLum
nubigenum	CTri EBou ECtt EDAr ELan EPot GAbr GArf GKev NBwr NHpl SIvy SLee SPlb SSim XLum XSen
- LIMONCELLO ('Wow312') (Wheels of Wonder Series) **new**	LBar
'Ruby Coral'	see *Ectotropis seanii-boganii*
sphalmanthoides	EDAr EPot GEdr NBwr NHpl NSla SPlb SRot SSim WJur
(Sundella Series) SUNDELLA APRICOT **new**	LBar
- SUNDELLA LAVENDER **new**	LBar
- SUNDELLA NEON **new**	LBar
SUNTROPICS COPPER **new**	CGBo

SUNTROPICS HOT PINK **new**	CGBo
SUNTROPICS PURPLE **new**	CGBo
SUNTROPICS RED **new**	CGBo
sutherlandii ♀H3	CCCN EAri EDAr EPfP NHpl SEdd
- 'Peach Star'	CCCN EDAr NHpl SSim WIce
TABLE MOUNTAIN	see *D.* 'John Proffitt'

Delphinium ✿ (*Ranunculaceae*)

'After Midnight'	LHom
'Alice Artindale' (d)	LHom
ambiguum	see *Consolida ajacis*
'Ann Woodfield'	CNMi LHom
'Ariel' ambig.	LRHS
Astolat Group	CBcs CTri EHyd ELan EPfP EWoo GMaP GMcL LCro LOPS LRHS MBel MGos NHol NLar NRHS SCob SGbt SPer SPoG SWvt WCAu
(Aurora Series) 'Aurora Deep Purple'	LBar LCro
- 'Aurora Lavender'	LBar LCro
'Austin's Dawn Chorus'	LHom
'Bambi'	CNMi
Belladonna Group	MACG
- 'Atlantis'	ECha EHyd NLar WCot WSpi
- 'Bellamosum'	EPfP LRHS MNrw WSpi
- 'Casa Blanca'	EPfP GMaP LRHS NLar WSpi
- 'Cliveden Beauty'	CWCL EPfP EWTr GMaP LRHS NLar SCoo SPoG WSpi
- 'Gute Nacht'	IPot LRHS
§ - 'Janny Arrow'	LRHS
- 'Moerheimii'	WSpi
- 'Piccolo'	ECha NLar SCoo SPoG
- 'Pink Sensation'	see *D.* × *ruysii* 'Pink Sensation'
- 'Völkerfrieden'	LRHS MNrw NLar WCot WSpi
'Berghimmel'	LRHS
'Beryl Burton'	CNMi
Black Knight Group	CBcs CKel CTri ECtt EHyd ELan EPfP EWoo GDam GMaP GQue LCro LRHS LSRN MACG MCot MGos NGdn NHol NLar NRHS SCob SGbt SPer SPlb SPoG SWvt WCAu WFar WHlf
'Black Velvet'	WNPC
'Black-eyed Angels' (New Millennium Series)	EHyd ELan EWTr IPot LRHS NRHS SBls SGbt WHlf
'Blue Arrow'	see *D.* (Belladonna Group) 'Janny Arrow', *D.* 'Blue Max Arrow'
Blue Bird Group	CBcs CTri CWal EHyd ELan EPfP GMaP GMcL LRHS MGos MPri NRHS SCob SEdd SGbt SPer SPoG WCAu
'Blue Butterfly'	see *D. grandiflorum* 'Blue Butterfly'
'Blue Dawn' ♀H5	CNMi LHom
Blue Fountains Group	LSRN SPoG SRms
Blue Jade Group	LHom
'Blue Jay'	EPfP LSRN MACG WHlf WSpi
'Blue Lace'	CDor CPla EHyd IPot SGbt
I 'Blue Lace' (New Millennium Series)	CAby ECtt EPfP LCro LOPS NLar SCoo SHar WSpi
§ 'Blue Max Arrow'	LRHS
'Blue Nile' ♀H5	CNMi LBar LHom LRHS NRHS SPoG
Blue Springs Group	NGdn
'Blue Tit'	CNMi LHom
'Blueberry Pie' (Highlander Series) (d)	LRHS SCob SPoG WCot
'Bolero'	EHyd EPfP LRHS MPri NRHS SCoo SPoG WCot
'Boudicca'	CNMi
'Bruce' ♀H5	LHom LRHS
brunonianum	GRum
'Butterball'	CNMi LHom
Cameliard Group	CBcs CKel ELan EPfP LCro LOPS NLar NRHS SPer SPoG
- Cameliard' (Pacific Hybrid Series)	CKel
cashmerianum	CSpe EBee GRum
'Cassius'	LHom
(Centurion Series) 'Centurion Sky Blue' ♀H5	LBar LCro
- 'Centurion White'	LCro LOPS
'Cha Cha'	CBcs EBee EHyd EPfP LRHS MPri NLar NRHS WCot WTor
'Chelsea Star'	LHom LRHS
'Cherry Blossom'	EHyd EPfP NLar WHlf
'Cherub' ♀H5	CRos EHyd LRHS NRHS
chinense	see *D. grandiflorum*
'Christel'	LRHS LSRN MCot NLar
'Claire'	CNMi
'Clifford Sky' ♀H5	CRos EHyd LRHS NRHS
'Cobalt Dreams' (New Millennium Series)	CDor LSun SGBe
'Conspicuous' ♀H5	LHom
'Constance Rivett'	LHom
'Crown Jewel'	LRHS
'Crystal Delight' (Highlander Series) (d)	EHyd ELan LRHS MBriF MPri NRHS SCob SPad SPoG WCot
'Cupid'	LHom
'Dark Blue Black Bee' (Excalibur Series)	SPoG
'Dark Blue Black' (Excalibur Series)	EPfP
'Dark Blue White Bee' (Excalibur Series)	EPfP GMcL LRHS SPoG WHlf
'Darling Sue'	CNMi LHom
'Diamant' PBR	LRHS
'Dreaming Spires'	SRms
'Dunsden Green'	LHom
Dusky Maidens Group	CAby CDor EHyd ELan EPfP LCro LOPS LRHS NLar SCoo SGbt SPoG
elatum (Aurora Series) 'Aurora Blue'	LBar LCro WWke
- - 'Aurora Light Blue'	LBar LCro
- - 'Aurora White'	LBar LCro
- 'Blushing Brides' (New Millennium Series)	EBee EHyd EPfP LRHS SPoG
- CINDERELLA ('Dd2011') **new**	LCro
- 'Dasante Blue'	LRHS
- 'Double Innocence' (New Millennium Series) (d)	CAby CDor EHyd ELan EPfP LRHS NLar NRHS SCoo
- 'Morning Lights' (New Millennium Series)	CDor EHyd EPfP LRHS NLar NRHS SCoo SPoG
- 'Sweethearts' (New Millennium Series) ♀H5	EBee ECtt EPfP LCro LOPS SBls SCoo SGBe
'Elizabeth Cook' ♀H5	LHom
'Elmfreude'	LRHS WSpi
'Emily Hawkins' ♀H5	CNMi LHom
exaltatum	CSpe
'Fanfare'	LHom
'Faust' ♀H5	CRos EHyd IPot LHom LRHS MCot MPri NRHS SCoo SPoG WSpi
'Fenella' ♀H5	CNMi CRos EHyd LHom LRHS NRHS
'Finsteraarhorn'	LRHS MAvo MCot WSpi
'Flamenco'	CBcs CMiW EHyd EPfP LRHS MBriF MPri NLar NRHS SCob SPad SPoG WCAu WCot WTor
'Foxhill Nina' ♀H5	LHom
Galahad Group	CBcs CKel ECtt EHyd ELan EPfP EWoo GMaP GMcL GQue LRHS MBel MCot NGdn NHol NRHS SCob SGbt SHar SPer SPlb SPoG WCAu WHlf
'Galahad' (Pacific Hybrid Series)	LCro LOPS MGos NLar
'Gemini'	LHom
'Gemma'	CNMi LHom
'Gillian Dallas'	LHom

	'Gordon Forsyth'	LHom
	'Gossamer'	CNMi NLar
§	***grandiflorum***	EBee
§	- 'Blue Butterfly'	CSpe EPfP LRHS NRHS SPlb SPoG
	- Delfix Series	CRos LRHS
	- 'Diamonds Blue' **new**	MDon
	- (Summer Series) 'Summer Blues'	EDAr
	- - 'Summer Colors'	EDAr
	- - 'Summer Nights'	CRos EDAr EHyd EPfP LRHS NRHS SCoo SPoG
	- 'White Butterfly'	EHyd LRHS NRHS
	'Green Twist' (New Millennium Series)	CDor EHyd EPfP LRHS NRHS SCob
	Guardian Series	WFar
	- 'Guardian Blue'	LRHS MACG NRHS SPoG
	- 'Guardian Lavender'	LRHS MACG NRHS SPoG
	- 'Guardian White'	LRHS MACG NRHS SPoG
	Guinevere Group	CBcs ECtt EPfP SPer SPoG
	'Guy Langdon'	CNMi
	HIGHLANDER BOLERO ('Coadelbol'PBR) (d) **new**	ELan
	hotulae	EBee
	iliense from Kyrgyzstan	GGro
I	'Independence'	LRHS
	'Innocence'	LRHS LSun SCob SGBe WSpi
	ithaburense	SPhx
	'Jill Curley' ♀H5	CRos EHyd LRHS NRHS
	kamaonense	GGro
	'Kennington Classic' ♀H5	LHom
	'Kestrel' ♀H5	CNMi LHom
	King Arthur Group	CBcs CTsd ELan EPfP LCro LOPS LSRN MBel MGos SCob SCoo SHar SPer SPoG WHlf
	'La Bohème'	WSpi
	'Langdon's Orpheus'	LHom
§	'Langdon's Royal Flush'	CRos EHyd LRHS NRHS
	'Lanzenträger'	LRHS
	'Lavengro' **new**	WHlf
	'Leonora'	CNMi
	'Light Blue White Bee' (Excalibur Series)	SPoG
	'Lillian Basset'	LHom
	'Loch Leven'	CNMi
	'Loch Nevis'	LHom
	'Lord Butler' ♀H5	CNMi EBee LHom LRHS
	'Lucia Sahin' ♀H5	CNMi LHom
	maackianum	GGro SBrt WCot
	Magic Fountains Series	GDam LRHS MACG MBros MDon SPlb SPoG SVic WWke
	- 'Magic Fountains Blue/White Bee'	CBod EPfP MBros SRms
	- 'Magic Fountains Bright Eye'	SRms
	- 'Magic Fountains Cherry Blossom'	CBod EPfP SPoG SRms
	- 'Magic Fountains Dark Blue'	CBod CWCL EPfP GMaP LSRN NLar SPoG SRms WFar
	- 'Magic Fountains Deep Blue'	SRms
	- 'Magic Fountains Deep Rose/White Bee'	SRms
	- 'Magic Fountains Lavender'	CWCL EPfP NLar NRHS SRms
	- 'Magic Fountains Lilac Pink'	CWCL EPfP SPoG SRms WFar
	- 'Magic Fountains Lilac Rose'	NRHS SCoo SPoG SRms
	- 'Magic Fountains Pure White'	CBod CWCL EPfP EWTr MBros NRHS SRms WFar
	- 'Magic Fountains Sky Blue'	EPfP SPoG SRms WFar
	- 'Magic Fountains The Blues'	SRms
	- 'Magic Fountains White Pixie'	SRms
	'Margaret' ♀H5	LHom
	'Marilyn Clarrissa'	CNMi
	'Melanie Avery'	LHom
	'Merlin' ambig.	LRHS
	'Michael Ayres' ♀H5	CNMi LHom
	'Mighty Atom'	CNMi LHom
	'Min' ♀H5	LHom
	'Misty Mauves' (New Millennium Series) (d)	EHyd EPfP LRHS NRHS SCoo WSpi
	'Molly Buchanan'	CNMi NLar
	'Moon Light'PBR (Highlander Series) (d)	ECtt EPfP LRHS LSun MPri SCob SPoG WCot XLum
	'Moonbeam'	LRHS SPoG
	'Moonlight Blues' (New Millennium Series)	EHyd LPla SGbt
	'Morgentau'	LRHS NLar
	'Morning Sunrise'PBR (Highlander Series) (d)	LPla LRHS LSun SCob SPoG WCot
	'Mrs Newton Lees'	LRHS
	'Mydark'	LHom
	'Ned Rose'	MAvo
	New Zealand hybrids	WFar
	nudicaule	SPlb
	- 'Laurin'	EDAr
	- 'Redcap'	CRos LRHS
	'Olive Poppleton' ♀H5	LHom
	'Oliver' ♀H5	LHom
	'Our Deb' ♀H5	LHom
	'Ouvertüre'	LRHS
	Pacific hybrids	EPfP LCro LOPS LSRN MHer SRms SWvt WCav
	'Pagan Purples' (New Millennium Series) (d)	CAby EHyd EPfP LCro LOPS LRHS MBros NLar NRHS SCoo WSpi
	Percival Group	EPfP LSto
	'Pericles'	LHom
	'Pink' (Excalibur Series)	SPoG
	'Pink Punch' (New Millennium Series)	ELan EPfP LRHS LSun WHlf
	'Pink Ruffles'	LHom
	'Plagu Blue'PBR	WSpi
	PRINCESS CAROLINE ('Odabar')	LRHS MPri
	'Pure White' (Excalibur Series)	EPfP SPoG
	'Purple Passion' (New Millennium Series)	CDor EHyd ELan EPfP LRHS LSun SBls SPoG WHlf
	'Purple Surprise' (Highlander Series) (d)	LRHS
	'Red Caroline'	SPeP WHlf
	requienii	CBgR CCBP CSpe SPhx WKif
	'Rose Butterfly' (d)	EHyd LRHS NRHS
	'Rosemary Brock' ♀H5	LHom
	'Royal Aspirations' (New Millennium Series)	EHyd ELan EPfP LRHS SGbt SPoG
	'Royal Flush'	see *D.* 'Langdon's Royal Flush'
	'Ruby'	CNMi
	'Ruby Tuesday'	CNMi
	'Ruby Wedding'	CNMi LHom
§	× ***ruysii*** 'Pink Sensation'	LRHS SGbt WSpi
	'Sandpiper'	LHom
	'Sarita'	WHlf
	'Schildknappe'	LRHS
	'Schönbuch'	LRHS
	'Secret'PBR	LRHS WCot
§	***semibarbatum***	EMor
	'Sherbet Lemon'	WHlf WTor
	'Shieldbearer'	LRHS
	'Sky Sensation'	LRHS
	'Snow Queen Arrow'	LRHS
	'Sommerabend'	LRHS
	'Sooty'	CNMi

'Spindrift' ♀H5	CNMi CRos EHyd LHom LRHS NRHS
'Starlight'PBR	LRHS
'Strawberry Fair'	LRHS MPri NLar NRHS SPoG
Summer Skies Group	CBcs CKel CTsd ELan EMor EPfP EWTr EWoo LCro LOPS LRHS MACG MGos SCob SHar SPer SPoG WCAu WHlf
'Summerfield Oberon'	LHom WCot
'Sungleam' ♀H5	CKel ECtt EWTr EWes IPot LHom NLar NRHS WHlf WSpi
'Sunkissed' ♀H5	CNMi LHom
'Sunny Skies' (New Millennium Series)	EHyd ELan LRHS
'Sweet Sensation'PBR (Highlander Series) (d)	EHyd ELan EPfP LPla LRHS LSun NLar NRHS SCob SPoG WCot WTor WTyc
'Sweetheart'	EHyd LRHS NRHS
'Tiger Eye'	LHom
'Titania'	LHom
'Trudy'	CNMi
'Turkish Delight'	LHom
uliginosum	SPlb
'Vanessa Mae'	CNMi LHom
variegatum	SBrt
vestitum	GGro
'Walton Benjamin'	LHom
'Walton Gemstone' ♀H5	LHom
'Wishful Thinking'PBR	CBcs
'Yvonne'	LRHS
zalil	see *D. semibarbatum*
'Zauberflöte'	LRHS

Dendranthema see *Chrysanthemum*

Dendriopoterium see *Sanguisorba*

Dendrobenthamia see *Cornus*

Dendrocalamus (*Poaceae*)

§ ***strictus***	SPlb

Dendromecon (*Papaveraceae*)

rigida	IDee WPGP

Dendropanax (*Araliaceae*)

cf. ***kwangsiensis*** FMWJ 13274	WCru
trifidus	WPGP
- B&SWJ 11230	WCru

Dendroseris (*Asteraceae*)

litoralis	CCCN

Dennstaedtia (*Dennstaedtiaceae*)

punctilobula	EHyd LRHS

Dentaria see *Cardamine*

pinnata	see *Cardamine heptaphylla*
polyphylla	see *Cardamine kitaibelii*

Deparia (*Woodsiaceae*)

japonica	WCot

Dermatobotrys (*Scrophulariaceae*)

saundersii	ECre WCot

Derwentia see *Parahebe*

Deschampsia ✿ (*Poaceae*)

cespitosa	CBod CEme CKel CKno CPud CWal EHeP EPPr EPfP GKev LCro LOPS LRHS MBel NBwr SCoo SEdd SPhx SPlb WCot XLum
- BRONZE VEIL	see *D. cespitosa* 'Bronzeschleier'
§ - 'Bronzeschleier'	CBWd CBod CDor CWCL EBee EGrl EHyd ELan ELon EMor EPPr EPfP GMaP LRHS LSto MAsh MHol NGdn NRHS NWsh SCob SPer SPhx SRms SWvt WCAu WFar WHlf XLum
- 'Cabana Buta'	LEdu SPhx WPGP
- 'Coral Cloud'	GQue
- 'Fairy's Joke'	see *D. cespitosa* var. *vivipara*
- 'Garnet Schist'	EPPr GQue LEdu LRHS SHor SPhx WPGP
- GOLD DUST	see *D. cespitosa* 'Goldstaub'
- GOLDEN DEW	see *D. cespitosa* 'Goldtau'
- GOLDEN PENDANT	see *D. cespitosa* 'Goldgehänge'
- GOLDEN SHOWER	see *D. cespitosa* 'Goldgehänge'
- GOLDEN VEIL	see *D. cespitosa* 'Goldschleier'
§ - 'Goldgehänge'	EPPr NBir XLum
§ - 'Goldschleier' ♀H6	CBar CBod CKel CRos CWCL EBee ECha EHyd ELon EMor EPPr EPfP GMaP LPal LRHS MAsh NGdn NRHS NWsh SCob SPer SPhx SWvt WFar WHlf WSpi XLum XSen
§ - 'Goldstaub'	EPPr
§ - 'Goldtau' ♀H6	Widely available
- 'Mill End'	CKno LEdu WPGP
- 'Morning Dew'	WFar
- 'Northern Lights' (v)	CSBt ELan EPfP LRHS SPoG SRms SWvt WPnP XLum
- 'Palava'	CKno EPPr
- 'Pixie Fountain'	EHyd EPfP GQue LRHS MNrw NDov NWsh SBls
- 'Schottland'	CKno EBee ECha EPPr GBin LEdu
- 'Tardiflora'	EBee SMHy XSen
- 'Tauträger'	ELon GQue SMHy
§ - var. ***vivipara***	EPPr NBro
- 'Waldschatt'	EBee ECha EPPr
- 'Willow Green'	SCoo
- 'Yunnan'	EPPr
flexuosa	CKno EHyd LRHS NBir NRHS NWsh SPhx
- 'Tatra Gold' ♀H6	CWCL ECha ECtt EHeP EHyd ELan GDam GMaP LRHS LSto MACG NBir NBro NLar NRHS NSti SCob SCoo SPer SPoG SRot SWvt
'Silver Mist' **new**	EBlo

Desfontainia (*Columelliaceae*)

§ ***spinosa*** ♀H4	CAbb CBcs CBod CDoC CKel CMac CPla CTri EBee EHyd ELan EPfP GAbr GArf GKev GKin GMcL IArd LRHS MAsh MBlu MGil NFav NLar SPer SPoG SRms SSha WFar WSHC
- 'Harold Comber'	CMac
- f. ***hookeri***	see *D. spinosa*

Desmodium (*Fabaceae*)

callianthum	CMac SBrt SMad WSHC
canadense	EAJP NLar SBls SPhx
§ ***elegans***	CBcs CExl EBee ELan EPfP LPar NLar NSti SBrt SMad SVen WSHC
- dark-flowered	EBee SMad WCFE WPGP
praestans	see *D. yunnanense*
tiliifolium	see *D. elegans*
§ ***yunnanense***	CExl WSHC

Deuterocohnia (*Bromeliaceae*)

sp.	WCot
brevifolia ♀H2	NCft SEdd WCot WPGP
lotteae	WCot

Deutzia ✿ (*Hydrangeaceae*)

bhutanensis HWJK 2180	WCru
'Bright Eyes'	WPGP

calycosa	MBlu
- BWJ 8007	WCru
- 'Dali'	CBcs CExl EHed EPfP IArd IDee NLar SDys SMad WKif
chunii	see *D. ningpoensis*
compacta	CBcs CMCN WPGP
- 'Lavender Time'	CDoC CExl CKel CMac EBee ELan EPfP EWTr GKev LRHS MAsh NLar SWvt WGob
cordatula B&SWJ 3720	WCru
- B&SWJ 6917	WCru
corymbosa	MRav
- GWJ 9202	WCru
- GWJ 9203	WCru
- GWJ 9339	WCru
- var. ***corymbosa***	WSpi
crenata B&SWJ 8886	WCru
- B&SWJ 8896	WCru
- B&SWJ 8924	WCru
- 'Flore Pleno'	see *D. scabra* 'Plena'
- var. ***heterotricha*** B&SWJ 5805	WCru
- - B&SWJ 8879	WCru
- var. ***nakaiana*** B&SWJ 11184	WCru
- - 'Nikko'	see *D. gracilis* 'Nikko'
§ - 'Pride of Rochester' (d) ♀H5	CBcs CBod CDoC CMCN CTsd ELan EPfP GKin ILea LSto MBlu MGil MMuc MRav NLar SCob SEle SPoG SWvt WLov
'Dark Eyes'	CExl GBin SChF SMad
discolor 'Major'	CExl WCru WGob
× ***elegantissima***	SRms
- 'Fasciculata'	CBod CKel EHyd ELan EPfP LRHS MGil NLar SPer SWvt WBor WLov WSpi
- 'Rosealind' ♀H5	CBcs CCCN CDoC CKel CMac CRos CTri EBee ELan EPfP GKin IArd LRHS LSRN MGil MRav SPer SRms SWvt WCFE WGob WHtc WKif WSpi
glabrata B&SWJ 617	WCru
- B&SWJ 8427	WCru
glomeruliflora	CMCN
- BWJ 7742	WCru
gracilis	CSBt ELan EPfP GArf GDam GKin LPar MAsh MGil MGos MRav MSwo NLar SNig SOrN SPer WFar WGob WHtc WSpi
- B&SWJ 8927	WCru
- 'Aurea'	CMac EPfP
- 'Carminea'	see *D. × rosea* 'Carminea'
§ - 'Marmorata' (v)	WAvo WHtc
§ - 'Nikko' ♀H5	Widely available
- var. ***ogatae*** B&SWJ 8911	WCru
- 'Rosea'	see *D. × rosea*
- 'Variegata'	see *D. gracilis* 'Marmorata'
hookeriana	CKel EHyd EPfP LRHS SBrt SWvt WGob
× ***hybrida*** 'Contraste' ♀H5	CMac WLov
- 'Iris Alford'	CKel CRos EHyd EPfP LRHS MGos WPGP WSpi
- 'Joconde' ♀H5	WFar
- 'Magicien' misapplied	see *D. × hybrida* 'Strawberry Fields'
- 'Magicien' ambig.	CBod CKel EGrl SGBe WAvo WSpi
- 'Magicien' Lemoine	CMac CRos CSBt EBee EHyd ELan EPfP LRHS MAsh MRav MSwo NBir SPer SRms SWvt WFar WKif WSpi
- 'Mont Rose' ♀H5	Widely available
- 'Perle Rose'	ILea NLar
§ - 'Strawberry Fields' ♀H5	Widely available
× ***kalmiiflora***	CBod CBrac CMac CSBt CTri EHeP ELan GDam GKin MAsh MGil MMrt MRav NLar SPer SRms SSha WFar WLov
× ***lemoinei***	WHtc
longifolia	CMCN WPGP
- 'Veitchii'	CSBt EPfP MGil MRav WCFE WSpi
- 'Vilmoriniae'	MRav
× ***magnifica***	ILea LIns MMrt SCob SGbt SGsty SRms
- 'Rubra'	see *D. × hybrida* 'Strawberry Fields'
maximowicziana B&SWJ 11567	WCru
monbeigii ♀H5	CExl CKel ELan EPfP LRHS MRav SWvt WGob WKif WSpi
- BWJ 7728	WCru
multiradiata	CExl EBee GBin LRHS MBlu MMrt NLar WPGP
§ ***ningpoensis***	CBcs CBod EBee ELan EPfP EWTr MBlu MGil NLar SPer WCFE WLov WPGP WSpi
paniculata B&SWJ 8592	ESwi WCru
parviflora var. ***barbinervis*** B&SWJ 8478	WCru
'Pink Pompon'	see *D.* 'Rosea Plena'
prunifolia B&SWJ 8588	WCru
pulchra	CBcs CDoC CEnd CKel CMCN EBee EHyd ELan EPfP LCro LRHS MGil MMuc MRav NLar SBrt SGBe SPer SPoG WGob WLov WPGP WSpi
- B&SWJ 1738	WCru
- B&SWJ 3870	WCru
- B&SWJ 3948 from the Philippines	WCru
- B&SWJ 6908	WCru
- pink-tinged	WPGP
purpurascens BWJ 7859	WCru
- 'Alpine Magician'	WKif
RASPBERRY SUNDAE ('Low 18'PBR)	LCro LRHS SGBe SRHi
§ × ***rosea***	CEnd CRos EGrl EHyd EPfP GJos LIns LRHS MAsh NRHS SRms WGob WKif
- 'Campanulata'	MSwo SRHi
§ - 'Carminea'	ILea MGil SDix SPlb SRms WFar WLov
§ 'Rosea Plena' (d)	CBod CEme CEnd CMac CSBt EHyd ELan EPfP GKin GMcL LBuc LRHS MAsh MGos NLar NRHS SEle SPoG SRms SWvt WFar WGob WHtc
× ***rosea*** YUKI CHERRY BLOSSOM ('Ncdx2')	CBcs EHed EPfP LBuc LCro LRHS MAsh NLar SGol
- YUKI SNOWFLAKE ('Ncdx1')	LCro LRHS MAsh NLar
scabra	CBrac CTri
- B&SWJ 11127	WCru
- B&SWJ 11168	WCru
- B&SWJ 11178	WCru
§ - 'Candidissima' (d) ♀H5	EHeP MGil MMuc MRav SEND SPer WFar WGob WLov
- 'Codsall Pink' ♀H5	EFPl MRav
§ - 'Plena' (d)	CBrac EPfP GKin LIns NBwr NLar SGsty SPer SPoG SRHi WCFE
- 'Pride of Rochester'	see *D. crenata* 'Pride of Rochester'
- 'Punctata' (v)	MAsh SRms
- 'Robert Fortune'	SPlb
- 'Variegata' (v)	CMac
setchuenensis	CMac MRav
- PAB 7449	LEdu
- var. ***corymbiflora*** ♀H5	CBcs CExl CKel CMCN CTri EBee ECre EHyd ELan EPfP GKev LRHS MSwo NLar SAko SChF SEle SPoG

	SWvt WFar WGob WHtc WKif WLov WPGP WSpi
- - NJM 11.096	WPGP
- - 'Kiftsgate'	CExl WPGP
taiwanensis	CMCN EBee EPfP WPGP
- B&SWJ 6858	WCru
- CWJ 12443	WCru
- CWJ 12459	WCru
× ***wellsii***	see *D. scabra* 'Candidissima'
× ***wilsonii***	SRms

Dianella ✿ (*Hemerocallidaceae*)

caerulea	CMac EBee MMrt NBir NLar SMrm
- 'Caspar Blue'	LPal
- CASSA BLUE ('Dbb03'[PBR])	CBcs CCht CEme EHyd EPfP LRHS MHol NRHS
- LITTLE JESS ('Dcmp01'[PBR])	EBee
- 'Variegata'	see *D. tasmanica* 'Variegata'
nigra	LEdu
- 'Margaret Pringle' (v)	SSha
revoluta	CBor
§ - 'Allyn Citation'[PBR]	CBcs XSte
- 'Blue Stream'	EBee
- COOLVISTA	see *D. revoluta* 'Allyn Citation'
- LITTLE REV ('Dr5000'[PBR])	CBod CCht EBee EPfP SEle SSha WSHC XSte
'Streetscape'	EBee
tasmanica	CAbb CBor CElw CKno CMac CTri CTsd CWal ECre ELan EPfP EShb GBin LEdu LPal SMad SRms SSha SVen WAvo WSHC
- DESTINY ('Tas100')	CCht CPla ELan LRHS MCot SMrm
- 'Emerald Arch'	LEdu
- 'Little Devil'	SSha
- TASRED ('Tr20'[PBR])	CBcs CBod CCht ELan EPfP MBNS SCob SIvy
§ - 'Variegata' (v)	CCCN CDTJ

Dianthus ✿ (*Caryophyllaceae*)

from Uzbekistan **new**	EPPr
'Aicardi' (pf)	CNMi
'Alan Titchmarsh' (p)	EPfP MGos SPoG SWvt
'Alice Forbes Improved' (b) **new**	NGKc
'Alice Lever' (p)	WAbe
§ 'Allen's Maria' (p)	LShi
'Allspice' (p)	WHoo
(Allwoodii Group) 'Alice' (p)	CCal EBtc
- 'Alyson' (p)	LShi
- 'Bobby' (p)	LShi
- 'Bovey Belle' (p)	LShi
- CHERRY DAIQUIRI ('Wp15 Pie42'[PBR]) (Cocktails Series) (p)	CCal EHyd EPfP LRHS MPri NRHS SGBe SRGP WCot
- 'Dennis' (p)	LShi
- 'Doris' pre-1932 (p)	LShi
- 'Doris' pre-1954 (p) $\mathbb{Y}^{H6}$	CAby CBcs CCal ECtt EGrI EHyd EPfP GMaP GQue LCro LOPS LRHS LSRN LShi MGos MHer MRav NGdn NRHS SCob SEND SPer SPlb SPoG SRGP SRms SWvt WCAu WCFE WGwG
- 'Doris Majestic' (p)	LShi
- 'Eileen' (p)	LShi
I - 'Fiona' (p)	LShi
- 'Hope' Allwood, pre-1932 (p) **new**	LShi
- 'Hope' Allwood, 1946 (p)	CCal LShi
- 'Purple Jenny' (p)	LShi
- SHIRLEY TEMPLE ('Wp15 Pie44'[PBR]) (Cocktails Series) (p)	CCal EHyd EPfP LRHS NRHS SGBe
- 'Susan' (p)	CCal
- TEQUILA SUNRISE ('Wp15 Pie45'[PBR]) (Cocktails Series) (p)	CCal EHyd LRHS MPri NRHS SGBe SRGP
Allwoodii Alpinus Group (p)	NGdn SRms XLum
alpinus $\mathbb{Y}^{H6}$	GJos MMuc NSla
- 'Albus' (p)	GArf NWad
- 'Darcies Love' (p)	EDAr
- 'Joan's Blood' (p) $\mathbb{Y}^{H6}$	NHpl
- 'Millstream Salmon' (p)	WFar
- red-flowered	NSla
amurensis	EPPr SPhx XLum
- 'Siberian Blue' (p)	EPPr
anatolicus	CBor CCal CRos EBou EHyd GJos GQue LRHS MBel MHer NGdn NRHS XLum XSen
'Anders Fay Seagrave' (p)	LShi
'Anders Irene Ann' (pf)	CNMi
'Anders Melody' (p)	LShi
'Anders Old Trafford' (p) **new**	CNMi
'Anders Our Meg' (p) **new**	CNMi
'Anders Patricia Griffiths' (p)	CNMi LShi
'Anders Red Devil' (p) **new**	CNMi
'Anders Supernova' (p)	CTri
'Anders Victoria Louise' (pf) **new**	CNMi
'Angela Carol' (pf)	CNMi
'Ann Franklin' (pf) $\mathbb{Y}^{H2}$	CNMi
'Anne S. Moore' (b)	NGKc
'Annette' (p)	CCal CRos EDAr EHyd LRHS NGdn NHol NRHS SLee SRGP SRot SWvt
'Annie Claybourne' (pf)	CNMi
'Annie Harmer' (pf) **new**	CNMi
ARCTIC STAR	see *D.* 'Devon Arctic Star'
arenarius	NGdn SBls SPlb
- 'Little Maiden' (p)	CCal CSpe EDAr MACG NGdn SBls SHar SLee
- 'Snow Flurries' (p)	ITim
'Argus' (p)	LShi
armeria	CAby CBgR NAts WHer WOut
arpadianus var. ***pumilus***	EPot
'Arthur Holmes' (pf)	CNMi
§ × ***arvernensis*** (p) $\mathbb{Y}^{H6}$	ECha SGro
'Ashley Reay' (p)	CNMi
'Audrey Robinson' (pf)	CNMi
'Auvergne'	see *D.* × *arvernensis*
'Averiensis'	see *D.* 'Berlin Snow'
AZTEC STAR ('Wp19 Nam02') (p) **new**	SHar
'Bailey's Celebration' (p)	CCal SRms WHlf
'Banana' (pf) **new**	CNMi
barbatus	MPri
- ***albus***	LSto
- AURICULA EYED MIXED (p,a)	LSto
- Dash Series (p,a)	MHol
- - 'Dash Crimson' (p,a)	MHol
- - 'Dash Magician' (p,a)	CBod MHol MPri SCob WHil
- 'Diabunda Purple Picotee' (Diabunda Series) (p,a)	SCob
- - 'Diabunda Red' (p,a)	SCob
- - 'Diabunda Rose' (p,a)	SCob
- double-flowered (p,a/d) **new**	LSto
- EXCELSIOR MIXED (p,a) **new**	LSto
- Festival Series (p,a)	MBros
- - 'Festival Raspberry' (p,a)	SCob

	- - 'Festival Red' (p,a)	SCob
	- - 'Festival White Flame' (p,a)	SCob
	- GREEN TRICK ('Temarisou'^{PBR}) (p,a)	LCro LOPS WNPC
	- 'Heart Attack' (p,a)	WCot WMal
	- Indian Carpet Group (p,a)	LCro MBros
	- Messenger Group (p,a)	SVic
	- 'Monksilver Black' (p,a)	CBod CSpe EBee ECha ECtt GElm LEdu LShi LSun MPie NCou NSti SIvy SMad SPad WBrk WCot WMal WSHC WTyc
	- Nigrescens Group (p,a) 🏆^{H7}	CSpe LBar SPhx
	- - 'Sooty' (p,a)	GJos LSto NCth SAng WFar WHer
	- 'Sweet Black Cherry' (Sweet Series) (p,a) **new**	WWke
§	'Bat's Double Red' (p)	LShi
	'Beamish Cherry' (b) **new**	NGKc
	'Beamish Cherry Ripple' (b) **new**	NGKc
	'Beamish Devil' (b) **new**	NGKc
	'Beamish Wood' (b) **new**	NGKc
	'Becky Robinson' (p) 🏆^{H6}	CNMi LShi
	'Belle of Bookham' (b)	NGKc
§	'Berlin Snow' (p)	CRos EDAr EHyd EPot GArf ITim LRHS LShi NRHS
	'Betty Morton' (p) 🏆^{H6}	CBor EHyd LRHS NRHS
	'Betty's Choice' (pf)	CNMi
	'Binsey Red' (p)	SBut SGro
	'Black and White Minstrels' (p,a)	CCal
	'Blackberry Ice' (pf) **new**	CNMi
	'Blue Hills' (p)	GKev
	'Blush'	see *D.* 'Souvenir de la Malmaison'
	BLUSHING STAR ('Wp19 Nam01') (p) **new**	SHar WTor
	'Bob's Highlight' (pf)	CNMi
	'Bofield Emily' (b)	NGKc
	'Bombardier' (p)	ECtt GMaP
	'Braeside Boy' (b) **new**	NGKc
	brevicaulis	CCal GJos
	BRIDAL STAR ('Wp18 cas06') (p) **new**	NDov
	'Bridal Veil' (p)	CCal LShi SBut SGro SRGP WHer WHlf
	'Brilliant'	see *D. deltoides* 'Brilliant'
	'Brilliant Star' (p) 🏆^{H6}	ECtt EHyd LRHS NRHS SBut SWvt WIce
	'Brockenhurst' (pf)	CNMi
	'Bruce' (pf) **new**	CNMi
	'Brympton Red' (p)	CCal CFis ECha LShi
	BUBBLEGUM ('Wp15val12') (p)	CCal
§	'Caesar's Mantle' (p)	EPPr
	caesius	see *D. gratianopolitanus*
	'Calypso Star' (p)	ECtt SPoG
	'Can-can' (pf)	ECtt
	CANDY FLOSS	see *D.* 'Devon Flavia'
§	'Carmine Letitia Wyatt'^{PBR} (p) 🏆^{H6}	CCal CRos ECtt EHyd NRHS SCoo SPoG
	CARMINE VALDA	see *D.* 'Devon Louise'
	carthusianorum	Widely available
	- W&B BGL-1	WCot
	- subsp. ***carthusianorum*** **new**	GElm
I	- 'Rupert's Pink' (p)	CCal LSto NGdn SHar SWvt
	- tan-flowered (p)	SMHy
	caryophyllus	CLau ENfk SVic
	'Charles' (p)	LShi
	'Charles Edward' (p)	LShi
	'Charles Musgrave'	see *D.* 'Musgrave's Pink'
	'Chastity' (p)	CCal ECtt LShi WHoo
	Cheddar pink	see *D. gratianopolitanus*
	CHERRY BURST ('Wp19 Mou01') (p) **new**	LCro SHar
	'Cheryl'	see *D.* 'Houndspool Cheryl'
	'Chetwyn Ruth Gillies' (pf)	CNMi
	CHILI	see *D.* CRACKER
	chinensis 'Black and White' (p,a)	CCal CWCL
I	- 'Valentine' (p,a)	LRHS
	'Chomley Farran' (b)	CSpe
	cintranus subsp. ***cintranus***	WCot
	'Clara's Choice' (pf) **new**	CNMi
	'Clare' (p)	LShi
	'Claret Joy' (p) 🏆^{H6}	ECtt LShi MMuc SEND
	'Cleopatra' (pf)	EMal
§	'Cockenzie Pink' (p)	CCal LShi SGro WHer
	COCONUT SUNDAE ('Wp 05 Yves'^{PBR}) (Scent First Series) (p) 🏆^{H6}	CCal CSBt ECtt EHyd ELan ELon EPfP LBar LRHS LSRN MCot NRHS SCob SCoo SGBe
	'Constance' (p)	LShi
	'Constance Finnis'	see *D.* 'Fair Folly'
	'Conwy Silver' (p)	WAbe
	'Conwy Star' (p)	EPot WAbe
	'Coral Reef'^{PBR} (Scent First Series) (p)	CCal ECtt EHyd ELan LRHS NRHS SGBe SPoG WHlf
	'Corona Blueberry Magic' (p,a)	LRHS
	'Corona Iceberry Magic' (p,a)	EHyd LRHS NRHS
	'Corona Lavender Magic' (p,a)	LRHS
	'Corona Raspberry Magic' (p,a)	LRHS
	'Corona Strawberry Magic' (p,a)	LRHS
	'Coronation Ruby' (p) 🏆^{H6}	LShi
	corsicus	XSen
	COSMOPOLITAN ('Wp15 Pie43'^{PBR}) (p)	CCal CRos EHyd EPfP LRHS MPri NRHS SGBe
	'Coste Budde' (p)	WSHC
§	CRACKER ('Wp10 Sab06'^{PBR}) (Early Bird Series) (p)	CCal EHyd LRHS NRHS
	'Cranberry Crush' (pf)	CNMi
	'Cranmere Pool' (p) 🏆^{H6}	CBcs CCal ECtt EHyd ELan EPfP GQue LCro LRHS LShi NFav NRHS SCoo SEND SPoG SWvt WCAu WFar
	'Crimson Warrior' (pf)	CNMi
	'Crompton Classic' (pf)	CNMi
	'Crompton Princess' (pf)	CNMi
	cruentus	Widely available
	'Cumbria' (pf)	CNMi
	'D.D.R.'	see *D.* 'Berlin Snow'
	'Dad's Favourite' (p)	LShi
	'Dainty Dame' (p) 🏆^{H4}	CRos CSpe CTri ECtt EHyd EPfP LRHS MNHC NRHS SCoo SGro SLee SPoG
	'Dancing Geisha'	EDAr LBar MACG SBls WHil WMal
	'Dante' (Sprint Series) (pt)	LRHS
	'David' (p)	EHeP LShi SCob
	'Dedham Beauty' (p)	SEND WCot
	deltoides 🏆^{H6}	EGrI ENfk EPfP EWld EWoo GQue LCro LEdu LOPS MBow MNHC SCob SDix SPlb SRms WFar WWild
	- 'Albus' (p)	ECha EPfP LShi NGdn
	- 'Arctic Fire' (p)	CCal CGBo EPfP NFav NGdn NHol NSla SBls SPeP WFar
	- 'Bright Eyes' (p)	CCal
	- 'Bright Spark' (p) **new**	CBor
§	- 'Brilliant' (p)	CCal GJos LShi NGdn NHol SRms SVic
	- 'Broughty Blaze' (p)	LShi

	- FLASHING LIGHT	see *D. deltoides* 'Leuchtfunk'
§	- 'Leuchtfunk' (p)	CCal ECha EHyd EPfP LShi LSto NRHS NSla SMHy SPoG WFar
I	- 'Luneburg Heath Maiden Pink' (p)	EPfP NGdn
	- 'Nelli' (p)	NGdn
	- 'Roseus' (p)	GJos
	- 'Shrimp' (p)	ECtt NGdn
	'Desmond'	ELon
	'Devon' (pf) **new**	CNMi
§	'Devon Arctic Star' (Early Bird Series) (p)	CCal CRos EHyd ELan EPfP GMaP LRHS NBwr NRHS SEdd SPoG SRms SWvt WIce
	'Devon Cream' (p)	CCal ELan LRHS SCoo SPoG WHlf
	'Devon Dove' PBR (p) 𝕐 H6	CAby CCal ECtt EHyd ELan EPfP LRHS LSto NDov NRHS SGbt
	'Devon Esther'	see *D.* POP STAR
	'Devon Fatima'	see *D.* ICED GEM
§	'Devon Flavia' PBR (Scent First Series) (p) 𝕐 H6	CCal CRos EHyd GDam LRHS NRHS SCob SCoo SEdd SGBe SPoG WHlf
	'Devon Flores'	see *D.* SHOOTING STAR
	'Devon General' PBR (p)	CCal
§	'Devon Louise' PBR (p)	WFar
	'Devon Magic' PBR (p) 𝕐 H6	CCal ECtt LRHS
	'Devon Sapphire'	see *D.* MYSTIC STAR
§	'Devon Winnie' PBR (p)	CCal
	'Devon Wizard' (p) 𝕐 H6	CAby CCal ECtt EHyd EPfP LCro LOPS LRHS MBel MRav MSpe NDov NRHS SGbt WCAu WHlf
§	'Devon Xera' (p) 𝕐 H6	CCal GDam SEND
§	'Devon Yolande' PBR (Scent First Series) (p)	CCal EBee EHyd EPfP LRHS LSRN NRHS SCoo SPoG WHlf
	'Dewdrop' (p)	CCal EHyd LShi MAsh MMuc NBir SEND
	'Diana'	see *D.* DONA
	'Diane' (p) 𝕐 H6	ELon EPfP LPal LShi SPoG SRGP SWvt WFar
	'Dianne' (pf)	SRms WFar
	DIANTICA EARLY LOVE ('Kledg18267') (pt)	CRos
	DIANTICA PEACH PARTY ('Kledg12163') (pt)	CRos EPfP LCro LRHS MPri
	DIANTICA PURPLE WEDDING ('Kledg18274') (pt)	CRos LRHS
	DIANTICA STRAWBERRY CREAM ('Kledg15176' PBR) (pt)	EPfP LRHS
	DIANTICA WHITE WITH EYE ('Kledg11116') (pt)	EHyd LRHS NRHS
§	DONA ('Brecas') (pf)	XLum
	'Dora' (p)	EHyd LSto NRHS
	'Doreen Hodgson' (p)	LShi
	'Doris Allwood' (pf)	CNMi EMal
	'Doris Elite' (p)	LShi
	'Doris Ruby'	see *D.* 'Houndspool Ruby'
	'Doris Supreme' (p)	LShi
	'Double North' (p)	CTri
	'Dreamer' (p) **new**	CBor
	'Duchess of Roxburghe' (pf)	EMal
	'Duchess of Westminster' (M)	EMal LShi
	'Duke of Norfolk' (pf)	EMal
	'Earl Kelso' (pf)	EMal
	'Earl of Essex' (p)	LShi SBut
	'Edenside Scarlet' (b)	LShi
	'Eileen Lever' (p)	GArf WAbe WHoo
	'Eira Wen' (p)	EPot WAbe
	'Eleanor Parker' (p)	WAbe
	'Eleanor's Old Irish' (p)	CFis ECtt LRHS LShi WCot WHer
	'Elizabethan' (p)	CAby CFis GBin MCot SGro SRms WTor
*	'Elizabethan Pink' (p)	CCal LShi
	'Elsie Ketchen' (pf)	CNMi
	'Emile Paré' (p)	LShi
	'Emmeline Pankhurst' (pf)	CNMi
	'Emperor'	see *D.* 'Bat's Double Red'
	erinaceus	GArf GJos LShi
	- var. ***alpinus***	EPot ITim LShi
	- Duguid's	WAbe
	'Evening Star' (p) 𝕐 H6	CCal CRos CTri EHyd LRHS NRHS SPoG SWvt
	'Eve's Holly' (pf)	CNMi
§	'Fair Folly' (p)	CCal LShi WHer
	'Farnham Rose' (p)	LShi
	ferrugineus	EPPr LEdu LRHS SBrt SPhx
	'Fettes Mount' (p)	WAvo WBrk WCot WMal
	'Feuerhexe' (p)	XLum
	'Fimbriatus' (p)	WHoo
	FIRE STAR	see *D.* 'Devon Xera'
	'Firestar' (p)	CCal CTri EHyd ELan GMaP MAsh NGrs NRHS SWvt
	FIZZY ('Wp08 Ver03' PBR) (Early Bird Series) (p)	CRos EHyd ELan EPfP LRHS NRHS
	'Fleur' (p)	CCal
	'Florence Ellen' (p) **new**	CNMi
	'Florence Franklin' (pf)	CNMi
	'Flutterby' (p)	EPfP MDon WIce WTor
	'Fragrant Ann' (pf) 𝕐 H6	EMal
	'Frances Isabel' (p)	LShi
	'Frank Bruno' (pf)	CNMi
	'Freda Woodliffe' (p)	WAbe WHoo
	FRENCH RED (pf)	EMal
	freynii	GKev LShi WAbe
	FRILLY ('Wp08 Ulr03' PBR) (Early Bird Series) (p)	CCal CRos LRHS
	fringed pink	see *D. superbus*
	'Fusilier' (p)	CCal CRos CTri EBou ECtt EHyd EPfP EWoo GDam GMaP LRHS LShi MAsh NRHS SCoo SPoG SWvt
	giganteus	LRHS SHar SPhx WCot
	'Gingham Gown' (p)	CCal ECtt EPot LShi NBir
	glacialis	CCal
	'Glynis Taylor' (p) **new**	CNMi
	'Gold Dust' (p)	ECtt EPot EWTr GArf LShi
	'Gold Embrace' (pf)	CNMi
	'Golden Cross' (b) 𝕐 H6	NGKc
	'Grandma Calvert' (p)	LShi
	'Gran's Favourite' (p) 𝕐 H6	CAby CBcs CCal ECtt EGrI EHyd ELan EPfP LBar LCro LOPS LRHS LSRN LShi MBow MCot MGos MHol MMuc NGdn NRHS SEND SPlb SPoG SRGP SRms SWvt WHer WHlf
§	***gratianopolitanus*** 𝕐 H6	CBod CCal CTri ENfk EPfP GJos GKev GQue LShi MBow MHer NBid
	- from Cheddar	WWild
	- 'Albus' (p)	MHer
	- 'Babi Lom' (p)	LShi
	- dwarf	WAbe
*	- 'Karlik' (p)	GQue
	- 'Rosenfeder' (p)	XLum
§	- 'Tiny Rubies' (p)	EDAr LShi
	'Greensides' (p)	LShi
	Grenadin Group	CCal
	'Grey Dove' (b) 𝕐 H6	NGKc
	'Gypsy Star' (p)	SPoG
	haematocalyx	GArf GJos
	- 'Alpinus'	see *D. haematocalyx* subsp. *pindicola*
§	- subsp. ***pindicola***	EPot GKev WAbe
	'Hamish Berry' (p)	CNMi
	'Hampshire' (pf)	CNMi
	'Hannah Gertsen' (p)	LShi
	'Harlequin' (p)	LShi

	HAYTOR	see *D.* 'Haytor White'
	'Haytor Rock' (p) ♀H6	CCal EPfP LRHS LShi
§	'Haytor White' (p) ♀H6	CBcs CCal EGrI EHeP LCro LOPS LRHS LShi NBir SCgs SCob WCAu WFar WHlf
	'Heath' (p)	LShi
	'Heaven Scent' (p)	SCgs
	'Helen' (p)	LShi
	'Helena Allwood' (pf)	EMal
	'Hercules' (pf)	CNMi
	'Hereford Butter Market' (p)	EBee SBut
	'Hidcote' (p)	CTri EHyd LRHS NRHS
	'Highland Fraser' (p)	WKif
	'Hot Spice' (p)	SPoG
§	'Houndspool Cheryl' (p) ♀H6	CBcs CCal ECtt EHyd EPfP LRHS LShi NRHS SCoo SPoG SRGP SRms WCAu WFar
§	'Houndspool Ruby' (p) ♀H6	CBcs CCal EPfP GQue LSRN LShi SRGP
	hyssopifolius	CCal GQue LShi
§	ICED GEM ('Wp06 Fatima'PBR) (Scent First Series) (p)	ELan LSRN SPoG
	'Icomb' (p)	WHoo
	'Ike' (Sprint Series) (pt)	LRHS
	'Inchmery' (p)	CCal LRHS LShi WHer WHoo
	'India Star'PBR (p) ♀H6	CCal CTri EHyd EPfP LRHS NRHS
	'Inshriach Dazzler' (p) ♀H6	CCal ECtt EPot GArf GEdr GMaP LRHS MAsh MHer NHol NSla SLee SRot WTor
	'Irene Ann' (pf) **new**	CNMi
	× ***isensis***	GEdr SBut
	'James Muir' (M)	EMal
	'Janelle Welch' (pf)	CNMi
	'Janet Walker' (p)	GMaP
	japonicus	CSpe
	'Jean Knight' (b) ♀H6	NGKc
	'Jess Hewins' (pf)	CNMi
	'Joanne' (pf)	CNMi
	'Joanne's Highlight' (pf)	CNMi
	'John Ball' (p)	SBut
	'Josephine' (pf)	CNMi
	'Joy' (p) ♀H6	CCal LShi SPoG
	'Judy Ann' (pf) **new**	CNMi
	'Julie Martin' (pf)	CNMi
	'Just Jodie' (pf)	CNMi
	'Kahori' (p)	CBod MACG SCoo SPoG WWke
	'Kelly's Kiss' (p)	CNMi
	'Kent' (pf)	CNMi
	'Kessock Rose Blush' (p)	CCal LShi
	'Kesteven Kirkstead' (p) ♀H6	CBor GAbr LShi MNrw
	knappii	ECha EDAr LDai LRHS MACG SBut SDix SHar SPhx XLum
	- 'Yellow Harmony' (p,a)	CCal GQue
	'Kristina' (pf) ♀H2	CNMi
	'La Bourboule' (p) ♀H6	CCal ECtt EHyd EPot GMaP LShi NRHS SEdd
	'La Bourboule Alba' (p) ♀H6	CTri LShi MAsh
	'Laced Joy' (p)	LShi
	'Laced Monarch' (p)	CBcs CCal ECtt EGrI EHyd ELan EPfP LRHS LShi NRHS SMrm SPlb SPoG SRms WHer WHlf
	'Laced Mrs Sinkins' (p)	CCal LShi WHer
	'Laced Prudence'	see *D.* 'Prudence'
	'Laced Romeo' (p)	LShi
	'Laced Treasure' (p)	CCal LShi
	'Lady Granville' (p)	CCal LShi SBut
	LADY IN RED ('Wp04 Xanthe'PBR) (p)	CCal ECtt EHyd ELan EPfP LRHS NBir NRHS SCoo SPoG SRms
	'Lady Windermere' (M)	EMal
	'Lancing Supreme' (p)	LShi WHer
	'Langford Manor' (pf)	CNMi

	'Lavender Lady' (pf)	CNMi
	'Lawley's Red' (p)	LShi
	'Layla Jane' (p)	CNMi
	'Leatham Pastel' (pf)	CNMi
	'Lemsii' (p) ♀H6	NGdn
	'Leslie Rennison' (b)	NGKc
	'Letitia Wyatt' (p) ♀H6	CCal CRos EGrI EHyd ELan EPfP LRHS LShi NRHS SCgs SPoG SRGP SRms WHlf
	'Leuchtkugel' (p)	EPot WAbe
	LILY THE PINK ('Wp05 Idare'PBR) (p) ♀H6	CCal EHyd LRHS NRHS SRGP WHlf
	'Lime Crush' (pf)	CNMi
	LIMONI ('Kolim') (pt)	LRHS
	'Linfield Annie's Fancy' (pf)	CNMi
	'Linfield Dorothy Perry' (p) ♀H6	LShi
	'Linfield Pink Margaret' (p)	CNMi
	'Little Ben' (p)	LShi
	'Little Jock' (p)	CCal ECtt EHyd EPot GQue LRHS LShi LSto MAsh NRHS SLee SPlb SRms
	'London Brocade' (p)	LShi
	'London Delight' (p)	LShi
	'London Glow' (p)	LShi
*	'London Joy'	LShi
	'London Lovely' (p)	LShi SBut
	'London Poppet' (p)	ECtt LShi
	'Lord Nuffield' (b)	NGKc
	'Loveliness' (p,a)	CTtf
	lumnitzeri	LShi XLum
	'Madrid' (pf) **new**	CNMi
	'Mandy' (p)	LShi
	'Mandy Gamble' (p) **new**	LShi
	'Manon des Sources' (pf)	CNMi
I	'Margaret's Choice' (p) **new**	CNMi
	'Maria'	see *D.* 'Allen's Maria'
	'Marian Allwood' (pf)	EMal
	'Marilyn's Highlight' (pf)	CNMi
	'Marmion' (pf)	EMal LShi
	'Ma's Choice' (p)	LShi
	'Matthew' (p)	WHoo
	'Maxine' (pf)	CNMi
	'Maybush' (pf)	CNMi
	MEMORIES ('WP11 Gwe04'PBR) (Scent First Series) (p)	CCal CRos EBee EHyd ELan EPfP LBuc LRHS MPri NRHS SCob SCoo SGBe SPoG WCot WFar WTor
	MENDLESHAM MINX ('Russmin'PBR) (p)	CCal EHyd ELan EPfP LRHS NRHS SWvt
	'Messines Pink' (p)	LShi WHer
	microlepis	EDAr LShi NGdn
	- f. ***albus***	NSla
*	- var. ***degenii***	WAbe
	- ED 791562	NGdn
	- 'Rivendell' (p)	WAbe
	'Miss Farrow' (p)	EHyd SHar
	'Miss Sinkins' (p)	CTri
	MOJITO ('Wp15 Pie41'PBR) (p)	CCal EHyd LRHS MPri NRHS SGBe WCot WMal
	'Monica Wyatt' (p) ♀H6	CCal ECtt EHyd ELan EPfP LRHS NRHS SPoG
	'Montrose Pink'	see *D.* 'Cockenzie Pink'
	'Monty Allwood' (p)	LShi
	'Monty's Pink' (pf)	EMal
	'Moor Editha' (p)	CNMi
	MORNING STAR	see *D.* 'Devon Winnie'
	'Morrissey' (pf)	CNMi
	'Moulin Rouge' (p) ♀H6	CAby CBcs CCal CTri ECtt EHyd ELan EPfP LCro LRHS MBow NRHS SPoG SRms WHlf
	'Mrs McBride's Old Irish' (p)	LShi
	'Mrs Sinkins' (p)	Widely available

	'Murray Douglas' (p)	LShi SBut
	'Murray's Laced Pink' (p)	SBut
§	'Musgrave's Pink' (p)	ECha LShi WHer
	'Musgrave's White'	see *D.* 'Musgrave's Pink'
	'My Love' (pf) **new**	CNMi
	myrtinervius	CCal GPSL NGdn WAvo
	'Mystic Dawn' (b)	NGKc
	'Mystic Ray Knight' (b) **new**	NGKc
§	MYSTIC STAR ('WP 05 Saphire') (p) 🏆H6	CCal ELan NGrs WIce
	'Napoleon III' (p)	LShi WMal
	nardiformis	XLum
	'Nautilus' (b)	LShi
	neglectus misapplied	see *D. pavonius*
	'Neon Star'PBR (p) 🏆H6	CCal CRos CTri EHyd ELan GEdr GKev LRHS NGrs NRHS SEdd SPoG
	'Nichola Ann' (b) 🏆H6	NGKc
	'Night Star' (p) 🏆H6	CCal CGBo CPla CRos EHyd ELan EPfP LRHS NRHS NSla SEND
	nitidus	LShi
	'Nomie' (pf)	CNMi
	'Nora' (pf) **new**	CNMi
	'Northland' (pf)	CNMi EMal
	'Nyewoods Cream' (p)	EPfP GArf GMaP LShi MHer NGdn NWad SGro SLee
	'Oakwood Erin Mitchell' (p)	CNMi
	'Oakwood Sweetheart' (p)	LShi
	'Odessa Red' (Odessa Series) (pt)	SRms
	'Old Blush'	see *D.* 'Souvenir de la Malmaison'
	'Old Clove Red' (b)	WKif
	'Old Fringed White' (p)	EWTr
	'Old Mother Hubbard' (p)	SGro
	'Old Red Clove' (p)	ECtt NFav WCot
	'Old Rose' (pf)	EMal
§	'Old Square Eyes' (p)	CCal EPPr EWTr LShi MNrw SHar WHer WMal
	'Old Velvet' (p)	CCal LShi
*	'Olivia' (pf)	WHlf
	'Oscar' (b)	SCob
	'Owston Third Avenue' (p)	LShi
	'Oxford Magic' (p)	LShi
	'Painted Lady' (p)	LShi
	'Paisley Gem' (p)	LShi SBut
	PASSION ('Wp Passion'PBR) (Scent First Series) (p)	CCal CRos EBee ECtt EHyd ELan EPfP LBar LRHS MHer NRHS SCob SCoo SEND SGBe SPoG WCot WHlf
§	***pavonius***	CCal EHyd EWes LRHS NGdn NRHS
	'Peach' (p)	SEND
	'Pendle Doris Delight' (p)	CNMi LShi
	'Peppermint Magic'	LRHS
§	***petraeus***	EWes NGdn XLum
§	- subsp. ***noeanus***	MACG
	'Petticoat Lace' (p)	LShi
	'Pheasant's Eye' (p)	LShi WHer
*	'Picton's Propeller' (p)	EPPr
	PIERROT ('Kobusa') (pf)	CNMi
	'Pike's Pink' (p) 🏆H6	CRos CSpe CTri EHyd ELan EPfP EPot EWTr LRHS LShi MAsh MMuc NBir NGdn NRHS SCoo SEND SPoG
	PINBALL WIZARD ('Wp15mow08') (p)	CCal EHyd LRHS NRHS SCoo SPoG
	pindicola	see *D. haematocalyx* subsp. *pindicola*
	pinifolius	CBod EDAr LShi SBrt
	'Pink Doris' (pf)	CNMi
	'Pink Jewel' (p)	ECha EPot MAsh MNHC SLee XLum
	PINK KISSES ('Kledg12163') (pt)	CRos EHyd LCro LOPS LRHS MPri NGrs NRHS SPoG
	'Pink Mrs Sinkins' (p)	CCal LShi
	'Pixie' (b)	EPot
	'Pixie Star'PBR (p) 🏆H6	CCal EWoo SPoG
	plumarius	CWal LShi MACG SBls SBut XLum
	- 'Albiflorus' (p)	XLum
	- Ipswich Pinks Group (p)	CCal
	- 'Maischnee' (p)	ECha
§	POP STAR ('Wp04 Esther'PBR) (p)	CCal LRHS SGbt WIce
	'Pretty' (p)	ECtt
	PRETTY FLAMINGO	see *D.* 'Carmine Letitia Wyatt'
	'Prince Charming' (p)	MAsh
	'Princess of Wales' (M)	EMal LShi
	'Priory Pink' (p)	LShi
§	'Prudence' (p)	LShi
	'Pudsey Prize' (p)	EPot
	'Purple Frosted' (pf)	EMal
	pygmaeus CMBTW 1678 **new**	GGro
	- NMWJ 14561	WCru
	pyrenaicus **new**	MMuc
§	'Queen of Henri' (p)	CRos EHyd LRHS LShi NRHS
	'Queen of Sheba' (p)	LShi WHer WKif
	'Rachel' (p)	ELon LShi
	'Rainbow Loveliness' (p,a)	CCal CWal
	RAINBOW LOVELINESS IMPROVED MIXED	WHil
	'Raspberry Ripple' ambig. (p)	NWad
	RASPBERRY SUNDAE	see *D.* 'Devon Yolande'
	'Ray' (Sprint Series) (pt)	LRHS
	REBEKAH ('Wp09 Mar05'PBR) (Early Bird Series) (p) 🏆H6	CCal CRos EHyd ELan LRHS NRHS
	'Red Dwarf'	see *D.* 'Red Star'
§	'Red Star'PBR (p) 🏆H6	CCal EHyd LRHS MAsh NRHS WIce
	'Reine de Henri'	see *D.* 'Queen of Henri'
	'Ringwood Belle' (pf)	CNMi
	'Robert Allwood' (pf)	EMal
	'Robert Smith' (b)	NGKc
	'Robin Ritchie' (p)	WHoo
	'Robina's Daughter' (p)	GAbr
	'Romance' (pf) **new**	MPri
	ROMANCE ('Wp09 Wen04'PBR) (Scent First Series) (p) 🏆H6	CCal CRos EHyd EPfP LBar LRHS NRHS SCob WHlf
	'Romsey' (pf)	CNMi
	'Roodkapje' (p)	XLum
	'Rose de Mai' (p)	CFis CNMi LShi SBut WHer WHoo
	'Rose Joy' (p) 🏆H6	SRGP
	ROSEBUD ('Wp08 Ros03'PBR) (Early Bird Series) (p)	CCal EHyd NRHS
	'Royal Crimson' (pf)	EMal
I	'Royal Purple' (pf) **new**	CNMi
	'Royal Salmon' (pf)	EMal
	'Ruby'	see *D.* 'Houndspool Ruby'
	'Ruby Doris'	see *D.* 'Houndspool Ruby'
	rupicola	CSpe WCot
	'Saint Nicholas' (p)	WThu
	'Sam Barlow' (p)	LShi
	SCARLET BEAUTY ('Hilbeau')	LSto
	seguieri	WOut
	'Seraphina' (pf)	CNMi
	serotinus	EPot LShi WCot
	SHERBET ('Wp08 Nik03'PBR) (Early Bird Series) (p)	EPfP
	'Shire Delight' (p) **new**	LShi
§	SHOOTING STAR ('Wp04 Flores'PBR) (p)	CCal ELan LRHS SRms WIce
	'Shot Silk' (pf)	EMal
	'Show Aristocrat' (p)	CCal LShi
	'Show Harlequin' (p)	LShi

	Name	Suppliers
	SHOWGIRL ('Wp08 Uni02') (Scent First Series) (p)	EPfP
	SILVER STAR ('Wp10 Hel01'PBR) (p)	CCal CTri EHyd EPfP LRHS NRHS
	simulans	SRot
	'Singapore Girl' (Kiwi Series) (p)	EWTr
	'Sir David Scott' (p)	SBut
*	'Six Hills' (p)	NWad
	SLAP 'N' TICKLE ('Wp 05 Pp 22'PBR) (Scent First Series) (p) ♀H6	CRos ECtt EHyd EPfP LRHS LSRN NRHS SCoo SPoG
	'Snowshill Manor' (p)	LShi
	'Solomon' (p)	CCal LShi
	'Somerset' (pf)	CNMi
	'Sops-in-wine' (p)	CCal ECha ECtt LShi MSCN
	'Sops-in-wine 2' (p) **new**	LShi
§	'Souvenir de la Malmaison' (M)	EMal LShi
	spiculifolius	EPot LShi MMuc
	'Spinfield Joy' (b) ♀H6	NGKc
	Spooky Group (p)	CCal
	'Square Eyes'	see *D.* 'Old Square Eyes'
	squarrosus	EPot LShi SRot WAbe
	- 'Nanus'	see *D.* 'Berlin Snow'
	'Starburst'PBR (p)	CCal CPla WHlf
	STARGAZER ('Wp13 Gil05'PBR) (Whetman Stars Series) (p)	CCal EWoo NGrs
	'Starlette'PBR (Star Double Series) (p)	CCal EHyd LRHS NRHS SCoo SGBe WIce
	STARLIGHT ('Hilstar') (pf)	CCal SRms
	STARLIGHT ('Wp 06 Parnia'PBR) (p)	CCal EWoo
	'Starry Eyes' (p) ♀H6	CCal CRos EHyd ELan EWTr EWoo GMaP LRHS NRHS SRms SWvt WIce
	'Storm' (pf)	EMal
	'Strawberries and Cream' (p)	ECtt SPoG
	strictus	WCot
*	- subsp. ***pulchellus***	GEdr NSla WFar
	subacaulis	EWTr MMuc SBut XLum
	- subsp. ***brachyanthus***	GJos
	suendermannii	see *D. petraeus*
	SUGAR PLUM ('Wp08 Ian04'PBR) (Scent First Series) (p)	CCal EBee ECtt EHyd ELan EPfP LBar LRHS MPri NRHS SCob SCoo SGBe WHlf
	'Summerfield Blaze' (p)	LShi
	'Summerfield Blush' (p)	LShi
	SUNFLOR CHARMY ('Hilcharm') (Sunflor Series) (pt)	LRHS
§	***superbus***	CCal EPPr EWld LRHS SBrt SPhx SPtp WHer
	- BO 15-070	GGro
	- from Japan	GGro
	- var. ***longicalycinus*** dark-flowered	GGro
	- - white-flowered	GGro
I	- 'Primadonna' (p)	SHar
	SUPERNOVA ('Wp11 Tyr04'PBR) (pf) ♀H6	CCal WHlf
	SUPERTROUPER AMY ('Kledp15187'PBR) (pt)	LRHS
	SUPERTROUPER CARMEN ('Kledp11106'PBR) (pt)	LRHS
	SUPERTROUPER CARMEN PURPLE (pt)	LRHS
	SUPERTROUPER CARMEN RED ('Kledp16214') (pt)	LRHS
	SUPERTROUPER DIWALI ('Kledcp05070') (pt)	LRHS
	SUPERTROUPER ELISE ('Kledp07093') (pt)	LRHS
	SUPERTROUPER GRACE ('Kledp16188') (pt)	LRHS
	SUPERTROUPER MARIE (pt)	LRHS
	SUPERTROUPER SISSY ('Kledp07088'PBR) (pt)	LRHS
	'Sweet Cecille' (pf)	CNMi
	SWEETNESS (mixed) (p)	CCal
	sylvestris	GArf GJos
	'Tatra' (pf)	NQui WMal
	'Tatra Blush' (p)	EPPr EWTr LShi
	'Tatra Fragrance' (p)	EPPr LShi
	'Tayside Red' (M)	EMal
	the Bloodie pink	see *D.* 'Caesar's Mantle'
	THE WESSEX PINK ('Wp15val11') (p)	CCal ECtt EPfP
	'Thora' (M)	EMal
	'Thunderstorm' (pf)	CNMi
	tianschanicus	GKev LRHS
	TICKLED PINK ('Devon Pp 11'PBR) (Scent First Series) (p) ♀H6	CCal CTri EBee ECtt EHyd ELan EPfP LRHS LSRN MPri NRHS SCoo SGBe SPoG
	'Tiny Rubies'	see *D. gratianopolitanus* 'Tiny Rubies'
	'Tony's Choice' (pf)	CNMi
	'Treasure' (p)	LShi
	'Trevor' (p)	LShi
	tristis	XLum
	'Tudor'	MNrw
	'Tudor Rose' (b)	MNrw
	'Unique' (p)	CCal CFis LShi
	'Urpeth Carol-Anne' (b) **new**	NGKc
	'Urpeth Ian Costen' (b) **new**	NGKc
	'Urpeth Rhiannon' (b) **new**	NGKc
	'Valda Wyatt' (p) ♀H6	CBcs CCal EPfP SEND SPoG SWvt WFar
	'Velvet Pelargonium' (pf)	EMal
	'Vic Masters' (p)	SGro
	'W.A. Musgrave'	see *D.* 'Musgrave's Pink'
	'Waikiki Pink' (pt)	SEdd
	'Waithman Beauty' (p)	CCal LShi WHoo
	'Waithman's Jubilee' (p)	CCal SGro
	'Warden Hybrid' (p)	CBor CCal CRos CTri ECtt EHyd EPfP LRHS LShi MNHC NRHS NWad SHar SPoG SWvt
	'Waterloo Sunset'PBR (p)	CCal
	'Weetwood Double' (p)	SGro
	'Welton Thunder' (p) **new**	CNMi
	'Wessex' (pf)	CNMi EHyd LRHS NRHS
	'Whatfield Anona' (p)	CCal
	'Whatfield Beauty' (p)	ECtt
	'Whatfield Brilliant' (p)	LShi
	'Whatfield Cancan' (p) ♀H6	CCal CGBo CRos ECtt EHyd ELan EPfP EPot GMaP LRHS LShi MNHC NFav NGdn NHol NRHS NSla SGro SPoG SWvt WCAu
	'Whatfield Cyclops' (p)	CCal LShi
	'Whatfield Dorothy Mann' (p)	CCal WIce
	'Whatfield Gem' (p)	CCal CPla ECtt ELan LShi MNHC NGdn SLee SWvt WCav WIce WWke
	'Whatfield Joy' (p)	CBor CCal CRos ECtt EHyd ELan EPfP LRHS LShi NGdn NRHS SLee
	'Whatfield Magenta' (p) ♀H6	CRos ECtt EHyd ELan EPot LRHS LShi NRHS SLee SPoG SRms
	'Whatfield Mini' (p)	LShi SRot
	'Whatfield Miss' (p)	LShi
	'Whatfield Misty Morn' (p)	ECtt
	'Whatfield Peach' (p)	CCal LShi
	'Whatfield Pom-pom' (p)	LShi
	'Whatfield Ruby' (p)	LShi
	'Whatfield White' (p)	CCal ECtt LShi

'Whatfield Wisp' (p)	ECtt EPfP EPot GArf LShi NBir
'White Champagne' (b) **new**	NGKc
'White Joy'[PBR] (p) 🏆H6	MRav
'White Ladies' (p)	LShi
'Widecombe Fair' (p) 🏆H6	CCal LShi SPoG WHlf

Diapensia (*Diapensiaceae*)

lapponica var. ***obovata***	GArf

Diarrhena (*Poaceae*)

obovata	EPPr

Diascia (*Scrophulariaceae*)

'Andrew'	SGro
'Appleby Appleblossom'	CPla
'Aurora Apricot' (Towers of Flowers Series)	EHyd EPfP LRHS NRHS
'Aurora Cherry Blossom' (Towers of Flowers Series)	ELan LRHS
'Aurora Dark Pink' (Towers of Flowers Series)	ELan LRHS
'Aurora Light Pink' (Towers of Flowers Series)	ELan LRHS
barberae	MBros
- 'Belmore Beauty' (v)	EWes
- 'Blackthorn Apricot' 🏆H4	EBee ECha EHyd EPfP MBow NDov NRHS SPlb SPoG SRms SWvt
§ - 'Fisher's Flora'	WFar
§ - 'Ruby Field'	EBee ECha EHyd EPfP LRHS NFav NRHS SMad SPoG SRms SWvt
BLUE BONNET ('Hecbon')	SWvt
'Bluebelle' (Maritana Series)	ECha NDov
'Blush'	see *D. integerrima* 'Blush'
(Breezee Series) BREEZEE APPLE BLOSSOM	LSou NLar SMrm WHlf
- BREEZEE APRICOT ('Diaspritwo'[PBR])	NLar SMrm
- BREEZEE ORANGE	WHlf
- BREEZEE RED	NLar WHlf
- BREEZEE SNOW ('Inndiabzsno'[PBR])	ELan NLar SMrm
'Coldham'	WGoo WMal
CORAL BELLE ('Hecbel'[PBR]) 🏆H3	CRos EHyd LRHS NRHS
§ 'Coral Spires'	CDor CSpe CTtf WCot WMal WSHC
cordata misapplied	see *D. barberae* 'Fisher's Flora'
cordata ambig.	WFar
cordifolia	see *D. barberae* 'Fisher's Flora'
'Denim Blue'	ECtt EDAr WFar
'Diamond Fuchsia'	LCro LSou
'Diamond Light Pink' **new**	LCro
'Diamond White Blush' **new**	LCro
(Divara Series) 'Divara Blush' **new**	NLar
- 'Divara Deep Red' **new**	NLar
- 'Divara Orange'	LSou NLar
- 'Divara Pink'	NLar
- 'Divara White' **new**	NLar
elegans misapplied	see *D. fetcaniensis*, *D. vigilis*
'Emma'	NDov SMHy SWvt WGoo WMal
felthamii	see *D. fetcaniensis*
§ ***fetcaniensis***	CKel EBee EPfP EShb GBee GElm LEdu LRHS MCot NDov NLar SIvy SWvt WSHC
- 'Daydream'	LShi MNrw MPie SGro WCFE WFar
flanaganii misapplied	see *D. vigilis*
(Flying Colours Series) FLYING COLOURS ANTIQUE ROSE ('Diastu'[PBR])	SPoG
- FLYING COLOURS APPLEBLOSSOM ('Diastara')	SPoG
- FLYING COLOURS APRICOT ('Diastina')	SPoG
- FLYING COLOURS DEEP SALMON IMPROVED ('Dala Depsam'[PBR])	SPoG
- FLYING COLOURS RED ('Diastonia')	SPoG
'Hector Harrison'	see *D.* 'Salmon Supreme'
'Hector's Hardy'	XLum
§ 'Hopleys'	CSpe ECha EHyd EPPr MAvo MHCG MPie MSCN NCth NLar NRHS SMHy SWvt WAvo WFar
ICE CRACKER ('Hecrack')	CRos EHyd ELan LRHS NRHS SRms
ICEBERG ('Hecice')	NDov SWvt
§ ***integerrima***	ECha MCot SMHy
- from Lesotho	SMrm
- 'Alba'	see *D. integerrima* 'Blush'
§ - 'Blush'	CSpe NDov WGoo
- 'Ivory Angel'	see *D. integerrima* 'Blush'
integrifolia	see *D. integerrima*
'Jacqueline's Joy'	NPer
'Joyce's Choice' 🏆H3	CRos EHyd LRHS NRHS SRms
'Katherine Sharman' (v)	EWes
'Lilac Belle' 🏆H3	EDAr EHyd ELan EPfP LRHS NBir NRHS SPlb SPoG SRms
'Lilac Mist'	NPer
LITTLE DANCER ('Pendan'[PBR])	ELan NLar WHlf
LITTLE DREAMER ('Pender'[PBR])	NLar
LITTLE DRIFTER ('Pendrif'[PBR])	NLar WHlf
LITTLE MAIDEN ('Penmaid'[PBR])	NLar
LITTLE TANGO ('Pentang'[PBR])	NLar SRms WHlf
'Monhop White'	ECtt
personata	Widely available
- 'Hopleys'	see *D.* 'Hopleys'
- orange-flowered	see *D.* 'Coral Spires'
'Peter'	NDov
PINK PANTHER ('Penther')	SWvt
RED ACE ('Hecrace')	MBow NPer SWvt
REDSTART ('Hecstart')	SWvt
rigescens 🏆H3	CBod CCBP CEme CWCL ECtt EPfP MBow NLar NPer SChF SPer SPlb SPoG SWvt WAbe WAvo WCFE WSHC WSpi
§ - 'Anne Rennie'	LRHS SWvt
- pale-flowered	see *D. rigescens* 'Anne Rennie'
'Ruby Field'	see *D. barberae* 'Ruby Field'
'Rupert Lambert' 🏆H3	NDov
§ 'Salmon Supreme'	EHyd EPfP LRHS NPer NRHS SPoG SRms
(Sundiascia Series) SUNDIASCIA BLUSH PINK ('Sunjodipi'[PBR])	WHlf
- SUNDIASCIA ORANGE ('Sunjodiora')	WHlf
- SUNDIASCIA SAKURA PINK ('Sunjodi 042'[PBR]) **new**	WHlf
- SUNDIASCIA UPRIGHT BRIGHT PINK ('Sunjodiblupi'[PBR])	CWCL
'Twinkle' 🏆H3	CRos EHyd LRHS NBir NPer NRHS SRms
§ ***vigilis*** 🏆H3	EBee EHyd EMor EPot NBro NCth NRHS SRms

Dicentra ✿ (*Papaveraceae*)

'Adrian Bloom'	EPfP SWvt WFar
(Amore Series) 'Amore Pink'	CMiW CWGN EMor NLar
- 'Amore Rose'[PBR]	CWGN GBin NBPC NHpl

'Aurora'	CBcs CMac CMiW ECha ECtt EMor EPfP GMaP ILea LCro LOPS LRHS MRav NBPC NGdn NLar NRHS SCob SPer SPoG SWvt WBrk WCAu WJam
'Boothman's Variety'	see *D.* 'Stuart Boothman'
'Bountiful'	CMac ECtt EHyd LRHS MRav NGdn NRHS SWvt
'Burning Hearts' PBR	CMiW CWGN ECtt EGrI EMor GEdr LBar LRHS MHol NCth NSti SPer SPoG WCAu
canadensis	CMiW EBee LEdu MAvo MNrw WAbe WFar WPGP
'Candy Hearts' PBR	EBee ECtt ELan EMor LBar NCth SCob
cucullaria	CElw CMiW CWCL EBee EHyd EMor EPPr EPot GAbr GArf GEdr GLet LAma LEdu LRHS MNrw MRav NBir NHpl NLar NRHS WAbe WFar
- 'Carl Gehenio'	GEdr
- 'Little Angels' (d)	WFar
- 'Pink Punk'	EBee EMor EPPr LEdu NLar WFar WMal
- 'Pittsburg'	CMiW EBee EPPr LEdu MNrw
eximia misapplied	see *D. formosa*
eximia ambig.	CMac EPfP GPSL WFar
eximia (Ker Gawl.) Torr.	GJos
- 'Alba'	see *D. eximia* (Ker Gawl.) Torr. 'Snowdrift'
§ - 'Snowdrift'	CDor EHeP SRms WFar
'Filigree'	CSpe ECha LEdu SPVi
'Firecracker'	MPnt
§ ***formosa***	CBcs CEme CToG CTri ECha EGrI EHyd ELan EPfP GGro GMcL LRHS MNHC NBro NGdn NRHS SPlb SRms WCAu
- f. ***alba***	CToG CTri ECha GLog NBir SRms WCru WFar WKif
- 'Bacchanal' 🏆H5	Widely available
- 'Cox's Dark Red'	GBin NHpl NLar
- 'Langtrees' 🏆H5	CMac CRos ECha EHyd EMor EPfP LEdu LRHS MAvo MRav NBro NLar NRHS SRms SSut SWvt WCru WFar WSpi
- 'Moorland Mist'	WFar
- 'Moorland Pearl'	WFar
- subsp. ***oregana***	EGrI EPPr LEdu
- SNOWFLAKES ('Fusd')	MRav
- 'Spring Gold'	ECha EGrI EMor EPPr LBar LSou NLar WFar
- 'Spring Magic'	CRos EBlo ECtt EHyd EMor EPPr EPfP LRHS LSou MRav NLar NRHS WSpi
'Golden Tears'	see *Dactylicapnos* 'Golden Tears'
'Ivory Hearts' PBR	CWGN EBee ELan EMor LBar NCth NLar NSti SCob SPeP SPer WHil
§ 'Katie'	EPPr
'Katy'	see *D.* 'Katie'
'King of Hearts'	Widely available
'Love Hearts' PBR	EMor LBar MHol NCth WHil
'Luxuriant' 🏆H5	CBcs CBod CRos EBee ECtt EHyd ELan EMor EPfP EShb LAma LBar LRHS LSRN MCot MGos MRav NBPC NRHS SPer SPoG SRms SWvt WCAu WFar WPnP
macrantha	see *Ichthyoselmis macrantha*
'Pearl Drops'	EBlo EHyd GLog GMcL LRHS MCot MHCG MMrt NBid NLar NRHS SRms WFar
peregrina	GEdr WAbe
- ***alba***	GEdr
'Red Fountain' PBR	CWCL EMor MPnt
scandens	see *Dactylicapnos scandens*
spectabilis	see *Lamprocapnos spectabilis*
'Spring Morning'	CDor CElw EMor EPPr LEdu NGdn WSpi
§ 'Stuart Boothman' 🏆H5	CMac CWCL ECtt EPfP GBin GMaP LEdu LRHS MCot MRav NBro NGdn NLar NQui SPer SPoG SRms SWvt WBrk WCAu WFar WKif
'Sulphur Hearts' **new**	GLet LBar MNrw SPad
thalictrifolia	see *Dactylicapnos scandens*
ventii	see *Dactylicapnos ventii*

Dichelostemma (*Asparagaceae*)

capitatum 'Ginny's Giant'	CSpe
congestum	CAvo CBor GKev SDeJ WHlf
§ ***ida-maia***	CAby CAvo CBor CWCL EPot GKev LAma SDeJ
- 'Pink Diamond'	CAvo CBor GKev LAma SDeJ
multiflorum	NRog
volubile	GKev NRog
- 'Pink Giant'	SDeJ

Dichondra (*Convolvulaceae*)

argentea 'Silver Falls'	EShb MBros MPri SCoo SPer SPoG
§ ***micrantha***	CKel EShb
repens misapplied	see *D. micrantha*

Dichroa (*Hydrangeaceae*)

B&SWJ 7177 from Thailand **new**	WCru
PAB 8488	LPla
from Guizhou, China	EHed EWld WCot WPGP
cyanea	LRHS
- B&SWJ 2367	WCru
- NJM 13.104	WPGP
daimingshanensis BWJ 15621 **new**	WCru
febrifuga B&SWJ 9734	WCru
- B&SWJ 9753	WCru
- NJM 10.042	WPGP
- PAB 8639	LEdu
hirsuta	LRHS
- NJM 10.051	WPGP
- B&SWJ 8207 from Vietnam	WCru
- BWJ 16315 from Vietnam **new**	WCru
aff. ***hirsuta*** B&SWJ 8371 from Laos	WCru
'Long March'	LEdu WPGP
yunnanensis	WPGP
- BWJ 15644 **new**	WCru
aff. ***yunnanensis*** B&SWJ 9734	WCru

Dichroa × *Hydrangea* see × *Didrangea*

Dichromena see *Rhynchospora*

Dichrostachys (*Fabaceae*)

cinerea	SPlb

Dicksonia ✿ (*Dicksoniaceae*)

antarctica 🏆H3	Widely available
berteriana	IKel
fibrosa 🏆H3	CDTJ CKel CTrC ETod IKel LRHS XSte
sellowiana	CDTJ CKel ETod IKel WPGP
squarrosa 🏆H3	CBdn CCCN CDTJ CKel ETod LRHS XSte
youngiae	CDTJ CKel IKel

Dicliptera (*Acanthaceae*)

§ ***sericea***	CCCN ECtt EShb EWld SEND SGro SRkn WSHC XLum XSen
suberecta	see *D. sericea*

Dictamnus (*Rutaceae*)

	albus	CBcs CKel CSpe EBee ECha EHyd ELan EMor EPfP GKev LBar LRHS MBel MCot MHoo MRav NRHS SMHy SMad SPer SPoG SWvt WCAu WSpi
	- var. ***albus*** $\mathbb{Y}^{H6}$	CDor EBlo EPfP EWoo SWvt
§	- var. ***purpureus*** $\mathbb{Y}^{H6}$	CSpe EBee EBlo ECha EHyd EMor EPfP GBin GKev ILea LRHS MBel MHoo MRav NGBl NRHS SPer SPoG SRms SWvt WCAu WKif WSpi
	fraxinella	see *D. albus* var. *purpureus*

Dictyosperma (*Arecaceae*)

album var. ***rubrum*** **new**	NPlm

× *Didrangea* (*Hydrangeaceae*)

versicolor	CAbb CBcs CBod CDoC CHll CKel CMCN EBee EPfP ESwi EWld IDee LRHS MGil SBrt SEdd SIvy SPoG SWvt WCru WJek WPGP
ytiensis B&SWJ 11790	WCru

Didymochlaena (*Dryopteridaceae*)

	lunulata	see *D. truncatula*
§	***truncatula***	CDoC

Dieffenbachia (*Araceae*)

'Camille' (v) $\mathbb{Y}^{H1a}$	LCro
'Compacta' (v)	NHrt
'Maroba' **new**	NHrt
'Reflector' (v) **new**	LCro
'Tropic Snow' (v) $\mathbb{Y}^{H1a}$ **new**	LCro

Dierama ✿ (*Iridaceae*)

	CD&R 192	CElw
	adelphicum	CElw EWes GAbr GKev WHil WSHC
	ambiguum	CElw EBee XLum
	argyreum	CBcs CBor CCCN CElw CMiW CTsd EBee EPri EWoo GKev ITim NLar SPoG WGob XSte
	atrum	EBee
	'Autumn Dazzler'	CPla
	Barr hybrids	CBro WHil
	'Blackberry Bells'	CAby CBod CBor CDor CPla CWCL CWGN CWnw EBee ELan EPfP EPri GKev LBar LLWG LRHS MAvo NLar SChF SMrm SPad SPoG WHoo WSpi WWke
	BLUE BELLE ('Rowblu'PBR)	CBor EBee ECtt GBin
	'Candy Stripe'	EBee IBal
	'Carmine'	CWCL
	'Cinnamon Fairy'	EBee EPfP IBal
	cooperi	CBor EBee EPfP NBir
	'Coral Belle'	IBal LRHS
	'Coral Bells'	CCCN IBal MNrw WPGP
	'Cosmos'	EPri LRHS LShi NBPC WFar
	'Dark Angel'	GAbr
§	***dracomontanum***	CBor CBro CCCN CElw CRos CWCL EBee EHyd EPfP EPri GKev GMaP LRHS MBel NBPC NBir NLar NRHS SPeP WFar WGob WGwG WHil WHoo XLum
	- dwarf, pink-flowered	GArf
	dracomontanum × ***pulcherrimum***	GDam SMad
	ensifolium	see *D. pendulum*
	erectum	CBcs CBor CCCN CWCL EPri LBar NBPC NLar WGob WHil WHlf XSte
	formosum	EBee
	galpinii	CCCN CPla CWCL EPri
	grandiflorum	WSHC
	'Guinevere'	CBor CCBP CDor CWCL CWGN EBee EPri GKev GMaP LEdu LRHS MCot MRav NBir NChi NGdn NQui SCob SMrm SPoG SVen WFar WGwG WHoo WSHC
	igneum	Widely available
	insigne	CCCN CPla CTsd CWCL EBee EPPr GAbr MHtn NWad SChF WCot
	jucundum	EMor EPri EWes LRHS WCot
	'Kilmurry White'	IBal
	'Lancelot'	EBee ECtt GMcL IBal LRHS NBir SCob SWvt WCot WFar WKif WSHC
	luteoalbidum	GKev
	'Miranda'	CBcs EBee ECtt ELan GMcL IBal LRHS NLar WWke
	mossii	CBcs CBor CCBP CCCN CTsd CWCL EPfP EPri LEdu LRHS NLar NQui NWad SPlb SPoG SVen WGob WPGP XLum
	nixonianum	GAbr MHer
	'Painted Lady'	IBal
	pauciflorum	CCCN CRos CTsd CWCL EBee EPri LRHS NBir NLar NSla WAbe WCot WGob WSHC
§	***pendulum***	CBro CElw GElm GKev LRHS MRav SWvt WCot WFar
	- 'Album'	WPGP
	pendulum × ***pulcherrimum***	GKev
	'Pink Dragon'	LRHS
	'Pink Fairies' **new**	CBor
	'Pink Rocket'	CBor CMiW CPla LLWG LRHS MHer MHtn NHol SPad SRkn XSte
	Plant World hybrids	ELon WFar
	PLANT WORLD JEWELS	CWCL NWad WFar
	'Puck'	MRav
	pulcherrimum	Widely available
	- var. ***album***	CAby CBor CCCN CEme CWCL CWnw EShb GKev LBar LLWG MAvo MHer MNrw NCth NLar NQui WHlf
	- 'Blackbird'	CAby CBcs CBor CCCN CPla CWCL EBou ELan EPri LLWG LRHS LSRN MHer NBPC NHol NLar SChF SPeP SPoG SWvt WFar WGob WHlf WPGP WWke
	- dark cerise-flowered	GKev IPot
	- dark pink-flowered	GAbr
	- 'Flaring Tips'	GKev LRHS
	- 'Merlin'	CDor EBee ECtt EShb GMcL IBal LRHS NBir SCob SVen SWvt WFar
	- pale-flowered	ECha ESgI GAbr
	- purple-flowered	CSpe ESgI
	- Slieve Donard hybrids	CWCL WFar
	pumilum misapplied	see *D. dracomontanum*
	'Queen of the Night'	EPri
	reynoldsii	CBor CCCN CPla CTsd EPri EWoo GBin NBPC NWad SPlb SPoG SVen WFar WKif WSpi
	robustum	CAbb CBod CCCN CPla CTsd CWCL EBee EShb EWes GAbr LRHS WCot WFar WPGP
	'Senlisse'	LRHS
	'Spring Dancer'	CPla EBee MHer NHol SPlb
	'Tiny Bells'	EDAr ESgI IBal WSHC
	'Titania'	GBin IBal
	trichorhizum	CCCN CElw CPla CWCL EPri GKev LPla LRHS NWad XLum
	white-flowered	MBel
	Wildside hybrids	WSHC

Diervilla (*Caprifoliaceae*)

	middendorffiana	see *Weigela middendorffiana*
	rivularis HONEYBEE ('Diwibru01'PBR)	CSBt LCro LOPS MMrt NEoE NLar SGBe SGol SPoG WHtc
	- 'Troja Black'	EPPr EPfP MBlu NLar SGol
§	***sessilifolia***	CBrac CMac EBee EPPr EWTr MBlu MRav WCot
	- 'Butterfly'	CMac EPPr LCro LOPS NLar WFar
	- COOL SPLASH ('Lpdc Podaras'PBR) (v)	CMac EBee NEoE SPoG SWvt
	× ***splendens***	CBrac EBee EHyd EPPr EPfP EWTr IDee LRHS MBNS MBlu MGil MSwo NLar SIvy SPer SPoG SWvt
	- DIVA	see *D.* × *splendens* 'El Madrigal'
§	- 'El Madrigal'PBR	LCro LRHS MMrt NEoE NLar NSti WHlf

Dietes (*Iridaceae*)

	bicolor	CAbb CBor CExl CPbh CSpe EBee EPri ESwi EWoo LEdu SBrt SChr SPoG WCFE WSHC
	grandiflora	CAbb CExl ESwi EWoo SChr SVen WCFE WCot
§	***iridioides***	CSpe EPri ESwi WGob XLum
	robinsoniana	WCot

Digitalis ✿ (*Plantaginaceae*)

	NJM 13.013	WPGP
	'Albino'	CRos EHyd EPfP LRHS NRHS
	ambigua	see *D. grandiflora*
	apricot hybrids	see *D. purpurea* 'Sutton's Apricot'
	canariensis	CAbb CBcs CCCN CCht CDTJ CHll CKel CSpe CTsd EAri EShb MEch MGil MMrt SEle SIvy SPad SPlb SVen WCFE
	ciliata	LShi
	davisiana	CExl CPla GLog MNHC
	'Elsie Kelsey'	EPfP SWvt WHlf
	eriostachya	see *D. lutea*
	ferruginea ♀H6	CCBP CDor CElw CSpe CWnw EBee ECha ECtt ELan EMor EPPr EPfP GArf GKev GQue LEdu LRHS LSto MRav NBir NGdn NRHS SCob SRms SVen WBrk WCAu WKif
	- B&SWJ 15395	WCru
	- 'Gelber Herold'	CDor CElw EMor GKev GMaP SBls SCob SMrm WFar WSpi
	- 'Gigantea' ♀H7	CAby CWnw ECtt ELan EMor EPfP EWoo GAbr LBuc LEdu LRHS LShi MBNS NDov SHar SPlb WHlf WPGP
	× ***fucata*** 'Foxy Apricot' (Foxy Series)	see *D.* × *fucata* 'Miranda'
§	- 'Miranda'	SWvt
	'Glory of Roundway' ♀H6	CBod CDor EBee ECtt EShb LCro MNrw NCou NLar SCob WCAu WCot
§	GOLDCREST ('Waldigone'PBR)	CBcs CRos CWGN ECtt EHyd EPfP LBar LBuc LRHS LSou NRHS SHar SPoG WHil WNPC
§	***grandiflora*** ♀H6	Widely available
	- 'Carillon' ♀H5	CBod EAJP EBee EHyd ELan EMor EPfP GDam LDai LRHS WCAu WCav WHoo WPnP
	- 'Cream Bell'	EPfP LBar
	- 'Dwarf Carillon'	EMor WHlf
	heywoodii	see *D. purpurea* subsp. *heywoodii*
	Illumination Series	see *D.* × *valinii* Illumination Series
	isabelliana	CBod CCCN CFis LDai WKif
	- BELLA ('Isob007') **new**	CSpe LCro
	'John Innes Tetra'	CTtf MBriF MMrt MNrw SPtp WOut
	kishinskyi	see *D. parviflora* Jacq.
	laevigata	CTtf EBee LEdu LShi MMrt NBro SEND
	- white-flowered	WCot
	lamarckii misapplied	see *D. lanata*
§	***lanata***	CRos EBou ECtt EHyd ELan EPfP LRHS MBNS MHol MNHC MPie NGdn NRHS SGbt SPlb SRms WGwG WOut
	- 'Café Crème'	CDor EMor LSto
	'Lemoncello' **new**	SCgs
	'Lucas'	LBar
§	***lutea*** ♀H6	Widely available
I	- 'Aurea'	LPla
§	- subsp. ***australis***	LDai
	× ***mertonensis*** ♀H5	Widely available
	- 'Summer King'	CChe CDor CWnw ECtt ELan GJos LSRN MBow SBls SPtp WFar
	micrantha	see *D. lutea* subsp. *australis*
	minor	EWes LShi
	obscura	CCCN CDor EAJP GKev SPlb SVen
*	- 'Dusky Maid'	WHlf
	- 'Sunset'	SBut
	orientalis	see *D. grandiflora*
§	***parviflora*** Jacq. ♀H5	CBod ECha ECtt EPPr EPfP GKev LCro LPal LRHS LShi MBNS MHer MMrt NBro NChi SEND SEdd
	- 'Milk Chocolate' ♀H5	CAby CBod CDor CElw CSpe ECtt ELan EMor EPfP ETod GKev LRHS LSRN MBros NFav NHpl NLar SBls SEdd SPtp
	'Pink Panther' **new**	LCro MPri
	(Polkadot Series) 'Polkadot Petra'	WHil
	- 'Polkadot Pippa'	LBar WHil WHlf
	- 'Polkadot Polly'	MBriF WHlf
	purpurea	Widely available
	- 'Alba'	see *D. purpurea* f. *albiflora*
§	- f. ***albiflora***	Widely available
	- - 'Anne Redetzky'PBR	CSpe LBar LRHS
	- 'Apricot Delight'	EBee MNHC SBut WCAu
	- Camelot Series	MBros SHar SVic
	- - 'Camelot Cream' ♀H5	EHyd ELan EPfP SCoo SPoG SWvt
	- - 'Camelot Lavender' ♀H5	EHyd ELan EPfP MACG SWvt
	- - 'Camelot Rose' ♀H5	EHyd ELan EPfP MACG SWvt
	- - 'Camelot White' ♀H5	EHyd ELan EPfP
	- 'Campanulata'	LShi
	- 'Cream Carousel' (Carousel Series)	EBee EHyd LRHS NRHS
	- Dalmatian Series	SCob
	- - 'Dalmatian Crème' ♀H7	CRos EPfP LBar LRHS MACG MDon MPri NRHS SCob SCoo WHil
	- - 'Dalmatian Peach' ♀H5	CBod ELan EPfP LBar LCro LRHS MACG MBros MDon WHil WHlf
	- - 'Dalmatian Purple' ♀H5	ELan EPfP LBar LCro LOPS LRHS MACG MPri SCob SCoo WHlf
	- - 'Dalmatian Rose' ♀H5	CBod CRos ELan EPfP LBar LCro LRHS MACG MDon MPri NRHS SCob SCoo
	- - 'Dalmatian White' ♀H5	CBod ELan EPfP LBar LCro LOPS LRHS MACG MBros MDon MPri SCob SCoo WWke
	- Excelsior Group	CBcs CDor CMac CRos CSBt CTri CWal ECtt EHyd EPfP GJos GMaP LCro LOPS LRHS NHol NMir NRHS SCob SGbt SPer SPoG SRms SVic SWvt
	- - (Suttons; Unwins)	ECtt MRav
	- - white-flowered	CTri
	- Foxy Group	EPfP GMcL LRHS MACG MNHC SPoG
	- Giant Spotted Group	CRos ECtt EHyd EPfP LRHS NRHS SPoG

§ - subsp. ***heywoodii***	CSpe EAJP LBar
- - 'Silver Fox'	NRHS SCob
- 'Lavender Carousel' (Carousel Series)	EHyd LRHS NRHS
- subsp. ***mariana***	CSpe
- 'Orchid Carousel' (Carousel Series)	EHyd LRHS NRHS
- 'Pam's Choice' ♀H7	CAby CChe CDor CKel CRos CSpe EAJP EBee ECtt EHyd ELan EPfP EWTr GBin LBar LCro LOPS LRHS LSRN LSun NCth NHol NLar NRHS SCob SCoo SPer WCAu
- 'Pam's Split'	LBar SCob
- 'Pink Gin' **new**	LBar
- 'Primrose Carousel' (Carousel Series)	NCou NLar SCob SCoo
- 'Purple Carousel' (Carousel Series)	EHyd LRHS NRHS
- 'Serendipity'	EHyd LRHS NRHS
- 'Snow Thimble'	CAby CDor EAJP EHyd ELan EPfP LBar LRHS LSun MACG MBros NLar NRHS SCoo
- 'Sugar Plum'	LBar WHlf
§ - 'Sutton's Apricot'	Widely available
- (Virtuoso Series) 'Virtuoso Cream'	LRHS
- - 'Virtuoso Lavender'	LRHS
- - 'Virtuoso Red'	GMcL
- - 'Virtuoso Rose Compact'	LRHS
- - 'Virtuoso Rose'	GMcL
- - 'Virtuoso White'	GMcL LRHS
- 'White Carousel' (Carousel Series)	EHyd LRHS NRHS
sceptrum	CCCN CTsd SIvy SPlb SVen
'Silver Cub'	WHlf
'Spice Island'	CCht EBee ECtt EPfP EWes LCro LOPS LPal LRHS LSou LSun MNrw NLar SPad WCot WSpi WTor
* ***stewartii***	CElw EWes LDai
thapsi	EAJP EPfP
- 'Spanish Peaks'	GEdr LBar
trojana	GKev LShi NBir
- 'Helen of Troy'	WSpi
× ***valinii*** 'Berry Canary'	CCht EPfP LBar LRHS NCou SPad SPoG
- 'Firebird'	CRos LBuc LCro SHar WCot
- 'Firecracker' **new**	LBar LBuc MPri
- Foxlight Series	LBuc
- - FOXLIGHT PLUM GOLD ('Takfoplgo'[PBR])	CWGN ECtt LBar LCro LOPS LRHS MAsh MDon SCoo WHil
- - FOXLIGHT ROSE IVORY ('Takforoiv'[PBR])	LBar LRHS MDon WHil
- - FOXLIGHT RUBY GLOW ('Takforugl'[PBR])	LBar LRHS LSou MAsh WHil WWke
§ - Illumination Series	CKel EAri EHyd LRHS SCob
§ - - 'Harkstead Apricot'	CCCN EPfP LRHS MNHC NHpl SEle
§ - - 'Harkstead Flame'[PBR]	CCht CRos EHyd EPfP LRHS NHpl NRHS SCoo SPad SPoG WHil
- - 'Harkstead Red'	CCCN EBee EPfP MHtn
- - ILLUMINATION APRICOT	see *D.* × *valinii* (Illumination Series) 'Harkstead Apricot'
- - ILLUMINATION CHERRY BRANDY	see *D.* ILLUMINATION RUBY SLIPPERS
- - ILLUMINATION FLAME	see *D.* × *valinii* (Illumination Series) 'Harkstead Flame'
- - ILLUMINATION PINK ('Tmdgfp001'[PBR]) (Illumination Series)	CAbb CRos EBee EPfP LBuc LCro LOPS LRHS NHpl SPoG WCot WHlf
§ - - ILLUMINATION RUBY SLIPPERS ('Tmdg1204'[PBR])	CRos EBee EHyd EPfP LRHS NHpl NRHS SOrN WHil
Vesuvius Group	LShi
viridiflora	CSpe GQue
'Walberton's Goldcrest'	see *D.* GOLDCREST

dill see *Anethum graveolens*

Dionaea ✿ (*Droseraceae*)

muscipula	CHew LCro LOPS SHmp SPlb WSSs WTyc
- 'Akai Ryu' ♀H3	NWac SHmp WSSs
- 'B52'	NWac WSSs
- 'Big Mouth'	NWac
- 'Bohemian Garnet'	WSSs
- 'Cross Teeth'	CHew
- 'Darwin'	NWac WSSs
- (Dentate Traps Group) 'Dentate Traps'	CHew WSSs
- 'Great White Shark' **new**	NWac
- 'Mk1979'	WSSs
- 'Red Piranha'	CHew
- 'Royal Red'	CHew NWac WSSs
- 'Sawtooth'	NWac WSSs
- shark-toothed	NWac
- 'South West Giant' ♀H3	NWac WSSs
- 'Spider'	NWac
- 'Tiger Fangs'	NWac WSSs

Dionysia (*Primulaceae*)

archibaldii	WAbe
aretioides ♀H4	WAbe
- 'Bevere'	EPot WAbe
bryoides	WAbe
'Charlson Emma'	WAbe
'Charlson Pip'	WAbe
'Corona'	WAbe
curviflora	WAbe
'Eric Watson'	WAbe
esfandiarii **new**	WAbe
gaubae	WAbe
'Geist'	WAbe
'Inka Gold'	WAbe
'Judith Bramley'	WAbe
'Lycaena'	WAbe
'Mike Bramley'	WAbe
'Monika'	WAbe
revoluta **new**	WAbe
sarvestanica	WAbe
'Schneeball'	WAbe
tapetodes	EPot WAbe
- 'Brimstone'	WAbe
'Tess'	WAbe
'Yellowstone'	WAbe
'Zdeněk Zvolánek'	WAbe

Dioon (*Zamiaceae*)

argenteum	CBrP
califanoi	CBrP
caputoi	CBrP
edule ♀H1b	CBrP LPal SPlb
- var. ***angustifolium***	CBrP
merolae	CBrP
rzedowskii	CBrP
spinulosum	CBrP CCCN NPlm

Dioscorea (*Dioscoreaceae*)

BO 15-072	GGro
bulbifera	SPlb
japonica	CAgr CLau GGro LEdu
opposita	GGro
polystachya	CAgr CRHN GPoy LEdu
sylvatica	SPlb
villosa	GGro LEdu

Diosma (*Rutaceae*)

ericoides L.	GAbr SWvt
hirsuta new	WHlf
- 'Silver Flame'	CBod EGrl
'Pink Fountain'	see *Coleonema pulchellum* 'Pink Fountain'
'Sunset Gold'	see *Coleonema* 'Sunset Gold'

Diosphaera (*Campanulaceae*)

asperuloides	see *Trachelium asperuloides*

Diospyros (*Ebenaceae*)

austroafricana	SPlb
glabra	SVen
* ***hyrcanum***	NLar
kaki (F)	CBcs CMCN EPfP NLar WCot WJur
- 'Fuyu' (F)	CAgr
- 'Kostata' (F)	CAgr
- 'Mazelii' (F)	CAgr WPGP
- 'Pendula' (F) new	NPlm
- 'Rojo Brillante' (F)	SVic
lotus	CAgr CBcs CMCN LEdu NLar SPlb WJur WKor
- FMWJ 13164	WCru
- PAB 10032	LEdu WPGP
- (f)	LMaj
- 'Albert' (m)	CAgr
- 'Browny' (f/F)	CAgr
lycioides	CPbh SPlb
'Mount Goverla' (F)	CAgr
'Nikita's Gift' (F)	CAgr
'Nikita's Russian' (F)	CAgr
'Nikshoo' (F)	CAgr
ramulosa	SPlb
rhombifolia	NLar
'Russian Beauty' (F)	CAgr
'Russian Red' (F)	CAgr
virginiana (F)	CBcs CMCN EBee NLar SPlb WJur WKor
- 'Morris Burton' (F)	CAgr
- 'Nc-10' (F)	CAgr

Dipelta (*Caprifoliaceae*)

floribunda ♀H5	CBcs CExl CMCN CSBt EHyd EPfP IDee MBlu MGil SWvt WPGP
ventricosa	CBcs CExl EHyd EPfP IDee LRHS MBlu MGil NLar SBrt SPoG WPGP
yunnanensis	CBcs CCCN CExl CKel EBee EHyd EPfP IArd IDee MBNS NLar SMad SPoG SWvt WPGP

Diphylleia (*Berberidaceae*)

cymosa	ECha GEdr LEdu LPla MNrw MRav SPhx WCot WCru WOld
grayi	GEdr LEdu WCru
sinensis	LEdu WCru

Diplacus see *Mimulus*

Dipladenia see *Mandevilla*

Diplarrena (*Iridaceae*)

§ ***latifolia***	CNor LRHS NCth SGBe
moraea	CDor CElw CMac CTsd CWCL EBee EGrl ITim MBel SMHy SPlb WSHC
- West Coast form	see *D. latifolia*

Diplazium (*Woodsiaceae*)

caudatum	WPGP

Diplopanax (*Cornaceae*)

stachyanthus B&SWJ 11803	WCru

Diplotaxis (*Brassicaceae*)

erucoides	CArg
tenuifolia	CAgr CBod ENfk EWhm LCro MHoo MNHC SRms

Dipsacus (*Caprifoliaceae*)

asper PAB 8884	LEdu
- from Ghangzhou, China new	ESwi
asperoides	GGro
dipsacoides	LEdu WPGP
§ ***fullonum***	CBod CHab CMac CPud ENfk EPfP GQue LCro LOPS MNHC NGrd NLar NMir SDix SEdd SRms WHer WSFF WWild
inermis	ECha GGro NBid
japonicus HWJ 695	SPhx WCru
pilosus	CBgR NDov
pinnatifidus PAB 2845	LEdu
sativus	SPhx
strigosus	SPhx
sylvestris	see *D. fullonum*

Dipteracanthus see *Ruellia*

Dipteronia (*Sapindaceae*)

sinensis	CBcs CMCN MBlu SMad WLov

Disa (*Orchidaceae*)

aurata	NDav
Bride's Dream gx	NDav
Child Safety Transvaal gx	NDav
- 'Sonia'	NDav
Colette Cywes gx 'Blush'	NDav
Constantia gx	NDav
Diores gx	NDav
- 'Inca City'	NDav
- 'Inca Gold'	NDav
- 'Inca Princess'	NDav
- 'Inca Warrior'	NDav
Diorosa gx	NDav
Foam gx	NDav
- 'Zoe'	NDav
Glasgow Orchid Conference gx	NDav
Ivan Watson gx	NDav
Kalahari Sands gx	NDav
- 'Tina'	NDav
Kewbett gx	NDav
- 'Pink Gem'	NDav
Kewdior gx	NDav
Kewensis gx 'Alice'	NDav
- 'Ann'	NDav
- 'May'	NDav
- 'Milkmaid'	NDav
- 'Ruth'	NDav
Reheat gx	NDav
Riette gx	NDav
Robert Parkinson gx	NDav
Sealord gx	NDav
Tracey Parkinson gx	NDav
tripetaloides	NDav
Unidiorosa gx 'Tracey'	NDav
uniflora	NDav SPlb
- carmine-flowered	NDav
- pink-flowered	NDav
- red-flowered	NDav
Unifoam gx	NDav

- 'Firebird'	NDav
Unilangley gx	NDav
Watsonii gx 'Bramley'	NDav
- 'Candy'	NDav
- 'Don'	NDav
- 'Sandra'	NDav

Disanthus (*Hamamelidaceae*)

cercidifolius ♀H5	CBcs CMCN CMac EGrl EHyd EPfP GKin LRHS MBlu SPoG WMat WPGP
- 'Ena-nishiki' (v)	MBlu WPGP
ovatifolius	WPGP
- B&SWJ 11706	WCru
- FMWJ 13365	WCru
- WWJ 11933	WCru
- WWJ 11994	WCru

Dischidia (*Apocynaceae*)

'Geri'	EShb
'Pangolin Kisses' **new**	LCro
ruscifolia	CDoC

Diselma (*Cupressaceae*)

archeri 'Read Dwarf'	CKen

Disepalum (*Annonaceae*)

petelotii FMWJ 13375	WCru

Disocactus (*Cactaceae*)

crenatus **new**	EAri
martianus **new**	EAri

× *Disophyllum* (*Cactaceae*)

'Odalisque' **new**	EAri

Disphyma (*Aizoaceae*)

australe	GKev

Disporopsis (*Asparagaceae*)

	B&SWJ 229 from Taiwan	ESwi WCru
	B&SWJ 1864 from Taiwan	WCru
	aspersa	CAvo CBro EPPr EPot ESwi EWld ITim LEdu MAvo MBriF MNrw NBir SSut WCru WFar WPGP
	- tall	CBct ESwi MACG WCru
	bodinieri	CDor
	- FMWJ 13457	WCru
	- KWJ 12277	ESwi WCru
	fuscopicta	CBct EHed EPPr LEdu MACG MAvo WCru
	longifolia B&SWJ 5284	WCru
	luzoniensis	WPGP
	- B&SWJ 3891	CBct EPPr ESwi GEdr LEdu WCru
	'Min Shan'	ELon
*	***nova***	EPPr ESwi MAvo
§	***pernyi***	Widely available
	- B&SWJ 1864	EPPr GEdr
	- 'Bill Baker'	CBct EBee EPPr ESwi LEdu MAvo WSHC
	aff. ***pernyi***	MBriF NBPC
	taiwanensis	EBee LEdu
	- B&SWJ 3388	CBct GEdr WCru
	undulata	CBct EBee EMor EPPr EPot ESwi GGro ILea LEdu NBid SHar WCru WPGP

Disporum (*Colchicaceae*)

	bodinieri	CTtf ELan EMor EPfP GElm GKev ILea IPot LAma SBea
	- DJHC 765	WCru
	aff. ***bodinieri***	EMor WHlf
	calcaratum BWJ 15552 **new**	WCru
	cantoniense	CBct LEdu SDir SPlb WFar WHil WPnP
	- B&L 12512	CExl
	- B&SWJ 1424	WCru
	- B&SWJ 9715	WCru
	- DJHC 98485	LEdu WOld WPGP
	- PAB 8339	LEdu
I	- 'Aureovariegata'	CBct EPfP ESwi LEdu WCot WSHC
	- 'Blueberry Bere'	LEdu
	- var. ***cantoniense***	WCru
	f. ***brunneum*** B&SWJ 5290	
	- 'Leigong'	WPGP
	- 'Leigong Chocolate'	LEdu
	- 'Moonlight' PBR (v)	CBct EBee EHed ELan EMor LEdu LRHS SMad XSte
	- var. ***sikkimense*** B&SWJ 2337	WCru
	- - B&SWJ 2358	LEdu WCru
	- - PAB 13.1711	LEdu
	- var. ***y-tiense*** HWJ 1045	WCru
	hookeri	see *Prosartes hookeri*
	kawakamii B&SWJ 350	WCru
	- RWJ 10103	CBct WCru
	lanuginosum	see *Prosartes lanuginosa*
	leschenaultianum B&SWJ 9484	WCru
	- B&SWJ 9505	WCru
	leucanthum	EBee ECha EHed WCru
	- B&SWJ 2389	WCru
	longistylum	EBee EHed LEdu
	- B&SWJ 2859	WCru
	- BWJ 8128	WCru
	- L 1564	CBct EHed EPfP ESwi LRHS WCru WOld
	- 'Green Giant'	CBct CBod CDor CExl CMiW CSpe CTtf EBee EHed ELan EMor EPfP GEdr GKev ILea LEdu LPla LRHS MCot NCth NHar NLar SBea SHar SMad WFar WHil WHlf WSHC XSte
	- 'Night Heron' ♀H6	CDor CExl CTtf ECha EHed EHyd EMor GElm GKev IPot LCro LEdu LRHS LSto NRHS SHar SMHy WCot WFar XSte
	aff. ***longistylum***	EMor
	- NJM 11.011	WPGP
	lutescens	EBee EPot LEdu WCru WPGP
	maculatum	see *Prosartes maculata*
	megalanthum	CBct CExl CMiW EBlo EMor ILea LEdu MBel NHar WCru WFar WPGP
	- CD&R 2412B	CDor CExl EBee EHed ELan IPot MACG MMrt NCth SHor WHlf
	menziesii	see *Prosartes smithii*
	nantouense B&SWJ 359	LEdu WCru
	- B&SWJ 6812	WCru
	oreganum	see *Prosartes hookeri* var. *oregana*
	sessile	EBee LEdu NBir WCru
	- B&SWJ 2824	WCru
I	- 'Aureovariegatum' (v)	EPPr WCru
	- 'Awa-no-tsuki' (v)	GEdr GKev
	- 'Kinga' (v)	LEdu
	- f. ***macrophyllum*** B&SWJ 4316	WCru
I	- 'Robustum Variegatum' (v)	SHar
	- 'Snow Stream' (v)	GEdr WFar
	- 'Variegatum' (v)	CDor CExl CTtf EBee EBlo ECha EHed EHyd ELan ELon EMor EPPr EPfP ESwi LBar LEdu LRHS MNrw NBir NHpl NLar NQui NRHS SPhx WCru WFar WHil WPGP WSHC
	- var. ***yakushimense***	LEdu
	- yellow-margined variegated (v)	GKev

shimadae	GKev
smilacinum	EMor NLar WCru
- B&SWJ 713	CBct WCru
* - 'Aureovariegatum' (v)	LEdu WCru
- 'Dai-setsurei' (v)	WCot
- 'Ki-naka-fu' (v)	WFar
- 'Koutei' (v)	WFar
- pink-flowered	CBct LEdu WCot WCru WSHC
smithii	see *Prosartes smithii*
taiwanense	LEdu
- B&SWJ 1513	WCru
- B&SWJ 2018	WCru
tonkinense B&SWJ 11814	WCru
trabeculatum	CBct CDor WCru
- 'Nakafu' (v)	WCru
uniflorum	CBct CBor CMiW CRos EHyd EMor EPfP GKev IPot LBar LEdu LRHS MHid MMrt MNrw NBid NRHS WSHC
- B&SWJ 651	CBct ESwi LEdu WCru
- B&SWJ 872	WCru
- B&SWJ 4100	WCru
- MSF 800	LEdu
viridescens	CBct EBee EBlo EMor EPPr LEdu WCru
- B&SWJ 4598	EPot ESwi WCru

Distyliopsis (*Hamamelidaceae*)

tutcheri	CJun

Distylium (*Hamamelidaceae*)

BLUE CASCADE ('Piidist-ii')	CBcs LRHS NLar XSte
myricoides	NLar
racemosum	CBcs CCCN CMac EBee EPfP MBlu NLar SSta

Dittrichia (*Asteraceae*)

viscosa	WCot

Diuranthera see *Chlorophytum*

Dizygotheca see *Schefflera*

Docynia (*Rosaceae*)

delavayi	SPtp

Dodecatheon (*Primulaceae*)

alpinum	NHar
'Aphrodite' PBR	ECtt NLar
austrofrigidum	GEdr LEdu SBrt WFar
clevelandii	EDAr GEdr
- subsp. ***patulum***	EHyd NRHS
'Comet'	CBor WFar
cusickii	see *D. pulchellum* subsp. *cusickii*
dentatum	GEdr LEdu NHar NRya SBrt WAbe WFar
- subsp. ***ellisiae***	GKev
- subsp. ***utahense***	GEdr NHar NRya WFar
frigidum	GEdr GKev
§ ***hendersonii***	GKev
integrifolium	see *D. hendersonii*
§ ***jeffreyi***	ECtt EDAr EPPr EPfP GEdr GKev MBNS MHol MNrw NBPC NLar SRkn WFar XLum
- subsp. ***pygmaeum***	EBee GKev
- 'Rotlicht'	EHyd LRHS NRHS
§ ***meadia*** 🏆H5	Widely available
- from Cedar County, USA	WAbe
- f. ***album*** 🏆H5	CBro CRos CTtf EDAr EHyd ELan EMor EPot EWoo LAma LEdu LRHS NHol NHpl NRHS SDir SPer SWvt WFar WPnP WSpi WTyc
- 'Aphrodite'	WFar
- 'Blush' **new**	CBor
- 'Goliath'	GAbr
- membranaceous	WAbe
- 'Queen Victoria'	LBar LEdu NLar WFar
'Meteor'	CBor WFar
pauciflorum misapplied	see *D. pulchellum*
pauciflorum (Dur.) E. Greene	see *D. meadia*
poeticum	SPlb
§ ***pulchellum*** 🏆H5	EBee EGrI EHyd GEdr GKev LEdu LLWG LRHS MNrw NRHS NRya WIce
- ***album***	WCav
§ - subsp. ***cusickii***	ECha LEdu
- subsp. ***pulchellum*** 'Red Wings'	CBor CTtf EBee EGrI ELan EPot EWoo GKev LAma LEdu LRHS NHar NHpl NLar WBor WCav WTyc
§ - Radicatum Group	CRos LRHS
- 'Sooke Variety'	NRya WAbe
radicatum	see *D. pulchellum* Radicatum Group
'Stellar Pink'	GEdr
tetrandrum	see *D. jeffreyi*

Dodonaea (*Sapindaceae*)

viscosa	EPfP SPlb
- 'Purpurea'	CBcs CBod CCht CTsd EBee LPal LRHS MGil MHtn SEdd SEle SGBe SGsty SIvy SPoG SVen

Doellingeria (*Asteraceae*)

scabra	see *Aster scaber*
umbellata	CBWd CKno ECha EPPr GQue LEdu LRHS LSto MMuc NBir NDov NLar SEND WCot WOld
- 'Weisser Schirm'	MNrw

Dolichandra (*Bignoniaceae*)

§ ***unguis-cati*** 🏆H3	CCCN CRHN EShb WJur

Dolichothele see *Mammillaria*

Dombeya (*Malvaceae*)

wallichii	CCCN

Dondia see *Hacquetia*

Doodia (*Blechnaceae*)

aspera	CLAP IKel NBro
- 'Rough Ruby'	CBct CBdn CMiW CTsd EHed MAsh NBro SIvy SMrm SPad XSte
§ ***caudata***	NBro
media	CAbb CAby CBct CBdn CBod CBrP CKel CLAP CMiW EBee EHyd GQue IKel LBar LEdu LLWG LPar LRHS NBro NRHS SMrm SPeP SPlb WCot
squarrosa	see *D. caudata*

Dorema (*Apiaceae*)

ammoniacum	SDix SPhx

Doronicum (*Asteraceae*)

austriacum	GJos MSCN NBid
caucasicum	see *D. orientale*
§ ***columnae***	CBcs
cordatum	see *D. columnae*
§ × ***excelsum*** 'Harpur Crewe'	EBee LEdu LShi MRav NPer SHar
'Finesse'	CRos EPfP GJos LRHS NRHS SRms
'Little Leo'	ELan EPfP GJos GMaP LRHS LSRN MTin NFav NLar SCob SEdd SGBe SPoG SRms WFar

§ ***orientale***	EHeP ELan EPfP GJos MBel MPri SPoG
- 'Leonardo'	CBod CRos EHyd EMor EPfP GMcL LRHS NGrd NRHS
- 'Leonardo Compact'	GArf MPri SCoo
- 'Magnificum'	CRos CSBt EHyd EPfP LBar LRHS NGBl NRHS SCob SPoG SRms WCAu WFar WHlf
pardalianches	GJos LPla MMuc NFav WBrk
- 'Goldstrauss'	EBee
plantagineum	MMuc
- 'Excelsum'	see *D.* × *excelsum* 'Harpur Crewe'

Doryanthes (*Doryanthaceae*)

palmeri	CBrP

Dorycnium see *Lotus*

Douglasia see *Androsace*

vitaliana	see *Vitaliana primuliflora*

Doxantha see *Macfadyena*

Draba (*Brassicaceae*)

acaulis	WAbe
aizoides	CRos EBou EHyd GJos LRHS NRHS SPlb SRms
aizoon	see *D. lasiocarpa*
§ ***aspera***	GJos
aurea var. ***leiocarpa***	CBor
bertolonii Boiss.	see *D. loeseleurii*
bertolonii Nyman	see *D. aspera*
bruniifolia	EDAr
'Buttermilk'	EPot WAbe
compacta	see *D. lasiocarpa* Compacta Group
* ***condensata***	GJos
cretica	GJos ITim
cusickii	CPla
dedeana	EPot GJos ITim WAbe
hispanica	CPla ITim
'John Saxton'	EPot WAbe
kotschyi	SPlb
§ ***lasiocarpa***	GJos SPhx
§ - Compacta Group	ITim
§ ***loeseleurii***	GJos
longisiliqua ♀H5	EPot WAbe
mollissima	EPot SPlb WAbe
- 'Göteborg'	EPot
nivalis	SPlb
norvegica	ITim
oligosperma	EDAr GJos
ossetica	WAbe
paysonii	ITim
polytricha	NSla
rigida var. ***bryoides*** compact	EPot WAbe
* - var. ***imbricata***	NBwr NSla
rosularis	EPot GJos WAbe
scardica	see *D. lasiocarpa*
sphaeroides	GJos NSla SPlb
yunnanensis	WAbe

Dracaena ✿ (*Asparagaceae*)

cochinchinensis	SPlb
congesta	see *Cordyline congesta*
'Dracaena'PBR **new**	NHrt
draco ♀H1c	CCCN CMCN EAri NPlm SPlb
fragrans	NHrt
- Compacta Group **new**	LCro NHrt
- - 'White Jewel'PBR	LCro LOPS NHrt
- (Deremensis Group) 'Lemon Lime' (v) ♀H1b	LCro LOPS NHrt NPlm
- - 'Warneckei' (v) ♀H1b	NHrt NPlm
- 'Janet Craig'	LCro LOPS NHrt
- 'Janet Lind' (v)	LCro LOPS NHrt
- 'Massangeana' (v) ♀H1b	NHrt
indivisa	see *Cordyline indivisa*
marginata (v) ♀H1b	LCro LOPS NHrt
- 'Bicolor' (v) **new**	LCro
- 'Magenta' (v) **new**	LCro
- 'Sunray'PBR (v) **new**	LCro
'Red Edge' **new**	NHrt
surculosa **new**	LCro
- 'Florida Beauty' (v) ♀H1b	LCro
- 'Mike' (v) **new**	LCro

Dracocephalum (*Lamiaceae*)

argunense	CAby LShi SPhx SRms
- 'Fuji Blue'	CPla EDAr EPfP EWes MHol SBut SPoG SVic WIce WMal WTor
- 'Fuji White'	EDAr SBut
austriacum	SBrt
calophyllum	GKev
forrestii	CPla
grandiflorum	GEdr SPhx WCot
moldavica	LRHS SPhx
nutans	SPhx
peregrinum 'Blue Dragon'	SPhx
prattii	see *Nepeta prattii*
rupestre	CSpe EAJP EMor MHol SBls SPhx
ruyschiana	EBee
- 'Blue Moon'	MHol
sibiricum	see *Nepeta sibirica*
virginicum	see *Physostegia virginiana*

Dracunculus (*Araceae*)

canariensis	EBee ESwi WCot
muscivorus	see *Helicodiceros muscivorus*
§ ***vulgaris***	CAby EBee EHyd EPfP EPot ESwi GKev ISha LAma LRHS NRHS NRog SEND SPlb WCot
- white-flowered	WCot

Drapetes (*Thymelaeaceae*)

dieffenbachii	GArf

Dregea (*Apocynaceae*)

sinensis	CBcs CBct CCCN CHll CKel CRHN CRos EBee ECre EGrl ELan EPfP EWes EWld LRHS MRav SEND SPoG SWvt WHil WPGP WSHC
- 'Brockhill Silver'	CKel EPfP GKev SPoG SWvt
- 'Variegata' (v)	CCCN EWes WHlf

Drepanostachyum (*Poaceae*)

falconeri J.J.N. Campbell. ex D. McClintock	see *Himalayacalamus falconeri*
hookerianum	see *Himalayacalamus hookerianus*

Drimiopsis (*Asparagaceae*)

maculata	CBor EAri EShb

Drimys (*Winteraceae*)

andina	MGil MMuc
aromatica	see *Tasmannia lanceolata*
colorata	see *Pseudowintera colorata*
granadensis	WCru
var. ***grandiflora*** B&SWJ 10777	
winteri ♀H4	CBcs CKel CMac CSBt CSde CTri EBee EGrl EHyd ELan EPfP EWTr GBin GKin LEdu LRHS LSRN MBlu MGil MGos NQui SArc SEle SGol SPer SPlb SPoG SWvt WFar WPav
§ - var. ***chilensis***	CBcs EHyd EPfP LRHS WCru WPGP

	- Latifolia Group	see *D. winteri* var. *chilensis*
	- var. ***winteri***	SRms

Drosanthemum (*Aizoaceae*)

	eburneum	SSim
	flammeum	SSim
	floribundum	SSim
	hispidum	CRos EHyd ELan EPot ITim LRHS MAsh NRHS SPlb SPoG SRot SSim WIce
	micans	SSim
*	***sutherlandii***	SRot

Drosera ✿ (*Droseraceae*)

	adelae	CHew
	admirabilis	CHew
	aliciae 🏆H3	CHew NWac SHmp
	'Andromeda'	CHew
	anglica	NWac
	ascendens	CHew
	binata	CHew NWac SHmp
§	- subsp. ***dichotoma*** 🏆H3	NWac SHmp
	capensis	CHew LCro LOPS NWac SHmp SPlb
	- 'Albino' 🏆H3	CHew SHmp
	- red	NWac
	cuneifolia	CHew
	dichotoma	see *D. binata* subsp. *dichotoma*
	filiformis	NWac
	- var. ***filiformis***	CHew SHmp SPlb
	- var. ***floridana***	CHew
	hamiltonii	CHew
	intermedia	NWac
	latifolia	CHew
	madagascariensis	NWac SHmp
	nidiformis	CHew NWac
	regia	CHew NWac
	rotundifolia	NWac SHmp
	schizandra	CHew
	scorpioides	NWac SHmp
	slackii 🏆H3	CHew
	spatulata	CHew NWac SHmp

Drosophyllum (*Drosophyllaceae*)

	lusitanicum	CHew

Dryandra see *Banksia*

	quercifolia	see *Banksia heliantha*

Dryas (*Rosaceae*)

	caucasica new	GKev
	drummondii	GKev
	integrifolia 'Greenland Green'	WAbe
	octopetala 🏆H7	CPla EDAr EHyd GArf GKev LRHS NFav NRHS SPoG SRms SWvt WAbe WHoo
§	- 'Minor' 🏆H7	EPot GArf WAbe
	× ***suendermannii*** 🏆H7	EPot GArf GBin GEdr NHar WAbe
	tenella misapplied	see *D. octopetala* 'Minor'

Drymonia (*Gesneriaceae*)

	chiribogana new	SBrt

Drynaria (*Polypodiaceae*)

	baronii	LEdu WCot WPGP
	propinqua	LEdu

Dryopteris ✿ (*Dryopteridaceae*)

	aemula	EFer LEdu
§	***affinis*** 🏆H5	Widely available
	- 'Angustata Crispa'	EBee EMor ISha SRms
	- 'Congesta Cristata'	CWCL ECtt EFer EMor GMaP LEdu LPal SCob
	- Crispa Group	CLAP EHyd EMor EPfP ISha LRHS NRHS WBrk
	- 'Crispa Congesta Grandiceps'	MAsh
§	- 'Crispa Gracilis' 🏆H5	CAby CKel CLAP CMiW CSta EHyd ELan ISha LPal LRHS MTin NBir NHol NLar NRHS
*	- 'Crispa Gracilis Congesta'	CBod EMor LLWG MRav NGdn WFib
§	- 'Cristata' 🏆H5	Widely available
	- 'Cristata Angustata' 🏆H5	CKel CLAP EFer ELan EMor EPfP LLWG NBid NBro NGdn NHol SCob WFib
	- 'Cristata The King'	see *D. affinis* 'Cristata'
	- 'Grandiceps Askew'	WFib
	- 'Linearis Cristata'	NBwr
	- 'Pinderi'	CAby CLAP EAJP EBee EMor EPfP GBin ISha LEdu LPar MPie MPnt NLar NRHS SCob WCot WSpi
	- Polydactyla Group	ISha SPlb
	- - 'Polydactyla Dadds'	CLAP EBee EMor NLar WCot
	- - 'Polydactyla Mapplebeck' 🏆H5	NBid WFib
	- 'Revolvens'	EFer
	atrata misapplied	see *D. cycadina*
	atrata (Wall. ex Kunze) Ching	CAby CDTJ CKel CPla CWCL EHyd ELan LLWG LPal LRHS NLar NRHS SEdd SPoG
	× ***australis***	CLAP EHed ISha
	austriaca	see *D. dilatata*
	buschiana	EBee EMor EWTr LPal MRav NLar
	carthusiana	EBee EFer EMor NLar WSpi XLum
	- 'Cristata'	EFer
	celsa	EBee ISha
	championii	CCCN CLAP EBee EHyd ELan EMor ISha LEdu NBid NBro NLar NRHS SRot
	clintoniana	EBee ECtt EFer EHyd GQue ISha ITim LPla MPie NRHS
	× ***complexa***	CBdn CLAP ISha
	- 'Stablerae' 🏆H7	CLAP EFer WFib
	- 'Stablerae' crisped 🏆H7	WFib
	coreanomontana	EMor NLar
	crassirhizoma 🏆H6	CBdn CCCN CLAP CRos EBee ECtt EHyd ELan EMor EPfP ISha LEdu LPla LRHS LSun NLar NRHS SCoo SPoG WCot WPGP WSpi
	cristata	CLAP CWCL EBee EPfP ISha
§	***cycadina*** 🏆H4	CBcs CBdn CLAP CRos EBee EFer EHyd ELan EMor EPfP EShb GBin ISha LEdu LPar LRHS MAsh MGos NBid NBir NRHS SCob SPlb WCot WFib WLov
§	***dilatata*** 🏆H6	CLAP ECha EFer EHyd ELan EMor EPfP ISha LPal LRHS MMuc MRav NRHS WFib WShi
	- 'Crispa Whiteside' 🏆H6	CAby CDor CLAP CMiW CRos CSde CWCL EAJP EBee EFer EHyd ELan EMor EPfP EShb ISha LRHS MRav NBro NLar NRHS SCoo SPlb SPoG SRot WFib WLov
	- 'Cristata'	LSun
	- 'Grandiceps'	CMac EFer GBin WFib
	- 'Jimmy Dyce'	CLAP CRos EBee EHyd EMor ISha LEdu LRHS MAsh NBro NRHS
I	- 'Lepidota Crispa'	EHyd LRHS NRHS
	- 'Lepidota Crispa Cristata'	CLAP EBee EMor
	- 'Lepidota Cristata' 🏆H6	CKel CMiW CWCL ELan EMor GBin GKev ISha LEdu NBro SCoo WFib
*	- 'Recurvata'	CLAP NLar
	erythrosora 🏆H4	Widely available
	- 'Brilliance' 🏆H5	CBcs CBct CBdn CBod CCCN CDoC CLAP CRos EBee ECtt EHyd

	ELon EMor ISha LEdu LRHS LSun MAsh MAvo MPie NCou NRHS SCoo SEdd WCot
- dwarf	CBod CMiW LEdu WHlf
- var. ***koidzumiana***	EHyd ISha LEdu LRHS NRHS WCot
- var. ***prolifica***	Widely available
- 'Radiance'	ISha
filix-mas ♀H7	Widely available
- 'Barnesii'	CEme CKel CLAP CRos CWCL EFer EHyd ELan EMor GBin LRHS MAsh NLar NRHS SEND SPlb WFar WLov
- 'Crispa'	CRos EHyd EPfP ISha LEdu LRHS MPnt NRHS WFib
- 'Crispa Congesta'	see *D. affinis* 'Crispa Gracilis'
- 'Crispa Cristata' ♀H7	CBod CChe CKel CLAP CRos CSta CWCL EBee ECtt EFer EHed EHyd ELan EMor EPfP GMaP ISha LEdu LLWG LRHS NBid NBir NBro NRHS SCob SPoG WFib
- 'Crispatissima'	EBee
- 'Cristata' ♀H7	CChe CLAP CSde EBee ECtt EFer ELan EMor LCro LLWG LOPS NBro SEND XSte
- Cristata Group	EFer
* - - 'Cristata Grandiceps'	EFer
- - 'Cristata Jackson'	SPlb
- - 'Cristata Martindale'	CLAP EBee NBid WFib
- - 'Fred Jackson'	WFib
- 'Depauperata'	CLAP
- 'Furcans'	CRos EBee ECtt EHyd LRHS NRHS
- 'Grandiceps Wills' ♀H7	NBid WFib
- 'Linearis'	EFer EHyd ELan EMor EWoo LPfP LRHS MGos NRHS WFib
- 'Linearis Polydactyla' ♀H7	Widely available
- 'Parsley'	CLAP EBee ISha NBro
* - Polydactyla Group	EMor MRav
I - 'Revolvens'	WFib
formosana	CBdn WPGP
goldieana	CBdn CBod CDTJ CLAP CRos ECha ECtt EFer EHyd ELan EMor EWTr GMaP ISha LLWG LRHS NBid NBir NLar NRHS SPlb WFar WFib WPnP WSpi XLum
hirtipes misapplied	see *D. cycadina*
intermedia	CBdn
kuratae	EMor LEdu LLWG NBro NLar WBrk WCot WPGP
labordei	CLAP
lepidopoda	CBcs CBdn CDoC CDor CLAP CRos EBee ECtt EHyd EMor ISha ITim LEdu LPal LRHS MAsh MPie NBro NRHS SPoG WCot WPGP WSpi
ludoviciana	CRos EBee EHyd LEdu LRHS NLar NRHS WSpi
marginalis	CDTJ EHyd EMor ISha NLar NRHS SCob
namegatae	WCot
oreades	WCot
pseudofilix-mas	ISha
pseudomas	see *D. affinis*
pulcherrima	CLAP CRos EHyd LRHS NRHS
pycnopteroides	CLAP
× ***remota***	CLAP EFer LRHS
sichotensis	EMor SPlb
sieboldii ♀H6	Widely available
stewartii	CAby CBdn CBod CLAP EMor ESwi ISha NBro NLar
submontana	CRos EHyd LRHS MAsh NRHS
tokyoensis ♀H6	CDTJ CLAP EHyd NLar NRHS WSpi
uniformis	CLAP EFer
wallichiana ♀H5	Widely available
- JURASSIC GOLD ('Hollasic')	CBct CBdn LCro LEdu NLar SMrm WHlf WPnP

Duchesnea (*Rosaceae*)

chrysantha	see *D. indica*
§ ***indica***	MRav SEND WKor

Dudleya (*Crassulaceae*)

calcicola	SPlb
cymosa	SPlb
lanceolata	SPlb

Dugaldia (*Asteraceae*)

hoopesii	see *Hymenoxys hoopesii*

Dulichium (*Cyperaceae*)

arundinaceum	LLWG
- 'Tigress'	LLWG

Dunalia (*Solanaceae*)

australis	see *Eriolarynx australis*

Duranta (*Verbenaceae*)

§ ***erecta***	CCCN CHll EShb
§ - 'Geisha Girl'	CCCN EShb
- 'Sapphire Swirl'	see *D. erecta* 'Geisha Girl'
- 'Variegata' (v)	CCCN
- white-flowered	EShb SVen
plumieri	see *D. erecta*
repens	see *D. erecta*
serratifolia	CCCN

Duvernoia see *Justicia*

Dyckia (*Bromeliaceae*)

brevifolia	WCot
'Burgundy Ice'	WCot
'Cherry Coke'	WCot
floribunda	EShb
frigida	WCot
goehringii	WCot
jonesiana	WCot
leptostachya	EAri SEND SPlb WCot
'Morris Hobbs'	WCot
remotiflora	EAri SChr
'Tarzana' **new**	SEdd

Dypsis (*Arecaceae*)

§ ***decaryi***	CCCN LPal NPlm SPlb
decipiens	NPlm
lanceolata **new**	NPlm
§ ***leptocheilos***	NPlm
lutescens ♀H1a	LCro LOPS LPal LWaG NHrt NPlm SPlb
pembana **new**	NPlm
pilulifera **new**	NPlm

Dysosma see *Podophyllum*

Dystaenia (*Apiaceae*)

takesimana	CAgr EBee GGro LEdu SPhx

E

Ecballium (*Cucurbitaceae*)

elaterium	CDTJ LWaG WCot

Eccremocarpus (*Bignoniaceae*)

scaber	CBcs CWCL EAri ELan ELon EShb NPer SPlb SPoG
- 'Carmineus'	EPfP
- 'Coccineus'	CPla

	- red-flowered	CWCL EPPr
	- 'Tangerine'	CSpe
	- (Tresco Series) 'Tresco Cream'	EPPr WHil
	- - 'Tresco Gold'	CSpe

Echeveria ✿ (*Crassulaceae*)

	sp.	LCro LOPS
	affinis	CBod CDTJ MHer SEdd SPlb WCot
	'Afterglow'	EAri
	agavoides ♀H2	CDTJ CDoC EAri LCro LOPS MRav SIvy
	- 'Ebony'	NMen WCot WOld
	- 'Jade Galaxy' **new**	SEdd
	- 'Lipstick'	EAri WCot WOld
	- 'Red Edge'	EAri NMen SSim
	- 'Red Taurus' **new**	NMen WOld
	alpina	see *E. secunda*
	amoena	CBod EAri NMen SEdd
	'Apollo'	SEdd
	'Apus' PBR **new**	SEdd
	bicolor	SEdd
	- B&SWJ 14388	WCru
	- B&SWJ 14849	WCru
*	'Black Knight'	CBod CSpe EGrI LRHS NLar SEdd SIvy SSim
	'Black Prince'	CDTJ CDoC ELan LCro NPer SPlb SRms WCot WOld
	'Blondie' **new**	EAri
	'Blue Bird'	CDoC
	'Blue Mayes' **new**	SEdd
	'Blue Waves'	SEdd WCot
	× ***bombycina*** ♀H2 **new**	SIvy
	cante ♀H2	SEdd SPlb
	chihuahuaensis ♀H2	CAbb CSBt EAri NCft SEdd SRms
	- 'Raspberry Dip'	SEdd WOld
	chilonensis **new**	SEdd
*	***chinensis*** **new**	SEdd
	'Chocolate' **new**	SEdd
	'Chrissy 'n' Ryan'	SEdd
	coccinea	ELan
	colorata f. ***colorata*** **new**	SEdd
	- - 'Mexican Giant' **new**	NMen SEdd
	- 'Desert Harmony' **new**	SEdd
	- 'Haage' **new**	SEdd
	colorata × ***desmetiana***	SMrm
	compressicaulis **new**	SEdd WOld
	'Corymbosa'	WCot
	crassicaulis **new**	SPlb
	'Crystal Rose' **new**	SEdd
	'Cubic Frost' **new**	EAri
	cuencaensis **new**	SEdd
	'Curly Locks'	CAbb EBee SEdd SIvy WCot WOld
	cuspidata × ***setosa*** var. ***ciliata***	SSim
	derenbergii ♀H2	MHCG SEdd
	× ***derosa***	CDTJ
	- 'Hertzblut' **new**	SEdd
	- 'Worfield Wonder'	SEdd
§	***desmetiana***	MHer SEdd SMrm SPlb WCot
	- variegated (v) **new**	SEdd
	'Dondo'	SCoo SEdd SPoG
	'Doris Taylor'	NMen SEdd
	'Duchess of Nuremberg'	CBod CPla CSBt EAri SEdd SIvy SPlb SSim
	'Easter Bonnet'	SSim
	'Ed Hummel' **new**	SEdd
	elegans ♀H2	CDTJ CDoC CKel CPla CSBt EAri EPfP EWes EWoo NCft SEND SEdd SIvy SPlb SRms SSim
	- var. ***simulans*** 'Waves' **new**	NMen
	'Elsa' **new**	SEdd

	'Fantastic Fountain' **new**	SEdd
	'Fireball'	WOld
	'Fireglow' **new**	SIvy
	'Frank Reinelt'	SEdd
	'Fred Wass'	CPbh
	'Frida Kahlo'	SEdd WOld
	funkii **new**	SEdd
	'Giant Blue'	CDoC
§	***gibbiflora*** 'Metallica'	SMrm SRms
	× ***gilva*** ♀H2	SEdd
*	- 'Red'	CAbb EAri EBee LSun SEdd WCot
	glauca Baker	see *E. secunda* f. *secunda*
	'Green Gollum' **new**	SEdd
	'Green Pearl' PBR	LCro
	'Gungekkan' **new**	SEdd
	halbingeri var. ***sanchez-mejoradae*** **new**	SEdd
	harmsii	SEdd
	harmsii × ***setosa*** **new**	SMrm
	'Hercules' PBR **new**	SEdd
	humilis **new**	WOld
	'Ileen'	SEdd
	'Imbricata'	NLar SRms
	'J. van Keppel'	SEdd
	'Latte Rose' **new**	SEdd
	'Lemon Light' **new**	SEdd
	'Lepus'	SEdd WOld
	lilacina ♀H2	CDoC CPla CSBt CSpe EAri EShb LCro MHol NCft NMen SEdd SPlb SRms SSim
	'Lincoln Frost' **new**	NMen
	'Lincoln Ghost' **new**	NMen
	'Lincoln Harlequin' **new**	NMen
	'Lincoln Mystery' **new**	NMen
	'Lincoln Mystique' **new**	NMen
	'Lincoln Razzamatazz' **new**	NMen
	'Lincoln Ruby Glow' **new**	NMen
	lobed leaves **new**	CSBt
	'Mahogany'	WCot
	'Mauna Loa'	CAbb EAri MHer MHol SEdd WCot WOld
	maxonii B&SWJ 10396	WCru
	'Mebina' variegated (v) **new**	SEdd
	'Mexecensis'	EAri SEdd
	'Mexicana' **new**	SEdd
	minima ♀H2	NMen SEdd SPlb
	'Mira' PBR **new**	SEdd
	montana B&SWJ 10277	WCru
	nodulosa	SEdd SIvy SMrm WCot
	- 'Nicolas Bravo'	SSim
	'Pastel Rose' **new**	SEdd
	'Peach Pride' **new**	SEdd
	'Perle von Nürnberg' ♀H2	CAbb CCBP CDoC EShb LCro LOPS LRHS MHer NMen SMad
	pilosa **new**	SEdd
	pringlei var. ***parva*** × 'Rain Drops' **new**	SEdd
	prolifica	SEdd SPlb
	pulidonis ♀H2	MHer NFav SEdd SSim
	pulvinata ♀H2	MHCG SEdd
	- 'Frosty'	SEdd SRms
I	- 'Rubra'	SPlb
	purpusorum	CDoC EAri NMen SPlb
	quitensis B&SWJ 14393	WCru
	'Rainbow' **new**	SEdd
	'Ramillette'	SEdd WMal
	'Red Prince'	CDoC SEdd
	'Reinelt's Cross' **new**	SEdd
	'Ron Evans'	SEdd
	rosea ♀H2	MHer SPlb SSim WCot WMal
	runyonii ♀H2	CDoC SRms
	- 'Topsy Turvy' ♀H2	CDTJ CSBt EAri MHer SEdd SIvy SRms SSim WCot

'Sagitta'PBR **new** SEdd
'Scorpio' WOld
§ ***secunda*** CAbb EAri SPlb
- var. ***glauca*** see *E. secunda* f. *secunda*
§ - f. ***secunda*** CDTJ CDoC ELan EShb GAbr NCft NFav SEdd SIvy WCav
- - 'Compton Carousel' ♀H2 SEdd SSim WCot WOld
* - - 'Gigantea' NPer
'Serrana' **new** EAri
'Set-Oliver' × ***setosa*** SEdd
× ***setorum*** 'Victor' **new** SEdd
setosa ♀H2 CDTJ EAri NCft SPlb
- var. ***ciliata*** EShb SEdd
- var. ***deminuta*** EAri SIvy
- var. ***oteroi*** **new** SEdd SPlb
'Shark Skin' **new** SEdd
shaviana ♀H2 CDTJ EAri SIvy SRms SSim WCot
- 'Pink Frills' SIvy
'Silver Shine' **new** SEdd
'Son of Pearl' MHtn
'Steve's Pelt' **new** SEdd
subcorymbosa **new** NMen
subsessilis see *E. desmetiana*
'Suryeon' **new** SEdd
'Tarantula' SEdd WOld
'Telstar' SEdd
tolimanensis **new** SPlb
tolucensis **new** SEdd
'Trumpet Pinky' **new** SEdd
'Van Breen' **new** SEdd
'Venus' **new** SEdd
'Victor Reiter' **new** SEdd
'Violet Queen' EShb
xichuensis SSim
'Yoda' **new** SEdd
'Zodiac' SEdd
'Zonnestraal' EGrI

Echeveria × *Graptopetalum* see × *Graptoveria*

Echeveria × *Pachyphytum* see × *Pachyveria*

Echeveria × *Sedum* see × *Sedeveria*

Echinacea (*Asteraceae*)

§ 'After Midnight'PBR (Big Sky Series) EGrI
'Aloha'PBR LRHS NRHS SPad SPoG WCAu
'Amazing Dream'PBR CAbb CWGN EBee LCro LOPS LRHS NCth NRHS SEdd WSpi
angustifolia ENfk LRHS MHoo SPhx
§ 'Art's Pride'PBR EGrI
'Big Kahuna'PBR CAbb CPar CWGN LBar LRHS SCob SEdd SPad SPeP SRHi
'Blackberry Truffle' (Cone-fections Series) (d) **new** LBar
'Butterfly Kisses'PBR (Cone-fections Series) (d) LCro LOPS LRHS NCth NLar SEdd SGBe WSpi
'Cantaloupe' (Supreme Series) (d) CWGN LBar SPad
'Caribbean Green' EBee
CHERRY FLUFF ('Echcher298'PBR) (Cone-fections Series) (d) CWGN LRHS
CHEYENNE SPIRIT (mixed) CDoC CDor EBlo ELan EPfP GMcL LEdu LRHS MACG MBros MHoo SPhx WFar WHil WHlf WSpi WTor WWke
'Chiquita'PBR (Prairie Pixie Series) LSou SPoG
'Cinnamon Cupcake' SPoG
'Cleopatra'PBR (Butterfly Series) CWGN EBee EPfP LAlb LRHS MBel NCth NLar SCoo SEdd SGBe SPoG WCot WHlf
'Colorburst Orange' (Colorburst Series) (d) CWGN
'Daydream'PBR CWGN EBee WSpi
DELICIOUS CANDY ('Noortdeli'PBR) (d) CPar CWGN LAlb LBar LCro LPla LSun MHtn MPri SEdd SRkn WCot WHil WTor WTyc
DELICIOUS NOUGAT ('Noecthree'PBR) (d) LBar MPri SPeP
(Dixie Series) 'Dixie Belle' CAbb WSpi
- 'Dixie Scarlet'PBR CAbb
(Double Scoop Series) DOUBLE SCOOP BUBBLEGUM ('Balscblum'PBR) (d) LRHS
- DOUBLE SCOOP CRANBERRY ('Balscanery'PBR) (d) LBar LRHS MACG WWke
- DOUBLE SCOOP MANDARIN ('Balscandin') (d) LRHS
- DOUBLE SCOOP ORANGEBERRY ('Balscoberr'PBR) (d) LRHS
- DOUBLE SCOOP RASPBERRY ('Balsceras'PBR) (d) LBar LRHS
'Eccentric'PBR (d) CAby CPar CWGN LBar LRHS NCth SEdd SMad WSpi WTor
ECCENTRIC YELLOW ('Noectwo'PBR) (d) CBod CWGN LBar NCth
'Emily Saul' see *E.* 'After Midnight'
'Evan Saul' see *E.* 'Sundown'
EVENING GLOW ('Eglow'PBR) CWGN EBee LRHS WSpi
'Ferris Wheel' (Carnival Series) WSpi
'Flame Thrower'PBR LCro LOPS SMad
FLAMINGO (Fine Feathered Series) **new** LBar
'Flamingo'PBR (Supreme Series) (d) CPla SPad
(Fountain Series) 'Fountain Light Purple' LBar SPad
- 'Fountain Orange Bicolour' **new** LBar
- 'Fountain Pink Eye' **new** LBar WHil
- 'Fountain Red' **new** WSpi
'Fourth of July'PBR EHyd LRHS NRHS
'Funky White' CWGN EPfP LBar NCth SPeP
'Funky Yellow' CAby CWGN LBar WCot
'Glowing Dream' LBar NCth SEdd
GOLDEN SKIPPER ('Echgol243'PBR) (Butterfly Series) ECtt EHyd LRHS MAvo NRHS
'Green Envy'PBR CBcs CWGN EBee EHyd ELan EMor EPfP EWoo GMaP LAlb LCro LOPS LRHS MBel MCot MNrw NLar NRHS WCAu WHlf WTor
'Greenline'PBR EBee NLar
'Guava Ice'PBR (Cone-fections Series) (d) CWnw LBar
§ 'Harvest Moon'PBR (Big Sky Series) EBee EGrI EPfP LRHS MBNS SWvt
'Hot Lava'PBR CWGN EBee EHyd LCro LRHS NLar NRHS SCob
'Hot Papaya'PBR (Cone-fections Series) (d) CPla CWCL CWGN CWnw ECtt ELan EMor EPfP LCro LOPS LRHS MHol NCth SCob SMad SMrm SPoG SWvt
'Hot Summer'PBR CBcs CWGN EBee EGrI EHyd EWoo LBar LEdu LRHS SGbt
'Indian Summer' EBee
'Irresistible'PBR (d) CWGN EBee EMor LBar LCro LOPS WTor
'JS Ivo's Poem' **new** IPot

'JS Stiletto' **new**	IPot
'Julia'^{PBR} (Butterfly Series)	ECtt EMor LBar LRHS SEdd SGBe SHar SPad WHlf
'Katie Saul'	see *E.* 'Summer Sky'
(Kismet Series) KISMET INTENSE ORANGE ('Tnechkio') **new**	LBar
- KISMET RED ('Tnechkrd') **new**	LBar
'Leilani'^{PBR}	CAbb WCAu
'Mac 'n' Cheese'^{PBR}	EBee EMor LRHS SCob
'Mama Mia'^{PBR}	CAbb CWGN LBar LCro MACG SEdd SGbt
'Marmalade'^{PBR} (Cone-fections Series) (d)	CAby CBcs CWGN EBee EMor EWTr LAlb LBar LRHS MHtn SCob SCoo SPoG WCAu WHlf
'Matthew Saul'	see *E.* 'Harvest Moon'
'Maui Sunshine'^{PBR}	CAbb
'Maya Raya'	LBar
'Meditation'^{PBR}	WCot
'Mellow Yellow'	see *E. paradoxa* 'Yellow Mellow', *E. purpurea* 'Mellow Yellows'
(Meteor Series) 'Meteor Pink'^{PBR} (d)	LRHS
- 'Meteor Red'^{PBR} (d)	CRos ECtt EHyd LRHS NRHS
MINI BELLE ('Minbel252'^{PBR}) (Cone-fections Series) (d) **new**	LAlb SEdd
(Mooodz Series) MOOODZ AWAKE ('Hilmoooawak')	LRHS NRHS
- MOOODZ COSY ('Hilmoocosy')	LRHS MPri
- MOOODZ COURAGE ('Hilmoocour')	MPri
- MOOODZ PEACE ('Hilmoopea')	MPri
- MOOODZ SHINY ('Hilmooshin')	LRHS MPri NRHS
- MOOODZ SYMPATHY ('Hilmoosymp') **new**	MPri
'Mozzarella' (d)	EBee
'Now Cheesier'^{PBR}	LCro
ORANGE MEADOWBRITE	see *E.* 'Art's Pride'
ORANGE PASSION ('Orpass'^{PBR})	CWGN EGrI LRHS WCAu
ORANGE SKIPPER ('Echor273'^{PBR}) (Butterfly Series)	CRos EGrI EHyd EPfP LRHS NRHS SHar
'Pacific Summer'	CWGN WSpi
pallida	Widely available
- 'Hula Dancer'	CBWd CDor CWnw EAJP EMor EWTr MACG NGdn SBut SPhx
(Papallo Series) 'Papallo Classic Rose'	EPfP LRHS
- 'Papallo Compact Pink'	LRHS
- 'Papallo Compact White'	LRHS
- 'Papallo Power Coral Orange'	LRHS
- 'Papallo Semi-Double Peach' (d) **new**	LBar
- 'Papallo Semi-double Pink' (d) **new**	EPfP
paradoxa	CBcs ECha EHyd ELan EMor EPfP LDai LRHS LSto NRHS SPer SPhx SPlb SWvt WCAu
- var. ***paradoxa***	CCBP MACG
§ - 'Yellow Mellow'	EWTr
'Parrot' (Fine Feathered Series)	LBar LCro SMad SPad
'Pineapple Sundae'^{PBR}	CWGN WHlf
'Pink Pearl' (Pearl Series) **new**	LBar NMen
'Pink Tip'	LBar LPla SPad

PIXIE MEADOWBRITE ('CBG Cone 2')	CWGN
POSTMAN ('Post301'^{PBR}) (Butterfly Series)	CPar NLar SPoG WSpi
'Purple Emperor'^{PBR} (Butterfly Series)	ECtt SGBe WSpi
§ ***purpurea***	Widely available
I - 'Alba'	CRos CWal ECha EHyd EPfP GMcL LRHS NRHS WCot WFar XLum
- 'Amber Mist'^{PBR} (Mistical Series)	EBee
- 'Augustkönigin'	EBee LRHS WCAu WCot
- 'Avalanche'^{PBR} (Butterfly Series)	CBod CWGN LPla SMrm
- 'Baby Swan Pink'	CBod CRos EBlo EHyd LRHS NLar NRHS
- 'Baby Swan White'	CBod CRos CWnw EBee EHyd ELan EPfP GQue LRHS LSto NLar NRHS
- Bressingham hybrids	CBod CRos EHyd LRHS LSou MArl MPie NRHS SGbt SPer WGwG
- 'Catharina'^{PBR}	CWGN ECtt
- CHUNKY PURPLE ('Noecone'^{PBR})	MHtn SEdd
- 'Coconut Lime'^{PBR} (Cone-fections Series) (d)	CWGN EMor EPfP LCro LOPS WCAu
- DOPPELGANGER	see *E. purpurea* 'Doubledecker'
§ - 'Doubledecker'	ELan EPfP NGdn SGbt SPeP SSut
- ELTON KNIGHT ('Elbrook'^{PBR}) $\heartsuit^{H5}$	LRHS SWvt WCot
- 'Fatal Attraction'^{PBR}	CBcs CWGN EHyd ELan EMor EPfP EWTr GMaP LEdu LPla LRHS LSRN LSou MBNS MRav NLar NRHS SCob SEdd SPad SPoG SWvt WCot
- 'Firebird'^{PBR}	SGbt SPoG
- 'Fragrant Angel'^{PBR}	LRHS MBNS NLar SWvt
- 'Green Eyes'	EBee LBar WCAu
- 'Green Jewel'^{PBR}	Widely available
- 'Green Twister'	CBod CDor CWGN CWnw EAJP EDAr EMor EWTr LAlb LBar LPla LSto MBel MHoo SPad WGwG WHil
- 'Happy Star'	CDor CRos EAJP EBee EHyd EPfP LRHS LSou NRHS SBls SCoo SGbt SPoG
- 'Hope'^{PBR}	LBar MBel NLar WCAu
- INNOCENT MEADOW MAMA ('Whites331'^{PBR}) (Meadow Mama Series) **new**	LBar
- 'Jade'	EBee LSRN
- 'Kim's Knee High'^{PBR}	ELan EPfP EWoo GMaP LRHS MTin NLar SPer SPoG SWvt
- 'Kim's Mop Head'	EPfP NLar
- LEMON DROP ('Drop352'^{PBR}) (Cone-fections Series) (d) **new**	LBar
§ - 'Leuchtstern'	CKno EHyd ELan EPfP LRHS NBir NGdn NRHS
- 'Little Magnus'^{PBR}	SCob SPoG
- 'Lucky Star'	ELan EPfP
- 'Magnus'	Widely available
- 'Magnus Superior'	CBod CDor CRos CSpe EAJP EBee EHyd EPfP LRHS LSou LSto LSun MHer MNrw NRHS SBut SEdd SGbt SMrm SWvt
- 'Maxima'	LRHS
- 'Mellow Yellows'	CDor EAJP EDAr SBls
- 'Meringue'^{PBR} (Cone-fections Series) (d)	SGBe
- 'Merlot'^{PBR}	LBar
- 'Milkshake'^{PBR} (d)	CWGN EBee EMor SMrm WSpi
- 'Pica Bella'	CRos CWGN EHyd EPfP LRHS NRHS SPad

- 'Pink Double Delight'PBR (Cone-fections Series) (d)	EGrI LCro LOPS LRHS MRav NGdn
- 'Pink Glow'	NDov
- 'Pink Parasol'	SBls
- 'Pink Sorbet'PBR (Cone-fections Series) (d)	SCob
- (PowWow Series) PowWow White ('Pas709018')	CBod CWGN SCob SPoG WTor
- - PowWow Wild Berry ('Pas702917'PBR)	CBod CRos CWGN EBee EDAr EHyd EPfP LRHS MBros MHol NRHS SPoG WFar WHil WTor
- (Prairie Splendor Compact Series) Prairie Splendor Compact Rose **new**	MNHC
- - Prairie Splendor	EPfP GMcL LPar SPhx
- (Primadonna Series) 'Primadonna Deep Pink'	EPfP
- - 'Primadonna Deep Rose'	CGBo ELan LEdu LRHS MACG NGBl SVic
- - 'Primadonna White'	CGBo CKel CSpe EHyd EPfP LRHS LSun MACG SRms
- 'Profusion'	WSpi
- 'Purity'PBR	SPoG
- Rainbow Marcella ('Rainb299'PBR) (Butterfly Series)	LRHS WHlf WSpi
- 'Razzmatazz'PBR (d)	CMac EBee EMor SCoo SPoG SWvt WCot
- 'Red Knee High'PBR	NLar
- 'Robert Bloom'	NBir SWvt WSpi
- Robin Hood ('Jsroho'PBR)	IPot SPeP
- 'Rubinglow'	ECtt LCro LOPS LSou NBir NLar SWvt
- 'Rubinstern'	Widely available
- 'Ruby Giant' ♀H5	EHyd ELan EWoo GBin GMaP LRHS LSRN LSou NLar NRHS SEdd SGbt WCot
- 'Sensation Pink'PBR	CAby CBod CKno CPar CWGN EHyd EPfP LAlb LRHS LSou MDon MMrt MPri NRHS SHar XLum
- 'Southern Belle'PBR (Cone-fections Series) (d)	CDor CNor CWCL CWGN ELan EMor MBNS MHol SCoo SMad SMrm WSpi
- 'Summer Salsa'PBR	CWGN WCot
- 'The King'	CRos EHyd LRHS NGdn NLar NRHS WSpi
- 'Vanilla Cupcake'PBR (d)	EPfP LRHS SCoo SPoG
- 'Vintage Wine'PBR	CRos EGrI ELan EPfP LCro LOPS LRHS NSti SPoG SWvt WCAu
- 'Virgin'PBR	CBod LCro LOPS MAvo MBel NDov SCob SEdd SPad WCAu
- 'White Double Delight'PBR (Cone-fections Series) (d)	LRHS
- 'White Lustre'	SRms
- 'White Swan'	Widely available
'Raspberry Truffle'PBR (Cone-fections Series) (d)	EPfP EWTr LBar LRHS NCth
'Red Pearl' (Pearl Series)	WSpi
'Rosita'PBR	LRHS
(Secret Series) 'Secret Affair' (d)	EHyd EMor LRHS
- 'Secret Glow'PBR (d) **new**	ECul NCth
- 'Secret Lust'PBR (d)	NCth
- 'Secret Passion'PBR (d)	CWGN SGbt WSpi
- 'Secret Romance'PBR (d)	LBar WCAu
simulata	EBee MACG
'Solar Flare'PBR (Big Sky Series)	EBee LRHS NLar WSpi
(Sombrero Series) Sombrero Adobe Orange ('Balsomador'PBR)	CBcs CBod MACG WHil
- Sombrero Baja Burgundy ('Balsombabur'PBR)	LRHS
- Sombrero Blanco ('Balsomblanc')	LBar LRHS LSou
- Sombrero Flamenco Orange ('Balsomenco'PBR)	LRHS MAvo
- Sombrero Granada Gold ('Balsomold'PBR) **new**	LBar
- Sombrero Hot Coral ('Balsomcor'PBR)	LRHS
- Sombrero Lemon Yellow ('Balsomemy')	LBar MACG
- Sombrero Lemon Yellow Improved ('Balsomemyim'PBR) **new**	CBod
- Sombrero Salsa Red ('Balsomsed'PBR)	CBcs LRHS SEdd
- Sombrero Sangrita ('Balsomanita'PBR) **new**	MACG WHil
- Sombrero Tres Amigos ('Balsomtresgo') **new**	CBod MACG MDon
'Starlight'	see *E. purpurea* 'Leuchtstern'
'Strawberry and Cream' (d) **new**	CBod LBar
'Summer 3000'	LRHS
'Summer Cloud'	CWGN EHyd LBar LCro LRHS NCth NRHS SMad WTor
'Summer Cocktail'PBR	CWGN EHyd ELan LBar LCro LOPS LRHS SEdd SPoG WHlf WSpi
'Summer Fire'	LRHS
'Summer Passion'	CWGN
§ 'Summer Sky'PBR (Big Sky Series)	EPfP
'Summer Sun'PBR	SPoG
§ 'Sundown'PBR (Big Sky Series)	EBee EHyd EPfP LCro LOPS NLar SCob SEdd SGbt SWvt WCAu
'Sunrise'PBR (Big Sky Series)	CAby EBee EHyd ELan EPfP GMaP LRHS MBNS NSti SCob SGbt SPoG SWvt WCAu WHlf
(SunSeekers Series) SunSeekers Coral **new**	LBar
- SunSeekers Magenta ('Apecssima'PBR)	LBar LRHS MPri WFar WTor
- SunSeekers Mellow ('Apecssime')	LBar
- SunSeekers Orange ('Apecssior'PBR)	LBar LRHS MPri WHlf WTor
- SunSeekers Pink ('Apecssipi')	LBar MPri
- SunSeekers Purple ('Apecssipu')	CRos EPfP LBar LRHS
- SunSeekers Rainbow ('Ifecssra') **new**	LBar
- SunSeekers Red ('Apecssired')	CRos LBar LRHS MHtn
- SunSeekers Salmon ('Ifecsssal')	CAby LBar LCro MACG MDon MPri SEdd WFar WTor WWke
- SunSeekers White ('Apecssiwh')	CAby EPfP LBar LRHS WFar WTor
- SunSeekers Yellow ('Apecssiye'PBR)	CRos LBar LRHS MPri
'Sunset'PBR (Big Sky Series)	ELan LDai LSRN SWvt
'Sweet Sixteen' (Cone-fections Series) (d)	LRHS
'Tangerine Dream'PBR	EBee EHyd EMor EPfP LRHS NCth SCob WCAu WSpi
tennesseensis 'Rocky Top'	EHyd GPSL LRHS MBNS MGos SBut

'Tiki Torch' PBR	CAby CWnw EMor LCro LOPS LRHS SCob SPoG SWvt WCot WTor
'Tomato Soup' PBR	CAby CBcs CBod CRos CWGN EBee ECtt ELan EMor EPfP LCro LOPS LPla LRHS LSRN MNrw SCob SEdd SGbt SPeP SPoG SRHi SWvt WCAu WCot WTor
'Twilight' PBR (Big Sky Series)	EGrI
'White Meditation' PBR	CBcs CBod CKno EHyd EMor EPfP LRHS MPri NRHS SEdd SPoG

Echinocactus (Cactaceae)

grusonii 🏆H1c **new**	EAri NHrt NPlm
- spineless **new**	NHrt

Echinocereus (Cactaceae)

acifer subsp. ***huitcholensis*** **new**	NMen
- - LAU 768 **new**	NMen
'Mark 2' **new**	NMen
melanocentrus	see *E. reichenbachii* subsp. *fitchii*
nivosus **new**	NMen
pectinatus **new**	EAri
§ ***reichenbachii***	NMen
subsp. ***fitchii*** **new**	
triglochidiatus	EAri
viereckii	NMen
subsp. ***morricalii*** **new**	
viridiflorus	SPlb

Echinops (Asteraceae)

B 191 **new**	NMen
§ ***bannaticus***	CBcs CMac CWal MAsh NBid
* - 'Albus'	WCAu WHlf
- 'Blue Globe'	CRos EGrI EHyd ELan EPfP GMcL LRHS LSRN MBriF MCot MGos NGdn NHol NRHS SCob SEdd SGbt SPoG WCAu WFar WHoo
- 'Blue Glow'	CBod LSun NLar SBls SCoo SPhx WCAu
- 'Blue Pearl'	SMHy
- 'Star Frost'	CBod CRos EBee EHyd ELan EPfP GJos LRHS NLar NRHS SBls SCob SPeP SRms WFar
- 'Taplow Blue'	Widely available
- 'The Giant'	CBod
chantavicus from Kyrgyzstan **new**	GGro
karatavicus from Kyrgyzstan **new**	GGro
maracandicus	LPla WCot
ritro misapplied	see *E. bannaticus*
§ ***ritro*** L.	Widely available
- ***alba***	GJos
- 'Baby Globes'	GQue
- 'Blue Cloud'	EBee
- subsp. ***ruthenicus*** 🏆H7	MRav WCot
- - 'Platinum Blue'	CRos EBee ECtt ELan LRHS NLar SCoo SGBe SPhx SRms
- 'Veitch's Blue' misapplied	see *E. ritro* L.
- 'Veitch's Blue'	Widely available
sphaerocephalus	GJos NBir SMrm SPlb
- 'Arctic Glow'	Widely available
tjanschanicus	CPla CRos EBee EHyd EWes GJos GPSL LDai LRHS MMuc NLar NRHS SEND

Echinopsis ✿ (Cactaceae)

§ ***ancistrophora*** 🏆H2 **new**	EAri LCro NCft
arachnacantha 🏆H2 **new**	EAri SPlb
- subsp. ***torrecillasensis*** **new**	EAri
atacamensis subsp. ***pasacana***	NPlm
bridgesii **new**	EAri
CARNIVAL (mixed) **new**	NMen
cinnabarina 🏆H2 **new**	EAri
'Damisa' **new**	SPlb
'Dark Melody' **new**	SPlb
formosa subsp. ***kieslingii*** **new**	NMen
huascha **new**	NPlm
'Kawinai' **new**	SPlb
'Lincoln Giant' **new**	NMen
'Lincoln Saffron' **new**	NMen
'Lincoln Storm' **new**	NMen
'Lincoln Tornado' **new**	NMen
macrogona **new**	NPlm
pachanoi **new**	EAri NPlm
peruvianus **new**	EAri NPlm
'Pink Flamingo' **new**	SPlb
pygmaea	see *Rebutia pygmaea*
red-orange-flowered **new**	SPlb
'Snowstorm' **new**	NMen
subdenudata	see *E. ancistrophora*
tanjensis subsp. ***bertramiana*** **new**	NPlm
terscheckii	LPal NPlm
thionantha **new**	NMen

Echium ✿ (Boraginaceae)

aculeatum	MEch
amoenum	CSpe CWCL EHyd LBar LRHS MEch NRHS SPhx
angustifolium Mill.	MEch SPhx
asperrimum	MEch
bethencourtianum	MEch SVen
'Blue Steeple'	CPla CWCL MEch
boissieri	CCCN MEch
brevirame	MEch
callithyrsum	MEch
candicans 🏆H1c	CAbb CBcs CBod CCCN CKel CPbh CPla CTrC CTsd ECre ELan MEch SVen WOut
- 'Dwarf Blue'	CCCN
decaisnei subsp. ***decaisnei***	MEch SVen
fastuosum	CCht CDoC CKel CWCL LBar SArc SBls SEND XVPe
gentianoides	MEch SPlb SVen
giganteum	MEch
hierrense	MEch
italicum	CCCN MEch
lusitanicum	CCCN
nervosum	MEch
onosmifolium	MEch SVen
'Pearce's Grey'	SVen
pininana 🏆H3	CAbb CBcs CBod CCht CDoC CPbh CPla CTrC CTsd CWal EAri ECre ELan LRHS LWaG MEch NLar SArc SChr SEND SPhx SVen WHlf XSte
- 'Snow Tower'	CCCN CDTJ CPla CTrC CWCL EAri ELan LBar LRHS MEch
pininana × 'Red Rocket'	CPla EAri
pininana × ***wildpretii***	CPla MEch
'Pink Fountain'	CBod CCCN CDTJ CKel CPla CTrC CWCL ELan LBar LRHS MEch SPhx WHlf
'Red Rocket'	CCCN CDTJ
rosulatum	CCCN
russicum	CCCN CSpe CTsd EHyd ELan EPfP LWaG MEch MHoo SBls SBut SPad SPhx SPlb XSen
sabulicola	MEch
simplex 🏆H1c	MEch
strictum	CCCN MEch

	sventenii	MEch SPlb
	tuberculatum	EWld LRHS MEch SPhx
	virescens	MEch SVen
	vulcanorum	MEch
	vulgare	CCCN CHab CSpe CTtf ELan ENfk GQue LCro LOPS LWaG MEch MHer MHoo MNHC NGrd NMir SBut SPhx WSFF WTre WWild
	- from Armenia	WCot
	- 'Blue Bedder' 🏆H7	CSpe MEch SPhx WSFF
	- 'Pink Bedder'	MEch
	- 'White Bedder'	MEch
	webbii	CKel MEch MMrt SVen
	wildpretii 🏆H2	CBcs CBod CCCN CCht CDTJ CDoC CPla CTsd CWCL EAri ECre ELan ESgI LAlb LBar MEch NLar SBls SEND SPhx SPlb SVen
	- subsp. ***wildpretii***	MEch

Ectotropis (*Aizoaceae*)

§	***alpina***	EWes GEdr
§	***seanii-hoganii***	CRos ECtt EHyd EPot EWes GEdr LRHS NBwr NRHS NSla SLee SPlb WAbe XLum

Edgeworthia (*Thymelaeaceae*)

§	***chrysantha***	CBcs CCCN CDoC CKel CRos EBee EHyd ELan EPfP GKev LCro LEdu LOPS LPal LPar LRHS MGos MHtn MVil NLar NRHS SArc SCob SEWo SGsty SPoG SWeb SavN WHlf WLea
I	- 'Grandiflora'	CBcs CDoC CWnw ELon ESwi IDee LCro LPar LRHS MGos NCth NLar SJap SMad WPGP XSte
	- 'Nanjing Gold'	LRHS
§	- 'Red Dragon'	CBcs GKev LCro LRHS SavN WHlf XSte
	- f. ***rubra*** hort.	see *E. chrysantha* 'Red Dragon'
	- 'Winter Liebe'	LRHS NLar
	papyrifera	see *E. chrysantha*

Edraianthus (*Campanulaceae*)

	croaticus	see *E. graminifolius*
	dalmaticus albus	GKev
	glisicii	GKev
§	***graminifolius***	GEdr
	- from Durmitor, Montenegro	NSla
	- ***albus***	see *E. graminifolius* subsp. *niveus*
	- subsp. ***graminifolius***	GKev
§	- subsp. ***niveus***	GEdr
	niveus	GEdr GKev NSla
	pilosulus	GKev
	pulevicii	GKev
§	***pumilio*** 🏆H5	EPot GArf GEdr GJos NSla SRms WAbe
	- silver-leaved	EPot
	sutjeskae	GKev
	tenuifolius	CSpe GKev
	zogovicii	see *E. graminifolius*

Egeria (*Hydrocharitaceae*)

§	***densa***	CBen

Ehretia (*Boraginaceae*)

§	***acuminata***	WPGP
	ovalifolia	see *E. acuminata*
	rigida	SPlb
	thyrsiflora	see *E. acuminata*

Elaeagnus (*Elaeagnaceae*)

	angustifolia	CAgr CArg CBcs EHeP EPfP IDee LMaj LPar MCoo MGos NWea SPer SRms WKor XSen
	- Caspica Group	see *E.* 'Quicksilver'
	argentea Pursh	see *E. commutata*
§	***commutata***	CMac EPfP MBlu MCoo SPer
I	- 'Aurea'	NLar
	- 'Zempin'	CKel CWnw LPar LRHS NLar
	× ***ebbingei***	see *E.* × *submacrophylla*
	macrophylla	EBee EPfP LRHS
	multiflora	MBlu NLar SPer WJur WKor WPGP XVPe
	- 'Sweet Scarlet'	CAgr XVPe
	parvifolia	CCCN ELan
	pungens 'Argenteovariegata'	see *E. pungens* 'Variegata'
	- 'Aureovariegata'	see *E. pungens* 'Maculata'
	- 'Dicksonii' (v)	CBod EHyd EPfP LRHS NLar SPer SRms WFar
	- 'Forest Gold' (v)	EHyd EPfP LRHS
	- 'Frederici' (v)	CBod CCCN CDoC CEnd CMac EBee EHyd ELan ELon LRHS MAsh MRav NLar SCob SPer SWvt WAvo WHtc
	- 'Hosoba-fukurin' (v)	CKel EBee ELan EPfP NLar WHtc
§	- 'Maculata' (v)	Widely available
§	- 'Variegata' (v)	CBcs CMac GMcL SPer SavN
§	'Quicksilver'	Widely available
§	× ***submacrophylla*** 🏆H5	Widely available
	- 'Coastal Gold' (v)	CBcs CBod CCCN CCoa CDoC CEme EBee EHeP EPfP LSRN LSto MGos SGol SRms WAvo WFar WHtc
I	- 'Compacta'	CBod CCCN CCoa CKel EBee ELan EPfP LCro LRHS LSou MGos SCob SGsty WHtc WReH
	- 'Gilt Edge' (v) 🏆H5	Widely available
	- GOLD SPLASH ('Lannou') (v)	CKel CMac EPfP SGol SWvt
	- 'Limelight' (v)	Widely available
	- MARYLINE ('Abrela')	MAsh NLar
	- 'Moonlight'	MAsh
	- 'Salcombe Seedling'	CCCN
	- 'Svelte Edge'	NLar
	- 'Viveleg' PBR (v)	CCVT CDoC CRos CWnw EHyd ELan EPfP LPar LRHS MAsh MGos NLar NRHS SCob SEWo SGsty WHtc
	umbellata	CBcs CEnd EBee EPfP IDee LEdu LMaj MAsh MBlu NLar SPer WJur WKor WLov WSHC
	- 'Amber' (F)	CAgr NLar
	- 'Big Red' (F)	CAgr
	- var. ***borealis*** 'Polar Lights'	NLar
	- 'Brilliant Rose' (F)	CAgr
	- 'Garnet' (F)	CAgr
	- 'Hidden Springs' (F)	CAgr LEdu WPGP
	- 'Jewel' (F)	CAgr
	- 'Late Scarlet' (F)	CAgr
	- 'Le Vasterival' **new**	MAsh
	- 'Newgate' (F)	CAgr
	- POINTILLA SWEET'N'SOUR (Pointilla Series) (F)	EGrI
	- 'Red Cascade' (F)	CAgr LEdu MBlu NLar
	- var. ***rotundifolia*** CWJ 12835	WCru
	- 'Ruby' (F)	CAgr NLar
	- 'Sweet 'n' Tart' (F)	CAgr LEdu WLov WPGP

Elatostema (*Urticaceae*)

	CHB 14 **new**	GGro
	CHBMV 1511 **new**	GGro
	from Yunnan CHB **new**	GGro
	umbellatum 'Dents de Kyoto'	EWld GGro
	- 'Ogon' **new**	GGro
	- 'Snow Patch' (v)	GGro

elderberry see *Sambucus nigra*

Elegia (*Restionaceae*)

capensis 𝕐^{H3}	CCCN CDTJ CPbh CTrC LRHS SPlb XSte
elephantina 𝕐^{H4}	CBod CCht CPbh CTrC LRHS XSte
equisetacea 𝕐^{H3}	CPbh
grandis	SPlb
macrocarpa	CCCN CPbh SPlb
tectorum 𝕐^{H2}	CCht CEme CPbh CTrC CTsd LRHS SPlb SPoG XSte
- dwarf 𝕐^{H4}	CPbh LRHS
- 'Fish Hoek'	CPbh LRHS

Eleocharis (*Cyperaceae*)

acicularis	CPud GQue LLWG LPfP
palustris	CPud CWat LLWG LPfP

Eleorchis (*Orchidaceae*)

japonica	NLAp
* - f. ***alba***	NLAp

Elettaria (*Zingiberaceae*)

cardamomum	EShb GPoy LEdu SPre WJek

Eleutherococcus (*Araliaceae*)

divaricatus B&SWJ 5027	WCru
giraldii BWJ 8091	WCru
hypoleucus B&SWJ 5532	WCru
aff. ***leucorrhizus*** PAB 8119	WPGP
pictus	see *Kalopanax septemlobus*
senticosus	GPoy
- B&SWJ 4568	WCru
septemlobus	see *Kalopanax septemlobus*
sessiliflorus B&SWJ 4528	ESwi WCru
- B&SWJ 8457	WCru
- B&SWJ 8618	WCru
sieboldianus	MRav SEND
- 'Variegatus' (v)	CCCN EBee EHed EPfP ESwi LRHS MGil MRav NLar SPoG WCFE
trifoliatus RWJ 10108	WCru

Ellisiophyllum (*Plantaginaceae*)

pinnatum B&SWJ 197	WCru

Elmera (*Saxifragaceae*)

racemosa	GAbr

Elodea (*Hydrocharitaceae*)

canadensis	LLWG NBir WMAq
densa	see *Egeria densa*

Elsholtzia (*Lamiaceae*)

flava PAB 13.012	WPGP
- 'Dzhouku Choc'	LPla
stauntonii	CBcs CKel EBee ECha ELan EMor EPPr LCro LRHS MGil MHer NLar NQui SRms SWvt WJek XLum XSen

Elymus (*Poaceae*)

arenarius	see *Leymus arenarius*
canadensis	EPPr
dahuricus from Olomouc	EPPr
glaucus misapplied	see *E. hispidus*
§ ***hispidus*** 𝕐^{H6}	MBlu NDov SCob SPer WCot
hystrix	LRHS
§ ***magellanicus***	Widely available
- 'Blue Sword'	EHyd ELan MGos NRHS SPtp SRkn SRms
riparius	EPPr
villosus	EPPr
- var. ***arkansanus***	EPPr
virginicus	EPPr

Embothrium ✿ (*Proteaceae*)

coccineum	CPla EPfP GBin GDam GMcL MGil SPlb WPGP XSte
- Lanceolatum Group	CEnd CTrC CTsd EAri EPfP GAbr MBlu SArc SSha SSta SWvt XSte
- - 'Inca Flame'	CCCN CJun CTrC EPfP LRHS SWvt
- Longifolium Group	CCCN WPGP

Emilia (*Asteraceae*)

coccinea	CSpe

Emmenopterys (*Rubiaceae*)

henryi	CBcs CMCN EPfP MBlu

emperor's mint see *Micromeria*

Empetrum (*Ericaceae*)

nigrum	GPoy WKor
- 'Bernstein'	GArf
rubrum	MGil

Empodium (*Hypoxidaceae*)

namaquensis	NRog
plicatum	CBor GKev NRog

Encephalartos ✿ (*Zamiaceae*)

altensteinii	CBrP LPal
chimanimaniensis new	EAri
concinnus new	EAri
ferox	CBrP EAri LPal
- blue-leaved new	EAri
- subsp. ***emersus*** new	EAri
horridus	CBrP
kanga new	EAri
lebomboensis	CBrP LPal
lehmannii	CBrP LPal
manikensis new	EAri
munchii new	EAri
natalensis	CBrP LPal
senticosus	LPal
villosus	LPal

endive see AGM Vegetables Section

Endymion see *Hyacinthoides*

Engelmannia (*Asteraceae*)

peristenia	EPPr WHil

Enkianthus ✿ (*Ericaceae*)

campanulatus 𝕐^{H5}	Widely available
- var. ***campanulatus*** f. ***albiflorus***	GKin NLar
- 'Miyama-beni'	NLar
I - 'Pagoda'	CBcs IArd IDee NLar
- var. ***palibinii***	CBcs EHyd EPfP GAbr GKin LRHS MAsh NLar
- PRETTYCOAT ('Jww10') new	CBcs MMrt
- 'Red Bells'	CBcs CBod EGrI EPfP GKin MAsh NLar SGol SMDa SPad SRHi SWvt WFar XSte
- 'Red Velvet'	GKin NLar
- 'Ruby Glow'	CBcs NLar SAko
- 'Showy Lantern'	NLar
- var. ***sikokianus***	CBcs NLar
- 'Sinsetu'	NLar
- 'Tokyo Masquerade' (v)	EHyd LRHS SPoG
- 'Venus'	CBcs EPfP GKin NLar
- 'Victoria'	CBcs NLar
- 'Wallaby'	CBcs GKev IDee NLar WAbe
cernuus f. ***rubens*** 𝕐^{H5}	CBcs CMac NLar

	chinensis	CRos EHyd EPfP LRHS MAsh SPoG
	deflexus	CBcs EHyd LRHS WPGP
	perulatus ♀H5	CBcs CBod CCCN CEnd EBee EPfP LPar LRHS MGil SPer
	serrulatus	GGGa

Ennealophus (*Iridaceae*)

	fimbriatus	GKev

Ensete (*Musaceae*)

	glaucum	CDTJ LPal
§	***ventricosum*** ♀H2	CCCN CDTJ LWaG SArc
§	- 'Maurelii' ♀H2	CBod CCCN CCht CDTJ CDoC CSBt CTsd EAri ELan ESwi ETod LCro LOPS LPal MHtn MPri NPlm SChr SDix SEND SPoG WHlf XSte
	- 'Rubrum'	see *E. ventricosum* 'Maurelii'
	- 'Tandarra Red'	CAbb

Entelea (*Malvaceae*)

	arborescens	EShb SPlb

Eomecon (*Papaveraceae*)

	chionantha	CBor CExl CMiW CPla CTtf EBee EBlo EWld GAbr GEdr GGro LEdu LRHS MAvo MPie MRav NBro NHpl NQui NSti SBrt WCru WFar WPGP WPnP XLum

Epacris (*Ericaceae*)

	paludosa	GArf
	serpyllifolia	WThu

Ephedra (*Ephedraceae*)

	sp.	MPie SArc
	altissima	XSen
	chilensis	GKev
	distachya	GPoy WKor
	equisetina RCB/TQ K-1	WCot
	fedtschenkoi	GKev
	fragilis	XSen
	gerardiana	LEdu LRHS MHtn
	- CC 3925	WCot
	- var. ***sikkimensis***	GGro XSen
§	***major***	XSen
	monosperma	WCot WThu
	nebrodensis	see *E. major*

Epilobium (*Onagraceae*)

	angustifolium	see *Chamaenerion angustifolium*
	- f. ***leucanthum***	see *Chamaenerion angustifolium* 'Album'
	californicum misapplied (Z)	see *E. canum*
§	***canum*** (Z)	ECha EDAr MBrN SRms SWvt WKif XLum XSen
	- 'Albiflorum' (Z)	ECha
§	- 'Dublin' (Z) ♀H4	Widely available
	- 'Ed Carman' (Z)	CKel ECha ECtt MGil WLov WMal WOld
§	- subsp. ***garrettii*** (Z)	SDys XLum
	- 'Glasnevin' (Z)	see *E. canum* 'Dublin'
§	- subsp. ***latifolium*** (Z)	XLum XSen
	- 'Olbrich Silver' (Z)	ECha WKif WMal XSen
	- 'Solidarity Pink' (Z)	WMal
	- 'Western Hills' (Z) ♀H4	CFis ECha EPot EWld LRHS MHer MMuc MRav SEND SPhx SRms SWvt WOld WPGP XLum XSen
	dodonaei	see *Chamaenerion dodonaei*
	glabellum misapplied	NSla
	hirsutum 'Album'	EWTr MACG
	microphyllum (Z)	see *E. canum*
I	'Pumilio' (Z)	EPot MHer
	rosmarinifolium	see *Chamaenerion dodonaei*
	septentrionale (Z)	WAbe
	villosum (Z)	see *E. canum*
	'White Wonder Bells' PBR	GMcL

Epimedium ✿ (*Berberidaceae*)

from Jian Xi, China	GEdr
from Yunnan, China	WPGP
acuminatum	CWCL EMor ESMi GEdr GPSL LEdu MNrw NLar NSum WFar WPGP WSHC
- L 575	CDor CElw CExl CSta
- 'Galaxy'	CExl LEdu
- 'Night Mistress' ♀H6	CSta CTtf EMor ESMi GPSL LEdu SPVi WPGP
- white-flowered **new**	CDor
- yellow-flowered	SPVi WPGP
- - CC 01141	CSta
'Akebono'	Widely available
ALABASTER ('Conalba')	CBar CKel EBee ECtt EWld GPSL SPer WFar
alpinum	CBod CMac EBee EBlo EHed EHyd EPfP GBin GKev GLog LEdu LRHS NChi NRHS SPVi SPer SRms WFar WHil
- 'Samobor'	LEdu
'Amanogawa'	CSta CTtf GEdr LEdu WCot
'Amber Queen' PBR ♀H6	Widely available
'Ambrosine' **new**	CMil
'André Charlier'	CElw CMil CSta WCAu
'Anju'	GEdr
'Arctic Wings' PBR	CSta CTtf CWCL EBee EPfP GEdr LEdu LPla NCth NGdn SPVi SWvt
'Asiatic Hybrid'	WCAu WFar XSte
'Beni-goromo'	GEdr
'Beni-kujaku'	EBee EMor GEdr GPSL SHar SPad WCot WFar
'Beni-yushima'	GEdr
'Bieke'	SMHy
'Black Sea'	CBWd CDor CElw CMil CSpe CWCL EBee EMor EPPr ESMi GBin LBar LEdu LRHS MBriF MNrw MPnt NLar NSum SPVi WBor WFar WHlf WPnP
brachyrrhizum	CDor CExl CTtf EMor NLar NSum
brevicornu	CSta GEdr WPGP
- Og 82.010	CExl SPVi
- Og 88.010	CDor SPVi
'Buckland Buzz'	EBee
'Buckland Spider'	CBor CFis CMil CSta EBee EHed EMor EPPr GEdr LEdu MNrw SPVi WCot WFar WPGP
'Buff Beauty'	CSta ESMi
'Buttered Popcorn'	EBee
campanulatum	CDor
- Og 93.087	CExl EBee
× ***cantabrigiense***	CBro CDor CMac CWCL ECtt EGrI EPPr GKev GMaP GPSL LPla MRav NHpl NLar SRms WCAu XLum
chlorandrum	CDor EBee EPPr LEdu WPGP
creeping yellow	CDor EBee ELan EMor EWTr MNrw WFar WHil
cremeum	see *E. grandiflorum* subsp. *koreanum*
'Dark Secret'	ESMi SPVi
'Darrell's Pink'	EBee
davidii	CBor CDor CSta CTtf EBee EMor EPPr ESMi GEdr LEdu MNrw NLar NSum SPVi WHil WHoo WPGP WSHC
- CPC 960079	CExl
- EMR 4125	CElw CExl

- dwarf	CExl
diphyllum	CExl EBee EPfP GEdr WPGP
dolichostemon	CElw EMor GPSL NChi
- Og 81.010	WPGP
'Domino' 🏆H6	CBWd CTtf ESMi GPSL LBar LEdu MAvo SPVi WPGP
'Double Cream' (d) **new**	SPVi
ecalcaratum	EBee LEdu WCot WPGP
- Og 93.082	CExl
'Egret'	CSta CTtf EBee LEdu SMHy SPVi WPGP
elongatum	ESwi
'Emperor'	see *E.* 'Phoenix'
'Enchantress'	CDor CElw CMiW CSta EMor ESMi LPla MNrw NLar NSum SPVi
epsteinii	CDor CMil CSta EBee EHed EMor EPPr ESMi EWld GEdr GGro LEdu MNrw SBrt WCot WPGP WSHC
- CPC 940347	CElw CExl
fangii	CExl
fargesii	CBor CDor CExl EBee GEdr LEdu MNrw NCth NSum SPVi WCAu WPGP WSHC
- 'Pink Constellation' 🏆H6	CDor CExl CSta CTtf EBee GEdr LEdu MNrw SGro SMHy SPVi WCot WPGP
'Fire Dragon'PBR	CBor ECtt EMor EPfP MBNS MNrw SPVi SPoG WFar
flavum	EBee WPGP
- Og 92.036	CExl EBee
'Flowers of Sulphur'PBR	CDor CSta EBee EHed EMor EPfP GDam GEdr SPVi WFar WSpi XSte
franchetii	CElw CExl CSta CTsd GEdr
- 'Brimstone Butterfly' 🏆H6	CBor CDor CExl CFis CTtf EHed EMor EPPr ESMi GEdr GPSL LEdu LPla NLar NSum SPVi WCot WHoo WPGP WSpi
'Fukujuji'	GEdr
'Golden Eagle'	CElw CExl CSta EBee EWes MNrw SPVi
§ ***grandiflorum***	CBcs CElw CRos CSta CTri CTsd CWCL EGrI EHed ELan ELon EMor EPfP EWTr GLog LRHS NBir NHpl NLar SEdd SGBe SPVi WCAu WFar WPnP
- 'Akagi-Zakura' 🏆H6	CSta SPVi
- 'Akakage'	CExl
- 'Album'	EMor
- 'Beni-chidori'	GEdr NSum
- 'Bronze Trim'	SMHy
- 'Circe' 🏆H6	ESMi SPVi
- 'Cranberry Sparkle'	EBee
- 'Crimson Beauty'	CTtf ECha WHoo WSHC
- 'Dark Beauty'	LBar SMad
- 'Elfenkönigin'	EBee NLar
- 'French Braid'	EBee
- 'Freya'	CExl EBee ECha ESMi LEdu NSum SMHy SPVi WSHC
§ - var. ***higoense***	GEdr SPVi WPGP
- - 'Bandit'	GEdr GPSL NCth SPVi
- 'Jennie Maillard'	ELon ESMi WCot
- 'Koji'	EBee GKev NLar SEdd SMad WHil WSHC
§ - subsp. ***koreanum***	ECha ESMi GEdr LPla NSum
- 'Kourin'	CSta GEdr
- 'La Rocaille'	CElw CSta SMHy SPVi
- 'Lilafee'	Widely available
- 'Mount Kitadake'	SPVi WAbe
- 'Mugawa-gen-pan'	SPVi
- 'Nanum'	EBee EMor ESMi GArf MCot MNrw NHar NSum NWad SPlb WAbe WHoo WPGP
- 'Pierre's Purple' **new**	LBar
- pink-flowered	MCot
- 'Purple Pixie'PBR	CDTJ ECtt ELan EMor GPSL LSou MBel NLar SCob SCoo SPer WCAu WFar WHil
- 'Purple Prince'	CExl EBee SPVi WPGP
- 'Queen Esta'	CExl EBee ECha ESMi LEdu MNrw MRav NSum SPVi WPGP WSHC
- 'Red Beauty'	Widely available
- 'Red Queen'	WCAu
- 'Rose Queen'	CWCL EBee EGrI ELan EMor EPfP ESMi LEdu LRHS MNrw MRav NBir NSti NSum SEdd SPVi SWvt WCAu WFar WPGP
- 'Roseum'	CMac CMil GMaP GPSL SWvt
- 'Rubinkrone'	CWCL GMaP MNrw
- 'Spring Wedding'	CMil
- var. ***thunbergianum***	CSta
- f. ***violaceum***	CElw EBee NSum WCFE
- 'Waterfall'	CSta SPVi
- 'White Beauty'	EMor WSHC
- 'White Queen'	EBee EPPr EPfP ESMi MBel WCot
- 'Wildside Red'	WSHC
- 'Yellow Princess'	CElw EBee
- 'Yubae'	CSta GEdr NLar SPVi
'Hagoromo'	GEdr
'Hakubai'	GEdr
'Harugasumi'	GEdr
higoense	see *E. grandiflorum* var. *higoense*
'Hina Matsuri'	GEdr
ilicifolium	CDor CSta CTtf LEdu WCot WPGP
'Jean O'Neill'	CDor CSta ECha EHed EMor EPPr EPri ESMi LEdu WCot WPGP WSHC
'Jenny Pym'	EBee EBtc
'Jinto Shan'	EHed
'Kaguyahime'	CElw EPPr GPSL LEdu WSHC
'King Prawn'	CSta ESMi LEdu SMHy SPVi WMal WPGP
'Knight Star'	CSta ESMi
'Kodai Murasaki' 🏆H6	SPVi
'Koki'	CBor GEdr
'Korin'	SPVi
'Kotobuki'	GEdr
latisepalum	CMil EBee ESMi EWld GEdr LEdu MNrw WCot WSHC
'Lemon Zest'	EBee ESMi SPVi
leptorrhizum	CDor CElw CExl CSta CWCL EBee EHed EMor EPPr ESMi EWld GEdr LEdu MNrw NCth NLar NSum SBrt WCot WHlf
- Og Y44	CExl WSHC
- 'Mariko'	CExl CMil CTtf LEdu MNrw SPVi
lishihchenii	CExl CMiW GEdr WPGP
- CC 96024	SPVi
'Little Shrimp'	CTri EBee EBlo EHed ELon GMaP GPSL MNrw NLar NSum WSHC
macranthum	see *E. grandiflorum*
macrosepalum	GEdr GPSL SPVi WPGP
'Mandarin Star'	CWCL EHed EMor ESMi GEdr GPSL NCth SMad SPVi WHlf
'Marchant's Sulphur Queen'	SMHy
'Marchant's Twin Set'	ESMi SMHy SPVi
membranaceum	EBee EGrI ESMi GEdr LEdu NCth WPGP
- Og 93.047	CExl EPPr GEdr LEdu
mikinorii	CExl GEdr GGro
- CC 990001	LEdu WPGP
'Milky Way'	MNrw
'Mine-no-fubuki'	GEdr
'Moonlight'	SPVi
'Myojo'	EBee GEdr
myrianthum	CDor EBee GEdr GPSL LEdu WPGP
'Never the Red Rooster'	CSta

ogisui	CDor CElw CMil CTtf EHed ESMi LEdu MRav SPVi WPGP
- Og 91.001	CExl EBee MNrw
- 'Diane'	LEdu SPVi
§ × ***omeiense*** 'Akame'	CExl CMil EPPr GEdr LEdu MNrw SPVi
- 'Emei Shan'	see *E.* × *omeiense* 'Akame'
- 'Myriad Years'	SPVi
- 'Pale Fire Sibling'	GEdr
- 'Stormcloud'	CElw CExl CMiW CMil CSta CTtf EHed EMor EPPr LEdu
parvifolium	LEdu
'Pathfinder'	CSta EHed ESMi GEdr
pauciflorum	EBee EMor EPPr GEdr LEdu LPla WPGP
- Og 92.123	CExl
× ***perralchicum***	CBro CKel CTri ECha LRHS NLar WSHC
- 'Fröhnleiten'	Widely available
- 'Lichtenberg'	EBee EWes
- 'Nachfolger'	SPVi
- 'Wisley'	CDor CElw EWes SPVi
perralderianum	CMac CSta CWCL EBee EHeP GMaP MBel MCot MNrw SRms WCAu
- 'Weihenstephan'	CDor CRos CWCL LEdu LRHS NLar WPnP
aff. ***perralderianum***	MPnt
'Perrine's Pink' (Magique Elfes Series)	WCot
'Persian Carpet'	EWld
§ 'Phoenix'	CDor CExl CSta CTtf ESMi WCot WMal
'Pink Champagne' ♀^{H6}	CSta CTtf EMor EPfP ESMi GEdr GKev LBar LEdu NBPC NCth SCob SPVi WCot WFar WMal WPGP
'Pink Elf'^{PBR}	Widely available
pinnatum	EBee GMaP XLum
§ - subsp. ***colchicum*** ♀^{H7}	CTtf CWCL ELan EMor EPfP GLog GQue LEdu LRHS MBel MCot MRav NGdn SCob SDix SPVi SPer WCAu WCot WFar WMal WPnP WSpi
- - L 321	WPGP
- - 'Thunderbolt'	EBee WCot
- ***elegans***	see *E. pinnatum* subsp. *colchicum*
platypetalum	ESMi SBrt WCot
- Og 93.085	CExl EBee
'Pretty in Pink'	CSta EHed EPfP LBar NCth
pubescens Og 91.003	CExl EBee WPGP
- from Shaanxi, China	ESMi SPVi
pubigerum	CDor CRos CWCL EBee ECha EGrI EHed EMor ESMi GLog ILea LEdu LPla LRHS MMuc NHpl NLar NSum SEND SIvy SPVi SRms SWvt WCAu WFar WSpi
'Red Maximum' ♀^{H6}	ESMi LEdu SPVi WCot WPGP
reticulatum	GEdr
rhizomatosum	CDor EPPr ESMi GEdr WPGP WSHC
- Og 92.114	LEdu WCot WPGP
'Rhubarb and Custard'	ESMi
'Royal Purple' ♀^{H6}	LEdu SPVi
× ***rubrum*** ♀^{H7}	Widely available
- 'Galadriel'	CBor CDor EMor EPfP ESMi ESwi GBin GPSL LBar SPad SPeP WCAu WFar WHil WHoo
- 'Sweetheart'	GEdr
sagittatum 'Warlord'	ESMi SPVi WPGP
'Sakura-maru'	CBor GEdr
'Sam Taylor'	SPVi
'Sasaki'	CBor CMil CWCL ESMi ESwi GBin GKev GPSL LBar NLar
'Scarlotti Biscotti' **new**	SPVi
sempervirens 'Candy Hearts'	WCot

- 'Creamsickle' (v)	GEdr WCot
- 'Okuda's White'	EBee
× ***setosum***	ESMi NLar NSum SPlb
'Shiho'	CWCL EBee GKev GPSL MAvo NLar
'Shiro-chiri-fu' (v) **new**	CSta
shuichengense	GEdr
'Simple Beauty'	CSta
'Sparkler' **new**	ESMi
'Sphinx Twinkler'	see *E.* 'Spine Tingler'
§ 'Spine Tingler' ♀^{H6}	Widely available
'Spinners'	EBee ESMi WCot
'Starcloud'	EBee
stellulatum	GEdr
- long-leaved	ESMi MACG
- 'Wudang Star'	CBWd CDor CExl CRos EBee EMor EPfP EWTr EWes GEdr GPSL LEdu LRHS MCot NSum SEdd SPVi WFar WHil WHlf WSHC
sulphureum 'Plena'	see *E.* × *versicolor* double-flowered
'Sunny and Share'	EMor GBin LBar
'Sunshowers'	CSta
'Suzuka'	GEdr LEdu WPGP
'Tama-no-genpei'	CSta GEdr LEdu WCot
'Tanima-no-yuki'	GEdr
'The Giant'	SPVi WCot WPGP
'Togen'	SPVi WCot
'Tokiwa-gozen'	GEdr
'Totnes Turbo'	CSta EBee ESMi WMal
trifoliolatobinatum CC 950046	LEdu
'Valor'	WCot
× ***versicolor***	CExl EShb SSut
- 'Cherry Tart'	CDor ESMi SPVi
- 'Cupreum'	CDor CFis CWCL EGrI EMor GPSL LEdu LRHS SHar SPVi WCAu WFar WHil
§ - 'Discolor'	CDor CElw CMiW CSta ECha EPPr NBir SMHy WCot
§ - double-flowered (d)	MHol
- 'Neosulphureum'	CBro CDor CTtf CWCL EBee EPPr LRHS WFar WPGP WSHC WThu
- 'Sulphureum' ♀^{H7}	Widely available
- 'Versicolor'	see *E.* × *versicolor* 'Discolor'
× ***warleyense***	Widely available
- 'Orangekönigin'	Widely available
'Wildside Amber'	CSta
'Wildside Ruby'	CSta CTtf ESMi SPVi WMal
'William Stearn'	CExl CSta EWld GEdr LEdu SPVi WCot WPGP
'Windfire'	EBee
'Winter's End' ♀^{H6}	SPVi WMal
wushanense	EBee EHed EPPr ESMi GEdr LEdu
- CC 14193	WPGP
- Og 93.019	CDor CExl WPGP
- 'Caramel'	CExl CSta EHed GEdr GPSL LEdu NSum WCAu WCot WSHC
- 'Cardiff Star'	CSta WMal
- 'Sandy Claws'	CSta SPVi WCot
- spiny-leaved	ESMi SPVi WCot WFar XLum
- - CC 014631	WPGP
'Yachimata-hime'	GEdr
'Yokihi'	CSta GEdr SPVi
× ***youngianum*** 'Beni-kujaku'	EWTr WFar
- 'Capella'	SPVi
- 'Fairy Dust'	EBee
- 'Grape Fizz'	EBee
- 'Marchacos Sprite'	EBee
- 'Merlin'	CDor CElw CWCL EBee EMor EPPr EPfP ESMi EWTr GEdr GPSL LSou MGos NLar NSti NSum WFar WSHC
- 'Niveum'	Widely available
- 'Roseum'	Widely available

- 'Ruby Tuesday' EBee
- 'Shikinomai' CExl
- 'Tamabotan' GEdr MNrw MRav WHil
§ - 'Typicum' CElw WSHC
- 'Youngianum' see *E.* × *youngianum* 'Typicum'
zhushanense EBee ESMi GEdr LEdu WCot WPGP
- CC 022403 **new** SPVi WPGP
- CC 02885 SPVi

Epipactis (*Orchidaceae*)

Catalina gx CJun EDAr GEdr MNrw NLAp
gigantea CBor CJun CPla EBee ECha EGrl ELan EWld GEdr GKev LAma MHer MNrw MRav NDav NLAp
- 'Serpentine Night' CJun LAma NLAp
- 'Serpentine Night' × ***thunbergii*** NLAp
helleborine WHer
Lizzy Lou gx CJun NLAp
Lowland Legacy gx CJun
- 'Edelstein' MNrw WFar
palustris CBor ELan IPot MBNS MNrw NLAp WHer WPnP
Passionata gx Light Royals Group CJun
Renate gx CJun NLAp
royleana CJun GEdr
Sabine gx CJun NLAp WHlf
- 'Frankfurt' EWld GEdr MNrw
thunbergii × ***veratrifolia*** NLAp

Epiphyllum ✿ (*Cactaceae*)

anguliger **new** EAri LCro NHrt
'Arcadia' **new** EAri
'Bliss' **new** EAri
'Clarence Wright' **new** EAri
crenatum **new** EAri
'Dante' **new** EAri
'Firewell' **new** EAri
'Frühlingsgold' **new** EAri
'Gardenia' **new** EAri
hookeri **new** EAri
- subsp. ***guatemalense*** **new** NPlm
'Hugletts' **new** EAri
'Marie Josephine' **new** EAri
'Meda' **new** EAri
'Mexico City' **new** EAri
pumilum **new** NPlm
'Red Tip' **new** EShb
'Reward' **new** EAri
'Royal Rose' **new** EAri
'Space Rocket' **new** EAri
'Tele Ann' **new** EAri
'Three Oranges' **new** EAri
tricolour-flowered **new** EAri

Epipremnum (*Araceae*)

§ ***aureum*** ♀H1b LCro LOPS NHrt NPlm
N'JOY ('Hansoti12'PBR) (v) **new** LCro
pinnatum MARBLE PLANET ('Ppiepi003'PBR) **new** LCro

Episcia (*Gesneriaceae*)

dianthiflora see *Alsobia dianthiflora*
'San Miguel' see *Alsobia* 'San Miguel'

Equisetum ✿ (*Equisetaceae*)

'Bandit' (v) WPGP
* ***camtschatcense*** CBod CEme EShb MNHC SArc SMad SPlb XLum
fluviatile CPud
giganteum 'El Tabacal' GGro
hyemale CBen CWal CWat EWat GQue LLWG LPfP NBro NPer NSti SBls SPlb WCot XLum
§ - var. ***affine*** CBdn EBee ELan LEdu WMAq WPGP
- var. ***robustum*** see *E. hyemale* var. *affine*
ramosissimum var. ***japonicum*** CPud SEdd WPGP
scirpoides EFer EWat LLWG MWts NPer NWad WMAq XLum
telmateia LEdu SMad WPGP
variegatum EBee EFer GGro

Eragrostis (*Poaceae*)

curvula CBod CElw CKno CWCL ECha EHyd EPPr EPfP EWTr LRHS MAvo NBir NGdn NWsh SEND SPhx XLum
- S&SH 10 CElw EPPr SMHy WPGP
- 'Totnes Burgundy' CAby CKno CRos CSde EHyd ELan EMor EPPr EPfP LEdu LRHS MAsh MAvo NRHS NWsh SPhx SRms WPGP XSen
elliottii CSpe ECha EPPr EShb LRHS MAvo SEND
- 'Wind Dancer' CSde EBee NWsh SRms XSen
spectabilis CBod CKno CSde EAJP EBee ECha EHyd ELan EPfP LDai LEdu LRHS MACG NGdn SBls WCot XLum XSen
trichodes CBod CKno ECha LDai LEdu NWsh XSen

Eranthemum (*Acanthaceae*)

pulchellum ♀H1b ECre

Eranthis (*Ranunculaceae*)

albiflora GKev
cilicica see *E. hyemalis* Cilicica Group
§ ***hyemalis*** ♀H6 CArg CBod CBro CRos CWCL EHyd ELan EMor EPfP EWoo GKev LAma LCro LOPS LRHS MPri NHpl NRHS NRog SDeJ SDir SWvt WCot WHlf WHoo WShi WTor
§ - Cilicica Group EHyd EPot ETay GEdr GKev GMaP LAma LRHS NBir NLar NRHS NRog SDeJ SDir SPer SPlb WCot WShi
- 'Flore Pleno' (d) GEdr GKev LAma NRog WCot
- 'Grünling' CAvo WCot
- 'Grünspecht' GEdr
- 'Orange Glow' EPot GEdr GKev LAma
- 'Schwefelglanz' CAvo CBor CBro EPot GEdr GKev WCot
§ - Tubergenii Group EPot GKev
- - 'Guinea Gold' ♀H6 GEdr NRog
- - 'Sachsengold' GKev
pinnatifida GEdr GKev
× ***tubergenii*** see *E. hyemalis* Tubergenii Group

Ercilla (*Phytolaccaceae*)

volubilis CBcs CBod CHll CRHN CWGN EGrl EPfP EShb EWld IDee MGil SBrt WCru WSpi

Eremophila (*Scrophulariaceae*)

longifolia SPlb

Eremurus (*Asphodelaceae*)

'Apricot Yellow' **new** LAma
bungei see *E. stenophyllus* subsp. *stenophyllus*
'Charleston' LAma

'Foxtrot'	GKev IPot LAma SDeJ
fuscus	GKev
'Helena'	LAma LRHS SDir SPhx
himalaicus	ELan EPot ERCP GBin GKev GMaP ILea LAma LRHS NLar NRog SDeJ SDir SPhx
'Image'	NRog
× ***isabellinus*** 'Cleopatra'	CBod EGrl EHyd EPfP EPot ERCP GKev GMaP IPot LAma LCro LOPS LRHS MBNS MHer NChi NLar NRog SDeJ SPeP SPhx SPoG WCot
- 'Emmy Ro'	GKev LRHS NRog
- 'Obelisk'	EPfP NRog
- 'Pinokkio'	ETay GKev LAma LCro LOPS LRHS NLar NRog SDeJ
- Ruiter hybrids	CBod ELan EPfP GKev LAma MGos NLar NRog SCob SDeJ SPhx
- Shelford hybrids	CBcs CBod ELan GKev MBros NRog SDeJ
- 'Tropical Dream'	GKev LRHS
'Jeanne-Claire'	LAma SDir
'Joanna' ♀H6	LAma LCro LOPS NLar SDir
'Lemon Fizz'	LAma NLar SDir
'Line Dance'	EHyd EPfP ETay GKev LAma LRHS NRHS
'Moneymaker'	LAma NRog
'Oase'	EHyd EPfP NRog SDeJ
'Pink Fizz' **new**	LAma NLar
'Pink Persuasion'	NLar
'Rexona'	GKev NRog SDeJ
robustus ♀H6	CBcs ELan EPot ERCP GKev LAma NLar NRog SDeJ SDir SPeP SPhx SPlb WCot
'Roford'	NRog
'Romance'	EHyd ERCP ETay LAma LRHS NBwr NRHS NRog SDeJ
'Rumba'	LAma NLar SDir
'Samba'	LAma
'Sarah Cato'	GKev LAma SPhx
stenophyllus ♀H6	EPot ERCP ETay GKev LAma LCro LOPS NLar SCob SDeJ SDir SPoG WCot
§ - subsp. ***stenophyllus***	CBcs EPfP GMaP LRHS MHer MNrw NPer NRog SPer
'Tap Dance'	GKev NLar
'White Beauty Favourite' PBR	ERCP LCro LOPS MHer SDeJ SPeP
'White Sensation'	LAma LRHS NLar SDir
'Yellow Giant'	GKev

Erepsia (*Aizoaceae*)

lacera	EAri SPlb

Erianthus see *Saccharum*

Erica ✿ (*Ericaceae*)

aestiva	SPlb
alopecurus	SPlb
andevalensis f. ***albiflora***	CFst
arborea	CTsd GDam SPlb XSen
- var. ***alpina*** ♀H4	CTri EPfP
§ - - f. ***aureifolia*** 'Albert's Gold' ♀H4	CBcs CDoC CRos CSBt CTri ELan EPfP GAbr GArf LCro LRHS MAsh MGos NHol NRHS SCoo SPer SPoG
- 'Arbora Gold'	see *E. arborea* var. *alpina* f. *aureifolia* 'Albert's Gold'
- 'Arnold's Gold'	see *E. arborea* var. *alpina* f. *aureifolia* 'Albert's Gold'
- f. ***aureifolia*** 'Golden Smile' **new**	CFst
- 'Estrella Gold' ♀H4	CBcs CDoC CKel CRos CSBt CTri EHyd ELan EPfP LRHS MAsh NHol NRHS SCoo SPer SPoG
australis 'Holehird'	CDoC
- 'Riverslea' ♀H4	CDoC CRos CTri EHyd LRHS NRHS SPoG
caffra	SPlb
canaliculata ♀H3	CBcs ECre
carnea 'Adrienne Duncan' ♀H6	GPer SCoo SRms
- f. ***alba*** 'Golden Starlet' ♀H6	CFst CSBt CTri MAsh NHol SCoo SRms
- - 'Ice Princess' ♀H6	ELan MAsh SCoo SRms
- - 'Isabell' ♀H6	CBcs CSBt MAsh SCoo SRms
- - MADAME SEEDLING	see *E. carnea* 'Weisse March Seedling'
- - 'Rosalinde Schorn'	SRms
- - 'Schneesturm'	SRms
- - 'Snow Queen'	SRms
- - 'Snowbelle' PBR	CFst
- - 'Springwood White' ♀H6	CFst CSBt CTri ELan MAsh MMuc NHol SPer SRms
- - 'Whitehall'	CFst LCro LOPS MAsh SCoo SRms
- - 'Winter Snow' ♀H6	CBcs CFst CSBt ELan SCoo SPer SRms
- 'Ann Sparkes' ♀H6	CBcs CFst CSBt CTri ELan GPer MAsh NHol SCoo SRms SVic
- f. ***aureifolia*** 'Aurea'	MAsh SCoo SRms
- - 'Barry Sellers'	SRms
§ - - 'Bell's Extra Special'	SRms
- - 'Dorset Sunshine'	CFst
- - 'Foxhollow' ♀H6	CBcs CFst CTri IArd MAsh NHol SCoo SPer SRms SVic
- - 'Gelber Findling'	SRms
- - 'Hilletje'	SRms
- - 'January Sun'	SRms
- - 'Westwood Yellow' ♀H6	CSBt MAsh NHol SRms
- 'Aztec Gold'	CFst SPer
- 'Beoley Pink'	SRms
- 'Branton Bamford'	CFst
- 'C.J. Backhouse'	SRms
- 'Challenger' ♀H6	ELan GPer MAsh SCoo SRms SVic
- 'Clare Wilkinson'	SRms
- 'Claribelle'	CFst
- 'Corinna' PBR	CFst
- 'December Red'	CFst ELan MAsh MMuc SCoo SEND SRms SVic
- 'Diana Young'	SCoo
- 'Dømmesmoen'	SRms
- 'Early Red'	SRms
- 'Eileen Porter'	MMuc
- 'Eva' ♀H6	CBcs CFst SRms
- 'Foxhollow Fairy'	SRms
- 'Gracilis'	SRms
- 'Heathwood'	SRms
- 'James Backhouse'	CFst CTri
- 'Jason Attwater'	SRms
- 'Jennifer Anne'	SRms
- 'John Kampa'	SRms
- 'John Pook'	SCoo SRms SVic
- 'King George'	CTri SRms
- 'Lohse's Rubin'	SRms
- 'Loughrigg' ♀H6	CTri MAsh NHol SCoo SRms SVic
- 'March Seedling' ♀H6	CFst MAsh NHol SCoo SRms
- 'Margery Frearson'	SRms
I - 'Martin'	SRms
- 'Myretoun Ruby' ♀H6	CBcs CFst CSBt CTri GPer LCro LOPS MAsh NHol SCoo SRms
- 'Nathalie' ♀H6	CFst CSBt MAsh SCoo SRms
- 'Pink Beauty'	see *E. carnea* 'Pink Pearl'
- 'Pink Cloud'	CFst
- 'Pink Mist'	SRms
§ - 'Pink Pearl'	CFst
- 'Pink Spangles' ♀H6	CBcs CFst CSBt CTri MAsh SCoo SPer SRms
- 'Pirbright Rose'	SRms
- 'Polden Pride'	SRms

	- 'Praecox Rubra'	NHol SCoo SRms
	- 'Queen Mary'	SRms
	- 'Queen of Spain'	SRms
	- 'R.B. Cooke'	MAsh SCoo SRms
	- 'Robert Jan'	SRms
	- 'Rosalie' 🏆H6	CFst IArd MAsh SCoo SPer SRms
	- 'Rosantha'	SRms
	- 'Rosea'	SPlb
	- 'Rosy Morn'	SRms
	- 'Rotes Juwel'	SRms
	- 'Rubinteppich'	SRms
	- 'Ruby Glow'	NHol
	- 'Sally'	CFst
	- 'Saskia'	CFst
	- 'Scatterley'	SRms
	- 'Schatzalp'	SRms
	- 'Sherwood Creeping'	SRms
	- 'Smart's Heath'	SRms
	- 'Springwood Pink'	CSBt GPer MAsh NHol SRms
	- 'Tanja'	CFst
	- 'Viking'	MAsh
	- 'Vivellii' 🏆H6	CTri GPer MAsh NHol SCoo SRms
	- 'Walter Reisert'	SRms
§	- 'Weisse March Seedling'	CFst
	- 'Wentwood Red'	SRms
	- WHISKY	see *E. carnea* f. *aureifolia* 'Bell's Extra Special'
	- 'Winter Beauty'	NHol
	- 'Winter Rubin'	CFst SRms
	- 'Winterfreude'	CFst
	- 'Wintersonne' 🏆H6	MMuc SRms
	cerinthoides 🏆H2	CPbh
	- 'Albertina'	CPbh
	ciliaris f. ***albiflora*** 'Stoborough'	CFst
	- 'Corfe Castle'	CFst
	- 'David McClintock'	CFst
	- 'Wych'	CFst
	cinerea f. ***alba*** 'Alba Minor'	CFst MAsh
	- - 'Hookstone White'	CFst
	- - 'White Dale'	CFst
	- 'Atrosanguinea Smith's Variety'	CFst
	- f. ***aureifolia*** 'Fiddler's Gold'	MAsh
	- - 'Golden Drop'	CFst MAsh
	- - 'Goldilocks'	CFst
	- 'Bucklebury Red'	CFst
	- 'C.D. Eason' 🏆H7	CFst CTri GJos GPer SCoo
	- 'Cevennes'	GPer
	- 'Champs Hill'	CFst
	- 'Creepy Crawly'	CFst
	- 'Discovery'	CFst
	- 'Eden Valley'	CFst GPer SCoo
	- 'Glencairn'	GPer
	- 'John Ardron'	CFst
	- 'Joseph Murphy'	CBcs CFst
	- 'Joyce Burfitt'	CFst
	- 'Katinka'	CBcs CFst GJos GPer
	- 'Lady Skelton'	CFst
	- 'Lilac Time'	CFst GJos GPer
	- 'Mrs E.A. Mitchell'	GPer SPlb
	- 'My Love'	CFst SPer
	- 'P.S. Patrick'	GJos
	- 'Pentreath'	GPer
	- 'Pink Ice' 🏆H7	CFst CTri GPer MAsh NHol
	- 'Providence'	CFst
	- 'Purple Beauty'	GPer
	- 'Romantic Scotland'	GJos GPer
	- 'Rosea'	GPer
	- 'Rosita'	CFst
	- 'Sandpit Hill'	CFst
	- 'Sherry'	NHol
	- 'Stephen Davis' 🏆H7	CFst GPer NHol SCoo
	- 'Velvet Night' 🏆H7	GPer NHol
	- 'Vivienne Patricia'	CFst
	cooperi	SPlb
	curviflora	SPlb
	× ***darleyensis*** 'Alba'	see *E.* × *darleyensis* f. *albiflora* 'Silberschmelze'
	- f. ***albiflora*** 'Ada S. Collings'	MAsh SRms
	- - 'Bing'	SCoo
	- - 'N.R. Webster'	SRms
§	- - 'Silberschmelze'	CKel CSBt CTri CWnw GJos MAsh MMuc SCoo SRms SVic
	- - 'White Glow'	CTri MAsh SRms
	- - 'White Perfection' 🏆H5	CBcs CDoC CFst CKel CWnw IArd MAsh MNHC NHol SCoo SPoG SRms SVic WFar
	- 'Archie Graham'	SRms
	- 'Arthur Johnson' 🏆H5	CFst CTri MAsh SRms
§	- f. ***aureifolia*** 'Eva Gold' PBR	CBcs CFst
	- - 'Golden Perfect'	CFst
	- - 'Jack H. Brummage'	CSBt CTri MAsh SRms
	- - 'Mary Helen'	CSBt MAsh NHol SCoo SRms SVic WFar
	- - 'Moonshine'	CFst SRms
	- - 'Tweety'	CFst CSBt SRms
	- 'Aurélie Brégeon'	SRms
	- 'Cherry Stevens'	see *E.* × *darleyensis* 'Furzey'
§	- 'Darley Dale'	CEme CKel CSBt CWnw ELan GJos GPer MAsh MMuc MNHC SCoo SPoG SRms SVic WFar
	- 'Epe'	CFst SRms
	- 'Eva'	see *E.* × *darleyensis* f. *aureifolia* 'Eva Gold'
§	- 'Furzey' 🏆H5	CSBt GPer LCro LOPS MAsh NHol SCoo SRms
	- 'George Rendall'	MAsh SCoo SRms
	- 'Ghost Hills' 🏆H5	CEme CKel CSBt LCro LOPS MAsh SCoo SPoG SRms
	- 'Irish Treasure'	CFst
	- 'J.W. Porter' 🏆H5	CEme CKel MAsh SCoo SRms
	- 'James Smith'	SRms
	- 'Jenny Porter' 🏆H5	ELan SCoo
	- 'Katia' PBR (Winter Belles Series)	CFst SPer
	- 'Kramer's Rote' 🏆H5	CEme CFst CKel CSBt CTri CWnw ELan NHol SCoo SPoG SRms SVic WFar
	- 'Lucie' PBR (Winter Belles Series)	CFst GJos
	- 'Margaret Porter'	SCoo SVic
	- MOLTEN SILVER	see *E.* × *darleyensis* f. *albiflora* 'Silberschmelze'
	- 'Phoebe' PBR (Winter Belles Series)	CBcs CFst
	- 'Pink Perfection'	see *E.* × *darleyensis* 'Darley Dale'
	- 'Rubina' PBR	CKel
	- 'Spring Surprise' PBR 🏆H5	CFst SCoo
	- 'W.G. Pine'	SRms
	- 'Winter Surprise'	CFst
	- 'Winter Treasure'	CFst
	discolor	CPbh
§	***erigena***	XSte
	- f. ***alba*** 'W.T. Rackliff' 🏆H5	CBcs CSBt GPer MAsh NHol SCoo SRms
	- f. ***aureifolia*** 'Golden Jubilee'	CFst
	- - 'Golden Lady'	CSBt MAsh NHol SCoo SRms
	- - 'Thing Nee'	CFst SRms
	- 'Brightness'	CSBt NHol SCoo
	- 'Irish Dusk' 🏆H5	CBcs CSBt CTri GPer MAsh MMuc SCoo SRms
	- 'Superba'	SRms

	formosa	CPbh
	glauca var. ***glauca***	SPlb
	gracilis	CDoC NBir
	× ***griffithsii*** 'Ashlea Gold'	CFst
	- 'Elegant Spike'	CFst
	- 'Jacqueline'	CFst
	- 'Valerie Griffiths'	CFst GPer NHol
	hibernica	see *E. erigena*
	lusitanica f. ***aureifolia*** 'George Hunt'	CFst EHyd ELan LRHS
	- GREAT STAR	see *E. lusitanica* 'Le Vasterival'
§	- 'Le Vasterival'	XSte
	- 'Sheffield Park'	EHyd LRHS NRHS SPoG
	mackayana f. ***eburnea*** 'Shining Light'	CFst
	mammosa 🏆H2	CPbh SPlb
	manipuliflora 'Elegant Spike'	CFst
	mediterranea misapplied	see *E. erigena*
	multiflora	XSen
	oatesii	CPbh
	× ***oldenburgensis*** 'Ammerland' 🏆H5	SCoo SRms
	'Pat Turpin'	CFst
	patersonia	SPlb
	perspicua	SPlb
	platycodon	CFst
	subsp. ***maderincola*** f. ***aureifolia*** 'Levada Gold'	
§	***scoparia*** 'Minima'	CCCN
	- 'Pumila'	see *E. scoparia* 'Minima'
	straussiana	SPlb
	× ***stuartii*** 'Irish Lemon' 🏆H5	CFst GPer NHol
	- 'Irish Orange'	EPot GPer NHol
	terminalis 'Thelma Woolner'	CFst
	tetralix f. ***alba*** 'Alba Mollis' 🏆H6	CFst GJos GPer MAsh
	- f. ***aureifolia*** 'Ruth's Gold'	NHol
	- 'Con Underwood'	CFst GPer
	- 'Hookstone Pink'	CFst
	- 'Ken Underwood'	CFst
	- 'L.E. Underwood'	CFst
	- 'Riko'	CFst
	- f. ***stellata*** 'Pink Star' 🏆H6	CFst NHol
	vagans f. ***alba*** 'Cornish Cream' 🏆H5	GJos GPer NHol
	- - 'Diana's Gold'	SRms
	- - 'Golden Triumph'	CFst
	- - 'Kevernensis Alba' 🏆H5	GPer
	- - 'Lyonesse' 🏆H5	MAsh MMuc NHol
	- f. ***aureifolia*** 'Valerie Proudley' 🏆H5	GPer MAsh NHol
	- - 'Yellow John'	CFst SRms
	- 'Birch Glow' 🏆H5	CFst
	- 'Keira'	CFst SRms
	- 'Mrs D.F. Maxwell' 🏆H5	CBcs CFst GPer MMuc NHol
	- 'Mrs Donaldson'	CFst
	- 'Saint Keverne'	CFst IArd MAsh MMuc NHol
	- 'Summertime'	CFst
	× ***veitchii*** 'Exeter' 🏆H4	CDoC CFst CRos CSBt EHyd ELan EPfP LRHS MAsh NRHS SPer SPoG
	- 'Gold Tips' 🏆H4	CFst CSBt
	versicolor 🏆H2	CPbh SPlb
	verticillata	CPbh
	× ***watsonii*** 'Cherry Turpin'	CFst
	- 'Claire Elise'	CFst
	- 'Dorothy Metheny'	CFst
	× ***williamsii*** 'Ken Wilson'	CFst GPer
	'Winter Fire'	CDoC CPbh
	woodii	SPlb

Erigeron (*Asteraceae*)

	'Adria'	CAby CRos EHyd ELon LBar LRHS MBel MHol NRHS
§	***alpinus***	SLee
	annuus	CKel CSpe ECha MHol MNrw NDov SDix SPhx WBrk WHoo WMal
	aurantiacus	CBcs CSpe ELan EPfP GKev SMad
	aureus 'Canary Bird' 🏆H4	EPot NSla WAbe WIce
	- 'The Giant'	WAbe
	AZURE FAIRY	see *E.* 'Azurfee'
§	'Azurfee'	CSBt ELan EPfP GMaP MACG NBir NLar SPer SPoG SWvt WFar
	BLACK SEA	see *E.* 'Schwarzes Meer'
	'Blue Beauty'	CMac CRos EHyd EPfP LRHS NRHS SRms
	'Charity'	MHCG MRav
	chrysopsidis	GKev
	- 'Grand Ridge'	EHyd EPot NRHS WAbe
	compositus	SRms
§	- var. ***discoideus***	NSla SLee SPlb
	- 'Rocky'	NSla
	DARKEST OF ALL	see *E.* 'Dunkelste Aller'
	'Dignity'	CAby EBee ELan LBar MBrN MPie MRav NHol SSut SWvt
	'Dimity'	ECha NBir WFar
	'Dominator'	CWGN LBar MHol WCot WFar
I	'Dunkelste Aller'	CAby CBcs EHyd ELan EPfP GAbr GLog GMaP LBar LRHS LSou MAsh MBel MHol MPie MRav NLar NRHS NSti SGbt SPoG SRms SWvt WCAu WFar WTor
	elegantulus	EDAr
	flettii	GKev
	'Foersters Liebling' 🏆H5	EBee LBar
	'Four Winds'	ECtt ELan EWes NGdn NHpl WIce
	glaucus	CCCN CSBt CWal GQue NGdn SEND SMad WBrk
	- 'Albus'	ELon NLar WFar
	- 'Elstead Pink'	CTri ECtt ELan WFar WSHC
	- large-flowered	ELon
	- 'Roger Raiche'	CFis MHol
	- 'Roseus'	SEND
	- 'Sea Breeze'	Widely available
	- 'Sennen'	MHCG NFav
	- 'Viewpoint Blue'	ELon
	grandiflorus	MHol
	howellii	MHol
	'Karminstrahl'	ELon
§	***karvinskianus*** 🏆H5	Widely available
	- 'Kew Profusion'	CKel CRos EHyd LCro LRHS NGrs NRHS SEdd WHil
	- 'Lavender Lady'	CSpe CTtf ECha EMor GBee LBar LCro LPla MAvo MHol SMrm SPhx WCot WMal WNPC WTor
	- pink-flowered **new**	SHor
	- 'Sea of Blossom'	CBod CCht CGBo CKel CWnw LRHS LSou LSun MBow MHol MPri NCou SCoo SPoG
	- 'Stallone'	NLar SBls WWke
	leiomerus	EDAr GEdr GKev
	linearis	CPla EDAr GEdr
	'Mrs F.H. Beale'	GBin LBar WCot
	mucronatus	see *E. karvinskianus*
	'Nachthimmel'	NGdn
	nanus	GEdr
	philadelphicus	CElw MNrw NBir NBro
	PINK JEWEL	see *E.* 'Rosa Juwel'
	PINK TRIUMPH	see *E.* 'Rosa Triumph'
	pinnatisectus	GArf NFav
	'Profusion'	see *E. karvinskianus*

	pulchellus	WBrk
	pumilus	WGoo
	pyrenaicus misapplied	see *E. alpinus*
	pyrenaicus Rouy	see *Aster pyrenaeus*
	'Quakeress'	CAby CTtf ECtt ELon EPri GAbr GMaP GQue LBar LSou MBel MHol MMuc MNrw MRav NGdn SDix SMrm SSut SWvt WFar WGwG
§	'Rosa Juwel'	CSBt ECtt EHeP EHyd ELan EPfP GBin GMaP LRHS MRav NBir NLar NRHS SPer SPoG SRms SWvt WCAu WFar
§	'Rosa Triumph'	EBee
	'Rotes Meer'	CMac EBee MRav
	rotundifolius 'Caerulescens'	see *Bellis caerulescens*
	salsuginosus misapplied	see *Eurybia sibirica*
§	'Schneewittchen' ♀^{H5}	CCBP CNor CRos EBee ECha ELan ELon EPfP LBar MACG MBNS MBel MHol MPie MRav NCth NRHS SRms SWvt WGwG
§	'Schwarzes Meer'	ELon WCot
	scopulinus	EDAr EPot GEdr WAbe
	simplex	EHyd LRHS NRHS
	'Snow Queen'	SWvt
	SNOW WHITE	see *E.* 'Schneewittchen'
	'Sommerneuschnee'	EBee LBar LPla NDov SHar WCAu WTor
	'Synehurst'	WCot WFar
	trifidus	see *E. compositus* var. *discoideus*
	uniflorus	MAsh SRms
	'Violetta'	SPoG
	'Wayne Roderick'	CRos EHyd ELan EPfP GBee LBar LRHS MACG NRHS SCoo WFar
	'White Quakeress'	CFis MHCG MRav SMrm WCot WFar

Erinacea (*Fabaceae*)

§	***anthyllis*** ♀^{H5}	EDAr GArf SBrt WAbe
	pungens	see *E. anthyllis*

Erinus (*Plantaginaceae*)

	alpinus ♀^{H6}	ECtt EDAr GAbr GJos GKev MAsh NBir NGrd SLee SRms SRot
	- var. ***albus***	GMaP SRms WHoo
	- 'Doktor Hähnle'	EDAr GJos SRms WHoo

Eriobotrya (*Rosaceae*)

	'Coppertone'	see × *Rhaphiobotrya* 'Coppertone'
	deflexa	WJur
	japonica (F) ♀^{H4}	CCCN CDoC CKel CTsd CWnw EGrl EHyd ELan EPfP LPal LPar LRHS MGos MMuc MNic NLar SArc SCoo SEND SGsty SPer SPlb SSta SVic SWeb WJur WKor WLea WPGP
	- 'Mrs Cookson' (F)	CAgr WMat
	- 'Oliver' (F)	CAgr WMat
	- 'Rose-Anne' (F)	WPGP

Eriobotrya × *Rhaphiolepis* see × *Rhaphiobotrya*

Eriocapitella see *Anemone*

Eriocephalus (*Asteraceae*)

	africanus	CBod SPlb WJek

Eriogonum (*Polygonaceae*)

	cespitosum	WAbe
	giganteum	EPot WMal
	grande var. ***rubescens***	WHil
	ovalifolium Wellington form	GEdr
	umbellatum	GKev
	- var. ***humistratum***	SLee WAbe
	wrightii var. ***subscaposum***	GKev

Eriolarynx (*Solanaceae*)

§	***australis*** ♀^{H3}	CBcs CCCN CDow CSpe EAri ELan LSRN MGil NGKo NSti SEND SIvy SMad SPlb SPoG SPtp SVen WCot WFar WHlf WPGP
§	- 'Andean Snow'	CCCN CDow CHll CSpe EShb MGil NGKo WHil WPGP
§	- 'Bill Evans'	CHll
	- blue-flowered	see *E. australis* 'Bill Evans'
	- purple-flowered	CDow
	- white-flowered	see *E. australis* 'Andean Snow'

Eriophorum (*Cyperaceae*)

	angustifolium	CBen CPud CTtf CWat EWat LLWG LPfP MWts SBls SPlb WMAq WPnP
	chamissonis	MWts
	latifolium	LLWG MACG
	rousseauianum	LLWG
	vaginatum	EWat LLWG MACG

Eriophyllum (*Asteraceae*)

	lanatum	ECha EPfP NBid NGBl SHar

Eriostemon (*Rutaceae*)

	myoporoides	see *Philotheca myoporoides*

Eriosyce (*Cactaceae*)

	chilensis var. ***albidiflora*** FK 192 **new**	NMen
	senilis ♀^{H2} **new**	NMen
	subgibbosa	NMen
	subsp. ***clavata*** **new**	
	- subsp. ***wagenknechtii*** **new**	NMen
	taltalensis violet-flowered **new**	SPlb

Eritrichium (*Boraginaceae*)

	aretioides	SPlb
§	***canum***	GKev
	pectinatum	GKev
	rupestre	see *E. canum*
	strictum	see *E. canum*

Erodium (*Geraniaceae*)

	absinthoides	EHyd EPot NRHS XSen
	- var. ***amanum***	see *E. amanum*
§	***acaule***	ECha EPPr
	'Almodovar'	WCot WFar
§	***amanum***	EWes GMaP
	balearicum	see *E.* × *variabile* 'Album'
	'Caroline'	WHoo
§	***castellanum***	EWld GBee NGrd NLar
	celtibericum 'Peñagolosa'	XSen
	chamaedryoides	see *E. reichardii*
	- 'Roseum'	see *E.* × *variabile* 'Roseum'
§	***cheilanthifolium***	SLee SRot
	chrysanthum	CAby CTri EBou ECha ECtt EDAr EGrl ELan EPfP EPot EWTr EWoo LShi MMuc MPnt MRav NBwr NChi NLar SEND SLee SPtp SWvt WKif WMal XLum XSen
	- (f)	SRot WFar
	- (m)	NRya
	- 'Arcadia'	SPhx
	'County Park'	ECha SBut SHar SRms WFar XLum XSen
	daucoides misapplied	see *E. castellanum*
	'Eileen Emmett'	EPot NBwr
	foetidum hybrids	SRot

	'Fran's Delight'	EDAr EPot SGro WAbe WFar WHoo
	'Freedom'	CBor WFar WIce
	'Fripetta'	WIce
	'Gini's Choice'	WCot
§	***glandulosum*** ♀H5	EBee EDAr EPfP MMuc SEND SPtp SRms WFar WKif XLum XSen
	'Grey Blush'	WKif
	gruinum	SPhx
	guttatum misapplied	see *E.* 'Katherine Joy'
	guttatum (Desf.) Willd.	CAby CWGN EPot EWTr EWoo GMaP MAvo NLar SRms
	hymenodes L'Hér.	see *E. trifolium*
	'Julie Ritchie'	WHoo
§	'Katherine Joy'	CBor EDAr EWes LShi MHer SRot WFar
	× ***kolbianum***	WAbe WCot WFar WHoo WMal
	- 'Natasha'	CBor ELan EPot EWes MHer MMuc SRot WIce WKif XLum
	'Las Meninas'	WCot
	× ***lindavicum***	MHer NChi
	macradenum	see *E. glandulosum*
	manescavii ♀H5	Widely available
	'Marchants Mikado'	WKif
	'Maryla'	CBor WFar WIce
	'Merstham Pink'	SRms
	'Milly'	EDAr
	paularense	GKev
	pelargoniiflorum	CAby CCht CRos CSpe EBee EHyd ELan EMor EPfP EWoo LRHS MCot MNHC NCou NRHS SAko SMrm SRms SWvt WCAu WFar WHil WKif
	'Peter Vernon'	MHer
	petraeum subsp. ***crispum*** misapplied	see *E. cheilanthifolium*
	- subsp. ***petraeum***	EPot
	'Pippa Mills'	EDAr WAbe
	'Purple Haze'	EHyd ELan EMor EPfP SLee SRms WFar
§	***reichardii***	CRos CTri ECtt EHyd LRHS MBrN NRHS SPoG SRms WCav
	- 'Album'	CRos EHyd EPfP LCro MAsh NGrs NHpl NRHS SLee SPoG WFar WHoo XLum
	- 'Bianca'	ELan EPfP
	- 'Jenny'	NHpl
	rodiei	EWes
	romanum	see *E. acaule*
§	***rupestre***	SRms WIce
	'Sans-culottes'	EWes
	'Spanish Eyes'	EBee SMad SRot SWvt WAbe WCot WFar WKif XLum
	'Special Rose'	CSpe ECtt EDAr MMuc SLee XLum
	'Stephanie'	CBor ELan EWes LShi MHer MMuc NBwr NLar WIce XSen
	supracanum	see *E. rupestre*
	'Tiny Kyni'	WFar
	trichomanifolium misapplied	see *E. cheilanthifolium*
	trichomanifolium L'Hér.	EWes
§	***trifolium***	MHer WBrk
	× ***variabile***	WFar
	- 'Album'	see *E.* × *variabile* 'Joe Elliott'
	- 'Bishop's Form'	see *E.* × *variabile* 'William Bishop'
	- 'Candy'	CBor ECtt MHer NHpl SLee SRot
	- 'Flore Pleno' (d)	CRos CTri EHyd ELan EPfP EWes LLWG LRHS MHer NHpl NRHS SLee SMrm SPoG SRms SRot WFar
§	- 'Joe Elliott'	CBor CRos EDAr EHyd EPfP EPot GKev GMaP LRHS MHer NGrd NRHS NRya SRms SRot SWvt WFar WTor
	- 'Red Rock'	CTri
§	- 'Roseum' ♀H5	ECtt ELan EWoo LLWG LRHS NCou SLee SPlb SRms
§	- 'William Bishop'	CBod CBor CGBo CRos ECha EDAr EHyd EPfP EPot GJos GMaP LCro LLWG LRHS LShi MAsh MBow NQui NRHS NRya SMrm SPoG SRms SRot SWvt WAbe WBrk WFar WHoo WIce

Erophila (*Brassicaceae*)

verna	SPhx

Erpetion see *Viola*

Eruca (*Brassicaceae*)

vesicaria	ENfk
- subsp. ***sativa***	CBod CSpe GPoy MHer MNHC SRms SVic

Eryngium (*Apiaceae*)

§	***agavifolium***	Widely available
	- giant	WPGP
	alpinum	CBod CPla CSpe ECha EWld GMaP GMcL LBar LRHS MGos MSCN NBir SPer SPhx SRms WCAu WFar
	- 'Amethyst'	EMor
	- 'Blue Star'	CBWd EBee ECtt EDAr ELan EPri GJos NLar WCAu WFar WSpi
	- 'Slieve Donard'	see *E.* × *zabelii* 'Donard Variety'
	- 'Superbum'	ECtt EMor MBriF SRms
	amethystinum	CPla EPri EWes LRHS NFav SPhx SPtp XLum
	'Blue Jackpot'	EBee ECtt EPfP EWes MAsh MBros MNrw
	bourgatii	Widely available
	- Graham Stuart Thomas's selection	CDor CEme CRos CSpe ECtt EHyd ELan EPPr GAbr GMaP LRHS MAvo MBel NBir NLar NRHS SPad SRms WCAu WCot WHoo WKif WSpi
	- 'Oxford Blue'	NLar NSla SPtp SWvt
	- PICOS AMETHYST ('Mackpam'PBR)	Widely available
	- 'Picos Blue'PBR ♀H5	Widely available
	bromeliifolium misapplied	see *E. agavifolium*, *E. eburneum*
	campestre	SPhx SPtp
	'Cobalt Star'	MAvo MRav SMHy
	creticum	MNrw
	cymosum	SPtp
	- B&SWJ 10267	ESwi WCru
	decaisneanum misapplied	see *E. pandanifolium*
	Dove Cottage hybrid	WHoo
	ebracteatum	CSpe EMor LEdu WPGP
	- var. ***poterioides***	ELan ILea IPot LCro LPla LRHS NDov SEdd SMad SPhx SPtp
§	***eburneum***	CBod ECha EGrI ELan EMor EWes GMaP ILea LRHS MSpe SMad SPtp
	- 'Fromefield Rapier'	SPtp
	aff. ***eburneum***	CMac
§	***giganteum*** ♀H6	Widely available
	- 'Silver Ghost' ♀H6	CAby CPla CSpe CTtf ECtt EDAr EPfP GMaP LBar LCro LOPS LRHS NDov NGdn NLar SBls SPhx SWvt WAvo WCot WFar WHlf WSpi
	glaciale	GKev
	gracile B&SWJ 10441	WCru
	'Green Jade'	NRHS
	guatemalense B&SWJ 10397	ESwi WCru
	horridum misapplied	see *E. eburneum*
	horridum ambig.	ECha EWes NLar SArc
	horridum Malme	WCot
	humboldtii B&SWJ 14342	WCru

	aff. ***humboldtii*** B&SWJ 14367	WCru
	humile	MHol
	- B&SWJ 10464	WCru
	- var. ***brevibracteatum*** B&SWJ 14735	WCru
	leavenworthii	EMor
	- 'Purple Sheen'	EDAr
	longifolium B&SWJ 14786	WCru
	maritimum	CEls CSpe GPoy NFav SPhx SPlb SRms
	Miss Willmott's ghost	see *E. giganteum*
	× ***oliverianum*** 🏆 H5	CDor CTri ECtt ELan EMor EPfP LRHS MAvo MCot MRav NBir NLar SPoG SWvt WCot
§	***pandanifolium*** 🏆 H4	EAri EBee ELan EMor EWes MNrw SArc SBls SEND SMHy SPlb SPoG SWvt WPGP
	- 'Physic Purple'	CAby CDor CSpe ECha ELan EMor LRHS MAvo NCth SDix SPtp WCot
	paniculatum	ECha
	- B&SWJ 14367	WCru
	- B&SWJ 14826	WCru
	'Pen Blue'	CAvo CDor CSpe CTtf ECha ECtt EPfP EWoo LBar LRHS MGos MHol MNHC MNrw NCth NDov SAko SPoG WCAu WCot WHlf WHoo WTor
	planum	Widely available
§	- 'Blauer Zwerg'	GMaP LRHS NLar WFar
	- 'Blaukappe'	CBod CRos EBee EBlo ECha EHyd ELan ELon EPfP GJos LDai LRHS LSto LSun MMuc NLar NRHS SCoo SEND SMHy SPhx SRms WFar
	- BLUE DWARF	see *E. planum* 'Blauer Zwerg'
	- 'Blue Glitter'	CDor EBee GJos NLar SWvt
	- 'Blue Hobbit'	Widely available
	- 'Flüela'	CBod ECtt EHyd EPfP EWes LRHS LSRN MACG NRHS
	- 'Jade Frost' PBR (v)	Widely available
	- 'Little Blue Wonder' PBR	NHol
	- (Magical Series) MAGICAL ANITA ('Kolmanita' PBR)	LBar MHol NLar
	- - MAGICAL BLUE GLOBE ('Kolmaglo')	NLar
	- - MAGICAL BLUE LAGOON ('Kolmblula' PBR)	LBar LRHS MHol NLar SMrm SRkn XSte
	- - MAGICAL PURPLE FALLS ('Kolmapufa' PBR)	MHol NLar
	- - MAGICAL SILVER ('Kolmagsil' PBR)	LRHS NLar
	- - MAGICAL SYMPHONY ('Kolmasy')	EPfP LRHS MHol NLar XSte
	- - MAGICAL WHITE FALLS ('Kolmwhifal')	MHol NLar
	- 'Naughty Jackpot' (v)	NLar
	- 'Paradise Jackpot' PBR	SRms
	- 'Seven Seas'	ECtt EHyd LRHS MBNS NRHS
	- 'Silver Salentino'	CBod GPSL
	- 'Silver Stone'	LDai SRms
	- 'Tetra Petra'	LRHS SRms WMal
	- 'Tiny Jackpot'	GMaP NLar
	- 'White Glitter'	CBod EBee ELan EPfP SCoo SPoG
	proteiflorum	CDor LRHS NDov SPlb WFar
	serra	EBlo EWes LDai SPtp
	spinalba	EDAr
	tricuspidatum	CDoC CRos EBee EBlo ECtt EHyd EPfP LRHS NRHS
	× ***tripartitum*** 🏆 H5	CBcs CBod CTri EBee ECha ECtt EHyd EMor EPfP GJos GMaP LRHS LSRN MBel MNrw MRav NBro NLar NRHS SWvt WCAu WHoo
	variifolium	Widely available
	- 'Miss Marble'	EBou EPfP LSun NGrd SBls SRms WFar
	venustum	EMor GGro NFav SMad SPtp WPGP
	vesiculosum	SPlb
	yuccifolium	CBWd CBod CSpe EBee ECha EMor EPfP EWes LRHS MAvo SDix SPeP SPhx SPlb SPtp SWvt WCAu XLum
	- 'Kershaw Blue'	EBee WPGP
	× ***zabelii***	ECha
	- 'Big Blue' 🏆 H5	Widely available
	- 'Blue Waves'	LRHS MBNS NCth
§	- 'Donard Variety'	EHyd ILea LRHS MAvo MCot NLar
	- 'Forncett Ultra'	MNrw
	- 'Jos Eijking'	CAvo CDor EBee ECtt EMor EPfP EPri GBin GMaP GMcL IPot LBar LCro LEdu LOPS LRHS LSRN MBel MRav NCth NHol NLar NSti SCob SEdd SPoG SWvt WCot WHoo
	- 'Neptune's Gold' PBR	Widely available
	- 'Violetta'	CDor CSpe EBee ECha ECtt EHyd EMor EPfP EPri LRHS MACG MCot MNrw NDov NLar NRHS WCAu WFar

Erysimum ✿ (*Brassicaceae*)

	allionii misapplied	see *E.* × *marshallii*
	alpinum misapplied	see *E. hieraciifolium*
*	***altaicum*** var. ***humillinum***	GEdr
	'Apricot Delight'	see *E.* 'Apricot Twist'
§	'Apricot Twist'	CBcs CBod CWCL CWGN CWal ECtt EHyd ELan ELon EPfP LDai LRHS LShi MAsh MCot MDon MPri NLar NRHS SCoo SPer SPoG SRms SWvt WCav WFar WHoo WMal WTor
	arkansanum	see *E. helveticum*
	'Audrey's Pink'	CCBP WMal
	bonanianum	WCot
	'Bowles's Mauve' 🏆 H4	Widely available
	'Bowles's Purple'	SRms SWvt
	'Bowles's Yellow'	LShi MHCG NFav WCot
	'Bredon'	NPer WKif WMal
	'Canaries Yellow'	GMcL LRHS
	'Caribbean Island'	LBar LShi SGBe
	cheiri	LShi MHer MPri NGrd
	- 'Baden-Powell' (d)	EPPr
	- 'Blood Red'	CArg CSpe LCro LOPS
	- 'Bloody Warrior' (d)	CElw WCot WMal
	- 'Cloth of Gold'	CArg CKel
	- 'Fire King'	CArg CKel LCro LOPS
	- 'Giant Pink'	CKel
	- 'Gold Dust'	CBod
	- 'Harpur Crewe' (d)	CFis NPer SRms WHer WMal
	- 'Ivory White'	CKel
	- 'Persian Carpet' (mixed) 🏆 H5	CKel LCro
	- Sunset Series	MBros
	- 'Vulcan'	CArg
	'Constant Cheer'	CElw CSBt EHyd ELan LBar LShi MAvo MBow MCot MRav NLar NPer SCoo SPoG SRGP SRms SWvt WBor WCav WHlf WHoo WKif WMal WSpi XLum
	CORAL ('Er0509-01') (Glow Series) **new**	CWCL
	'Cotswold Gem' (v)	ELon LDai MHer NPer SWvt
	'Desert Island'	CKel ECtt SGBe
	'Dorothy Elmhirst'	see *E.* 'Mrs L.K. Elmhirst'
	'Early Sunrise' (Sky Series) **new**	LBar WHlf
	'Gogh's Gold' (Artist Series)	LShi NLar WHlf WMal
	'Golden Jubilee'	ECtt SGBe SRms WCav WIce

	'Hector's Gatepost'	MAvo
§	***helveticum***	EDAr LShi SRms
§	***hieraciifolium***	LShi
	'Honeyberry'	LRHS
	'Jacob's Jacket'	ECha EWld LShi MHer NPer
	'Jenny Brook'PBR	XLum
	'John Codrington'	ECha GBin NPer WSpi
	'Joseph's Coat'	MHCG
	kotschyanum	CBor EBou EPot GEdr LShi NBwr NSla SRms WAbe WIce
	'Lady Roborough'	NQui
	'Lemon Light'	WHoo
	linifolium	SRms
	- 'Little Kiss Lilac'	MACG
	- STARS 'N' STRIPES ('Yastrip'PBR) (v)	ECtt SRkn
§	- 'Variegatum' (v)	CCCN CFis CSBt ECtt EDAr ELan EPfP LBar LShi MCot NPer SHar SPer SPoG WCav WHer XLum
	- 'Variegatum' peach-flowered (v)	LRHS NQui
§	× ***marshallii***	LShi SPhx
	'Monet's Moment' (Artist Series)	LBar LShi SCoo SGBe SPoG WHlf
	'Moonlight'	GMaP MRav SRms SRot WHoo
§	'Mrs L.K. Elmhirst'	NPer
	mutabile	ECha EHyd EPfP LShi
	'Night Skies' (Sky Series) **new**	LBar NLar WPnP
	'Orange Flame'	CBor ECha EPot GArf LShi MHer NPer WHoo
	'Orange Zwerg'	LRHS MMuc WIce
	'Paint Box' (Artist Series)	CBod SCob SCoo SGBe WHlf
	'Parish's'	CCBP CElw CFis CSpe ECha LShi WFar WGoo WHoo WMal
	'Parkwood Gold'	EPot NHpl
	'Pastel Patchwork'	ECtt EPfP LCro LRHS MDon NRHS WFar WWke
	Perry's hybrid	NPer
	'Perry's Peculiar'	NPer
	'Perry's Surprise'	NPer
	'Perry's Variegated' (v)	NPer
	pieninicum **new**	LShi
	'Plant World Lemon'	NLar WHlf
	'Primrose Dame'	CKel
§	***pulchellum***	ECha EPot
	pumilum DC.	see *E. helveticum*
	'Purple Jep'	LRHS
	'Purple Shades'	CKel
	'Red Jep'	CDoC EHyd ELan EPfP LRHS LShi NRHS SAdn SAng SCoo SPer WCot WHlf WNPC WTor
	rupestre	see *E. pulchellum*
	'Ruston Royal'	CElw ECha WKif WMal
	RYSI COPPER	CRos EHyd EPfP LRHS NRHS SCoo SPoG
	RYSI MOON	WHlf WTor
	scoparium	LShi
	'Sissinghurst Variegated'	see *E. linifolium* 'Variegatum'
	'Spice Island'	ECtt SCob SGBe
	'Sprite'	NPer
	Sugar Rush Series	MBros
	SUNBURST ('Listrace') (v)	CWCL ECtt LShi MBNS WCot
	'Sweet Sorbet'	EPfP NLar SRkn SWvt
*	'Tricolor'	LWaG
	'Tropical Sunset' (Sky Series) **new**	LBar
	'Variegatum' ambig. (v)	SGBe SRot
	WALBERTON'S FRAGRANT STAR ('Walfrastar'PBR) (v)	EHyd EPfP LRHS MAsh NRHS SCoo SPoG SRms
	WALBERTON'S FRAGRANT SUNSHINE ('Walfrasun')	CRos EHyd EPfP LBar LRHS MPri NRHS SCoo SPoG
	'Wenlock Beauty'	CFis LDai SRms
	'Winter Joy'	ELan EPfP LRHS
	'Winter Light'	LRHS WHlf
	WINTER ORCHID	CWGN EPfP GMaP LCro LRHS SAng SGBe WHlf WTor
	'Winter Party'	LRHS
	'Winter Passion'	CRos CWCL EHyd EPfP LRHS NLar SCoo SPoG
	WINTER ROUGE	WHlf
	WINTER SORBET ('Inneryws'PBR)	ECtt ELan LRHS SGBe WTor

Erythraea see *Centaurium*

Erythrina (*Fabaceae*)

	abyssinica	SPlb
	amazonica	SPlb
	arborescens	SPlb
	× ***bidwillii***	CCCN WPGP XVPe
	crista-galli ♀H3	CBcs CCCN CDTJ CHll CKel CSpe EAri EHyd ELan EPfP LAlb LRHS MGil MVil SArc SPlb WPGP XSen XVPe
	- 'Compacta'	LRHS XSte XVPe
	flabelliformis	SPlb
	guatemalensis	SPlb
	herbacea	SPlb
§	***humeana***	SPlb
	latissima	SPlb
	lysistemon	SPlb
	princeps	see *E. humeana*
	rubrinervia	SPlb
	speciosa	SPlb
	vespertilio	SPlb

Erythronium ✿ (*Liliaceae*)

	albidum	GEdr GKev LAma NRog
	americanum	GKev LAma MAvo MNrw NRog WAbe
	- 'Cincinnati'	NRog
	'Bryn Meifod'	WAbe
	californicum	CWCL EBee EHyd GKev LEdu MAvo MNrw NRHS NRog WAbe
	- 'Brimstone'	MCor
	- 'Sonoma'	NRog
	- 'White Beauty' ♀H5	Widely available
	californicum × ***citrinum***	NRog
	caucasicum	EPot GKev
	- from Krasnodar	NRog
	'Citronella'	MAvo NRog
	cliftonii hort.	see *E. multiscapideum* Cliftonii Group
	dens-canis	Widely available
	- from Montenegro	NRog
	- from NE Spain	NRog
	- 'Charmer'	GEdr MNrw NRog
	- dark	CBor GLet
	- 'Frans Hals'	EPot GEdr GKev LAma LEdu NRog WAbe
	- 'Lilac Wonder' ♀H5	CBor EBee EPot GEdr GKev GMaP LAma LEdu MNrw NRog SDeJ
*	- 'Moerheimii' (d)	GEdr GKev NRog
	- var. ***niveum***	GEdr NRog
	- 'Old Aberdeen' ♀H5	CAvo CRos EHyd LRHS MAvo NLar NRHS NRog WAbe
	- 'Pink Perfection'	CBor EBee GEdr GKev LAma LEdu MNrw NRog SDeJ WAbe
	- 'Purple King'	CBor EBee EPot GEdr GKev GMaP ISha LAma LEdu MNrw NHol NHpl NRog SDeJ WAbe
	- 'Rose Queen'	CBor EGrI EPot GEdr GKev GMaP LEdu MAvo MNrw NLar NRog SDeJ WHlf WHoo

- 'Snowflake'	CAvo CBor CRos EHyd EPot GEdr GKev ISha LAma LEdu LRHS MNrw NBir NHol NHpl NLar NRHS NRog SDeJ WAbe
- 'Valerie Wollaston'	MAvo
- 'White Splendour'	EPot GEdr LEdu MAvo MNrw NRog
elegans	NHpl NRog
§ ***grandiflorum***	EBee GKev NRog
- subsp. ***chrysandrum***	see *E. grandiflorum*
'Harvington April Sunrise'	LRHS
'Harvington Snowgoose'	CRos EHyd LRHS MCor NHar NRHS
'Harvington Sunshine'	LRHS NHar
helenae	MNrw
hendersonii ♀H5	EHyd LRHS MAvo NRHS NRog SPlb WAbe
hendersonii* × *klamathense	NRog
'Hidcote Beauty'	CRos EHyd LRHS NRHS
howellii* × *revolutum	LRHS
'Janice' ♀H5	MCor
japonicum	CMiW EPot GKev MNrw NRog
'Jeannine'	GKev NRog WAbe
'Joanna' ♀H5	CTtf GEdr MAvo MCor MNrw NHar NRog WAbe
'John Brookes'	MCor
'Keith'	MCor
'Kinfauns Pink'	CBor CWCL EBee EMor GBin GEdr GKev GLet GMaP LAma NRog
'Kondo'	CBcs CBor EPfP ETay MAvo NBir NHol NLar NRog SCob SDeJ
'Margaret Mathew'	LEdu WAbe
'Miss Jessopp'	NRog
§ ***multiscapideum***	EMor GKev MNrw NRog WAbe
- from Pulga, California	NRog
§ - Cliftonii Group ♀H4	MAvo WAbe
oregonum	CRos CWCL EBee EHyd GBin GKev LRHS MAvo MNrw NHpl NRHS NRog
'Pagoda' ♀H5	Widely available
purdyi	see *E. multiscapideum*
revolutum	CAvo CBro CTtf CWCL EHyd GBin GEdr GKev GMaP LAma LRHS MNrw NHar NHpl NRHS NRog SChF
- from God's Valley, Oregon	MNrw
- giant pink-flowered	NRog
- Johnsonii Group	EPot WAbe
- 'Knightshayes'	CRos EHyd LRHS NRHS
- 'Knightshayes Pink'	CAvo WShi
- 'Pink Beauty'	GKev NRog
- 'Rose Beauty'	NRog
- 'Wild Salmon'	EHyd LRHS MAvo NHar NRHS
'Rosalind'	NHar NRog WAbe
sibiricum	GKev LAma NHpl NRog
- subsp. ***altaicum***	NRog
- 'Gornaya Shoria'	NRog
- 'Kemerov'	NRog
- 'Lilac Cloud'	NRog
- subsp. ***sibiricum***	NRog
- 'Tomsk'	NRog
- white-flowered	NRog
'Sundisc' ♀H4	CBro ECha MAvo NRog
'Susannah'	EHyd MCor NRHS
tuolumnense	CAvo CWCL EMor GEdr GMaP MCor MCot MNrw NHpl NRog SDeJ WAbe
- EBA clone 2	MCor
- 'Spindlestone'	CRos EHyd GEdr LRHS NHar NRHS WAbe
umbilicatum	EPot GEdr GKev NHpl NRog

Erythrostemon (*Fabaceae*)

§ ***gilliesii*** ♀H3	CBcs EAri LRHS SPlb WCot

Escallonia (*Escalloniaceae*)

'Apple Blossom' ♀H4	Widely available
§ ***bifida*** ♀H3	CRos EHyd ELan EPfP EWes LRHS MAsh NRHS WPGP
'C.F. Ball'	CBrac CTri ELan GMcL MAsh MSwo NBwr NWea SGol SRms
'Donard Beauty'	CBrac NWea SRms
'Donard Brilliance'	SGol SRms
'Donard Radiance' ♀H4	CBrac CEnd CMac CSBt EHeP NLar NWea SCob SGbt SGol SPoG SRms SWvt WFar
'Donard Red'	NBwr
'Donard Seedling'	CBcs CBrac CCVT CRos EDir EHeP EHyd ELan EPfP GArf GDam GMcL LPar LRHS LSto MAsh MGos MMuc MSwo NBwr NPer NRHS NWea SCob SPer SRms SWvt WFar
'Donard Star'	NLar NWea WCFE
'Donard White'	NBwr NLar SPoG
'Edinensis'	EPfP NLar SRms WSpi
× ***exoniensis***	SRms
GLOWING EMBERS ('Lowat21')	CBod LCro LRHS MAsh SCoo SGBe WHtc
GOLDEN CARPET ('Alcaura'PBR)	CBod EHyd ELan EPfP LPar LRHS MAsh NRHS SCob SNig SPoG WHlf WNPC
'Hopleys Gold'	see *E. laevis* 'Gold Brian'
illinita	WPav
'Iveyi' ♀H4	Widely available
§ ***laevis***	NLar
§ - 'Gold Brian'	CMac EHyd EPfP GMcL LRHS MAsh MGos NBwr NRHS SPer
- 'Gold Ellen' (v)	CBrac CDoC CEme CRos CSBt CTri EHyd ELan EPfP GMcL LRHS MAsh MGos MRav MSwo NBwr NHol NLar NRHS SCob SCoo SGBe SNig SPer SPoG SRms SSha SWvt
- PINK ELLE ('Lades'PBR)	CBod CDoC CKel CRos CSBt EBee EDir EHyd ELan EPfP LCro LOPS LPar LRHS MAsh MGos NRHS SCob SCoo SGBe SPoG SWvt WFar WHlf WNPC
'Langleyensis' ♀H4	CTri SRms
× ***mollis***	SPer
montevidensis	see *E. bifida*
myrtilloides B&SWJ 14329	WCru
organensis	see *E. laevis*
'Peach Blossom' ♀H4	CBar CBcs CDoC CEnd CKel CRos EBee EHeP EHyd ELan EPfP GMcL LRHS MAsh MSwo NHol NRHS SCob SCoo SGbt SGol SPer SRms WFar
'Pink Carpet' **new**	NLar
'Pride of Donard' ♀H4	CSBt EHeP LRHS SCob SGsty SRms
pulverulenta	WPav
RED CARPET ('Loncar'PBR)	CBcs CBod SCob WNPC
'Red Dream'	CSBt EFPl EHeP EPfP GMcL LPar LRHS MAsh MGos MSwo SCob SCoo SGsty SPoG SRms SWvt WAvo WFar
'Red Elf'	CMac CRos EHeP EHyd ELan EPfP GKin GMcL LPar LRHS MAsh MGos NBwr SPlb SRms SWvt WFar
'Red Hedger'	CBod CSBt CTsd EHeP ELan LPar MRav SRms
'Red Knight'	CEnd EHyd LRHS MAsh NHol NLar NRHS WNPC
resinosa	CMCN SPlb SRms SVen WPav
revoluta	CTri MGil WPav
rubra 'Crimson Spire' ♀H4	CBar CBcs CBod CBrac CEnd CSBt CTri EHeP EPfP GKin GMcL LSRN

		MAsh MGos MMuc MRav NBwr NWea SCob SEND SGbt SNig SPer SPlb SRms SSha
	- 'Ingramii'	EHeP NWea SEND
	- var. ***macrantha***	Widely available
	- 'Pygmaea'	see *E. rubra* 'Woodside'
§	- 'Woodside'	CMCN SRms
	'Show Stopper' **new**	CBod
	'Silver Anniversary'	MSwo
	'Slieve Donard'	CBrac CMac EHeP MRav NWea SRms
	'Tall Boy'	LRHS
	tucumanensis	SPlb
	'Ventnor'	SPlb SVen
	virgata	WPav

Eschscholzia (*Papaveraceae*)

californica	MBel
- 'Alba'	CSpe
- 'Apricot Chiffon' (Thai Silk Series) ♀H3	LCro LOPS
- 'Ivory Castle'	CKel SMrm SPhx
- var. ***maritima***	CSpe
- 'Mission Bells'	LCro
- 'Orange King'	LRHS SPhx
- 'Peach Sorbet' **new**	LCro
- 'Red Chief'	CSpe LRHS SMrm SPhx

Espostoa (*Cactaceae*)

blossfeldiorum **new**	NCft
guentheri	see *Vatricania guentheri*
lanata ♀H2 **new**	NPlm SPlb

Esterhuysenia (*Aizoaceae*)

alpina	EAri SPlb

Etlingera (*Zingiberaceae*)

elatior	EAri

Eucalyptus ✿ (*Myrtaceae*)

	aggregata	EBee SArc SKin WGrf
	alpina	SPlb
	amygdalina	SPlb
	apiculata	WGrf
	approximans	SKin WGrf
	archeri	CDTJ CDoC CTsd ELan EPfP MGos MHtn SKin WGrf WHtc
§	***bridgesiana***	WGrf
	caesia ♀H2	SPlb
	- subsp. ***magna***	WGrf
	camaldulensis	LMaj SPlb WGrf
	camphora	CCCN SKin WGrf
	cinerea	CTsd SKin SPlb SWeb WGrf
	citriodora	see *Corymbia citriodora*
	coccifera	CBod CDoC CTsd EBee EPfP IDee MNHC NPer SEdd SKin SPlb SSha WGrf WLov
	cordata	CDoC EBee EPfP IDee SKin WGrf
	crenulata	CCht EBee SEdd SKin WGrf
	crucis subsp. ***crucis***	SPlb
	cypellocarpa	SPlb
	dalrympleana ♀H5	CDoC CMac IPap LSRN MGos MMuc NPer SEND SKin SLim SPer SPlb WGrf WHlf WHtc WPGP
	deanei	WGrf
	debeuzevillei	see *E. pauciflora* subsp. *debeuzevillei*
	deglupta	WGrf
	delegatensis	NPer WGrf
	denticulata	WGrf
	divaricata	see *E. gunnii* subsp. *divaricata*
	elliptica	WGrf
	erythrocorys	SPlb
	eximia	see *Corymbia eximia*
	ficifolia	see *Corymbia ficifolia*
	fraxinoides	SPlb
	gamophylla	SPlb
	glaucescens	CAbb LPar SArc SKin WGrf
	globulus	CWCL SPlb
	- subsp. ***bicostata***	WGrf
	- coastal	WGrf
	goniocalyx	WGrf
§	***gregsoniana***	EBee EPfP SKin SMad SPlb WGrf
	gunnii ♀H5	Widely available
	- AZURA ('Cagire'PBR)	CDoC IBal LCro LOPS LPar LSRN MTrO NLar NOrn SCob SLim SRHi WGrf WMat XSte
§	- subsp. ***divaricata***	SKin WGrf
	- FRANCE BLEU ('Rengun'PBR)	CBod CDoC CKel CWnw LSRN NCth NOrn WCot WGrf WHlf XSte
	- 'Silbertropfen'	CBod
*	- 'Silver Drop'	WFar
	- SILVERANA ('Lon40')	CKel CWnw SGsty WGrf
	johnstonii	ELan SEdd SKin SPer WGrf
	kitsoniana	SKin WGrf
	kruseana	SPlb
	kybeanensis	SKin WGrf
§	***lacrimans***	WGrf
	leucoxylon	SKin SPlb WGrf
	subsp. ***megalocarpa***	
	ligustrina	SKin WGrf
	'Little Boy Blue'	WGrf
	macrocarpa	SPlb WGrf
	mitchelliana	LAlb SEdd SKin WGrf
	moorei	CDTJ
	- var. ***moorei***	WGrf
	neglecta	SKin WGrf
	nicholii	CBcs CDoC CSpe CTsd EBee EPfP MGos SCoo SKin SPoG SSha WGrf WPGP
	niphophila	see *E. pauciflora* subsp. *niphophila*
	nitens	CDTJ SKin SPlb WGrf
§	***nitida***	SKin WGrf
	obliqua	WGrf
	paliformis	WGrf
	parviflora	CBod SKin
	parvula ♀H5	CCCN CMac CTsd MMuc SEND SSha WGrf
	pauciflora	CCCN EBee SCob SEdd SPer SSha
§	- subsp. ***debeuzevillei*** ♀H5	CAbb CBod EPfP NOrn SArc SKin WGrf WPGP
	- var. ***nana***	see *E. gregsoniana*
§	- subsp. ***niphophila*** ♀H5	Widely available
	- - from Mount Bogong, Australia	WGrf
	- - 'Pendula'	see *E. lacrimans*
	- subsp. ***pauciflora***	WGrf
	- - from Mount Buffalo, Australia	WGrf
	perriniana	CEme CEnd EHeP ELan EPfP MGos MHtn MTrO SKin SPer SPlb SPoG SSha SWvt WFar WGrf WHtc WMat
	pulchella	WGrf
	pulverulenta	CMac SPlb WFar WGrf
	- 'Baby Blue'	CTsd SGBe SKin SWvt WFar WGrf
	regnans	SKin WGrf
	risdonii	WGrf
	robusta **new**	WGrf
	rodwayi	WGrf
	rossii	SPlb
	rubida	CCCN SKin WGrf
	saxatilis	SKin WGrf
	'Shannon Blue'	WGrf
	sideroxylon	SPlb
	- 'Rosea'	SPlb
	simmondsii	see *E. nitida*
	stellulata	SKin WGrf

stricta	SKin WGrf
stuartiana	see *E. bridgesiana*
sturgissiana	WGrf
subcrenulata	CDoC CTsd SKin WGrf
tetraptera	SPlb
torquata	SPlb
urnigera	CTsd EPfP SMad WGrf
vernicosa	SKin WGrf
viminalis	SKin

Eucharidium see *Clarkia*

Eucharis (*Amaryllidaceae*)

§ ***amazonica*** 🏆[H1b]	CCCN LAma SDeJ SDir
grandiflora misapplied	see *E. amazonica*

Eucomis ✿ (*Asparagaceae*)

sp.	MPtr
ALOHA	see *E.* 'Leia'
autumnalis misapplied	see *E. zambesiaca*
§ ***autumnalis*** (Mill.) Chitt.	CBro EAri EPot ERCP GKev LRHS SDeJ SDir SPlb WCot
- subsp. ***amaryllidifolia***	CBro WCot
bicolor 🏆[H4]	Widely available
- 'Alba'	CBro CTca GKev
§ ***comosa***	CAvo CBro CTca EAri EBee EShb GKev LAma MPtr NGKo SBls SDeJ SDir WCot
- 'Can Can'	LRHS XSte
- 'Cornwood'	CAvo CBro CTca EAri EPPr GKev
- dark-stemmed **new**	EPPr
- 'Indian Summer' **new**	GKev
- 'Johannesburg'	CBro EAri GKev
- 'Kilimanjaro'	EAri
- 'Lotte'	CTca
- 'Oakhurst'	CChe CPla EAri ESwi GMcL LRHS WCot
- purple-leaved	CAvo EShb
- 'Sparkling Burgundy'	Widely available
- 'Sparkling Rosy'	GKev IPot LAma LCro MPtr NGKo SCoo SDir SPoG WFar
- var. ***striata***	EBee
'Dark Star'	ECtt IPot LRHS XSte
'Erundu' **new**	SDir
'Etanga' **new**	SDir
'Freckles'	EAri EPPr NGKo SPoG SRms
'Glow Sticks'	CWGN ECtt
humilis 'Twinkle Stars'	EWld GKev LAma SDeJ WFar
'Joy's Purple'	CBro CPar CTca EAri EPri
§ 'Leia'[PBR] (Aloha Lily Series) 🏆[H4]	CAvo CBod CBro CTca EPfP EShb LSou SGBe SPad
MAUI ('Gsalkele'[PBR]) (Aloha Lily Series) 🏆[H3]	CBro EShb LSou SGBe
montana	CBro CPla CTca EAri EBee EPot EWld GKev LAma SDeJ SDir WCot
NANI ('Gsalipol'[PBR]) (Aloha Lily Series) 🏆[H4]	CAvo CBro EShb LSou SGBe WHil
pallidiflora 🏆[H3]	CAvo EAri LEdu NGKo WPGP
§ - subsp. ***pallidiflora***	CBro CPar CTca EAri EGrI EPPr EPri EShb EWld GKev LAma LRHS MRav NGKo SDeJ SDir SMrm SPeP SPtp WAvo WSHC XSte
- - pink-flowered	CPar
- subsp. ***pole-evansii*** misapplied	see *E. pallidiflora* subsp. *pallidiflora*
'Pink Gin'	CAvo CBro EAri GKev IPot LAma SDir SPeP
'Playa Blanca'	CTca EPri GKev LAma LRHS XSte
punctata	see *E. comosa*
regia JCA 3.230.709	WCot
'Swazi Pride'	NGKo
'Tugela Jade'	LRHS XSte
undulata	see *E. autumnalis* (Mill.) Chitt.
vandermerwei 🏆[H3]	CBro CTca EBee EGrI EPot LAma LEdu NGKo SDeJ SDir SPlb
- 'Octopus'	CCCN CTca ELan EPfP GKev WFar XSte
§ ***zambesiaca***	CAvo CBro CPla CTca GKev NGKo SMHy
- JCA 3.230.709	WCot
- JCA 3.231.010	WCot
- 'White Dwarf'	CBcs EPri LAma WFar WGwG
'Zeal Bronze'	CTca EAri WAvo WCot
'Zulu Flame'	LRHS

Eucommia (*Eucommiaceae*)

ulmoides	CBcs CMCN MGil NLar WJur

Eucrosia (*Amaryllidaceae*)

Harry Hay's hybrid **new**	WMal

Eucryphia ✿ (*Cunoniaceae*)

cordifolia	CBcs CMac IDee LRHS MBlu MGil NLar
§ ***cordifolia*** × ***lucida***	CCCN
glutinosa 🏆[H4]	CCCN EHyd EPfP GGGa GKev IDee LRHS MAsh MGil SAko SCob WJur
× ***hillieri***	WSpi
- 'Winton'	CBct EBee SChF WPGP
× ***intermedia***	CCCN CDoC CMac NLar SRms SSta
- 'Miniature'	EPfP
- 'Rostrevor' 🏆[H4]	CBcs CJun CMac EHyd ELan EPfP GGGa GKev IArd LRHS LSRN MAsh MBlu NLar SChF SSta WPGP XSte
'Leatherwood Cream' (v)	ELon WSpi
lucida	CBod CCCN EHyd ELon LRHS MMuc NLar NRHS WSpi XSte
- 'Ballerina' 🏆[H4]	CBcs CJun CMac CPer CRos EBee EHed EHyd ELan EPfP GKin LRHS MAsh NLar NRHS SAko SChF SCoo SMad SPoG WPGP
- 'Carousel'	CRos MAsh
I - 'Chaplin's Variety'	WPGP
- 'Dumpling'	WPGP
- 'Gilt Edge' (v)	CBcs CRos EHyd LRHS MAsh NRHS SPoG XSte
- 'Pink Cloud'	CBcs CBod CCCN CDoC CJun CKel CMac CPer CRos EGrI EHed EHyd ELan ELon EPfP GKev GKin LRHS LSRN MAsh MBlu MGil MGos MMrt NLar NRHS SPer SWvt WPGP
- 'Spring Glow' (v)	CRos EHyd LRHS MAsh NLar NRHS
milliganii	CCCN CDoC CKel CMac EHyd ELon EPfP GKev LRHS MBlu MRav SPer SRms SSta WPGP WSpi
moorei	CCCN CMac IDee LRHS WPGP
× ***nymansensis***	CPer SArc SRms WSpi
- 'George Graham'	GGGa IArd WPGP
- 'Nymans Silver' (v)	CBcs CDoC CJun CKel CMac CPer EHyd ELan EPfP GGGa LRHS MAsh MMrt SPer SPoG SSta
- 'Nymansay' 🏆[H4]	Widely available
'Penwith' misapplied	see *E. cordifolia* × *lucida*
'Penwith' ambig.	CJun IDee NLar

Eugenia (*Myrtaceae*)

uniflora	CCCN

Eunomia see *Aethionema*

Euodia (*Rutaceae*)

daniellii	see *Tetradium daniellii*
hupehensis	see *Tetradium daniellii* Hupehense Group

Euonymus ✿ (*Celastraceae*)

	B&L 12543	EWes
	NJM 09.109	CRHN
	NJM 10.106	WPGP
	from Kachin, Burma	WPGP
§	***aculeolus*** new	IArd
	alatus	Widely available
	- B&SWJ 8794	WCru
	- var. ***apterus***	EPfP SPtp
	- 'Blade Runner'	CAco CDoC CRos EDir EHed EHyd EPfP ESwi GKin LRHS MBlu MGos NLar NRHS SGol
	- CHICAGO FIRE	see *E. alatus* 'Timber Creek'
	- 'Ciliodentatus'	see *E. alatus* f. *striatus*
	- 'Compactus' ♀H6	Widely available
	- 'Fastigiata'	CJun
§	- 'Fire Ball' ♀H6	CJun
*	- 'Macrophyllus'	CJun
	- 'Rudy Haag'	CJun EPfP
	- 'Select'	see *E. alatus* 'Fire Ball'
	- 'Silver Cloud'	NLar
§	- f. ***striatus***	CJun
	- - B&SWJ 11051	ESwi WCru
§	- 'Timber Creek'	EPfP MBlu
	americanus	EPfP MBlu NLar SMad
	- var. ***angustifolius*** B&SWJ 12905	ESwi WCru
	bungeanus	EPfP WLov
	- B&SWJ 8782 from South Korea	WCru
	- 'Dart's Pride'	CJun EHed EPfP NLar WLov
	- 'Fireflame'	CJun NLar WCot
	- 'Pendulus'	MBlu
	- var. ***semipersistens***	CJun NLar WCru
§	***carnosus*** ♀H5	CJun CMCN
	- CWJ 12425	WCru
	- NMWJ 14515	WCru
	- 'Belmonte'	CJun EPfP NLar
	- 'Red Wine'	CJun EBee EPfP LEdu LRHS MBlu NLar WCot WLov
	- 'Trompenburg Lustre'	CJun NLar
§	***clivicola***	EPfP SMad SPtp WCru WPGP
	aff. ***clivicola*** HIRD 103	SBrt
	cornutus	SPtp WJur WPGP
	- var. ***quinquecornutus*** ♀H6	CMCN CSpe EBee EHed ELan EPfP ESwi IArd MBlu MGil SPoG WPGP
	'Den Haag'	EPfP LRHS
	europaeus	Widely available
	- from Slovakia	WCru
	- f. ***albus***	EPfP NLar SMad SPoG
	- 'Atropurpureus'	CMCN EPfP
	- 'Atrorubens'	CJun
	- 'Aucubifolius' (v)	CMac
	- 'Brilliant'	CJun EPfP LRHS NLar
	- 'Chrysophyllus'	EPfP MBlu
	- var. ***intermedius***	CJun EPfP MBlu NLar
	- 'Miss Pinkie'	CEnd NOrn
	- 'Red Cascade' ♀H6	Widely available
	- 'Scarlet Wonder'	CJun EPfP LRHS MAsh NLar WHtc WMat
	- 'Thornhayes' ♀H6	EPfP
	farreri	see *E. nanus*
	fimbriatus	CJun
	fortunei	CCCN SavN
	- BLONDY ('Interbolwi') (v)	CBcs CEme CRos EHyd ELan EPfP GMcL LRHS MAsh MDon MGos MMuc MSwo NRHS SCob SCoo SGBe SGol SLim SPer SPoG SRms SavN WCot
	- 'Canadale Gold' (v)	CMac EHyd EPfP LRHS MAsh NHol NRHS SGsty SPer
	- 'Coloratus'	EPfP MBlu MSwo SEND WFar
	- 'Country Gold'	WFar
	- DAN'S DELIGHT ('Dandel'PBR) (v)	EFPl LCro LOPS MThu SGol SPoG
	- 'Dart's Blanket'	EBee EHeP ELan EPfP GMcL MRav SCob SavN
	- 'Emerald Cushion'	EHeP
	- 'Emerald Gaiety' (v) ♀H5	Widely available
*	- 'Emerald Green'	SavN
	- 'Emerald 'n' Gold' (v) ♀H5	Widely available
	- 'Gold Spot'	see *E. fortunei* 'Sunspot'
	- 'Gold Tip'	see *E. fortunei* 'Golden Prince'
	- GOLDEN HARLEQUIN ('Hoogi'PBR) (v)	CBcs CBod CEme EBee EFPl EPfP GMcL MAsh MThu NWad SGBe SPoG SWvt
§	- 'Golden Pillar' (v)	GMcL
§	- 'Golden Prince' (v)	CMac MRav MSwo SRms
	- GOLDY ('Waldbolwi'PBR)	CBod EFPl EPfP NLar SPoG
	- 'Harlequin' (v)	CBcs CBrac CKel CMac CSBt EFPl EHyd ELan EPfP LBuc LCro LPar LRHS LSRN MAsh MBlu MGos MRav NRHS SCob SGBe SGol SPer SPoG SRms SWvt SavN WFar
	- 'Heins Silver'PBR	EBee
	- 'Hort's Blaze'	EBee NLar
	- 'Kewensis' ♀H5	CBod CMac CWCL EHyd ELan LRHS LWaG SArc SPoG WCFE WCru
	- 'Kewensis Variegatus' (v)	MRav
	- 'Minimus'	CSpe EFPl EPPr MSwo WPGP XLum
*	- 'Minimus Variegatus' (v)	EPPr SPlb
	- 'Perrolino'	SavN
	- 'Prince John'	CSBt
	- 'Sheridan Gold'	MRav
	- 'Silver Gem'	see *E. fortunei* 'Variegatus'
	- 'Silver Queen' (v)	Widely available
	- 'Silverstone'PBR (v)	CKel EPfP SPoG
	- 'Sunshine' (v)	CKel CRos EHyd EPfP LRHS MAsh SPoG WAvo
§	- 'Sunspot' (v)	CBcs CBod CMac EBee MMuc MSwo NBwr SGol SRms
§	- 'Variegatus' (v)	SRms
	- var. ***vegetus***	WFar
	- 'Wolong Ghost' ♀H5	CBcs CBod CCCN CCoa CDoC CExl CKel CMCN CRos CWCL EBee EHyd ELan EPPr EWld GGro LPla LRHS MBlu MMuc NLar NRHS SBrt SWvt WCot WLov
	frigidus KWJ 12275	WCru
	- var. ***elongatus*** GWJ 9378	WCru
	grandiflorus misapplied	see *E. carnosus*
§	***grandiflorus*** Wall.	CJun EPfP NLar SCoo WCot
	- f. ***salicifolius*** misapplied	see *E. grandiflorus* Wall.
	- 'Ruby Wine'	CBcs EHed EPfP LRHS MGos MPkF MTrO WHtc WMat XSte
	hamiltonianus	CMCN ELan EPfP LRHS MMuc SMad WLov
	- 'Fiesta'	CJun NLar
	- subsp. ***hians***	see *E. hamiltonianus* subsp. *sieboldianus*
	- 'Indian Summer'	CJun EHyd EPfP EWTr LRHS MAsh MTrO NLar SPoG WLov WMat
	- 'Koi Boy'	CJun EPfP LSRN MAsh MTrO NLar SPoG WMat
	- 'Miss Pinkie'	CJun EPfP LRHS NLar WLov
	- 'Pink Delight' ♀H6	CJun
	- 'Poort Bulten'	CJun
	- 'Popcorn'	CJun EPfP LRHS WLov
	- 'Rainbow'	CJun EPfP
	- 'Red Chief'	CJun
	- 'Red Elf'	CJun NLar
	- 'Rising Sun'	CJun EPfP NLar
§	- subsp. ***sieboldianus***	EPfP MRav WLov
	- - B&SWJ 10941	WCru

	- - PAB 5337	LEdu
	- - 'Calocarpus'	CJun EPfP
	- - 'Coral Charm'	CBcs CJun EPfP WLov
	- 'Snow' (v)	WCot
	- 'Winter Glory'	CJun
§	***huangii***	CJun CMCN WLov
	- B&SWJ 3700	WCru
	japonicus	CBcs CBod CCoa CDoC CMac CPer EHeP EPfP GMcL LRHS MNic SArc SCob SEND SEWo SGsty SPer SWeb SavN WReH
	- B&SWJ 11159 **new**	WCru
	- 'Albomarginatus' (v)	CTri EHeP EPfP MPri SCob SEND SRms
	- 'Argenteovariegatus' (v)	SGsty
§	- 'Aureomarginatus' (v)	CAco CBod CBrac CCVT CKel GMcL LRHS MPri MSwo NBwr SWeb
	- 'Aureopictus'	see *E. japonicus* 'Aureus'
	- 'Aureovariegatus'	see *E. japonicus* 'Ovatus Aureus'
§	- 'Aureus' (v)	CBcs CDoC CKel CSBt EHeP EPfP GMcL MPri NRHS SCob SCoo SEND SPer
	- 'Benkomasaki'	LRHS LSRN SEWo SGsty
	- 'Bravo' (v)	Widely available
	- 'Charles'PBR	SPoG
	- 'Chollipo' (v) ♀H5	CKel EBee ELan EPfP SEND SPoG WAvo
	- 'Compactus'	SCoo
	- 'Duc d'Anjou' misapplied	see *E. japonicus* 'Viridivariegatus'
	- 'Duc d'Anjou' Carrière (v)	CKel EBee EHeP ELan EPfP EWes MRav SEND SPoG
	- 'Elegantissimus Aureus'	see *E. japonicus* 'Aureomarginatus'
	- EXSTASE ('Goldbolwi'PBR) (v)	MAsh WCot
	- 'Francien' (v)	EBee EHyd LRHS NLar NRHS
	- 'Gold Queen'	MPri NLar
	- 'Golden Maiden' (v)	CKel EBee ELan EPfP MAsh SCoo SLim SPoG SRms SWvt
	- 'Golden Pillar'	see *E. fortunei* 'Golden Pillar'
	- GREEN MILLENIUM ('Minmil'PBR)	LRHS
	- 'Green Rocket'	CBod CCCN CCVT CCoa CEme CEnd CKel CRos EBee EHyd ELan EPfP GBin LCro LRHS LSRN LSto MGos MNic MPri MRav NRHS SPoG SSta SWvt WCot WFar WLov
	- 'Green Spider'	SPoG
	- 'Green Spire'	CDoC CEnd CKel CWnw LSRN MNic NLar SWvt
	- 'Happiness'PBR	CBod MTin
	- 'Kathy'PBR	CKel CRos CWnw EHyd ELan ELon EPfP LPar LRHS LSRN MAsh NLar NRHS SPoG SavN
§	- 'Latifolius Albomarginatus' (v)	CGBo CKel ELan EPfP MRav MSwo SPer SWvt
	- 'Luna'	see *E. japonicus* 'Aureus'
	- 'Macrophyllus'	SSha SavN
	- 'Macrophyllus Albus'	see *E. japonicus* 'Latifolius Albomarginatus'
	- 'Maiden's Gold'	CSBt
	- 'Marieke'	see *E. japonicus* 'Ovatus Aureus'
	- 'Mediopictus'	LPar
	- 'Microphyllus'	CMac EHeP LPar MNic MRav SArc SGol SRms
§	- 'Microphyllus Albovariegatus' (v)	CBod CKel CMac CSBt CTri EDAr EHeP EHyd ELan EPfP LRHS MGos SCob SRms SWvt WAvo WFar
§	- 'Microphyllus Aureovariegatus' (v)	CMac CRos CSBt EHyd ELan EPfP LRHS MAsh MMuc NLar NRHS SGsty
	- 'Microphyllus Aureus'	see *E. japonicus* 'Microphyllus Pulchellus'
	- 'Microphyllus Gold Dust'	CBod
§	- 'Microphyllus Pulchellus' (v)	CBcs CDoC CKel CMac CSBt EPfP LRHS MGos MMuc SPoG SWvt
	- 'Microphyllus Variegatus'	see *E. japonicus* 'Microphyllus Albovariegatus'
§	- 'Ovatus Aureus' (v) ♀H5	Widely available
	- PALOMA BLANCA ('Lankveld03'PBR)	CRos EHyd EPfP LCro LOPS LPar LRHS NRHS SCoo SPoG SavN WFar
	- 'Président Gauthier' (v)	CDoC EBee EHeP ELan GArf GMcL LPar LRHS SCob SCoo SGsty SPer SWeb SWvt
	- 'Pulchellus Aureovariegatus'	see *E. japonicus* 'Microphyllus Aureovariegatus'
	- 'Robustus'	CBod CCCN
	- 'Rokujo'	GEdr NWad
	- 'Silver King'	CMac SGsty
	- 'Silver Krista' (v)	NLar
	- 'Susan' (v) ♀H5	CMac MAsh SGsty
§	- 'Viridivariegatus' (v)	LRHS WAvo
	- 'White Spire'PBR (v)	LCro LRHS MAsh MGos MHtn SCoo SPoG WCot WLea
	kachinensis B&SWJ 11668	WCru
	kiautschovicus 'Berry Hill'	NLar
	- 'Manhattan'	NLar
	latifolius	CJun CMCN EPfP IDee LEdu WCru
	aff. ***latifolius*** NJM 13.024	WPGP
§	***laxiflorus*** GWJ 9351	WCru
	- HWJ 890	WCru
	lucidus	IDee
	macropterus	CJun CMCN IArd
	- B&SWJ 12591	WCru
	- 'Mount Fuji' **new**	IDee
	morrisonensis	see *E. huangii*
	myrianthus	CJun EHed EPfP IDee LRHS MBlu MPkF NLar SPtp
	aff. ***myrianthus*** slim-leaved NJM 11.016	WPGP
§	***nanus***	NLar WLov
	- var. ***turkestanicus***	EPfP MVil NLar SBrt SMad SRms
	obovatus	SBrt
	occidentalis	SBrt
	oxyphyllus	CJun CMCN ELan EPfP LRHS MMuc NLar SPtp WCru WHtc WLov
	- 'Waasland'	CJun EPfP NLar
	phellomanus ♀H6	CBcs CKel EBee ELan EPfP GKev GKin IDee LAlb LPar LRHS MBlu MGil MGos MMuc MPkF MRav MTrO NLar NOrn SCoo SPer SPoG SWvt WMat WPGP
	PIERROLINO ('Heespierrolino'PBR)	MRav NLar SCoo
§	***planipes***	Widely available
	- B&SWJ 8660	WCru
	- 'Dart's August Flame'	CJun
	- 'Sancho' ♀H6	CJun EPfP LRHS NLar WMat
	porphyreus B&SWJ 13914	WCru
	- GWJ 9377	WCru
	quelpaertensis	CJun
	'Rokojō'	EPot
	'Rokojō Variegated' (v)	WCot
	rosmarinifolius	see *E. nanus*
	rubescens	see *E. laxiflorus*
	sachalinensis misapplied	see *E. planipes*
	sachalinensis (F. Schmidt) Maxim. B&SWJ 10835	WCru
	sacrosanctus	CJun MBlu
	sanguineus	CJun NLar
	semenovii	WPGP
	sieboldianus var. ***sanguineus*** B&SWJ 11140	WCru

- - B&SWJ 11386	WCru
spraguei	EPPr NFav SBrt
- CWJ 12446	WCru
tingens	CJun CMCN WPGP
tonkinensis FMWJ 13350	WCru
trapococcus	SPtp
vagans misapplied	see *E. aculeolus*
vagans Wall.	WCot
velutinus	SPtp
verrucosus	CJun NLar
- NJM 13.024	WPGP
wilsonii	EWTr MBlu NLar
yedoensis	see *E. hamiltonianus* subsp. *sieboldianus*

Eupatoriadelphus see *Eupatorium*

Eupatorium ✿ (*Asteraceae*)

B&SWJ 9052 from Guatemala	WCru
FMWJ 13428 from Northern Vietnam	WCru
album misapplied	see *Ageratina altissima*
album L.	NBid
altissimum	SRms
amabile NMWJ 14456	WCru
aromaticum	see *Ageratina aromatica*
atrorubens	see *Bartlettina sordida*
cannabinum	CBod CHab CPla CPud EBee EGrI GPoy GQue LLWG LPfP LShi MBNS MHer MMuc MWts NAts NBir NMir NPer SEND SPhx WHer WSFF
§ - f. ***albiflorum***	SPhx
- 'Album'	see *E. cannabinum* f. *albiflorum*
- f. ***cannabinum*** 'Flore Pleno' (d)	CMac ECtt ELan ELon MHer MRav NBir NGdn NLar SDix WCot WFar WSFF WWtn
- - 'Spraypaint' (v)	WSFF
capillifolium 🏆H3	CTtf EBee ECtt ESwi EWes MPie SDix SHar SMrm
- 'Elegant Plume'	EBee
coelestinum	see *Conoclinium coelestinum*
dubium 'Baby Joe'PBR	Widely available
- 'Little Joe'	CBod CTtf GBin LEdu MDon MNHC WCAu WSFF
fistulosum	EBee
- f. ***albidum***	ECha EWhm
- - 'Bartered Bride'	CKno EBee ECtt EPPr EWes LPla MBel NLar SPeP WCot WSFF
- - 'Ivory Towers'	CBod CDor CRos EBee ECha EHyd LBar LRHS MACG NRHS SBls SPtp WCot
- - 'Massive White' 🏆H7	EMor EShb MNrw NBir NSti
- 'Berggarten'	LEdu WSFF
fortunei 'Capri' (v)	LBar WCot WHil
- 'Fine Line' (v)	WSFF
- 'Pink Elegance' (v)	CBod CToG EBee ECtt EHyd EMor EShb LBar LRHS LShi LSou LSto MNrw NBPC NLar NRHS SGbt SMrm SPoG SRms
- 'Pink Frost' (v)	EWTr MWts NGdn SCob SPeP
japonicum	GPoy
ligustrinum	see *Ageratina ligustrina*
lindleyanum	LEdu WSFF
- var. ***trisectifolium*** B&SWJ 12742	WCru
maculatum	NGdn NLar
- Atropurpureum Group	Widely available
- - 'Ankum's August'	EBee LBar LPla SMHy
- - 'Gateway'	CBod CDor EBee EBlo ECtt ELon EPPr EPfP LEdu LRHS NBid NLar SWvt WHil WSFF
- - 'Glutball'	CKno EBlo ELon LPla LRHS LSun MNrw NChi SMad SPeP
- - 'Little Red'	WSFF
- - 'Orchard Dene' 🏆H7	IPot LEdu SMHy
- - 'Phantom'PBR	CRos EBee ECtt EHyd ELon EMor EWTr EWoo GBin LRHS MHol NBPC NCth NLar NRHS SAko SMad SPoG WFar WSFF
- - 'Prairie Giant'	MAvo NDov
- - 'Purple Bush' 🏆H7	CDor CKno EBee ECtt EHyd ELon EPfP GBee GQue LCro LRHS MHer NDov NGrd SDix SWvt WSFF
- - 'Red Dwarf'	CBWd CKno ECtt EHyd ELon EPfP GQue LBar LEdu LRHS MCot MHer MPie NFav NLar NRHS SGBe SMDa SPoG SWvt WHil WHoo
- - 'Riesenschirm' 🏆H7	Widely available
- 'J.S. Humble'	IPot LRHS MNrw
- 'Snowball'PBR	CBod ECtt EPfP LBar
makinoi	WCru
var. ***oppositifolium*** B&SWJ 8449	
'Mask'	IPot MNrw NLar
micranthum	see *Ageratina ligustrina*
perfoliatum	EMor GPoy MMuc NLar WSFF
purpureum	CBcs CBod CHby ECha ECtt ELon GDam GMaP GMcL GPoy LLWG MHer MHoo NBro NChi NGdn SCob SMrm SPer SPlb SRms WCAu WHer WSFF
- 'Album'	CTri LEdu SWvt
rugosum	see *Ageratina altissima*
* 'Snowball'	CBWd LSou NDov SPoG
weinmannianum	see *Ageratina ligustrina*
yakushimaense	GEdr WCot

Euphorbia ✿ (*Euphorbiaceae*)

'Abbey Dore' 🏆H7	ECha GBin MAvo SPhx WCot WSHC
aeruginosa	EAri
amygdaloides	ECtt SWvt XSen
- 'Bob's Choice'	WSHC
- 'Craigieburn'	CKel EHyd LRHS MRav NRHS
- 'Frosted Flame'PBR	LLWG MHol WCot
§ - 'Purpurea'	Widely available
§ - var. ***robbiae*** 🏆H6	Widely available
- - dwarf	EWes
- - 'Redbud'	EWes
- 'Rubra'	see *E. amygdaloides* 'Purpurea'
- 'Variegata' (v)	NCth
* × ***arendsii***	ECha SMHy
biglandulosa Desf.	see *E. rigida*
BLACKBIRD ('Nothowlee'PBR)	CBcs CMac CWGN ECtt EPfP LBar LCro LPal LRHS MAvo MGos MRav NLar SCob SMad SWvt WSpi XSen
'Blue Haze'	ECha LPla WCot WFar WSHC WSpi
cactus	CDoC
caerulescens	EAri
canariensis	EAri
capitulata	SBrt
cashmeriana CC&McK 607	EWes
ceratocarpa 🏆H4	CSpe ECha ECtt ETod EWes EWoo GMaP MBNS SMad WAvo WCAu WCot WSHC WSpi WTor XSen
characias	CBcs CMac EHyd EPfP EWoo MCot MRav NPer NRHS SPer SRms SWvt WBrk WCot XSen
- 'Ascot Moonbeam'	LRHS SGBe SPoG
- 'Black Pearl'	CBcs CEme CKel CRos ECtt EHyd ELan EPfP GMcL LBar LRHS MAvo MBel MHol NLar NRHS SCob SGBe SGbt SPoG SRkn SWvt WSpi

- 'Blue Wonder'	CSpe ECtt EPfP EWes GMaP LRHS NFav NLar SCob WCot WNPC XSen
- 'BQ'	WCot
- subsp. ***characias***	EPfP NLar SEND
- - 'Burrow Silver' (v)	ELon EPfP EWoo LDai MRav SWvt WNPC
- - 'Humpty Dumpty'	CBod CRos EBee ECtt EHyd ELan EPfP GMaP LRHS LSRN NLar NPer NRHS SCob SPer SRms SWvt WFar WMal XSen
- - 'Joshua'	WCot
- 'Eye-catcher'	WCot
- 'Forescate'	EBee EHyd EPfP NRHS
- 'Glacier Blue'PBR (v)	CRos CSpe CTsd CWGN EBee ECha EHyd ELan EPfP GKev LRHS LSRN MAsh MHol NHpl NLar NRHS SCob SCoo SGBe SHeu SPeP SPoG SRHi SRms WCot WNPC
- 'Goldbrook'	EPfP LRHS MBriF MRav NRHS
- 'Kestrel' (v)	WCot
- 'Portuguese Velvet'	CBod CRos ECtt EHyd ELan EPfP LBar LRHS MCot MHol MRav NLar NRHS SArc SEdd SPtp WCot XLum XSen
- 'Silver Edge' (v)	EAJP ELan EPfP LSou MHol NLar NSti SCoo SGBe WNPC XSte
- SILVER SWAN ('Wilcott'PBR) (v)	Widely available
- 'Tasmanian Tiger'PBR (v) ♀H4	CBcs CBod CRos CWGN EBlo EPfP EWes GMaP LBar LRHS LSRN MAvo MGos MHol NHpl NLar NRHS SCob SGBe SHeu SPoG SRms SWvt WCot WNPC WSpi
- 'Variegata' (v)	CKel CWnw
- subsp. ***wulfenii***	Widely available
- - 'Bosahan'	CExl
- - 'Emmer Green' (v)	ECtt EWes NSti WCot
- - 'Jayne's Golden Giant'	SMad
- - 'Jimmy Platt' ♀H4	SRms WCot
§ - - 'John Tomlinson'	EGrI EWes MRav SPtp WAvo WSpi
- - Kew form	see *E. characias* subsp. *wulfenii* 'John Tomlinson'
- - 'Lambrook Gold'	MRav NLar NPer SCob WSpi
- - 'Lambrook Gold' seed-raised	see *E. characias* subsp. *wulfenii* Margery Fish Group
§ - - Margery Fish Group	CFis EHyd EPfP EWoo LRHS MCot NBir NChi NLar NRHS SPer
- - 'Perry's Tangerine'	NPer
§ - - 'Purple and Gold'	MAvo NCth NLar SGBe SWvt XLum XSen
- - 'Purpurea'	see *E. characias* subsp. *wulfenii* 'Purple and Gold'
- - 'Shorty'	EBee ECtt EHyd EPfP LRHS NLar NRHS SGBe SPoG XSen
- - 'Silver Shadow' (v)	EBee NGBl WCot
- - 'Thelma's Giant'	MAvo
- - 'Westacre Giant'	EWes
clavarioides	WAbe
- var. ***truncata***	WCot
'Copton Ash'	CBcs EBee ECha ECtt GBin SPhx XSen
corallioides	ECha EPfP NLar NPer NSti WHer WNPC
§ ***cornigera*** ♀H5	CDor EBee ECha EGrI EHyd EPfP LRHS NBid NGdn NLar NRHS NSti SMHy SPhx WCAu WCru WFar
- 'Goldener Turm'	ECha ECtt EHyd EPfP GMcL LCro LRHS LSou SPer SPhx
corollata	CSpe
cyparissias	ECha ELan EWoo GQue MRav NBir NGdn NLar SRms WBrk WFar XLum XSen
- 'Betten'	see *E.* × *gayeri* 'Betten'
- 'Clarice Howard'	see *E. cyparissias* 'Fens Ruby'
- clone 2	WCot
§ - 'Fens Ruby'	Widely available
- 'Orange Man'	CBcs CBod CKel CRos ECtt EHyd ELan EPfP EWes LBar LRHS LSou MAsh NGdn NLar NRHS SPoG SVen SWvt WBrk WFar
- 'Purpurea'	see *E. cyparissias* 'Fens Ruby'
- 'Red Devil'	CDor
- 'Tall Boy'	EBee EWes
decaryi	EAri
deflexa	ECha EWes MAvo NLar WMal
dendroides	CKel SPtp
'Despina'PBR	SGBe
§ ***donii***	ECha EWes MAvo NFav SMHy SPtp WSpi
- HWJK 2405	WCru
- 'Amjillasa'	ECha SDix SMHy WKif
dulcis	NBro
- 'Chameleon'	CDor CMiW ECtt EGrI ELon EPfP GQue MGos MRav NBid NBir NFav NLar NPer SCob SPlb SWvt WBrk WCAu WCot WFar WSpi
'Efanthia'PBR	CRos EWes GMcL LRHS NRHS SGBe
enopla	EAri LCro
§ ***epithymoides***	Widely available
- 'Bonfire'PBR	ECha EGrI EMor GBin LBar MAvo MHer MHol NGBl NLar SDix SMad SPer SPoG WCot WHil
§ - 'Candy'	CBod ECha LBar LPla MAsh MHol SMHy SMrm WFar
- 'First Blush' (v)	NLar WCot WFar
§ - 'Lacy' (v)	EWes WFar
§ - 'Major' ♀H6	EBee ECha SDix WKif
- 'Midas'	GBin MNrw SDix SMHy SMrm WMal
- 'Senior'	CRos EHyd EPfP LRHS MNrw NRHS SEdd
EXCALIBUR ('Froeup'PBR)	CEme CMac ELan ELon LSRN MBNS MMuc MRav NBir NLar NRHS NSti SEND SIvy SPtp SWvt
fischeriana B&SWJ 8575	WCru
flanaganii ♀H2 **new**	NHrt
§ × ***gayeri*** 'Betten'	EBee EWes NLar XSen
'Golden Foam'	see *E. stricta*
graminea 'Glitz'	SPhx
grandicornis **new**	EAri
'Grey Hedgehog'	CKel
griffithii	GQue LEdu NBro WFar
- 'Dixter'	Widely available
- 'Fern Cottage'	EWes WCot
- 'Fireglow'	Widely available
- 'King's Caple'	EWes LRHS NLar SPoG WCru
- 'Wickstead'	EMor NLar WCot
'Helena'PBR (v)	LSRN SWvt
henryi	see *E. sieboldiana*
heptagona	SEND
hierosolymitana	SBrt
horrida ♀H2	LCro SPlb
hypericifolia DIAMOND FROST ('Inneuphe'PBR)	CKel CSpe LCro LOPS LSou SRkn WCot
- 'Diamond Star'	LSou
- 'Silverfog'PBR	LSou
- STARPLEASURE	LSou
× ***inconstantia*** **new**	EAri
ingens	NPlm SEND
I - 'Marmorata' (v) **new**	NPlm
jacquemontii	MRav NLar WCot
'Jade Dragon'	LRHS SMHy SWvt
'Jessie'	NLar
jolkinii	CExl

KALIPSO ('Innkalff') EPfP NLar
lathyris NLar NPer SRms SVic WHer
lenewtonii new EAri
longifolia misapplied see *E. cornigera*
longifolia D. Don see *E. donii*
longifolia Lam. see *E. mellifera*
margalidiana ♀H4 EBee ECha EWes GBin WCot
marginata CSpe
× ***martini*** Widely available
- 'Aperitif' LPal SPoG
- 'Ascot Rainbow'PBR (v) ♀H5 Widely available
- 'Baby Charm' CRos EPfP LLWG LRHS LSRN MGos NGdn NLar NRHS SCob SGBe SRms WNPC XSen
- 'Helen Robinson' ♀H5 WCot
- 'Kolibri' EHyd EPfP LRHS NRHS SCoo SWvt
- 'Rudolph'PBR CBod CKel ELan LBar LLWG NLar SPoG
- TINY TIM ('Waleutiny') CBod EBee ECtt EHyd EPfP LRHS MDon NChi NFav NRHS SRms SWvt
- 'Walberton's Red Flush' EHyd LRHS NRHS
- WALBERTON'S RUBY GLOW ('Waleuphglo') EPfP LRHS SPeP
mauritanica EShb
mayuranathanii new EAri
§ ***mellifera*** ♀H3 Widely available
milii var. ***milii*** LCro
myrsinites ♀H5 Widely available
nereidum ♀H5 EWes WMal
nicaeensis EBee LRHS SPhx WCot XSen
obesa ♀H1c EAri
oblongata CSpe EGrI ELan LCro LRHS NLar SEND SPhx WCot
palustris ♀H7 Widely available
- 'Teichlaterne' GBin NLar SAko
- 'Walenburg's Glorie' EBee ECha ELon EWTr GBin LCro LOPS LRHS MNrw MRav NLar NSti SHar SMad WKif XLum
- 'Woodchippings' WCot
- 'Zauberflöte' SRms
paniculata subsp. ***monchiquensis*** new CSpe
paralias WHer
§ × ***pasteurii*** CBcs CDTJ CKel EHed EMor EPfP EWes GMaP LCro LShi MNrw MRav NBir SIvy SPhx WCot WKif WMal WPGP
- Brown's strain EWoo LPla LRHS SEdd WCot
- 'Honey Pot' ♀H6 CDoC EPfP LRHS
- 'John Phillips' ♀H4 CBct CExl EBee EGrI EPfP LRHS MAvo NLar SChF WPGP
- 'Phrampton Phatty' ♀H4 LRHS MAvo WCot WPGP
- 'Roundway Titan' ♀H6 CKel ELan EPfP LRHS SWvt
- 'Skinny Bere' LEdu
pentagona SVen
phosphorea new EAri EShb
pilosa 'Major' see *E. epithymoides* 'Major'
pithyusa CPla ECha EGrI ELan SEND SPlb WSHC XSen
- subsp. ***cupanii*** 'Ponte Leccia' NLar
polychroma see *E. epithymoides*
- 'Purpurea' see *E. epithymoides* 'Candy'
- 'Variegata' see *E. epithymoides* 'Lacy'
portlandica EGrI SVen WHer
REDWING ('Charam'PBR) CBcs CMac ELan GMcL LSou LSun MAvo MHol MNrw MRav NLar SGBe SPoG SWvt WCot
reflexa see *E. seguieriana* subsp. *niciciana*
resinifera WCot
§ ***rigida*** ♀H6 CBro CKel ECha EWes WCot WMal WSpi XSen
robbiae see *E. amygdaloides* var. *robbiae*
sarawschanica ECha GKev LPla MAvo SPhx
schillingii ♀H5 CDor CRos EBee ELan EPfP EWoo GBin GMaP GMcL GQue IPot LRHS LSRN MMuc MRav NLar SPhx SPlb SPoG SPtp SRms SWvt WCAu WCru WFar WSHC WSpi
schoenlandii SPlb
seguieriana ECha EGrI EWes SAng
§ - subsp. ***niciciana*** EWTr GBin LCro LRHS MAvo SMHy SPhx WCAu WHoo XSen
serrulata Thuill. see *E. stricta*
§ ***sieboldiana*** MHol
sikkimensis ♀H5 ECha EHyd EWes GLog GMcL LPla LRHS NLar NPer NRHS SBrt SRms WFar
- 'Crûg Contrast' MAvo WCru WFar
spinosa CKel SPlb XLum
§ ***stricta*** CBgR CSpe WSpi
stygiana CBcs CBod CDTJ CExl ECre EGrI ELan EPfP EWes GBin LPla LRHS LShi MCot MHol MNrw NLar SAko SHor SMad SPlb WCot WCru WPGP WSHC
- 'Pico' new WPGP
- subsp. ***santamariae*** CDTJ NLar SPeP WMal WPGP WSHC XVPe
- subsp. ***stygiana*** EBee WPGP
- 'Torridge' ♀H4 WCot
tirucalli EAri EShb NHrt
tortilis new EAri
triangularis LCro
trigona new EAri
- f. ***rubra*** new EAri
valdevillosocarpa GJos LPla NLar SPhx WFar
'Velvet Ruby' LSRN NLar SWvt XSen
wallichii misapplied see *E. donii*
wallichii Kohli see *E. cornigera*
wallichii ambig. EWoo LOPS LRHS MCot MRav NLar NSti
wallichii Hook. f. CExl EPfP LCro LOPS MNrw WCot
'Whistleberry Garnet' ♀H7 CBar CKel CMac ELan EPfP GBin LRHS MMuc SWvt WNPC
xylophylloides new EAri

Euptelea (*Eupteleaceae*)

franchetii see *E. pleiosperma*
§ ***pleiosperma*** CBcs EWTr NLar
polyandra EBee EPfP NLar SBrt WPGP

Eurya (*Pentaphylacaceae*)

japonica IDee
- 'Moutiers' (v) CBcs LRHS MGil MPkF XSte
- 'Variegata' misapplied see *Cleyera japonica* 'Fortunei'

Eurybia (*Asteraceae*)

§ ***divaricata*** Widely available
§ - 'Eastern Star' LPla WCot WFar WOld WSpi
- Raiche form see *E. divaricata* 'Eastern Star'
- 'Tradescant' MNrw NLar SMad
§ ***furcata*** XLum
§ × ***herveyi*** Widely available
§ ***macrophylla*** CFis EHyd ELan EWoo GQue LRHS MHol NLar NRHS SPhx WFar WOld
- 'Albus' EPPr WFar
- 'Twilight' see *E.* × *herveyi*
§ ***radula*** ECha EPPr EWes MACG MAvo MNrw NLar NWsh WOld WSHC
- 'August Sky' CBod CKno EBee EMor EPPr GBee LRHS NDov NLar SPhx WCot WFar WHoo

§ ***schreberi*** CDor ECha EPPr EWes LEdu LPla MACG MAvo MHol MNrw MPie MSpe NWsh SRms WCot WFar WHoo WOld WPGP
§ ***sibirica*** EBou WOld
§ ***spectabilis*** EBou WFar
- 'JS Macho Blue' IPot MNrw WFar WOld

Euryops (*Asteraceae*)

abrotanifolius CCCN SVen
§ ***acraeus*** ♀H4 ECtt ELan EPot EWes WAbe
brachypodus SVen
§ ***chrysanthemoides*** CCCN CSde EShb SEND SSha SVen
- 'Sonnenschein' ECre
evansii Schltr. see *E. acraeus*
'Jamaica Sunshine' **new** CGBo
lateriflorus SPlb
pectinatus ♀H3 CBcs CBod CCCN CCht CDTJ CDoC CExl CKel CRos CSBt CSde CTri CTsd CWal EHyd ELan EPfP EShb GQue LRHS MGil MSCN NFav SEND SGBe SVen SWvt
- double-flowered (d) CCCN
tenuissimus SVen
tysonii ELon EWes SPlb SVen
virgineus CBod CCCN CExl CKel EPfP SPlb SVen

Euscaphis (*Staphyleaceae*)

japonica B&SWJ 11359 WCru
- B&SWJ 12739 WCru

Eustachys (*Poaceae*)

§ ***distichophylla*** XLum

Eustephia (*Amaryllidaceae*)

coccinea WCot
darwinii WCot

Eutrema (*Brassicaceae*)

§ ***japonicum*** GGro GPoy LEdu MHoo
- 'Monzen' GPoy

Eutrochium see *Eupatorium*

Ewartia (*Asteraceae*)

planchonii SPlb WAbe WFar

Exbucklandia (*Hamamelidaceae*)

populnea WPGP
tonkinensis KWJ 12209 WCru

Exochorda (*Rosaceae*)

alberti see *E. korolkowii*
giraldii var. ***wilsonii*** CExl CKel CMac EBee ELan EMil EPfP MBlu MHtn MMuc MRav NLar SWvt WCFE
§ ***korolkowii*** MAsh NLar
× ***macrantha*** EDir ILea
§ - 'Niagara'PBR CAco CBcs CBod CDoC CKel CMac CRos CWnw EBee EHyd EPfP GKev LCro LOPS LRHS LSRN MGos NLar NRHS SCob SPoG SavN WHlf
- SNOW DAY SURPRISE see *E.* × *macrantha* 'Niagara'
- 'The Bride' ♀H6 Widely available
racemosa EPfP NLar SPer WJur
- BLUSHING PEARL ('Huibl') **new** SRHi
- MAGICAL SNOWDROPS ('Kolmagisno'PBR) LRHS
- MAGICAL SPRINGTIME ('Kolmasprit'PBR) EPfP LRHS MPkF MThu NLar SCoo WFar

serratifolia CBcs CKel EBee ELan EMil EPfP LRHS SPoG
- 'Snow White' CEnd CJun EWes GKin IDee ILea LRHS MBlu NLar SWvt

F

Fabiana (*Solanaceae*)

imbricata CPbh EPfP MGil SPlb WPav
- 'Prostrata' SVen WPav
- f. ***violacea*** hort. ♀H4 CBod CMac CSBt CTri ELan EPfP LRHS MMuc SGBe SPad SWvt WAvo WHlf WKif WPav
- - dark-flowered CBcs

Fagopyrum (*Polygonaceae*)

cymosum see *F. dibotrys*
§ ***dibotrys*** CSpe EBee ECha EWld LEdu XLum
I - 'Cally Form' ESwi

Fagraea (*Gentianaceae*)

ceilanica FMWJ 13099 WCru

Fagus ✿ (*Fagaceae*)

from Guangxi, China WPGP
from Vietnam WPGP
§ ***crenata*** CMCN CMen MBlu
- 'Mount Fuji' CAco CMen
engleriana CExl LRHS WHtc
grandifolia subsp. ***mexicana*** WPGP
longipetiolata CBcs CExl CMCN EPfP WPGP
- NJM 11.036 WPGP
lucida CExl CMCN MBlu
orientalis CBcs CMCN
- 'Iskander' IArd IDee MBlu SGol SMad
sieboldii see *F. crenata*
sylvatica ♀H6 Widely available
- 'Albovariegata' (v) CLnd
- 'Aniek' SGol
- 'Asterix' MBlu
§ - Atropurpurea Group Widely available
- - 'Purpurea Latifolia' CAco
- - 'Purpurea Pendula' Widely available
- - 'Riversii' ♀H6 CAco CBcs CEnd CLnd CMCN ELan EPfP GKin MGos MNic MTrO NLar NOrn NRog NWea SGsty SPer WMat
- - 'Swat Magret' CAco EPfP
- 'Aurea Pendula' CEnd MBlu SMad
- 'Bicolor Sartini' (v) MBlu
- 'Birr Zebra' CEnd
- 'Black Swan' CAco CLnd CMCN EBee ELan LPar LSRN MAsh MBlu MGos MTrO NHol NOra NOrn SPoG WHtc WMat WMou
- 'Bornyensis' MBlu
- 'Brathay Purple' MBlu
- 'Cochleata' CMCN
- 'Cockleshell' MBlu
- 'Cristata' MBlu
§ - 'Dawyck' ♀H6 CAco CBcs CLnd CMac EBar ELan EPfP LMaj LPar MGos NLar NRog NWea SCob SGol SLau SPer
- 'Dawyck Gold' ♀H6 Widely available
- 'Dawyck Purple' ♀H6 Widely available
- 'Fastigiata' misapplied see *F. sylvatica* 'Dawyck'
- 'Franken' (v) CAco MBlu
- 'Green Obelisk' MBlu

- 'Greenwood'	MBlu
- var. ***heterophylla***	CLnd NRog NWea
- - 'Aspleniifolia' ♀H6	CEnd CMCN CMac CPer EPfP GBin GKin LMaj LPar MBlu MGos MTrO NLar SCoo SGol SLau SPer SPoG WHtc WMat WMou
- - (Atropurpurea Group) 'Ansorgei'	CEnd MBlu
- - 'Incisa'	MBlu
- - f. ***laciniata***	CPer MBlu
- - 'Mercedes'	CAco CMCN MBlu WLov
- 'Horizontalis'	MBlu
- 'Pendula' ♀H6	CAco CBcs CCVT CEnd CLnd CMCN CMac CSBt ELan EWTr LPar MGos MSwo NOra NRog NWea SGol SLau SPer WMat WMou WTSh
- 'Purple Fountain' ♀H6	CAco CEnd CMCN ELan LPar MAsh MBlu MGos MTrO NLar NOra NOrn NWea SLau SWeb WMat
- Purple-leaved Group	see *F. sylvatica* Atropurpurea Group
§ - 'Purpurea Tricolor' (v)	CAco CEnd CMCN CMac EBee MBlu MGos MTrO NOra NRog NWea SCoo WMat
- 'Red Obelisk'	see *F. sylvatica* 'Rohan Obelisk'
- 'Rohan Gold'	CAco CEnd CMCN SGol
§ - 'Rohan Obelisk'	CAco CEnd CMCN LMaj LPar MBlu
I - 'Rohan Pyramidalis'	CEnd CMCN
- 'Rohan Trompenburg'	CMCN MBlu
- 'Rohan Weeping'	CAco MBlu NLar
- 'Rohanii'	CAco CBcs CEnd CMCN CSBt EPfP GKin MGos NRog SLau
- 'Roseomarginata'	see *F. sylvatica* 'Purpurea Tricolor'
- 'Rotundifolia'	LMaj MBlu
- 'Spaethiana'	CAco GKin
- 'Striata'	CAco
- f. ***tortuosa***	MBlu MPkF
- - 'Rot Süntel'	CAco MTrO
- 'Tricolor' misapplied (v)	see *F. sylvatica* 'Purpurea Tricolor' (v)
- 'Tricolor' ambig. (v)	SLau
- 'Tricolor' (v)	CAco CBcs CLnd CSBt LMaj NHol NLar NOra SGol
- 'Tur'	SMad
- 'Zlatia'	CAco CMCN CSBt LPar MBlu MGil MGos NRog SGol SLau

Falcaria (*Apiaceae*)

vulgaris	WCot

Fallopia (*Polygonaceae*)

aubertii	see *F. baldschuanica*
§ ***baldschuanica***	CBcs CBod CBrac CDoC CMac CRos CSBt CTri EBee EHyd ELan EPfP GMcL LBuc LCro LOPS LRHS MAsh MGos MSwo NRHS SEND SGbt SNig SOrN SPer SPlb SPoG SWvt WFar
multiflora	see *Reynoutria multiflora*

Farfugium (*Asteraceae*)

§ ***japonicum***	CDTJ GGro XVPe
- B&SWJ 884	WCru
- B&SWJ 14699	WCru
- 'Argenteum' (v)	CDTJ EMil SMad WCot
§ - 'Aureomaculatum' (v) ♀H3	CDTJ XVPe
- 'Bumpy Ride'	WCot
- 'Crispatum'	LEdu LPla SChr XLum XSte XVPe
- double-flowered (d)	WCru
- var. ***formosanum*** NMWJ 14574	WCru
- var. ***giganteum***	CDTJ XSte XVPe
- - B&SWJ 15122 **new**	WCru
- 'Kagami-jishi' (v)	CDTJ
- 'Kaimon Dake' (v)	WCot
- 'Kinkan' (v)	WCot
- 'Shishi Botan'	CDTJ XSte
I - 'Tsuwa-buki'	CDTJ WCot
- 'Wavy Gravy'	XSte
'Last Dance' PBR	EBee ECtt
tussilagineum	see *F. japonicum*

Fargesia (*Poaceae*)

from Jiuzhaigou, China	CDTJ GMcL LPal MAvo MMuc MWht NLar SBGi SCoo WPGP
adpressa	MWht
apicirubens 'White Dragon'	CDTJ
demissa 'Gerry'	CKel CWnw
denudata	CBct CDTJ ESwi NLar SBGi
- L 1575	MWht
denudata Xian 1	CDTJ
dracocephala 'Green Dragon'	CBdn GBin MMuc MWht NLar SBGi
'Jiuzaighou 9'	CDoC GDam SBGi
§ ***murielae*** ♀H5	CAgr CBdn CDoC CEme EDir EGrI ELan EPau EPfP GArf LCro LOPS LPar LSto MACG MAsh MGos MMuc MWht NBwr NFav NWea SArc SBGi SCob SPlb WFar
- 'Bimbo'	CDoC EPfP LPal LPar NLar SWvt
- 'Dana Jumbo'	EHyd LRHS NRHS
- 'Dino'	EMil
- 'Grüne Hecke'	MWht
- 'Harewood'	GMcL MWht SWvt
- 'Joy'	GBin NLar
- 'Jumbo'	CBcs CBod CDoC CSBt EAri ELon EPfP GDam GMcL LPal MAvo MGos MWht NGdn NLar NRHS SGsty SPer SRms SWvt
- 'Luca' PBR	LRHS
- 'Mae'	CDTJ MWht
- 'Novecento'	SCoo SPoG
- 'Panda' PBR	EHyd LRHS NRHS SBGi
- 'Simba'	EHeP EHyd EPfP GBin GDam GMaP GMcL LMaj LPal LPar LRHS LSRN MAsh MBrN MGos MWht NGdn NLar NRHS SBGi SCob SGsty SPer SPlb SPoG SWeb SWvt WFar WPGP
- 'Vampire'	MAsh SCoo SPoG
murieliae BLUE DRAGONSCALE	see *F. murieliae* BLUE LIZARD
§ - BLUE LIZARD ('Japo 72' PBR)	MWht SCoo
- RED ZEBRA ('Japo 51' PBR)	MWht SBGi
- 'Smaragd' PBR **new**	NBwr
- 'Superjumbo' PBR	LPal
§ ***nitida***	CAbb CBcs CEme CEnd CWnw EHyd ELan EPfP GArf LRHS MAsh MGos MWht NRHS SBGi SCob SCoo SPoG SRms SWvt WPGP
- 'Black Pearl'	CDoC GDam LPar MAsh MAvo SCoo SPoG WPGP
- 'Great Wall'	CDTJ CDoC CSBt ELan GBin LPal MAsh NLar SCoo SPoG
- Jiuzhaigou 1	see *F.* RED PANDA
- 'Jiuzhaigou 2'	MWht SBGi
- 'Jiuzhaigou 4'	CDTJ CExl WPGP
- 'Jiuzhaigou Genf'	CDTJ MWht NLar WPGP
- 'Nymphenburg'	MAsh
- 'Pillar'	MAsh
- 'Volcano'	CDoC MAsh SBGi SCoo
'Obelisk' PBR	LPar
§ RED PANDA ('Jiu') ♀H4	LCro LOPS LPal MWht SPoG SWvt
robusta ♀H5	CAbb CBod CDTJ CSBt ELan EPfP MAvo MBrN MMuc MWht NGdn NLar SBGi SCob SSut WPGP

- 'Asian Wonder'	CBod CKel CWnw LCro LOPS LPar LRHS MHtn NFav NLar SBGi SEdd SGsty SPeP XSte
- 'Campbell'	CBdn CDoC ELon LPal LPar NLar SGsty
- 'Ming Yunnan'	LEdu WPGP
- 'P. King'	MWht
- 'Pingwu'	CBdn CBod CDTJ CDoC EAri GDam GMcL LPal LPar MGos MWht SBGi SGsty
- 'Red Sheath'	CDTJ CExl MWht WPGP
- 'Wenchuan'	CKel CWnw
- 'Wolong'	CBdn CExl LPar MWht NLar WPGP
rufa 🏆H4	CAbb CBcs CBdn CBod CDoC CKel CSBt EAri ELan ELon EPfP EShb LCro LOPS LPal LSRN MAvo MBlu MBrN MGos MMuc MPri MWht NFav NLar SCob SWeb WFar WPGP XSte
similaris KR 4175	MWht
spathacea misapplied	see *F. murielae*
utilis	MMuc MWht SEND
'Winter Joy'	SBGi SCoo WPGP
yulongshanensis	MWht

Farsetia (*Brassicaceae*)

clypeata	see *Fibigia clypeata*

Fascicularia (*Bromeliaceae*)

andina	see *F. bicolor*
§ ***bicolor***	Widely available
- subsp. ***bicolor***	CDoC CMac
- subsp. ***canaliculata***	ELon LEdu MNrw SChr SIvy SPad WPGP
kirchhoffiana	see *F. bicolor*
litoralis	see *Ochagavia litoralis*
pitcairniifolia misapplied	see *F. bicolor*
pitcairniifolia (Verlot) Mez	see *Ochagavia litoralis*

× *Fatshedera* (*Araliaceae*)

lizei 🏆H3	CBcs CMac CRos CSde CTri EBee ELon EPfP GBin LRHS MAsh MRav SArc SDix SEND SPer SPlb SPoG SRms SWvt WAvo WHtc
§ - 'Annemieke' (v) 🏆H3	CBcs CBod CKel EHyd ELan ELon EPfP LRHS MMuc MRav SEND SEle SPer SPoG WAvo WHtc
§ - 'Aurea' (v)	CRos
- 'Aureopicta'	see × *F. lizei* 'Aurea'
- compact	CKel EPfP
- 'Lemon and Lime'	see × *F. lizei* 'Annemieke'
- 'Maculata'	see × *F. lizei* 'Annemieke'
- 'Variegata' (v) 🏆H3	CSde EBee ELan ELon EPfP LRHS SDix SEND SPer SRHi SWvt WAvo WHtc
- 'Variegata' compact (v)	SPoG

Fatsia (*Araliaceae*)

§ ***japonica*** 🏆H5	Widely available
- 'Camouflage'	see *F. japonica* 'Murakumo-nishiki'
- 'Moseri'	CBod ELon ESwi LEdu MBNS SMrm SWvt WCot
§ - 'Murakumo-nishiki' (v)	LCro
- 'Spider's Web'	see *F. japonica* 'Tsumugi-shibori'
§ - 'Tsumugi-shibori' (v)	Widely available
- 'Variegata' (v) 🏆H5	CMac ELan EPfP LPar MAsh MGos MRav SCob SEND SPoG WCot
I 'Megafatsia'	CDTJ
papyrifera	see *Tetrapanax papyrifer*
polycarpa	CDTJ CDoC CExl EAri
- B&SWJ 1776	WCru
- B&SWJ 3467	WCru
- B&SWJ 7144	WCru
- RWJ 10133	WCru
- from Tregye	IKel
- deeply cut leaf	GBin IKel SMad WCot WPGP
- GREEN FINGERS	ELan LAlb LCro LRHS NLar

Fatsia × *Hedera* see × *Fatshedera*

Faucaria (*Aizoaceae*)

bosscheana **new**	EAri
tigrina 🏆H2	EAri
tuberculosa 🏆H2	CBod CPbh SEdd SSim

Fauria see *Nephrophyllidium*

Feijoa see *Acca*

Felicia (*Asteraceae*)

§ ***amelloides***	CCCN CPbh CWal SPlb
- 'Santa Anita'	CTri NWad SVen
§ - variegated (v)	CCCN ECtt NPer
§ ***amoena***	CTri
- 'Variegata' (v)	CCCN CTri
capensis	see *F. amelloides*
coelestis	see *F. amelloides*
echinata	CCCN
FELICITARA BLUE ('Wigetablue'PBR)	SPoG
filifolia blue-flowered	SVen
natalensis	see *F. rosulata*
pappei	see *F. amoena*
§ ***petiolata***	CFis CTri EBee EWes MMuc MNrw NSti WSHC
§ ***rosulata***	CAby CBor EDAr GArf GEdr LShi MAsh MHol NBro NLar SBrt WFar WIce
uliginosa	EWes SBrt SPlb WIce
wrightii	GEdr

Fenestraria (*Aizoaceae*)

rhopalophylla **new**	EAri
- subsp. ***aurantiaca*** 🏆H2	SSim

fennel see *Foeniculum vulgare*

fenugreek see *Trigonella foenum-graecum*

Ferocactus (*Cactaceae*)

emoryi **new**	EAri
glaucescens 🏆H2 **new**	EAri NPlm
gracilis	NPlm
subsp. ***coloratus*** **new**	
herrerae **new**	EAri
histrix **new**	EAri
latispinus 🏆H2 **new**	EAri
peninsulae **new**	NMen
pilosus **new**	NMen NPlm
robustus **new**	EAri

Ferraria (*Iridaceae*)

§ ***crispa***	CBor GKev LAma NRog WCot
- var. ***nortieri***	NRog WCot
divaricata	NRog WCot
- subsp. ***arenosa***	NRog
schaeferi	CBor NRog WCot
undulata	see *F. crispa*
variablis	CBor WCot

Ferula (*Apiaceae*)

assa-foetida	LDai WJek
chiliantha	see *F. communis* subsp. *glauca*
§ ***communis***	CElw CKel CSpe ECha ELan EPri EWes GBin GPoy LEdu LRHS LShi LWaG SDix SEND SPad SPhx SPlb SPoG SPtp WJek XSen

	- 'Cretan Giant'	WPGP
	- 'Gigantea'	see *F. communis*
§	- subsp. ***glauca***	CSpe EBee ECha EWes LEdu SDix SMHy SPhx SSut WCot WPGP
	- - B&SWJ 12999	WCru
	'Giant Bronze'	see *Foeniculum vulgare* 'Giant Bronze'
	tingitana B&SWJ 14005	WCru
	- 'Cedric Morris'	ECha SDix SPhx WCot

Ferulago (*Apiaceae*)

	cassia	WCot
	nodosa	SPhx
	stellata	WCot
	sylvatica	SPhx
	- PAB 2875	LEdu

Festuca (*Poaceae*)

	actae	XLum
	amethystina	CBod CKel CKno EShb LCro LOPS LRHS MBel MMuc NGdn SCob SEND SPhx
	- 'Aprilgrün'	XLum
	arundinacea	CHab MMuc SEND
	californica	XLum
	curvula	EShb
	subsp. ***crassifolia***	
	elegans	EPPr
	eskia	XLum
	filiformis	CHab
§	***gautieri***	CPla EHeP NWsh WSpi XLum
	- 'Pic Carlit'	NLar XLum
	gigantea	CHab MMuc SEND
	glacialis	XLum
	- 'Czakor'	XLum
	glauca Vill.	CBcs GMaP MBNS MGos NGdn SPer SPlb SRms WCAu XSen
I	- 'Auslese'	EShb NGdn
	- 'Azurit'	EWes LShi NLar SCob SPoG SRms
§	- 'Blaufuchs'	CBod CEme CSBt EHeP EHyd ELan EPfP EWes GMaP LRHS MAsh MAvo MBlu MGos NLar NRHS NWsh SCob SPer SPlb SWvt WFar WSpi XLum
§	- 'Blauglut'	SCob SRms
	- BLUE FOX	see *F. glauca* 'Blaufuchs'
	- BLUE GLOW	see *F. glauca* 'Blauglut'
	- 'Blue Select'	LSun
	- 'Elijah Blue'	Widely available
	- 'Golden Toupee'	EBlo ECha EHeP EHyd ELan EPfP LRHS MBlu MGos NLar NRHS SPer SPlb SWvt XLum
	- 'Harz'	XLum
	- INTENSE BLUE ('Casblue'[PBR]) ♀H5	CBrac CKno CPla CRos EBee EHyd ELan EPfP EWes GMcL LCro LOPS LRHS LSRN MAsh MGos NRHS NWsh SCoo SMad SPeP SPoG SRms
*	- ***minima***	CCCN NWsh
	- SEA URCHIN	see *F. glauca* 'Seeigel'
§	- 'Seeigel'	NRHS
	- SELECT	see *F. glauca* 'Auslese'
	- 'Seven Seas'	see *F. valesiaca* 'Silbersee'
	- 'Solling'	XLum
	'Hogar'	LPal
	idahoensis 'Tomales Bay'	CKno
	liviensis	XSen
	mairei	CBod ECha EPPr LPla XLum
	ovina	CHab SPhx WSFF
	- var. ***gallica***	NWsh
	- 'Söhrewald'	EPPr
*	- 'Tetra Gold'	SWvt
	paniculata	CKno
	pratensis	CHab
	punctoria	MMuc
	rubra	CHab CKno WSFF
	scoparia	see *F. gautieri*
	'Siskiyou Blue'	CAby
	tatrae	MMuc SEND
	valesiaca var. ***glaucantha***	CBod LRHS NGdn XLum
§	- 'Silbersee'	SRms
	- SILVER SEA	see *F. valesiaca* 'Silbersee'
	vivipara	NBid XLum
*	- ***glauca*** new	NBwr
*	'Willow Green'	SPlb

Fibigia (*Brassicaceae*)

§	***clypeata***	CSpe LDai
	eriocarpa	LRHS SPhx

Ficaria (*Ranunculaceae*)

	fascicularis	GKev MNrw NRog NRya WCot
	verna	GKev
	- Alba Group	LEdu NRya
	- anemone-centred	see *F. verna* 'Collarette'
§	- Aurantiaca Group	CDor NLar NRya
	- var. ***aurantiacus***	see *F. verna* Aurantiaca Group
	- 'Bowles's Double'	see *Ficaria verna* 'Double Bronze'
	- 'Brambling'	EBee LEdu NBPC
	- 'Brazen Child'	SHar
	- 'Brazen Hussy'	Widely available
	- subsp. ***bulbilifer***	see *F. verna* subsp. *verna*
§	- subsp. ***chrysocephala***	EBee ECha MNrw WCot
	- 'Coffee Cream'	NSum WFar
§	- 'Collarette' (d)	EBee ELan EMor LEdu LLWG MHer NBir NLar NRog NRya NSum WFar
	- 'Coppernob'	CDor CFis WCot WFar
	- 'Cupreus'	see *F. verna* Aurantiaca Group
§	- 'Double Bronze' (d)	LEdu NBir NRya NSum WFar
§	- 'Double Mud' (d)	EPPr LEdu NRya NSum SHar WFar
	- double white-flowered (d)	NRog
	- - cream-flowered	see *F. verna* 'Double Mud'
	- - yellow-flowered	see *F. verna* Flore Pleno Group
	- 'Dusky Maiden'	NLar NRya NSum WFar
	- 'E.A. Bowles'	see *F. verna* 'Collarette'
§	- Flore Pleno Group (d)	CBod CDor CMac CTri ELan EPPr EPfP LShi NRya NSum SHar SRms WCot WFar
	- 'Fried Egg'	LShi NSum WFar
	- 'Green Petal' (d)	EPPr NBir NRya NSum SHar WFar WHer
	- 'Hyde Hall'	NLar WCot WFar
	- 'Ken Aslet Double' (d)	EPPr MHer NSum
	- 'Lemon Dazzler'	EBou
	- subsp. ***major***	see *F. verna* subsp. *chrysocephala*
	- 'Montacute' (d)	CDor WFar
	- 'Old Master'	WCot
	- 'Orange Sorbet' (d)	NSum WFar
	- 'Primrose'	NRya NSum
	- 'Randall's White'	CDor ECha EPfP NSum SHar WFar
	- 'Rita Pirouet'	WCot
	- 'Salmon's White'	EPPr NBir NRog NRya NSum SHar WFar
	- 'Silver Collar' (d)	LEdu
	- 'Tortoiseshell'	EPPr WOut
§	- subsp. ***verna***	CTri WSFF WShi
	- - 'Chedglow'	WCot
	- 'Wisley Double'	see *Ficaria verna* 'Double Bronze'
	- 'Yaffle'	WBor

Ficinia (*Cyperaceae*)

§	***nodosa***	SPlb
	truncata	CBor WCot
	- 'Ice Crystal' (v)	EHyd ELan LCro LEdu LRHS MHtn NRHS SMad SPoG

Ficus (*Moraceae*)

	afghanistanica 'Silver Lyre'	EBee EPfP SMad SVen WPGP
	'Amstel' **new**	NHrt
	benghalensis	NHrt
	- 'Audrey' **new**	LWaG NHrt
	benjamina ♀H1c	NHrt
	- 'Danielle'PBR	LCro LOPS NHrt
	- 'Exotica'	LCro
	- 'Twilight' **new**	LCro
I	***binnendijkii*** 'Alii'	CDoC NHrt NPlm
	- 'Amstel King' **new**	NHrt
	carica (F)	CCCN ERom LPar SArc SEWo SPad WJur
	- 'Adam' (F)	CCCN LEdu NLar NRog SEND SVen WPGP
I	- 'Aranysárga Óriásfüge' (F) **new**	WJur
	- 'Babits' (F) **new**	WJur
I	- 'Bauern Feige' (F)	SRms
	- 'Beall' (F)	CCCN
	- 'Black Ischia' (F)	CCCN SDix SMHy
	- 'Bornholm' (F)	CCCN SPre SWeb
	- 'Bourjassotte Grise' (F)	CAgr XSen
	- 'Brogiotto Nero' (F)	NRog
	- 'Brown Turkey' (F) ♀H4	Widely available
	- 'Brunswick' (F)	CAgr CBod CCCN CDoC CEme CRHN CTri ELan EPfP EPom EShb LEdu MTrO NLar NRHS NRog SBmr SCoo SDix SEND SKee SPoG SRms SVen WCot WFar WLov WMat WTyc
	- 'Califfo Blue' (F)	SBmr SRms
	- 'Cambridge Builder' (F)	SVen
	- 'Castle Kennedy' (F)	CCCN
	- 'Celeste' (F)	SRms
	- 'Chicago Hardy' (F)	NRog
	- 'Col de Dame Blanc' (F)	NRog XSen
	- 'Col de Dame Noir' (F)	XSen
	- 'Colummaro Black Apulia' (F)	CCCN
	- 'Colummaro White Apulia' (F)	CCCN
	- 'Dalmatie' (F)	CAgr CCCN CDoC ELan EPfP LRHS MTrO NOra NRog SEND SRms WMat WPGP XSen
I	- 'Digitata' (F)	MBlu
	- 'Dorée' (F)	EPom NRog XSen
	- 'Dorée de Porquerolles' (F)	CCCN
	- 'Early Violet' (F) **new**	WJur
	- 'Ed's Teacup' (F) **new**	WCot
	- 'Filacciano' (F)	CCCN
	- 'Fiorone Verde' (F)	SVen
	- 'Flanders' (F)	CCCN
	- 'Gianchetta'	SVen
	- 'Goutte d'Or' (F)	CAgr CCCN EPfP EPom
	- 'Green Sweet'	see *F. carica* Zöld Aszalódó
	- 'Grise de Marseille' (F)	CCCN
	- 'Grise de Saint Jean' (F)	NRog XSen
	- 'Ice'	see *F. carica* 'Jégfüge'
	- 'Ice Crystal' (F) ♀H5	CBod CDoC CKel CRos EBee ELan EMil EPfP IDee LAlb LEdu LPar LRHS MBlu MPie MTrO NLar NOra SCoo SMad SPoG SRms SVen WCot WMat
I	- 'Jégfüge' (F) **new**	WJur
	- 'Jordan' (F)	LRHS MTrO NOra SCoo SPoG
	- 'Kadota' (F)	NRog SVen
§	- 'Lila Pogácsa' (F) **new**	WJur
	- 'Longue d'Août' (F)	NRog WJur XSen
	- 'Lupo' (F)	SVen
	- 'Madeleine des Deux Saisons' (F)	EPom SEND SKee XSen XSte
	- 'Marseillaise' (F)	XSen
	- 'Melanzana' (F)	WJur
	- 'Morena' (F)	SRms
	- 'Napolitana' (F)	EDir NPlm
	- 'Negretta' (F)	SVen
	- 'Nero' (F)	SGsty
	- 'Newlyn Harbour' (F)	ELon
	- 'Noire de Barbentane' (F)	XSen
	- 'Noire de Bellone' (F) **new**	IDee
	- 'Noire de Caromb' (F)	CAgr CCCN CLnd EPfP LRHS MTrO NPlm SKee SRms WJur WMat XSen
	- 'Noire de Provence'	see *F. carica* 'Reculver'
	- 'Osborn's Prolific' (F)	EPfP SEND SGol SWvt WCot XSen
	- 'Panachée' (F)	CCCN EPom LCro MTrO NLar NOra SCoo SPoG SRms WJur
	- 'Pastilière' (F)	XSen
	- 'Perretta' (F)	LRHS
§	- 'Pesti Sárga' (F) **new**	WJur
	- 'Peter's Honey' (F)	NRog
	- 'Précoce de Dalmatie' (F)	CCCN CKel EPfP LEdu NLar SRms WCot
§	- 'Reculver' (F)	SEND
	- 'Ronde de Bordeaux' (F)	CCCN EPfP NRog SEND SWeb XSen
	- 'Rouge de Bordeaux' (F)	CAgr CBod CCCN CTsd EDir EPom LRHS SKee SPlb SRms SSta XSte
	- 'Rubado' (F)	SVen
	- 'San Piero' (F)	SVen
	- 'Scone'	see *F. carica* 'Lila Pogácsa'
	- 'Signora' (F) **new**	WJur
	- 'Sucre Vert' (F)	NRog
	- 'Sultane' (F)	CAgr EPom IDee SVen WPGP XSen
	- 'Tayip 1' (F)	CAgr
	- 'Tayip 2' (F)	CAgr
	- 'Tena' (F)	NRog
	- 'Verdal' (F) **new**	NPlm
	- 'Violette Dauphine' (F)	CBod EPfP LEdu NLar NRog SEND SKee WLov
	- 'Violette de Sollies' (F)	XSen
	- 'Violette Normande' (F)	SEND XSte
	- 'White Adriatic' (F)	CAgr CCCN CDoC NLar NRog SRms WLov
	- 'White Genoa'	see *F. carica* 'White Marseilles'
§	- 'White Marseilles' (F)	CAgr CCCN CMac CRHN EPfP MTrO NRog SCoo SEND SKee SPoG SRms WMat WPGP
	- 'Yellow Budapest'	see *F. carica* 'Pesti Sárga'
	- 'Yellow Giant'	see *F. carica* 'Aranysárga Óriásfüge'
	- 'Zamoreica' (F)	SEND
§	- Zöld Aszalódó (F) **new**	WJur
	carica × pumila	WPGP
	cyathistipula	LCro NHrt
	elastica	NHrt
	- 'Abidjan'	LCro NHrt
	- 'Belize'PBR (v) **new**	CDoC
	- 'Melany'PBR **new**	NHrt
§	- 'Pemela' **new**	LCro
	- PETITE MELANY	see *F. elastica* 'Pemela'
	- 'Robusta'	CDoC LCro LOPS LWaG NHrt NTrD
	- 'Tineke' (v)	CDoC LCro LOPS
	lyrata ♀H1b	CDoC LCro LWaG NHrt NTrD
	- 'Bambino'PBR	LCro LOPS LWaG NHrt
	microcarpa	CDoC LCro LPal NHrt
	- 'Moclame'PBR **new**	LCro NHrt
	aff. ***oligodon***	SVen
	pumila ♀H2	CDoC CTsd EShb IDee LWaG
	- 'Nana'	NWad
	- 'Sonny' (v)	LWaG NWad
	- 'Variegata' (v) ♀H2	EShb
	- 'White Sunny' (v) **new**	LWaG
	punctata	EShb
	retusa (F)	NGKo

tikoua	IArd
vaccinioides	WPGP

fig see *Ficus carica*; see also AGM Fruit Section

filbert see *Corylus maxima*

Filipendula (*Rosaceae*)

	alnifolia 'Variegata'	see *F. ulmaria* 'Variegata'
	camtschatica	EBee ECha ELan LPla LRHS MMuc NBid NFav NLar WPGP WWtn
	- B&SWJ 10987	WCru
	- RBS 0224	NLar
	- 'Rosea'	CTtf
	digitata 'Nana'	see *F. multijuga*
	hexapetala	see *F. vulgaris*
	- 'Flore Pleno'	see *F. vulgaris* 'Multiplex'
	'Kahome'	CRos CTtf EHyd ELon EMor EShb EWhm GAbr GLog GMaP LRHS NBid NBir NGdn NLar NRHS NSti SCob SPer WFar WPnP
	kamtschatica 'Moe-ki-fukurin-fu' (v)	GGro
	kiraishiensis	EBee
	- B&SWJ 1571	WCru
	koreana	CRos EBlo EHyd LRHS NRHS
§	***multijuga***	EBee EGrl EWhm NHol NLar NWad
	- B&SWJ 10950	WCru
	- 'Hjördis'	CBod CKel ELon EMor LBar MBel MSCN SPeP WHoo
	- var. ***yezoensis*** B&SWJ 10828	WCru
	palmata	ECha EGrl WFar
	- 'Digitata Nana'	see *F. multijuga*
	- dwarf	GRum
	- 'Elegantissima'	see *F. purpurea* 'Elegans'
	- 'Göteborg'	EBee NLar
	- 'Nana'	see *F. multijuga*
	- 'Rosea'	CMac EMor NBir
	- 'Rubra'	CRos EBee EBlo EHyd EPfP LRHS MRav NGdn NRHS
	purpurea	EBee ECha GQue ILea LCro LLWG MMuc SCob SEND SRms WCru WFar WTyc
	- f. ***albiflora***	ILea
§	- 'Elegans'	EBee EGrl ELon EWTr ILea NBid NHol NWad SCob SPer SRms WFar WPnP WTyc
*	- 'Plena' (d)	NLar
	- 'Rhapsody'	LPla
§	***rubra*** 'Venusta' ♀H5	Widely available
	- 'Venusta Magnifica'	see *F. rubra* 'Venusta'
	rufinervis	LPla
	- B&SWJ 8469	WCru
	- B&SWJ 8611	WCru
§	***ulmaria***	Widely available
	- 'Aurea'	CDor CMac CTri CWCL EBee ECha ECtt EGrl EHyd ELan EMor EWhm GBin GMaP LEdu LRHS MHol MRav NBid NFav NLar SPer SRms WCot WFar WSHC
	- 'Corinne Tremaine'	WHer
	- 'Flore Pleno' (d)	MRav NBid SPer WCot WFar WHrl
	- 'Rosea'	EHyd LEdu LLWG LRHS MHoo
§	- 'Variegata' (v)	CWCL EBee ECtt EHyd ELan EWhm GQue LBar LRHS MHol NBid NGdn NLar NRHS SRms WFar WHer XLum
§	***vulgaris***	CDor CHab CKel GLog LEdu LRHS MBow MMuc MNHC NAts NBro NGrd NMir NQui SPhx WHer
	- 'Devon Cream'	MAvo
	- 'Flore Pleno'	see *F. vulgaris* 'Multiplex'
	- 'Grandiflora'	EGrl
§	- 'Multiplex' (d)	CBod CDor CMac CSpe CTtf ECha EHyd ELan EMor EPfP GMaP LLWG LRHS MHer MMrt MMuc MRav MSCN NBid NBir NLar NRHS NRya NSti SCob SRms WFar
	- 'Plena'	see *F. vulgaris* 'Multiplex'
	- 'Rosea'	EMor

Firmiana (*Malvaceae*)

simplex	EBee ESwi LEdu MBlu SBrt SMad WJur WPGP

Fitzroya (*Cupressaceae*)

cupressoides	CAco CBcs IArd IDee LRHS SLim WPav
- 'Borde Hill' (f)	CAco

Flueggea (*Phyllanthaceae*)

suffruticosa	SBrt

Foeniculum (*Apiaceae*)

	vulgare	Widely available
§	- var. ***azoricum*** 'Fino'	EKin MCtn NRob
	- - 'Orion' ♀H2	EKin
	- 'Bronze'	see *F. vulgare* 'Purpureum'
	- var. ***dulce***	ENfk
§	- 'Giant Bronze'	CBod CKel LCro LEdu LOPS LRHS SCob SPhx WSpi XSen
§	- 'Purpureum'	Widely available
	- 'Smoky'	ECha MRav
	- 'Sweet Florence'	LCro SVic
	- 'Zefa Fino'	see *F. vulgare* var. *azoricum* 'Fino'

Fokienia (*Cupressaceae*)

hodginsii	CAco

Fontanesia (*Oleaceae*)

fortunei	EBtc

Fontinalis (*Fontinalaceae*)

sp.	CPud
antipyretica	CPud LPfP

Forsythia (*Oleaceae*)

'Arnold Dwarf'	NLar SRms
'Beatrix Farrand' ambig.	CTri EPfP NBwr NWea SEND SRms
'Beatrix Farrand' K. Sax	LRHS MMuc NLar
'Fiesta' (v)	CBod ELon EPfP LRHS MAsh MDon MRav MSwo NLar NWad SPer WCot WFar
giraldiana	MSwo SRms
GOLD TIDE	see *F.* MARÉE D'OR
'Golden Nugget'	CBod CMac ELan EPfP MAsh SPoG WCFE WFar
'Golden Times' (v)	CMac CRos EHyd GMcL LRHS MAsh MDon MSwo NEoE NHol NRHS SPoG SWvt WAvo WCot WFar WHtc
'Goldstream' (v)	NWad
× ***intermedia***	CWal
- 'Arnold Giant'	MBlu
- 'Goldrausch'	CRos EBee EHyd EShb GMcL LCro LOPS LPar LRHS MAsh MDon NLar NRHS SAko WHtc
- 'Goldzauber'	CBrac
- 'Lynwood Variety' ♀H5	Widely available
- 'Lynwood Variety' variegated (v)	CMac MTrO
- MIKADOR ('Minfor6'PBR) **new**	LCro
- MINIGOLD ('Flojor')	CBrac CMac CSBt ELan MSwo NLar SRms WHlf

	- 'Nimbus'^{PBR}	CBod EBee EPfP LRHS MAsh MMrt NLar WFar
	- SHOW OFF ('Mindor'^{PBR})	LRHS
	- 'Spectabilis'	CBod CBrac EDir EHeP EPfP LBuc MAsh NBwr NWea SCoo SGol SLim SRHi WFar
	- 'Spectabilis Variegated' (v)	NEoE
	- 'Spring Glory'	MHer WAvo WSpi
	- 'Susan Gruninger' (v)	WCot
	- 'Variegata' (v)	CBrac SRms
	- WEEK END ('Courtalyn') 🏆^{H5}	CDoC CEme CEnd CRos EHyd ELan EPfP LBuc LCro LOPS LPar LRHS MAsh MMuc NHol NLar NRHS SCob SCoo SEND SGol SGsty SPlb SavN WFar
	'Kanarek'	NLar
	× ***mandschurica***	CBcs
§	MARÉE D'OR ('Courtasol') 🏆^{H5}	CRos EPfP LRHS MAsh MRav NLar NRHS SPer SPoG WFar WHlf
	MÊLÉE D'OR ('Courtaneur')	SGol WBor
	'Northern Gold'	MBlu
	ovata 'Ottawa'	WHtc
	'Paulina'	EDAr WCot
	suspensa	CMac CTri EPfP ESwi NWea SPlb SRms WSpi
	- f. ***atrocaulis***	NWea WSpi
	- 'Nymans'	EPfP EWTr MRav NLar NSti SBrt SEND SPer
§	- 'Taff's Arnold' (v)	WSpi
	- 'Variegata'	see *F. suspensa* 'Taff's Arnold'
	viridissima	NWea WJur
	- 'Bronxensis'	NBir WAbe WCot
	- CITRUS SWIZZLE ('Mckcitrine'^{PBR})	NLar WCot
	- var. ***koreana*** 'Kumsom' (v)	LRHS NLar
	- 'Weber's Bronx'	ELon GKev NLar NWea

Fortunella see *Citrus*

Fothergilla (*Hamamelidaceae*)

	gardenii	CBcs CJun EHyd EPfP MBlu MRav NLar SPer SWvt
	- 'Blue Mist'	CCCN CEnd CJun EBee EHyd ELan EPfP LRHS MAsh NLar SPer SPoG SSta WFar
	- 'Carolina' **new**	NLar
	- 'Suzanne'	CJun NLar
	- 'Zundert'	NLar
	× ***intermedia*** BEAVER CREEK ('Klmtwo')	NLar
	- 'Blue Shadow'	CBcs CBod CCCN CJun LPar LRHS MGos NLar NRHS SRHi WFar
	- 'Mount Airy' 🏆^{H5}	CJun CMCN EPfP LRHS NLar SSta XSte
	- 'Red Licorice'	CBcs CJun EPfP NLar
	- 'Sea Spray'	CJun NLar
	- 'Windy City'	CJun NLar
	major 🏆^{H5}	CBcs CDoC CEme CJun EBee EGrI EHyd ELan EPfP LCro LOPS LPar LRHS MAsh MBlu MGil MGos MPri MRav NLar SPer SRHi SWvt WFar WHlf WTSh XSte
	- 'Bulkyard'	CJun
	- Monticola Group	CEnd CJun CRos EHyd EPfP LRHS MAsh MMuc SCob SGbt SSta
	- - 'Huntsman'	CCCN CJun EPfP SPer SSta

Fouquieria (*Fouquieriaceae*)

	columnaris	SPlb
	splendens	SPlb

Fragaria ✿ (*Rosaceae*)

	alpina 'Alba'	see *F. vesca* 'Semperflorens Alba'
	× ***ananassa*** 'Albion'^{PBR} (F)	CArg CMac LCro LOPS LSRN NRog
	- 'Alice'^{PBR} (F) 🏆^{H6}	CAgr CMac EPom SCgs
§	- 'Anablanca' (F)	LRHS
	- 'Anaïs' (F)	LRHS
	- 'Aromel' (F)	CTri MAsh
	- bubbleberry (F)	LCro LRHS
	- 'Buddy'^{PBR} (F)	CArg EPom
	- 'Cambridge Favourite' (F) 🏆^{H6}	CAgr CArg CMac CRos CSBt CTri EHyd EMil EPfP EPom GDam GQue LBuc LCro LOPS LRHS MAsh MGos MPri NBwr NRHS NRog SBmr SCgs SEdi SPlb
	- 'Cambridge Vigour' (F)	MAsh NBwr NRHS
	- 'Charlotte'^{PBR} (F)	LRHS
	- 'Christine' (F)	CAgr CArg EPom NBwr
	- 'Cupid'^{PBR} (F)	CArg EPom LCro NRog
	- 'Darselect'^{PBR} (F)	EPom
	- 'Delia' (F)	CRos EHyd LRHS NRHS
	- 'Delician' (F)	LRHS
	- DELIZZ ('Liza'^{PBR}) (F)	EHyd LRHS NRHS
	- 'Elan'^{PBR} (F)	NRHS SCoo
	- 'Elegance'^{PBR} (F)	CArg EPom NRog
	- 'Elsanta' (F)	CArg CRos CSBt EHyd EPfP EPom GDam IArd LBuc LCro LRHS MBros MPri NBir NBwr NRHS NRog SBmr SEdi SPer
	- 'Everest'^{PBR} (F)	NRHS
	- 'Fenella'^{PBR} (F)	CArg CMac EPom LCro
	- 'Finesse' (F) 🏆^{H6}	CSBt NRHS NRog
	- 'Flamenco'^{PBR} (F)	CArg EPom LEdu NRog SBmr
	- 'Florence'^{PBR} (F) 🏆^{H6}	CAgr CArg CRos CSBt EHyd EPom LRHS NRHS NRog SBmr SPer
	- 'Florian' (F)	LEdu
	- (Fragoo Series) FRAGOO DEEP ROSE ('Tarpan') (F)	CRos EHyd LRHS NRHS
	- - FRAGOO PINK ('Pikan') (F)	CRos EHyd LRHS NRHS
	- - FRAGOO WHITE ('Belton') (F)	CRos EHyd LRHS NRHS
	- Fraise des Bois	see *F. vesca*
	- 'Framberry' (F)	EPom LEdu LRHS
	- 'Frau Mieze Schindler' (F)	LEdu
*	- 'Fresca' (F)	EHyd LRHS NRHS
	- 'Gariguette' (F)	EPom LRHS
	- 'Gorella' (F)	LRHS
	- 'Hapil' (F) 🏆^{H6}	EPfP EPom GDam LBuc NRog
	- 'Honeoye' (F) 🏆^{H6}	CAgr CArg CMac CSBt EPfP EPom GDam LBuc LCro LEdu LOPS LRHS NBwr NRog SPer
	- 'Judibell'^{PBR} (F)	NRog
	- JUST ADD CREAM ('Tmstr14pnk'^{PBR}) **new**	LCro
	- 'Korona'^{PBR} (F)	CMac EPom LRHS
	- 'Leo Alba' (F)	CArg
	- 'Loran' (F)	LRHS MBros SCoo
	- 'Lucy'^{PBR} (F)	CMac
	- 'Mae'^{PBR} (F)	CArg LEdu
	- 'Magnum' (F)	LRHS
	- 'Malling Centenary'^{PBR} (F) 🏆^{H6}	EPom LRHS NRog
	- 'Malling Opal'^{PBR} (F)	EPom NRog
	- 'Malwina'^{PBR} (F)	EPom NRog SVic
	- 'Manille' (F)	EPom
	- 'Marshmello' (F)	EPom
	- 'Mount Everest' (F)	LCro LRHS
	- 'Ostara' (F)	MBros
	- 'Pandora' (F)	LEdu
	- 'Pegasus' (F) 🏆^{H6}	CAgr CRos CSBt EHyd EPfP EPom LRHS NRHS
	- pineberry (F)	EWhm LEdu
	- PINK PANDA ('Frel') (F)	CBod CMac EBee EHyd ELan GDam GMcL LRHS MBel MHer MRav

		NGdn NLar NRHS SGbt SIvy SPer SPoG WBor WCAu WCav
	- pink-flowered (F)	GAbr
	- 'Red Dream' (F)	LCro
	- 'Red Glory'PBR (F)	NRHS
	- 'Red Princess'PBR (F)	NRHS
	- RED RUBY	see *F.* × *ananassa* 'Samba'
	- 'Redgauntlet' (F)	CRos EHyd EPfP LRHS NBwr NRHS NRog
	- 'Rhapsody' (F) 🏆H6	CRos EHyd LRHS LSRN NRHS
	- 'Roman' (F)	SCoo
	- 'Royal Sovereign' (F)	CMac CTri EPfP EPom LRHS NBir SVic
	- 'Ruby Ann' (F)	SCoo
§	- 'Samba'PBR (F)	CBod EBee EHyd ELan GLog LRHS MBel NGdn NRHS SGbt SMrm
	- 'Senga Sengana' (F)	SVic
	- SNOW WHITE ('Hansawhit'PBR) (F)	EPom LEdu LRHS SVic
	- 'Sonata'PBR (F)	ELan EPom LRHS
	- 'Sweet Ann'PBR (F)	LRHS
	- 'Sweet Eve'PBR (F)	LRHS
	- 'Sweetheart' (F)	EPfP EPom LCro NRog
	- 'Symphony'PBR (F) 🏆H6	CAgr CRos CSBt EHyd EPfP EPom LBuc LRHS LSRN NRHS SCoo
	- 'Temptation' (F)	CRos EHyd LRHS MBros NRHS SVic
	- 'Toscana'PBR (F)	SCoo
	- 'Totem' (F)	NBwr
§	- 'Variegata' (v)	LDai LRHS MHoo SGbt SPer SPoG
	- 'Vibrant'PBR (F) 🏆H6	EPom NRog
	- 'White Dream' (F)	LCro
	'Bowles's Double'	see *F. vesca* 'Multiplex'
	chiloensis (F)	LEdu WKor
	- 'Chaval' (F)	ECha MRav WMal
	- 'Variegata' misapplied	see *F.* × *ananassa* 'Variegata'
	indica	see *Duchesnea indica*
	'Lipstick'	EBee MHoo NFav NLar SIvy WCAu WSpi
	moschata	CAgr CLau WKor
	nubicola	CAgr GPoy
	'Variegata'	see *F.* × *ananassa* 'Variegata'
§	***vesca*** (F)	Widely available
*	- var. ***albescens***	CLau
	- 'Alexandria' (F)	CLau ENfk NPol
	- 'Alpina Scarletta' (F)	ENfk
	- 'Ana Blanca'	see *F.* × *ananassa* 'Anablanca'
	- 'Baron Solemacher' (F)	NPol SPhx WHer
	- 'Capron Royale' (F)	CAgr
	- 'Flore Pleno'	see *F. vesca* 'Multiplex'
	- 'Fructu Albo' (F)	CAgr
	- 'Golden Alexandra' (F)	ECha EWhm NPol NWad
	- 'Mara des Bois' (F)	EPom LRHS SPer SVic
	- 'Mignonette' (F)	CLau EWhm NPol
	- 'Monophylla' (F)	LEdu NPol WHer
§	- 'Multiplex' (d)	EPPr NPol WHer WOut
§	- 'Muricata'	LEdu
	- 'Patchwork' (v)	NPol
	- 'Pineapple Crush' (F)	NPol WHer
	- 'Plymouth Strawberry'	see *F. vesca* 'Muricata'
	- 'Reine des Vallées' (F)	LRHS
	- 'Rügen' (F)	NPol
	- 'Scarlet Beauty' (F)	EPom NPol
§	- 'Semperflorens Alba' (F)	CAgr LShi NWad
	- 'Variegata' misapplied	see *F.* × *ananassa* 'Variegata'
	- 'White Soul' (F)	NPol
	- 'Yellow Wonder' (F)	LRHS NPol
	virginiana	CAgr WKor
	viridis	CAgr WKor

Francoa ✿ (*Francoaceae*)

	appendiculata	ILea MGil NBir NFav NWad SDix SFra SGBe SHeu WHer WPav
	'Confetti'	SHar
*	dwarf purple	CElw SFra
	'Lady Ann Palmer' **new**	SFra
	'Purple Spike'	see *F. sonchifolia* Rogerson's form
	ramosa	CTri EBee GKev ILea NBir NBro SDix SFra SMrm WKif
	sonchifolia	Widely available
	- 'Alba'	EBee SFra
	- 'Cally Dwarf Purple'	SHeu
	- 'Culm View Lilac'	CKel EBee LRHS SFra WBrk
	- 'Molly Anderson'	SFra
	- 'Petite Bouquet'	CKno EWes LBar SFra SOrN SRms WNPC
	- 'Pink Bouquet'	CAbb CKno CMac CWGN EBee LRHS LSRN MHol NBPC SFra SHeu SRkn WFar WHlf XSte
	- 'Pink Giant'	CBod CPla CSpe EHyd EPfP EWhm EWoo GAbr GKev LBar LRHS MBel MPie NBPC NRHS NWad SFra SHeu WFar
§	- Rogerson's form	CElw CMiW CRos CTri EHyd EShb GBin GGro LRHS NBPC NBir NChi NRHS SDix SFra SHeu SMrm SPeP WFar

Frangula (*Rhamnaceae*)

§	***alnus***	CArg CBTr CCVT CHab CPer CTri EPfP LBuc LPar MBlu MGos NBwr NWea SCob SEWo SavN WFar WMou WSFF WTSh
	- 'Aspleniifolia'	EPfP IDee LMaj LRHS MBlu MGil MMuc MRav NLar WCFE WLov WPGP
	- 'Minaret'	MBlu
	- 'Ron Williams'	CRos EHyd ELan EPfP LRHS MBlu MPkF NLar SPoG SavN
	californica B&SWJ 14057	WCru

Frankenia (*Frankeniaceae*)

laevis	CKel SRms
thymifolia	CKel CTri EBou ECtt EPfP MAsh MHer SLee SPlb WHoo XLum

Franklinia (*Theaceae*)

alatamaha	CBcs IDee LRHS MBlu MGil WPGP XSte

Franklinia × *Gordonia* see × *Gordlinia*

Fraxinus ✿ (*Oleaceae*)

angustifolia 'Raywood'	NBwr
bungeana	WJur
excelsior	EDir NBwr
- 'Jaspidea'	NBwr
- 'Westhof's Glorie'	NBwr
ornus	NBwr
uhdei	GKev

Freesia (*Iridaceae*)

alba Foster	see *F. lactea*
alba (G.L.Mey.) Gumbl.	CPbh
'Algarve' (d)	NRog
andersoniae	NRog
'Anouk'	NRog
'Athene'	NRog
'Ballerina'	NRog
'Bloemfontein'	NRog
'Blue Bayou' (d)	NRog
'Blue Moon'	LCro LOPS
'Blue Sky'	NRog
'Calgary'	NRog
'Chiron'	NRog
'Clazina'	NRog
'Corona'	NRog

corymbosa	NRog
- cream-flowered	NRog
- pink-flowered	NRog
- white-flowered	NRog
'Delta River'	EPfP SPoG
'Epona'	NRog
'Fantasy' (d)	NRog
fergusoniae	NRog
'Figaro' (d)	NRog
'Fragrant Sunburst'	CRos EPfP SCoo SPoG
fucata	CPbh
'Gold River'	SPoG
'Golden Melody'	NRog
grandiflora	CBor
subsp. ***grandiflora*** new	
'Jessica'	NRog
§ ***lactea***	CBor
'Lady Brunet' (d)	NRog
§ ***laxa*** 🏆H3	CBor CPbh CSpe CTri CTtf EPri GKev LEdu LRHS NHpl WFar WHlf
- var. ***alba*** 🏆H3	CBor CPbh EPri GKev SChr WFar
- subsp. ***azurea*** new	CBor
- 'Joan Evans'	CBor CTtf WFar
- ***viridiflora***	CTtf
leichtlinii subsp. ***alba*** new	SChr
(Lovely Series) 'Lovely Blue'	CRos LRHS
- 'Lovely Cream'	CRos LRHS
- 'Lovely White'	CRos LRHS
'Oberon'	NRog
'Pink Fountain'	NRog
'Purple Rain' (d)	NRog
'Red Beauty' (d)	NRog
'Red River'	SPoG
refracta	CPbh
'Romany' (d)	NRog
'Royal Blue'	NRog
'Santorini'	NRog
'Sevilla'	NRog
sparrmannii	NRog
'Striped Pearl'	NRog
'Troubadour' (d)	NRog
viridis	CBor NRog
'White River'	EPfP SPoG
xanthospila	NRog

Fremontodendron (*Malvaceae*)

'California Glory' 🏆H4	Widely available
californicum	CTri EBee ELan LPar NLar SEND SPlb WFar
- subsp. ***decumbens***	SBrt
'Pacific Sunset'	MGos MRav

Freylinia (*Scrophulariaceae*)

cestroides	see *F. lanceolata*
§ ***lanceolata***	CBcs CCCN EBee SPlb SVen
tropica	MGil
visseri	SVen

Frithia (*Aizoaceae*)

pulchra 🏆H2	EAri

Fritillaria ✿ (*Liliaceae*)

acmopetala 🏆H4	CAvo CBor CMiW CWCL EMor EPot ERCP GArf GKev ITim LAma MBow MNrw NRog SDeJ SDir SHar WCot WHlf WIce WSHC
- 'Brunette'	NRog
- subsp. ***wendelboi***	NRog
- - 'Zwanenburg'	GKev
affinis	NHpl
- yellow-flowered	CBor CWCL
alburyana	NRog
amana	CBor CWCL EMor ERCP GKev LAma NRog WCot
- 'Cambridge'	WCot
arabica	see *F. persica*
assyriaca	EPot
aurea	NRog
- 'Golden Flag'	SDeJ
ayakoana	GKev
biflora 'Martha Roderick'	SDeJ
§ ***bithynica***	ITim NRog
bucharica	EPot GKev LAma NRog
- 'Hodji-obi-Garm'	NRog
camschatcensis	CBor EMor EPot ERCP GArf GBin GEdr GKev GMaP LAma NBir NHpl NLar NRog SDeJ WCot WTyc
- 'Alaska'	GArf NHar
- 'Aurea'	GRum NHar
- black-flowered	NHar
- double-flowered (d)	GKev
- dwarf	GRum
- f. ***flavescens***	GEdr GKev LAma
carduchorum	see *F. minuta*
carica	CBor NRog
cirrhosa	NRog
citrina	see *F. bithynica*
crassifolia	ISha
- subsp. ***crassifolia***	GKev NRog
§ - subsp. ***kurdica***	ITim NRog
davidii	NDry
davisii	EPot GKev ISha LAma NRog SDeJ
eduardii	GKev NRog
- 'Castor'	EPot GKev
- 'Pollux'	GKev LAma
elwesii	CAby CAvo EPot ERCP GKev ISha ITim LAma NLar NRog SDeJ SDir WIce
* ***glauca*** 'Golden Flag'	NRog SDeJ
- 'Goldilocks'	SDeJ
graeca	GKev ITim NRog SDeJ
grandiflora	NRog
hispanica	see *F. lusitanica*
hupehensis	SBrt
imperialis 🏆H7	CKel GKev WHlf
- 'Argenteovariegata' (v)	GKev LAma NRog
- 'Aureomarginata' (v)	GKev LAma NRog SDir
- 'Aureovariegata' (v)	SDir
- 'Aurora'	CBcs CRos EHyd EPot ERCP ETay GKev GMcL LAma LRHS MPtr NBwr NLar NPer NRHS SCob SDeJ SPer WPhe
- 'Bach' (Rascal Series)	GKev ISha
- 'Beethoven' (Rascal Series)	GKev ISha NRog WCot
- 'Brahms' (Rascal Series)	GKev ISha
- 'Chopin' (Rascal Series)	CAvo GKev NRog
- 'Double Gold' (d) new	GKev LAma NLar
- 'Early Dream' new	GKev LAma
- 'Early Fantasy'	GKev
- 'Early Magic'	GKev LAma NRog
- 'Early Passion'	GKev SDir
- 'Early Sensation' new	GKev LAma
- 'Garland Star'	CRos EHyd GKev LAma LRHS NLar NRHS NRog SDeJ SDir
- 'Helena' new	NLar
- var. ***inodora***	GKev
- 'Inodora Purpurea'	LAma
- 'Lutea'	CAvo CRos EHyd ERCP GKev LAma LCro LRHS MPtr NBwr NRHS SCob SPoG WPhe
- 'Mahler' (Rascal Series)	GKev
- 'Maxima'	see *F. imperialis* 'Rubra Maxima'
- 'Maxima Lutea' 🏆H7	CRos EHyd ELan EPfP EPot ERCP ETay GKev GMcL LRHS NBwr NLar NRHS SDeJ SPoG

	- 'Orange Beauty'	CRos EHyd GKev LAma LRHS NRHS NRog SDeJ WPhe
	- 'Prolifera'	GKev LAma NRog SDeJ SPeP
	- 'Rubra'	EHyd ERCP ETay GKev LAma LCro LOPS LRHS MPtr NLar NRHS SCob WFar WPhe
§	- 'Rubra Maxima'	CRos EHyd ELan EPot ERCP GKev GMcL LRHS NRHS SDeJ WHlf
	- 'Satie' (Rascal Series)	GKev
	- 'Slagzwaard'	GKev LAma NRog
	- 'Striped Beauty'	EPot SDeJ SDir WPhe
	- 'Sulpherino'	LAma NRog
	- 'Sunset'	GKev LAma NLar
	- 'The Premier'	GKev LAma NRog SDeJ
	- 'Vivaldi' (Rascal Series)	EPot GKev NRog
	- 'William Rex'	CAvo CRos CWCL EHyd EPfP EPot ERCP GKev LAma LBuc LRHS NLar NRHS NRog SDir SPoG
	involucrata	WCot
	karadaghensis	see *F. crassifolia* subsp. *kurdica*
	koidzumiana	GKev
	latakiensis	CBor EPot GKev NRog
§	***lusitanica***	ITim
	meleagris 🏆H5	Widely available
	- var. ***unicolor*** subvar. ***alba*** 🏆H5	ERCP GKev ILea LCro LOPS NHol NLar NRog SDeJ SHar SPer SPhx WPnP WShi
	- - - 'Aphrodite'	EPot LAma NBir WCot
§	***messanensis***	ITim
	- subsp. ***gracilis***	ITim
	michailovskyi	CAvo CRos EHyd EPot ERCP ETay GKev LAma LRHS MNrw NHpl NRHS NRog SDeJ SRms WFar WPhe
	- 'Multiflorum'	GKev
§	***minuta***	NRog SDeJ
	montana	NRog
	nigra Mill.	see *F. pyrenaica*
	olgae	NRog
	olivieri	GKev
	pallidiflora 🏆H5	CAvo CBor CMiW CWCL EPot ERCP GKev ISha LAma NBir NHpl NRog SDeJ SPhx
§	***persica***	CAvo CBcs CBor CKel CPla ECha ECul EHyd EPfP EPot ERCP ETay ISha LAma LCro LOPS LRHS MHtn NLar NRHS NRog SPeP SPhx WHlf WPhe
	- 'Adiyaman' 🏆H4	SDeJ
	- 'Alba'	CAvo GKev NRog SDeJ SPeP SPhx WHlf
	- 'Bicolor'	LAma
	- 'Green Dreams'	ELan GKev LAma NLar
	- 'Ivory Bells'	EPot ERCP GKev LAma LCro LOPS NLar NRog SDeJ WPhe
	- 'Magic Bells'	LAma
	- 'Midnight Bells'	NRog
	- 'Pastel'	NRog
	- 'Purple Dynamite' **new**	LAma
	- 'Purple Favorite'	GKev
*	- 'Senkoy'	GKev NRog
	- 'Twin Towers Tribute'	GKev LAma NLar
	pontica 🏆H4	CAvo EPfP EPot ERCP GKev ITim LAma NHpl NRog SDeJ SPhx WCot
	pudica 'Giant'	NRog SDeJ
§	***pyrenaica*** 🏆H5	NRog
	raddeana	CAvo EMor EPot ERCP GKev LAma LCro NLar NRog SDeJ SPhx WCot WHlf
	roylei	ITim
	rubra major	see *F. imperialis* 'Rubra Maxima'
	sewerzowii	EPot GKev LAma NRog WCot
	sphaciotica	see *F. messanensis*
	stenanthera	CBor EPot GKev LAma NRog WHlf
	- 'Cambridge'	NRog
	- 'Ihnatschai'	NRog
	- 'Ugam'	NRog
	stribrnyi	EPot NRog
	thunbergii	GKev ISha LAma NRog WCot
	uva-vulpis	CAby CRos EAJP EHyd EPot ERCP EWoo GKev ISha LAma LCro LRHS LSto MBow MNrw NBir NRHS NRog SDeJ WFar WShi
	verticillata	ECha
	- 'Urdzhar'	NRog
	whittallii	NRog

Fuchsia ✿ (*Onagraceae*)

	'A.M. Larwick'	SLBF
	'Abbé Farges' (d)	CLoc CRos EHyd EPts LRHS NRHS SLBF SVic WRou
	'Abigail' (d)	WRou
	'Abundance'	EHDe
	'Achievement' 🏆H4	CLoc MJac SVic
	'Adinda' (T) 🏆H1c	EPts MHer WRou
	'Adrienne' (d)	EPts WRou
	'Aileen Foreman' **new**	MJac
	'Aisen'	WRou
	'Alan Swaby' **new**	SLBF
	'Alan Titchmarsh' 🏆H2	EPts SLBF
	'Alaska' (d)	CLoc
	'Alderford'	EHDe SLBF
	'Alfie' (d)	SLBF
	'Alfonso' (d)	SLBF
	'Alice Hoffman' (d) 🏆H4	Widely available
	'Alicia Sellars'	WRou
	'Alison Ewart'	CLoc SVic
	'Alison Patricia' 🏆H2	EHDe MJac SLBF SVic
	'Alison Reynolds' (d)	WRou
	'Alison Ruth Griffin' (d)	MJac
	'Alison Sweetman' 🏆H2	MJac
	'All Summer Beauty' (T)	SLBF WRou
	'Allen Jackson'	SLBF WRou
	'Alyssa May Garcia' (d)	EPts MJac SLBF WRou
	'Amazing Maisie' (d)	SLBF
	'Amelia Rose'	SLBF
	'Amelie Aubin'	CLoc WRou
	'Amy'	MJac
	'Amy Lye'	CLoc EHDe SVic
§	'Andenken an Heinrich Henkel' (T)	CLoc
	'Andrew Carnegie' (d)	CLoc
	'Angela' (d)	WRou
	'Angela Dawn'	WRou
	'Angela King'	WRou
	'Angela Leslie' (d)	SVic
	'Angel's Kiss' (E)	SLBF
	'Anita'	CLoc EPts MJac SLBF WRou
	'Ann Howard Tripp'	CLoc EPts MJac SVic WRou
	'Ann Reid'	SLBF
	'Anna Sunshine' (T)	EPts WRou
	'Annabel' (d) 🏆H4	CLoc CTri EPts MJac SLBF SVic WRou
	'Annie Brookfield' (d) **new**	SLBF
	'Annie Earle'	EHDe
	'Annie M.G. Schmidt'	EPts WRou
	'Anthea Day' (d)	CLoc
	'Anthonie Sherwood' (T)	WRou
	'Antigone'	EHDe SLBF
	'Antoinette Peeters' (d)	WRou
	'Applause' (d)	CLoc EPts SLBF
	aprica misapplied	see *F.* × *bacillaris*
	aprica Lundell	see *F. microphylla* subsp. *aprica*
	'Apricot Ice'	CLoc SVic
	'Arabella Improved'	EHDe
	arborea	see *F. arborescens*

§	***arborescens***	CBcs CCht CDow CHll CLoc CTsd CWCL ECre EHDe EWld LSou MCot SDys SIvy SVic WOld WRou
	– B&SWJ 10475	WCru
	'Arcady'	CLoc
	'Arctic Challenger' **new**	EPts
	'Ariel' (E)	LRHS SVic
	'Arkie'	MJac
	'Army Nurse' (d) 𝕐H4	CBod CEnd CLoc CRos EHDe EHyd ELan ELon EPfP EPts LCro LRHS MAsh MGos NBir NBwr NLar NRHS SGBe SGol SLBF SVic WHlf WLov WRou
	'Ashtede'	SLBF
	'Ashville'	SLBF WRou
	'Atlantic Star'	MJac
	'Aubergine'	see *F.* 'Gerharda's Aubergine'
	'Auenland'	MJac
	'Auntie Jinks' 𝕐H2	MJac
	'Aurora Superba'	CLoc SLBF
	'Autumnale' 𝕐H2	CLoc EHDe EPts SLBF SPoG WRou
	'Avalanche' ambig. (d)	EHDe SLBF
	'Avocet'	CLoc
	'Avon Celebration' (d/v)	CLoc
	'Avon Gem'	CLoc
	'Avon Glow' (d)	CLoc
	'Avon Gold'	CLoc
	'Awake Sweet Love' (T)	EPts
	'Aylisa Rowan' (E)	SLBF WRou
	'Azure Sky' (d)	MJac
	'Baby Blue Eyes' 𝕐H4	CBod CLoc CRos EHDe EHyd ELan LRHS LSRN MAsh NRHS SLBF SVic WRou
	'Baby Bright'	SLBF
	'Baby Thumb' (v)	EPts
§	× ***bacillaris*** (E)	CAbb CChe CGBo EPPr EWes SEle SIvy SLBF SPoG WHer WLov XLum
§	– 'Cottinghamii' (E)	EWld ILea WRou WSHC
§	– 'Reflexa' (E)	CCCN CTrC NQui
	'Bagworthy Water'	CLoc
	'Balkonkönigin'	CLoc
	'Ballerina Girl' (E)	SLBF WRou
	'Ballet Girl' (d) 𝕐H2	CLoc EHDe SLBF
	'Bambini'	EPts
	'Banks Peninsula'	GBin
	'Barbara'	CLoc EPts MJac SVic
	'Barbara Reynolds'	MJac WRou
	'Barbara Windsor'	MJac
	'Barry's Queen'	see *F.* 'Golden Border Queen'
	'Bart Comperen' (d)	WRou
	'Bashful' (d)	EPts SVic
	'Beacon'	CLoc CMac CRos EHDe EHyd EPfP EPts LRHS MAsh MJac NRHS SGol SLBF SPoG SVic WRou
	'Beacon Rosa' 𝕐H4	CLoc EHyd EPfP EPts LRHS MAsh MJac NRHS SLBF SPoG SVic WRou
	'Bealings' (d)	SLBF
	'Beauty of Bath' (d)	CLoc
	'Beauty of Clyffe Hall' Lye	EHDe
	'Beauty of Prussia' (d)	CLoc
	'Beauty of Swanley'	EHDe
	'Beauty of Trowbridge'	EHDe
	'Bella Rosella' (California Dreamers Series) (d) 𝕐H2	CLoc EPts LCro MBros MJac SCgs SCoo WRou
	'Belvoir Beauty' (d)	CLoc
	'Ben de Jong'	SLBF WRou
	'Ben Jammin'	CDoC CLoc EPfP EPts SVic
	'Ben-Ben'	SLBF WRou
	'Bernice Elizabeth' (d)	WRou
	'Bernie's Big-un' (d)	SLBF
	'Bernisser Hardy' 𝕐H4	EPts LRHS NQui SLBF XLum
	'Betsy Huuskes'	SLBF
	'Beverley'	EPts

	'Bicentennial' (d)	CLoc EPts LCro MBros MJac SLBF
	'Billy Green' (T) 𝕐H2	CLoc EHDe EPts MHer MJac SVic
	'Blacky' (d)	CCCN CPla SDix SDys WRou
	'Bland's New Striped'	CLoc EPts SLBF
§	'Blauer Engel' (d)	LCro MJac WHlf WRou
	'Blaze Away' (d)	MJac WRou
	BLUE ANGEL	see *F.* 'Blauer Engel'
	'Blue Bush'	EPts MJac SVic XLum
I	'Blue Danube' Blackwell (d)	CLoc
	'Blue Gown' (d)	CLoc SVic
	'Blue Lace' (d)	SVic
	'Blue Mirage' (d)	CLoc SVic
	'Blue Veil' (d)	CLoc MJac SCoo
	'Blue Waves' (d)	CLoc SVic
	'Blush o' Dawn' (d)	CLoc SVic
	'Bobby's Girl'	EPts
	'Bob's Best' (d)	EPts
	boliviana ambig.	EAri EHDe IDee MHer
§	***boliviana*** Carrière	CHll EGrI EPPr WCru WRou
	– B&SWJ 14871 **new**	WCru
§	– var. ***alba*** 𝕐H2	CHll CLoc CRHN EPts WFar
	– var. ***boliviana***	CRHN
	– var. ***luxurians*** 'Alba'	see *F. boliviana* Carrière var. *alba*
	– 'Pink Cornet'	WRou
	– f. ***puberulenta*** Munz	see *F. boliviana* Carrière
	'Bon Accorde'	CLoc EHDe EPts SLBF SVic
	'Boogie Nights' **new**	SLBF
I	'Boogie Woogie'	EPts MJac SLBF WRou
	'Borde Hill' (d)	EPts
	'Border Queen' 𝕐H4	CLoc EHDe EPts MJac SLBF SVic
	'Börnemann's Beste'	see *F.* 'Georg Börnemann'
	'Bouquet' (d)	EHDe SLBF
	'Bow Bells'	CLoc MJac
	'Boy Marc' (T) 𝕐H1c	SLBF
	'Brandt's 500 Club'	CLoc
	'Breevis Minimus'	SLBF
	'Brenda White'	CLoc
	'Brian McFetridge' (d)	WRou
	'Brilliant' ambig.	EHDe
	'Brilliant' Bull, 1865	CLoc
	'Brookwood Belle' (d) 𝕐H3	EPts MJac SLBF
	'Brutus' 𝕐H4	CLoc EHDe EHyd EPfP EPts LRHS MAsh NRHS SCoo SLBF SVic WFar WRou
	'Bryan Breary' (E)	WRou
	'Bryn Derw'	WRou
	'Bryn Seren'	SLBF WRou
	'Bryn-y-Baal'	WRou
	'Campo Thilco'	WRou
	campos-portoi	EBee MGil WPGP
	'Candy Bells' (d)	CSBt
	'Canny Bob'	MJac
	'Cara Mia' (d)	CLoc
	'Caradela' (d)	CLoc MJac
	'Cardinal'	CLoc
	'Cardinal Farges' (d)	CLoc SLBF SVic WRou
	'Careless Whisper'	SLBF
	'Carla Johnston' 𝕐H2	CLoc EPts MJac SVic WRou
	'Carmel Blue'	CLoc SCob SVic WRou
	'Carnoustie' (d)	EHDe
	'Carol Grace' (d)	CLoc
	'Caroline'	CLoc EPts SVic
	'Caroline's Joy'	MJac SCoo
	'Cascade'	CLoc EPts MJac
	'Cecile' (d)	CCCN EPts MJac SLBF
	'Celebration' (d)	CLoc
	'Celia Smedley' 𝕐H3	CLoc CRos EHDe EHyd EPts LCro LRHS MJac NRHS SLBF SVic WRou
	'Ceri'	CLoc WMal
	'Champagne Celebration'	CLoc
	'Chang' 𝕐H2	CLoc SLBF SVic WRou
	'Chantelle Garcia' (d)	EPts MJac SLBF
	'Chapel Rossan' (E)	SLBF WRou

'Charles Welch'	EPts
CHARLIE DIMMOCK ('Foncha'PBR) (d)	CLoc
'Charming'	CLoc EHDe EHyd LRHS MAsh MJac NRHS SVic
'Chatt's Delight'	SLBF
'Checkerboard' ♀H3	CLoc EHDe EPts MHer MJac SLBF SVic WRou
'Chelsea Louise'	EPts
'Cherry Lee'	SLBF WRou
'Cherry Pop' (E)	WRou
'Chessboard'	CLoc
'Chillerton Beauty' ♀H4	CLoc CTri EHDe EHyd ELan ELon EPts LRHS MJac NLar NRHS SLBF SVic WFar WRou
'Chilli Red'	CBcs EHDe EHyd EPts LCro LRHS NRHS
'China Lantern'	CLoc SVic
'Chloe Christina' (E)	WRou
'Chris and Kath' (d) **new**	SLBF
'Chris Bright'	MJac WRou
'Chris Tarrant' (d)	EPts
cinerea	EHDe
'Cinnabarina' (E)	CLoc SLBF SVic
'Citation'	SVic
'City of Adelaide' (d)	CLoc
'Clair de Lune'	SLBF
'Claudia' (d)	EPts MBros MJac SLBF WRou
'Cliff's Hardy'	SVic
'Cliff's Own'	SVic
'Cliff's Unique' (d)	EPts
'Clifton Beauty' (d)	MJac
'Clifton Charm'	EPts MJac SVic
'Clifton Pride'	MJac WRou
'Clipper'	EHDe
'Cloth of Gold'	CLoc EHDe MJac SLBF SVic
'Cloverdale Pearl'	MAsh SPoG
'Coachman' ♀H4	CLoc EHDe EPts MBros SLBF WRou
coccinea	CSde SVic
'Colette Kelly'	SVic
'Collingwood' (d)	CLoc
'Colne Fantasy' (v)	SLBF
'Colne Raider'	WRou
'Conchetta Garcia'	WRou
'Connie' (d)	SVic XLum
'Connor's Cascade'	SLBF
'Conspicua' ♀H4	LRHS SIvy SLBF SVic WRou
'Constance' (d)	CLoc MJac SLBF SVic
'Constance Comer'	MJac SVic WRou
'Coralle' (T) ♀H1c	CCCN CLoc EPts MBros MJac SLBF WRou
'Corallina' ♀H4	CLoc SVic
* ***cordata*** B&SWJ 9095	WCru
– B&SWJ 10325	WCru
cordifolia misapplied	see *F. splendens*
'Core'ngrato' (d)	CLoc
'Cornish Blue'	CLoc
'Cornwall Calls' (d)	EHDe
corymbiflora misapplied	see *F. boliviana* Carrière
'Costa Brava'	CLoc
'Cotta Christmas Tree' (E)	SLBF WRou
'Cottinghamii'	see *F.* × *bacillaris* 'Cottinghamii'
'Cotton Candy' (d)	CLoc SVic WRou
'Countdown Carol' (d)	EPts
'Countess of Aberdeen'	EHDe SLBF
'Countess of Maritza' (d)	CLoc
'Cover Girl' (d)	EPts
'Crackerjack'	CLoc
'Crescendo' (d)	CLoc
'Crinkley Bottom' (d)	EPts MJac SLBF
'Crosby Serendipity'	CLoc
cylindracea misapplied	see *F.* × *bacillaris*
'Daisy Bell'	CLoc MJac
'Dana Samantha'	EPts
'Dancing Bloom'	EPts
'Dancing Flame' (d) ♀H3	CLoc EHDe EPts MBros MJac SLBF WRou
'Daniel Pfaller' (d)	MJac
'Danny Boy' (d)	CLoc
'Dark Eyes' (d) ♀H4	CLoc LCro MJac SLBF
'David' ♀H4	CLoc EHDe ELan ELon EPts LSRN MJac SLBF SPoG WAvo WCot WLov WRou
'David Clifford'	EHDe
'David Lockyer' (d)	CLoc
'Dawn Fantasia' (v)	CLoc EPts
'Dawn Star' (d)	CLoc
'Deborah Street' (d)	CLoc
'DebRon's Black Cherry'	SLBF
'DebRon's White Linen' (d)	WRou
'Deep Purple' (d)	CLoc EPts MJac SCoo WRou
'Delia Smith' (d)	EPts
'Delicate Blue'	SLBF
'Delicate Purple'	EHDe EPts SLBF WFar WMal WRou
'Delphobe'	EPts
'Delta's Bride'	SLBF
'Delta's Groom'	SLBF
'Delta's Paljas'	SLBF
'Delta's Sara'	Widely available
§ ***denticulata*** ♀H2	CLoc EAri EHDe EHyd EPts LRHS MHer NRHS SLBF SVic
'Desperate Daniel'	EPts
'Devonshire Dumpling' (d) ♀H2	CLoc EPts MJac SLBF WRou
'Diamond Wedding'	SVic
'Diana Wright'	WAvo WLov
'Diane Stephens'	WRou
'Dipton Dainty' (d)	CLoc SVic
'Display' ♀H4	CLoc CRos EHDe EHyd EPfP EPts LRHS MGos MJac MPri NPer NRHS SCob SGBe SGol SLBF SPoG SVic WRou
'Diva'	WCot
'Doc'	EPts SVic
'Docteur Topinard'	CLoc
'Doctor'	see *F.* 'The Doctor'
'Doctor Foster' ♀H4	CLoc CTri EHDe MAsh SVic
'Doctor Olson' (d)	CLoc
'Doctor Robert'	EPts MJac
'Doctor Sat Sandilands' (d)	WRou
'Dodo'	SLBF
§ 'Dollar Prinzessin' (d) ♀H4	CLoc CMac CRos EHDe EHyd EPfP EPts EShb LCro LRHS MBros MGos MJac MPri NPer NRHS SGol SLBF SLim SPlb SVic WFar WHlf WRou
'Dominyana'	EHDe
'Dopy' (d)	EPts SVic
'Doray'	EPts
'Doreen Redfern'	CLoc SVic
'Doris Joan'	SLBF
'Dorothea Flower'	CLoc
'Dorothy'	EPts SLBF
'Dorothy Ann'	SLBF
'Dorothy Day' (d)	CLoc
'Dorothy Hanley' (d)	CCCN CLoc EPts MJac SCob SLBF SVic WRou
'Drake 400' (d)	CLoc
'Drame' (d)	EHDe SVic
'Duchess of Albany'	CLoc EHDe
'Duchess of Cornwall' (d)	EPts
'Duke of Wellington' Haag, 1956 (d)	CLoc
'Dunrobin Bedder'	EHDe SLBF
'Dusky Rose' (d)	CLoc MJac
'Dutch Mill'	CLoc

	'Dying Embers' ♀H4	CLoc CMil EShb GBin MAsh MHer SDix SVen WRou
	'East Anglian'	CLoc
	'Easter Belle'	EHyd LRHS NRHS
	'Ebbtide' (d)	CLoc
	'Eden Lady'	CLoc
	'Eden Rock' (d)	CLoc
	'Edith' ambig.	EPts
	'Edith' Brown (d)	SLBF
	'El Cid'	CLoc SVic
	'Ela'	WRou
	'Elaine Ann'	EPts MJac
	'Elaine Cosgrove'	WRou
	ELECTRIC LIGHTS ('Nufu1'PBR)	LRHS
	'Elfin Glade'	CLoc SVic
	'Elfriede Ott' (T) ♀H1c	CLoc WRou
	'Elma'	MJac WRou
	'Elsa' (d)	SVic
	'Elsie Lowis Kay'	WRou
	'Emily Bright'	EHDe
	'Emily Eve' (d)	EPts MJac SLBF
	'Emma Payne'	SLBF
	'Empress of Prussia' ♀H4	CLoc EHDe EPPr EPts SLBF SVic
	encliandra (E)	NWad
	- subsp. ***encliandra*** (E)	NWad
§	'Enfant Prodigue' (d)	CLoc SDix SLBF SVic XLum
	'Eppsii'	SLBF
	'Eric's Majestic' (d)	MJac
	'Ernie'PBR	EPts SLBF WRou
	'Eruption' (T)	CLoc CPla CWCL MJac
	'Esmay'	WRou
	'Estelle Marie'	CLoc WRou
	'Eternal Flame' (d)	EPts
	'Eternity' (d)	WRou
	'Ethel May' (d)	MJac
	'Eva Boerg' ♀H4	CCCN CLoc CTri EPts MBros WKif WRou
	'Evensong'	CLoc SVic
	'Evita'PBR (Bella Series)	LCro LOPS
	excorticata	CBcs CCCN CTsd ESwi SIvy SPlb WBor
	'Fairy Lights'	CBcs
	'Falklands' (d)	EHDe EPts SLBF
	'Falling Stars'	CLoc
	'Fancy Pants' (d)	CLoc SVic
	'Felicity Kendal' (d)	SCoo
	'Festival Lights' (E)	SLBF WRou
	'Ffion'	EPts WRou
	'Finn'	EPts
	'Fiona'	CLoc SVic
	'Fiona Pitt' (E)	SLBF
	'Fire Mountain' (d)	CLoc
	'Firecracker'	see *F.* 'John Ridding'
	'Flair' (d)	CLoc
	'Flamingo Wings' (d)	EPts
	'Flanders Field'	SLBF WRou
	'Flash' ♀H4	CLoc CTri EHyd ELan EPts LRHS MJac NRHS SLBF SPoG SVic WOld WRou
	'Flashlight'	EWld MAsh MJac SCoo
	'Flat Jack o' Lancashire' (d)	SLBF
	'Fleur de Picardie'	SLBF
	'Flirtation Waltz' (d)	CLoc MJac SVic
	'Flocon de Neige'	SLBF
	'Florentina' (d)	SVic
	'Florrie's Gem' (d)	SLBF
	'Flying Cloud' (d)	CLoc SVic
	'Flying Scotsman' (d)	CLoc EPts SCoo SVic WRou
	'Forget-me-not'	CLoc SVic
	'Four Farthings' (d)	EPts WRou
	'Foxgrove Wood' ♀H4	EPts LRHS SLBF SVic
	'Frances Haskins'	WRou
	'Frank Saunders'	SLBF WRou
	'Frank Unsworth' (d)	EPts MJac
	'Frankfurt 2006'	MJac
	'Frankie Boy'	SLBF
	'Frankie's Magnificent Seven' (d)	EPts
	'Frans Boers'	SLBF
	'Frau Hilde Rademacher' (d)	EPts SLBF SVic WRou
	'Fred's First' (d)	SVic
	'Friendly Fire' (d)	CLoc
	'Frosted Flame'	CLoc MJac SLBF
	'Frozen Tears'	EPts
	'Fuchsiade '88'	CLoc
	'Fuchsiarama '91' (T) ♀H2	SLBF
	'Fuji-san'	ELon EPts
	fulgens (T) ♀H2	CHll CWal EPPr WRou
*	- 'Variegata' (T/v)	EPts WRou
	'Fulpila'	SLBF
	'Gail Barber'	WRou
	'Galadriel'	SLBF
	'Garden News' (d) ♀H4	CBod CEnd CLoc CRos EHyd EPfP EPts LRHS MAsh MBow MBros MJac NBir NPer NRHS SCob SLBF SVic WFar WHlf WRou
	'Gartenmeister Bonstedt' (T) ♀H1c	CLoc EWld WRou
	'Gary Rhodes' (d)	SCoo
	'Gay Fandango' (d)	CLoc
	'Gay Spinner' (d)	CLoc
	'Gemma Fisher' (d)	EPts
	GENE ('Goetzgene'PBR) (Shadowdancer Series)	SCoo
	'Général Monk' (d)	EPts
	'Genii' ♀H4	Widely available
	'Geoff Oke'	WRou
	'Geoffrey Smith' (d)	EPts
§	'Georg Börnemann' (T) ♀H2	CLoc MJac
	'George Barr'	EHyd LRHS NRHS
§	'Gerharda's Aubergine'	CLoc
	'Giant Pink Enchanted' (d)	CLoc
	'Gilt Edge' (v)	CLoc
	'Gina Bowman' (E)	EPts SLBF WRou
	GINGER ('Goetzginger'PBR) (Shadowdancer Series)	SCoo
	'Ginny B' **new**	MJac
	'Gipsy Princess' (d)	CLoc
	'Gladiator' (d)	CMac EHDe
	'Gladys Lorimer'	EHyd EPts LRHS NRHS
	glazioviana ♀H2	CSde EPPr EPts SLBF SVen
§	'Globosa'	CAgr
	'Glowing Embers'	WRou
	'Glowing Lilac' (d)	EPts
	'Golden Anniversary' (d)	CLoc
§	'Golden Border Queen'	CLoc EHDe
	'Golden Dawn'	CLoc SVic
	'Golden Girl'	SLBF
	'Golden Herald'	EHDe SLBF
	'Golden Marinka' (v) ♀H2	CLoc EHDe
	'Golden Swingtime' (d)	MJac
	'Golden Treasure' (v)	CLoc
	'Good as Gold'	WRou
	'Göttingen' (T)	SLBF
	gracilis	see *F. magellanica* var. *gracilis*
	'Graf Witte'	EPPr SVic
	'Grandma Sheila'	WRou
	'Grandma Sinton' (d)	CLoc
	'Grandpa Jack' (d)	SLBF
	'Grayrigg'	ELon EPPr EPts EShb LSRN MHer SGBe SLBF SVic WRou
	'Great Ouse' (d)	EPts
	'Great Scott' (d)	CLoc
	'Green 'n' Gold'	EHDe
	'Greenpeace'	SLBF

'Grumpy'	EPts SVic
'Gruss aus dem Bodethal'	CLoc EPts
'Gunton Park' (T)	EHDe
'H.G. Brown'	SLBF
'Hannah Louise' (d)	EPts
'Happy'	EPts MHer SVic
'Happy Anniversary'	CLoc
'Happy Birthday' (d) **new**	MAsh
'Happy Fellow'	CLoc WRou
'Happy Wedding Day' (d)	CLoc EPts SCoo SVic
'Hapsburgh'	EHDe
'Harbour Lites'	SLBF
'Harlow Car'	EPts
'Harriet Lye'	EHDe
'Harry Gray' (d) 🏆H2	CLoc EPts MJac SLBF WRou
'Harry Taylor' (d)	EPts
'Harry's Sunshine'	SLBF
hartwegii	MHer
'Harvey's Reward'	SLBF
'Hastings'	SLBF
hatschbachii 🏆H2	CBcs EBee EHDe EPPr EShb EWes LRHS MCot SBrt SDix SEle SGBe SIvy SPlb SVen WFar WPGP
'Haute Cuisine' (d)	CLoc
'Hawaiian Sunset' (d)	CLoc EPts SLBF
'Hawkshead' 🏆H4	Widely available
'Hayley Jackson'	MJac
'Hayley Jay' (d)	SLBF
'Hazel Elizabeth'	WRou
'Heidi Ann' (d) 🏆H4	CLoc CRos EHyd EPts LRHS MAsh MBros NRHS SLBF SVic
§ 'Heidi Weiss' (d)	CLoc
'Heinrich Henkel'	see *F.* 'Andenken an Heinrich Henkel'
'Helen Clare' (d)	CLoc
'Helen Storer'	MJac
'Hemsleyana'	see *F. microphylla* subsp. *hemsleyana*
'Her Majesty's Crown' (T)	SLBF
'Herald' 🏆H4	CRos EHDe EHyd LRHS MGos SLBF SVic
'Herbé de Jacques'	see *F.* 'Mr West'
'Heritage' (d)	CLoc
'Hermiena'	CLoc EPts MHer SLBF SVic
'Herps Pierement'	SLBF
'Herps Serang'	SLBF
'Hi Di'	SLBF WRou
'Hidcote Beauty' 🏆H2	CLoc EHDe SLBF
'Hobson's Choice' (d)	SLBF
'Holly's Beauty' (d)	CLoc EPts WRou
'Hot Coals'	EPts MJac SVic WRou
'Howlett's Hardy' 🏆H4	CLoc SVic
'Hula Girl' (d)	MJac
'Huntsman' (d)	CCCN
'I Love You'	WRou
'Ian Storey'	EHyd LRHS NRHS WRou
'Icecap'	SVic
'Iced Champagne'	CLoc MJac
'Ichiban' (d)	CLoc
'Icicles Chandelier'	SLBF
'Igloo Maid' (d)	CLoc
'Imogen Faye' (d)	SLBF WRou
'Impudence'	CLoc
'Impulse' (d)	CLoc
'Insulinde' (T)	EHDe EPts MHer MJac SLBF
'Iona'	WRou
'Irene Sinton' (d)	MJac
'Isn't She Lovely'	SLBF
'Italiano' (d)	MJac
'Ivana van Amsterdam'	WRou
'Jac Damen'	SLBF
'Jack Shahan' 🏆H2	CCCN CLoc EPts MBow MJac WRou
'Jack Siverns'	WRou
'Jan Everett' (d)	SLBF
'Janice Perry's Gold' (v)	MJac
'Janie' (d)	EHyd EPfP LBuc LRHS MAsh NRHS SVic
'Jasper's Formidable' (T)	SLBF
'Jasper's Lightning' (T)	EHDe SLBF
'Jasper's Unbelievable'	WRou
'Jean Frisby'	CLoc
'Jean Harper'	WRou
'Jean Taylor'	EPts WRou
'Jean Webb' (v)	WCot
'Jeanie J'	WRou
'Jef van der Kuylen' (d)	WRou
'Jennifer'	MJac
'Jennifer Ann'	MAsh NRHS SLBF WRou
'Jenny Carr'	WRou
'Jenny May'	CLoc EPts
'Jess'	SLBF
'Jessica Reynolds'	WRou
'Jester' Holmes (d)	CLoc
'Jet'	MJac
'Jiddles' (E)	SLBF
'Jill Holloway' (T)	SLBF
'Jim Dodge' (d)	EPts
'Jimmy Cricket' (E)	WRou
'Joan Cooper'	CLoc SLBF SVic
'Joan Knight'	CLoc
'Joan Margaret' (d)	MJac
'Joan Morris'	SLBF
'Joanna Lumley' (d)	EPts
'Jo-Anne Fisher' (d)	EPts
'Joanne Jackson'	MJac
'John Bartlett'	CLoc
'John Egan'	WRou
'John Galea'	SLBF WRou
'John Grooms' (d)	WRou
'John Hitchcock' (d)	WRou
'John Lockyer'	CLoc
'John Maynard Scales' (T) 🏆H2	MJac WRou
§ 'John Ridding'PBR (T/v) 🏆H1c	SPoG
'Johnny Boy'	SLBF WRou
JOLLIES FORCE BONDY	WRou
JOLLIES FORCE PARIS ('Brfu 09721'PBR)	WRou
JOLLIES MACON ('Brfu 12811')	WRou
JOLLIES MENTON ('Brfu 0543'PBR)	WRou
JOLLIES NANCY ('Brfu 07951'PBR)	WRou
JOLLIES REIMS	WRou
JOLLIES TARBES ('Brfu 0582')	WRou
JOLLIES TRAILING BELFORT ('Brfu 10681'PBR)	WRou
'Jon Oram'	CLoc
I 'Joy'	SLBF
'Joy Patmore'	CLoc SLBF
'Joyce Sinton'	CLoc
'Juella'	WRou
'Julie Marie' (d)	MJac
'June Marie Shaw'	MJac
'Just Donna' **new**	SLBF
'Just Pat'	MJac
'Just Terry' (d)	EHDe SLBF
'Kaley Jackson'	MJac WRou
'Karen Isles' (E)	SLBF WRou
'Karen Louise' (d)	CLoc
'Kate Taylor' (d)	SLBF
'Kath van Hanegem'	CLoc
'Katie Alice'	WRou

	'Katie Coast'	WRou
	'Katie Rogers'	EPts
	'Katjan'	EHDe GBin SLBF WFar WRou
	'Katrina Thompsen'	CLoc EPts SLBF
	'Ken Tudor'	MJac
	'Kenny Walkling' ♀H2	MJac SLBF
	'Kimberly' (d)	MJac
	'King's Ransom' (d)	CLoc
	'Kit Oxtoby' (d)	CLoc MJac
	'Knight Errant'	EHDe SLBF
	'Kobold'	MJac
	'Kolding Perle'	SLBF
	'Kuniko Atarashi' (d)	WRou
	'Kwintet'	MJac
	'La Campanella' (d) ♀H2	CCCN CLoc EHDe EPts MBros MJac
	'Lady Boothby' ♀H4	Widely available
	'Lady Framlingham' (d)	EPts
	'Lady in Black' (d)	CBcs ELan ELon LSou SIvy SPoG WLov WTyc
	'Lady in Red' (d)	WRou
	'Lady Isobel Barnett'	CLoc MJac SLBF
	'Lady Rebecca' (d)	CLoc
	'Lady Thumb' (d) ♀H3	Widely available
	'Lambada'	CLoc WRou
	'Lancashire Lad' (d)	MJac
	'Land van Beveren'	SLBF
	'Lassie' (d)	CLoc
	'Last Chance' (E)	SLBF
	'Laura' ambig.	SVic WRou
I	'Laura' (Dutch)	CLoc EPts SLBF
	'Laura Cross' (E)	SLBF WRou
	'Lauren'	WRou
	'Lechlade Gordon'	EHDe
	'Lechlade Gorgon'	EHyd LRHS NRHS SLBF
	'Lechlade Magician'	EPts SEND SLBF WMal WRou
	'Lechlade Tinkerbell' (E)	EHDe
	'Lena' (d) ♀H2	CLoc CMac CTri EHDe EPts MJac SLBF SMrm SPlb SVic
	'Lena Dalton' (d)	CLoc
	'Leonora'	CLoc SLBF SVic WRou
	'Lesley's Wonder'	MJac
	'Leslie Bowman' ♀H2	EHDe SLBF WRou
	'Lett's Delight' (d)	EPts
	'Letty Lye'	EHDe
	'Leverhulme'	see *F.* 'Leverkusen'
§	'Leverkusen' (T)	CLoc MJac SLBF
	'Liebriez' (d) ♀H4	SVic WRou
	'Lilac Lustre' (d)	CLoc SVic
	'Lilian'	MJac
	'Lillian Annetts' (d) ♀H2	EHDe MJac SLBF WRou
	'Lillibet' (d)	CLoc
	'Lincoln Castle'	WRou
	'Linda Grace'	MJac
	'Linda Hinchliffe'	EHDe EPts MJac SLBF WFar WRou
	'Lindisfarne' (d)	CLoc MJac
	'Lionel'	WRou
	'Lisa' (d)	EPts
	'Little Beauty'	SVic
	'Little Boy Blue'	EPts
	'Little Brook Gem'	SLBF
	'Little Catbells' (E)	SLBF
	'Little Cracker'	SPoG
	'Little Jessica' (E)	MJac SLBF WRou
	'Little Tony'	SLBF WRou
	'Loeky'	CLoc SVic
	'Logan Garden'	see *F. magellanica* 'Logan Woods'
	'London 2000'	CLoc EHDe MJac SLBF WRou
	'London in Bloom'	SLBF
	'Lonely Ballerina' (d)	CLoc
	'Lord Byron'	CLoc
	'Lord Lonsdale'	EPts WRou
	'Lord Roberts'	CLoc EHDe SLBF
	'Lorna Swinbank'	SVic

	'Lottie Hobby' (E) ♀H3	CLoc CMac EGrI EHyd ELan EPts ITim NWad SVic WCot WRou
	'Louise Emershaw' (d)	MJac
	'Louise Nicholls'	MJac
	'Loveliness'	CLoc EHDe SVic
	'Lovely Linda'	SLBF
	'Love's Reward' ♀H2	CLoc MJac SLBF SVic
	loxensis misapplied	see *F.* 'Speciosa'
	'Lucy Locket'	MJac
	'Lye's Elegance'	EHDe
	'Lye's Excelsior'	EHDe
	'Lye's Favourite'	EHDe
	'Lye's Own'	EHDe SLBF
	'Lye's Perfection'	EHDe
	'Lye's Unique' ♀H3	CLoc EHDe EPts MJac SLBF SVic
	'Lyndon'	MJac
	'Lyndon Clements'	MJac
	'Lynette' (d)	CLoc
	'Lynne Patricia' (d)	EPts
	'Machu Picchu'	CLoc EPts WRou
	'Madame Cornélissen' (d) ♀H4	CLoc CMac CRos CTri EHDe EHeP EHyd ELan EMor EPfP EPts LRHS MAsh NLar NRHS SCoo SEND SLBF SLim SPer SVic WFar WLov WRou XLum
	magellanica ♀H4	CBcs CWal EHyd GArf LRHS MAsh MGil NPer NRHS NWea SPer SVic WCAu WFar WGwG WOld WSpi
	- 'Alba'	see *F. magellanica* var. *molinae* 'Alba'
	- 'Alba Variegata' (v)	SPer WFar
	- 'Angel's Teardrop'	WRou
	- 'Arauco'	SBrt
	- 'Folius Aureus'	WFar
	- 'Gold Mountain'	CBod WFar
§	- var. ***gracilis*** ♀H4	CAgr CLoc CTri EPfP NBro
	- - 'Aurea' ♀H4	CBcs CKel CMac EHeP EHyd ELan ELon EPPr EPfP LRHS MHer MRav NRHS SCoo SDix SLBF SPer SRms SVic WAvo WRou XLum
	- - 'Purple Mountain'	CBod LPla
	- - 'Variegata' (v) ♀H4	EHyd EPfP MGos MRav SVic
§	- - 'Versicolor' (v) ♀H4	Widely available
	- 'Lady Bacon'	CBcs CBod CMil EBee EHDe EHyd ELon EPts EShb EWes LRHS MCot MHer NLar NRHS SDys SEND SLBF SPoG WBor WMal WOld WPGP WRou WSHC WTyc
§	- 'Logan Woods'	EBee ELon EPfP GKin MBlu SLBF SMrm WPGP
	- 'Lyonesse Lady'	WRou
	- var. ***molinae***	CTri EBee ELan EPfP EShb GBin MBlu MNrw MSwo NBid NPer SCob SPer SPlb WFar
§	- - 'Alba' ♀H4	CBod CDoC EHDe EHeP EPts EWld GArf GMcL MNHC MPie SGol WFar WGwG WSpi
I	- - 'Alba Aureovariegata' (v)	CBcs CMac WFar
	- - 'Golden Sharpitor' (v)	CCCN WFar
	- - 'Mr Knight's Blush'	WSpi
§	- - 'Sharpitor' (v) ♀H4	CDoC CKel EBee ECha ELan ELon EPfP LRHS NChi NPer SPer SPoG WFar WKif WLov WRou WSHC
	- 'Pumila'	EPot EWes GArf MAsh MHer SMHy WAbe WFar
	- 'Purpurea'	LRHS SGBe
§	- 'Thompsonii' ♀H4	EHDe SMHy
	- 'Variegata Aurea' (v)	EHeP SGBe WFar
	'Magic Flute'	CLoc MJac
	'Mandarin Cream'	CLoc
	'Mantilla' (T)	MJac
	'Maori Maid' (d)	LCro MJac

'Marble Crepe' (T)	SLBF
'Marcia'^{PBR} (Shadowdancer Series)	CLoc
'Marcus Graham' (d)	CLoc SLBF WRou
'Margaret' (d) ♀^{H4}	CLoc CTri ELon EPts SLBF SVic WFar WRou
'Margaret Brown' ♀^{H4}	CLoc CTri EHyd LRHS NRHS SLBF SVic WRou
'Margaret My Own'	EPts
'Margaret Roe'	MJac
'Margaret Viscountess Thurso'	SLBF
'Margarite Dawson' (d)	SVic
'Maria Landy'	MJac SLBF
'Maria Mathilde' (d)	SLBF
'Maria Shaw'	EPts
'Mariana' **new**	EPts
'Marin Glow' ♀^{H3}	CLoc SVic
'Marina Kelly'	WRou
'Marinka' ♀^{H2}	CLoc EHDe EPts MBros MJac SLBF
MARISKA ('Bf01'^{PBR}) (Bella Series)	CLoc LCro LOPS
'Marlies de Keijzer' (E)	EPts NWad SLBF SVen WRou
'Mart'	SLBF
'Martha Adcock'	MJac SLBF WRou
'Martin's Yellow Surprise' (T)	SLBF
'Mary' (T) ♀^{H1c}	CLoc EPts MJac SLBF WCot
'Mary Lockyer' (d)	CLoc
'Mauve Beauty' (d)	EHDe SLBF
'Mauve Wisp' (d)	SVic
'Mavis Enderby'	MJac SLBF
'Max Cobi'	MJac SLBF WRou
I 'Maxima'	CLoc EPts SLBF WRou
'Maxine's Smile'	MJac SLBF
'Meditation' (d)	CLoc
'Melting Moments' (d)	SCoo WRou
'Mephisto' ♀^{H2}	LRHS
'Mercurius' ♀^{H4}	LRHS XLum
'Mersty' (d)	SLBF WRou
I 'Mexicali Rose' Machado	CLoc
'Michael' (d/v)	EPts
'Michael Wallis' (T)	SLBF
michoacanensis misapplied	see *F. microphylla* subsp. *aprica*
michoacanensis Sessé & Moç. B&SWJ 9148 (E)	WCru
'Micky Goult' ♀^{H2}	CLoc EPts MJac
microphylla (E)	CBcs CBod CElw CLoc CTsd CWal EBee GBin GQue MGil SDix SMHy SMad SRkn SVic WAbe XSte
- B&SWJ 10331	WCru
§ - subsp. ***aprica*** (E) B&SWJ 9101	WCru
- - 'Dolly's Dress' (E)	WCru
§ - subsp. ***hemsleyana*** (E)	SVic
- - B&SWJ 10478	WCru
- - 'Silver Lining' (E)	CCCN CTsd EPPr MBros NCou SDix SWvt WCot WCru WFar WNPC XSte
- 'Variegata' (E/v)	EWes
§ 'Mieke Meursing' ♀^{H2}	CLoc MJac SLBF SVic
'Millennium'	CLoc EPts MJac SCoo SVic WRou
'Millfield Alpha'	EPts
'Millfield Bravo'	EPts
'Millfield Charlie'	EPts
'Millfield Delta'	EPts
'Millfield Echo'	EPts WRou
'Millfield Foxtrot'	EPts
'Ming'	CLoc
'Miniature Jewels' (E)	SLBF
minimiflora misapplied	see *F.* × *bacillaris*
'Minipani'	SLBF
'Minirose'	EHDe EPts SLBF

'Miramere'	EPts
'Miranda' (Bella Series)	WRou
'Mischief'	SVic
'Misha Charlotte'	SLBF
'Miss California' (d)	CLoc
'Miss Lye'	EHDe
'Miss Muffett' (d)	EPts
'Mission Bells'	CLoc EPts SVic
'Misty Mease'	MJac
'Molesworth' (d)	MJac
'Money Spinner'	CLoc
'Mood Indigo' (d)	CLoc
'Moody Blues'	WRou
'Moonbeam' (d)	CLoc
'Moonglow' (d)	MJac
'Moonlight Sonata'	CLoc
'More Applause' (d)	CLoc
'Morning Light' (d)	CLoc
'Mountain Mist' (d)	SVic
'Mr A. Huggett'	CLoc EPts SLBF
§ 'Mr West' (v)	CEme SCob WFar XSte
'Mrs Audrey Berkley' (d)	SLBF
'Mrs B.' (E)	MJac
'Mrs Churchill'	CLoc
'Mrs Grant'	EHDe
'Mrs J Bright'	EHDe
'Mrs Lee Belton' (E)	SLBF
'Mrs Marshall'	EMal SLBF
'Mrs Popple' ♀^{H4}	Widely available
'Mrs W. Castle'	SVic
'Mrs W.P. Wood' ♀^{H4}	CBod CLoc EHDe ELon MSCN SVic WRou
'Mrs W. Rundle'	CLoc SLBF
'Mrs Wilks' ♀^{H1c}	SLBF WRou
'Multa'	WRou
'Muriel' (d)	CLoc
'My Charlotte'	EHDe SLBF
'My Dad'	SLBF
'My Grandchildren'	SLBF WRou
'My Little Cracker'	MJac WRou
'My Little Dream' (d)	WRou
'My Little Fairy'	WRou
'My Little Fat Friend' **new**	SLBF
'My Little Gem'	WRou
'My Little Sparkler'	WRou
I 'My Mum' Dobson	SLBF
'My Mum' Rolt **new**	WRou
'My Pat'	SLBF
'My Sacha'	SLBF
'Myriad'	SLBF
'Nancy Lou' (d)	CLoc MJac SLBF SVic
'Natasha Sinton' (d)	CCCN MJac
'Nathan Rhys'	EPts
'Neil B' **new**	MJac
'Nell Gwyn'	CLoc
'Nellie Nuttall' ♀^{H2}	CLoc EHDe EPts
'Neopolitan' (E)	CLoc EHDe EPts SVic
'Nephele'	EPts WRou
'New Millennium' (d)	LCro
'Nice 'n' Easy' (d)	MJac WRou
'Nicki's Findling'	EPts MJac WRou
'Nicola Jane' (d)	EPts MAsh MJac SLBF SVic WRou
'Nicola Storey'	WRou
'Nicolette'	MJac
§ ***nigricans*** B&SWJ 10664	WCru
'Nora'^{PBR} (Bella Series)	WRou
'Northern Jewel'	EPts SLBF
'Northilda'	SVic
'Northway'	CLoc
'O Sole Mio'	SVic
obconica (E)	EHDe
'Obcylin' (E)	EPts MHer
'Ocean Beach'	EPts

'Oetnang' (d)	CTri SCoo
'Old Somerset' (v)	CCCN
'Olga Storey'	EHyd LRHS NRHS
'Olive Smith'	EHDe EPts MJac
OLIVIA ('Bf06'PBR) (Bella Series)	WRou
'Olympic Sunset'	SVic
'Opalescent' (d)	CLoc
'Orange Crush'	CLoc
'Orange Crystal'	MJac SLBF SVic
'Orange Drops'	CLoc EPts WRou
'Orange Flare'	CLoc SLBF
'Orange King' (d)	CLoc WHlf
'Orange Mirage'	CLoc
'Orange Star' (E)	SLBF WRou
'Orangeblossom'	SLBF
'Orient Express' (T) ♀H1c	CLoc
'Ornamental Pearl' (v)	CLoc SLBF
'Other Fellow'	EPts MJac SLBF
'Oulton Empress' (E)	SLBF WRou
'Oulton Fairy' (E)	SLBF
'Oulton Painted Lady' (E)	WRou
'Oulton Red Imp' (E)	SLBF
'Oulton Travellers Rest' (E)	SLBF WRou
'Our Carol'	SLBF WRou
'Our Claire'	WRou
'Our Hilary'	SLBF
'Our Michelle'	SLBF
'Our Nan' (d)	MJac
'Our Spencer'	SLBF
'Our Ted' (T)	EPts
'Over the Waves' (d)	CLoc
'Overbecks'	see *F. magellanica* var. *molinae* 'Sharpitor'
'Overbecks Ruby'	WCot
'P and C' **new**	SLBF
'P.E. King' (d)	SLBF
'Pam and Ted Love'	WRou
'Pam Plack'	SLBF
'Pan'	SLBF
paniculata (T) ♀H2	CCCN CRHN EGrI EHDe EPts MCot MHer SLBF WCru
'Papoose' (d)	SLBF SVic WRou
'Party Frock'	CLoc
parviflora misapplied	see *F.* × *bacillaris*
'Pat Meara'	CLoc
'Pathétique' (d)	CLoc
'Patience' (d)	SLBF
'Patio Princess' (d)	CLoc EPts SCob WRou
'Patricia Hodge' (Buds of May Series)	MDon WRou
'Patty Sue' (d)	EPts WRou
'Paula Jane' (d) ♀H2	EHDe MAsh MJac SLBF SVic WRou
'Pauline Rawlins' (d)	CLoc
'Paulus'	WRou
'Pavilion Princess'	SLBF WRou
'Peachy' (California Dreamers Series) (d)	CLoc SCoo WRou
'Peacock' (d)	CLoc
'Peasholm'	WRou
'Pee Wee Rose'	EHDe SVic WRou
'Peloria' (d)	CLoc
'Peppermint Chip' (d) **new**	SLBF
'Peppermint Stick' (d)	CLoc
'Perky Pink' (d)	EPts
'Perogers 70'	WRou
'Perry Park'	MJac SVic
'Perry's Jumbo'	NPer
'Peter Meredith'	MJac WRou
petiolaris B&SWJ 10675	WCru
'Pharaoh'	CLoc
'Phénoménal' (d)	SLBF
'Phryne' (d)	SVic
'Phyllis' (d) ♀H4	CLoc EHyd EPts LRHS MJac NRHS SLBF SVic WRou XLum
'Piet van der Sande'	SLBF WRou
'Pink Aurora'	CLoc
'Pink Ballet Girl' (d)	CLoc SVic
'Pink Bon Accord'	CLoc SVic
'Pink Cloud'	CLoc
'Pink Darling'	CLoc
'Pink Elephant' (d)	CLoc WRou
'Pink Fandango' (d)	CLoc
'Pink Fantasia' ♀H2	CLoc EPts MJac SVic WRou
PINK FIZZ ('Fngenfu01'PBR)	WHlf
'Pink Galore' (d) ♀H2	CLoc MJac
'Pink Goon' (d)	SLBF SVic
'Pink Haze'	SVic
'Pink Ice' (d)	MBros
'Pink Marshmallow' (d) ♀H4	CLoc MJac SCgs SLBF
'Pink Pearl' Bright (d)	EHDe
'Pink Quartet' (d)	CLoc
'Pink Rain'	MJac
'Pink Slippers'	CLoc
'Pink Spangles'	see *F.* 'Mieke Meursing'
'Pink Temptation'	CLoc
'Pinwheel' (d)	CLoc
'Piper's Vale' (T)	MJac
'Pixie'	CLoc EHDe MJac SLBF SVic
'Playboy' (d)	SVic
'Popsie Girl' (v)	EHDe SLBF WRou
'Posset Sparkler' **new**	SLBF
'Powder Puff' Hodges (d)	CLoc
'Prelude' Blackwell	CLoc
'President Arthur Phillips' (d)	WRou
'President Barrie Nash'	CLoc
'President Derek Luther' **new**	SLBF
'President George Bartlett' (d) ♀H2	CLoc EPts MJac SLBF WRou
'President Joan Morris' (d)	SLBF
'President John Porter'	MJac SLBF WRou
'President Leo Boullemier'	MJac
'President Margaret Slater'	CLoc
'President Moir' (d)	SLBF
'President Peter Holloway'	EPts SLBF WRou
'President Stanley Wilson' (d)	EPts
'Preston'	CMac
'Preston Guild' ♀H3	CLoc NPer SDys SRms SVic WFar WRou
'Prince of Orange'	CLoc SVic
'Princess Dollar'	see *F.* 'Dollar Prinzessin'
procumbens	CBcs CBod CCCN CCht CLoc EAri EHDe ELon EPfP EPts EShb IDee MHer SIvy SLBF WKor WRou
- 'Argentea'	see *F. procumbens* 'Wirral'
- grey-leaved	ESwi SBrt
- 'Variegata'	see *F. procumbens* 'Wirral'
§ - 'Wirral' (v)	CLoc CTsd EAri EHDe EShb ESwi MHer SLBF
'Prodigy'	see *F.* 'Enfant Prodigue'
'Prosperity' (d) ♀H3	CKel CLoc EHyd EPts LRHS MAsh MJac NRHS SLBF SPoG SVic
'Pumila'	CMac EPfP LRHS SDix SVic
'Purple Emperor' (d)	CLoc
'Purple Heart' (d)	CLoc
'Purple Lace'	SVic
'Purple Prince' (d)	SVic
'Purple Rain'	EPts WRou
'Pussy Cat' (T)	CLoc
'Putney Pride'	EPts
'Put's Folly' ♀H2	MJac
'Quasar' (d)	CLoc EPts MBros MJac SLBF WRou
'Queen Mary'	CLoc EHDe
'Queen of Bath' (d)	SVic
'Queen of Mercia' (d)	MJac
'Queen Victoria' Smith (d)	EHDe

'Query'	SVic
'R.A.F.' (d)	CLoc EHDe EPts
'Radings Gerda' (E)	SLBF WRou
'Radings Karin'	WRou
'Radings Michelle' (E)	WRou
'Rambling Rose' (d)	CLoc
'Raspberry' (d)	CLoc
'Reading Ruby'	EPts MJac
'Reading Show' (d)	EPts SLBF
'Rebecca Ward'	SLBF
'Red Rain'	SLBF
'Red Shadows' (d)	CLoc
'Red Spider'	CLoc SCoo SLBF
'Red Tyrol' **new**	MPri
'Red Wing'	CLoc
'Reflexa'	see *F.* × *bacillaris* 'Reflexa'
'Reg Gubler'	SLBF
'Regal'	CLoc
regia	SLBF WMal
- subsp. ***regia***	EHDe XLum
- subsp. ***reitzii***	SBrt XLum XVPe
- subsp. ***serrae***	WPGP
'Remember Carole Anne' (d)	SLBF WRou
'Remembering Claire'	EPts MHer SLBF
'Remembrance' (d)	EPts SLBF WRou
'Rhapsody' ambig.	SVic
'Riccartonii' ♀^{H6}	Widely available
'Riccartonii Variegated' (v)	EHDe
'Richard John' (v)	SVic
'Ridestar' (d)	CLoc
'Rijs 2001' (E)	SLBF
'Ringwood Market' (d)	SCoo SLBF
'Rita May' (E)	WRou
'Rivendell'	EPts WRou
'Rocket Fire' (California Dreamers Series) (d)	SVic
'Roesse Blacky'	WHlf
'Roger de Cooker' (T)	CLoc EPts MJac SVic
'Rohees New Millennium' (d)	SLBF
'Roman City' (d)	CLoc
'Romany Rose'	CLoc
'Ronald L. Lockerbie' (d)	CLoc
'Roos Breytenbach' (T)	MJac WRou
'Rosalien'	CLoc WRou
'Rosamunda' (d)	CLoc
'Rose Churchill' (d)	MJac
'Rose Fantasia' ♀^{H2}	CLoc EHDe EPts MJac SLBF WRou
'Rose of Castile'	CLoc EHDe EPts MJac SLBF SVic WRou
'Rose of Castile Improved' ♀^{H4}	LRHS MJac SLBF
'Rose of Denmark'	CLoc EHDe MJac SCoo SLBF
'Rose Winston' (d)	SCoo
rosea misapplied	see *F.* 'Globosa'
'Rosecroft Beauty' (d/v)	EHDe
'Rosemarie Higham' (v)	MJac SCoo
'Rosemary Day'	CLoc
'Rosy Frills' (d)	MJac
'Roualeyn's White Gold' (d) ♀^{H2}	WRou
'Rough Silk'	CLoc
'Royal Academy' (d)	EPts
'Royal Mosaic' (California Dreamers Series) (d)	LCro MJac
'Royal Velvet' (d) ♀^{H2}	CLoc EHDe EHyd EPts LRHS SLBF SVic WRou
'Rubra Grandiflora'	SIvy WRou
'Ruby Tuesday' (d)	MJac
'Ruby Wedding' (d)	SLBF
'Rufus' ♀^{H4}	CLoc CMac EPts MJac SLBF SVic WRou
'Ruth'	SVic
'Ryan'	SLBF

	'S'Wonderful' (d)	CLoc
	'Saartje'	WRou
	'Sabrina'	SLBF WRou
	'Sailor'	EPts
	'Salmon Cascade'	EPts MJac SLBF
	'Salt 'n' Pepper' (E)	SLBF WRou
	'Sam Sheppard'	EHDe
	'Samantha's Smile' (d)	SLBF
	'Santa Cruz' (d)	CMac SLBF SVic
	'Santa Lucia' (d)	CLoc
	'Sappho Phaoon' (T)	EPts WRou
	'Sara Helen' (d)	CLoc
	'Sarah'^{PBR} (Bella Series)	LCro WRou
	'Sarah Brightman' (d)	CLoc
	'Sarah Eliza' (d)	SCoo
	'Sarcoma UK'	WRou
	'Satellite'	CLoc
	'Saturnus' ♀^{H4}	CRos LRHS SPoG WMal WRou
	'Scarcity'	EHDe SVic
	'Scarlet Jester'	EPts SLBF WRou
	'Schneewitcher'	EPts
	'Sealand Prince'	SVic
	'Sebastopol' (d)	CLoc
	serratifolia Ruíz & Pav.	see *F. denticulata*
	'Seventh Heaven' (d)	CLoc MJac SCoo WRou
	'Sharpitor'	see *F. magellanica* var. *molinae* 'Sharpitor'
	'Shatzy B'	EPts SLBF WRou
	'Shelford'	CLoc EPts MJac SCob SLBF SVic
	'Shell Pink'	SVic
	'She's a Beauty' (d)	MJac
	'Shirley Teece'	EPts
	'Shrimp Cocktail'	CKel CLoc LRHS WFar WHlf
	'Siberoet' (E)	SLBF
	'Sid Garcia'	SLBF
	'Sierra Blue' (d)	CLoc
	'Silver Chime'	WRou
	'Silver Surfer'	EPts MJac SLBF
	'Silverdale'	EPts
	simplicicaulis	EHDe
	'Sincerity' (d)	CLoc
	'Siobhan Evans' (d)	SLBF
	'Sir Alfred Ramsey'	EHDe
	'Sir Matt Busby' (d)	EPts MJac WRou
	'Sister Ann Haley'	EPts
	'Sister Sister' (d)	SLBF
	'Skater's Waltz' (d)	CLoc
	'Sleepy'	EPts SVic
	'Sleigh Bells'	CLoc SVic
	'Small Pipes'	SLBF
	'Sneezy'	EPts SVic
	'Snow Burner' (California Dreamers Series) (d)	CLoc MBros
	'Snowbird' (d)	SLBF
§	'Snowcap' (d) ♀^{H4}	CCCN CChe CLoc EHDe ELon EPts GKin MAsh MGos MJac NPer NRHS SCob SCoo SGBe SLBF SLim SPoG SVic WFar WRou
	'Snowdrift' Colville (d)	CLoc
	'Snowfire' (d)	CLoc
	'Snowflake' (E)	EPts WRou
	'Soila'^{PBR} (Bella Series)	CLoc WRou
	'Son of Thumb' ♀^{H4}	CLoc CRos EHyd EPts LRHS MJac NRHS SGol SLBF SLim SPer SVic WRou
	'Sonata' (d)	CLoc
	'Sophia'^{PBR} (Bella Series)	CLoc LCro LOPS WRou
	'Sophie Louise'	EPts MJac WRou
	'Sophisticated Lady' (d)	EPts
	'South Gate' (d)	CLoc SVic
	'Space Shuttle'	CLoc SLBF
	SPARKLING SILVER ('Lowssil') (d/v)	LRHS SGBe

	'Sparky' (T)	CLoc EHDe EPts MHer SLBF WRou
	'Speciana'	EPts
§	'Speciosa'	EAri EGrI WRou
§	***splendens*** 🏆H2	CCCN CDow CLoc CWal MCot NPer SLBF WRou
	- B&SWJ 10469	WCru
	'Sporting Chance'	WRou
	'Spring Bells' (d)	EHyd LRHS NRHS
	'Squadron Leader' (d)	EPts
	'Squirtie'	SLBF
	'Stanley Cash' (d)	CLoc
	'Star Wars'	CLoc EHDe EPts MJac WRou
	'Stardust'	WRou
	'Stella Ann' (T)	EPts
	'Stoke Poges Jewel'	WRou
	'Stokie'	WRou
	'Straat Futami' (E)	EPts
	'Straat Magelhaen'	EAri
	'Strawberry Delight' (d)	CLoc
	'Strawberry Split'	CDoC EPfP LRHS
	'Strawberry Sundae' (d)	CLoc
	'String of Pearls'	CLoc MJac SLBF SVic
	'Stuart Lockyer' (d)	CLoc
	'Sue'	SLBF
	'Sue Kylymnik'	SLBF WRou
	'Suffolk Splendour' (d)	EPts WRou
	'Sugar Plum Fairy' (E)	WRou
	'Sunray' (v)	CBcs CEnd CKel CLoc CMac CRos EHDe EHyd ELon EPfP LBuc LCro LRHS MAsh MGos NCou NRHS SCoo SGBe SLBF SPoG SVen WCot WRou
	'Sunset'	CLoc
	'Susan Green'	MJac
	'Susan Hampshire'	SLBF
	'Susan McMaster'	CLoc
	'Susan Travis'	CLoc SVic
	SUSANNA ('Bf02'PBR) (Bella Series)	WRou
	'Swanley Beauty'	EHDe
	'Swanley Gem' 🏆H2	CLoc SLBF SVic
	'Swanley Pendula'	CLoc
	'Swanley Yellow'	EHDe
	'Sweet Sarah' (E)	EPts
	'Sweet Willow'	EPts
	'Swingtime' (d) 🏆H2	CLoc EPts LCro MBros MJac SLBF WRou
	sylvatica misapplied	see *F. nigricans*
	'Sylvia Barker' 🏆H2	SLBF
	'Sylvia's Choice'	WRou
	'Symphony'	CLoc
	'Syreme' (d)	EHDe SLBF
	'T.I.S. Herentals'	SLBF WRou
	'Taddle'	SLBF
	'Taffeta Bow' (d)	CLoc SLBF
	'Tamerus Nandoe'	WRou
	'Tamworth'	CLoc MJac SVic
	'Tangerine'	CLoc SVic
	'Tarra Valley'	EAri EHDe
	'Tausendschön' (d)	WRou
	'Ted Ness'	WRou
	'Ted's Tribute'	SLBF
	'Temptation' Peterson	CLoc
	'Ten Cents'	SLBF
	'Tennessee Waltz' (d) 🏆H2	CLoc EPts SLBF SVic
	'Tess'	EPts
	tetradactyla misapplied	see *F.* × ***bacillaris***
	'Texas Longhorn' (d)	CLoc
	'Thalia' (T) 🏆H1c	CCCN CLoc CWCL EPts LSRN MHer MJac SCob SGBe SIvy SLBF SPlb SPoG WHlf WLov WOld WRou
	'Thamar'	CLoc EPts SVic WRou
	'That's It' (d)	SVic

	'The Aristocrat' (d)	CLoc
§	'The Doctor'	CLoc
	'The Tarns'	SVic WRou
	'Thelma Copestake'	MJac SLBF
	'Thomas' (d)	EPts
	'Thompsonii'	see *F. magellanica* 'Thompsonii'
	'Thornley's Hardy'	SVic
	'Three Cheers'	CLoc
	thymifolia (E)	CKel CMil EHyd LRHS MHer SDys SEND SGro WCot WKif
	- subsp. ***thymifolia*** (E)	CDoC SEle
	'Tia Clements'	MJac WRou
	'Tickled Pink'	WRou
	'Tillingbourne' (d)	SLBF
	'Time After Time'	CLoc MBros SLBF WRou
	'Timlin Brened' (T)	WRou
	'Timothy Titus' (T) 🏆H1c	EHDe SLBF
	'Ting-a-ling'	CLoc SVic
	'Tinker Bell' Hodges	SVic
	'Tinytobes'	MJac
	'Toby Bridger' (d)	CLoc
	'Toby Foreman'	SLBF
	'Toby S' (d)	SLBF
	'Tom Thumb' 🏆H4	Widely available
	'Tom West' misapplied	see *F.* 'Mr West'
	'Tom West' ambig.	CBod CKel SVic
	'Tom West' Meillez (v) 🏆H2	CChe CDoC CLoc CWCL EHDe EHyd EPts LRHS MAsh MBros MHer MJac MRav MSCN NRHS SGol SLBF WFar WRou
	'Tom Woods'	WRou
	'Ton Ten Hove'	EHDe
	'Tony Talbot'	MJac
	'Tony's Treat' (d)	EPts
	'Torch' (d)	CLoc
	'Torchlight'	EPts
	'Torvill and Dean' (d)	CLoc EPts MJac SLBF
	'Tracid' (d)	SVic
	'Trail Blazer' (d)	CLoc MJac
	'Trailing Queen'	MJac
	'Trase' (d)	SVic
	'Traudchen Bonstedt' (T) 🏆H1c	CLoc
	'Tricolor'	see *F. magellanica* var. *gracilis* 'Versicolor'
	'Trientje'	SLBF
	'Trimley Bells'	SLBF
	triphylla (T)	MHer
	'Tristesse' (d)	CLoc
	'Tropicana' (d)	CLoc
	'Troubador' Waltz (d)	CLoc
	'Trudi Davro'	MBros SCoo
	'Trudy'	EPts SVic
	'True Love'	CLoc
	'Truly Treena' (d)	SLBF
	'Trumpeter' Reiter (T)	CLoc EPts MJac
	'Tuonela' (d)	CLoc
	'Tupence'	WRou
	'Turkish Delight'	WRou
	'Tutti-frutti' (d)	CLoc
	'Twinkling Stars'	MJac
	'Twinny'	SLBF
	'Twist and Shout'	EPts WRou
	'University of Liverpool'	CLoc MJac
	'Valerie Bradley'	EPts
	'Valerie Jane'	SLBF
	'Vanessa Jackson'	CLoc MJac SVic
	'Vanessa Wright'	EHyd LRHS NRHS
	'Variegated Procumbens'	see *F. procumbens* 'Wirral'
	'Veenlust'	MJac
	'Velvet Crush'	EPts WRou
	'Venus Victrix'	EHDe
	venusta	EHDe

'Vera'[PBR] (Bella Series)	WRou
'Vera Garcia'	EPts MJac SLBF WRou
'Versicolor'	see *F. magellanica* var. *gracilis* 'Versicolor'
'Vicky J'	WRou
'Violet Bassett-Burr' (d)	CLoc
'Violet Gem' (d)	CLoc
VIOLETTA ('Goetzviol') (Shadowdancer Series)	SCoo
'Vivien Colville'	CLoc SVic
'Voodoo' (d)	CLoc EPts MBros SCoo
'Wagtails White Pixie'	EHDe
'Wake the Harp'	SLBF
'Waldfee' (E)	WRou
'Waldis Grafin'	WRou
'Waldis Isobel'	WRou
'Waldis Maja'	WRou
'Walz Jubelteen' 🏆[H2]	CLoc CWCL ELan ELon EPts LCro MJac SAdn SEle SGBe SLBF SVen SVic WCot WRou
'Walz Lucifer'	SLBF
'Walz Luit'	WRou
'Walz Polka'	SLBF
'Wapenveld's Bloei'	EPts SLBF
'Water Color'	SLBF
'Water Nymph'	CLoc MHer SLBF SVic WRou
'Wattenpost'	SLBF
'Waveney Gem'	CLoc MJac SLBF
'Waveney Sunrise'	EHDe MJac
'Welsh Dragon' (d)	CLoc
'Wendy' Catt	see *F.* 'Snowcap'
'Wendy Bendy'	EPts MJac
'Wendy Jane Webster'	EPts
'Wendy's Beauty' (d)	CLoc EPts MJac
'Westminster Chimes' (d)	CLoc SLBF
'Whaley Thorns' (d)	MJac
'Wharfedale' 🏆[H4]	EHyd ELon EPts LRHS MJac NRHS SLBF SVic WRou
'What's-it' (E)	SLBF
'Whirlaway' (d)	CLoc
'Whispering Dawn'	WRou
'White Academy'	EPts
'White Ann'	see *F.* 'Heidi Weiss'
'White Clove' (E)	SVic WRou
'White King' (d)	CLoc WRou
'White Pixie' 🏆[H4]	EPPr EPts MJac SLBF SVic
'White Queen' ambig.	EHDe
'White Spider'	CLoc
'Whiteknights Amethyst'	SVic
'Whiteknights Blush'	CKel EBee EPfP EWes LRHS SMrm
'Whiteknights Cheeky' (T)	EPts SVic
'Whiteknights Glister' (v)	WRou
'Whiteknights Pearl' 🏆[H4]	ECha EHDe ELon EPts MHer SDys SGol SLBF SVic
'Whiteknights Ruby' (T)	SLBF
'Whoopee' (d)	EPts MJac SLBF WRou
'Wicked Queen' (d)	SVic
'Widnes Wonder'	MJac SLBF WRou
'Wigan Peer' (d)	EPts MJac WRou
'Wight Magic' (d)	MJac
'Wilson's Colours'	EPts
'Wilson's Joy'	MJac
'Wilson's Pearls' (d)	SLBF
'Wilson's Sugar Pink'	EPts MJac
'Win and Walt'	WRou
'Windhapper'	SLBF
'Windsor Castle' **new**	SLBF
'Winifred Glass'	EHDe
'Winston Churchill' (d) 🏆[H2]	CLoc EHDe EPts MBros MJac SCob SCoo SVic
'Winter's Tale'	SLBF
'Woodside' (d)	SVic
'Wyre Light' (E)	SLBF
'Yattendon Lady'	SLBF
'Zifi'	SLBF

Fumana (*Cistaceae*)

procumbens	EDAr

Fumaria (*Papaveraceae*)

capreolata	WSFF
lutea	see *Corydalis lutea*

Furcraea (*Asparagaceae*)

bedinghausii	see *F. parmentieri*
§ ***foetida***	CCCN
gigantea	see *F. foetida*
longaeva misapplied	see *F. parmentieri*
macdougalii	SPlb
§ ***parmentieri***	CBcs CCCN CDoC CDTJ CTsd EShb GBin LEdu LRHS NCft NGKo SChr SPlb SVen XSte
selloa var. ***marginata*** (v)	NCft SIvy

G

Gahnia (*Cyperaceae*)

sieberiana	SPlb

Gaillardia (*Asteraceae*)

'African Sunset'	GMcL
APRICOT HONEY	LBar SHar SMad
aristata misapplied	see *G.* × *grandiflora*
aristata Pursh 'Maxima Aurea'	EHyd EPfP SPhx
GOBLIN	see *G.* × *grandiflora* 'Kobold'
× ***grandiflora*** 'Amber Wheels'	ELan
- 'Arizona Apricot'	EHyd MBNS SCob SGBe
- 'Arizona Red Shades'	EAJP EHyd GPSL SCob SGBe
- 'Arizona Sun'	EAJP EHyd LPal MNHC SCob SGBe SVic WCav
- 'Bijou'	EBou SWvt
- 'Burgunder'	CMac CSBt CSpe EAJP EHyd ELan EPfP LRHS LSou MBow NLar SBls SGbt SMad SOrN SPer SPhx SPoG SWvt WPnP
- 'Celebration'[PBR]	CRos EHyd LBar LRHS MPri NLar SCoo SGBe
- 'Dazzler' 🏆[H5]	CSBt EBee EHyd ELan EPfP LRHS SGbt SPer SPoG
- 'Fanblaze'[PBR]	CBod EHyd GMcL LRHS NRHS SCob WFar
- 'Fanfare'[PBR]	CWGN EHyd EPfP LBar LRHS NRHS SCoo
- (Gallo Series) GALLO DARK BICOLOR ('Kiegaldab'[PBR])	LRHS
- - GALLO PEACH ('Kiegalpea'[PBR])	NRHS
- - GALLO YELLOW ('Kiegalyel')	LRHS
§ - 'Kobold'	CBcs CMac CRos CSBt EBee EHeP EHyd ELan EPfP GMaP GMcL LBuc LRHS NLar NRHS SCob SGbt SHar SOrN SPer SPlb SPoG SWvt WPnP
- (Mesa Series) MESA BRIGHT BICOLOUR ('Pas888652')	CBod LBar MDon WHlf
- - MESA PEACH ('Pas907056')	LBar MDon WHlf
- - MESA RED ('Pas953516')	LBar MDon MPri NLar WHlf
- - MESA YELLOW ('Pas888653')	LBar MDon
- Monarch Group	WFar

§ - 'Oranges and Lemons'	SHar
- 'Red Sun'PBR	CWGN
- (SpinTop Series) SPINTOP COPPER SUN **new**	LBar
- - SPINTOP ORANGE HALO ('Bargaispinor') **new**	LBar
- - SPINTOP RED **new**	LBar
- - SPINTOP RED SUNBURST	LBar SPad
- - SPINTOP YELLOW TOUCH ('Bargaispinyel'PBR) **new**	LBar
- (Sunburst Series) SUNBURST BURGUNDY	WFar
- - SUNBURST BURGUNDY PICOTEE ('Granretip')	GMcL
- (Sunset Dwarf Series) 'Sunset Cutie'	LBar LRHS MPri NRHS SPoG
- - 'Sunset Flash'	LRHS MPri SGBe SPoG
- - 'Sunset Snappy'	LBar MPri SPoG
- - 'Sunset Sunrise'	EPfP LRHS SPoG
- (Sunset Medium Series) 'Sunset Mexican'	LRHS
- - 'Sunset Popsy'	LRHS
- - 'Sunset Spice'	EPfP LRHS
- 'Tokajer'	EBee EHyd ELan EPfP EWTr LRHS NRHS SBls SPhx
SAINT CLEMENTS	see *G.* × *grandiflora* 'Oranges and Lemons'

Galactites (*Asteraceae*)

tomentosa	CPla EGrI EWTr LDai SPhx
- white-flowered	SPhx

Galanthus ✿ (*Amaryllidaceae*)

'Acton Pigot No. 3'	CElw WOld
'Ailwyn' (d) ♀H5	ELon GEdr NDry WOld
'Alison Hilary'	CAvo CTtf GEdr LEdu MCor
× ***allenii***	EPot EPri
'Amy Doncaster's Double' (d)	MCor
'Anne of Geierstein'	MHCG
'Ann's Millennium Giant'	CBro GEdr
'Armine'	CElw EPfP LRHS WCot
'Art Nouveau'	CElw CTtf
'Atkinsii' ♀H5	CAvo CBro CElw CRos EAri ECha EHyd EMor EPot EWoo GAbr GEdr GKev LAma LRHS MAsh MAvo NBir NRHS SDir SDix WCot WFar WHoo WOld WShi
'Autumn Beauty'	EHyd LRHS NRHS
'Autumn Belle'	LRHS
'Babraham Scented'	GEdr
'Backhouse Spectacles'	GEdr
'Ballerina' (d)	GEdr MAsh NDry WCot WOld
'Barbara's Double' (d)	EWes GEdr
'Basisgrüner'	NDry
'Baylham'	MCor
'Beethoven'	LAma
'Benhall Beauty'	CBro CElw EWes GEdr
'Benton Magnet'	EPot MCor
'Bertram Anderson' ♀H5	EPot GEdr WCot WOld
'Bess'	CElw GEdr
'Betty Hansell' (d)	CAvo MCor WOld
'Bill Bishop'	CBro CElw ECha ELon GEdr WCot
'Bitter Lemons'	CAvo
'Bitton' ambig.	GEdr NPol
'Blewbury'	ECha LEdu
'Bloomer'	MCor
'Brenda Troyle'	CBro CElw CRos ECha EHyd EMor EPot EPri GEdr LRHS MAsh NPol NRHS WCot WFar
'Brigadier Mathias'	EPot
'Bright Eyes'	MAsh
'Bungee'	CTtf GEdr
'By Gate'	GEdr
'Byfield Special'	MCor
byzantinus	see *G. plicatus* subsp. *byzantinus*
cabardensis	see *G. transcaucasicus*
'Caryl Baron'	CAvo
caucasicus misapplied	see *G. elwesii* var. *monostictus*
caucasicus ambig.	GAbr NPol
- 'Comet'	see *G. elwesii* 'Comet'
- var. ***hiemalis*** Stern	see *G. elwesii* Hiemalis Group
- 'John Tomlinson'	see *G. elwesii* 'John Tomlinson'
'Chequers'	GEdr
'Cicely Hall'	CTtf GEdr
'Cinderella'	MCor
'Cliff Curtis'	GEdr MAsh
'Compu.Ted'	CAvo
corcyrensis spring-flowering	see *G. reginae-olgae* subsp. *vernalis*
- winter-flowering	see *G. reginae-olgae* subsp. *reginae-olgae* Winter-flowering Group
'Cordelia' (d)	CElw GEdr MCor
'Corrin'	GEdr
'Cotswold Beauty'	CAvo
'Cowhouse Green'	GEdr MAsh MCor NDry
'Curly'	CAvo CElw CTtf EAri EWes GEdr
'Daglingworth'	EPri GEdr
'Daphne's Maximus'	MCor
'David Baker'	EPot GEdr
'Desdemona' (d)	EPot GEdr GMaP ITim WCot WFar
'Ding Dong'	CTtf GEdr MAsh MHCG
'Dionysus' (d)	ECha EMor EPot EWes GEdr GKev ITim LAma MAsh NBir NWad SDeJ WBrk WFar WShi
'Dodo Norton'	GEdr MAsh
'Dragonfly'	CAvo
'Dryad Artemis'	GEdr NDry
'Dryad Gold Bullion'	GEdr NDry
'Dryad Gold Charm'	GEdr NDry
'Dryad Gold Medal'	GEdr NDry
'Dryad Gold Sovereign'	GEdr NDry
'Dryad Gold Star'	GEdr NDry
'Early to Rize' **new**	MAsh
'Eilys Elisabeth Hartley'	NDry
'Eliot Hodgkin'	GEdr
§ ***elwesii*** ♀H5	CRos CTri EAri EGrI EHyd ELan EMor EPot ETay GQue LAma LCro LRHS MAsh NBir NPol NRHS NRog SDeJ SDir SPer SRms WCot WFar WHoo WShi
- 'Abington Green'	EPot
- 'Athenae'	CBro
- 'Beany'	CAvo MAsh
- 'Beluga'	GKev LRHS MThu
- 'Benjamin Britten'	GEdr GKev LAma
- 'Bo Bette'	GEdr NRog
- 'Broadwell'	MAsh
- 'Cedric's Prolific'	CElw ECha EMor EWoo GEdr MCor NRya WBrk WFar
- 'Chantry Green Twins'	GEdr MAsh
§ - 'Comet' ♀H5	CElw CTtf ELon GEdr GKev MAsh MAvo MCor MNrw WFar
- 'Daphne's Scissors'	CElw GEdr
- 'David Shackleton'	CElw GEdr
- 'Deer Slot'	CAvo CTtf MAsh
- 'Early Twin'	WCot
- 'Echoes'	WCot
- 'Edith' **new**	CAvo
- (Edward Whittall Group) 'Phil Bryn'	MAsh
- - 'Two Eyes'	GEdr
- 'Elmley Lovett'	CElw MAvo
- var. ***elwesii*** 'Big Boy'	GEdr MCor

	- - 'Fenstead End'	CAvo GEdr MAsh
	- - 'Fred's Giant'	GMaP
	- - 'Kite'	EWoo GEdr
	- - 'Maidwell L'	CBro EPot MAsh
	- - 'Paradise Giant'	GEdr ITim
	- - 'Pat Mason'	MCor
	- - 'Sibbertoft Magnet'	GEdr
	- - 'Spring Greens'	GEdr
*	- 'Flore Pleno' (d)	NPol
	- 'Godfrey Owen' (d) ♀H5	CAvo CElw CFis CTtf ELon EPot EPri GEdr LAma MAsh MCor WBrk WOld
	- 'Green Brush'	CAvo CBro CTtf EWes GKev LAma LRHS MCor
	- 'Grumpy'	EPri GEdr
	- 'Helen Tomlinson'	SHar
§	- Hiemalis Group	CBro ECha EPri GKev LAma WCot
	- - 'Barnes' ♀H5	CFis ECha ELon GEdr MCor WCot
	- - 'Donald Sims' Early' **new**	ELon
	- - 'Earliest of All'	CBro
	- - 'Highdown'	GKev
	- - 'Rainbow Farm Early'	WCot
	- 'Jessica'	CAvo EWoo GEdr
§	- 'John Tomlinson'	GEdr MAsh
	- 'Jonathan'	MAsh
	- 'Kencot Kali'	CAvo CTtf
	- 'Kyre Park'	GEdr
	- 'Ladybird'	GEdr MAsh
	- late-flowering	GEdr
	- 'Long 'drop'	GEdr
	- 'Louise Ann Bromley'	CAvo MCor
	- 'Maidwell'	GEdr MAsh MCor
	- 'Mandarin'	CAvo CElw EWes
	- 'Margaret Biddulph'	MCor
	- 'Margaret Owen'	MCor MNrw
	- 'Marielle'	GEdr
	- 'Marjorie Brown'	CAvo CElw CFis CTtf ECha EPot GEdr ITim MAvo MCor
	- 'Marlie Raphael'	CAvo
	- var. ***maximus***	see *G. elwesii* 'Yvonne Hay'
	- 'Milkwood'	see *G. elwesii* 'Mrs Macnamara'
	- 'Miss Mowcher'	WCot
§	- var. ***monostictus*** ♀H5	CBro ECha EHyd GKev LRHS NRHS WBrk WFar
	- - 'B. Britten'	LRHS
	- - 'G. Handel'	LAma LRHS
	- - 'G. Verdi' **new**	LAma
	- - 'Grayswood'	GEdr
	- - 'H. Purcell'	EBee EMor GEdr LAma LRHS
	- - 'Kryptonite'	CAvo
	- - 'Lord Monostictus'	EWoo
	- - 'Mozart'	LAma LRHS
	- - 'Rogers Rough'	SDys
	- - 'Smaragdsplitter'	CAvo
	- - 'Warwickshire Gemini'	MAvo MHCG
	- aff. var. ***monostictus***	WFar
	- 'Morgana' **new**	CAvo
	- 'Moses Basket'	CAvo CTtf
	- 'Moya's Green'	CAvo
	- 'Mr Blobby'	MCor
	- 'Mr Omer'	WCot
	- 'Mr Peggotty'	WCot
§	- 'Mrs Macnamara' ♀H5	CElw CFis ECha EPri EWoo GEdr MCor WBrk WFar WOld
	- November-flowering	WCot
	- 'Penelope Ann'	ECha GEdr NRya
	- 'Peter Gatehouse'	CTtf MCor
	- poculiform	CTtf
	- 'Polar Bear'	CAvo CElw CTtf EAri GEdr GKev LRHS MThu
	- 'Pyramid'	CTtf MCor
§	- 'Ransom's Dwarf'	GEdr MCor
	- 'Remember, Remember'	CTtf GEdr MAsh
	- 'Rosemary Burnham'	CAvo CElw MCor NDry
	- 'Ruth Birchall'	MCor
	- 'Selborne Green Tips'	CTtf
	- 'Sickle'	MAsh
	- 'Sir Edward Elgar'	EBee LAma LRHS
I	- 'Snowwhite'	NDry
	- 'The Bride'	NDry
	- 'Three Leaves'	CElw
	- 'Washfield Colesbourne'	see *G.* 'Washfield Colesbourne'
	- 'Yashmak'	CAvo
§	- 'Yvonne Hay'	GEdr
	- 'Zwanenburg'	CTtf
	'Ermine House' (d)	GEdr MCor
	'Ermine Lace'	CAvo WOld
	'Erway'	CTtf
	'Falkland House'	CElw EPot GEdr
	'Faringdon Double' (d)	CAvo CTtf EPot EPri
	'Feodora'	CAvo
	'Fieldgate Forte'	CAvo
	'Fieldgate Prelude'	CFis EWoo GEdr NDry
	'Fieldgate Superb'	CAvo NDry
	'Fly Fishing'	CAvo CTtf GEdr MCor WCot
	'Forge Double' (d)	GEdr MCor
	fosteri	CTtf GEdr NDry NRog
	fosteri × ***koenenianus***	NDry
	'Franz Josef'	CAvo MAsh
	'Friar Tuck'	MCor
	'G71' (d)	MCor
	'Gabriel'	CAvo EPot GEdr
	'Galadriel'	EPri GEdr
	'Galatea'	CBro ECha EMor EPri EWes GAbr ITim MAsh MCor NRya SDys WBrk WFar
	'George Elwes'	CTtf GEdr
	'George Proverbs'	MAsh
	'Gill Gregory'	GEdr
	'Ginns'	WBrk
	'Glenchantress'	GEdr
	(Gold Group) 'Ronald Mackenzie'	GEdr NDry
§	***gracilis***	GEdr LRHS NPol WCot
	- 'Highdown'	CElw CTtf
	- Kew	CElw
	- 'Vic Horton'	CElw CTtf GEdr WOld WThu
	graecus misapplied	see *G. gracilis*
	graecus Orph. ex Boiss.	see *G. elwesii*
	'Gravity'	CAvo
	'Grayling'	see *G. plicatus* 'Percy Picton'
	'Green Arrow'	CElw
	'Green Eyes'	CAvo MAsh
	'Green Man'	CAvo GEdr WFar
	'Green Necklace'	CTtf EWes GEdr
	'Green Ribbon'	MCor
	'Greenfields'	GEdr ITim WBrk
	'Greenfinch'	CAvo MCor
	green-tipped double (d)	GEdr
	'Hans Guck in die Luft'	NDry
	'Headbourne'	ECha MCor
	'Heffalump' (d)	EPri GEdr MCor
	'Hercule'	MCor
	'Hill Poë' (d)	CBro CElw CTtf GEdr MCor WHoo
	'Hippolyta' (d)	CAvo CBro CElw CTtf ECha EMor EPot GEdr GKev LAma LEdu LRHS MAvo MCor NPol WCot WHoo WShi
	'Hobson's Choice'	GEdr
	'Homersfield'	CElw ELon EPri
	'Honeysuckle Cottage'	CAvo MCor
	'Hörup'	GEdr
	'Hoverfly'	MCor
	× ***hybridus*** 'Merlin' ♀H5	CBro CElw CTtf EPri GEdr WCot WFar

- 'Pieces of Eight' **new**	CAvo
- 'Robin Hood'	CAvo EAri GEdr GKev NRog
'Icicle'	CElw GEdr
§ ***ikariae*** Bak.	GEdr ITim
- 'Emerald Isle'	NDry
- subsp. ***ikariae*** Butt's form	NPol
- Latifolius Group	see *G. platyphyllus*
- subsp. ***snogerupii***	see *G. ikariae* Bak.
'Imbolc'	CTtf GEdr MCor
(Imperial Group) 'Shepton Merlin'	CElw
'Ivy Cottage Corporal'	CAvo GEdr MAsh
'Jacquenetta' (d)	CBro CElw EWes GEdr GKev ITim LAma LRHS MAsh
'James Backhouse'	ECha EMor MCor WShi
'Jennifer Hewitt'	CElw
'John Gray' ♀H5	EPri EWes GEdr
'June Boardman'	CAvo
'Kath Dryden'	EPot
'Kersen'	CAvo
'Ketton'	CBro CElw CTtf GEdr MAvo NRya
'Kildare'	CAvo GEdr LEdu
'Kingston Double' (d)	GEdr MAsh
'Kinn McIntosh'	WCot
'Lady Beatrix Stanley' (d) ♀H5	CAvo CBro CElw EAri ECha EPfP EPot GEdr MAsh NWad WCot WFar WOld
lagodechianus	CBro GEdr MCor NRog
'Lapwing'	CTtf EPot GEdr MAsh MCor
latifolius Rupr.	see *G. platyphyllus*
'Lavinia' (d)	CElw CTtf EAri EWes GEdr WFar WOld
'Limetree'	CElw EPri EWes GEdr MAvo NPol WFar
'Little Ben'	CElw GEdr GMaP MCor
'Little Dorrit'	GEdr MAsh
'Little John'	EPot GEdr WBrk
'Little Magnet'	CAvo
'Little Poppet' **new**	WCot
'Long John Silver'	CAvo
'Longnor Hall' (d)	MCor
'Longstowe'	MAsh
'Lord Lieutenant'	GEdr
'Lucy'	CAvo
lutescens	see *G. nivalis* Sandersii Group
'Lyn'	CBro EMor GEdr NBir
'Magic' **new**	CAvo
'Magnet' ♀H5	CAvo CBro CElw CFis CTtf CWCL EAri EBee EHyd EMor EPot EWoo GAbr GEdr GKev LAma LEdu LRHS MAsh MCor MNrw NBir NPol NRHS WBrk WCot WFar WShi
aff. 'Magnet'	GMaP SDir WFar
'Martha MacLaren'	CAvo
'Matt Bishop'	CAvo
'Megan'	GEdr
'Melanie Broughton'	CElw EPot EWes GEdr MAsh MCor
'Midas'	CAvo
'Midge' **new**	GEdr
'Midwinter'	CAvo
'Mighty Atom'	CBro GAbr WBrk
'Mill House'	CTtf
'Miss Prissy' (d)	NDry
'Miss Willmott'	MAsh
'Moby Dick'	EWes
'Moccas'	CElw CFis
'Modern Art'	CAvo CTtf EPot GEdr MCor MHCG
'Moortown'	CAvo GEdr MAsh
'Mother Goose' **new**	CAvo LAma
'Mr Stinker'	CAvo
'Mr Taylor' **new**	CAvo
'Mr Thompson'	EPot

'Mrs Backhouse No 12'	MCor
'Mrs Thompson'	CElw CTtf ECha GEdr MNrw
'Mrs Wrightson's Double' (d)	GEdr
'Muku' (d)	NDry
'Natalie Garton'	CFis CTtf GEdr MCor
'Neill Fraser'	EPri GEdr
'Nerissa' (d)	EPfP GEdr LRHS
nivalis ♀H5	Widely available
- 'Courteenhall' Wyatt	CTtf EPri
- 'Alan's Treat'	GEdr MCor WOld
- 'Alburgh Claw'	MAsh
- 'Angelina'	CAvo
- 'Anglesey Abbey'	CElw EWes EWoo GEdr MCor
- 'April Fool'	GEdr
- 'Ballynahinch'	GEdr ITim
- 'Bitton'	GEdr
- 'Blonde Inge'	CAvo CTtf EPot GEdr MCor
- 'Chedworth'	CAvo CElw EAri GEdr WBrk
- 'Christmas Wish'	GKev
- 'Cornwood'	GEdr
- dwarf	ITim
- 'Elfin'	CAvo CElw CTtf EWes GEdr WCot
- 'Elworthy Bumble Bee' (d)	CElw GEdr
- Estonian Spirit Group	NDry
- 'Flocon de Neige'	CAvo
- 'Fuzz'	MCor
- 'Gloucester Old Spot'	GEdr
- 'Green Diamond'	CElw
- 'Green Tear'	GEdr MCor
- 'Greenish'	CTtf MCor
- 'Héloïse des Essourts' (d) **new**	CAvo
- subsp. ***imperati***	WBrk
- 'Irish Green'	MAsh
- 'Kullake'	NDry
- 'Lady Putman' **new**	CAvo
- 'Lutescens'	see *G. nivalis* Sandersii Group
- 'Major Pam' (d)	GEdr
- 'Margery Fish'	CAvo
- 'Melvillei'	CAvo EWoo
- 'Munchkin'	CTtf
- 'Pagoda' **new**	CAvo
- 'Pewsey Vale'	WBrk
- f. ***pleniflorus*** (d)	CBor EAri GKev MPri SPoG
- - 'Bagpuize Virginia' (d)	GEdr
- - 'Blewbury Tart' (d)	CAvo CBro CElw CTtf ELon EPri EWes GEdr MAsh MCor WBrk WCot WFar WHoo
- - 'Doncaster's Double Charmer' (d)	MAsh
- - 'Flore Pleno' (d) ♀H5	CArg CBro CWCL EGrI ELan EMor EPfP EPot EWoo GBin LAma LCro LOPS LRHS MMuc NHpl NRog NRya SDeJ SEND SPer SRms WBrk WCot WShi
- - 'Lady Elphinstone' (d)	CElw EAri GEdr MCor NPol NRya WCot
- - 'Octopussy' (d)	GEdr MAsh MCor
- - 'Pusey Green Tips' (d)	CElw CTtf EPot GAbr NPol WCot
- - Scharlockii Group double (d)	CTtf
- - 'Walrus' (d)	ELon GEdr WBrk
- Poculiformis Group	CElw
- - 'Angelique'	CTtf NDry
- - 'Francesca de Grammont'	NDry
- - 'Gloria'	CAvo
- - 'Henry's White Lady'	GEdr MCor
- - 'Moreton Mill'	CAvo
- cf. Poculiformis Group	CElw
- 'Puck'	GEdr
- 'Rosemary Mitchell'	MAvo
§ - Sandersii Group	GEdr GMaP MCor WFar
- - 'Lowick'	CTtf

- - 'Norfolk Blonde'	CTtf GEdr
§ - Scharlockii Group	CElw ECha ELon GKev MCor NRog WBrk
- - 'Selina Cords'	CElw
- 'Sibbertoft White'	EPri WBrk
- 'Tiny'	GEdr WFar
- 'Tiny Tim'	EPot GEdr ITim MCor NRya WFar
- 'Tippy Green'	CElw GKev
- 'Viridapice' 🏆H5	CAvo CBor CBro CElw CTtf CWCL EAri ECha EGrI EMor EPot GAbr GKev GMaP LAma LCro MCor NBir NPol NRog NWad SDeJ SDir WCot WFar WShi
- 'Warei'	CElw EPri
- 'White Cloud'	GKev
- 'White Dream'	CElw GEdr
'North Star' (d)	CElw
'One Drop or Two'	CAvo
'Ophelia' (d)	CBro EAri ECha GAbr GEdr MCor NPol WBrk WFar WHoo
'Orion'	CFis
'Peardrop'	GEdr
'Peg Sharples'	CAvo GEdr
peshmenii	LEdu
- 'Kastellorizo'	NDry
'Phantom'	CAvo
'Philippe André Meyer'	CAvo MCor
§ ***platyphyllus***	EPfP
plicatus 🏆H5	CBro CElw EHyd EMor GAbr GKev LAma LRHS MCot NPol NRHS WBrk WCot WShi
- from Coton Manor	MCot
- 'Amy Doncaster'	CTtf GEdr MCor
- 'Augustus' 🏆H5	CBro CElw EPot EWes GEdr MAsh WCot WHoo
- 'Barbara Buchanan's Late'	CElw
- 'Baxendale's Late'	EAri GEdr GKev
- 'Beth Chatto'	EPot MCor
- 'Bolu Shades'	GKev
§ - subsp. ***byzantinus***	CBro LAma MHCG WThu
- - 'Ariadne'	CAvo
- - 'Conquest'	CBro
- - 'Patricia Ann'	CElw
- 'Clun Green Plicate'	CElw
- 'Colossus'	CBro CElw EPfP EWes GKev LRHS MAsh WCot
- 'Diggory' 🏆H5	CAvo CTtf EPri GEdr MAsh MCor MHCG WCot
- 'Duckie'	GEdr WFar
- 'E.A. Bowles' 🏆H5	CAvo GEdr MAsh WOld
- 'Eric Fisher' **new**	LAma
- 'Florence Baker'	GEdr
- 'Gerard Parker'	GEdr
- 'Glenorma'	CAvo GEdr
- 'Gold Edge'	EPot GEdr
- 'Golden Fleece' **new**	GEdr
- 'Green Hayes'	GEdr MCor
- 'Green Teeth'	CElw GEdr
- 'Jenny's Pearl' **new**	CAvo
- 'John Long'	EPot GEdr MCor
- 'Josie'	GEdr
- 'Lambrook Greensleeves'	CFis MCor
- 'Madeleine'	CElw CTtf GEdr MCor NDry
§ - 'Percy Picton'	CAvo EWes EWoo GEdr
- 'Phil Cornish'	CAvo GEdr MAsh
- 'Sally Pasmore'	CAvo
- 'Seraph'	CAvo
- 'Sibbertoft Manor'	CElw
- 'Sophie North'	CElw CTtf GEdr
- 'The Pearl'	GEdr
- 'Three Ships' 🏆H5	GEdr MAsh MCor NHar
- 'Trimmer'	GEdr
- 'Trinity'	CAvo
- 'Trym'	CElw CTtf EPri GEdr NDry NPol WFar
- 'Trymlet'	CAvo EPot EWoo GEdr MAsh
- 'Trympostor'	CAvo CElw GEdr MCor
- 'Warham'	CBro CElw EAri EPot GAbr ITim WCot
- 'Wendy's Gold'	CAvo CBro CTtf EPot EPri EWes GEdr LRHS MAsh MCor NDry NRHS WBrk WFar
'Pride o' the Mill'	CTtf GEdr MAsh
'Primrose Warburg'	CElw EPot EWes GEdr MAsh MAvo MCor WFar
'Ransom's Dwarf'	see *G. elwesii* 'Ransom's Dwarf'
reginae-olgae	GKev LRHS NDry
- 'Blanc de Chine'	NDry
- subsp. ***reginae-olgae*** 'Tilebarn Jamie'	MCor WCot
§ - - Winter-flowering Group	CBro
§ - subsp. ***vernalis***	LEdu WCot
- - 'Christine'	CElw
- - 'Miss Adventure'	CAvo
'Reverend Hailstone'	CTtf EWes GEdr MCor
'Richard Ayres' (d)	CElw EPri GEdr MCor NRHS
rizehensis	CAvo CBro GKev
- Baytop 34474	GEdr
'Robyn Janey' **new**	CAvo
'Rodmarton'	EPot EPri GEdr
'Rodmarton Arcturus'	CElw GEdr
'Rodmarton Regulus'	GEdr
'S. Arnott' 🏆H5	CAvo CBro CElw EAri EBee ECha EHyd EPfP GAbr GKev GMaP LAma LCro LOPS LRHS MAvo MCor NBir NPol NRHS NRog NRya NSla SDeJ WBrk WCot WFar WHoo WShi
'Saint Anne's'	CAvo CElw GEdr
'Sally Wickenden'	CTtf EPot
'Sally's Double' (d)	MCor
'Santa Claus' **new**	ELon
'Scharlockii'	see *G. nivalis* Scharlockii Group
'Seagull'	CElw CFis GEdr MCor MNrw
'Sentinel'	CAvo CElw EPot GEdr
'Shimmer' **new**	CAvo
'Shropshire Queen'	GEdr
'Silverwells'	GEdr
'Sir Henry B-C'	GEdr MAsh
'Sir Herbert Maxwell'	GEdr
'Snow Angel'	CAvo
'Snow Fox'	GEdr GKev LRHS MThu SDir
'South Hayes' 🏆H5	CAvo EPot GEdr
'Spindlestone Surprise' 🏆H5	GEdr ITim
'Sprite'	CAvo CElw
'Starling'	CAvo
§ 'Straffan' 🏆H5	CAvo CBro CElw EAri ECha EMor EPot EPri MCor NPol WBrk WCot WFar
'Sutton Courtenay'	GEdr WOld
'The Apothecary'	CElw
'The Linns'	GEdr
'The O'Mahoney'	see *G.* 'Straffan'
'The Wizard'	CAvo
'Titania' (d)	CElw CTtf ELon GEdr MCor WHoo
§ ***transcaucasicus***	GEdr
'Treasure Island' **new**	CAvo
'Trotter's Merlin'	CElw
'Trumpolute'	MAsh MCor
'Trumps' 🏆H5	CAvo EPri GEdr MAsh MCor
'Trym Baby'	GEdr
'Trymming'	GEdr
'Tryzm'	CAvo
'Tubby Merlin'	CElw MAsh
'Turncoat'	CAvo
'Under Cherry Plum'	CAvo
× ***valentinei***	MCor

- 'Celia's Double' (d) **new**	CAvo
- 'Compton Court'	CBro GEdr ITim
- double-flowered (d) **new**	WHlf
- 'Northern Lights' **new**	CAvo
'Veronica Cross'	CAvo
§ 'Washfield Colesbourne'	CElw ECha EWoo
'Washfield Warham'	CElw ECha EPri EWoo MCor
'Wasp'	CAvo CTtf EPot EPri GEdr MAsh MCor WCot
'Welshway'	GEdr
'White Dreams'	GEdr
'White Swan' Ballard (d)	CElw EWes GEdr MCor WBrk
'William Thomson'	EWes
'Winifrede Mathias'	CElw MCor
'Wisley Magnet'	MCor
woronowii ♀H5	CArg CAvo CBro CElw CTri CTtf EPot ETay EWoo GAbr LAma LCro LEdu LRHS MAvo MCor NBir NRog SDeJ SDix WBrk WFar WShi
- 'Elizabeth Harrison'	GEdr MAsh
- 'Rodmarton Capella'	MCor

Galatella (*Asteraceae*)

§ ***linosyris***	CBod EBee EWes MAvo MHol NLar SPer SPhx WFar WOld WSHC
- 'Goldilocks'	see *G. linosyris*
§ ***sedifolia***	CBod CTtf EHyd ELon EPPr EShb LEdu LRHS LSou MAvo NBid NRHS NSti SPoG WCot WOld
- subsp. ***dracunculoides*** RCBAM 5	WCot
§ - 'Jean Polignier'	LEdu LPla
- 'Nana'	EBee MRav NBir NLar NWsh SPer WCAu WCot WFar WOld XLum

Galax (*Diapensiaceae*)

aphylla	see *G. urceolata*
§ ***urceolata***	MNrw NHar

Galega (*Fabaceae*)

bicolor	NBir SRms
× ***hartlandii***	LShi
- 'Alba' ♀H7	EWes GBin LRHS LShi MArl MRav WCAu WCot WHoo WSHC
- 'Lady Wilson' ♀H7	EMor EWes GBin MArl MAvo MHol MMrt SRms WCot WFar WKif
'Her Majesty'	see *G.* 'His Majesty'
§ 'His Majesty'	EBee LEdu MAvo MCot SMrm WCot
officinalis	CCBP CHby CTri EBee ELan EMor ENfk EPfP GMaP GPoy LBar LRHS LSun MAvo MHer MNHC MNrw MRav NBir NGrd NRHS NSti SBut SEND SPer SRms WCAu WFar WSpi
- 'Alba'	CCBP ELan EMor EPfP LEdu LRHS MACG MAvo MBrN MHer SBls SBut SEND SMrm SPer SPhx SRms WCAu WKif WSpi WTre
- COCONUT ICE ('Kelgal') (v)	SGBe SPoG
- 'Norfolk Gold' **new**	EWes
orientalis	EBee EWes LEdu MArl MAvo MCot MRav SBrt WCot WPGP WSHC
- PAB 6771	WPGP

Galeobdolon see *Lamium*

Galeopsis (*Lamiaceae*)

tetrahit	WSFF

Galium (*Rubiaceae*)

boreale	SPhx
cruciata	see *Cruciata laevipes*
glaucum	SPhx
mollugo	CHab
§ ***odoratum***	Widely available
verum	CHab EBee EBou ENfk GJos GPoy GQue LCro LOPS LShi MHer MMuc MNHC NAts NGrd NMir SEND SPhx SRms WFar WHlf WWild

Galtonia (*Asparagaceae*)

candicans ♀H4	Widely available
- 'Moonbeam' (d)	GKev
princeps	ECha EHyd LRHS NRHS WPGP
regalis	CTca WPGP
viridiflora	CBor CBro CTca CTtf ECha EGrl EPPr EWTr EWoo GBin GKev GQue LAma LRHS MHol MNrw SDeJ SDir SGBe

Galvezia (*Plantaginaceae*)

speciosa	CCCN

Gamblea (*Araliaceae*)

ciliata B&SWJ 13907	WCru
pseudoevodiifolia B&SWJ 11707	WCru

Garcinia (*Clusiaceae*)

mangostana	CCCN

Gardenia (*Rubiaceae*)

augusta	see *G. jasminoides*
florida L.	see *G. jasminoides*
grandiflora	see *G. jasminoides*
§ ***jasminoides*** ♀H1c	CBcs CCCN LCro MPri SGsty
- 'Crown Jewel'PBR (d)	CBcs EHyd EPfP LCro LOPS LRHS MAsh NRHS SPoG WCot XSte XVPe
- HEAVEN SCENT ('Magda 1') **new**	XVPe
- 'Kleim's Hardy'	Widely available
- PINWHEEL ('Piiga-I')	LCro LOPS XVPe
- SUMMER SNOW ('Bab1183')	XVPe
'Perfumed Petticoats'	XSte XVPe

garlic see *Allium sativum*; also AGM Vegetables Section

garlic, elephant see *Allium ampeloprasum* 'Elephant'

Garrya ✿ (*Garryaceae*)

congdonii	IDee
elliptica	CBcs CCCN CDoC CKel CMac CRos EBee EHeP EPfP ERom GDam LMil LRHS LSRN LSto MAsh MGos MPri NCth NRHS SCob SGsty WAvo WHtc
- (f)	MPri MSwo SGbt SWvt WSpi
- (m)	CTri NLar SGol WSpi
- 'James Roof' (m) ♀H4	Widely available
× ***issaquahensis***	CRos ELan IArd LRHS SCoo SPoG
'Glasnevin Wine' (m) ♀H4	WSpi
× ***thuretii***	CBcs CBod EBee EPfP GMcL IDee MMuc NLar SGol WFar WSpi

× *Gasteraloe* (*Asphodelaceae*)

beguinii	NCft
'Flow'	NCft
'Green Ice'	NCft NMen
'Grey Ghost'	NCft
'Thaise'	NCft
'Tiki Zilla'PBR	SPad
'Wonder'	NCft

Gasteria ✿ (*Asphodelaceae*)

acinacifolia	SPlb
batesiana ♀H2	NCft SEND
batesiana* × *nitida var. ***nitida*** new	SPlb
bicolor new	EAri
- var. ***liliputana*** ♀H1c	EAri NCft SPlb
- - 'Variegata' (v) new	SPlb
brachyphylla var. ***bayeri*** new	SPlb
- variegated (v) new	EAri
carinata new	EAri SPlb
- var. ***verrucosa***	EShb SEND SPlb SSim
disticha	EAri SPlb
- var. ***disticha*** f. ***monstruosa*** new	SPlb
- - 'Striata' (v) new	SPlb
'Dragon Skin'	SPad
ellaphieae	SPlb
glauca new	SPlb
glomerata new	SPlb
glomerata* × *rawlinsonii new	SPlb
'Little Warty' ♀H2	NCft SPad SSim
marmorata	see *G. obliqua*
nitida var. ***nitida*** variegated (v)	WCot
obliqua 'Variegata' (v) new	SPlb
rawlinsonii	NCft
'Rumpelstiltskin'	NCft
'Salad Cream'	NCft
'Smokey'	EShb

× *Gaulnettya* see *Gaultheria*

Gaultheria ✿ (*Ericaceae*)

antarctica	WThu
cuneata	EHyd LRHS MAsh NRHS WThu
aff. ***dumicola*** NJM 10.032	WPGP
forrestii BWJ 7809	WCru
itoana	GKev
'Jingle Bells'	LCro SCoo
'John Saxton'	WAbe
miqueliana	GEdr NLar WThu
mucronata	CDoC EGrI EPfP GKev MAsh NWea SCob WFar
- (f)	CKel
- (m)	CBod CMac CSBt CTri EPfP GMcL MGos SPer SRms WFar WPav
- 'Alba' (f)	WPav
- 'Bell's Seedling' (f/m) ♀H6	CBcs CBod CBrac CKel CTri ELan EPfP GMcL MAsh NBir NLar SGbt SPer SPoG WFar
- 'Cherry Ripe' (f)	WPav
- 'Crimsonia' (f) ♀H6	CBcs CMac EPfP SPer SRms
- 'Lilacina' (f)	CMac MAsh
- 'Lilian' (f)	CSBt EPfP
- MOTHER OF PEARL	see *G. mucronata* 'Parelmoer'
- 'Mulberry Wine' (f) ♀H6	CBcs CBod CSBt ELan NHol SGbt SPer
§ - 'Parelmoer' (f)	CSBt
- 'Pink Pearl' (f) ♀H6	CEme SRms
- pink-berried (f)	GDam GMcL
- red-berried (f)	GMcL
- 'Rosea' (f)	WPav
§ - 'Signaal' (f)	CBcs CBod ELan MAsh NLar SPer
- SIGNAL	see *G. mucronata* 'Signaal'
§ - 'Sneeuwwitje' (f)	CBcs CBod ELan EPfP LRHS MAsh SPer WFar
- SNOW WHITE	see *G. mucronata* 'Sneeuwwitje'
- 'Thymifolia' (m)	ELan EPfP
- white-berried (f)	GMcL SCob
- 'Wintertime' (f) ♀H6	CMac SRms
§ ***myrsinoides***	GKev WThu
nummularioides	NHar
'Pearls'	EPot GArf NWad WAbe
phillyreifolia	MGil
procumbens ♀H5	CAgr CBcs CDTJ CDoC CMac CRos EGrI EHeP EHyd ELan EPfP GEdr GKev GMcL LRHS MAsh MBlu MGos NGrs NRHS NWea SCob SPer SPlb SPoG SRms SWvt WFar WHlf
- BIG BERRY ('Gaubi'PBR)	CDoC LCro LOPS LRHS SCoo
- GAULTHIER PEARL ('Specgp11'PBR) new	LCro
- VERY BERRY ('Kieverber')	EShb NBir NWad
prostrata	see *G. myrsinoides*
pyroloides	GArf
shallon	CAgr CBrac EHeP EPfP GDam GMcL MCoo NLar NWea SCob SPer SRms SWvt WFar
sinensis	GArf NHar
thymifolia	NWad
trichophylla	GArf NHar
× ***wisleyensis***	CRos EHyd LRHS NRHS SRms
- 'Pink Pixie'	CRos EHyd LRHS MAsh NRHS
- 'Ruby'	CMac
- 'Wisley Pearl'	EPfP NLar SCoo WFar

Gaura see *Oenothera* (G)

coccinea	see *Oenothera suffrutescens*
longiflora	see *Oenothera filiformis*
sinuata	see *Oenothera sinuosa*

Gazania (*Asteraceae*)

'Aztec' ♀H2	CCCN
'Bicton Orange'	CCCN ECtt SCoo SVen
'Big Kiss White Flame' (Kiss Series)	CRos LBuc
'Big Kiss Yellow Flame' (Kiss Series)	CRos LBuc
'Blackberry Ripple'	CCCN SCoo SGBe
'Blackcurrant Ice'	MCot
'Christopher'	SCoo
'Christopher Lloyd'	CCCN SMrm WCav
'Cornish Pixie'	CCCN
'Cream Beauty'	MCot
CREMAZU (Sunbathers Series) new	EPfP
Daybreak Series	MBros MDon
- 'Daybreak Red Stripe'	SCob
- 'Daybreak Rose Stripe'	SCob
FROSTY KISS MIXED (Kiss Series)	SCob
'Katua' (Sunbathers Series)	ELan
Kiss Series	MBros
krebsiana	CCCN
'Lemon Beauty'	ECtt
linearis 'Colorado Gold'	EDAr SGBe
'Magic'	CCCN ELan SCoo WCav
NAHUI ('Suga119') (Sunbathers Series)	CCCN
rigens 'Variegata' (v) ♀H2	CCCN
RUMI ('Suga116') (Sunbathers Series)	CCCN
Sunbathers Series	SCob
Sunburst Series	LCro LOPS
SUNSET JANE ('Sugaja'PBR) (Sunbathers Series)	CCCN
SUNSET JANE LEMON SPOT ('Sugajale') (Sunbathers Series)	CCCN NRHS
Talent Series ♀H3	LCro LOPS
TIGER EYE ('Gazte') (v)	CCCN ELan MPri
TIGER STRIPES MIXED	MBros

TIKAL (Sunbathers Series) SCob
TOPTOKAI ('Suga407') (Sunbathers Series) CCCN NRHS
TOTONACA ('Suga212') (Sunbathers Series) CCCN ELan EPfP NRHS

Geissorhiza (*Iridaceae*)

aspera CPbh
inflexa CBor WHil
radians WHil
tulbaghensis CBor CPbh

Gelsemium (*Gelsemiaceae*)

rankinii WCot
sempervirens ♀H3 CBcs CCCN CRHN EBee EShb LSRN MGil SBrt SNig SPoG WCot

Genista (*Fabaceae*)

aetnensis ♀H5 EWes LRHS SArc SPer SPtp SRms WLov WSpi
§ ***canariensis*** ♀H3 CSBt
decumbens see *Cytisus decumbens*
fragrans see *G. canariensis*
hispanica CBcs CBrac CDoC CSBt EHeP ELan EPfP GMcL MAsh MMuc NBwr NLar SCob SPer SRms SWvt WCFE
horrida NLar
humifusa see *G. pulchella*
lydia ♀H5 Widely available
§ ***maderensis*** MPri
pilosa SRot
- 'Goldilocks' MMuc
- var. ***minor*** NLar WAbe
- 'Procumbens' ♀H5 CBrac EDAr GEdr NWad
- 'Vancouver Gold' CMac ELan EPfP SPer SRms
§ 'Porlock' ♀H3 CBcs CBod CDoC CEme CKel CMac CRos CSBt CTri EBee EHyd EPfP LRHS MAsh MRav NRHS SEND SSha
§ ***pulchella*** WAbe
sagittalis SPer
§ × ***spachiana*** ♀H1c CTri NBwr SPoG WHlf
tinctoria CCBP CHab GPoy GQue MMuc NAts WHer
§ - 'Flore Pleno' (d) ♀H6 EBtc GEdr
- 'Humifusa' EPot GEdr
- 'Moesiaca' WAbe
- 'Plena' see *G. tinctoria* 'Flore Pleno'
- 'Royal Gold' ♀H6 MRav NLar NWad SPer SPlb
villarsii see *G. pulchella*

Genlisea (*Lentibulariaceae*)

hispidula CHew

Gennaria (*Orchidaceae*)

diphylla GKev

Gentiana ✿ (*Gentianaceae*)

§ ***acaulis*** ♀H5 CBor CRos EHyd EPot GArf GEdr GKev GMaP ITim LRHS MAsh NGdn NHar NLar NRHS NSla SPlb SRms WAbe WHoo
- f. ***alba*** 'Snowstorm' GKev
- 'Arctic Fanfare' EPot GEdr
- 'Coelestina' WThu
- 'Krumrey' EPot GEdr GKev GRum
- 'Luna'PBR NLar WIce
I - 'Maxima Enzian' GEdr GRum
- 'Rannoch' EPot GEdr NLar
- 'Stumpy' GEdr
- 'Trotter's Variety' GArf GEdr WAbe
- 'Velkokvensis' EPot GEdr
'Alex Duguid' CRos EHyd GEdr LRHS NHar
'Amethyst' CRos EHyd GEdr LRHS WAbe
andrewsii SBls
angulosa misapplied see *G. verna* 'Angulosa' hort.
angulosa M. Bieb. see *G. verna* subsp. *pontica*
angustifolia GAbr GKev WAbe
- Frei hybrid NSla
'Ann's Special' GEdr
asclepiadea ♀H5 CBcs CSpe EBee ECha EHyd ELan EMor GAbr GEdr GKev GMaP GQue LEdu LRHS MBel MNrw NBid NBir NCth NFav NHar NLar NRHS SBls SPer SRms WCAu WCFE WHoo WKif
- 'Alba' EBee EHyd EMor GEdr GKev GMaP LEdu NBid NFav NLar NRHS SPer SRms WCFE WHoo
- dark blue-flowered WPGP
- 'Knightshayes' EBee GKev LEdu NLar
I - 'Nana' EBee GKev
- 'Phyllis' EBee GKev
- 'Pink Swallow' EMor GEdr
- 'Rosea' GEdr GKev
- 'White Swallow' GEdr
- 'Whitethroat' EBee GKev
'Balmoral'PBR GMaP NHar
'Barbara Lyle' WAbe
bavarica var. ***subacaulis*** SPlb
× ***bernardii*** see *G.* × *stevenagensis* 'Bernardii'
'Berrybank Dome' CRos EHyd GMaP LRHS
'Berrybank Sky' CRos EHyd GEdr GMaP LRHS NHar
'Berrybank Snowflakes' GMaP
'Berrybank Star' CRos GEdr LRHS
bisetaea SRms
'Blauer Diamant' GEdr
'Blauer Kobold' GEdr
'Blauer Zwerg' GEdr
'Blue Flame' GEdr
'Blue Heaven' GEdr
'Blue Magic'PBR NLar
'Blue Sea' CRos EHyd LRHS
'Blue Silk' ♀H5 CBor CRos EHyd EPfP GEdr GKev LRHS NHar NRHS SPoG WAbe
brachyphylla WAbe
'Braemar'PBR GMaP NHar
* ***burrowthii*** GEdr
'Cairngorm' CRos EHyd GEdr LRHS
calycosa GArf
'Carmen' GEdr
× ***caroli*** WAbe
clusii CPla GKev
'Compact Gem' GEdr NHar WAbe
§ ***cruciata*** CBor ELan GEdr NLar SBls
'Crystal Ashiro' (Ashiro Series) **new** LBar
§ ***dahurica*** EBee NGdn NLar SPtp
'Dark Hedgehog' GEdr
David Sturrock's dark seedling NHar
depressa CPla EPot WAbe
'Devonhall' GEdr NHar
'Diana'PBR NLar
dinarica 'Colonel Stitt' WThu
'Dumpy' GEdr
'Elehn' GEdr NHar
'Elizabeth' GEdr
'Ettrick' GEdr
'Eugen's Allerbester' (d) CAby CBor CRos EHyd GEdr GKev GMaP LBar LRHS NHar NHol NLar SPer WAbe WFar
'Eugen's Bester' NHar
farreri WAbe
- Silken Star Group WAbe
'Faszination' GEdr
'Gellerhard' GEdr

	'Gewahn'	GEdr
I	'Glamis Strain'	CRos EHyd GEdr LRHS NHar SPer
	'Glen Moy'	GEdr
	'Glendevon'	GEdr
§	***gracilipes***	GEdr SPlb SRms
	grossheimii	GKev
	'Hamburg'	GEdr
	'Henry'	GEdr
	Inshriach hybrids	EHyd LRHS
	'Inverleith'	EPfP GEdr NHol SPlb
	'Iona' PBR	NHar
	'Joan Ward'	CRos EHyd LRHS SPer
	'John Aitken'	GEdr
	'Juwel'	GEdr
	'Kobold'	GEdr
	kochiana	see *G. acaulis*
	kurroo var. ***brevidens***	see *G. dahurica*
	lagodechiana	see *G. septemfida* var. *lagodechiana*
	'Lapis Lazuli' **new**	GEdr
	ligustica	EPot
	'Lipstick Ashiro' (Ashiro Series) **new**	LBar
	'Little Diamond' PBR	NLar
	'Lucerna'	EHyd GEdr GKev LRHS
	lutea	CBod EBee EMor GKev GPoy NFav NHar NLar SMad SRms WCAu
	× ***macaulayi*** 'Blue Bonnets'	GEdr
	- 'Kidbrooke Seedling'	GEdr WAbe
	- 'Kingfisher'	EHyd GEdr WAbe
§	- 'Praecox'	EBou
	makinoi 'Marsha' PBR	SPoG
	'Margaret'	GEdr
	'Maryfield'	GEdr
	'Melanie'	GEdr
	'Moonlight'	GKev
	'Multiflora'	EHyd
	newberryi	GArf
	'Oban' PBR	GMaP NHar
	occidentalis	CPla WAbe
	ornata	GArf WAbe
	'Orva'	LRHS
	paradoxa ♀H5	GKev NSla SBrt
	- 'Blauer Herold'	EDAr GKev
	phlogifolia	see *G. cruciata*
	pneumonanthe	NLar SPlb
	prolata	GArf
	pumila subsp. ***delphinensis***	WAbe
	pumila × ***verna***	NCth
	purdomii	see *G. gracilipes*
	robusta CC 7494	EBee
	'Sapphire Blue'	EBee GEdr
	saxosa	CBor LRHS NBir NHpl NRHS NSla WAbe
	scabra 'Little Pinkie' PBR	GEdr
	'Selektra'	GEdr
	septemfida ♀H5	EHyd GAbr GKev LRHS MAsh NBir NBwr NHpl NRHS NSla SPlb SRms WHoo WIce WKif
*	- var. ***kuznetzovii***	GKev
§	- var. ***lagodechiana*** ♀H5	GEdr GKev SRms WFar XLum
	'Serenity'	CAby CBor EHyd GEdr NHar WAbe
	'Shot Silk' ♀H5	CRos EHyd GEdr LRHS MGos NBwr NHol NHpl SPer SPoG WAbe WIce
	sikokiana	GArf
	'Silken Giant'	GEdr WAbe
	'Silken Glow'	WAbe
	'Silken Night'	GEdr WAbe
	'Silken Seas'	CBor GEdr NHar WAbe
	'Silken Skies' ♀H5	GEdr WAbe
	'Silken Surprise'	WAbe
	sino-ornata ♀H5	CAby EBou EPfP GKev GMaP GQue LCro LRHS MAsh NHpl NRHS SCoo SEdd SPoG SRms WAbe WIce
	- SDR 5127	MGos
	- 'Angel's Wings'	GEdr
	- 'Bellatrix'	GEdr
	- 'Blautopf'	GEdr
	- 'Brin Form'	SRms
	- 'Downfield'	EHyd GKev
	- 'Edith Sarah'	GEdr
	- 'Gorau Glas'	WAbe
	- 'Mary Lyle'	GEdr
	- 'Oha'	GEdr
	- 'Praecox'	see *G.* × *macaulayi* 'Praecox'
	- 'Purity'	EHyd GEdr WAbe
	- 'Starlight'	GEdr GKev NHar
	- 'Weisser Traum'	EHyd GEdr LRHS NHar NHol NLar
	- 'White Wings'	GEdr
	'Sir Rupert'	GEdr NHar
	'Stardust'	GKev
	'Sternschuppe'	GKev
	× ***stevenagensis***	EHyd
§	- 'Bernardii'	GEdr
	- dark-flowered	WAbe
	straminea	EBee GKev
	'Strathmore' ♀H5	CBor CRos EHyd GEdr GKev GMaP LRHS NBir SPlb WIce
	'Suendermannii'	GKev
	'Surprise'	GEdr
	syringea	WAbe
	ternifolia 'Cangshan'	GEdr
	- 'Dali'	GEdr
	'The Caley'	GEdr GMaP LRHS NHar
	tibetica	GPoy LEdu WCAu WPGP XLum
	- PAB 2357	LEdu WPGP
	Tough's form	GEdr
	triflora 'Shine Blue Ashiro' PBR (Ashiro Series) **new**	LBar
	'Troon'	GMaP NHar
	veitchiorum	EPot GArf
	verna	CBor CRos EHyd EPfP EPot EWes GKev LCro LOPS LRHS NBwr NHpl NRHS NSla SPlb SPoG WAbe WHoo
	- 'Alba'	GEdr NLar NSla WAbe
§	- 'Angulosa' ♀H5	MAsh
§	- subsp. ***pontica***	WIce
	- subsp. ***tergestina***	GKev
	'Violette'	EHyd GEdr LRHS
	waltonii	EWes
	zekuensis	WCot

Geranium ✿ (*Geraniaceae*)

	aconitifolium misapplied	see *G. palmatum*
	aconitifolium L'Hér.	see *G. rivulare*
	'Alan Mayes'	CBWd CBod CMac ECtt EHyd EPPr EWoo GBin GKin GPSL LHGe LRHS MBel NBPC NGdn NRHS WCra WFar WPnP
	'Alan's Blue'	EBee
	albanum	CElw EPPr GElm GLog GPSL SRGP
	albiflorum	EBee
	'Allendale Gem'	EBee
	anemonifolium	see *G. palmatum*
	'Ann Folkard' ♀H7	Widely available
	'Ann Folkard' × ***psilostemon***	LSRN
	'Anne Thomson' ♀H7	Widely available
	'Ant Chilly'	EBee LHGe
	× ***antipodeum*** 'Chocolate Candy' PBR	LBar LBuc NCth SCoo SPoG
	- 'Pink Spice' PBR	CWGN GKin GMcL LBuc SPoG SRms

- 'Purple Passion'PBR	LBuc SPoG
- 'Stanhoe'	MHCG
- (*G. sessiliflorum* subsp. *novae-zelandiae* 'Nigricans' × *G. traversii* var. *elegans*)	SRms
argenteum	NSla
aristatum	EBee EPPr GElm MNrw MRav SGbt WCru
armenum	see *G. psilostemon*
asphodeloides	CElw MNrw NBid NBir SGbt SHar WBrk WFar
- subsp. ***sintenisii***	EPPr
- 'Starlight'	NBid
atlanticum Hook. f.	see *G. malviflorum*
'Azure Rush'	CDoC CDor CKel CRos CWGN EBee EBlo ECtt EHyd ELon EPfP GMaP IPot LBar LRHS MACG MHol MPri NCth NDov NRHS NSti SPer SPoG SRms WCAu WCra WFar WPnP WSpi
'Azurro'	EBee
'Baby Blue'	see *G. himalayense* 'Baby Blue'
'Bertie Crûg'	ECtt ELon GMcL LLWG NBir NCou NLar SRms SRot SWvt
'Bloomtime'	ECtt LBar LRHS MACG WCra
'Blue Boy'	NLar
'Blue Cloud' ♀H7	Widely available
'Blue Pearl'	EPPr NBir NSti
§ BLUE SUNRISE ('Blogold'PBR) ♀H7	Widely available
'Blue Thunder'	EPPr
'Blushing Turtle'PBR	CBod CKel CWnw ECtt ELan EMor EPfP LBar LRHS MAvo MHol MPri NDov NLar SCoo SPoG WCAu WCra WNPC WTor
'Bob's Blunder'	CRos EAri ECtt EMor LRHS MBNS MBel MHol MNrw MSCN NBPC NLar SAko SPeP SPoG SRms SWvt WCot WCra WFar WHoo
bohemicum	WHer
- 'Orchid Blue'	SWvt
'Brookside' ♀H7	Widely available
'Buckland Beauty'	CExl EWes SGro
'Buxton's Blue'	see *G. wallichianum* 'Buxton's Variety'
caeruleatum	NLar
canariense	see *G. reuteri*
§ × ***cantabrigiense***	CMac CRos EBee EBou ECtt EHyd EMor EPfP GMcL LRHS MHer MNrw NBir NBro NLar NPer NRHS NSti SCob SRms WBor WBrk WCru
- 'Berggarten'	EBee EPPr GBin NLar SAko SRGP WBrk WCra WJam
- 'Biokovo'	Widely available
- 'Cambridge'	CBod EBee ECha ECtt EGrI EHeP ELan EMor EPPr EPfP GAbr GKin LHGe LRHS MBow MRav MSwo NRHS SCob SPer SPoG SRms SWvt WBrk WCra WFar WFib XSen
- CRYSTAL ROSE ('Abpp')	EBee EHyd EPPr EPfP LRHS NRHS NSti SRGP WCot
- 'Hanne'	CDor EBee ECha ECtt EPPr EWes WCra
- 'Harz'	CDor EPPr SAko WCra
- 'Hilary Rendall'	EBee ECha ECtt EPPr WCra
- 'Karmina'	CDor EBee EBlo EHyd EPPr EPfP GBin GPSL LRHS NFav NLar NRHS WCra WFar WHoo WSpi XLum XSen
- 'Rosalina'	EPPr
- 'Show Time'	EPPr

- 'St Ola'	Widely available
- 'Vorjura'	EBee EPPr SAko
- 'Westray'PBR	CBod CDor CMac CWnw ECtt GJos GLog LCro LOPS LSou MHol MMuc NBir NCou NGdn NLar NRya NSti SEND SRms SWvt WCra WFib WIce WPnP
'Chantilly'	EBee ECtt EPPr EWTr LHGe MAvo NBir NChi NLar WCru WFib WGwG
'Chipchase Castle'	NChi
christensenianum B&SWJ 8022	WCru
cinereum	NSla
- 'Apple Blossom'	see *G.* × *lindavicum* 'Apple Blossom'
- 'Sateene'PBR	CAby CBor GMaP NLar SRms
(Cinereum Group) 'Alice'PBR	CAby CBor EBee LRHS NLar SRms WCra WFar
- 'Ballerina' ♀H5	Widely available
- 'Carol'	CAby CBor CWGN EWes GKin LSRN MRav NRHS SWvt WCra WFar
I - 'Heather'	CBor WFar
- 'Janette'	CBor NRHS
- JOLLY JEWEL CORAL ('Noortjjcor')	WCot
- JOLLY JEWEL HOT PINK ('Noortjjhpi')	LCro LOPS
- JOLLY JEWEL LILAC ('Noortlil'PBR)	CWGN GEdr LBar NSti WCot WCra
- JOLLY JEWEL NIGHT ('Noortnight'PBR)	CWGN ECtt GEdr LBar LRHS MAvo MPnt MThu NLar SHeu WCAu WCot WCra WHlf
- JOLLY JEWEL PURPLE ('Noortpur'PBR)	CWGN GEdr LCro LOPS LRHS MPri NHar SHeu WCot WCra WHlf
- JOLLY JEWEL RASPBERRY ('Noortjjrab')	CWGN WCot
- JOLLY JEWEL RED ('Noortimpred')	EMor LBar MPnt MPri NCou NHar NLar NSti SHeu WCAu WCot WCra
- JOLLY JEWEL SALMON ('Noortsal'PBR)	CWGN EMor GEdr LCro LOPS MHol MThu SHeu WCot WHlf
- JOLLY JEWEL SILVER ('Noortjjsil')	LBar LRHS MPri NSti WCot WCra
- JOLLY JEWEL VIOLET ('Noortvio')	WCot
- 'Lambrook Helen'	CAby CBor CExl
- 'Laurence Flatman'	CAby CBor CExl CSpe ECtt EHyd EPfP EPri EWoo GMaP LHGe LRHS MCot MPnt NBid NBwr NChi NDov NQui NRHS NSla SPoG SRms WCra
- 'Lizabeth'PBR	CBor NLar WCot
- 'Melody'PBR	CAby CBor
- 'Pandora'	CBor
- 'Penny Lane'PBR	CBor MHol WCra
- 'Purple Pillow'	CBor CWGN EGrI ELan LSRN LShi NChi NFav SAko SPer SRms SWvt WFar
- ROTHBURY GEM ('Gerfos'PBR) ♀H5	EGrI IPot MRav SWvt WCra
- 'Signal'	ELon EPot MPnt
- 'Sophie'PBR	CBor EHyd LRHS NRHS
§ - 'Thumbling Hearts'	CBor CWGN EBee EGrI GPSL LBar LCro LLWG MAsh NCth SAko WCot WCra WFar
- THUMPING HEART	see *G.* (Cinereum Group) 'Thumbling Hearts'
'Claridge Druce'	see *G.* × *oxonianum* 'Claridge Druce'
clarkei	SBut
§ - 'Kashmir White'	Widely available
- 'Mount Stewart'	CExl EBee EPfP
- Purple-flowered Group	WCav
- - 'Kashmir Purple'	Widely available
- Raina 82.83	MNrw

clarum B&SWJ 10246	WCru
collinum	EPPr
'Color Carousel'	EBee
'Coombland White'	CBod CExl EBee ECtt EHyd EPau EWTr EWes EWoo GQue LHGe LSun MAvo NCou NRHS SPoG SRGP WCot WCra WFar WNPC WSpi
'Copper Tiger'	LEdu WPGP
'Coquet Island'	EPPr
'Criss Canning'	EPPr WCra
'Curly Girly'	EBee
'Cyril's Fancy'	EBlo
'Daily Purple'	CWGN
dalmaticum ♀H5	Widely available
- 'Album'	EBee EHyd EMor EPot GDam MRav NRHS SRGP SRms WAbe
- 'Bressingham Pink'	CBor ECtt EPPr
- 'Bridal Bouquet'	CTtf ECtt NBwr NSla WHoo
- 'Stade's Hellrosa'	EPPr
dalmaticum* × *macrorrhizum	see *G.* × *cantabrigiense*
'Danny Boy' ♀H7	EBee LHGe
'Dark Eyes' **new**	LBar WNPC
'Deep Purple'	CTtf EBee
delavayi misapplied	see *G. sinense*
'Deux Fleurs'	IPot MAvo MNrw
'Devon Pride'	CElw EBee EPPr LHGe
'Dilys' ♀H7	CBor EBee ELan EPPr GElm LHGe MAvo MNrw NBir NChi NDov NGdn NGrd NLar NSti WCra WFar WPnP WSpi
'Distant Hills'	EBee EPPr
'Diva'	EBee EPPr
'Doctor Geert Lambrecht'	EBee
'Double Jewel'	see *G. pratense* 'Double Jewel'
DRAGON HEART ('Bremdra'PBR)	Widely available
drakensbergense	WFar
DREAMLAND ('Bremdream'PBR)	CBod CDor CSpe CWGN EBee ECtt EMor EPfP GMaP LCro LHGe LOPS LPla LRHS LSRN MAvo MBNS MBel NLar SEdd SGBe SMrm WCAu WCot WCra
'Dusky Crûg'	CBod CSBt ECtt EHyd ELan EMor EPfP EShb GDam GElm GMaP GMcL LRHS LSto MAsh MBel MPie NFav NHpl NSti SDix SGBe SPoG SRot SWvt WCot WCra WFar WSpi WWke
'Dusky Rose'	CAby CDor CKel ECtt EWoo GJos GKev GMcL GPSL NLar SHar SRGP WFar
'Dylis'	WCAu
'Elke'	Widely available
'Elworthy Eyecatcher'	CDor CElw MAvo MNrw
'Elworthy Tiger'	CElw EBee MAvo
endressii	CBod CWCL ECha EPfP GMaP GMcL LHGe LShi MBNS MMuc NBro NPer NPol SEND SPlb SRms SWvt WCra WFar WHlf XLum
- 'Album'	see *G.* 'Mary Mottram'
- 'Prestbury White'	see *G.* × *oxonianum* 'Prestbury Blush'
I - 'Rose'	MAvo
- 'Wargrave Pink'	see *G.* × *oxonianum* 'Wargrave Pink'
erianthum	GLog GMaP NLar WCru
- 'Axeltree'	WCot
- 'Blues in the Night'	EBee
- 'Calm Sea'	WCru
- 'Neptune'	WCru
- 'Pale Blue Yonder'	EBee EWes
eriostemon Fischer	see *G. platyanthum*
'Eureka Blue'	CRos ECha ECtt EHyd EPfP GAbr LPla LRHS MHol NLar NRHS NSti SEdd SPoG WCot WCra WPnP
'Eva'	WCra
'Expression'	see *G.* 'Tanya Rendall'
'Farncombe Cerise Star'	CElw
§ ***farreri***	CBor CExl EHyd EPot GGro LRHS NBir NRHS NSla WMal
'Fay Anna'	CBct CBod CWGN EMor EPfP GBee GBin LHGe MBros MHol MPnt SCob SPeP SPoG WFar
'Finnish Pink'	NGrd
'Foundling'	IPot
gracile	EBee EBlo EHyd EPfP GMaP LRHS MNrw NBir NChi NRHS WBrk WCru
- 'Blanche'	EPPr
- 'Blush'	EPPr EWes
- 'Golden Gracile'	see *G.* 'Mrs Judith Bradshaw'
grandiflorum	see *G. himalayense*
gymnocaulon	EBee EPfP LRHS NLar WCru
gymnocaulon* × *platypetalum	EBee
'Harmony'	EBee EPPr
harveyi	EWes EWld NChi SPhx WKif
§ ***hayatanum***	EHyd
- B&SWJ 164	NLar WCru
'Hexham Velvet'	ECtt LBar LHGe MHol MNrw WCra WSpi
§ ***himalayense***	CBcs CBod ECha EHeP EHyd ELan EMor EPfP LRHS MBNS MMuc MRav NBir NBro NGrd NRHS SEND SPlb SRms WCav WCra WFar XLum
- CC 1957 from Tibetan border	CExl EPPr
- HPA 1347	GGro
- ***alpinum***	see *G. himalayense* 'Gravetye'
§ - 'Baby Blue'	CElw CRos EBee ECtt EHyd ELon EPPr LBar LRHS MAvo MBel MNrw NGdn NLar NRHS NSti SRGP WBrk WCAu WCra WCru WFib WPnP
- 'Birch Double'	see *G. himalayense* 'Plenum'
- 'Derrick Cook'	CDor CElw EBee ECha ECtt EPPr EPfP EWTr EWoo GAbr GBin GElm LBar LHGe LPla LRHS MAvo MBel MNrw NGrd NLar NSti WBrk WCAu WCra WHoo WJam WPnP WSpi
- 'Devil's Blue'	EPPr MAvo SRGP WCAu
§ - 'Gravetye'	Widely available
- 'Irish Blue'	CDor CElw EBee EPPr EWoo GElm GMaP LBar NLar NPol NSti SRGP WCra WFib
- ***meeboldii***	see *G. himalayense*
- 'Pale Irish Blue'	EBee EPPr
§ - 'Plenum' (d)	Widely available
'Hola Guapa'	GPSL
ibericum misapplied	see *G.* × *magnificum*
ibericum ambig.	NFav SRms WCAu
ibericum Cav.	CTri EHyd LRHS NRHS
- 'Black and Blue'	EBee WHlf
- subsp. ***ibericum***	CMac WCra
- subsp. ***jubatum***	MNrw SGbt SRms
- - 'White Zigana'	EBlo ECtt NLar SRms WGwG
- subsp. ***jubatum* × *renardii***	SWvt
- var. ***platypetalum*** misapplied	see *G.* × *magnificum*
- var. ***platypetalum*** Boiss.	see *G. platypetalum* Fisch. & C.A.Mey.
§ - 'Ushguli Grijs'	EPPr NLar WCot
incanum	CAby CCht CSpe EBee LLWG NBir NHpl SRGP SVen WCFE WSpi
- var. ***incanum***	SGro

	'Ivan' ♀H7	CAby CBod CElw CFis CWCL EBee ECha ECtt EHyd EPPr EPau LPla LRHS MBel NChi NLar NRHS WCot WCra WCru WFib
	'Ivybridge Eyeful'	WSHC
	'Japfu' **new**	LBar
	'Jean Armour'	CBod ECtt EHyd EPPr GBee LRHS LSou MAvo MBel NLar NRHS SPoG WFar WGwG
	× ***johnsonii***	WFib
	- 'Johnson's Blue'	Widely available
	'Jolly Bee'	see *G.* ROZANNE
	'Joy'	CDor CRos CTtf CWGN EBee EHyd ELon EPfP EWoo GElm LHGe LSun MRav NBPC NBir NDov NLar NRHS NSti SRGP SRms WCot WCra WFib WGwG WHil WMal WPnP
	'JS Matu Vu'	CDor CWGN ECtt GPSL LBar NDov SPoG WCAu WCra WSpi
§	'Kanahitobanawa'	MAvo WSHC
	'Karen Wouters'	EPPr
	'Kashmir Blue'	CExl CRos EHyd ELan EPfP GMaP LRHS NLar NRHS SWvt WCAu WCra WFar WKif
	'Kashmir Pink'	Widely available
§	'Khan'	CElw ECha EPPr EWes EWoo MAvo NEoE NLar SDys SMHy SRGP WCru
	'Kirsty'	EWes MAvo NChi
	kishtvariense	GGro MRav NSti WCru
	koraiense	WFar
	- B&SWJ 797	WCru
	- B&SWJ 878	CExl EBee WCru
	koreanum misapplied	see *G. hayatanum*
	koreanum ambig.	NLar
	- B&SWJ 602	CExl WCru WHoo
	krameri	NLar
	- B&SWJ 1142	CExl WCru
	'Lakwijk Star'	CBod CFis ECtt EMor EPPr EPfP GPSL ILea LHGe LRHS NLar SPoG SRms WCAu WCra WMal
	'Larch Cottage Velvet'	MAvo
	libani	CDor EPPr MCot NBid NSti WBrk WCot WSHC
	- RCB RL B-2	WCot
	- 'Kew Gardens'	EPPr
	'Light Dilys'	EBee EPPr LCro LHGe LOPS NDov
	'Lilac Ice'	CWGN EBee ECtt EHyd EPfP GMaP IPot LCro LOPS LPla LRHS MNrw NCth NDov NLar NRHS NSti SGbt WCra
§	× ***lindavicum*** 'Apple Blossom'	EPot LRHS WAbe WFar
	- 'Gypsy' ♀H5	WMal
	linearilobum subsp. ***transversale*** 'Foundling's Friend'	CCht CWGN CWnw EMor IPot LBar LHGe SCoo SRGP WCot WSpi
I	- - 'Laciniatum'	WCot
§	'Little David'	CFis GPSL LHGe MBel NLar WCra
	'Little Devil'	see *G.* 'Little David'
	'Little Gem'	CRos EBee EHyd GPSL LRHS MAvo NDov NRHS SGro WFar WHoo
	lucidum	WSFF
	'Lydia'	SRGP XSen
§	***macrorrhizum***	CBod CSBt EGrI EHeP GBin GJos GKev GKin GMcL LCro LEdu LOPS LRHS LSun LWaG MCot MRav MSCN NBro SRms WCAu WFar WSFF XLum XSen
	- 'Album'	CDor ECha EHeP EHyd EMor EPPr EWoo GMaP LRHS LShi MBel MSwo NBid NBro NChi NRHS SAko SRGP WBrk WCAu WCot WCra WCru WFar WFib WJam
	- 'Bevan's Variety'	Widely available
	- 'Bulgaria'	EPPr
	- 'Cham Ce'	ECtt EPPr
	- 'Czakor'	CBod CDor CGBo CMac EBee EBlo ECtt ELan ELon EMor EPPr EPfP LHGe MCot MRav MSpe NGdn NLar SAko SCob SEdd SRGP SRms SWvt WBrk WCot WCra WCru WFar XLum
I	- 'De Bilt'	EPPr EWes
	- 'Freundorf'	EPPr EWes GQue SAko
	- 'Glacier'	ECha EPPr EWes
	- 'Ingwersen's Variety' ♀H7	Widely available
	- 'Lohfelden'	EPPr EWes WBrk WCru
	- 'Montasch'	NLar
	- 'Morris Minor'	EWes
	- 'Mount Olympus'	see *G. macrorrhizum* 'White-Ness'
	- 'Mytikas'	EPPr
	- 'Olympos'	EPPr NLar
	- 'Pastis'	SPoG
	- 'Pindus'	EBee EHyd EPPr EWes LRHS NLar NRHS NSti SPtp SRGP WCru WFar
	- 'Prionia'	EBee EPPr NLar SAko
	- 'Purpurrot'	EPPr WBrk
	- 'Ridsko'	EPPr SRGP WBrk WCru
	- ***roseum***	see *G. macrorrhizum*
	- 'Rotblut'	EPPr WBrk
	- 'Sandwijck'	EPPr WBrk WCra
	- 'Snow Sprite'	CKel EPPr GJos MHer NEoE NLar WBrk WHrl XLum
	- 'Spessart'	Widely available
	- 'Variegatum' (v)	ELan GMaP GMcL MBriF NBir SRGP SRms WCot WFar
	- 'Velebit'	EPPr WCru XLum
	- 'Vitalis'	CBod
§	- 'White-Ness' ♀H7	Widely available
	macrostylum	WCot
	- 'Leonidas'	EPPr
	- 'Talish'	EPPr
	- 'Uln Oag Triag'	EPPr
	maculatum	EHyd LRHS MCot MMrt MNrw MRav NLar NRHS NSti SRGP WCru
	- from Kath Dryden	EPPr
	- f. ***albiflorum***	CElw EBee EHyd ELan ELon EMor EPPr EPfP EWoo LHGe LRHS MBel MNrw NChi NLar NSti SRGP SSut WBrk WCra WCru WFar WPnP
	- 'Beth Chatto'	Widely available
	- 'Elizabeth Ann' PBR ♀H7	CWGN EBee ECtt EWoo LHGe LSou MBel MHol MNrw NGdn NLar NSti SDix WCot WCra WFar WFib WPnP
	- 'Espresso'	Widely available
	- 'Putnam County'	EBee EPPr
	- 'Schokoprinz'	SAko
	- 'Shameface'	EBee EBlo EHyd EPPr EPfP LRHS NRHS WCra
	- 'Silver Buttons'	EBee
	- 'Smoky Mountain'	EPPr
	- 'Spring Purple'	CDor CElw EBee EPPr MAvo NChi NLar WFar
	- 'Sweetwater'	EPPr
	- 'Vickie Lynn'	CCBP EBee EPPr EWTr MAvo MBel NDov NLar WCAu WCra
	maderense ♀H3	Widely available
	- 'Guernsey Pink' **new**	LBar
	- 'Guernsey White'	CBod CCCN CPla CSpe CTrC CTsd LBar LRHS SPhx WKif WOut
	- white-flowered	CWCL EAri LDai
	maderense × ***palmatum***	LWaG
	MAGICAL ALL SUMMER BLUE ('Bokramasum') **new**	LBar

	MAGICAL ALL SUMMER DEEP BLUE **new**	LBar
	MAGICAL ALL SUMMER PINK **new**	LBar
§	× ***magnificum*** ♀H7	Widely available
I	- 'Anemoniflorum'	WCra
	- 'Blue Blood'	CBod CKel EBee ECtt EPPr EPfP GAbr GMcL LBar LHGe NBPC NGdn NLar NSti SCob SRms SWvt WCot WCra WFar
	- 'Ernst Pagels'	CBod CDor GBin
	- 'Peter Yeo'	WCra
	- 'Rosemoor'	CAby CBod CElw CRos ECtt EHyd ELan EPPr EPfP LCro LHGe LOPS LRHS LSto NLar NRHS SPer WBor WCra WFar WFib WHoo WSpi XLum
	- 'Vital'	LHGe XLum
	magniflorum	EBee EWes GKev NBid SHar
	- LA VETA LACE ('P0135')	LRHS
	'Maître Hugo'	EBee NChi
§	***malviflorum***	CAby CFis ECha NSti WCot
	- from Spain	EWes
	- pink-flowered	EPPr WSHC
§	'Mary Mottram'	CElw LDai MAvo
	'Mavis Simpson' ♀H6	Widely available
	'Maxwelton'	EBee
	'Melinda'	CDor EBee ECtt GElm WCot WFib
	'Memories'PBR	CBor LSRN SRms
	'Menna Bach'	MAvo WFar
	'Meryl Anne'	MAvo
	'Midnight Star'	EBee EPPr EWes LHGe
	molle	WSFF
	× ***monacense***	CCBP EBee EHyd LEdu LRHS NRHS WCru WFar WGwG
	- var. ***anglicum***	CDor EHyd EPPr EPfP LRHS NLar
	- 'Anne Stevens'	EBee
	- 'Claudine Dupont'	CDor CElw ECha EPPr GQue MSpe WCot WFib
	- dark-flowered	WFar
	- 'Emma White'	EBee EPPr NChi NGrd
	- 'Jackie'	EBee EPPr NChi
	- var. ***monacense*** 'Breckland Fever'	EBee EPPr WCra
§	- - 'Muldoon'	NBir SRGP WChS WFar
	- 'Spotted in the Pass'	EBee
	'Mourning Widow'	see *G. phaeum* 'Lady in Mourning'
	'Mrs Jean Moss'	EBee EPPr EWes MAvo NChi WCra
§	'Mrs Judith Bradshaw'	EPPr
	napuligerum misapplied	see *G. farreri*
	'Natalie'	EBee LSRN MAvo NChi SWvt WJam WWke
	nepalense	SRGP SRms
	'Nicola'	CElw CRos EBlo EHyd EPPr LRHS MAvo NLar NRHS SRGP
	'Nimbus' ♀H7	Widely available
	nodosum	Widely available
	- 'Blueberry Ice'	CDor CElw MAvo
	- 'Clos de Coudray'	EBee ELon EMor EPPr EPfP ESwi GPSL LHGe LRHS MAvo NFav NLar NSti SHar SRGP WCAu WCra WFar WPnP
	- 'Dark Heart'	MCot
	- dark-flowered	see *G. nodosum* 'Swish Purple'
	- 'Darkleaf'	EBee
	- 'Eton Mess'	WCot
	- 'Fielding's Folly'	CElw LEdu
	- 'Hexham Big Eye'	CDor CElw EBee EWes LPla MAvo WBrk WFar
	- 'Hexham Face Paint'	EBee WCra
	- 'Hexham Feathers'	CDor CElw
	- 'Hexham Freckles'	EBee EPPr
	- 'Hexham Lace'	CDor CElw EPPr
	- 'Hexham Whitethroat'	EBee
	- 'Julie's Velvet'	CElw LEdu SGro WHoo
	- lilac-flowered	EGrl
	- pale-flowered	see *G. nodosum* 'Svelte Lilac'
	- 'Pascal'	EPPr
	- 'Silverwood'	Widely available
	- 'Simon'	ESwi NLar WCra
§	- 'Svelte Lilac'	CBod CRos ECtt EHyd EMor EPPr EPfP EWoo LHGe LPla LRHS LSou NBro NHol NRHS NSti SPoG SRGP WBrk WChS WCru WFar WFib WPnP
§	- 'Swish Purple'	EPPr NLar WCru
	- 'Tony's Talisman'	EBee WBrk
	- 'Whiteleaf'	CDor CElw CFis CMac EHyd EPPr GBin GElm LRHS NChi NRHS SBut SRGP WCru WFar
	- 'Wreighburn House White'	EBee EPPr MAvo
	'Nora Bremner'	EBee
	'Nunwood Purple'	EBee EPPr MAvo
	'Old Rose'	EHyd LRHS WCru
	onaei f. ***yezoense***	GGro
	oreganum	EBee
§	***orientalitibeticum***	CExl CSpe EBee GKev MBow MCot MMuc NBid NRya SBrt SEND SMad WCot WSHC
	'Orion' ♀H7	Widely available
	'Orkney Blue'	CElw EPPr NChi WCra WCru
	ORKNEY CHERRY ('Bremerry'PBR)	CMac CTsd CWnw EMor EPfP GJos GPSL LCro LOPS LRHS MBel MNrw SCob SGBe SHeu SRkn SRms WCra WNPC WPnP
	'Orkney Dawn'	LHGe
	'Orkney Flame'	EBee EPPr NChi WCra
	'Orkney Mist'	MAvo
	'Orkney Pink'	ECtt EHyd EPfP
	× ***oxonianum***	EGrl GQue
	- 'A.T. Johnson' ♀H7	CAby CBcs CBod CEme CSde CTri CWCL EBee ECtt EHyd ELan EPPr EPfP EShb GKin GMaP LRHS MRav NBir NLar NRHS NSti SPer SPoG SRms SWvt WCru WFar WSpi
	- 'Alice'	SRGP
	- 'Alison Redpath' **new**	WCra
	- 'Ankum's White'	EBee EPPr EWes
	- 'Beholder's Eye' ♀H7	CBod EPPr MMuc NLar WPnP
	- 'Breckland Sunset'	EBee NLar SRGP
	- 'Bregover Pearl'	SMHy
	- 'Bressingham's Delight'	CRos EBlo EHyd EPfP LRHS NRHS SRGP
I	- 'Cally Seedling'	EWes
	- 'Cam Beauty'	MAvo
	- 'Chocolate Strawberry'	EBee EPPr
§	- 'Claridge Druce'	CMac CTri ECha ELan EPau EPfP GKin GMaP LHGe MRav NBir NGdn NGrd NLar NRHS SPer SRms WCra WFar XLum
	- 'Cream Chocolate'	EPPr LHGe
	- 'David Rowlinson'	CDor EPPr
	- 'Dawn Time'	CDor
	- 'Ella'	CWGN
	- 'Elworthy Misty'	CElw CFis EPPr SRGP WCra
	- 'Frank Lawley'	NBid NChi WFar
§	- 'Fran's Star' (d)	WCru
	- 'Frilly Gilly'	EBee
	- 'Glynis'	SRGP
	- 'Hexham Pink'	EBee WCra
	- 'Hexham White'	EBee EPPr
	- 'Hollywood'	EPPr NLar NPer SAko SRms WFar
	- 'Iced Green Tea'	EBee
	- 'Irene Hatwell'	EPPr LShi
	- 'Julie Brennan'	EBee
	- 'Kate Moss'	NSti

	- 'Katherine Adele'	CKel CKno CSpe ECha ECtt EMor EPPr EPfP EShb EWes GBee GElm LBar LSou MMuc MPnt NLar NSti SBut SEND SMrm SRGP SRms WCAu WFar WFib
§	- 'Kingston'	EPPr
	- 'Königshof'	EPPr EWes
	- 'Kurt's Variegated'	see *G.* × *oxonianum* 'Spring Fling'
	- 'Lace Time'	CAby CBod CKel CRos ECtt EHyd EMor EPPr EPfP GKin LHGe LRHS LSRN NLar NRHS SMHy SMrm SPer SPoG SRGP SRms WCAu WCra WJam WPnP WTyc
	- 'Lady Moore'	EPfP LHGe LRHS SRGP
	- 'Lambrook Gillian'	CFis SRGP
	- 'Lasting Impression'	EPPr
	- 'Laura Skelton'	CElw EBee
	- 'Little John'	EPPr EWes
	- 'Maurice Moka'	EBee MSpe NLar
	- 'Miriam Rundle'	WCru
	- 'Miss Heidi'	EPfP LCro LRHS
	- 'Music from Big Pink'	EBee EPPr EWes
	- 'Patricia Josephine'	WCAu
	- 'Phantom'	EBee EPPr
	- 'Phoebe Noble'	CRos EBee EHyd EPPr LRHS MNrw NRHS WFib
	- 'Phoebe's Blush'	NChi
§	- 'Prestbury Blush'	CElw
	- 'Prestbury White'	see *G.* × *oxonianum* 'Prestbury Blush'
	- 'Raspberry Ice'	EBee EWes
	- 'Rebecca Moss'	CAby CBod ECha ECtt EHyd ELan GAbr GPSL LRHS LSRN NChi NRHS NSti SAko SBut WCru WFar WFib WGwG
	- 'Red Sceptre'	EBee
	- 'Rose Clair'	CBod EHyd ELan LHGe LRHS NBir NLar NRHS SRGP WCAu WCru
	- 'Rosenlicht'	EBee GKin MRav WCru XLum
	- 'Rothbury Sarah'	EBee EPPr
	- 'Sandy'	EBee EPPr
	- 'Something Special'	EBee EPPr
§	- 'Spring Fling' (v)	CDor ECtt EWes MSpe NWad WFar
	- 'Stillingfleet Keira'	EBee EPPr NSti
	- 'Summer Surprise'	EPPr EWes WCru
	- 'Susan'	EPPr EWes
	- 'Susie White'	EPPr WCru
	- 'Tess'	ECtt MHol WHoo
§	- f. ***thurstonianum***	CMac EHyd EPPr EPfP EPri EWoo LRHS MRav NBid NBir NBro NRHS SPoG SRms WBrk WCru WFar WSHC WSpi XLum
	- - 'Armitageae'	SRGP
	- - 'Breckland Brownie'	EBee EPPr EWes SRGP
	- - 'Crûg Star'	WCru
	- - 'David McClintock'	EBee EPPr SRGP WFar
	- - 'Robin's Ginger Nut'	EBee EWes
	- - 'Sherwood'	CSde EPPr GElm LHGe MSpe NSti WFar
	- - 'Southcombe Double' (d)	ECtt ELan SRGP SRms WCra WFar
§	- - 'Southcombe Star'	EBee EBlo EPPr GAbr NGdn WCru
	- - 'Sue Cox' (d)	EPPr
	- - 'White Stripes'	EBee EPPr LHGe
	- 'Trevor's White'	CDor EBee EPPr LRHS WCAu WCra WCru WPnP
	- 'Tyne Salmon'	EBee
	- 'Venus'	EWes
	- 'Wageningen' ♀H7	EBee EHyd LRHS NGdn NLar SEND WCot WCru WFar
	- 'Walter's Gift'	CBod ECtt EHyd EMor EPPr EPfP EPri EShb GElm LHGe LRHS LSou MAvo MPie MRav NBPC NBir NChi NLar NPer NRHS SAko SRGP WChS WCru WFar WHoo WPnP
§	- 'Wargrave Pink'	Widely available
	- 'Waystrode'	EBee SRGP
	- 'Westacre White'	ECha EPPr EWes
	- 'Whiter Shade of Pale'	EBee
	- 'Winscombe'	NChi NLar
	× ***oxonianum*** × ***sessiliflorum*** subsp. ***novae-zelandiae*** 'Nigricans'	EMor
§	***palmatum*** ♀H4	Widely available
	palustre	EBee EPPr EPfP GLog LHGe LRHS MMuc MNrw NLar WCAu WCot WCra
	'Pastel Clouds'	WFar
	PATRICIA ('Brempat') ♀H7	Widely available
	peloponnesiacum	EWes MNrw NLar NWad
	phaeum	Widely available
	- 'Advendo'	EPPr
	- 'Album'	Widely available
	- 'Alec's Pink'	EBee LHGe NSti SHar WCAu WPnP
	- 'All Saints'	LEdu
	- 'Angelina'	EBee EPPr EWoo WBrk
	- 'Anita' **new**	WCra
	- 'Anita Alice' **new**	NGrd WCot
	- 'Ann Logan'	EBee WCra
	- 'Aureum'	see *G. phaeum* 'Golden Spring'
	- 'Basket of Lavender'	EBee LHGe
	- 'Blauwvoet'	EPPr LHGe NChi
	- 'Blue Shadow'	EPPr LEdu LPla
	- 'Brown Sugar'	EBee
	- 'Calligrapher'	EPPr GElm NChi NGrd
	- 'Chocolate Biscuit'	EBee EPPr LHGe
	- 'Chocolate Chip'	EPPr WCot
	- 'Conny Broe' (v)	CDor EShb WSHC
	- 'Dark Angel'	EBee
	- 'Dark Dream'	EBee NGrd
	- 'David Bromley'	NChi WCru
	- 'David Martin'	EPPr
	- 'Enid'	EPPr
	- 'Garage Door'	EBee
	- 'George Stone'	NChi NGrd
	- 'Golden Samobor'	CElw EHeP EPPr WCot
§	- 'Golden Spring'	EPPr LBar LHGe NChi NEoE NLar SRGP WCra WFar
	- 'Green Ghost'	EBee EPPr
	- 'Hector's Lavender'	EBee
	- 'Hexham Halo'	EBee
	- var. ***hungaricum***	EBee EPPr
	- 'James Haunch'	CDor EPPr WCra
	- 'Jenson's Purple'	EBee
	- 'Joanna Mac' **new**	WOut
	- 'Joseph Green' (d)	CBor EBee ESgI MAvo NGrd WCot WCra WFar
	- 'Judith's Blue'	EBee NChi
	- 'Klepper'	EPPr GBin LHGe
§	- 'Lady in Mourning'	CExl EBee NChi SRms WCra WCru WFar
	- 'Lavender Pinwheel'	CDor GPSL LHGe MSpe SMHy SPer WCot
*	- 'Lilacina'	ECha
	- 'Lily Lovell'	Widely available
	- 'Lisa' (v)	CDor CElw ECha EPPr EWoo LHGe MAvo MBriF MNrw MSpe SPtp WCot WFar WHoo
	- 'Little Boy'	EPPr NEoE
	- var. ***lividum***	GMaP LRHS MACG MRav SRms WFar XLum
	- - 'Joan Baker'	CDor EBee MBriF MNrw MSpe NChi NGdn NSti SDys WCru WFar WFib

	Name	Suppliers
	- - 'Majus'	EBee EHyd ELan EMor EPPr EPfP LRHS NRHS WFar
	- 'Lustige Witwe' (v)	WCot
	- 'Margaret Wilson' (v)	CElw CWGN ECha EMor EWes GBee GElm LEdu LHGe MSpe NBir NEoE NGdn NLar NSti WCot WCra WFar WSHC
	- 'Mierhausen'	CElw EBee EPPr EWoo WCra
	- 'Misty Samobor'	CKel ECha NGrd WCra
	- 'Mojito' (v)	ECha MAvo WCot
	- 'Moorland Dylan'	WFar WOut
	- 'Mottisfont Rose'	CDor CElw SGro
	- 'Mourning Widow'	see *G. phaeum* 'Lady in Mourning'
	- 'Mrs Charles Perrin'	CFis
	- 'Night Time'	EBee EPPr
	- 'Nightshade'	EBee EPPr
	- 'Our Pat' 🏆H7	EBee EPPr LHGe NGrd WCot
	- var. ***phaeum*** 'Langthorns Blue'	CRos EBee EBlo EHyd ELan EPPr EPfP LEdu LRHS MNrw NRHS SWvt
	- - 'Samobor'	Widely available
	- 'Phantom of the Opera' (v)	CElw EBee EMor EPPr
	- 'Pink Palava'	LEdu
I	- 'Ploeger de Bilt'	EBee
	- 'Purple Moon'	EPPr
	- 'Rachel's Rhapsody'	EBee EPPr MSpe WCra
	- 'Raven'	CBWd CBod CBor CDor ECtt EMor EPPr EWoo LBar LHGe LRHS MACG MBel NChi NGrd NLar SCob SPer WCAu WCra WFar
	- 'Ray of Light'	EPPr
	- 'Rise Top Lilac'	EBee WCra
	- 'Robin's Angel Eyes'	EBee ECha LHGe WCra
	- 'Rose Air'	WFar
	- 'Rose Madder'	CCBP CDor CElw LEdu MBriF MNrw NChi NLar SMHy SPhx WCru
	- 'Rothbury Cherry' **new**	WCra
	- 'Rothbury Ruby'	EBee LHGe
	- 'Sarah'	WOut
	- 'Saturn'	EPPr
	- 'Séricourt'	MSpe WCot WCra WFib
	- 'Shadowlight'	EPPr NEoE NLar
	- 'Springtime' PBR	CAby CDor EBee EMor GPSL LHGe MSpe NBPC NGdn NLar SRms WCAu WCra WFib
	- 'Stillingfleet Ghost'	EBee LEdu MBriF MNrw NChi NSti
	- 'Taff's Jester' (v)	NHol WCot
	- 'Tyne Mist'	EBee EPPr
§	- 'Variegatum' (v)	CMac EBee ELan GElm MSpe NBir WFar
	- 'Vintage Dave'	WOut
	- 'Walküre'	EMor EPPr EWes EWoo LBar LHGe MBriF MSpe NChi NGrd NLar WCra
	- 'Waterer's Blue'	CDor ECha NGrd WCra
	- 'Wendy's Blush' **new**	ESgI WCot
	'Philippe Vapelle'	Widely available
	'Pink Delight'	CElw MAvo SGro WHoo WMal
	'Pink Penny'	CBct CBod CDor CSde CWCL ECtt EPfP GJos LHGe LPla LRHS LSRN MHol MNrw NLar NSti SCob SCoo SEdd SGBe SPoG SRms WCAu WCra WFar WHlf WNPC WPnP WTor
	'Pink Petticoats'	MPri NCou
§	***platyanthum***	EWld GGro WCru
	- 'Ankum'	EBee
	- 'Russian Giant'	EPPr
	platypetalum misapplied	see *G. × magnificum*
	platypetalum Franch.	see *G. sinense*
§	***platypetalum*** Fisch. & C.A. Mey.	EHyd EPPr LRHS NBir NRHS XLum
	- 'Dark Side of the Moon'	EBee EPPr
	- 'Genyell'	EBee EPPr MAvo NChi
	- 'Turco'	EBee EPPr EPfP LHGe NLar WCAu WCra
§	***pogonanthum***	GLog NBir
	- BO 16-049	GGro
	polyanthes	EWes GGro NChi
	pratense	CCBP CHab CMac CWal EHeP EPPr EWoo GJos GMaP GQue MBow MHer MNHC NAts NMir SCob SPer SPlb SPoG SRms WCot WCra WFar WSFF WShi XLum
	- 'Algera Double'	CFis ECtt ELan EMor EPfP LBar LRHS MAvo NBPC WCAu WCra
	- 'Bittersweet'	EPPr
	- 'Black 'n' White'	ELan LBar LRHS MAsh NCth SHeu WCot
	- 'Blue Lagoon'	EPPr
*	- 'Blue Skies'	WFar
	- 'Blue Sky Thinking'	EBee
	- 'Boom Chocolatta' **new**	LBar
	- 'Catforth Cadenza' (v)	MAvo
	- 'Cloud Nine' PBR (d)	CWGN EWTr GPSL LBar MBel NCth SHar WCra WPnP WSHC WTyc
	- 'Cluden Sapphire'	EBee EPPr GElm LBar NHol WCAu WCra WCru
	- 'Delft Blue'	CBod LBar
	- 'Delft Blue Butterfly'	WCra
§	- 'Double Jewel' (d)	CWGN EPfP IPot NBir NCth NLar WFar
	- 'Else Lacey' (d)	CElw EBee NLar NSti WCot
	- 'Flore Pleno'	see *G. pratense* 'Plenum Violaceum'
	- 'Hexham Spook'	EBee
I	- 'Himalayanum'	NLar
	- 'Hocus Pocus'	CRos CWGN EHyd ELan EWoo LBar LRHS MAsh MNrw NBro NCth NLar NRHS NSti SCob SGBe WCAu WCra WFar
	- 'Hoo House'	WHoo
	- 'Ilja'	EPPr MNrw
	- 'Janet's Special'	WHoo
	- 'Juliana' (d)	NGrd
	- 'Marshmallow'	CDor CFis EBee ECtt EPPr EPfP GElm GPSL LBar LPla MBriF NCth NLar NSti SCoo SEdd SPoG WCAu WCot WCra WMal
	- 'Milou'	NLar WCra
	- 'Moondance'	CBor
	- 'Mrs Kendall Clark' 🏆H7	Widely available
	- 'Pink Splash'	LBar WFar
	- 'Plenum Caeruleum' (d)	CTtf MRav NBid NChi WSHC
§	- 'Plenum Violaceum' (d) 🏆H7	CMiW CWCL ECtt EHyd ELan GMaP GMcL LRHS MRav NBir NChi NRHS NSti SGbt SRms SWvt WCra WCru WFar WSHC
	- 'Pope's Purple'	see *G. pratense* (Victor Reiter Group) BLACK BEAUTY
	- var. ***pratense*** f. ***albiflorum***	ECha EPPr EWoo GMaP LRHS NBid SDix SGbt SPer WCra WFar WSpi
	- - - 'Galactic'	ECtt GElm GPSL LBar LRHS MACG MBriF NBir NLar SPoG WCot WCru WFib WPnP
	- - - 'Laura' PBR (d)	CExl EBee ECtt EMor EPfP EWes LBar LHGe LSRN MBel MHol NCth NGdn NLar NSti WCra WFar WHlf WPnP WSHC WTyc
	- - - 'Plenum Album' (d)	EBee ELan EMor EPPr EWes LRHS MNrw MRav NGdn NLar SGbt SRms SWvt WCot WFar WGwG WNPC WSpi
	- - - 'Silver Queen'	CFis EBee ECtt EHyd EPPr GPSL LRHS NBir NRHS SMrm SPoG WGwG WPnP

	- 'Purple Ghost'	CBcs CSpe CWGN EHyd EPfP GPSL LBar LRHS LSou MACG MAsh MMrt NEoE NLar NRHS NSti SCob SMrm SPoG WCra WFar WPnP WSpi
	- 'Rectum Album'	see *G. clarkei* 'Kashmir White'
	- 'Robin's Grey Beard'	EBee EPPr MAvo WCra
§	- 'Rose Queen'	NBir SGbt WCru
	- 'Roseum'	see *G. pratense* 'Rose Queen'
	- 'Southease Celestial'	SMHy WGoo
	- 'Splish-splash'	see *G. pratense* 'Striatum'
	- 'Stanton Mill'	NBid
	- var. ***stewartianum***	MRav
	- - 'Elizabeth Yeo'	ECtt EPPr WCra WCru
	- - 'Raina'	EPPr
§	- 'Striatum'	Widely available
	- variegated, white-flowered (v)	WCot
§	- (Victor Reiter Group) BLACK BEAUTY ('Nodbeauty'[PBR])	CAby CExl CPla CWGN EBee EPfP EWes LBar LBuc LRHS MAvo MGos MPnt NHpl NLar SGBe SPoG SRkn WCra WFar WSpi
	- - 'Kaya'	ECtt EWes LBar LHGe NLar WCot WCra
	- - 'Midnight Blues'	CWGN
	- - 'Midnight Clouds'	CWGN EBee EPfP WFar
	- - MIDNIGHT GHOST ('Midnightlyona'[PBR])	EPfP MAsh WSpi
	- - 'Midnight Reiter'	CExl CWGN EBee EGrl EHed ELan EPfP GPSL LBar LRHS MACG MBow NBro NChi NHpl NLar NQui SBls SCob SCoo SDys SPoG SWvt WCAu WCra WFar WTor
	- - 'New Dimension'	WFib WSpi
	- - 'Purple Heron'	CBor NRHS
	- - 'Purple-haze'	WFar WSHC
§	- - 'Victor Reiter'	CDor CSpe EPPr LEdu NBir NChi NHpl WCot WCra
	- 'Wisley Blue'	EPPr
	- 'Yorkshire Queen'	NGdn NSti WCru
	'Prelude'	CDor CElw EBee ELon EPPr LPla NBir NEoE NLar SHar WCAu WFib WMal
	procurrens	CTri GAbr WBrk WCru
§	***psilostemon*** ♀H7	Widely available
	- 'Bressingham Flair'	CDor CTri EBlo ECtt LHGe LRHS MRav NBid NChi NLar SRms WCru WFar
	- 'Catherine Deneuve'[PBR]	CWGN EBee EPfP EWes GPSL LBar NLar NSti WCAu WCra
	- 'Coton Goliath'	EBee EPPr EWes MAvo
	- 'Harry' **new**	WCot WCra
	- 'Jason Bloom'	CRos EBlo EHyd EPPr LRHS NRHS
	- 'Madelon'	LHGe NLar
	- 'Rosefinch'	EBee EPPr WCot WCra
	- 'Snowfinch'	CDor
	pulchrum	EWes
	punctatum hort.	see *G.* × *monacense* var. *monacense* 'Muldoon'
	- 'Variegatum'	see *G. phaeum* 'Variegatum'
	'Purple Rain'	EBee EPPr NChi WCra
	pylzowianum	NBid
	pyrenaicum	GAbr NSti
	- f. ***albiflorum***	GAbr MNrw NBir SPhx SRGP WBrk WCot WFar
	- 'Barney Brighteye'	SRGP
	- 'Bill Wallis'	Widely available
	- 'Isparta'	ECha EPPr MNrw SHar SPhx SRGP WBrk WGoo
	- 'Summer Sky'	SRGP SWvt
	- 'Summer Snow'	GPSL SBut WFar WTor
	'Rainbow'[PBR]	LBar WCra
	Rambling Robin Group	ECre EWes
*	- 'Silver Shadow'	SPhx
	rectum	EPPr NLar WCru
	- 'Album'	see *G. clarkei* 'Kashmir White'
	'Red Admiral'	Widely available
	'Red Propellers'	CElw CPla WSHC
	reflexum 'Katara Pass'	NChi
	refractoides	GGro WCot
	refractum	CExl
	regelii	EPfP WCru
	renardii ♀H6	Widely available
	- 'Beldo'	MAvo
	- 'Tcschelda'	ECha ECtt EPPr LRHS NBir NLar SRms WCra WFar
	- 'Zetterlund'	EBee EHyd EPPr EPfP EPri EWTr LRHS NQui NSti WFar
§	***reuteri***	LDai SAng SChr WCru
	'Richard Nutt'	EBee
	richardsonii	CBod EBee EHyd EWoo GKev LRHS MNrw NBir NRHS NWad SPoG WCru WGwG
	- white-flowered	NChi
	× ***riversleaianum*** 'Russell Prichard' ♀H4	Widely available
§	***rivulare***	GLog NLar
	robertianum	ENfk EPPr GQue LWaG SPhx SRms WSFF
§	- 'Album'	EPPr SHar SPhx SRms WHer
	- f. ***bernettii***	see *G. robertianum* 'Album'
	- 'Celtic White'	EMor EPPr MMuc
	'Robin's Black Heart'	EBee LHGe
	robustum	EPri GLog NBir SBut SPlb WGoo WKif
	'Rosetta'[PBR]	CBod EPfP LBar WCAu
	'Rosie Crûg'	SWvt
	Rosie's *sanguineum* hybrid	LPar
	'Rothbury Red'	EBee NChi WCra
§	ROZANNE ('Gerwat'[PBR]) ♀H7	Widely available
	rubescens	see *G. yeoi*
	rubifolium	WCru
	rubifolium × ***wallichianum*** 'Buxton's Variety' **new**	CBod
	SABANI BLUE ('Bremigo'[PBR])	CMac CWGN EBee ECtt EWes EWoo GElm LBar LCro LHGe LOPS MHol NLar NSti SPer WCot WCra WNPC WSHC WSpi
	'Salome'	CBcs CBod CDor CWGN EBee ECtt GLog LHGe LRHS NBir NLar NSti SRms SWvt WCot WCra WGwG WKif
	'Sandrine'[PBR]	CWGN LBar LRHS MBriF MNrw NSti SPoG SRms WCot WCra WPnP
	sanguineum	Widely available
	- ALAN BLOOM ('Bloger')	EBee EHyd LRHS NLar NRHS WCra WFib
	- 'Album' ♀H7	Widely available
	- 'Alpenglow'	EBee ELon EPPr WBrk
	- 'Ankum's Pride' ♀H7	CDor EAJP EHyd EPPr EPfP LHGe LRHS LSou MBel MBros NChi NGdn NLar NRHS NSti SGro SRGP WBrk WCra WCru WFib WPnP XSen
	- 'Apfelblüte'	ELon EPPr EWTr GPSL LHGe MCot NLar WCAu WCra WPnP
	- 'Aviemore' ♀H7	EPPr GBin GQue NLar
	- 'Barnsley'	EPPr NBro
	- 'Belle of Herterton'	EPPr NChi NEoE WBrk WCru
	- 'Bloody Graham'	EPPr LRHS SPhx WBrk
	- 'Canon Miles'	ECtt EPPr IPot LHGe NLar SRms WCra WSpi
	- 'Catforth Carnival'	EPPr MAvo
	- 'Cedric Morris'	CElw ECha ELon EPPr NLar SGro WBrk WCra WCru WPnP

	- 'Compactum'	EPPr XLum
	- dark purple-flowered	SSut
	- dwarf	WAbe
	- 'Elsbeth'	CElw CRos EBee ECha ECtt EHyd ELan ELon EPPr EPfP EWes GBin LRHS LSou MBel NGdn NLar NRHS NSti SMrm SPoG WBrk WCru WFar WFib WPnP XLum XSen
	- 'Feu d'Automne'	EBee ELon EPPr NLar WBrk
	- 'Fran's Star'	see *G.* × *oxonianum* 'Fran's Star'
	- 'Glenluce'	CDor CWnw ECtt EHyd ELon EPPr EPfP EShb LHGe LRHS LSto MAsh MRav NBPC NChi NDov NGdn NGrd NLar NRHS NWad SPoG SRms WBrk WFar WPnP
	- 'Hampshire Purple'	see *G. sanguineum* 'New Hampshire Purple'
	- 'Holden'	ELon EPPr WBrk
	- 'Inverness'	EBee EPPr WCra XLum
	- 'Joanna'	ELon EPPr WBrk
	- 'John Elsley'	EBee ECtt EHyd EPPr GPSL LBar LRHS LSou NBro NEoE NGdn NRHS NSti WCra WPnP
	- 'John Innes'	EPPr
	- 'Jubilee Pink'	WCru
	- 'Kristin Jacob'	EPPr
	- var. ***lancastrense***	see *G. sanguineum* var. *striatum*
	- 'Leeds Variety'	see *G. sanguineum* 'Rod Leeds'
§	- 'Little Bead' ♀H7	EPPr NHpl NWad WBrk XLum
	- 'Max Frei'	Widely available
	- 'Nanum'	see *G. sanguineum* 'Little Bead'
§	- 'New Hampshire Purple'	EBee ECtt EHyd ELon EPPr GAbr LBar LRHS MAvo NBro NGdn NLar SRGP SRms WBrk WCra WFib
	- 'Nyewood'	EBee ECtt EHyd EPPr LRHS NBPC NGdn SEND WBrk WCru WFib
	- 'Pink Diadem' **new**	LBar
	- 'Pink Pouffe'	CBct CWGN CWnw EBee ECtt EHyd ELon GPSL LHGe LRHS NCou NLar NRHS SCob SCoo SHeu WCra
	- 'Pink Summer'	EBee EWTr LBar SGBe
	- 'Prado'	XLum
	- var. ***prostratum*** (Cav.) Pers.	see *G. sanguineum* var. *striatum*
	- 'Purple Flame'	see *G. sanguineum* 'New Hampshire Purple'
	- 'Red Robin'	EBee EPPr
§	- 'Rod Leeds'	EBee ELon
	- 'Sandra'	SRGP
§	- 'Shepherd's Delight'	EPPr
	- 'Shepherd's Warning' misapplied	see *G. sanguineum* 'Shepherd's Delight'
	- 'Shepherd's Warning' ♀H7	ECtt IPot MMuc MRav NBir NLar SEND WCru WFib WHoo WIce
	- 'Shooting Star'	EPPr IPot NLar
	- 'South Nutfield'	CElw NChi
§	- var. ***striatum*** ♀H7	Widely available
	- - deep pink-flowered	CSBt MSwo SWvt
	- - 'Mottisfont'	SGro
	- - 'Reginald Farrer'	WCru
	- - 'Splendens' ♀H7	CRos EHyd EPPr LRHS NBid NChi NRHS SAko WCru
	- (Vision Series) 'Vision Light Pink'	CBod EPPr MHol WFar
	- - 'Vision Violet'	CBod CBor CSpe EBee EBou LRHS MAvo NGrd SRms SWvt WBrk WFar WPnP
	'Sanne'	EWes LRHS LSou STPC WCot WCra WFar WFib
	'Scapa Flow'	EPPr GAbr MAvo NChi WCra
	schlechteri	EWes MMuc SEND WBrk WMal
	'Sea Pink'	EBou
	'Sea Spray'	CTri GMcL
	sessiliflorum	EMor
	subsp. ***novae-zelandiae***	
I	- - 'Nigricans'	ECha EMor EPfP SCob WFar
§	- - 'Porters Pass'	EWes NHpl SPlb WFar
	- - red-leaved	see *G. sessiliflorum* subsp. *novae-zelandiae* 'Porters Pass'
	'Sheilah Hannay'	SHar
	shikokianum	GArf GKev GLog NLar WCra WPnP
	- var. ***kaimontanum***	WCru
	- var. ***quelpaertense***	CFis EBee
	- - 'Crûg's Cloak'	WCru
	'Shocking Blue'	NLar WFib
	'Shouting Star'	see *G.* 'Kanahitobanawa'
	'Simonside'	EBee EPPr
§	***sinense***	CExl GGro LSou XLum
	'Sirak' ♀H7	Widely available
	soboliferum	CFis CPla LBar NBir NDov NLar WCru WFar
	- Cally strain	EBee EPPr LPla WHoo
	- var. ***kiusianum***	CElw
	- 'Rothbury Star'	WCra
	- 'Starman'	EWoo LBar NBPC NLar WCra WSHC WSpi
	'Solitaire'	EBee MAvo WCot
	'Southcombe Star'	see *G.* × *oxonianum* f. *thurstonianum* 'Southcombe Star'
	'Spinners'	CElw CMac EBee ECtt EHyd EPPr EPfP GElm GMaP LRHS MAvo MRav NBid NBir NGdn NLar NRHS NSti SPer WCru WFar WFib WPnP
	stapfianum var. ***roseum***	see *G. orientalitibeticum*
	'Stephanie'	CCBP CElw EHyd EPPr EWes LHGe LPla LRHS LSRN MAvo MBNS MNrw MRav MSpe NChi NGdn NLar NRHS NSti WCAu WCra WPnP WSHC
	'Storm Chaser'	EBee LBar LRHS MMrt NSti WHlf
	subcaulescens ♀H4	CAby EAJP EBee EHyd ELan EPfP LRHS LSRN NBid NLar NRHS NRya SBut SPhx SRms SWvt WAbe WCFE WFar WIce
	- 'Giuseppii' ♀H5	CExl CRos ECtt EGrI EHyd ELon EPfP EPot EWoo LBar LHGe LRHS LSou NBir NDov NRHS SCoo SPoG SWvt WCra WHoo WKif
	- 'Splendens' ♀H5	CSpe CTri ECtt EHyd GMcL LRHS MHer NRHS NSla SRms WCra WFar
	'Sue Crûg'	CEme EBee ECtt EHyd ELan LRHS NChi NRHS WCra WCru
	'Sue's Sister'	WCru
	'Summer Cloud'	EPPr
	SUMMER SKIES ('Gernic'PBR) (d)	Widely available
	suzukii B&SWJ 016	CExl
	- NMWJ 14518	WCru
	'Sweet Heidy'PBR	CDor EBee ECtt EPfP LPla MHol MNrw MPnt MPri NGdn NLar NSti SGBe WBor WCAu WCra WFar WPnP
	sylvaticum	MBow NGdn NGrd NMir SBut WFar WShi
	- f. ***albiflorum***	NSti WCru
	- - 'Cyril's Superb White'	EBee EPPr
	- 'Album' ♀H7	Widely available
	- 'Amanda'	EBee WCra
	- 'Amy Doncaster'	CBod CDor CElw CExl EBee ECtt EHyd ELan EPPr LRHS MRav NBir NLar NSti SPer WCot WFar WFib WHoo WPnP

- 'Angulatum'	CElw EPPr NChi
- 'Arthur' **new**	WCra
- 'Birch Lilac'	CElw EBee EPPr EPri NLar WCra WFib
- 'Coquetdale Lilac'	CDor EBee EPPr
- 'Greek Fire'	EBee MAvo NSti
- 'Ice Blue'	EPPr NChi WCAu
- 'Immaculée'	EPPr MRav
- 'Jonah P'	EBee
- 'Kanzlersgrund'	CElw EPPr
- 'Lilac Eyes'	EBee
- 'Lilac Time'	EPPr
- 'Master Charles Wilson'	EBee WCra
- 'Master Niall Lawson'	EBee WCra WFar
- 'Mayflower' ♀H7	Widely available
- 'Miss Connie Wilson'	EBee
- f. ***roseum***	NLar
- - 'Baker's Pink'	EPPr GElm MNrw MRav NBir WCAu WCru WFar WPnP
§ 'Tanya Rendall'PBR	ELan GMcL NLar SRGP SRms WCot WCra WFar WFib WPnP
'Terre Franche'	LHGe MAvo NLar SPhx WCAu WCra
§ ***thunbergii***	GGro SBut SRGP WFar XLum
- 'Jester's Jacket' (v)	GMcL LBar LShi MNrw WFar
- pink-flowered	EPPr
- white-flowered	EPPr
thurstonianum	see *G.* × *oxonianum* f. *thurstonianum*
'Tinpenny Mauve'	MAvo MNrw WCra WMal
'Tiny Monster'	Widely available
'Tod the Whippet'	NChi
transbaicalicum	XLum
traversii var. ***elegans***	EHyd LRHS NRHS
tuberosum	CCBP CDor CElw ECha GKev MRav NBir NGdn NQui SPhx WCra WFar
- subsp. ***linearifolium***	EPPr
- 'Richard Hobbs'	EPPr
- 'Rosie's Mauve'	EPPr MAvo
'Ushguli Grijs'	see *G. ibericum* Cav. 'Ushguli Grijs'
'Vectis'	CElw
'Verguld Saffier'	see *G.* BLUE SUNRISE
versicolor	CBcs CEme EBee EPfP GAbr GPSL LRHS MHer NLar SHar SRms WCAu WCra WFar WPnP
- 'Kingston'	see *G.* × *oxonianum* 'Kingston'
§ - 'Snow White'	EPPr SBut WCru WFib
- 'The Bride'	EPPr
- 'White Lady'	see *G. versicolor* 'Snow White'
'Victor Reiter'	see *G. pratense* (Victor Reiter Group) 'Victor Reiter'
violareum	see *Pelargonium* 'Splendide'
viscosissimum	WFib
wallichianum	EBee GElm NBir NChi NSti
- HPA 1373	GGro
§ - 'Buxton's Variety'	Widely available
- 'Crystal Lake'PBR	CWGN EBee ECtt EPfP EWoo LBar LHGe MBNS MHol MNrw NBir NDov NGdn NSti SCob WCAu WCra WFar WHil WPnP
- DAILY BLUE ('Nogetwo'PBR) **new**	LBar
- 'Happy Buxton'	LBar MHol
- HAVANA BLUES ('Noorthava'PBR)	EBee ECha ECtt EPfP ILea IPot LCro LHGe LOPS LRHS NLar NSti SCob SDix SEdd WCot WCra WFar
- 'Pink Buxton'	EWes NLar
- pink-flowered	WCru
- 'Rise and Shine'PBR	CWGN EBee ECtt ELan LCro LHGe LOPS LRHS MBriF NCth NSti SRms WCAu WCot WCra
- 'Rosetta'	WCAu
- 'Rosie'	SRGP
- 'Syabru'	EBlo MNrw
- 'Sylvia's Surprise'PBR	CDor EBee ECtt EHyd LBar LRHS MPri NCth NRHS SCob WCAu WCra
'Wednesday's Child'	WFar
'Westacre Halo' **new**	WCot
'White Doves'	MAvo NDov
wilfordii misapplied	see *G. thunbergii*
Wisley hybrid	see *G.* 'Khan'
wlassovianum	Widely available
- from Crûg Farm	NLar WCra
- 'Blue Star'	MRav NEoE SBut SRGP WCra WFar
- 'Martyn and Emma'	SRGP
- 'Zeppelin'	NLar WCra
§ ***yeoi***	NSti WCru
yesoense	GGro NSti WFar
- var. ***nipponicum***	EMor
yoshinoi misapplied	see *G. thunbergii*
yoshinoi Makino	SBut
yunnanense misapplied	see *G. pogonanthum*

Gerbera (*Asteraceae*)

(Garvinea Sweet Series)	LBar
GARVINEA SWEET CAROLINE ('Garsweetcaro')	
- GARVINEA SWEET DREAMS ('Gardreams'PBR)	LBar
- GARVINEA SWEET GLOW ('Garglow'PBR)	LBar LRHS NRHS SPeP
- GARVINEA SWEET HEART ('Garheart')	LRHS NCth
- GARVINEA SWEET HONEY ('Garho'PBR)	SGBe SPeP
- GARVINEA SWEET LOVE ('Garswlove')	LRHS
- GARVINEA SWEET MEMORIES ('Garsweetmemo'PBR)	LBar LRHS SPad
- GARVINEA SWEET SIXTEEN ('Garsixteen'PBR) **new**	LBar
- GARVINEA SWEET SMILE ('Garsmile')	LBar LRHS SGBe
- GARVINEA SWEET SPICE ('Garspice'PBR) **new**	LBar
- GARVINEA SWEET SUNSET	see *G.* (Garvinea Sweet Series) 'Sweet Sunset'
- GARVINEA SWEET SURPRISE ('Garsurprise')	LBar LRHS SPeP
§ - 'Sweet Sunset'	LRHS
REVOLUTION BICOLOR MIX (Revolution Series) **new**	WWke

Gerrardanthus (*Cucurbitaceae*)

macrorhizus	NCft

Gesneria (*Gesneriaceae*)

cardinalis	see *Sinningia cardinalis*

Geum ✿ (*Rosaceae*)

'Abendsonne'	CElw MAvo MNrw MRav MSpe NBPC NEoE WFar
'Alabama Slammer' (Cocktails Series)	Widely available
alpinum	see *G. montanum*
'Apricot Beauty'	CWCL
'Apricot Crush'	MNrw
'Apricot Delight'	CTtf NEoE
'Apricot Pearl' (Censation Series) (d)	CBod CWGN ECtt LBar MHol
'Baked Beans'	GElm NEoE
'Banana Daiquiri' (Cocktails Series)	CRos CWCL EBee ECtt ECul EGrI EHyd ELan EMor EPfP GKev LRHS

	LSto MBriF MPri NRHS SCob SHeu WFar
'Beech House Apricot'	CDor CWCL ECtt EHyd EMor EWes LRHS MNrw MPie MRav NBro NEoE NHol NLar
'Beech's Double'	EWes
'Bell Bank'	Widely available
'Belle Beauté' **new**	CBod
'Birkhead's Creamy Lemon'	EBee MHCG NBir
'Blazing Sunset' (d)	Widely available
'Blood Orange'	CTtf ECtt EHyd EPPr EPfP GKev LRHS MAvo MBriF MCot NEoE NRHS SPoG WFar
'Bohema Pink' (d) **new**	LBar
'Borisii'	Widely available
'Bremner's Nectarine'	CElw EPPr MNrw MSpe NChi NEoE SHar
'Broomrigg Beauty'	NEoE
'Brown Sugar'	NEoE
bulgaricum	EBee NBir NLar NRya WFar XLum
'Can-can' (d)	CDor CElw CTtf EMor LBar MACG MAvo MSCN WCAu WHoo WMal
'Cantamos'	NEoE
capense	NLar SPlb
'Centurion'	NEoE
chiloense 'Red Dragon'	SBut SWvt
'Chipchase'	CElw NChi NWad
coccineum ambig.	EWTr GArf GKev
coccineum Sibth. & Sm.	GLog WHoo
- 'Ann'	EPri
- 'Cooky'	EHyd EMor GMcL GPSL LRHS MBriF NBro NGrd NLar NRHS SRms SWvt WFar
- 'Eos'	CSpe CTtf CWCL EBee ECtt EWes GElm LEdu LRHS MBriF MHol MNrw MPnt MRav NBPC NGdn NLar NSti SHeu SPoG SRms WGwG
- 'Koi'	CBod CKel CWnw EAJP EBee EDAr EPfP EWTr GBin LEdu LRHS LSto LSun MACG MBros MDon MHol NEoE NGrd STPC SVic WFar WPnP
- 'Queen of Orange'	CRos CSBt CWal ECul LRHS NGrd SRms WFar
- 'Werner Arends'	GElm MAvo MNrw MRav WCot WFar
'Copper Pennies'	CElw NEoE
'Coppertone'	CElw CWCL EGrI ELan EPri GElm MRav NBir NChi
'Coral Pearl' (Censation Series) (d)	LBar LCro
'Coral Tempest' (Tempest Series) **new**	LBar MAvo WNPC
'Cosmopolitan' (Cocktails Series)	Widely available
'Cotton Candy'	NEoE
'Country Rock'	NEoE
'Country Rock Star'	WFar
'Cream Crackers'	NEoE WBrk
'Cumbrian Candy'	NEoE
'Cumbrian Cheddar'	NEoE
'Cumbrian Cherrypie'	NEoE WFar
'Cumbrian Cherrytart'	NEoE
'Cumbrian Cream'	NEoE
'Custard Tart'	NEoE
'Dark and Stormy' (Cocktails Series)	LRHS MAvo NEoE
'Dawn'	NEoE SMHy
'Dawntreader' (Valley Hi Series) **new**	NEoE
'Deano's Delight'	NEoE
'Diamond White'	EWhm

'Diana'	GElm MNrw NLar
'Dingle Apricot'	ECtt GAbr MNrw MRav NBir
'Dolly North' (d)	CElw CWCL EPPr EWhm GBee GElm MHol MRav MSpe NBro NGdn SHar WBrk WCAu WJam
'Double Sunrise' (d)	WFar
'East of Eden'	GElm NEoE
'Eden Apricot'	NEoE
'Eden Rising'	NEoE
'Eden Valley Angel'	GElm NChi NEoE WWtn
'El Wano'	NEoE
'Elworthy Amber'	CElw
'Elworthy Coppernob'	CElw
'Emory Quinn'	EPPr EWes LRHS NEoE NSti WHrl
'Fancy Frills'	CElw ECtt MAvo WHoo
'Farmer John Cross'	CElw CTtf EBee EBlo ECtt EPPr EPri LShi MBriF MHol MSpe NLar WFar WJam WWtn
'Feuermeer'	CElw NLar
'Fiery Tempest' (Tempest Series) **new**	SPad WNPC
'Fire Opal' (d) 🏆H7	CBor CElw CWCL EAJP EMor MNrw NBir
'Fire Storm'[PBR]	CBod CWGN EBee ECtt EHyd EMor EPfP GAbr GElm LBar LRHS LSun MHol MNrw MPnt NEoE NLar SPad SPoG SRms WCot WFar WMal WNPC
'Fireball'	CFis CWCL ECtt EShb LRHS MArl MAsh MBNS MMuc MNHC NLar
'Firefinch'	NEoE
'Flame'	NLar
'Flames of Passion'[PBR]	Widely available
'Flower of Darkness'	NEoE
'Georgenberg'	CRos ECtt EPfP GElm GMaP LRHS MACG MBel MHer MNrw NBir NFav NGdn NHol NLar NRHS NWad SPer SRms SWvt WCAu WFar WWke
'Gimlet' (Cocktails Series)	CWGN ECtt EMor EPri GBin GPSL LEdu LRHS NLar WTyc
'Golden Joy'	CBor CDor CElw MAvo MNrw NEoE WHoo
'Goldfinch'	WFar
'Hannay's'	GElm MHCG MNrw MPie MSpe SHar SPtp
'Harvest Moon'	NEoE
'Hearts in Amber'	NEoE WFar
'Herterton Lemon'	CElw WCot
'Herterton Primrose'	CCBP CElw CWCL ECtt EPPr GBee GElm LLWG MNrw NBPC NBid NSti WFar
'Hilltop Beacon' (d)	CDor CElw CTtf MAvo NEoE NLar SGro WFar WGoo WHoo
* ***hybridum luteum***	NSti
× ***intermedium***	NGdn NLar
- 'Diane'	NChi
- 'Hofrennydd'	NWad
'Jolly Roger'	NEoE
'Karlskaer'	CBod CToG CWCL EBlo ECtt EHyd EWes EWoo GElm GQue LPla LRHS MBel MBow MCot MNrw NBPC NGdn NLar NRHS WFar WGwG WWtn
'Lady Stratheden' (d) 🏆H7	Widely available
'Lemon Delight'	CDor CElw LEdu MAvo WMal
'Lemon Drops'	Widely available
'Lemon Frilled'	CTtf
'Lemon Sorbet' **new**	CBor
'Limoncello'	EMor LRHS SHeu
'Lionel Cox'	CWCL ELan GAbr GElm GMaP MBow MRav NBir NBro NChi NGdn NLar SRms WFar

	'Lipstick Sunset'	NEoE SCoo SPoG
	'Lisanne'	CCBP CElw CWCL EBee EMor GElm GKev LSto MACG MAvo MNrw MPnt NDov NLar SHar SMHy SPtp WCAu WFar
	'Little Lottie'	NEoE
	'Little Twister'	NEoE
	'Maddy Prior'	NEoE
	magellanicum	CSpe EWes NLar WMal
	'Magic Toybox'	NEoE
	'Mai Tai'PBR (Cocktails Series)	Widely available
	'Mandarin' (d)	CDor GElm SHar WMal
	'Mango'	MBros NDov
	'Mango Lassi'	CElw CTtf ECtt EMor EShb GBin GElm MACG NCth NEoE NLar SHar WCAu
	'Marmalade'	ECtt EHyd EWhm GElm LLWG LPla LRHS MAvo MNrw MRav NFav NLar NRHS SHar SSut WFar WHrl WKif
	'McClure's Magic'	NEoE
§	***montanum*** $\mathbb{Y}^{H6}$	CRos EBee EHyd GKev GLog LRHS MMuc NBir NRHS NSla SRms XLum
	'Moonlight Serenade'	CBod CWCL EBee ECtt EHyd EPPr EPfP LRHS LSto NEoE NRHS WFar
	'Moorland Sorbet'	WFar
	'Mr Mojo'	NEoE
	'Mrs J. Bradshaw' (d) $\mathbb{Y}^{H7}$	Widely available
	'Mrs W. Moore'	CWCL EBee GQue LDai MNrw MPnt MRav NBPC NBir NBro NChi NLar NQui WOut
	'Nonna'PBR	MAvo SPad WHil
	'Nordek'	CElw ECha ECtt GAbr GQue MNrw MRav NGdn SPoG WFar
	'Norwell Lemon Lamp'	MNrw
	pentapetalum	see *Sieversia pentapetala*
	'Pineapple Crush'	GElm
	'Pink Fluffy' (Censation Series)	ECtt MAsh MBros MHol
	'Pink Frills'	CElw ECtt EMor EPPr EPri EWTr EWes EWhm GAbr GBin GQue LEdu LLWG MAvo MPie MRav NBPC NLar SGbt SMHy SPtp
	'Pink Petticoats'	CBod CWCL EMor LBar MBNS MBros SPad WHlf WHoo
	'Poco'	CFis CRos CToG CWCL EHyd EPfP EWes EWhm LRHS MAvo MNrw MSpe NEoE NRHS WFar
	'Prairie Dancer'	GElm NEoE
	'Present'	NChi
	PRETTICOATS PEACH ('Tngeupp') (Pretticoats Series)	SPad WNPC
	'Primrose'	EWhm NBro NGdn NLar
	'Primrose Cottage'	EBee EMor GQue LBar LRHS SCoo WCAu WNPC
	'Prince of Orange' (d)	CElw CRos EHyd GAbr LRHS MNrw MRav NRHS SWvt WFar
	'Prinses Juliana'	Widely available
	'Proud's Pearl'	NEoE WMal
	pyrenaicum	GKev
I	'Rearsby Hybrid'	CElw MRav SHar SPlb
	'Red Wings' (d)	CFis CWCL GElm GMaP LRHS MNrw MRav NBir SHar WGwG
	'Rijnstroom'	EPPr LDai MNrw NBPC SHar WFar
	'Rise and Shine'	NEoE
	rivale	Widely available
	- 'Album'	Widely available
	- 'Barbra Lawton'	LEdu NBPC WJam
	- 'Cream Drop'	LLWG MCot NChi SHar
	- 'Leonard's Variety'	Widely available
	- 'Marika'	EBee
	- 'Marmalade'	CElw CWCL MBriF MPnt NBPC NChi WCav
I	- 'Nana'	CBor
	- pink-flowered	EGrI
	- 'Snowflake'	CDor CElw MSpe NChi NEoE NLar WJam
	'Roger's Rebellion'	NEoE WFar
	'Rubin'	GBin NDov NSti SGro
	'Rusty Young'	CBWd CBod CToG CWCL EBee ECtt EPPr EPfP EWes GBee GElm LRHS MBel MNrw NEoE NRHS SGbt
	'Savanna Sunrise'	MNrw
	'Savanna Sunset'	CToG EBee ECtt EHyd EMor EPPr EWes EWoo GElm LRHS LShi LSto MBel MHer NEoE NRHS WHrl
	SCARLET TEMPEST ('Macgeu001'PBR) (Tempest Series)	Widely available
	'Sea Breeze' (Cocktails Series)	EPfP LRHS
	'Shannara' (d)	CElw GElm NEoE
	'Sigiswang'	LEdu MNrw MRav WFar
	'Smokey Peach' (d) **new**	CElw
	'Snowdrop'	NEoE
	'Spanish Fly' (Cocktails Series)	LRHS LSou
	'Spellbound'	NEoE
	'Spider Muffin'	NEoE
	'Stacey Proud'	NEoE
	'Stacey's Sunrise'	CBod CToG ECtt EHyd EMor EPPr EWes LRHS MAvo MBel MHCG MNrw NEoE NLar NRHS SPoG WFar
	'Star of Bethlehem'	NEoE
	'Starker's Magnificum'	WCot
	'Stevie Nicks'	MBriF NEoE
	'Strawberries and Cream'	NEoE
	'Sundrud Star'	NEoE
	'Sunkissed Lime'PBR	EMor LRHS LSou MPnt NEoE NSti
	'Sunrise' (d)	CKel ECha EDAr EHyd LRHS LSto MACG MDon MHol NRHS SVic
	'Sweet and Sour' **new**	GElm
	'Sweet Angel Dar'	NEoE
	'Sweet Stacey'	NEoE
	'Tangerine'	EPri MRav
	'Tangerine Dream'	EMor LRHS
	(Tempo Series) TEMPO ORANGE ('Tngeuto') (d) **new**	LBar
	- TEMPO ROSE ('Tngeutr') (d) **new**	LBar WNPC
	'Tequila Sunrise' (Cocktails Series)	CBcs CElw CRos CWGN EBee ECtt EHyd ELan EMor EPPr EPfP GBin ILea LRHS LSto MNrw MPnt MPri NEoE NGdn NHpl NRHS SCob SEdd WCAu WNPC
	'The Giant Peach'	NEoE
	'Tinkerbell'	NEoE
	× ***tirolense***	EBee
	'Toast of Cumbria'	NEoE
	'Toffee Apples'	NEoE
	'Tosai'	CBod CBor CKel LRHS NEoE
	'Totally Tangerine'PBR	Widely available
	triflorum	CSpe EMor EWes GEdr GGro LEdu MNrw NDov NGrd SHar SPhx
	- SDR 8121	GKev
	- var. ***campanulatum***	NEoE
	- 'Peace Pipe'	MNrw
	'Turbango'	NEoE
	'Turbango Twister'	NEoE
	'Turnpike Tales'	NEoE
	'Turnpike Troubadour'	NEoE
	'Tutti Frutti'	MAvo
	'Two Tone Pearl' (Censation Series) (d)	CWGN NLar

urbanum	ENfk NMir WHer
- 'Corinne Tremaine'	WHer
'Wet Kiss' (Cocktails Series)	LRHS SHeu
'Wish Song' (Valley Hi Series) **new**	NEoE
'Wyn's Wish'	NEoE

Gevuina (*Proteaceae*)

avellana	WPGP

Gilia ✿ (*Polemoniaceae*)

achilleifolia	SPhx

Gillenia (*Rosaceae*)

stipulata	IPot LEdu LRHS MNrw SPhx WPGP
trifoliata ♀H7	Widely available
- 'Pink Profusion'	CAbb CBod CMiW CSpe EBee EMor GBin GEdr IPot LBar LEdu LPla LRHS MACG MBel MMrt MNHC MNrw NBid NCth NLar SCob WCAu WCot WFar WHil WHlf WSHC WTor XSte

Gingidia (*Apiaceae*)

montana	EMor WHil

Ginkgo ✿ (*Ginkgoaceae*)

biloba	Widely available
- B&SWJ 8753	WCru
- 'Anny's Dwarf'	MBlu
- 'Autumn Gold' (m) ♀H6	CBcs CEnd CMCN ELan MBlu MGos MPkF SLim WMat
- 'Baldii'	NLar
- 'Barabits' Fastigiata'	LRHS MBlu
- 'Barabits' Nana'	CAco MBlu
- 'Beijing Gold'	CAco MBlu MPkF NLar
- 'Blagon'	LRHS SGol WHtc
- 'Buddy'	SLim
- 'California Sunset'	MBlu SLim
- 'Chase Manhattan'	MPkF
- 'Chotek'	MBlu SMad
- 'Chris's Dwarf'	LRHS
- 'Clica'	NLar
- 'Conica'	CAco
- 'David'	SLim
- 'Eastern Star' (f)	CAgr
- 'Eiffel'	LPar
- 'Everton Broom'	CMac CMen MBlu SLim SRms
- 'Fabulous Underwear'	SLim
- 'Fairmount' (m)	MBlu
- 'Fastigiata' (m)	CAco CMCN EPfP MBlu
- 'Fastigiata Blagon'	CAco CCVT ERom LMaj LPar LRHS
- 'Finger'	SLim
- 'Globosa'	CAco LIns MBlu
- 'Gnome'	LSRN MPkF
- 'Goethe'	MBlu
- 'Golden Dragon'	MBlu
- 'Golden Globe'	MPkF
- 'Gresham'	MPkF
- 'Horizontalis'	CAco MBlu SGsty
- 'Jade Butterflies' ♀H6	MBlu SLim
- 'Jehosaphat'	MBlu
- 'Jerry Vercade'	MPkF
- 'King of Dongting' (f)	CAco CAgr MBlu SLim
- 'Lakeview' (m)	CAco MPkF
- 'Landliebe'	MBlu
- 'Lil' Matthew'	SLim
- 'Long March'	CAgr
- 'Magyar'	MBlu
- 'Mariken' ♀H6	CAco CWGN EHed ELan EPfP LMaj LPar LRHS MGil MPkF NLar SGsty SLim
- 'Mayfield' (m)	CAco EPfP MBlu
- 'McFarland'	CAgr
- 'Menhir'PBR	CAco CBcs EBee ELan EPfP ILea LRHS MGos MPkF MTrO WCot WMat
- 'Obelisk'	CAco SGsty SLim SMad
- Ohazuki Group (f)	CAgr
- 'Palo Alto'	CAco
- Pendula Group	CEnd CMCN EBee IDee MBlu MPkF WMat
- 'Princeton Sentry' (m) ♀H6	CAco ELan EPfP IPap MBlu
- 'Pyramidalis'	CAco
- 'Robbie's Twist'	MPkF NLar SLim
- 'Roswitha' (v)	NLar
- 'San José'	CAco
- 'Santa Cruz'	CAco
- 'Saratoga' (m) ♀H6	CAco CAgr CBcs CEnd CLnd CMCN EBee EPfP MBlu MPkF NOrn SLim SMad SRms WMat
- 'Shangri-La' (m)	MBlu
- 'Sinclair'	MPkF
- 'Survivor'	SMad
- 'Talon Variegated' (v)	MBlu
- 'Thelma'	SLim
- 'Tit'	CAco CEnd CMCN EPfP LPar MBlu MPkF SLim WLea
- 'Todd'	MBlu
- 'Tremonia'	CMCN EPfP MBlu MPkF
- 'Troll' ♀H6	CAco EPfP LRHS MAsh MBlu MGil SCoo SLim SMad SPoG
- 'Tubifolia'	CMCN ESwi IDee MBlu MPkF NLar SLim WPGP
- 'Umbrella'	SLim
- Variegata Group (v)	MPkF
- - 'Variegata' (v)	CAco
- 'W.B.'	MPkF

ginseng see *Panax ginseng*

Gladiolus (*Iridaceae*)

'Adi'	WCot
'Ajax'	WPhe
alatus	CBor NRog
'Alba' (N)	WPhe
'Amanda Mahy' (N)	WCot WMal WPhe
'Antica' (L)	WPhe
'Astarte' (L)	WPhe
'Atom' (S/P)	CAvo CBor GKev LAma SDeJ WPhe
aurantiacus	WCot
'Avalanche' (B)	SDeJ
'Azurro'	WPhe
'Bach'	WPhe
'Bibi' (Tub) **new**	LAma
'Black Jack' (L)	SDeJ
'Black Surprise'	WPhe
'Blue Frost' (L)	SDeJ
'Blue Mountain'	WPhe
'Bocelli' (M)	WPhe
'Bonfire' (G)	WPhe
'Boone'	GBin SMrm
'Brahms' (L)	WPhe
byzantinus	see *G. communis* subsp. *byzantinus*
callianthus	see *G. murielae*
cardinalis	WCru
'Careless' (L)	WPhe
carinatus	NRog
- blue-flowered **new**	CBor
- pink-flowered **new**	CBor
carinatus* × *orchidiflorus	WCot
'Carine' (N)	EBee NRog SDeJ WPhe
carmineus	CBor NRog WCot

carneus	CBor CBro EPot LAma NRog SDeJ
'Carolina Primrose'	GBin
'Casablanca'^{PBR}	LRHS
caucasicus	GKev
'Charm' (N/Tub)	LAma SDeJ WPhe
'Charming Beauty' (Tub)	GKev NRog SDeJ WPhe
'Charming Henry' (Tub)	LAma
'Charming Lady' (Tub)	LAma NRog SDir WPhe
'Chopin' (L)	WPhe
'Columbine' (P)	SDeJ
× ***colvillii*** 'Frozen Sparks' **new**	GKev SDir
- 'Galaxian'	GKev LAma SDir
- 'Irish Gold' **new**	GKev SDir
communis	WCot
§ - subsp. ***byzantinus*** 𝕐H5	Widely available
'Coral Lace' (L)	SDeJ
'Côte d'Azur' (G)	SDeJ
crassifolius	CPbh
'Cream Perfection' (L)	SDeJ WPhe
cruentus	WCot
§ ***dalenii***	CDor CPbh CSpe
- 'Boone'	LPla WCot
§ - subsp. ***dalenii***	CBor CPbh SChr WCot
- red-flowered	WHil
'Dark Ruby' (*papilio* hybrid)	LEdu WMal WPGP
'David Hills' (*papilio* hybrid)	CAvo CBor CBro CDor CTtf ECha LPla NCth SMHy WCot WHoo WSHC
ecklonii	CPbh CTtf
'Elvira' (N)	GKev LAma WPhe
'Emerald Spring' (S)	WCot
equitans	CBor
'Espresso'^{PBR} (S)	ERCP
'Esta Bonita' (G)	WPhe
'Evergreen'	ERCP
'Far West' (L)	ERCP
'Farandole' (S)	SDeJ
'Fergie' (B)	ERCP
'Fidelio' (L)	SDeJ
'Fiona'	LAma
'Fiorentina' (L)	ERCP SDeJ
'Flame'	WPhe
flanaganii	CBor CBro CPbh CSpe CTtf EBee EPot EPri GArf GEdr GKev MNrw NHpl NSla SBrt WAbe WPav
'Flevo Bambino' (S)	EPri
floribundus hort.	NRog
'Fortarosa' (L)	WPhe
× ***gandavensis*** hort.	WCot
garnieri	see *G. dalenii* subsp. *dalenii*
geardii	WCot
grandis	see *G. liliaceus*
'Green Star' (L)	LCro LOPS SDeJ WPhe
'Greyhound' (L)	WPhe
griseus	NRog
'Halley' (N)	GKev LAma NLar NRog WPhe
'Hansnett'	WCot WSHC
'Happy Weekend' (L)	SDeJ
'Haydn' (L)	WPhe
'Himalaya' (L)	WPhe
'Holland Pearl' (B)	SDeJ
huttonii	CBor NRog
huttonii × ***tristis*** var. ***concolor***	WCot
illyricus	CBor GKev SPlb
imbricatus	CBor MHer
'Impressive' (N)	GKev LAma NLar NRog SDeJ WPhe
'Indian Summer'^{PBR} (L)	ERCP WPhe
'Invitation'	SDeJ
§ ***italicus***	CKel EBee ETay GKev
'Jacksonville Gold' (L)	SDeJ
'Jester' (L)	SDeJ
'Judy'^{PBR} (M)	WPhe
'Karaoke' (L)	WPhe
'Kazimir' (L)	WPhe
'Lakeland'^{PBR} (L)	WPhe
'Las Vegas' (P)	LAma WPhe
'Laura Jay' (P)	LAma
'Lennon' (L)	WPhe
§ ***liliaceus***	NRog
'Limelight' (L) **new**	CBor
'Lucifer'^{PBR} (L)	WPhe
'Mademoiselle de Paris'	CBro
'Magma' (L)	WPhe
'Mantovani'	WPhe
'Marina' (P)	WMal
'Matanzas' (M)	WPhe
'Match Point' (L)	SDeJ
meliusculus	NRog
'Messina' (M)	WPhe
'Mexico' (L)	SDeJ
miniatus	CBor NRog
'Mirella' (N)	CAvo LAma WPhe
'Modena' (M)	WPhe
'Mon Amour'^{PBR} (L)	LRHS SDeJ WPhe
'Monsieur Piquet' (P)	EPri WCot
'Mount Everest'	WPhe
§ ***murielae*** 𝕐H3	CAby CAvo CBor CBro CCBP CRos CTtf CWal EGrI EHyd EPfP ERCP EShb GBin GKev LAma LCro LOPS LRHS MACG MCot MHol NRHS SCoo SDeJ SDir SPeP SPer SPlb SRms
'Mylena' (M)	WPhe
natalensis	see *G. dalenii*
'Natan' (L)	WCot
'Nathalie' (N)	CAvo NRog SDeJ WPhe
'Nijmegen' (L)	WPhe
'Nova Lux' (L)	SDeJ SDir
'Nymph' (N)	CAvo GKev LAma LCro LDai LOPS NBir SDeJ SDir WPhe
§ ***oppositiflorus***	CPbh CSpe LEdu SPlb WSHC
- subsp. ***salmoneus***	see *G. oppositiflorus*
'Orangerie' (L)	WPhe
'Oscar' (G)	ERCP SDeJ
palustris	WAbe
papilio	Widely available
- 'Peachy'	CTtf
§ - Purpureoauratus Group	CBro SRms WSHC
- yellow-flowered	CTtf SMad
'Passos'^{PBR} (S)	ERCP
'Peach Blossom' (N)	WCot
'Penny Lane' (M)	WPhe
'Pescara' (M)	WPhe
'Peter Pears' (L)	ERCP LCro SDeJ SDir
Pilbeam hybrids	WCot
'Pink Lady' (L)	SDeJ
'Plum Tart' (L)	LCro LOPS LRHS MBros SDeJ
'Pop Art'	SDeJ
'Prima Verde' (L)	WPhe
primulinus	see *G. dalenii*
'Prins Claus' (N)	EShb GKev SDeJ SDir WPhe
priorii	CBor NRog
'Priscilla' (L)	MBros SDeJ SDir
'Purple Flora'	ERCP
'Purple Mate'	CBor LCro LOPS
purple-striped	WHil
purpureoauratus	see *G. papilio* Purpureoauratus Group
'Raspberry Sorbet' (S)	WPhe
'Rigoletto' (L)	WPhe
'Robinetta' (*recurvus* hybrid) 𝕐H3	GArf GKev LAma LCro LDai LOPS SDeJ WPhe
'Rosalina' (L)	WPhe
'Rosiebee Red'^{PBR} (G)	LRHS

'Rostov' **new**	ERCP
'Rotary'PBR (L)	WPhe
'Roussel'	WPhe
'Ruby' (*papilio* hybrid)	Widely available
'Salmon Star' (L)	WPhe
'San Siro'PBR (M)	WPhe
saundersii	EBee LEdu
scullyi	NRog
segetum	see *G. italicus*
'Sogno' (M)	WPhe
'Sourire' (S)	SDeJ
'Spic and Span' (L)	SDeJ
splendens	CBor NRog
'Sugar Plum'	ERCP
'Thalia'	WPhe
'That's Love' (L)	SDeJ
'The Bride'	CAvo CBro EWoo ITim LAma LCro LDai LOPS MPie NLar SDeJ SDir
'Trevor Edwards' **new**	WCot
tristis	CAvo CBor CBro CElw CSpe EAri ELon MHer SMHy WAbe
- var. ***concolor***	CPbh WCot
- var. ***tristis***	NRog
undulatus	NRog WCot
'Vasto' (M)	WPhe
'Venezia' (M)	WPhe
venustus	CPbh NRog
'Vesuvio' (L)	WPhe
virescens	NRog
'Vivaldi' (L)	WPhe
'Volcano' (N)	WPhe
'Wagner' (L)	WPhe
watermeyeri	CBor CPbh WHil
watsonius	NRog
'White Prosperity' (L)	ERCP LCro LOPS
'Wine and Roses' (L)	SDir
woodii	WCot
'Yellow Star' (L)	WPhe
'Ziporra' (S)	EPri
'Zizanie' (L)	SDeJ

Glandora (*Boraginaceae*)

§ 'Alba'	CBod CWCL CWnw GJos SPoG
§ 'Compacta'	WAbe
diffusa misapplied	see *G. prostrata*
§ ***diffusa*** ambig.	SRot
- 'Alba'	see *G.* 'Alba'
- 'Compacta'	see *G.* 'Compacta'
§ ***diffusa*** (Lag.) D.C.Thomas 'Picos'	WAbe
§ ***oleifolia*** ♀H4	CBor EHyd GEdr LRHS NBir NRHS
§ ***prostrata*** 'Grace Ward' ♀H5	CBod CKel CWnw ECtt ELan EPfP GArf GJos LBar LRHS MPri NRHS SEdd SGbt WIce
§ - 'Heavenly Blue' ♀H5	Widely available
- 'Star'PBR	CBod EHyd ELan EPfP GJos GMaP LBar LLWG LRHS MACG NHpl NLar NRHS SCoo SEdd SPoG SWvt WFar WIce
§ ***rosmarinifolia***	EHyd LRHS NRHS WCFE

Glandularia (*Verbenaceae*)

'Abbeville'	WCot WMal
§ (Aztec Series) AZTEC PEARL ('Balazpearl'PBR)	SCoo
- AZTEC RED ('Balazred')	SCoo
- AZTEC SILVER MAGIC ('Balazsilma'PBR)	MBros SCoo
BABYLON PINK ('Morena') (Babylon Series)	MTrO
§ 'Claret' ♀H3	CMac EBee ECtt EHyd ELan EPfP LCro LOPS LRHS NRHS SBut SCoo SPoG
corymbosa	ECha EPPr LRHS MACG MSpe SMrm SPer SPhx
'Diamond Merci'	WMal
'Edith Eddleman'	CMac EHyd EPfP LRHS NGrs NRHS SPoG
elegans	NDov
(Enchantment Series) ENCHANTMENT RED	MPri
- ENCHANTMENT VIOLET EYE **new**	MPri
ESTRELLA VOODOO RED STAR ('Wesverevoo'PBR)	LSou
'Hammerstein Pink'	EBee EPfP
'Homestead Purple'	CMac EBee EBlo EHyd ELan EPfP EShb LCro LDai LOPS LRHS NRHS SDix SRkn SRms SWvt WHlf WNPC
'Jennys' Wine'	see *G.* 'Claret'
'La France'	ECha EHyd EPfP LRHS NRHS SMHy SMad SPhx SPoG SRkn
'Little Annie'	WNPC
'Lois' Ruby'	see *G.* 'Claret'
'Merci'	NDov
§ ***peruviana***	EBou EHyd EPot LRHS NRHS SRms XLum
- ENDURASCAPE PINK BICOLOR ('Balendpibi') (Endurascape Series) ♀H2	WHlf
'Pink Bouquet'	see *G.* 'Silver Anne'
'Pink Parfait'	EPfP
§ Quartz Series ♀H2	MBros MPri
- 'Quartz Red Polka Dot'	EPfP
(Samira Series) SAMIRA PURPLE WING	LSou
- SAMIRA ROSE	LSou
SEABROOK'S LAVENDER ('Sealav'PBR)	EPfP NRHS SCoo SHar SRkn SRms SWvt
(Showboat Series) 'Showboat Magenta'	LSou
- 'Showboat Mango Orange' **new**	MPri
- 'Showboat Midnight'	LSou WWke
- 'Showboat Salmon'	LSou
- 'Showboat White'	LSou
§ 'Silver Anne' ♀H3	LDai
§ 'Sissinghurst' ♀H3	ECtt SAng SDix SEdd SMrm SRms WHlf
'Strawberry Kiss'	EPfP SPoG
'Tenerife'	see *G.* 'Sissinghurst'
VECTURA LAVENDER (Vectura Series)	EHyd LRHS LSou NRHS
VEPITA BLUE VIOLET ('Invebluvio'PBR) (Vepita Series)	MHol

Glandularia × *Verbena* (*Verbenaceae*)

METEOR SHOWER ('Invebrutow')	LBar LCro WHil

Glaucidium (*Ranunculaceae*)

palmatum ♀H5	CExl CPla EMor EWld GEdr GGro GKev NHpl NSla WCru WFar
- 'Album'	see *G. palmatum* var. *leucanthum*
§ - var. ***leucanthum***	EMor GEdr GKev LAma NHpl

Glaucium (*Papaveraceae*)

§ ***corniculatum***	CAby CSpe EBlo ECha EHyd EPfP LRHS NRHS SPhx
flavum	CKel ECha LRHS MHer NFav SPhx WHer XSen
- ***aurantiacum***	see *G. flavum* f. *fulvum*
§ - f. ***fulvum***	CKel EMor EPPr MNrw WHil
- orange-flowered	see *G. flavum* f. *fulvum*

- red-flowered	see *G. corniculatum*
grandiflorum	SPhx
phoenicium	see *G. corniculatum*

Glaucosciadium (*Apiaceae*)

cordifolium PAB 9003	LEdu

× *Glebianthemum* (*Asteraceae*)

§ GRANDAISY YELLOW ('Bonmax 1228') (Grandaisy Series)	MBros SCob

Glebionis (*Asteraceae*)

coronaria	MNHC SRms
§ ***segetum***	CBod CHab LCro LOPS MBow NBir

Glechoma (*Lamiaceae*)

hederacea	GPoy NMir SPhx WHer
§ - 'Variegata' (v)	MPri SPer XLum

Gleditsia (*Fabaceae*)

caspia	LEdu
- NJM 13.019	WPGP
japonica	NLar
koraiensis	LEdu
triacanthos	CMCN LPar NRog SPlb WJur WTSh
- 'Calhoun'	CAgr
- 'Elegantissima' (v)	SPer
- 'Emerald Cascade'	CEnd
- f. ***inermis***	LPar
- - SKYLINE ('Skycole')	LIns LMaj LPar SGsty
- - 'Sunburst'	Widely available
- 'Millwood'	CAgr
- 'Rubylace'	CBod CCVT CEnd CMCN CMac EBee ELan LMaj MAsh MBlu MDon MRav MSwo NRog SPer WMat

Globba ✿ (*Zingiberaceae*)

marantina	EAri
racemosa	EAri
- var. ***hookeri*** HWJCM 471	ESwi WCru WSHC
radicalis	MHid WPGP

Globularia (*Plantaginaceae*)

alypum	CKel IDee
bellidifolia	see *G. meridionalis*
bisnagarica	WCot
cordifolia ♀H5	EBou EHyd EPot GEdr GKev LRHS MMuc NBir NHpl NRHS SHar SRms WHoo XSen
- RCB UA 30	WCot
- 'Alba'	XSen
incanescens	GEdr
§ ***meridionalis***	CAby CBor EPot EWes GKev
- 'Blue Bonnets'	GEdr NBwr
- 'Hort's Variety'	NSla WAbe
nana	see *G. repens*
nudicaulis	EPot GEdr GKev SWvt
orientalis	XSen
punctata	GEdr GKev MACG SRms WFar
pygmaea	see *G. meridionalis*
§ ***repens***	GEdr WAbe
trichosantha	GEdr GKev MACG SRms XSen
valentina	CPla GEdr
vulgaris	XSen

Gloriosa (*Colchicaceae*)

lutea	see *G. superba* 'Lutea'
rothschildiana	see *G. superba* 'Rothschildiana'
superba ♀H1c	SDeJ SDir
- 'Bordeaux'	GKev LAma
- 'Carsonii'	GKev LAma SDeJ SDir
- 'Greenii'	GKev LAma SDeJ SDir
§ - 'Lutea'	GKev LAma SDeJ
§ - 'Rothschildiana'	CBcs CDoC EAri GKev LAma LCro LOPS SDeJ SDir SRms
- 'Rothschildiana Salmon'	SDir
- 'Sparkling Striped'	GKev LAma SDir
- 'Tomas de Bruyne'	GKev LAma
- 'Tricolor'	SDir

Gloxinella (*Gesneriaceae*)

§ ***lindeniana***	WDib

Gloxinia (*Gesneriaceae*)

gymnostoma	see *Seemannia gymnostoma*
lindeniana	see *Gloxinella lindeniana*
nematanthodes	see *Seemannia nematanthodes*
sylvatica	see *Seemannia sylvatica*

Glumicalyx (*Scrophulariaceae*)

flanaganii	CPbh GArf SPlb
goseloides	CPbh
nutans	CPbh SPlb

Glyceria (*Poaceae*)

aquatica variegata	see *G. maxima* var. *variegata*
maxima	CPud LPfP NPer SPlb
§ - var. ***variegata*** (v)	CBen CPud CToG CWat ECha EHyd ELan EPfP GMaP GMcL LLWG LPfP LRHS MMuc NBir NRHS SRms SVic WMAq XLum
spectabilis 'Variegata'	see *G. maxima* var. *variegata*

Glycyrrhiza (*Fabaceae*)

echinata	CAgr
§ ***glabra***	CAgr CBod CCCN CHby CLau CSpe EMor ENfk GPoy MHer MHoo SPlb SRms WJek
glandulifera	see *G. glabra*
uralensis	CAgr ELan EPPr
yunnanensis	CBor CSpe ECha EPPr MHer SDix SMHy

Glyptostrobus (*Cupressaceae*)

pensilis	CAco CExl IDee LRHS WPGP
- 'Wooly Mammoth'	CAco IArd LRHS

Gmelina (*Lamiaceae*)

hystrix	CCCN

Gnaphalium (*Asteraceae*)

'Fairy Gold'	see *Helichrysum thianschanicum* 'Goldkind'

Godetia see *Clarkia*

Goeppertia (*Marantaceae*)

burle-marxii	NHrt
concinna	CDoC LCro
§ ***crocata*** ♀H1a	CDoC
- 'Tassmania'	LCro LOPS
FLAMESTAR ('Twyca0018'PBR) **new**	NHrt
'Freddie'	CDoC
§ ***insignis***	CDoC LCro NHrt
kegeljanii NETWORK ('Pp0005'PBR) **new**	LCro
majestica 'Sanderiana' **new**	NHrt
§ ***makoyana*** ♀H1a	CDoC
'Maui Queen'	CDoC
§ ***ornata*** **new**	LCro
§ ***roseopicta*** ♀H1a	NHrt
- 'Little Princess' (v) **new**	LCro

- 'Surprise Star' **new** NHrt
§ ***rufibarba*** ♀H1a NHrt
- 'Wavestar' CDoC LCro
§ ***truncata*** CDoC WLea
veitchiana 'Medaillon' LCro LOPS NHrt
warscewiczii CDoC
'Whitestar' LCro LOPS
§ ***zebrina*** ♀H1a CDoC LCro NHrt

goji berry see *Lycium barbarum*, *L. chinense*

Gomphocarpus (*Apocynaceae*)

§ ***fruticosus*** EAri SVen
§ ***physocarpus*** CBod

Gompholobium (*Fabaceae*)

scabrum SPlb

Gomphostigma (*Scrophulariaceae*)

virgatum CBod CCBP CCCN CSpe ELan EPPr EPfP EShb GMaP LLWG MPie SMrm SPhx SPlb WCFE WCot WFar WSHC WTor
- 'White Candy' GBin LRHS MGil MPkF SVen XSte

Gomphrena (*Amaranthaceae*)

globosa CCCN
- 'Lizard Light' CCCN

Goniolimon (*Plumbaginaceae*)

collinum GEdr
- 'Sea Spray' NFav
cuspidatum from Kyrgyzstan **new** GGro
incanum 'Blue Diamond' GJos NFav NHpl WCot
§ ***tataricum*** EBee EPPr GJos MMrt
§ - var. ***angustifolium*** SRms

Goodia (*Fabaceae*)

lotifolia CCCN

Goodyera (*Orchidaceae*)

repens NLAp

gooseberry see *Ribes uva-crispa*; see also AGM Fruit Section

× *Gordlinia* (*Theaceae*)

grandiflora MPkF XSte XVPe

Gordonia (*Theaceae*)

axillaris see *Polyspora axillaris*

Gorgonidium (*Araceae*)

intermedium SBrt WCot

granadilla see *Passiflora quadrangularis*

granadilla, purple see *Passiflora edulis*

granadilla, sweet see *Passiflora ligularis*

grape see *Vitis*; see also AGM Fruit Section

grapefruit see *Citrus* × *aurantium* Grapefruit Group

Graptopetalum (*Crassulaceae*)

sp. CSBt
bellum ♀H2 NMen SPlb
filiferum SEdd SPlb
§ ***paraguayense*** SEdd SVen
- subsp. ***bernalense*** NWad SChr
suaveolens SEdd SPlb

Graptopetalum × *Sedum* see × *Graptosedum*

× *Graptosedum* (*Crassulaceae*)

'Darley Sunshine' NWad SEdd SIvy
'Francesco Baldi' **new** SEdd
'Mediterranean Mystery' **new** SEdd

× *Graptoveria* (*Crassulaceae*)

'Abbey Brook' SEdd
'Albert Baynes' **new** SEdd
'Douglas Huth' **new** EAri
'Ghostly' SEdd WCot
hybrid (*Echeveria agavoides* × *Graptopetalum filiferum*) **new** SEdd
'Kew Marble' **new** SEdd
'Lulu' **new** SEdd
'Milky Way' **new** SEdd
'Moonglow' **new** SEdd
'Mrs Richards' SEdd
'Pik Ruza' **new** EAri SEdd
'Pistachio' **new** SEdd
'Silver Mist' **new** NMen
'Titubans' MHer

Gratiola (*Plantaginaceae*)

officinalis CBen LLWG LPfP MHer MHoo

Greenovia (*Crassulaceae*)

aizoon SEdd SPlb
§ ***aurea*** SPlb
§ ***diplocycla*** CPbh SEdd
- 'Gigantea' SEdd SPlb

Grevillea (*Proteaceae*)

* ***alba*** SEle
alpina EGrI WPGP
'Angie' **new** CCCN
banksii 'Canberra Hybrid' see *G.* 'Canberra Gem'
- var. ***forsteri*** SPlb
'Big Red' **new** IDee
'Bon Accord' CTsd
'Bronze Rambler' CBcs CCCN XSte
§ 'Canberra Gem' ♀H4 Widely available
'Clearview David' CCCN CCht CDoC CKel CSde LEdu LRHS MMuc SEle SGBe SVen
'Coconut Ice' CTsd
crithmifolia SPlb
'Cvd White' CCCN
'Fireworks' **new** CCCN
'Ivanhoe' CCCN
johnsonii WHlf
juniperina CBcs CCCN CEme CHll CMac EPfP IDee LPar SArc SCoo SEle SGsty SLim SSha SVen XSen
- 'Molonglo' CTsd
- f. ***sulphurea*** CBcs CBod CCCN CKel CTsd EGrI ELon MGil MMuc SEdd SEle SIvy SPer SPlb WLov
- - prostrate CTrC
'Lady O' CCCN
lanigera 'Celia' **new** CCCN
- 'Mount Tamboritha' CBcs CBod CCCN CCht CDoC CMac CPbh CSde CTsd EGrI EPfP LRHS SEle SPoG SSha WCot WFar XSte
- 'Pepito' **new** CCCN
- prostrate WAbe
lavandulacea 'Black Range' WCot
- 'Penola' CCCN

leucopteris SPlb
'Little Robyn' CTsd
'Mason's Hybrid' CTsd
miqueliana CBcs CTsd
  subsp. ***moroka***
'Moonlight' SEdd
'Murray Valley Queen' WCot WPGP
'New Blood'PBR CBcs XSte
'Olympic Flame' CBcs CBrac CCCN CCht CDoC CEnd CExl CKel CSBt CTrC CWnw EGrI EPfP LRHS MGos MMuc SAko SCob SEdd SEle SGBe SIvy SPoG SSha
paniculata SPlb
'Pink Lady' CBcs CCCN CKel ELon EPfP SEle
'Poorinda Constance' WCot
'Poorinda Queen' CCCN
robusta 🏆H2 EShb SPlb
'Robyn Gordon' CCCN
'Rondeau' CCCN
rosmarinifolia 🏆H4 CBcs CCCN CEme CMac CSBt CTri CWal ELan GKin SArc SEle SPer SPlb SSta WFar
- 'Jenkinsii' CCCN CCht CDoC CKel CMac CSBt CSde CTsd EGrI ELan EPfP LRHS SEle SGBe SIvy SLim SSha WCot
§ × ***semperflorens*** CCCN CCht CSde CTsd EHyd SEle SPlb
'Spider Man' CCCN
thelemanniana 'Baby' CTsd
tolminsis see *G.* × *semperflorens*
victoriae CBcs CCCN CCht CDoC CJun CKel CSde CTsd EAri EPfP LRHS MBlu MHtn SAko SChF SEdd SEle SPlb SSha WCot WHlf WPGP
- subsp. ***victoriae*** CExl
williamsonii CBcs CBod CCht CTsd SEle SIvy SSha

Grewia (*Malvaceae*)

occidentalis ECre LRHS XSte

Greyia (*Melianthaceae*)

sutherlandii SPlb

Griffinia (*Amaryllidaceae*)

espiritensis NRog
liboniana NRog
rochae GKev

Grindelia (*Asteraceae*)

§ ***camporum*** SPlb WHil
chiloensis SMad
hirsutula new WHil
integrifolia EBee GQue XLum
robusta see *G. camporum*

Griselinia ✿ (*Griseliniaceae*)

littoralis 🏆H5 Widely available
- 'Bantry Bay' (v) CCCN CSde EBee EHyd ELan LRHS MAsh NLar SMad SPoG SWvt WFar WHtc
- 'Brodick Gold' ELon GKin
- 'Dixon's Cream' (v) CBcs CCCN CKel CMac CSBt EHyd ELan EPfP LRHS MRav SGBe SRms SVen
- 'Emerald' SGsty
- 'Green Favor' EBee EDir
- GREEN HORIZON ('Whenuapai'PBR) CBod CKel ELan IBal LPar LRHS SCob SCoo SPer SPoG WHtc
- 'Green Jewel' (v) CBod CCCN EPfP NLar WHtc
- 'Variegata' (v) 🏆H4 Widely available

racemosa new IDee
ruscifolia CBcs EBee LEdu
scandens CCCN SEND WCot

guava, common see *Psidium guajava*

guava, purple or strawberry see *Psidium littorale* var. *longipes*

Guichenotia (*Sterculiaceae*)

macrantha SPlb

Gunnera ✿ (*Gunneraceae*)

cordifolia LLWG
densiflora GEdr
hamiltonii CBct ECha EPot LEdu SRms WFar XLum
killipiana B&SWJ 9009 WCru WFar
magellanica Widely available
- (f) SRms
- 'Osorno' EBee
manicata Widely available
perpensa CBcs CBen CCCN EBee ESwi WCot WFar
prorepens CBod CExl CMac EBee ECha ILea NWad SRms WFar
saint-johnii B&SWJ 14708 WCru

Guzmania (*Bromeliaceae*)

dissitiflora NCft
HOPE ('Durahop'PBR) 🏆H1b new LCro
'Tempo'PBR NPic
'Torch'PBR 🏆H1b NPic
'Voila' new LCro

Gymnadenia (*Orchidaceae*)

conopsea LAma NLAp

Gymnocalycium (*Cactaceae*)

anisitsii EAri NCft
  subsp. ***damsii*** new
baldianum 🏆H2 new EAri NCft NMen
denudatum 'Southfield Pink' new NMen
erinaceum R 726B new NMen
eytianum see *G. marsoneri* subsp. *matoense*
grandiflorum see *G. monvillei*
horstii new NCft
- subsp. ***buenekeri*** 🏆H2 new NMen
§ ***marsoneri*** NMen
  subsp. ***matoense*** new
§ ***monvillei*** new SPlb
multiflorum see *G. monvillei*
pflanzii new NCft
§ - subsp. ***zegarrae*** new NMen
riograndense see *G. pflanzii* subsp. *zegarrae*
saglionis 🏆H2 new SPlb
spegazzinii subsp. ***cardenasianum*** new NMen

Gymnocarpium (*Woodsiaceae*)

dryopteris 🏆H5 CDor CLAP EFer GArf GKev GMaP GQue LRHS WCot WFib WPGP WShi
- PAB 1757 LEdu
- PAB 8351 LEdu
- 'Plumosum' 🏆H5 CBod CLAP CRos EBee EHyd EMor GEdr ISha LEdu LRHS MAsh NHar NLar NRHS WFar WFib
oyamense 🏆H5 EShb SPlb
robertianum EFer EWld LEdu

Gymnocladus (*Fabaceae*)

chinensis WPGP
dioica CBcs CLnd CMCN ELan EPfP LEdu LMaj MBlu SMad SPer WJur WPGP WTSh

Gynandriris see *Moraea*

Gynerium (*Poaceae*)

argenteum see *Cortaderia selloana*

Gynostemma (*Cucurbitaceae*)

pentaphyllum CAgr LEdu SRms WCot WJek
- B&SWJ 570 WCru

Gypsophila (*Caryophyllaceae*)

acutifolia EBee
aretioides EHyd EPot LRHS NRHS SPlb SRot WAbe
cerastioides see *Acanthophyllum cerastioides*
dubia see *G. repens* 'Dubia'
elegans SVic
fastigiata 'Silverstar' EHyd EPfP LRHS
(Festival Series) 'Festival' SGbt
§ - 'Festival Pink Lady' LBar WFar
gracilescens see *G. tenuifolia*
'Jolien' (v) WIce
muralis see *Psammophiliella muralis*
nana EWes
pacifica ECha GQue
paniculata CBod LShi MRav NFav SRms XLum
- 'Bristol Fairy' (d) CDor CSBt ECha ELan EPfP GDam GMaP GMcL LRHS NLar SCob SPoG SWvt WCAu WFar XLum
- 'Compacta Plena' (d) ECtt EPfP GMaP LRHS MRav NGdn SGbt SRms
- double white-flowered (d) XLum
- FESTIVAL STAR ('Danfestar'PBR) (Festival Series) GMcL
- 'Flamingo' (d) CBcs CDor ECha MACG NLar SCob SCoo SEdd SPer SPoG SWvt WFar XLum
- MY PINK ('Dangypink') SMad
- 'Pacific Pink' EBee
- 'Perfect Alba' LRHS
- 'Perfekta' CBcs SPer
§ - 'Schneeflocke' (d) CBod CKel CSpe EBou MACG SRms
- SNOWFLAKE see *G. paniculata* 'Schneeflocke'
- SUMMER SPARKLES ('Esm Chispa'PBR) CRos EHyd LRHS NRHS
- WHITE FIRE ('Dangypwhifa') EBee
§ ***petraea*** GKev
'Pink Festival' (Festival Series) (d) CDor ECha ECtt EHyd EPfP LRHS NRHS SPoG
repens ♀H5 ECtt GBin GJos GKev LShi MAsh SPlb SWvt WCav WFar WWke XLum XSen
- 'Dorothy Teacher' ECtt WAbe WFar
§ - 'Dubia' EBou ECha EPot EWTr MAsh MHer SLee SRms SRot WIce WSHC
- 'Filou Rose' EBou EDAr GJos LRHS MACG WHil
- 'Filou White' EDAr LBuc LRHS MACG
- PINK BEAUTY see *G. repens* 'Rosa Schönheit'
§ - 'Rosa Schönheit' ECha ECtt EPot NDov SPer WFar XLum
- 'Rosea' CTri EBee EBou ECtt EDAr ELan EPfP EWTr GArf GJos GMaP ITim LShi MMuc NDov NGdn NHpl NSla SBut SEND SLee SPer SPoG SRms SWvt WFar WHoo WIce WWke XLum
- 'Ruby Gems' CBor WFar
- 'Silver Carpet' (v) EBee ELan
- white-flowered ECha NGdn SWvt WFar
§ 'Rosenschleier' (d) ♀H6 CDor EBee ECha ECtt ELan EPfP GKev GMaP LCro LOPS LRHS MBel MRav NDov NGdn SGbt SPer SRms SWvt WCAu WSHC XLum
I 'Rosenschleier Variegata' (v) EBee ELan EPfP
'Rosy Veil' see *G.* 'Rosenschleier'
§ ***tenuifolia*** EPot EWld GArf GMaP ITim NHpl WAbe
transylvanica see *G. petraea*
§ ***vaccaria*** SPhx
VEIL OF ROSES see *G.* 'Rosenschleier'
'White Festival'PBR (Festival Series) (d) EHyd EPfP LBar LRHS NRHS SHar SPoG WTor
'White Flare' (Festival Series) **new** SPeP

H

Habenaria (*Orchidaceae*)

tridactylites GKev

Haberlea (*Gesneriaceae*)

ferdinandi-coburgii see *H. rhodopensis*
§ ***rhodopensis*** ♀H5 ELan EPPr EPot GArf GEdr NHar NHpl NSla SRms WAbe WThu XLum
- 'Connie Davidson' GEdr GKev
- 'Virginalis' CElw GEdr NSla WThu

Hablitzia (*Amaranthaceae*)

tamnoides CAgr

Habranthus (*Amaryllidaceae*)

andersonii see *H. tubispathus*
brachyandrus SRms WCot
gracilifolius CPla WAbe
martinezii ♀H2 EDAr
§ ***robustus*** ♀H2 CBor CCCN EPot EShb EWld GKev LAma
§ ***tubispathus*** ♀H2 CBor EDAr GKev SBrt

Hacquetia see *Sanicula*

Haemanthus (*Amaryllidaceae*)

albiflos ♀H2 CPrp EAri ELan EPri EShb GKev LAma NGKo NSti SDir SRms
amarylloides WCot
barkerae WCot
carneus WCot
coccineus ♀H2 EPri WCot
humilis WCot
- subsp. ***hirsutus*** WCot
kalbreyeri see *Scadoxus multiflorus* subsp. *multiflorus*
katherinae see *Scadoxus multiflorus* subsp. *katherinae*
natalensis see *Scadoxus puniceus*
nortieri WCot
pubescens WCot
sanguineus WCot

Hakea (Proteaceae)

	baxteri	SPlb
§	***drupacea***	CPbh
	epiglottis	CTrC
	laurina	CCCN CPbh SPlb
§	***lissosperma***	CBcs EBee EPfP SPlb WPGP
	nodosa	CCCN
	oleifolia	CPbh
	platysperma	SPlb
§	***salicifolia***	CCCN SPlb
	saligna	see *H. salicifolia*
	sericea misapplied	see *H. lissosperma*
	sericea Schrad. & J.C.Wendl. pink-flowered	SPlb
	suaveolens	see *H. drupacea*
	teretifolia	CTrC
	victoria	SPlb XSte

Hakonechloa ✿ (Poaceae)

	macra ♀H7	Widely available
§	- 'Alboaurea' (v) ♀H7	CExl CKno CRos CSde EBlo EHyd ELan EPfP GArf GMcL LCro LOPS LRHS LSRN MGos MHol NRHS SCob SCoo SRms
	- 'Albovariegata' (v)	CAbb CAby CDoC CKno EBee EMor LCro LEdu LOPS NLar SCob SMHy WAvo
§	- 'All Gold'	Widely available
	- 'Aureola' ♀H7	Widely available
	- 'Beni-kaze'	CKno CMiW EBee ECtt EHed ELan ELon EMor MNrw NDov NLar SCob SCoo SMHy WPnP
	- 'Fubuki' (v)	EBee
	- 'Greenhills'	EMor LEdu
	- 'Mediovariegata' (v)	EBee ECha
	- 'Naomi' (v)	CMiW CWnw EBee EHed ELan EMor GArf LPla SMHy SPer WFar WPnP XSte
	- 'Nicolas'	CBod CDor CExl CMiW CWnw EBee ECtt EHed ELan ELon EMor EPfP EWes GMcL LCro LEdu LOPS LPla LRHS LSRN LSou NLar SCoo SEle SPer SPoG WFar WNPC WPnP XSte
	- 'Ogon'	see *H. macra* 'All Gold'
	- 'Samurai' (v)	CKno EPPr EPfP LRHS
	- 'Stripe It Rich' (v)	CCht EBee ECtt EMor EWes LPla NLar SMrm
	- SUNFLARE ('Habsfl007')	CAby CBcs CBod CKno CMiW CSde CWGN EBee EMor LCro LEdu LLWG LOPS LPla NLar NPol SMrm WNPC WPnP
	- 'Sunny Delight' (v)	EBee EMor
	- 'Variegata'	see *H. macra* 'Alboaurea'

Halenia (Gentianaceae)

	elliptica	GKev

Halesia ✿ (Styracaceae)

§	***carolina***	Widely available
	- Monticola Group	CBcs CCVT CLnd CMac CPer ELan EPfP LMaj LSRN NLar SWvt WHtc
	- - 'Arnold Pink'	EHed
I	- - 'Variegata' (v)	EPfP MBlu NLar SSta
	- 'Uconn Wedding Bells'	CJun MBlu WTSh
	- Vestita Group ♀H5	CAco EPfP MAsh MBlu MGil MRav NLar SSta WLov
	- - 'Rosea'	EPfP MBlu NLar
	diptera	MBlu
	- Magniflora Group	CJun EPfP MBlu NLar SSta
	macgregorii	see *Perkinsiodendron macgregorii*
	tetraptera	see *H. carolina*

× Halimiocistus (Cistaceae)

	algarvensis	see *Halimium ocymoides*
§	'Ingwersenii' ♀H4	CBod ELan NLar SPer SRms XLum
	revolii misapplied	see × *H. sahucii*
§	***sahucii*** ♀H4	CBcs CBod CDoC CRos CSBt CTri ECha ELan EPfP ILea LCro LRHS MAsh MBNS MPri MRav MSwo NLar SGBe SPer SPoG SRms SWvt WLov XLum
	- ICE DANCER ('Ebhals'PBR) (v)	EBee MAsh SCob SPer SWvt WFar
	'Susan'	see *Halimium* 'Susan'
§	***wintonensis*** ♀H4	CBcs CBod CRos EGrl EHyd ELan EPfP LRHS MAsh MGil MMrt NLar SPer SRms WLov
§	- 'Merrist Wood Cream' ♀H4	CBcs CBod CBrac CDoC CKel CSBt CSde EBee EGrl ELan EPfP LSRN MAsh MGil MMrt MRav MSwo NLar SCob SGBe SPer SPoG SWvt WFar WLov WMal WSHC

Halimodendron see Caragana

Halimione (Amaranthaceae)

§	***portulacoides***	CEls

Halimium (Cistaceae)

	'April Snow' **new**	NLar
	'April Sun' **new**	NLar
§	***atriplicifolium***	XSen
§	***calycinum***	CBcs CBod CBor CDoC CKel CRos EGrl EHyd ELan EPfP LCro LRHS MAsh MMuc NBwr NRHS SCob SCoo SGBe SPad SPer SPoG SWvt WCav WLov
	commutatum	see *H. calycinum*
	halimifolium misapplied	see *H.* × *pauanum*
§	***halimifolium*** Willk.	WMal XSen
§	***lasianthum***	CMac CSBt LCro MRav WMal
	- 'Concolor' ♀H4	MAsh MSwo SWvt
	- subsp. ***formosum***	EHyd ELan EPfP LRHS MAsh SChF
	'Sandling' ♀H4	SPoG SRms WPGP
	libanotis misapplied	see *H. calycinum*
§	***ocymoides***	LRHS MSwo SGBe WFar
§	× ***pauanum***	EHyd LRHS NRHS
§	'Susan' ♀H4	CBcs EBee EHyd ELan EPfP LRHS MMrt NRHS SCoo SGBe SPer WAbe WLov
§	***umbellatum***	EPfP
	wintonense	see × *Halimiocistus wintonensis*

Halleria (Stilbaceae)

	lucida	CBcs CCCN EBee EGrl SEle SPlb SVen WKor

Haloragis (Haloragaceae)

	erecta	SPlb SVen XLum
	- 'Rubra'	WCot
	- 'Wellington Bronze'	CExl CPla CSpe CWal EBee EGrl ELan EWld LEdu SBls WHer XLum

Hamamelis ✿ (Hamamelidaceae)

	'Amethyst'	CJun MBlu NCth
	'Brevipetala'	CEnd CJun LMaj
	'Danny'	CJun
	'Dishi'	CJun
	'Fire Blaze'	CJun MBlu NLar
	× ***intermedia*** 'Advent' ♀H5	CJun MAsh
	- 'Allgold'	SCob
	- 'Amanda'	NLar
	- 'Andre'	WPGP
	- 'Angelly' ♀H5	CJun EHed MBlu NLar

- 'Anne' ♀H5	WPGP
- 'Aphrodite' ♀H5	CBcs CJun CRos EHyd GDam GMcL LRHS LSRN MAsh MBlu MGos MRav NLar NOra NRHS SPer WHlf
- 'Arnold Promise' ♀H5	Widely available
- 'Aurora' ♀H5	CJun EPfP LRHS MBlu NLar NOra WPGP
- 'Barmstedt Gold' ♀H5	CDoC CJun CRos EHyd EPfP LRHS LSRN MGos MRav NOra NRHS SAko SPer SPoG SRms
- 'Bernstein'	CJun
- 'Birgit'	NCth NLar
- 'Carmine Red'	CJun CMac LRHS
- 'Copper Beauty'	see *H.* × *intermedia* 'Jelena'
- 'Cyrille'	MMuc
- 'Diane' ♀H5	Widely available
§ - 'Feuerzauber'	CTri EGrI EPfP LMaj LRHS MAsh MHtn NLar NOrn SGsty SMad SPer SRHi SWvt WFar
- FIRE CRACKER	see *H.* × *intermedia* 'Feuerzauber'
- 'Foxy Lady'	MBlu
- 'Frederic' ♀H5	CJun EPfP
- 'Gingerbread' ♀H5	CJun EPfP
- 'Glowing Embers'	CJun
- 'Harry' ♀H5	CJun MAsh NLar
- 'Heinrich Bruns'	CJun
- 'Hiltingbury'	LRHS MGos
§ - 'Jelena' ♀H5	Widely available
- 'Limelight'	CJun MBlu MMuc
- 'Livia'	CJun CRos EHyd EPfP LRHS MAsh NRHS SCoo WPGP
- MAGIC FIRE	see *H.* × *intermedia* 'Feuerzauber'
- 'Moonlight'	CJun
- 'Nina'	EPfP LRHS
- 'Orange Beauty'	CBcs CBod CJun CRos EBee EGrI EHyd LCro LRHS MBlu MDon MGos NLar NOrn NRHS SAko SCoo SPer SRHi WPGP
- 'Orange Peel'	CJun EBee EPfP NLar WPGP
- 'Ostergold'	CJun
- 'Pallida' ♀H5	Widely available
- 'Primavera'	CJun CLnd
- 'Ripe Corn'	CJun MBlu
- 'Robert' ♀H5	CJun CRos EHyd ELan EPfP LRHS NRHS
- 'Rubin' ♀H5	CBcs CJun CRos EHyd EPfP GMcL LRHS MGos NLar NRHS SCoo SPer
- 'Rubinstar'	CJun
- 'Ruby Glow'	CRos EHed EHyd LRHS LSRN MAsh MGos NLar NRHS NWea SCoo SPer SPoG SWvt
- 'Savill Starlight'	CJun
- 'Spanish Spider'	CJun MBlu
- 'Strawberries and Cream'	CJun
- 'Sunburst'	CJun CRos EHyd EPfP LRHS MBlu MGos NLar
- 'Swallow Hayes'	LRHS
- 'Twilight'	CJun NCth NLar
- 'Vesna' ♀H5	CJun MAsh MBlu SCoo
- 'Westerstede'	CJun CLnd CWnw EHed GMcL LCro LMaj LRHS LSRN MGos NHol NLar NWea SCoo SEWo SGsty WFar
- 'Wiero'	CJun
- 'Zitronenjette'	CJun
japonica	WJur
- 'Brentry' **new**	CBcs
- 'Pendula'	MBlu
- 'Rubra'	EGrI
- 'Zuccariniana'	NLar
mollis	Widely available
- 'Boskoop'	MMuc NLar
- 'Coombe Wood'	CJun LRHS NOra
- 'Imperialis'	CJun
- 'Iwado'	CJun
- 'Jermyns Gold' ♀H5	CBcs CJun CRos EHyd EPfP LMil LRHS MAsh NRHS
- 'Kort's Yellow'	CJun
- var. ***pallida***	CBrac SEWo SRHi SWvt
- 'Wisley Supreme' ♀H5	CJun ELan EPfP LRHS MGos SRHi
'Rochester'	CJun
vernalis	WJur
- purple-flowered	MBlu
- 'Quasimodo'	MBlu
- 'Sandra'	CMCN MBlu MGos MRav NOra
virginiana	CAgr CMCN EGrI GPoy IDee LPar LSto MMuc NWea WHlf WJur
- 'Mohonk Red'	CJun
'Yamina'	CDoC CRos ELan LMil LRHS MAsh NLar SGol

Hamelia (*Rubiaceae*)

patens	CCCN

Hanabusaya (*Campanulaceae*)

§ ***asiatica***	WFar

Haplocarpha (*Asteraceae*)

rueppellii	NHpl SRms

Haplopappus (*Asteraceae*)

coronopifolius	see *H. glutinosus*
§ ***glutinosus***	ECha EPot MMuc SLee SPlb SRms
macrocephalus **new**	EDAr

Hardenbergia (*Fabaceae*)

violacea ♀H3	CCCN CHll CRHN CTsd EAri ELan SEND SEdd WCot WHlf
- f. ***alba***	CHll CKel EAri ELan SEND WLov
- - 'White Wanderer'	CCCN
- 'Bliss' **new**	CCCN
- CANDY WRAPPER ('H2 206'PBR) **new**	CCCN
- 'Happy Wanderer'	CCCN SIvy
- f. ***rosea***	CCCN CHll

Harrisia (*Cactaceae*)

tetracantha **new**	NPlm

Hasteola (*Asteraceae*)

§ ***suaveolens***	LEdu

Hastingsia (*Asparagaceae*)

alba	WSHC

Haworthia ✿ (*Asphodelaceae*)

attenuata	EAri EShb NCft
- 'Super Zebra'	WCot
'Big Band'	LCro
'Black Prince'	EShb
coarctata ♀H2	SEND
cooperi	NCft
- var. ***truncata*** **new**	SEdd
cymbiformis	EAri NCft SPlb
- variegated (v)	NCft
elizeae **new**	SEdd
fasciata	EPfP EWoo SEND
- 'Concolor'	CDoC EAri SPlb SSim
glabrata var. ***concolor***	EAri EShb
'Jack Brown'	NCft
limifolia	EShb NCft SPlb
- SPIDER WHITE ('Lock01'PBR)	LCro
- var. ***ubomboensis***	NCft
margaritifera	NCft SSim

marumiana	NCft
- var. ***batesiana***	NCft
- var. ***reddii***	NCft
mirabilis var. ***badia*** **new**	SPlb
nigra **new**	SPlb
obtusa 'Turu Pika' **new**	SEdd
pumila ♀H2	SEND
- subsp. ***minima*** **new**	SPlb
pygmaea var. ***acuminata*** **new**	SEdd
- f. ***major*** **new**	SPlb
reinwardtii ♀H2	WSFF
- var. ***brevicula***	NCft
retusa ♀H2	WOld
- 'Grey Ghost'	NCft
× ***revendettii***	NCft
'Sakura Cristal' **new**	SEdd
starkiana	NCft
tesselata	see *H. venosa* subsp. *tesselata*
tortusa	NCft
truncata ♀H2	NCft
variegata var. ***modesta***	NCft
§ ***venosa*** subsp. ***tesselata*** ♀H2	SEND
'Window Light' **new**	SEdd

hazelnut see *Corylus*; see also AGM Fruit Section

Hebe ✿ (*Plantaginaceae*)

albicans ♀H4	Widely available
- prostrate	see *H. albicans* 'Snow Cover'
§ - 'Snow Cover'	EWes
- 'Snow Drift'	see *H. albicans* 'Snow Cover'
'Amanda Cook' (v)	NPer
'Amethyst Mist'	GDam GMcL
§ 'Amy'	ELon EShb GMcL LRHS NPer SPer SWvt WCot
× ***andersonii***	CDoC
§ - 'Andersonii Variegata' (v)	SRms
- 'Argenteovariegata'	see *H.* × *andersonii* 'Andersonii Variegata'
anomala misapplied	see *H.* 'Imposter'
'Aoira'	see *H. recurva* 'Aoira'
§ ***armstrongii***	MMuc
armstrongii* × *selaginoides	WKif
'Autumn Glory'	CBrac CDoC CGBo EHyd ELan EPfP GMcL LCro LRHS LSRN MAsh MRav MSwo NBir NRHS SCob SGBe SPer SPlb SPoG SRGP SWvt WSpi XLum
'Autumn Joy'	SWvt
'Azurens'	see *H.* 'Maori Gem'
'Baby Boo' (v)	CDoC LRHS NBwr SCob
'Baby Marie'	CDoC CGBo CSBt EHyd ELan EPfP GJos GKin GMcL LBuc LRHS LSRN MSwo NLar NPer NRHS SCoo SGBe SPoG SRms SWvt WFar
'Beverley Hills' PBR	CSBt EHyd
'Bicolor Wand'	CCCN
'Black Beauty'	EHyd EPfP GDam GMcL LRHS MAsh NRHS SCob
'Black Panther'	ELon GMcL
'Blue Clouds' ♀H4	CRos EHyd EPfP LRHS MSwo NRHS NWad SPer WCFE WMal
BLUE ELEGANCE ('Lowgeko' PBR) (Garden Elegance Series)	ELan LCro LRHS SGBe
§ 'Blue Gem'	CCoa CDoC CMac GMcL LPar NLar SGBe SGsty
BLUE HAZE ('Lowchi' PBR) (Garden Beauty Series)	SGBe
BLUE ICE ('Lowapb') (Garden Beauty Series)	LRHS SGBe
'Blue Shamrock'	SWvt
BLUE STAR ('Vergeer 1' PBR)	CDoC CRos EPfP GJos LBuc LRHS MAsh NRHS SPoG SRms
BLUSH ELEGANCE ('Lowele') (Garden Elegance Series)	ELan LCro LRHS SGBe
'Boscawenii'	WHer
'Bouquet' PBR	CBod LSou
§ 'Bowles's Hybrid'	CBrac CGBo MRav MSwo SCob SEND SRms
brachysiphon	CTri SEND SPer SRms SVen
brevifolia	SGBe
BRONZE GLOW ('Lowglo') (Garden Beauty Series)	CDoC CGBo LBuc LRHS SGBe
'Bronzy Baby' PBR (v)	MAsh SPoG
buchananii	MHer NPer
§ - 'Fenwickii'	WHoo
- 'Minor' ambig.	GQue WAbe
- 'Minor' Hort. NZ	EPot
'Burgundy Blush'	LBuc SPoG
'Burning Heart' (v)	LBuc LRHS
buxifolia	see *H. odora*
§ 'Caledonia' ♀H4	CBcs CDoC CRos EGrI EHyd ELan EPfP LCro LOPS LRHS LSRN MAsh MGos NPer NRHS SCoo SGBe SPoG SRms SWvt WCav XLum
'Carl Teschner'	see *H.* 'Youngii'
'Carnea Variegata' (v)	EHyd GMcL LRHS NRHS SPer SRms
catarractae	see *Parabebe catarractae*
'Celebration' PBR (v)	CBod LRHS
'Celine'	CCoa EHyd EPfP LRHS MAsh NRHS
'Champagne'	CBrac CDoC CGBo EHyd ELan EPfP LCro LOPS LPar LRHS LSRN MAsh MBlu NLar NRHS NWad SCoo SGBe SRms XLum
'Champagne Ice'	LBuc
CHAMPION ('Champseiont' PBR)	GJos GMcL MSwo NLar SCoo
'Charming White'	CChe CEme CGBo
chathamica	EBtc
'Christabel'	CGBo
'Claret Crush' PBR	SCoo SPoG
'Clear Skies'	SRms
'Cobb Valley'	LRHS
'Conwy Knight'	SRms
corstorphinensis	EBtc
'County Park'	GMcL
cupressoides 'Boughton Dome'	ELan EPot EShb GJos MCot MHer WAbe WHoo
- 'Golden Dome'	SGsty
'Dark Angel'	LBuc SCoo
DARK STAR ('Lowgamma') (Garden Beauty Series)	SGBe
darwiniana misapplied	see *H. glaucophylla*
'Dazzler' (v)	MAsh
decumbens	EWes GArf GBin
'Diamond'	SCob SRms
dieffenbachii	SVen
diosmifolia	CBod CDoC CGBo NRHS NWad
- 'Wairua Beauty'	CDoC LRHS SGBe
× ***divergens***	SPlb
'Dorothy Peach'	see *H.* 'Watson's Pink'
'E.B. Anderson'	see *H.* 'Caledonia'
'Edington'	SPer WCFE
elliptica	CDoC
- 'Variegata'	see *H.* 'Silver Queen'
'Emerald Dome'	see *H.* 'Emerald Gem'
§ 'Emerald Gem' ♀H4	CBod CGBo CRos CTri EGrI EHeP EHyd ELan EPfP GDam GMcL LPar LRHS LSRN MAsh MGos MHer MMuc MSwo NBwr NRHS SCob SGBe SPlb SPoG SRot

	'Emerald Green'	see *H.* 'Emerald Gem'
§	'Eveline'	CRos CSBt CTri LRHS
	'Evelyn'	SPer
	evenosa	EBtc
	'Eversley Seedling'	see *H.* 'Bowles's Hybrid'
	'Eyecatcher'^{PBR} (v)	LSou
	'Fairfieldii'	WAbe WAvo WMal WSHC
	'First Light'^{PBR}	CDoC CKel LSou NLar SRms
	'Fragrant Jewel'	SEND
	× ***franciscana***	CGBo NCou
	- 'Blue Gem' ambig.	CBrac CGBo EHeP EHyd ELan LRHS MAsh MMuc MRav NBir NPer NRHS SCob SEND SPer SPlb SPoG SRms WSpi XLum
	- 'Foreness Pink'	SEND
	- lime variegated (v)	SEND
	- 'Purple Tips' misapplied	see *H. speciosa* 'Variegata'
	- 'Variegata'	see *H.* 'Silver Queen'
I	- 'White Gem'	SRms
	'Frozen Flame' (v)	ELan LBuc MAsh SPoG WMal
	(Garden Beauty Series)	CDoC CSBt LBuc LCro LOPS LRHS
	GARDEN BEAUTY BLUE ('Cliv'^{PBR})	LSou MAsh SCoo SGBe SRms WSpi
	- GARDEN BEAUTY PINK ('Lowpito')	CDoC SGBe SRms
§	- GARDEN BEAUTY PURPLE ('Nold'^{PBR})	CSBt EHyd EPfP LBuc LCro LOPS LRHS LSou MAsh NRHS SGBe WSpi
	- GARDEN BEAUTY WHITE ('Lowhi')	LRHS SGBe
	'Gauntlettii'	see *H.* 'Eveline'
§	***glaucophylla***	XLum
I	- 'Variegata' (v)	EHyd LRHS NRHS SCoo SPer WKif
§	'Gloriosa'	SCob
	'Gold Beauty' (v)	SRms
	'Gold Pixie'	LBuc
	GOLDEN ANNIVERSARY ('Lowag'^{PBR}) (Garden Beauty Series)	LRHS
	'Goldrush'^{PBR} (v)	MAsh SPoG
	'Goliath' **new**	SGBe
	gracillima	EBtc SEle
	'Great Orme' $\mathbb{Y}^{H4}$	CBrac CGBo CRos EHeP EHyd ELan EPfP GBin GLog LSRN MAsh MRav MSwo NPer NRHS SCob SEND SGBe SPer SPlb SPoG SRms SWvt WCFE WSFF
	'Green Globe'	see *H.* 'Emerald Gem'
	'Greensleeves'	EHyd
	'Grethe'	EHyd NRHS SCob SEND
	'Hadspen Pink'	CDoC
	'Hanne'	EHyd LRHS NRHS
§	'Hartii'	MRav
	'Havens Green'	GMcL
	'Headfortii'	EBtc EGrI
	'Heartbreaker'^{PBR} (v)	CDoC CRos EHyd ELan EPfP GMcL LBuc LCro LOPS LRHS MAsh MGos MPri NRHS SCob SCoo SGBe SPoG SWvt
	HEBEDONNA ANNA ('Zebora'^{PBR}) **new**	GDam
	'Helena' (Addenda Series)	CDoC
	'High Voltage'^{PBR}	GJos MHtn NEoE WHtc WSpi WTyc
	'Highdown Pink'	EBtc
	HIGHLAND JUBILEE	see *H.* 'Ruthie Gray'
	'Hinderwell'	NPer
	hookeriana	see *Parahebe hookeriana*
	hulkeana	MGil MHer MMrt SMHy WAbe WHoo WKif
§	'Imposter'	SRms
	'Inspiration'	CGBo NWad SCob SRms
	'James Stirling'	see *H. ochracea* 'James Stirling'
	'Jewel of the Nile'^{PBR} (v)	EShb MMrt NFav SCob SGBe SPoG WFar
	'Joan Mac'	EBee ELan MHtn SCoo
	'John Collier'	SEND
	'Johny Day'	CGBo
	'Karna'	SCob
	'Katrina' (v)	CDoC
	'Killiney Variety'	EBtc
	'Kirkii'	EHeP ELan MSwo NLar XLum
	'Knightshayes'	see *H.* 'Caledonia'
	'Lady Ann'^{PBR} (v)	CRos EHyd EPfP GMcL LBuc LRHS MAsh NRHS NWad SCob SPoG
	'Lady Ardilaun'	see *H.* 'Amy'
	latifolia	see *H.* 'Blue Gem'
	lavaudiana	EBtc WMal
	'Lavender Spray'	see *H.* 'Hartii'
	leiophylla	EBtc
	LEOPARD ('Lowand') (Garden Beauty Series)	ELan LRHS MPri SGBe
	'Leopard Spot' (v)	LCro LRHS SCoo SGBe
	'Lilac Fantasy'	LRHS SGBe
	'Linda'	SEND
	'Lisa'	EHyd LRHS NRHS
	'Liz'	LBuc SPoG
	'Louise'	SCob
	lyallii	see *Parahebe lyallii*
	lycopodioides 'Aurea'	see *H. armstrongii*
	'Lynash'	CGBo
	mackenii	see *H.* 'Emerald Gem'
	macrantha $\mathbb{Y}^{H4}$	GArf GBin GMcL SRms
	macrocarpa	CDoC LRHS SGBe
	- var. ***latisepala***	CDoC LRHS SGBe
	'Magic Summer'^{PBR}	LBuc MAsh NRHS SPoG
§	'Maori Gem'	MRav
	'Margret' $\mathbb{Y}^{H4}$	CDoC CSBt EBee EHyd EPfP GArf GMcL LRHS LSRN MAsh MGos NBwr NRHS SCoo SGBe SPer SPoG SRms WSpi
	'Maria'	SCob
	'Marie Antoinette'	CBod
	'Marilyn Monroe'^{PBR}	CBod LSou MAsh WTyc
	'Marjorie'	CMac EHeP ELan EPfP GBin LRHS LSRN MSwo NPer NRHS NWea SCob SPer SPoG SRms SWvt WFar
	'Marshmallow'	SCoo
	matthewsii 'Turkish Delight'^{PBR}	GJos NEoE
	MATTY BROWN ('Tull 303'^{PBR})	LSou MAsh MHtn
	'McKean'	see *H.* 'Emerald Gem'
	'Merlot Memories'^{PBR}	SCoo
	'Mette'	MAsh
	MIDNIGHT SKY ('Lowten'^{PBR}) (Garden Beauty Series)	CDoC LCro LOPS LRHS MPri SCoo SGBe SPoG WCot
	'Midsummer Beauty' $\mathbb{Y}^{H4}$	EHyd EPfP GBin GDam GMcL LRHS LSRN MRav NBir NRHS SCob SEND SPer SPlb SPoG SRms SWvt WSFF XLum
	'Milmont Emerald'	see *H.* 'Emerald Gem'
§	'Mohawk'^{PBR}	EHeP GJos NRHS SCoo SPoG WSpi
§	'Mrs Winder' $\mathbb{Y}^{H4}$	CBrac CGBo CMac EHeP EHyd ELan EPfP GDam GMcL LPar LRHS LSRN MAsh MGos MRav MSwo NBwr NPer NRHS SCob SCoo SGBe SGbt SGsty SPer SPoG SRGP SWvt WSpi
	'Nantyderry'	CDoC CGBo MGil
§	'Neil's Choice' $\mathbb{Y}^{H4}$	ELon LRHS
	'New Zealand'	CKel CWnw GDam GMcL XLum
	'Nicola's Blush' $\mathbb{Y}^{H4}$	CDoC CGBo CMac CRos EBee EHeP EHyd ELon EPfP EShb GBin GMcL LRHS LSRN MCot MRav MSwo NBwr NLar NRHS SCob SEND SPer SPoG SRGP SRms SWvt SavN WMal

	ochracea	EHyd EPfP LRHS NRHS
§	– 'James Stirling' ♀H4	CBcs CMac CSBt EHeP ELan GArf GDam GJos LCro LOPS LSRN MAsh MGos MSwo NBwr NLar NWad SCob SCoo SGBe SPlb SPoG SWvt WFar WSpi
§	***odora***	ELan LSto NWea WSpi XLum
I	– 'Nana'	MMuc
	– 'New Zealand Gold'	CRos EHeP EHyd EPfP GJos LRHS MMuc NRHS NWad
	– prostrate	SRms
	– 'Summer Frost'	CDoC CSde
	'Oratia Beauty' ♀H4	CDoC CGBo EHeP LSRN MRav NBwr SEND
	'Orphan Annie' (v)	CDoC CGBo
	'Pacific Paradise'PBR	SPoG
	parviflora misapplied	see *H.* 'Bowles's Hybrid'
	parviflora Vahl. Cockayne & Allan var. ***angustifolia***	see *H. stenophylla*
	– 'Holdsworth'	CBod
	'Pascal' ♀H4	EHyd ELan EPfP GMcL LCro LOPS LRHS LSRN MAsh MGos NRHS SCoo SGBe SPer SPoG SRms SWvt WFar
	'Pastel Blue'	LRHS
	'Patti Dossett'	see *H. speciosa* 'Patti Dossett'
	pauciramosa	SRms
	'Pearl of Paradise'PBR	LBuc NRHS NWad SPoG
	perfoliata	see *Parahebe perfoliata*
	'Perry's Rubyleaf'	NPer
	'Petra's Pink'	EHyd
	'Pewter Dome' ♀H4	CCoa EPfP GMcL MGos MRav SCob SDix SRms SWvt XLum
	pimeleoides	GMcL WAbe
	– 'Glauca'	NPer
	– 'Quicksilver' ♀H4	CRos CSBt EHyd ELan EPfP GArf GJos LRHS LSRN MGil MGos MRav NBwr NPer NRHS SCob SCoo SGBe SLee SPer SRms WAvo WSpi XLum
	pinguifolia	NLar SPlb
	– 'Pagei' ♀H5	Widely available
	– 'Sutherlandii'	CBcs CBrac CDoC EHeP EHyd EPfP GMcL LPar LRHS LSRN MAsh MGos MSwo NBwr NRHS NWea SArc SCob SCoo SGsty SWvt WFar XLum
	PINK CANDY ('Tulpink'PBR)	CBod MSwo WTyc
	'Pink Elephant' (v) ♀H4	CDoC LBuc LRHS SGBe SPoG
	'Pink Fantasy'	NWad SGbt
	'Pink Goddess'	EHyd EPfP LRHS NRHS SEND
	'Pink Lady'PBR	ELan GMcL SPoG
	'Pink Paradise'PBR	ELan GMcL NLar NRHS NWad SPoG SRms
	'Pink Payne'	see *H.* 'Eveline'
	'Pink Pearl'	see *H.* 'Gloriosa'
	'Pink Pixie'	LBuc MAsh SCoo SPoG SRms
	'Pinocchio' (v)	LRHS MAsh
	'Polly Moore'	EBtc
	poppelwellii	GQue NLar
	'Porlock Purple'	see *Parahebe catarractae* 'Delight'
I	'Prostrata'	CSBt
	'Purple Emperor'	see *H.* 'Neil's Choice'
	'Purple Paradise'PBR	GDam GMcL LSou NLar SPoG
	'Purple Pixie'	see *H.* 'Mohawk'
	'Purple Princess'	CGBo EHyd EPfP LRHS NRHS
	PURPLE SHAMROCK ('Neprock'PBR) (v)	CDoC CRos EHyd EPfP GJos GMcL LRHS LSou MAsh NLar NRHS SCoo SGBe SPoG SRms SWvt WHtc
	'Purple Tips' misapplied	see *H. speciosa* 'Variegata'
§	***rakaiensis*** ♀H4	Widely available
	– 'Golden Dome'	see *H. rakaiensis*
	ramosissima	EPot GAbr GBin

	raoulii	SRms WAbe
	RASPBERRY RIPPLE ('Tullyraspb'PBR)	GMcL
	'Raven'	CDoC CGBo
	recurva	CCoa CGBo CTri SRms
§	– 'Aoira'	SPlb
	– 'Boughton Silver' ♀H4	CEme LRHS LSRN MMuc SGBe
	'Red Edge' ♀H4	Widely available
	'Red Ruth'	see *H.* 'Eveline'
	RHUBARB AND CUSTARD ('Tull 302'PBR)	GJos LBuc LCro MAsh MMrt SCoo SPoG WCot
	ROSE ELEGANCE ('Lowtop') (Garden Elegance Series)	LCro LRHS SGBe
	'Rosie'	LBuc LSRN NRHS SCoo SPer SRot SWvt
	'Royal Blue'	SCob
	'Ruby Port'PBR	SCoo
§	'Ruthie Gray'PBR (v)	GMcL
	salicifolia	CMac CTca EHeP EHyd ELan EPfP IDee LRHS MRav NBwr NRHS NWad SEND SPer SPlb SRms WFar WSpi XLum
	– pale blue-flowered	SEND
	'Sandra Joy'	LSRN
	'Sangria Sensation'PBR	SCoo
	'Santa Monica'	GMcL WCot
	'Sapphire' ♀H4	EHyd EPfP GMcL LRHS MAsh NRHS SCoo SRms SWvt
	'Shiraz'	EHyd
	'Silver Dollar' (v)	CBcs GArf GMcL LRHS LSou NRHS NWad SCob SGBe SPoG SRms
§	'Silver Queen' (v) ♀H3	CBcs CBod CBrac CCoa CDoC CEme CGBo CKel CMac CSBt CWnw EHeP EHyd ELan GMcL LCro LOPS LRHS MAsh MMuc NLar NPer NRHS SEND SGBe SGsty SPer SPoG SRms
	'Simon Délaux'	SEND WCot
	'Sparkling Sapphires'	LRHS SGBe SPoG
	speciosa	CPla
	– 'La Séduisante'	CTri LRHS SEND WSpi
§	– 'Patti Dossett'	CDoC CGBo
	– 'Red Hugh'	SEND
§	– 'Variegata' (v)	CRos CSBt EHyd LRHS NBwr NPer NRHS SCob
	'Spender's Seedling' misapplied	see *H. stenophylla*
	'Spender's Seedling' ambig.	MCot MMuc NBwr WSpi
	'Spender's Seedling' Hort.	CGBo LRHS MRav NBwr SEND SPoG SRms
	'Spring Glory'	CRos EHyd EPfP LRHS NRHS
	STARLIGHT ('Marklight') (v)	LBuc LCro MSwo SGBe WHlf
§	***stenophylla***	EShb LRHS LSRN NBwr NLar SArc SDix SPer SPlb WOut
	– 'White Lady'	GJos
	stricta	CGBo SEND
	– var. ***macroura***	CBrac
	– var. ***stricta***	CDoC SPlb
	subalpina	CSBt
	'Summer Blue'	MBlu
	'Sunrise' **new**	LCro
	'Sunset Boulevard'PBR	CBod
	'Super Red'	CEme CSBt SGBe
	'Sweet Dreams'	MAsh
	'Sweet Kim' (v)	LBuc LRHS NRHS SGBe SPoG
	tetrasticha	GRum WAbe
	'Tiptop' (v)	LSou
	topiaria ♀H4	CAgr CBod CDoC CEme CGBo CKel CMac CSBt CWnw EBou EPfP GMcL LRHS MBrN MMuc MRav MSwo NBir NFav NLar NWad SCoo SEND SGbt SPer SPoG WAbe WSpi XLum

- 'Doctor Favier'	SRms
'Tricolor'	see *H. speciosa* 'Variegata'
'Trixie'	EHeP WSpi
'Trudi'	SCob
'Valentino'PBR	SCoo
vernicosa 𝕐H4	CCoa CDoC CEme CKel CWnw EHeP EHyd GDam GMcL MGos MHer NBwr NFav NWad NWea SCob SCoo SGsty SPer SPlb SPoG SWvt WAbe WSpi
'Waikiki'	see *H.* 'Mrs Winder'
§ 'Warley'	CBrac CDoC CGBo EHyd LRHS NRHS WSpi
'Warleyensis'	see *H.* 'Warley'
§ 'Watson's Pink'	SPer WKif
'White Gem' (*brachysiphon* hybrid) 𝕐H4	GMcL NLar NPer SPer
'White Heather'	CRos EHyd EPfP LRHS NRHS
'White Paradise'PBR	SPoG
'White Quartz' (Gemstone Series) **new**	NLar
'White Spritzer'PBR	SCoo
'Wild Romance'	CDoC LBuc MAsh SPoG
'Willcoxii'	see *H. buchananii* 'Fenwickii'
'Wingletye' 𝕐H4	EHyd LRHS WAbe XLum
'Wiri Blush'	CBrac CGBo SWvt
'Wiri Charm'	CBcs CBrac CCoa CDoC CGBo CMac CRos CSBt EBee EGrl EHyd ELon EPfP GArf LRHS MSwo NLar NRHS SEND SPer
'Wiri Cloud' 𝕐H4	CBcs CBod CDoC CEme CMac EGrl EHyd EPfP LRHS MMuc MSwo NRHS SCob SEND SRms
'Wiri Dawn' 𝕐H4	EGrl EHyd ELan EPfP NRHS SRms SWvt XLum
'Wiri Icing Sugar'	CGBo
'Wiri Image'	CBcs CCoa CSBt EHyd NRHS SEND
'Wiri Joy'	EHyd EPfP LRHS NRHS SEND
'Wiri Mist'	CBcs EHyd ELan LPar LRHS NBwr NRHS WOut XLum
'Wiri Prince'	SCob
'Wiri Splash'	CRos EHyd LRHS NRHS
'Wiri Vision'	CBrac CGBo CSBt SEND
§ 'Youngii' 𝕐H4	Widely available

Hebenstretia (*Scrophulariaceae*)

dura	WFar
- variegated (v) **new**	WCot

Hechtia (*Bromeliaceae*)

sp.	WCot
argentea	EAri

Hedeoma (*Lamiaceae*)

ciliolata	WAbe

Hedera ✿ (*Araliaceae*)

§ ***algeriensis***	SArc WFib
- 'Bellecour'	WFib XLum
- 'Ghost Tree' (v)	GMcL
§ - 'Gloire de Marengo' (v) 𝕐H5	Widely available
- 'Marginomaculata' (v)	EHyd EPfP EShb LRHS MAsh SMad SPoG WFib
- 'Montgomery'	EHyd LRHS LSRN NRHS
- 'Ravensholst' 𝕐H5	CMac MRav SCob WFib
§ ***azorica***	EShb WCot WFib
- amber-fruited	WCot
- 'Pico'	EShb WFib
- 'Saiga'	WCot
- 'Variegata' (v)	WCot
canariensis misapplied	see *H. algeriensis*
- 'Variegata'	see *H. algeriensis* 'Gloire de Marengo'
canariensis Willd. var. ***azorica***	see *H. azorica*
chinensis	see *H. nepalensis*
- typica	see *H. nepalensis*
§ ***colchica***	EHeP NWea WFib
- 'Arborescens'	NWea
* - 'Arborescens Variegata' (v)	WCot
- 'Batumi'	MBNS WFib
- 'Dendroides'	EWTr
- 'Dentata' 𝕐H5	CBod MRav WFar WFib
- 'Dentata Aurea'	see *H. colchica* 'Dentata Variegata'
§ - 'Dentata Variegata' (v) 𝕐H5	Widely available
- 'Dentata Variegata' arboreal (v)	WCot
- 'My Heart'	see *H. colchica*
- 'Paddy's Pride'	see *H. colchica* 'Sulphur Heart'
§ - 'Sulphur Heart' (v) 𝕐H5	Widely available
- 'Variegata'	see *H. colchica* 'Dentata Variegata'
cristata	see *H. helix* 'Parsley Crested'
helix	CBTr CCVT CMac EHeP GDam LCro LOPS LPar MBros NBwr NWea SCob SWeb WSFF XLum
- 'Adam' (v)	LSRN WFib
- 'Amber Waves'	WFib
- 'Anita'	EHeP GBin WFib
§ - 'Anna Marie' (v)	WFib
- 'Arborescens'	CKel EShb LPar NLar WSFF
- 'Ardingly' (v)	WFib
- 'Atropurpurea'	GBin MMuc SEND WFib
- (Aureovariegata Group) 'Chrysophylla' (v)	MSwo
- 'Baltica'	WFib
- 'Bettina' (v)	WCot
- 'Bill Archer'	GBin WFib
- 'Bird's Foot'	see *H. helix* 'Pedata'
- 'Boskoop'	WFib
- 'Bredon'	MRav
- 'Brimstone' (v)	WFib
§ - 'Brokamp'	WFib
- 'Buttercup' 𝕐H5	CBod CMac CRos ELan EPfP GMcL GQue LCro LRHS LSRN LSto MAsh MGos MMuc NLar SCob SEND SPoG SRms SWvt WCFE WFib
- 'Caecilia' (v) 𝕐H5	EPfP MSwo SWvt WFib
- 'Caenwoodiana'	see *H. helix* 'Pedata'
- 'Caenwoodiana Aurea'	WFib
§ - 'Calico' (v)	WFib
- 'Calypso' (v)	WFib
- 'Carolina Crinkle'	GBin
- 'Cathedral Wall'	WFib
§ - Cavendishii Group (v)	SRms WFib
- 'Cavendishii'	see *H. helix* Cavendishii Group
§ - 'Ceridwen' (v) 𝕐H5	CSBt SCob SPlb WFib
- 'Cheeky'	WFib
- 'Chester' (v)	WFib
- 'Chicago'	WFib
- 'Chicago Variegated' (v)	WFib
§ - 'Classy Lassie' (v)	WFib
- 'Clotted Cream' (v)	CDoC CRos GMcL LRHS LSto MAsh WFib
- 'Cockle Shell'	EPPr WFib
- 'Colin'	GBin
§ - 'Congesta' 𝕐H5	CMac CTsd EPPr SRms WFib
- 'Conglomerata'	ELan SRms WFib
- 'Courage'	WFib
- 'Crenata'	WFib
- 'Crispa'	MRav
- 'Cristata'	see *H. helix* 'Parsley Crested'
- 'Curleylocks'	see *H. helix* 'Manda's Crested'
- 'Curley-Q'	see *H. helix* 'Dragon Claw'
- 'Curvaceous' (v)	WCot WFib
- 'Cyprus'	see *H. pastuchovii* subsp. *cypria*

- 'Dealbata' — see *H. hibernica* 'Dealbata'
- 'Deltoidea' — see *H. hibernica* 'Deltoidea'
- 'Discolor' — see *H. helix* 'Minor Marmorata'
§ - 'Donerailensis' — MBlu WFib
§ - 'Dragon Claw' — WFib
- 'Duckfoot' ♀H5 — EShb GBin WCot WFib
- 'Dyinnii' — ELan EPot LShi NLar NSla SPlb SPtp WAbe WCot
- 'Eileen' (v) — WFib
§ - (Elegantissima Group) 'Marginata Elegantissima' (v) — EDir SGsty
- - 'Tricolor' (v) — CMac CTri EPfP LRHS SPoG WCFE WFib
- 'Elfenbein' (v) — WCot WFib
- 'Erecta' — ELan EPPr GAbr IDee LCro MBlu MHer NHol NRya NWad SDix SMad SPer SPlb WCFE WFib XLum
- 'Ester' (v) — CSBt SCob
- 'Eva' (v) — EDir WFib
- 'Fantasia' (v) — WFib
- 'Feenfinger' — WFib
- 'Filigran' — WFib
- 'Flashback' (v) — WFib
- 'Flavescens' — WFib
- 'Fluffy Ruffles' — GKev WFib
- 'Francis' — WFib
- 'Frosty' (v) — WFib
- 'Garland' — WFib
- 'Gavotte' — WFib
- 'Gilded Hawke' — WFib
- 'Glache' (v) — MRav WFib
- 'Glacier' (v) ♀H5 — Widely available
- 'Glymii' — GBin WFib
- 'Gold Harald' — see *H. helix* 'Goldchild'
- 'Gold Ripple' — see *H. helix* 'Golden Starlight'
§ - 'Goldchild' (v) ♀H5 — CBcs CKel CMac CSBt EBee EDir EHeP EHyd EPfP GMcL LCro LOPS LRHS MAsh MGos MMuc MRav MSwo NBir NHol NRHS SCob SLim SPer SPoG SWvt WFib
- 'Golden Ann' — see *H. helix* 'Ceridwen'
- 'Golden Arrow' — see *H. helix* 'Goldfinger'
§ - 'Golden Curl' (v) — CMac EHyd EPfP LRHS WFib
- 'Golden Ester' — see *H. helix* 'Ceridwen'
- 'Golden Gate' (v) — WCot
- 'Golden Girl' (v) — WFib
§ - 'Golden Ingot' (v) ♀H5 — CSBt EHyd LRHS WFib
- 'Golden Jytte' — see *H. helix* 'Classy Lassie'
- 'Golden Kolibri' — see *H. helix* 'Midas Touch'
§ - 'Golden Starlight' (v) — CSBt EDir ELan NLar SEND WFib
- 'Goldfinch' — WFib
§ - 'Goldfinger' — EHyd LRHS WFib
- 'Goldheart' — see *H. helix* 'Oro di Bogliasco'
- 'Goldstern' (v) — MRav WFib
- 'Gracilis' — see *H. hibernica* 'Gracilis'
- 'Green Finger' — see *H. helix* 'Très Coupé'
- 'Green Man' — WFib
- 'Green Ripple' — CBcs CKel CRos EDir EHeP EHyd ELan EPfP GDam GMcL LCro LRHS MBlu MGos MMuc MSwo MWht NRHS NWea SCob SEND SGsty SPer SPlb SRms SWvt WFib
- 'Halebob' — WFib
- 'Hamilton' — see *H. hibernica* 'Hamilton'
- 'Harald' (v) — WFib
- 'Hazel' (v) — WFib
- 'Hedge Hog' — WFib
- 'Heise' (v) — WFib
- 'Heise Denmark' (v) — WFib
- 'Helvig' — see *H. helix* 'White Knight'
- 'Henriette' — WFib
- 'Hispanica' — see *H. iberica*
- 'Hite's Miniature' — see *H. helix* 'Merion Beauty'
- 'Ice Cream' (v) — GKev WCot
- 'Imp' — see *H. helix* 'Brokamp'
- 'Ingelise' (v) — GMcL
- 'Ingrid' (v) — SRms
- 'Ivalace' — CKel EDir EPPr MSwo SCob SRms WFib XLum
- 'Jake' — WFib
- 'Jara' arboreal — WCot
- 'Jasper' — WFib
- 'Jersey Doris' (v) — WFib
- 'Jerusalem' — see *H. helix* 'Calico'
- 'Jester's Gold' — EHeP
- 'Jubilee' (v) — WFar WFib
- 'Kaleidoscope' (v) — WFib
- 'Kevin' — WFib
- 'Kolibri' (v) — EDir EHeP NWea SCob SRms WFib
- 'Königer's Auslese' — WFib
- 'Lalla Rookh' — MRav WFib
- 'Leo Swicegood' — WFib
- 'Lightfinger' — EHeP WFib
- 'Little Diamond' (v) — CKel CMac ELan GMcL SCob SRms SWvt WFib
- 'Little Luzii' (v) — WFib
§ - 'Lucida' — SDix
- 'Luzii' (v) — EHeP WFib
- 'Maculata' — see *H. helix* 'Minor Marmorata'
§ - 'Manda's Crested' ♀H5 — ELan NLar WFib
- 'Maple Leaf' ♀H5 — WFib
- 'Marginata Elegantissima' — see *H. helix* (Elegantissima Group) 'Marginata Elegantissima'
I - 'Marmorata' Fibrex — NBwr WFib
- 'Mathilde' (v) — WFib
- 'Melanie' — ECha WCot WFib
- 'Meon' — WFib
§ - 'Merion Beauty' — WFib
§ - 'Midas Touch' (v) ♀H5 — CKel ELan GMcL NWea WFib
- 'Mini Ester' (v) — CSBt
- 'Minikin' (v) — WCot
* - 'Minima' misapplied — GEdr GQue
- 'Minima' Hibberd — see *H. helix* 'Donerailensis'
- 'Minima' M.Young — see *H. helix* 'Congesta'
§ - 'Minor Marmorata' (v) — EPPr XLum
- 'Minty' (v) — EPPr WFib
- 'Misty' (v) — WFib
- 'Modern Times' — LPal
- 'Needlepoint' — XLum
- 'Niagara Falls' — LRHS
- 'Nigra Aurea' (v) — WFib
- 'Obovata' — WFib
§ - 'Oro di Bogliasco' (v) — Widely available
- 'Ovata' — WFib
§ - 'Parsley Crested' ♀H5 — CDoC ELan WFib
- 'Patent Leather' — WFib
§ - 'Pedata' — MSwo SRms WFib
- 'Perkeo' — WCot WFib
- 'Peter' (v) — WFib
- 'Pink 'n' Curly' — WCot WFib
- 'Pink 'n' Very Curly' — WCot
§ - 'Pittsburgh' — EDir WFib
- 'Plattensee' — EDir
- 'Plume d'Or' — WFib
- f. ***poetarum*** — MBlu WCot WFib
- - 'Poetica Arborea' — EShb
- 'Poetica' — see *H. helix* 'Lucida'
- 'Raleigh Delight' (v) — WCot
- 'Ray's Supreme' — see *H. helix* 'Pittsburgh'
- 'Rhizomatifera' — WFib
- 'Richard John' — see *H. helix* 'Golden Curl'
- 'Ritterkreuz' — WFib
- 'Romanze' (v) — WCot WFib
- 'Russelliana' — EPPr WCFE WFib
- 'Sagittifolia' ambig. — EHeP LRHS MAsh MBlu SPoG

	- 'Sagittifolia Variegata' (v)	WFib
	- 'Saint Agnes'	see *H. helix* 'Golden Ingot'
	- 'Sally'	WFib
	- 'Salt and Pepper'	see *H. helix* 'Minor Marmorata'
	- 'Schäfer Three' (v)	WFib
	- 'Seabreeze'	WFib
	- 'Shamrock' ♀H5	WFib
	- 'Shannon'	WFib
	- 'Silver Ferney' (v)	EPPr EShb WFib
	- 'Silver King' (v)	WCot WFib
§	- 'Snow Cap' (v)	WFib
	- 'Spetchley'	see *H. hibernica* 'Spetchley'
	- 'Splashes' (v)	WFib
	- 'Sunrise'	WFib
	- 'Suzanne'	see *H. nepalensis* 'Suzanne'
	- 'Tanja'	WFib
	- 'Teardrop'	WFib
	- 'Telecurl'	WFib
	- 'Temptation' (v)	WFib
	- 'Teneriffe' (v)	WFib
	- 'Topazolite' (v)	WFib
§	- 'Très Coupé'	MMuc SArc SEND
	- 'Trinity'	WFib
	- 'Tripod'	WFib
	- 'Triton'	WFib
	- 'Troll'	WFib
	- 'Ursula' (v)	WFib
	- 'Very Merry'	WFib
	- 'Vitifolium'	see *H. hibernica* 'Vitifolia'
§	- 'White Knight' (v) ♀H5	WFib
	- 'White Mein Herz'	see *H. helix* 'Snow Cap'
	- 'White Ripple' (v)	SGsty WFib
	- 'White Wonder'	LCro LOPS SPoG
	- 'Williamsiana' (v)	WFib
	- 'Woerneri'	see *H.* × *soroksarensis* 'Woerneri'
	- 'Wonder'	LCro
	- 'Yellow Ripple'	see *H. helix* 'Golden Starlight'
	- 'Zebra' (v)	WFib
	hibernica	CBcs CKel CSBt EHeP EPfP EWTr GDam GMcL LBuc LCro LPal LRHS MRav MSwo NBwr NWea SCob SEWo SGsty SPer SWeb SWvt WFib
	- 'Angularis Aurea' ♀H5	WFib
	- 'Anna Marie'	see *H. helix* 'Anna Marie'
	- 'Arbori Compact'	LPar
	- 'Betty Allen'	WFib
§	- 'Crûg Gold'	WCru
§	- 'Dealbata' (v)	CMac SRms WFib
§	- 'Deltoidea' ♀H5	MWht WCFE WFib
	- 'Digitata Crûg Gold'	see *H. hibernica* 'Crûg Gold'
	- 'Ebony'	see *H. hibernica* (Hibernica Group) 'Ebony'
	- 'Glengariff'	WFib
§	- 'Gracilis'	WFib
§	- 'Hamilton'	WFib
§	- (Hibernica Group) 'Ebony'	WFib
§	- - 'Rona' (v)	GQue WFib
	- - 'Sulphurea' (v)	WFib
	- - 'Variegata' (v)	WFib
	- 'Lobata Major'	SRms
	- 'Palmata'	WFib
	- 'Rona'	see *H. hibernica* (Hibernica Group) 'Rona'
	- 'Sagittifolia'	CKel EPfP SCob
§	- 'Spetchley' ♀H5	CMac GKev MRav NLar NPer NWad SLee WCot WFib
I	- 'Vitifolia'	WFib
§	***iberica***	WFib
	maderensis	WFib
	maroccana 'Morocco'	WFib
	- 'Spanish Canary'	WFib
§	***nepalensis***	WFib
	- KWJ 12345	WCru
	- 'Marbled Dragon'	WFib
	- 'Roy Lancaster' **new**	EPPr
	- 'Sino Bart' **new**	EPPr
§	- 'Suzanne'	WFib
	pastuchovii	EShb WFib
	- from Troödos, Cyprus	see *H. pastuchovii* subsp. *cypria*
	- 'Ann Ala' ♀H5	EPPr MBlu WAvo WCot WFib
§	- subsp. ***cypria***	EPPr WFib
	- 'Lagocetti'	see *H. pastuchovii* 'Lagodekhi'
§	- 'Lagodekhi'	WFib
§	***rhombea***	WCot WFib
	- 'Japonica'	see *H. rhombea*
	- 'Variegata' (v)	WFib
§	× ***soroksarensis*** 'Woerneri'	NLar WFib

Hedychium ✿ (*Zingiberaceae*)

	KR **new**	SEdd
	PAB 10111 **new**	WFar
	W&O 7118	GGro
	W&O 7120	GGro
	from Ziyadum, Myanmar	WFar WPGP
	'Anne Bishop'	EAri SEND
	aurantiacum	CBcs CCCN CDTJ CTsd EAri ELan ETod LAma LEdu MCot WFar XLum
	aureum	LEdu WPGP
	'Ayo'	EAri
	brevicaule B&SWJ 7171	WCru
	'C.P. Raffill'	see *H.* × *moorei* 'Raffillii'
	chrysoleucum	CCCN
*	'Clarkei'	CCCN
	coccineum	CDTJ CTsd EAri LPal MHid
	- B&SWJ 5238	WCru
	- from Mizoram, India	WPGP
	- var. ***angustifolium***	WPGP
	- 'Hungphung Stripe'	LEdu WPGP
	- 'Khangkhui Tall Boy'	LEdu MHid WPGP
	- 'Khonoma Silver'	LEdu WPGP
	- 'Shillong Ghost'	LEdu WPGP
	coronarium ♀H1c	CAbb CAvo CCCN CDTJ CTsd CWal ELan ETod LAma MHid XLum
	- B&SWJ 3745	WCru
	- 'Gold Spot'	CCCN CDTJ CTsd EAri LAma
	- var. ***urophyllum***	see *H. flavum* Roxb.
	'Coronata Cream' **new**	EAri
	deceptum	EAri LRHS SChr XSte
	densiflorum	CAbb CCCN CDTJ CTsd EAri EBee ECha LAma LCro LEdu LOPS MHid SRms WCot WCru WFar WPGP XLum
	- EN 562	CExl
	- LS&H 17393	CExl
	- from Gongshan, China **new**	SEdd
	- 'Assam Orange'	CAvo CBcs CBct CCCN CExl CTsd EAri EWld IDee LEdu MHid SEND SMHy SPlb WCru WPGP
	- 'Sorung'	CDTJ CExl LEdu SChr WPGP
	- 'Stephen'	CAvo CCCN CDTJ CExl EBee LEdu LRHS MNrw SEdd SPlb WFar WPGP XSte
	'Devon Cream'	CCCN CDTJ CExl CTsd LRHS SChr WFar XSte
	'Doctor Moy' (v)	CDTJ EAri MHid NGKo WCot XSte
	'Elizabeth'	EAri
	ellipticum	CAbb CCCN CDTJ CTsd ETod LAma SDir XLum
	- B&SWJ 8354	WCru
	- PAB 7867	LEdu WPGP
	'Filigree'	CExl EAri
§	***flavescens***	CCCN CDTJ CTsd EAri EBee ELan LAma LCro LOPS
	flavum misapplied	see *H. flavescens*
§	***flavum*** Roxb.	CAbb CBcs EAri XLum

- HWJ 604	WCru
forrestii misapplied	see *H.* 'Helen Dillon'
forrestii Diels	CSpe CTsd IDee SPlb
- KWJ 12314	WCru
gardnerianum ♀^{H2}	CAbb CDTJ CExl CTsd EBee EPPr ETod LAma LCro LEdu LOPS LPal LRHS MHid MNrw MSCN NGKo SArc SChr SDeJ SDir SPlb WCru WFar XLum XSte
- B&SWJ 12533	WCru
- NJM 13.079	WPGP
'Giant Yellow'	CDTJ
'Gold Flame'	EBee
gomezianum	LEdu
gracile	WCru
greenii	CBcs CBct CCCN CDTJ CSpe CTsd EAri EBee EWld LAma LEdu LPal MNrw MPie SDir SPlb WBor WCru WFar XLum
- 'Mhui Fang'	WPGP
griffithianum	CCCN CDTJ LAma XLum
- white-flowered	CCCN
§ 'Helen Dillon'	CCCN CDTJ CExl ESwi LEdu LRHS SEdd WCru WPGP
'Keneggy'	SVen
'Lemon Sherbet'	EAri
'Luna Moth'	EAri WPGP
luteum	CTsd
maximum	CDTJ EAri SChr SMad WPGP
- B&SWJ 8261A	WCru
- HWJ 810	WCru
§ × ***moorei*** 'Raffillii'	WCru
'Pink Princess'	CDTJ
'Pink V'	LRHS
'Pradhan'	EAri
'Samsheri'	CCCN EAri
spicatum	CAbb CAvo CCCN CDTJ CExl CTsd GPoy LEdu MNrw MRav SMHy WFar WPGP
- B&SWJ 7231	WCru
- CC 1705	CExl
- P. Bon. 57188	CExl WPGP
- PAB 13.0718	LEdu
- from Ciaojiang	SBrt
- 'Himalayan Lipstick'	EBee LAma SDir
- 'Huani'	LEdu
- 'Liberty'	WCru
- 'Shirui Steps'	LEdu
- 'Singalila'	LEdu SEdd WCru WPGP
- 'Troglodyte'	LEdu WFar WPGP
'St Martin's'	CCCN
stenopetalum	EAri MHid WPGP
- B&SWJ 7155	WCru
'Tahitian Flame' (v)	EAri
(Tai Series) 'Tai Pink Princess'	EAri
- 'Tai Sunlight' **new**	EAri
'Tara' ♀^{H4}	CAvo CBct CCht CDTJ CExl EAri EPfP LEdu LRHS MGil MNrw SArc SMHy SMad SPad SPlb WCru WPGP XSte
'Tara' red **new**	EAri SChr
tengchongense 'Trum Trom'	WCru
- 'YTý'	WCru
thyrsiforme	CDTJ CTsd LAma WCru XLum
'Vanilla Ice' (v)	EAri
'Verity' (v) **new**	EAri
villosum	EAri
- var. ***tenuiflorum***	CDTJ EAri MHid WPGP
- - KWJ 12305	WCru
wardii	CDTJ CExl CTsd EAri ESwi LRHS MHid SEdd WCot WCru WPGP
× ***wilkeanum***	CBct
yunnanense	EAri LEdu SBrt SChr SEdd SPlb WPGP
- B&SWJ 9717	WCru
- BWJ 7900	ESwi WCru
- L 633	CExl
- PAB 7361 **new**	WFar
- 'Iago'	WCru

Hedysarum (*Fabaceae*)

coronarium	CSpe ELan LShi SMHy SPoG WKif
hedysaroides	GArf
multijugum	MBlu WSHC

Heimia (*Lythraceae*)

salicifolia	EBee ECre MGil SBrt WPGP

Helenium (*Asteraceae*)

'Adios'	WFar
'Amber'	ECtt MAvo MSpe WFar
'Amber Dwarf'	SAko
autumnale	CSBt CTri CWal EPfP LDai LSRN MNHC NChi SWvt WFar XLum
- 'All Gold'	SWvt
- 'Bandera'	CBod ECtt MSCN NCth NRHS SPad
- 'Fuego'^{PBR} (Mariachi Series)	CBod CMac CRos CWGN ECtt EHyd LCro LOPS LRHS LSou MBel MHol MNrw MPri NCth NRHS SCob SRms SWvt WCAu WNPC
§ - Helena Series	CGBo CRos SBls SWvt WFar
§ - - 'Helena Gold'	CBod EPfP LSto MACG WPnP
- - 'Helena Rote Töne'	CBod CChe CSpe EHyd EPfP GDam LRHS LSun MACG MHol NRHS SCoo WBor
- - 'Helena Yellow'	EHyd EPfP LRHS NRHS WCav
- 'Ranchera'^{PBR} (Mariachi Series)	ECtt IPot LRHS NLar NRHS SPad
- 'Salsa'^{PBR} (Mariachi Series)	CBod CKno CMac CRos CSpe ECtt EHyd ELan LCro LOPS LRHS LSou MAvo MNrw NCth NLar NRHS SPad SRms SWvt WNPC
- 'Short and Sassy'^{PBR}	CBcs ECtt EHyd ELan LBar LRHS LSou MNrw MPri NLar NRHS SCoo SOrN SPad SPoG SRms WHil WNPC
- 'Siesta'^{PBR} (Mariachi Series)	CBcs CRos ECtt EHyd LRHS MNrw NLar NRHS SRms WHil
- 'Sombrero'^{PBR} (Mariachi Series)	CBcs CBod CMac ECtt EMor LCro LRHS NEoE NSti SPoG WNPC
'Baudirektor Linne' ♀^{H7}	ECtt ESwi SHar WCAu WPGP
'Betty'	CBod EBlo ECtt LSou MAsh MNrw MSCN MSpe WCAu
'Biedermeier'	MNrw MSpe SAko SPer WCAu
bigelovii	XLum
'Blütentisch' misapplied	see *H.* 'Riverton Beauty'
'Blütentisch' Foerster ♀^{H7}	EHyd GMaP LRHS NLar NRHS
'Bressingham Gold'	MHCG MNrw MSpe WAvo WHrl
'Bruno'	CRos EBlo EHyd LRHS MArl NRHS SHar SMrm
'Butterpat' ♀^{H7}	CDor EBlo ECtt EHyd GMaP LRHS MArl MNrw MRav MSpe NCth NRHS WCav
'Can Can'	CRos ECtt EHyd ELon EPfP IPot LRHS MHer MNrw NGdn NRHS SRms WCAu WFar WGoo WHlf
'Carmen' (UFO Series)	EBlo MSpe WHlf
'Chelsey'	ECtt ELan EPfP GQue LCro LRHS LSRN MBNS MNrw MRav MSpe NBPC NLar NSti SPoG SRms WPnP
'Chipperfield Orange'	CWCL ECtt GMaP MArl NBPC NBir NGdn WOld
'Coppelia'	EBlo GElm NBir NGdn WFar
COPPER SPRAY	see *H.* 'Kupfersprudel'

'Crimson Beauty'	EBlo
DARK BEAUTY	see *H.* 'Dunkle Pracht'
'Dauerbrenner'	ECtt IPot MAvo SHar
'Double Trouble'PBR	CWnw ECtt EHyd LBar LRHS MBNS MHol NFav NGdn NHpl NRHS SGbt SRms WCot WFar
§ 'Dunkle Pracht' ♀H7	EBee EBlo ECtt EWTr LSRN MSpe NLar WFar WOld
'El Dorado'	CBWd CRos CWCL EBee EBlo ECtt EHyd ELon IPot LBar LEdu LRHS MAvo MSpe NDov NRHS NSti SRms WCot WFar
'Fancy Fan'	MSpe
'Fata Morgana'	ECtt MAvo MHer MSpe
'Festival'	ECtt
'Feuersiegel' ♀H7	CRos EBlo ECtt EHyd LRHS NRHS SAko
'Fiesta'	ECtt MAvo WFar
'Flamenco'	MSpe WFar
'Flammendes Käthchen'	CRos EBee EBlo ECtt EHyd LRHS NRHS SAko SHar SMrm
'Flammenrad'	EBee SAko
'Flammenspiel'	EBlo ECtt MNrw
'Gartensonne' ♀H7	LPla MAvo SMrm WAvo
'Gelbe Waltraut'	MAvo
GOLD FOX	see *H.* 'Goldfuchs'
'Gold Intoxication'	see *H.* 'Goldrausch'
GOLDEN YOUTH	see *H.* 'Goldene Jugend'
§ 'Goldene Jugend'	ECtt ELon WCot
§ 'Goldfuchs'	WCot
§ 'Goldlackzwerg'	LRHS WMal
§ 'Goldrausch'	EBee ECtt EPfP GBin MMrt MNrw NGdn SAko WCAu WFar WOld
'Goldriese'	MSpe
'Helena' misapplied	see *H. autumnale* 'Helena Gold'
hoopesii	see *Hymenoxys hoopesii*
'Hot Lava'	CBod CWGN ECtt IPot MNrw SCoo SPoG
'Indianersommer'	CBWd CDor ECtt GMaP LDai MNrw NLar SMrm SPer SSut WCFE WGoo WSpi
'Julisamt'	LEdu
'Kanaria'	CBar CBod CDor CKel CRos CWnw EBee EBlo EHyd EPfP GBin GElm LRHS MAvo MBel MRav MSpe NLar NRHS NSti SMrm WHil
'Karneol' ♀H7	EBlo EHyd EPfP LRHS NRHS
'Königstiger' ♀H7	CRos EBlo ECtt EHyd GBee LRHS MHCG MNrw NRHS SAko WFar
'Kugelsonne'	GBin NLar SAko WCAu
§ 'Kupfersprudel'	SAko WCot
'Kupferzwerg'	EAJP ELan LSto SAko
'Lemon Queen'	WSpi
'Lemon Sundae' (Sundae Series) **new**	LBar
'Little Orange'	NDov WGoo
'Loysder Wieck'	EBee ECtt LRHS MBNS MBel MSpe NGdn SPeP WCAu WTor
'Luc' ♀H5	ECha ELon GBin MAvo WCot WMal
§ 'Mahagoni'	IPot
MAHOGANY	see *H.* 'Mahagoni'
'Mahogany'	see *H.* 'Goldlackzwerg'
MARDI GRAS ('Helbro')	CAby CKel EBee ECtt EHyd ELan EMor EPfP GElm LRHS LSou MAvo MBel MHol MSpe NCth NRHS SOrN SPoG SRms SWvt WCAu WNPC WTor
'Marion Nickig'	WFar
'Meranti'	MSpe NDov SWvt WCot
'Moerheim Beauty' ♀H7	Widely available
'Monique' (UFO Series)	CBod EBlo MACG MSpe
'Oldenburg'	WCot
'Pat's Promise'	SWvt
'Peach Sundae' (Sundae Series) **new**	LBar WNPC
PIPSQUEAK ('Blopip')	EBee EBlo LRHS SRms WCAu
'Poncho'	IPot LBar LRHS SRms
'Potter's Wheel'	CBod EBee ECtt LBar MSpe NCth NGdn NLar SRms
puberulum	EHyd LRHS NBir NGrd NRHS WPnP
'Pumilum Magnificum'	EHyd ELan EPfP GQue MSpe NBPC NFav SMad WFar XLum
'Ragamuffin'	ECtt SWvt WCot
'Rauchtopas'	CBWd ILea IPot LCro LEdu LPla LSou MBel MMrt MSpe NDov NLar SAko SMrm WGoo WPGP
RED AND GOLD	see *H.* 'Rotgold' Foerster
'Red Army'	ECha ECtt ELon EMor GBee LEdu MSpe NGdn SRkn SRms SWvt
'Red Jewel'	Widely available
'Ring of Fire' ♀H7	SMHy
§ 'Riverton Beauty'	ECha ECtt LSto MNrw NChi SDix WCot WHoo
'Riverton Gem'	EBlo ECtt GBee MHCG
'Rotgold' misapplied	see *H. autumnale* Helena Series
§ 'Rotgold' Foerster	SRms WPnP
'Rouge Foncé'	WFar
'Rubinzwerg' ♀H7	Widely available
'Ruby Charm'	ECtt EPfP MACG MBros MNrw WCot WFar WHlf
§ 'Ruby Thuesday'	Widely available
'Ruby Tuesday'	see *H.* 'Ruby Thuesday'
'Sahin's Early Flowerer' ♀H7	Widely available
'Septemberfuchs'	LEdu SAko WPGP
'Septembergold'	LBar
'Sonnenwunder'	EBlo
'Sophie zur Linden'	ECha ECtt MSpe
'Strawberry Sundae' (Sundae Series) **new**	LBar
'Sunshine Superman'	MSpe
'The Bishop'	CBod EBee EHyd EPfP LCro LOPS LRHS MRav NHol NRHS SCob SGbt SPer SWvt WFar WGwG
'Tie Dye'	CBod EBee ECtt EPfP LBar NBPC NGdn SPoG WFar
'Tijuana Brass'	ECtt IPot NLar
'Tip Top'	EHyd EPfP LRHS SGBe
'UFO Tom' (UFO Series)	LBar MSpe NDov
'Vicky'	ECtt MHCG SHar
'Vivace'	ELon LEdu WCot WPGP
'Wagon Wheel'	WFar
'Waldhorn'	WPGP
'Waltraut' ♀H7	Widely available
'Wesergold' ♀H7	CMac CRos EBee EBlo EHyd EWTr LRHS MRav NDov NRHS NSti SPoG WCAu
'Westerstede'	EBlo LRHS
'Wonnadonga'	IPot
'Wyndley'	CBcs CDor CRos EBlo ECtt EHyd ELan EMor EPfP EShb ETod GElm GMaP LRHS LSto MBel MHer MRav NBir NGdn NLar NRHS SGbt SPer SRms WCAu WCav WFar
'Zimbelstern'	EBlo ECha ECtt MAvo MCot MSpe NLar WCot WFar WPGP

Heliamphora (*Sarraceniaceae*)

nutans	SHmp

Helianthella (*Asteraceae*)

§ ***quinquenervis***	EBee EBlo EHyd EMor EPfP LRHS NLar NRHS WFar

Helianthemum (*Cistaceae*)

'Alice Howorth'	WIce
'Amabile Plenum' (d)	GBin LBar LShi

	'Amy Baring' ♀H5	CRos CTri ECtt EHyd LRHS NRHS SRms WHoo
	'Annabel' (d)	CRos ECtt EHyd GAbr GBin LRHS NRHS WFar
	apenninum	LPla SBut SEND SRms WAbe XSen
	'Apricot'	CTri ECtt
	'Apricot Blush'	WAbe
	'Baby Buttercup'	LShi
	'Beech Park Red'	CTri ECtt EPot WAbe WFar WHoo WIce WKif
	'Ben Afflick'	CRos ECtt EHyd LRHS MAsh NGrs NRHS NSla SRms
	'Ben Alder'	ECtt
	'Ben Dearg'	ECtt SRms
	'Ben Fhada'	Widely available
	'Ben Heckla'	CRos ECtt EHyd GAbr LRHS NRHS SRms XLum
	'Ben Hope'	CRos CTri ECtt EHeP EHyd ELan EPfP EWTr EWoo LCro LRHS NGrs NRHS SCob SRms WHoo XLum XSen
§	'Ben Ledi'	CBcs ECtt ELan GJos GMaP LRHS MAsh MAvo NHol SCob SGbt SPoG SRms SRot WAbe WFar
	'Ben More'	CAvo CBcs CKel CRos ECtt EHyd ELan EPfP GJos GMaP LRHS MAsh MBros MRav MSwo NBir NRHS SCob SCoo SPoG SRms WFar WHoo WIce
	'Ben Nevis'	CTri GAbr SRms
	'Ben Vane'	CRos ECtt EHyd LRHS NRHS SRms
	'Boughton Double Primrose' (d)	WAbe WFar
	'Bunbury'	EBou ECtt ELon EPfP GJos GQue NBir SEdd SPoG SRms WFar
I	'Butter and Eggs'	SRms
	'Captivation'	NHol
	'Cerise Queen' (d)	CTri ECha ECtt EPfP GKev LBar LCro LRHS MSwo SEND SRms WFar
	chamaecistus	see *H. nummularium*
	'Cheviot'	ECha NBir WHoo XLum
	'Chocolate Blotch'	CRos EHyd LRHS NRHS SEND SRms
	'Coachman's Salmon Coral'	ECtt
	'Cornish Cream'	ECtt NHol SRms
	cupreum	GKev
	'David'	NHol
	'David Ritchie'	WHoo
	'Diana'	ECtt EPot WIce
	double apricot-flowered (d)	CPla LRHS
	'Elfenbeinglanz'	WFar
	'Everton Ruby'	see *H.* 'Ben Ledi'
	'Fair Aubrie' **new**	ECha
	'Fairy'	EHyd ELan EPfP
§	'Fire Dragon' ♀H4	CAvo CRos ECha ECtt EHyd ELan EPfP GAbr GMaP LRHS MAsh NBir NRHS SGbt SRms WAbe XLum XSen
	'Fireball'	see *H.* 'Mrs C.W. Earle'
	'Georgeham'	CAvo EBou ECtt ELon GAbr NBir NHol SRms WHoo XLum
§	'Golden Queen'	CBod EBou ECtt EHeP EPfP LBar MAsh MSwo SRms WFar
	'Hampstead Orange'	CTri
	'Hartswood Ruby'	CRos EHyd GMaP LRHS NRHS SAko SRms WAbe WFar
	'Henfield Brilliant' ♀H4	CKel CRos EAJP ECha ECtt EHyd ELan ELon EPfP EWoo GAbr LRHS MRav NBir NBwr NHol NRHS NSla SBut SMad SPoG SRms WCav WCot WHoo WSHC XLum
	'Highdown'	SRms
	'Highdown Apricot'	CRos ECtt EHyd ELon GAbr LRHS NRHS SPoG SRms
	'Honeymoon'	ECtt
	'Jubilee' (d) ♀H4	CTri ECtt GAbr GJos MAsh MAvo MHol NBir NChi NHol SPoG SRms WCav
	'Karen's Silver'	WAbe
	'Kathleen Druce' (d)	ECtt
	'Kathleen Mary'	WIce
	'Lawrenson's Pink'	CBod CRos ECtt EHeP EHyd GJos LRHS NRHS SRms WCAu WFar XSen
	'Lemon Queen'	ECtt WCAu
	'Lucy Elizabeth'	ECtt
	lunulatum	CRos EHyd LRHS NRHS SRms WAbe
	'Marianne'	ECtt
	'Mead Sunset'	ECtt
§	'Mrs C.W. Earle' (d) ♀H4	CTri ECtt EHyd ELan EPfP GKev LRHS MBros NRHS SRms
	'Mrs Clay'	see *H.* 'Fire Dragon'
	'Mrs Croft'	SRms
	'Mrs Hays'	ECtt
	'Mrs Lake'	GAbr
	'Mrs Moules'	SRms
	mutabile	SPlb SVic WFar
§	***nummularium***	CBee ENfk GPoy GQue MHer MNHC NAts NMir SPhx SRms WAbe WIce WSFF WWild
§	– subsp. ***tomentosum***	GAbr
	oelandicum	NSla SRms WAbe
	– subsp. ***alpestre***	EBou
	– subsp. ***incanum***	WAbe
	– subsp. ***italicum***	WAbe
	– subsp. ***piloselloides***	EPot WAbe
	'Old Gold'	ECtt SRms WAbe
	'Orange Phoenix' (d)	ECtt
	'Ovum Supreme'	NHol
	pannosum	WAbe
	'Peach'	CTri
	'Pink Angel' (d)	SRms WAbe WFar
	'Praecox'	CTri SRms
	'Prima Donna'	EHyd ELan EPfP
	'Prostrate Orange'	SRms
	'Raspberry Ripple'	CRos EBou EHyd ELan EPfP EPot LRHS NBwr NRHS SPoG SRms
	'Razzle Dazzle' (v)	SRms
	'Red Dragon'	EPot WAbe
	'Red Orient'	see *H.* 'Supreme'
	'Regenbogen' (d)	ECtt SEND
§	'Rhodanthe Carneum' ♀H4	CKel CRos EBou ECha ECtt EHyd ELan EPfP EWTr EWoo GDam GJos GKev GMaP LRHS LSto MRav MSwo NBir NRHS SCob SEND SPoG SRms WAbe WCAu WCav WKif WTor
§	'Rosakönigin'	EBou ECtt NHol SEND WAbe
	'Rose of Leeswood' (d)	ECtt GJos MHol SPoG SRms WHoo WKif XLum
	ROSE QUEEN	see *H.* 'Rosakönigin'
	'Roxburgh Gold'	SRms
	'Saint John's College Yellow'	EHyd LRHS NRHS SRms
	'Salmon Queen'	CRos ECtt EHyd LRHS NRHS SEND SRms
	'Shot Silk'	ECtt EWes SRms
	'Snow Queen'	see *H.* 'The Bride'
	'Sterntaler'	GAbr SRms WFar
	'Strawberry Fields'	ECtt NSla
	'Sudbury Gem'	CRos CTri ECha ECtt EHyd LRHS NRHS SRms
	'Sulphur Moon'	CRos EHyd LRHS NRHS SRms
	'Summertime'	NGrs

	'Sunbeam'	ECtt SRms
§	'Supreme'	ECtt ELan EPfP EWes GArf SRms XSen
§	'The Bride' ♀H4	Widely available
	'Tigrinum Plenum' (d)	EWes
	'Tomato Red'	ECtt
	tomentosum	see *H. nummularium* subsp. *tomentosum*
	umbellatum	see *Halimium umbellatum*
	'Voltaire'	ECtt GAbr
	'Welsh Flame'	ECtt NHol WAbe
	'Wisley Orange'	NGrs
	'Wisley Pink'	see *H.* 'Rhodanthe Carneum'
	'Wisley Primrose' ♀H4	Widely available
	'Wisley Rose'	EHyd NGrs NRHS
	'Wisley White'	CKel CTri ECha ECtt ELan SHar
	'Wisley Yellow'	ECtt
	'Yellow Queen'	see *H.* 'Golden Queen'

Helianthus (Asteraceae)

	angustifolius	SDix
	'Anne'	ELon LPla NDov
	annuus	LRHS SVic
	- 'Claret' ♀H4	LCro LOPS
	- 'Garden Statement'	LCro LOPS
	- 'Lemon Queen'	LBar WCav
	- 'Moonbright'	SVic
	- 'Ms Mars' **new**	LCro
	- 'Ring of Fire'	SVic
	- 'Sonja'	SVic
	- SUNBELIEVABLE BROWN EYED GIRL ('Sunbeliv01') (Sunbelievable Series)	CWGN MBros WHil
	- 'Sunbright' ♀H4	SVic
	- 'Sunrich Orange' (Sunrich Series)	SVic
	- 'Sunsation Yellow' (Sunsation Series) ♀H4 **new**	LCro
	- 'Teddy Bear' (d) ♀H4	LCro
	- 'Valentine' ♀H4 **new**	LCro
	atrorubens	MHol MRav NBro
	'Bitter Chocolate'	LEdu MSpe SMDa WPGP
	'Capenoch Star' ♀H5	ECtt GMaP LEdu MArl MAvo MNrw MRav MSpe NBro NLar SDix SWvt WCAu
	'Capenoch Supreme'	ECtt
	'Carine'	ECha ELon GBin LEdu MNrw NLar WCot WFar
	'Cotswold Queen'	WCot
	debilis subsp. ***cucumerifolius***	SVic
	- 'Vanilla Ice'	LCro
*	***decapetalus*** 'Kastle Kobena'	CDor
	- MORNING SUN	see *H.* 'Morgensonne'
	'Dorian Roxburgh'	ECha ECtt LPla MAvo MHol WCot WHoo
	'Double Whammy' (d)	ECtt LBar WTyc
	'Flying Saucers'	CBod CKno ECtt LBar
	giganteus	ECha SHar
	- 'Sheila's Sunshine'	CElw CTtf EBee ECtt EHyd EPPr EWes ILea LEdu LPla LRHS MNrw NDov NRHS SAko SHar SMHy SPhx WFar WHrl WOld
	'Gullick's Variety' ♀H5	ECtt NBro NChi NLar SPhx SWvt WFar WOld XLum
	'Happy Days' ♀H5	CTtf ECtt EPfP EWes GBin LSou LSun MAvo MHol MSpe NCth NGBl NSti SBea SMad SPeP SRms WCot WFar WHoo WOld
	× ***kellermanii***	EBee MAvo SPhx
§	× ***laetiflorus***	GPSL MACG NLar SEND
	- 'Daniel Dewar'	MMuc
	- var. ***rigidus***	see *H. pauciflorus*
§	'Lemon Queen' ♀H4	Widely available
	'Limelight'	see *H.* 'Lemon Queen'
	'Loddon Gold' ♀H5	CBod ECtt EHyd ELan EPfP EShb LRHS MArl MBel MHer MRav MSpe NBir NFav NRHS SMrm SWvt WBor WCot WFar
§	***maximiliani***	CBod ELan ELon EMor LDai LSun MMuc SBls SMad SPhx SPtp
	microcephalus	EBee ELon MMuc NDov
	- 'JS Straffe Prairie Gast'	MNrw WFar
	'Miss Mellish' ♀H5	EBee ECtt LEdu LPla SMad WBor WBrk WCot WFar WHoo
	mollis	CBod MACG SBrt SPhx WFar
	'Monarch' ♀H5	EBee EWhm MHol MRav NLar SMad SMrm WCot WFar WOld
§	'Morgensonne'	GQue WCot
	'O Sole Mio'	WCot WFar
	occidentalis	SPhx
	orgyalis	see *H. salicifolius*
§	***pauciflorus***	EBee
	quinquenervis	see *Helianthella quinquenervis*
	'Razzmatazz'	SAko
	rigidus misapplied	see *H.* × *laetiflorus*
	rigidus (Cass.) Desf.	see *H. pauciflorus*
§	***salicifolius***	Widely available
	- 'Low Down'PBR	SCob SMad SWvt
	- 'Table Mountain'PBR	LRHS NLar SMad SWvt
	- very fine-leaved	WCot
	scaberrimus	see *H.* × *laetiflorus*
	'Soleil d'Or'	ECtt SRms WFar WWFP
	strumosus	MHol WCot
	'Suncatcher Pure Gold' **new**	LBar
	'Triomphe de Gand'	NDov WFar
	tuberosus	EBee GPoy
	- 'Bleu Patate'	LEdu
	- 'Drago'	LEdu
	- 'Dwarf'	LEdu
	- 'Fuseau'	LCro LOPS SVic
	- 'Garnet'	LEdu
	- 'Sakhalinski'	LEdu
	- 'Sugarball'	LEdu

Helichrysum (Asteraceae)

	adenocarpum	SPlb
	alveolatum	see *H. splendidum*
	ambiguum	CFis
	amorginum 'Amber Cluster'PBR	SCoo
	- 'Pink Bud'	MMuc
	- RUBY CLUSTER ('Blorub'PBR)	LBar SCob SRms
	angustifolium	see *H. italicum* subsp. *italicum*
	- from Crete	see *H. microphyllum* (Willd.) Cambess.
§	***arwae***	EDAr WAbe
	basalticum	EDAr
	bellidioides	see *Anaphaloides bellidioides*
	bracteatum	see *Xerochrysum bracteatum*
	coralloides	see *Ozothamnus coralloides*
	'County Park Silver'	see *Ozothamnus* 'County Park Silver'
	'Dargan Hill Monarch'	see *Xerochrysum bracteatum* 'Dargan Hill Monarch'
	'Elmstead'	see *H. stoechas* 'White Barn'
	frigidum	EPot WAbe
	heldreichii	WMal
	hookeri	see *Ozothamnus hookeri*
§	***hypoleucum***	SDix
	'Icicles'	ELan GBin LRHS SEdd
	italicum	CBod CCBP CKel CSBt EBou ECha EGrI EHeP ENfk GBin GMaP GPoy

		GQue LCro LShi MHer MHoo MNHC SArc SEND SPoG SRms SVen SVic WHer XLum XSen
	- 'Dartington'	ENfk GBin SRms
§	- subsp. ***italicum***	CSBt SEdi
	- 'Korma'PBR	CBod CKel CPla CRos EHyd ELan EPfP EWhm GBin LRHS MAsh MHol NRHS SRms
	- subsp. ***microphyllum***	see *H. microphyllum* (Willd.) Cambess.
	- 'Nanum'	see *Plecostachys serpyllifolia*
§	- subsp. ***serotinum***	CBcs EPfP GPoy LCro MRav SPer SRms SWvt
	lanatum	see *H. thianschanicum*
	ledifolium	see *Ozothamnus ledifolius*
	marginatum misapplied	see *H. milfordiae*
	microphyllum misapplied	see *Plecostachys serpyllifolia*
	microphyllum ambig.	SRms
§	***microphyllum*** (Willd.) Cambess.	CCBP ENfk MHoo MNHC SEND
§	***milfordiae*** ♀H4	EDAr GArf ITim SPlb SRms WAbe
	orientale	EPot GKev XSen
	pagophilum	GKev WAbe
	petiolare ♀H3	ECtt MCot SPer SPoG
	- 'Aureum'	see *H. petiolare* 'Limelight'
	- 'Goring Silver' ♀H3	SPoG
§	- 'Limelight' ♀H3	ECtt SPer SPoG
	- 'Variegatum' (v) ♀H3	ECtt MCot SPoG
	populifolium misapplied	see *H. hypoleucum*
	rosmarinifolium	see *Ozothamnus rosmarinifolius*
§	'Schwefellicht'	EBee ECha EPfP MRav SPer WSHC
	selago	see *Ozothamnus selago*
	serotinum	see *H. italicum* subsp. *serotinum*
	serpyllifolium	see *Plecostachys serpyllifolia*
	sessilioides	EPot WAbe
§	***splendidum*** ♀H4	EPPr NBro XSen
	stoechas	XSen
	- 'Silverball'	LRHS
§	- 'White Barn'	ECha EPPr LShi MAvo WCot WMal WSHC XLum
	SULPHUR LIGHT	see *H.* 'Schwefellicht'
§	***thianschanicum***	SRms XLum
	- GOLDEN BABY	see *H. thianschanicum* 'Goldkind'
§	- 'Goldkind'	NBir XLum
	- 'White Wonder'	EHyd EPfP LRHS NRHS
	trilineatum misapplied	see *H. splendidum*
	tumidum	see *Ozothamnus selago* var. *tumidus*
	withergense	WAbe
	woodii	see *H. arwae*

Helicodiceros (*Araceae*)

§	***muscivorus***	NGKo WCot

Heliconia ✿ (*Heliconiaceae*)

	psittacorum	CCCN
	rostrata	CCCN
	schiedeana	CHII

Helictotrichon (*Poaceae*)

	cantabricum new	XSen
	planiculme	EPPr
	pratense	CHab
§	***sempervirens*** ♀H5	Widely available
I	- 'Pendulum'	CEme XSen
	- 'Saphirsprudel'	EBee EHyd EPfP NSti WCot WPGP

Heliophila (*Brassicaceae*)

	coronopifolia	CSpe

Heliopsis (*Asteraceae*)

	helianthoides	CPla CRos LRHS WCav WFar
	- 'Limelight'	see *Helianthus* 'Lemon Queen'
	- LORAINE SUNSHINE ('Helhan'PBR) (v)	CBod CWGN GMcL LRHS MHol NWsh SIvy SPoG WCot WFar
	- 'Red Shades' new	CBod
	- var. ***scabra***	NHol
	- - 'Asahi'	CBod EBee ECtt MHol
	- - BALLERINA	see *H. helianthoides* var. *scabra* 'Spitzentänzerin'
	- - 'Benzinggold' ♀H6	MRav SMrm
	- - 'Bleeding Hearts'	CGBo CSpe EAJP EDAr EWTr MNrw SBls
	- - 'Bressingham Doubloon' (d)	LRHS
	- - 'Burning Hearts'	CWGN EDAr GElm LBar LRHS MCot NCth NLar SBea SMad SRms SVic WHil
	- - GOLDEN PLUME	see *H. helianthoides* var. *scabra* 'Goldgefieder'
§	- - 'Goldgefieder' ♀H6	MSpe WFar
	- - 'Mars'	WFar
	- - 'Patula'	EBee
	- - 'Prairie Sunset'PBR	EBee ECtt MHol
§	- - 'Sommersonne'	CSBt ECtt EHyd ELan EMor EPfP GMcL LRHS NGBl NPer SPer SRms
§	- - 'Spitzentänzerin' ♀H6	EBee ECtt MSpe
	- - 'Summer Nights'	EBee ELan EPfP EWTr GElm LCro LDai LOPS MNrw NSti SBut SDix SPhx WFar WSpi
	- - SUMMER SUN	see *H. helianthoides* var. *scabra* 'Sommersonne'
	- - 'Sunburst' (v)	CRos EHyd LRHS NRHS
	- - 'Venus'	CBod EBee ECtt EHyd LBar LRHS MAsh SRms
	- 'Summer Pink' (v)	CWGN SIvy SPoG WCot WFar
	- 'Sunstruck'	LBar
	- 'Tuscan Sun'PBR	EBee SMad

Heliotropium ✿ (*Boraginaceae*)

§	***amplexicaule***	SDys SMHy
	anchusifolium	see *H. amplexicaule*
§	***arborescens***	ENfk EPfP EShb MCot
	- 'Chatsworth' ♀H1c	CAby CCCN ECre ECtt
	- 'Dame Alice de Hales'	ECtt
	- 'Florence Nightingale'	WMal
	- 'Gatton Park'	ECtt WMal
	- 'Lord Roberts'	ECtt WMal
	- 'Marine'	SPhx
	- MARINO BLUE ('Kleha07520'PBR)	LSou MBros
	- 'Mary Fox'	ECtt
	- 'Mrs J.W. Lowther'	ECtt
	- 'Nautilus Power Blue' (Nautilus Power Series) new	WHlf
	- 'Princess Marina' ♀H1c	LCro LOPS NLar
	- 'Reva'	ECtt
	- SCENTROPIA BLUE ('Heliovi')	MPri
	- 'White Lady'	CCCN CSpe ECtt SAng
	- 'White Queen'	ECtt WMal
	- 'Woodcote'	ECtt
	'Butterfly Kisses'	CRos SPoG
	peruvianum	see *H. arborescens*

Helipterum see *Syncarpha*

Helleborus ✿ (*Ranunculaceae*)

	abruzzicus WM 0227	MPhe
	abschasicus	see *H. orientalis* Lam. subsp. *abchasicus*
	ANGEL GLOW ('Blt02'PBR)	CRos LBar LRHS MAsh NRHS SGBe
§	***argutifolius*** ♀H5	Widely available

- HGC SNOW FEVER ('Coseh 900'PBR)	SCoo
- mottled-leaved	see *H. argutifolius* 'Pacific Frost'
§ - 'Pacific Frost' (v)	CDor
- 'Silver Lace'	ELan EPfP GKev LDai LRHS LSRN NBir SGBe SPoG
- variegated (v)	GKev
atrorubens misapplied	see *H. orientalis* Lam. subsp. *abchasicus* Early Purple Group
atrorubens Waldst. & Kit. WM 9028 from Slovenia	MPhe
- WM 9805 from Croatia	MPhe
- spotted	MPhe
× ***ballardiae*** 'Candy Love'PBR	CRos EHyd EPfP LCro LEdu LOPS LRHS MAvo MCot NRHS SCob
- HGC CAMELOT ('Coseh 940'PBR)	CRos ECtt EHyd EPfP LRHS MAsh NLar NRHS
- HGC CHAMPION ('Coseh 730'PBR)	LRHS MAsh
- HGC MAESTRO ('Coseh 890'PBR)	CRos EHyd EPfP LRHS NRHS
- HGC MERLIN ('Coseh 810'PBR)	CRos LRHS MAsh NLar SCoo SPoG
- HGC SNOW DANCE ('Coseh 800'PBR)	CRos EHyd EPfP LRHS NRHS SPoG
× ***belcheri*** 'Pink Ice'	MAsh
§ ***bocconei***	EBee
- WM 1332 from Sicily	MPhe
- WM 1334 from Calabria, Italy	MPhe
- WM 9905 from Sicily	MPhe
- subsp. ***bocconei***	see *H. bocconei*
colchicus	see *H. orientalis* Lam. subsp. *abchasicus*
corsicus	see *H. argutifolius*
croaticus WM 9810	GKev MPhe
'Crystal Love'	LRHS
dumetorum	GKev
- WM 1306 from Hungary	MPhe
- WM 1309 from Slovenia	MPhe
- WM 9209	MPhe
§ × ***ericsmithii***	LRHS LSRN MAsh WSpi
- 'Bob's Best'	SRms SWvt
- HGC JOKER ('Coseh 740'PBR)	LRHS SPoG
- HGC MARLON CREAM ('Coseh 980'PBR)	LRHS NRHS
- HGC MONTE CRISTO ('Coseh 860'PBR)	CRos EHyd EPfP LRHS NRHS SCoo
- HGC SHOOTING STAR ('Coseh 790'PBR)	CRos EHyd EPfP LRHS NRHS SCoo
- 'HGC Silvermoon'PBR	LRHS NLar
§ - 'Ivory Prince'PBR	CRos EHyd EPfP LRHS MAsh MCot NGrs NRHS SPoG
- 'Pink Beauty'PBR	CEnd EPfP LBar NLar SEdd SPoG WCot
- 'Pirouette'PBR	ECre EPfP LCro LOPS LRHS MAsh NRHS
- RUBY GLOW ('Blt01')	EPfP
- 'Snow Love'PBR	CRos EHyd EPfP EWoo LRHS NLar NRHS
- 'Winter Moonbeam'PBR	CEnd CMil ECre ECtt EPfP LBar LBuc LRHS LSRN LSou NRHS SGBe SPoG SRms WCot
- 'Winter Sunshine'PBR	EGrI EPfP LBar LBuc LRHS NRHS SGBe SPoG SRms
foetidus ♀H7	Widely available
- 'Gold Bullion'	SPoG
- 'Harvington Pewter'	EHyd LRHS NRHS
- 'Ruth'	EWoo MAsh
- Wester Flisk Group	CBod EPfP GKev LEdu LRHS MNHC NHol NPer SPoG SPtp WAvo WSpi
Gold Collection	see *Helleborus* with names starting HGC
'Harvington Rebekah'PBR	EHyd NRHS
HELLO HELLEBORUS DACAYA ('Hiljwlsdaca') **new**	CBod LBar
HGC CINNAMON SNOW ('Coseh 700'PBR)	ECre EShb LRHS MAsh NGrs NLar NRHS SCoo
HGC ICE 'N' ROSES RED ('Coseh 4100'PBR)	LRHS MAsh
HGC ICE 'N' ROSES ROSE ('Coseh 4200'PBR)	LRHS MAsh
HGC ICE 'N' ROSES WHITE ('Coseh 4500'PBR)	LRHS
HGC MADAME LEMONNIER ('Lem 100'PBR)	EHyd ELan EPfP LRHS MAsh NRHS
HGC PARADENIA ('Coseh 960'PBR)	CRos LRHS
HGC PINK FROST ('Coseh 710'PBR)	CRos ECtt EHyd LRHS MAsh MPri NLar NRHS SCoo SEdd SPoG
§ × ***hybridus***	CBod CBro CKel CMac ECha EHyd ELan GMaP LCro LOPS LRHS MCot MGos NBid NRHS SCob SMrm SPer SRms WAvo WBrk WCAu WCot WJam WPnP
- anemone-centred	CBod EGrI LEdu MNrw WFar
- - yellow	EWTr LRHS
- 'Angellier'	EBee
- 'Apple Blossom'	WFar
- 'Apricot Blush' (Winter Jewels Series)	CWGN
- apricot-flowered	WFar
- 'Ashwood Blushing Bride'	MAsh
- 'Ashwood Elegance Pearl'	MAsh
- (Ashwood Evolution Group) 'Ashwood Yellow Hammer'	MAsh
- - 'Lunar Neon'	MAsh
- 'Ashwood Fascination'	MAsh
- Ashwood Garden hybrids	ELan MAsh MRav SRms
- - anemone-centred	MAsh
- - double-flowered (d)	MAsh
- - - green-spotted (d)	EGrI
- Ballard's Group	CKel WFar
- Barnhaven hybrids, anemone-centred	XBar
- - apricot	XBar
- - dark purple	XBar
- - double (d)	XBar
- - green	XBar
- - picotee	XBar
- - pink	XBar
- - red and green	XBar
- - slate	XBar
- - spotted	XBar
- - yellow	XBar
- BLACK BEAUTY ('Blck1'PBR)	CKel WSpi
- black-flowered	GMaP WFar
- 'Blue Lady' (Lady Series)	CBcs GDam GKev LRHS MBNS NCou NGdn SPer
- 'Blue Metallic Lady' (Lady Series)	EHyd EPfP GKev LRHS MBNS MHol NRHS SPer WSpi
- Bradfield hybrids	MCot
- 'Burgundy'	EGrI
- 'Cherry Blossom' (Winter Jewels Series)	CWGN
- 'Cherry Frost'	MAsh
- 'Chocolate Truffle'	CBor
- 'Cinderella'PBR (d)	LRHS SCoo SPoG
- 'Circe'	EBee
- 'Clare's Purple'	MACG MNHC

- cream-flowered WFar
- 'Dark as Night' CBor WTyc
- dark-flowered WFar
- - picotee WFar
- - purple-flowered WFar
- - red-flowered WFar
- deep red-flowered MHol WFar
- double-flowered (d) MNrw WFar
- - black-flowered (d) LEdu WFar
- - dark purple-flowered (d) EGrI WFar
- - green-flowered (d) CBod EGrI WFar
- - picotee (d) WFar
- - pink-flowered (d) EMor WCAu WFar
- - purple-flowered (d) CBod EBou EPfP WFar
- - red-flowered (d) CBod WFar
- - spotted (Lady Series) (d) EGrI
- - white-flowered (d) LRHS WCAu WFar
- - - picotee (d) CBod EPfP GAbr LRHS NRHS
- - yellow-flowered (d) CWCL WFar
- - - cream-speckled (d) CBod EHyd LRHS NRHS SEdd
- 'Double Black' (d) CWCL EGrI EPfP EWTr LBar
- 'Double Ellen Green' (d) LBar LSto
- 'Double Ellen Picotee' (d) CWGN EGrI LCro LOPS NCth
- 'Double Ellen Pink' (d) EGrI LCro LSto NCth
- 'Double Ellen Pink Spotted' (d) EGrI LCro LOPS LSto
- 'Double Ellen Purple' (d) LBar LCro LOPS LSto
- 'Double Ellen Red' (d) EGrI LBar LCro LOPS LSto
- 'Double Ellen Red Splash' (d) EGrI
- 'Double Ellen White' (d) CWGN EGrI EPfP LBar LCro LSto NCth SCob
- 'Double Ellen White Spotted' (d) EGrI LCro LSto SCob WCAu
- 'Double Ellen Yellow' (d) EGrI LBar
- Farmyard anemone-centred WFar
- - apricot WFar
- - black WFar
- - cream WFar
- - - spotted WFar
- - dark pink WFar
- - double apricot (d) WFar
- - - black (d) WFar
- - - cream (d) WFar
- - - - spotted (d) WFar
- - - pink (d) WFar
- - - - spotted (d) LRHS WFar
- - - primrose (d) WFar
- - - - spotted (d) WFar
- - - red (d) WFar
- - - slate-grey (d) EGrI LEdu WFar
- - - waterlily (d) EGrI
- - - white (d) WFar
- - - - spotted (d) WFar
- - green WFar
- - - spotted WFar
- - picotee WFar
- - pink WFar
- - - spotted WFar
- - plum WFar
- - primrose WFar
- - - dark-eyed WFar
- - - spotted WFar
- - red WFar
- - slate spotted WFar
- - slate-grey WFar
- - white WFar
- - - dark-eyed WFar
- - - splash WFar
- - - spotted WFar
- 'Farmyard Appleblossom' WFar
- 'Farmyard Woodland' WFar
- 'Gold Red Star' GAbr LBar MACG SPeP WSpi
- 'Golden Lotus' (d) CWGN WHlf
- 'Green Ripple' WFar
- green-flowered WFar
- Harvington apricot CRos EHyd LCro LOPS NBir NLar NRHS
- - double apricot (d) CRos EHyd LCro LRHS NRHS
- - - blush (d) CRos EHyd LRHS NRHS
- - - chocolate (d) CRos EHyd LCro LOPS LRHS NRHS
- - - cream speckled (d) CRos EHyd LRHS NRHS SEdd SPoG
- - - dark purple (d) EHyd NRHS
- - - lilac speckled (d) LCro LRHS
- - - lime-green (d) EHyd LCro LRHS NRHS
- - - pink (d) CRos EHyd LCro LOPS LRHS NRHS SPoG
- - - - speckled (d) CRos EHyd LCro LOPS LRHS NRHS
- - - purple (d) EHyd LRHS NBir NLar NRHS SPoG
- - - - cascade (d) CRos EHyd EPfP LRHS NRHS
- - - red (d) CRos EHyd LCro LOPS LRHS NBir NLar NRHS
- - - - speckled (d) SPoG
- - - white (d) CRos EHyd LCro LOPS LRHS NBir NLar NRHS SPoG
- - - - speckled (d) EHyd LCro LRHS
- - - yellow (d) CRos EHyd LCro LRHS NBir NLar NRHS
- - - - speckled (d) CRos EHyd LRHS NRHS
- - dusky CRos EHyd LCro LRHS NRHS
- - lime EHyd LCro LOPS NRHS
- - picotee CRos EHyd LCro LRHS NBir NLar NRHS SPoG
- - pink CRos EHyd LRHS NLar NRHS
- - - speckled LCro LOPS NLar SPoG
- - red CRos EHyd LCro LOPS LRHS NLar NRHS SPoG
- - - speckled CRos EHyd LRHS NRHS
- - white CRos EHyd LCro LOPS LRHS NLar NRHS SPoG
- - - speckled LCro LOPS
- - yellow CRos EHyd LRHS NLar NRHS SPoG
- - - speckled CRos EHyd EPfP LCro LOPS LRHS NLar NRHS SPoG
- - - with maroon eye LCro
- 'Harvington Black' EHyd EPfP LCro LRHS NRHS
- 'Harvington Blush Picotee' SRms
- 'Harvington Petticoat' LRHS NRHS
- 'Harvington Shades of the Night' CRos EHyd EPfP LCro LOPS LRHS NLar NRHS SPoG
- 'Harvington Smokey Blues' CRos LCro LRHS
- 'Harvington Special' LRHS
- Hillier hybrids anemone-centred, pink EGrI
- - burgundy LEdu
- - slate LRHS
- - yellow, magenta eye EHyd LRHS NRHS
- 'Lucy Black' LRHS
- maroon-flowered WFar
- mauve freckled, double (d) WFar
- 'Mrs Betty Ranicar' (d) ILea SRms
- nearly black-flowered WFar
- 'Onyx Odyssey' CWGN
- pale pink-flowered WFar
- 'Pamina' SMHy

§ - Party Dress Group (d) LSRN NLar WFar
- Picotee Group NLar WFar WHoo
- pink freckled, double (d) WFar
- 'Pink Lady' (Lady Series) CBcs CBod CSBt EGrI EHyd EPfP GMcL LRHS NCou NRHS SPer
- 'Pink Lady Spotted' (Lady Series) EGrI SCob
- pink-flowered SDeJ WHoo
- pink-red-flowered WFar
- plum-flowered MMuc SEND

- 'Pluto'	WFar
- 'Pretty Ellen Pink'	GKev LCro LOPS
- 'Pretty Ellen Purple'	EGrI
- 'Pretty Ellen Red'	LCro LOPS SCob
- 'Pretty Ellen White'	GKev LCro LOPS
- 'Primrose Picotee'	WFar
- primrose-flowered	EWTr
- purple-flowered	WFar
- 'Queen of the Night' (Queen Series)	EGrI WSpi
- 'Red Lady' (Lady Series)	CBcs EGrI EHyd EPfP LRHS LSRN MBNS NHol NRHS SPer
- red-flowered	LEdu WFar WHoo
- 'Scheherazade' **new**	CBor
- 'Single Burgundy' **new**	LBar
- slate-grey	CBod EGrI
- slaty blue-flowered	LEdu SEND
- 'Smokey Blue'	EHyd ELan LRHS NRHS
- smokey purple-flowered	LSRN SGbt
- (Spring Promise Series) SP ALICE ('Hlr 270') (d)	SCoo
- - SP ANJA OUDOLF ('Hlr 200')	CRos LRHS
- - SP CONNY ('Hlr 160'PBR)	CRos EHyd EPfP LRHS MBNS MHtn NRHS SCoo
- - SP ELLY ('Hlr 190'PBR) (d)	SCoo
- - SP FRILLY ISABELLE (d)	SCoo
- - SP FRILLY KITTY (d)	SCoo
- - SP JOHN HOPKINS ('Hlr 220')	CRos EHyd LRHS NRHS SCoo
- - SP LILY ('Hlr 210') (d)	EPfP LRHS MBNS
- - SP MARY LOU ('Hlr 150'PBR)	EHyd LRHS SCoo
- - SP RACHEL	EHyd EPfP SCoo
- - SP REBECCA	LRHS
- - SP SALLY ('Hlr 250')	EPfP LRHS SCoo
- - SP SOPHIE ('Hlr 260')	NLar SCoo
- - SP SUE	SCoo
§ - spotted	WCot WFar WHoo
- - cream	NBir WFar
- - double, pink (d)	EGrI WFar
- - - white (d)	CBod WFar
- - - yellow (d)	CBod EGrI WCAu WCot WFar
- - green	WFar
- - ivory	WFar
- - light purple	WFar
- - pink	CBod EHyd LEdu LRHS MBNS NBir NRHS SCob SEND WFar WHoo
- - primrose	ELan SGbt WFar
- - white	CBod MMuc NBir SCob SEND WBor WCAu WFar
- - yellow	EWTr SCob WCAu WFar
- 'Tutu'PBR	EPfP LBar NRHS SGBe SPeP SPoG SRms
- 'Ushba'	CSpe
- Washfield double-flowered (d)	EGrI LEdu SCob SPer SRkn WBor WHil
- 'White Lady' (Lady Series)	CBcs MBNS NCou SPer
- 'White Lady Spotted' (Lady Series)	CBar CBod EGrI EHyd EPfP GKev LRHS NCth NHol NRHS SPer
- white-flowered	EPfP GMaP WFar WHoo
- white-veined	WFar
- Wilgenbroek hybrids black	EWoo
- - double white (d)	EWoo
- - red	EWoo
- - slaty blue	EWoo
- - white	EWoo
- 'Winter Joy Bouquet'	EBee
- 'Yellow Lady' (Lady Series)	CBar CBcs CKel EGrI EHyd GMcL LRHS MBNS NCth NRHS SPer
- yellow-flowered	GMaP SEND WFar WHoo
- - freckled, double (d)	LEdu
- Zodiac Group	CBod LRHS WGwG
liguricus WM 0230	MPhe
lividus	CRos EBee EHyd EPfP EWes GKev LAma LRHS NBir NRHS SBrt SDeJ SDir SRms
- subsp. ***corsicus***	see *H. argutifolius*
- 'Purple Ear'	LRHS
- 'Purple Rose'	SRms
- 'Rose Green'	MHtn
- 'White Marble'	LAma LRHS MAsh
- white-flowered	GKev
'Marshmallow'	MHol MNrw WCot
'Moonshine'PBR	NHol NLar
multifidus	NBir
- WM 1316	MPhe
- subsp. ***hercegovinus*** WM 0622	MPhe
- subsp. ***istriacus***	CBro
- - WM 9322	MPhe
- - WM 9324	MPhe
- subsp. ***multifidus*** from Croatia WM 9833	MPhe
niger	Widely available
- Ashwood strain	MAsh
- 'Christmas Carol'	CKel EHyd EWoo GMcL LCro LRHS NRHS SCoo SOrN
- double-flowered (d)	CDor
- Harvington hybrids	EHyd LRHS MAsh NRHS
- - double-flowered (d)	LCro LOPS SPoG
- HGC GOLDMARIE ('Coseh 2020'PBR)	ELan
- 'HGC Jacob'PBR	ELan EPau LSRN MHtn NRHS SRms
- HGC JACOB ROYAL ('Coseh 240'PBR)	EBee EPau
- HGC JASPER ('Coseh 1010'PBR)	ELan MAsh
- HGC JESKO ('Coseh 1000'PBR)	ELan MAsh
- HGC JOEL ('Coseh 210'PBR)	CRos ECtt EHyd EPfP LRHS NLar NRHS SCoo
- HGC JOHN ('Coseh 3090'PBR) **new**	MAsh
- HGC JONAS ('Coseh 220'PBR)	CRos ECtt EHyd EPfP LRHS NRHS SCoo
- 'HGC Josef Lemper'PBR	LRHS LSRN NLar SRms
- HGC SNOW FRILLS ('Coseh 230'PBR)	EHyd LRHS MAsh NLar NRHS SCoo
- HGC WINTERGOLD ('Coseh 2010'PBR)	CRos ECtt EHyd EPfP LRHS NRHS SCoo
- 'Ivory Prince'	see *H.* × ***ericsmithii*** 'Ivory Prince'
- 'Little Star' **new**	LBar
- 'Mini Blanc'	CRos EHyd LRHS NRHS
- 'Mini Star'	LRHS
- 'Mont Blanc'	EBee EPfP LRHS MCot WCot
- 'Potter's Wheel'	CRos EHyd EPfP GKev LRHS NBir NRHS
- 'Praecox'	CKel EHyd ELon EPfP
- SNOW CRYSTAL ('Hilnelsncr')	LRHS
- 'Snow Moon'	CBor
× ***nigercors*** 'Emma'PBR	CEnd CRos ECtt EHyd EPfP EWoo GMaP LRHS MCot MHol NLar NRHS SEdd SHar SPoG WCot
- 'HGC Green Corsican'	NRHS
- HGC ICE BREAKER FANCY ('Coseh 820')	EHyd EPfP LRHS MAsh NRHS SCoo
- HGC ICE BREAKER MAX ('Coseh 750'PBR)	EHyd EPfP LRHS MAsh NRHS SCoo
- HGC ICE BREAKER PICO ('Coseh 840')	ECre EPfP
- HGC ICE BREAKER PRELUDE ('Coseh 830'PBR)	NRHS
- 'Pink Beauty'	CBcs NLar

- 'Winter Passion'PBR EPfP
× *nigristern* see *H.* × *ericsmithii*
odorus CBro EBee XLum
- WM 0312 from Bosnia MPhe
- WM 9018 from Kosovo **new** MPhe
- WM 9415 MPhe
- WM 9728 from Hungary MPhe
- subsp. ***cyclophyllus*** WM 1508 **new** MPhe
odorus* × *orientalis GDam
orientalis misapplied see *H.* × *hybridus*
orientalis ambig. CBar CTsd EGrI EHeP EWoo GMcL MPri WHil
orientalis Lam. CBcs CEme EHyd EWes LPal LRHS MPhe MSwo NRHS XLum
§ - subsp. ***abchasicus*** (A. Braun) B. Mathew CBro EBee MAsh WSpi
§ - - Early Purple Group CTri SRms
- subsp. ***guttatus*** misapplied see *H.* × *hybridus* spotted
purpurascens CBro GKev LCro LOPS NBir
- WM 0815 from Romania MPhe
- WM 9211 from Hungary MPhe
- WM 9412 MPhe
(Rodney Davey Marbled Group) ANNA'S RED ('Abcrd02'PBR) (Frostkiss Series) CBcs CRos EBee EPfP LCro LOPS LRHS MAsh NRHS SCoo SEdd SPoG
- CHARMER ('Epb 21') MAsh
- CHERYL'S SHINE ('Epb 31') CBcs LRHS NLar SCoo SEdd SPoG
- DANA'S DULCET ('Epb 30') MAsh SCoo SPoG WCot
- 'Dorothy's Dawn' (Frostkiss Series) CBcs MAsh SPoG
- MOLLY'S WHITE ('Epbrd01'PBR) CBcs CRos LRHS MAsh
- MOONDANCE ('Epb 20') LRHS MAsh
- PENNY'S PINK ('Abcrd01') CBcs CRos ECtt EPfP LCro LRHS LSRN MAsh MHol SEdd SPoG WCot
- PIPPA'S PURPLE ('Rd09') LRHS MAsh
- REANNA'S RUBY ('Epb 32') MAsh
- SALLY'S SHELL ('Epb 12') (Frostkiss Series) CBcs MAsh SEdd SPoG
× ***sahinii*** 'Winterbells'PBR CBod EBee EGrI LBar LCro LOPS LRHS LSou MAsh NRHS SCoo SPoG SRms
× ***sternii*** CBcs CBod CKel CRos CTri EHyd ELan EPfP EWoo GKev GMaP LCro LRHS LSto MNrw NLar NRHS SPoG
- Aberconwy strain MAsh
- 'Ashwood Silver' MAsh
- Ashwood strain EBee MAsh
- Blackthorn Group LRHS SWvt
- 'Boughton Beauty' EBee ELan WSpi
- pewter-flowered CSpe
- 'Silver Dollar' EBee LRHS LSRN SGBe SMad SPoG SRms
thibetanus MAsh WAbe
torquatus MPhe
- WM 0609 from Montenegro MPhe
- WM 0617 from Serbia MPhe
- WM 9820 from Bosnia MPhe
- 'Dido' (d) WFar
- double-flowered, from Montenegro (d) WM 0621 MPhe
- Party Dress Group see *H.* × *hybridus* Party Dress Group
'Verboom Beauty' CDoC EHyd LCro LOPS LRHS MAsh NRHS
viridis EBee LEdu SRms XLum
- WM 0444 from Italy MPhe
- WM 1303 from Slovenia MPhe
- WM 9723 from Italy MPhe
- subsp. ***occidentalis*** GKev
- - WM 1340 from Germany MPhe
- - WM 1344 from Spain MPhe
- - WM 9501 from Wales MPhe
WALBERTON'S ROSEMARY ('Walhero'PBR) ♀H7 CRos EHyd EPfP LRHS MAsh NRHS SHar SPoG WSpi
'White Beauty'PBR EPfP NLar NRHS SGBe SPoG WCot

Helminthotheca (*Asteraceae*)

§ ***echioides*** WHer

Helonias (*Melanthiaceae*)

bullata EMor

Heloniopsis (*Melanthiaceae*)

acutifolia B&SWJ 218 WCru
- B&SWJ 6817 WCru
- B&SWJ 6836 WCru
japonica see *H. orientalis*
leucantha B&SWJ 11148 WCru
§ ***orientalis*** CBct CBor CTtf
- B&SWJ 6278 WCru
- var. ***breviscapa*** GEdr LEdu SMad WCru
- - B&SWJ 5635 WCru
- - B&SWJ 5873 WCru
- - B&SWJ 5938 WCru
- - 'A-so' LEdu WCru
- 'Dark Single' GEdr
- var. ***flavida*** 'Snow White' GEdr GKev
tubiflora GEdr
- B&SWJ 822 WCot
- 'Temple Blue' CBct EBee WCru
umbellata EBee EPfP WSHC
- B&SWJ 1839 WCru
- B&SWJ 3732 **new** EBee

Helosciadium (*Umbelliferae*)

§ ***nodiflorum*** CPud

Helwingia (*Helwingiaceae*)

chinensis CBcs CCCN CKel CTsd ESwi EWTr EWld GBin GEdr MGil MHtn MPie MPkF MVil NLar SBrt SEND SMad SPoG SSha WBor WLov WPGP XSte
- broad-leaved EBee EHed LAlb NLar SIvy SMad WPGP
- narrow-leaved ESwi
himalaica CExl ESwi MPkF MVil SBrt SMad XSte
japonica EWld MVil NLar
- broad-leaved WPGP

Helxine see *Soleirolia*

Hemerocallis ✿ (*Hemerocallidaceae*)

'A Bodacious Pattern' EStr
'A Groovy Kind of Love' EStr
'A Lady Named Hank' EStr
'A Small Multitude' EStr
'Aabaa' EWoo
'Aabachee' CBgR EStr
'Aaron Brown' EStr
'Ablazing Rimfire' SDay
'Above the Clouds' EWoo
'Absolute Ripper' EStr
'Absolute Treasure' EStr
'Absolute Zero' SDay
'Addie Branch Smith' SDay
'Admiral' WNHG
'Admiral's Braid' EWoo SDay
'Adoration' SPer
'Adrienne's Surprise' **new** SDay
'Aerea' MHol

'Aerial Display'	EStr SDay
'African Chant'	ELan
'After the Riot' (d)	EStr
'Ageless Beauty'	ELon EStr LAma SDir
'Ahoy Matey'	EStr
'Ahoya'	CBgR EStr
'Airs and Graces'	SDay
'Alabama Jubilee'	WNHG
'Alan'	CRos EBlo EHyd LRHS MRav NRHS
'Alan Adair'	SDay
'Alayne Clare'	EStr
'Alec Allen'	SDay
'Aleta Everett Adams'	EStr
'Alexander the Great'	WHrl
'Alien DNA'	EStr
'Alien Fingerprint'	EStr
'Aliens in the Garden'	EStr
'All American Baby'	EStr
'All American Chief' 𝕐H6	EStr SDay
'All American Plum'	WHrl
'All American Tiger'	SDay
'All American Windmill'	CBgR EStr WHrl
'All Fired Up'	ELon EStr SDay
'All the Magic'	SDay
'All Too Beautiful' **new**	SDay
'Allegheny Skyline'	EStr
'Allegiance'	WNHG
'Alli Sheldon'	ECha
'Alluring Peach'	EStr
'Almond Puff'	SDay
'Almost an Angel' **new**	EStr
'Alpine Mist'	SDay
'Al's Peach Tower' **new**	EStr
'Alta Vista' **new**	SDay
'Alternate Universe'	EStr
altissima	EStr EWoo MNrw SDix XLum
'Always Afternoon' 𝕐H6	CBgR CBod EGrI EPfP EStr LBar MNrw SDay WCAu WHrl XSen
'Amadeus'	EStr SCob SDay
'Amazon Amethyst'	WCAu
'Ambassador'	CBgR
'Amber Classic'	ELon
'American Freedom'	SDay
'American Revolution'	CBgR EGrI ELon EStr EWoo GBin GQue LSun MAvo MBNS MCot MHol NChi SBea SCoo SDys SEdd SMad SPoG SSut WCot WHrl WPnP WSpi XLum
'America's Most Wanted'	EStr SDay
'Amerstone Amethyst Jewel'	EStr
'Amerstone Saffron Jewel'	SDay
'Amethyst Tears' **new**	SDay
'Amy Michelle' (d)	EStr
'Amy's Rainbow'	EStr
'Anastasia'	SDay
'Angel Artistry'	SDay
'Angel in Oz'	EStr
'Angel Rodgers'	EStr
'Angelic Messenger' **new**	SDay
'Angels in America'	EStr
'Angelus Runaway'	EStr
'Angelwalker'	EStr
'Anna Rubinina'	EStr
'Anna Warner'	ELon MMuc SEND
'Annabelle's Ghost'	CBgR
'Annie Golightly'	SDay
'Annie Welch'	ELon
'Antique Lavender'	WCAu
'Antique Linen' **new**	LLWG
'Antique Rose'	EStr SDay
'Anzac'	CBro ECha ECtt EStr GArf LShi NGdn SWvt
'Apache Uprising'	SDay
'Apollodorus'	SDay WHrl WNHG
'Apple Court Chablis'	EStr
'Apple Court Damson'	EStr
'Apple Court Ruby'	ELon
'Apple Swirl'	EStr
'Apple Tart'	SDay
'Applique'	EStr
'Après Moi'	NLar
'Apricot Beauty' (d)	WSpi
'Apricot Velvet'	CBgR
'April Fools'	EStr
'April in Paris'	SDay
'Aquamarine'	SDay
'Aquarelle'	EStr
'Arabian Magic'	EStr
'Arctic Snow' 𝕐H6	CBgR CBro CMac ECrc ECtt EHyd EStr GJos LAma LPar LRHS MCot MNrw NRHS SDay SDir WPnP
'Arles Sultry Eyes'	EStr
'Armed and Dangerous'	EStr
'Arpeggio'	EStr SDay
'Ar-Range You a Pretty' **new**	EStr
'Art Gallery Curly-Q'	EStr
'Art Gallery Quilling'	EStr
'Arterial Blood' **new**	EStr
'Arthur Moore'	SDay
'Artificial Evolution'	EStr
'As the World Purrs' **new**	EStr
'Asheville Pink Lady'	EStr
'Asheville White Winged Dove'	EStr
'Ashton's Giggles'	EStr
'Asian Artistry'	WNHG
'Asiatic Pheasant'	SDay
'Asterisk' 𝕐H6	EStr SDay
'Astolat'	EBee
'Aten'	CBgR SDay
'Atlanta Bouquet'	SDay
'Atlanta Cover Girl'	SDay
'Atlanta Fringe Benefit'	SDay
'Atlanta Full House'	SDay
'Atlas'	WGwG
'Augenstern'	EStr
'August Frost' 𝕐H6	EStr SDay
'August Morn'	CBgR
'Augusto Bianco'	SDay
'Autumn Minaret'	EStr
'Autumn Prince'	EWoo
'Autumn Red'	CBcs CBgR EStr GKin MMuc MNrw NBir SCob SEND WCot
'Autumn Wood'	SDay
'Ava Michelle'	SDay
I 'Avant Garde' Moldovan	EStr
'Avant Garde' Russell	EStr WCAu
'Avon Crystal Rose'	WNHG
'Awakening Dream'	SDay
'Awash with Color'	EStr SDay
'Awesome Blossom'	EStr GBin MBNS MNrw WHrl
'Awesome Candy'	EStr
'Aztec Beauty'	EStr
'Aztec Furnace'	EStr SDay
'Aztec Gold'	EStr
'Baby Betsy'	EStr SDay
'Baby Blues'	SDay
'Baby Darling'	SDay
'Baby Red Eyes'	EStr WFar
'Backseat Debutante' **new**	EStr
'Bad Medicine'	EStr
'Baja'	WFar
'Bakabana'	CBod EHyd LRHS NRHS
'Bald Eagle'	EStr MNrw
'Bali Hai'	EStr LBar SRms WHrl WSpi
'Bali Watercolor'	EStr

'Bama Bound'	EStr
'Bamboo Blackie'	CBgR SDay
'Banana Cream Beauty'	SDeJ WSpi
'Banana Man'	EStr
'Banana Smoothie'	EStr
'Bandit Man'	EStr SDay
'Barbara Alsop'	EStr SDay
'Barbara Mitchell'	EStr EWTr EWoo SDay SDeJ WCAu WNHG
'Barbary Corsair'	EStr SDay
'Baroni'	ECha LShi
'Bas Relief'	EStr
'Bat Signal'	EWoo
'Batgirl'	EStr
'Battle Hymn'	WCAu
'Bayou Bride'	SDay
'Be Bop a Lula'	EStr
'Bea'	EStr
'Beat the Barons'	SDay
'Beautiful Design'	EStr
'Beautiful Edgings'	EStr SDay
'Beauty Marked' **new**	SDay
'Beauty to Behold' 🏆^{H6}	SDay
'Becky Lynn'	EStr SDay
'Bed of Nails'	EStr
'Bed of Roses'	EStr
'Bedarra Island'	SDay
'Bee's Big Ben'	SDay
'Before You Accuse Me'	EStr
'Beijing'	SDay
'Bela Lugosi'	CBgR ECrc EHyd ELon EPfP EStr EWoo GQue ILea LRHS LSRN MBNS NBro NChi NQui NRHS SCob SDay SPer WHrl WNHG
'Believe It'	WNHG
'Bella Isabella'	EStr
'Belladonna Starfish'	EStr
'Bellini'	SDay
'Belly Button Slipknots'	EStr
'Beloved Deceiver'	SDay
'Ben Adams'	SDay
'Ben Bachman'	EStr
'Benchmark'	SDay
'Bengal Bay'	SDay
'Bengal Fire'	WNHG
'Berlin Lemon Crepe'	GBin
'Berlin Red'	ECha ELon GBee MNrw SDay SSut WFar
'Berlin Red Velvet'	GBin
'Berlin Tallboy'	SDay
'Berlin Yellow'	EStr
'Berliner Premiere'	EStr
'Bernard Thompson'	SDay
'Berry Blitz'	EStr
'Berry Patch'	EStr
'Berrylicious'	CBod
'Bertie Ferris'	EStr EWoo NLar SDay
'Beside Still Waters'	EStr
'Best Seller'	CBod LAma WCAu
'Bette Davis Eyes'	CBgR EStr SDay
'Betts Allen'	EStr
'Betty Benz'	SDay
'Betty Jenkins'	EStr
'Betty Powell' **new**	SDay
'Betty Warren Woods'	SDay
'Betty Woods' (d)	SDay
'Bettylen'	EStr
'Beyond Riches'	EStr
'Beyond Thunder Dome'	EStr
'Bi-colored Blues'	EStr
'Big Apple'	EStr SDay
'Big Beautiful Babe'	EStr
'Big Bird'	EStr MBNS SDay

'Big Blue'	EStr SDay
'Big Honking Bahama Richie'	EStr
'Big Honking Cream Smoothie' **new**	EStr
'Big Kiss' (d)	ELon
'Big Ogeeche'	EStr
'Big Red Wiggles'	EStr
'Big Smile'	MBNS MNrw SDeJ
'Big Snowbird'	SDay
'Big Time Happy'	CBod EHyd LRHS SCob SEdd SPoG
'Big World'	CBgR
'Bill Norris'	SDay
'Birthday Honours'	SDay
'Bitsy'	ELon
'Black Adder'	SDay
'Black Ambrosia'	EStr SDay
'Black Arrowhead'	EStr MACG WCAu
'Black Emanuelle'	LDai LSun MNrw NLar WFar XSen
'Black Eye'	SDay WNHG
'Black Eyed Belle'	EWoo WNHG
'Black Eyed Stella'	WSpi
'Black Eyed Susan'	CBod ECtt EStr
'Black Friday'	EStr
'Black Handlebars'	EWoo
'Black Ice'	ELon SDay
'Black Knight'	EWoo NLar SRms
'Black Magic'	CBro CTri ECtt EHyd EPfP EStr GKin GMaP LRHS LSRN MHer MRav NBir NGdn NRHS SPer WHrl WNHG
'Black Plush'	EWoo
'Black Prince'	CBgR EShb MBNS
'Black Stockings'	EBee ELon EPfP EStr EWes LAma MHol MNrw SCob SDeJ SDir SMrm
'Blackberries and Cream'	EStr
'Blackberry Candy'	ECtt EHyd EStr GKin LRHS MHol NHol NRHS NWad SDay WCAu
'Blackberry Sherbert'	NCth WFar
'Blackberry Sundae'	EStr
'Blacky'	EStr
'Blazing Cannons'	EStr
'Blazing Romance'	EStr
'Blessed Again'	SDay
'Blessing'	EStr SDay
'Blessing in Disguise'	EStr
'Blizzard Bay'	EPfP EStr SDay WFar
'Blizzard Blast'	EStr
'Blonde is Beautiful'	SDay
'Blood Spot'	SDay
'Blue Balloon'	EStr
'Blue Deva'	EStr
'Blue Diana'	SDay
'Blue Orchid' **new**	SDay
'Blue Ridge Butterfly' **new**	SDay
'Blue Sheen'	CBgR CMac ECtt EStr GMaP MHol WFar WSpi
'Blue Stardust'	EStr
'Blue Venture' **new**	SDay
'Blue Wrangler'	EStr
'Blueberry Breakfast'	EStr WNHG
'Blueberry Candy'	ECtt EStr GJos ILea
'Blueberry Frost'	CBgR
'Blueberry Sundae'	CWat MACG
'Bluethroat'	EStr
'Blufftop Volunteer'	EStr
'Blushing Belle'	NBro SDay
'Bob Faulkner'	EStr
'Bob Marley' **new**	EStr
'Bobby's Lavender Eyes'	EStr
'Bobo Anne'	EStr
'Bogeyman'	CBod EStr LBar
'Bohemian Rhapsody'	EStr
'Boitzer Helicopter'	EStr

'Bold Courtier'	CBgR
'Bonanza'	CBcs CBgR CBro CRos CTri EBlo ECha ECtt EGrl EHyd EStr GMcL LPal LRHS MRav NBir NBro NGdn NLar NRHS SCob SEND SPer SWvt WCAu WCot WFar
'Bone China'	WNHG
'Boney Maroney'	CBgR
'Bonfire Heart'	EStr
'Bonibrae Blue-eyed Baby'	EStr
'Bonibrae Heartbreaker'	EStr
'Bonibrae Maggie Anne'	EStr
'Bonibrae Smoke and Mirrors'	EStr
'Bonibrae the Freak' **new**	EStr
'Bonnie Boy'	XLum
'Booger'	SDay
'Booroobin Magic'	EStr EWoo
'Border Lord'	EStr EWoo
'Border Music'	EStr
'Borgia Queen'	EStr SDay
'Boss Hogg'	EStr
'Both Sides Now'	ECtt
'Boulderbrook Serenity'	SDay
'Bourbon Kings'	SDeJ WHrl WWtn
'Bowl of Cream'	EStr
'Bowl of Roses'	EStr WCAu
'Brass Buckles'	see *H.* 'Puddin'
'Breath of Blue Air'	EStr
'Breathing in Snowflakes'	EStr
'Breathless Beauty'	WNHG
'Breathless Charm'	EStr
'Brenda Newbold'	EStr SDay
'Brer Rabbit's Baby'	EStr
'Bridget'	ELan
'Bright and Morning Star'	EStr
'Bright Beacon'	SDay
'Bright Eyed and Bushy Tailed'	EStr
'Bright Side'	CBgR
'Bright Spangles'	SDay
'Brilliant Circle'	ECtt
'Broadway Accent' **new**	SDay
'Broadway Last Mohican'	EStr
'Brocaded Gown'	ELan SDay
'Brookgreen Plantation'	EStr
'Brooklyn Twist'	EStr SDay
'Brown Billows'	EWoo
'Brown Exotica'	EWoo
'Brown Witch'	ELon EWoo
'Brown-Eyed Girl'	SDay
'Browns Ferry Royalty'	EStr WFar
'Bruce'	EStr
'Bruno Müller'	SDay
'Brutus'	WHrl
'Bubbling Brown Sugar'	EStr SDay
'Bubbly'	SDay
'Bucksport'	EStr
'Buckyballs'	SDay
'Bud Producer'	CBgR
'Budding Oddity' **new**	SDay
'Buddy's Wild and Wonderful'	EStr
'Buffys Doll'	SDay
'Bug's Hug'	EStr
'Bumble Bee'	ECtt EStr SDay
'Burgundy Love'	EStr LLWG
'Burlesque'	SDay WCot
'Burmese Buddha'	SDay
'Burning Daylight' ♀H6	CAby CBgR CRos EBlo ECtt EHeP EHyd EPfP EStr LBar LRHS MNrw MRav NRHS SCob SPer SRms WCAu WCot WFar
'Burning Inheritance'	SDay
'Burning So Brightly'	EStr
'Burnished Ruffles'	EStr
'Bursting Bubble'	SDay
'Bust a Move' **new**	EStr
'Butterfly Charm'	SDay
'Butterfly Love'	EStr
'Butterpat'	SDay
'Butterscotch'	WFar
'Butterscotch Ruffles'	SDay
'Button Box'	SDay
'Buzz Bomb'	CFis ECrc ECtt EHyd ELon EMor EStr GBee GKin LRHS LSRN MHol NGdn NRHS SPer WFar
'By Myself'	SDay
'Byzantine Emperor'	EHyd LRHS NRHS
'Caballero'	EStr
'Cabbage Butterfly'	EStr
'Cabbage Flower'	SDay
'Cabernet Caberet' **new**	SDay
'Cajun Gambler'	EStr SDay
'Calgary Stampede'	EStr
'Calico Jack'	EStr SDay SPad
'Calico Spider'	EStr
'California Sunshine'	SDay
'Caliph's Robes'	SDay
'Call Girl'	SDay
'Calligraphy'	EStr
'Camden Ballerina'	SDay
'Camden Gold Dollar'	SDay
'Camelot Green'	WNHG
'Cameroons'	EStr SDay
'Campfire Embers'	EStr
'Canadian Border Patrol'	CWCL EStr NLar SCob SDay SPer
'Canary Chaos'	EStr
'Canary Feathers'	SDay
'Canary Glow'	CTri WFar
'Canary Wings'	CBgR
'Candide'	SDay
'Candor'	SDay
'Candy Cane Dreams'	EStr
'Candy Gram'	EStr
'Canopy of Heaven'	SDay
'Can't Fault Ya'	EStr
'Cape Breton'	EStr MHol
'Cape Cod'	SDay
'Captain America'	EStr
'Capulina'	EWoo
'Cara Mia'	CBgR EStr NBir WFar
'Caramba'	CBgR
'Caramel Taffy'	WHrl
'Caribbean Frank League'	SDay
'Caribbean Purple Spires'	EStr
'Carlotta'	SDay
'Carmine Monarch'	EStr
'Carnal Emporium'	EStr
'Carolicolossal'	ELon SDay
'Carolina Cool Down'	EStr
'Carolina Cranberry'	ELan
'Carolina Dynamite'	EStr
'Carolina Lemon Squeezer'	EStr
'Caroline Taylor'	WHrl
'Carrick Wildon'	CBod EBee EPfP LBar MBros WFar
'Carrot'	SDay
'Cartwheels'	ECha EGrl EHyd EShb EStr GBee GKin GMaP LRHS MRav NBro NRHS SCoo SRms SSut WCAu WFar
'Casino Gold'	SDay
'Castile'	SDay
'Catawampus'	EStr
'Catherine Neal'	EStr SDay
'Catherine Woodbery'	Widely available

'Cathy's Sunset'	ECtt EHyd EWhm GBee GKin LRHS LSRN MBNS NBro NGdn NRHS NWad
'Cause for Pause'	EStr
'Caviar'	SDay
'Cedar Waxwing'	MNrw
'Cee Tee'	SDay
'Celebration of Angels'	EStr MHol SDay
'Celestial City'	SDay
'Celestial Eyes'	SDay
'Cerulean Warbler'	EStr
'Challenger'	SDay
'Chance Encounter'	NHol SDay
'Changing Latitudes'	WHrl
'Chantilly'	EStr
'Charles Johnston'	CBgR EStr EWoo MSpe SDay
'Charleston Strong'	EStr
'Charlie Pierce Memorial'	EStr SDay
'Charm Alarm'	EStr
'Charming Manners'	EStr
'Chartwell'	EWoo
'Chasing Moonbeams' **new**	SDay
'Checkerboard Curls'	EStr
'Cheerful Note'	WNHG
'Cheese and Wine'	EPfP MHol
'Cherokee Star'	EStr
'Cherries Are Ripe' **new**	SDay
'Cherry Cheeks'	EBlo ECtt EHyd ELan ELon EPfP EStr LRHS MHol MNrw MRav NRHS WCAu WCot WFar WWtn
'Cherry Eyed Pumpkin' ♀H6	EStr SDay WCAu
'Cherry Grove Beach'	EStr
'Cherry Peacock'	EStr
'Cherry Stripes'	EStr
'Cherry Swizzler' **new**	EStr
'Cherry Tiger'	EStr
'Cherry Valentine'	ELon SPad
'Cherrystone'	EStr
'Chesapeake Crablegs'	EStr SDay
'Chesières Lunar Moth'	CBgR ELon SDay
'Chester Cyclone'	SDay
'Chestnut Mountain'	SDay
'Chevron Spider'	EStr
'Chicago Antique Tapestry'	SDay
'Chicago Apache'	ELon EPfP EStr EWoo LLWG NBir SCob SDay SPer WSpi XSen
'Chicago Aztec'	ELon
'Chicago Blackout'	ECtt GKev MACG WCot
'Chicago Cardinal'	EStr
'Chicago Cherry'	WNHG
'Chicago Fire'	EPfP
'Chicago Firecracker'	XLum
'Chicago Heirloom'	WCAu
'Chicago Jewel'	ELon NSti
'Chicago Knobby'	EStr SDay
'Chicago Knockout'	ELan EPfP EWoo
'Chicago Peach'	NBir WCAu
'Chicago Petticoats'	WFar
'Chicago Picotee Memories'	SDay
'Chicago Picotee Pride'	SDay
'Chicago Picotee Promise'	WNHG
'Chicago Picotee Queen'	WNHG
'Chicago Queen'	SDay WNHG
'Chicago Rainbow'	CBgR
'Chicago Royal Blue'	CTri
'Chicago Royal Crown'	ECtt EMor
'Chicago Royal Robe'	CWCL EBlo ELon LRHS NBid SDay SPer SRms WCot WWtn
'Chicago Silver'	SDay SMrm
'Chicago Star'	WNHG
'Chicago Sugarplum'	SDay
'Chicago Sunrise'	CBgR CRos EBlo EHyd ELon GMaP LLWG LRHS MRav NGdn NRHS SDay SWvt WCot WNHG

'Chick Flick'	EStr
'Chick Magnet'	EStr
'Chicka Chicka Boom Boom' **new**	EStr
'Chicken Coop Madonna'	EStr
'Chicken on the Run' **new**	EStr
'Chief Four Fingers'	EWoo
'Chief Sarcoxie'	SDay
'Chief Sequoia'	EStr
'Child of Fortune'	SDay
'Children's Festival'	CMac CRos EBlo ECtt EStr GMaP LRHS MRav NLar SDay SWvt WFar
'China Bride'	EStr SDay
'China Lake'	SDay
'Chinese Autumn'	EStr
'Chinese Cloisonne'	EStr SDay
'Chinese Coral'	EWoo
'Chinese Imp'	NLar SDay
'Chinese New Year'	EStr
'Chinese Temple Flower'	SDay
'Chipmunk' **new**	EStr
'Chiricahua Warrior'	EWoo
'Chocolate Candy'	EStr
'Chocolate Dude'	SDay
'Chocolate Splash'	SDay
'Chokecherry Mountain'	EStr EWoo LBar
'Chorus Line'	SDay WNHG
'Christina's Pink Parasol'	EStr
'Christine Lynn'	WNHG
'Christmas Is'	CBgR CMac CPar CWGN ECtt ELon EStr GKin GMcL NHol NRHS SDay WCot WHrl WNHG
'Christmas Ornament'	EStr
'Christmas Wishes'	EStr
'Ciao'	SDay
'Ciarra Vonnie'	SDay
'Cimarron Knight'	CBgR
'Cindy's Eye'	EStr SDay WCot
'Cinnamon Stick'	EStr
'Cinnamon Sunrise'	EStr
citrina ♀H6	CBgR CEme CMac EBee EStr EWoo GKev MBel MCot WCAu WCot WHoo WHrl XLum XSen XSte
citrina × (× ***ochroleuca***)	WCot
'Citrus Juices' **new**	EStr
'Civil Law'	SDay
'Civil Rights'	SDay
'Classic Caper'	WNHG
'Classic Edge'	SDay
'Claudine'	ELon
'Claudine's Charm'	EStr
'Clearly a Thrill'	EStr
'Cleo'	WHrl
'Cleopatra'	ELon MSpe SDay
'Clothed in Glory'	EStr WCot
'Clownfish'	EStr
'Cobalt Dawn' **new**	SDay
'Cobraskin Necktie'	EStr
'Coburg Fright Wig'	EWoo
'Cocktail Party'	EStr
'Codie Wedgeworth' **new**	SDay
'Colonel Joe'	WNHG
'Colonel Mustard'	EStr
'Comanche Eyes'	SDay
'Coming Up Roses'	CAby CBod CPar ELon SCoo
'Concorde Nelson'	ELon EStr SDay
'Condilla' (d) ♀H6	EStr SDay
'Conspicua'	CBgR
'Contessa'	CBro EBlo EHyd LRHS NRHS
'Conway Red Light'	EStr
'Cool It'	EStr MPie NLar SCob SDeJ WHrl
'Cool Jazz'	EStr SDay
'Cooler Than Me'	EStr

'Copper Dawn'	EStr NChi
'Copper Windmill'	CBgR ELon EStr SDay WNHG
'Copperhead'	EStr
'Coral Majority'	EStr
'Coral Mist'	ECrc
'Coral Sparkler'	WNHG
'Corinthian Pink'	SDay
'Corky'	CAby CBro ECha ELan ELon EMor EPfP GMaP GMcL LSRN MBel MNrw NGdn NLar SMrm SPer SPhx SSut WCAu WFar WSpi XLum
'Cornwall'	EStr
'Cosmic Blast'	EStr
'Cosmic Hummingbird'	EBou ECtt EStr SDay
'Cosmic Legacy'	EStr
'Cosmik Debris'	EStr
'Cosmopolitan'	GBin
'Country Club'	GMaP
'Country Melody'	SDay
'Court Magician'	EStr EWoo SDay
'Court Troubadour'	ELon
'Coyote Moon'	EStr SDay
'Crackling Fire'	EStr
'Cranberry Baby'	ECtt EStr LRHS MHol MTin SCoo WHoo WNHG
'Cranberry Coulis'	CWat
'Crawleycrow'	SDay
'Crayola Violet'	EStr SDay
'Crazy Awesome'	EStr
'Crazy Ivan'	EStr
'Crazy Larry'	EStr
'Crazy Mr Jim'	EStr
'Crazy Pierre'	EWoo SDay WHrl
'Cream Drop'	ECtt EPPr GMaP GQue LRHS MBriF MCot MRav NBro NGdn NLar NRHS NSti SDay SPer WCot WFar WHrl
'Creative Edge'	SDay
'Crimson Icon'	SDay
'Crimson Pirate'	CBgR CMac ECrc ELon EPfP EStr EWoo GKev GLog GQue ILea LPar LRHS LSRN MSpe NBir NEoE NQui NRHS SCob SPer SPlb WCAu WFar WHrl WWtn XLum
'Crimson Wind'	EStr
'Cripple Creek'	EStr
'Croesus'	SRms
'Crooked Smile'	EStr
'Crystal Pinot'	ELon EStr
'Cumulus Sunset'	EStr
'Cupid's Gold'	SDay
'Curls'	CBgR SDay
'Curly Cinnamon Windmill' ♀H6	EStr SDay
'Curly Rosy Posy'	SDay
'Curt's Gift'	EStr
'Custard Candy' ♀H6	CWCL CWGN ECtt EHyd EPfP EStr EWoo GKin LCro LRHS MBriF NHol NRHS WCAu WNHG
'Cute as Can Be'	EStr
'Cyber Zone'	EStr
'Cyclone Twister'	EStr
'Cyclone Whirlaway'	EStr
'Cynthia Lucius'	EStr
'Cynthia Mary'	ECtt GKin SRGP
'Czarina'	EStr
'Daddeeo Segrest'	EStr
'Daddy's Catfish Stew'	EStr
'Dad's Best White'	EStr
'Daily Bread'	SDay
'Daily Dollar'	NGdn
'Dallas Spider Time'	SDay
'Dallas Star'	EStr SDay WHrl
'Dan Mahony'	EStr
'Dan Patch' **new**	EStr
'Dan Tau'	SDay
'Dance Ballerina Dance'	SDay
'Dance Fever'	SDay
'Dance with Somebody'	EStr
'Dances with Giraffes'	EStr
'Dancing Crab'	CBgR
'Dancing Dragon' **new**	SDay
'Dancing Dreams'	EStr
'Dancing Dwarf'	SDay
'Dancing Elf'	EStr
'Dancing for Dixie'	EStr
'Dancing in the Rain'	EStr
'Dancing Lions'	SDay
'Dancing on Air'	ECtt SMrm SPeP
'Dancing on Ice'	EStr
'Dancing Shiva'	SDay
'Dancing Summerbird'	ELon EStr LBar SDay
'Dancing with Linda'	EStr
'Daring Deception'	ECtt EGrI EHyd ELon EPfP LRHS MNrw NRHS SDay SDeJ
'Daring Dilemma'	EStr SDay
'Daring Reflection'	SDay
'Darius'	WNHG
'Dark Angel'	NRHS
'Dark Magician'	EStr
'Dark Monkey'	EStr
'Dark Sprite'	EWoo
'Darker Shade'	EStr
'Darrell'	SDay
'Dash Dash'	EStr
'David Holman'	WNHG
'David Kirchhoff'	EStr SDay
'Davidson Update'	WNHG
'Davi's Dilemma'	EStr
'Daylight'	WNHG
'De Colores'	EStr SDay
'Dearest Mahogany'	EStr
'Debary Canary'	EWoo
'Debussy'	EStr
'Decatur Ballerina'	WNHG
'Decatur Captivation'	WNHG
'Decatur Cherry Smash'	SDay
'Decatur Dictator'	WNHG
'Decatur Festival'	WNHG
'Decatur Imp'	SDay WHrl
'Decatur Jewel'	WNHG
'Decatur Piecrust'	EStr
'Decatur Rhythm'	WNHG
'Decatur Supreme'	WNHG
'Decatur Treasure Chest'	WNHG
'Decidedly Happy'	EStr
'Deep Impact' **new**	EStr
'Defuniak Peach Blossom'	EStr
'Delicate Design'	SDay
'Delightsome'	SDay
'Deloris Gould'	SDay
'Demetrius'	CWat EStr
'Dervish' **new**	SDay
'Desdemona'	EStr XLum
'Desert Dreams'	WCot
'Desert Icicle'	SDay
'Designer Gown'	EStr SDay
'Designer Jeans'	EStr SDay
'Designer Rhythm'	EStr
'Desirable Duchess'	EStr
'Desire of Nations'	EStr
'Desperate Housewife'	EStr
'Destined to See'	CBro ECtt ELon EStr EWhm LDai MNrw NBir NBro SPad SPer WCot WHrl

'Devon Cream'	SPer
'Devon Ruby'	SDay
'Devonshire'	EStr
'Diamond Dust'	LSRN NLar SPer WSpi
'Diana Grenfell'	CBgR
'Dick Kitchingman'	CBgR SDay
'Different for Girls'	EStr
'Digital Dynamics'	EStr
'Dipped in Ink'	EStr
'Dipped in Pink'	EStr
'Discarded Beauty'	EStr
'Disco Inferno'	EStr
'Distant Galaxy'	EStr WCAu
'Distinguished Gentleman' **new**	EStr
'Diva Bride'	EStr
'Diva in Zebra'	EStr
'Diva's Choice'	EStr
'Divertissment'	CBgR ELon EWoo SDay WHrl
'Dizzy Miss Lizzy'	EStr
'Do the Twist'	SDay
'Do You Know Doris'	SDay
'Doc Holliday'	EStr
'Doctor Doom'	EStr
'Doctor Freckles Mr Hyde'	EStr
'Doctor McGregor's Garden'	EStr
'Doctor Strangelove'	EStr
'Dominic'	CBgR EWoo MACG MSpe SDay WFar
'Don Stevens'	WHrl
'Don's Wild Heather'	EStr
'Don't Leave Empty-handed'	EStr
'Dorethe Louise'	CBgR SDay
'Dorothy McDade'	EWoo MNrw
'Dory's Big Heart'	EStr
'Dot Paul'	ELan
'Double Action' (d)	ELon SDay
'Double Cream' (d)	WCot
'Double Cutie' (d)	EHyd EStr LRHS NLar NRHS SDay SRms
'Double Delicious' (d)	WCot
'Double Doubloon' (d)	XLum
'Double Dream' (d)	EGrI EStr WHrl
'Double Firecracker' (d)	MBNS NBro NLar
'Double Gardenia' (d)	EStr WNHG
'Double Honey' (d)	EStr
'Double Oh Seven' (d)	ELon
'Double Pompon' (d)	EStr
'Double Red Royal' (d)	EGrI EStr
'Double Red Whirlwind' (d) **new**	EStr
'Double River Wye' (d)	CBgR EShb EStr GBee MACG MHer MNrw NGdn WBrk WCot WFar WHoo WHrl
'Dowager Queen'	WNHG
'Dragon Dreams'	SDay
'Dragon Fire Breath'	EStr
'Dragon Flight'	LLWG
'Dragon King'	SDay
'Dragon Lore'	EStr
'Dragon Seeker'	EStr
'Dragon's Eye'	EHyd EWoo LBar LRHS NRHS SDay WNHG
'Dragon's Orb'	SDay
'Dragon's Token' **new**	SDay
'Dream Awhile'	SDay
'Dream Keeper'	EWoo
'Dream Legacy'	SDay
'Dreamliner'	EStr
'Dresden Doll'	SPer
'Driving Me Wild'	SDay
'Drooling Lizard'	EStr
'Droopy Drawers'	ELon SDay

'Drop Cloth'	EStr
'Druid's Chant'	EWoo
'Duke of Durham'	EStr EWoo
'Duke of Earl'	CBgR
dumortieri	CAgr CBro EBee EBlo ECha EWhm EWoo GGro MMuc MRav NBid NBir NSti SCob SEND SPer WCot WWtn XSen
– B&SWJ 1283	WCru
'Dumpy'	EStr
'Dune Needlepoint'	EStr WHrl
'Dunkle Prinzessin'	GBin
'Dutch Art'	SDay
'Dutch Beauty'	WFar
'Dutch Gold'	MHCG MNrw
'Dynasty Pink'	SDay
'Earl of Warwick'	CBgR
'Earlianna'	EStr
'Earnest Yearwood'	SDay
'Earth Fire'	SDay
'Easter Star'	EStr
'Easy Ned'	ELon EWoo SDay
'Eat Our Wake Pintaheads'	EStr
'Echo Echo'	EStr
'Ed Brown'	SDay
'Ed Kirchhoff'	XLum
'Ed Murray'	EStr SDay WCAu
'Edgar Brown'	WCot
'Edge Ahead'	CMac ECtt EHyd GKin GMcL LRHS NCth NHol NRHS SDay WCAu WHrl
'Edge of Darkness'	CWGN NLar NSti SDay WFar
'Edith Marie'	EStr
'Edith Vaughan'	EStr SDay
'Edna Spalding'	CRos EHyd LRHS NRHS SDay
'Eenie Allegro'	CBro SPer
'Eenie Fanfare'	EStr NBir
'Eenie Weenie'	CBro ELon EStr GKev NBro SRms WWtn
'Eenie Weenie Non-stop'	ECha EGrI EPPr
'Eggplant Electricity'	EWoo
'Eggplant Escapade' ♀^{H6}	CBgR ELon EStr MSpe SDay WHrl
'Egyptian Ibis'	EWoo WNHG
'Egyptian Queen'	CBgR SDay
'Eight Miles High'	EStr SDay
'Eighteen Karat'	EStr
'El Desperado'	CBgR ECtt EHyd ELon EStr EWoo GQue ILea LRHS MBNS MHol MNrw NRHS WCAu WCot WHrl
'El Glorioso'	CWat EStr
'Elaine Farrant'	SDay
'Elaine Strutt'	SDay SWvt WCot WSpi
'Electric Marmalade Magic'	SDay
'Elegance Supreme' **new**	SDay
'Elegant Candy' ♀^{H6}	CBgR CMac EPfP EStr EWoo WCAu
'Elegant Girls'	EStr
'Eleonor'	WFar
'Elf Power' **new**	EStr
'Elfin Illusion'	EStr
'Elizabeth Salter'	CWCL EStr NLar SDay
'Eloquent Silence'	SDay
'Elsie Stelter'	EStr
'Elva White Grow'	SDay
'Elven Elegance'	EStr
'Emerald Dew'	SDay
'Emerald Empress'	EStr
'Emerald Eye'	SDay
'Emerald Starburst'	EStr
'Eminent Domain'	SDay
'Emperor's Choice'	SDay
'Emperor's Dragon'	EStr SDay
'Enchanted Empress'	SDay
'Enchanted Forest'	EStr WCAu
'Enchanter's Spell'	SDay

'Enchanting Blessing'	EStr SDay
'Endurance Emperor' **new**	LLWG
'English Cameo'	SDay
'English Skies'	EStr
'Entransette'	SDay
'Entrapment'	CBod ECtt EStr SDeJ WFar
'Entwined in the Vine'	EStr
'Erica Nichole Gonzales'	SDay
'Erin Prairie'	EStr
'Etched Eyes'	EWoo
'Eternal Blessing'	SDay
'Eternity Road'	EStr
'Etruscan Tomb'	EStr
'Evelyn Claar'	CMac
'Evelyn Lela Stout'	SDay
'Evening Enchantment'	EStr SDay
'Ever So Ruffled'	EStr SDay
(EveryDaylily Series) EVERYDAYLILY BRONZE **new**	LBar
- EVERYDAYLILY CERISE ('Ver00157'PBR) **new**	LBar
- EVERYDAYLILY CREAM ('Ver00112'PBR)	EStr LBar
- EVERYDAYLILY PINK CREAM ('Ver00323'PBR) **new**	LBar
- EVERYDAYLILY PINK WING ('Ver00213'PBR) **new**	LBar
- EVERYDAYLILY PUNCH YELLOW ('Ver00204'PBR) **new**	LBar
- EVERYDAYLILY RED RIBS ('Ver00322'PBR) **new**	EStr LBar LCro MNrw
- EVERYDAYLILY ROSE ('Ver00198'PBR) **new**	LBar
'Exotic Love'	SDay
'Exotic Spider'	EStr
'Exotic Star'	EStr
'Exotic Treasure'	EStr
'Exploded Pumpkin'	EBee EStr
'Exploding Galaxy'	EStr
'Explosion in the Paint Factory'	EStr
'Eye of the Hurricane'	EStr SDay
'Eye on a String'	EStr
'Eye on America'	EBee ELon EStr
'Eyes are Mosaics'	EStr
'Eyes Bright'	EStr
'Eyes That See' **new**	SDay
'Ezekiel'	SDay WHrl
'Fabergé'	SDay
'Face the Music' **new**	SDay
'Facemaker'	EStr
'Fairest Love'	LDai MNrw WHrl
'Fairest of Them'	CBgR
'Fairy Charm'	SDay
'Fairy Jester'	SDay
'Fairy Summerbird'	SDay
'Fairy Tale Pink'	EStr SDay
'Fall Farewell'	WNHG
'Fall Guy'	SDay
'Fama'	EStr SDay
'Fantasia'	EWoo
'Farmer's Daughter'	CBgR SDay
'Father James Foster'	EStr
'Feather Down'	SDay
'Fellow'	EStr
'Femme Fatale'	SDay
'Femme Osage'	EStr SDay
'Ferengi Gold'	SDay
'Ferris Wheel'	EWoo
'Fiestaville'	EStr
'Final Touch'	CBgR EStr MSwo NBro
'Finders Keepers'	EStr
'Fire and Fog'	EStr
'Fire Bird Suite'	EStr
'Fire Dance'	ELon
'Fire from Heaven'	WHrl
'Fire Tree'	CBgR ELon EStr
'Firestorm'	EStr
'First Formal'	SPer
'First Knight'	EStr SDay
'Flaming Firebird'	EStr
'Flaming Sword'	WBrk
'Flamingo Carousel' **new**	EStr
'Flamingo Parade'	EStr
'Flash Mob'	EStr
flava	see *H. lilioasphodelus*
'Fleeting Fancy'	SDay
'Flight of the Dragon'	SDay
'Flip Fiasco'	EStr
'Flip, Flop and Fly' **new**	EStr
'Flirty Edna' **new**	SDay
'Florentine Silk'	EStr
'Florissant Miss'	EStr
'Flower Basket' (d)	EStr
'Flower Pavilion'	SDay
'Floyd Cove'	SDay
'Fly Catcher'	CBgR SDay
'Flying Saucer Blues'	SDay
'Flying Trapeze'	EStr
'Fooled Me' ♀H6	ECtt EHyd EStr LRHS NRHS SDay
'For the Good Times'	EWoo
'Forbidden Desires'	EStr
'Forest Phantom'	EStr
'Forever Red'	EStr
'Forever Redeemed'	EStr SDay
forrestii	GKev
'Forsooth'	CBgR
'Forsyth Ace of Hearts'	CBgR
'Forsyth Evening Glow'	EStr
'Forsyth Lemon Drop'	SDay
'Forsyth White Buds'	EStr
'Fortress of Solitude'	EStr
'Fortune's Dearest'	SDay
'Forty Second Street'	EStr
'Foxfire Light' **new**	SDay
'Fragrant Bouquet'	EStr
'Fragrant Pastel Cheers'	SDay
'Fragrant Reflections'	EStr MAsh
'Fragrant Returns'	CKel ECtt EGrI LEdu SPoG
'Frank Smith'	WCAu
'Frankly Scarlet'	EStr
'Frans Hals'	Widely available
'Fred Manning'	EStr
'Free Wheelin''	EStr SCob
'French Connection'	SDay
'French Fare'	EStr
'French Lingerie'	EStr
'French Pavilion'	SDay
'French Porcelain'	SDay
'Fresh Air'	MNrw
'Fried Green Tomatoes'	EStr
'Friends with Benefits'	EStr
'Frills and Furbelows'	SDay
'Frilly Bliss'	EStr
'Fritz Schroer'	CBgR
'Froggy'	EStr
'Frosted Encore'	SDay
'Frosted Pink Ice'	SDay
'Frosted Vintage Ruffles'	EBee EStr EWes MNrw WCAu
'Frosty White'	SDay
'Frozen Arrowhead'	EStr
'Frozen Jade'	EHyd LRHS NRHS SDay
'Fuchsia Fashion'	SDay
'Full Grown'	EStr
'Fully Blessed'	EStr

fulva	CTri GPSL MMuc NBir SEND SRms WBrk WHrl XSen
– B&SWJ 8647	WCru
– 'Flore Pleno' (d)	CAvo CMac CTri ELan GBin MBriF MHer MRav NBir NBro NGdn NSti SMad SPer SRms WBrk WCAu XSen
§ – 'Green Kwanso' (d)	CBgR ECha EHyd ITim LRHS NRHS WFar WPnP WWtn
– var. ***kwanso***	WWtn
– – B&SWJ 6328	WCru
– 'Kwanso' ambig. (d)	GKev
– var. ***littorea***	CMac XLum
– var. ***rosea***	EBlo LRHS WCot
§ – 'Variegated Kwanso' (d/v)	ELon MRav NBir WCot WFar WHer WHrl
– yellow-variegated (v)	WCot
'Fun Fling'	EStr
'Funicular'	EStr
'Furgalisus'	EStr
'Gadsden Goliath'	SDay
'Gadsden Light'	EStr SDay
'Galaxy Ranger'	EStr
'Gale Storm'	WNHG
'Galena Holiday'	EWes
'Galileo'	EStr
'Garden Butterfly'	EStr
'Garden Crawler'	CBgR
'Garden Portrait'	EWoo SDay
'Garrett Allen'	EStr
'Gary Colby'	EStr
'Gaudy Grasshopper'	EStr
'Gavin Petit' **new**	SDay
'Gay Octopus'	CBgR EStr MSpe WHrl
'Gay Rapture'	SPer
'Gay Troubadour'	EWoo
'Geltonoji Žvaigdže' **new**	EStr
'Gemini'	SDay
'Gender Equality'	EStr
'Geneva Firetruck'	EStr WHrl
'Gentle Country Breeze'	SDay
'Gentle Rose'	EStr SDay
'Gentle Shepherd'	Widely available
'Gentle Thoughts'	SDay
'George Cunningham'	EBlo ECtt EGrI EHyd ELan LRHS MRav NBir NRHS SDay WFar
'George David'	WHrl
'Georgette Belden'	ECtt GKin MSpe NHol SPeP
'Georgia Cream' (d)	NLar
'Georgina May' **new**	SDay
'Gerda Brooker'	EStr
'Get All Excited'	ELon
'Ghost Baby' **new**	EStr
'Ghost Pattern'	EStr
'Giant Moon'	CBgR CRos EBlo ECtt EHyd ELan EStr LRHS NRHS SDay SRms
'Giddy Go Round'	EWoo SDay
'Gimme a Pigfoot' **new**	EStr
'Ginger Twist'	EStr
'Gingham Maid' **new**	SDay
'Give Me Eight'	EWoo
'Glacier Bay'	CBgR EWoo SDay
'Glazed Heather Plum'	EStr SDay
'Gleber's Top Cream'	EStr SDay
'Gleeman Song'	CBgR
'Glendevon'	EStr
'Glittering Treasure'	SDay XLum
'Glow Appeal'	EStr
'Go Seminoles'	EStr
'Going Bananas'[PBR]	WCot
'Gold Elephant'	SDay
'Gold Fever'	SDay
'Golden Bell'	NGdn
'Golden Chance'	WCAu
'Golden Chimes'	Widely available
'Golden Compass'	EStr
'Golden Firefly'	SDay
'Golden Ginkgo'	SDay WNHG
'Golden Peace'	SDay
'Golden Prize'	NGdn SDay WCot XSen
'Golden Scroll'	SDay
GOLDEN ZEBRA ('Malja'[PBR]) (v)	CEme CWGN ELan EPfP MRav NLar SRms
'Goldie Hicks'	SDay
'Golliwog'	CBgR EStr
'Gorgeous Smile'	EStr
'Got Milk'	EStr
'Gothic Butterfly'	EStr
'Gothic Window'	SDay
'Grace and Favour'	SDay
'Graceful Eye'	SDay
'Graceland'	SDay WHrl
'Grand Masterpiece'	EStr NGdn SDay WFar
'Grand Palais'	ELon SDay
'Granite City Towhead'	ELon EWoo
'Granny's Smokehouse'	EStr
'Grape Arbor'	WNHG
'Grape Harvest'	WNHG
'Grape Magic'	MSpe WCot
'Grape Velvet'	CSpe EStr EWoo MHer NSti SRms WCAu WNHG WWtn
'Grapes of Wrath'	EStr
'Great Auntie Picklebottom'	EStr
'Green Arrow'	EStr
'Green Dolphin Street'	SDay
'Green Dragon'	SDay
'Green Eyed Lady'	SDay
'Green Eyes Wink'	MHol
'Green Flutter'	CBgR EStr GBee GBin GQue LPla NBir NGdn NSti WSpi
'Green Fringe'	SDay
'Green Goddess'	XLum
'Green Gondola' **new**	EStr
'Green Icon'	EStr
'Green is Good' **new**	EStr
'Green Lines'	EStr
'Green Mystique'	EStr SDay
'Green Nautilus'	EStr
'Green Puff'	SDay
'Green Spider'	CBgR SDay
'Green Token' **new**	EStr
'Green Widow'	EWoo SDay
'Greenland'	ECtt EHyd EStr LRHS NRHS
'Greywoods Cowgirl Casanova'	EStr
'Greywoods Fashionista'	EStr
'Greywoods Fingers Malone'	EStr
'Greywoods Katz Kando'	EStr
'Greywoods Nautical Nellie'	EStr
'Groove-billed Ani'	EStr
'Groovy Green'	SDay
'Grumbly'	ELan WPnP
'Gryphon Hankow Legacy'	EStr
'Gryphon Prague Gothic'	EStr
'Guardian Angel'	WCFE
'Guardian Light' **new**	SDay
'Gwen Leman'	EStr
'Gypsy Sweetheart'	WNHG
'Hail Mary'	SDay
'Halloween Green'	EStr
'Hamlet'	SDay WNHG
'Handsome Devil'	EStr
'Happy Apache'	EStr
'Happy Medium'	EStr

'Happy Returns'	CBgR CRos CSBt CTri EBlo ECha EHyd ELan EPfP EStr EWoo LCro LRHS LSRN MBel NGdn NHol NRHS SRms WCAu XLum
'Harbor Blue'	ELon SDay
'Harbor Gate'	SDay
'Harrods'	EStr
'Harry Barras'	XLum
'Harvest Hue'	SDay
'Having Fun'	EStr
'Hawaiian Nights'	WNHG
'Hawk'	ELon SDay
'Hawkwoman'	EStr
'Hazel'	EStr
'Hazmatter's Ball'	EStr
'Heady Wine'	EStr SDay
'Heart Wishes'	EStr
'Heartless'	EStr
'Heavenly Angel Ice'	ELon EPfP EStr MACG
'Heavenly Beginnings'	EStr
'Heavenly Black Bird'	EStr
'Heavenly Curls'	EStr SDay
'Heavenly Fire and Ice'	EStr
'Heavenly Flight of Angels'	EStr SMrm
'Heavenly Mr Twister'	EStr
'Heavenly Orange Blaze'	EStr EWoo
'Heavenly Pink Butterfly'	EStr SDay
'Heavenly Spider Monkey' **new**	EStr
'Heavenly Thunderbird'	EStr
'Heavenly Treasure'	SDay
'Heavenly United We Stand'	EStr
'Heavenly Way Big'	EStr
'Heidi Eidelweiss'	EWoo
'Heirloom Lace'	SDay WCAu
'Helen Sever'	EStr
'Helen Shooter'	EStr
'Helena Seabird'	EStr SDay
'Helix'	EPfP EStr MBros SDay
'Helle Berlinerin'	SDay SEdd
'Hello Screamer'	EStr
'Helter Skelter'	SDay
'Heman'	EStr
'Henry D. Allnutt'	EStr
'Her Best Bloomers' **new**	EStr
'Her Majesty's Wizard'	CBgR ELan ELon
'Here Lies Butch'	EStr
'Here Lies Jimmy Hoffa' **new**	EStr
'Hermitage Newton'	SDay
'Hexagon'	EStr
'Hey There'	SDay
'Hiding Place'	EStr
'High Profile'	EStr
'High Tor'	ELon EStr SDay WHrl WOld
'High Water Mark'	EStr
'Highland Lord' (d)	EStr MSpe SDay WCAu
'Highland Summerbird'	SDay
'Hingucker' **new**	SDay
'His Highness' **new**	SDay
'Hold Your Horses'	SDay
'Holiday Delight'	EStr
'Holiday Mood'	ELan
'Holly Dancer' ♀H6	EStr
'Homeward Bound'	SDay
'Honey Redhead'	SDay
'Honeysuckle Rose'	EStr
'Honor Flight'	EStr
'Hooked on Romance'	EStr
'Hope Diamond'	SDay
'Hope Floats'	EStr
'Hoping for Hugs'	EStr
'Hornby Castle'	CBro CRos EBlo EHyd LRHS NRHS
'Hortensia'	SDay
'Hot Pink Fury'	EStr
'Hot Tamales and Red Hots'	EStr
'Hot Town'	ELan
'Hot Wheels'	CBgR
'Hot Wire'	SDay WNHG
'Hotheaded Woman' **new**	EStr
'Houdini'	SDay WCAu
'House of Orange'	EStr SDay
'How Beautiful Heaven Must Be' **new**	SDay
'Hubbles Buddy'	EWoo
'Humdinger'	EStr SDay WCot
'Hummingbird'	EStr
'Humungousaur'	EStr
'Hunker Down'	EStr
'Huntress'	EStr
'Hybridizer's Truffle'	EStr
'Hymn'	SDay
'Hyperion'	CAby CBgR CMac CTri ECha ECtt ELon EShb EStr EWoo GKin GMcL LEdu LRHS MACG MHol MRav NBid NGdn SDay SMrm SPer SWvt WCAu WCot WWtn
'I Gotta Be Me'	EStr
'I Love to Tell the Story'	EStr
'I See Stars' **new**	EStr
'Ice Carnival'	EStr LDai NGdn NLar SCob SWvt WSpi
'Ice Castles'	CTri SDay
'Ice Cool'	SCob
'Ice Planet'	SDay
'Icecap'	CBgR
'Icy Lemon'	EStr SDay
'Ida Duke Miles'	SDay
'Ida Mae Norris'	EStr
'Ida Wimberly Munson'	SDay
'Ida's Magic'	EStr SDay
'Identity Crisis'	EStr
'Iditarod'	EStr
'Igor'	SDay
'Ikebana Star'	EStr
'Iktomi'	EStr
'Illini Jackpot'	SDay
'I'm a King Bee'	EStr
'Imperial Lemon'	GBin
'Impromptu'	SDay
'In Depth' (d)	EWoo NBro NLar WCot WHrl
'In Her Shoes'	EStr
'In Search of Angels'	EStr
'In Strawberry Time'	WNHG
'Inca Puzzle'	SDay
'Inchon'	EStr
'Increased Complexity'	EStr
'Incy Wincy Spider' **new**	EStr
'Indian Giver'	SDay
'Indian Paintbrush'	ELon MACG NBir WNHG
'Indian Sky'	SDay
'Indy Heart Stopper'	EStr
'Inner View'	ECtt EStr SDay
'Innocent Blush'	EStr
'Inspired Word'	SDay
'Interstellar' **new**	EStr
'Invitation to Immortality'	EWoo LSun
'Iridescent Jewel'	SDay
'Irish Elf'	ELon GBin SDay SHar
'Irish Mixup'	EStr
'Irish Veil'	EStr
'Iron Gate Glacier'	EPPr EStr LRHS MBNS SDay XLum
'Irresistible You'	EStr
'Irving Schulman'	SDay
'Isaac'	EStr
'Isabelle Rose'	EStr SDay
'Isle of Dreams'	SDay

'Isle of Wight'	SDay
'Islesworth'	EWoo SDay
'Isolde'	CBgR EStr
'It's My Party' **new**	EStr
'It's Soul Time'	EStr
'Itsy Bitsy Spider'	CBgR EWoo
'Itza Mirage'	EStr
'Ivelyn Brown'	EStr SDay
'Ivory Cloud' (d)	EStr
'Ivory Coast'	SDay
'J.T. Davis'	EStr
'Jack O'Lantern Smile' **new**	EStr
'Jamaican Jammin''	SDay
'Jamaican Me Crazy' ♀H6	SDay
'James Marsh'	CBgR EWoo MNrw NSti SDay WCAu WCot WFar WNHG
'James the Dragon Slayer' **new**	EStr
'Jane Trimmer'	SDay
'Jane's Prism'	EStr
'Janet Gayle' **new**	SDay
'Janice Brown'	CWCL ECtt EGrl EMor EStr EWoo GBee NHol NLar NRHS SDay WHrl
'Janie Wilson'	WNHG
'Jan's Twister'	EStr MNrw SDay WHrl
'Jason Salter'	EStr SDay
'Jay Turman'	SDay
'Jealous Sky'	EStr
'Jean'	EStr SDay
'Jean Swann'	EStr
'Jedi Codie Wedgeworth'	SDay
'Jedi Dot Pierce'	EStr SDay
'Jedi Rose Frost'	SDay
'Jellyfish Jealousy' ♀H6	EStr SDay
'Jennie Sivyer'	EStr
'Jenny Wren'	EPPr EWoo NBro
'Jerry Hyatt'	EStr
'Jersey Breeze'	EStr
'Jersey Jim'	EWoo
'Jerusalem'	SDay
'Jeune Tom'	CBgR
'Jewel Case'	WNHG
'Jim McKinney'	EStr
'Joan Derifield'	EStr
'Joan Senior'	Widely available
'Job Creator'	EStr
'Jock Randall'	SDay
'Jockey Club' (d)	ECtt EStr WHrl
'Jogolor'	EStr
'John R. Pike'	EStr
'Johnny Come Lately'	EStr
'Joie de Vivre'	EWoo
'Jolly Lad'	SDay
'Jolyene Nichole'	SDay
'Jordan'	LSRN SWvt
'Jordan's Jazz'	EStr
'Josephine Marina'	EStr
'Journey to Oz'	EWoo
'Journey's End'	SDay
'Jovial'	EStr SDay
'Joyful Occasion'	SDay
'Joyful Participation'	EStr
'Juanita's Picotee Delight'	SDay
'Judah'	SDay
'Judge Roy Bean'	EStr SDay WHrl
'Judy Davidson'	WNHG
'Judy Farquhar'	EStr
'Julie Covington' **new**	EStr
'Julie Newmar' ♀H6	SDay
'June Melody'	WNHG
'June Wine'	SDay
'Jungle Beauty'	CBgR SDay
'Jungle Jack Joiner'	SDay
'Just Celebrate'	SDay
'Just My Size'	EBee EStr
'Just Whistle'	EStr
'Justin George'	SDay
'Justin June'	WHrl
'Kaleidoscopic Intrigue'	EStr
'Kansas Kitten'	EStr EWoo SDay
'Karen's Curls' ♀H6	SDay
'Kasia'	WHrl
'Kate Carpenter'	EStr SDay
'Kathleen Salter'	EStr EWoo SDay
'Kathryn June Wood'	SDay
'Katie Elizabeth Miller'	SDay
'Katisue Herrington'	EStr
'Kazuq'	SDay
'Kecia'	SDay
'Keene'	EWoo
'Kelly's Girl'	SDay
'Kempion'	CBgR
'Kermit's Scream'	EStr
'Key to my Heart'	CBgR
'Key West Sunset'	EStr
'Kharma Police'	EStr
'Kickin' Chicken'	EStr
'Killer Purple'	SDay
'Kimberly Sue'	EStr
'Kindly Light'	EWoo
'King Crab'	EStr
'King George'	EStr SDay
'King Kahuna' (d)	EStr SDay
'King of Anything'	EStr
'King's Gold'	EStr
'King's Throne'	WNHG
'Kiowa Sunset'	SDay
'Kirsten My Love'	EStr
'Kiss Kiss Kiss'	EStr
'Kiss the Sky'	EStr
'Kissed by Moonlight'	EStr
'Knights in White Satin'	EStr SDay
'Kokomo Queen'	EStr
'Kristin Dalton'	EStr
'Kung Fu Panda'	EStr
'Kwanso Flore Pleno'	see *H. fulva* 'Green Kwanso'
'Kwanso Flore Pleno Variegata'	see *H. fulva* 'Variegated Kwanso'
'La Fenice'	EStr
'La Peche'	SDay
'Lacy Doily'	EStr WCAu
'Lacy Marionette'	ELon EWoo SDay
'Lady Betty Fretz'	EBee EStr
'Lady Fingers'	CBgR WHrl
'Lady Inara'	EStr
'Lady Liz'	SDay WNHG
'Lady Mischief'	EStr SDay
'Lady Neva' ♀H6	CBgR ELon MSpe
'Lady Tiger'	WNHG
'Ladybug Hawk'	EStr
'Ladybug's Two Moons' (d)	EStr
'Ladykin'	ELon SDay
'Lake Norman Spider'	EWoo SDay
'Lambada'	EStr
'Lamplighter's Circle'	EStr
'Land of Enchantment'	EStr
'Land of Our Fathers' **new**	SDay
'Land's End'	EStr
'Lark Song'	EBlo EHyd LRHS NRHS WFar WHrl
'Larry's Candy Stripe Swizzle'	EStr
'Last Snowflake' **new**	SDay
'Last Song'	EStr
'Late Report'	EStr
'Late Summer Rose'	WNHG
'Laughing Giraffe'	EStr WCot

'Laughton Tower'	SMHy
'Lauradell'	SDay
'Lauren Leah'	SDay
'Lava Burst'	EStr
'Lava Stream'	EStr
'Lavender Blue Baby'	CBod EPfP EStr MHol SPer
'Lavender Bonanza'	SDay
'Lavender Deal'	MNrw WNHG
'Lavender Handlebars'	SDay
'Lavender Memories'	EStr SDay WNHG
'Lavender Showstopper'	WCAu
'Lavender Spider'	CBgR
'Lavender Stardust'	SDay
'Lavender Tonic'	SDay WNHG
'Lavender Tutu'	ECtt EStr MBros
'Lazy Hazy Days'	EStr
'Leading Edge'	SDay
'Ledgewood's Frequent Flyer'	EStr
'Ledgewood's Irish Spirit'	EStr
'Ledgewood's Sunday Dessert'	EStr
'Lee Reinke'	EStr
'Leila Mantle'	CBgR
'Lemon Bells'	CWat EBou ECha EHyd EPfP EStr GKev GKin GMaP LEdu LRHS MAvo NBro NCth SDay SHar WCAu WSpi
'Lemon Custard'	EStr
'Lemon Dessert'	ELon
'Lemon Fellow'	EWoo
'Lemon Madeline'	EStr
'Lemon Mint'	ELon
'Lemon Soldier'	EStr
'Lemonora'	SDay
'Lenox'	SDay
'Leonard Bernstein'	EStr SDay
'Leprechaun's Curls'	EStr
'Let it Rip'	EWoo
'Let Loose'	EStr
'Let Love Rejoice'	EStr
'Let Me Be Clear' **new**	EStr
'Lies and Lipstick'	EStr
'Life is a Highway'	EStr
'Life Unlimited'	EStr
'Light the Way'	ECha SEdd SPoG WCot
'Light Years Away'	ELon MBNS MNrw
'Lightning Strikes Twice'	EStr
'Like a Gee Six'	EStr
'Lilac Lady'	EStr
'Lilac Wine'	ECha WBor
§ ***lilioasphodelus***	Widely available
'Lillian's Good Intentions'	EStr
'Lilly Dache'	EStr EWoo
'Lilting Belle'	MSpe
'Lilting Lady'	EStr SDay
'Lilting Lavender'	ELon SDay WCAu
'Lily Munster'	EStr
'Lime Frost' ♀H6	CBgR EStr SDay
'Lime Painted Lady'	CBgR
'Limetree'	CBgR EStr
'Limited Edition'	EWoo
'Limoncello'	SDay
'Lin Wright'	EWoo
'Linda'	MRav
'Linda Sierra'	EStr
'Linda the Green Eyed Lady'	EStr
'Lines of Splendor'	EWoo
'Lip Smack'	EStr
'Lipstick on a Pig'	EStr
'Lisa My Joy' **new**	SDay
'Litchfield Plantation'	EStr
'Little Anna Rosa'	ECtt EStr LLWG
'Little Audrey'	EStr
'Little Big Man'	SDay
'Little Bugger'	ELon
'Little Bumble Bee'	LRHS WWtn
'Little Business'	SDay
'Little Cadet'	XLum
'Little Cranberry Cove'	GBin
'Little Deeke'	SDay WHrl
'Little Dream Red'	SDay
'Little Fairy' **new**	LBar
'Little Fantastic'	ELon SDay WWtn
'Little Fat Cat'	EStr
'Little Fellow'	EStr
'Little Girl'	ELon
'Little Grapette'	ELon EPfP EStr GQue LLWG LPla NLar NSti SCob
'Little Greenie'	SDay
'Little Gypsy Vagabond'	CBgR CWat EStr
'Little Heavenly Angel'	EStr
'Little Isaac'	EStr
'Little Kiki'	SDay
'Little Lassie'	CBgR
'Little Maggie'	SDay
'Little Men'	WCAu
'Little Miss Lucy'	EStr
'Little Miss Manners'	EStr NLar
'Little Missy'	CBgR EStr SDay WNHG
'Little Monica'	SDay
'Little Music Maker' (d)	EStr
'Little Paul'	EStr
'Little Red Hen'	ECha EHyd GKin LRHS NBir NBro NGdn SDay WFar
'Little Show Stopper'	NBro NLar
'Little Showoff'	SDay
'Little Surfer Girl'	EStr
'Little Swain'	SDay
'Little Sweet Talk'	ELon
'Little Swirling Shadows'	EStr
'Little Tawny'	ELon
'Little Toddler'	SDay
'Little Velma'	EStr
'Little Violet Lace'	SDay
'Little Wart'	CBgR SDay WHrl
'Little William'	EStr
'Little Wine Cup'	CAby CMac CRos ECrc ELon EStr GKin GMaP LRHS MRav MTin NBir NGdn NRHS SCoo SMrm SPer SRms
'Little Women'	SDay WHrl
'Little Zinger'	SDay
'Littlest Angel'	SDay
'Littlest Clown'	SDay
'Living in Amsterdam'	EStr
'Lobo Lucy'	ELon EStr
'Loch Ness Monster'	EStr
'Lochinvar'	MRav
'Loco Bo'	EStr
'Lois Burns'	EWoo SDay
'Lola Branham'	EStr EWoo
'Lonely Heart'	EStr
'Long John Silver'	ELon EStr
'Long Stocking'	EStr SDay WCot
'Long Tall Sally'	EStr
'Longfields Anwar'	EGrl EWoo
'Longfields Bandit'	EWoo
'Longfields Beauty'	EWoo MSpe
'Longfields Dress Pink'	EStr
'Longfields X Factor'	EStr LAma
'Longfields Glory'	EHyd ITim LRHS NRHS
'Longfields Maxim' (d)	EStr MHol SDeJ
'Longfields Pearl'	EStr ITim LBar
'Longfields Pride'	EStr SRms
'Longfields Purple Eye'	NLar
'Longfields Think Pink'	EStr

'Longfields Tropica'	EStr
'Longfields Twins'	MBNS WCot WFar
'Longfields Whoopy'	EGrl ELon LAma SDir
longituba B&SWJ 4576	WCru
'Look at Me'	ELan
'Look Lucky'	EStr
'Lost in the Toy Store'	EStr
'Lost in the Translation'	EStr
'Loth Lorien'	EHyd EStr LRHS SDay
'Lots of Hoopla'	EStr
'Lotta Dotta'	EStr
'Lotus Land'	SDay
'Lotus Position'	EBee
'Loud Girls' **new**	EStr
'Louis McHargue'	SDay
'Lourice Abdallah'	EStr
'Love Those Eyes'	EStr
'Love to Dance' **new**	SDay
'Lovely Margie'	EStr
'Lovely Miss Laucius'	EStr
'Lovely Rita'	EStr
'Loverboy'	EStr
'Loving Memories'	SDay
'Lowcountry Gem'	EStr
'Lucille Lennington'	WNHG
'Lullaby Baby'	ELan NLar SDay WNHG
'Luminous Jewel'	SDay
'Lunar Sea'	EStr
'Lupita Vindaz'	EStr
'Luscious Honeydew'	WNHG
'Lusty Lealand'	SDay
'Lusty Little Lulu'	SDay
'Luxury Lace'	CAgr EBee EHyd ELan EStr GKin LRHS LSRN MACG NBir NGdn NHol NLar NWad SPer WFar WHrl WWtn XLum
'Lydia Bechtold'	EStr SDay
'Lynn Hall'	NLar WSpi
'Mabel Fuller'	CBgR MRav SPer WHrl
'Mabel Nolen'	EStr
'Mable Lewis Nelson'	EStr
'Macbeth'	EGrl EStr LAma MNrw SDir
'Mad Max'	EStr EWoo SDay
'Madeline Nettles Eyes'	EBee ELon EStr
'Madmoiselle Constanza'	SDay
'Mae Graham'	SDay
'Maestro Puccini'	SDay
'Maggie Fynboe'	CBgR
'Magic Amethyst'	CBgR
'Magic Carpet Ride'	EStr
'Magic Dancer'	EStr
'Magic Elf' **new**	EStr
'Magic Filigree'	SDay
'Magic Lace'	EStr
'Magic Masquerade'	SDay
'Magic of Oz'	EStr SDay
'Magical Messenger'	EStr
'Mahogany Magic' ♀H6	ELon EStr
'Majestic Dark Eyes'	EStr
'Malachite Prism'	EStr
'Malaysian Monarch'	EStr SDay WNHG
'Malaysian Spice'	WNHG
'Maleny Canary'	EStr
'Maleny Chantilly Lace'	EStr
'Maleny Debutante'	EStr
'Maleny Kiwi Dazzler'	EStr
'Maleny Mite'	EWoo
'Maleny Tiger'	SDay
'Mallard'	CAby CBgR EBlo ECha ECtt EStr LRHS MHer MRav NBir SDay SPer WCot
'Malmaison Plum'	EStr SDay
'Mama Sophia'	EStr

'Mama's Pajamas'	EStr
'Man on Fire'	WNHG
'Manchurian Apricot'	SDay
'Marble Faun'	SDay
'Margaret Perry'	MNrw NLar
'Margaret Seawright'	EStr
'Margo Reed Indeed'	EStr SDay WNHG
'Marietta Charmer'	SDay
'Marietta Delight'	EStr
'Marietta Snowflake' **new**	SDay
'Marietta Trilogy' **new**	EStr
'Marilyn Lee Bock'	EStr
'Marilyn Morss Johnson'	EStr
'Marion Vaughn'	ECha ECtt ELan EPfP GKin GMaP MBel MRav NSti SDix SRGP SWvt WCAu WCot WFar WHoo WSHC
'Mariska'	EStr SDay WNHG
'Marked by Lydia'	ELon
'Marshall McLuhan'	EStr
'Martha Adams'	SDay
'Martie Everest'	EWoo
'Martina Verhaert'	CWGN EStr
'Mary Alice Stokes'	EStr
'Mary Ethel Anderson'	EStr SDay
'Mary Todd'	EBee GMcL WCAu XSen
'Mary's Baby'	EStr
'Mary's Gold' ♀H6	SDay
'Masada'	WNHG
'Mask of Time'	EStr
'Mask of Zorro'	EStr
'Mata Hari'	SDay
'Matchless Fire'	EStr
'Maude's Valentine'	SDay
'Mauna Loa'	CSBt ECha ELon EPfP EStr GQue MNrw NLar SDeJ SWvt WCAu WCot
'May May'	CBgR ELon SDay
'Mayan Poppy'	EStr
'Meadow Mist'	CBgR ELon
'Meadow Sprite'	SDay WCot
'Mean Mister Mustard'	EStr
'Medieval Guild'	EStr
'Mema's Dingaling'	EStr
'MeMe's Alter Ego'	EStr
'MeMe's Guilty Pleasure'	EStr
'MeMe's Indulgence'	EStr
'MeMe's Lovin' the Limelight'	EStr
'MeMe's Merlot'	EStr
'MeMe's Pink Flamingo'	EStr
'Memory Number One'	EStr
'Mephistopheles'	EWoo
'Merry Jo's Delight'	EStr
'Merry Moppet'	EStr EWoo
'Merry Witch'	EStr
'Metaphor'	MHol SDay
'Michael Poliga'	EStr
'Michael's Sword'	EStr
'Michele Coe'	ECtt GKin NBro NGdn SDay WCAu WFar WHrl
'Mico'	ELon
middendorffii	CMac EBlo EStr EWoo GGro GKev GMaP LPla NSti WHrl WSpi WThu
'Middle of Nowhere'	EStr
'Midnight Confession'	EStr
'Midnight Magic'	SDay
'Midnight Mantis'	SDay
'Midnight Raider'	EWoo
'Midnight Rambler'	SDay
'Midnight Rendezvous'	EStr
'Mighty Goliath' **new**	EWoo
'Mighty Shogun'	SDay
'Mikado'	CBgR CMac EStr

'Mike Reed'	EStr
'Milady Greensleeves'	EStr EWoo SDay WHrl
'Milanese Mango'	EStr SDay
'Mildred Mitchell'	CBgR ELon EStr GKev NLar WHrl
'Military School'	EStr
'Millie Schlumpf'	SDay
'Mimosa Umbrella'	EStr
'Ming Lo'	SDay
'Ming Porcelain'	SDay WCAu WNHG
'Mini Pearl'	CAby ECtt ELon EStr LRHS MPie NRHS SDay SPer
'Mini Stella'	CBro ECtt LBar SDay WFar
'Minnie Wildfire'	EStr
minor	EBlo EHyd EPPr LRHS NRHS SRms
- B&SWJ 8841	WCru
'Miracle Maid'	WNHG
'Miss Atomic Bomb'	EStr
'Miss Jessie'	EStr EWoo MSpe SDay
'Miss Mayhem' **new**	EStr
'Miss North Carolina'	EStr
'Miss Piggy'	EStr
'Missenden'	CBgR EStr MNrw
'Missouri Beauty'	SWvt
'Mister Lucky'	EStr
'Mojave Sunset'	EStr
'Mokan Butterfly'	MSpe SDay
'Monica Marie'	EStr SDay
'Mont Royal Demitasse'	ELon
'Mood Elevator' **new**	SDay
'Moon Snow'	SDay
'Moon Witch'	SDay
'Moonlight Mist'	SDay
'Moonlight Orchid'	WHrl
'Moonlit Caress'	CBgR EBee ECtt NBro SDay
'Moonlit Crystal'	EStr
'Moonlit Masquerade' ♀H6	CBgR CWGN ECtt ELon EStr MAvo MBNS MNrw NLar SDay SEND SRms WHrl
'Moonlit Summerbird'	EStr SDay
'Moontraveller'	WCot
'Morgen le Fay'	EStr
'Mormon Spider'	EStr
'Morning Face'	EStr
'Morning Sun'	WCot
'Morocco Red'	CBro ELan MHCG
'Morphin Time'	EStr
'Morpho Butterfly'	EStr
'Morticia' **new**	SDay
'Mosel'	SDay
'Moses' Fire'	ECtt EStr MHol NLar SPeP WFar
'Mossy Glade'	CBgR
'Mount Echo Sunrise'	EWoo
'Mount Herman Intrigue' **new**	EStr
'Mount Joy'	EStr
'Mountain Laurel'	ECtt EHyd EStr GKin LDai LRHS MRav NRHS WFar WGwG
'Mountain Top Experience'	SDay
'Moussaka'	CWGN EStr WCAu WFar
'Move over Moon'	EStr SDay
'Mr and Mrs Bubbs'	EStr
'Mrs Hugh Johnson'	CChe EShb NFav WHrl
* 'Mrs Lester'	SDay
'Muddy Creek Magic'	EStr
'Muffet's Little Friend'	WHrl
'Multiple Multiplications'	EStr
'Mumbo Jumbo'	SDay
'Munchkin Moonbeam'	SDay
'Muriel Rhem'	EStr
'Murphy's Law'	EStr
'Muscle and Blood'	EWoo
'Muscle Man'	EStr
'Music Show' **new**	SDay
'My Belle'	SDay
'My Darling Clementine'	EStr SDay WNHG
'My Friend Kammy'	EStr
'My Happy Valentine'	SDay
'My Heart Belongs to Daddy'	EStr
'My Melinda'	SDay
'My Place or Yours'	EStr
'My Reggae Tiger'	EStr
'Mynelle's Starfish'	MSpe SDay WHrl
'Mystical Rainbow'	SDay
'Nabis'	SDay
'Nacogdoches Lady'	SWvt
'Nagasaki' (d)	SDay
'Nairobi Dawn'	SDay
* 'Nana Wallich'	EStr
'Nanuq'	ELon SDay
'Naomi Ruth'	EStr
'Nashville'	CBro ELan WHrl
'Nashville Lights'	CBgR EStr SDay
'National Memento'	EStr
'Native Reflection'	EStr
'Natty Man'	EStr
'Naughty Red'	EStr MACG
'Navajo Jewel'	EStr
'Navajo Pony'	EStr
'Navajo Princess'	SDay
'Neal Berrey'	EStr SDay
'Nefertiti'	CBgR ELon NBir WCAu
'Neon Flamingo'	EStr
'Neon Sunshine'	EStr
'Neon Yellow'	EStr
'Neutron Star'	EStr
'Never Ending Fantasy'	EStr
'Never Get Away'	EStr
'New Design'	EStr
'New Wine'	WNHG
'New York Follies'	EStr
'Neyron Rose'	EHyd GKin LRHS NGdn NRHS WWtn XLum
'Night Beacon'	CBgR ECtt EGrl ELon EStr EWoo GKin LLWG MNrw MPie NLar SCob SDay SDeJ WCAu WHrl
'Night Embers'	ECtt ELon EPfP EStr EWTr EWoo LAma MBel NGdn NLar SDir SPad WCAu WHrl
'Night Raider'	CBgR EStr SDay WNHG
'Nile Crane'	CBgR ELon EStr MNrw SDay SPer
'Nile Plum'	EStr SDay
'Nina Winegar'	EStr
'Ninja Storm'	EStr
'Nivia Guest'	SDay
'Nob Hill'	EBlo ELon EStr LRHS WHrl XLum
'Nona's Garnet Spider'	ELon
'Nordic Night'	CBgR SDay
'North Wind Dancer' ♀H6	EWoo
'North Wind Drifter'	EStr
'Norton Beauté'	WCot
'Norton Eyed Seedling'	WNHG
'Norton Orange'	EStr
'Nosferatu'	SDay
'Not Forgotten'	WNHG
'Nothing is Easy'	EStr
'Notify Ground Crew'	EStr SDay
'Nova'	ELon SDay
'Now Go Hide' **new**	EStr
'Nowhere to Hide'	EStr
'Nuit Parisienne'	EStr
'Nuka'	XLum
'Numinous Moments'	SDay
'Nutmeg Elf'	CBgR SDay
'Oakes Love'	EWoo MNrw
'O'Bannon Orchid'	EStr
'Obsidian'	SCoo

'Ocean Ice' **new**	SDay
'Ocean Rain'	EStr SDay WNHG
'Ocean Spirit'	EStr
'Oceanside' **new**	SDay
'Octopus Hugs'	EStr
'Ojo de Dios'	EWoo
'Oke-She-Moke-She-Pop'	EStr
'Old San Juan'	EStr
'Old Tangiers' ♀H6	EStr SDay WNHG
'Olfactory Evidence' **new**	EWoo
'Olive Bailey Langdon'	EStr SDay WCot
'Olive's Odd One'	ELon EStr
'Oloroso'	CBgR
'Olympic Gold'	EStr
'Olympic Showcase'	EStr SDay
'Omomuki'	SDay
'On and On'	EStr GQue MBros MNrw
'On Pointe'	EStr
'On Silken Thread'	SDay
'One Above You'	EStr
'One Eye Willie' **new**	EStr
'One Last Straw'	EWoo
'One Step Beyond' **new**	SDay
'One Strange Cookie'	EStr
'Oodles'	WHrl
'Open Hearth'	EStr SDay WHrl
'Open my Eyes'	EStr
'Orange Dream'	SDay
'Orange Empire'	SDay
'Orange Exotica'	CBgR EStr
'Orange Fizz' (d)	EStr
'Orange Nassau'	EStr WCAu WFar
'Orange Velvet'	SDay
'Orangeman' misapplied	NGdn
'Orchid Candy'	EStr GMcL NBir
'Orchid Corsage'	ELon EStr SDay
'Orchid Lady Slipper'	EStr EWoo
'Oriental Impressions'	EStr
'Oriental Ruby'	SDay
'Ornamental Focus' **new**	SDay
'Osterized'	EStr
'Ostrich Plume'	EStr
'Ouachita Beauty'	CBgR ELon
'Our Kirsten'	EStr SDay
'Out of Balance'	EStr
'Outrageous'	CBgR EStr SDay WNHG
'Outrageous Ramona'	WNHG
'Over the Mountain' **new**	SDay
'Oy Vey'	EStr
'Paige's Pinata'	EStr
'Painted Lady'	EGrl WNHG
'Painted Pink'	SDay
'Painter's Touch'	SDay
'Palace Garden Beauty'	EWoo
'Palace Pagoda'	WNHG
'Pale Behemoth' **new**	SDay
'Pale Moon Windmill'	SDay
'Panda Bear'	EStr
'Pandora's Box'	CTri CWat ECtt EGrl ELan EStr MNrw NBir NGdn NLar SDeJ SWvt WBor WFar
'Pantherette'	ELon
'Papa Goose'	EStr
'Papa Goose Gets Jiggy'	EStr
'Paper Butterfly'	EStr SDay
'Papilion'	EStr
'Papoose'	XLum
'Paprika Flame'	EStr MHol
'Parade of Peacocks'	CBgR
'Paradise Bar and Grill'	EStr
'Paradise Lost'	EStr
'Pardon Me'	CAby CBWd CBro EBee ECtt EGrl EHyd ELan ELon EStr GJos GKin GMaP LRHS MPie NCth NGdn NLar NRHS SCoo SDeJ SWvt WCAu WFar
'Parfait'	CBgR EStr EWoo WHrl WNHG
'Parlor Game' **new**	SDay
'Parrot Tattoo'	EStr
'Parson's Robe'	SDay
'Part-time Princess'	EStr
'Party Pants'	EStr
'Party Queen'	SDay
'Passion for Red'	SDay
'Passive Aggressive'	EStr
'Pastel Ballerina'	SDay
'Pastel Classic'	SDay
'Pat Mercer'	SDay
'Patchwork Puzzle'	EStr EWoo
'Patricia Gentzel Wright'	EWoo
'Patricia Snider Memorial'	SDay
'Patrick Starfish'	EStr
'Patriotic Flavor'	EStr
'Patsy Bickers'	ELon EWoo
'Pattern Breaker'	EStr
'Patterns'	WNHG
'Patti Neyland'	EStr
'Paul Weber'	SDay
'Paula Goes Prime Time'	EStr
'Paula Nettles'	EStr
'Paulette Miller' **new**	SDay
'Paw Print'	EStr
'Pawn of Prophecy'	EStr SDay
'Peach Float'	EWoo
'Peach Jubilee'	EStr
'Peach Magnolia' (d)	EStr
'Peach Margarita'	EStr
'Peach Whisper'	EStr SDay
'Peacock Frills' **new**	EStr
'Peacock Maiden'	EStr EWoo WHrl
'Peacock Tale' **new**	EStr
'Pear Ornament'	SDay
'Pearl Anniversary'	EStr
'Pearl Jam'	SDay
'Pearl Lewis'	EStr SDay
'Peggy Jeffcoat'	EStr
'Penelope Vestey'	CBgR EStr NBir SDay
'Pennypurrs'	EStr
'Penny's Worth'	CRos EBlo LEdu LRHS WCot WFar XLum
'Peppermint Ice'	EStr
'Perfect Control' **new**	SDay
'Persian Melon Plus'	WCAu
'Persian Ruby'	EStr SDay WNHG
'Petite Ballerina'	SDay
'Phial of Galadriel' **new**	SDay
'Phill Warbasse'	EStr
'Photon Torpedo'	MACG
'Phyllis Cantini'	SDay
'Piano Man'	EStr WNHG
'Piccadilly Princess'	EStr SDay
'Pickin' and Grinnin''	EStr
'Piece of the Action'	EStr
'Pigment of Imagination'	EStr
'Pinhill Navajo Beauty'	EStr
'Pink Ambrosia'	EStr
'Pink Charm'	CEme CMac CWal ECha ECtt EHyd EPPr GKin GMaP NBro NRHS
'Pink Circle'	SDay
'Pink Cotton Candy'	SDay
'Pink Damask' ♀H6	Widely available
'Pink Dazzler'	WNHG
'Pink Delight'	MPie
'Pink Dream'	CBgR NBir
'Pink Embrace' **new**	SDay
'Pink Flirt'	SDay

'Pink Lady'	GDam MNrw MRav SRms
'Pink Monday'	SDay WNHG
'Pink Puff'	NBir NLar
'Pink Scintillation'	SDay
'Pink Spider'	SDay
'Pink Stripes'	EStr
'Pink Sundae'	WHrl
'Pink Super Spider'	EWoo SDay
'Pink Thunderbird'	EStr
'Pink Whip Tips'	EStr
'Pink Windmill'	ELon SDay
'Pinky Promise'	EStr
'Pirate King' **new**	SDay
'Pirate Treasure'	EStr SDay
'Pirates of Penzance' **new**	EStr
'Pirate's Patch'	EWoo SDay WCot
'Pixie Dragon'	EStr
'Pixie Parasol'	WNHG WSpi
'Pixie Princess'	EStr
'Pizza'	SDay
'Playing with Crayons'	EStr
'Pleated Petticoats'	EStr
'Pledge a Grievance' **new**	EStr
'Plum Beautiful'	EStr
'Plum Beauty'	NLar
'Plumas Lake'	WNHG
'Poetic Pattern'	EStr
'Poinsettia'	EStr
'Point of View'	EStr
'Pojo'	EStr SDay
'Polar Vortex'	EStr
'Polka Dot Bikini'	EStr
'Pony'	ELon SDay
'Porcelain Pleasure'	SDay
'Possum in a Sack'	CBgR
'Post Time'	EStr
'Powerpuff Girls'	EStr
'Prague Spring'	EStr SDay WCAu WHrl WNHG
'Prairie Belle'	NLar
'Prairie Blue Eyes'	EStr SDay SPlb WBor WCot WHrl
'Prairie Charmer'	SEND WHrl
'Prairie Moonlight'	NLar
'Prankster'	EStr
'Precious d'Oro'	GQue NFav SCob
'President Hadley'	SDay
'Pretty Face Nice Legs'	EStr
'Pretty Miss'	ECtt EStr WGwG
'Pretty, Pretty Please'	EStr
'Preview Party'	WNHG
'Primal Scream' ♀H6	EStr LSun MHol NLar SDay SMad SPoG WCot
'Prince of Midnight'	SDay
'Prince of Purple'	ELon
'Prince Poppycock'	EStr
'Prince Redbird'	SDay
'Princess Charming'	EStr
'Princess Summerbird'	SDay
'Princeton Eye Glow'	SDay
'Princeton Silky'	ELon
'Printmaker'	EStr
'Prize Picotee Deluxe'	SDay
'Prize Picotee Elite'	SDay
'Protocol'	ELon SDay
'Proud Mary'	SDay
'Ptarmigan'	CBgR EStr SDay
'Pterodactyl Eye'	EStr SDay
§ 'Puddin'	SDay
'Pueblo Dancer'	EStr
'Pug Yarborough'	EStr SDay
'Pullin' Strings'	EStr
'Pumpkin Kid'	SDay
'Pumpkin Prince'	EStr
'Punxsutawney Phil'	EStr
'Puppet Show'	SDay
'Pure and Simple'	SDay
'Purgatory Mountain' **new**	EStr
'Purple Avenger'	SDay
'Purple Badger' **new**	EStr
'Purple Bicolor'	WHrl
'Purple Flame'	EStr
'Purple Oddity'	SDay
'Purple Ostrich' **new**	EStr
'Purple Passion's Promise'	EStr
'Purple Penguin'	EStr
'Purple Rain'	CWat MPie SDay SWvt
'Purple Waters'	WPnP
'Purpleicious'	EStr NLar
'Pursuit of Excellence'	SDay
'Pushamataha'	SDay
'Putting on the Ritz'	EStr
'Pygmy Plum'	SDay
'Pyrotechnics'	EStr
'Quality of Mercy'	SDay
'Quartzitic Scintillation'	EStr
'Queen Charlotte'	EStr
'Queen Empress'	WNHG
'Queen Kathleen'	EStr
'Queen Lily'	WNHG
'Queen of Green'	EStr
'Queen of May'	MNrw WCot
'Queen of Spades'	SDay
'Queensland'	SDay
'Quick Results'	SDay
'Quiet Moment' **new**	SDay
'Quiet Riot'	EStr
'Quietly Awesome'	SDay
'Quietness'	SDay
'Quilt Patch'	EStr
'Quinn Buck'	SDay
'Ra Hansen'	EStr SDay
'Radiant Moonbeam' ♀H6	CBgR EStr
'Raging Bull'	EStr
'Raging Tiger'	SDay WHrl
'Rainbow Candy'	CWGN
'Rainbow Maker'	EStr
'Rainbow Spangles'	SDay
'Rajah'	CBgR CMac EStr NBro SPer WHrl
'Raspberry Candy'	CBro EStr SDay SRms WHrl
'Raspberry Star'	EStr
'Raspberry Wine'	ECha
'Raspberry Winter'	EStr
'Razzle'	EStr
'Reach for the Heavens'	EStr
'Real Life Drama'	EStr
'Real Wind'	EStr SDay
'Reason for Laughter' **new**	SDay
'Red Admiral'	EBlo
'Red Bull'	EStr
'Red Butterfly'	SDay
'Red Grace'	EStr
'Red Pennant'	SDay
'Red Precious' ♀H6	MAvo MNrw SMHy WCot
'Red Rain'	EStr EWoo SDay WHrl
'Red Ribbons'	ELon EWoo
'Red Rum'	CBgR MSwo NBro NRHS
'Red Spider Mite' **new**	EStr
'Red Squirrel'	EStr
'Red Suspenders'	ECtt EStr MBNS SDay
'Red Tallboy'	EStr
'Red Twister'	ELon EStr SDay
'Red Volunteer'	EStr SDay
'Redheaded Hussy'	EStr
'Regal Finale'	SDay
'Regal Giant'	EStr
'Regency Dandy'	SDay
'Regency Heights'	EStr

	'Regency Masquerade'	SDay
	'Renee'	MNrw
	'Renie's Delight'	SDay
	'Respighi'	EStr
	'Rest Beyond the River'	EStr
	'Return Trip'	ELon
	'Rhubarb Wine'	EStr
	'Rhythm of Love'	EStr
	'Ribbonette'	EStr
	'Rich Girls'	EStr
	'Richfield Wonder'	SDay
	'Ricky Rose'	SDay
	'Rigamarole'	SDay
	'Riley Barron'	SDay
	'Rise of the Phoenix'	EStr
	'Robespierre'	SDay
	'Rock Solid'	SDay
	'Rocket Booster'	EStr SDay
	'Rocket City'	ELan EStr WNHG
	'Rococo'	SDay
	'Roger Grounds'	CBgR LRHS SDay
	'Roll with It'	EStr
	'Rollin' and Tumblin'' **new**	EStr
	'Rolling Hill'	SDay
	'Rolling Raven'	EStr
	'Roman Toga'	CBgR SDay
	'Romanian Rendevous'	EStr
*	'Romantic Rose'	MBNS NLar WHrl
	'Romeo is Bleeding'	EStr
	'Ron Azzanni'	EStr
	'Root Beer'	GQue WCAu WHrl
	'Rorschach Test'	EStr
	'Rose'	SDay
	'Rose Corsage'	LAma SDir
	'Rose Emily'	CBgR EStr SDay
	'Rose F. Kennedy'	EStr
	'Rose Fever'	EWoo
	'Rose Tattoo'	EStr
	'Roseate Spoonbill'	EWoo
	'Roses in Snow'	EStr SDay
	'Rosewood Snowflakes'	SDay
	'Roswitha'	EStr
	'Rosy Lights'	EWoo
	'Rosy Returns'	LRHS NLar WNHG
	'Roy Likes Em Hot'	EStr
	'Royal Braid'	NLar SPer WCot
	'Royal Celebration'	WCot
	'Royal Diana'	SDay
	'Royal Elk'	EWoo
	'Royal Heritage'	EHyd EStr LRHS NRHS SDay
	'Royal Parade'	SDay
	'Royal Robe'	CTri
	'Royal Saracen'	SDay
	'Royal Thornbird'	CBgR
	'Ruby Corsage'	EStr
	'Ruby Sentinel'	SDay WNHG
	'Ruby Spider' ♀H6	ELon EStr EWoo SDay
	'Ruby Storm'	EStr
	'Ruby Sullivan'	SDay
	'Ruffled Apricot'	WNHG
	'Ruffled Carousel'	WNHG
	'Ruffled Dude'	EStr
	'Ruffled Ivory'	SDay
	'Ruffled Lemon Lace'	EStr
	'Ruffled Magic'	SDay
	'Ruffled Perfection'	SDay
	'Rumble Seat Romance'	WNHG
	'Running for the Border'	EStr
	'Running Late' ♀H6 **new**	SDay
	'Russian Easter'	EStr SDay
	'Russian Ragtime'	ELon EStr
	'Russian Rhapsody' ♀H6	SDay
	'Ruth Love'	WNHG

'Ruth Oliver'	EStr
'Sabie'	EStr
'Sabine Baur'	EStr MNrw NLar SDay WFar
'Sabra Salina'	EStr SDay WNHG
'Sacred Drummer'	SDay
'Saffron Glow'	SDay
'Sahara Sand Storm'	EStr
'Sahara Song'	EStr
'Saintly'	EWoo
'Sallie Brown'	EStr SDay
'Salmon Sheen'	SPer
'Sammy'	EStr SDay WHrl
'Sammy Russell'	Widely available
'Samuel Bell'	EWoo
'Sandra Elizabeth'	SDay
'Sandy Beckman'	EStr
'Santa's Little Helper'	EStr SDay
'Santa's Pants' **new**	EWoo
'Saratoga Belle'	EStr
'Sariah'	SDay
'Satin Glass'	CRos EBlo EHyd LRHS NRHS
'Satin Glow'	ECha
'Saved Soul'	EStr
'Say Yes'	EStr
'Scarlet Flame'	ECha
'Scarlet Oak'	SDay
'Scarlet Orbit'	EWoo SDay
'Scarlet Prince'	WNHG
'Scarlet Ribbons'	EStr
'Scarlock'	SDay
'School Girl'	EBlo EHyd LRHS NRHS
'Scorchio'	EStr
'Scorpio'	CBgR SDay WHrl
'Screamcicle'	EStr
'Screaming Demon'	EStr SDay WCot
'Sea Swept Dreams'	SDay
'Seal of Approval'	EBee EStr
'Seal the Deal'	EStr
'Sebastian'	SDay
'Secretary's Sand'	EWoo
'Seductive Fairy Tale'	EStr
'Seductor' **new**	SDay
'Seeing Stars'	SDay
'Seismic Force' **new**	SDay
'Self Determination'	SDay
'Selma Longlegs' ♀H6	EStr MSpe SDay
'Seminole Blood'	SDay
'Seminole Wind'	EWoo SDay
'Semiramide'	CBgR WNHG
'Serena Lady'	SDay
'Serena Sunburst' ♀H6	EHyd EStr LRHS NRHS SDay
'Serene Madonna'	ELan ILea
'Serenity Bay'	EStr
'Serenity Morgan'	CBgR EWoo
'Serge Rigaud'	WHrl
'Sergeant Major'	SDay
'Seuss on the Loose'	EStr
'Shadow Cabinet'	EStr
'Shadowed Pink'	WNHG
'Shady Lady'	SDay WNHG
'Shaggy Pumpkin'	EStr
'Shaman' Gates	SDay
'Shards of Kryptonite'	EStr
'Shark Attack'	EStr
'Sharky' (d)	EStr
'She Devil'	EStr
'Shelly Victoria'	SDay
'Sherry Lane Carr'	EStr SDay
'Sherwood Gladiator'	WNHG
'She's So Outrageous'	EStr
'Shimek September Morning'	EStr
'Shimmering Elegance'	SDay

'Shinto Etching'	EStr
'Shinto Shrine'	WNHG
* 'Shocker'	EWoo
'Shotgun'	EStr
'Shreddy'	EStr
'Shuffle the Deck'	EStr SDay
'Sigudilla'	WNHG
'Silent Sentry'	EStr WCAu
'Silent Thunder'	EStr
'Silken Fairy'	CBgR SDay
'Silken Touch'	CBgR EStr SDay
'Silly Wabbit'	EStr
'Silly Whimsey'	EStr
'Siloam Amazing Grace'	SDay
'Siloam Angel Blush'	ECtt MHol SDay
'Siloam Baby Talk'	ELon NBir SDay WPnP
'Siloam Bo Peep'	SDay
'Siloam Button Box'	SDay WHrl
'Siloam Bye Lo'	SDay
'Siloam Cinderella'	SDay
'Siloam David Kirchhoff'	SDay
'Siloam Doodlebug'	CBgR NLar SDay
'Siloam Double Classic' (d)	EStr SDay
'Siloam Dream Baby'	ELon
'Siloam Ethel Smith'	SDay
'Siloam Fairy Ruffles'	WNHG
'Siloam Fairy Tale'	SDay
'Siloam Flower Girl'	SDay
'Siloam French Doll'	NLar
'Siloam French Marble'	SDay
'Siloam Frosted Mint'	SDay
'Siloam Gold Coin'	SDay
'Siloam Helpmate'	WNHG
'Siloam John Yonski'	SDay
'Siloam June Bug'	CBgR ELan SHar WCot
'Siloam Little Girl'	ECtt SDay
'Siloam Mama'	SDay
'Siloam New Toy'	EStr WHrl
'Siloam Nugget'	EStr
'Siloam Orchid Jewel'	SDay
'Siloam Paul Watts'	EGrl EStr GMcL SDay
'Siloam Peewee'	ELon
'Siloam Pink Glow'	SDay
'Siloam Pocket Size'	SDay
'Siloam Red Toy'	EHyd LRHS NRHS SMHy
'Siloam Ribbon Candy'	SDay WNHG
'Siloam Rose Dawn'	SDay
'Siloam Royal Prince'	SDay
'Siloam Ruffled Infant'	SDay
'Siloam Show Girl'	CWGN GKin MSpe
'Siloam Space Age'	WNHG
'Siloam Spizz'	EStr SDay
'Siloam Sugar Time'	ELon
'Siloam Theresa Moore'	SDay
'Siloam Tiny Mite'	SDay WHrl
'Siloam Tom Thumb'	CBgR
'Siloam Ury Winniford'	CBro CMac GMcL NLar SDay WHoo WHrl
'Siloam Virginia Henson'	SDay WWtn
'Silver Ice'	SDay
'Silver Lance'	EStr SDay WNHG
'Silver Quasar'	SDay
'Silver Run' **new**	SDay
'Silver Sides'	EStr
'Silver Sword'	EStr
'Silver Veil'	SDay
'Simmons Overture'	ECtt EStr MNrw
'Simple Twist of Fate'	EStr
'Sinbad Sailor'	NLar
'Singapore Sunrise'	EStr
'Sings the Blues'	SDay
'Sink Into Your Eyes'	EStr WHrl
'Sips of Sin'	EStr
'Sir Blackstem'	ELon SDay
'Sir Galahad'	EStr
'Sir Modred' ♀H6	EStr SDay WNHG
'Sissy Pants'	EStr
'Sister Grace'	SDay
'Sister Sally's Blessing' **new**	EStr
'Sitting on a Rainbow'	EStr
'Skinny Dipper'	EStr
'Skinwalker'	EStr
'Sky over Schuyler' **new**	EStr
'Skylight'	EStr
'Slapstick'	EStr SDay
'Sleepy'	ECha
'Sleepy Hollow'	EStr SDay
'Slender Lady'	ELon
'Slipping Into the Abyss'	EStr
'Small Wonder' **new**	EStr
'Small World Eye of the Cat'	EStr
'Smith Brothers'	ELon
'Smoke on the Water'	EStr
'Smoke Scream'	EStr
'Smoking Gun'	SDay
'Smoky Mountain Autumn'	EStr SDay WHrl
'Smoky Mountain Bell'	SDay
'Smooch Hollow'	CBgR EStr
'Smuggler's Gold'	EStr GJos SDay
'Smurfette'	EStr
'Snaggle Tooth'	EStr LLWG
'Snake in the Grass Boo'	EStr
'Snow Elf' **new**	SDay
'Snowed In'	EWoo
'Snowy Apparition'	ECrc ECtt EHyd EMor EPfP EStr GKev GKin LRHS NRHS NWad SWvt
'Snowy Eyes'	GKin WHrl
'Snowy Morning'	SDay
'Snufalufagus' **new**	SDay
'So Cold'	EStr
'So Excited'	SDay
'So Lovely'	EWoo XLum
'So Many Stars'	SDay
'Soft Cashmere'	XLum
'Solar Blast' (d) **new**	EStr
'Solid Geometry'	EStr
'Solid Scarlet'	EStr
'Solomon's Robes'	SDay
'Sombrero Way'	EHyd LRHS NRHS SDay
'Someone Special'	EStr SDay
'Somerset Fandango'	CBgR
'Something Wonderful' **new**	SDay
'Song Sparrow'	CBro
'Sonic Duck'	EStr
'Soraya Seline'	CBgR
'Sorcerer's Song'	SDay
'Sound of Color'	EStr
'South Carolina Peach'	EStr
'South Seas'	EStr
'Southern Cotton'	EStr
'Southern Shiner'	EStr
'Southern Wind'	SDay
'Sovereign Queen'	WNHG
'Spacecoast Dream Catcher'	EStr
'Spacecoast Freaky Tiki'	EStr
'Spacecoast Irish Illumination'	EStr
'Spacecoast Rose Queen'	EStr
'Spacecoast Scrambled'	NLar
'Spacecoast Starburst'	EStr SDay WCot
'Spacecoast Sweet Eye'	EStr
'Spacecoast The Green Mile'	EStr
'Spanish Fandango'	EStr
'Sparkling Dawn'	EStr
'Sparkling Orange'	SDay

'Spartan Warrior'	EStr
'Spartanburg'	EStr
'Spectral Elegance' **new**	SDay
'Speedo' **new**	SDay
'Spider Breeder'	CBgR ELon EStr
'Spider Man' ♀H6	ELon EStr MSpe SDay WCAu
'Spider Miracle'	EWoo SDay
'Spider Red'	CWGN EWTr
'Spider Web'	EStr SDay
'Spin Master'	EStr
'Spindazzle'	CBgR SDay
'Spinne in Lachs'	EStr
'Spinneret'	EStr
'Spiral Nebula'	EStr
'Spiral Sun'	EStr
'Spirit Folk'	EStr
'Spirit Weaver'	SDay
'Splatter'	EStr
'Splendid Touch'	SDay
'Split Review' **new**	EStr
'Splittin' Hairs'	EStr
'Spode'	SDay
'Spooner'	CBgR
'Spoons for Escargot'	EStr
'Spotted Fever'	EStr
'Spring Willow Song'	SDay
'Springfield Clan'	EStr
'Springmaid Beach'	EStr
'Spunky Monkey'	EStr
'Square Dancer's Curtsy'	SDay
'Stack the Deck'	EStr
'Stafford' ♀H6	Widely available
'Staghorn Sumac'	GKin NHol WCAu
'Star Asterisk'	SDay
'Star of India'	EStr
'Star of Kryptonite'	EStr
'Star Poly'	EStr
'Star Twister'	SDay
'Stargate Portal'	EStr
'Starling'	CWnw EWes EWoo NChi WSpi WWtn
'Starman's Quest'	EStr
'Starstruck'	WNHG
'Startle'	ELon EStr MNrw WCot WHrl
'Statuesque'	EWoo
'Steely Blue Eyes'	EStr
'Stella de Oro'	Widely available
'Stella in Purple'	LBar
'Stella in Red'	CBod LBar
'Stella Russell'	LRHS
'Stellar Masquerade'	WNHG
'Stewart Mandel'	EStr
'Stoke Poges'	CBgR CBro ELon EPPr EShb EStr GBin MMuc WHrl WNHG
'Stop the Car'	EStr
'Stop the Insanity'	EStr
'Stoplight'	CBgR EHyd ELon EStr LRHS SDay SMHy WHrl
'Storm Damage'	EStr
'Storm of the Century'	CBod
'Straight No Chaser' **new**	EStr
'Strasbourg'	CMac
'Strawberry Candy' ♀H6	CBgR CMac CSBt ECtt EHyd ELon EPfP EStr EWoo LAma LLWG LRHS MAvo MPie NGdn NLar NRHS SDay SDir SPer WCAu WHrl WNHG WSpi
'Strawberry Fields Forever'	EStr EWoo NLar SDay
'Strawberry Lemonade'	EStr
'Strider Spider'	EStr
'Strike Up the Band' **new**	SDay
'Strikingly Dramatic'	EStr
'String Bikini'	EStr
'Strutter's Ball'	EStr EWoo MCot NGdn SDay SPer WCAu WHrl
'Stupid in Love'	EStr
'Stupidville USA'	EStr
'Stu's Old Pink Spider'	CBgR
'Suburban Golden Eagle'	EStr
'Sue Strickfaden'	EStr
'Sugar Cookie'	EWoo SDay
'Sugar Magnolia'	EStr
'Sugar Paint' **new**	WCAu
'Summer Dragon'	EStr
'Summer Interlude'	WFar
'Summer Star'	EStr
'Summer Wine'	CBgR CRos CSBt ECtt EGrl ELon EPfP EWTr GMaP LRHS MBel MCot NBir NChi NHol NLar NRHS NSti SCob SPer SSut SWvt WCAu WCot WHoo WHrl WSpi XLum
'Sun Dazzle'	EStr
'Sun Dial'	EStr
'Sun Scream'	EStr
'Sunday Gloves'	WNHG
'Sunday Morning'	SDay
'Sungold Candy'	EStr
'Sunray Brilliance'	EWoo
'Sunset Lagoon'	EStr
'Sunset Rays'	EStr
'Sunshine on My Shoulders'	EStr
'Superlative'	EStr SDay
'Supermodel'	EStr
'Susan Weber'	SDay
'Svengali'	SDay
'Swagger and Style'	EStr
'Swallow Tail Kite'	SDay
'Swan Dance'	EStr SDay
'Sweet Country Luvin''	EStr
'Sweet Goldoni'	EStr
'Sweet Home Louisiana'	EStr
'Sweet Hot Chocolate'	LRHS MNrw
'Sweet Pea'	EStr
'Sweet Reason' **new**	SDay
'Sweet Sugar Candy'	ECtt SDeJ
'Sweetie Time' **new**	SDay
'Swirling Spider'	CBgR EWoo
'Swirling Water'	SDay
'Symphony of Praise'	EStr
'Tachibana'	SDay
'Taffy Tot'	SDay
'Taj Mahal'	ELon EWoo GQue SDay
'Tang Porcelain'	SDay
'Tangerine Tango'	EWoo
'Tangerine Twist'	EStr
'Tango Dos' **new**	EStr
'Tani'	SDay
'Taos'	EStr SDay
'Tapestry of Dreams'	SDay
'Tar and Feather'	EStr
'Tarantula'	ELon
'Taruga'	EWoo SDay
'Tasmania'	SPer
'Tattooed Lady'	SDay
'Technical Knockout'	EWoo
'Techny Peach Lace'	EStr SDay
'Techny Spider'	EStr
'Teenie Girl'	EStr
'Tejas'	ELon SPer WOld
'Tennessee Afterglow'	EStr
'Tennessee Flycatcher'	EWoo WHrl
'Tennyson'	SDay
'Tequila and Lime'	EStr MACG SPeP
'Tet Set'	WNHG
'Tetraploid Siloam Red Toy'	SDay
'Tetraploid Stella de Oro'	SDay

'Tetrina's Daughter'	CBgR LRHS SDay
'Texas Blue Eyes'	EStr WNHG
'Texas Feathered Fancy' **new**	EStr
'Thank Your Lucky Stars'	EStr
'The Bird is the Word'	EStr
'The Blessing of Freedom'	EStr
'The Color of Wonderful'	EStr
'The Dragon Reborn' **new**	SDay
'The Future of Desire'	EStr
'The Ghosts of Boyfriends Past'	EStr
'The New Normal'	EStr
'The Senator'	EStr
'The Ultimate Sacrifice'	EStr
'Thelma Douglas'	EStr
'Thelma Perry'	LEdu
'There's a Place'	EStr
'Thermal Overload'	EStr
'Thin Man'	EStr SDay
'Think Pink'	EBee
'This World Aflame'	EStr
'Thomas Tew'	EStr
'Thorhalla'	EStr SDay
'Thousand Voices'	EStr
'Thrill Ride'	SDay
'Thumbelina'	ECha EGrI XLum
§ ***thunbergii***	ECha XLum
'Thunder and Lightning'	EStr
'Thundercat'	EStr
'Thundering Ovation'	CWGN
'Thy True Love'	SDay
'Tidewater Snowflake'	EStr
'Tie-dye Illusion'	EStr
'Tiger Blood'	EPfP EStr LAma LLWG SDir
'Tigereye Spider'	EStr EWoo
'Tigerling'	EStr
'Tiger's Eye'	SDay
'Tigger'	EGrI EStr GJos SDeJ SPad WCAu
'Tiki God'	EStr
'Till I Turn Purple'	EStr
'Time Lord'	SDay
'Time of Angels'	EStr
'Time Together'	EStr
'Time Window'	EStr
'Tiny Talisman'	SDay
'Tiny Temptress'	SDay
'Tip of the Iceberg'	EStr
'Tis Midnight'	WNHG
'Tixie'	EStr
'Tom Barnes'	EStr
'Tom Collins'	SDay
'Tom Wise'	EStr
'Tone Poem'	WNHG
'Tonia Gay'	SDay
'Tooth'	EStr
'Toothpick'	EWoo WHrl
'Tootsie'	SDay
'Tootsie Rose'	SDay
'Topguns Aztec Vision'	EStr
'Topguns Bandit's Bandana'	EStr
'Topguns Cactus Jack'	EStr
'Torpoint'	CBgR MRav SDay
'Touch of Magic'	EStr
'Touch of Summer' **new**	SDay
'Towhead'	MRav SDay WCot
'Toyland'	NBir NGdn NLar
'Trahlyta'	CBgR ELon EStr EWoo SDay WHrl
'Tramps Like Us'	EStr
'Trance'	EStr
'Transatlantic Flutter'	EStr
'Treasure Map'	EStr
'Treasure That I Seek'	EStr
'Triade'	EStr
'Tribute to Joe'	EStr
'Trickster'	EStr
'Tripped Out'	EStr
'Trog'	EStr
'Trond'	SDay
'Trooping the Colour'	SDay
'Tropic Sunset'	SDay
'Tropical Depression'	EWoo
'Tropical Fusion'	EStr
'Tropical Hot Flash'	EStr
'Tropical Passion'	EStr
'Tropical Toy'	SDay
'Troubled Sleep'	EWoo
'Troubled Waters'	SDay
'True Gertrude Demarest'	SDay WHrl
'Trump Card'	EStr
'Tune the Harp'	EStr
'Tupac Amaru'	EStr
'Turkish Tapestry'	CBgR
'Turkish Turban'	SDay
'Turn the Other Cheek'	EStr
'Turtle Island'	EStr
'Tuscawilla Charlie Baker'	SDay
'Tuscawilla Darrel Apps' **new**	SDay
'Tuscawilla Princess'	EStr
'Tuscawilla Tigress'	EStr GKin MNrw SDay WHrl
'Tutankhamun'	EStr SDay
'Tuxedo'	SDay
'Tuxedo Junction' ♀H6	EStr
'Tuxedo Whiskers'	EStr
'Twilight Swan'	WNHG
'Twirling Pinata'	EWoo
'Twist of Lemon'	SDay
'Twitter Bug' **new**	EStr
'Two Part Harmony'	WHrl
'Ultra Persuasion'	SDay
'Umbrella Parade'	EStr
'Unchartered Waters'	SDay
'Uncle Bryan'	SDay
'Uncle Lurch'	EStr
'Undefinable'	EStr
'Unforgetable Fire'	SDay
'Unlock Your Dreams'	EStr
'Up the Wazoo'	EStr
'Upper Class Peach'	EStr SDay
'Uptown Girl'	EStr SDay
'Valiant'	WHrl
'Valley Monster'	SDay
'Valley Sprite'	EStr
'Vanessa Arden'	SDay
'Vanilla Fluff'	EStr
'Vanishing Mist'	EStr
'Varsity'	EHyd LRHS NBir NRHS SPer
'Vectis Amy Hiscock'	EStr
'Vectis Jean Merritt'	EStr SDay
'Vectis Jean Peirce'	EStr
'Vectis Joan Morey'	EStr
'Vectis Nora Malone'	EStr SDay
'Vegas Show Girl'	EStr
'Veins of Truth'	CBgR EBee EStr WCAu
'Velvet Eyes'	EStr
'Velvet Ribbons'	SDay
'Velvet Shadows'	CBgR SDay
'Velvet Web'	EStr
'Vendetta'	WNHG
'Venusian Mirage'	EStr
'Vera Biaglow'	EStr SDay
'Vernal Tutone'	WNHG
'Very Berry Ice'	EStr
vespertina	see *H. thunbergii*
'Vesuvian'	SDay
'Vi Simmons'	EStr SDay
'Vicountess Byng'	WWtn

'Victoria Aden'	CBro
'Victoria Elizabeth Barnes'	WNHG
'Victorian Lace'	SDay
'Victorian Violet'	SDay
'Video'	SDay
'Vie en Rose'	EStr
'Viewpoint'	SDay
'Villa Vanilla'	EStr WFar
'Vino di Notte'	EStr
'Vintage Bordeaux'	ELan SDay
'Vintage Burgundy'	CBgR WNHG
'Vintage Passion'	EStr
'Vintage Wine'	WNHG
'Violent Thunder'	EStr
'Violet Cuckoo'	EStr
'Violet Hour'	EStr SDay
'Violet Patch'	SDay
'Violet Stained Glass'	WNHG
'Viracocha'	WNHG
'Virgin's Blush'	SPer
'Visual Intrigue' **new**	SDay
'Vohann'	SDay
'Volcanic Eruption'	EStr
'Volcano Queen'	EStr WFar
'Voodoo Dancer'	EGrI EPfP EStr SCoo SPoG
'Waggle Dance'	EStr
'Waiting in the Wings'	SDay
'Walking on Sunshine'	EStr WCot
'Walnut Hill'	EStr
'Walt Disney'	GKin
'Walter Kennedy'	EStr
'Wanda Evans'	EStr
'War Paint'	EStr SDay
'Warp Drive'	SDay
'Watch Tower'	CBgR
'Watchyl Dancing Spider'	EStr
'Water Witch'	CWat SDay
'Watermelon Man'	CBgR EWoo
'Waxen Splendor'	EStr
'Wayne Johnson'	WNHG
'Wayside Green Imp'	MNrw
'We Can Dance' **new**	EStr
'Web Browser'	EStr SDay
'Web Crawler'	EStr
'Webster's Aggie'	EStr
'Webster's Pastel Beauty'	EStr
'Webster's Pinched Peach'	EStr
'Webster's Pink Wonder'	EStr SDay
'Webster's Yellow Wonder' **new**	EStr
'Wedding Band'	SDay
'Wee Willie Winkie'	WNHG
'Welfo White Diamond'	SDay
'Wesley Lee Kirby'	EStr
'What a Day for a Daydream'	EStr
'When I Dream'	EStr
'When You Get to Asheville'	EStr
'Which Way Jim'	SDay
'Whichford'	CBgR CBro EBee EBlo ECha ECtt EHyd ELan EPfP EWoo GKin LRHS NRHS SDay SPer SSut WGwG
'Whip City Fancy Free'	EStr
'Whipped Chocolate'	EStr
'Whirling Fury'	ELon
'Whiskey on Ice'	SDay
'Whisper My Name'	EStr
'White Coral'	LSRN NBro SCoo
'White Edged Madonna'	WHrl
'White Ensign'	SDay
'White Eyes Pink Dragon'	EStr
'White Ibis'	SDay
'White Magician'	EStr
'White Mountain' **new**	SDay

'White Pansy'	SDay
'White Temptation'	CWnw EPfP EStr ILea LSun SDay WNHG XSen
'White Tie Affair'	SDay
'White Zone'	SDay
'Whiter Shade'	SDay
'Whooperee'	SDay
'Whoopie'	WHrl
'Wicked Ways'	EStr
'Wideyed'	XLum
'Wiggle Butt'	EStr
'Wigglesworth'	EStr
'Wild and Wonderful'	EWoo LSun SDay WFar
'Wild at Heart'	EStr
'Wild Horses'	MNrw NLar SCob SDay SMad WHrl
'Wild Mustang'	EStr
'Wild Planet'	EStr
'Wild Wookie'	SDay
'Wildest Dreams'	SDay
'Wildfire Tango'	SDay
'Wilson Spider'	EStr
'Wind Beneath My Sails'	EWoo
'Wind Frills'	EStr SDay
'Wind Song'	ELon SDay
'Wind Storm'	EStr
'Windblown Sands'	SDay
'Windham Blueberry Mojito'	EStr
'Windmill Yellow'	EWoo SDay
'Window Dressing'	EWoo SDay
'Wineberry Candy'	EStr NLar SDay
'Winged Migration'	EStr
'Winnie'	EStr
'Winnie the Pooh'	SDay
'Winsome Lady'	ECtt GKin WBor WHrl
'Winter Dreams'	SDay
'Winter Masquerade'	SDay
'Winter Wolf'	EStr
'Winyah Eye'	EStr
'Wired'	EStr
'Wisest of Wizards'	SDay WHrl
'Wishful Dreaming'	EStr
'Wishing Well'	WCot
'Wisk Me Away'	EStr
'Wispy Rays'	EStr
'Witch Hazel'	WCAu WWtn
'Witch Hollow'	EStr
'Witch Stitchery'	EStr SDay
'Witches Brew'	CBgR
'Witches Coven'	SDay
'Without Warning'	CBgR
'Womanizer'	EStr
'Wonder of it All'	EStr
'Wonders Never Cease'	SDay
'Wood Duck'	EStr
'Woodland Spider'	SDay
'Woodside Ruby'	WNHG
'World of Peace'	SDay
'Wounded Heart'	SDay
'Wyatt's Cameo'	SDay
'Wyoming Wildfire'	CBgR
'Xia Xiang'	SDay
'Xochimilco'	WNHG
'Ya Ya Girl'	EStr
'Yabba Dabba Doo'	EStr SDay
'Yankee Pinstripes'	EStr
'Yazoo Elsie Hintson'	EStr
'Yazoo Wild Violet'	EStr
'Yellow Angel'	ELon WCot
'Yellow Green Monarch'	SDay
'Yellow Rain'	WCot
'Yellow Ribbon'	EStr
'Yellow Submarine'	MHol

'Yes Man'	EStr
'Yesterday Memories'	SDay
'Yesterday, Today and Tomorrow'	SDay
yezoensis	EBtc
'You Angel You'	LAma SDir
'You are Mine'	EStr
'You Had Me at Woof'	EStr
'You Social Thing'	EStr
'Yum Yum Plum'	EStr SDay
'Yuma'	WNHG
'Zachary S. Hickey'	EStr
'Zagora'	EStr WCAu
'Zampa'	CBgR EStr SDay
'Zappa'	SDay
'Zara'	EStr SPer
'Zenobia'	EStr
'Zero Dark Thirty'	EStr
'Zig Zag Jazz'	EStr
'Zip Boom Bah'	EStr
'Zuni Mountains'	WNHG

Hemiboea (*Gesneriaceae*)

bicornuta	GEdr
- PB 07-1108	GGro WFar
strigosa	WPGP
- PB	GGro WFar
- PB 374338	GGro
subcapitata	SBls SBrt WCot WFar WPGP

Hemionitis (*Pteridaceae*)

arifolia	SPlb

Hemipilia (*Orchidaceae*)

§ ***graminifolia***	GKev SDir
- white-flowered	SDir

Hemiptelea (*Ulmaceae*)

davidii	SMad

Henckelia (*Gesneriaceae*)

speciosa 'Crûg Cornetto'	WCru

Hepatica ✿ (*Ranunculaceae*)

acutiloba	EMor EPot GAbr GEdr GKev LAma MAsh NBir NLar SDir WPnP
- blue-flowered	MAsh
- white-flowered	MAsh NLar
acutiloba* × *nobilis	LBar
americana	EMor GEdr MAsh NBir NLar
- Eco Group seedlings	MAsh
- var. ***obtusa*** 'Ashwood Marble'	MAsh
angulosa	see *H. transsilvanica*
falconeri	MAsh
(Forest Series) 'Forest Pink'	GKev
- 'Forest Purple'	EBee GKev LCro
- 'Forest Red'	GKev LBar LCro
- 'Forest White'	GKev LBar LCro
* 'Gerani' × ***nobilis*** var. ***glabrata***	MAsh
'Hazelwood Froggie' **new**	NDry
henryi	GEdr MAsh
- blushed pink-backed-flowered	MAsh
insularis	GEdr MAsh
maxima	EWld GEdr MAsh MBriF NDry
× ***media*** 'Ballardii'	GEdr NDry
- 'Blaue Stunde'	GEdr
- Dryad Blush Group	NDry
- 'Harvington Beauty'	GEdr NBir NDry WSHC
- 'Holzdorfe Silver'	GEdr
- 'Kim'	GEdr NDry
- 'Millstream Merlin'	GEdr NHpl
- 'Silberprinzessin'	GEdr
§ ***nobilis*** ♀H6	Widely available
- 'Acrux' (Star Series) **new**	GEdr
- 'Adara' (Star Series) **new**	GEdr
- 'Alabaster' seedlings	MAsh
- 'Alkes' (Star Series) **new**	GEdr
- 'Baby Rosa'	GEdr
- 'Bibo'	MAsh
- 'Bibo' seedlings, red-flowered	MAsh
- blue-flowered	MAsh MAvo NSla SPlb WAbe
- 'Brockman' (d)	GEdr
- 'Cobalt'	GEdr NSla
- compact evergreen	NDry
- 'Cremar'	GEdr NDry
- 'Crenatiloba'	MAsh
- dark-blue-flowered	NDry
- 'Elkofener Heidi'	GEdr
- 'Flamingo'	GEdr
* - var. ***glabrata***	MAsh
- - dwarf white-flowered	NDry
- indigo-flowered	MAsh
- var. ***japonica***	EWes GEdr ITim NBir NDry NSla
- - 'Aikawa' (5/d)	GEdr
- - 'Akane' (1)	GEdr
- - 'Akanezora' (6/d)	GEdr
- - 'Akebono' (9/d)	GEdr
- - 'Anjyu' (9/d)	GEdr
- - 'Aozora' (1)	GEdr
- - 'Asahi' (7/d)	GEdr
- - 'Asahizuru' (6/d)	GEdr
- - 'Benifusya' (1)	GEdr
- - 'Benihagure' (9/d)	GEdr
- - 'Benikanzan' (1)	GEdr
- - 'Benikujyaku' (7/d)	GEdr
- - 'Benioiran' (3)	GEdr
- - 'Benisuzume' (1)	GEdr
- - 'Benitaiko' (9/d)	GEdr
- - 'Bojyou' (5A/d)	GEdr
- - 'Daishihou' (9/d)	GEdr
- - 'Dewa' (9/d)	GEdr
- - 'Ebisu-no-hana' (5A/d)	GEdr
- - 'Echigobijin' (1)	GEdr NDry
- - 'Fukujyu' (9/d)	GEdr
- - 'Gosho-zakura' (5A/d)	GEdr
- - 'Gyousei' (1)	GEdr
- - 'Hakurin' (6/d)	GEdr
- - 'Hakusetsu' (9/d)	GEdr
- - 'Hanagoromo' (9/d)	GEdr
- - 'Haruka' (2)	GEdr
- - 'Harumo-no-Gatari' (8/d)	GEdr
- - 'Haruno-awajuki' (9/d)	GEdr
- - 'Hatsune' (5/d)	GEdr
- - 'Hidamari' (5/d)	GEdr
- - 'Hohobeni' (9/d)	GEdr
- - 'Hokutosei' (7/d)	GEdr
- - 'Hoshizora' (2)	GEdr
- - 'Hosyun' (1)	GEdr
- - 'Isaribi' (1)	GEdr NDry
- - 'Junissen' (6/d)	GEdr
- - 'Kagura' (5A/d)	GEdr
- - 'Kansashi'	NDry
- - 'Kasumino' (1)	GEdr
- - 'Kiko' (9/d)	GEdr
- - 'Kimon' (9/d)	GEdr
- - 'Koshi-no-maboroshi' (7/d)	GEdr
- - 'Kotobuki-hime' (5/d)	GEdr
- - 'Kouen' (6/d)	GEdr
- - 'Kougyoku' (9/d)	GEdr
- - 'Kurotaiyou' (d)	GEdr
- - 'Kuukai' (8/d)	GEdr

- - f. ***magna***	MAsh
- - - 'Murasaki-shikibu' (9/d)	GEdr
- - 'Manazuru' (9/d)	GEdr
- - 'Minamo' (5/d)	GEdr
- - 'Miwaku' (1)	GEdr
- - 'Miyoshino' (1)	GEdr NDry
- - 'Miyuki' (9/d)	GEdr
- - 'Murasaki-sakama' (9/d)	GEdr
- - 'Nanakubo' (1)	GEdr
- - 'Notaniyama'	GEdr
- - 'Noumurasaki' (1)	GEdr
- - 'Oboryo' (1)	GEdr
- - 'Odoriko' (9/d)	GEdr
- - 'Okesabayashi'	GEdr
- - 'Okina' (9/d)	GEdr
- - 'Ō-murasaki' (1)	GEdr
- - 'Orihime' (9/d)	GEdr NDry
- - 'Reeka' (1)	GEdr
- - 'Ryokurei' (5A/d)	GEdr
- - 'Ryokusetsu' (9/d)	GEdr
- - 'Ryokuun' (9/d)	GEdr NDry
- - 'Sadobeni' (1)	GEdr
- - 'Saichou' (7/d)	GEdr
- - Sandan Group (7/d)	GEdr
- - 'Satsuma' (5A/d)	GEdr
- - 'Sayaka' (1)	GEdr
- - 'Seizan' (9/d)	GEdr
- - 'Senhime' (9/d)	GEdr
- - 'Sen-nin' (6/d)	GEdr
- - 'Sennin-buraku' (8/d)	GEdr
- - 'Setsudu' (7/d)	GEdr
- - 'Shikouden' (9/d)	GEdr
- - 'Shikouryuu' (9/d)	GEdr
- - 'Shio' (9/d)	GEdr
- - 'Shirayuki' (9/d)	GEdr
- - (Shiun Group) 'Shihou' (9/d)	GEdr
- - 'Shoujyouno-homare' (9/d)	GEdr
- - 'Sougetsu' (6/d)	GEdr NDry
- - 'Souhou' (1)	GEdr
- - 'Soushyunka' (9/d)	GEdr
- - 'Subaru' (9/d)	GEdr
- - 'Suien' (9/d)	GEdr
- - 'Syouchikubai' (7/d)	GEdr
- - 'Syunryuu' (9/d)	GEdr
- - 'Taeka' (9/d)	GEdr
- - 'Takase' (9/d)	GEdr
- - 'Takumi' (9/d)	GEdr NDry
- - 'Tamahime' (8/d)	GEdr
- - 'Tamakujyaku' (6/d)	GEdr
- - 'Tamasaburou' (1)	GEdr
- - 'Tenjinbai' (1)	GEdr NDry
- - 'Tenjin-ume' (1)	GEdr
- - 'Tennyonomai' (6A/d)	GEdr
- - 'Toki' (9/d)	GEdr
- - 'Tori-no-saezuri'	NDry
- - 'Touen' (9/d)	GEdr
- - 'Touhou' (9/d)	GEdr
- - 'Touryoku' (9/d)	GEdr
- - 'Toyama-chiyo-iwai' (7/d)	GEdr
- - 'Umezono' (1)	GEdr
- - 'Unabara' (9/d)	GEdr
- - 'Usugesyou' (9/d)	GEdr
- - 'Wakakusa' (9/d)	GEdr
- - 'Yaegoromo' (6/d)	GEdr NDry
- - 'Yahiko' (5/d)	GEdr
- - 'Yahikomurasaki' (1)	GEdr
- - 'Yamahibiki' (9/d)	GEdr
- - 'Yellow Shades'	GEdr
- - 'Yukishino' (2)	GEdr
- - 'Yumes' (7/d)	GEdr

	- - 'Yuunagi' (9/d)	GEdr
	- - 'Yuunami' (1)	GEdr
	- - 'Yuuzen' (5/d)	GEdr
	- - 'Yuzuru' (9/d)	GEdr
	- var. ***japonica*** × ***nobilis*** var. ***nobilis***	NDry
	- large, pale blue-flowered	NSla
	- lavender-flowered	MAsh
	- 'Lilac Picotee'	NSla
	- 'Matar' (Star Series) **new**	GEdr
	- 'Oelands Doppelstern' **new**	GEdr
	- 'Oeland's Nacht'	GEdr
	- Ohleila Group	MAsh
	- pale pink-flowered	MAsh
	- 'Papillion' seedlings	MAsh
	- patterned leaf	NSla
	- 'Polens Weisse' **new**	GEdr
	- var. ***pubescens***	MAsh NSla
	- Pygmy Group	MAsh
*	- var. ***pyrenaica***	EWld GKev LEdu MAsh NSla WAbe WThu
*	- - 'Apple Blossom'	GEdr MAsh NBir
*	- - 'Harold Bawden'	GEdr
	- - 'Harold Bawden' seedlings	MAsh
*	- - 'Pyrenean Princess'	MAsh
*	- - white-flowered	NBir
	- 'Pyrenean Marbles'	NBir
	- 'Rosa Elite'	GEdr MAsh
	- 'Rubra Plena' (d)	GEdr MAsh NDry NSla
	- 'Stained Glass'	EWld
	- 'Susanne' **new**	GEdr
	- 'Tabby'	NDry
	- 'Talitha' (Star Series) **new**	GEdr
	- 'White Sands'	GBin GEdr
	- white-flowered	GAbr LRHS MAsh
	- 'Zartila'	MAsh
	'Noubeni'	GEdr
	'Professor Friedrich Hildebrandt'	GEdr
	× ***schlyteri***	MAsh NDry
	- Ashwood hybrids	MAsh
	- blue-flowered	MAsh NDry
	- Silver Shadow Group	MAsh
	- 'The Bride'	GEdr MAsh
	× ***schlyteri*** 'The Bride' × ***transsilvanica***	MAsh
§	***transsilvanica*** ♀H5	GEdr MAsh MCot WCot
	- 'Ada Scott'	GEdr
	- 'Blue Eyes'	GBin GEdr NCth
	- 'Blue Jewel'	ELan GBin GEdr
	- blue-flowered	MAsh
	- 'Buis'	ECha GEdr NLar
	- 'Connie Greenfield'	GEdr NSla
	- 'Donner Wolke'	GEdr
	- 'Eisvogel'	GEdr NDry
	- 'Elison Spence' (d)	GEdr
	- 'Fuchs'	GEdr
	- 'Grethe' seedlings	GEdr
	- 'Karpati Krönen'	GEdr
	- 'Lilacina'	GEdr MAsh NDry
	- 'Loddon Blue'	GEdr NDry
	- 'März'	GEdr
	- 'Praecox'	GEdr
	- 'Supernova'	GEdr
	- white-flowered	GEdr MAsh
	triloba	see *H. nobilis*
	aff. ***yamatutai***	MAsh

Heptacodium (*Caprifoliaceae*)

	jasminoides	see *H. miconioides*
§	***miconioides*** ♀H7	Widely available
	- TIANSHAN ('Minhep'^{PBR})	LRHS MPkF SGol WCot

Heptapleurum see *Schefflera*

Heptaptera (*Apiaceae*)

triquetra CKel CSpe

Heracleum (*Apiaceae*)

dissectum new GGro
dulce EBee
lehmannianum WPGP
sphondylium LAlb WSFF
- pink-flowered SBls
stevenii WCot
wallichii B&SWJ 13931 WCru

Herbertia (*Iridaceae*)

§ **lahue** SBrt WAbe

Hereroa (*Aizoaceae*)

glenensis EAri EDAr EHyd LRHS NRHS SLee SPlb

Hermannia (*Malvaceae*)

flammea SPlb
stricta WAbe

Herminium (*Orchidaceae*)

monorchis NLAp

Hermodactylus see *Iris*

Herniaria (*Caryophyllaceae*)

glabra GPoy GQue

Hertia (*Asteraceae*)

§ **cheirifolia** CCCN CSde EWes EWld SEND WSHC XLum

Hesperaloe (*Asparagaceae*)

funifera XSen
malacophylla EBee
parviflora CPla CSpe EAJP ELan ESwi LAlb LEdu SEND SPlb XSen

Hesperantha ✿ (*Iridaceae*)

bachmanii CBor
§ **baurii** CBor CPbh GArf GBin NHpl
coccinea CBcs CMac CPla CToG CTri EBee EPfP GBin GKev LAma LRHS MBow NChi NFav NGdn NHol NLar SCob SDeJ SDir SGbt WFar WMAq XLum
- f. **alba** Widely available
- 'Anne' NLar WFar
- 'Autumn's Dawn' ECtt WFar
- 'Ballyrogan Giant' WFar WHer WSHC
- 'Big Moma' WFar
- 'Cardinal' NHol WFar
- 'Caroline' ECtt WFar
- 'Cindy Towe' CAbb CKno ELon LSou SPoG WFar WWke
- 'Elburton Glow' WFar
- 'Eric's Early' ELon WFar
- 'Fenland Daybreak' Widely available
- 'Gigantea' see *H. coccinea* 'Major'
- 'Good White' ECha NBir SMHy WFar
- 'Grandiflora' see *H. coccinea* 'Major'
- 'Hilary Gould' ECtt ELon WAvo
- 'Ice Maiden' CAbb CTtf ECtt LRHS LSou MAvo NSti SGBe SPoG WNPC
- 'Jack Frost' EBee ECtt ELon WFar
- 'Jazz' MAvo
- 'Jennifer' ♀H4 CBor CBro CDor CElw CMac CTri CTtf EBee ECha ECtt EHyd ELon EPfP GAbr GArf LBar LRHS MMuc MRav NLar NWad SRms SWvt WAvo WFar WSHC
- 'Maiden's Blush' ECtt LEdu NLar SRms WFar
§ - 'Major' ♀H4 Widely available
- 'Marchants Seedling' SMHy
- 'Marietta' WFar
- 'Mollie Gould' CAvo ECtt EHyd EPfP LBar LRHS MNrw MPie NBPC NCth NHol NLar NWad NWsh SCoo SGbt SRms WAvo WBrk WFar
- 'Mrs Hegarty' CEme ELon EPfP GDam GMaP GMcL MACG MGos MHer NBid NBir NFav NHol NLar NQui SDeJ SPer SPlb SPoG SRms SWvt WFar WPnP
- 'November Cheer' CMac ECtt NBir NLar
- 'Oregon Sunset' CBcs CBod CKel CKno CPla EAri ECtt ELon LBar LLWG LRHS LSou SGBe SMrm SPad SPeP WFar WHil WHoo WKif WWke
- 'Pallida' CMil ECtt ELon NBir WFar
- 'Pink Marg' ECtt ITim WFar
- 'Pink Princess' see *H. coccinea* 'Wilfred H. Bryant'
- 'Professor Barnard' CCCN CKel EBee ECtt ELon EPfP EPri MBNS MNrw NBir NFav NLar WBrk WFar WNPC
- 'Red Arrow' EWes
- 'Red Dragon' ECtt NHol WHoo
I - 'Rosea' GKev LAma MPie SDeJ WFar
- 'Ruth' ECtt WFar
- 'Salmon Charm' ECtt WFar
- 'Salmon's Leap' WFar
- 'Salome' CBor CDor ECtt WFar WMal
- 'Scarlet Queen' WFar
- 'Simply Pink' LBar SPad
- 'Snow Drift' WFar
- 'Snow Maiden' CBod CElw EBee ECtt LBar LRHS NLar WFar WMal
- 'Strawberry' WFar
§ - 'Sunrise' ♀H4 CBcs CBro CExl CSBt CWCL EBee ECha EHyd ELan EPfP EShb GAbr LRHS MRav MSpe NBPC NBir NCth NGdn NLar NRHS NWad SGbt SPer SWvt WFar WHoo WKif
- 'Sunset' see *H. coccinea* 'Sunrise'
- 'Tambara' ECtt WFar XLum
- 'Vibrant Scarlet' WFar
- 'Viscountess Byng' CTri EBee MNrw NBir
* - 'White Admiral' WFar WOut
§ - 'Wilfred H. Bryant' ♀H4 Widely available
- 'Zeal Salmon' CBro CElw ECha EGrl ELon NBir WFar WNPC
cucullata CPbh
'Halloween Pink' new LBar
'Halloween Red' new LBar
huttonii EPPr GEdr ITim NBir WFar
mossii see *H. baurii*
pauciflora CPbh
vaginata CBor CPbh

Hesperis (*Brassicaceae*)

matronalis Widely available
- **alba** see *H. matronalis* var. *albiflora*
§ - var. **albiflora** CAby CBod CCBP CLau CSpe CTtf ELan EPfP EWoo LCro LEdu LOPS MACG MHoo MNHC NGdn NLar SBut SPer SPhx WBrk WTor
- - 'Alba Plena' (d) CRos EBee LRHS SMad WCAu WCot WHlf
- double-flowered (d) CTtf
nivea LEdu
steveniana LRHS SPhx

Hesperochiron (*Boraginaceae*)

californicus	SBrt

× *Hesperotropsis* see × *Cuprocyparis*

Heteromeles (*Rosaceae*)

arbutifolia	see *H. salicifolia*
§ ***salicifolia***	GKev LEdu SBrt

Heteromorpha (*Apiaceae*)

arborescens	SPlb SVen

Heteropolygonatum (*Asparagaceae*)

'Mikinori Ogisu'	EBee
roseolum	EWld
urceolatum	WCru

Heteropterys (*Malpighiaceae*)

glabra	WCru

Heterotheca (*Asteraceae*)

subaxillaris	WCot
villosa 'Golden Sunshine'	MAvo

Heuchera ✿ (*Saxifragaceae*)

'Alan Davidson'	MPnt
'Alison'	MPnt
'Amber Waves'PBR	LRHS MBros MDon MPnt NBir SCob SWvt
§ ***americana***	CWal LRHS MRav NBir SHar SHeu SSut SWvt
- var. ***americana***	MPnt
- Dale's strain	GPSL MPnt SBls SHeu SPlb SWvt
- 'Harry Hay'	EPPr EPri LEdu LPla MPnt SHeu WPGP WSHC
- 'Marvellous Marble'	EPfP EShb LRHS MDon MPnt SHeu
- 'Ring of Fire'	EHeP MPnt SHeu SRms SWvt
'Amethyst Myst'	EPfP LSRN MCot MPnt SCob SCoo SHeu
'Apple Crisp'PBR	ECtt EPfP LCro LRHS MPnt MTin NLar SCob SHeu SWvt WNPC
'Apple Souffle'	MPnt SHeu
'Apple Twist'PBR (Dolce Series)	EPfP SHeu
'Appletini' (Dolce Series) **new**	SHeu
'Apricot'	CWGN MPnt
'Autumn Glow' (Seasonal Selection Series)	CRos EHyd LRHS MPnt NRHS SHeu WCot WNPC
'Autumn Haze'PBR	MPnt SHeu
'Autumn Leaves'PBR	CKel CWal CWnw ECtt ELan LCro LOPS MPnt NLar SCoo SEdd SHeu SPoG SWvt
'Baby's Breath'	MPnt
'Bardot'	MPnt
'Beaujolais'PBR	MNrw MPnt NBir SHeu WCot WNPC
'Beauty Colour'	ELan GMaP MRav NGdn NRHS SHeu SPer SWvt WJam
'Bella Notte'PBR	MPnt NLar SHeu WNPC
'Berry Marmalade'PBR	CBod EBee EPfP LRHS MAsh MPnt SCoo SHeu SOrN SPoG SWvt WNPC
'Berry Smoothie'PBR	CPla CRos CWGN EBee EHyd ELan EPfP LRHS LSRN MBNS MCot MGos MHol MPnt NHol NLar NPer NRHS SCob SCoo SEdd SHeu SPer SPoG SWvt
'Berry Timeless'PBR	LBar SHeu
(Big Top Series) 'Big Top Bronze'	SHeu
- 'Big Top Burgundy'	SHeu
- 'Big Top Gold'	CWGN SHeu
'Bilberry' (Indian Summer Series)	MPnt SHeu
'Binoche'PBR	CRos EBee EHyd ELan LBar LRHS MPnt MPri NRHS SCob SHeu WCot WNPC
'Birkin'	LRHS MPnt
'Black Cherry' (Heucheraholics Series)	SHeu
'Black Pearl' (Primo Series)	CPla EPfP LBar LCro LOPS LRHS MBros MDon MPnt MPri NLar SCoo SHeu SPad WTor
'Black Sea'	ECtt EPfP GQue LRHS MPnt SEdd WCot WNPC
'Black Taffeta'PBR	CBod CWGN EBee LBuc MPnt SHeu SPad WNPC
'Blackberry'	EPfP LBar SHeu
'Blackberry Crisp'PBR	EBee LBuc MPnt SHeu WNPC
'Blackberry Jam' ♀H6	CBar CKel CRos EHyd ELan EPfP GMcL LRHS LSou MPnt NBir NHol NRHS SCoo SEdd SGBe SHeu SWvt WFar
'Blackbird'	MPnt SHeu SWvt WFar WSpi
'Blackout'	ECtt MNrw MPnt SHeu
'Blondie'PBR (Little Cutie Series)	CBcs CWGN ECtt EHyd EPfP GJos LBar LCro LRHS MPnt MPri NLar NRHS SEdd SHeu SPad SPoG WCot WNPC
'Blondie in Lime' (Little Cutie Series) ♀H6	CRos EHyd EPfP LBar LCro LRHS MPnt MPri NLar NRHS SHeu WNPC
'Blood Red'	SHeu
'Blood Vein'	MPnt SHeu
'Blushing Dawn'	LRHS
'Blushing Down'	MPnt
'Bouquet'	MPnt SHeu
'Boysenberry'PBR (Indian Summer Series)	EBee ELan EPfP LRHS MPnt SHeu
bracteata	MPnt XLum
'Bressingham Glow'	MPnt SHeu
Bressingham hybrids	CSBt EPfP SRms SVic
'Bressingham Spire'	MPnt
'Bright and Breezy' (Seasonal Selection Series)	CRos EHyd EPfP LRHS MPnt NRHS SHeu
'Bronze Beauty'	MPnt SHeu WBrk WCot
'Brown Sugar'	MPnt SHeu
'Brownfinch'	CElw LPla MPnt SBrt SHeu SSut WCot
'Brownies'	MPnt SHeu WHrl
'Burgundy Bill' (Fox Series)	MPnt
'Burgundy Frost'	MPnt SHeu
'Café Olé' ♀H6	ECtt MPnt SHeu WHer
'Cajun Fire'PBR	CWGN ELan MPnt SHeu
'Can-can' ♀H6	CRos CTri EHyd ELan LRHS MAvo MNrw MPnt NBir NRHS SCob SCoo SHeu SWvt WCAu WSpi
'Candy Honey'	LRHS
'Canyon Duet'	MPnt SHeu
'Cappuccino'	EBee ELan MPnt MRav SCob SHeu SWvt
'Caramel'PBR	CMac CRos CWGN EBee ECtt EHyd ELan EMor GDam GMaP LCro LOPS LPal LRHS MAsh MNrw NRHS SCob SGbt SHeu SPer SPoG SWvt WCAu WCot
'Carmen'	MPnt SHeu
'Carmencita'	SHeu
(Carnival Series) CARNIVAL BLACK OLIVE	LRHS
- CARNIVAL COCOMINT ('Balcarcint'PBR)	SHeu
- CARNIVAL COFFEE BEAN ('Balcarcean'PBR)	EHyd GJos LRHS NRHS

- CARNIVAL FALL FESTIVAL **new**	GJos
- CARNIVAL LIMEADE ('Balcarmade'PBR)	ELan LRHS SHeu
- CARNIVAL PEACH PARFAIT ('Balcarpait')	EHyd LRHS NRHS SHeu
- CARNIVAL PLUM CRAZY ('Balcarulm'PBR)	GJos SHeu
- CARNIVAL ROSE GRANITA	LRHS SHeu
- CARNIVAL WATERMELON ('Balcarmelo')	LRHS MHol
'Cascade Dawn'	EBee MPnt NBir SWvt
'Cassis'	LRHS MPnt SHeu WCot
'Celtic Sea'	LRHS
'Cézanne' (Master Painters Series)	MPnt SHeu
'Champagne Bubbles'	CWGN MPnt SHeu
CHAMPAGNE ('Tnheucha'PBR)	CBod LBar MPnt NLar SHeu WNPC
CHARLES BLOOM ('Chablo')	MPnt SHeu
'Charlotte' (Fox Series) **new**	MPnt
'Chatterbox'	MPnt SHeu
'Checkers'	see *H.* 'Quilter's Joy'
'Cherries Jubilee'PBR	GMaP MPnt SHeu
'Cherry Cola'PBR ♀H6	Widely available
'Cherry Truffles' (Dolce Series)	CBod LBar SHeu WNPC
'Chiqui'	MPnt SHeu
chlorantha	MPnt
'Chocolate Limes'	MPnt SHeu WNPC
'Chocolate Ruffles'PBR	CBcs CKel CRos CWnw ECha EHeP ELan EPfP EShb EWoo GDam GMaP LRHS LSRN MCot MGos MHer MHol MRav NDov NRHS SCob SPer SPoG SRkn SRms SWvt WCav WFar WSpi
'Chocolate Veil'	MPnt
'Christa'	MPnt SHeu
'Cinnabar Silver'PBR	LBar MPnt NLar
'Circus'PBR	MPnt SHeu WNPC
'Citronelle'	CWGN ECtt EGrI EHyd EPfP LRHS MPnt NRHS SHeu SWvt WCot WNPC
'City Lights'	SHeu
'Coco'PBR (Little Cutie Series)	EBee EHyd EPfP LBar LRHS MPnt MPri NRHS SHeu WNPC
'Color Dream'PBR	MPnt SHeu
'Cool Dude' (Fox Series)	MPnt
coral bells	see *H. sanguinea*
'Coral Bouquet'	MPnt SHeu
'Coral Cloud'	MPnt SHeu
'Coral Frost'	LRHS MDon
'Coral Sea'	WCot
'Coralberry'PBR (Indian Summer Series)	ELan LBar LRHS MPnt SHeu
'Corallion'	MPnt
'Cranberry' (Indian Summer Series)	ELan EPfP LRHS LSou MHol MPnt SHeu SOrN WNPC WTor
'Crazy Rasta'	WNPC
CRÈME BRÛLÉE ('Tnheu041') (Dolce Series)	CChe CRos CWnw EHyd ELan EPau EPfP GDam LRHS MGos NCou NLar NRHS SCoo SEdd SHeu SPoG SWvt
'Crème Caramel'	MPnt
'Creole Nights'PBR	MPnt SHeu
'Crimson Curls'	EHyd ELan LRHS MPnt NRHS SHeu SRms SWvt
'Crispy Curly'	MPnt SHeu
cylindrica	EPfP GKev MPnt SHeu
- var. ***alpina***	GKev
- 'Cream'	MPnt
- 'Francis'	MPnt
- 'Greenfinch'	EHeP ELan EWTr GKev GLog GMaP LRHS MPnt MRav NBir SHar SHeu SHor SWvt XLum

- 'Hyperion'	MPnt SHeu
'Da Vinci' (Master Painters Series)	MPnt SHeu
'Damask'	MPnt SHeu
'Dark Beauty'PBR	SCob SEdd SHeu SOrN SPer WNPC
'Dark Magic'	SHeu
'Dark Secret'PBR	EBee LRHS MPnt SHeu WHlf
'Dark Storm' (Seasonal Selection Series)	CRos EHyd EPfP LRHS MPnt NRHS SHeu
'David'	MPnt SHeu WBrk
'Delta Dawn'PBR	CPla CWGN EBee EPfP LBar LRHS MPnt NSti SCoo SGBe SHeu SPoG SWvt WNPC
'Dennis Davidson'	see *H.* 'Huntsman'
'Dizzi Blonde'	SHeu
'Earth Angel'	MPnt SHeu
EBONY AND IVORY ('E and I'PBR)	EBee EShb GMaP MPnt SHeu SRms SWvt WSpi
'Eden's Aurora'	MPnt
'Electra'PBR	EPfP GMcL LCro LRHS MPnt NLar SHeu SWvt
'Electric Lime'	ELan LBar MPnt NLar SHeu SPoG WNPC
'Elworthy Rusty'	CElw
'Emperor's Cloak'	CKel CWal GLog GQue SHeu SWvt
'Emperor's Cloak' green-leaved	CKel EWTr
'Encore'PBR	MPnt SHeu
'Fairy Dance'	MPnt
'Fantasia'	SHeu
'Fire Alarm'PBR	CWGN EHyd ELan EPfP LBuc LRHS MPnt NRHS SCob SHeu WNPC
'Fire Chief'PBR	Widely available
'Firebird'	MPnt
FIREFLY	see *H.* 'Leuchtkäfer'
'Fireworks'PBR	MPnt MRav NLar SCob SHeu
'Fleur' (Fox Series)	LBuc MPnt WNPC
'Florist's Choice'	MPnt SHeu
(Forever Series) 'Forever Purple'	CWGN EBee EHyd EPfP GJos GPSL LBar LBuc LRHS LSRN LSou MHol MPnt NLar NRHS SCoo SHeu SPoG WFar WNPC WTor
- 'Forever Red'	CWGN LBar LCro MPnt SGBe SHeu WNPC
'French Quarter'	MPnt SHeu
'Frilly Lizzie' (Fox Series)	WNPC
'Frost' (Little Cutie Series)	EPfP MDon MPnt SHeu WNPC
'Frosted Violet'	see *H.* 'Frosted Violet Dream'
§ 'Frosted Violet Dream'PBR	EPfP LRHS LSRN MPnt SHeu SWvt WNPC
'Galaxy'PBR	CWGN MPnt SHeu
'Gauguin' (Master Painters Series)	MPnt SHeu
'Georgia Peach'PBR	CPla CWGN EBee ELan EPfP LBar MNrw MPnt NBir SHeu SWvt WFar WNPC
'Georgia Plum'	CWGN EBee EHyd ELan EPfP LBar LRHS MPnt NRHS SHeu WNPC
'Ginger Ale'PBR	CKel CWGN EBee EHyd ELan EWes EWoo GMcL LBar LRHS MDon MHol MPnt NHol NRHS NSti SCoo SGBe SHeu SPer SPoG SWvt
'Ginger Peach'PBR	EPfP MPnt SCob SHeu WNPC
'Ginger Snap'PBR (Little Cutie Series)	LRHS MPnt SHeu WNPC
glabra	MPnt SHeu
glauca	see *H. americana*
'Glitter'PBR ♀H6	CWGN EBee ECtt EPfP LBuc MPnt SHeu SPoG WNPC
'Gloire d'Orléans'	MPnt XLum
'Gloriana'	EHyd

'Gojiberry' (Indian Summer Series)	EBee EPfP MPnt SHeu
'Gotham'PBR	MPnt SHeu WNPC
(Grande Series) GRANDE AMETHYST ('Tnhega')	SHeu
- GRANDE BLACK ('Tnheugb')	SHeu
'Grape Expectations' **new**	LBar SHeu
'Grape Soda'PBR (Soda Series)	CWGN MPnt SHeu WNPC
'Grape Timeless' **new**	WNPC
'Green Goddess' (Heucheraholics Series)	SHeu
'Green Ivory'	MPnt SHeu XLum
'Green Sashay'	MPnt SHeu
'Green Spice' ♀H6	Widely available
'Guacamole' ♀H6	MPnt SHeu
'Guardian Angel'	MPnt SHeu SRGP
'Gypsy Dancer'PBR (Dancer Series)	MPnt SHeu
'Hailstorm' (v)	MPnt
hallii	EDAr MPnt SPlb
'Happy Autumn'	LRHS
'Happy Flames'	SHeu
'Happy Moon'	WCot
HARVEST BURGUNDY ('Balheubur')	MPnt SHeu
HARVEST SILVER ('Balheusil')	EPfP MPnt SHeu
'Havana'PBR	EHyd LRHS MPnt NRHS SHeu
'Helen Dillon' (v)	EShb GMaP MPnt SHeu SWvt WGwG
'Hercules'PBR	MPnt SHeu
'High Hopes'	MPnt SHeu
hispida	MPnt
'Hocus Pocus'	SHeu
'Hollywood'PBR	EBee GJos GMcL LRHS MDon MGos MPnt NBir NHol SHeu SPoG
'Hot Stuff'	SHeu
HUCKLEBERRY ('Ifhehb'PBR) (Indian Summer Series)	LBar SHeu
§ 'Huntsman'	MPnt MRav SHeu
Indian Summer Series	LRHS
'Iron Maiden'	SHeu
'Isabella' (Fox Series)	LRHS MPnt WNPC
'Isla' (Heucheraholics Series)	SHeu
'Jade Gloss'PBR	MPnt MPri SHeu SWvt WNPC
'Jooles Green Giant' (Heucheraholics Series)	SHeu
'June Bride'	MPnt
'Kadastra'	MPnt SHeu
'Kassandra'PBR	EHyd LRHS MPnt NRHS SHeu SWvt
KEY LIME PIE ('Tnheu042'PBR) (Dolce Series)	CWGN ECtt EHyd EMor LRHS MGos NHol NRHS SCoo SHeu SRms SWvt WFar WHlf
'King Kong'	MPnt
Kira Series	MPnt
- 'Kira Purple Rain Forest'	SHeu
'Lady Romney'	XLum
'Lemon Chiffon'	EHyd LRHS MPnt NRHS SHeu
'Lemon Love'	CBod EPfP LBar MDon MPnt SHeu WNPC
§ 'Leuchtkäfer'	EBou EHyd EPfP EWTr GMaP MHer MPnt MRav NBir SBls SCob SHeu SPlb SRms WJam XLum
LICORICE ('Tnheu044'PBR) (Dolce Series)	CRos ECtt EHyd GMcL LRHS MBNS MGos MPnt NRHS SHeu SPoG SWvt WFar
'Lily the Pink'	SHeu
'Lime Marmalade' ♀H6	Widely available
'Lime Rickey'PBR	CWGN EHyd LRHS MGos NGBl SCob SHeu SWvt WCot
'Lime Ruffles'PBR	MPnt SHeu WNPC

'Lime Swizzle' (Baby Bells Series) **new**	LBar SHeu
'Lipstick'PBR ♀H6	CWGN EBee MPnt SHeu SWvt
'Little Tinker'	MPnt SHeu
'Lune Rousse'	MPnt SHeu
'Madison Bride' (Fox Series) ♀H6	CBod LRHS MPnt WCot WNPC
'Magic Flute'	SHeu
'Magic Wand' ♀H6	SHeu
'Magma'	SHeu
'Magnum'	CWGN MPnt SHeu
'Mahogany'PBR	LRHS LSou MPnt MPri SHeu SWvt WHoo
'Mahogany Monster' (Primo Series)	SHeu
'Malachite'	CRos EHyd LRHS MPnt NRHS SHeu
'Mango'	MPnt SHeu
'Marmalade'PBR ♀H6	Widely available
'Maroon Blush'	SHeu
'Mars'	CRos EHyd LRHS MPnt NRHS SHeu
'Mary Rose'	MPnt SHeu
maxima	CBod MPnt SHeu
'Mega Caramel'	MPnt SHeu
'Mega Citronelle'	MPnt
'Megan' (Heucheraholics Series)	SHeu
'Melting Fire'	CChe EHyd GMcL GPSL LRHS MPnt SBls SHeu
'Mercury'	SHeu
'Metallic Shimmer' (Fox Series) ♀H6	CBod MPnt WNPC
'Metallica'	GJos SHeu
micans	see *H. rubescens*
micrantha	MPnt SHeu SRms
- var. ***diversifolia*** misapplied	see *H. villosa*
- 'Martha's Compact'	MPnt
§ - 'Ruffles'	ECha MPnt SHeu
'Midas Touch'	CWGN MPnt
'Midnight Bayou'	CPla ELan GMcL MPnt NLar NPer SHeu SWvt
'Midnight Rose'	Widely available
'Midnight Rose Select'	MPnt SHeu
'Midnight Ruffles'PBR	MPnt SHeu WFar
'Milan'PBR	EHyd ELan LBar LRHS MDon MPnt NRHS SHeu WNPC
'Mini Caramel'	MPnt
'Mini Mouse'	MPnt SHeu
'Mint Frost'PBR	EHeP ELan LRHS MPnt SHeu SWvt
'Mint Julep'PBR	SHeu
'Miracle'PBR	MPnt SHeu
'Mocha'PBR	MNrw MPnt SHeu SWvt
'Molly Bush'	SHeu
'Morello'	MPnt SHeu WNPC
'Mother of Pearl'	MPnt SHeu
'Mulberry' (Indian Summer Series)	EPfP LRHS SHeu WFar WTor
'Muscat'	MPnt SHeu
'Mysteria'PBR	MPnt SHeu
'Mystic Angel'	MPnt SHeu
'Neptune'	MPnt SHeu
(Northern Exposure Series) NORTHERN EXPOSURE AMBER ('Tnheunea'PBR)	MPnt SHeu
- NORTHERN EXPOSURE BLACK ('Tnheuneb')	SHeu
- NORTHERN EXPOSURE LIME ('Tnheunel'PBR)	MPnt SHeu
- NORTHERN EXPOSURE PURPLE ('Tnheunep')	SHeu
- NORTHERN EXPOSURE RED ('Tnhheuner'PBR)	MPnt SHeu

- NORTHERN EXPOSURE SILVER ('Tnheunes'^{PBR})	SHeu
'Oakington Jewel'	MPnt
'Obsidian'^{PBR} 🏆^{H6}	Widely available
'Orange Dream'	MPnt SHeu
'Orangeberry'	LBar MPnt SHeu
'Orphée'	MPnt NChi
'Paprika'^{PBR}	CKel CRos CWGN EBee EHyd LCro LRHS MPnt NRHS SCob SHeu WCot WFar WNPC WTor
'Paris'^{PBR} 🏆^{H6}	CDoC CRos CWGN EHyd EMor EPfP LBar LRHS LSRN MAsh MBel MDon MGos MPnt NHol NRHS SEdd SGBe SHeu SPer SPoG WCot WNPC
parishii NNS 93384	MPnt
parvifolia var. ***nivalis***	MPnt
- var. ***utahensis***	MPnt
'Pauline' (Fox Series)	CWGN EHyd LBuc LRHS MPnt NRHS SHeu WNPC
'Peach Crisp'^{PBR}	CWGN MPnt SHeu WNPC
'Peach Flambé'^{PBR}	CPla CRos CWGN CWnw EGrI EHyd ELan LRHS MBNS MDon MGos MHer MPnt MPri NRHS SCob SCoo SHeu SPoG SWvt WHer
PEACH MELBA ('Tnheu043'^{PBR}) (Dolce Series)	MDon MPnt SHeu
'Peach Pie'	MPnt
'Peachberry Ice' (Dolce Series)	LBar MPnt SHeu WNPC
'Peachy Keen'	SHeu
'Pear Crisp'	LBar MPnt SHeu
'Penelope'	LRHS MPnt SHeu
'Peppermint' (Little Cutie Series)	CBod EPfP LBar LBuc MPnt SHeu WCot WNPC
'Peppermint Spice'^{PBR} (21st Century Collection Series)	MDon MPnt SHeu
'Persian Carpet'	LRHS MPnt NBir NRHS SHeu SWvt
(Petite Series) 'Petite Marbled Burgundy'	MPnt SHeu SWvt
- 'Petite Pearl Fairy'	EGrI MPnt SHeu SWvt
- 'Petite Pink Bouquet'	MPnt SHeu
'Pewter Moon'	EHeP GMaP MPnt NBir SHeu WFar
'Pewter Veil'	MPnt SHeu
'Phoebe's Blush' (Fox Series)	EPfP MHtn MPnt WNPC
'Picasso' (Master Painters Series)	MPnt SHeu
'Pilley Pink'	SHeu
'Pilley Pumpkin'	SHeu
pilosissima	XLum
'Pink Dancer' (Fox Series) **new**	MPnt
'Pink Panther' (Heucheraholics Series)	MPnt SHeu WNPC
'Pink Pearls'^{PBR}	CWGN EHyd EPfP LRHS MPnt NRHS SHeu WCot WNPC
'Pinot Bianco'	MPnt SHeu
'Pinot Gris'^{PBR}	CWGN MPnt SHeu WNPC
'Pinot Noir'	MPnt SHeu
'Pistache'	MPnt SHeu WCot WNPC
§ 'Pluie de Feu'	EShb MPnt MRav SHeu XLum
'Plum Pudding'^{PBR}	Widely available
'Plum Royale'^{PBR}	EHyd ELan LRHS MGos MPnt SHeu SWvt
'Pretty Perinne'^{PBR}	MPnt SHeu
'Pretty Pistachio' (Primo Series) **new**	LBar SHeu
'Pretty Polly'	MPnt SHeu
'Prince'	EHyd ELan LRHS MPnt NRHS SEdd SHeu SWvt
'Prince of Orange'	SHeu
'Prince of Silver'	MPnt SHeu
pringlei	see *H. rubescens*
pubescens	MPnt SHeu XLum
- 'Alba'	MPnt
pulchella	EBou EDAr GKev GLog MHer MPnt SHeu SPlb SRms
'Purple Crinkle'	MPnt SHeu WNPC
'Purple Petticoats' 🏆^{H6}	CBcs ELan LRHS MDon MGos MPnt SCoo SHeu SPoG
'Quick Silver'	EHyd MPnt NBir NRHS SWvt
§ 'Quilter's Joy'	MPnt
'Rachel'	EHyd EPfP GMaP LRHS LSRN MPnt MRav NGdn NRHS SEdd SHeu SWvt WHlf XLum
RAIN OF FIRE	see *H.* 'Pluie de Feu'
'Raspberry' (Fox Series)	MPnt
'Raspberry Ice'^{PBR}	MPnt SHeu
'Raspberry Regal'	MPnt MRav NBir SHeu SWvt WCot
'Raspberry Sea'	LRHS
'Rave On'^{PBR}	CWGN EBee ELan MPnt NHol SHeu SPer SWvt
'Red Dress'	MPnt SHeu
'Red Lightning'^{PBR}	CWGN LBar MPnt SHeu
'Red Pearls'	LRHS MPnt NCth SHeu WNPC
'Red Sea'	EHyd EPfP LRHS LSun MPnt NRHS SHeu WCot WNPC
'Red Spangles'	MPnt NBir SHeu
'Regina' 🏆^{H6}	EHyd MPnt NRHS SHeu SWvt WNPC
'Renoir' (Master Painters Series)	CWGN MPnt SHeu
(Rex Series) 'Rex Lime'	LBar SPad
- 'Rex Purple'^{PBR} **new**	LBar
- 'Rex Red' **new**	LBar
richardsonii	MPnt SHeu XLum
'Rickard'	MPnt
'Rio'^{PBR}	CWGN EPfP LBar MHtn MPnt SHeu WNPC
'Robert'	MPnt
'Root Beer'^{PBR}	EHyd MHol MPnt NRHS SHeu WNPC
'Rose Quartz' **new**	LBar
ROSEMARY BLOOM ('Heuros')	SHeu
§ ***rubescens***	NBro
- var. ***versicolor***	GKev
'Ruffles'	see *H. micrantha* 'Ruffles'
'Sanbrot'	MPnt
§ ***sanguinea***	CMac EGrI MPnt MRav NBir
- 'Alba'	EShb MPnt SMHy
- 'Coral Forest'	SHeu
- 'Coral Petite'	EDAr EHyd LRHS NRHS SHeu
- 'Dew Drops'^{PBR} (v)	SHeu
- 'Frosty'	EHyd LRHS NRHS
- 'Geisha's Fan'	GArf MPnt SHeu SWvt
- 'Monet' (v)	MPnt SHeu
- var. ***pulchra***	GKev
- 'Ruby Bells'	EHyd GMcL LSRN MPnt NRHS SHeu SRms
- 'Sioux Falls'	GPSL SHeu
- 'Snow Storm' (v)	ELan MPnt SHeu SRms
- 'Splendens'	EHeP MPnt XLum
- 'Taff's Joy' (v)	MPnt
- 'White Cloud' (v)	ECha EPfP EWTr LSto MPnt SHeu SHor SRms XLum
'Sashay' 🏆^{H6}	CBod GBin LPla MPnt SHeu WCot WNPC
'Saturn'	MPnt SHeu SWvt
'Schneewittchen'	MPnt MRav SHeu
'Scintillation'	MPnt
'September Morn' (Seasonal Selection Series)	CRos EHyd EPfP LRHS MPnt NRHS SHeu WNPC

'Shanghai'[PBR]	CWGN EBee EHyd EPfP LRHS LSRN MDon MPnt NRHS SHeu SWvt WFar WNPC
'Shenandoah Mountain'	MPnt
'Shere Variety'	MPnt
'Silver Celebration' (Fox Series) [♀H6]	LBuc MPnt WNPC
'Silver Dollar'	CWGN EBee MPnt SHeu
'Silver Gilt'	SHeu
'Silver Gumdrop' (Dolce Series)	CPla EPfP LBar LCro MHtn MPnt SEdd SHeu SOrN SRkn WNPC WTor
'Silver Heart'	EBee EHyd LRHS MPnt NRHS
'Silver Indiana'	MPnt SHeu
'Silver Light'[PBR]	MPnt SHeu
'Silver Lode'[PBR]	MPnt SHeu
'Silver Scrolls'[PBR]	CMac CRos EHyd EPfP GMaP LCro LOPS LRHS LSRN MBel MGos MPnt MRav NRHS SCob SCoo SEdd SOrN SPoG SWvt WCot
'Silver Shadows'	MPnt SHeu
'Silver Streak'	see × *Heucherella* 'Silver Streak'
'Sioux Falls'	MPnt
'Slater's Pink' (Fox Series)	MPnt WCot WNPC
'Sloeberry' (Indian Summer Series)	LBar SHeu
'Snow Angel'	CWGN MPnt SEdd SHeu SPoG WCot WNPC
'Snowfire' (v)	MPnt SHeu
'Southern Comfort'[PBR]	CPla CWGN EBee MPnt NHol NPer SCoo SHeu SPoG SWvt
'Sparkler'	MPnt
'Sparkling Burgundy'	ELan LPal LRHS MPnt SHeu SWvt
'Spearmint' **new**	SHeu WNPC
'Spellbound'[PBR]	CWGN MPnt SHeu SPoG WNPC
'Starry Night'	MPnt
'Steel City'	MPnt SHeu
'Stormy Seas'	EBee EGrI EHyd ELan LRHS MPnt MRav NBir NRHS SCob SHeu SRGP SWvt WCAu
'Strawberries and Cream' (v) [♀H6]	MPnt SHeu
'Strawberry Candy'[PBR]	CWGN MPnt NLar SCob SHeu
'Strawberry Swirl'	CElw ELan EWTr GMaP MPnt MRav NBir SHeu SWvt WCAu
'Sugar Berry'[PBR] (Little Cutie Series)	EHyd EPfP LBar LBuc LRHS MPnt NRHS NSti SEdd SHeu WCot WNPC
SUGAR FROSTING ('Pwheu0104'[PBR])	CKel CRos EHyd ELan EPau GJos LRHS LSRN MGos MPnt NCou NHol NRHS SHeu SWvt
'Sugar Plum'[PBR]	CWGN EBee ELan EPfP GMcL LBuc LRHS LSRN MPnt SHeu WHoo WNPC
'Summer Sundae' **new**	CBor
'Sunrise' (Seasonal Selection Series)	MPnt SHeu WNPC
'Sweet Berry'	MPnt
'Sweet Caroline' (Fox Series)	MPnt WNPC
'Sweet Tart'[PBR] (Little Cutie Series)	CRos EHyd EPfP LBar LCro LRHS MDon MPnt NLar NRHS SHeu SPoG WNPC
'Swirling Fantasy'[PBR]	EGrI MPnt SHeu WFar
'Tangerine Wave' (Fox Series) [♀H6]	EPfP LRHS MPnt SHeu WNPC
'Tara'	MPnt SHeu
'Tayberry' (Indian Summer Series)	LRHS SHeu
'Thomas' (Fox Series) [♀H6]	CBod MPnt NSti SHeu WCot WNPC
'Timeless Night' **new**	LBar MPnt SHeu WNPC
'Timeless Treasure' **new**	LBar SHeu WNPC
'Tiramisu'[PBR]	CWGN MPnt SHeu SWvt WNPC
'Tokyo'[PBR] (City Series)	CWGN LBar LRHS MAvo MPnt NLar SHeu SPoG
'Topaz Jazz'	LBar MPnt SHeu WNPC
'Van Gogh' (Master Painters Series)	MPnt SHeu
'Vanilla Spice'	MPnt SHeu
'Velvet Night'	MDon MPnt NBir SHeu SPlb
'Venus' [♀H6]	CWGN EHyd LPal LRHS MPnt NRHS SHeu WCFE WCot WHoo
'Vesuvius'	MPnt SHeu
'Vienna'[PBR] (City Series)	MPnt SHeu WNPC
§ ***villosa***	ECha LEdu MPnt MRav XLum
- 'Autumn Bride'	CElw EWTr LSto MPnt SDix SHeu SMHy
- BRESSINGHAM BRONZE ('Absi'[PBR])	EHyd MPnt SHeu
- 'Chantilly'	LBar MPnt SHeu
- var. ***macrorhiza***	CBod EShb MPnt XLum
- 'Palace Purple'	Widely available
- 'Palace Purple Select'	CMac CTri GDam LSun MBow MCot SSut SWvt WSpi
- 'Plumpower'[PBR]	SHeu
- Purpurea Group	LRHS
- 'Royal Red'	ECha
'Violet Shimmer' (Fox Series)	CBod MPnt WNPC
'Virginale'	MPnt
'Walnut' (Fox Series) [♀H6]	MPnt SHeu WNPC
'White Marble'	MPnt SHar SHeu
'White Spires'	MPnt SHar SHeu
'White Swirls'	MPnt
'Wild Rose' (Primo Series)	EMor LBar LCro LRHS LSou MDon MPnt SHeu WNPC
'Wildberry' (Dolce Series)	CBod EBee EPfP LBar MHtn MPnt SHeu WNPC
'William How'	MPnt SHeu
'Winter Joy' (Seasonal Selection Series)	CRos EHyd LRHS MPnt NRHS SHeu WNPC
'Winter Red'	MPnt SHeu
(World Caffé Series) WORLD CAFFÉ AMERICANO ('Jmb 14/11')	LBar SPad
- WORLD CAFFÉ ROMANO ('Jmb 14/14') **new**	LBar
'XXL'	MPnt SHeu
'Zabeliana'	MPnt SHeu
'Zipper'[PBR]	CWGN LBar MPnt SHeu WNPC

Heuchera × *Tiarella* see × *Heucherella*

× *Heucherella* ✿ (*Saxifragaceae*)

'Alabama Sunrise'[PBR]	CRos CTsd ELan EMor EPfP EWhm GMcL LBar LRHS MPnt NLar NPer NRHS SHeu SWvt WFar
alba 'Bridget Bloom'	EHyd EPfP GMaP LRHS MPnt MRav SEdd SHeu SRms WCAu WFar XLum
§ - 'Rosalie'	GMcL MPnt MRav SHeu SPlb WSHC
'Art Deco'	MPnt SHeu
'Art Nouveau'	EMor LRHS LSou MPnt SHeu WCot WNPC
'Autumn Cascade'[PBR] (Cascade Series)	MPnt SHeu
'Berry Fizz'	MPnt SHeu SWvt
'Birthday Cake'	MPnt SHeu
'Blue Ridge'	LSou MPnt WTor
'Brass Lantern'[PBR] [♀H6]	CPla CRos CSBt EMor EPfP GJos LRHS LSou MAsh MPnt NHol NRHS SCob SCoo SHeu SPoG SRms SWvt WCot WNPC
'Burnished Bronze'[PBR]	EMor MPnt NLar SCob SCoo SHeu SPoG SWvt
'Buttered Rum'[PBR]	CWGN EBee EMor LBar MPnt SHeu SPad WNPC
'Butterscotch' **new**	WCot
'Catching Fire'	MPnt SHeu WNPC
'Chocolate Lace'[PBR]	MPnt SHeu

'Cinnamon Bear'	MPnt SHeu
'Citrus Shock'	EMor MPnt SCoo SHeu SPoG
'Copper Cascade'PBR (Cascade Series)	ELan LBar LRHS LSou MPnt SHeu WNPC WTor
'Cracked Ice'PBR	EMor LBar LRHS MPnt SCob SHeu WNPC
'Dayglow Pink'PBR	GMaP LSRN LSou MPnt NLar SHeu
'Eye Spy' (Fun and Games Series)	LBar SHeu WNPC WTor
'Fan Dancer'	MPnt SHeu
'Fire Frost'PBR	LSou MPnt SHeu
'Firecracker' **new**	WNPC
'Glacier Falls' (Falls Series)	SHeu WNPC
'Gold Cascade'PBR (Cascade Series)	ELan EPfP LRHS MPnt WNPC
GOLD STRIKE ('Hertn041')	EMor MBNS MPnt SHeu
'Golden Zebra'PBR	CWGN EMor MPnt NLar SHeu SWvt WTor
'Great Smokies'	MPnt SHeu
'Gunsmoke'PBR	EMor LSou MPnt SCob SHeu SWvt WFar
HAPPY HOUR LIME ('Tnherhhl')	EMor LBuc MPnt SHeu WNPC
'Heart of Darkness'PBR	MPnt SHeu
'Honey Rose'PBR	EBee LBar LSou MPnt SCob SCoo SHeu SPoG WNPC
'Hopscotch' (Fun and Games Series)	LBar SHeu WNPC
'Hot Spot'PBR	MPnt SHeu
'Infinity'PBR	LBar LSou SHeu
'Kimono'PBR 🏆H6	CBod CRos EHyd ELan EMor EPfP EWoo GMaP GMcL LRHS LSRN LSto MAvo MPnt NLar NRHS NSti SCob SCoo SHeu WJam
'Leapfrog' (Fun and Games Series)	LCro SHeu
'Mojito'	MPnt SHeu
'Ninja'	see *Tiarella* 'Ninja'
'Onyx'	EBee EMor LBar LBuc SHeu WNPC
'Party Time'PBR	SHeu
'Pink Fizz'	CBod LBar MPnt MPri SHeu WNPC WTor
PINK WHISPERS ('Hertn042')	LSou MPnt SHeu
'Plum Cascade'PBR (Cascade Series)	LBar LBuc MPnt SHeu SPeP WNPC
'Quicksilver'	CBcs EMor EPfP GMaP MPnt SHeu SWvt
'Red Rover' (Fun and Games Series)	LBar MPnt MPri SHeu WNPC
'Redstone Falls'PBR (Falls Series)	EBee EPfP GJos LBar MNrw MPnt MSCN SHeu SPoG SWvt WCot WNPC
'Ring of Fire'	SWvt
§ 'Silver Streak'	EHyd LRHS MPnt NRHS SHeu SWvt
'Solar Eclipse'	CBcs CKel CRos CTsd EBee EHyd EMor LBar LCro LOPS LRHS MAsh MPnt NLar NRHS NSti SCob SCoo SHeu SPad SPoG SWvt WFar WNPC
'Solar Power'PBR	CRos CWGN EBee EHyd ELan EMor EPfP LRHS MPnt MPri NRHS SHeu SWvt WFar WNPC
'Stoplight'PBR	CRos CWGN ECha ELan EMor EPfP GMaP LRHS MGos MPnt MRav NBir NHol NSti SCob SHeu SWvt WFar WNPC
'Summer Snowflake'	SHeu
'Sunrise Falls'PBR (Falls Series)	EBee MPnt MSCN SHeu SWvt WFar WNPC
'Sunspot'PBR (v)	EMor NBro SHeu SRms WHer
'Sweet Tea'PBR	Widely available
'Tapestry'PBR 🏆H6	Widely available
tiarelloides	SRms
'Twilight'PBR	EMor LSou MPnt SHeu
§ 'Viking Ship'	MPnt NBir SHeu
'Yellowstone Falls'PBR 🏆H6	GMcL LBar MPnt MSCN NCou SHeu SWvt WNPC

Hexastylis see *Asarum*

Hibbertia (*Dilleniaceae*)

aspera	CAbb CBcs CBod CCCN CKel CRHN CTsd LRHS WCot WFar WKif WSHC
§ ***cuneiformis***	CCCN
pedunculata	WAbe
procumbens	ITim
§ ***scandens*** 🏆H1c	CAbb CBcs CCCN CHll CRHN EShb
tetrandra	see *H. cuneiformis*
volubilis	see *H. scandens*

Hibiscus (*Malvaceae*)

'Cherry Cheesecake' **new**	MPkF
coccineus	EShb LRHS SBrt SPlb XSte
- white-flowered	SBrt
'Cranberry Crush'PBR	CWGN ELan MNrw
'Fireball'PBR	SPoG
FULL BLAST	see *H.* 'Resi'
hamabo	CCCN IPap SGbt SNig WHlf
huegelii	see *Alyogyne huegelii*
'Jazzberry Jam'PBR	ELan MNrw SPoG
'Kopper King'PBR	MNrw SPoG
'Midnight Marvel' **new**	MPkF XSte
moscheutos	SBrt SVic XLum
- CAROUSEL JOLLY HEART ('Tahi56'PBR)	LCro
- CAROUSEL PINK CANDY ('Tahi12'PBR)	CWGN SPad
- CAROUSEL PINK PASSION ('Tahi16'PBR)	LCro
- CAROUSEL RED WINE ('Tahi61'PBR) **new**	SPeP
- 'Galaxy'	EAJP
- 'Old Yella'PBR	ELan SPoG
- PLANET GRIOTTE ('Tangri'PBR)	MPkF XSte
- 'Royal Gems'PBR	ELan
'Newbiscus Pink'	CCCN
'Newbiscus Red'	CCCN
'Newbiscus White'	CCCN
paramutabilis	EWes
'Plum Crazy'PBR	MHtn
§ 'Resi'PBR	EBar
rosa-sinensis	CDoC SPre
- 'Apple Blossom'	WFib
- 'Arcadian Spring'	WFib
- 'Aunty Di' **new**	WFib
§ - 'Bari' (Sunny Cities Series)	CCCN
- 'Blues Man'	WFib
- 'Blush' **new**	WFib
§ - 'Bordeaux'PBR (Sunny Cities Series)	CCCN
- 'Byron Metts'	WFib
- 'Cajun Cocktail'	see *H. rosa-sinensis* 'Jambalaya'
- 'Candy Floss' (d)	WFib
- 'Carmen Keene'	WFib
- 'China Town'	WFib
- 'Cloud Nine'PBR	WFib
- 'Cockatoo'	WFib
- 'Cooperi' (v) 🏆H1b	WFib
- 'Courier Mail'	WFib
- 'Dorothy Brady'	WFib
- 'Enid Lewis' (d)	WFib
- 'Fifth Dimension'	WFib
- 'Gabriel'	WFib

	- 'Georgia Peach'	WFib
	- 'Gwen Mary'	WFib
	- 'Holly's Pride'	WFib
	- 'Hot Bikini'	WFib
§	- 'Jambalaya'	WFib
	- 'Jayella'	WFib
	- 'June's Joy'	WFib
	- 'Key West Thunderhead' (d)	WFib
	- 'Königer'	WFib
	- 'Lemon Chiffon'	WFib
	- 'Linda Pear' (d)	WFib
	- 'Madame Dupont'	WFib
	- 'Me Oh My Oh'	WFib
	- 'Mrs Andreasen' (d)	WFib
	- 'Rhinestone'	WFib
	- 'Roman Candle'	WFib
	- 'Rose Flake'	WFib
	- 'Rum Runner'	WFib
	- 'Soft Shoulders'	WFib
	- 'Spanish Lady'	WFib
	- 'Sprinkle Rain'	WFib
	- 'Sunny Bary'	see *H. rosa-sinensis* 'Bari'
	- (Sunny Cities Series) 'Sunny Bordeaux'	see *H. rosa-sinensis* 'Bordeaux'
	- - SUNNY CANCUN ('Hican'PBR)	CCCN
	- - SUNNY TORINO ('Hirio'PBR)	CCCN
	- 'Susan Schlueter'	WFib
	- 'Tahitian Christmas'	WFib
	- 'Tahitian Desert Sands'	WFib
	- 'Tarantella'	WFib
	- 'The Path'	WFib
	- 'Velvetine' **new**	WFib
	- 'Vermillion Queen'	WFib
	- 'Weekend'	WFib
	- 'White Swan'	WFib
	ROSE MOON ('Walhirosmo'PBR)	CRos EHyd LBuc LRHS NRHS SPoG XVPe
	schizopetalus ♀H1b	WFib
	sinosyriacus 'Lilac Queen'	CKel EHyd EPfP LRHS WCot WPGP
	- 'Ruby Glow'	CKel EPfP LRHS LSRN WPGP
	'Sunny Premiere'	CCCN
	syriacus	CCCN LMaj LPal SChr SWeb SavN WJur
§	- 'America Irene Scott'PBR	LCro SPoG
	- 'Aphrodite'	SRHi SSta
	- 'Ardens' (d)	CEnd EBee LPar SPoG WFar WHtc
§	- AZURRI BLUE SATIN ('Dvpazurri'PBR)	SSta
	- 'Azzurri'	see *H. syriacus* AZURRI BLUE SATIN
	- BLUE BIRD	see *H. syriacus* 'Oiseau Bleu'
	- BLUE CHIFFON ('Notwood3'PBR) (Chiffon Series) (d) ♀H5	CSBt EHyd ELan EPfP LCro LOPS LPar LRHS NRHS SPoG SRHi
	- 'Bredon Springs'	SSta
	- CHINA CHIFFON ('Bricutts') (Chiffon Series) (d)	LPar MMuc SEND SPer SPoG
	- 'Diana' ♀H5	CBcs CBod CDoC CRos EBee EHyd ELan ELon EPfP LRHS LSRN MAsh NRHS SCob SCoo SPer SSta WHlf WLov
	- 'Dorothy Crane'	CKel LRHS SSta
	- 'Duc de Brabant' (d)	CCCN CSBt LPar MBlu
	- 'Elegantissimus'	see *H. syriacus* 'Lady Stanley'
	- 'Freedom' (d)	LRHS
	- 'Gandini van Aart'PBR	LPar LRHS SGol
	- 'Hamabo' ♀H5	CBod CBrac CRos CSBt CTri EBee EHyd ELan ELon EPfP LRHS LSRN MAsh MGos MMuc NLar NRHS SCoo SEND SPer SPoG SWvt WFar WLov
	- 'Helene'	LRHS LSRN MBlu SSta WHtc
	- 'Honghwarang'	SSta
§	- 'Lady Stanley' (d)	CBod CCCN CDoC CMac CSBt SCoo SNig
	- LAVENDER CHIFFON ('Notwoodone'PBR) (Chiffon Series) (d) ♀H5	CSBt EHyd ELan EPfP EWes LCro LOPS LPar LRHS LSRN MMuc NRHS SCoo SEND SPer SPoG
	- 'Leopoldii' (d)	EBee
	- MAGENTA CHIFFON ('Rwoods5'PBR) (Chiffon Series)	EHyd LCro LOPS LRHS NRHS SPoG
	- 'Marina'	CBod CCCN CDoC EHed ELan ELon EPfP LCro LPar MACG MBlu MRav SNig SPer WFar WLov WTyc
	- 'Mathilde'	SSta
	- 'Mauve Queen'	SSta
	- 'Meehanii' misapplied	see *H. syriacus* 'Purpureus Variegatus'
	- 'Meehanii' (v) ♀H5	CEnd EBee EPfP LRHS SCoo SPer SPoG SSta WHtc
	- 'Melrose'	SSta
	- 'Monstrosus'	LPar NLar
§	- 'Oiseau Bleu' ♀H5	Widely available
	- PINK CHIFFON ('Jwnwood4'PBR) (Chiffon Series) (d)	CSBt EHyd ELan LCro LOPS LPar LRHS NRHS
	- PINK GIANT ('Flogi')	EPfP LPar SPer SSta
	- PINKY SPOT ('Minspot'PBR)	EHed
	- PURPLE PILLAR ('Gandini Santiago'PBR)	LCro LPar LRHS SCoo SGol SWeb
	- PURPLE RUFFLES ('Sanchoyo') (d)	CDoC EPfP SPoG WHtc
§	- 'Purpureus Variegatus' (v)	CMac EHyd
	- 'Red Heart' ♀H5	CBod CEnd CMac CRos CSBt CTri EHyd ELan EPfP LCro LPar LRHS MAsh MGos MMuc NRHS SCob SEND SGbt SPer SPoG SRms SSta SWvt WCFE
	- RUSSIAN VIOLET ('Floru')	CEnd CKel EPfP LRHS
	- 'Snowdrift'	SSta
I	- 'Speciosus' (d)	LPar SPoG WFar
	- STARBURST CHIFFON ('Rwoods6') (Chiffon Series)	CRos LCro LOPS LRHS SCoo
	- SUGAR TIP	see *H. syriacus* 'America Irene Scott'
	- SUP'HEART ('Minomb'PBR)	EHed EPfP SGsty
	- 'Totus Albus'	LPar SSta
	- ULTRAMARINE ('Minultra'PBR)	CDoC EPfP SGsty
	- 'Variegatus'	see *H. syriacus* 'Purpureus Variegatus'
	- WHITE CHIFFON ('Notwoodtwo'PBR) (Chiffon Series) (d) ♀H5	CSBt EHyd ELan EPfP EWes LCro LOPS LPar LRHS LSRN MRav SCoo SPer SPoG
	- 'William R. Smith' ♀H5	LPar MSwo SSta
	- 'Woodbridge' ♀H5	Widely available
	trionum	CSpe WKif
	- 'Sunny Day'	ELan

hickory, shagbark see *Carya ovata*

Hieracium (*Asteraceae*)

	aurantiacum	see *Pilosella aurantiaca*
	brunneocroceum	see *Pilosella aurantiaca* subsp. *carpathicola*
	laevigatum subsp. ***nivale***	MMuc
§	***lanatum***	GJos NBir NWad
	maculatum Sm.	see *H. spilophaeum*
	pannosum	WCot
	pilosella	see *Pilosella officinarum*
	scullyi	EPPr WFar
§	***spilophaeum***	GGro MMuc NBid NPer

- 'Blue Leaf'	WCot
- 'Leopard'	GJos
villosum	GJos WHer
welwitschii	see *H. lanatum*

Hierochloe (*Poaceae*)

odorata	EPPr GPoy LEdu SBls XLum

Himalayacalamus (*Poaceae*)

asper	CDTJ
§ ***falconeri***	SDix WCot
§ ***hookerianus***	EPfP LAma SChr
- 'Himalaya Blue'	SBGi

Himantoglossum (*Orchidaceae*)

robertianum	GKev

× *Hippeasprekelia* (*Amaryllidaceae*)

'Durga Pradhan'	WCot
'Red Beauty'	CBor WCot
'Red Star'	CCCN

Hippeastrum ✿ (*Amaryllidaceae*)

× ***acramannii*** 🏆H2	CAvo WCot
blossfeldiae	LAma
(Butterfly Group) 'Exotic Star'PBR	WPhe
(Colibri Group) 'Baby Star' 🏆H2	GKev SDeJ
- 'Balentino'PBR	GKev
- 'Rapido'	LCro LOPS
- 'Veneto'	SDeJ
cybister **new**	WCot
(Diamond Group) 'Charisma' 🏆H2	ETay LAma SDeJ WPhe
- 'Christmas Star' **new**	ETay
- 'Fairytale' 🏆H2	LCro LOPS SDeJ
- 'Lemon Star'	WPhe
- 'Picotee' 🏆H2	GKev LAma LCro LOPS SDeJ
- 'Pyjama Party' **new**	LAma
- 'Red Fire'	GKev
§ - 'Tierra' **new**	LCro
- 'Très Chic'	ETay WPhe
(Double Diamond Group) 'Alfresco'PBR (d)	ETay GKev SDeJ
(Double Galaxy Group) 'Amarantia'PBR (d)	GKev
- 'Aphrodite' (d)	ETay LAma WPhe
- 'Blossom Peacock' (d)	WPhe
- CHERRY NYMPH ('Chernym'PBR) (d)	WPhe
- 'Clown' 🏆H2	SDeJ WPhe
- 'Double Delicious' (d)	WPhe
- 'Double Dragon'PBR (d)	LAma
- 'Double Record' (d)	SDeJ
- 'Elvas' (d)	WPhe
- 'Ice Queen' (d)	LAma WPhe
- 'Lady Jane' (d)	LAma SDeJ
- 'Marilyn'PBR (d)	LAma
- 'Nymph' (d)	GKev LAma WPhe
- 'Red Peacock' (d)	SDeJ
(Galaxy Group) 'Ambiance'	LAma WPhe
- 'Apple Blossom' 🏆H2	GKev LAma LCro LOPS SDeJ WPhe
- 'Apricot Parfait'	GKev
- 'Barbados'	LAma WPhe
- 'Benfica'	LAma WPhe
- 'Black Pearl'	LCro LOPS
- 'Christmas Gift'	GKev LAma LCro LOPS WPhe
- DAPHNE ('94 B6')	WPhe
- 'Desire'	WPhe
- 'Flamenco Queen' 🏆H2	LAma WPhe
- 'Gervase'	GKev LAma WPhe
- 'Grand Diva'	GKev LAma
- 'Hercules'	SDeJ
- 'Lagoon'PBR 🏆H2	LCro LOPS
- 'Liberty'	SDeJ
- 'Limona'PBR	LCro LOPS
- 'Luna'	LAma WPhe
- 'Minerva'	LAma SDeJ WPhe
- 'Mont Blanc'	LAma SDeJ
- 'Monte Carlo'PBR 🏆H2	WPhe
- 'Orange Souvereign'	WPhe
- 'Park Red'	GKev
- 'Pink Princess' **new**	LAma
- 'Pink Surprise'	WPhe
- 'Popov'PBR	WPhe
- 'Purple Rain'	WPhe
- 'Red Lion' 🏆H2	GKev LAma LCro LOPS WPhe
- 'Red Pearl'PBR	WPhe
- 'Rilona'	GKev LAma SDeJ WPhe
- 'Royal Velvet' 🏆H2	LAma WPhe
- 'Samba' **new**	LAma
- 'Showmaster'	WPhe
- 'Spartacus'PBR	WPhe
- 'Susan'	SDeJ WPhe
- 'Temptation' **new**	LAma
- 'Tosca'	WPhe
× ***johnsonii*** 🏆H2	WCot
'McCann's Double' (d) **new**	LAma
papilio	CPla GKev LCro LOPS SDeJ
psittacinum	WCot
puniceum	GKev
'Royal Red'	LCro
'San Antonio Rose'	WCot
'Snow Queen'	ETay LCro LOPS
(Sonatini Group) 'Eye Catcher'	GKev
- 'Pink Rascal'	GKev
- 'Red Rascal'	GKev
- 'Sonatini Valentino'	WCot
- 'White Rascal'	GKev
(Spider Group) 'Bogota'	GKev LAma LCro LOPS
- 'Carmen'	WPhe
- 'Chico' 🏆H2	GKev LAma
- 'Emerald'	LAma WCot
- 'Evergreen' 🏆H2	LCro LOPS WPhe
- 'Sumatra'PBR	LCro LOPS
striatum	WCot
stylosum	LAma WCot
TERRA MYSTICA	see *H.* (Diamond Group) 'Tierra'
'Toughie'	EBee
(Trumpet Group) 'Estella'	ETay
- 'Santiago'	LAma
- 'Swan Lake'PBR	SDeJ
vittatum	GKev

Hippeastrum × *Sprekelia* see × *Hippeasprekelia*

Hippocrepis (*Fabaceae*)

§ ***comosa***	NAts NSla SPhx WAbe
§ ***emerus***	CBcs CCCN CDoC CKel CMac ELan EPfP IArd LPar MAsh MGil MGos MMuc SEND SNig SVen WSpi

Hippophae (*Elaeagnaceae*)

rhamnoides	Widely available
- (m)	EPom
- 'Askola' (f/F)	CAgr
- 'Dorana' (f/F)	CAgr
- 'Freisendorf Orange' (f/F)	CAgr
- 'Frugna' (f/F)	CAgr NLar
- 'Hergo' (f/F)	CAgr LPar NLar XVPe
- 'Hikul' (m)	CAgr CKel CWnw LPar NLar
- 'Juliet' (f/F)	CAgr
- 'Leikora' (f/F) 🏆H7	CAgr ELan EPfP MBlu NLar SPer

- ORANGE ENERGY ('Habego'PBR) (f/F) CAgr
- 'Pollmix' (m) ♀H7 CAgr ELan EPfP MBlu NLar SPer
- 'Pollmix 1' (m) new XVPe
- 'Sirola' (f/F) CAgr
salicifolia CAgr WKor
- 'Streetwise' EHyd LRHS
sinensis LS&E 15724 WPGP

Hippuris (Plantaginaceae)

vulgaris CBen CPud CWat EWat GQue LLWG LPfP NPer WMAq XLum

Hirpicium (Asteraceae)

armerioides SPlb

Histiopteris (Dennstaedtiaceae)

incisa LEdu SPlb WPGP

Hoheria ✿ (Malvaceae)

'Ace of Spades' CAbb CDoC CKel EHyd ELan ELon EPfP LRHS MGil MMrt NLar SEND SPer SWvt WSpi
§ **angustifolia** EBee EPfP IDee MVil SVen WPGP
angustifolia × sexstylosa WPGP
'Borde Hill' CAbb CBcs CBod CDoC CJun CKel CMac CTrC EBee EGrI EHyd ELan ELon EPfP LRHS LSRN MAsh MGil SEND SMad SPer SWvt WCFE WPGP WSpi
glabrata CMac CTrC EPfP GBin IDee NBir
'Glory of Amlwch' ♀H4 CAbb CBcs CDoC CJun CKel ELan EPfP GGGa LRHS LSRN SChF SPoG SWvt WKif WPGP WSpi
§ **lyallii** ♀H4 CCCN CKel LSRN SPer SVen WSpi
microphylla see *H. angustifolia*
populnea CBcs CCCN CTsd
- 'Sunshine' (v) CDoC SPoG
sexstylosa CAbb CTri CWal EPfP LEdu LRHS LSRN SMad SPer SPlb SVen SWvt WFar WJur WSpi
- 'Crataegifolia' EBee MGil NLar WSpi
- 'Pendula' CMac
- 'Stardust' ♀H4 Widely available
'Snow White' LRHS LSRN MGos MNic MTrO NOra SPoG SRHi WMat

Holarrhena (Apocynaceae)

pubescens 'Snowflake' CDoC

Holboellia (Lardizabalaceae)

FMWJ 13055 WCru
angustifolia WCru
- subsp. **angustifolia** WCru
- - H&M 1504 WPGP
- subsp. **linearifolia** BWJ 8004 WCru
- subsp. **obtusa** DJHC 506 WCru
brachyandra HWJ 1023 WCru WPGP
aff. **chapaensis** B&SWJ 7250 WCru
coriacea CBcs CBod CCCN CKel CRHN EBee EHyd EPfP LEdu LRHS MGil MRav NLar NQui SEND SPer WCFE WCru WJur
- B&SWJ 2818 WCru
aff. **grandiflora** FMWJ 13333 WCru
latifolia CBcs CCCN CKel CMac CRHN CRos CTri EBee EGrI EHyd ELan EPfP LEdu LRHS MGil NLar SAdn SArc SNig SPer SPoG SWvt WBor WCru WPGP WSHC
- DJHC 98442 WCru
- HWJCM 008 WCru
- HWJK 2014 WCru
- subsp. **chartacea** dark-flowered HWJK 2213D WCru
- - pale-flowered HWJK 2213C WCru
- lanceolate-leaved WPGP
- - HWJK 2419 WCru

Holcus (Poaceae)

lanatus WSFF
mollis 'Albovariegatus' (v) CWCL EBou ECha EPPr GMaP NBid NBro NPer NSti SPlb SRms WPnP XLum
- 'White Fog' (v) MMuc NWad

Holmskioldia (Lamiaceae)

* **lutea** CCCN
sanguinea CCCN

Holodiscus (Rosaceae)

discolor CBcs EBee EHyd ELan EPfP EWes LRHS MBlu MGil MMuc MRav NLar NQui SPer SPlb
- var. **ariifolius** WHlf

Homalocladium (Polygonaceae)

§ **platycladum** EShb

Homeria (Iridaceae)

breyniana var. **aurantiaca** see *Moraea collina*

Homoglossum see *Gladiolus*

Hordeum (Poaceae)

jubatum ♀H6 CDor CKel CKno CSpe CTtf CWCL EAJP EWes GBee LEdu MAsh NGdn NGrd SEdd SMrm SPhx SRot WPnP
- 'Early Pink' NDov
marinum new WCot
secalinum CHab WWild

Hormathophylla (Brassicaceae)

spinosa 'Roseum' ♀H5 CTri ECha EDAr ELan EPot GArf XLum
- 'Rubrum' XSen

Horminum (Lamiaceae)

pyrenaicum LShi MHol MMuc SBut SEND SRms
I - f. **alboviolaceum** EWhm SBrt SBut
- dark-flowered SBrt WSHC

Hornungia (Brassicaceae)

alpina GEdr MACG NBwr NSla XLum

horseradish see *Armoracia rusticana*

Hosta ✿ (Asparagaceae)

AGSJ 302 WCot
'A Many-Splendored Thing' IBal
'Abana' (v) IBal
'Abba Dabba Do' (v) CDor ECtt ELon EMic IBal LBar MHost NSue SSien
'Abba Showtime' IBal
'Abby' (v) EMic IBal MHost NSue SSien WFar
'Abiqua Ariel' EMic
'Abiqua Blue Crinkles' IBal NBir
'Abiqua Blue Edger' IBal MHost SSien
'Abiqua Blue Madonna' IBal

'Abiqua Blushing Recluse'	SSien
'Abiqua Delight' (v)	EMic
'Abiqua Drinking Gourd' 🏆[H7]	CBdn CDor ECtt ELon EMic EMor GMaP IBal MHost NLar NSue SArc SSien
'Abiqua Elephant Ears'	IBal
'Abiqua Ground Cover'	IBal
'Abiqua Moonbeam' (v)	EMic IBal MHost NGdn SSien
'Abiqua Recluse'	EMic IBal
'Abiqua Trumpet'	EMic IBal LRHS NGdn NLar NNor SSien
'Abraham Lincoln'	IBal
'Academy Flora'	IBal
'Academy Mavrodaphne'	EMic
'Ada Reed'	IBal
'Adorable'	EMor IBal NSue SSien
aequinoctiiantha	EMic IBal SSien
'Afterglow' (v)	IBal SSien
'Alabama Gold'	EMic
'Alakazaam' (v) 🏆[H7]	EMic IBal SSien WFar
'Alan Titchmarsh'	IBal MHost NSue
albomarginata	see *H.* 'Paxton's Original' (*sieboldii*)
§ 'Albomarginata' (*fortunei*) (v)	CBcs CMac EBlo EHeP NBir NGdn NNor SSien SWvt WFar
'Alex Summers'	EMic IBal SSien WFar
'Alice in Wonderland' (v)	IBal
'All That Jazz' (v)	IBal
'Allan P. McConnell' (v) 🏆[H7]	EMic IBal LRHS LSta MHost MNrw NSue SSien WFar WOld
'Allegan Emperor' (v)	IBal SSien
'Allegan Fog' (v)	EMor EShb GEdr IBal LRHS LSta NHpl NSue SSien
'Alligator Alley' (v)	EMic IBal SSien
'Alligator Shoes' (v)	EMic IBal
'Almost'	IBal
'Alpine Aire'	EMic IBal
'Alpine Dream'	IBal
'Alternative'	IBal
'Alvatine Taylor' (v)	EMic IBal NGdn SSien
'Amalia'[PBR] (v)	ESwi IBal NSue SSien
'Amanuma'	EMic IBal NSue
'Amazing Grace' (v)	EMic IBal
'Amazone' (v) **new**	EHed
'Amber Tiara'	EMic IBal MHost NSue SSien
'American Choo Choo'	EMic
'American Dream' (v)	EMic IBal LSta SSien
'American Gothic' (v)	IBal
'American Halo'	EMic IBal MHost NLar NSti NSue SSien
'American Icon'	EMic IBal
'American Sweetheart'	EMic IBal SSien
'Americana' (v)	IBal SSien
'Amethyst Gem'	IBal NSue
'Amos'	IBal SSien
'Amy Elizabeth' (v)	EMic IBal
'Andorian'	IBal NSue
'Andrew'	SSien
'Andy Murray' (v)	MHost
'Angel Falls' (v)	SSien
'Angel Feathers' (v)	IBal SSien
'Angelique' (v)	IBal SSien
'Anglo Saxon' (v)	IBal
'Ani Machi' (v) 🏆[H7]	NSue
'Ann Kulpa' (v)	CBdn EMic ESwi IBal MHost NGdn SSien
'Annabel Lee'	IBal
'Anne' (v)	IBal NSue SSien
'Ansly' (v)	IBal
'Antioch' (*fortunei*) (v)	EMic GLog IBal MRav NLar NNor SSien
'Aoki' (*fortunei*)	EMic IBal
'Aoki Variegated' (v)	EMic
'Aomori Select'	EMic
'Aphrodite' (*plantaginea*) (d)	EPfP EWTr SMad SMrm SSien
'Apollo'	NNor
'Apple Candy' (v)	IBal NSue SSien
'Apple Green'	EMic GKev IBal
'Apple Pie'	IBal MHost
'Appletini'	IBal NSue
'Aqua Velva'	IBal
'Arc de Triomphe'	ECtt EMic EMor IBal MHost NLar SSien
'Arch Duke'	IBal SSien
'Arctic Blast'	EMic IBal
'Arctic Circle' (v)	EMic
'Argentea Variegata' (*undulata*)	see *H. undulata* var. *undulata*
'Aristocrat' (Tardiana Group) (v)	EMic EMor IBal NGdn NNor SSien WFar
'Arnold Black' **new**	SSien
'Asian Pearl' (v)	IBal
'Aspen Gold' (*tokudama* hybrid)	EMic
'Astral Bliss'	IBal
'Athena' (v)	SSien
'Atlantis'[PBR] (v)	CBod EMic EMor IBal NGdn NSue SSien
'Atom Smasher'	NSue
'Atomic Elvis'	CBdn IBal NSue
'August Beauty'	EMic IBal SSien
'August Moon'	CRos ECtt EGrI ELan ELon EMic GBin GMaP GMcL IBal LRHS LSto MHost MRav NBir NChi NGdn NLar NNor NRHS SCob SCoo SEdd SPer SPoG SRms SSien SWvt WFar XLum
'Aureafolia'	see *H.* 'Starker Yellow Leaf'
'Aureoalba' (*fortunei*)	see *H.* 'Spinners'
'Aureomaculata' (*fortunei*)	see *H. fortunei* var. *albopicta*
'Aureomarginata' ambig. (v)	CEme SCoo SSien
'Aureomarginata' (*montana*) (v)	CMac EBlo ELan EMic GMaP IBal MMuc NGdn NLar NSue WFar
§ 'Aureomarginata' (*ventricosa*) (v) 🏆[H7]	EMic GAbr IBal NBir NGdn WFar
'Aureostriata' (*tardiva*)	see *H.* 'Inaho'
'Austin Dickinson' (v)	ECtt EMic ESwi IBal LSta SSien
'Autumn Frost' (Shadowland Series) (v) 🏆[H7]	EMic EMor IBal NSue
'Avalanche'	SSien
'Avocado'	ELon EMic EWTr IBal NLar NSue SSien WFar
'Ayesha' (v)	SSien
'Azure Snow'	IBal
'Azuretini'	IBal NSue
'Babbling Brook'	IBal NSue
'Baby Blue' (Tardiana Group)	EMic
'Baby Blue Eyes'	EMic IBal NSue
'Baby Booties' (v)	CBdn ESwi IBal NSue
'Baby Bunting'	IBal MHost NBro NLar NNor NSue SSien
'Baby Doll' (v)	IBal
'Baby Kim'	EMic
'Backyard Monster' (v)	IBal
'Bailey's Cream' (v)	IBal
'Baja White'	IBal SSien
'Bali-Hai'	IBal
'Ballerina'	IBal
'Bam Bam Blue'	CBdn IBal
'Banana Muffins'	IBal
'Band of Gold'	EMic IBal MHost SSien
'Banyai's Dancing Girl'	EMic IBal
'Barbara Ann' (v)	CBdn EMic IBal ITim MHost NGdn SSien
'Barbara May'	IBal
'Barney Fife'	IBal

'Battle Star' (v)	NSue SSien
'Beach Boy' (v)	IBal MHost MNrw NLar NSue SSien
'Bea's Colossus'	IBal
'Beauty Little Blue'	IBal NSue
'Beauty Substance'	IBal NNor SSien
'Beckoning'	EMic IBal MHost NSue SSien
'Bedazzled' (v)	CBdn IBal SSien
'Bedford Blue'	CBdn EMic IBal MHost SSien
'Bedford Rise and Shine' (v)	EMic ESwi IBal LRHS LSta MHost SSien
'Bedford Wakey-Wakey'	IBal MHost
'Behemoth'	IBal NSue
'Bell Bottom Blues'	IBal
bella	see *H. crassifolia*
'Bells of Edinburgh'	IBal SSien
'Ben Vernooij' (v)	CBdn IBal MHost SSien
'Bennie McRae'	IBal
'Best of Twenty'	IBal NSue
'Betcher's Blue'	EMic IBal
'Betsy King'	CMac MRav NLar
'Bette Davis Eyes'	IBal
'Betty'	IBal MHost NSue
'Beyond Glory' (v)	EMic
'Biddy's Blue'	IBal
'Big Beauty' (v)	ESwi IBal
'Big Boy' (*montana*)	EWTr IBal LRHS LSta NSue
'Big Daddy' (*sieboldiana* hybrid) (v)	Widely available
'Big John' (*sieboldiana*)	IBal NSue
'Big Mama'	EMic IBal MNrw NGdn NSue SSien
'Big Performer' (v)	IBal
'Big Top'	IBal SSien
'Bigfoot'	IBal
'Biggie'	IBal
'Bill Brinka' (v)	IBal SSien
'Bill Dress's Blue'	EMic SSien
Binny sport (*sieboldii*)	GBin
'Birchwood Blue Beauty'	IBal
'Birchwood Gem'	IBal
§ 'Birchwood Parky's Gold'	ECtt EMic GMaP IBal MHost NGdn NHol NLar NNor SMrm SSien
'Birchwood Ruffled Queen'	EMic SSien
'Bitsy Gold'	EMic
'Bitsy Green'	NSue
'Bitter Lemons' **new**	NSue
'Bix Blues'	IBal
'Bizarre'	EMic
'Black Beauty'	IBal
'Black Hills'	EMic IBal
'Black Light' **new**	IBal SSien
'Blackfoot'	IBal
'Blackjack' (*sieboldiana*)	IBal SSien WFar
'Blarney Stone'	IBal SSien
'Blaue Venus'	IBal
'Blaze of Glory'	IBal
'Blazing Saddles' (v)	CBdn EMic IBal SSien
'Blonde Elf'	EMic IBal NGdn NHol NNor
'Blue Angel' misapplied	see *H. sieboldiana* var. *elegans*
'Blue Angel' (*sieboldiana*) ♀^{H7}	Widely available
'Blue Arrow' ♀^{H7}	IBal LRHS LSta NNor NSue
'Blue Baron'	EMic IBal
'Blue Belle' (Tardiana Group)	EMic IBal MHost NEoE NGdn
'Blue Blush' (Tardiana Group)	EMic IBal MHost NGdn
'Blue Boy'	EMic NNor SSien
'Blue Cadet'	CBcs CMac CPud CRos EBee EMic EShb GKev GQue LRHS LSto MHost NBir NGdn NLar NRHS NSue NWad SCoo SSien WFar
'Blue Canoe'	IBal MHost
'Blue Cascade'	EMic IBal NSue
'Blue Chip'	EMic
'Blue Circle'^{PBR}	EMic IBal
'Blue Clown'	IBal
'Blue Cup' (*sieboldiana*)	EMic MRav SRms
'Blue Danube' (Tardiana Group)	ECha EMic IBal MHost
'Blue Diamond' (Tardiana Group)	EMic NNor NSue WFar
'Blue Dimples' (Tardiana Group)	IBal MHost
'Blue Dolphin'	IBal SSien
'Blue Edger'	IBal MHost NBir SSien
'Blue Eyes'	EMic NSue
'Blue Flame'	ECtt EMic IBal
'Blue Frost'	IBal
'Blue Haired Lady'	IBal
'Blue Hawaii'	IBal NSue SSien
'Blue Heart' (*sieboldiana*)	ECha EMic IBal
'Blue Ice' (Tardiana Group)	SSien
'Blue Impression'	EMic
'Blue Ivory' (v)	EBee ECtt EHed ELon EMor NGdn NSue SPad
'Blue Jay' (Tardiana Group)	EMic IBal
'Blue Lady'	EMic IBal
'Blue Lollipop'	GEdr
'Blue Magic'	MHost
'Blue Mammoth' (*sieboldiana*) ♀^{H7}	EMic EMor EPfP IBal NLar NSue SEdd SSien
'Blue Maui'	IBal
'Blue Monday'	EMic SSien
'Blue Moon' (Tardiana Group)	EMic IBal MHost NGdn NLar SSien
'Blue Mountains'	IBal
'Blue Mouse Ears' ♀^{H7}	Widely available
'Blue Plate Special'	ESwi
'Blue River' (v)	EMic ESwi IBal
'Blue Seer' (*sieboldiana*)	EMic SSien
'Blue Shadows' (*tokudama*) (v)	ESwi GMcL NLar NSue SSien WFar
'Blue Skies' (Tardiana Group)	EMic IBal MHost
'Blue Sliver'	SSien
'Blue Splendor' (Tardiana Group)	IBal
'Blue Umbrellas' (*sieboldiana* hybrid)	ECtt ELan EPfP GAbr GMaP IBal MHost NGdn NLar NNor SSien
'Blue Vision'	ECtt IBal
'Blue Wedgwood' (Tardiana Group)	EMic GQue IBal LRHS MHost NGdn SCob SSien
'Blue Wonder'	IBal
'Blue Wu'	EMic IBal
'Blueberry à la Mode'	IBal
'Blueberry Cobbler'	IBal MHost
'Blueberry Muffin'	EMic MHost NSue
'Blueberry Tart'	IBal
'Bluetooth'	IBal
'Blushing Blue'	CBdn
'Bob Deane' (v)	EMic IBal SSien
'Bob Olson' (v)	CBdn ESwi IBal MHost SSien WFar
'Bobbie Sue' (v)	IBal SSien
'Bobcat'	IBal
'Bogie and Bacall' (v)	IBal
'Bold and Brassy' **new**	ESwi
'Bold Edger' (v)	CBdn EMic IBal
'Bold Intrigue' (v)	IBal
'Bold Ribbons' (v)	EMic SSien
'Bolt out of the Blue'	EMic
'Bonanza'	EMic
'Bonfire'	EMic
'Border Bandit' (v)	IBal
'Border Street' (v)	SSien
§ 'Borwick Beauty' (*sieboldiana*) (v)	ELon EMic IBal LSou NGdn NLar SPer SSien
'Bottom Line' (v)	IBal

'Bountiful'	EMic IBal NSue
'Bounty' (v) **new**	SSien
'Boyz Toy'	EMic IBal NSue WOld
'Branching Out'	IBal
'Brandywine'	IBal
'Brash and Sassy'	IBal
'Brave Amherst' (v)	IBal
'Brenda's Beauty' (v)	EMic IBal
'Bressingham Blue'	CRos CSBt EBlo ECtt ELon GQue IBal LAma LPfP LRHS MHost MRav NLar NNor SPer SSien SWvt WFar
'Bridal Falls'[PBR] (v)	CBdn ESwi IBal NSue SSien
'Bridal Veil'	EMic IBal MHost
'Bridegroom'	EMic ESwi IBal SSien
'Bridgeville'	IBal
'Brigadier'	IBal
'Brigham Blue'	IBal
'Bright Glow' (Tardiana Group)	EMic IBal
'Bright Lights' (*tokudama*) (v)	EMic NGdn SSien WFar
'Bright Star' (v)	CBdn IBal NSue SSien
'Brim Cup' (v)	CDor ECtt ELon EPfP EShb GMcL LAma MACG MNrw NBro NGdn NNor SMrm SPer SSien
'Broadband' (v)	GBin IBal
'Broadway' (v)	EMic EMor IBal
'Bronx Bomber' (v)	IBal NSue
'Brooke'	EMic IBal
'Brother Ronald' (Tardiana Group)	EMic IBal LRHS LSta MHost
'Brother Stefan'	CBdn EHed IBal MHost NGdn NSue SSien
'Brutus'	IBal
'Buckshaw Blue'	EBlo EMic EMor IBal MHost NBir NEoE NGdn NNor SSien WHrl
'Bulletproof'	CBod EPfP IBal LBar NGdn
'Bumblebee'	CBdn SSien
'Bunchoko'	IBal NNor
'Burke's Dwarf'	IBal
'Butter Rim' (*sieboldii*) (v)	IBal
'Buttered Popcorn' (v)	SSien
'Cally Atom'	GBin IBal MHost
'Cally Colossus'	IBal MHost
I 'Cally Strain' (*nigrescens*)	MHer
'Cally White' (*nigrescens*)	IBal MHost
'Calypso' (v)	EMic ESwi IBal MNrw NGdn NSue NWad WFar
'Camelot' (Tardiana Group)	IBal MHost NGdn NSue
'Cameo'	GEdr SSien
'Camouflage'	EMic IBal MHost
'Canadian Blue'	ECtt EMic IBal LCro LSou NLar NNor NSue SPeP SSien WFar
'Candle Wax'	IBal MHost
'Candy Dish'	IBal NSue SSien
'Candy Hearts'	EMic IBal NNor SSien
capitata	NNor
- B&SWJ 588	WCru
'Captain Kirk' (v) 🏆[H7]	EMic ESwi IBal MHost NGdn NSue SSien WFar
'Captain's Adventure' (v)	EMic EMor IBal LBar LCro NSue SPeP SSien WFar
caput-avis	see *H. kikutii* var. *caput-avis*
'Carder Blue'	EMic IBal
'Carl'	SSien
'Carnival' (v)	EMic ESwi IBal LSta NGdn NHpl SPoG SSien
'Carol' (*fortunei*) (v)	IBal LSta MHost NGdn NLar NNor NSue SSien
'Carolina Blue'	IBal
'Carolina Sunshine' (v)	SSien
'Carousel' (v)	EMic IBal SSien
'Carry On' (v) **new**	SSien
'Cascades' (v)	EMic IBal NGdn SSien
'Cathedral Windows' (v) 🏆[H7]	CLAP EMic IBal MHost NSue SSien
'Catherine'	CBdn ELon EMic EMor IBal MHost NLar NSue SSien WFar
'Cat's Eyes' (*venusta*) (v)	IBal SSien
'Cavalcade' (v)	EMic
'Celebration' (v)	EBlo ELan EMic IBal
'Celestial'	IBal
'Celtic Dancer'	EMic IBal SSien
'Celtic Uplands'	EMic IBal
'Center of Attention'	CBdn EMic EMor IBal NGdn SSien
'Centerfold'	NSue
'Cha Cha Cha'	IBal
'Chabo-unazuki' (*kikutii* var. *caput-avis*)	EMic
'Chain Lightning' (v)	CBdn ECtt EMic IBal MHol NSue SSien
'Challenger'	EMic
'Chameleon' (v)	EMic
'Champagne for All' (v)	IBal
'Champagne Toast' (v)	IBal NSue
'Change of Tradition' (*lancifolia*) (v)	EMic
'Chanticleer' **new**	CBdn
'Chantilly Lace' (v)	EMic IBal
'Chariots of Fire' (v)	IBal
'Chartreuse Waves'	IBal
'Cheatin' Heart'	CBdn IBal MHost NSue WFar
'Chelsea Babe' (*fortunei*) (v)	IBal MHost SSien
'Cherish'	NGdn NHpl WFar
'Cherokee' (v)	CBdn IBal SSien
'Cherry Berry' (v)	CLAP CWGN EBee ECtt EHed EMor EShb ESwi GBin IBal LBar LRHS MACG MBNS MHer MHost MNrw NBro NEoE NGdn NLar NNor NRHS NWad SCob SPeP SPoG SSien WFar
'Cherry Flip'	SSien
'Cherry Tart'	IBal SSien
'Cherub' (v)	EMic IBal SSien
'Chesapeake Bay'	CBdn EMic IBal
'Chesterland Gold'	IBal
'Chief Sitting Bull'	IBal
'Childhood Sweetheart' (v)	IBal NSue
'China Girl'	EMic ESwi IBal
'Chinese Sunrise' (v)	EMic GBin GMcL IBal NNor SRms SSien
'Chionea' (v)	IBal
'Chiquita'	IBal
'Chi-town Classic' (v)	IBal
'Chodai Ginba'	IBal
§ 'Chōkō-nishiki' (*montana*) (v)	CDor IBal LRHS NGdn NNor NRHS SSien
'Choo Choo Train'	EMic SSien
'Chopsticks'	EMic SSien
'Christmas Candy'[PBR]	ECtt EMic IBal MHost NSue SSien
'Christmas Charm' (v)	IBal
'Christmas Cookies'	IBal SSien
'Christmas Island'	NSue
'Christmas Pageant' (v)	EMic IBal
'Christmas Tree' (v) 🏆[H7]	ECtt EMic EMor ESwi IBal LSta MHost NGdn NLar NRHS NSue SSien
'Church Mouse'	EMic IBal NSue SSien
'Cinderella'	IBal MHost SSien
'Cinnamon Sticks'	IBal NSue
'Citation' (v)	IBal
'City Lights'	ECtt EHyd EMic LRHS NRHS
'City Slicker' (v)	IBal
clausa	EMic
- var. ***normalis***	IBal NBir NGdn NLar
'Clear Fork River Valley'	EMic IBal SSien

'Cleopatra' (v)	SSien
'Clifford's Forest Fire'	ECtt EMic EMor IBal NLar SSien WFar
'Clifford's Stingray' (v)	EMic IBal NSue SSien
'Climax' (v)	EMic IBal SSien
'Cloudburst'	EMic IBal
'Clovelly'	IBal
'Clown's Collar' (v)	EMic IBal SSien
'Coal Miner'	IBal SSien
'Coast to Coast' (Shadowland Series)	SSien
'Coastal Treasure' (v)	IBal
'Coconut Custard'	CBdn EMic
'Cody'	IBal NSue
'Cold Heart'	EMic IBal
'Collector's Banner'	IBal
'Collector's Choice'	IBal
'Color à la Mode' (v)	IBal
'Color Festival' (v)	CDor ELon EMic IBal LLWG NLar NNor NSue SSien WFar
'Color Glory'	see *H.* 'Borwick Beauty'
'Colored Hulk' (v)	EHed EMic EMor IBal SSien
'Colossal'	EMic IBal
'Columbus Circle' (v)	EMic IBal
'Con Te Partiro' (v)	GEdr MHost NSue SSien WFar
'Confused Angel' (v)	IBal
'Cookie Crumbs' (v)	EMic GEdr IBal NNor NSue
'Cool as a Cucumber' (v)	CBdn IBal NSue
'Coquette' (v)	EMic IBal
'Corn Belt' (v)	EMic IBal
'Corn Muffins'	EMic
'Corona' (v)	EMic
'Corryvreckan'	IBal MHost
'Cotillion' (v)	EMic GEdr IBal NSue
'Count Your Blessings' (v)	EMic IBal
'Country Mouse' (v)	EMor GBin GEdr IBal NHpl NSue SPoG SSien WFar WPnP
'County Park'	IBal MHost
'Cowrie' (v)	IBal
'Cracker Crumbs' (v) ♀H7	CBdn EMic GEdr IBal LRHS LSta MNrw NHpl NNor NSla NSue SSien WAbe WCot WFar WOld
'Craig's Temptation'	IBal NRHS
'Cranberry Wine'	IBal SSien
§ ***crassifolia***	EMic IBal SSien XLum
'Cream Cheese' (v)	IBal
'Cream Delight' (*undulata*)	see *H. undulata* var. *undulata*
'Cream Edger' (v)	MHost SSien
'Crepe Soul' (v)	IBal
'Crepe Suzette' (v)	IBal NNor SSien
'Crested Reef'	EMic SSien
'Crested Surf' (v)	EMic IBal
'Crinkled Leather' **new**	SSien
'Crinoline Petticoats'	IBal
§ ***crispula*** (v)	CDor EBlo EHyd IBal LRHS MCot MRav NChi NRHS
'Crocodile Socks' (v)	IBal
'Crown Prince' (v)	IBal NGdn
'Crown Royalty'	EMic IBal
§ 'Crowned Imperial' (*fortunei*) (v)	EMic IBal
'Crumb Cake'	NSue
'Crumples' (*sieboldiana*)	IBal MHost
'Crusader' (v)	CBdn ELon EMic IBal LRHS LSta MMuc SEND WFar
'Crystal Dixie'	EMic GBin IBal NSue SSien WFar
'Cumulonimbus'	IBal LSta MHost
'Cup of Grace'	IBal MACG
'Curlew' (Tardiana Group)	EMic IBal MHost
'Curls'	EMic IBal
'Curly Fries'	IBal MHost NSue SSien
'Curtain Call'	IBal
'Cutting Edge'	EMic IBal NSue

'Cuyahoga' (v)	IBal
'Dab a Green'	IBal
'Dance with Me' (v)	EMic IBal NSue SSien
'Dancing in the Rain' (v)	CWGN GMcL NBro WFar
'Dancing Mouse' (v)	GEdr IBal NSue WFar
'Dancing Out of Time'	NSue
'Dancing Queen'	EMic IBal NSue SSien
'Danish Mouse'	IBal
'Dark Shadows'	EMic IBal NGdn NSti WFar
'Dark Star' (v)	EMic IBal MHost NGdn NSue
'Dark Victory'	EMic
'Dartmoor Forest'	IBal MHost
'Dawn'	EMic IBal MHost NSue NWad
'Dawn's Early Light'	EMic IBal NSue
'Dax'	IBal
'Daybreak' ♀H7	EMic IBal NBro
'Day's End' (v)	EMic IBal SSien
'Deane's Dream' ♀H7	EMic IBal MHost SSien
'Decorata'	EMic
decorata var. ***normalis***	EMic
'Deep Blue Sea'	EMic IBal NNor NSue
'Deep Pockets'	IBal
'Dee's Golden Jewel'	EMic SSien
'Déjà Blu' (v) ♀H7	EMic IBal NSue
'Delicious' (v)	IBal
'Deliverance'	EMic ESwi IBal NSue
'Delta Dawn' (v)	EMic IBal NGdn
'Delta Desire'	IBal
'Derek Coxs'	EMic IBal
'Desert Mouse'PBR (v)	GEdr IBal NSue SSien
'Designer Genes'	EMor IBal LRHS LSta SSien WFar
'Devil's Advocate'	IBal
'Devon Blue' (Tardiana Group)	EMic IBal LSta MHost NNor SSien
'Devon Cloud'	MHost SSien
'Devon Desire' (*montana*)	IBal MHost NLar SSien
'Devon Discovery'	IBal MHost
'Devon Giant'	EMic MHost NNor SSien
'Devon Gold'	EMic GAbr IBal MHost SSien
'Devon Green' ♀H7	Widely available
'Devon Hills'	MHost
'Devon Mist'	IBal LSta MHost NNor SSien
'Devon Tor'	EMic IBal MHost
'Dew Drop' (v)	MHost
'Dewed Steel'	CBdn IBal SSien
'Diamond Lake' **new**	IBal SSien
'Diamond Tiara' (v)	EMic IBal LRHS LSta MHost NBir NGdn NSue SSien
'Diamonds are Forever' (v)	IBal NSue
'Diana Remembered'	CDor EMic EMor IBal MHost NGdn NNor NSue SSien WFar
'Dick Ward'	EMic IBal
'Dilithium Crystal'	ESwi IBal NSue WFar
'Dillie Perkeo'	IBal
'Dilys'	EMic MNrw
'Dimple'	EMic
'Dinky Donna' (v)	EMic IBal MHost NHpl NSue
'Dinner Jacket' (v)	EMor IBal LRHS LSta MHost SSien
'Dinner Mint' (v)	IBal
'Dino' (v)	IBal
'Dixie Chick' (v)	EMic GEdr IBal LRHS MHost NHpl NNor NSue SSien
'Dixie Chickadee' (v)	EMic SSien
'Dixie Cups'	CBdn IBal
'Dixieland Heat'	IBal
'Doctor Fu Manchu'	IBal
'Domaine de Courson'	EMic IBal MHost NSue WFar
'Don Stevens' (v)	IBal LRHS SSien
'Dorothy'	EMic
'Dorset Blue' (Tardiana Group)	EMic IBal MHost SSien
'Dorset Charm' (Tardiana Group)	EMic MHost

'Dorset Flair' (Tardiana Group)	EMic IBal MHost
'Double D Cup'	SSien
'Doubled Up'	CBdn IBal
'Doubloons'	EMic SSien
'Dracula'	MHost SSien
'Dragon Tails' 𝕐^{H7}	EMic GEdr IBal LRHS LSta NHpl NNor NRHS NSue WAbe WFar
'Dragon Warrior' (v)	IBal
'Drake's Tail'	IBal NLar
'Dream Queen' (v)	CDor ECtt EMor IBal MHost MSCN NLar SPad SSien
'Dream Weaver' (v)	ELon IBal MBrN MNrw NBro NGdn NSue SPer SPoG SSien WFar
'Dress Blues'	CMac EMic IBal
'Drip Drop' (v)	SSien
'Drummer Boy'	EMic IBal MHost
'Duchess' (*nakaiana*) (v)	EMic IBal
'Duke of Cornwall' (v)	IBal
'DuPage Delight' (*sieboldiana*) (v)	EMic IBal NGdn NLar
'Dust Devil' (*fortunei*) (v)	IBal MHost SSien
'Dusty Waters'	IBal SSien
'Dutch Flame' (v)	NLar NSue
'Eagle's Nest' (v)	IBal
'Early Times'	IBal MHost SSien
'Earth Angel'^{PBR} (v)	EMic IBal LSta MHost NGdn SSien
'Eastern Spires'	EMic
'Ebony Towers'	EMic IBal
'Eclipse' (v)	LRHS
'Eco Mirror'	IBal
'Edge of Night'	EMic IBal
'Edwin Bibby'	EMic MHost
'El Capitan' (v)	EMic IBal
'El Niño'^{PBR} (Tardiana Group) (v) 𝕐^{H7}	CBdn CDor CWGN EMic EPfP IBal LRHS MHost MNrw NBro NGdn NLar NSue SCoo SPoG SSien WFar
§ 'Elata'	EMic
'Elatior' (*nigrescens*)	IBal SSien
'Elbridge Gerry' (v)	IBal
'Eldorado'	see *H.* 'Frances Williams'
'Eleanor Lachman' (v)	IBal
'Eleanor Roosevelt'	IBal
'Electrocution' (v)	ESwi GEdr NSue SSien
'Elegans'	see *H. sieboldiana* var. *elegans*
'Elisabeth'	EMic IBal
'Elizabeth Campbell' (*fortunei*) (v)	EMic IBal MHost SSien
'Elkheart Lake'	EMic IBal SSien
'Ellen'	EMic
'Ellerbroek' (*fortunei*) (v)	EMic
'Elsley Runner'	IBal LSta NSue
'Elvis Lives'	EMic IBal LSta NGdn NLar NNor SSien
'Embroidery' (v)	EMic
'Emerald Carpet'	IBal
'Emerald Charger' (v)	IBal SSien
'Emerald Crown'	EMic IBal
'Emerald Edger'	EMic MHost
'Emerald Emperor'	IBal SSien
'Emerald Necklace' (v)	EMic IBal
'Emerald Paisley'	IBal
'Emerald Ruff Cut'	CBdn EMic IBal SSien
'Emerald Tiara' (v)	CBdn EMic IBal LRHS LSta MHost NLar NSue SSien WFar
'Emeralds and Rubies'	EMic ESwi IBal NNor NSue SSien
'Emily Dickinson' (v)	ECtt EMic IBal LRHS LSta NNor
'Emma' (v)	SSien
'Empress Wu'^{PBR}	Widely available
'Enchiladas' (v)	SSien
'Encore'	IBal
'Enduring Beacon'	NSue
'English Sunrise' (Tardiana Group)	IBal
'Enterprise' (v)	EMic EMor IBal NGdn NSue SSien
'Envy' (v) **new**	SSien
'Eola Sapphire'	EMic IBal
'Eos'	IBal NLar
'Eric Smith' (Tardiana Group)	EMic IBal MHost SHar WFar
'Eric Smith Gold'	GKev
'Eric's Gold'	IBal MHost SSien
'Erie Magic' (v)	EMic IBal SSien
'Eskimo Pie' (v)	WFar
'Essence of Summer'	EMic IBal
'Essence of Sunset' (v)	IBal SSien
'Eternal Flame'	CBdn NSue SSien
'Everlasting Love' (v)	EMic IBal
'Excitation'	EMic IBal
'Exotic Presentation' (v)	EMic IBal SSien
'Extasy' (v)	EMic IBal NGdn NSue WFar
'Eye Candy' (v)	IBal
'Eye Catcher'	EMic SSien
'Eye Declare' (v)	IBal
'Fair Maiden' (v)	NHpl
'Faith'	EMic SSien
'Faithful Heart' (v)	EMic IBal MHost NSue
'Fall Dazzler' (v)	IBal SSien
'Fall Emerald'	EMic
'Fan Dance' (v)	IBal
'Fantabulous' (v)	ELan IBal SSien
'Fantasy Island' (v)	EMor IBal MHost NSue SSien WFar
'Fat Boy'	IBal
'Fat Cat'	SSien
'Fatal Attraction'	IBal SSien
'Feather Boa'	CBdn EMic IBal LRHS LSta MHost NSue WFar
'Feng Shui'	IBal
'Fenman's Fascination'	EMic IBal
'Fiesta' (v)	IBal SSien
'Final Summation' (v)	EMic IBal NSue
'Final Victory' (v)	IBal SSien
'Finlandia'	IBal
'Fire and Ice' (v)	Widely available
'Fire Dance' **new**	IBal
'Fire Island' 𝕐^{H7}	CDor ECtt ELan ELon EMic EMor GBin IBal MACG MHost MNrw NPoe NSue SMad SPeP SSien WCot XSte
'Fire Opal' (v)	IBal
'Firefly' (v)	IBal SSien
'Fireplace' (v)	IBal SSien
'Fireworks' (v) 𝕐^{H7}	CDor EAri ECtt EMor EWoo GEdr GMcL LBar LBuc MBNS MBel MNrw NBro NCou NNor NSue SMad SSien WCot
'Firn Line' (v)	EMor IBal MHost NGdn SSien
'First Blush'	CBdn ESwi IBal NSue SSien WCot
'First Frost' (v) 𝕐^{H7}	CRos ECtt EHyd ELan ELon EMic EMor EPfP IBal LRHS LSta MAvo MBros MHost MNrw NGdn NLar NRHS NSue SCoo SPoG SSien
'First Love' (*montana*)	EMic IBal NSue SSien
'First Mate' (v)	IBal SSien
'Five O'Clock Shadow' (v)	IBal
'Five O'Clock Somewhere' (v)	IBal
'Flamenco Mouse'	NSue
'Flapjack' (v)	IBal
'Fleet Week'	EMic IBal
'Flemish Angel' (v)	CBdn IBal NSue SSien
'Flemish Design'	IBal
'Flemish Gold'	IBal
'Flemish Master' (v)	EMic IBal SSien
'Flemish Sky'	ECtt EMic IBal NGdn NLar
'Flemish Steel'	IBal

	Name	Suppliers
	'Floradora'	EMic IBal MHost NSue
	'Floratini'	NSue
	'Florence Nightingale' **new**	IBal SSien
	'Flower Power'	NNor
	'Fluted Fountain'	EMic
	'Fog Light'	IBal SSien
	'Fool's Gold' (*fortunei*)	EMic IBal
	'Forbidden Fruit'[PBR] (v) ♀H7	CBdn EMic EMor IBal MHost NSue SSien
	'Forest Fireworks' (v)	SSien
	'Forest Shadows'	EMic IBal
	'Formal Attire' (*sieboldiana* hybrid) (v)	EMic IBal LRHS LSta
	'Forncett Frances' (v)	IBal MHost
	'Fortis'	see *H. undulata* var. *erromena*
	fortunei	EMic GMcL SSien WFar
§	- var. ***albopicta*** (v)	CBcs CPud EBlo ECha EGrl EHeP ELan EMic EPfP GMaP LCro LRHS MHost MRav NChi NLar NNor NRHS SPer SRms SSien WBrk WFar
	- - f. ***aurea***	CMac ECha GMcL MHost MMuc NLar SRms SSien WFar
	- - f. ***viridis***	NNor
§	- var. ***aureomarginata*** (v) ♀H7	CBod CKel CPud CRos CTri ECha ELan ELon EMic EPfP EShb GMaP GMcL IBal LRHS MHost MMuc NGdn NLar NNor NRHS SCob SEND SPlb SSien WFar
	- var. ***gigantea***	see *H. montana*
	- var. ***hyacinthina***	EMic IBal MRav NGdn NLar SSien XLum
	- - variegated	see *H.* 'Crowned Imperial'
	- var. ***stenantha***	EMic
	'Fountain of Youth' (*kikutii*)	IBal
	'Fourteen Carats'	EMic
	'Fourth of July'	NSue
	'Foxfire Night Skye' (v)	IBal SSien
	'Foxfire Palm Sunday' (v)	IBal
	'Fragrant Blue'	CTsd EHyd ELan ELon EPfP IBal LBuc MHost NBro NGdn NHpl NNor SPoG XLum
	'Fragrant Blue Ribbons' (v)	IBal SSien
	'Fragrant Bouquet' (v) ♀H7	CDor ECtt ELan EMic EMor IBal LRHS LSRN LSta MHost NGdn NHol NLar NNor NSue SSien WFar
	'Fragrant Dream'	IBal NLar NSue SSien
	'Fragrant Fire'	EMic IBal
	'Fragrant Gold'	EMic
	'Fragrant King'	IBal
	'Fragrant Queen'[PBR] (v)	EMic IBal NSue SSien
	'Fragrant Star'	EMic IBal MHost
	'Fragrant Surprise' (v)	NSue SSien
	'Fran Godfrey'	EMic IBal MHost SSien
	'Francee' (*fortunei*) (v) ♀H7	Widely available
§	'Frances Williams' (*sieboldiana*) (v)	Widely available
	'Francheska' (v)	EMic IBal
	'Frank Lloyd Wright'	IBal
	'Free Jazz' (v)	IBal
	'Fresh' (v)	CBdn EMic IBal NSue
	'Fried Bananas' ♀H7	CBod CDor EHed EMic IBal ITim MHost SSien
	'Fried Green Tomatoes'	EMic IBal MHost NLar NNor
	'Friends' (v)	EMic SSien
	'Fringe Benefit' (v)	EMic MHost SSien
	'Frisian Pride'	EMic IBal NSue
	'Frisian Waving Steel'	EMic IBal
	'Frosted Dimples'	EMic IBal MHost
	'Frosted Frolic' (v)	EMic IBal SSien WFar
	'Frosted Jade' (v)	EMic EPfP IBal LRHS MMuc NLar SEND
	'Frosted June'	CBdn IBal
	'Frosted Lollipop' (v)	IBal
	'Frosted Mini Hearts'	IBal NSue
	'Frosted Mouse Ears'[PBR]	GEdr IBal LSta NHpl NSue SSien
	'Frozen Margarita'	EMic IBal NLar NSue SSien
	'Fruit Punch'	EMic IBal MHost SSien
	'Fujibotan' (v)	EMic IBal
	'Fukurin-Fu' (*venusta*) (v)	GEdr
	'Fulda'	EMic IBal
	'Full Moon'	EMic
	'Funky Monkey'	EMic IBal SSien
	'Funny Bones'	CBdn
	'Funny Frolic' (v)	IBal
	'Funny Mouse' (v)	CBdn EMic IBal LBar NHpl NSue SSien WFar
	'Futura' (v)	IBal
	'Gabriel's Wing' (v)	IBal
	'Gaiety' (v)	ECtt EMic IBal
	'Gaijin' (v)	EMic IBal NSue WOld
	'Garden Party' (v)	IBal NSue SSien
	'Garden Treasure'	SSien
	'Garnet Prince'	CBdn IBal
	'Gay Blade' (v)	IBal LPla
	'Gay Feather' (v)	EMic SSien
	'Gay Search' (v)	IBal MHost NWad
	'Geisha' (v)	IBal LRHS NEoE NGdn NNor NSue SSien
	'Geisha Satin Ripples'	IBal
	'Gemstone'	CBdn MHost NSue
	'Gene's Joy'	EMic
	'Gentle Giant'	CBdn IBal
	'Gentle Spirit' (v)	IBal
	'George M. Dallas' (v)	IBal
	'George Smith' (*sieboldiana*)	EMic IBal MHost SSien
	'Georgia Sweetheart' (v)	IBal SSien
	'Get Nekkid' **new**	ESwi
	'Ghost Spirit' (v)	IBal NSue SSien WFar
	'Ghostmaster' (v)	IBal WFar
	'Giantland Mouse Cheese'	IBal NSue
	'Giantland Sunny Mouse Ears'	GEdr IBal NSue SSien
	'Gig Harbor'	IBal
	'Gigantea' (*sieboldiana*)	see *H.* 'Elata'
	'Gilded Teacup' (v)	NSue
	'Gilt by Association'	EMic IBal
	'Gilt Edge' (*sieboldiana*) (v)	EMic
	'Gin and Tonic' (v)	NSue
	'Gingee'	EMic IBal NSue SSien
	'Ginko Craig' (v)	CMac CRos EHyd ELan EMic EPfP GEdr GMaP IBal LRHS MRav NBir NGdn NLar NRHS SPer SPoG SSien WFar
	'Ginrei'	IBal
	'Ginsu Knife' (v)	EMic IBal
	'Glacial Towers' (v)	IBal SSien
	'Glad Rags' (v)	ECtt IBal LBar
	'Glad Tidings'	IBal
	'Glamour'	IBal SSien
	'Glass Hearts'	EMic IBal NNor NWad
	glauca	see *H. sieboldiana* var. *elegans*
	'Glen Triumph'	SSien
	'Glitter'	EMic IBal
	'Glockenspiel'	EMic IBal MHost
I	'Gloriosa' (*fortunei*) (v)	IBal NSue
	'Glory'	CBdn IBal SSien
	'Glory Hallelujah'	EMic IBal
	'Goddess of Athena' (*decorata*) (v)	IBal
	'Gold Bug'	SSien
	'Gold Drop' (*venusta* hybrid)	EMic IBal MHost NHol NSue
	'Gold Edger'	CDor CMac EBlo EHyd EMic EShb GMaP IBal LRHS MHost MRav NBir NGdn NLar NNor NRHS NSti WFar
	'Gold Edger Surprise' (v)	EMic

'Gold Flush' (*ventricosa*)	EBlo EMic
§ 'Gold Haze' (*fortunei*)	CDor IBal MHost NBir SSien
'Gold Leaf' (*fortunei*)	IBal MHost
'Gold Pressed Latinum'	IBal
'Gold Regal'	EHyd EMic GBin IBal LRHS WFar
'Gold Rush'	EMic MHost SSien
'Gold Standard' (*fortunei*) (v)	Widely available
'Goldbrook' (v)	EMic IBal MHost
'Goldbrook Galleon'	IBal
'Goldbrook Gayle' (v)	MHost
'Goldbrook Gaynor'	IBal MHost
'Goldbrook Genie'	IBal MHost
'Goldbrook Girl'	IBal MHost
'Goldbrook Glamour' (v)	IBal MHost SSien
'Goldbrook Gleam' (v)	IBal MHost
'Goldbrook Glimmer' (Tardiana Group) (v)	IBal LSta MHost
'Goldbrook Glory'	CBdn IBal MHost SSien
'Goldbrook Gold'	IBal MHost
'Goldbrook Good Gracious' (v)	IBal
'Goldbrook Grace'	IBal MHost
'Goldbrook Gratis' (v)	IBal MHost
'Goldbrook Grayling'	ECtt EMic IBal LRHS MHost NRHS
'Goldbrook Grebe'	IBal LSta MHost
'Goldbrook Greengage' (v)	IBal MHost
'Goldbrook Greenheart'	IBal
'Golden Age'	see *H.* 'Gold Haze'
'Golden Empress'	NSue
'Golden Fountain'	EMic
'Golden Friendship'	SSien
'Golden Gate'	CBdn IBal
'Golden Goal'	IBal
'Golden Guernsey' (v)	EMic
'Golden Isle'	IBal MHost
'Golden Meadows'PBR (*sieboldiana*)	CBdn CDor ECtt EMic IBal NGdn NSue SSien WFar
'Golden Medallion' (*tokudama*)	CRos EBee EBlo ECtt EHyd EMic LRHS NGdn NRHS WFar
'Golden Mouse'	NHpl
'Golden Nakaiana'	see *H.* 'Birchwood Parky's Gold'
'Golden Needles' (v)	IBal NSue SSien
'Golden Oriole'	LRHS LSta MHost NNor
'Golden Prayers' (*tokudama*)	ECtt ELan GAbr GMcL MRav NBir NBro NGdn NLar WFar WSHC
'Golden Regal'	WFar
'Golden Scepter'	EMic IBal LRHS LSta MHost NNor SRms SSien WFar
'Golden Spades'	EMic NSue
'Golden Spider'	EMic MHost NNor SSien
'Golden Sunburst' (*sieboldiana*)	ECha ECtt NGdn NLar XLum
'Golden Sweetie'	EMic
'Golden Tiara' (v) ♀H7	Widely available
'Golden Tusk'	IBal
'Golden Waffles'	ECtt EMic EMor SPeP
'Golden Wedding' (*venusta*) **new**	CBor
'Goldene Woge'	SSien
'Goldpfeil'	MHost
'Goldsmith'	EMic MHost
'Gone Fishin'' (v)	IBal
'Gone with the Wind' (v)	IBal SSien
'Goober'	IBal MHost
'Good as Gold'	CBdn
'Good Times' **new**	SSien
'Goodness Gracious' (v)	IBal SSien
'Gorgeous George'	IBal
'Gosan' (*tardiva*)	EMic
'Gosan Gold Midget'	EMic
'Gosan Leather Strap'	ESwi IBal
'Gosan Mina'	EMic
'Gosan Shining'	EMic

gracillima	IBal NWad
'Granary Gold' (*fortunei*)	MHost
'Grand Canyon'	EMic SSien
'Grand Finale'	IBal
'Grand Marquee' (v)	CDor EMic IBal NGdn NLar WFar
'Grand Master'	IBal
'Grand Prize' (v)	EMic IBal NSue SSien
'Grand Rapids'	EMic IBal
'Grand Slam'	IBal NSue
'Grand Tiara' (v)	CDor EMic IBal MHost NGdn NSue SSien
'Grand Total'	IBal
'Grant Park'	IBal
'Grape Fizz'	IBal
'Gray Cole' (*sieboldiana*)	EMic IBal ITim SSien
'Great Arrival'	EMic IBal
'Great Escape'PBR (v)	EMic IBal SSien
'Great Expectations' (*sieboldiana*) (v)	Widely available
'Great Lakes Gold'	IBal
'Green Acres' (*montana*)	EMic IBal LEdu WFar
'Green Angel' (*sieboldiana*)	IBal
'Green Cheese'	EMic IBal
'Green Dwarf'	WFar
'Green Eyes' (*sieboldii*) (v)	IBal NSue WFar
'Green Fountain' (*kikutii*)	EMic IBal
'Green Gold' (*fortunei*) (v)	EMic
'Green Guppy'	NSue
'Green Lama'	EMic IBal
'Green Mouse Ears'	CBdn GEdr NHpl NSue SSien WFar
'Green Piecrust'	EMic
'Green Platter'	EMic
'Green Sheen'	EMic
'Green Sleeve'	EMic
'Green Velveteen'	CDor IBal
'Green with Envy' (v) ♀H7	CBdn EMic GEdr IBal MBrN MHost NNor NSue NWad SSien WOld
'Greenie Weenie Bikini'	MHost NSue SSien
'Greenrush'	SSien
'Greensleeves' (v)	IBal
'Grey Ghost'	EMic
'Grey Glacier' (v)	IBal
'Grey Goose' (Tardiana Group)	EMic MHost
'Groo Bloo'	IBal
'Ground Master' (v)	CMac ELan EPfP GMaP MRav NBro NGdn NLar NNor NSti SPer WFar
'Ground Sulphur'	EMic NSue SSien
'Grover Cleveland'	IBal
'Grünherz'	IBal
'Grunspecht' (Tardiana Group)	IBal
'Guacamole' (v) ♀H7	CBcs CDor CRos CTsd EBee ECha ECtt EHyd ELon EMic EMor EPfP EWTr GBin IBal LRHS LSta MBrN MHost MPri NGdn NLar NNor NRHS SCgs SCob SPoG SSien WFar WPnP
'Guardian Angel' (*sieboldiana*)	EMic IBal NSue SSien
'Gum Drop'	EMic NNor
'Gun Metal Blue'	IBal
'Gunther's Prize' (v)	IBal
'Gunther's Rim' (v)	IBal
'Gypsy Rose' ♀H7	EMic EShb IBal LSta NGdn NLar NSue SSien WFar
'Hacksaw'	EMic IBal MHost NSue SSien
'Hadspen Blue' (Tardiana Group) ♀H7	CBdn CDor CSBt CWCL EBee ELan EMic EPfP GMaP IBal LRHS MBrN MGos MHost MRav NBir NBro NGdn NHol NLar NNor SCob SPoG SSien WSpi

'Hadspen Hawk' (Tardiana Group)	IBal MHost
'Hadspen Heron' (Tardiana Group)	EMic IBal MHost NWad XLum
'Hadspen Nymphaea'	IBal MHost
'Hadspen Pink' **new**	CBdn
'Hadspen Rainbow'	EMic IBal
'Hadspen Samphire'	CBdn EMic IBal MHost NBir NBro SSien
'Hadspen White' (*fortunei*)	CBdn EMic IBal MHost NLar NSue
'Haku-chu-han' (*sieboldii*) (v)	EMic NHpl
'Hakujima' (*sieboldii*)	IBal
'Hakumuo' (v)	IBal SSien
§ 'Halcyon' (Tardiana Group) 🏆H7	Widely available
'Half and Half'	EMic IBal NSue SSien
'Halo'	NNor
'Hammurabi' **new**	IBal
'Hampshire County' (v)	EMic IBal SSien
'Hands Up' PBR (v) 🏆H7	CBdn EMor EPfP IBal MHost NGdn NNor NSue SSien
'Hanja's Crazy Mouse' (v)	IBal
'Hanky Panky' (v)	EMor IBal NGdn NSti NSue SSien WFar
'Hannibal Hamlin' (v)	IBal
'Happily Ever After' (v)	IBal
'Happiness' (Tardiana Group)	EMic IBal MHost MRav SSien
'Happy Camper' (v)	IBal
'Happy Dayz' (v)	IBal SSien
'Happy Hearts'	EMic MHost
'Happy Valley' (v)	IBal NSue SSien
'Harmony' (Tardiana Group)	EMic MHost
'Harold Read' (v)	CDor
'Harpoon' (v)	EMic
'Harriette Ward'	IBal
'Harry van de Laar'	EMic IBal MHost SSien
'Harry van Trier' 🏆H7	EMic MHost SSien
'Hart's Tongue'	IBal
'Harvest Delight'	EMic
'Harvest Glow'	IBal
'Hawaiian Luau' (v) **new**	SSien
'Hawkeye' (v)	IBal
'Hazel'	EMic IBal
'Heart and Soul' (v)	EMic IBal NSue
'Heart Broken'	IBal MHost
'Heart of Chan'	IBal
'Heart Throb'	EMic MHost
'Heartbeat' (v)	NSue SSien
'Heartleaf'	EMic
'Heart's Content' (v)	IBal SSien
'Heartsong' (v)	CBdn EMic IBal
'Heat Wave' PBR (v)	CBdn EMic IBal SSien
'Heavenly Beginnings' (v)	IBal
'Heavenly Tiara' (v)	NSue SSien
'Heavy Duty'	IBal SSien
'Heideturm'	IBal
'Helen Doriot' (*sieboldiana*)	EMic IBal
'Helen Field Fischer' (*fortunei*)	IBal NLar
helonioides f. ***albopicta*** misapplied	see *H. rohdeifolia*
'Herifu' (v)	EMic
'Hertha' (v)	EMic
'Hida-no-hana' (*montana*) (v)	IBal
'Hidden Cove' (v)	IBal NSue SSien
'Hidden Treasure' (v)	IBal
'Hideout' (v)	IBal
'High Kicker'	IBal
'High Noon'	SSien
'High Society' (v)	GEdr IBal MNrw NHpl NNor NSue SSien
'High Tide'	IBal
'High Voltage' (v)	IBal SSien
'Hi-ho Silver' (v)	IBal NSue SSien
'Hilda Wassman' (v)	IBal
'Hillbilly Blues' (v)	EMic NSue
'Hippodrome' (v)	EMic IBal
'Hirao Elite'	IBal
'Hirao Majesty'	IBal
'Hirao Supreme'	EMic IBal
'Hirao Tetra'	SSien
'His Honor' (v)	EMic IBal SSien
'Holar Arches Park'	IBal
'Holar Garnet Crow' **new**	IBal
'Holar Ice Empress'	IBal
'Holar Purple Flash'	IBal
'Holar Red Spear' **new**	SSien
'Holar Red Wine' **new**	IBal
'Holar Rising Flame' **new**	IBal
'Holar Wild Side'	IBal
'Hollywood Lights' (v)	IBal NGdn NSue
'Holstein'	see *H.* 'Halcyon'
'Holy Molé' (v)	EMic IBal
'Holy Mouse Ears' PBR	GEdr IBal NSue SSien
'Honey Moon'	EMic IBal NNor SSien
'Honeybells'	CBcs CDor CMac EBee ECha ELan EMic GBin GQue IBal LEdu MBros MCot MHost MRav NBid NGdn NNor NSti SPer WCAu WFar XLum
'Honeysong' (v)	EMic IBal MHost NNor SSien
'Hoosier Dome'	EMic
'Hoosier Harmony' (v)	EMic
'Hope' (v)	NLar
'Hot Air Balloon'	IBal SSien
'Hotcakes'	EMic IBal
'Hudson Bay' (Shadowland Series) (v)	IBal
'Humpback Whale'	EMic IBal NSue SSien
'Hush Puppie'	EMic IBal MBrN MHost MNrw NHpl NSue SSien WFar
'Hyacintha Variegata' (*fortunei*) (v)	CMac NNor
'Hydon Gleam'	EMic IBal MHost NSue
'Hydon Sunset'	CRos EBee EBlo EHyd EMic ESwi GEdr IBal LRHS MHost MNrw NBir NLar NNor NRHS NSti NSue SSien
hypoleuca	IBal
'Hyuga-urajiro' (v)	EMic GEdr IBal NSue SSien WFar
'Ice Cream' (*cathayana*) (v)	IBal NGdn NSue SSien
'Ice Cube' (v)	IBal SSien
'Ice Prancer'	EMic IBal
'Iced Lemon' (v) 🏆H7	CBdn EMic GEdr IBal MHost NHpl NNor NSue SSien WFar
'Illicit Affair'	CBdn ECtt EMic IBal MHost NHpl NNor NSue SSien
'Imp' (v)	IBal
§ 'Inaho'	LRHS NSue
'Inca Gold'	IBal NSue
'Incoming'	IBal
'Independence' (v)	EMic IBal MHost NBro NSue SPoG SSien WFar
'Independence Day' (v)	EMic
'Inniswood' (v)	CDor CWCL ECtt EMic IBal NBro NGdn NLar NSti SSien WFar
'Invincible'	CDor ECtt EMic EMor IBal MHost NBid NGdn NLar NNor SSien WFar
'Invincible Spirit'	CDor IBal SSien
'Iona' (*fortunei*)	EMic IBal MHost NNor SSien
'Irische See' (Tardiana Group)	IBal
'Irish Eyes' (v)	EMic IBal SSien
'Irish Luck'	EMic IBal NSue
'Iron Gate Delight' (v)	NNor
'Iron Gate Glamour' (v)	CDor

'Iron Gate Special' (v)	EMic
'Iron Gate Supreme' (v)	EMic
'Iron Sky'	IBal
'Island Charm' (v)	EBlo EHyd EPfP IBal LRHS NHpl NLar NNor SCob SSien WFar
'Itty Gold'	IBal
'Ivory Coast' (v)	ECtt EHyd EMic EMor IBal LRHS MHol NRHS NSue SSien
'Ivory Necklace' (v)	IBal SSien
'Ivory Queen' (v)	IBal NSue SSien
'Iwa Yara Moto'	IBal
'Jack Berry'	CBdn IBal
'Jack of Diamonds'	IBal SSien
'Jade Beauty'	EMic
'Jade Cascade'	CDor EMic GBin IBal NBir NLar WFar
'Jade Scepter' (*nakaiana*)	EMic MHost
'Jadette' (v)	NSue
'Jane Ward' (v)	SSien
'Janet Day' (v)	EMic
'Janet' (*fortunei*) (v)	NGdn NNor SSien
'Janet's Gold Sox' **new**	EMic
'Janet's Green Sox'	EMic
'Japan Boy'	see *H.* 'Montreal'
'Jason and Katie' (v)	EMic IBal
'Java' **new**	SSien
'Jaws'	EMic IBal NSue SSien
'Jaz'	IBal SSien
'Jennifer' (v)	IBal
'Jennifer Bailey' (v)	SSien
'Jerry Landwehr'	EMic IBal
'Jewel of the Nile' (v)	CDor IBal
'Jiminy Cricket'	NSue
'Jimmy Crack Corn'	EMic IBal NGdn
'Jingle Bells'	IBal
'John Wargo'	IBal
'Joker' (*fortunei*) (v)	CBdn NNor
'Jolly Green Giant' (*sieboldiana* hybrid)	EMic
'Joseph'	EMic IBal MHost
'Josephine' (v)	SSien
'Joshua's Banner' (v)	SSien
'Journeyman'	EMic IBal MHost
'Journey's End' (v)	EMic IBal NSue
'Joyce Trott' (v)	SSien
'Joyful' (v)	IBal
'Jubilee' (v)	EMic IBal
'Judy Rocco'	IBal
'Juha' (v)	EMic
'Jules'	IBal
'Julia' (v)	EMic IBal NSue SSien
'Julie Morss'	EMic GMaP IBal MHost SSien
'Jumbo' (*sieboldiana*)	SSien
'June' PBR (Tardiana Group) (v) ♀H7	Widely available
'June Fever' PBR (Tardiana Group) ♀H7	CDor EHed ELon EMic EMor ESwi IBal NBro NGdn NLar NSue SPoG SSien WFar
'June Moon' (v)	ESwi SSien
'June Spirit' (v)	CBdn EMic IBal SSien
'Jurassic Park'	GMcL IBal LLWG LRHS MNrw NLar NNor NSue SSien
'Just So' (v)	IBal NNor SSien
'Justine' PBR	IBal NSue SSien
'Kabitan'	see *H. sieboldii* var. *sieboldii* f. *kabitan*
'Kabuki'	IBal NSue
'Kalamazoo' (v)	CBdn EMic IBal SSien
'Kaleidochrome' (v)	IBal
'Kanzi' (v)	NSue SSien
'Karin'	EMic IBal
'Katherine Lewis' (Tardiana Group) (v)	EMic IBal LRHS LSta MHost NHol SSien

	'Kath's Gold'	EMic
	'Katie Q' (v)	EMic IBal SSien
	'Katsuragawa-beni' (v)	EMic IBal SSien
	'Kayak'	IBal
	'Kelly'	EMic
	'Kelsey'	EMic IBal
	'Kempen Magenta Blue' **new**	IBal
	'Kempen Waving Shadow'	IBal
	'Kenzie' (v)	EMic IBal
	'Key Lime Pie'	EMic IBal MHost SSien
	'Key West'	IBal SSien
	'Kifukurin' (*kikutii*)	see *H.* 'Kifukurin-hyuga'
§	'Kifukurin-hyuga' (v)	IBal
	'Kifukurin-kiyosumi'	IBal
	'Kifukurin-ko-mame' (*gracillima*) (v)	NSue
	'Kifukurin-otome' (*venusta*) (v)	EMic NSue SSien
	'Kifukurin-ubatake' (*pulchella*) (v)	EMic IBal
	kikutii	EMic IBal
§	- var. ***caput-avis***	EMic
§	- var. ***yakusimensis***	EMic GArf GEdr IBal SMad
*	'Kimidori Fukurin Otome' (*venusta*)	SSien
	'Ki-nakafu-otome' (*venusta*)	IBal SSien
	'Kinbotan' (*venusta*) (v)	EMic GEdr SSien
	'Kinbuchi Tachi' (*rectifolia*) (v)	IBal
	'King James'	CBdn IBal
	'King of Spades'	IBal
	'King Tut'	EMic
	'Kingfisher' (Tardiana Group)	LRHS LSta MHost
	'Kingsize'	EMic IBal NSue SArc SSien
§	'Kirishima'	EMic NHpl NSue NWad
	'Kisuji'	see *H.* 'Mediopicta'
	'Kitty Cat'	IBal MHost WFar
	'Kiwi Black Magic'	IBal
	'Kiwi Blue Baby'	EMic IBal NSue
	'Kiwi Blue Ruffles'	IBal
	'Kiwi Blue Sky'	IBal
	'Kiwi Canoe'	IBal
	'Kiwi Cream Edge' (v)	EMic
	'Kiwi Forest'	IBal
	'Kiwi Full Monty' (v)	CBdn CDor EMic EMor ESwi IBal NLar NSue SSien WFar
	'Kiwi Gold Rush'	CBdn SSien
	'Kiwi Hippo'	IBal NSue
	'Kiwi Jordan'	IBal
	'Kiwi Kaniere Gold'	IBal
	'Kiwi Minnie Gold'	IBal ITim
	'Kiwi Parasol'	IBal
	'Kiwi Skyscraper'	CBdn IBal
	'Kiwi Spearmint'	ECtt EMic WFar
	'Kiwi Sunshine'	CBdn IBal
	kiyosumiensis	IBal
	'Klopping Variegated' (v)	EMic
	'Knight's Journey'	IBal SSien
	'Knockout' (v)	MRav NBro NGdn NLar NNor
	'Kogarashi Nakafu' (*tortifrons*)	NSue
	'Komodo Dragon'	IBal MHost SSien
	'Konkubine'	EMic
	'Korean Snow'	IBal NSue
	'Koriyama' (*sieboldiana*) (v)	EMic
	'Krossa Cream Edge' (*sieboldii*) (v)	IBal
	'Krossa Regal' ♀H7	Widely available
	'La Donna'	IBal
	'Lacy Belle' (v)	CDor CSBt EMic EPfP IBal LRHS NBro NEoE NGdn NSue SSien

'Lady Godiva'	IBal
'Lady Guineverre'	CBdn EMic IBal LBar SSien
'Lady Helen'	EMic
'Lady in Red'	IBal
'Lady Isobel Barnett' ♀H7	IBal
'Lady Luck' (v)	IBal
laevigata	IBal
'Lake Hitchcock' (v)	IBal
'Lake Superior'	IBal
'Lake Tekapo' (v)	IBal NSue
'Lakeside Accolade'	IBal
'Lakeside Alex Andra' (v)	IBal
'Lakeside April Snow' (v)	EMic IBal NGdn SSien
'Lakeside Baby Face' (v)	EMic ESwi IBal LSta NHpl NSue SSien WFar
'Lakeside Banana Bay' (v)	IBal NGdn SSien
'Lakeside Beach Bum'	IBal NSue
'Lakeside Beach Captain' (v)	EMic SSien
'Lakeside Black Satin'	NNor WFar
'Lakeside Blue Cherub'	EMic IBal NNor
'Lakeside Breaking News' (v)	EMic IBal SSien
'Lakeside Butter Ball'	IBal
'Lakeside Cha Cha' (v)	EMic IBal NNor SPeP WFar
'Lakeside Cindy Cee' (v)	IBal
'Lakeside Circle O' (v)	IBal
'Lakeside Coal Miner'	NGdn NLar NSue SSien
'Lakeside Color Blue'	IBal
'Lakeside Contender'	IBal SSien
'Lakeside Cupcake' (v)	CBdn EMic IBal MHost NGdn NSue SSien
'Lakeside Cupid's Cup' (v)	EMic IBal
'Lakeside Dimpled Darling' (v)	EMic MHost NSue
'Lakeside Dividing Line' (v)	IBal
'Lakeside Doodad' (v)	IBal MHost NSue
'Lakeside Down Sized' (v)	CBdn EMic IBal MHost MNrw NSue SSien WFar
'Lakeside Dragonfly' (v)	ECtt ELon EMic EShb IBal MNrw NGdn NLar NSue SSien WFar
'Lakeside Elfin Fire'	GEdr
'Lakeside Fancy Pants' (v)	CBdn IBal
'Lakeside Feather Light' (v)	IBal
'Lakeside Foaming Sea'	IBal
'Lakeside Full Tide'	IBal
'Lakeside Hazy Morn' (v)	IBal
'Lakeside Hoola Hoop' (v)	IBal
'Lakeside Iron Man'	IBal
'Lakeside Jazzy Jane' (v)	IBal
'Lakeside Kaleidoscope'	CBdn EMic IBal NGdn NSue
'Lakeside Keepsake' (v)	IBal
'Lakeside Khum Kaw'	IBal
'Lakeside Legal Tender'	IBal
'Lakeside Lime Time'	IBal
'Lakeside Little Gem'	IBal MHost NSue
'Lakeside Little Tuft' (v) ♀H7	EMic IBal MHost NLar NSue SSien
'Lakeside Lollipop'	EMic IBal SSien
'Lakeside Love Affaire'	IBal WFar
'Lakeside Maestro'	IBal NLar NSue
'Lakeside Maverick'	IBal SSien
'Lakeside Meadow Ice' (v)	IBal SSien
'Lakeside Meter Maid' (v)	IBal NSue SSien
'Lakeside Midnight Miss'	IBal
'Lakeside Miss Muffett' (v)	EMic IBal NSue
'Lakeside Missy Little' (v)	IBal
'Lakeside Neat Petite'	IBal LRHS LSta NSue
'Lakeside Ninita' (v)	ECtt EMic IBal NNor NSue
'Lakeside Old Smokey'	IBal
'Lakeside Paisley Print' (v)	ECtt EHed EMic EMor EPfP IBal MHol MNrw NSue SSien WFar
'Lakeside Pebbles'	IBal
'Lakeside Premier'	EMic IBal
'Lakeside Prophecy'	IBal

'Lakeside Prophecy Fulfilled' (v)	IBal
'Lakeside Rhapsody' (v)	EMic IBal SSien
'Lakeside Ring Master' (v)	IBal
'Lakeside Ripples'	IBal
'Lakeside Rocky Top' (v)	IBal WFar
'Lakeside Roy El' (v)	IBal SSien
'Lakeside Sapphire Pleats'	EMic
'Lakeside Sassy Sally'	IBal
'Lakeside Scamp' (v) ♀H7	CBdn EMic GEdr IBal LSta MHost NSue SSien
'Lakeside Shadows' (v)	IBal
'Lakeside Shoremaster' (v)	IBal
'Lakeside Slick Chick' (v)	IBal
'Lakeside Sophistication' (v)	IBal
'Lakeside Sparkle Plenty' (v)	IBal
'Lakeside Spellbinder' (v)	CLAP EMic IBal LBar LRHS LSta
'Lakeside Spruce Goose' (v)	CBdn EMic IBal SCoo
'Lakeside Storm Watch'	EMic NLar SSien
'Lakeside Swan Pon' (v)	IBal
'Lakeside Symphony' (v)	EMic
'Lakeside Tee Ki' (v)	IBal
'Lakeside Whizzit' (v)	IBal NSue
'Lakeside Zesty Zeno' (v)	IBal
'Lakeside Zinger' (v)	EMic IBal MBrN MHost NNor NSue SSien
lancifolia	CMac EBee EMic GMaP IBal MHost MRav NGdn NSti SRms SSien WKif WSHC WThu
'Last Dance' (v)	IBal
'Last Train Home'	MHost SSien
'Laterna Magica' **new**	NSue
'Laura Lanier'	EMic IBal
'Laura Z'	IBal
'Lavender Doll'	IBal
'Leading Lady'	IBal
'Leapin' Lizard' **new**	CBdn
'Leather Gloss' **new**	IBal
'Leather Sheen'	EMic
'Leatherneck'	IBal
'Lederhosen'	EMic
'Lemon Delight'	EMic ESwi IBal LRHS LSta MHost NNor NRHS NSue SSien WFar
'Lemon Drop'	MHost
'Lemon Frost'	EMic IBal NSue
'Lemon Lime'	CDor ECtt EMic EMor IBal LRHS MBrN MHost MNrw NEoE NNor NRHS NSue SIvy SSien WAbe WCot WOld
'Lemon Meringue'	NSue SSien
'Lemon Twist'	CDor
'Lemon Zinger' (v) **new**	SSien
'Lemonade'	GBin IBal
'Lemontini'	MHost NSue SSien
'Leola Fraim' (v)	CBdn IBal LSta MHost NSue
'Let Me Entertain You'	EMic SSien
'Let's Twist Again' (v)	CBdn SSien
'Leviathan'	EMic
'Lewis and Clark'	IBal
'Libby'	EMic IBal MHost NSue
'Liberty' PBR (v) ♀H7	CBcs CBdn CDor CWGN ECtt EMic EPfP GMcL IBal MHost NBro NGdn NLar NNor NSue SAko SPer SSien
'Light of Zetar'	IBal
'Li'l Abner' (v)	IBal
'Lilac Giant' **new**	SSien
'Lilac Wine' (*venusta*) **new**	CBor
* ***lilacina***	WFar
'Lily Blue Eyes'	EMic MHost SSien
'Lime Fizz'	CBdn EMic IBal MHost NHpl NSue SSien WFar
'Lime Regal'	MHost

'Lime Shag' (*sieboldii* f. *spathulata*)	IBal MHost NSue SSien WFar
'Limetini'	MHost
'Limey Lisa'	EMic IBal NNor NSue
'Linda Sue' (v)	IBal
'Lionheart' (v)	IBal NSue
'Lipstick Blonde'	NSue SSien
'Little Aurora' (*tokudama* hybrid)	EMic IBal NSue WFar
'Little Bit'	EMic IBal MHost NSue
'Little Black Scape'	EMic IBal NGdn NLar NWad SSien
'Little Blue' (*ventricosa*)	EMic
'Little Bo Beep' (v)	IBal WFar
'Little Boy'	IBal
'Little Caesar' (v)	IBal LRHS NGdn NNor NSue SSien WFar
'Little Devil'	EMic MHost NSue SSien
'Little Doll' (v)	IBal
'Little Hobber'	EMic MHost NSue
'Little Ice Mouse' (v)	NSue SSien
'Little Jay' (v)	NSue SSien
'Little Maddie'	EMic SSien
'Little Miss Magic'	IBal
'Little Miss Muffett'	NSue
'Little Miss Sunshine'	IBal
'Little Prayer'	WFar
'Little Red Joy'	EMic IBal MHost SSien
'Little Red Rooster'	CBdn EMic GEdr IBal MHost NGdn NHpl NLar NNor NSue SSien WFar
'Little Star Struck'	NSue
'Little Stiffy'	IBal
'Little Sunspot' (v)	ECtt EMic NSue
'Little Treasure' (v)	IBal NSue SSien WFar
'Little White Lines' (v)	EMic GEdr GKev IBal MHost NRHS NSue SSien
'Little Wonder' (v) ♀H7	EMic ESwi LRHS LSta MHost NSue SIvy SSien
'Living Water'	EMic SSien
'Lizard Lick'	EMic IBal LSta NSue
'Lollapalooza' (v)	CBdn IBal
'London Fog' (v)	GBin GEdr
'Lonesome Dove' (v)	SSien
'Long Fellow' (v)	IBal
longipes	SSien
- B&SWJ 10806	WCru
- f. ***hypoglauca***	SSien
'Lost World'	EMic IBal
'Lothar the Giant'	IBal
'Louie Louie' (v) **new**	SSien
'Love of Life' (v)	SSien
'Love Pat' ♀H7	ECtt EMic IBal LBar LSRN LSta MBNS MRav NGdn NLar NNor NSue SSien
'Love Song'	IBal SSien
'Loyalist'[PBR] (v)	IBal NGdn NLar NNor SPoG SSien WFar
'Lucky Mouse'[PBR] (v)	EMic EMor GEdr IBal NSue SSien
'Lucky Number' (v)	MHost SSien
'Lucy Vitols' (v)	CDor EMic ESwi IBal
'Lullabye'	EMic
'Luna Moth'	CBdn CBod ECtt EMor EPfP ESwi IBal LBar NSue SSien
'Lunar Eclipse' (v)	EMic
'Lunar Orbit' (v)	SSien
'Machete'	IBal
'Mack the Knife'	EMic IBal NLar WFar
'Maculata Aurea'	NNor
'Made in Spades' (v)	NSue
'Maekawa'	IBal
'Magic Fire'[PBR] (v)	ECtt EMic IBal NLar SSien
'Magic Island'	CBdn IBal LCro MHol MHost NSue SSien
'Magica'	IBal

'Majesty'	EMic IBal MNrw NGdn SSien
'Major Tom'	IBal
'Majordomo'	EMic ESwi
'Malabar' (v)	EMic IBal SSien
'Mama Mia' (v)	EMic EPfP IBal LSou NBro NGdn NHol NWad SSien WFar
'Mango Salsa'	IBal
'Mango Smoothie'	MHost SSien
'Mango Tango' (v)	IBal SSien
'Maple Leaf' (*sieboldiana*) (v)	EMor
'Maraschino Cherry'	EMic EWTr GBin IBal LPla NGdn NSue
'Mardi Gras' (v)	EMic IBal
'Marge' (*sieboldiana* hybrid)	EMic
'Margie's Angel' (v)	NSue
'Margin of Error' (v)	IBal
'Marginata Alba' misapplied	see *H.* 'Albomarginata' (*fortunei*), ***H. crispula***
'Marilyn'	EMic IBal
'Marilyn Monroe' ♀H7	EMic GEdr IBal LSta MHost NSue SSien
'Marmalade on Toast'	EMic MHost
'Marquis' (*nakaiana* hybrid)	IBal
'Marrakech'	EMic IBal LSta NSue
'Marshmallow Sky' (v)	CBdn SSien
'Martini'	SSien
'Mary Joe'	EMic
'Mary Marie Ann' (*fortunei*) (v)	EMic IBal
'Masquerade' (v)	MHost NNor WAbe WFar WThu
'Mata Hari' (v)	NSue SSien
'Maui Buttercups'	EMic MHost NSue
'May'	EMic IBal
'Maya' (*fortunei*) (v)	EMic IBal
'Medieval Age' (v)	IBal
§ 'Mediopicta' (*sieboldii*)	EMic IBal
'Mediovariegata' (*undulata*)	see *H. undulata* var. *undulata*
'Medusa' (v)	MHost NGdn NSue
'Megan's Angel' (v)	SSien
'Memories of Dorothy'	EMic IBal MHost
'Mesa Fringe' (*montana*)	EMic NLar
'Metallica'	SSien
'Mid Afternoon'	IBal
'Midas Touch'	NLar
'Middle Ridge'	EMic
'Midnight at the Oasis' (v)	EMic IBal NSue SSien
'Midnight Oil'	ESwi
'Midnight Ride'	IBal SSien
'Midwest Magic' (v)	EMic IBal MHost NLar
'Mighty Mite'	IBal NSue
'Mighty Mouse' (v)	EMor IBal SSien
'Mikawa-no-yuki'	IBal
'Mike Shadrack' (v)	EMic IBal SSien
'Miki'	IBal
'Mildred Seaver' (v)	CBdn EMic IBal LSta
'Millennium'	ECtt EMic IBal
'Ming Jade'	CDor EMic
'Mini Skirt'	CBdn ESwi IBal SSien
I 'Minima Aurea'	IBal
'Minke' (v)	SSien
'Minnesota Wild' (v)	IBal SSien
'Minnie Bell' (v)	IBal
'Minnie Klopping'	EMic
minor misapplied f. ***alba***	see *H. sieboldii* var. *alba*
§ ***minor*** Maekawa	GEdr ITim LShi NWad WAbe WFar XLum
- B&SWJ 1209 from Korea	WCru
- B&SWJ 8775 from Korea	WCru
- B&SWJ 11103 from Japan	WCru
- from Japan	EMic LShi
- from Korea	IBal
'Minor' (*ventricosa*)	see *H. minor* Maekawa
'Mint Julep' (v)	IBal

	'Minuet' (v)	IBal
	'Minuta' (*venusta*)	MHost
	'Minuteman' (*fortunei*) (v) ♀H7	CBcs CBdn CDor EHyd ELon EMic EPfP EWoo GQue IBal MBNS MHost MMuc NGdn NHpl NLar NNor SEND SSien WFar
	'Minutini'	NSue
	'Miracle Lemony'	CBdn EMor EPfP IBal LBar NSue
	'Miss Linda Smith'	EMic IBal MHost
	'Miss Ruby'	EMic IBal SSien
	'Miss Saigon' (v)	IBal
	'Miss Susie'	IBal
	'Miss Tokyo' (v)	EMic IBal SSien
	'Mississippi Delta'	EMic
	'Mister Watson'	EMic IBal
	'Misty Waters' (*sieboldiana*)	EMic
	'Misweave' (v)	IBal
	'Moerheim' (*fortunei*) (v)	EMic MHost WFar
	'Mohegan'	EMic
	'Mohrchen'	EMic
	'Moi Marleen'	EMic
	'Mojito'	EMic
	'Monster Ears'	EMor EPfP IBal NSue
§	***montana***	WFar
	– B&SWJ 4796	WCru
	– B&SWJ 5585	LEdu WCru
	– f. ***macrophylla***	IBal NSue
	aff. ***montana***	SSien WFar
§	'Montreal'	SSien
	'Moody Blues' (Tardiana Group)	CBdn EMic
	'Moon Dance' (v)	IBal
	'Moon Lily'	EMic SSien
	'Moon River' (v)	EMic IBal
	'Moon Split' (v)	IBal NGdn SSien
	'Moon Waves'	IBal
	'Moonbeam'	EMic EShb
	'Moongate Flying Saucer'	EMic
	'Moonlight' (*fortunei*) (v)	EMic GMaP IBal LRHS NNor SSien
	'Moonlight Sonata'	CBdn EMic IBal SSien
	'Moonstruck'PBR (v)	ECtt EMic IBal NLar NSue SSien
	'Morning Light'	ECtt EMor GMcL IBal MHost NBro NGdn NLar SRkn SSien WFar
	'Morning Star' (v)	EMic IBal LCro NGdn NSue SSien WFar
	'Moscow Blue'	EMic
	'Moulin Rouge'	IBal NSue SSien
	'Mount Everest'	EMic IBal SSien
	'Mount Fuji' (*montana*)	IBal
	'Mount Kirishima' (*sieboldii*)	see *H.* 'Kirishima'
	'Mount Tom' (v)	IBal SSien
	'Mountain Green'	SSien
	'Mountain Snow' (*montana*) (v)	EMic SSien
	'Mourning Dove' (v) ♀H7	EMic IBal SSien
	'Mouse Capades' (v)	IBal
	'Mouse Party' (v)	IBal
	'Mr Big'	IBal NGdn WCot
	'Mr Blue'	IBal NSue
	'Mrs Minky' ♀H7	EMic EMor MHost SSien
	'Muffie' (v)	EMic NSue
	'Munchkin Fire' **new**	SSien
	'Munchkin' (*sieboldii*)	MHost SSien WFar
	'Muriel Seaver Brown' **new**	ESwi
	'My Child Insook' (v)	SSien
	'My Claire' (v)	IBal SSien
	'My Cup of Tea'	IBal SSien
	'My Marianne' (v)	SSien
	'My Precious' (v)	IBal NSue
	'Mystic Mouse'	IBal
	'Mystic Star'	IBal NSue
	nakaiana	CDor EMic
	'Nakaimo'	GBin IBal NLar
	'Nana' (*ventricosa*)	see *H. minor* Maekawa
§	'Nancy Lindsay' (*fortunei*)	CDor EMic IBal MHost NGdn NLar
	'Nancy Minks'	EMic IBal
	'Neat and Tidy'	IBal
	'Neat Splash' (v)	CWCL NBir SSien
	'Neat Splash Rim' (v)	SSien
	'Needlepoint'	IBal
	'Neelix'	IBal
	'Nemesis' (v)	IBal
	'Neptune'	EMic EMor IBal NSue SSien
	'Nesmith's Giant'	EMic
	'Niagara Falls' ♀H7	CBdn EMic IBal NGdn NSue SSien
	'Nicola'	CBdn EMic IBal MHost NSue
	'Nifty Fifty' (v)	SSien
	'Night at the Opera' (v) **new**	SSien
	'Night before Christmas' (v) ♀H7	EMic EMor EWTr IBal MHost MNrw NBro NGdn NHol NLar NNor SSien WHoo
	'Night Life'	EMic IBal NSue
	nigrescens	EMic IBal LSta NChi
	'Niko' (v)	IBal
	'Nippers'	EMic IBal NSue SSien
	'None Lovelier' (v)	EMic IBal
	'North Hills' (*fortunei*) (v)	EMic IBal NBir NGdn SWvt WFar
	'Northern Exposure' (*sieboldiana*) (v)	CDor ECha EMic IBal NGdn NLar SPoG SSien WFar
	'Northern Halo' (*sieboldiana*) (v)	CDor
	'Norwalk Chartreuse'	IBal
	'Number Nine'	IBal
	'Nutty Professor' (v)	IBal
	'Obscura Marginata' (*fortunei*)	see *H. fortunei* var. *aureomarginata*
	'Ocean Isle' (v)	IBal
	'October Sky'	EMic IBal SSien
	'Oder'	EMic IBal
	'Ogon Tsushima'	SSien
	'Ogon-chirifu-hime'	EMic IBal
	'Ogon-hime-tokudama'	IBal
	'Ogon-koba'	IBal
	'Ogon-tachi' (*rectifolia*) (v)	EMic IBal
	'Oh Cindy' (v)	EMic IBal
	'O'Harra'	CBdn EMic NSue SSien
	'Old Faithful'	EMic IBal
	'Old Glory'PBR (v)	ECtt EMic EPfP IBal MHol SSien
	'Olga's Shiny Leaf'	EMic
	'Olive Bailey Langdon' (*sieboldiana*) (v) ♀H7	CDor EMic IBal
	'Olive Branch' (v)	EMic IBal SSien
	'Olympic Edger'	EMic IBal
	'Olympic Glacier' (v)	EMic SSien
	'Olympic Gold Medal'	EMic IBal MHost SSien
	'Olympic Silver Medal'	EMic IBal MHost SSien
	'Olympic Sunrise' (v)	EMic IBal SSien
	'Olympic Twilight'	CBdn EMic IBal
	'On Stage'	see *H.* 'Chōkō-nishiki'
	'On the Border' (v)	IBal SSien
	'On the Marc'	SSien
	'On the Move'	EMic
	'One Iota' (v)	IBal
	'One Last Dance' (v)	NSue SSien
	'One Man's Treasure'	EMic IBal LSou MBel MHost NGdn NNor SSien
	'Ooh La La' (v)	EMic IBal NSue
	'Ophir'	EMic SSien
	'Ops' (v)	CBdn EMic GEdr IBal LSta SSien
	'Orange Crush' (v)	IBal
	'Orange Marmalade' (v) ♀H7	Widely available
	'Orange Star'PBR (v)	EMic IBal MHost NSue SSien
	'Oriana' (*fortunei*)	EMic MHost SSien
	'Orion's Belt' (v)	ESwi IBal MHost
	'Osprey' (Tardiana Group)	LSta MHost
	'Over the Waves'	IBal MHost NSue

'Oxheart'	EMic IBal
'Oze' (v)	SSien
pachyscapa	CBdn
'Pacific Blue Edger'	EMic MHost NNor WFar
'Painted Lady' (*sieboldii*) (v)	GKev
'Paisley Border' (v)	NSue
'Pamela Lee' (v)	EMic IBal NGdn SSien
'Pandora's Box' (v)	EMor GEdr NHar NHpl WCot WFar WPnP
'Papa' (v)	IBal
'Paradigm' (v) ♀H7	EMic IBal LRHS LSta MBrN MHost NGdn NLar SSien
'Paradise Backstage' (v)	EMic IBal
'Paradise Beach'	EMic IBal WFar
'Paradise Blue Sky'	IBal
'Paradise Expectations' (*sieboldiana*) (v)	EMic IBal SSien
'Paradise Glory' ♀H7	CBdn EMic IBal SSien
'Paradise Gold Line' (*ventricosa*) (v)	IBal
'Paradise Goldheart'	SSien
'Paradise Island' PBR (*sieboldiana*) (v)	ECtt EGrI EMic IBal NGdn NSue SSien WFar
'Paradise Joyce' PBR	EMic EMor GMcL IBal NLar NNor
'Paradise Ocean'	CBdn EMic IBal SSien
'Paradise on Fire' (v)	IBal SSien
'Paradise Parade' (v)	IBal
'Paradise Passion' (v)	IBal
'Paradise Power' PBR	EMic SSien
'Paradise Puppet' (*venusta*) ♀H7	EMic GEdr GKev IBal MHost NNor NSue NWad SSien
'Paradise Red Delight' (*pycnophylla*)	EMic IBal MHost SSien
'Paradise Sandstorm'	IBal MHost SSien
'Paradise Standard' (d)	EMic IBal
'Paradise Sunset'	EMic GEdr IBal MHost NHpl NNor NSue SSien WFar
'Paradise Sunshine'	EMic IBal
'Paradise Surprise' (v)	IBal SSien
'Paradise Tritone' (v)	EMic ESwi IBal
'Parasol' (v)	IBal
'Parky's Prize' (v)	CBdn IBal MHost NSue SSien
'Party Popper' (v)	MHost NSue
'Pastures Green'	IBal MHost
'Pastures New'	EMic MHost NSue
'Pathfinder' (v)	EMic SSien WFar
'Patricia'	EMic
'Patrician' (v)	IBal MHost
'Patriot' (v) ♀H7	Widely available
'Patriot's Fire' (v)	EHyd IBal NRHS SSien
'Patriot's Green Pride'	IBal
'Paul Revere' (v)	NSue
'Paul's Glory' (v) ♀H7	CBdn CDor EMic EPfP GLog GMaP IBal LBar LRHS MBros MHost MNHC NBir NGdn NNor NSue SCob SPoG SSien WFar
§ 'Paxton's Original' (*sieboldii*) (v)	SSien WWke
'Peace' (v)	CBdn IBal MHost
'Peacock Strut'	IBal
'Peanut'	IBal MHost NSue SSien
'Pearl Lake'	EMic IBal MHost NBir NGdn NHol NLar NNor
'Peedee Absinth'	EMic
'Peedee Elfin Bells' (*ventricosa*)	IBal
'Pelham Blue Tump'	EMic MHost SSien
'Peppermint Ice' (v)	EMic NGdn SSien
'Percy'	EMic SSien
'Peridot' (Tardiana Group)	IBal
'Permanent Wave'	IBal
'Perry's True Blue'	EMic IBal
'Peter Pan'	EMic IBal SSien

'Pete's Dark Satellite'	EMic IBal NSue
'Pewterware'	EMic IBal
'Phantom'	CBdn IBal
'Philadelphia'	EMic IBal
'Phoenix'	CDor ECha EMic IBal NLar SSien
'Photo Finish' (v)	IBal SSien
'Phyllis Campbell' (*fortunei*)	see *H.* 'Sharmon'
'Picta' (*fortunei*)	see *H. fortunei* var. *albopicta*
'Piecrust Power'	IBal
'Piedmont Gold'	EMic IBal SSien
'Pilgrim' (v)	CDor EBee EHyd EMic IBal LRHS MHol MHost MMuc NBro NGdn NHpl NRHS SEND SSien WFar
'Pinani Island Surf' (v)	CBdn SSien
'Pineapple Juice' (v) **new**	EMic
'Pineapple Poll'	EMic MHost NNor WFar WHoo
'Pineapple Upside Down Cake' (v)	EMic IBal NBro NLar NSue SSien
'Pinky'	IBal
'Pin-up' (v)	IBal NSue
'Pistache' (v)	IBal NSue
'Pixie Vamp' (v)	EMic IBal SSien
'Pizzazz' (v)	EMic IBal MHost NGdn NHol NLar SSien WFar
plantaginea	EGrI LEdu LSta SSien WFar WSpi
- var. ***grandiflora***	see *H. plantaginea* var. *japonica*
§ - var. ***japonica***	EBee ECha LRHS MNrw MRav SMHy WFar WSpi
'Platinum Tiara' (v)	EMic IBal NBir SSien
'Playmate' (v)	IBal
'Plug Nickel'	EMic IBal MHost NSue SSien
'Plum Creek'	SSien
'Pocketful of Sunshine' (v)	IBal NSue SSien
'Poker'	IBal
'Polar Moon' (v)	IBal
'Pole Cat' (v)	IBal
'Pooh Bear' (v)	EMic NSue SSien
'Popcorn'	CBdn IBal NSue SSien
'Popo' ♀H7	EMic IBal MHost NHpl NNor NSue SSien
'Porter' (*venusta*)	EMic IBal NSue
'Potomac Pride'	CDor EHyd EMic LRHS LSta MHost NRHS
'Powder Blue' (v)	EBee ELan IBal
'Powder Keg' (v)	IBal
'Prairie Magic' (v)	SSien
'Prairie Moon'	NSue SSien
'Prairie Sky'	CBdn ECtt EMic EMor GMcL IBal NGdn NLar SSien WFar
'Prairie Sunset' (v)	NSue
'Prairie's Edge' (v)	SSien
'Praying Hands' (v) ♀H7	Widely available
'Precious Metal'	IBal
'Prestige and Promise' (v)	IBal
'Pretty Flamingo'	EMic MHost
'Prima Donna'	CBdn EMic
'Prince of Wales'	CRos EHyd EMic IBal LRHS MHost NNor NRHS SMrm SPeP SPoG SSien XSte
'Private Dancer'	IBal
'Prom Queen' (v)	EMic IBal
'Proud Dragon' (v)	IBal SSien
'Proud Sentry'	CBdn EMic IBal SSien
'Punk Rock'	IBal
'Punky' (v)	EMic IBal SSien
'Purbeck Mist'	MHost SSien
'Purbeck Ridge' (Tardiana Group)	MHost
'Purple and Gold'	EMic SSien
'Purple Boots'	EMic IBal MHost SSien
'Purple Bouquet'	MHost
'Purple Dwarf'	EMic IBal NLar NNor WCru
'Purple Gem'	NNor

'Purple Glory'	CBdn EMic MHost SSien
'Purple Haze'	EMic IBal LPla NGdn WFar
'Purple Heart'	CBcs CWnw EBee ECtt EMic EMor EPfP EWoo GBin IBal LCro LEdu LLWG LOPS LPla LRHS MHer NEoE NHpl NSti NSue NWad SCoo SGBe SMrm SSien WNPC WPnP XSte
'Purple Passion'	EMic IBal LSta NSue
'Purple Profusion'	EMic IBal
'Purple Python'	IBal MHost
'Purple Sensation'	see *H.* 'Stirfry'
'Quarter Note' (v)	IBal
'Queen Josephine' (v)	CDor CRos ECtt EMic EPfP GMcL IBal LBar LRHS MHost NGdn NHpl NNor SMrm SSien WFar
'Queen of Islip' (*sieboldiana*) (v)	SSien
'Queen of the Seas'	EMic ESwi IBal NNor NSue
'Quill' ♀H7	EMic LSta NSue
'Quilting Bee'	EMic EMor IBal NNor NSue
'Radiant Edger' (v)	EMic IBal MHost NHol NRHS NSue
'Rain Dancer'	CBdn EMic IBal SSien
'Rain Forest'	EMic IBal
'Rainbow's End' (v)	ECtt EPfP IBal NLar NSue SSien
'Rainforest Sunrise' (v)	CBod ELon EMic IBal LSou NGdn NSue SSien WFar
'Randy Rachel' (v)	LRHS LSta
'Rare Breed' (v)	IBal
'Rascal' (v)	CDor EMic IBal SSien
'Raspberries and Cream' (v)	IBal
'Raspberry Sorbet' ♀H7	EHyd EMic IBal LRHS LSta MHost NRHS NSue SSien
'Raspberry Sundae' (v)	CTsd CWGN ECtt EHed EMor IBal LRHS MMrt NHpl NSti NSue SMrm SPoG SSien WBor WNPC WTyc
'Raucous Ruffles'	EMic
'Rebel Heart' (v)	IBal SSien
rectifolia	NNor
'Red Alert' (v)	IBal SSien
'Red Cadet'	EMic ESwi IBal MHost NSue SSien WFar
'Red Dog'	EMic NSue
'Red Dragon'	EMic IBal SSien
'Red Hot Flash' (v)	EMic IBal SSien
'Red Hot Poker'	IBal
'Red Neck Heaven' (*kikutii* var. *caput-avis*)	IBal
'Red October'	ECtt EMic EWTr EWoo GQue IBal LEdu LPal MBNS MHost NGdn NHpl NLar NNor SSien WBor WCAu WFar
'Red Salamander'	EMic ESwi IBal SSien
'Red Sox'	IBal
'Red Stepper'	EMic IBal SSien WFar
'Red Stilts'	IBal SSien
'Red Tubes' (*venusta*)	IBal
'Reflections' (v) **new**	ESwi
'Regal Rhubarb'	EMic IBal
'Regal Splendor' (v) ♀H7	CBdn CDor ECtt ELan ELon EMic IBal LCro LOPS LRHS LSta MHost NBro NGdn NNor NRHS NSue SCob SPoG SSien WFar WHoo
'Regal Supreme' (v)	IBal NSue SSien
'Regal Tot'	NSue
'Reginald Kaye'	EMic
'Rembrandt Blue'	EMic IBal
'Remember Me' PBR	ECtt ELan EMic GMcL LBuc LLWG LSRN MBNS MPnt NHol NLar NNor NSue SSien WFar
'Reptilian'	EMic IBal
'Resonance' (v)	IBal NGdn NLar NSue
'Restless Sea'	CBod EMic EMor NGdn NSue
'Reverend Mac'	IBal MHost

'Reversed' (*sieboldiana*) (v)	EMic EMor IBal LRHS LSta LSto NBro NGdn NNor WFar
'Revolution' PBR (v)	GKev IBal LSRN MACG MHost NBro NGdn NLar NSue SSien WFar
'Rhapsody' (*fortunei*) (v)	EMic IBal
'Rhein' (*tardiana*)	EMic IBal
'Rhinestone Cowboy' (v)	IBal
'Rhino Hide' (v)	IBal MHost SSien
'Rhythm and Blues'	IBal NSue
'Rich Uncle'	IBal
'Richland Gold' (*fortunei*)	EMic MHost
'Richmond' (v)	ESwi
'Rim Rock'	EMic IBal
'Ringtail'	EMic IBal NSue
'Ripple Effect' (v)	CBdn EMic EMor IBal MHost NLar NNor NSue SSien
'Rippled Honey'	EMic IBal MHost NEoE SPtp SSien
'Rippling Waves'	EMic
'Riptide'	EMic NGdn
'Risa'	IBal
'Risky Business' PBR (v) ♀H7	CBdn CWGN EMic EMor IBal NLar NSue SSien
'Road Rage' **new**	IBal
'Robert Frost' (v)	EMic IBal
'Robin Hood'	IBal
'Robin of Loxley'	EMic IBal
'Robusta' (*fortunei*)	see *H. sieboldiana* var. *elegans*
'Robyn's Choice' (v)	MHost
'Rock and Roll'	IBal SSien
'Rock Island Line' (v) ♀H7	EMic IBal MHost NSue NWad WFar
'Rock Princess'	IBal
'Rocket's Red Glare'	IBal
§ ***rohdeifolia*** (v) B&SWJ 10862	WCru
'Roller Coaster Ride'	IBal
'Ron Damant'	IBal MHost
'Rootin'-Tootin'' (v)	IBal
'Roseann Walter' (v)	EMic IBal
'Rosedale Buddy Holly' **new**	IBal
'Rosedale Knox'	IBal
'Rosedale Lost Dutchman'	IBal
'Rosedale Melody of Summer' (v)	IBal
'Rosedale Misty Magic' (v)	IBal
'Rosedale Richie Valens'	IBal
'Rosemoor'	EHyd IBal MHost
'Rossing's Pride'	EMic SSien
'Roxsanne'	EMic MHost
'Roy Klehm' (v)	EMic IBal
'Royal Charm'	IBal
'Royal Charmer' (v)	CBdn IBal
'Royal Flush' (v)	IBal
'Royal Golden Jubilee'	EMic IBal MHost
§ 'Royal Standard' ♀H7	Widely available
'Royal Tapestry' (v)	IBal
'Royal Tiara' (*nakaiana*) (v)	IBal
'Royal Wedding' (v)	SSien
'Royalty'	IBal MHost NSue SSien
'Rubies and Ruffles' (v)	IBal
'Ruffed Up'	EMic SSien
'Ruffled Mouse Ears'	IBal NSue
'Ruffled Pole Mouse' (v)	IBal NSue SSien
'Rufus Rider'	IBal
rupifraga	IBal SSien
'Rusty Bee'	IBal MHost
'Ryan's Big One'	IBal
§ 'Sagae' (v) ♀H7	EBlo EHyd EWhm GQue IBal LRHS MHost NGdn NNor NRHS NSue NWad SSien WFar
'Saint Elmo's Fire' (v)	CDor GBin IBal LRHS LSta
'Saint Fiacre'	EMic

'Saint John'	IBal NSue
'Saint Paul' 🏆[H7]	EMic IBal MNrw
'Saishu-jima' (*sieboldii* f. *spathulata*)	EMic GEdr ITim WCru
'Saishu-yahato-sito' (v)	IBal MHost NSue
'Salute' (Tardiana Group)	EMic SSien
'Samurai' (*sieboldiana*) (v)	EMor MRav NBir NBro NGdn NLar SSien
'Sandhill Crane' (v)	EMor LSou SSien
'Sarah Kennedy' (v)	MHost
'Sara's Sensation' (v)	IBal NSue
'Satisfaction' (v) 🏆[H7]	EMic IBal MAvo
'Savannah'	IBal
'Sazanami' (*crispula*)	see *H. crispula*
'Scallion Pancakes'	EMic
'Scarlet Ribbons' (v)	EMic IBal SSien
'Scheherazade' **new**	SSien
'School Mouse' (v)	CBdn IBal NSue SSien
'Schwan'	GBin
'Sea Beacon' (v)	ESwi
'Sea Current'	IBal
'Sea Dream' (v)	CBdn CDor EMic ESwi LRHS LSta NGdn NNor SSien
'Sea Fire'	IBal
'Sea Gold Star'	CDor
'Sea Grotto' **new**	ESwi
'Sea Gulf Stream'	EMic NSue
'Sea Lotus Leaf'	EMic NLar NNor
'Sea Mist' (v)	ESwi
'Sea Monster'	IBal
'Sea Thunder' (v)	CDor EMic EMor ESwi IBal LRHS SSien
'Sea Yellow Sunrise'	EMic ESwi IBal SSien
'Searing Flame' (v)	IBal
'Second Wind' (*fortunei*) (v)	EMic ESwi MHost SSien
'Secret Ambition'[PBR] (v)	IBal
'Secret Love'	EMic IBal
'Secret Treasure'[PBR] (v)	CBdn IBal NSue SSien
'Seducer' (v) 🏆[H7]	EMic ESwi IBal SSien
'See Saw' (*undulata*)	EMic IBal
'Semperaurea' (*sieboldiana*)	IBal
'September Sun' (v)	EMic IBal SSien
'September Surprise'	SSien
'Serena' (Tardiana Group)	IBal
'Serendipity'	CBdn EMic IBal
'Shade Beauty' (v)	EMic IBal SSien
'Shade Fanfare' (v)	CDor CRos ECtt EHyd ELan ELon EMic EPfP GQue IBal LRHS LSta MBNS MRav NBir NGdn NLar NNor NRHS NSti SSien WFar
'Shade Finale' (v)	IBal
'Shade Master'	EMic
'Shade Parade' (v)	EMic IBal
'Shady Affair'	EMic
§ 'Sharmon' (*fortunei*) (v)	ELon EMic MHost NLar SSien
'Sharp Dressed Man'	IBal
'Shazaam'	IBal
'Sheila West'	EMic MHost
'Shelleys' (v)	IBal
'Sherborne Profusion' (Tardiana Group)	EMic IBal MHost SSien
'Sherborne Songbird' (Tardiana Group)	CBdn IBal MHost
'Sherborne Swallow' (Tardiana Group)	EMic IBal MHost SSien
'Sherborne Swan' (Tardiana Group)	CBdn IBal MHost
'Sherborne Swift' (Tardiana Group)	EMic ESwi IBal LRHS LSta MHost NRHS SSien
'Shere Khan' (v)	IBal
'She's got the Moves'	CBdn
'Shimmy Shake'	EMic SSien
'Shining Tot'	IBal NNor
'Shiny Penny' (v)	EMic IBal MHost NSue
'Shiny Sonata'	ESwi IBal
'Shirley Levy'	IBal
'Showboat' (v)	EMic
sieboldiana	CAgr CMac CSBt ECha EGrl EMic GMaP MRav MSwo NChi SCob SPlb SRms XLum
§ - var. ***elegans*** 🏆[H7]	Widely available
- var. ***mira***	EMic
§ - var. ***sieboldiana***	NGdn SSien
sieboldiana* × *venusta	NGdn
sieboldii	MRav
§ - var. ***alba***	IBal
§ - var. ***sieboldii*** f. ***kabitan*** (v)	EMic IBal NGdn NSue SSien
- - f. ***shiro-kabitan*** (v)	EMic LRHS NSue
- f. ***spathulata***	EMic
'Sienna Susan'	SSien
'Silberpfeil'	EMic NSue
'Silk Road' (v)	IBal NSue
'Silver Bay'	EMic IBal SSien
'Silver Crown'	see *H.* 'Albomarginata'
'Silver Lance' (v)	EMic IBal
'Silver Lode' (v)	IBal
'Silver Moon'	EMic IBal
'Silver Serenity'	CBdn IBal SSien
'Silver Shadow' (v)	EMic NBir NGdn NLar NNor NSue NWad SSien
'Silver Spray' (v)	IBal SSien
'Silver Star' (v)	IBal
'Silver Threads and Gold Needles' (v)	IBal LSta NHpl NSue SSien
'Silverado' (v)	IBal
'Silvery Slugproof' (Tardiana Group)	IBal LRHS LSta MHost
'Simply Sharon' (v)	IBal
'Singing in the Rain' (v)	IBal NSue
'Sitting Pretty' (v)	IBal
'Sizzle'	IBal NSue SSien
'Sky Dancer'	ECtt EMic IBal NSue
'Skywriter' **new**	SSien
'Sleeping Beauty'	CWGN ECtt EMic IBal NGdn NSue SSien
'Sleeping Star'[PBR] (v)	IBal NSue SSien
'Slick Willie'	EMic
'Slim and Trim' 🏆[H7]	EMic GEdr IBal MHost NHpl NSue SIvy SSien
'Small Parts'	CBdn ECtt EMic IBal MHost NNor NSue SSien
'Small Sum'	IBal
'Smash Hit' (v)	IBal NSue
'Smiley Face'	NSue
'Smiling Mouse' (v) 🏆[H7]	IBal SSien
'Smoke Signals'	IBal
'Snake Eyes' (v) 🏆[H7]	CBdn ELon EMic EMor IBal MACG MAvo MBel NSue SSien
'Snow Boy' (v)	IBal NSue
'Snow Bunting' (v)	CBdn MHost
'Snow Cap' (v)	CDor ECtt EMic EMor IBal NEoE NGdn NLar NNor SPoG WFar
'Snow Crust' (v)	EMic SSien
'Snow Flakes' (*sieboldii*)	CMac NBro NEoE NGdn NLar NSue SCob WAbe
'Snow Mouse' (v)	IBal NHpl SSien WFar
'Snowden' 🏆[H7]	ECha EMic GMaP IBal LRHS LSta MHost NBir NGdn NNor NRHS SSien WCru
'Snowy Lake' (v)	IBal SSien
'So Sweet' (v)	CRos ECtt EHyd ELan ELon EMic EMor EWoo GEdr GLog LRHS MHost NBro NGdn NHol NNor NRHS SSien WFar
'Something Blue'	EMic IBal

'Something Else'	EMic
'Sorbet' (v) **new**	SSien
'Southern Gold'	EMic
'Space Odyssey'	IBal NSue SSien
'Sparkler' (v)	IBal
'Sparkling Burgundy'	EMic LSta
'Sparky' (v)	IBal
'Spartacus' (v)	EMic IBal MHost NSue SSien
'Spartan Arrow'	NSue
'Spartan Glory' (v)	IBal SSien
'Special Blend' (v)	IBal
'Special Gift'	EMic IBal MHost SSien
'Spellbound' (v)	CBdn IBal
'Spilt Milk' (*tokudama*) (v)	EMor IBal SSien WHoo
'Spinach Souffle' (v)	IBal
§ 'Spinners' (*fortunei*) (v)	ECha EMic IBal MHost NNor
'Splendid Sarah' (v) **new**	SSien
'Spock's Ears'	IBal
'Spring Break' (v)	EMic
'Spring Fling'	EMic IBal SSien
'Spring Love'	IBal
'Spring Morning'	EMor SMad
'Spritzer' (v)	CBdn CDor EMic MNrw NSue SSien
'Squash Casserole'	IBal
'Stag's Leap' (v)	IBal SSien
'Stained Glass' (v) ♀H7	CBcs CDor EBee ECtt EHyd ELon EMic EMor EPfP IBal LAma LBar MHost NGdn NNor NSue SMad SSien WBor WFar
'Stand by Me' (v)	CBdn EMic GEdr IBal MHost NSue SSien
'Stand Corrected' (v)	IBal SSien
'Star Kissed'	IBal
'Star Light Star Bright'	EMic IBal
'Star Wars'	NSue
'Starburst' stable (v)	IBal
'Stardust'	IBal
'Stargate'	IBal
§ 'Starker Yellow Leaf'	EMic
'Starship' (v)	EMic IBal
'Steffi' (v)	IBal
'Step Sister'	EMic IBal
'Stepping Out' (v)	EMic IBal NSue
'Stetson' (v)	EMic IBal
'Stiletto' (v)	ELon EMic GEdr GKev IBal LRHS LSta MBNS MHost MNrw NBro NEoE NGdn NHpl NLar NNor NSue SPoG SSien SWvt WFar WSHC
'Stimulation'	IBal
'Sting' (v)	CBdn EMor EPfP LBar LCro NSue SEdd
'Stir It Up'	SSien
§ 'Stirfry'	CBod EMic LBar NGdn NLar SSien
'Stone's Valentine'	EMic
'Strawberry Surprise' (v)	EMic IBal
'Strawberry Yoghurt'	NSue
'Striker' (v)	IBal NSue
'Striptease' (*fortunei*) (v)	CBdn CDor CMac EMic EMor ESwi GLog IBal LRHS LSta MBNS MHost MNrw NGdn NHol NLar NSue SSien WFar
'Stuck in Time'	CBdn IBal SSien
'Subcrocea'	SSien
'Sugar and Cream' (v)	EMic IBal NGdn NNor
'Sugar and Spice' (v)	CBod ELon EMic IBal MHost SSien
'Sugar Babe' (v)	EMic
'Sugar Daddy'	EMic EMor IBal MAvo MHost SSien
'Sugar Mama' (v)	SSien
'Sugar Plum'	ESwi IBal
'Sugar Snap' (v)	SSien
'Sulphur Glory'	SSien
'Sultana' (v)	IBal SSien

'Sum and Substance' ♀H7	Widely available
'Sum and Subtle' (v)	IBal
'Sum Cup-o-Joe' (v)	EMic
'Sum of All' (v)	EMic NSue
'Summer Breeze' (v)	EMic IBal LBar NGdn NSue
'Summer Dress'	GBin NSue
'Summer Fragrance'	ECtt EMic GBin IBal
'Summer Gold'	EMic
'Summer Joy'	CDor
'Summer Lovin'' (v)	IBal SSien
'Summer Music' (v) ♀H7	CDor CWCL EMic IBal LBar SSien
'Summer Serenade' (v)	EMic NGdn NSue SSien
'Summer Squall'	IBal
'Sumsational' (v)	EMic IBal
'Sun Catcher'	EMic
'Sun Mouse'	CBdn IBal NSue SSien
'Sun Power'	ELon EMic NBro NLar SSien
'Sun Worshipper'	IBal
'Sundance' (v)	IBal
'Sunlight Child'	CBdn EMic IBal MHost NSue WAbe
'Sunny Delight'	CBdn
'Sunny Disposition'	SSien
'Sunny Smiles' (v)	EMic
'Sunnybrook' (v)	SSien
'Sunset Grooves' (v)	EMic IBal
'Sunshine Glory' ♀H7	CDor EMic IBal NSue
'Super Bowl'	IBal
'Super Nova' (v)	IBal SSien
'Super Sagae'	CDor EMic IBal MHost SSien WFar
'Surfer Girl'	NSue
'Surprised by Joy' (v)	IBal MHost NHpl NNor NSue SSien
'Susan' (v)	NSue
'Susy'	IBal
'Sutter's Mill'	IBal
'Suzuki Thumbnail'	EMic
'Swamp Thing' (v)	IBal
'Sweet Bo Beep'	EMic IBal LSta
'Sweet Bouquet'	EMic
'Sweet Home Chicago' (v)	EMic IBal LAma SSien
'Sweet Innocence' (v)	EMic IBal SSien
'Sweet Marjorie'	IBal
'Sweet Susan'	CRos EBee EBlo EHyd LRHS NNor NRHS SPer SSien SWvt
'Sweet Tater Pie'	EMic IBal
'Sweetheart'	EMic
'Sweetie' (v)	CDor EMic IBal
'Sweetness'	IBal
'Swirling Hearts'	IBal
'Swirls Design' **new**	ESwi
'Swizzle Sticks'	EMic
'T Dawg' (v)	EMor NLar
'T. Rex'	CBod CDor EHed ELon EMic EMor IBal NSue SSien WFar
takudama	see *H. sieboldiana* var. *sieboldiana*
'Tall Boy'	GBin IBal NBir NNor
'Tamborine' (v)	EMic EMor IBal LRHS LSta
'Tango'	EMic IBal
'Tappen Zee' (v)	EMic IBal SSien
Tardiana Group	NGdn NNor
tardiflora	IBal LRHS
tardiva	EMic NLar
'Tattle Tails'	CBdn EMic IBal NHpl NSue SSien
'Tattoo'[PBR] (v)	CWGN NLar SSien
'Tea at Bettys' ♀H7	CBdn EMic IBal MHost NSue SSien
'Teacher's Pride'	IBal MHost NSue
'Tears of Joy'	WFar
'Teaspoon'	EMic IBal LSta MHost NHpl NNor NSue SSien
'Teatime' (v)	EMic IBal NSue SSien
'Teeny-weeny Bikini' (v)	NSue SSien WFar
'Templar Gold'	IBal SSien
'Temple Bells'	IBal

'Temptation'	EMic IBal
'Tequila Sunrise'	IBal
'Terpsichore'	EMic
'Terry Wogan'	IBal MHost
'Thank You'	SSien
'The British are Coming' **new**	SSien
'The Devil's Edge' (v)	SSien
'The King' (v)	ECtt IBal NSue SSien
'The Leading Edge' (v)	IBal
'The Razor's Edge'	IBal WFar
'The Right One' (v)	IBal
'The Shining'	IBal
'The Twister'	EMic
'Theo's Blue'	EMic IBal LSta SSien
'Theo's Red'	IBal
'Thomas Hogg'	see *H. undulata* var. *albomarginata*
'Thumb Nail'	EMic GEdr IBal MHost NNor NWad SMHy
'Thumbelina'	EHyd EMic IBal LRHS NGdn NRHS NSue SSien WAbe
'Thunderbolt' PBR (*sieboldiana*)	ECtt EHed EMor IBal LBuc MBNS MHol NGdn NLar SPeP SSien WFar WNPC
tibae	IBal
'Tick Tock' (v)	ECtt EMic IBal NSue SSien
'Tickle Me Pink'	CBdn EMic IBal WFar
'Tidewater'	IBal
'Tilt-a-Whirl'	IBal
'Time Tunnel' (*sieboldiana*) (v)	EMic IBal
'Timeless Beauty' (v)	CBdn EMic EMor IBal MBNS MHost NSue SSien WFar
'Timothy' (v)	IBal
'Tiny Tears'	SSien
'Titanic' PBR	EMic IBal SSien
'Titanium'	CBdn IBal NSue SSien
'Toasted Waffles'	WFar
tokudama	EBlo EMic IBal NBir NGdn WFar XLum
§ - f. ***aureo-nebulosa*** (v)	IBal MHost NGdn SRms SSien
- f. ***flavocircinalis*** (v)	CBod ELon EMic EPfP GMaP IBal MHost NBro SSien WFar WHoo
'Tokyo Smog' (v)	NSue
'Toledo'	IBal
'Tom Schmid' (v) ♀H7	CBdn EMic IBal MHost NSue SSien
'Tom Thumb'	EMic IBal MHost NNor NSue SSien
'Tongue of Flame' (v)	NSue
'Tongue Twister'	IBal
'Topaz'	IBal
'Topscore'	NNor
'Torchlight' (v)	IBal LRHS LSta NSue
tortifrons	IBal SSien
'Tortilla Chip'	IBal WFar
'Tot Tot'	CBdn EMic IBal LSta MHost NSue
'Totally Twisted'	EMic IBal NSue
'Touch of Class' PBR (v) ♀H7	CDor ECtt EGrI EHed EMor GBin GMcL IBal LBar MACG MHost NGdn NHol NNor NSue SCgs SSien WFar WTyc
'Touchstone' (v)	SWvt
'Toy Soldier' ♀H7	EMic ESwi GEdr IBal MHost NGdn NLar NSue SSien
'Trail's End'	EMic
'Tranquility' (v)	EMic
'Tremors'	EMic IBal
'Triple Ripple' (v)	SSien
'Trixi' (v)	IBal
'Tropical Dancer'	IBal
'Tropical Storm' (v)	IBal SSien
'Tropicana' (v)	SSien
'True Blue'	ECtt EMic
'Tsugaru Komachi'	EMic
'Tsugaru Komachi Kifukurin' (v)	IBal
'Tugaux' (v)	IBal
'Turnabout' (v)	IBal
'Turning Point'	IBal
'Twiggie'	EMic MHost
'Twilight' (*fortunei*) (v)	CAby CBdn ECtt EGrI EHyd EMic EMor EShb IBal LRHS MBNS MHol MHost NGdn NLar NRHS NSue SSien SWvt WFar
'Twilight Time'	CBdn IBal
'Twinkle Toes'	EMic IBal NSue
'Twist of Green'	MHost
'Twist of Lime' (v) ♀H7	EMic GKev IBal LRHS LSta MHost NGdn NNor NRHS NSue SSien WCot WOld
'Twitter'	ESwi IBal
'Tycoon' (v)	SSien
'UFO'	EMic IBal NSue WFar
'Ultramarine'	IBal
'Ultraviolet Light'	IBal SSien
'Ulysses S. Grant'	IBal
'Unchained Melody'	IBal
undulata (v)	NNor WFar
§ - var. ***albomarginata*** (v)	CMac EHeP EHyd EMic EPfP GMaP LRHS LSRN MHost MRav NBid NBir NGdn NLar NRHS SCob SPer SRms SWvt WFar XLum
§ - var. ***erromena***	CRos EBlo EHyd GMaP LRHS NNor NRHS XLum
§ - var. ***undulata*** (v) ♀H7	CDor EBlo EHyd EMic GMaP IBal LRHS MRav NGdn NLar NNor NRHS SPer
- var. ***univittata*** (v)	ECha EMic NBir NEoE SRms WFar
'Unforgettable'	EMic IBal SSien
'Unruly Child'	ESwi IBal NSue SSien
'Upper Crust' (v)	IBal
'Uprising' (v)	IBal SSien
'Urajiro' (*hypoleuca*)	IBal
'Urajiro-hachijo' (*longipes* var. *latifolia*)	IBal
'Valentine Lace'	EMic IBal
'Valley's Blue Curaçao'	IBal
'Valley's Cathedral'	IBal
'Valley's Chute the Chute'	EMic IBal LSta MHost SSien
'Valley's Glacier' (v)	ECtt IBal WFar
'Valley's Lemon Squash'	IBal
'Valley's Paparazzi' (v)	IBal
'Valley's Red Scorpion' **new**	IBal
'Valley's Sushi' (v)	IBal SSien
'Valley's Vanilla Sticks'	EMic IBal MHost SSien
'Van Wade' (v)	EMic IBal MHost
'Vanilla Cream' (*cathayana*)	EMic IBal NNor NRHS WFar
'Variegata' (*gracillima*)	see *H.* 'Vera Verde'
'Variegata' (*tokudama*)	see *H. tokudama* f. *aureo-nebulosa*
'Variegata' (*undulata*)	see *H. undulata* var. *undulata*
'Variegata' (*ventricosa*)	see *H.* 'Aureomarginata' (*ventricosa*)
'Variegated' (*fluctuans*)	see *H.* 'Sagae'
'Velvet Moon' (v)	ECtt EMic IBal MBNS SSien
'Venetian Skies' (v)	IBal SSien
ventricosa	CMac EMic GMcL IBal WFar XLum
- BWJ 8160 from Sichuan	WCru
ventricosa* × *venusta	NWad
'Venus' (d)	ITim LEdu NGdn WCot WFar
'Venus Star'	EMic MHost
venusta	CRos EBee EBlo EHyd EMic EPfP GBin GEdr IBal LRHS MHost MRav NBid NBir NNor NRHS NSue NWad SSien WAbe WFar
- B&SWJ 4389	WCru
- dwarf	IBal SSien
- ***yakusimensis***	see *H. kikutii* var. *yakusimensis*
§ 'Vera Verde' (v)	EBlo NBir NSue

'Verdi Valentine'	EMic IBal
'Verkade's One'	IBal NSue
'Vermont Frost' (v)	IBal NSue
'Verna Jean' (v)	EHyd EMic IBal LRHS NRHS
'Veronica Lake' (v)	ECtt EHyd EMic GEdr IBal LRHS LSta MHost NNor NRHS NSue SSien
'Vibrant Hope'	SSien
'Victory' ΨH7	EHyd IBal LRHS MHost NRHS NSue SSien
'Viking Ship'	CBdn EMic IBal SSien
'Vilmoriniana'	EMic
'Vim and Vigor'	EMic IBal SSien
'Vina'	IBal
'Virginia Reel' (v)	IBal NSue SSien
'Viridis Marginata'	see *H. sieboldii* var. *sieboldii* f. *kabitan*
'Volcano Island'[PBR] (v) ΨH7	CBdn EMic IBal NSue SSien
'Vulcan' (v)	CBdn EMic EMor IBal SSien
'Wagtail' (Tardiana Group)	IBal MHost NNor SSien
'Wahoo' (*tokudama*) (v)	IBal
'Waiting in Vein' **new**	IBal
'War Paint' ΨH7	EMic IBal ITim NNor NSue SSien WFar
'Warwick Comet' (v)	EMic IBal SSien
'Warwick Curtsey' (v)	EMic EPri IBal
'Warwick Delight' (v)	NSue
'Warwick Edge' (v)	EMic IBal SSien
'Warwick Essence'	EMic IBal
'Warwick Sheen'	IBal
'Watermark' (v)	EMic
'Waterslide'	NSue SSien
'Waukon Glass'	EMic IBal
'Waukon the Moon'	CBdn
'Waukon Thin Ice'	EMic IBal
'Waukon Water'	EMic IBal
'Wave Runner' (v) **new**	SSien
'Waving Winds' (v)	EMic IBal
'Waving Wuffles'	EMic
'Wayne' (v)	EMic
'Wayside Blue'	EMic
'Wayside Perfection'	see *H.* 'Royal Standard'
'Weihenstephan' (*sieboldii*)	EMic IBal
'Well Shaked' (v)	IBal
'Weser'	IBal
'Wheaton Blue'	EMic
'Wheaton Thunder' (v)	EMic
'Wheee!' (Shadowlands Series)	CBdn IBal NSue SSien
'Whirligig' (v)	CBdn EMic SSien
'Whirling Dervish' (v)	IBal
'Whirlwind' (*fortunei*) (v) ΨH7	CBdn CDor ECtt ELan EMic IBal MBros MHost MNrw MRav NBro NGdn NLar NNor NSue SPoG SPtp SSien WBor WCAu WFar WHoo
'Whirlwind Tour' (v)	IBal
'Whiskey Sour'	IBal
'White Bikini' (v)	IBal LSta NNor SSien
'White Ceiling'	IBal
'White Christmas' (*fortunei*) (v)	NGdn SSien
'White Christmas' (*undulata*) (v)	SSien
'White Dove' (v)	EPfP IBal LBar
'White Edger'	EMic
'White Elephant' (v)	IBal
'White Fairy' (*plantaginea*) (d)	EMic
'White Feather' (*undulata*)	CWGN EPfP LAma LBar LCro LOPS LSou MNrw NBir NEoE NGdn NLar SMad SPeP SPoG SSien WFar
'White Gold'	EMic SSien
'White Jewel' (v)	IBal
'White Knight'	IBal
'White On' (*montana*)	EMic
'White Trumpets'	EMic
'Wide Brim' (v) ΨH7	Widely available
'Wiggles and Squiggles'	CBdn ESwi IBal SSien
'William Lachman' (v)	IBal NLar
'Wily Willy'	ESwi IBal SSien
'Wind River Gold'	EMic
'Windfall' (v) **new**	IBal
'Windsor Gold'	see *H.* 'Nancy Lindsay'
'Winfield Blue'	EMic IBal NBir
'Winfield Gold'	EMic MHost
'Winfield Mist' (v)	IBal
'Winsome' (v)	EMor IBal LRHS NSue SSien
'Winter Lightning' (v)	NNor
'Winter Snow' (v) ΨH7	CBdn CDor EMic IBal NSue SSien WFar XSte
'Winter Warrior' (v)	EMic IBal SSien
'Wintergreen' (v)	SSien
'Wishing Well'	ESwi SSien
'Wogon' (*sieboldii*)	EMic GKev GMaP ITim NNor
'Wogon's Boy'	CDor EMic LRHS
'Wolverine' (v)	CBod ECtt EMic EMor MBNS NGdn NNor NSue SSien SWvt WAbe WFar
'Wonderful'	NSue
'Wonderful Life' (v)	IBal
'Woodland Elf' (v)	IBal NSue SSien
'Woolly Mammoth' (v)	IBal NSue
'Woop Woop' (v)	IBal
'World Cup'	IBal SSien
'Worldly Treasure'	IBal
'Wrinkle in Time' (v) **new**	CBdn SSien
'Wrinkles and Crinkles' (v)	EMic
'Wu-La-La' (v)	ESwi IBal SSien
'Wunderbar' (v)	IBal SSien
'Wylde Green Cream'	IBal NGdn SSien
'Xanadu' (v)	IBal NSue
'X-rated' (v)	NSue
'X-ray' (v)	NSue SSien
'Yakushima-mizu' (*gracillima*)	EMic
'Yankee Blue'	IBal NSue SSien
'Yellow Boa'	EMic ESwi NSue
'Yellow Edge' (*fortunei*)	see *H. fortunei* var. *aureomarginata*
'Yellow Edge' (*sieboldiana*)	see *H.* 'Frances Williams'
'Yellow Polka Dot Bikini' (v)	CBdn EMic EPfP IBal SSien
'Yellow River' (v) ΨH7	CBdn EBee EMic ESwi IBal MHost NGdn NNor NSue SSien WFar
'Yellow Splash' (v)	ECha EMic NNor
'Yellow Splash Rim' (v)	EMic SSien
'Yellow Splashed Edged' (v)	EMic
'Yellow Waves'	SSien
'Yesterday's Memories' (v)	EMic IBal SSien
'Yin' (v)	EMic IBal SSien
yingeri	WPGP WSHC
– B&SWJ 546	LEdu WCru
'You're So Vein'	IBal
'Yucca Ducka Do' (v)	EMic IBal SSien
'Zager Blue'	EMic
'Zager Green'	EMic
'Zager White Edge' (*fortunei*) (v)	CBdn EMic IBal SSien
'Zebra Stripes' (v)	IBal
'Zig Zag' (v)	IBal
'Zion's Hope'	EMic
'Zita' **new**	SSien
'Zitronenfalter'	IBal
'Zodiac' (*fortunei*) (v)	IBal
'Zorro'	CBdn ESwi IBal MHost
'Zounds'	CBdn EBee EBlo ECtt EHyd EMic EShb IBal LRHS MRav NGdn NLar SRms SSien WFar

Hottonia (*Primulaceae*)

palustris	CBen CPud LCro LLWG LPfP NPer

Houstonia (Rubiaceae)

	caerulea misapplied	see *H. michauxii*
	caerulea L.	EBou SPlb SRot
	- var. ***alba***	EWes SPlb SRot
	- 'Millard's Variety'	GQue LCro WIce
§	***michauxii***	NBwr
	- 'Fred Mullard'	EWes NBwr

Houttuynia (Saururaceae)

	cordata	CAgr CMac GPoy LEdu LLWG NSti SDix WFar XLum
§	- 'Boo-Boo' (v)	CMac CPud CToG CWat LPfP
§	- 'Chameleon' (v)	Widely available
	- 'Fantasy' (v)	LLWG
	- 'Flame' (v)	CKel CPla EBee GMcL LLWG LRHS MBNS MHol SMrm WFar
	- 'Flore Pleno' (d)	CBen CBod CMac CPla CWat ECha EWld LCro LLWG LOPS MRav MSCN NBir NPer SBls SPer SPlb SRms XLum
	- 'Joker's Gold'	ECtt ELan EMor EPPr EPfP WFar
	- 'Pied Piper' (v)	LBar NBir SPad
	- 'Terry Clarke'	see *H. cordata* 'Boo-Boo'
	- 'Tricolor'	see *H. cordata* 'Chameleon'
	- Variegata Group (v)	LLWG NBro

Hovea (Fabaceae)

	montana	SPlb

Hovenia (Rhamnaceae)

	dulcis	CAgr CBcs EBee EPfP LAlb LEdu MBlu MVil NLar WJur WKor XVPe
	- B&SWJ 11024	WCru
	- NJM 11.003	WPGP

Howea (Arecaceae)

§	***forsteriana*** ♀H1a	CCCN EAri LCro LOPS LPal NHrt NPlm SArc SPlb

Hoya (Apocynaceae)

§	***australis***	EShb LCro
	bella	see *H. lanceolata* subsp. *bella*
	carnosa ♀H2	CHll CRHN CTtf EAri EOHP EShb NHrt WWFP
	- 'Albomarginata' (v) **new**	EAri
§	- 'Compacta Regalis' (v)	NPer
	- HINDU ROPE	see *H. carnosa* 'Compacta Regalis'
	- 'Krinkle 8'	NPer
	- 'Tricolor' (v)	CCCN CDoC EAri LCro NCft NHrt NPer
	- 'Variegata' (v)	CHll EShb
*	***compacta*** 'Tricolor'	NPer
	'Dapple Grey' **new**	EAri
	darwinii misapplied	see *H. australis*
	gracilis	CCCN LCro LWaG
	kerrii	CDoC
	lacunosa	CCCN
§	***lanceolata*** subsp. ***bella*** ♀H1c	CCCN CDoC EShb LCro
	linearis	CDoC EAri LCro NCft
	longifolia	EAri
	pubicalyx	EAri EShb LCro
	- 'Splash' (v) **new**	EAri
	wayetii **new**	EAri LCro

Huernia (Apocynaceae)

	zebrina ♀H1b	WOld

Humata (Davalliaceae)

	tyermanii ♀H3	CCCN CDoC CMen EShb ISha LCro LEdu SBrt SPlb WCot WFib
	- 'Bunny'	CCCN LCro LOPS
	- 'Selcka'	CMen

Humea see Calomeria

	elegans	see *Calomeria amaranthoides*

Humulus ✿ (Cannabaceae)

	lupulus	CBcs CDoC EPfP GPoy GQue LPar NLar SRms WSpi
	- 'Aureus' ♀H6	Widely available
	- 'Aureus' (f)	CRHN GKev MGil MHtn MNHC SPoG WCot
	- 'Bramling Cross' (f)	SEsH
	- 'Brewer's Gold' (f)	SEsH
	- 'Bullion' (f)	SEsH
	- 'Cascade' (f)	SEsH
	- 'Centennial' (f)	SEsH
	- 'Chinook' (f)	SEsH
*	- ***compactus***	GPoy
	- 'Early Choice' (f)	SEsH
	- 'Fuggle'	CAgr GPoy SEsH
	- 'Galena' (f)	SEsH
	- 'Glacier' (f)	SEsH
	- 'Golden Tassels' (f)	CBod CKel ELan ELon MGil MGos MHtn MMuc MNHC NLar SEND SNig SPer SPoG SRms WBor WFar
	- (Goldings Group) 'Amos' Early Bird' (f)	SEsH
	- - 'Calais Golding' (f)	SEsH
	- - 'Cobbs'	SEsH
	- - 'Eastwell Golding' (f)	SEsH
	- - 'Mathons'	SEsH
	- - 'Redsell's Eastwell' (f)	SEsH
	- - 'Whitbread Golding' (f)	SEsH
	- 'Hallertau' (f)	SEsH
	- 'Hallertau Tradition' (f)	SEsH
	- 'Hersbrucker' (f)	SEsH
	- 'Late Cluster' (f)	SEsH
	- 'Liberty' (f)	SEsH
	- 'Magnum' (f)	LCro LOPS SEsH
	- 'Mount Hood' (f)	SEsH
	- 'Northern Brewer' (f)	CAgr EBee NLar SEsH
	- 'Nugget' (f)	SEsH
	- 'Omega' (f)	SEsH
	- 'Perle' (f)	SEsH
	- 'Phoenix' (f)	SEsH
	- 'Prima Donna'	CAgr CMac ELan LEdu MGil NLar SEsH SPer SPoG SWvt
	- 'Progress' (f)	SEsH SVic
	- 'Record' (f)	SEsH
	- 'Saaz' (f)	SEsH
	- 'Santium' (f)	SEsH
	- 'Styrian Golding' (f)	SEsH
	- 'Tettnanger' (f)	SEsH
	- 'Willamette' (f)	SEsH
	- 'Wye Challenger'	CAgr GPoy MHer SEsH
	- 'Wye Northdown'	CAgr SEsH SVic
	- 'Wye Target' (f)	SEsH
	- 'Yeoman' (f)	SEsH
	- 'Zenith' (f)	SEsH

Hunnemannia (Papaveraceae)

	fumariifolia	CSpe

Huodendron (Styracaceae)

	biaristatum	IDee

Huperzia (Lycopodiaceae)

	lucidula	CBrP

Hutchinsia see Hornungia

Hyacinthella (*Asparagaceae*)

glabrescens	WCot
leucophaea	GKev WCot

Hyacinthoides (*Asparagaceae*)

aristidis	WCot
'Bakkum Blue'	GKev LAma SDir
ciliolata	CBro GKev SGro WAbe WCot
§ ***hispanica***	NBir SEND WCot
- 'Alba'	LAma
- subsp. ***algeriensis***	WCot
- 'Dainty Maid'	GKev NRog WCot
- 'Excelsior'	GKev LAma NRog
- 'Miss World'	GKev WCot
- 'Queen of the Pinks'	GKev NRog WCot
- 'White City'	GKev NRog WCot
§ ***italica*** $\mathbb{Y}^{H6}$	GKev WCot WShi
lingulata	EDAr NDry WAbe WCot
mauritanica	GKev LAma NRog
§ ***non-scripta***	Widely available
- 'Alba'	CAvo EGrI GKev LAma MMuc NBir NRog SDir SEND SRms
- 'Bracteata'	WCot
- long-bracteate, white-flowered	CAvo WCot
- 'Mill House Blue' (d)	WCot
- 'Mill House Pink' (d)	WCot
- 'Mill House White' (d)	WCot
- 'Rosea'	CAvo EGrI GKev ILea NRog
- 'Wavertree'	GKev NRog WCot
reverchonii	NRog WCot
§ ***vincentina***	GKev

Hyacinthus ✿ (*Asparagaceae*)

amethystinus	see *Brimeura amethystina*
azureus	see *Muscari azureum*
comosus 'Plumosus'	see *Muscari comosum* 'Plumosum'
orientalis	LAma NRog
- 'Aida' $\mathbb{Y}^{H4}$	ERCP
- 'Aiolos'	ETay GKev LAma SDeJ SDir
- var. ***albulus*** 'Roman Blue'	ERCP GKev LAma
- - 'Roman White'	ERCP GKev LAma
- 'Amsterdam'	NRog
- 'Anastasia'	CAvo
- 'Anna Liza'	LAma NRog SDeJ
- 'Anna Marie' $\mathbb{Y}^{H4}$	LAma NRog SDeJ
- 'Apricot Passion'	ERCP GKev NRog SDeJ
- 'Atlantic'	LAma
- 'Blue Eyes'	SDeJ
- 'Blue Festival' $\mathbb{Y}^{H4}$	GKev LAma LCro SDeJ SDir
- 'Blue Giant'	SDeJ
- 'Blue Jacket' $\mathbb{Y}^{H4}$	ECul ETay GKev LAma NRog SDeJ
- 'Blue Magic'	SDeJ
- 'Blue Pearl' ^{PBR}	GKev LCro LOPS SDeJ
- 'Blue Star'	LCro SDeJ SDir
- 'Blue Tango'	ERCP LAma
- 'Carnegie'	CArg CAvo EPfP ERCP ETay GKev LCro LOPS NRog SDeJ
- 'Chestnut Flower' (d)	LAma NRog SDeJ SDir
- 'China Pink'	CRos EHyd LRHS NRHS SDeJ
- 'City of Haarlem' $\mathbb{Y}^{H4}$	CArg CRos EHyd ETay GKev LAma LCro LOPS LRHS NRHS NRog SDeJ WHlf
- 'Crystal Palace' (d)	LAma NRog SDeJ
- 'Dark Dimension'	ERCP LAma LCro SDir
- 'Delft Blue' $\mathbb{Y}^{H4}$	CArg CAvo CRos EHyd EPfP ETay GKev LAma LCro LOPS LRHS LSto NRHS NRog SDeJ WShi
- 'Distinction'	SDir
- 'Eros'	SDeJ
§ - 'Fairly' ^{PBR} $\mathbb{Y}^{H4}$	SDir
- FAIRY WHITE	see *H. orientalis* 'Fairly'
- 'Fondant'	CArg EHyd ETay LAma LCro LOPS LRHS NRHS SDeJ
- 'General Köhler' (d)	SDeJ
- 'Gipsy Princess'	LAma
- 'Gipsy Queen' $\mathbb{Y}^{H4}$	CAvo ETay GKev LAma NRog SDeJ SDir WCot
- 'Hollyhock' (d) $\mathbb{Y}^{H4}$	LAma NRog SDeJ SDir
- 'Jan Bos' $\mathbb{Y}^{H4}$	CArg EHyd ETay GKev LAma LCro LOPS LRHS NRHS NRog SDeJ WHlf
- 'Lady Derby'	SDeJ
- 'L'Innocence' $\mathbb{Y}^{H4}$	LSto
- 'Madame Sophie' (d)	LAma SDeJ
- 'Miss Saigon' $\mathbb{Y}^{H4}$	ECul ERCP LAma LRHS NRog SDeJ
- multi-flowered	CAvo SDeJ
- 'Odysseus'	LAma SDeJ
- 'Paul Hermann' $\mathbb{Y}^{H4}$	NRog SDeJ
- 'Peter Stuyvesant'	ERCP LCro LOPS NRog SDeJ SDir
- 'Pink Elephant'	ETay
- 'Pink Festival' $\mathbb{Y}^{H4}$	GKev LAma SDeJ
- 'Pink Pearl'	CRos EHyd ETay GKev LAma LCro LOPS LRHS NRHS NRog SDeJ
- 'Pink Surprise'	ERCP WHlf
- 'Prince of Love' ^{PBR} (d)	ERCP LAma WHlf
- 'Purple Beauty' **new**	LAma
- 'Purple Sensation' ^{PBR}	LCro LOPS NRog SDeJ
- 'Purple Star'	LCro LOPS
- 'Red Magic'	SDeJ
- 'Rosette' (d)	LAma SDeJ
- 'Royal Navy' (d) $\mathbb{Y}^{H4}$	ERCP ETay LAma SDeJ WHlf
- 'Sky Jacket'	LCro LOPS NRog
- 'Snow Crystal' (d)	ERCP WHlf
- 'Splendid Cornelia'	EPfP ERCP NRog SDeJ WHlf
- 'White Festival' $\mathbb{Y}^{H4}$	GKev LAma SDeJ
- 'White Pearl'	CRos EHyd GKev LCro LOPS LRHS NRHS NRog SDeJ WHlf
- 'Woodstock'	CAvo EPfP ERCP ETay GKev LAma LCro LOPS LSto NRog SDeJ SDir WHlf
- 'Yellow Queen' $\mathbb{Y}^{H4}$	NRog
- 'Yellowstone'	SDeJ

Hydrangea ✿ (*Hydrangeaceae*)

angustipetala	see *H. scandens* subsp. *chinensis* f. *angustipetala*
anomala subsp. ***anomala*** BWJ 8052 from China	WCru
- - HWJK 2065 from Nepal	WCru
§ - - 'Winter Glow'	CKel EBee ELan EPfP ESwi LBuc MRav SGol WCru WFar
- subsp. ***glabra***	LRHS
- - B&SWJ 6804	WCru
- - 'Crûg Coral'	CMac LCro MHtn MThu NLar SGol SPoG WCru
§ - subsp. ***petiolaris*** $\mathbb{Y}^{H5}$	Widely available
- - B&SWJ 5996 from Yakushima	WCru
- - B&SWJ 6337	WCru
§ - - - var. ***cordifolia***	CBcs LSto NBro NBwr NFav NLar
- - - B&SWJ 6081	WCru
- - - B&SWJ 11487	WCru
§ - - - 'Brookside Littleleaf'	ETho IDee MGos NBro NLar WFar
- - dwarf	see *H. anomala* subsp. *petiolaris* var. *cordifolia*
- - 'Early Light' (v)	SGbt
- - 'Flying Saucer'	LCro LRHS NLar
- - var. ***megaphylla*** B&SWJ 4400	WCru
- - - B&SWJ 8497	WCru
* - - var. ***minor*** B&SWJ 5991	WCru
- - 'Mirranda' (v)	CBcs CKel CMac CRHN ELan EPfP LPar MGos NBro NBwr NLar SGol SPer SPoG SRms SWvt
§ - - var. ***ovalifolia***	CRHN ESwi

- - - B&SWJ 8799	WCru
- - - B&SWJ 8846	WCru
- - 'Silver Lining'PBR	CBcs CCCN CKel CMac CRos CWGN EBee EHyd EPfP LCro LOPS LRHS MDon MGos NLar NRHS SCoo SGol SGsty SMad SPoG SRms
- - 'Summer Snow' (v)	EHyd LRHS NRHS SPoG SRHi
- - var. ***tiliifolia***	see *H. anomala* subsp. *petiolaris* var. *ovalifolia*
- - 'Yakushima'	WCru
- subsp. ***quelpartensis***	see *H. anomala* subsp. *petiolaris* var. *ovalifolia*
- 'Winter Surprise'	see *H. anomala* subsp. *anomala* 'Winter Glow'
§ ***arborescens***	MRav WPGP
- 'Annabelle' ♀H6	Widely available
- 'Bounty'	MAsh MBlu SGol WLov
- CANDYBELLE BUBBLEGUM ('Grhyar1407')	LCro SGol
- CANDYBELLE MARSHMALLOW ('Grhyar1406')	LCro MAsh SGol
§ - subsp. ***discolor***	GBin
- - 'Sterilis'	NLar WLov
- 'Eco Pink Puff'	SEdd
- 'Emerald Lace'	CBcs CMil MBlu SEdd SGol WLov XSte
- 'Golden Annabelle' (v)	SGol
§ - 'Grandiflora'	CBcs CEme EPfP LRHS NBro NLar
- 'Hayes Starburst'PBR	CDoC CRos EBee EHyd ELan EPfP LRHS MMrt SGol SPoG SWvt WBor XSte
- 'Hills of Snow'	see *H. arborescens* 'Grandiflora'
- INCREDIBALL	see *H. arborescens* STRONG ANNABELLE
- INCREDIBALL BLUSH	see *H. arborescens* SWEET ANNABELLE
- INVINCIBELLE RUBY	see *H. arborescens* RUBY ANNABELLE
- INVINCIBELLE SPIRIT	see *H. arborescens* PINK ANNABELLE
- LIME RICKEY ('Smnhalr'PBR)	LCro LOPS LRHS NLar SGol
- MAGICAL PINKERBELL ('Kolpinbel') (Magical Series)	LRHS NLar SGol SRHi
- 'Picadilly'	NLar
§ - PINK ANNABELLE ambig.	Widely available
- 'Pink Pincushion'	NBro NLar WFar
- 'Puffed Green'	NLar
- subsp. ***radiata***	EHyd LRHS MRav SGol WFar WPGP
- - 'Robusta' **new**	SSha
- - 'Samantha'	EBee EPfP LRHS SPoG WLov WPGP
§ - RUBY ANNABELLE ('Ncha3'PBR)	LCro LOPS MMrt NLar SEdd SMad
- 'Ryan Gainey'	LEdu WSpi
- 'Sheep Cloud'	MBlu
- 'Strong Annabelle'	see *H. arborescens* STRONG ANNABELLE
§ - STRONG ANNABELLE ('Abetwo'PBR)	CBcs CDoC CEme CRos EHyd ELan EPfP LCro LRHS LSRN MAsh MBlu NLar NRHS SCob SGol SGsty SPoG WSpi
§ - SWEET ANNABELLE ('Ncha4'PBR)	LCro LOPS LRHS NLar SMad
- 'Vasterival'	NLar
- 'Visitation'	CTsd MACG WFar
- WHITE DOME ('Dardom'PBR)	NBro
aspera	CMac SSta WCru WKif WPGP
- HWJCM 452	WCru
- from Gongshan, China	CExl CMil WPGP
- 'Anthony Bullivant' ♀H5	CBcs CDoC CKel EPfP IArd IDee LRHS MAsh NLar SGol SHyH SWvt WKif WLov XSte
- 'Bellevue'	IArd MBlu NLar WPGP XSte
- Farrell form	EPfP MBlu WPGP
- HOT CHOCOLATE ('Haopr012'PBR)	CBcs CBod CDoC CKel CMil CTsd CWnw EBee EHed ELan EPfP LPar LRHS MBlu MGos MRav MThu NLar NSti SCob SGol SPoG WLov
- Kawakamii Group	CExl CKel CSpe EPfP ESwi NLar SGol SWvt WCru WPGP
- - B&SWJ 3456	WCru
- - B&SWJ 3527	WCru
- - B&SWJ 6702	WCru
- - B&SWJ 6714	WCru
- - B&SWJ 6827	WCru
- - B&SWJ 6996	WCru
- - B&SWJ 7101	WCru
- - 'August Abundance'	WCru
- - 'Formosa'	WCru
- - 'Maurice Mason'	CExl
- - 'September Splendour'	WCru
- Kawakamii Group × ***involucrata***	EPfP WPGP WSpi
§ - 'Koki'	LRHS WPGP
- 'Macrophylla' ♀H5	EBee ELan EPfP GKin MBlu MGil MGos MRav NLar SPer SWvt WCru WPGP WSpi
- 'Mauvette'	CKel EHyd EPfP GKin LRHS MBlu NBro NLar SGol SHyH SPer WCru
- 'Peter Chappell' ♀H5	CExl CKel CMac MBlu NLar WLov WPGP
- PURPLE PASSION	see *H. aspera* 'Koki'
§ - subsp. ***robusta***	CExl EBee LRHS WPGP WSpi
- - B&SWJ 13999	WCru
- - GWJ 9430	WCru
- - KR 10735	EBee WPGP
- - WWJ 11888	WCru
- 'Rocklon'	ESwi NLar SGol
- 'Rosthornii'	see *H. aspera* subsp. *robusta*
- 'Sam MacDonald'	CExl EHyd EPfP LRHS NCth NLar WPGP WSpi
§ - subsp. ***sargentiana***	Widely available
- - GOLD RUSH ('Giel')	CRos LCro LRHS MMrt MThu NLar SRHi
- - 'La Fosse'	MBlu WPGP
- - large-leaved	CExl WCru
- 'Spinners'	NLar
- subsp. ***strigosa***	CExl CKel CSde EHyd EPfP GKev SWvt WCru WPGP
- - B&SWJ 8201	WCru
- - KWJ 12151 from northern Vietnam	WCru
- - from Gong Shan, China	CExl
- - 'Elegant Sound Pavilion'	WPGP
- - 'Gongshan'	WPGP
- - 'Sapa'	WPGP
- 'Taiwan Pink'	NLar SGol
- 'The Ditch'	ESwi NLar
- 'Titania'	WPGP
§ - Villosa Group	Widely available
- - 'Trelissick'	WPGP
- - 'Velvet and Lace' ♀H5	EPfP GMcL MGos NLar WSpi XSte
asterolasia B&SWJ 10481	WCru
§ 'Blue Deckle' (L)	CMac MAsh MGos MRav NBro SDys SGol WBor WLov XSte
cinerea	see *H. arborescens* subsp. *discolor*
davidii B&SWJ 8307	WCru
- B&SWJ 11692	WCru
- B&SWJ 11717	WCru
- f. ***purpurascens*** KWJ 12233B	WCru
'Dharuma'	GKin LRHS SCoo SGol

EARLY SENSATION ('Bulk'[PBR])	CBcs CCVT CDoC CEme CEnd CKel EBee EHed EHyd EPfP EShb GBin GKin LRHS MAsh MSwo NRHS SGol SPoG WFar WPGP
'First Red'	CEnd
'Garden House Glory'	CExl CMil SAko WPGP
glabrifolia	see *H. scandens* subsp. *chinensis*
glandulosa B&SWJ 4031	WCru
'Glyn Church'	EPfP MAsh SAko SChF WPGP
aff. ***gracilis*** B&SWJ 3942	WCru
§ ***heteromalla***	CMCN LEdu NBro WPGP
- B&SWJ 2142 from India	WCru
- BWJ 7657 from China	WCru
- GWJ 9337 from Sikkim	WCru
- HWJ 526 from Vietnam	WCru
- HWJ 938 from Vietnam	WCru
- HWJCM 180	WCru
- HWJK 2127 from Nepal	WCru
- KR 9913 from India	WPGP
- Bretschneideri Group	EBee EPfP GKin SHyH WCru
- 'Fan Si Pan'	WCru
- 'Gidie' **new**	NLar
- 'Jermyns Lace'	NLar
- 'June Pink'	NLar
- 'Long White'	NLar
- 'Morrey's Form'	WCru
- 'Nepal Beauty'	EBee EPfP ESwi NLar SGol WPGP
- 'Snow in June'	GGGa
- 'Snowcap'	NLar
- f. ***xanthoneura*** NJM 11.009	WPGP
- - 'Wilsonii'	WCru
- 'Yalung Ridge'	WCru
aff. ***heteromalla***	SGol WSpi
'Hidcote Pink'	see *H. macrophylla* 'Juno'
hirta	MBlu
- B&SWJ 5000	WCru
- B&SWJ 11022	WCru
indochinensis B&SWJ 8307	WCru
- WWJ 11609	WCru
* - f. ***purpurascens***	MGil
integerrima	see *H. serratifolia*
integrifolia	WPGP
- B&SWJ 022	WCru
- B&SWJ 6967	WCru
involucrata	CSde EPfP LRHS SGol WSpi
- B&SWJ 4790	WCru
- B&SWJ 11578	WCru
- 'Hortensis' (d)	CMac NLar SMad WCru WKif WPGP WSpi
- var. ***idzuensis***	WCru
- 'Late Love'	XSte
- 'Mihara-kokonoe'	SGol WPGP
- 'Multiplex' (d)	ESwi MBlu WCru
- 'Oshima'	MBlu WPGP
- 'Plena' (d)	CKel EPfP NLar WPGP WSpi
- 'Plenissima' (d)	WCru
- 'Sterilis'	EPfP WCru WSpi
- 'Tokada Yama'	CMil IArd IDee NLar
- 'Viridescens' ♀[H4]	CBcs NLar WCru WPGP
- 'Yohraku-tama' (d) ♀[H4]	EPfP NLar SGol WCru WPGP XSte
- 'Yokudanka' (d)	IArd IDee NLar WPGP
kawagoeana	WCru
var. ***grosseserrata*** B&SWJ 11500	
- - B&SWJ 11511	WCru
lobbii	see *H. scandens* subsp. *chinensis*
longifolia CWJ 12413	WCru
longipes	CExl WCru
- var. ***fulvescens*** B&SWJ 8188	WCru
- var. ***longipes***	CExl
- - NJM 11.084	WPGP
luteovenosa	EBee WCru
- B&SWJ 5647	WCru
- B&SWJ 5929	WCru
- B&SWJ 6220	WCru
- B&SWJ 6317	WCru
macrophylla 'AB Green Shadow'[PBR] (H)	MAsh SGol
- 'Adria' (H)	ILea NLar SGol
- 'Aduarda'	see *H. macrophylla* 'Mousmée'
- ADULA ('H211901'[PBR]) (H)	LRHS
- 'All Summer Beauty' (H)	CSBt ELan ELon GBin MAsh MHtn
- ALPEN GLOW	see *H. macrophylla* 'Alpenglühen'
§ - 'Alpenglühen' (H)	CBcs CSBt NLar SHyH
- 'Altona' (H) ♀[H5]	CBcs CBrac CCVT EHyd EPfP GMcL IArd LCro LOPS LRHS MAsh MGos MRav NBir NLar SPer SRms SSha
- 'Amethyst' (H/d)	LRHS XSte
- 'Ami Pasquier' (H)	CBcs CDoC CEme CKel CMac CSBt CSde CTri EGrI EHyd ELan ELon EPfP EShb LRHS LSRN MRav MSwo SAko SCob SCoo SHyH SPoG SRms SWvt WLov
- 'Amor' (H)	SCob SCoo SGol
- 'Amour Toujours' (Rendez-vous Series) (H)	LRHS MPri
- 'Angélique' (Rendez-vous Series) (H)	LRHS
- 'Aureovariegata' (L/v)	WCot
- 'Ave Maria' (H)	GBin NLar
§ - 'Ayesha' (H)	Widely available
- 'Bachstelze' (Teller Series) (L)	GEdr MAsh WLov WPGP
- 'Baron Pourpre' (H)	MAsh
- 'Bavaria'[PBR] (H)	GKin SGol WFar
- 'Beauté Vendômoise' (L)	CMil LRHS NLar XSte
- 'Bel Alexandre' (H) **new**	SGol
- 'Bela'[PBR] (H)	MAsh XSte
- 'Benelux' (H)	CBcs
- 'Benxi'[PBR] (L)	LRHS SCoo SOrN
- 'Bergfink' (Teller Series) (L)	NLar
- BERLIN ('Rabe'[PBR]) (City-line Series) (H)	SGol
- BIANCO ('Hbabia'[PBR]) (H)	LRHS
- 'Bicolor'	see *H. macrophylla* 'Harlequin'
- Black Steel Series (H)	LRHS NRHS
- - 'Black Steel Zambia' (H)	LCro LOPS SGol WCot
- - 'Black Steel Zaza' (H)	EPfP
- 'Black Trombone' (H)	SGol
- BLACKBERRY PIE ('Makz') (Flair & Flavours Series) (L)	EHyd EPfP LRHS SPoG
§ - 'Blanc Bleu' (L)	EPfP LSRN WFar
§ - 'Blauer Prinz' (H)	NLar SHyH SRms
§ - 'Bläuling' (Teller Series) (L) ♀[H5]	CDoC GKin LSRN MAsh SEdd SGbt SGol XSte
§ - 'Blaumeise' (Teller Series) (L) ♀[H5]	Widely available
- 'Blue Bonnet' (H)	ELon EPfP LRHS LSRN MRav SCob SHyH
- BLUE BUTTERFLY	see *H. macrophylla* 'Bläuling'
- BLUE PRINCE	see *H. macrophylla* 'Blauer Prinz'
- BLUE SKY	see *H. macrophylla* 'Blaumeise'
- BLUE TIT	see *H. macrophylla* 'Blaumeise'
- 'Blue Wave'	see *H. macrophylla* 'Mariesii Perfecta'
- BLUEBIRD	see *H. macrophylla* 'Bläuling'
- 'Bluebird' misapplied	see *H. serrata* 'Bluebird'
§ - 'Blushing Bride' (H)	LCro LOPS
- 'Bodensee' (H)	CCVT CMac NBwr NLar SGsty WFar WSpi XSte
- 'Bottstein' (H)	CCVT
- 'Bouquet Rose' (H)	ECtt EDir ELon MMuc NLar SHyH
- 'Brestenburg' (H)	MAsh
- 'Bristol Red' (H) **new**	SGol
- 'Brügg' (H) ♀[H5]	LRHS MAsh SAko SGol SPer

- 'Buchfink' (Teller Series) (L) XSte
- CAIPIRINHA ('H212907'PBR) (H) SCoo SGol
- 'Cameroun' (H) SGol
- 'Camilla'PBR (H) SGol WFar
- 'Camino' (L) EPfP SGol
- CARDINAL see *H. macrophylla* 'Kardinal' (Teller Series)
§ - 'Cardinal Red' (H) CRos ECre EHyd EPfP LRHS NRHS WFar
- CHARM ('Hbachar'PBR) (H) LRHS MPri SGol
- (Charming Series) CHARMING CLAIRE see *H. macrophylla* (Magical Series) MAGICAL CLEOPATRA
- - CHARMING LISA see *H. macrophylla* (Magical Series) MAGICAL AQUAREL
- - CHARMING SOPHIA see *H. macrophylla* MAGICAL FLAMENCO
- CHIQUE ('Hbachi'PBR) (H) NRHS
- 'Choco Chic' (L) LRHS MAsh MPri SGol
- 'Choco Pur' (Rendez-vous Series) (H) XSte
- CLARISSA ('Hba 208901'PBR) (H) SCoo
- 'Cocktail' (Rendez-vous Series) (H) LRHS MPri SGol
- COCO ('W002095'PBR) (Beautensia Series) (H/d) NRHS
- 'Coco Blanc' (Beautensia Series) (H/d) SGol
- COLOR FANTASY see *H. macrophylla* 'Merveille Sanguine'
- 'Cordata' see *H. arborescens*
- 'Cotton Candy Two' (L) CMil EPfP LRHS MMrt NRHS
- CURLY SPARKLE ('H213901'PBR) (H) LRHS
- CURLY WURLY ('Hbacurl'PBR) **new** NBwr
- 'Dark Angel' (Black Diamonds Series) (L) CMac ELan LCro LOPS LPar MGil NLar NRHS SCoo SGol
- DEEP PURPLE DANCE ('Schrolla02'PBR) (Music Collection) (H) EPfP LRHS MGos
- DESIRE ('H213'PBR) (H) SGol
- 'Deutschland' (H) CTri
- 'Doctor Jean Varnier' (L) CKel EMil EPfP NLar
- DOLCE CHIC ('Hore0034'PBR) (Rembrandt Series) (H) SGol
- DOLCE FARFALLE ('Dolfarf'PBR) (H) WCot
- DOLCE FRAGOLA ('Dolfrag'PBR) (H) **new** CWnw
- DOLCE GIPSY ('Dolgip'PBR) (L) EPfP MGos SGol
- DOLCE KISS ('Dolkis'PBR) (L) EHed EPfP MGos SGol
- 'Domotoi' see *H. macrophylla* 'Setsuka-yae'
- 'Doppio Bianco' see *H. macrophylla* 'Wedding Gown'
- DOPPIO NUVOLA ('Kaho'PBR) (H/d) **new** LCro SGol
- 'Doppio Rosa' (L/d) LCro LOPS SGol
- 'Doris' (H) SCob SGol
- DRAGONFLY see *H. macrophylla* 'Libelle'
- 'Draps Wonder' see *H. macrophylla* 'Forever Pink'
- EARLY BLUE/EARLY PINK ('Hba 202911'PBR) (H) CDoC LCro LRHS MAsh MPri SCob SCoo SGol SPoG XSte
§ - 'Early Sensation' (Forever and Ever Series) (H) CMac GKin
§ - 'Eisvogel' (L) ELon
- 'Elbtal'PBR (H) LRHS
- 'Eldorado' (H) CBod ELon MGil SHyH SNig WLov WSpi
- 'Elégance' (Rendez-vous Series) (L) LRHS MAsh SGol
- ELEGANT ROSA ('Hore0031'PBR) (Rembrandt Series) (H) SGol
- ENDLESS SUMMER ('Bailmer') (H) ELan SEWo SGsty
- ENDLESS SUMMER BLUSHING BRIDE see *H. macrophylla* 'Blushing Bride'
§ - 'Enziandom' (H) CBcs CSBt MAsh SGol
- 'Etoile Violette' (L/d) ♀H5 CDoC SGol XSte
- 'Eugen Hahn' (H) SGsty XSte
- 'Europa' (H) CBcs CBrac CDoC NLar SHyH
- EXPRESSION ('Rie 06'PBR) (Double Delights Series) (H/d) SGol
- 'Fanfare'PBR (H) SGol
§ - 'Fasan' (Teller Series) (L) MAsh NBro SGol WFar XSte
- FIRELIGHT see *H. macrophylla* 'Leuchtfeuer'
- FIREWORKS see *H. macrophylla* 'Hanabi'
- FIREWORKS BLUE see *H. macrophylla* 'Jōgasaki'
- FIREWORKS PINK see *H. macrophylla* 'Jōgasaki'
- FIREWORKS WHITE see *H. macrophylla* 'Hanabi'
- FIRST WHITE ('Hba 202903'PBR) (H) MAsh XSte
- FOREVER ('Youmeone'PBR) (H/d) CBod CSBt EPfP LRHS MPri SCoo
- (Forever and Ever Series) FOREVER & EVER see *H. macrophylla* 'Early Sensation'
- - FOREVER & EVER DOUBLE PINK ('Rie 09') (H/d) SGol
- - FOREVER & EVER PEPPERMINT ('Rie 13'PBR) (H) CBod CSBt MBros SGol
- - FOREVER & EVER TOGETHER ('Rie 05') (H/d) ♀H5 CSBt EHyd LRHS MAsh SCoo SGol SPoG
§ - 'Forever Pink' (H) MAsh NLar SGol WHtc
§ - 'Frau Mariko' (Lady Series) (H) MRav SGol
§ - 'Frau Nobuko' (Lady Series) (H) XSte
- 'French Cancan' (Rendez-vous Series) (L) LRHS MAsh MPri SGol
- 'Frillibet' (H) MRav NLar
- FRISBEE ('H211903'PBR) (L) SGol
- FRISBEE PETTICOAT ('H213903'PBR) (L) **new** NLar
- 'Ganku Bo Chokens' (L) WCot
- 'Garden Romance' (L) **new** LCro
- GEMINI ('Stramini'PBR) (H) SGol
§ - 'Générale Vicomtesse de Vibraye' (H) ♀H5 CBcs CChe CDoC CEnd CKel CSde CTri EBee EHyd ELan ELon EPfP GBin LRHS MAsh MGil NBir NRHS SHyH SPer SPoG WBor WFar WLov XSte
- GENTIAN DOME see *H. macrophylla* 'Enziandom'
- 'Geoffrey Chadbund' see *H. macrophylla* 'Möwe'
- 'Gerda Steiniger' (H) GMcL
- 'Gimpel' (Teller Series) (L) MAsh
§ - GLAM ROCK ('Horwack'PBR) (H) CBcs CDoC EGrI LCro LOPS MPkF SCoo SGol SGsty XSte
- 'Glowing Embers' (H) IArd
- GOLDRUSH ('Nehyosh') (L/v) CEme GMcL NHol SRms WCot
- 'Goliath' (H) ELon
- GRÄFIN COSEL ('Horcos'PBR) (Saxon Series) (H) LRHS SGol XSte

§ - 'Grant's Choice' (L) — NBro
- GREAT STAR — see *H. macrophylla* 'Blanc Bleu'
- GREEN LIPS ('Hba215910'PBR) (H) — SGol
- 'Grünes Gewölbe' (H) — SGol
- 'Hamburg' (H) — CBcs CTri ECtt EHeP EPfP GMcL SDix SHyH WFar
§ - 'Hanabi' (L/d) — CBcs MBlu MGil NLar SGol WSpi XSte
§ - 'Harlequin' (H) — CMac SGol
- 'Hatsu-shime' (L) — NLar
- 'Heinrich Seidel' (H) — CBcs CTri
- 'Hercule Poirot' (H) — SGol
- (Hovaria Series) 'Hobella'PBR (L) — CBcs SGol WFar
- - 'Hobergine'PBR (H) — LAlb SGol XSte
- - 'Holibel'PBR (H) — LAlb SGol
- - 'Homigo'PBR (H) — SGol
- - 'Hopaline'PBR (H) — WPGP
- - 'Hopcorn'PBR (H) — LAlb SGol XSte
§ - 'Hörnli' (H) — XSte
- HOT RED ('Agrihydradrie'PBR) (H) — CDoC EHyd LCro LOPS LRHS MAsh NRHS SCoo SPoG XSte
- 'Immaculata' (H) **new** — WLov
- 'Inspire'PBR (H) — MPri SGol XSte
- 'Izu-no-hana' (L/d) — CAbb CBcs CBod CKel CMil EHed ELan EMil EPfP GBin MBlu MGil MMrt NLar SGol SHyH SPoG WBor WLov WSpi
- 'Izu-no-odoriko' (L) — SGol
- 'James Grant' — see *H. macrophylla* 'Grant's Choice'
- JIP ('H213910') (H) — LRHS SGol
- 'Jofloma' (H) — MMrt NLar
§ - 'Jōgasaki' (L/d) — CBcs CSde MBlu NLar SDys SHyH WPGP
- 'Jomari' (Fireworks Series) (L/d) — SGol
- 'Joseph Banks' (H) — CBcs CTri
- 'Julisa' (H) — CWnw MMrt MPkF XSte
§ - 'Juno' (L) — CKel SGol XSte
- (Kanmara Splendour Series) KANMARA SPLENDOUR IN CHAMPAGNE ('H212904'PBR) (H) — LRHS SCoo
- - KANMARA SPLENDOUR IN LILAC ('H211906'PBR) (H) — LRHS SCoo
- - KANMARA SPLENDOUR IN ROSE ('H211904'PBR) (H) — LRHS
- - KANMARA SPLENDOUR IN STRONG PINK (H) — LRHS SCoo
- - KANMARA SPLENDOUR IN WHITE ('H211907'PBR) (H) — LRHS SCoo
- 'Kardinal' (H) — see *H. macrophylla* 'Cardinal Red' (H)
§ - 'Kardinal' (Teller Series) (L) ♀H5 — MAsh SGol SPoG
- 'Kardinal Violet' (L) — LCro LOPS MAsh
- 'King George' (H) — CBar CBcs CBod CBrac CDoC CEme CKel CRos CSBt ECtt EHyd ELon EPfP GMcL LRHS LSto MGil MGos MMuc NHol NRHS SAdn SAko SGol SHyH SPer SPoG SWvt WFar
- KINGFISHER — see *H. macrophylla* 'Eisvogel'
§ - 'Klaveren' (L) ♀H5 — MAsh NBro XSte
- 'Kluis Superba' (H) — CTri SHyH
- 'Koria'PBR (L) ♀H5 — CKel CRos LRHS MPkF NRHS SCoo SEdd SGol SPoG
§ - 'Kumico' (H) — SCob SGol
- 'L.A. Dreamin' (H) — SGol
- 'La France' (H) — CBod CTri EHyd LRHS MGil SHyH SNig SPoG
- 'La Marne' (H) — LRHS XSte
- 'La Vie en Rose' (Rendez-vous Series) (H) — LRHS MPri SCob SGol XSte
- 'Lady in Red' (L) — EHyd EPfP LRHS NRHS SPoG
- 'Lady Mariko' — see *H. macrophylla* 'Frau Mariko'
- 'Lady Nobuko' — see *H. macrophylla* 'Frau Nobuko'
- 'Lady Oshie' (Teller Series) (L) — SGol
- 'Lanarth White' (L) ♀H5 — Widely available
- 'Lemon Wave' (L/v) — NLar SGol
§ - 'Leuchtfeuer' (H) — ELon GMcL MGil SGol SHyH WLov XSte
§ - 'Libelle' (Teller Series) (L) ♀H5 — CBcs CBod CEnd CMac EHyd ELan ELon EPfP GDam GMcL LMil LPar LRHS MGos MMuc MRav NBir NLar NRHS SCob SEND SGol SGsty SPer SPoG WSpi XSte
- LIGHT-O-DAY ('Bailday') (L/v) **new** — SGol
- 'Lilacina' — see *H. macrophylla* 'Mariesii Lilacina'
- 'Little Blue' (H) **new** — LCro
- 'Little Pink' (H) **new** — LCro
- 'Little Purple' (H) **new** — LCro
- 'Little White' (H) **new** — LCro
- LOVE ('Youme H1917'PBR) (H/d) — CRos EPfP LOPS LRHS SGol SPer SPoG
- 'Love You Kiss'PBR (Hovaria Series) (L) — CBcs CDoC CEnd LAlb LRHS NLar NRHS SCoo SGol SPoG WCot
- 'Lutin'PBR (L) — CDoC
§ - 'Maculata' (L/v) — WGwG
- 'Madame A. Riverain' (H) — EPfP NLar SHyH
- 'Madame Emile Mouillère' (H) ♀H5 — Widely available
- 'Madame Plumecocq' (H) — LRHS XSte
- 'Mademoiselle' (Rendez-vous Series) (H) — LRHS MAsh
- (Magical Series) MAGICAL AMETHYST ('Hokomathyst'PBR) (H) — CBcs CDoC MPkF SGol XSte
- - MAGICAL AMORE ('Hortmamore') (H) **new** — SGol
§ - - MAGICAL AQUAREL ('Hortmaqua') (H) — LRHS
- - MAGICAL BLUEBELLS ('Hortmabluebel') (H) **new** — SGol
- - MAGICAL BRIDE ('Hortmabrid'PBR) (H) — CBod SGol WFar
- - MAGICAL CANDY ROCK ('Hortmacaro') (H) **new** — SGol
§ - - MAGICAL CLEOPATRA ('Hortmaclepa') (H) — LRHS SGol
- - MAGICAL COLOURDREAM ('Hortmacodre'PBR) (H) ♀ **new** — CBod SGol
- - MAGICAL CORAL ('Hokomac'PBR) (H) — CBcs SGol XSte
- - MAGICAL CRYSTAL ('Ankong'PBR) (H) — SGol
§ - - MAGICAL FLAMENCO ('Hortmaflam'PBR) (H) **new** — SGol
- - MAGICAL GREEN CLOUD ('Hortmagreclo') (H) **new** — SGol
- - MAGICAL GREEN DELIGHT ('Hokomagrede') (H) **new** — LCro

- - MAGICAL GREENFIRE ('Qufu') (H)	SGol
- - MAGICAL HARMONY ('Hortmahar'[PBR]) (H) ♀H5	NLar XSte
- - MAGICAL JADE ('Hortmaja'[PBR]) (H)	MBlu MPkF NLar WCot XSte
- - MAGICAL NOBLESSE ('Hokomano'[PBR]) (H)	CBcs LCro SGol XSte
- - MAGICAL OCEAN ('Hortmoc'[PBR]) (H)	NLar
- - MAGICAL RED AMETHYST ('Hokomareda') (H)	SGol
- - MAGICAL REVOLUTION ('Hokomarevo'[PBR]) (H) ♀H5	CBcs CDoC LCro SGol XSte
- - MAGICAL RHAPSODY ('Hortmarhso'[PBR]) (H) ♀H5	CBod SGol WFar
- - MAGICAL RUBY RED ('Kolmaru'[PBR]) (H)	CBod SGol WFar
- - MAGICAL RUBY TUESDAY	see *H. macrophylla* 'Ruby Tuesday'
- - MAGICAL SPOTLIGHT ('Hortmaspoli') (H) **new**	SGol
- - MAGICAL SUNSHINE ('Hortmasun') (H) **new**	SGol
- - MAGICAL WINGS ('Hortmawin'[PBR]) (H) ♀H5	MBlu
- 'Maréchal Foch' (H)	CTri NLar
- 'Mariesii' (L)	CBod CTri ELan GBin LSto MGil MSwo NBwr NLar SCob SHyH SPer
§ - 'Mariesii Grandiflora' (L)	CMac EDir EPfP MMuc NBro NBwr SCob SGol SGsty SRms WFar
§ - 'Mariesii Lilacina' (L) ♀H5	MMuc SEND WFar WSpi
§ - 'Mariesii Perfecta' (L)	Widely available
- 'Marina' (H)	LRHS MAsh
- 'Masja' (H)	CBar CBcs CCVT EDir EGrl ELon GKin IArd MGos MMuc MRav MSwo NBro NLar SAko SGol WBor
- 'Mathilde Gütges' (H)	CCVT SCob SGsty XSte
- 'Merveille' (H)	NBro
§ - 'Merveille Sanguine' (H)	Widely available
- 'Mini Hörnli'	see *H. macrophylla* 'Hörnli'
- 'Mini Penny'[PBR] (H)	SGol
- MINTY ICE ('Es11'[PBR]) (Flair & Flavours Series) (H)	SGol
- 'Mirai'[PBR] (H)	CBcs EPfP ESwi NRHS SEdd WCot WPGP
- 'Miss Belgium' (H)	CMac CTri GKin GMcL
§ - 'Mousmée' (L)	SHyH XSte
- 'Mousseline' (H)	LRHS
§ - 'Möwe' (Teller Series) (L) ♀H5	CBcs ECtt EGrl ELon EPfP GBin MGil MMuc NLar SCob SCoo SDix SEdd SGol SHyH SPer SRms WLov WSpi
- MRS KUMICO	see *H. macrophylla* 'Kumico'
- 'Mrs W.J. Hepburn' (H)	CSBt SPer
§ - 'Nachtigall' (Teller Series) (L) ♀H5	EPfP MAsh SHyH WLov WPGP
- 'Nadeshiko-gaku' (L)	SHyH
- 'Nanping'[PBR] (Sturdy Series) (L)	SPoG
- 'Niedersachsen' (H)	CTri MRav SHyH
- NIGHTINGALE	see *H. macrophylla* 'Nachtigall'
- 'Nigra' (H)	CBcs CKel CMac CWal EHyd ELan ELon EPfP EWTr GBin LRHS MGil MGos MMuc MRav NBro NLar NRHS SAdn SDix SEND SHyH SPer WGwG WLov XSte
- 'Nikko Blue' (H)	CBcs GKin NLar SGol SHyH SOrN
§ - 'Nymphe' (H)	SGsty
- 'Oregon Pride' (H)	EPfP MAsh WFar
- 'Otaksa' (H)	CMil NLar
- 'Papagei' (Teller Series) (L)	SPer
- 'Pax'	see *H. macrophylla* 'Nymphe'
§ - 'Perfection' (Double Delights Series) (H/d)	SGol
- 'Pfau' (Teller Series) (L)	ELon MAsh MGil WSpi XSte
- PHEASANT	see *H. macrophylla* 'Fasan'
- 'Pia' (H)	CMac CMil ELon ESwi MAsh MRav NLar SPer SRms WLov WSpi
- PIGEON	see *H. macrophylla* 'Taube'
- 'Pink Lollipop' (Flair & Flavours Series) (H)	SGol
- 'Pink Sensation'[PBR] (H)	MAsh
- 'Pink Sky' (H) **new**	MPri
- 'Pirate's Gold' (L/v)	WFar
- 'Prinses Beatrix' (H)	SHyH
- 'Purple Prince' (H)	EGrl
- 'Quadricolor' (L/v)	CDow CMac CMil MRav SAdn SDix SHyH SPlb SRms WCot
- 'Queen Elizabeth' (H)	GKin
- 'R.F. Felton' (H)	CBcs SHyH
- 'Radiant' (H)	SRms
- RATHEN ('Horath'[PBR]) (Saxon Series) (H)	SGol
- 'Red Ace' (H)	SCob
- 'Red Angel' (Black Diamonds Series) (H)	LCro NRHS SCoo SGol
- 'Red Baron'	see *H. macrophylla* 'Schöne Bautznerin'
- 'Red Beauty'[PBR] (H)	SGol
- 'Red Red' (H)	MAsh
- 'Red Riding Hood' (H)	EGrl
- REDBREAST	see *H. macrophylla* 'Rotkehlchen'
- 'Regula' (H)	SHyH
- 'Renate Steiniger' (H)	CBrac CSBt MRav SGol WLov WSpi XSte
- ROCO BLACK KNIGHT ('Roco131801') (H) **new**	SGol
- ROMANCE ('Youmenine'[PBR]) (H/d)	CRos EHyd GMcL LRHS MAsh MPri NRHS SCob SCoo SGol SPoG WCot
- 'Romantique' (H)	MAsh
- 'Rosita' (H)	CBrac NBir SGol SGsty XSte
- ROSSO GLORY ('Hore0007') (Rembrandt Series) (H)	SGol
- 'Rotdrossel' (Teller Series) (L)	GBin
§ - 'Rotkehlchen' (Teller Series) (L)	CBod CEnd GArf MMrt NLar SGol SPlb SWvt
- 'Rotschwanz' (Teller Series) (L) ♀H5	CDoC CMil ELon GBin MAsh NLar SCob SHyH WBor WCot WLov WPGP XSte
- 'Rouge Baiser' (H)	SGol
- ROYAL RED ('Hbarore'[PBR]) (H)	LRHS MPri SGol XSte
- 'Royal Red Lilac' (Teller Series) (L)	MAsh
§ - 'Ruby Tuesday'[PBR] (H)	LCro SGol WFar
- 'Sabrina' (Dutch Ladies Series) (H)	CBcs CBod CChe CEnd CRos EGrl EHyd EPfP LRHS NRHS SCob SGol SHyH SRkn WFar
- 'Saint Claire' (H)	CBcs
- SALSA ('Sidsalimp'[PBR]) (Dutch Ladies Series) (H/d)	CBrac CRos EHyd LRHS MMrt NRHS SCob SCoo SGol
- 'Sandra' (Dutch Ladies Series) (L)	CBcs CRos ELon EPfP LRHS MBros WFar
- SASKIA ('Sidsaskimp'[PBR]) (Dutch Ladies Series) (H)	SCob SGol

	– SCHLOSS WACKERBARTH	see *H. macrophylla* GLAM ROCK
	– 'Schneeball' (H)	ELon LCro MAsh SCoo SGol WLov XSte
§	– 'Schöne Bautznerin' (H) ♀H5	CCVT CDoC CEnd EGrI ILea LRHS WFar WLov WSpi
	– 'Sea Foam' (L)	NLar
	– 'Selina' (Dutch Ladies Series) (L)	CBcs EPfP LSRN SCoo SGol WHtc WLov
	– 'Selma' PBR (Dutch Ladies Series) (L)	CBcs EPfP SGol
	– 'Semperflorens' (H)	XSte
	– 'Sensation' (H)	CBcs
§	– 'Setsuka-yae' (L/d)	SGol
	– 'Shakira' (H)	SGol
	– 'Shamrock' (L)	SHyH
	– 'Sheila' (Dutch Ladies Series) (L)	CBcs EPfP LCro LOPS LSRN
	– 'Shin-ozaki' (H)	NLar
	– 'Shooting Star' PBR (L)	LRHS
	– 'Sibilla' (H)	SGol SHyH SPlb WFar
	– 'Silver Star' (H) **new**	SGol
	– SISTER THERESE	see *H. macrophylla* 'Soeur Thérèse'
	– SO LONG EBONY ('Monmar') (H)	NCth SGol
	– SO LONG ROSY ('Coumont') (H)	NCth SGol
	– SO LONG SUNNY ('Tk02') (H)	CKel CWnw NCth SGol
§	– 'Soeur Thérèse' (H)	CBar CBcs CSBt EPfP LPar MAsh MMuc NLar SGol SGsty SWvt WGwG XSte
	– SPEEDY RED IMPROVED ('Hba215911' PBR) (H)	LRHS
	– 'Spike' PBR (H)	NRHS
	– STAR GAZER ('Kompeito' PBR) (Double Delights Series) (L/d)	SGol XSte
	– STRAWBERRIES 'N' CREAM ('Mak2' PBR) (L)	CRos EPfP LRHS SPoG
	– STYLE PINK ('Horpink') (Saxon Series) (H)	LRHS
	– subsp. ***stylosa***	WCru WFar WPGP
	– – MF 942115	WPGP
*	– 'Sunset' (L)	CBcs
	– 'Sweet Fantasy' (Hovaria Series) (H)	ELan EPfP SGol
	– 'Tandem' (H)	LRHS XSte
§	– 'Taube' (Teller Series) (L)	CBcs CBod ELan MAsh SGol SHyH SWvt
	– Teller Series (L)	CDoC
	– 'Teller Pink'	see *H. macrophylla* 'Taube'
	– 'Teller Red'	see *H. macrophylla* 'Rotkehlchen'
	– Teller variegated	see *H. macrophylla* 'Tricolor'
	– Teller Weiss	see *H. macrophylla* 'Libelle'
	– THREE SISTERS (mixed) (H)	LPar
	– TIFFANY ('H211902' PBR) (Flair & Flavours Series) (L)	SCoo SGol
	– 'Tinkerbell' PBR (L/d) **new**	SGol
§	– 'Tivoli' PBR (H)	LCro NRHS SCoo SGol WFar
	– TIVOLI BLUE	see *H. macrophylla* 'Tivoli'
	– TIVOLI PINK	see *H. macrophylla* 'Tivoli'
	– 'Tokyo Delight' (L) ♀H5	CMac ESwi MAsh SDys SHyH
	– 'Tovelit' (H)	SGol XSte
§	– 'Tricolor' (L/v)	CBcs CTri EShb MGos MPkF NLar SGol SHyH SPer WAvo WFar WHtc XSte
	– 'Variegata'	see *H. macrophylla* 'Maculata'
	– 'Veitchii' (L) ♀H5	CBcs CMil CSBt ECre EHyd EPfP MGos MRav MSwo SDix SHyH SPer WBor
	– VIBRANT VERDE ('Hore0046') (Rembrandt Series) (H)	SGol
	– 'Vicomte de Vibraye'	see *H. macrophylla* 'Générale Vicomtesse de Vibraye'
	– 'Warabe'	see *H. serrata* 'Warabe'
§	– 'Wedding Gown' PBR (Double Delights Series) (L/d) ♀H5	MPkF SGol
	– 'Weisse Königin' (H)	SHyH
	– 'Westfalen' (H)	CMac SDix SHyH
	– 'White King' PBR (H)	SGol
	– 'White Spirit' (L)	SGol
	– 'White Wave'	see *H. macrophylla* 'Mariesii Grandiflora'
	– white-flowered	LRHS
	– 'Wudu' PBR (H)	SCoo SGol
	– 'Xian' PBR (Sturdy Series) (H)	SGol
	– 'Yamato' (H)	XSte
	– 'Yola' (H)	NBro WFar
	– YOU & ME TOGETHER ('Youmefive' PBR) (H/d)	CKel EMil LCro LOPS MPri
	– 'Zebra' PBR (Black Steel Series) (H)	ELan ESwi LCro LOPS SGol SPer WCot
	– 'Zhuni Hito' (L)	NLar
	– 'Zorro' PBR (L) ♀H5	Widely available
	aff. ***mangshanensis*** BWJ 8120	WCru
	MISS SAORI ('H2002' PBR) (d)	CBcs CBod CKel CRos CSBt CWGN EBee EGrI EMil EPfP LCro LOPS LRHS MBros MPkF MPri NRHS SPoG XSte
	paniculata	CMCN GDam LMaj SavN WBor
	– B&SWJ 3556 from Taiwan	WCru WFar
	– B&SWJ 5413 from Japan	WCru
	– B&SWJ 8894 from Japan	WCru
	– 'Ammarin'	MAsh
	– ANGEL'S BLUSH	see *H. paniculata* 'Ruby'
	– BABY LACE ('Piihpi' PBR)	SGol SRHi
	– 'Big Ben' ♀H5	CRos EHed EHyd EPfP GGGa LRHS MAsh NRHS SGol
	– BOBO ('Ilvobo' PBR)	CDoC CWGN EBee ECul EHyd EPfP ERom LPar LRHS MACG MAsh MGos MPkF NRHS SCob SEdd SGol XSte
	– 'Bombshell' PBR	CKel EBee EMil LCro LOPS NLar NRHS SCob SGol SOrN WSpi
	– 'Brussels Lace'	CKel EMil EPfP LRHS LSRN MRav NLar NRHS SCoo SGol SHyH SSta WLov
	– 'Burgundy Lace'	MBlu NLar
	– CANDLELIGHT ('Hpopr013' PBR)	EFPl LPar NLar SGol SOrN
	– 'Chantilly Lace'	CKel EBee
	– CONFETTI ('Vlasveld 02' PBR)	EFPl LCro LOPS MAsh SCoo SGol SNig
	– DART'S LITTLE DOT ('Darlido' PBR)	GBin NLar WFar WPGP
	– DENTELLE DE GORRON ('Rencri' PBR)	SGol
	– DIAMANT ROUGE ('Rendia' PBR)	CCVT ECul EFPl EGrI EHed ELan LCro LOPS LPar LRHS MGos MPkF NRHS SCob SGol SOrN WHlf XSte
	– DIAMANTINO ('Ren101' PBR)	SGol WHlf
	– 'Dolly'	CRos EHyd EPfP LRHS LSRN NBwr SGol SPoG
	– EARLY HARRY ('Hpopr018')	CBod CTsd EBee WCot WLov
	– 'Everest'	CBod CCVT CRos EHyd EPfP LRHS NLar NRHS SPoG
	– FIRE LIGHT ('Smhpfl' PBR)	LCro NCth

	- 'Floribunda'	CRos EHyd ELan EPfP LRHS NRHS SChF WFar
	- FRAISE MELBA ('Renba'PBR)	MMrt MPkF SGol XSte
	- GRAFFITI ('Rou201406') **new**	LCro SGol
	- 'Grandiflora'	Widely available
	- GREAT STAR	see *H. paniculata* 'Le Vasterival'
	- 'Greenspire'	CRos EHyd EPfP LRHS MBlu MRav NRHS WFar
	- 'Harry's Souvenir'	NLar
§	- 'Jane'PBR	Widely available
	- 'Kyushu'	Widely available
	- 'Last Post'	NRHS
§	- 'Le Vasterival'PBR	CEnd CKel EHed SCob WSpi
	- 'Levana'PBR	EHed EWTr NLar SGol SHar SHyH WFar
	- 'Limelight'PBR ♀H5	Widely available
	- LITTLE FRAISE ('Rou201306')	SGol
	- LITTLE LIME	see *H. paniculata* LITTLE LIME
	- LITTLE QUICK FIRE ('Smhplqf'PBR)	LCro SGol
	- LITTLE SPOOKY ('Grhp08')	LCro SGol
	- (Magical Series) MAGICAL CANDLE ('Bokraflame'PBR)	CDoC ELan EPfP MAsh NRHS SGol WFar
	- - MAGICAL FIRE ('Bokraplume'PBR)	MPkF NLar NRHS SGol WFar WSpi
	- - MAGICAL FLAME ('Bokratorch'PBR)	ELan
	- - MAGICAL HIMALAYA ('Kolmahima'PBR)	MGos NLar SGol WFar
	- - MAGICAL MATTERHORN ('Bokomaho')	NLar
	- - MAGICAL MONT BLANC ('Kolmamon'PBR)	EBee LCro SGol
	- - MAGICAL MOONLIGHT ('Kolmagimo'PBR)	SCoo SGol
	- - MAGICAL STARLIGHT	see *H. paniculata* PERLE D'AUTOMNE
	- - MAGICAL SUMMER ('Bokrathirteen')	EFPl SGol WFar
	- - MAGICAL VESUVIO ('Kolmavesu'PBR)	EBee MGos NLar SGol
	- 'Mathilde'	SGol
	- 'Melody'	NLar
	- MOJITO ('Grhp10') **new**	SGol
	- 'Mount Aso'	NBro SGol
	- 'October Bride'	CEnd NLar WPGP
	- 'Papillon'	SGol WPGP
	- PASTELGREEN ('Renxolor'PBR)	EHed SGol
	- 'Pee Wee'	NLar
§	- PERLE D'AUTOMNE ('Degustar')	SGol
	- 'Phantom' ♀H5	Widely available
	- PINK DIAMOND ('Interhydia') ♀H5	Widely available
	- 'Pink Lady'	NBro SOrN
	- PINKY-WINKY ('Dvppinky'PBR) ♀H5	Widely available
	- 'Polar Bear'PBR	CBcs CBod CWGN EBee EHed NLar SCob SEdd SGol SHar WLov
§	- POLESTAR ('Breg14'PBR)	EHed LCro NLar
	- 'Praecox'	MRav WCru
	- PRIM'WHITE ('Dolprim')	EBee MBlu NLar WHlf
	- 'Rosy Morn'	CRos EHyd LRHS
§	- 'Ruby'	EPfP LSRN NLar SGol
	- 'Silver Dollar' ♀H5	CDoC CKel CRos EHed EHyd EPfP GBin LCro LMil LOPS LRHS LSRN MAsh MBros MGos NBwr NLar NRHS SCob SEdd SGol SHyH SNig SWvt WCot WFar WSpi
	- SKYFALL ('Frenne')	CBcs LCro SGol
	- 'Sparkling'	SGol
	- 'Starlight'	LEdu MPkF
	- 'Starlight Fantasy'	see *H. paniculata* PERLE D'AUTOMNE
	- SUNDAE FRAISE ('Rensun'PBR)	CCVT CChe CDoC CEme CEnd CKel CWGN EBee EHyd EPfP EShb GGGa LPar LRHS MAsh MGos MPkF NRHS SCob SEdd SGol SGsty SRHi XSte
	- SWITCH OPHELIA	see *H. paniculata* POLESTAR
	- 'Tardiva'	CBcs CBod EBee EHeP EPfP GKin LCro LOPS LSto MGos NBro SDix SGol SHyH SPer SRms SWvt WFar WLov WPGP
	- 'Tender Rose'	NLar
	- 'The Slooten Rocket'	ESwi
	- 'Unique'	CBcs CCVT CKel CRos EBee EDir EHyd ELan EPfP LRHS LSRN MAsh MRav MSwo NBro NLar NRHS SCoo SGol SHyH SPer SSta WAvo WFar WLov WPGP
	- VANILLE FRAISE ('Renhy'PBR)	Widely available
	- 'White Goliath'	NLar
	- 'White Lace'	NLar
	- 'White Lady'	CBcs NRHS SGol
	- 'White Moth'	CKel GGGa LEdu NBro NLar
	- 'Wim's Red'PBR	Widely available
	- 'Yuan-Yang'	WCru
	peruviana var. ***oerstedii*** B&SWJ 10750	WCru
	- - B&SWJ 10752 **new**	WCru
	peruviana* × *seemannii	CEnd GKin IArd SSta
	peruviana* × *serratifolia	CRHN
	petiolaris	see *H. anomala* subsp. *petiolaris*
	'Preziosa' ♀H4	Widely available
	quercifolia	Widely available
	- 'Alice'	CDoC CKel CMac EBee EHyd ELan EPfP ESwi IDee LMil LRHS LSRN MAsh NLar SChF SGol SHyH WPGP
	- 'Alison'	SGol
I	- 'Amethyst' Dirr	NLar SGol
	- 'Applause'	EBee EHyd ELan EPfP LRHS NLar SGol WPGP
	- 'Back Porch'	NLar SGol
	- 'Burgundy'	CBcs CMil EBee EPfP ESwi IArd LRHS MBlu NLar SGol WPGP WSpi
	- 'Flore Pleno'	see *H. quercifolia* SNOWFLAKE
	- 'Harmony'	CKel CMil EBee EHyd ELan ELon EPfP ESwi IDee LRHS MGos NLar NRHS SGol SHyH SSta WLov WPGP XSte
	- ICE CRYSTAL ('Hqopr010'PBR)	CDoC CKel EBee ELan EPfP ESwi LRHS NLar NSti SGol SGsty SRHi WAvo WHlf WPGP WSpi
	- 'Lady Anne'	WPGP
	- 'Little Honey'PBR	CBcs LCro MAsh NLar SGol WPGP XSte
	- 'Munchkin'	CDoC CKel CWnw LCro LRHS MGos SGol SHor XSte
	- 'Pee Wee'	CBcs CDoC CKel CMac EBee EHyd ELan EPfP LRHS MAsh MMrt SAko SGol SHyH SPoG SSta SWvt WLov WPGP
	- 'Queen of Hearts'	ESwi LRHS MGos SRHi
	- 'Ruby Slippers'	CDoC ESwi LRHS MGos MThu NLar SCoo SGol SRHi WSpi
	- 'Sike's Dwarf'	ELan MRav NLar SGol SSha WCFE WLov
	- 'Snow Giant' (d)	SGol SRHi
	- SNOW QUEEN ('Flemygea') ♀H5	Widely available

§	- SNOWFLAKE ('Brido') (d) ♀H5	CBcs CDoC CEnd CKel CMac CRos CSde CWGN ELan EPfP LCro LOPS LRHS MAsh MGos MRav NLar NRHS SCoo SEdd SGol SHyH SMad SPer SPoG WLov WPGP WSpi XSte
	- 'Tennessee Clone'	EBee LRHS NLar SGol
	RUNAWAY BRIDE SNOW WHITE ('Ushyd0405')	CBcs EPfP LAlb LCro LRHS MSwo NLar SGol SMad WHlf XSte
	sargentiana	see *H. aspera* subsp. *sargentiana*
	scandens	NBro
	- B&SWJ 5448	WCru
	- B&SWJ 5481	WCru
	- B&SWJ 5496	WCru
	- B&SWJ 5523	WCru
	- B&SWJ 5602	WCru
	- B&SWJ 5725	WCru
	- B&SWJ 5893	WCru
	- B&SWJ 6159	WCru
	- B&SWJ 6317	WCru
§	- subsp. ***chinensis***	CBcs
	- - B&SWJ 1488	WCru
	- - B&SWJ 3214	WCru
	- - B&SWJ 3410 from Taiwan	WCru
	- - B&SWJ 3420	WCru
	- - B&SWJ 3423 from Taiwan	WCru
	- - B&SWJ 3487 from Taiwan	WCru
	- - B&SWJ 3869	WCru
	- - BWJ 8000 from Sichuan	WCru
	- - BWJ 8035	WCru
§	- - f. ***angustipetala***	WPGP
	- - - B&SWJ 3454	WCru
	- - - B&SWJ 3553	WCru
	- - - B&SWJ 3667	WCru
	- - - B&SWJ 3733	WCru
	- - - B&SWJ 3814	WCru
	- - - B&SWJ 6038 from Yakushima	WCru
	- - - B&SWJ 6041 from Yakushima	WCru
	- - - B&SWJ 6056 from Yakushima	WCru
	- - - B&SWJ 6787	WCru
	- - - B&SWJ 6802	WCru
	- - - B&SWJ 7121	WCru
	- - - B&SWJ 7128	WCru
§	- - - 'Golden Crane'	CBcs EBee EPfP WCru WFar WPGP
	- - - 'Monlongshou'	see *H. scandens* subsp. *chinensis* f. *angustipetala* 'Golden Crane'
	- - 'Big White'	EBee WPGP
	- - f. ***formosana***	CMil
	- - - B&SWJ 1488	WCru
	- - - B&SWJ 7097	WCru
	- - f. ***macrosepala*** B&SWJ 3423	ESwi WCru
	- - - B&SWJ 3476	WCru
	- - - CWJ 12441	WCru
	- - f. ***obovatifolia*** B&SWJ 3487b	WCru
	- - - B&SWJ 3683	WCru
	- - - B&SWJ 3869 from the Philippines	WCru
	- - - B&SWJ 7121	WCru
	- subsp. ***liukiuensis***	WCru
	- - B&SWJ 6022	WCru
	- - B&SWJ 11471	WCru
	- 'Mine-no-yuki'	SGol
	seemannii	Widely available
	- 'Roger Grounds' (v)	WCot
	aff. ***seemannii***	CBod CEnd GKin NGrs WSpi
	SEMIOLA ('Inovalaur'PBR)	CBcs EBee EHyd EPfP LRHS NRHS SGol SRHi
	serrata	CTri

	- B&SWJ 6184	WCru
	- B&SWJ 6241	WCru
	- PAB 4757	LEdu
	- 'Acuminata'	see *H. serrata* 'Bluebird'
	- 'Aigaku' (L)	CExl CMil
	- 'Akabe-yama' (L)	NBro NLar
	- 'Aka-tsanayama' (L)	LRHS
	- 'Akishino-temari' (L)	WPGP
	- Amacha Group (L)	SGol
	- - 'Amagi-amacha' (L)	CMil NBro NLar
	- - 'Ō-amacha' (L)	WPGP
	- 'Amagyana' (L)	CExl
	- subsp. ***angustata***	WCru
	- 'Ao-yama' (L)	WPGP
	- AVELROZ ('Dolmyf'PBR) (L)	SGol
	- 'Belladonna' (L)	LRHS NBro
	- 'Belle Deckle'	see *H.* 'Blue Deckle'
	- 'Beni-gaku' (L)	CExl ECre EHyd LRHS MAsh MBlu NBro NLar NRHS SGol
	- 'Beni-temari' (L)	LRHS NBro
	- 'Beni-yama' (L) ♀H4	CMil
	- 'Betu-ko-temari' (L)	LRHS
	- 'Bleuet' (L)	XSte
	- 'Blue Billow' (L)	NBro NLar SGol
	- BLUEBERRY CHEESECAKE	see *H. serrata* TUFF STUFF
§	- 'Bluebird' (L) ♀H4	Widely available
I	- 'Boothii' (L)	CMac
	- 'Cap Sizun' (L)	SChF SGol WPGP XSte
	- 'Chiba Cherry-lips' (L)	ESwi LSto WCru
	- 'Chiri-san Sue' (L/d)	WCru
	- COTTON CANDY	see *H. serrata* TUFF STUFF
	- 'Crûg Bicolor' (L)	WCru
	- 'Crûg Caerulean' (L)	WCru
	- 'Crûg Cobalt' (L)	ESwi WCru
	- 'Crûg Sô Cool' (L)	ESwi WCru
	- 'Diadem' (L) ♀H4	CAbb CBod CExl CSde EHed ELon EPfP GKev LRHS NBro SEdd
	- 'Forget Me Not' (L)	NBro
	- 'Fuji Waterfall'	see *H. serrata* 'Fuji-no-taki'
	- 'Fuji-no-shirayuki' (L/d)	LRHS
§	- 'Fuji-no-taki' (L/d) ♀H4	GEdr NLar WPGP
	- 'Golden Showers' (L)	NBro
	- 'Golden Sunlight'PBR (L)	NLar SGol SWvt
	- 'Graciosa' (L)	XSte
	- 'Grayswood' (L) ♀H4	CBcs CBod CDoC CExl CKel CMac CSBt EHyd ELan EPfP EWTr LRHS MAsh MGil MRav NBro NRHS SCob SDix SGol SHyH SNig SPer WBor WKif WLov WPGP XSte
	- 'Hakucho' (L/d)	NBro WPGP
	- 'Hallasan' misapplied	see *H. serrata* 'Maiko', 'Spreading Beauty'
	- 'Hallasan' R. & J. de Belder (L)	WPGP
	- 'Hime-benigaku' (L)	CMil MBlu WFar
	- 'Hoshi-kuzu'	SGol
	- 'Impératrice Eugénie' (L)	LRHS NLar XSte
	- 'Intermedia' (L)	CExl NBro
	- 'Kiyosumi' (L) ♀H4	CBcs CBrac CExl CKel EBee ECre ELon EMil EPfP GEdr NBir NLar SBrt SSha WBor WCru WFar WLov WPGP
	- 'Klaveren'	see *H. macrophylla* 'Klaveren'
	- 'Koreana' (L)	SAko SGol
	- 'Kujuusan' (L)	CMil
	- 'Kurenai' (L)	EBee EPfP NBro NLar WFar WPGP
	- 'Kurohime' (L)	EBee NBro WFar WPGP
	- 'Macrosepala' (L)	WPGP
§	- 'Maiko' (L)	IArd
	- 'Midori' (L)	CExl
	- 'Mikamba'	see *H. serrata* 'Mikanba-gaku'
§	- 'Mikanba-gaku' (L)	SGol

- 'Mikata-yae' (L/d)	CMil WPGP
- 'Miranda' (L) 🏆H4	CExl CMil EHyd EPfP LRHS MAsh NBro NLar SDys SGol WFar
- 'Miyama-yae-murasaki' (L/d) 🏆H4	CExl CMil SGol SRms WPGP
- 'Momobana' (L)	CMil
- 'Momo-beni-yama' (L)	NBro
- 'Mont Aso' (L)	CMil EWld IArd NLar
- 'Niji' (L)	WPGP
- 'Odoriko-amacha' (L)	EBee SChF WPGP
- 'Otsu-hime' (L)	NLar
- 'Pretty Maiden'	see *H. serrata* 'Shichidanka'
- 'Ramis Pictis' (L)	NBro NLar
- 'Rosalba' (L) 🏆H4	CExl ECre NBro
- 'Santiago'PBR (L)	EPfP SGol WPGP
- 'Sekka' (L)	EBee MBlu SChF SEdd WPGP
§ - 'Shichidanka' (L/d)	CMil NBro
- 'Shichidanka-nishiki' (L/d/v)	CExl
- 'Shikoubai' (L) **new**	GEdr
- 'Shinonome' (L/d)	CExl
- 'Shirahuzi' (L/d)	SGol
- 'Shirofuji' (L/d) 🏆H4	CMil EWld
- 'Shiro-gaku' (L)	NBro NLar
- 'Shiro-maiko'	WPGP
- 'Shirotae' (L/d)	CExl LRHS SGol
- 'Shōjō' 🏆H4	CMil EBee MAsh MBlu NBro SGol WPGP XSte
§ - 'Spreading Beauty' (L)	WPGP
- 'Suzukayama-yama' (L)	WPGP
* - var. ***thunbergii*** 'Plena' (L/d)	WCru
- 'Tiara' (L) 🏆H4	CAbb CExl CKel CMil EBee EHyd EPfP GGGa GKev LSRN MAsh NBir NBro NLar NRHS SDix SDys SEdd SGol SHyH SPoG WPGP XSte
§ - TUFF STUFF ('Mak 20'PBR) (L)	EPfP LPar LRHS NRHS SGol SPoG XSte
- 'Veerle' (L)	CBcs CMil EHed ILea NBro NLar SGol
- 'Vicomte de Kerlot' (L)	XSte
§ - 'Warabe' (L)	CMil SGol
- 'Yae-no-amacha' (L/d)	CBcs CExl NBro NLar
- subsp. ***yezoensis***	EWld NLar SGol
§ ***serratifolia***	CBcs CExl IArd IDee SSta WPGP
- HCM 98056	WCru
sikokiana B&SWJ 5035	WCru
- B&SWJ 5855	WCru
- B&SWJ 11174	WCru
- B&SWJ 11381	WCru
'Silver Slipper'	see *H. macrophylla* 'Ayesha'
steyermarkii B&SWJ 10501	WCru
tiliifolia	see *H. anomala* subsp. *petiolaris* var. *ovalifolia*
'Victoria'	GMcL
villosa	see *H. aspera* Villosa Group
xanthoneura	see *H. heteromalla*
aff. ***zhewanensis*** MF 93117	WCru

Hydrastis (*Ranunculaceae*)

canadensis	GPoy LEdu

Hydrocharis (*Hydrocharitaceae*)

morsus-ranae	CBen CHab CPud CWat EWat LLWG LPfP MWts NPer WPnP

Hydrocotyle (*Araliaceae*)

asiatica	see *Centella asiatica*
novae-zeelandiae **new**	LPfP
sibthorpioides 'Crystal Confetti' (v)	LLWG LPfP WHil
vulgaris	CWat EWat

Hydrophyllum (*Boraginaceae*)

canadense	SBrt
virginianum	LEdu WPGP

Hylomecon (*Papaveraceae*)

hylomeconoides	EWld WCru
§ ***japonica***	CMiW EBee EHyd ELan GArf GEdr GGro GKev GLog GMaP LEdu LRHS NBir NHar NHpl NQui NRHS NRya WCot WPGP

Hylotelephium (*Crassulaceae*)

§ 'Abbey Dore'	CBod EBee ECtt ELan ELon EPfP LRHS MSpe NBir SPhx WCAu
AMBER ('Florseamb')	WCot
§ ***anacampseros***	GQue MMuc NDov NRya NWad XLum
'Angelina's Teacup' (SunSparkler Series) **new**	LBar
'Aquarel'	GBin
'Autumn Charm'	see *H.* (Herbstfreude Group) 'Lajos'
§ 'Bertram Anderson' 🏆H7	Widely available
'Birthday Party' (Birthday Party Series)	SPoG
'Blade Runner'	LRHS
'Blue Elf'PBR (SunSparkler Series)	LBar XSte
'Blue Pearl'PBR (SunSparkler Series)	EBee LBar LCro LOPS MPnt NCth SPoG
§ 'Carl' 🏆H7	Widely available
§ ***cauticola*** 🏆H5	EPot MAsh MRav NWad SRms WIce XLum
- 'Coca-Cola'	Widely available
- 'Lidakense' 🏆H5	CAby CTri ECha EGrI EPot MAsh MAvo MHer NHol NLar NWad SHar SPlb SRot XLum XSen
- 'Robustum'	see *H.* 'Ruby Glow'
'Cherry Tart'PBR (SunSparkler Series)	LBar LRHS
'Chocolate Cherry'	EPfP GKev LRHS LSou MPri NDov SHeu
'Chocolate Drop'PBR	CWGN IPot MAvo NLar SHeu SRms
'Chocolate Sauce'	MAvo
'Class Act'PBR	ECtt EHyd LBar LRHS MNrw MPri NLar NRHS SPoG SRms
'Cloud Walker'PBR	ECtt SPoG WFar
'Crazy Ruffles'	WCot
cyaneum 'Sakhalin'	CRos EHyd LRHS MHer NRHS
'Dark Jack'	ECtt GQue NGdn SMrm WCot
'Dazzleberry'PBR (SunSparkler Series)	EPfP IPot LBar LCro LOPS LRHS
§ ***erythrostictum***	GBin XLum
- B&SWJ 11384	WCru
- 'Frosty Morn' (v)	Widely available
§ - 'Mediovariegatum' (v)	CDor ELan LRHS MHer SWvt WFar XLum
§ ***ewersii***	MAsh NBro NLar SPhx SPlb SRot
- CC 5288	GKev
- var. ***homophyllum*** 'Rosenteppich'	CDoC EHyd EPPr EPfP LRHS MAsh MPri NBir NRHS SPoG SRms SWvt WAvo
'Firecracker'PBR (SunSparkler Series)	LBar LOPS LRHS LSou MPnt SCoo WHil WNPC
'Frosted Fire'	LBar MACG MAsh SRms WFar WHoo
'Green Expectations'	MRav
§ Herbstfreude Group	EHyd EWoo GQue LRHS SEdd SGbt SMrm WCav WHlf WMal
- 'Autumn Fire'	EBee MAsh
- 'Beka' (v)	NFav
- 'Elsie's Gold' (v)	CTtf EBee ECtt EPfP MNrw NLar SRms

§	- 'Herbstfreude' ♀H7	Widely available
	- 'Jaws'PBR	CKno EBee ECtt LSou NLar WCot WFar XLum
§	- 'Lajos' (v)	CBod LBar LRHS MAsh NFav WCot WFar
	- 'Mini Joy'	ELon MNrw
	'Ice Ruffles' (v)	SPoG WFar
	'Jade Tuffet'PBR (SunSparkler Series)	LBar LRHS
	'José Aubergine'PBR	CBod CKno CTtf EBee ECha ECtt EHyd EPfP EWoo LCro LPla LRHS MAsh MAvo MBel MRav NDov NHol NLar NRHS NSti SCob SHeu SPoG SRms WCAu
§	'Joyce Henderson'	CDor CElw EHyd ELan EPfP GBin LRHS MCot MRav NChi NLar SPer SRGP SRms WAvo WBrk WCot XSen
	'Lac d'Oô'	GBin
	'Lemonjade' (Rock 'N Grow Series) **new**	LBar
	'Lime Twister' (SunSparkler Series) (v) **new**	LBar LCro WHil
	'Lime Zinger'PBR (SunSparkler Series)	CPla CRos CSBt EPfP LCro LOPS LRHS LSou MPri SEdd SPad WNPC
I	'Marchants Best Red' ♀H7	MNrw MRav NCth SPhx WCot WMal
§	'Matrona' ♀H7	Widely available
§	'Mr Goodbud'PBR ♀H7	CAby ECtt GPSL LRHS MAsh MAvo MHer MNrw MPri NBir NLar NRHS SCob SHeu SPoG SRms WCAu WCot WSpi WTor
	'Munstead Purple'	MCot
§	'Munstead Red'	Widely available
§	'Oriental Dancer'	LBar LRHS MThu
	'Pinky'	EBee
	PLUM DAZZLED ('Pldaz2018') (SunSparkler Series)	LBar
§	***pluricaule***	CDor EHyd EPot LRHS NBro NHol NRHS NWad SLee SPlb SRms WCav
	'Pool Party'PBR (Party Hardy Series)	CRos EHyd EPfP NLar NRHS SRms
§	***populifolium***	ECha GQue MHer MMuc NLar WMal XLum
	- 'Em's Variegated' (v) **new**	ECha
§	'Red Cauli' ♀H7	Widely available
	'Red Setter'	SPhx WMal
	'Red Sparkle'	EPfP LRHS
§	'Ruby Glow' ♀H5	Widely available
	Seduction Series **new**	CBod
§	***sieboldii***	SRms
	- 'Dragon'	MHCG MPri
	- 'Mediovariegatum'	see *H. sieboldii* 'Misebaya-nakafu'
§	- 'Misebaya-nakafu' (v) ♀H3	MHer MRav SPlb XLum
§	***spectabile*** ♀H7	CBod CTri CWnw EHyd ELan EPfP GJos LRHS MCot MHer MRav NGdn NRHS SGbt SPlb SRms WBor WBrk WFar WGwG WSFF
	- BLACK BEAUTY ('Florseblab')	ECtt
	- Brilliant Group	CBar CRos EGrl EHeP LCro LRHS SCob SRms WCAu
	- - 'Abendrot'	ECha
	- - 'Brilliant' ♀H7	CBcs CBod CKel CSBt CTri ECha ECtt EHyd ELan EPfP LCro LOPS LPal LRHS MAvo MGos MHol MRav NFav NGdn NLar NWsh SCob SPer SPoG SWvt WFar WSpi
	- - 'Carmen'	NBir XLum
	- - 'Hot Stuff'	ECtt EHyd ELan EPau EPfP LRHS MBNS NCou NRHS SCoo SPoG SRms WCot
	- - 'Lisa'	ECha NLar
	- - 'Meteor'	MRav NLar SMrm
	- - 'Neon'	EPfP LRHS MAsh MAvo MBros
	- - 'Pink Fairy'	MNrw
	- - 'Rosenteller'	SMrm WBrk
§	- - 'Septemberglut'	CRos EHyd LRHS NRHS WSpi XLum
	- - 'Steven Ward'	EWes
	- 'Crystal Pink'PBR	LBar LRHS MNrw MPri NLar
	- 'Humile'	XLum
	- 'Iceberg'	CBod CTtf EBee ECha ECtt EGrl EHyd EPfP GBin LRHS LShi LSto MAsh MGos MRav NCth NGdn NLar NRHS SPhx SWvt WCAu WFar WSFF WSpi XLum XSen
	- 'Pink Chablis' (v)	WCot
	- SEPTEMBER GLOW	see *H. spectabile* (Brilliant Group) 'Septemberglut'
	- 'Stardust'	CDor CRos CTri EBee EHyd EPfP GBin GKev GMaP LCro LRHS LSou MBNS NBPC NCth NFav NRHS SCob SRms WBrk WFar WHlf XLum
	- 'Variegatum'	see *H. erythrostictum* 'Mediovariegatum'
	- WALBERTON'S PIZAZZ	EHyd EPfP LRHS NRHS SPoG
§	'Stewed Rhubarb Mountain'	CKno EBee ECha ECtt EHyd ELan EPfP LDai MBNS MRav NLar NRHS SGbt SMrm WCAu
	'Sunset Cloud'	EWes LPla MRav
§	***tatarinowii***	WCot
§	***telephium***	NBir SIvy SRms WSFF XLum
§	- Atropurpureum Group	MRav NLar SWvt
	- - 'African Pearl'	EGrl
	- - 'Arthur Branch'	EHyd LRHS NChi
	- - 'Bon Bon'	EPfP MBros NLar SPoG
	- - 'Bressingham Purple'	CRos EBee EHyd LRHS NRHS
	- - 'Chocolate'	GPSL NLar
	- - 'Dark Knight'	CRos EHyd EPfP GPSL LRHS NRHS
	- - 'El Cid'	EWes
	- - 'Karfunkelstein' ♀H7	CDor CKno EBee ECha ECtt GBee GBin GLog GQue LCro LOPS LRHS MAvo NBir NDov SPhx WCot XLum
	- - 'Lynda Windsor'	ECtt NLar SWvt
	- - 'Möhrchen'	EGrl GMaP GMcL MRav NGdn NLar
	- - 'Picolette'	ECtt EHyd LRHS NGdn NRHS SPoG SRms WCot
	- - 'Postman's Pride'PBR	CWGN ECtt NGdn
§	- - 'Purple Emperor' ♀H7	Widely available
	- - 'Ringmore Ruby'	MNrw WCot
	- - 'Xenox'PBR ♀H7	CBct CWGN EBee ECtt EHyd EPfP GBin IPot LDai LRHS MAsh MAvo MCot MNrw NLar NRHS NWad SCoo SPoG SRms WAvo WCAu
	- 'Cherry Truffle'PBR	LBar SHeu
	- 'Coral Reef'PBR	LBar
	- 'Dark Magic'PBR	LBar LRHS MPri SIvy
	- 'Desert Black'PBR	LSou MBNS SEdd
	- Emperor's Waves Group	ELan MNHC NGdn NWad SBls
§	- subsp. ***fabaria***	MRav NWsh SMrm WCot
	- - var. ***borderei***	ECha LPla SPhx
	- 'Jennifer'	EBee ECtt SGro WCAu WCot
	- 'Marina'PBR	NLar
	- subsp. ***maximum***	XSen
	- - 'Atropurpureum'	see *H. telephium* Atropurpureum Group
	- - 'Gooseberry Fool'	EBee ECtt ELan EPfP GMaP LRHS LSou MACG MBriF NEoE SRms WCAu
	- 'Moonlight Serenade'PBR	EBee ECtt SRms

- 'Orange Xenox' PBR	EPfP
- 'Raspberry Truffle'	EPfP LRHS SHeu
§ - subsp. ***ruprechtii***	CDor ECha ECtt EGrl EHyd GMaP GMcL LRHS MCot MRav NLar NRHS SPer SPhx
- - 'Citrus Twist'	LPla LRHS MRav
- - 'Hab Gray'	EBee ECtt EWes EWld LRHS NLar SMrm SRms SSut XSen
- - 'Pink Dome'	ECha LPla
- 'Strawberries and Cream'	CMac EBee ECha EHyd ELan ELon EPfP EShb GMaP LCro LRHS MAsh MBNS MBel MMuc MRav NGdn NLar NRHS SGbt SMrm
- 'Sunkissed' PBR	CBod ECtt LBar NLar WHil
- 'Surrender Red' **new**	WCAu
- (Touchdown Series) 'Touchdown Breeze' PBR	CKno
- - 'Touchdown Flame' PBR	SHeu
- - 'Touchdown Teak' PBR	CKno CTtf EBee ECha EHyd EPfP IPot LEdu LRHS MAsh NRHS SCob SEdd SHeu WTor
- 'Twinkling Star' PBR	MNrw NLar
- YELLOW MATRONA ('Eline' PBR)	ECtt LCro LRHS MAsh MBNS NLar
- 'Yellow Xenox' PBR	IPot NLar
'Thundercloud' PBR	EPfP GJos LBar NWad SCob SRms
'Thunderhead' PBR	NCth SHar SHeu WHlf
§ ***ussuriense***	GBin GPSL NBir
- 'Chuwangsan'	WCru
'Veluwse Wakel'	GBin
§ 'Vera Jameson' 🏆H5	CBod CRos CWal ECha ECtt EHyd ELan EPfP EShb GKev LRHS LSRN MCot MRav NBir NHol NRHS NWsh SMrm SPer SRms SWvt WHoo WKif WSpi
§ ***verticillatum***	LShi
§ ***viviparum***	NLar
- B&SWJ 8662	WCru
WALBERTON'S PINK WHISPER	EHyd EPfP LRHS NRHS SPoG
'Washfield Purple'	see *H. telephium* (Atropurpureum Group) 'Purple Emperor'
'Wildfire' (SunSparkler Series) **new**	LBar LCro SPad

Hymenanthera see *Melicytus*

Hymenocallis (*Amaryllidaceae*)

× ***festalis***	see *Ismene* × *deflexa*
harrisiana	CCCN LAma SDeJ
longipetala	see *Ismene longipetala*
'Sulphur Queen'	see *Ismene* 'Sulphur Queen'

Hymenolepis (*Asteraceae*)

parviflora	see *Athanasia parviflora*

Hymenoxys (*Asteraceae*)

grandiflora	see *Tetraneuris grandiflora*
§ ***hoopesii***	CMac EHeP EHyd EPfP GDam GMaP GMcL LRHS LShi NBir NGrd NLar NRHS SRms WFar XLum

Hyophorbe (*Arecaceae*)

indica	EAri
lagenicaulis	LPal NPlm
verschaffeltii	LPal NPlm

Hyoscyamus (*Solanaceae*)

niger	GPoy WSFF

Hypericum ✿ (*Hypericaceae*)

aegypticum	CTri EPot MHer NBwr SLee SPlb WAbe WThu
androsaemum	ECha ELan GAbr MMuc MSwo NPer SCob WFar
§ - 'Albury Purple'	ELan EShb ESwi LDai XLum
- 'Autumn Blaze'	CBcs
- 'Excellent Flair'	NLar
§ - f. ***variegatum*** 'Mrs Gladis Brabazon' (v)	CMac EShb NBir WCot
'Archibald'	EWes
athoum	SLee WThu
balearicum	ELan MMuc SBrt WAbe WIce XSen
§ ***beanii***	WCFE
bellum	SPtp
calycinum	CBod CBrac CMac CTri EHeP ELan EPfP GDam GMcL LBuc MDon MGos MRav NLar NWea SCob SEND SPer SRms SWvt WFar XLum
- 'Brigadoon'	SGol
- CARNIVAL	see *H. calycinum* FIESTA
§ - FIESTA ('Crowthyp' PBR) (v)	LRHS LSou NEoE
cerastioides	CTri EDAr EWes GJos NGdn SRms WCot
coris	EWes SRms
cuneatum	see *H. pallens*
× ***cyathiflorum*** 'Gold Cup'	CMac EHyd LRHS MAsh
'Daybreak'	CRos EHyd LRHS MAsh NEoE SGol SPoG
× ***dummeri*** 'Peter Dummer' 🏆H5	NLar WSpi
'Eastleigh Gold'	CMac
elodes	CWat LLWG LPfP
'Fancy Pants'	LEdu WPGP
forrestii 🏆H5	MMuc SEND
fragile misapplied	see *H. olympicum* f. *minus*
frondosum 'Sunburst'	EPfP
grandiflorum	see *H. kouytchense*
henryi L 753	SRms
'Hidcote'	see *H.* × *hidcoteense* 'Hidcote'
§ × ***hidcoteense*** 'Hidcote' 🏆H5	Widely available
- 'Hidcote Variegated' (v)	SRms
hirsutum	CHab
× ***inodorum*** 'Albury Purple'	see *H. androsaemum* 'Albury Purple'
- 'Autumn Surprise' PBR	NWad
- 'Dream'	NLar
- 'Elstead'	EPfP MRav NBwr NWea WSpi
- GOLDEN BEACON ('Wilhyp' PBR) 🏆H5	CSpe ESwi GMcL MAsh MHer MMuc MNrw NBir NWad SEND WCot
- (Magical Series) MAGICAL BEAUTY ('Kolmbeau' PBR)	CBod NBid NEoE NLar SGbt SPoG
- - MAGICAL CHERRY ('Kolmcherrip' PBR)	ELan SCob
- - MAGICAL GRACE ('Kolmagrace' PBR)	CBod LRHS LSou SCob
- - MAGICAL INNOCENCE ('Kolmaginno' PBR) **new**	NEoE
- - MAGICAL LIGHTNING ('Kolmligh' PBR)	CBod LRHS LSou NEoE NLar WHtc
- - MAGICAL PUMPKIN ('Kolmapuki' PBR)	CBod LRHS LSou NEoE SCob
- - MAGICAL RED ('Kolmred')	EPfP NEoE NLar SPoG
- - MAGICAL SUNSHINE ('Kolmasun' PBR)	MMrt NEoE SCob WHtc
- - MAGICAL UNIVERSE ('Kolmuni' PBR)	CBod GDam LRHS LSou NEoE NLar WHtc
- - MAGICAL WHITE ('Kolmawhi' PBR)	CBod ELan GDam LSou MMrt NEoE SPoG
- 'Rheingold'	MAsh NLar
- 'Ysella'	MRav
kalmianum	IDee SBrt

	- 'Gemo'	IArd
	kamtschaticum	XLum
	kazdaghense	EWes
§	***kouytchense*** ♀H5	EHyd EPfP EWes GBin LRHS MAsh MMuc MRav SEND SPoG SWvt WKif WSpi
	lancasteri ♀H5	CRos EHyd EPfP ESwi LRHS SPoG SPtp
	leschenaultii misapplied	see *H.* 'Rowallane'
	maclarenii	EWes
	MAGICAL FLAME ('Kolmagif')	MMrt
	MAGICAL RED FLAME ('Kolmaref'PBR)	EPfP
	(Miracle Series) MIRACLE ATTRACTION ('Alldiablo'PBR)	CDoC CRos LRHS MGos SRms
	- MIRACLE BLIZZ ('Allblizz')	CRos EHyd LRHS MGos NLar NRHS
	- MIRACLE BLOSSOM ('Allblossom'PBR)	CRos EHyd LRHS NLar NRHS
	- MIRACLE FANTASY ('Hymirfan')	NLar
	- MIRACLE MARVEL ('Allmarvel'PBR)	CDoC MGos
	- MIRACLE NIGHT ('Allmadne'PBR)	NLar
	- MIRACLE SUMMER ('Hymirsum')	NEoE NLar
	- MIRACLE WONDER ('Hymirwon')	LRHS NLar
	× ***moserianum*** ♀H4	CMac CRos EHyd EPfP EWes LRHS NPer SCob SPer SRms WFar WHtc
	- LITTLE MISSTERY ('Dunnehyp'PBR) (v)	CDoC CKel CRos EHyd EMil EPfP LBar LRHS MAsh NEoE NRHS SCob SPoG
§	- 'Tricolor' (v)	CBcs CBod CBrac CGBo CKel CMac CSBt CTri EHeP EHyd ELan ELon EPfP LCro LOPS LRHS MAsh MGos MRav MSwo NBwr NRHS SCob SGol SPer SPlb SPoG SWvt WFar
	- 'Variegatum'	see *H.* × *moserianum* 'Tricolor'
	'Mr Bojangles'	SCob
	'Mrs Brabazon'	see *H. androsaemum* f. *variegatum* 'Mrs Gladis Brabazon'
	olympicum ♀H4	CRos CTri ECha EHyd ELan EPot GJos LRHS NRHS SEND SPer SRms SWvt WIce XLum XSen
	- 'Grandiflorum'	see *H. olympicum* f. *uniflorum*
§	- f. ***minus***	CTri EPfP GRum NGdn NHpl SPlb SRms
§	- - 'Sulphureum'	CChe CRos EHyd ELon EWes GMaP LRHS NBir NRHS SPer SRms SWvt WCFE WCav WFar
	- - 'Variegatum' (v)	EWes NBir SWvt
§	- f. ***uniflorum***	CBod EBou MMuc NBro NSla SLee WCav WIce
	- - 'Citrinum' ♀H5	CBcs CBod CMil CSpe ECha ECtt EPot LBar LPla MHol MMrt MMuc MRav SEND SMad WAbe WCot WFar WHoo WKif XSen
	orientale	EWes GLog NWad
§	***pallens***	WAbe
	patulum	SPtp
	- var. ***henryi*** Rehder & hort.	see *H. pseudohenryi*
	- var. ***henryi*** Veitch ex Bean	see *H. beanii*
	perforatum	CBod CCBP CHab CHby ENfk EPfP GJos GPoy IRos MGil MHer MHoo MNHC NGrd NLar NMir SEND SRms WHer WSFF
	polyphyllum misapplied	see *H. olympicum* f. *minus*
	- 'Citrinum'	see *H. olympicum* f. *minus* 'Sulphureum'
	- 'Grandiflorum'	see *H. olympicum* f. *uniflorum*
§	***pseudohenryi*** ♀H5	MMrt SPtp
	pulchrum	SBrt
	quadrangulum L.	see *H. tetrapterum*
	reptans misapplied	see *H. olympicum* f. *minus*
	reptans Hook.f. & Thomson ex Dyer	EWes NWad
	revolutum PAB 3861	LEdu
§	'Rowallane' ♀H3	CTri LRHS NLar SDix SPoG SSha SWvt
	'Sungold'	see *H. kouytchense*
	'Sweet Lion'	CMac
	tenuicaule	IDee
§	***tetrapterum***	CPud LPfP
	trichocaulon	EWes ITim
	uralum	SPtp
	- HWJ 520	ESwi WCru
	- NJM 10.097	WPGP
	wilsonii	WCFE

Hypocalyptus (*Fabaceae*)

sophoroides	SPlb

Hypochaeris (*Asteraceae*)

radicata	CHab NMir

Hypocyrta see *Nematanthus*

Hypoestes (*Acanthaceae*)

aristata	SVen

Hypolepis (*Dennstaedtiaceae*)

ambigua	SPlb
dicksonioides new	LEdu WPGP
glandulifera	LEdu
millefolium	CBrP LEdu LRHS SPlb WCot WPGP

Hypoxis (*Hypoxidaceae*)

	hirsuta	CBor CCCN
	krebsii	CBor
	longifolia	MAsh
	parvula	CBor XLum
	- var. ***albiflora***	NWad
§	- - 'Hebron Farm Biscuit'	CCCN EWes GEdr NWad WFar
	villosa	GKev

Hypoxis × *Rhodohypoxis* see × *Rhodoxis*

H. parvula × ***R. baurii***	see × *Rhodoxis hybrida*

Hypsela (*Campanulaceae*)

	longiflora	see *H. reniformis*
§	***reniformis***	CBor EBou EDAr ITim LLWG MAsh NHpl SLee

Hyssopus ✿ (*Lamiaceae*)

officinalis	Widely available
- f. ***albus***	ECha ELan ENfk EPfP MHer MHoo MNHC SBls SRms WFar WHer XLum XSen
- subsp. ***aristatus***	ELon ENfk EPfP GPoy LCro MHer MHoo MNHC SPoG WHoo XLum XSen
- 'Caeruleus'	EPPr
- subsp. ***officinalis***	XSen
- 'Roseus'	CBod EBou ECha ELan ENfk EPPr EPfP GPoy MHer MHoo MNHC SPoG WHer XLum XSen
- f. ***ruber***	CLau
- white-flowered	SEdi

Hystrix (*Poaceae*)

patula	CBod EMor EPPr MNrw SBls SPlb XLum

I

Iberis (*Brassicaceae*)

ABSOLUTELY AMETHYST ('Ib2401')	CBod ELan GBin LBar LRHS MCot SPoG WFar WHlf WIce
candolleana	see *I. violacea* Candolleana Group
commutata	see *I. sempervirens*
DWARF FAIRY MIX (Fairy Series)	LCro
gibraltarica	SRms
- 'Betty Swainson' ♀H4	CElw CSpe SHar SMrm
jordanii	see *I. violacea*
'Masterpiece'[PBR]	CBod CDoC CKel EHyd ELan EPfP LBar LCro LRHS NPer NRHS SCoo SPoG WFar WHlf
'Pink Ice'	CRos EHyd ELan EPfP LBar LRHS MACG MCot MPri NRHS SCob SEdd SHar SRHi WFar WHlf WIce WTor
pruitii	see *I. violacea*
saxatilis	CRos EHyd ITim LRHS NRHS SRms WThu
semperflorens	WAvo WBrk
§ ***sempervirens***	CTri CWal EBou EHeP ELan EPfP MAsh MMuc NBro SAdn SBut SCob SEND SHar SRms WCFE XSen
- 'Appen-Etz'	CRos EHyd EPfP GMaP LRHS NRHS NWad SRms WFar
- 'Fischbeck'	SRms SRot
- 'Golden Candy'	CTri MHer NHpl SPoG SRms WFar WIce XSen
- 'Little Gem'	see *I. sempervirens* 'Weisser Zwerg'
- 'Nevina'	CBod
- SCHNEEFLOCKE	see *I. sempervirens* 'Snowflake'
- 'Snow Cushion'	EPfP
§ - 'Snowflake' ♀H5	CWnw EBou EPfP EPot GKev GMaP LCro LOPS LPal LRHS MACG MHer SCob SMrm SPer SPoG SRms SWvt WHlf WIce XLum
§ - 'Weisser Zwerg'	EBou ECha ELan GMaP MHer MRav NBwr SRms
- 'Whiteout'	CBod LBar MACG WFar
'Snowball'	SRms
'Summer Snowdrift' **new**	LBar
§ ***violacea***	NSla SPlb
§ - Candolleana Group	GEdr

Ichthyoselmis (*Papaveraceae*)

§ ***macrantha***	EBlo ECha EPot LEdu NLar WCru WFar WSHC

Idesia (*Salicaceae*)

polycarpa	CBcs EBee EGrl EPfP ESwi LEdu SChF WJur WKor WPGP
- CWJ 12837	WCru

Ilex ✿ (*Aquifoliaceae*)

× ***altaclerensis*** 'Balearica' (f)	CJun
§ - 'Belgica Aurea' (f/v) ♀H6	CBcs CJun EPfP MSwo NHol WAvo WHtc
- 'Camelliifolia' (f) ♀H6	CBcs CJun LIns LPar MBlu SGol SPer WSpi
- 'Camelliifolia Variegata' (f/v)	CMac
- 'Golden King' (f/v) ♀H6	Widely available
- 'Hodginsii' (m)	CJun
- 'Howick' (f/v)	CJun
- 'Lawsoniana' (f/v) ♀H6	Widely available
- 'Mundyi' (m)	EBtc
- 'Purple Shaft' (f)	CJun CMCN MRav
- 'Ripley Gold' (f/v)	CBrac CJun CMac CRos LRHS MAsh MRav NLar NWea SSha WAvo WHtc
- 'Silver Sentinel'	see *I.* × *altaclerensis* 'Belgica Aurea'
- 'W.J. Bean' (f)	CJun
- 'Wilsonii' (f)	NLar
aquifolium ♀H6	Widely available
- 'Alaska' (f)	Widely available
- 'Amber' (f) ♀H6	CJun CPer NLar
- 'Ammerland' (f)	CJun
- 'Angustifolia' (f)	CJun
- 'Angustifolia' (m or f)	CRos EPfP LRHS SPoG
- 'Angustimarginata Aurea' (m/v)	MTrO
§ - 'Argentea Marginata' (f/v) ♀H6	Widely available
§ - 'Argentea Marginata Pendula' (f/v)	CRos ELan EPfP LRHS MAsh NOra SRms WFar
- 'Argentea Pendula'	see *I. aquifolium* 'Argentea Marginata Pendula'
- 'Argentea Variegata'	see *I. aquifolium* 'Argentea Marginata'
- 'Atlas' (m)	CBcs LBuc SWvt
- 'Aurea Marginata' (f/v)	CMac EHeP EPfP MGos NOra NWea SCob SEWo WCFE WFar WMat
- 'Aurea Regina'	see *I. aquifolium* 'Golden Queen'
- 'Aureomaculata'	NLar
- 'Aurifodina' (f)	CJun WAvo WHtc
- 'Bacciflava' (f)	CBcs CJun CMac CTri ELan ELon EPfP IArd MBlu MRav NLar SPer SRms SWvt WFar
- 'Bowland' (f/v)	NLar
- 'Calypso' (f/v) **new**	CJun
- 'Chris Whittle'	LRHS NLar
- 'Crassifolia' (f)	EBee
- 'Crispa' (m)	CBod
- 'Elegantissima' (m/v)	CBrac CJun
- 'Fastigiata Sartori'	NLar
- 'Ferox' (m)	CJun CRos EHyd ELan EPfP LRHS
- 'Ferox Argentea' (m/v) ♀H6	Widely available
- 'Ferox Aurea' (m/v)	CBrac CDoC CJun ELon MAsh
§ - 'Flavescens' (f)	MBlu WCot
- 'Frogmore Silver' (m/v)	CJun
- 'Glanzzwerg'	SAko
- 'Gold Flash' (f/v)	CJun
- 'Golden Milkboy' (m/v)	CBrac CJun CMac EDir EPfP MAsh WAvo WCot WLov
§ - 'Golden Queen' (m/v) ♀H6	SRms
- 'Golden Tears' (f/v)	CJun
- 'Golden van Tol' (f/v)	CBcs CJun CSBt CTri EBee EDir EFPl ELan ELon EPfP EShb ETod GMcL MAsh MBlu MDon MGos MSwo MTrO NBwr NLar SCoo SGol SPer SRms WFar
- 'Green Minaret'	SAko
§ - 'Green Pillar' (f)	LRHS
- 'Green Spire'	see *I. aquifolium* 'Green Pillar'
- 'Handsworth New Silver' (f/v) ♀H6	Widely available
- 'Harpune' (f)	IArd SAko
- 'Hastata' (m)	IArd
- HECKENZWERG ('Hachzwerg'[PBR])	SAko
- 'Heterophylla Aureomarginata' (m/v)	WHtc
- 'Ingramii' (m/v)	MAsh MSwo NLar
- 'J.C. van Tol' (f) ♀H6	Widely available
- 'Latispina' (f)	CJun
- 'Lichtenthalii' (f)	CJun IArd
- 'Madame Briot' (f/v) ♀H6	Widely available
- 'Monstrosa' (m)	CJun
- moonlight holly	see *I. aquifolium* 'Flavescens'
- 'Myrtifolia' (m)	CBod CDow CJun CMac ELan EPfP LSto NLar SWvt WPav

	- 'Myrtifolia Aurea' (m/v)	SWvt
	- 'Myrtifolia Aurea Maculata' (m/v)	CBod CDoC CJun CRos CTri EHyd ELan LRHS MAsh MRav SPoG SWvt WCot WLov
	- 'Northern Lights' (v)	MSwo SGsty
	- 'Pendula' (f)	MRav
	- 'Pyramidalis' (f) ♀H6	CBcs CJun CMac CRos CTri EHeP ELan GMcL LRHS MAsh MGos NLar NWea SCob SGol SRms WFar
	- 'Pyramidalis Aureomarginata' (f/v)	WHtc
	- 'Pyramidalis Fructu Luteo' (f) ♀H6	MAsh
	- 'Recurva' (m)	CJun CMac
	- 'Rubricaulis Aurea' (f/v)	CJun GMcL
	- 'Scotica' (f)	CJun NWea
	- SIBERIA ('Limsi'PBR) (f)	LMaj
	- 'Silver King'	see *I. aquifolium* 'Silver Queen'
	- 'Silver Lining' (f/v)	CJun
	- 'Silver Milkboy' (f/v)	MBlu WFar
	- 'Silver Milkmaid' (f/v)	CJun CRos EHyd LRHS MAsh NLar NRHS SLim SWvt
§	- 'Silver Queen' (m/v) ♀H6	CBar CBcs CCVT CDoC CEnd EDir EPfP LCro LOPS LRHS MAsh MGos MRav MSwo MTrO NHol NLar NOra NWea SGbt SLim SPer SPoG SSha SWvt WHtc WLov WMat
	- 'Silver Sentinel'	see *I.* × *altaclerensis* 'Belgica Aurea'
	- 'Silver van Tol' (f/v)	CDoC CJun CLnd EBee EDir ELan EPfP EShb ETod GMcL MAsh MDon MRav NLar NPer WFar
	- 'Somerset Cream' (f/v)	CJun
*	- 'Variegata' (v)	SArc SWeb
	- 'White Cream' (m/v)	SAko
	- 'Zig Zag' (f)	CJun
	× ***aquipernyi*** DRAGON LADY ('Meschick') (f) ♀H6	CBod IArd LRHS
	- 'San Jose' (f)	CJun
	× ***attenuata***	WFar
	- 'Sunny Foster' (f/v)	CBcs CMCN SAko WFar
	× ***beanii***	CJun
§	***bioritsensis***	CMCN
	cassine L.	CMCN
	chapaensis HWJ 946	WCru
	'Clusterberry' (f)	CJun
	colchica	CMCN IArd IDee
	cornuta	EPfP ESwi
	- B&SWJ 8756	WCru
§	- 'Dazzler' (f)	CJun
	- 'Ira S. Nelson' (f)	IArd
	- 'Mercury' (f)	CJun
	- 'O. Spring' (f/v)	CJun CMac
	crenata	CAco CDoC CMCN CTri EDir ERom GDam LCro LOPS LPar LRHS LWaG MGos NHol NWea SArc SCob SGsty SPer SSha SWeb WFar WHtc WLea
*	- 'Akagi'	WFar
	- 'Aureovariegata'	see *I. crenata* 'Variegata'
	- 'Blondie'PBR (f)	LPar SWeb
	- 'Carolina Upright' (m)	EBee LIns LPar SEWo SSta
	- 'Cherokee' (m)	LMaj
	- 'Convexa' (f) ♀H6	CJun EHeP EHyd EPfP GMcL LIns LPar LRHS LSto MAsh MRav NRHS NWea SEWo SGsty SJap SWeb
	- 'Convexed Gold' (f/v)	EPfP NLar NWad SPoG WFar
	- DARK GREEN ('Icoprins11'PBR)	CAco CDoC ELan EPfP LBuc LCro LOPS LRHS LSRN NWea SCob SGsty SVic SWeb WReH
	- 'Dwarf Pagoda' (f)	SAko
	- 'Eden's Paradise'PBR	SGsty
	- Fastigiata Group	CRos LRHS SCob SSha WFar
	- - 'Fastigiata' (f) ♀H6	CAco CBod CRos EHyd EPfP LRHS LSRN MAsh MGos NGrs NLar SMad SPer SPoG
	- - 'Sky Pencil' (f)	CMCN
	- 'Glorie Gem' (m)	SJap
*	- 'Glory Gem' (f)	CBcs LRHS LSRN NPlm SGsty
	- 'Golden Gem' (f/v) ♀H6	CBod CJun CMac CRos CSBt CTri EHeP ELan EPfP GArf GMcL LCro LRHS LSto MAsh MDon MGos MSwo NLar NRHS NWad NWea SJap SPer SPoG SSha SWvt WFar WHtc
	- 'Green Hedger' ♀H6	CLnd EPfP LIns LMaj MGos NLar SGsty
	- 'Green Lustre' (f)	LPar LSRN
	- 'Kinme' (f)	LPal LRHS NPlm SGsty SWeb
	- 'Luteovariegata'	see *I. crenata* 'Variegata'
	- LUXUS GLOBE ('Annys5'PBR) (m)	LCro NLar
	- 'Mariesii' (f)	CMac EBee MBlu
I	- 'Pyramidalis' (f)	CMac MRav NWea
	- 'Samurai'PBR **new**	NLar
§	- 'Shiro-fukurin' (f/v)	CJun CMCN CRos EHyd ELan EPfP LRHS NRHS SPoG
	- 'Snowflake'	see *I. crenata* 'Shiro-fukurin'
	- 'Stokes' (m)	CBod CDoC LPar MSwo NLar
§	- 'Variegata' (v)	CMCN CMac CRos EHyd EPfP LRHS NRHS
	cyrtura (f)	EBtc
	'Dazzler'	see *I. cornuta* 'Dazzler'
	dimorphophylla 'Somerset Pixie' (f)	CJun
	dipyrena	SAko
	'Doctor Kassab' (f)	CMCN
	'Elegance' (f)	MBlu WFar
	excelsa	CMCN
	fargesii subsp. ***fargesii*** var. ***fargesii***	WPGP
	aff. ***gagnepainiana*** FMWJ 13168	WCru
	'Good Taste' (f)	CJun NLar WFar
	'Hohman' (f)	CJun
	'Indian Chief' (f)	CJun
	× ***koehneana***	CCVT LPar MMuc SDix SEND WHtc
	- 'Chestnut Leaf' (f) ♀H5	CBcs CBod CCVT CDoC CJun CLnd CMCN ELan EPfP LMaj LRHS LSto MRav NLar NSti SMad WFar
	laevigata	CMCN
	latifolia	MMuc NLar
	'Leonardo'	EBee
	'Malcolm S. Whipple' (m) **new**	IDee
	'Mary Nell' (f)	CJun
	maximowicziana **new**	LIns
§	× ***meserveae*** 'Anny's Dwarf' (m)	LRHS NLar
	- BLUE ANGEL ('Conang') (f)	CBod CBrac CCCN CDoC CMac CSBt EBee EHeP ELan EPfP GMcL LIns LMaj LPar LRHS LSto MDon MRav NFav NLar NRHS NWea SPer SPoG SRms WAvo WFar WHtc
	- BLUE MAID ('Mesid') (f)	CCCN CDoC LIns LMaj LOPS LPar LRHS MGos NRHS SWeb
	- BLUE PRINCE ('Conablu') (m) ♀H7	CAco CBcs CBrac CCCN CDoC CMCN CMac EHeP ELan EPfP GMcL LBuc LIns LPar MBlu NBwr NHol NLar NWea SArc SCob WFar
	- BLUE PRINCESS ('Conapri') (f) ♀H7	CAco CBcs CBod CBrac CCVT CMCN CMac EDir ELan EPfP GBin GMcL LBuc LMaj LPar MBlu MGos MRav NBwr NLar NWea SCob SCoo SPer WFar

- CASTLE SPIRE ('Hachfee'PBR) (f) — CLnd LIns LPar LRHS SWeb WFar
- CASTLE WALL ('Hecken Star'PBR) (m) — CLnd LMaj LRHS NLar SEWo WFar
- GENTLE — see *I.* × *meserveae* 'Anny's Dwarf' (m)
- GOLDEN GIRL ('Mesgolg') (f) — SGsty
- 'Goliath' (f) — WFar
- 'Heckenpracht'PBR (m) — LPar WFar
- LITTLE RASCAL ('Mondo') (m) — CBod CKel CWnw EHed EPfP ESwi LRHS MGos NLar SGsty XSte
- 'Little Sensation' — LRHS MBlu NLar SPoG

myrtifolia — CDoC MAsh MRav NHol
'Nellie R. Stevens' (f) — CCVT CDoC CJun CKel CLnd EBee EHeP ELan EPfP ILea LIns LMaj LPar LSRN NLar SEWo SGsty SWeb WAvo WHlf WHtc WMat
opaca — CMCN
pedunculosa — MBlu NLar
perado subsp. ***azorica*** B&SWJ 12526 — WCru
- subsp. ***platyphylla*** — CMCN EBee MBlu SArc
pernyi — CJun CMCN IArd WHtc
- var. ***veitchii*** — see *I. bioritsensis*
rotunda — LEdu WPGP
rugosa — CMCN
'September Gem' (f) — CJun CMCN
serrata — CMac CMen
- 'Leucocarpa' (f) — CMac
sikkimensis — LEdu
spinigera — CBcs NWea
sugerokii var. ***longipedunculata*** B&SWJ 10856 — WCru
'Tanager' (f) — CJun
triflora var. ***kanehirae*** — LIns NLar
verticillata — CMCN NFav NWea SBrt WFar WLea
- (f) — CBcs EPfP MMrt NLar
- (m) — EPfP MMrt NLar
- f. ***chrysocarpa*** (f) — NLar
- 'Compacta' — see *I. verticillata* 'Nana'
- 'Maryland Beauty' (f) — CJun NLar
§ - 'Nana' (f) — CJun
- 'Red Sprite' — see *I. verticillata* 'Nana'
- 'Scarlett O'Hara' (f) — CJun
- 'Southern Gentleman' (m) — CJun MBlu
- 'Winter Gold' (f) — CJun MBlu
- 'Winter Red' (f) — CJun CMCN MBlu
vomitoria — CMCN EBtc
× ***wandoensis*** — CJun WFar
'Washington' (f) — IArd LIns WFar
'William Cowgill' (f) — CJun
yunnanensis — EBee IArd IDee

Iliamna see *Sphaeralcea*

Illicium (*Schisandraceae*)

anisatum — CBcs CCCN CExl EPfP LEdu SSta WPGP
- B&SWJ 8411 — WCru
floridanum — CBcs CCCN NLar SSta WJur
aff. ***griffithii*** WWJ 11911 — WCru
- WWJ 11971 — WCru
- WWJ 11974 — WCru
henryi — CExl EBee EPfP LRHS NLar WPGP
aff. ***henryi*** — CBcs IDee
jiadifengpi — NLar
lanceolatum — CExl
- KWJ 12245 — WCru
macranthum B&SWJ 11809 — WCru
majus WWJ 11919 — WCru
aff. ***majus*** — WCru
- WWJ 12017 — WCru
merrillianum HWJ 1015 — WCru
mexicanum — CExl
oligandrum — CBcs CExl EBee NLar WPGP
philippinense — CBcs
- CWJ 12466 — WCru
simonsii — CExl MBlu WCot WPGP
- BWJ 8024 — WCru
tashiroi CWJ 12468 — WCru
'Woodland Ruby' — EPfP WPGP

Ilysanthes see *Lindernia*

Impatiens ✿ (*Balsaminaceae*)

P1961 — EPPr ESwi
W&O 8071 **new** — GGro
from China, Darrell Probst collection — GGro WFar
from Sikkim **new** — GGro
apiculata — WFar
arguta — CExl EBee EWld GGro SBrt WBor WFar
- 'Alba' — CExl CSpe EPPr GGro MPie SIvy WFar
- big blue-flowered — EPPr ESwi SIvy
- dark violet-flowered **new** — GGro
- tall — GGro WFar
auricoma × ***bicaudata*** — CDTJ MPie WDib
balansae — CDTJ EBee GGro SBrt WPGP
bicaudata — SPlb
congolensis — CCCN
DIVINE LAVENDER ('Pas425593') (Divine Series) (NG) — MBros
ernstii — CExl
flanaganae — CDTJ ESwi EWld SBrt SIvy WFar WPGP
forrestii — GGro
gomphophylla — CDTJ WFar
hawkeri Divine Series — MBros MDon
hochstetteri — WFar
insignis — EBee EPPr GGro SBrt
keilii — WDib
kerriae — WFar
kilimanjari subsp. ***kilimanjari*** — CDTJ CSpe ECre MPie
kilimanjari × ***pseudoviola*** — CDTJ CSpe ECre MPie WDib WFar
- - , white-flowered **new** — CDTJ
- - , dark pink-flowered — WFar
- - , pale pink-flowered — ECre MPie WFar
langbianensis HWJ 1054 — WCru WFar
aff. ***langbianensis*** HWJ 1054 — GGro
macrophylla B&SWJ 10157 — WCru WFar
mengtszeana PB 02-519 — GGro WFar
- trailing — GGro SBrt WFar
namchabarwensis — CCCN
niamniamensis ♀H1b — CHll CWal EShb NCft WDib WFar
- 'Congo Cockatoo' — CDTJ NPer SRms
- 'Golden Cockatoo' (v) — CDTJ CHll EShb WFar
noli-tangere — WSFF
nyimana CHB 14 **new** — GGro
omeiana — CCCN CDTJ CPla CSpe EBee ELan EPPr ESwi EWld GGro LEdu MNrw MSCN NFav NLar SPtp WCru WFar WPGP
- DJHC 98492 — GGro WCru WFar WMal
- 'High Voltage' — GGro WFar
- 'Ice Storm' — CDTJ EBee EPPr ESwi EWld GEdr GGro IPot LEdu NBro NLar WCot WCru WFar WPGP
- long-leaved — WFar

- 'Pink Nerves'	CTsd EBee ESwi GGro LEdu MPie WFar
- 'Red Leaf'	EPPr ESwi
- 'Sango'	CPla CSpe EWld GGro LEdu WFar WMal
- 'Silver Pink'	GGro
- variegated (v)	GEdr
oxyanthera	GGro WFar
- 'Milo'	GGro SBrt WFar
parasitica	WDib
pianmaensis CHB 14 new	GGro
§ ***prainii*** new	WPGP
- CHBMV 15 new	GGro
pritzelii	CDTJ
- 'Sichuan Gold'	CDTJ EPPr ESwi LEdu WFar
puberula	GGro WFar
- HWJK 2063	EBee ESwi EWld SBrt WCru
qingchengshanica 'Emei Dawn'	CExl EBee EPPr ESwi WCru WFar
repens ♀H1b	WDib
rhombifolia	GGro
rothii	EBee ESwi WCot WPGP
scabrida	CSpe
§ 'Secret Love'	CCCN CDoC
sodenii ♀H1c	CDTJ EShb ESwi SIvy WDib WFar
- 'Flash'	WFar
- 'Ravishing Rhi' new	WFar
- white-flowered	WFar
- - red eye	WFar
stenantha	EBee ESwi EWld GEdr GGro SBrt WFar WPGP
sultani	see *I. walleriana*
(SunPatiens Series)	MPri
SUNPATIENS COMPACT BLUSH PINK ('Sakimp013'^{PBR}) (NG) ♀H1b new	
- SUNPATIENS COMPACT ELECTRIC ORANGE ('Sakimp025'^{PBR}) (NG) ♀H1b	MBros MPri
- SUNPATIENS VIGOROUS BLUSH PINK ('Sakimp023'^{PBR}) (NG)	MBros
- SUNPATIENS VIGOROUS CLEAR WHITE ('Sakimp036'^{PBR}) (NG) new	MBros
- SUNPATIENS VIGOROUS LAVENDER ('Sakimp006') (NG)	MBros
- SUNPATIENS VIGOROUS MAGENTA ('Misato Fg3') (NG)	MBros
- SUNPATIENS VIGOROUS ORANGE ('Misato Fg2') (NG)	MBros
- SUNPATIENS VIGOROUS WHITE IMPROVED ('Sakimp010'^{PBR}) (NG)	MBros
taronensis	see *I. prainii*
tinctoria	CAbb CAby CDTJ CExl CHll CSpe EBee EPPr ESwi EWld IPot SBrt
- from Cherangani, Kenya	EPPr
tuberosa	WDib
uniflora	GGro SBrt
VELVETEA	see *I.* 'Secret Love'
§ ***walleriana***	MBros
- BEACON SELECT MIXTURE (Beacon Series) new	MBros MDon
- DeZire Series	MBros MPri
- - 'DeZire Red'	MBros
- - 'DeZire White'	MBros
- 'Salsa Red' (Fiesta Series) (d)	SCob

Imperata (*Poaceae*)

cylindrica	CMen CWal XLum
- 'Red Baron'	see *I. cylindrica* 'Rubra'
§ - 'Rubra'	Widely available

Incarvillea (*Bignoniaceae*)

arguta	XLum
- W&O 7122	GGro
brevipes	see *I. mairei*
'Brighton Pride'	SBrt
compacta	GKev
- var. ***qinghaiensis***	GKev
delavayi	CAby CBcs CSBt CTsd ECha EDAr EGrl ELan EPfP GArf GKev LAma LBar LRHS MGos MSCN NRHS SDeJ SGBe SRms SVen SWvt WAvo WFar XLum
- 'Alba'	see *I. delavayi* 'Snowtop'
- 'Bees' Pink'	EPfP GEdr LBar LPla
§ - 'Snowtop'	CAby CBcs CTsd EBee EDAr ELan EPfP GBin GKev LAma LBar SDeJ SWvt WBor WCot WFar
cf. ***delavayi***	CEme GMcL
diffusa	GKev
forrestii	GKev
grandiflora	EBee GKev
lutea	GKev
§ ***mairei***	CRos EBee EHyd GKev LBar LRHS NRHS SRms
- var. ***mairei*** f. ***multifoliata***	see *I. zhongdianensis*
olgae	EAJP EBee ELan WPGP
'Snowdrop'	EMor
§ ***zhongdianensis***	EBee EPri GArf GEdr GKev
- BWJ 7692	WCru
- BWJ 7978	WCru
- W&O 7127	GGro

Indigofera (*Fabaceae*)

NJM 9166	WPGP
§ ***amblyantha***	CBcs CCCN EHed EHyd EPfP GKev LRHS LShi MAsh MBlu MGil NLar NRHS NSti SPlb WCFE WHlf WSHC WSpi
aff. ***amblyantha***	MMrt
balfouriana Craib BWJ 7851	WCru
bungeana	CCCN MGil MHer SRms
cassioides	WCru
§ 'Claret Cascade' ♀H5	EPfP LRHS WSHC
dielsiana	CCCN EHyd ELan EPfP WSHC WSpi
'Dosua'	SEND
fortunei new	WSHC
- 'Alba' new	WSHC
gerardiana	see *I. heterantha*
hancockii	EPfP SChF
hebepetala	EPfP SBrt WCFE WSHC
§ ***heterantha*** ♀H5	Widely available
heterophylla	CCCN
himachalensis	EBee NLar WSHC
- H&M 1818	WPGP
himalayensis	EBee MGil WCFE
- 'Silk Road'	CCCN CKel CRos EBee EHed EHyd ELan EPfP GKev LCro LRHS MBlu MGil MGos MSCN NLar NRHS SPoG WSpi
§ ***howellii*** 'Reginald Cory' ♀H5	CExl EBee EPfP ESwi LRHS MBlu WCru WPGP WSHC
§ ***howellii × pendula*** new	WPGP

kirilowii	CCCN EHyd ELan EPPr EPfP LRHS MBlu NLar WPGP WSHC WSpi
- var. ***alba***	CKel EBee EPfP LRHS WPGP
§ ***pendula***	CCCN CExl CMac CSde CWGN EBee EHyd ELan EPfP ESwi LRHS MGil SBrt SPoG WCFE WKif WPGP WSHC WSpi
- B&SWJ 7741	WCru
potaninii misapplied	see *I. howellii* 'Reginald Cory', *I. amblyantha*, *I.* 'Claret Cascade', *I. pendula*
potaninii ambig.	CBcs CExl CMac WHer
aff. ***pseudotinctoria***	CCCN
subverticillata misapplied	see *I. howellii* 'Reginald Cory'
szechuensis	CKel CSde LPla LRHS MGil NLar WSHC
tinctoria	CCCN MAvo

Indocalamus (*Poaceae*)

latifolius	MWht
solidus	see *Bonia solida*
§ ***tessellatus*** ♀H5	CBcs CBod ELon LPal MWht NGdn NPlm SMad
- f. ***hamadae***	MWht

Inula (*Asteraceae*)

acaulis	WCot
conyzae	WSFF
dysenterica	see *Pulicaria dysenterica*
ensifolia	CBcs EHyd ELan EPfP MSCN NLar SMrm WCav WHlf WHoo XLum
- 'Gold Star'	EBee MHol MRav NBid NBir WAvo WCot WFar
glandulosa	see *I. orientalis*
helenium	CCBP CHab CHby EBou ENfk GGro GPoy ILea LCro LEdu LOPS MHer MHoo MNHC NBid NBir NGrd NLar SRms WCot WHer WJek WShi
hirta	XLum
hookeri	CChe ECha ELan EShb GBin GMaP ILea LEdu LLWG LShi MBel MHer MHol MMuc MSpe NBid NChi NDov NLar NPer NSti SAdn SBls SDix SEND WBrk WCAu WCav WWtn
- GWJ 9033	WCru
- 'Mude'	EBee
macrocephala misapplied	see *I. royleana*
magnifica	Widely available
- 'Sonnenstrahl' ♀H6	EPPr LEdu NLar SPhx
oculus-christi	EWes LShi WCot
§ ***orientalis***	CRos EBee EHyd GJos ILea LRHS MHol NGBl NLar NRHS SPad SRms XLum
- B&SWJ 15379	WCru
- 'Grandiflora'	EShb LShi
racemosa	EHyd EPPr EWes GBin GGro GJos GQue LRHS MACG MNrw NRHS SPlb SRms WBor
- 'Sonnenspeer'	CBod NBid NLar
§ ***royleana***	MNrw MRav
salicina	EBee

Inulanthera (*Asteraceae*)

calva	WCot WFar

Iochroma (*Solanaceae*)

australe	see *Eriolarynx australis*
cyaneum	CCCN CDow CHll EAri ECre SPlb SVen
- purple-flowered	CCCN NGKo
§ - 'Trebah'	NGKo
fuchsioides	CHll EAri NGKo
gesnerioides 'Coccineum'	CCCN CHll EShb
grandiflorum	see *Trozelia grandiflora*
violaceum hort.	see *I. cyaneum* 'Trebah'
warscewiczii	see *Trozelia grandiflora*

Ipheion (*Alliaceae*)

'Alberto Castillo' ♀H5	Widely available
'Alice'	WCot WMal
'Diana'	WCot
hirtellum	see *Nothoscordum hirtellum*
'Jessie'	CAby CBor CBro CTtf ECha EHyd EPot ERCP EWes GKev LAma LHWs LRHS MNrw NHpl NRHS SDeJ WBrk WMal WTor WTyc
'Judy'	WCot
'Rolf Fiedler' ♀H4	CBro CTri EBee EHyd ELan EPfP EPot ERCP ETay EWes GKev LAma LRHS NRHS NRog NRya SDeJ SHar SRms WFar WHil
sellowianum	CTtf
sessile	EBee
'Tessa'PBR	CBor EBee ECha ERCP EWes GKev LHWs NHpl WTor
§ ***uniflorum***	CBor CBro CTri ECha EGrI GKev ITim LAma NRog SEND SRms WBrk WCav WCot WShi WTyc XLum
- f. ***album***	CBro EBee ECha EHyd EWes GArf LRHS NRHS NRog WBrk WCot WHil WMal
- 'Charlotte Bishop'	CAvo CBor CBro CRos EBee ECha EGrI EHyd ELon ERCP EWes GKev LAma LHWs LRHS MNrw MPie NBir NHpl NRHS NRog NRya SDeJ SRms WBrk WCav WCot WHoo WMal WTyc
- 'Froyle Mill' ♀H5	CAvo CBro EHyd ELon EPot ERCP EWes GKev LRHS NHpl NRHS NRog SDeJ SRms WCot WHoo
- 'Hoo House'	WHoo WMal
- 'Miss Hannah'	WMal
- subsp. ***tandiliense***	EPPr
- 'Wisley Blue' ♀H5	CBod CBro CRos CTri CWCL ECha EHyd ELan ELon EPot ERCP GKev LAma LRHS MBros MRav NRHS NRog NRya SDeJ SPoG SRms WCot
- 'Wisley Star'	GKev

Ipomoea (*Convolvulaceae*)

acuminata	see *I. indica*
alba	CCCN CSpe EShb
batatas	CCCN
- 'Beauregard'	SVic
- 'Bonita'PBR	LRHS
- (Bright Ideas Series) BRIGHT IDEAS BLACK ('Floipobib'PBR)	EShb
- - BRIGHT IDEAS LIME ('Floipobil'PBR)	EShb
- 'O'Henry'	SVic
- (Sweet Caroline Series) 'Sweet Caroline Light Green'PBR	MPri
- - SWEET CAROLINE SWEETHEART JET BLACK ('Ncornsp-021shjb') **new**	MPri
cairica	WCot
carnea	CCCN
coccinea var. ***hederifolia***	see *I. hederifolia*
§ ***hederifolia***	CCCN

× ***imperialis*** 'Sunrise Serenade'	CCCN
§ ***indica*** ♀H1c	CCCN CRHN ECre EShb SPer
learii	see *I. indica*
leptophylla	EDAr
lindheimeri	SMad
§ ***lobata*** ♀H1c	CSpe LCro LOPS
mauritiana	CCCN
'Milky Way'	CCCN
muellerii	CCCN
× ***multifida***	CSpe
purpurea 'Kniola's Black Night'	CSpe
- 'Star of Yelta'	LCro
quamoclit	CSpe
tricolor 'Heavenly Blue' ♀H1c	LCro LOPS
versicolor	see *I. lobata*

Iresine (*Amaranthaceae*)

herbstii ♀H1c	EShb
- 'Aureoreticulata'	EShb

Iris ✿ (*Iridaceae*)

AGSJ	EPPr
KR 3739	GEdr
'Abbey Chant' (IB)	XSen
'Ablaze' (MDB)	EDAr
'About Town' (TB)	WCAu
'Absolute Treasure' (TB)	WCAu
'Acacia Rhumba' (La)	LLWG
'Ace' (MTB)	EWoo
'Acropole' (TB) **new**	EWoo
'Action Front' (TB)	CBod CEnd CKel CRos ECtt EHyd ESgI EShb EWoo GBin LRHS MGos NRHS SDeJ WCAu WGwG
'Action Packed' (TB) **new**	WCAu
'Actress' (TB)	CRos ECtt EHyd EPfP LRHS LSRN MGos NRHS WGwG
acutiloba × ***afghanica***	GKev
'Adobe Rose' (TB)	EWoo XSen
'Adventuress' (TB)	XSen
'Afternoon Delight' (TB)	ESgI
'Afternoon in Rio' (TB)	WCAu
'Again and Again' (TB)	EWoo
'Agatha Christie' (IB)	CKel WCAu
'Aggressively Forward' (TB)	WCAu
'Agnes James' (CH)	CBro MAvo
'Ahwahnee Princess' (SDB)	ELon
'Aichi-no-kagayaki' (SpH)	WCot XLum
'Al Segno' (TB)	GKev
'Alabaster Unicorn' (TB)	ESgI
albicans ♀H5	CBro EPot GKev LEdu SBrt
- 'Blue Pygmy'	LSto MPie
'Alcazar' (TB)	EWoo GDam GMcL
'Alice Harding' (TB)	ESgI
'Alida' (Reticulata)	EHyd EPot ERCP EShb ETay EWoo GKev LAma LCro LOPS LRHS MBNS NBir NRHS NRog SDeJ WBrk
'Alien Mist' (TB)	EIri
'Alizes' (TB) ♀H7	CKel ESgI LRHS WViv XSen
'All Night Long' (TB)	EWoo
'Ally Oops' (SpH)	CDor LLWG WCAu
'Always Lovely' (BB) **new**	WCAu
'Amadora' (TB)	EIri
'Amanda Jane' (AB)	EWld
'Amas' (TB)	EWoo
'Amazing Grace' (TB)	EWoo
'Ambassadeur' (TB)	EWoo
'Amber Beauty' (Dut)	NRog
'Amber Queen' (SDB)	CKel ECtt NBir SCob SDeJ WGwG
'Ambroisie' (TB) ♀H7	ESgI
'Amethyst Flame' (TB)	SRms
'Amherst Blue' (IB)	EIri
'Amherst Caper' (SDB)	EIri
'Amherst Glacier' (IB)	WCAu
'Amigo' (TB)	EWoo
'Amoena' (TB) **new**	EWoo
'Among Friends' (MTB) ♀H7 **new**	EWoo
'Amphora' (SDB)	CBro
'Ancient Echoes' (TB)	ESgI
'Andalou' (TB) ♀H7	CWCL ESgI WViv XSen
anglica	see *I. latifolia*
'Ann Chowning' (La)	CPud CWat EBee EPri LAma LCro LPfP MWts SDir WHil WPnP
'Annabel Jane' (TB)	ELon WCAu
'Anne Elizabeth' (SDB)	CBro
'Anne Troflar' **new**	WCAu
'Annemarie Troeger' (Sib) ♀H7	ELon
'Annick' (Sib)	EBlo MMrt XSen
'Antarctique' (IB)	ESgI
'Antiope' (Rc)	GKev
'Aphrodisiac' (TB)	XSen
aphylla	GBin SBrt WAbe
- 'Aslet's Purple'	GBin
'Apollo' (Dut)	CAvo LAma NRog
'Appointer' (SpH)	EWoo NChi
'Apricorange' (TB)	SRms WCot
'Apricot Blaze' (TB)	ESgI
'Apricot Drops' (MTB) ♀H7	ESgI EWoo WCAu
'Apricot Frosty' (BB)	XSen
'Apricot Silk' (IB)	CKel NQui WCot
'Apricot Topping' (BB)	SIri
'Aquamarine' (IB)	MHol
'Arabian Bayou' (La) **new**	LPfP
'Archie Owen' (Spuria)	WCAu
'Arctic Night' (IB)	WCAu
'Arctic Sunrise' (TB)	CKel ESgI
arenaria	see *I. humilis*
'Argus Pheasant' (TB)	ESgI
'Around Midnight' (TB)	CBor
'Arpège' (TB)	CKel LCro XSen
'Arrows' (La)	LLWG
'Art Deco' (TB)	SIri XSen
'As de Coeur' (TB)	XSen
'Ascension Crown' (TB)	ESgI
'Ask Alma' (IB)	EWoo SIri XSen
'Astro Flash' (TB)	ESgI
'Attention Please' (TB)	SBea
attica	CBro GEdr GKev
- blue-flowered	GKev WAbe
- lemon-flowered	EPPr GKev SBrt WAbe WThu
- violet-flowered	GKev
§ ***aucheri*** ♀H4	EPot EWoo GKev LAma NRog XSen
- 'Leylek Ice'	NRog
'Audition' (La)	LLWG
'Aunt Josephine' (TB)	ESgI
'Aunty Ruth' (CH)	MAvo
'Aurélie' (TB)	WViv
'Austrian Sky' (SDB)	CFis CKel CMac ECtt ELon EPfP SDeJ WCot
'Autumn Apricot' (TB)	EWoo
'Autumn Circle'	WCAu
'Autumn Echo' (TB)	ESgI LRHS XSen
'Autumn Encore' (TB)	CKel GMcL SRms WHlf
'Autumn Princess' (Dut)	ERCP GKev LAma SDeJ
'Autumn Riesling' (TB)	WCAu
'Autumn Tryst' (TB)	ESgI WCAu
'Avalon Sunset' (TB)	EIri
'Avanelle' (IB)	GBin
'Awesome Blossom' (TB)	ESgI
'Az Ap' (IB)	ELon WCAu
'Aziyadé' (TB) **new**	EWoo
babadagica	GEdr WAbe

'Babbling Brook' (TB)	CKel ESgI EWoo XSen
'Baby Bengal' (BB)	XSen
'Baby Blessed' (SDB)	CBro WCAu
'Baby Sister' (Sib)	EBlo ELon EWoo GBin GMcL LSRN NBro WFar
'Badlands' (TB)	WCAu
'Baie Rose' (IB)	SIri
'Bal Masqué' (TB)	ESgI WViv XSen
'Ballerina Pink' (BB)	WCAu
'Ballet Lesson' (SDB)	ESgI
'Ballyhoo' (TB)	WCAu XSen
'Baltic Star' (TB)	EWoo WCAu
'Banbury Beauty' (CH) ♀H4	NLar
'Banbury Gem' (CH)	NLar
'Banbury Melody' (CH)	MAvo
'Banbury Ruffles' (SDB)	ESgI LRHS NLar WCAu
'Bangles' (MTB) ♀H7	WCAu
'Banish Misfortune' (Sib)	EPri LLWG WGob
'Bar de Nuit' (TB)	ESgI EWoo
'Barbara May' (TB)	WCAu
'Barbara My Love' (TB)	WCAu
barbatula	SBrt
– BWJ 7663	ESwi WCru
'Barcoo' (La)	LLWG
'Batik' (BB)	WCot XSen
'Bayberry Candle' (TB)	CKel
'Be My Baby' (BB)	WCAu
'Beach Girl' (TB)	EWoo
'Beauty Becomes Her' (TB)	WCAu
'Beauty Mark' (SDB)	SIri
'Bedtime Story' (IB)	LBar XSen
'Bee Wings' (MDB)	EDAr ESgI
'Before the Storm' (TB)	CKel CTsd ELan ELon ESgI LRHS WCAu WLov XSen
'Being Busy' (SDB)	ESgI
'Bel Avenir' (TB)	ESgI
'Bel Azur' (IB)	ESgI LRHS
'Beleni' **new**	WCAu
'Belgian Princess' (TB)	SIri WCAu
'Belise' (Spuria)	WCot
'Belle Aude' (TB) **new**	ESgI
'Belle de Nuit' (TB)	EWoo WViv
'Benbow' (TB)	WMil
'Benton Ankaret' (TB)	EWoo
'Benton Apollo' (TB)	CEnd ECha ETod EWoo
'Benton Argent' (TB)	CMil ECha ESgI ETod EWoo
'Benton Arundel' (TB)	CBWd CEnd ECha EGrI ESgI ETod EWoo NCth SIri
'Benton Bluejohn' (TB)	ECha
'Benton Caramel' (TB)	CBWd CFis CMil ECha ECtt EPfP ETod EWoo LRHS MBriF NCth NRHS SIri
'Benton Cordelia' (TB)	ECha ECtt EPfP EWoo MBriF
'Benton Daphne' (TB)	ESgI EWoo
'Benton Dierdre' (TB)	CCBP CMil ECha ECtt ELan ELon EPfP ESgI ETod EWoo LRHS MBriF NRHS SRms WGwG
'Benton Duff' (TB)	CBWd CFis ECha ESgI ETod EWoo NRHS
'Benton Evora' (TB)	ECha ESgI
'Benton Farewell' (TB)	CMil ECha EPfP ETod
'Benton Judith' (TB)	ECha
'Benton Lorna' (TB)	CBWd ECha ECtt ELan EPfP ETod EWoo MBriF MHol NCth NRHS WGwG
'Benton Menace' (TB)	CMil ECha EPfP ETod EWoo LBar
'Benton Nigel' (TB)	CBWd CMil EBee ECha ECtt ELan EPfP ETod EWoo LRHS MBriF SBea WGwG
'Benton Old Madrid'	CBWd CMil ECha EPfP ETod EWoo
'Benton Olive' (TB)	ECha EWoo NRHS
'Benton Opal' (TB)	CBWd ECha ESgI ETod EWoo WCAu WGwG
'Benton Pearl' (TB)	CEnd CMil ECha ESgI ETod EWoo WCAu
'Benton Primrose' (TB)	CEnd CMil ESgI ETod EWoo NCth NRHS SBea WGwG
'Benton Sheila' (TB)	CCBP CKel ECha ELan ELon EWoo WCot
'Benton Susan' (TB)	CEnd CMil ECha ECtt ESgI ETod EWoo MBriF NRHS WGwG
'Beotie' (TB)	EWoo
'Berkeley Gold' (TB)	CRos CSBt ECtt ELan EWes LRHS NRHS SCob SDeJ SPer WGwG
'Berlin Bluebird' (Sib)	SMHy
'Berlin Purple Wine' (Sib)	EPri ESgI WGob
'Berlin Ruffles' (Sib) ♀H7	EWes
'Berlin Sky' (Sib)	EWes
'Berlin Tiger' (SpH) ♀H7	CBen EPPr EWTr EWoo LLWG LPfP MSCN NLar SDix WCAu
'Berlin Violetta' (SpH)	GBin
'Best Bet' (TB)	ESgI WCAu
'Bet the Farm' (TB) **new**	WCAu
'Bethany Claire' (TB)	ESgI WCAu
'Better Believe It' (La)	LLWG
'Better Together' (TB)	WCAu
'Betty Cooper' (Spuria)	WCAu
'Betty Simon' (TB)	EWoo XSen
'Beverly Sills' (TB)	CKel CRos ECtt EHyd EPfP EWoo LCro LRHS MNHC MRav NCth NRHS SBls SDeJ WCAu WLov XSen
'Bewilderbeast' (TB)	XSen
'Bianco' (TB)	EWoo WCAu WHil
'Bibury' (SDB) ♀H7	WCAu
bicapitata	WAbe
'Bickley Cape' (Sib)	GBin
'Big Blue' (Sib)	WFar
'Big Heart' (Sib)	EIri
biglumis	see *I. lactea*
biliottii	CBro GAbr
'Bishop's Robe' (TB)	CKel EWoo LCro LOPS LRHS
'Black as Night' (TB)	XSen
'Black Aura'	NWad
'Black Cherry Delight' (SDB)	ESgI
'Black Dragon' (TB)	CKel EGrI GMcL WSpi XSen
'Black Flag' (TB)	XSen
'Black Gamecock' (La)	CAby CPud CWCL CWat ECtt EGrI EPfP EShb GKev LAma LCro LLWG LOPS LPfP MHer MNrw MSCN MWts NLar SBls WCAu WFar WMAq WPnP
'Black Hope' (TB)	EWoo
'Black is Back' (TB)	WCAu
'Black Joker' (Sib)	CAby ELon EPfP LCro LLWG MHol NCth WGob WTor
'Black Knight' (TB)	EGrI EHeP LRHS MRav NQui SCob SEdd WKif WSpi
'Black Magic' (IB)	EWoo
'Black Night' (IB)	GKev
'Black Suited' (TB)	SIri
'Black Swan' (TB)	CBor CEme CKel CMac ECha ECtt EHyd ELan EPfP ESgI EShb ETod EWoo LCro LOPS LRHS LSRN NQui NRHS SBea SCob SOrN SPeP SPer SPoG SRms WCot WTor XSen
'Black Taffeta' (TB)	WSpi
'Black Tie Affair' (TB)	CBod CEnd CKel ECtt EHyd ELan EPfP ESgI EWoo LBar LRHS MAsh NCth NRHS XSen
'Black Watch' (IB)	CKel LCro LOPS LRHS
'Blackbeard' (BB) ♀H7	WCAu
'Blackbeard's Ghost' (AB)	WCAu
'Blackberry Tease' (TB)	WCAu
'Blackberry Towers' (TB)	ESgI
'Blackcurrant' (IB)	WCAu
'Blackout' (TB)	ESgI

'Blatant' (TB) ESgI XSen
'Blaue Milchstrasse' (Sib) ESgI MMrt
'Blazing Light' (TB) XSen
'Blenheim Royal' (TB) ESgI XSen
bloudowii WAbe
'Blue Admiral' (TB) GBin
'Blue Bird' (Sib) ECtt MBros SCoo SPoG WFar WGob
'Blue Boy' (IB) EWoo
'Blue Burgee' (Sib) ECha
I 'Blue Butterfly' (Sib) EPfP NGdn
'Blue Denim' (SDB) ECtt ELon EPfP GMaP MHol MRav NBir NLar SCob WCot
'Blue Eyed Blond' (IB) CKel MBriF SBea
'Blue Eyed Brunette' (TB) ESgI
'Blue Gown' (TB) EWoo
'Blue Hendred' (SDB) NBir
'Blue Hill' (Reticulata) ERCP GKev LAma NRog
'Blue Ice' (Reticulata) GKev LAma
'Blue King' (Dut) SCob
'Blue King' (Sib) CBod CDor CKel ELan EPfP GMaP MNHC MRav NBro NGdn SPer
'Blue Magic' (Dut) ♀H5 CAvo
'Blue Mere' (Sib) MCot MHol
'Blue Moon' (Sib) ELon WFar
'Blue Mountain Mist' (La) LLWG
'Blue my Mind' (TB) WCAu
'Blue Nile' (TB) **new** EWoo
'Blue Note' (Reticulata) EHyd EPfP EPot ERCP EWoo GKev LAma LBar LRHS NRHS NRog WHoo
'Blue Note Blues' (TB) WCAu
'Blue Pennant' (Sib) NLar
'Blue Pigmy' (SDB) CBod CWat ECtt EGrI EPfP MRav MTin NLar SDeJ WGwG
'Blue Reverie' (Sib) ELon
'Blue Rhythm' (TB) CEnd EHyd ELan ELon EPfP EWoo GBin GMaP GMcL LRHS MRav NRHS SCoo SDeJ SPer WCAu
'Blue Sapphire' (Dut) MHol
'Blue Sapphire' (TB) CKel ESgI
'Blue Shimmer' (TB) CBod CMac EBee ECha ECtt ELan EPfP ESgI EShb ETod EWoo LRHS LSRN NCth NRHS SDeJ SPer SRms WCAu WGwG
'Blue Splash' (IB) WCAu
'Blue Staccato' (TB) ESgI WCAu XSen
'Blue Suede Shoes' (TB) ESgI EWoo LSRN XSen
'Blue Trill' (TB) WCAu
'Blueberry Fair' (Sib) CDor
'Bluebird Wine' (TB) CKel
'Blushing Pink' (TB) CKel
'Bold Encounter' (TB) WCAu
'Bold Pretender' (La) CBod ECtt EGrI ELon EPri GKev MBros MHol NLar WHil
'Bold Print' (IB) CBod CKel CRos ECtt EHyd ELon GMaP LRHS LSRN MGos MHer NCth NRHS SMad SOrN SPeP SPoG WCAu WLov
'Bonanza' (TB) **new** EWoo
'Boo' (SDB) SIri WCAu XSen
'Border Town' (Spuria) WCAu
'Bottled Sunshine' (IB) LRHS
'Bound for Glory' (La) LLWG
'Bournemouth Beauty' (Sib) ♀H7 CDor
'Bouzy Bouzy' (TB) ESgI XSen
bracteata EBee
'Braithwaite' (TB) CKel CRos CWGN EHyd ELan EPfP ESgI EShb EWoo LRHS NRHS SBea SCob SDeJ SHar SMrm SPer SRms WCAu WGwG WTor
'Brannigan' (SDB) NBir NSti
'Brasilia' (TB) NBir
'Brassie' (SDB) CBro EHeP XSen
'Breakers' (TB) ♀H7 ESgI WCAu
'Brenchley' (IB) SIri
§ 'Bride' (DB) NLar
'Bride's Halo' (TB) XSen
'Bridesmaid' (TB) **new** EWoo
'Bright Button' (SDB) ESgI
'Bright Vision' (SDB) ESgI
'Bright White' (MDB) CBro
'Bright Yellow' (DB) MRav
'Brighteyes' (IB) SRms
'Brindisi' (TB) XSen
'Bring it On' (MTB) **new** EWoo
'Brise de Mer' (TB) XSen
'Brising' **new** EWoo
'Bristo Magic' (TB) XSen
'Bristol Gem' (TB) XSen
'Broadleigh Angela' (CH) CBro
'Broadleigh Carolyn' (CH) ♀H5 CElw WSHC
'Broadleigh Lavinia' (CH) CBro CPla
'Broadleigh Nancy' (CH) CBro
'Broadleigh Peacock' (CH) CElw NLar WMal WSHC
'Broadleigh Penny' (CH) MAvo NLar
'Broadleigh Rose' (CH) CBro CElw CTtf EGrI EPri MAvo MBrN MCot WSHC
'Broadway Baby' (IB) ESgI
'Broadway Star' (TB) CKel
'Bronzaire' (IB) EIri WCAu
'Bronze Beauty' (Dut) NRog
'Bronze Beauty' (TB) SDeJ
'Bronze Beauty' van Tubergen (*boogiana* hybrid) NBir SDeJ
'Brother Carl' (TB) XSen
'Bruno' (TB) EWoo LSRN NLar WMil
'Brussels' (TB) ESgI
bucharica misapplied see *I. orchioides* Carrière
bucharica ambig. CAvo ECha EWoo GKev MNrw NHpl SDeJ XSen
§ ***bucharica*** Foster ♀H5 CBro EPot EWoo LAma
– 'Princess' (J) NRog
* – 'Top Gold' (J) GKev
'Buckwheat' (TB) EWoo SIri
'Buisson de Roses' (TB) XSen
bulleyana CBro GKev SRms
– BWJ 7912 WCru
– black-flowered GKev NWad
– – SDR 1792 EBee
'Bumblebee Deelite' (MTB) ♀H7 CBor CKel WCAu WMal
'Bundle of Joy' (Sib) ECtt WGob
'Bundle of Love' (BB) WCAu
'Burgermeister' (TB) XSen
'Burgundy Party' (TB) XSen
'Burka' (TB) ESgI
'Burmese Dawn' (TB) CKel
'Burnt Toffee' (TB) ESgI EWoo SIri XSen
'Buto' (TB) EWoo
'Butter and Cream' (Sib) CToG
'Butter and Sugar' (Sib) Widely available
'Buttermere' (TB) SRms
'Butterpat' (IB) ESgI
'Butterscotch Kiss' (TB) CMac EHyd ELon LDai LRHS MGos MRav NBir NLar NRHS SDeJ SPeP SPer WLov
'Buzzword' (SDB) WCAu
'By Jeeves' (TB) **new** WCAu
'Bye Bye Blues' (TB) ESgI XSen
'Cabaret Royale' (TB) ESgI XSen
'Cable Car' (TB) CKel ESgI EWoo
'Caesar' (Sib) SRms
'Caesar's Brother' (Sib) CKel CRos EHyd ELan EWoo GBee GKev LCro LOPS LRHS LSto MGos

	Name	Suppliers
		NHol NLar NRHS SPer WBrk WCAu WFar
	'Cajun Rhythm' (TB)	CKel XSen
	'Calaeno' (Reticulata)	GKev
	'Caldron' (TB)	CKel
	'Caliente' (TB)	EHeP MRav WCAu XSen
	'California Style' (IB)	CKel XSen
§	Californian hybrids	CElw CMac NBir NSla WCot
	'Calm Stream' (TB)	WCAu
	'Calypso Beat' (TB)	SIri
	'Calypso Mood' (TB)	XSen
	'Cambridge' (Sib) 🏆H7	CAvo EHyd EIri EPfP LRHS NRHS WFar WGob
	'Cameliard' (TB)	EWoo
	'Camelot' (TB)	WMil
	'Camelot Rose' (TB)	XSen
	'Cameo Blush' (BB)	XSen
	'Cameo Wine' (TB)	ESgI XSen
	'Cameroun' (TB)	ESgI EWoo
	'Campbellii'	see *I. lutescens* 'Campbellii'
	canadensis	see *I. hookeri*
	'Canadian Streaker' (TB/v)	EWoo
	'Canary Bird' (TB)	ESgI
	'Candy Rock' (IB)	EWoo WCAu
	'Cannington Ochre' (SDB)	CBro
	'Cantab' (Reticulata)	EHyd LRHS NBir NRHS SDeJ
	'Canterbury' (TB)	LRHS
	'Cape Cod Boys' (Sib)	CDor WGob
	'Caprice' (TB)	EWoo
	'Captain Indigo' (IB)	ESgI WCAu
	'Captive Sun' (SDB)	CKel ECtt ELan EPfP MAsh SIri WGwG WTor
	'Caramel' (TB)	XSen
	'Cardinal' (TB)	WMil
	'Care to Dance' (TB)	WCAu
	'Careless Sally' (Sib)	WCAu
	'Carfax' (TB)	WMil
	'Caribbean Dream' (TB)	NLar XSen
	'Carmen' (Dut) **new**	ETay
	'Carnaby' (TB)	CEnd CKel EHyd ELon EPfP ESgI EShb LBar LRHS MRav NRHS SDeJ WGwG XSen
	'Carnival Time' (TB)	CBod CKel CMac CRos CWGN ECtt EHyd EPfP ESgI ETod LDai LRHS MBriF MHer NRHS WHoo WLov WTor XSen
	'Carolina' (Reticulata)	EHyd GKev LAma NRHS
	'Carolina Gold' (TB)	CKel XSen
*	'Caronte' (IB)	ESgI
	'Carriage Trade' (TB)	LRHS
	'Cartouche' (BB)	SIri
	'Casbah' (TB)	XSen
	'Cascade Springs' (TB)	XSen
	'Cascade Sprite' (SDB)	SRms
	'Casque d'Or' (TB)	LCro LOPS
	'Catalyst' (TB)	XSen
	'Caterina' (TB) 🏆H7 **new**	EWoo
	'Cat's Eye' (SDB)	SIri
	'Catwalk Idol' (La)	LLWG
	caucasica	CMac
	'Cayenne Capers' (TB)	ESgI
*	'Cedric Morris'	EWes
	'Cee Cee' (TB)	XSen
	'Cee Jay' (IB) 🏆H7	EWoo
	'Celebration Song' (TB)	ESgI WCAu XSen
	'Celestial Glory' (TB)	XSen
	'Center Line' (TB) **new**	WCAu
	'Cerdagne' (TB)	XSen
	chamaeiris	see *I. lutescens* subsp. *lutescens*
	'Champagne Elegance' (TB)	CKel EIri NBir XSen
	'Champagne Encore' (IB)	ELon EWoo
	'Champagne Frost' (TB)	XSen
	'Champagne Waltz' (TB)	XSen

	Name	Suppliers
	'Chance Beauty' (SpH) 🏆H7	CBen GBin
	'Change of Pace' (TB)	ESgI WCAu XSen
	'Chanted' (SDB)	WCAu XSen
	'Chantilly' (TB)	CBod EWoo LBar LRHS MRav NBir NGdn NLar NRHS SPer
	'Chapeau' (TB)	ESgI WCAu
	'Charlotte's Tutu' (La)	LLWG
	'Charmaine' (TB)	XSen
	'Charming Billy' (Sib)	ECtt LBar MHol NCth NLar WGob
	'Chartreuse Bounty' (Sib)	CDor ECtt ELan EPri EWes GMaP MHol NLar WFar WGob
	'Chasing Rainbows' (TB)	WCAu
	'Cheap Frills' (TB)	WCAu
	'Cher and Cher Alike' (TB) **new**	WCAu
	'Cherished' (TB)	CKel
	'Cherished One' (La)	LLWG
	'Cherry Blossom Song' (TB)	SIri
	'Cherry Garden' (SDB)	CBro CWat ECha ECtt EGrI ELan ELon EPfP EShb EWes GKev GMaP MBNS MRav MTin NBir NGdn NLar SCob SDeJ WCot WGwG WOld
	'Cherub's Smile' (TB)	ESgI XSen
	'Chicken Little' (MDB)	CBro EDAr
I	'Chieftain' (SDB)	MRav
	'Childhood Sweetheart' (La)	LLWG
	'Chilled Wine' (Sib)	ELon LRHS
	'Chimera' (IB) **new**	EWoo
	'China Dragon' (TB)	XSen
	'Chinese Coral' (TB)	XSen
	'Chinese Treasure' (TB)	XSen
	'Chinook Winds' (TB)	ESgI
	'Chivalry' (TB)	ESgI
	'Christmas Angel' (TB)	NLar WCAu
	Chrysofor Group	CAby
	chrysographes 🏆H6	Widely available
	- BWJ 7930	WCru
I	- 'Black Beauty'	EWoo
	- 'Black Gold'	CPla ECtt EPri ESgI LBar LRHS MHol NLar
I	- 'Black Knight'	CExl EPfP NChi NFav NLar SChF SMad
	- 'Black Magic' **new**	CBor
I	- 'Black Velvet'	GEdr WSpi
	- black-flowered	CAby EBee ELan GAbr GKev GKin LAma LCro LOPS LRHS LShi MNrw NGdn NHpl NRHS SBls SCob SPer WCAu WCru WFar WGwG WPGP WPnP WSHC WSpi
	- 'Bob's Fancy'	SDeJ
	- dark-flowered	GKev GMcL WFar
	- hybrid	ESgI WFar
	- 'Kew Black'	CExl GKev LEdu NBir
	- 'Mandarin Purple'	GQue SPer
	- yellow-flowered	WFar
	chrysographes* × *forrestii	NBir
	'Château d'Auvers-sur-Oise' (TB)	SIri WViv
	'Chubby Cheeks' (SDB)	WCAu
	'Ciel et Mer' (TB)	WViv
	'Cimarron Rose' (SDB)	ESgI
	'Cimarron Strip' (TB)	CKel WCot XSen
	'Cinque Terre' (TB)	WCAu
	'Circle of Light' (TB)	WCAu
	'Circus Stripes' (TB)	XSen
	'Citoyen' (TB)	XSen
	'Citronnade' (TB)	ESgI
	'City of Paradise' (TB)	ESgI
	'Clairette' (Reticulata)	CRos EHyd EPot GKev LAma LRHS NRHS NRog SDeJ
	'Clarence' (TB)	ESgI MHol XSen
	clarkei	EWoo WCAu

– B&SWJ 2122	MHol WCru
– CC 2751	CExl
– SDR 3819	GKev
'Class Ring' (TB)	WCAu
'Classic Look' (TB)	ESgI SIri
'Classic Navy' (BB)	ESgI
'Clear Blue Sky' (SDB)	WCAu
'Clematis' (TB)	WMil
'Cleo' (TB)	NSti
'Cleo Murrell' (TB)	ESgI EWoo
'Cleve Dodge' (Sib)	EPri EWoo WGob XLum
'Cliffs of Dover' (TB)	CKel EIri ESgI EWoo LCro LOPS MCot SCob SCoo SRms
'Cloudcap' (TB)	SRms
'Clownerie' (TB)	EWoo WViv
'Clyde Redmond' (La) ♀H5	WMal
'Coal Face' (TB)	WCAu
'Coal Seams' (TB)	WCAu
'Coalignition' (TB)	EWoo WCAu
'Codicil' (TB)	ESgI WViv XSen
colchica	LEdu
'Colette Thurillet' (TB)	CKel WCAu WViv XSen
'Colin's Pale Blue' (Sib)	NCth SMHy
'Color Glory' (TB)	SIri
'Color Me Blue' (TB)	WCAu
'Color Splash' (TB)	XSen
'Color Strokes' (TB)	WCAu
'Colorific' (La)	LAma NLar WGob
'Colortart' (TB)	XSen
'Coming Up Roses' (TB)	XSen
'Con Fuoco' (TB)	XSen
'Concertina' (IB)	WCAu
'Concoction' (IB)	GKev
'Concord Crush' (Sib)	CAby NCth NGdn WGob WPnP WTor WTyc
confusa ♀H4	EAri ESwi MACG MBriF SArc SMad SPlb XSen XSte
§ – 'Martyn Rix'	CAbb CBct CMac CWCL EGrI EPPr EPfP ESgI ESwi LRHS MACG MBriF MPie SBrt SEND SRms WGwG WMal
'Conjuration' (TB)	CKel SIri WCAu
'Constant Wattez' (IB)	CKel ESgI NLar
'Constantine Bay' (TB)	ESgI
'Contrast in Styles' (Sib)	ECtt EPri EWoo LAma MNrw MSCN NQui SDir WFar WGob
'Cool Change' (TB)	WCAu
'Copatonic' (TB)	ESgI WCAu
'Copper Capers' (TB)	ESgI
'Copper Classic' (TB)	ELon ESgI LSRN WCAu
'Coquet Waters' (Sib)	NBid
'Coraband' (TB)	NLar
'Coral Sunset' (TB)	XSen
'Cordoba' (TB)	WCAu XSen
'Corinthe' (TB) **new**	EWoo
'Coronation Anthem' (Sib)	EPri EWoo
'Côte d'Azur' (Sib)	CBor
'Côte d'Or' (TB)	XSen
'Country Charm' (TB)	WCAu
'Country Kisses' (TB)	WCAu
'County Town Red' (TB)	SIri
'Coup de Soleil' (TB)	EWoo WViv
'Cracklin' Burgundy' (TB)	XSen
'Crackling Caldera' (TB)	MMrt
'Cranapple' (BB) ♀H7	EIri ESgI WCAu
'Cranberry Ice' (TB)	ELon EWoo MNHC XSen
'Cranberry Sauce' (TB)	SIri
'Cranbrook' (IB) ♀H7	SIri
'Crathie' (TB)	CMil ECha EWoo
'Cream Beauty' (Dut)	LCro SDeJ
cretensis	see *I. unguicularis* subsp. *cretensis*
'Crimson King' (IB)	EWoo
'Crinoline' (TB)	CKel XSen
'Crispette' (TB)	EWoo
cristata	EPot GEdr NHpl SGro
– 'Abbey's Violet'	LBar SMad
– 'Alba'	SGro WAbe WHil
§ – 'Captain Collingwood'	WAbe
– 'Eco Little Bluebird' **new**	NLar
cristata* × *lacustris	GArf
crocea ♀H6	GBin
'Croftway Lemon' (TB)	ELon WSpi
'Crowned Heads' (TB)	WCAu XSen
'Crushed Ice' (La)	LLWG
'Crystal Gazer' (TB)	WCAu
'Crystal Glitters' (TB)	ESgI
'Cup Race' (TB)	XSen
'Curlew' (IB)	WCAu
'Currier' (Sib)	CBod LBar
'Cute or What' (SDB)	ESgI SIri
'Cutie' (IB)	EWoo
'Cyanea' (DB)	EGrI GKev
'Cyclamint' (La)	LLWG
cycloglossa	EPot GKev LAma NRog
'Daedalus' (Rc)	GKev
'Daemon Imp' (MTB)	EIri WCAu
'Daffy Duck' (TB) **new**	WCAu
'Dainty Lace' (La)	LLWG
'Dale Dennis' (DB)	XSen
'Dance Ballerina Dance' (Sib)	CWCL EBee EPri MRav NCth NFav NLar WFar
'Dance for Joy' (TB)	XSen
'Dance On' (Reticulata)	LAma
'Dance the Night Away' (TB)	WCAu
'Dance til Dawn' (TB) **new**	WCAu
'Dancer's Veil' (TB)	CKel CMac EBee ECtt EHyd ELon EPfP ESgI LRHS MRav NRHS SPer
'Dancing in the Dark' (TB) **new**	WCAu
'Dancing in the Moonlight' (IB) **new**	WCAu
'Dancing Lilacs' (MTB)	ESgI EWoo
'Dancing Star' (TB) **new**	WCAu
danfordiae	EHyd EPot EWoo GKev LAma LCro LOPS LRHS NHpl NRHS NRog SDeJ
'Dante's Inferno' (TB)	EWoo
'Daphne' (TB)	WMil
'Dardanus' (Rc)	EPot ERCP GKev LAma NRog SDeJ WCot
'Dark Circle' (Sib)	EBee WFar
'Dark Crystal' (SDB)	ESgI EWoo
'Dark Desire' (Sib)	MRav
'Dark Vader' (SDB)	ESgI SIri
'Darkness' (IB)	SIri
'Darkness' (Reticulata) **new**	LAma
'Darkside' (TB)	XSen
'Dating a Royal' (TB)	WCAu
'Daughter of Stars' (TB)	ELon
'Dauntless' (TB)	CCBP ESgI
'Dauphin' (IB) **new**	EWoo
'Dawn of Fall' (TB)	ESgI
'Dawn Waltz' (Sib)	CBro ELon EWoo NCth WFar WGob WHlf
'Dawning' (TB) ♀H7	ESgI
'Dazzling' (IB)	SIri WCAu
'Dazzling Gold' (TB)	CKel ESgI XSen
'Dear Delight' (Sib)	ELon MNrw NLar WFar
'Decadence' (TB)	WCAu
§ ***decora***	WAbe WCAu
'Deep Black' (TB)	CKel CRos CWGN EBee ECha ELan EPfP ESgI ETod EWoo GBin GMaP LRHS LSRN MBNS MBriF MCot MRav NLar NRHS NWad SDeJ SMrm SPer SPoG WCAu WGwG
'Deep Pacific' (TB)	WCAu
'Deepening Shadows' (CH)	MAvo

	'Deeper Meaning' (TB) **new**	WCAu
	'Deft Touch' (TB)	XSen
	delavayi 🏆^{H6}	EWes GGro
	- SDR 50	CExl GKev
	- 'Didcot'	CRos EBlo EHyd LRHS NRHS
	'Delirium' (IB)	SIri WCAu
	'Delta Butterfly' (La)	WMAq
	'Demi-Deuil' (TB)	EWoo
	'Demon' (SDB)	NBPC SMrm XSen
	'Demure Illini' (Sib)	MNrw
	'Depth of Field' (TB)	EGrI
	'Derwentwater' (TB)	SRms WCAu
	'Deseret' (TB) **new**	EWoo
	'Desert Echo' (TB)	GMcL WHlf XSen
	'Desert Song' (TB)	EGrI
	'Destination Fabulous' (TB) **new**	WCAu
	'Devil May Care' (IB)	ESgI
	'Dewful' (Sib)	WFar
	'Diabolique' (TB) 🏆^{H7}	XSen
	'Dipped in Dots' (TB) **new**	WCAu
	'Dirigo Black Velvet' (Sib)	ELon
	'Disco Jewel' (MTB)	ESgI
	'Discovered Treasure' (TB)	WCAu
	'Discovery'^{PBR} (Dut)	SDeJ
	'Disguise' (TB)	WCAu
	'Distant Music' (La)	LLWG
	'Ditto' (MDB)	EDAr ESgI
	'Ditzy' (SDB)	SIri
	'Diversion' (TB)	ESgI
	'Dividing Line' (MTB)	WCAu
	'Dixie Darling' (TB)	ESgI XSen
	'Dixie Pixie' (SDB)	WCAu
	'Dogrose' (TB)	EWoo
	'Dolce' (SpH)	WCAu
	dolichosiphon subsp. ***orientalis***	GKev
	'Dolly Madison' (TB)	ESgI EWoo
§	***domestica***	CBro CPla EAri EHyd EPPr EPfP EWoo MACG SMad SPlb SRms WSHC
	- 'Freckle Face'	CWCL LBar MHol
	'Dominion' (TB)	EWoo WMil
	'Don Juan' (TB)	EWoo
	'Dotted Swiss' (TB)	XSen
	'Double Byte' (SDB)	XSen
	'Double Espoir' (TB)	XSen
	'Double Lament' (SDB)	CBro EDAr
	'Double Standards' (Sib)	EPri LAma NLar SDir WFar WGob
	'Double Vision' (TB)	XSen
	'Douce Reverie' (TB)	WViv
	douglasiana	GKev
	'Dover Beach' (TB)	SIri
	'Dover Castle' (BB) 🏆^{H7}	SIri
	'Downtown Brown' (TB)	WCAu
	'Draco' (TB)	ECtt EPfP ESgI LBar SBea XSen
	'Dramatic Style' (TB) **new**	WCAu
	'Dream Indigo' (IB)	EWoo WCAu XSen
	'Dreaming Green' (Sib)	EBee ECha
	'Dreaming Late' (Sib)	EWoo WCAu
	'Dreaming Orange' (Sib)	ECtt EPri LAma SDir
	'Dreaming Rainbows' (TB)	WCAu
	'Dreaming Spires' (Sib)	GBin
	'Dreaming Yellow' (Sib)	CAby CAvo CBar CEnd CKel CPud CToG ECha EHyd EPri ESgI GBin GKin LRHS MRav NRHS SPer WCAu WGob WGwG
	'Duke of Bedford' (TB)	WMil
	'Dunkler Wein' (Sib)	EWes
	'Dunlin' (MDB)	CBro NBir SBut
	'Duplicity' (TB) **new**	WCAu
	'Dusky Challenger' (TB)	CBod CKel EBee ECtt EPfP ESgI EWoo LBar LCro LOPS LRHS MMrt SRms WCAu XSen

	'Dusky Evening' (TB)	XSen
	'Dutch Chocolate' (TB)	EWes EWoo LCro LOPS XSen
	'Dynamite' (TB)	XSen
	'Dyonisos' (TB)	SIri
	'Eagle's Flight' (TB)	XSen
	'Earl of Essex' (TB)	XSen
	'Early Light' (TB) 🏆^{H7}	EIri ESgI
	'Easter' (SDB)	SIri
	'Eastertime' (TB)	ESgI
	'Eastman Winds' (La)	LLWG
	'Easy' (MTB)	EIri
	'Ebony Echo' (TB)	EWoo
	'Echo de France' (TB)	ESgI SRms XSen
	'Eden's Paradise Blue' (Sib)	ELon
	'Edge of Winter' (TB)	XSen
	'Edith Wolford' (TB)	CKel GMcL LBar MMrt SBea SCob XSen
	'Edna Grace' (La)	LLWG
	'Ed's Blue' (DB)	ELan
	'Edward' (Reticulata)	EPfP NRog SDeJ
	'Edward of Windsor' (TB)	ELan EWoo GMaP LRHS NLar
	'Ego' (Sib)	ECha ELon EPri EWoo GMaP WFar
	'Eileen Louise' (TB) 🏆^{H7}	WCAu
	'Elaine's Wedding' (La)	LLWG
	'Eldorado' (TB)	EWoo
	'Eleanor Roosevelt' (IB)	EWoo
	'Eleanor's Pride' (TB)	EWoo SRms
	elegantissima	see *I. iberica* subsp. *elegantissima*
	'Elizabeth Poldark' (TB)	ESgI XSen
	'Elsa Sass' (TB)	ESgI EWoo
	'Elsie Petty' (IB)	SIri
	'Elvinhall'	CBro
	'Elysium' (IB) **new**	ESgI
	'Emperor' (Sib)	LRHS NSti
	'Empress of India' (TB)	EWoo
	'Endless Love' (TB)	EIri
	'English Charm' (TB)	ESgI XSen
	'English Cottage' (TB)	CKel CTsd ELon EShb EWoo GBin LBar LSRN MHer NLar SMrm SRms WCAu WSpi XSen
	'Ennerdale' (TB)	SRms
	'Enriched' (MTB) 🏆^{H7}	WCAu
§	***ensata***	CBcs CBro CRos EGrI ELan EPfP GArf LPfP LRHS LSun MNrw NLar NRHS SCob SPlb SRms SVic WBor WPnP
	- 'Activity'	ELon WFar
	- 'Alba'	ECha MMuc WCFE
	- 'Angel Mountain'	LBar LLWG MBNS WFar WGob
	- 'Angelic Choir'	LLWG
	- 'Apollo'	CToG
	- 'Asian Warrior'	WFar
	- 'Azuma-kagami'	MNrw
	- 'Azure'	LAma SDir WFar
I	- 'Blue King'	GDam NHol
	- 'Blue Mandarin'	ECtt
	- 'Blue Spritz'	LLWG
	- 'Carnival Prince'	WFar
	- 'Cascade Crest'	WFar
	- 'Celestial Emperor'	LLWG WGob
	- 'Center of Interest'	NBir
	- 'Christina's Gown'	WFar WGob
	- 'Crepe Paper'	WFar
	- 'Cry of Rejoice'	GMcL
	- 'Crystal Halo' 🏆^{H6}	EPfP MNHC WCAu
	- 'Dace'	GBin
	- 'Dancing Waves'	CToG
I	- 'Darling'	EPfP WFar WGob
	- (Dinner Plate Series) 'Dinner Plate Blueberry Pie' **new**	LBar
	- - 'Dinner Plate Cheesecake' **new**	LBar

	- - 'Dinner Plate Cupcake' **new**	LBar
	- - 'Dinner Plate Ice Cream' **new**	LBar
	- - 'Dinner Plate Jell-O' **new**	LBar
	- - 'Dinner Plate Tiramisu' **new**	LBar
	- 'Dirigo Editor'	LLWG
	- 'Dirigo Maiden's Blush'	LLWG
	- 'Dramatic Moment'	WFar WSpi
I	- 'Dresden China'	WFar
	- 'Eden's Paintbrush'	EShb
	- 'Eileen's Dream'	ECtt EPfP LBar LLWG LPfP SPeP
	- 'Electric Rays'	ELon LAma LLWG SDir WFar WOld
I	- 'Emotion'	CMac WFar
	- 'Flying Tiger'	GBin
I	- 'Fortune'	GBin LAma MSCN SDir
	- 'Freckled Geisha'	CBrac CMac ECtt ELon EPfP IPot MACG NBir NQui SRms WFar
	- 'Frilled Enchantment' 🏆H6	IPot WFar WGob WHlf
	- 'Frosted Pyramid'	CToG
	- 'Galatea Marx'	CBod WFar
	- 'Gipsy'	CBen CKel CMac LRHS
	- 'Gold Bound'	ECtt ELon LAma SDir SMad WGob
	- 'Good Omen'	ECtt WGob
	- 'Gracieuse'	CBor CMiW CTsd NLar WBor
	- 'Greywoods Catrina'	LLWG WFar WGob
	- 'Gusto'	CMac ELon EPfP LDai MNrw SRms WFar
	- 'Harlequinesque'	ECtt IPot SMad WFar WGob
	- 'Harpswell Chantey'	IPot
	- 'Hercule'	NBir WFar
	- 'Hoshi-akari'	WFar
	- 'Ike-no-sazanami'	LLWG
	- 'Imperial Velvet'	WFar
	- 'Indigo Delight'	LLWG
*	- 'Innocence'	NLar SRms WFar
	- 'Iso-no-nami'	WFar
	- 'Japanese Plum'	LLWG
	- 'Jeweled Kimono'	EWoo
	- 'Jocasta'	WFar
	- 'Jodlesong'	WFar
	- 'Jupiter'	EGrl
	- 'Kalamazoo'	WFar
	- 'Katy Mendez' 🏆H6	IPot
	- 'Kogesho'	NLar
	- 'Koh Dom'	SPer
	- 'Kongo-san'	NLar WFar
	- 'Kuma-funjin'	CToG
	- 'Kumo-no-obi'	CAby CEnd CFis CPud CToG ESgI GBin NHol SMrm WFar
	- 'Lady in Waiting'	ECtt EPfP LAma LRHS MSCN SDir WGob WOld WTyc
	- 'Laughing Lion'	ECtt EWoo WFar WGob
	- 'Light at Dawn'	LDai MBel
	- 'Lilac Blotch'	SPer
	- 'Loyalty'	EWoo SHar WFar
	- 'Michinoku-kogane'	CMiW
	- 'Mist Falls'	ESgI
	- 'Momogasumi'	ECtt LAma LLWG MNrw NQui SGro WHil
§	- 'Moonlight Waves'	CEnd CKel CMac CPud CRos CToG EBee ECha EHyd ELan EPfP EWoo GBin GKin GMaP IPot LRHS LShi MACG MHer MHol MRav NGdn NHol NRHS SMrm SRms WFar WGob WSpi
	- 'Murasame' 🏆H6	EShb
	- 'Neptune's Trident'	LLWG
	- 'Oku-banri'	EPfP WFar
	- 'Oriental Eyes'	NGdn
	- pale mauve-flowered	NBir
	- 'Pin Stripe'	NLar WFar
	- 'Pink Frost'	CFis EBlo EPfP ESgI MHer WFar WGob
	- 'Pleasant Earlybird'	WFar
	- 'Prairie Frost'	NLar
	- 'Pure Emotion'	LLWG
	- 'Purple Parasol'	ECtt LLWG WGob
	- purple-flowered	EWoo
	- 'Queen's Tiara'	ECtt ELon IPot WBor WGob WTyc
	- 'Rakka-no-utage'	NLar
	- 'Red Tessa'	LLWG
	- 'Returning Tide' 🏆H6	GBin
	- 'Rivulets of Wine'	LLWG
	- Rodionenko hybrids	WMal
§	- 'Rose Queen' 🏆H6	CDor CGBo CMac CRos CToG CTtf EBlo ECha EHyd ELan EPfP EWoo GBin GKin GMaP LPfP MRav NBir NGdn NHol NRHS SMrm SPer SRms WCAu WFar WGob XLum
	- 'Rowden'	CToG
	- 'Rowden Amir'	CToG
	- 'Rowden Autocrat'	CToG
	- 'Rowden Baronet' **new**	CToG
	- 'Rowden Begum'	CToG
	- 'Rowden Caesar'	CToG SGro
	- 'Rowden Caliph'	CToG
	- 'Rowden Chieftan'	CToG
	- 'Rowden Consul'	CToG
	- 'Rowden Dictator'	CToG
	- 'Rowden Empress'	CToG
	- 'Rowden Gaekwar' **new**	CToG
	- 'Rowden King'	CToG NChi
	- 'Rowden Knight'	CToG
	- 'Rowden Laird' **new**	CToG
	- 'Rowden Marquess'	CToG
	- 'Rowden Mikado'	CToG NChi
	- 'Rowden Naib'	CToG
	- 'Rowden Nuncio'	CToG
	- 'Rowden Queen'	CToG
	- 'Rowden Regent' **new**	CToG
	- 'Rowden Sovereign'	CToG
	- 'Rowden Sultan'	CToG
	- 'Rowden Tetrarch'	CToG
	- 'Rowden Viceroy' **new**	CToG
I	- 'Royal Banner'	ECtt EWoo WFar
	- 'Royal Crown'	XLum
I	- 'Ruby King'	CPud
	- 'Ruffled Dimity'	IPot
I	- 'Sensation'	ECtt GBin NLar SRms
	- 'Snowy Hills'	XLum
	- 'Sorcerer's Triumph'	WFar
	- 'Splish Splash'	GKev
	- var. ***spontanea*** B&SWJ 1103	WCru
	- - B&SWJ 8699	WCru
	- 'Stippled Ripples'	IPot
	- 'Strut and Flourish'	EWoo
	- 'Sugar Dome'	LLWG
	- 'Sunrise Ridge'	LLWG
	- 'Taketori-hime' (v)	XLum
	- 'Tensyukaku'	CMiW
	- 'Topas'	WFar WGob
	- 'Umi-kaze'	NLar
	- 'Variegata' (v) 🏆H6	CBct CEme CMac CRos EBee EBlo ECha EHyd ELri ELon EPfP GBin GMaP GMcL LPfP LRHS MHer MHol MMuc NLar NRHS SEND SMad SPoG SRms WFar WPnP
	- 'Velvety Queen'	ECtt
	- 'Waka-murasaki-uyeki'	EGrl
	- 'Wave Action'	EWTr IPot
I	- 'White Ladies'	CKel CSBt EShb GKev LRHS SPeP WBor WCAu WGob WSpi

- 'Wine Ruffles'	GKev
- 'Yako-no-tama'	WFar
- 'Yedo-yeman'	WFar
'Epicenter' (TB)	XSen
'Eramosa Skies' (SDB)	WCAu
'Eric the Red' (Sib)	ELon
'Erste Sahne' (Sib)	GBin
'Etcetera' (TB) **new**	WCAu
'Evadne' (TB)	WMil
'Evening Drama' (TB)	SIri
'Evening Gown' (TB)	XSen
'Ever After' (TB)	EWoo XSen
'Ever Again' (Sib)	ELon EWoo
'Everything Plus' (TB)	ESgI XSen
'Ewen' (Sib)	EWoo GKin GLog GMaP NGdn WCot
'Exotic Isle' (TB)	ESgI XSen
'Exotic Star' (TB)	CKel
'Experiment' (SDB)	EIri
'Extra Dazzle' (La)	LLWG
'Eye Catcher' (Reticulata)	EPot ERCP GKev IPot LAma NBir NRog
'Eye Magic' (IB)	XSen
'Eye of Tiger'	see *I.* 'Tigereye'
'Eyebright' (SDB) ♀H7	CBro
'Fabiola' (Reticulata)	EHyd EPot ERCP GKev LAma NRHS SDeJ
'Fabuleux' (TB)	SIri WViv
'Face of an Angel' (TB)	WCAu
'Fall Empire' (TB)	EWoo
'Fall Fiesta' (TB)	XSen
'Fanciful Whimsy' (IB)	WCAu
'Fancy Me This' (Sib) **new**	LBar
'Fancyancy' (TB) **new**	EWoo
'Fanfaron' (TB)	ESgI XSen
'Farleigh Damson' (SDB)	SBdl SIri
'Fashion Lady' (MDB)	CBro
'Fathom' (IB)	WCAu
'Faubourg-St John' (La)	LLWG
'Feather and Fan' (La)	LLWG
'Feel the Thunder' (TB) **new**	WCAu
'Feminine Charm' (TB)	MRav
'Festival's Acadian' (La)	LLWG
'Feu du Ciel' (TB) ♀H7	CKel ESgI SPeP XSen
'Few Are Chosen' (La)	LLWG
'Fidget' (SDB) **new**	WCAu
'Fiesta Time' (TB)	XSen
'Film Festival' (TB)	ECtt EPfP ESgI LRHS SPeP
'Finalist' (TB)	XSen
'Fingertips' (SDB) **new**	ESgI
'Finola' (Reticulata)	ERCP GKev LAma
'Fire and Ice' (TB) **new**	WCAu
'Firebug' (IB)	XSen
'Firecracker' (TB)	MRav
'First Interstate' (TB)	ESgI XSen
'First Movement' (TB)	ESgI
'First Violet' (TB)	ESgI
'Five Star Admiral' (TB)	XSen
'Flaming Dragon' (TB)	XSen
'Flaming Victory' (TB)	XSen
'Flash of Light' (TB) **new**	WCAu
'Flashy Show Girl' (TB) **new**	WCAu
flavescens	EWoo XSen
'Flecks and Specks' (AB) **new**	WCAu
'Fleece of White' (BB)	WCAu
'Flibbertigibbet' (SDB)	SIri
'Flight of Butterflies' (Sib) ♀H7	Widely available
'Flirting Again' (SDB) ♀H7	SIri
'Floorshow' (TB)	XSen
'Flora Zenor' (TB) **new**	EWoo
§ 'Florentina' (IB/TB) ♀H6	CBro CHby CKel EWoo GPoy LRHS MHer MNHC MRav NBid NBir NLar SEND SRms WCAu WLov XSen
'Florentine Silk' (TB)	WCAu
'Floridor' (TB)	EWoo
'Flumadiddle' (IB)	CBro
'Flutter-By' (TB)	EWoo
'Flûte Enchantée' (TB)	XSen
'Focus' (TB)	XSen
foetidissima ♀H6	Widely available
- 'Aurea'	WCot
- ***chinensis***	see *I. foetidissima* var. *citrina*
§ - var. ***citrina***	EPPr EPri EWld GAbr GKev LEdu LRHS NLar WGwG
- 'Fructu Albo'	WCot
- var. ***lutescens***	NSti
- 'Paul's Gold' **new**	GEdr
- 'Variegata' (v) ♀H6	NBir NPer
'Fogbound' (TB)	WCAu
'Foggy Dew' (TB)	EHyd EPfP EWoo LRHS NRHS SDeJ
'Folie Douce' (TB)	WViv
'Fond Kiss' (Sib)	CDor WCAu WGob
'Fondation Van Gogh' (TB)	XSen
'Foolish Fancy' (TB)	SIri
'Footloose' (TB)	XSen
'For Lovers Only' (TB) **new**	WCAu
'Forecasting Rain' (SDB)	SIri
'Foreign Legion' (TB)	WCAu
'Forest Light' (SDB)	CBro EDAr ESgI
'Forever and a Day' (TB) **new**	WCAu
'Forever Blue' (SDB)	WCAu
'Forever Gold' (TB)	XSen
'Forge Fire' (TB)	ESgI
formosana B&SWJ 3076	WCru
'Forrest Hills' (TB)	EPfP
forrestii ♀H6	CBro CMac EPfP GGro GKev GLog LRHS NBir
- black-flowered	GRum
'Fort Apache' (TB)	EWes EWoo
'Fortunata' (TB)	XSen
'Fortunate Son' (TB)	EWoo WCAu
'Fourfold Blue' (SpH)	GBin
'Fourfold Lavender' (Sib)	EWes NLar
'Fourfold White' (Sib)	ESgI
'Framboise' (TB)	XSen
'Frances Iva' (TB)	EWoo
'Francheville' (TB)	EWoo
'Francina' (TB)	WMil
'Frank Elder' (Reticulata)	EHyd EPot ERCP GKev LAma LRHS NRHS NRog SDeJ WAbe
'Frans Hals' (Dut)	NBir
'Frappe' (TB)	CKel
'French Buttercream' (SpH) **new**	LLWG
'French Can Can' (TB)	SIri
'Fresno Calypso' (TB)	CKel ESgI WCAu XSen
'Friends' Song' (La)	LLWG
'Frigiya' (Spuria)	GBin
'Frimousee' (TB)	WViv
'Frison-roche' (TB)	WViv
'Frisounette' (TB)	ESgI
'From this Moment' (La)	LLWG
'Frontier Marshall' (TB)	XSen
'Frost and Flame' (TB)	CBod CEnd CKel EBee ECtt EHyd ELan EWoo GBin GKev LCro LRHS MAsh MRav NBir NLar NRHS SDeJ SPer SPoG WGwG
'Frosted Angel' (SDB)	CBro
'Frosted Velvet' (MTB)	WCAu
'Frosty Jewels' (TB)	ESgI XSen
'Frozen Planet' (Reticulata)	ERCP LAma
'Fruit Cocktail' (IB)	XSen

'Full of Magic' (TB) **new**	WCAu
'Full Sun' (Spuria)	EWoo
'Full Tilt Boogie' (TB) **new**	WCAu
fulva 𝕐H5	EBee EGrI EPPr EPri EWat EWhm EWoo MMrt NBir NSti SBrt WCAu WCot
- 'Marvell Gold' (La)	EWat
× ***fulvala*** 𝕐H5	NBir NSti
'Funambule' (TB)	EWoo
'Furnaceman' (SDB)	CBro EDAr
'Futuriste' (TB)	SIri WViv
'Fuzzy' (MDB)	EPot
'Gai Luron' (TB)	CKel
'Gala Madrid' (TB) **new**	LBar
'Gallant Moment' (TB)	ESgI XSen
'Galway' (IB)	XSen
'Game Plan' (TB)	WCAu
'Gandalf the Grey' (TB)	ESgI
'Garnement' (TB)	WViv
'Garnet Storm Dancer' (La)	LLWG
'Gay Head' (TB)	EWoo
'Gay Parasol' (TB)	CKel
'Gelbe Mantel' (Sino-Sib)	NBir
'Gemstone Walls' (TB)	ESgI
'Gentius' (TB)	EWoo
'George' (Reticulata) 𝕐H7	CAby EHyd EPot ERCP EWoo GKev LAma LRHS NRHS NRog SDeJ WHlf
'George Smith' (TB)	ECtt
'Gerald Darby'	see *I.* × *robusta* 'Gerald Darby'
§ ***germanica***	ESgI GPoy SEND WCAu WCot WGwG
- var. ***florentina***	see *I.* 'Florentina'
§ - 'Nepalensis'	WCAu
- 'Shazam' (BB) **new**	LBar
- 'The King'	see *I. germanica* 'Nepalensis'
'Gertrude' (TB)	EWoo
'Ghost Train' (TB)	CKel ESgI EWoo SIri
'Ginger Twist' (Sib)	CBod CDor ELon LBar WGob
'Gingerbread Man' (SDB)	CBro EDAr ESgI EWld GEdr MBrN NSla SMrm SWvt WCAu
'Ginny's Choice' (La)	LLWG
'Girly Girl' (TB)	WCAu
'Glacier Gold' (TB)	XSen
'Glad Rags' (TB)	XSen
'Gladbeck Yellow' (TB)	EWoo
'Gladys Austin' (TB)	XSen
'Gleaming Gold' (SDB)	NLar
'Glenthorn' (TB)	SIri
'Glowing Embers' (TB)	ESgI EWoo
'Gnu' (TB)	XSen
'Goddess of Green' (IB)	EWoo
'Godfrey Owen' (TB)	WCAu
'Godinton' (TB)	SIri
'Going Home' (TB) 𝕐H7	SIri
'Going My Way' (TB)	CKel ESgI EWoo SBea SIri WCAu XSen
'Gold Burst' (TB)	XSen
'Gold Country' (TB)	XSen
'Gold Galore' (TB)	SIri
'Golden Alps' (TB)	SRms
'Golden Beauty' (SpH)	GKev LAma NRog SDeJ
'Golden Child' (SDB)	XSen
'Golden Edge' (Sib)	CBod ECtt GBin GQue LLWG NLar SMrm WCAu WFar WGob
'Golden Encore' (TB)	WCAu
'Golden Fireworks' (La)	LLWG
'Golden Immortal' (TB)	EIri EWoo WOld
'Golden Muffin' (IB)	CKel
'Golden Panther' (TB)	WCAu
'Golden Violet' (SDB)	ESgI
'Golden Zebra' (TB)	LCro MBros MHol
'Good Looking' (TB)	ESgI
'Good Show' (TB)	ESgI EWoo XSen
'Good Vibrations' (TB)	XSen
'Goodbye Heart' (TB)	EWoo
'Gordon' (Reticulata)	EHyd LRHS NRHS NRog
'Goring Butterfly' (SpH) **new**	CBro
gormanii	see *I. tenax*
'Gossip' (SDB)	CBro
'Got Milk' (TB)	MACG
'Goudhurst' (SDB)	SIri
'Gracchus' (TB)	EWoo
'Grace and Charm' (BB) **new**	WCAu
'Grace Sturtevant' (TB)	EWoo WMil
gracilipes 'Alba'	GArf GEdr
graeberiana	EPot GKev NRog SDeJ
graminea 𝕐H6	CBro CFis CMac EGrI EIri EPri GKev NBir NChi NSti WCot
- var. ***pseudocyperus***	GBin
graminifolia	see *I. kerneriana*
'Granada Gold' (TB)	SRms XSen
'Grand Amiral' (TB)	WViv
'Grand Illusion' (Spuria)	EWoo
'Grand Waltz' (TB)	XSen
'Grandis' (Sib)	GBin
'Great Lakes' (TB)	ESgI EWoo
'Grecian Skies' (TB)	ESgI
'Green Eyed Lady' (TB)	ESgI
'Green Ice' (TB)	LRHS MRav
'Green Jungle' (TB)	EWoo
'Green Pastures' (TB) **new**	EWoo
'Green Spot' (SDB) 𝕐H7	CBod CBro CKel ECha ECtt EHyd ESgI LRHS MBriF MRav NBir NLar NRHS SDeJ
'Greensand Way' (TB)	SIri
'Grenade' (TB)	EWoo SIri WViv
grey-flowered (Sib)	ELon
'Grooving' (BB)	ESgI
'Grosser Wein' (Sib)	GBin
'Guess Who I Am' (TB)	WCAu
'Gull's Wing' (Sib)	CAby EPfP LLWG LRHS MBel MHol NLar SMrm SPoG WGob WPnP
'Gypsy' (TB) **new**	EWoo
'Gypsy Beauty' (Dut)	ELan LCro LOPS MNrw NRog SDeJ
'Gypsy Jewels' (TB)	XSen
'Gypsy Lord' (TB)	WCAu
'Gypsy Queen' (TB) **new**	EWoo
'Gypsy Romance' (TB) 𝕐H7	SIri
'Gypsy Tart' (SDB)	SIri
'Habit' (TB)	EWoo WCAu
'Hail Mary' (La)	LLWG
halophila	see *I. spuria* subsp. *halophila*
'Happenstance' (TB)	WCAu
'Happiness' (Reticulata)	GKev LAma
'Happy Mood' (IB)	EIri
'Harbor Blue' (TB)	CKel EWoo NLar WCAu
'Harlow Gold' (IB)	ESgI
'Harmony' (Reticulata)	CAby CAvo EHyd EPfP EPot EWoo GKev LAma LCro LOPS LRHS NBir NRHS NRog SDeJ WBrk
'Harpswell Happiness' (Sib) 𝕐H7	CKel EBee ELan ELon EPfP EPri GBin LAma SDir WGob
'Harpswell Haze' (Sib)	ECha
'Harpswell Velvet' (Sib)	GBin
'Harriette Halloway' (TB)	CWGN EPfP EShb ETod EWoo LSRN NLar WCot
'Harry's Choice' (TB) **new**	SIri
'Harvest Home' (BB)	SIri
'Harvest King' (TB)	XSen
'Harvest of Memories' (TB)	ESgI EWoo GMcL SPoG
'Haut les Voiles' (TB)	EWoo WViv
'Haute Couture' (TB)	XSen
'Haviland' (TB)	XSen
'Having Fun' (Sib)	CDor NCth

	'Headcorn' (MTB) 🏆H7	SIri
	'Headline Banner' (BB)	WCAu
	'Heather Carpet' (SDB)	WCAu
	'Heather Stream' (La)	ELon
	'Helen Astor' (Sib)	CDor CToG ELon MRav
	'Helen Collingwood' (TB)	ESgI EWoo
	'Helen McGregor' (TB)	EWoo
	'Helen Proctor' (IB)	ESgI SIri WCot XSen
	'Helena Terry' (TB)	ESgI
	'Helene C.' (TB)	EWoo WViv XSen
	'Helga'	EGrI
	'Helicopter' (Sib)	LBar
	'Hello Darkness' (TB) 🏆H7	ESgI WCAu WCot XSen
	'Hell's Fire' (TB)	ELon WSpi
	'Hemstitched' (TB)	EWoo
	henryi	GKev WAbe
	'Her Royal Highness' (TB)	LAma LCro
	'Here Be Dragons' (Sib)	CDor WCAu WGob
	'Here Comes the Night' (TB)	WCAu
	'Here Comes the Sun' (TB)	WCAu
	'Hester Prynne' (TB)	WMil
	'Heure Bleue' (TB)	WViv
	'Hey True Blue' (TB)	WCAu
	'High Barbaree' (TB)	EWoo
	'High Blue Sky' (TB)	WCAu
	'High Octane' (TB) **new**	WCAu
	'Highland Mist' (La)	LLWG
	'Hildegarde' (Dut)	SDeJ
	'Hindenburg' (TB)	CKel
	'Hippolyta' (Rc)	GKev
	'His Royal Highness' (TB)	WCAu
	histrio	EPot
	- subsp. ***aintabensis***	NRog
	histrioides 'Halkis'	EHyd EPot LRHS NRHS SDeJ
	- 'Lady Beatrix Stanley'	CAvo CRos EHyd EPot ERCP GKev LAma LHWs LRHS MNrw NBir NRHS NRog SDeJ
	- 'Major'	NRog
	'Hoar Edge' (Sib)	EPri NChi
	'Hocus Pocus' (SDB)	CKel CWGN ECtt ESgI EWoo LRHS NRHS WGwG
	'Hohe Warte' (Sib) 🏆H7	EWoo GBin WCAu
	'Höhenflug' (Sib)	GBin
	'Holden Clough' (SpH) 🏆H7	CPla EBee ELan EPPr EPfP EWoo GBin GMcL LEdu MBriF MCot MMuc MNrw MRav NBir NChi NFav NGdn NSti NWad WBrk WFar WSHC WWke
	'Holden's Child' (SpH)	CWat LLWG WCAu
	'Holidaze' (IB) 🏆H7	EIri
	'Hollywood Ending' (La)	LLWG
	'Holy Night' (TB)	ESgI SRms
	'Honey Glazed' (IB)	ELon
	'Honey Mocha Lotta' (Spuria)	EWoo
	'Honey Stars' (La)	LLWG
	'Honeyplic' (IB) 🏆H7	SIri
	'Honington' (SDB)	WCAu
	'Honky Tonk Blues' (TB)	ESgI
	'Honorabile' (MTB)	EWoo
	hoogiana 🏆H5	GKev LAma
I	- 'Amphion'	GKev
I	- 'Antiope'	GKev
	- 'Purpurea'	GKev
	- 'Zethos'	GKev
§	***hookeri***	CBod CTsd EWoo GArf GMaP MACG MHol NHpl NLar NSla SPtp SRms WAbe WIce
	'Hopelessly Devoted' (La)	LLWG
	'Horizon Bleu' (TB)	EWoo
	'Horned Rosyred' (TB)	EWoo
	'Hortensia Rose' (TB)	WViv
	'Hot' (SDB)	ESgI
	'Hot and Spicy' (La)	LLWG
	'Hot Spiced Wine' (TB)	SIri
	'Hot to Trot' (TB)	ESgI
	'House of Cards' (TB) **new**	WCAu
	'How Audacious' (Sib)	ECtt LBar LCro MBros
	'Howard Weed' (TB)	EGrI
	'Hubbard' (Sib)	EPri LLWG MNrw SPoG WFar WGob
	'Huckleberry Fudge' (TB)	XSen
	'Hugs and Kisses' (TB) **new**	WCAu
§	***humilis***	LShi WAbe
	'Humors of Whiskey' (Sib)	WGob
	'Huntress' (Sib)	CDor
	hyrcana	NRog
	'Hysteria' (TB) **new**	WCAu
	'I Repeat' (TB)	XSen
	'I See Stars' (TB) **new**	LBar
§	***iberica*** subsp. ***elegantissima***	GKev
	'Ice Blue' (TB)	NRog
	'Ice Capades' (TB)	WCAu
	'Ice Etching' (SDB)	WCAu
	'Ila Crawford' (Spuria) 🏆H7	XSen
	'Illini Charm' (Sib)	WFar
	illyrica	see *I. pallida*
	'I'm Back' (TB)	WCAu
	'Immortality' (TB)	CBod CKel CRos CWGN EPfP ESgI EWoo GKev GMcL LRHS MHol SCob SRms STPC WCAu XSen
	'Imperative' (IB)	EWoo SIri
	'Imperator' (TB)	ELan
	'Imperial Bronze' (Spuria)	MNrw
	'Imperial Opal' (Sib)	ECtt NGdn WFar WGob
I	'Imperial Velvet' (Sib)	ELon WFar
	'Imprimis' (TB)	WCAu XSen
	'In Full Sail' (Sib)	CDor WGob
	'In Love' (TB)	XSen
	'In Town' (TB)	XSen
	'Indeed' (IB)	ESgI
	'Indian Chief' (TB)	CWCL ELan ESgI EWoo LCro MHer MRav
	'Indian Hills' (TB)	EWoo
	'Indigo Princess' (TB)	EWoo XSen
	'Indigo Seas' (TB)	EWoo
	'Inferno' (TB)	EWoo
	'Ink Patterns' (TB)	WCAu
	'Inn-Keeper' (La)	LLWG
	'Innocent Pink' (TB)	ESgI
	innominata	EHyd GArf GGro GKev LRHS NBir NBro NRHS NSla SRms WAbe
I	- 'Clotted Cream'	EGrI
	- 'Peacock'	EGrI
	- yellow-flowered	NRya
	'Inspired' (TB)	WCAu
	'Interpol' (TB)	ESgI EWoo XSen
	'Intrepid' (TB)	WViv
	'Invicta Celebration' (BB)	SIri
	'Invicta Daybreak' (IB)	SIri
	'Invicta Gold' (SDB)	SIri
	'Invicta Reprieve' (IB)	SIri
	'Invicta Sapphire' (TB)	SIri
	'Irisades' (TB)	SIri WViv
	'Irish Harp' (SDB)	ESgI
	'Isabelle' (Sib)	XSen
	'Island Sunset' (TB)	SIri
	'Isobel Rose' (TB)	SIri
	'Italian Ice' (TB)	EIri
	'Italian Velvet' (TB)	WCAu
	'It's Amazing' (IB)	WCAu
	'J.S. Dijt' (Reticulata)	EHyd EPfP EPot ERCP EWoo GKev LAma LCro LOPS LRHS MGos NRHS NRog SDeJ
	'Jacquessiana'	EWoo
	'Jac-y-do' (Sib)	EWes

	'Jamie Roo' (TB)	SIri
	'Jane Phillips' (TB) ♀H7	Widely available
	'Japanese Pinwheel'	WGob
	japonica ♀H4	CWal EWTr NLar NPer SPlb WCot WFar XLum XSen
	– B&SWJ 8921	WCru
	– 'Bourne Graceful'	CExl
	– 'Ledger'	CAby CExl CMac ECha MRav NCth SIvy SMad WWFP
	– 'Monty'	WWFP
	– 'Rudolph Spring'	EPPr WSHC
§	– 'Variegata' (v) ♀H4	CBcs CBct CBro ECha ESwi NPer NSti SArc WBrk WFar WWFP XSen
	'Java Bleue' (TB)	SIri
	'Jazz Festival' (TB)	SIri WCAu XSen
	'Jazz Hot' (La)	LLWG
	'Jazzed Up' (TB)	XSen
	'Jean Band' (CH)	GBin
	'Jean Cayeux' (TB)	ESgI EWoo
	'Jean Guymer' (TB)	ESgI
	'Jeanne Price' (TB)	ESgI EWoo
	'Jerry Murphy' (Sib)	ECtt EPfP LBar NCth SPeP WGob
	'Jesse's Song' (TB)	XSen
	'Jet Black' (TB)	EWoo
	'Jewel Baby' (SDB)	CBro
	'Jewels' (SDB) **new**	WCAu
	'Jiansada' (SDB)	CBro
	'Jigsaw' (TB)	XSen
	'Joanna' (TB)	EWoo NLar
	'Joie de Vivre' (La)	LLWG
	'Joyance' (TB) **new**	EWoo
	'Joyce' (Reticulata)	CRos EHyd GKev LRHS NRHS SDeJ
	'Joyce Cole' (Sib)	WCAu
	'Joyful Skies' (TB)	WCAu
	'Jubilant Spirit' (Spuria)	EWes EWoo
	'Jubilation' (TB)	EWoo
	'Jubilé Rainier III' (TB)	WViv
	'Juliet' (TB)	ESgI EWoo
	'June Prom' (IB)	EHyd EPfP ESgI LRHS NCth NRHS
	'June Rose' (IB)	CKel
	'Jungle Fires' (TB)	EWoo
	'Jungle Shadows' (BB)	ELon ESgI EWoo MRav NBir
	'Jurassic Park' (TB)	CKel SIri WCAu XSen
	'Just Dance' (IB)	ESgI
	'Just Imagine' (La)	LLWG
	'Just Jennifer' (BB)	WCAu
	'Kabluey' (Sib)	EBee ECtt NCth WFar WGob
	'Kaboom' (Sib)	MHol WFar
	kaempferi	see *I. ensata*
	'Kasim' (J)	GKev
	'Katharine Hodgkin' (Reticulata) ♀H7	CAby CAvo CRos EBee ECha EHyd EPfP EPot ERCP EWoo GAbr GKev LAma LCro LHWs LOPS LRHS MNrw NBir NHpl NLar NRHS NRog SDeJ WBrk WCot WFar WHil WHoo
	'Katharine's Gold' (Reticulata)	CAvo EPfP EPot ERCP ETay GKev LAma NRog WBrk WHoo
	'Kathleen Milne' (TB) **new**	ESgI
	'Katy Petts' (SDB)	ESgI
	'Keeper's Cottage' (TB) **new**	SIri
	kemaonensis PAB 8473	LEdu
	'Kent Compote' (IB)	SIri
	'Kent Pride' (TB)	Widely available
	'Kent Skylark' (IB)	SIri
	Kenta No Se129 (Sib)	EPri
	'Kentish Icon' (SDB)	SIri
	'Kentish Lad' (IB)	SIri
	'Kentucky Derby' (TB)	ESgI XSen
§	***kerneriana*** ♀H5	CBro GKev NBir
	'Kharput' (IB)	EWoo
	'Kildonan' (TB)	EWoo
	'Kimzey' (TB)	CKel

	'King Christian' (IB) **new**	EWoo
	'Kinshikou' (SpH)	LLWG
	kirkwoodii	GKev
	'Kiss of Summer' (TB) ♀H7	ESgI
	'Kiss the Girl' (Sib)	LLWG
	'Kissing Circle' (TB)	ESgI
	'Kita-no-seiza' (Sib)	CDor ECtt NCth NGdn WFar
	'Kiwi Slices' (SDB)	CWat
	'Knick Knack' (MDB)	CBro CKel ECtt EHyd ELan ELon GMaP LRHS MRav MTin NRHS SDeJ SPoG
	koreana	EPPr
	korolkowii	GKev
	'Kuh-e-Abr' (Reticulata)	GKev LAma NRog
	'La Meije' (TB)	WViv
	'La Senda' (Spuria)	WCot
	'Lace Legacy' (TB)	LSRN
	'Laced Cotton' (TB)	XSen
§	***lactea***	EPri SBrt SMHy XSen
	– CC 7174	GKev
	lacustris	WAbe WCot
	– 'Captain Collingwood'	see *I. cristata* 'Captain Collingwood'
	'Lady Belle' (MTB)	ESgI
	'Lady Byng' (TB)	WMil
	'Lady Friend' (TB)	WCAu XSen
	'Lady in Red' (SDB)	ESgI WCAu
	'Lady of the Night' (BB)	WCAu
	'Lady Paramount' (TB) **new**	EWoo
	'Lady Vanessa' (Sib)	EBee ELon MRav NSti WGob
	laevigata	CPud CRos CToG EWat ITim MRav NBro NPer SRms WFar WMAq WShi
	– var. ***alba***	CToG LLWG LRHS SRms
	– 'Atropurpurea'	LLWG
	– blue-flowered	CPud LLWG
	– 'Colchesterensis'	CPla CPud EWat NGdn NPer WMAq
I	– 'Dorothy'	NGdn
	– 'Dorothy Robinson'	EPfP MRav
*	– 'Elgar'	WMAq
	– 'Liam Johns'	CToG LLWG
	– 'Midnight'	see *I. laevigata* 'Weymouth Midnight'
	– 'Monstrosa'	EWat
	– 'Mottled Beauty'	LBar
	– 'Richard Greaney'	CToG EWat LLWG
	– 'Rose Queen'	see *I. ensata* 'Rose Queen'
	– 'Rowden Seaspray'	CToG
	– 'Rowden Starlight'	CToG LLWG
	– 'Royal Cartwheel'	LLWG
I	– 'Snowdrift'	CPud CToG EWat LLWG NBir NGdn NPer WCAu WFar WMAq
	– 'Variegata' (v) ♀H6	CPud CToG CWat ECha EPfP EWat LLWG NBro NGdn NPer SCob WMAq
	– 'Violet Garth'	EWat
	– 'Weymouth'	see *I. laevigata* 'Weymouth Blue'
§	– 'Weymouth Blue'	CToG EWat LLWG
§	– 'Weymouth Midnight'	LLWG
	– 'Weymouth Purity'	EWat
	laevigata × versicolor	WCAu
	– – Tamberg hybrid	LLWG
§	'Lake Niklas' (Sib)	ELon MHol
	'Langport Chapter' (IB)	ESgI
	'Langport Claret' (IB)	ESgI
	'Langport Curlew' (IB)	ESgI
	'Langport Duchess' (IB)	ESgI
	'Langport Fairy' (IB)	ESgI
	'Langport Flame' (IB)	ESgI
	'Langport Lord' (IB)	ESgI
	'Langport Minstrel' (IB)	ESgI
	'Langport Smoke' (IB)	WCAu
	'Langport Star' (IB)	ESgI
	'Langport Storm' (IB)	CFis EHyd ELon ESgI LRHS MBriF MRav NRHS SDeJ WTor
	'Langport Sun' (IB)	ESgI

'Langport Violet' (IB)	ESgI
'Langport Wren' (IB) ♀H7	CBro CKel ECtt EHyd ELon EPfP EPri ESgI EShb EWoo LRHS MBel MCot NBir NGdn NRHS WTor
'Langthorns Pink' (Sib)	MRav
'Lark Ascending' (TB)	MACG
'Late Hours' (TB) **new**	WCAu
§ ***latifolia***	EGrI WShi
- 'Duchess of York'	EBee
- 'Isabella'	NRog SDeJ
- 'King of the Blues'	EBee GKev SDeJ
- 'Montblanc'	NRog SDeJ
- 'Queen of the Blues'	SDeJ
'Latin Lark' (TB)	ESgI
'Laughing Clown' (TB) **new**	WCAu
'Laura Louise' (La)	LAma LLWG WGob
'Lavandulacea' (TB)	EWoo
'Lavender Bounty' (Sib)	GBin
'Lavender Landscape' (SpH) **new**	WCAu
lazica ♀H5	CBct CBod CBro CMac EBee EBlo ELan EPPr EPfP EPot EPri EWoo GBin GKev LRHS MMrt MPie MRav NBir NChi NCth NSti SBrt SEND SMHy SPlb SRms WGwG WMal WOld
- 'Joy Bishop'	EWoo
- 'Primrose Upward' **new**	WCot
* - 'Richard Nutt'	WCot WSHC
'Legato' (TB)	ESgI
'Lemon Flare' (SDB)	MRav SRms
'Lemon Ice' (TB)	ECha EWoo GBin LBar SCoo SDeJ SHar SPer SPoG WGwG WTor
'Lemon Pop' (IB)	WCAu
'Lemon Puff' (MDB)	CBro WCAu
'Lemon Veil' (Sib)	LAma NLar SDir WGob
'Lemon Whip' (IB)	EWoo
'Lena' (SDB)	CBro
'Lenora Pearl' (BB)	XSen
'Lent A. Williamson' (TB)	EWoo
'Lenzschnee' (TB)	EWoo
'Leo Hewitt' (Sib)	ELon
leptophylla	GKev
'Let's Elope' (IB)	WCAu
'Licorice Stick' (TB)	XSen
'Light Beam' (TB)	XSen
'Light Cavalry' (IB)	ESgI EWoo
'Light Rebuff' (TB)	EWoo
'Lilac Hymn' (TB) **new**	ESgI
'Lilac Times'	EWoo
'Lilli-white' (SDB)	CKel CWat EHyd ELon ESgI LRHS LSto MRav MTin NRHS SPoG WCAu
'Lilting' (TB)	XSen
'Limbo' (SpH)	LLWG
'Lime Fizz' (TB)	XSen
'Limelight' (TB)	SRms
lineata	GKev
'Lion King' (Dut) ♀H6	CAvo GKev LAma LCro LOPS MNrw MPie
'Little Black Belt' (SDB)	LRHS
'Little Blackfoot' (SDB)	WCot
'Little Blue' (Sib)	EBlo
'Little Blue-eyes' (SDB)	ESgI
'Little Bluets' (SDB)	ESgI
'Little Episode' (SDB)	CBro EDAr
'Little Nutkin' (La)	LLWG
'Little Rosy Wings' (SDB)	CBro
'Little Ruby Slippers' (La)	LLWG
'Little Shadow' (IB)	CWGN MRav SRms
'Little Sheba' (AB)	WCAu
'Little Showoff' (SDB)	ESgI
'Little Tilgates' (CH)	WCot WSHC
'Little Twinkle Star' (Sib)	MHer WFar
'Living Waters' (TB)	ESgI
'Local Color' (TB)	ESgI SIri XSen
'Lodore' (TB)	SRms
'Lohengrin' (TB)	EWoo
'Lollipop' (SDB)	ESgI
'London Pride' (TB)	EWoo
'Longhorn Pink' (TB) **new**	WCAu
longipetala	EPPr NBir
'Looking Forward' (TB)	ESgI
'Loop the Loop' (TB)	CKel CMac SPoG SRms
'Loose Valley' (MTB) ♀H7	SIri
'Lord Warden' (TB)	CBod CEnd ECtt LDai SHar WGwG
'Lorilee' (TB)	ESgI
'Lost in Love' (TB)	WCAu
'Lottie Lou' (TB)	SIri
'Lotus Land' (TB)	WCAu
Louisiana hybrids	LPfP
'Louvois' (TB)	CKel ESgI EWoo NLar
'Love Me Do' (La)	LLWG
'Love the Sun' (TB)	ESgI XSen
'Lovely Again' (TB)	GKev MRav WCAu
'Lovely Leilani' (TB)	ESgI
'Lovely Señorita' (TB)	WCAu
'Love's Tune' (IB)	CRos ECtt EHyd EPfP EWoo LRHS NRHS WTor
'Loyalist' (TB)	SIri
'Lucky Devil' (Spuria) ♀H7	WCAu
'Lugano' (TB)	EWoo
'Lullingstone Castle' (Kent Castles Series) (IB)	SIri
'Lumarco' (TB)	WViv
'Lumière d'Automne' (TB)	XSen
'Lurline' (TB)	WMil
lutescens ♀H7	EPot GArf GKev MHid WAbe
§ - 'Campbellii'	GArf
§ - subsp. ***lutescens***	XSen
- subsp. ***subbiflora***	WAbe
'Ma Mie' (IB)	WViv
maackii	GGro
'Mabel Coday' (Sib)	EBee EPri
'Mad Hat' (Sib) **new**	LBar
'Mad Magenta' (Sib)	GBin WCAu
'Madame Lynn' (Spuria)	EWoo
'Madeira Belle' (TB)	ECtt EHyd EPfP ESgI EWoo LRHS NRHS SPeP WCAu WGwG
'Mady Carriere' (TB)	EWoo
'Magharee' (TB)	ESgI
'Magic Man' (TB)	XSen
'Magic Masquerade' (TB)	WCAu
'Magical Encounter' (TB)	EWoo SIri
'Magneto' (SDB) **new**	WCAu
magnifica ♀H5	GKev LAma NRog
'Mahogany Lord' (Spuria)	WCAu
'Maid of Orange' (BB)	CKel WCAu
'Maisie Lowe' (TB)	ESgI EWoo
'Majestic' (TB)	WMil
'Majestic Overtures' (Sib)	LLWG
'Makin' Good Time' (TB) **new**	WCAu
'Mallow Dramatic' (TB)	CKel
I 'Mandarin' (TB)	ESgI
'Mandarin Purple' (Sino-Sib)	EBlo
'Mango Smoothy' (BB)	ESgI
'Man's Best Friend' (IB)	SIri
'Maranatha'	EWoo
'Marcus Perry' (Sib)	CToG
'Margot Holmes' (Cal-Sib)	WFar
'Margrave' (TB)	XSen
'Marilyn Holmes' (Sib)	GLog WCot
'Mariposa Autumn' (TB)	EWoo SIri WOld
'Marjaneh' (J)	GKev
'Marjorie' (TB)	SRms
'Marksman' (SDB)	SIri

'Marmalade Skies' (BB) WCAu
'Marry the Night' (TB) **new** WCAu
'Mars Landing' (Reticulata) EPot ERCP GKev LAma
'Marsh Marigold' (TB) WMil
'Martyn Rix' see *I. confusa* 'Martyn Rix'
'Mary Frances' (TB) CKel WCAu XSen
'Mary McIlroy' (SDB) ♀H7 CBro
'Marybill' (TB) SIri
'Master Touch' (TB) ELon WLov XSen
'Matinata' (TB) ELan EWoo XSen
'Matt McNames' (TB) EWoo
'Maui Moonlight' (IB) ♀H7 ESgI NLar WCAu
'May Allison' (TB) **new** EWoo
'Meadow Court' (SDB) CBro GEdr
'Medallion' (Spuria) EWoo
'Media Luz' (Spuria) WCAu
'Medici Prince' (TB) WCAu
'Medway Valley' (MTB) ♀H7 SIri
mellita see *I. suaveolens*
'Mellow Yellow' (TB) CEme
'Melon Honey' (SDB) ELon WCAu
§ 'Melton Red Flare' (Sib) EHyd ESgI EWoo GBin LRHS MBNS NRHS WAvo
'Memphis Memory' (Sib) EBee ELan ELon LRHS MHol NLar WFar WGob
'Men in Black' (TB) EWoo WCAu
'Mer du Sud' (TB) ♀H7 CBor CEnd ECtt EIri EPfP ESgI ETod EWoo LCro LRHS MACG SCob WCot WViv XSen
'Merchant Marine' (TB) **new** WCAu
* 'Merebrook Blue Lagoon' (La) WMAq
'Merebrook Jemma J' (La) WMAq
'Merebrook Purpla' (La) WMAq
'Merebrook Rum 'n' Raisin' (La) WMAq
* 'Merebrook Rusty Red' (La) WMAq
'Merebrook Sunata' (La) WMAq
'Merebrook Sunnyside Up' (La) WMAq
'Merebrook Symphony' (La) WMAq
'Merlot' (TB) ESgI
'Mesa Pearl' (Sib) CDor
mesopotamica see *I. germanica*
'Mexicana' (TB) **new** EWoo
'Mezza Cartuccia' (IB) ESgI
'Miami Beach' (TB) WCAu
'Michael Paul' (SDB) ♀H7 EGrI
'Mickey Gold' (Dut) **new** LAma
'Mickey Ocean' (Dut) **new** LAma
'Mickey Sea' (Dut) **new** LAma
'Midhurst White' (TB) SIri
I 'Midnight Blue' (MDB) CBro
'Midnight Caller' (TB) ESgI EWoo XSen
'Midnight Tryst' WCAu
'Midsummer Night's Dream' (IB) EWoo
'Midwest Star' (IB) CKel
'Mighty Mouse' (MDB) ELon
milesii ♀H3 CExl EPri GBin GKev NBir SBrt
'Millennium Falcon' (TB) SIri
'Millennium Sunrise' (TB) WCAu
'Mini-Agnes' (SDB) CBro EDAr
'Minisa' (TB) ESgI
'Miss Apple' (Sib) EPfP LBar WGob WTor
'Miss Nellie' (BB) CKel
'Mission Bay' (Sib) **new** LBar
'Mission Ridge' (TB) MHol
'Missouri Autumn' (Spuria) WCAu
missouriensis CMac EPPr GKev
'Mme Chéreau' (TB) EWoo
'Money in Your Pocket' (TB) **new** WCAu
'Monsieur-Monsieur' (TB) ESgI
Monspur Group WCot
'Moon Silk' (Sib) CBro ECtt ELon EPri EWes GBin LAma SCob WCot WFar WGob WHil
'Moonlight Masquerade' WCAu
'Moonlight Waves' see *I. ensata* 'Moonlight Waves'
'Moonlit Water' (TB) WCAu
'Morning Show' (IB) CKel
'Morning World' (TB) **new** WCAu
'Morwell' (TB) WMil
'Morwenna' (TB) ♀H7 ESgI
'Mother Earth' (TB) ESgI
'Mount Everest' (TB) LCro SDeJ
'Mountain Lake' (Sib) EBee EHyd ESgI EShb GBin LRHS MPie NRHS WFar WGob WSpi
'Mr Peacock' (Sib) WGob
'Mrs Horace Darwin' (TB) EWoo
'Mrs Rowe' (Sib) EIri ELon EPri ESgI MRav NFav WCAu WFar
'Mrs Tait' (Spuria) NChi
'Mrs Valerie West' (TB) WMil
'Muggles' (SDB) SIri
'Music' (SDB) SIri
'Music Maker' (TB) EGrI
'Mustard Falls' (SDB) **new** EDAr
'My Cher' (SDB) WCAu
'My Cher of Happiness' (BB) WCAu
'My Kayla' (SDB) ESgI
'My Seedling' (MDB) CBro
'Myra' (SDB) XSen
'Mysterieux' (TB) SIri
'Mystic' (TB) WMil
'Mystic Beauty' (Dut) LAma SDeJ
'Nada' (SpH) WCot
'Nancy Hardy' (MDB) CBro
'Naples' (TB) SIri
'Nassak' (TB) EWoo
'Natascha' (Reticulata) EPot GKev LAma NRog SDeJ
'Natchez Trace' (TB) CKel EPri LCro LOPS LRHS XSen
'Navajo Jewel' (TB) XSen
'Navy Brass' (Sib) EPri
'Needlecraft' (TB) XSen
'Needlepoint' (TB) ESgI
'Neglecta' (TB) **new** EWoo
'Neige de Mai' (TB) ESgI
* 'Nel Jupe' (TB) LRHS NLar
nepalensis see *I. decora*
'New Centurion' (TB) XSen
'New Face' (TB) WCAu
'New Idea' (MTB) CBro ESgI WCAu
'New Leaf' (TB) WCAu
'Nibelungen' (TB) CBor CBro ELan EPfP EWoo XSen
'Nickel' (IB) WCAu
nicolai 'Hissar' (J) NRog
'Night Breeze' (Sib) EPri
'Night Edition' (TB) ESgI XSen
'Night Game' (TB) XSen
'Night Owl' (TB) CKel CTsd EGrI ELon ESgI GDam GMcL MHer SBls
'Night Ruler' (TB) EWoo
'Nightfall' (TB) EBee NLar
'Nights of Gladness' (TB) ESgI
'Niklas Sea' see *I.* 'Lake Niklas'
'Ninja Turtles' (SDB) SIri
'No Restraint' (IB) **new** WCAu
'Noctambule' (TB) ♀H7 EWoo SIri WViv
'Noon Siesta' (TB) ESgI
§ × ***norrisii*** EHyd EPfP LRHS NRHS
– KIBA GIANTS (mixed) EAri SBls
'North Downs' (BB) SIri
'North Star' (Reticulata) **new** LAma
'North Star' (TB) GKev
'Not Quite White' (Sib) CBod

	'Now and Forever' (La)	LLWG
	'Nuit Blanche' (TB)	ESgI
	'Nuit de Noces' (TB)	SIri
	'Oblivion' (IB)	WCAu
	'Obsidian' (TB)	EWoo WCAu
	'Ochre Doll' (SDB)	CBro
	ochroleuca	see *I. orientalis* Mill.
	'October' (TB)	ESgI
	'October Storm' (IB)	EWoo
	'October Sun' (TB)	CKel ELan
	'Odin' (TB) **new**	EWoo
	'Oh Happy Day' (La)	LLWG
	'Oh Jamaica' (TB)	XSen
	'Oh So Cool' (MTB)	ESgI
	'Oklahoma' (TB)	EWoo
	'Oklahoma Bandit' (IB)	CKel
	'Oktoberfest' (TB)	XSen
	'Ola Kalá' (TB)	CRos EHeP EHyd ESgI EWoo GMaP GMcL LRHS MGos NLar NRHS SPeP SPer WCAu XSen
	'Old Black Magic' (TB)	ESgI XSen
	'Old Flame' (TB)	XSen
	'Olympiad' (TB)	ESgI XSen
	'Olympic Challenge' (TB)	ESgI MRav
	'Ombre' (TB) **new**	ESgI
	'Ominous Stranger' (TB)	ESgI MMrt
	'On Cloud Nine' (Reticulata) **new**	LAma
	'On Deck' (TB) **new**	WCAu
	'Once Again' (TB)	XSen
	'One Desire' (TB)	XSen
	'Open Sky' (SDB)	LRHS XSen
	'Orageux' (IB)	ESgI WMal
	'Orange Caper' (SDB)	CKel CMac ECtt EHyd ESgI LRHS MRav MTin NRHS SCob WCot
§	'Orange Chariot' (TB)	MBros
	'Orange Glow' (TB)	GKev
	'Orange Glow' (Reticulata) **new**	LAma
	'Orange Harvest' (TB)	ESgI XSen
	'Orange Jubilee' (TB) **new**	ESgI
	orchioides misapplied	see *I. bucharica* Foster
§	***orchioides*** Carrière	CAby ELan
	'Oregon Skies' (TB)	ESgI
	'Oriental Beauty' (TB)	SDeJ
	orientalis ambig.	ELan EWes MNrw WBor
§	***orientalis*** Mill. 🏆^{H6}	CAby GBin MMuc SEND SPtp WCot WCru XSen
	'Orinoco Flow' (BB) 🏆^{H7}	ESgI WCAu
	'Orloff' (TB)	ESgI
	'Orville Fay' (Sib)	GAbr WBor WCot
	'Ottawa' (Sib)	CWat EHyd WFar
	'Oulo' (TB)	XSen
	'Our House' (TB)	ESgI
	'Our Marcus' (TB)	SIri
	'Our Sassy' (La)	LLWG
	'Out of the Dark' (TB)	WCAu
	'Outer Edge' (IB) **new**	WCAu
	'Over in Gloryland' (Sib) **new**	WCAu
	'Overjoyed' (TB)	XSen
	'Owyhee Desert' (TB)	WCAu
	Pacific Coast hybrids	see *I.* Californian hybrids
	'Pacific Panorama' (TB)	ESgI XSen
	'Pagan Dance' (TB)	EWoo
	'Pagan Pink' (TB)	XSen
I	'Pageant' (Sib)	SMHy WCot WFar
	'Pageant' (TB)	WFar
	'Paint It Black' (TB)	EWoo XSen
	'Painted Lady' (Reticulata)	EPot ERCP GKev LAma LCro LOPS NCth WBrk
	'Painted Woman' (Sib)	CDor LLWG MBros
	'Pale Shades' (IB)	CBro
§	***pallida***	CBro CMac CPla EWoo GMaP LSun MRav SEND SRms WCAu XSen
§	- 'Argentea Variegata' (TB/v)	Widely available
	- 'Aurea'	see *I. pallida* 'Variegata' Hort.
	- 'Aurea Variegata'	see *I. pallida* 'Variegata' Hort.
	- subsp. ***cengialtii***	GKev
	- var. ***dalmatica***	see *I. pallida* subsp. *pallida*
§	- subsp. ***pallida***	CCBP CKel ECha EHyd ELan EPfP LRHS MHid NRHS SCob SCoo SHar SPer
	- 'Variegata' misapplied	see *I. pallida* 'Argentea Variegata'
§	- 'Variegata' Hort. (v) 🏆^{H7}	CBcs CBct CBro CEnd CKel CMac CWat ECha ELan EPfP LRHS MAsh MHol MRav NRHS NSti SDix SPeP SPer SPlb SPoG SRms SWvt WBrk WCot XSen
	'Palm Springs' (IB)	EPot LHWs SDeJ
	'Palm Springs' (Reticulata)	GKev LRHS NRHS SDeJ
	'Pamplemousse' (IB)	SIri
	'Pansy Purple' (Sib)	LRHS MNrw WHil
	'Panther' (SDB)	WCAu
	'Papillon' (Sib)	CBWd CTri EBlo ECtt EHyd ELan ELon EPri ESgI EWes EWoo LRHS NBir NGdn NRHS NSti SCob SDeJ SPer WFar
	'Paprikash' (Sib)	LBar LLWG NCth
	'Paradise' (TB)	NLar
	'Paradise Park' (TB) **new**	ESgI
	paradoxa	GKev
	'Paris Lights' (TB)	XSen
	'Parisian Dawn' (TB)	WCAu
	'Park Avenue' (TB) **new**	LAma
	'Parthenon' (TB) **new**	EWoo
	'Parting Glances' (IB)	WCAu
	'Party Dress' (TB)	CMac EBee ECtt EHyd ELan ESgI EShb LBar LRHS MRav NBir NLar NRHS NWad SCob SPer SPoG SRms WGwG
	'Party's Over' (TB)	WCAu
	'Pass the Wine' (TB) **new**	LBar
	'Pastel Accent' (La)	LLWG
	'Patches' (TB)	ESgI
	'Patina' (TB)	EIri EWoo LRHS
	'Patterdale' (TB)	NBir
	'Pauline' (Reticulata)	CAvo EPot ERCP EWoo GKev LAma LCro LRHS NRHS NRog
	'Pause' (SDB)	WCAu
	'Peaceful Waters' (TB)	XSen
	'Peach Eyes' (SDB)	CBro EDAr
	'Peach Picotee' (TB)	ESgI XSen
	'Peaches in Wine' (La)	LLWG
	'Peachy Face' (IB)	XSen
	'Pearly Dawn' (TB)	ECtt
*	'Pêche Melba' (TB)	XSen
	'Peebee and Jay' (MTB)	WCAu
	'Pelion Hills'	LRHS SGBe
	'Penguin Party' (TB) **new**	WCAu
	'Penny a Pinch' (TB)	CKel
	'Pennywhistle' (Sib)	LBar NLar
	'Percheron' (Sib)	EPri EWoo
	'Perfect Interlude' (TB)	EIri XSen
	'Perfect Vision' (Sib) 🏆^{H7}	MHCG
	'Performer' (MTB)	EIri
	'Perry's Blue' (Sib)	Widely available
	'Perry's Pigmy' (Sib)	ELon
	'Persian Berry' (TB)	XSen
	'Persimmon' misapplied	see *I.* 'Tycoon'
	'Persimmon' ambig. (Sib)	CAby CDor CKel ECtt EHyd GKin GQue LRHS MHer NRHS WFar WGwG
	'Peter Hewitt' (Sib) 🏆^{H7}	EPri MAvo WCAu WMal
	'Peter's Heir' (La)	LLWG
	'Pétillant' (TB)	EWoo

'Petit Tigre' (IB)	SIri
'Petite Charm' (IB)	WCAu
'Petite Monet' (MTB)	ESgI
'Petite Polka' (SDB)	NLar
'Petticoat Shuffle' (TB)	WCAu
'Pharaoh's Daughter' (IB)	EWoo
'Pigeon' (SDB)	XSen
'Pinewood Amethyst' (CH)	MAvo
'Pinewood Charmer' (CH)	CElw
'Pink Attraction' (TB)	ESgI XSen
'Pink Bubbles' (BB)	XSen
'Pink Charm' (TB)	ECtt EHyd ELan EPfP LRHS MHer NRHS SDeJ SPlb SPoG
'Pink Confetti' (TB)	XSen
'Pink Empress' (IB)	CKel
'Pink Haze' (Sib)	CBor
'Pink Horizon' (TB)	SPeP XSen
'Pink Kitten' (IB)	WCAu WGwG XSen
'Pink Lavender' (TB)	ELon SRms
'Pink Panther' (SDB) **new**	ERCP LAma
'Pink Parfait' (Sib)	CAby CWat MBNS NGdn WFar WGob WTor
'Pink Pele' (IB)	CKel ESgI
'Pink Pinafore' (TB)	EWoo
'Pink Quartz' (TB)	ESgI
'Pink Reprise' (BB)	EWoo
'Pink Swan' (TB)	XSen
'Pink Taffeta' (TB)	XSen
'Pinnacle' (TB)	EWoo
'Pioneer' (TB)	WMil
'Pipes of Pan' (TB)	ESgI MRav
'Pirate Ahoy' (TB)	WCAu
'Pirate Prince' (Sib)	NPer
'Pirate's Quest' (TB)	ECtt LBar MHer NCth XSen
'Piroska' (TB)	XSen
'Pixie' (DB)	GKev
'Pixie' (Reticulata) ♀H7	CAvo ELan EPot ERCP LAma LRHS NRog SDeJ
'Pleasures of May' (Sib)	ELon
'Pledge Allegiance' (TB)	ESgI
'Plickadee' (SDB)	CBro
'Plissée' (Sib) ♀H7	EWoo GBin
'Poesie' (TB)	WViv
'Pogo' (SDB)	CKel CMac CRos ECtt EHyd EWoo LRHS MHer MRav MTin NBir NRHS SDeJ SRms WGwG
'Polar Ice' (Reticulata)	LHWs
'Polar Ice' (TB)	EPot ERCP GKev LAma LRHS
'Polar Mist' (TB) **new**	WCAu
'Polvere di Stelle' (TB)	ESgI
'Poodle Parade' (TB)	WCAu
'Pop Culture' (IB)	WCAu
'Popped White' (TB) **new**	WCAu
'Port of Call' (Spuria)	EWoo
'Post Master' (La)	LLWG
'Potpourri Rose' (La)	LLWG
'Pounsley Purple' (Sib)	EPri
'Power Point' (TB)	WCAu
PRETTY IN BLUE (mixed) (Dut)	SDeJ
'Pretty Please' (TB)	ESgI
'Pretty Polly' (Sib)	CDor
'Pretty Reward' (MTB)	WCAu
'Primavera' (IB) **new**	EWoo
'Primrose Cream' (Sib)	GBin WCot
'Primrose Drift' (TB)	ESgI
'Prince Indigo' (TB)	MRav
'Prince of Burgundy' (IB)	WCAu
'Prince of Tuscany' (DB)	CBor
'Prince Victor' (IB) **new**	EWoo
'Princess Bride' (BB) ♀H7	WCAu
'Princess Leia' (La)	LLWG
'Princess Osra' (TB)	WMil
'Princesse Caroline de Monaco' (TB)	CKel EWoo WViv
'Prinzess Viktoria Luise' (IB) **new**	EWoo
prismatica	GArf GKev MHid SBrt
'Private Eye' (TB)	WCAu
'Professor Blaauw' (Dut) ♀H5	CAvo CWCL
'Project Runway' (TB) **new**	WCAu
'Prosper Laugier' (TB)	WCAu WLov
'Proud Tradition' (TB)	SIri XSen
'Provençal' (TB)	CKel ELon ESgI WCAu XSen
'Prussian Blue' (Sib) ♀H7	ESgI GBin SMHy
pseudacorus	Widely available
- B&SWJ 5018 from Japan	WCru
- 'Aketon Ivory' **new**	CToG
- 'Alba'	CBen CPud CWat LPfP MWts NGdn SRms
- var. ***bastardii***	CToG CWat ECha EGrI ELon EPfP EPri LCro LLWG LOPS LPfP NPer SPer WBrk WFar WPnP WWtn XLum
- 'Clotted Cream'	GLog
- 'Come in Spinner'	LLWG
- cream-flowered	NBir
- 'Crème de la Crème'	CToG ELon EPfP EWoo GBin LLWG NLar NSti NWad WFar
- 'Dragonfly Dance'	LLWG
- 'Esk'	EPPr
- 'Flore Pleno' (d)	CToG LPfP NLar NPer SRms WBrk WCot WFar WPnP
- 'Gigantea' **new**	CToG
I - 'Golden Fleece'	SPer
- 'Golden Queen'	CToG EWat LLWG
- 'Ivory'	CToG LLWG
- 'Kelis Choice'	LLWG
- 'Krill'	CDor EPPr EWoo LLWG
- 'Mini Mart'	LLWG
- 'Roccapina'	GBin
- 'Rowden Brimstone'	CToG
- 'Roy Davidson' ♀H7	CBro CToG LLWG MWts NLar WCot WFar WHil WWtn
- 'Spartacus'	EBee
- 'Sulphur Queen'	GBin LLWG NLar WCot
- 'Sun Cascade'	GBin
- 'Tiger Brother'	CBro LLWG WBrk
- 'Turnipseed'	WCot
- 'Variegata' (v) ♀H7	Widely available
* ***pseudocapnoides*** (J)	GKev
'Puddy Tat' (SDB)	WCAu
pumila	CRos EDAr EGrI EHyd ITim LRHS MBros NRHS NSla
- f. ***atroviolacea***	WAbe
* - 'Gelber Mantel'	NBir WFar
- 'Nicola'	EDAr
- 'Violacea' (MDB)	SRms
- yellow-flowered	EDAr WAbe
'Pure As Gold' (TB)	CWCL EIri ESgI WCot XSen
'Purple Gem' (Reticulata)	EHyd LRHS NRHS NRog
'Purple Hill' (Reticulata)	ERCP ETay GKev LAma
'Purple Mere' (Sib)	MHCG
'Purple Pleasure' **new**	WCAu
'Purple Sensation' (Dut)	SDeJ
'Purple Study' (MTB)	WCAu
'Pussycat Pink' (SDB)	ESgI WCAu
'Quaker Lady' (TB)	ESgI EWoo
'Quark' (SDB)	CBro
'Quechee' (TB)	CEnd EHyd EPPr EPfP ESgI ETod EWoo GMaP LBuc LDai LRHS MBriF MCot MRav NLar NRHS NWad SCob SCoo SDeJ SMrm SPer WGwG
'Queen Adelaide' (La)	LLWG
'Queen Flavia' (IB) **new**	EWoo
'Queen in Calico' (TB)	ESgI

	'Queen Jeanne' (La)	LLWG
	'Queen of Angels' (TB)	WCAu
	'Queen of Hearts' (TB)	XSen
	'Queen of May' (TB)	EWoo
	'Queen of the Mist' (TB)	WCAu
	'Queen's Circle' (TB) ♀H7	WCAu
	'Rabbit's Foot' (SDB)	SIri
	'Radiant Burst' (IB)	SIri
	'Rain Dance' (SDB) ♀H7	ESgI
	RAINBOW GRAND MIXTURE	SDeJ
	'Rainbow Rim' (SDB)	ESgI WCAu
	'Rajah' (TB)	CBod CEnd CRos EHyd ELan ESgI EWoo GMaP LRHS LSRN MCot MHer MNrw MRav NRHS SBea SCob SCoo SDeJ SMrm SPer SPoG WGwG WLov WSpi
	'Rambunctious' (Sib)	CDor
	'Rameses' (TB)	ESgI EWoo
	'Rancho Rose' (TB)	XSen
	'Ranman' (Sib)	CDor
	'Rare Edition' (IB)	CKel EWoo NBir XSen
	'Rare Quality' (TB)	XSen
	'Rare Treat' (TB)	XSen
	'Raspberry Acres' (IB)	MRav WCAu
	'Raspberry Blush' (IB) ♀H7	CKel ECha ECtt EGrI EHyd EPfP EWoo GBin LBar LRHS LSto MRav NBir NCth NRHS SBea SDeJ SMrm WGwG WHoo WTor XSen
	'Raspberry Tiger' (SDB)	WCAu
	'Raven Girl' (TB) **new**	WCAu
	'Ravissant' (TB)	WViv
	'Re La Blanche' (TB)	SIri
	'Realm' (TB)	EWoo
	'Rebellion' (TB) **new**	EWoo
	'Reckless Abandon' (TB) **new**	WCAu
	'Recurring Delight' (TB)	WCAu
	'Red Echo' (La)	LLWG
	'Red Ember' (Dut)	CAvo ERCP ETay GKev LAma LCro LOPS MNrw MPie SPeP WHil
	'Red Enigma' (TB)	SIri
	'Red Flare' (TB)	WFar
	'Redflare' (Sib)	see *I.* 'Melton Red Flare'
	'Red Flash' (TB)	ESgI
	'Red Heart' (SDB)	ELon ESgI MRav XSen
	'Red Orchid' (IB)	ELan EWoo LBar LRHS SRms
	'Red Revival' (TB)	EWoo MRav WCAu
	'Red Rufus' (TB)	CKel
	'Red Velvet Elvis' (La)	LLWG
	'Red Zinger' (IB)	CMac EWoo LRHS
	'Reddy Maid' (Sib)	LRHS
	'Redeemer's Crimson' (TB) **new**	ESgI
	'Redelta' (TB)	XSen
	'Redondo' (IB)	EWoo
	'Reflections of Love' (TB) **new**	WCAu
	'Reflets Safran' (TB)	XSen
	'Regal Surprise' (SpH) ♀H7	CToG EWat LLWG SBrt
	'Regality' (Sib)	MHer MMuc
	'Regard Sombre' (TB)	SIri
	'Regards' (SDB)	CBro XSen
	'Regency Belle' (Sib) ♀H7	GBin
	'Regency Buck' (Sib)	WFar WOld
§	***reichenbachii***	GKev WAbe
	'Remembering Vic' (Spuria)	EWoo
	'Rendez-Vous' (Dut)	SDeJ
	'Renee Fleming' (La)	LLWG
	'Repartee' (TB)	XSen
	reticulata	ELan ETay GKev LAma NRog SDeJ WHlf
	- var. ***bakeriana***	LAma NRog
	'Réussite' (TB)	EWoo
	'Rhapsody' (Reticulata)	EHyd EPot GKev LAma LRHS NRHS SDeJ
	'Rheingauperle' (TB)	ESgI EWoo
	'Rhinelander' (TB)	SIri WCAu
	'Rialgar' (IB) **new**	EWoo
	'Rigamarole' (Sib)	EGrI MWts WFar WGob
	'Rikugi-sakura' (Sib)	ELon EPri NCth NLar SHar WCot WGob WHil
	'Rimfire' (TB)	ELan MHol
	'Ringo' (TB)	EGrI MRav
	'Rio de Oro' (TB)	WViv
	'Rio Rojo' (TB)	WCAu
	'Rip City' (TB)	ESgI EWoo
	'Rive Gauche' (TB)	ESgI
	'Riveting' (SDB)	WCAu
	'Roanoke's Choice' (Sib)	CBro CElw ELon EWes LAma MNrw NCth SDir WFar
	'Roaring Jelly' (Sib)	CDor EPri EWes NLar WCot WGob
	'Robe d'Été' (TB)	WViv
§	× ***robusta*** 'Dark Aura' ♀H7	EBlo LLWG LRHS MAvo MWts WCot WHil WMal
§	- 'Gerald Darby'	Widely available
	- 'Mountain Brook'	CToG LLWG
	- 'Purple Fan'	LLWG
	'Rochester Castle' (Kent Castles Series) (IB)	SIri
§	'Rocket' (TB)	ECtt EHyd ESgI ETod EWoo GMaP LBar LBuc LRHS MRav NBir NCth NRHS SDeJ SPer
	'Roger Perry' (Sib)	CToG
	'Roku Oji' (Sib)	CDor
	'Romance' (TB)	EWoo
	'Romantic Evening' (TB)	EIri WCAu XSen
	'Romney Marsh' (IB)	SIri
	'Romola' (TB)	WMil
	'Roryu' (SpH)	LLWG
	'Rosace' (Sib)	EWoo
	'Rosalie Figge' (TB)	CMac EIri ESgI MHol WCAu WCot
	'Rosario' (Dut) **new**	SPeP
	'Rose Queen'	see *I. ensata* 'Rose Queen'
	'Rose Quest' (Sib) **new**	ESgI
	'Rose Unique' (IB)	EWoo
	'Rosebud Melody' (Sib)	GBin
	'Roseplic' (TB)	LRHS
	'Rosette Wine' (TB)	ESgI
	'Rosselline' (Sib)	MAvo
	'Rosy Bows' (Sib)	WCAu WFar
	'Rosy Veil' (TB)	ESgI
	'Rosy Wings' (TB)	ESgI
	'Roucoulade' (TB)	SIri
	'Rouge Gorge' (TB)	SIri WViv
	'Royal' (IB) **new**	EWoo
I	'Royal Blue' (Sib)	EBee ECha
	'Royal Crusader' (TB)	XSen
	'Royal Snowcap' (TB) **new**	WCAu
	'Roy's Repeater' (SpH)	ELon EWoo LLWG WCAu
	'Ruby Chimes' (IB)	ESgI WCAu
	'Ruby Contrast' (SDB)	CKel WCAu
	'Ruby Eruption' (SDB)	EIri ESgI
	'Ruby Wine' (Sib)	NLar
	rudskyi	see *I. variegata*
	'Ruffled Velvet' (Sib) ♀H7	CBcs CDor CElw CKel ECtt ELan EPfP EPri EWoo GBin GDam GLog GMaP GMcL LCro LRHS LSto MCot MRav NChi NLar SCob SPeP SPer WBor WCAu WFar
	'Ruffles and Flourishes' (Sib)	LLWG WCAu
	'Ruffles Plus' (Sib)	EPri WGob
	'Rumor Has It' (TB)	WCAu
	'Russian Kavelguard' (J)	CWCL
	'Rustler' (TB)	WCAu
	'Rusty Beauty' (Dut)	NRog SDeJ
	'Ruth Margaret' (TB)	CKel

'Ruth Rowlands' (TB)	ESgI EWoo
ruthenica	GArf
– var. ***nana***	CExl GEdr GKev
'Sable' (TB)	CKel CRos EHyd ELan EPfP ESgI ETod EWoo GMaP LBar LRHS MRav NCth NLar NRHS SCob SCoo SDeJ SHar SPer WCAu WGwG
'Sable Night' (TB)	ESgI
'Saint Crispin' (TB)	ECtt EHyd EPfP EWoo GMaP LRHS MRav NRHS SPer SPoG WGwG
'Salamander Crossing' (Sib) ♀H7	WCAu
'Salonique' (TB)	EWoo NLar
'Saltwood' (SDB)	CBro
'Saltwood Castle' (Kent Castles Series) (IB)	SIri
'Salvatore' (IB) new	LAma
'Sam Carne' (TB)	WCAu
× ***sambucina***	XSen
'San Diego' (TB)	ESgI
'San Francisco' (TB)	ESgI EWoo
'Sanctification' (TB) ♀H7	ESgI
'Sandy Caper' (IB)	WCAu
sanguinea 'Nana Alba'	GBin
§ – 'Snow Queen'	CBcs CEme CKel CToG CWat EGrI ELan EPfP EPri EWTr EWoo GBin GKev LPfP LRHS NBid NLar NQui NRHS NSti SPer WCAu WCot WFar
'Sapphire Beauty' (Dut)	GKev NRog SDeJ SPeP
'Sapphire Gem' (SDB)	ESgI
'Sapphire Hills' (TB)	LRHS XSen
'Sarah Taylor' (SDB) ♀H7	EWoo
'Sasha Borisovich' (TB)	ESgI
'Saturday Night Live' (TB)	EWoo
'Saturnus' (AB) new	LAma
'Savoir Faire' (Sib)	ECha
'Scent Sational' (Reticulata)	EPot ERCP GKev LAma
'Scented Wonder' (TB)	WCAu
schachtii	GArf
– purple-flowered	GArf WAbe
'Scramble' (Sib)	GMcL WCot WFar
'Scribe' (MDB)	CBro NBir
'Sea Breeze' (Reticulata)	EPot ERCP GKev LAma
'Sea Fret' (SDB)	CBro
'Sea Gull' (TB) new	EWoo
'Sea of Joy' (TB)	XSen
'Sea Shadows' (Sib)	EGrI EPri NBir
'Sea Wisp' (La)	EWoo LPfP
'Season Ticket' (IB)	XSen
'Second Look' (TB)	MBow XSen
'Second Wind' (TB)	EWoo WCAu
'Secret Affair' (TB) new	WCAu
'Secret Melody' (TB)	XSen
'Secret Service' (TB)	WCAu
'Semola' (SDB)	ESgI
'Senlac' (TB)	ELan EWoo NLar WMil
serbica	see *I. reichenbachii*
'Sespe' (TB) new	EWoo
setosa ♀H7	CMac CTri EAJP EGrI EHyd EPPr EPot EWTr GBin GKev LRHS MNrw NCth NHpl NRHS SGBe WFar
– var. ***arctica***	GKev LEdu
I – 'Baby Blue'	EHyd EPfP GKev LRHS MACG MBNS NRHS
– subsp. ***canadensis***	see *I. hookeri*
– dark violet-flowered	EPri
– ink-black seed pods	GGro
– var. ***nana***	see *I. hookeri*
'Shah Jehan' (TB) new	EWoo
'Shaker's Prayer' (Sib) ♀H7	ELon GAbr GBin LAma MNrw SDir WCAu WGob
'Shall We Dance' (Sib) ♀H7	CDor
'Shampoo' (IB)	EWoo

'Share the Spirit' (TB)	WCAu
'Sharp Dressed Man' (TB)	WCAu
'Sharrie Carrie' (TB)	SIri
'Sheer Excitement' (BB) new	EWoo
'Sheila Ann Germaney' (Reticulata)	CRos EHyd EPot ERCP ETay GKev LAma LHWs LRHS NRHS WBrk
'Shekinah' (TB) new	EWoo
'Sherbert' (TB) new	EWoo
'Sherbet Lemon' (IB) ♀H7	WCAu
'Shirley Chandler' (IB) ♀H7	SIri
'Shirley Pope' (Sib) ♀H7	EWes GBin LRHS NSti WFar WGob WPnP WSpi
'Shirley's Choice' (Sib)	ELon EPri
'Shiryukyo' (SpH)	WMal
'Short Distance' (IB)	EWoo
'Showdown' (Sib)	EBlo ECtt EHyd GMaP LRHS NRHS
'Shrawley' (Sib)	EWoo
shrevei	see *I. virginica* var. *shrevei*
'Shurton Inn' (TB)	SRms WCAu
sibirica	CAvo CTri CTsd GAbr GArf GBin GKev GQue LPfP MBros MCot MHid MMuc NChi NCth SBls SCob SPlb WBrk WFar WGwG WHer WPnP WShi
– PAB 6119	LEdu
– 'Snow Queen'	see *I. sanguinea* 'Snow Queen'
– white-flowered	ECha EPfP EPri GKev SRms WBrk WFar WWke
sichuanensis	CExl SPlb
'Side Effects' (TB)	WCAu
'Sierra Blue' (TB)	ESgI
'Sierra Grande' (TB)	XSen
'Sierra Nevada' (Spuria)	XSen
'Sign of Leo' (TB)	CKel EWoo XSen
'Silver Edge' (Sib) ♀H7	Widely available
'Silver Ice' (MTB) new	WCAu
'Silver Peak' (TB)	CKel
'Silverado' (TB)	ESgI GBin LRHS WCAu WSpi
'Silvery Beauty' (Dut) ♀H6	CAvo ELan GKev LAma LCro LOPS MPie NBir NRog SDeJ
'Silvery Princess' (Dut)	SDeJ
'Simply Coral' (TB)	WCAu
'Simply Irresistible' (La)	LLWG
'Simply Sensational' (TB) new	WCAu
sindjarensis	see *I. aucheri*
'Sinfonietta' (La)	LLWG WCot
'Sing to Me' (TB)	WCAu
'Sinister Desire' (IB)	EWoo SIri
sintenisii ♀H6	GKev WAbe XSen
'Sir Michael' (TB)	ESgI EWoo
'Siva Siva' (TB)	CKel ESgI MRav
'Sixteen Candles' (IB)	EWoo
'Skating Party' (TB)	ESgI XSen
'Skiers' Delight' (TB)	ESgI
'Sky Beauty' (Dut)	SDeJ
'Sky Hooks' (TB)	XSen
'Sky Wings' (Sib)	CToG ECha MArl WFar
'Skydancer' (SDB)	WCAu
'Skyfire' (TB)	CKel
'Skylark's Song' (TB)	EIri EWoo
'Small Sky' (SDB)	CBro
'Smart' (SDB)	WCAu
'Smart Aleck' (TB)	ESgI
'Smart Move' (TB)	ESgI
'Smiling Faces' (TB)	WCAu
'Smooth Orange'	see *I.* 'Orange Chariot'
'Snapshot' (TB) new	WCAu
'Snow Prince' (Sib)	CBWd EPri
'Snow Season' (SDB)	ESgI
'Snow Tracery' (TB)	ECtt EHyd EPfP EWoo LRHS NRHS
'Snow Troll' (SDB)	WCAu

'Snowcrest' (Sib)	CEnd CPud EBee EHyd ESgI GBin LRHS MRav NRHS WGob WHoo
'Snowmound' (TB)	CKel ESgI
'Snowy Owl' (TB)	WCAu
'Snugglebug' (SDB)	WCAu
'Social Event' (TB)	ESgI XSen
'Soft Blue' (Sib) ♀H7	CBWd ELon EPri NLar WCAu
'Solar Fusion' (Spuria)	EWoo
'Solid Mahogany' (TB)	MRav
'Song of Norway' (TB)	EIri EWoo XSen
songarica	MHid
sophenensis	EPot GKev LAma
'Sopra il Vulcano' (BB)	ESgI
'Sorbonne' (TB)	WCAu
'Sordid Lives' (TB)	WCAu
'Sostenique' (TB)	ESgI
'Southcombe White' (Sib)	SMHy
'Southland' (IB)	EWoo
'Souvenir de Madame Gaudichau' (TB)	ESgI EWoo
'Sparkling Rose' (Sib)	Widely available
'Sparkling Waters' (TB)	ESgI
'Spartan' (TB)	EWoo
'Speckled Hen' (La)	LLWG
I 'Speckles' (Sib)	EPPr
'Speeding Star' (Spuria)	WCAu
'Spellbreaker' (TB)	ELon SIri
'Spice Lord' (TB)	WCAu
'Spiced Custard' (TB)	EIri ESgI
'Spicy Cajun' (La)	LAma WHil
'Spindazzle' (Sib)	ECtt LBar
'Spirit of Memphis' (TB)	XSen
'Splashacata' (TB)	XSen
'Splish Splash' (Reticulata) **new**	LAma
'Spot On' (Reticulata)	CAvo EPot GKev LAma LRHS
'Spreckles' (TB)	CKel ESgI
'Spree' (SDB)	WCAu
'Spring Blush' (MTB) ♀H7	EIri
'Spring Madness' (TB)	WCAu
'Spring Time' (Reticulata)	SDeJ
spuria	CMac EWoo SBls
§ - subsp. ***halophila***	ECha GKev
- subsp. ***notha*** CC 725	WCot
- subsp. ***ochroleuca***	see *I. orientalis* Mill.
'Spy' (BB)	WCAu
'Sri Lanka' (AB) **new**	WCAu
'St Louis Blues' (TB)	ESgI XSen
'Stairway to Heaven' (TB)	ESgI WCAu
'Stapleford' (SDB)	CBro
'Staplehurst' (MTB) ♀H7	SIri
'Star Cluster' (Sib)	WFar
'Star in the Night' (TB)	WCAu
'Star Shine' (TB)	WCAu
'Starring' (TB)	EIri
'Starship' (TB)	XSen
'Starwoman' (IB) ♀H7	WCAu
'Staten Island' (TB)	ESgI SRms WCAu
'Stella Polaris' (TB)	ELon
'Stellar Lights' (TB)	EIri EWoo WCAu
'Stephen Wilcox' (Sib)	CDor EPri
'Stepping Out' (TB) ♀H7	CKel CMac CRos ECtt EHyd EPfP ESgI ETod EWoo GBin LBar LDai LRHS NCth NRHS SCob SDeJ SHar WCAu WHoo WTor
'Steve' (Sib)	CPar ESgI EWes NLar
'Steve Varner' (Sib)	EPri
'Steve's Choice' (TB) **new**	SIri
'Stingray' (TB)	ESgI
'Stitch in Time' (TB)	EIri
stolonifera	GKev NRog
- 'Augustus'	GKev
- 'Caligula' (Rc)	GKev
- 'Claudius'	GKev
- 'George Barr'	GKev
- 'Morning Coffee'	GKev
- 'Trajanus'	GKev
- 'Vespasianus'	GKev
- 'Zwanenburg Beauty'	GKev
'Stop the Music' (TB)	XSen
'Storrington' (TB)	CBWd CEnd CMil ECha ECtt ELan EPfP ETod WCAu
'Strathmore' (TB)	CMil ECha ETod EWoo
'Strawberry Fair' (Sib) ♀H7	GBin WCAu
'Strike it Rich' (TB)	ESgI
'Strongold' (Dut) ♀H6 **new**	LAma
'Strozzapreti' (TB)	ESgI
'Strut your Stuff' (TB)	WCAu
'Study in Black' (TB)	XSen
'Stylish Socialite' (La)	LLWG
stylosa	see *I. unguicularis*
§ ***suaveolens***	EDAr GEdr NHpl NWad
- var. ***flavescens***	see *I. suaveolens* yellow-flowered
- Hevolvus Group	WCot
§ - purple-flowered	EDAr GEdr GKev SGro WAbe
- var. ***violacea***	see *I. suaveolens* purple-flowered
§ - yellow-flowered	GArf GKev WAbe
'Succès Fou' (TB)	WViv
'Sugar' (IB)	NSti WCAu
'Sugar Magnolia' (TB)	SIri
'Sugarmouse' (BB)	SIri
'Sultan's Palace' (TB)	CBod CEnd CKel EBee ECtt EPfP EWoo LBar LCro LRHS MHer WCAu WSpi XSen
'Sultan's Ruby' (Sib)	EWoo
'Sultry Mood' (TB)	CKel
'Summer Holidays' (TB)	XSen
'Summer Olympics' (TB)	CKel
'Summer Revels' (Sib)	EPri EWes WGob
'Summer Sky' (Sib)	CDor ELon LEdu MHCG MSCN NCth WCot
'Summer's Day' (Reticulata) **new**	LAma
'Sun in Splendour' (SpH) **new**	CToG
'Sunadokei' (SpH)	LLWG
'Sunlit Shores' (La)	LLWG
'Sunny Delight' (TB)	ESgI
'Sunny Disposition' (TB)	XSen
'Sunnyside Up' (TB)	GKev
'Sunset Sky' (TB)	CKel CWGN
'Sunshine' (TB)	GKev
'Sunshine' (Reticulata)	EPot ERCP LAma SDeJ
'Superact' (Sib)	ELon
'Superstition' (TB) ♀H7	CKel CWGN EIri ELan EWes LCro LOPS LRHS MRav WCAu WHlf XSen
'Supreme Sultan' (TB)	ESgI SCob WCAu XSen
I 'Surprise' (Dut)	MNrw
'Susan Bliss' (TB)	ELan EPfP ESgI EWoo WCAu WMil
'Swain' (TB)	ESgI
'Swan Ballet' (TB)	ESgI
'Swans in Flight' (Sib)	WCAu
'Swazi Princess' (TB)	ELon SEdd SRms WSpi
'Sweet and Innocent' (SDB) **new**	WCAu
'Sweet Kate' (SDB)	ESgI
'Sweet Lavender' (TB)	WMil
'Sweet Lena' (TB)	ESgI
'Sweet Musette' (TB)	SChr SRms WCAu
'Sweet Surrender' (Sib)	EPri
'Sweeter than Wine' (TB)	MRav
'Swingtown' (TB)	WCAu
'Swirling Waters' (La)	LLWG
'Swiss Majesty' (TB)	WCAu
'Swizzle' (IB)	XSen
'Sybil' (TB)	GBin

	'Sylvan' (TB)	XSen
	'Symphony' (Dut)	ELan NBir SDeJ
	'Syncopation' (TB)	ELon ESgI XSen
	'Syrian Hills' (TB)	WCAu
	'Tabac Blond' (TB)	EWoo
	'Tact' (IB)	SIri
	'Taking Chances' (TB)	WCAu
	'Tamberg' (Sib)	CKel EWoo LSto NLar
	'Tamerlan' (TB)	EWoo
	'Tan Tingo' (IB)	XSen
	'Tangerine Sky' (TB)	LRHS MBriF
	'Tantara' (SDB)	XSen
	'Tantrum' (IB)	XSen
	taochia	WAbe
	'Tarn Hows' (TB)	ESgI EWoo SRms
	taurica	WAbe
	'Teal Velvet' (Sib)	ECha ELon EPfP EPri ESgI EWes EWoo GLog LRHS SCob WFar WGob
	'Tealwood' (Sib)	GBin WMal
	'Teapot Tempest' (BB)	WCAu
	'Teasaucer Hill' (MTB) ♀H7	SIri
	tectorum	EAri EWoo LRHS SGBe WCot WMal XLum XSen
	- BWJ 8191	WCru
	- from Yunnan	MHid
	- 'Alba'	WThu XSen
	- 'Cruella'	CKel MHol MSCN WSpi
	- 'Variegata' misapplied	see *I. japonica* 'Variegata'
	- 'Variegata' (v)	SRms
	'Tell Fibs' (SDB)	CBro
	'Teller of Tales' (La)	LLWG
	'Telstar' (Dut) **new**	LAma
	'Temper Tantrum' (Sib)	CBrac CToG EGrI
	'Temple Gold' (TB)	NPer
	'Temple Meads' (IB)	ESgI WCAu
	'Temple of Lights' (TB) **new**	WCAu
	'Temporal Anomaly' (TB) **new**	WCAu
	'Tempting Fate' (TB)	SIri
§	***tenax***	EDAr
	'Tenebrae' (TB)	WMil
	'Tenterden' (BB)	SIri
	tenuissima	EPot
	'Terra del Fuoco' (TB) **new**	ESgI
	'Teven' (La)	LLWG
	'Teverlae' (Sib)	EBee EHyd LRHS NRHS
	'Thaïs' (TB)	ESgI EWoo
	'That's All Folks' (TB) **new**	WCAu
	'That's Red' (MTB)	EIri
	'The Black Douglas' (TB)	EWoo
	'The Bride'	see *I.* 'Bride'
	'The Citadel' (TB)	ELon
	'The Red Douglas' (TB)	EWoo
	'The Rocket'	see *I.* 'Rocket'
	'Theodolinda' (TB)	EWoo
	'Third Charm' (SDB)	CBro EDAr
	'Third World' (SDB)	CBro
	'Thornbird' (TB) ♀H7	EIri ESgI SRms WCAu
	'Three Part Harmony' (TB)	WCAu
	'Three Quarters' (Sib)	ELon EWoo NChi
	'Thriller' (TB)	ESgI EWoo WCAu XSen
	'Thundercloud' (TB)	EWoo
	'Thundering Ovation' (TB)	WCAu
	'Tic Tac Toe' (MTB) **new**	WCAu
	'Tickety Boo' (SDB)	ECtt LBar MBros NBPC
	'Tiffany' (TB)	EWoo
§	'Tigereye' (Dut)	ERCP GBin GKev LAma LCro LOPS MNrw SDeJ SPeP
*	'Tiger's Eye' ambig.	CKel

	'Time Zone' (TB)	WCAu
	'Timescape' (TB)	EGrI
	timofejewii **new**	WAbe
	tingitana	GKev
	'Tinkerbell' (SDB)	EBee ECtt EHyd ESgI GMaP LRHS NBir NRHS SDeJ
	'Tiny Titan' (MDB) **new**	WOld
	'Tipped in Blue' (Sib) **new**	CBod LBar
	'Tishomingo' (TB)	EWoo
	'Titan's Glory' (TB) ♀H7	CBod CCBP CKel CMac ECtt EPfP LEdu MPie MRav SRms WCot WHoo WSpi
	'Tollong'	ILea
	'Tom Tit' (TB)	WCAu WMil
	'Tomato Bisque' (La)	LLWG
	'Top Flight' (TB)	ELan SRms
	'Top Gun' (TB)	ESgI
	'Torero' (TB)	SIri
	'Total Eclipse' (TB)	SRms
	'Touch of Mahogany' (TB)	WCAu
	'Town Flirt' (TB)	WCAu
	'Trapel' (TB)	ESgI
	'Trencavel' (TB)	ESgI
	'Trenwith' (TB)	ESgI
	'Triple Whammy' (TB)	ESgI XSen
	'Triplicate' (SDB)	SMrm
	'Tristram' (TB)	WMil
	'Tropic Night' (Sib)	Widely available
	tuberosa	CAvo CBor CBro CTri CWCL ECha ERCP EWoo LAma MHer SDeJ WShi
	- MS 76	WCot
	- MS 964	WCot
	- PB	GKev WCot
	'Tulip Festival' (TB)	CBor CKel
	'Tumble Bug' (Sib)	CDor ECtt LBar WGob
	'Tumultueux' (TB)	WViv
	'Tuxedo' (TB)	XSen
	'Twice Is Nice' (TB) **new**	WCAu
§	'Tycoon' (Sib)	EBlo EWoo GBin LCro NChi SPer
	typhifolia	GKev
	'Ultimate' (SDB)	ESgI WCAu
	'Unbuttoned Zippers' (Sib)	CDor NLar
	'Uncorked' (Sib)	CTtf ECtt EPfP LBar LLWG MSCN
	'Undercurrent' (TB)	WCAu
§	***unguicularis***	Widely available
	- 'Abington Purple'	EIri
	- 'Alba'	CAvo CExl XSen
	- subsp. ***angustifolia***	WSHC
§	- subsp. ***cretensis***	GKev WAbe
	- - white-flowered	WSHC
	- 'Diana Clare'	MAvo
	- 'Kilbroney Marble'	MAvo
	- 'Marondera'	CAvo CBct
	- 'Mary Barnard' ♀H5	CAvo CBro EGrI MHer WHoo
	- 'Peloponnese Snow'	CBro EPot GEdr
	- 'Speciosa'	CBro
§	- 'Walter Butt'	CAvo EBee MAvo WOld
	'Up in Flames' (TB)	SIri
	'Vague à l'Âme' (TB)	EWoo
	'Valda' (Sib)	ELon EWoo WOld
	'Vamp' (IB)	EWoo GBin XSen
	'Vanilla Mist' (La)	LLWG
	'Vanilla Skies' (TB)	WCAu
	'Vanity' (TB)	XSen
	'Vanity's Child' (TB)	WCAu XSen
§	***variegata*** ♀H7	CDor EBee EDAr GBin SCob XSen
	- from Podyjí, Moravia	SBrt
I	- var. ***reginae*** 'Davidowii'	MAvo
	'Velvet Dusk' (TB)	EWoo
	'Velvet King' (TB)	ESgI
	'Velvet Midnights' (TB) **new**	ESgI
	'Venus Vortex' (La)	LLWG

	versicolor	CBen CPud CToG CWat EWoo GBin GKev GMaP GMcL GPoy LPfP MMuc MNHC MWts SEND SPlb SRms WCAu WFar WMAq WPnP WShi
	- 'Algonquin'	LLWG
	- 'Bellerive Harmony'	LLWG
	- 'Between the Lines'	LLWG
	- 'Candystriper'	LLWG
	- 'China West Lake'	LLWG
	- 'Claret Cup'	EWoo
	- 'Dottie's Double'	CToG
	- 'Kermesina'	CEme CPud ECha ELan EWat EWoo GKev LCro LLWG LOPS LPfP NPer NSti SBls SRms WFar WMAq WPnP
	- 'Mint Fresh'	LLWG
	- 'Mysterious Monique'	LLWG MWts
	- 'Party Line'	CBen
	- purple-flowered	EWat
	- 'Raspberry Slurp'	LLWG
	- 'Rowden Allegro'	CToG LLWG
	- 'Rowden Anthem'	CToG
	- 'Rowden Aria'	LLWG
	- 'Rowden Cadenza'	CToG EWat LLWG
	- 'Rowden Calypso'	CToG LLWG
	- 'Rowden Cantata'	CToG LLWG
	- 'Rowden Concerto'	CToG LLWG
	- 'Rowden Electro'	LLWG
	- 'Rowden Jingle'	CToG
	- 'Rowden Lullaby'	CToG
	- 'Rowden Lyric'	LLWG
	- 'Rowden Madrigal' **new**	CToG
	- 'Rowden Melody'	LLWG
	- 'Rowden Minuet'	CToG
	- 'Rowden Pastorale'	CToG LLWG
	- 'Rowden Sonata'	CToG LLWG
	- 'Rowden Symphony'	CToG
	- 'Rowden Waltz'	LLWG
	'Very Special' (TB) **new**	WCAu
	'Vi Luihn' (Sib)	ECha ELon SAko WFar
	'Vibrations' (TB)	ESgI WCAu
	vicaria	NRog
	'Victoria Falls' (TB)	CKel ESgI MHol
	'Victorian Secret' (Sib)	EBee ELon
	'Victorine' (TB) **new**	EWoo
	'Viel Creme' (Sib)	ESgI
	'Viel Schnee' (Sib)	ELon EWoo
	'Vigilante' (TB)	EWoo
	'Vin Nouveau' (TB)	XSen
	'Vingolf' (IB) **new**	EWoo
	'Vino Rosso' (SDB)	ESgI
	'Violet Beauty' (Reticulata)	EHyd NRHS NRog
	'Violet Harmony' (TB)	ESgI
	virginica	LLWG
	- 'De Luxe'	see *I.* × *robusta* 'Dark Aura'
	- 'Lavender Lustre'	LLWG
	- 'Orchid Purple'	LLWG
	- 'Pale Lavender'	LLWG
	- 'Pink Perfection'	LLWG
	- 'Pond Crown Point'	CToG
§	- var. ***shrevei***	LLWG
	- 'Slightly Daft'	LLWG
	'Vishnu' (TB) **new**	EWoo
	'Vitafire' (TB)	ESgI
	'Vitality' (IB)	ELon ESgI
	'Vitrail' (IB)	WViv
	'Vivacious Beginnings' (Reticulata) **new**	LAma
	'Vive la France' (TB)	ESgI
	'Voilà' (IB)	ESgI
	'Volts' (SDB)	XSen
	'Voyage' (SDB)	XSen
	'Wabash' (TB)	CKel EWoo XSen
	'Waihi Wedding' (La)	LLWG
	'Walmer Castle' (Kent Castles Series) (IB)	SIri
	'Walter Butt'	see *I. unguicularis* 'Walter Butt'
	'War Chief' (TB)	ESgI MBriF MRav SPeP WCAu
	'War Sails' (TB)	SIri WCAu
	warleyensis	NRog
	'Warlsind' (J)	GKev
	wattii	CExl EPPr WGwG
	- KWJ 12172	WCru
	'Wealden Mystery' (Sib)	EPri
	'Wearing Rubies' (TB)	ESgI WCAu
	'Webelos' (SDB)	MRav
	'Webmaster' (SDB)	EPPr
	'Wedding Candles' (TB)	CKel
	'Wedding Vow' (TB)	EIri
	'Wedgwood' (Dut)	GBin
*	'Wedgwood Blue' (Sino-Sib)	GBin
	'Weisse Etagen' (Sib)	ELon
	'Welcome Return' (Sib)	LLWG MMuc SDir WGob
	'Welfenfürstin' (Sib)	GBin SAko
	'Well Suited' (SDB)	ESgI
	'Wench' (TB)	EWoo
	'Westwell' (SDB)	GEdr
	'What Again' (SDB)	XSen
	'What It's Worth' (TB)	WCAu
	'What's New Pussycat' (BB)	WCAu
	'Whee' (SDB)	WCAu
	'White Amber' (Sib)	ECtt LBar WGob
	'White Caucasus' (Reticulata)	EPot ERCP GKev LAma
	'White City' (TB)	CKel EHyd EPfP ESgI EWoo GMaP LRHS MRav NPer NRHS SDeJ SPer SRms WCAu
	'White Excelsior' (Dut)	SPeP
	'White Gem' (SDB)	ESgI
	'White Knight' (TB)	EBee EHeP SEdd WSpi
	'White Reprise' (TB)	XSen
I	'White Swan' (Sib)	EPri
	'White Swirl' (Sib)	CAvo CBar CBro CTri EBee ECha ECtt ELon EPfP ESgI GBin GLog GMaP GMcL LCro LRHS MRav NBro NLar NRHS NSti SCob SRms WFar WGob WPnP
	'White Triangles' (Sib)	ELon EWoo
	'White Umbrella' (La)	ECtt LLWG MBros
	'White van Vliet' (Dut)	SDeJ
	'White Wine' (MTB)	WCAu
	'Widow's Veil' (SDB)	ESgI
	'Wild' (BB)	WCAu
	'Wild Wings' (TB)	LRHS SGbt WCAu
	willmottiana 'Alba'	GKev
	wilsonii ♀H7	CExl GArf GKev NRya
	'Wine Wings' (Sib)	LRHS WGob
	'Winesap' (TB)	ESgI EWoo
	'Wings at Dawn' (TB) **new**	WCAu
	'Wink and Smile' (TB) **new**	WCAu
	winogradowii ♀H7	CBor EHyd EPot GKev NRHS NRog WAbe
	'Winter Olympics' (TB)	CKel CRos ECtt EHyd ELan LBar LRHS MRav NRHS SOrN SPer WGwG WTor
	'Winterfest' (TB)	WCAu
	'Wintry Sky' (TB)	WCAu
	'Wish Upon a Star' (SDB)	WCAu
	'Wishful Thinking' (TB)	SIri
	'Wizard's Return' (SDB)	SIri
	'Wondrous' (TB)	CEnd ECtt EPfP ESgI LBar WGwG
	'Word of Warning' (La)	LLWG
	'Wrangler' (IB)	SIri
	'Wynne Magnolia' (Sib) **new**	LBar

xiphioides	see *I. latifolia*
xiphium var. ***lusitanica***	GKev
'Yankee Consul' (Sib)	EPri
'Yaquina Blue' (TB)	ESgI WCAu
'Yarai' (SpH)	CBen LLWG
'Yasha' (SpH)	CBen LLWG
'Yellowtail' (Sib)	CBod EPfP LBar MSCN
'Yeoman' (TB)	WMil
'Yes' (TB)	ESgI
'Yippy Skippy' (SDB)	WCAu
'Yosemite Nights' (TB)	EWoo
'Yosemite Star' (TB)	EWoo
'Yo-yo' (SDB)	LBar
'Yukiyanagi' (SpH)	LLWG
'Yvonne Pelletier' (TB)	WCAu
'Zakopane' (Sib)	EWes
'Zantha' (TB)	XSen
'Zero' (SDB)	ESgI
'Zinger' (BB)	WSpi
'Zweites Hundert' (Sib)	WFar WKif

Isatis (*Brassicaceae*)

glauca	SPhx
tinctoria	CBod CCBP CHab CHby CKel CSpe ENfk GJos GPoy MHer MHoo MNHC SRms SVic WSFF XSen
– subsp. ***athoa***	WCot

Ismelia (*Asteraceae*)

carinata 'Bright Eye' new	WMal

Ismene (*Amaryllidaceae*)

§ × ***deflexa*** ♀H1c	CCCN EShb GKev LAma LCro LOPS SDeJ
– 'Zwanenburg'	GKev LAma
§ ***longipetala***	GKev LAma
§ 'Sulphur Queen' ♀H1c	CBor GKev LAma SDeJ SMrm

Isodon (*Lamiaceae*)

calycinus	SPlb
effusus	MHol MNrw WPGP
excisus	LPla
longitubus	LEdu MHol
– B&SWJ 11027	WCru

Isolatocereus see *Stenocereus*

Isolepis (*Cyperaceae*)

§ ***cernua***	CBen CPud CWat EWat LCro LLWG LOPS LPfP LRHS MACG MWts SCoo WCot WMAq
'Live Wire'	see *I. cernua*
nodosa (Rottb.) R. Br.	see *Ficinia nodosa*

Isoloma see *Kohleria*

Isomeris see *Cleome*

Isoplexis see *Digitalis*

Isopogon (*Proteaceae*)

anemonifolius	CCCN SPlb
anethifolius	SPlb
formosus	LRHS XSte
trilobus new	SPlb

Isopyrum (*Ranunculaceae*)

biternatum	LEdu
nipponicum	GGro
thalictroides	EBee EMor EPot LEdu NRya WCot

Isotoma (*Campanulaceae*)

§ ***axillaris***	CSpe NPer SCoo
– 'Fairy Carpet'	LLWG LRHS NCou NHpl SLee SRms WWke
– FIZZ 'N' POP GLOWING PURPLE ('Tmlu 1301') new	MDon
– 'Lauren Blue'	MPri
fluviatilis	NLar

Itea (*Iteaceae*)

ilicifolia ♀H5	Widely available
* – 'Rubrifolia'	ELan
virginica	CBcs CMCN EGrI LRHS MRav
§ – 'Henry's Garnet' ♀H5	CBod CDoC CEme CEnd CKel CMCN CMac EBee EGrI EPfP EShb EWhm GArf GBin MGil MGos NLar SCob SEle SGol SIvy SMad SPad SPer SPoG SRms SSha SWvt WLov WPGP
– LITTLE HENRY ('Sprich'PBR)	CBcs CKel CMac CSBt EBee EPfP ILea LRHS NLar XSte
– 'Long Spire'	NLar
– 'Merlot'	CBod EHed ELon MACG MBlu NLar SIvy
– 'Sarah Eve'	CMCN NLar
– 'Saturnalia'	NLar
– Swarthmore form	see *I. virginica* 'Henry's Garnet'
yunnanensis	CExl MBlu NLar

Ixeris (*Asteraceae*)

stolonifera	XLum

Ixia (*Iridaceae*)

bellendenii	NRog
'Blue Bird'	NRog SDeJ SPeP
'Castor'	EGrI NRog SPeP
'Giant'	CBor GKev LAma LShi NRog SDeJ
'Hogarth'	GKev LAma NRog
'Holland Glory'	NRog
'Jesse'	GKev LAma SDeJ
latifolia	CPbh
lutea	NRog
'Mabel'	CAvo CBor CWCL GKev LAma NRog
maculata 'Orange Peel' new	CBor
– yellow-flowered new	CBor
'Marquette'	CBor GKev LAma
paniculata	NRog
– 'Eos'	CBor GKev LAma NRog
'Panorama'	NRog
polystachya	CBor CPbh GKev NRog
pumilio	CBor
'Rose Emperor'	ECha GKev NRog SDeJ
scillaris	CBor CPbh
'Spotlight'	CAvo GKev LAma NRog
'Venus'	CBor CWCL EGrI GKev LAma NRog SDeJ
viridiflora	CBor NRog SPlb WHil
'Vulcan'	NRog
'Yellow Emperor'	CBor GKev LAma NRog SDeJ

Ixiolirion (*Ixioliriaceae*)

pallasii	see *I. tataricum*
§ ***tataricum***	EBee GKev NRog SDeJ
– Ledebourii Group	CAvo

J

Jaborosa (*Solanaceae*)

integrifolia	EBee LEdu SVen XLum

Jacaranda (*Bignoniaceae*)

	acutifolia misapplied	see *J. mimosifolia*
§	***mimosifolia*** ♀H1c	CBcs CCCN EShb SPlb WCFE WJur XVPe

Jacobaea (*Asteraceae*)

	candida	WCot
§	***maritima***	SCob SEND
	- 'Ramparts'	ECre
	- 'Silver Dust' ♀H4	MBros

Jacobinia see *Justicia*

Jamesia (*Hydrangeaceae*)

	americana	CBcs CMCN NLar SBrt WCru

× *Jancaemonda* (*Gesneriaceae*)

	vandedemii	NHar

Jasione (*Campanulaceae*)

§	***heldreichii***	NBir SRms
	jankae	see *J. heldreichii*
§	***laevis***	EHyd EPfP GAbr GArf SRms
§	- 'Blaulicht'	CBor CFis ECha EHyd EPfP GJos MHol NBwr NRHS SPlb WFar WWke
	- BLUE LIGHT	see *J. laevis* 'Blaulicht'
	montana	MNHC SRms WWild
	perennis	see *J. laevis*

Jasminum ✿ (*Oleaceae*)

	CW&T 6374	CMCN
	affine	see *J. officinale* f. *affine*
	angulare ♀H2	CRHN EShb SEND WFib
	azoricum ♀H2	CBcs CCCN CRHN CTsd EPfP EShb SEND SPre WFib
	beesianum	Widely available
	blinii	see *J. polyanthum*
	dispermum	CRHN NLar
	diversifolium	see *J. subhumile*
	farreri	see *J. humile* f. *farreri*
	fruticans	CMac EBee ELon GAbr MMrt SBrt SEND WCru WGob
	- RCB UA 22	WCot
	giraldii misapplied	see *J. humile* f. *farreri*
	grandiflorum misapplied	see *J. officinale* f. *affine*
	grandiflorum L. 'De Grasse'	CRHN EShb WFib
	heterophyllum	see *J. subhumile*
	humile	CExl MGil NBwr NLar SEND SPtp WJur WKif
§	- f. ***farreri*** Farrer 867	WPGP
	- var. ***glabrum***	see *J. humile* f. *wallichianum*
	- 'Pershore Purple'	WAvo
§	- 'Revolutum' ♀H5	CBcs CEme CMac CRHN CRos CSBt CWCL EBee EHyd ELan EPfP EShb GMcL LCro LPar LRHS MGos MRav NBwr NLar SEND SGbt SPoG SRms SWvt
§	- f. ***wallichianum*** B&SWJ 2559	WCru
	- - PAB 2534	LEdu
	- - PAB 9962	LEdu
	lanceolaria new	WPGP
§	***mesnyi*** ♀H3	CBcs CCCN CHll CMac CRHN EPfP EShb LSto SEND SGro SVen WCFE WJur
	multiflorum	CCCN
	multipartitum ♀H2	CCCN CHll EShb
§	***nudiflorum*** ♀H5	Widely available
	- 'Argenteum'	see *J. nudiflorum* 'Mystique'
	- 'Aureum'	CMac CRos ELan LRHS MAsh MRav NLar SPer SPoG SRms
*	- 'Compactum'	MAsh
§	- 'Mystique' (v)	CRos EHyd ELan LRHS NRHS
	odoratissimum ♀H2	WFib
	officinale	Widely available
§	- f. ***affine***	CBcs CCCN CKel CRHN CRos CTri EHyd ELan EPfP ETho LCro LRHS MAsh MRav NRHS SCoo SDix SRms SSut
§	- 'Argenteovariegatum' (v) ♀H5	CKel CMac CWGN ELan ELon EPfP LRHS LSRN MDon MGos MHer MMuc MRav SEND SMad SPer SPoG SWvt WLov WSHC WTyc
	- 'Aureovariegatum'	see *J. officinale* 'Aureum'
§	- 'Aureum' (v)	CBcs CBod CKel CMac CWCL ELan EPfP LRHS LShi MAsh MHer MNHC NFav SCoo SRms WLov
	- 'Clotted Cream'	see *J. officinale* 'Devon Cream'
	- 'Crûg's Collection'	WCru
§	- 'Devon Cream'PBR	Widely available
	- FIONA SUNRISE ('Frojas'PBR) ♀H5	Widely available
	- 'Grandiflorum'	see *J. officinale* f. *affine*
	- 'Inverleith' ♀H5	CBod CCCN CKel CRos EBee ECtt ELan EPfP ETho LCro LRHS MAsh MBNS MGil MGos MNHC MRav NRHS SCoo SMad SNig SPad SPer SPoG SSha WHtc
	- SUNBEAM ('Lowbeam')	CDoC CRos EBee EHyd LRHS NBwr NRHS SCoo SNig
	- 'Variegatum'	see *J. officinale* 'Argenteovariegatum'
	parkeri	CBcs CBor CCCN CKel CMac EBee EHyd ELon GMaP MGil NLar SEle
	- 'Bychan'	WAbe
§	***polyanthum*** ♀H2	CBcs CKel CRHN CSBt CSde ELan EPfP EShb ETho LCro LOPS NBwr SEND SGsty SPre SRms SWeb
	- dark red-leaved	CCCN CExl CKel EBee EPfP
	primulinum	see *J. mesnyi*
	reevesii hort.	see *J. humile* 'Revolutum'
	sambac ♀H2	CCCN CHll CRHN SPre WFib WHlf
	- 'Grand Duke of Tuscany' (d)	CCCN
	- 'Maid of Orleans' (d)	CCCN EShb
	sieboldianum	see *J. nudiflorum*
§	***simplicifolium*** subsp. ***suavissimum***	CHll CRHN
	stenalobium	WCot WFib
	× ***stephanense***	Widely available
	suavissimum	see *J. simplicifolium* subsp. *suavissimum*
§	***subhumile*** NJM 12.044 new	WPGP

Jatropha (*Euphorbiaceae*)

	cinerea	SPlb
	integerrima	CCCN
	multifida	CDoC SPlb
	podagrica ♀H1b	CDoC LAma LCro SPad

Jeffersonia (*Berberidaceae*)

	diphylla	CBor CRos EBee EHyd EMor EPPr EPot EPri GBin GKev ILea LAma LEdu LRHS MBel MNrw NBir NChi NRHS WAbe WFar WPnP WThu
	dubia	CRos EHyd EPot EWes EWld GBin GKev LEdu LRHS MNrw NBir NChi NRHS SBrt WAbe WCot WThu
	- 'Alba'	EPot WAbe
	- 'Sunago-fu' (v)	GEdr
	- variegated (v)	EPot

Jordaaniella (*Aizoaceae*)

	cuprea new	EAri

jostaberry see *Ribes × nidigrolaria*

Jovellana (*Calceolariaceae*)

punctata	CBcs CBod CCCN CTsd EAri EBee EMor EWld IArd IDee MHtn SPlb WLov
sinclairii	CTsd
violacea ♀H3	CAbb CBcs CCCN CExl CKel CMac CPla CTrC CTsd CTtf EBee EHyd EPfP EWld GMcL LRHS MGil SEle SPad SVen WPGP

Jovibarba ✿ (*Crassulaceae*)

§	***allionii***	CBod CGBo CTri EBou EDAr EPfP EPot LCro LRHS MHer MSCN NFav NHpl SRms SSim WAbe WFar WHoo
	- 'Oki'	CRos EDAr EHyd LRHS NRHS SRms
	allionii × hirta	NBwr SDys SPlb
	allionii × sobolifera	LRHS
§	***arenaria***	NMen XLum
*	***echiniformis***	XLum
	globifera 'Autumn Fires'	SSem
§	***heuffelii***	CRos EHyd GArf LRHS NFav NHpl NRHS WFar XLum
	- 'Achisia'	NMen
	- 'Adagdak'	NMen
	- 'Agaffa'	NMen
	- 'Aiolos'	NHol
	- 'Aldicia'	NMen
	- 'Alena'	NMen
	- 'Almkroon'	NHol NWad
	- 'Ambassadeur'	NMen
	- 'Angel Wings'	SRms WHoo
	- 'Ardysia'	NMen
	- 'Arnia'	NMen
	- 'Askja'	NMen
	- 'Atoll'	NMen
	- 'Atria'	NMen
	- 'Bandana'	NMen
	- 'Barbel'	NMen
	- 'Baripper'	NMen
	- 'Beacon'	NMen
	- 'Beacon Hill'	NMen
	- 'Belcore'	NMen XLum
	- 'Bermuda'	NMen
	- 'Biapho'	NMen
	- 'Bibiana'	NMen
	- 'Big Brother'	NMen
	- 'Big Red'	NHol NWad
	- 'Bolero'	NMen
	- 'Bora'	NWad
	- 'Brandaris'	SDys
	- 'Brocade'	NHol NMen NWad
	- 'Bronze Ingot'	NMen
	- 'Bulgarien'	NMen
	- 'Burgharis'	NMen
	- 'Cauvery'	NMen
	- 'Centaurus'	NMen
	- 'Charell'	NMen
§	- 'Cherry Glow'	NMen
	- 'Chocoleto'	NMen
	- 'Cimmanon'	NMen
	- 'Comanchero'	NMen
I	- 'Compacta'	NMen
	- 'Copper King'	NMen
	- 'Corbierie'	NMen
	- 'Coutanche'	NMen
	- 'Cover Girl'	NMen
	- 'Crill'	NMen
	- 'Deciso'	NMen
	- 'Dream'	NMen
	- 'Drechter Gem'	NMen
	- 'Dynosia'	NMen
	- 'Elmo's Fire'	NMen
*	- 'Emerald and Ruby'	WFar
	- 'Enicia'	NMen
	- 'Eos Moment'	NMen
	- 'Ernest'	NMen
	- 'Etysia'	NMen
	- 'Fan Joy'	NMen
	- 'Fandango'	NMen
	- 'Geronimo'	NHol NMen
	- 'Ghaysia'	NMen
	- 'Giuseppi Spiny'	NMen
	- var. ***glabra***	WHoo
	- - from Anaba Kanak, Bulgaria	NHol
	- - from Treska Gorge, Macedonia	SRms
§	- - 'Cameo'	NMen
	- 'Gladiator'	NMen
	- 'Gold Rand'	NHol NWad
*	- 'Golden Touch'	WFar
	- 'Grand Slam'	NMen
	- 'Green Land'	NMen
	- 'Greenstone'	NHol NMen NWad
	- 'Harmony'	NHol
	- 'Henry Correvon'	NMen
	- var. ***heuffelii***	NMen
	- 'Heulin'	NMen
	- 'Hot Bikini'	NMen
	- 'Hot Chocolate'	NMen
	- 'Hot Lips'	NMen
	- 'Idylle'	NMen
	- 'Ikaros'	NHol
	- 'Inferno'	NMen NWad
	- 'Ithaca'	NHol NWad
	- 'Iuno'	NHol
	- 'Jackpot'	NMen
	- 'Jade'	NMen
I	- 'Jovi King'	NMen
	- 'June's Choice'	NMen
	- 'King Sunny'	NMen
	- 'Konrada'	NMen
	- var. ***kopaonikensis***	NMen NWad
	- 'Lorelei'	NMen
	- 'Lucky Bell'	NMen
	- 'Machon'	NMen
	- 'Madera'	NMen
	- 'Major'	NMen
	- 'Mary Ann'	NMen
	- 'Miller's Violet'	NMen
	- 'Mink'	NMen
	- 'Minuta'	NMen
	- 'Misty'	NMen
	- 'Mystique'	NMen WHoo
	- 'Nannette'	NMen
	- 'Olivia'	NMen
	- 'Orion'	NMen XLum
	- var. ***patens***	NMen
	- 'Penponds'	NMen
	- 'Pink Skies'	NMen
	- 'Pink Star'	NMen
	- 'Prisma'	NMen
	- 'Pronker'	NMen
	- 'Purple Haze'	XLum
	- 'Purple Heide'	NMen
	- 'Quennevalis'	NMen
	- 'Red Rose'	NMen
	- 'Red Start'	NMen
	- 'Rhapsody'	NMen
	- 'Samares'	NMen
	- 'Sarabande'	NMen
	- 'Serenade'	NMen SRms
	- 'Silex'	NMen

- 'Springael's Choice' NMen
- 'Summer King' NMen
* - 'Sun and Silver Edge' WFar
- 'Sungold' NHol NWad
- 'Suntan' NWad
- 'Superduper' NMen
- 'Sylvan Memory' NMen
- 'Tancredi' NMen
- 'Torrid Zone' MBrN NMen
- 'Trinity' NMen
- 'Troon' NMen
- 'Try Me' NMen
- 'Tuxedo' NHpl NMen
- 'Violet' NMen SDys
- 'Yuppy Alone' NMen

§ ***hirta*** EDAr GKev SLee WFar XLum
- from Wintergraben, Austria SPlb SRms
- 'Belansky Tatra' NMen SRms
- subsp. ***glabrescens*** from High Tatra, Slovakia/Poland XLum
- - from Smeryouka, southern Carpathians EDAr NMen
- 'Hedgehog' EMul
- var. ***neilreichii*** CRos EDAr EHyd LRHS MHer NRHS SRms
- 'Purpurea' XLum

§ ***sobolifera*** EDAr EGrI EPot GArf GKev SPlb XLum
- 'Green Globe' CRos EDAr EHyd LRHS NRHS SDys SSem
- 'Miss Lorraine' XLum

Jubaea (*Arecaceae*)

§ ***chilensis*** 🏆H4 CPHo ETod LPal NPlm SArc SPlb
spectabilis see *J. chilensis*

Jubaeopsis (*Arecaceae*)

caffra new NPlm

Juglans ✿ (*Juglandaceae*)

§ ***ailanthifolia*** CMCN IDee
- B&SWJ 11026 WCru
- var. ***cordiformis*** (F) EBtc
- - 'Brock' (F) CAgr
- - 'Campbell Cw3' (F) CAgr
- - 'Fodermaier' seedling (F) CAgr
- - 'Imshu' (F) CAgr
- - 'Rhodes' (F) CAgr
- - 'Simcoe' (F) CAgr

ailanthifolia × cinerea see *J. × bixbyi*
§ **× *bixbyi*** CAgr
cinerea 'Beckwith' (F) CAgr
- 'Booth' (F) CAgr
- 'Booth' seedling (F) CAgr
- 'Chamberlin' (F) CAgr
- 'Craxezy' (F) CAgr
- 'Kenworthy' seedling (F) CAgr
- 'Myjoy' (F) CAgr

hindsii CMCN
mandshurica (F) CMCN WJur
- B&SWJ 12550 from Korea WCru
- BWJ 8097 from China WCru
- RWJ 9905 from Taiwan WCru

microcarpa × nigra CDoC LPar MTrO NRog
nigra (F) 🏆H6 Widely available
- 'Beineke 10'[PBR] (F) CAco
- 'Bicentennial' (F) CAgr
- 'Emma Kay' (F) CAgr
- 'Laciniata' EPfP MBlu
- 'Potsdam' (F) CAgr
- 'Thomas' (F) CAgr
- 'Weschke' (F) CAgr

regia (F) Widely available
- 'Apollo' (F) ELan MTrO
- 'Axel' (F) CAgr WMat
- 'Broadview' (F) CAgr CArg CBTr CBrac CEnd CMac CPer ELan EPom LBuc LCro LPar LRHS MBlu MGos MLod MTrO NOra NWea SCoo SEWo SKee SPoG SSFT SVic WMat
- 'Buccaneer' (F) CAgr CArg CMac CPer ELan EPom LPar MLod MTrO NOra SCoo SKee WMat
- 'Chandler' (F) CAgr
- 'Corne du Périgord' (F) CAgr
- 'Ferjean' (F) CAgr
- 'Fernette'[PBR] (F) CAgr MTrO NOra WMat
- 'Fernor' (F) CAgr MTrO WMat
- 'Franquette' (F) 🏆H6 CAgr MTrO NOra WMat
- 'Hansen' (F) CAgr
- 'Hartley' (F) CAgr
- 'Jupiter' (F) ELan MTrO
- 'Laciniata' 🏆H6 CMCN
- 'Lara' (F) 🏆H6 CAgr NOra SBmr WMat
- 'Mars' (F) ELan MTrO
- 'Mayette' (F) CAgr
- 'Meylannaise' (F) CAgr
- 'Mini Multiflora 14' (F) CAgr
- number 16 (F) WMat
- 'Parisienne' (F) CAgr
- 'Plovdivski' (F) WMat
- 'Proslavski' (F) WMat
- 'Purpurea' CMCN MBlu
- 'Rita' (F) LBuc
- 'Ronde de Montignac' (F) CAgr
- 'Saturn' (F) ELan MTrO
- 'Sychrov' (F) MTrO WMat

sieboldiana see *J. ailanthifolia*
sigillata LEdu

jujube see *Ziziphus jujuba*

Juncus (*Juncaceae*)

articulatus LLWG XLum
§ ***decipiens*** 'Curly-wurly' CBor CDoC EHyd EPfP LRHS NRHS
- 'Spiralis' see *J. decipiens* 'Curly-wurly'

effusus CBen CPud LCro LPfP LRHS NPer WMAq XLum
- 'Carman's Japanese' NSti
- 'Gold Strike' (v) LLWG

§ - f. ***spiralis*** CBen CPud CRos CSpe CTtf CWat EHyd EPfP EWat GQue LCro LOPS LPfP LRHS MAsh NBir NFav NRHS SBls SCob SPeP SPlb SVic WCot WMAq XLum

ensifolius CBen CMiW CWat EWat LLWG LPfP MWts NPer NSti WMAq
- 'Flying Hedgehogs' LPfP MACG

inflexus CPud CWat LLWG LPfP XLum
- 'Afro' NBro NWsh SPlb

maritimus LPfP
pallidus EPPr
patens 'Carman's Gray' CKno CWCL
- 'Elk Blue' CKno SPeP

subnodulosus LLWG
'Swarm of Hedgehogs' NWsh
TWISTED ARROWS (mixed) LRHS
'Twister' LRHS

Junellia (*Verbenaceae*)

azorelloides WAbe
congesta WAbe
coralloides WAbe
§ ***micrantha*** EPot WAbe
§ ***succulentifolia*** WAbe
thymifolia WAbe

Juniperus ✿ (*Cupressaceae*)

	ashei	CAco
	bermudiana	CAco
	chinensis	CAco CMen MAsh NWea
	- 'Aurea' 🏆H6	SEND
§	- 'Blaauw' 🏆H6	CMac CMen LRHS SLim
	- 'Blue Alps' 🏆H6	CAco LRHS MGos MMuc SCoo SEND SLim
	- 'Bokor'	CAco
	- 'Echiniformis'	CKen
	- 'Expansa Aureospicata' (v)	CMac EPfP SCoo SEND SPoG SRms
§	- 'Expansa Variegata' (v)	SLim
	- 'Itoigawa'	CAco CMen
§	- 'Kaizuka' 🏆H6	SLim
	- 'Kaizuka Variegata'	see *J. chinensis* 'Variegated Kaizuka'
	- 'Kék'	CAco
	- 'Keteleeri'	CAco
	- 'Kuriwao Gold'	see *J.* × *pfitzeriana* 'Kuriwao Gold'
	- 'Plumosa'	SLim
	- 'Plumosa Albovariegata' (v)	MAsh
	- 'Plumosa Aurea' 🏆H6	CAco
	- 'Plumosa Aureovariegata' (v)	CKen
	- 'Pyramidalis' 🏆H6	CBrac CEme EPfP GMcL MAsh SCob SCoo
	- 'San José'	CMen
§	- var. ***sargentii***	CMen
	- 'Shimpaku'	CKen CMen
	- 'Stricta'	CAco CSBt LRHS NBwr NOrn SLim
	- 'Sulphur Spray'	see *J.* × *pfitzeriana* 'Sulphur Spray'
	- 'Torulosa'	see *J. chinensis* 'Kaizuka'
§	- 'Variegated Kaizuka' (v)	SLim
	- 'Wilson's Weeping'	LRHS
	communis	CAco CHab CPer ELan GDam GPoy NWea SCob SPre SSha WKor WTSh XSen
	- 'Arnold'	NLar
	- 'Arnold Sentinel'	CKen
	- 'Barton'	EBtc
	- 'Brien'	CKen
	- 'Brynhyfryd Gold'	CKen GKev SLim
	- 'Compressa' 🏆H7	CBcs CEme CKen CMac CSBt EPfP EPot GMcL LBee LRHS MAsh MGos NHol NSla NWea SCob SCoo SLim SPer SPoG SSha
	- 'Corielagan'	CKen
	- 'Cracovia'	CKen
	- var. ***depressa***	GPoy SEND
	- 'Depressa Aurea'	CBrac CKen CSBt GMcL LBee SSha
	- 'Depressed Star'	SPoG
	- 'Effusa'	CKen
	- 'Gold Cone'	CBod CBrac CEme CKen ELan EPfP LBee MAsh MGos SLim SPoG SSha
	- 'Goldschatz'	CKen EPfP LRHS LSta SCoo SLim SPoG
	- 'Green Carpet' 🏆H7	CAco CKen ELan EPfP GKin GMcL LBuc LCro LRHS LSta MAsh MGos SCoo SGsty SJap SLim SPoG SVic
	- 'Greenmantle'	LPar LRHS MTrO WMat
	- 'Haverbeck'	CKen
	- 'Hibernica' 🏆H7	CBrac CSBt ELan EPfP EWTr GMcL LRHS MGos NBwr NWea SCob SGsty SLim SPer SPoG SSha
	- 'Hibernica Aurea'	CMac
	- 'Hornibrookii'	NWea SRms
	- 'Horstmann'	SMad
I	- 'Horstmann's Pendula'	NLar
	- 'Kenwith Castle'	CKen
	- 'Meyer'	CMac
	- 'Repanda' 🏆H7	CAco CBcs CBrac CKel CMac CSBt CWnw EHeP EPfP GMcL LCro LRHS MGos NLar NWea SCob SCoo SLim SPoG SSha WFar

§	- var. ***saxatilis***	CKen
	- 'Sentinel'	SLim
	- 'Sieben Steinhauser'	CKen NLar
	- 'Silver Mist'	CKen
	- 'Spotty Spreader' (v)	SLim
	- Suecica Group	NWea
	- - 'Suecica Aurea'	GMcL
	- - 'Suecica Nana'	SLim
	- 'Zeal'	CKen
	conferta	see *J. rigida* subsp. *conferta*
	- 'Blue Lagoon'	CAco
	- var. ***maritima***	see *J. taxifolia*
	convallium	CAco
	davurica 'Expansa Albopicta'	see *J. chinensis* 'Expansa Variegata'
	- 'Expansa Variegata'	see *J. chinensis* 'Expansa Variegata'
	deppeana	CAco
	var. ***zacatecensis***	
	drupacea	CAco
	excelsa	CAco
	- subsp. ***polycarpos***	CAco
	foetidissima	CAco
	- 'Karaca Blue'	CAco
	formosana	CAco
	× ***gracilis*** 'Blaauw'	see *J. chinensis* 'Blaauw'
	'Grey Owl' 🏆H7	CAco CBrac LRHS MMuc NWea SCob SEND SGsty SLim SRms
	horizontalis	NWea
I	- 'Andorra Variegata' (v)	CKen SCoo
	- 'Bar Harbor'	CMac
§	- 'Blue Chip'	CAco CKen ELan EPfP GDam GMcL LBee MGos SCob SCoo SGsty SLim SPoG WLea
	- 'Blue Moon'	see *J. horizontalis* 'Blue Chip'
	- 'Blue Rug'	see *J. horizontalis* 'Wiltonii'
	- 'Glauca'	CBrac CKel NWea SCob
	- 'Golden Carpet' 🏆H7	CAco CBod ELan LBuc LCro LOPS LPar LRHS LSta NLar
	- 'Grey Pearl'	CKen
	- 'Hughes'	LBee NWea
	- ICEE BLUE ('Monber') 🏆H7	CKel CKen CWnw ELan EPfP LRHS NLar SPoG
	- 'Limeglow' 🏆H7	CAco CBcs CBod CBrac ELan EPfP GMcL NLar SCoo SPoG SSha
	- 'Mother Lode'	CKen LPar
	- 'Neumann'	CKen
	- 'Plumosa'	CAco
	- 'Prince of Wales'	MAsh NWea WLea
	- var. ***saxatilis*** misapplied	see *J. communis* var. *saxatilis*
	- 'Turquoise Spreader'	CSBt
	- 'Villa Marie'	CKen SPoG
§	- 'Wiltonii'	EHeP LRHS NWea
	- 'Yukon Belle'	CKen
	× ***media***	see *J.* × *pfitzeriana*
	navicularis	CAco
	occidentalis	CAco
	oxycedrus	XSen
§	× ***pfitzeriana***	CMac GDam GMcL NWea SCob WFar
	- 'Blaauw'	see *J. chinensis* 'Blaauw'
	- 'Blue and Gold' (v)	CKen SPoG
§	- 'Carbery Gold' 🏆H6	CBcs CBrac CMac CSBt EPfP GKin LRHS MAsh MGos NBwr SCoo SLim SPoG SSha
	- 'Gold Coast'	CBod CBrac CKen CSBt LBee LRHS MAsh MGos
	- GOLD SOVEREIGN ('Blound')	LBee
	- 'Gold Star'	LRHS LSta MAsh WLea
*	- 'Golden Joy'	SLim
	- 'Golden Saucer'	MAsh

	- 'Goldkissen'	LRHS
	- 'King of Spring'	SLim
§	- 'Kuriwao Gold'	GKin GMcL MMuc SEND
	- 'Mint Julep'	CAco CBrac CKel CSBt EHeP EPfP GMcL LRHS MAsh NBwr SCob SCoo SGsty SLim
	- 'Old Gold' 🏆H6	CEme CKel CWnw EPfP GKin GMcL LBee LCro LOPS LPar LRHS LSta LSto MGos NBwr NWea SCob SCoo SEND SGsty SPer SPlb SVic WFar
	- 'Old Gold Carbery'	see *J.* × *pfitzeriana* 'Carbery Gold'
	- 'Pfitzeriana Aurea'	CBrac CEme CKel CMac NBwr NWea SCob
	- 'Pfitzeriana Glauca'	CKel
§	- 'Sulphur Spray' 🏆H6	LRHS MMuc SCob SEND SLim WCFE
	phoenicea	CKel XSen
	- subsp. ***turbinata***	XSen
	pinchotii	CAco
§	***pingii*** 'Glassell'	NLar
	- 'Hulsdonk Yellow'PBR	LPar SPoG
§	- var. ***wilsonii***	CKen
	procumbens 'Nana' 🏆H7	CBcs CEme CKen CMac CWnw EPfP GMcL LBee LPar LRHS MAsh MGos NHol NLar SCoo SGsty SJap SLim SPoG SSha SavN WCFE
	pseudosabina Fisch. & C.A. Mey.	CAco
	recurva	IDee
	- 'Castlewellan'	MGil NLar WFar
	- var. ***coxii***	CAco CMac LRHS MBlu NBwr NHol NLar SMad SRms
§	- 'Densa'	CKen
	- 'Nana'	see *J. recurva* 'Densa'
	rigida	CAco CMen
§	- subsp. ***conferta***	CMac SEND
	- - 'All Gold' 🏆H6	LRHS LSta SLim SPoG
*	- - 'Blue Ice'	CKen
	- - 'Blue Pacific'	CEme CKen LRHS SGsty SPoG SWeb
	- - 'Blue Tosho'	NLar
	- - 'Schlager' 🏆H6	SLim
	- - 'Silver Mist'	CKen
	sabina	NWea
	- 'Hicksii'	NWea
	- 'Skandia'	CKen
	- 'Tamariscifolia'	EHeP GKin GMcL LBee MAsh MGos MMuc NWea SArc SCob SEND SGsty SLim SPer SPoG
	saltuaria	CAco
	sargentii	see *J. chinensis* var. *sargentii*
	scopulorum 'Blue Arrow' 🏆H6	Widely available
	- 'Blue Banff'	CKen
	- 'Moonglow'	LPar SGsty
	- 'O'Connor'	CAco
	- 'Skyrocket'	CAco CBcs CBod CCVT CMac CSBt CWal EDir EHeP EPfP IPap LMaj MGos NBwr NWea SCob SPad SRms SSha SWeb
	- 'Springbank'	WCFE
	- 'Wichita Blue'	CCVT EPfP
	semiglobosa	CAco
§	***squamata***	SavN
	- 'Blue Carpet' 🏆H7	Widely available
	- 'Blue Spider'	SSha
	- 'Blue Star' 🏆H7	Widely available
	- 'Blue Star Variegated'	see *J. squamata* 'Golden Flame'
	- 'Blue Swede'	see *J. squamata* 'Hunnetorp'
	- 'Chinese Silver'	CAco
	- 'Dream Joy'	NLar
	- var. ***fargesii***	see *J. squamata*
	- 'Filborna'	LBee
	- 'Floreant'	SPoG
	- 'Glassell'	see *J. pingii* 'Glassell'
§	- 'Golden Flame' (v)	CKen
	- 'Holger' 🏆H7	CAco CEme CMac EPfP GMcL LBee LRHS MAsh MGos NBwr NHol NLar SCoo SLim SPoG WFar
§	- 'Hunnetorp'	WFar
	- 'Meyeri'	GMcL
	- 'Tropical Blue'	SPoG
	- 'Wilsonii'	see *J. pingii* var. *wilsonii*
§	***taxifolia***	CSBt
	thurifera	XSen
	tibetica	CAco
	virginiana	CAco
	- 'Burkii'	SArc
	- 'Frosty Morn'	CKen
	- 'Golden Spring'	CKen
	- 'Pendula'	CAco
	- SILVER SPREADER ('Mona')	CKen CSBt
	- 'Sulphur Spray'	see *J.* × *pfitzeriana* 'Sulphur Spray'

Jussiaea see *Ludwigia*

Justicia (*Acanthaceae*)

	adhatoda	EShb
	americana	LLWG SBrt
	aurea	EAri EShb SPlb
§	***brandegeeana*** 🏆H1b	CCCN EShb
	- 'Lutea'	see *J. brandegeeana* 'Yellow Queen'
	- variegated (v)	EShb
§	- 'Yellow Queen'	EShb
	- yellow-flowered	EShb
§	***carnea***	CHll EAri EMdy EShb WFar
	- 'Alba'	CCCN EAri WFar
	- dark-leaved	CHll EShb
	- 'Radiant'	SMad
§	***floribunda*** 🏆H1b	CBcs CCCN CHll MHtn MNHC SEle SSha WLov
	guttata	see *J. brandegeeana*
	pauciflora	see *J. floribunda*
	'Penrhosiensis'	EShb
	pohliana	see *J. carnea*
	rizzinii	see *J. floribunda*
	spicigera	CCCN EShb
	suberecta	see *Dicliptera sericea*

K

Kadsura (*Schisandraceae*)

coccinea B&SWJ 11793	WCru
- FMWJ 13489	WCru
heteroclita	WPGP
- FMWJ 13385	WCru
- WWJ 11947	WCru
japonica	CBcs
- B&SWJ 1027	WCru
- B&SWJ 4463 from Korea	WCru
- B&SWJ 11109 from Japan	WCru
- B&SWJ 14672	ESwi WCru
- 'Fukurin' (v)	NLar
- 'Variegata' (v)	CCCN CKel EBee EHyd EPfP LRHS
- white fruit	NLar
aff. ***japonica*** NMWJ 14550	WCru

Kaempferia ✿ (*Zingiberaceae*)

rotunda	CCCN LAma SDir

Kageneckia (*Rosaceae*)

oblonga	SPlb

Kalanchoe (*Crassulaceae*)

	beauverdii	EShb
	beharensis 🏆H1b	CCCN CDTJ CDoC ELan EShb NCft NPlm WCot
	– 'Fang' 🏆H1b	CDTJ ELan EShb SEdd WCot
	– 'Rusty'	CDTJ EShb
	blossfeldiana 'Don Nando'PBR (d) **new**	LCro
	daigremontiana	CSBt EShb
§	***delagoensis***	CCCN CDoC CSBt EShb EWoo
	'Dorothy'	EShb
	fedtschenkoi 'Variegata' (v)	EShb WCot
	hildebrandtii	EShb
	humilis	CDoC EShb WCot
	× ***kewensis***	EShb
	laciniata	EShb
	laetivirens	SSim
	luciae 🏆H1b	CDoC
	manginii 🏆H1b	EShb
	'Oak Leaf'	EShb
	orgyalis	EShb WCot
	'Partridge'PBR	LWaG
	pinnata	EShb
	'Prebella'	EShb
	pumila 🏆H1b	CDoC EShb SGro
	rosei var. ***variifolia***	EShb
	scandens 'Kalahari Survivor'	EShb
	serrata	EShb
	sexangularis	EShb
	'Tessa' 🏆H1b	EShb WCot
	thyrsiflora	CDoC EShb
	– 'Bronze Sculpture'	CAbb CBod MCot SEdd SIvy SSim XSte
	– RED LIPS ('Ubilips')	EAri LCro
	tomentosa 🏆H1b	CDoC CPbh EShb WCot
	– 'Chocolate Soldier' **new**	SEdd
	tubiflora	see *K. delagoensis*

kale, curly see AGM Vegetables Section

Kalimeris (*Asteraceae*)

	altaica	EPPr
§	***incisa***	CFis EBee MMuc SPhx
	– 'Alba'	EBee ECha ELon GMaP NLar SRms WCAu WFar
	– 'Blue Star'	CBod EBee ECha ELon GMaP GQue MNrw MSpe NLar WCAu WFar WSHC WTor
	– 'Charlotte'	ELon EWes LPla MACG MNrw NDov NHol SAko SDix SPoG WFar WGoo
	– 'Edo Murasaki'	GGro SBrt
	– 'Jürgen Wever'	LPla NDov
	– 'Madiva'	EBee ECha ELon GBee LPla NDov SAko SRms WGoo
	– 'Nana Blue'	EBee ECha ELon NDov SPoG SRms
	integrifolia 'Daisy Mae'	NDov
	'Mon Jardin'	EBee ELon SHar SRms WCot
§	***mongolica***	EBee ECha EPPr LEdu MMuc SAko SBut WFar WGoo WSHC
	– 'Antonia'	ECha LPla NDov NLar WCot
	– variegated (v)	WCot
§	***pinnatifida***	MHol
	– 'Hortensis'	MACG MHol MNrw WSHC
§	***yomena*** 'Shogun' (v)	CBod CDor CKel CMac EBee ECha ECtt EHyd ELon EPfP LEdu LRHS MACG MBel MHer MHol MNrw MPie NSti SMrm SPer SPoG SRms WFar XLum
	– 'Variegata'	see *K. yomena* 'Shogun'

Kalmia ✿ (*Ericaceae*)

	angustifolia 🏆H5	MGil WSpi
	– var. ***angustifolia*** f. ***candida***	LRHS
	– f. ***rubra*** 🏆H5	CBcs CCCN CDoC CRos EBee EHyd EPfP LCro LRHS MAsh NLar SCob SPer WFar WSpi
I	– 'Rubra Nana'	CMac
	latifolia	CBcs EBee EGrI EPfP GDam LPar LRHS NWea SPer SWvt
	– 'Alpine Pink'	WSpi
	– 'Bandeau'	XSte
	– BEACON	see *K. latifolia* 'Leuchtfeuer'
	– 'Black Label'	XSte
	– 'Bridesmaid'	MAsh
	– 'Bullseye'	MAsh SAko SPoG
	– 'Bumblebee'	XSte
	– 'Carousel'	CBcs CCCN MAsh
	– 'Clementine Churchill'	CMac
	– 'Freckles' 🏆H6	CMac MAsh SCob SPoG
	– 'Galaxy'	LRHS SAko
	– 'Ginkona'	MAsh SAko XSte
	– 'Heart of Fire'	MAsh
	– 'Kaleidoscope'	MAsh SCoo
	– 'Latchmin'	MAsh XSte
§	– 'Leuchtfeuer'	XSte
	– 'Little Linda' 🏆H6	MAsh
	– 'Minuet'	CBcs CCCN EHyd GMcL LRHS MAsh MGil SCoo SPoG SWvt XSte
	– 'Mitternacht'	GGGa MAsh
	– 'Moyland'	MAsh
	– f. ***myrtifolia*** 'Elf'	EHyd LRHS MAsh
	– 'Nani'	MAsh
	– 'Nipmuck'	CMac MAsh
	– 'Olympic Fire' 🏆H6	CBcs EGrI EHyd GGGa GMcL LRHS MAsh MGil SAko SWvt WSpi WTSh XSte
	– 'Olympic Wedding'	LRHS SPoG
	– 'Ostbo Red'	CBcs LRHS MAsh SCob SPoG SWvt
	– 'Peppermint'	GGGa LRHS MAsh
	– 'Pink Charm' 🏆H6	CMac SAko
	– 'Pinwheel'	LRHS MAsh MGil SAko SPoG
	– 'Sterntaler' **new**	MAsh
	– 'Tad'	MAsh
	– 'Tiddlywinks'	LRHS
	– 'Tofka'	XSte
§	***microphylla***	WAbe
	polifolia	CBcs CCCN CDoC LCro LOPS LRHS MGil SPer SavN WThu
	– 'Alba'	see *K. polifolia* f. *leucantha*
	– 'Glauca'	see *K. microphylla*
§	– f. ***leucantha***	LRHS WAbe
	– 'Newfoundland'	CBcs LRHS

Kalmiopsis (*Ericaceae*)

leachiana	EPot

Kalmiopsis × *Phyllodoce* see × *Phylliopsis*

Kalopanax (*Araliaceae*)

	pictus	see *K. septemlobus*
§	***septemlobus***	CBcs EPfP MMuc NLar SEND WJur
	– var. ***magnificus*** B&SWJ 10900	WCru
	– f. ***maximowiczii***	EPfP MBlu NLar

Keiskea (*Lamiaceae*)

japonica	GEdr
– pink-flowered	GGro SBrt

Kelseya (*Rosaceae*)

uniflora	WAbe

Kennedia (*Fabaceae*)

	coccinea	CCCN
	nigricans	CCCN
	rubicunda	CCCN

Kentia (*Arecaceae*)

	forsteriana	see *Howea forsteriana*

Kentranthus see *Centranthus*

Kerria (*Rosaceae*)

	japonica misapplied single	see *K. japonica* 'Simplex'
	japonica (L.) DC.	CBod EWld SGbt
	- (d)	see *K. japonica* 'Pleniflora'
	- 'Albescens'	NLar WCot
	- 'Golden Guinea' 🏆H5	CBod CBrac CMac CRos ELan EPfP EWTr GDam GMcL LCro LOPS LRHS MAsh MGos MRav NLar NRHS SCoo SPoG SRms SWvt WFar
§	- 'Picta' (v)	CMac EBee MGos MRav MSwo SRms WAvo WFar
§	- 'Pleniflora' (d) 🏆H5	CBar CBod CBrac CEme CMac CPla CRos CSBt EBee EHeP ELan EPfP GAbr GMcL LRHS MAsh MGos MRav MSwo NBwr NLar SCob SPlb SPoG SRms SWvt WFar
§	- 'Simplex'	CMac EShb NBwr SRms
	- 'Variegata'	see *K. japonica* 'Picta'

Keteleeria (*Pinaceae*)

	evelyniana	CAco
	fortunei	CAco

Khadia (*Aizoaceae*)

	acutipetala	CCCN

Kiggelaria (*Flacourtiaceae*)

	africana	SVen

Kirengeshoma (*Hydrangeaceae*)

	palmata	Widely available
	- 'Black Style'	EBee ILea IPot LBar
	- dwarf	WCot
	- Koreana Group 🏆H7	CExl EBee EHyd ELan EPPr GAbr GKev LEdu LRHS MBel MCot MHol MMuc MRav NBPC NBid NCou NGBl NHol NLar NRHS NSti SMrm SPad SPer WBor WCot WCru WFar WPGP

Kitaibela (*Malvaceae*)

	vitifolia	CSpe EWoo GElm LShi NBid SBls SMHy SPlb WAvo WFar WHer XSen

Kitchingia see *Kalanchoe*

kiwi fruit see *Actinidia deliciosa*

Klasea (*Asteraceae*)

§	***bulgarica***	ECha EPPr ESwi MPie NDov SBls SDix SHar SPhx WGoo WHil
§	***coronata***	LPla
§	- subsp. ***insularis*** B&SWJ 8698	WCru
	- - B&SWJ 12710 **new**	WCru
§	***lycopifolia***	WCot WMal
§	***radiata*** subsp. ***gmelinii***	EHyd EPPr LRHS NRHS

Kleinia (*Asteraceae*)

	abyssinica	EBtc
§	***anteuphorbium*** **new**	EAri
	articulata	see *Curio articulata*
	fulgens	ECre
§	***grantii***	CSpe EShb SGro SIvy WCot
§	***madagascariensis*** **new**	EAri
§	***neriifolia***	EShb NPlm SIvy
§	***picticaulis*** **new**	EAri
	repens	see *Curio repens*

Knautia (*Caprifoliaceae*)

§	***arvensis***	CBod CCBP CElw CHab EBee EHyd ELan EPfP EWoo GDam GJos GQue LCro LOPS MBow MHer MNHC NAts NLar NMir SPer SPhx SRms WCAu WHer WPnP WSFF WShi WWild XSen
	- white-flowered	SPhx
	dipsacifolia	SBut SHar
	drymeia	WOut
	'Jardin d'en Face'	LRHS WCav
§	***macedonica***	Widely available
	- 'Crimson Cushion'	CSpe
	- 'Mars Midget'	CBod CRos CSpe EBee EHyd ELan ELon EMor EPfP EShb GJos GMaP LRHS MGos MPie NBPC NLar NRHS SCob SPhx SPoG SWvt WCAu WCav WFar
	- Melton pastels	CChe CDoC CDor CRos EBee EGrI EHyd ELan EPPr EPfP GJos GMaP LRHS MGos NLar NPer NRHS SBls SCob SCoo SGBe SPhx SPoG SRkn SRms SWvt WCAu WCav WFar WTor
	- 'Midget Mauves' **new**	LBar
	- pink-flowered	SRms
	- 'Red Baron'	CChe
	- 'Red Cherries'	LSto
	- 'Red Knight'	CBod CDor CKel CRos EBee EHyd EPfP LPal LRHS MBNS NLar NRHS SCoo SRms WTor
	- tall, pale-flowered	SPhx
	- 'Thunder and Lightning'PBR (v)	CBct CBod CDoC CRos CSpe CWGN EBee ECtt EHyd ELan EPfP EWes LBar LRHS LSou MAvo MNrw MRav NLar NRHS SCob SCoo SEdd SGBe SPoG SRms WCAu WCot WFar WTor
	sarajevensis	MAvo MHol

Knightia (*Proteaceae*)

	excelsa	CBcs LRHS XSte

Kniphofia ✿ (*Asphodelaceae*)

	'Ada'	ELon LRHS
	albescens	SPlb
	'Alcazar'	CBcs ECtt EHeP ELon EPfP EWhm GMcL LCro LPal MAvo MBel MHer MSpe SCob SPer SWvt WCAu WCFE WFar
	'Amazing Fun'	CWGN NCth
	'Ample Dwarf'	ECtt WCot
	'Amsterdam'	GBin LBar
	angustifolia	SPlb
	'Apricot'	EBlo WCot
	'Apricot Souffle'	EPri WCot WMal
	BANANA POPSICLE ('Tnknibp') (Popsicle Series)	CBod LRHS
	'Barton Fever' 🏆H6	WCot
	baurii	SPlb
	'Bees' Jubilee'	MAvo NChi
	'Bees' Lemon'	Widely available
§	'Bees' Sunset' 🏆H5	CAvo CPrp CRos EBee EBlo ECha ECtt EHyd EPfP EPri LRHS MMuc

	NRHS SEND SMrm SPoG SWvt WSHC
'Border Ballet'	EHyd LRHS NBir NGdn NRHS XLum
brachystachya	LEdu SBrt SPlb
'Bressingham Comet'	CBor CRos EBee EBlo ECtt EHyd ELon LRHS NBir NRHS SRms WSpi
'Bressingham Gleam'	EBlo
BRESSINGHAM SUNBEAM ('Bresun')	CRos EBee EBlo ECtt EHyd LRHS NBir NRHS
'Bressingham Yellow'	ECtt
'Brimstone' Bloom ♀H5	CDor CRos EBlo ECtt EPfP EPri LEdu LRHS NBid NBir NRHS SCob SWvt WFar WMal
bruceae	SPlb SVen
'Buttercup' ♀H5	CAvo CPrp LSRN
'C.M. Prichard' misapplied	see *K. rooperi*
'C.M. Prichard' Prichard	WCot
'Candlelight'	ECtt MAvo WSHC
caulescens	Widely available
- 'Coral Breakers'	ECtt ELon GMaP LRHS MAvo NBPC SEND WCot
- early-flowering	WSpi
- 'John May'	EBee ECtt ESwi MAvo MHer SEdd SWvt WCot
- short	ECha
'Champagne'	WCot
'Chichi'	WCot
'Christmas Cheer'	EBee
citrina	CBod CSpe CTsd GKev GLog MBrN NGBl WCot XLum
'Cobra'	CDor CRos EBlo ECtt EHyd GMaP LRHS NRHS WCot
(Colour the Sky Series)	LBar
'Colour the Sky Lemon' **new**	
- 'Colour the Sky Sage' **new**	LBar
- 'Colour the Sky Sunset' **new**	LBar
'Coolknip' **new**	WMal
'Coral Flame' ♀H5	CRos EBlo EHyd LRHS NRHS
'Coral Sceptre'	WCot
'Corallina'	GBin
'Creamsicle' PBR (Popsicle Series)	ECtt WCot
CROWN HYBRIDS (mixed) **new**	CGBo
'Dingaan'	EBee ECtt GMcL MNrw NBir NLar
'Dorset Sentry'	CAby ECtt EHyd ELon EPfP EWoo LRHS MBel MGos MNrw NBPC NBir NLar WCAu WCot WFar
'Drummore Apricot'	CKno CPrp CRos EBee ECha ECtt ELon EPfP LBar LRHS LSRN MAsh MPie MSpe NBir NLar NRHS NWsh WCot WFar WGwG
'Early Buttercup'	NBPC WFar
'Ed's Findling' **new**	WCot
'Elvira' PBR	CRos EAri EBlo ECtt EHyd GElm IPot LRHS MHol NCth NLar NRHS SAko SPeP SPoG WCot
EMBER GLOW ('Tneg' PBR) (Glow Series)	CBod EBee ECtt LCro LOPS NLar WLov
ensifolia	NGdn SVen XLum
'Ernest Mitchell'	WCot
Express hybrids	XLum
'Feuerkerze'	SAko
'Fiery Fred' ♀H6	CPrp CRos EBee EBlo ECtt EHyd ELon EPfP EShb EWhm LRHS LSto MMuc MRav MSpe NLar NRHS SGbt WCot WHoo WSpi WWke
'Fire Brand'	WCot
FIRE GLOW ('Tnfg' PBR) (Glow Series)	NLar

'First Sunrise' PBR	ECtt
'Flamenco'	CKel EHyd ELon LRHS NGdn NRHS NWsh SCob SRms SVic WFar WLov
'Florence Bedecked'	WCot
foliosa Hochst.	LEdu
'Frances Victoria'	WCot
galpinii misapplied	see *K. triangularis* subsp. *triangularis*
'Gelbe Flamme'	SAko
'Gilt Bronze'	WCot
'Gladness'	MAvo MSpe NBir WCot
'Goldelse'	CRos EBee EHyd LRHS NBir NRHS
'Green and Cream'	MHCG WBrk
'Green Jade'	Widely available
'H.E. Beale'	WCot
'Happy Halloween'	CPrp LRHS MAvo
'Hen and Chickens'	ECtt NBPC SSut WCot WFar
hirsuta	SRms WSHC
- 'Fire Dance'	CEme CTsd EBou EHyd GAbr LRHS LSun NLar WFar WSpi
- 'Traffic Lights'	GDam GMcL
'Ice Queen'	Widely available
ichopensis	LEdu SVen WPGP
'Incandesce' ♀H5	EPPr EWhm GAbr LBar MNrw NBPC SPoG WCot WMal
'Innocence' ♀H4	CRos EBee EBlo EHyd EPfP LRHS NRHS
'Jane Henry'	CDor LEdu
'Jenny Bloom'	CPrp CRos ECtt EPfP EWTr EWoo GMaP LEdu LRHS LSto MRav NLar NRHS NSti SRms WFar WSpi
'Jess's Delight'	WCot
'John Benary'	CFis CMac CPrp EBee ECtt EHyd GLog GMaP LRHS MBel MSpe NBir NLar NRHS SRms WCAu WCot WGwG WKif
'Jonathan' ♀H5	WCot
laxiflora	WPGP
'Lemon Popsicle' PBR (Popsicle Series)	CAbb CBct CRos CWCL CWGN EHyd ELan EPfP LLWG LRHS MMrt NFav NRHS SCob SEdd SGBe SRms WFar WNPC XSte
'Light of the World'	see *K. triangularis* subsp. *triangularis* 'Light of the World'
'Limelight'	CBod CChe CPar ECtt LBar SPad WCAu
linearifolia	CExl EBee EBlo SPlb WCot WPGP XLum
'Little Elf'	CDor XLum
'Little Maid'	CBcs CBod CRos CSBt ECha ECtt EGrl EHeP EHyd ELan EPfP EPri GMaP GMcL LRHS MHer MRav NBPC NBir NLar NRHS SCob SPer SRms SWvt WCAu WCot WFar WSHC WSpi
'Lord Roberts'	MAvo MRav WCot
'Luna'	WCot
macowanii	see *K. triangularis* subsp. *triangularis*
'Mango Popsicle' PBR (Popsicle Series)	Widely available
'Mermaiden'	ECtt MAvo
'Minister Verschuur'	CRos EBee EBlo ECtt EHyd LRHS MSpe NRHS WSpi
'Moonstone' ♀H5	CBod CWCL EAri ECtt ELon EPPr GAbr GBin GKev LRHS LSun MACG MNrw NBPC NLar NSti SEND SEdd SPoG WCot WSpi
'Mount Etna'	WAvo
multiflora 'November Glory'	WCot WFar WMal
'Nancy's Red'	Widely available
nelsonii Mast.	see *K. triangularis* subsp. *triangularis*

	'New Sensation'	WCot
	'No Rhyme nor Reason'	WCot
§	'Nobilis' ♀H5	CExl CRos ECha ECtt ELan ELon EPfP GAbr GElm GMaP LRHS LSRN MAvo MHol MNrw MSpe NBPC NGdn SArc SDix SEND SHar SPer SRms SWvt WCAu WCot WSpi
	northiae ♀H4	CCht CExl CPla EAri EBee ELan EPri EWes GAbr GElm LRHS MNrw NLar SArc SEND SEdd SPad SPlb SWvt WCot WCru WPGP WSpi XLum
	'Old Court Seedling'	EBee WCot WFar
	'Orange Blaze' (Pyromania Series) **new**	LBar
	'Orange Fackel'	SAko
	'Orange Vanilla Popsicle'PBR (Popsicle Series)	CBct CBod CGBo CNor CRos CSBt CSpe ECtt EHyd ELon EMor EWTr IPot LEdu LLWG LRHS MBros MPnt MThu NLar NRHS SCob SEdd SPad SPoG WFar WHil WNPC WTyc XSte
§	'Painted Lady'	CDor CTri ECtt GMaP MNrw SEND SWvt WCot
	'Papaya Popsicle'PBR (Popsicle Series)	CBct CBod CGBo CRos CWGN EBee ECtt EHyd ELan ELon EPfP IPot LLWG LRHS LSou MNrw MPie MThu NLar NRHS SCob SPoG SRms WFar WSpi
	parviflora	EBee XLum
	pauciflora	CBor CPbh WCot WMal
	'Pencil Orange' **new**	LBar
	'Pencil White' **new**	LBar
	'Penny Rockets' ♀H6	CRos EBlo EHyd EPPr LRHS NRHS
	'Percy's Pride'	Widely available
	'Pfitzeri'	SRms
	'Pineapple Popsicle'PBR (Popsicle Series)	CPrp CTsd CWGN ECtt ELon EMor LRHS LSou MMrt MPnt NEoE NSti SRms WNPC
	(Poco Series) POCO ORANGE ('Tnknipo'PBR)	LBar NLar WHlf
	- POCO RED ('Tnknipr'PBR) **new**	LBar
	- 'Poco Sunset' **new**	LBar
	- POCO YELLOW ('Tnknipy'PBR)	CBod LBar WHlf
	'Primrose Upward' ♀H6	WCot
I	'Primulina' Bloom	EBlo EHyd LRHS NRHS
	'Prince Igor' misapplied	see *K.* 'Nobilis'
	'Prince Igor' Prichard	ECtt NBir
	'Red Rocket'PBR	EGrI GMcL LRHS WCot WHil
	'Redhot Popsicle'PBR (Popsicle Series)	CBod CTsd CWGN EHyd EPfP IPot LRHS MAvo MHol MNrw MPnt NBPC SGBe SPoG WCot WNPC
	'Rich Echoes' ♀H5	CWGN ECtt ELon EPPr ESwi EWhm LEdu MAvo MHol MNrw WCot WMal
	ritualis	CExl
	'Rocket's Red Glare' (Pyromania Series) **new**	LBar
§	***rooperi*** ♀H5	Widely available
	'Royal Castle'	CExl CRos CTsd EHeP EHyd GMaP LRHS NBir NGdn NRHS SCob SEND SRms WFar WWke XLum
	'Royal Standard' ♀H5	CBcs CRos EBee EBlo ECtt EHeP EHyd ELon EPfP GMaP LCro LOPS LRHS NRHS SCob SPer SPoG SWvt WCAu WFar WGwG WSpi
	rufa Baker	EPri LEdu WMal WPGP
	- 'Rasta'	CBcs CBod LBar WHlf
	aff. ***rufa***	ESwi
	'Safranvogel' ♀H5	EBlo ECtt LBar LRHS NBPC WCot
	'Samuel's Sensation' misapplied	see *K.* 'Painted Lady'
	'Samuel's Sensation' Samuel ♀H5	EBee EBlo ECtt EHyd LRHS NRHS SWvt WCot
	sarmentosa	CExl SPlb SVen WCot
	'Scorched Corn'	CBod LBar LEdu
	'Sherbet Lemon'	WCot
	'Shining Sceptre' misapplied	see *K.* 'Bees' Sunset'
	'Shiny Beast'	WCot
	'Springtime'	WCot
	'Star of Baden-Baden'	NBir SEND WCot
	Stark's early perpetual-flowering hybrids	CSBt XLum
	'Strawberries and Cream'	ECtt EGrI ELon NLar SGbt SWvt
	stricta	XLum
	'Sunningdale Yellow' ♀H5	ECha ECtt GMaP SRms WHoo WSpi
	'Sunset' ambig.	SRHi
	'Sweet Corn'	CBod LBar SMrm
	'Tawny King' ♀H5	Widely available
	'Tetbury Torch'PBR	CBod CExl CWGN ECtt EHyd GKev LRHS MAvo MHer NLar NRHS SPtp SWvt WCAu WSpi
	thomsonii	CExl
	- 'Kichocheo'	EPPr LEdu WCot
	- var. ***snowdenii*** misapplied	see *K. thomsonii* var. *thomsonii*
	- var. ***snowdenii*** ambig.	CExl XLum
§	- var. ***thomsonii***	LEdu SMHy WSHC
	- - 'Stern's Trip' ♀H4	WPGP
	'Timothy' ♀H5	Widely available
	'Toffee Nosed' ♀H5	Widely available
	'Torchbearer'	WCot
	triangularis	EBlo EPfP SGBe WFar XLum
§	- subsp. ***triangularis***	EHyd LRHS NRHS SRms SVen XLum
§	- - 'Light of the World'	ECtt GAbr NBPC NBir SWvt WCot WFar
	'Tuckii' misapplied	SRms
	typhoides	NBir SPlb
	tysonii	EBlo SPlb XLum
	uvaria	EHyd EWld LCro LOPS LPal LPar LRHS NBir NRHS SBls SCob SPer SRms WCAu WCot XLum XSen
	'Vanilla'	EWTr LRHS MMuc NLar SEND
	'Vesta'	CRos EBee EBlo EHyd LRHS NRHS
	'Vincent Lepage'	NLar
	'Wol's Red Seedling'	CAvo ECtt MNrw NBPC WCot WGwG
	'Wrexham Buttercup' ♀H6	CDor EBee ECtt ELan EMor EPfP EWTr EWhm GElm GMaP IPot LSRN LSun MHol MNrw MSpe NBPC NLar SCob SEND SRkn WCot WFar WSpi
	'Yellow Cheer'	WCot WMal
	'Yellow Hammer' Slieve Donard	MMuc SEND

Koeleria (*Poaceae*)

	cristata misapplied	see *K. macrantha*
	glauca	CAby CRos EBee ECha EHyd EPfP EShb GMaP GMcL LRHS MBNS NBwr NGdn NRHS NWsh SCob SPlb SWvt WFar XSen
§	***macrantha***	EPPr
	vallesiana 'Mountain Breeze'	ECha EPPr

Koelreuteria (*Sapindaceae*)

bipinnata	IDee LRHS SSha
- var. ***integrifoliola***	WJur
elegans subsp. ***formosana***	CMCN
paniculata	Widely available

- 'Coral Sun'PBR ♀H5	CDoC EBee EPfP LPar LRHS MBlu MGos MMrt NOra NOrn WHtc WMat
- 'Fastigiata'	EBee ELan EPfP MBlu SCoo
- 'Rosseels'	NLar
- 'September'	MBlu

Kohleria (*Gesneriaceae*)

'Ampallang'	WDib
'An's Nagging Macaws'	WDib
'Brazil Gem'	WDib
'Bristol's Evil Storm'	WDib
'Cybele'	WDib
'Dark Velvet'	WDib
digitaliflora	see *K. warszewiczii*
'Flashdance'	WDib
'Hcy's Jardin de Monet'	WDib
'Heartland's Blackberry Butterfly'	WDib
'Jester' ♀H1b	WDib
'Lilla Gubben'	WDib
lindeniana	see *Gloxinella lindeniana*
'Manchu'	WDib
'Marquis de Sade'	WDib
'Queen Victoria'	WDib
I ***sciadotydaea***	WDib
'Silver Feather'	WDib
§ 'Sunrise'	WDib
'Sunshine'	see *K.* 'Sunrise'
'Texas Rainbow'	WDib
§ ***warszewiczii*** ♀H1b	WDib
'Yf's Elin'	WDib
'Yf's Emma'	WDib
'Yf's Josse'	WDib
'Yf's Lotta'	WDib
'Yf's Torun'	WDib

Kolkwitzia (*Caprifoliaceae*)

amabilis	CSBt CTri ELan EPfP GBin GDam GMcL LIns LPar NBwr NWea SGol SPlb SRHi SRms SavN WCFE WJur
- DREAM CATCHER ('Maradco')	CMac EPfP MAsh MRav NEoE NLar SGol WHtc WSpi
- 'Pink Cloud' misapplied	see *K. amabilis* 'Rosea'
- 'Pink Cloud' ♀H6	Widely available
§ - 'Rosea'	CBrac

kumquat see *Citrus japonica*

Kunzea (*Myrtaceae*)

ambigua	CBcs SPlb
- pink-flowered	SEle
'Badja Carpet'	SEle SSha
baxteri	CPbh
ericifolia	SPlb
§ ***ericoides***	CBee GAbr GPoy
parvifolia	SPlb
pauciflora	SPlb
pomifera	CBee

L

Lablab (*Fabaceae*)

purpureus 'Ruby Moon'	CSpe

+ *Laburnocytisus* (*Fabaceae*)

'Adamii'	CMac EBee EPfP LPar LSRN MGos NLar NOrn SPer WHtc

Laburnum ✿ (*Fabaceae*)

alpinum	NRog NWea SPlb SavN WJur
§ - 'Pendulum'	CAco CCVT ELan LCro LSRN MAsh MGos MRav NOrn NRog SPoG
§ ***anagyroides***	EDir GDam IPap LMaj LPar MMuc NBwr NWea SEND SNig SRms WHlf WJur WMou
- 'Erect'	SPoG
- 'Yellow Rocket'	CBTr CBcs CDow EBee EPfP LCro LRHS MAsh MTrO NOrn WMat
'Famous Walk'	see *L.* × *watereri* 'Vossii'
'Pendula'	see *L. alpinum* 'Pendulum'
vulgare	see *L. anagyroides*
× ***watereri***	MTrO
- 'Sunspire'	LCro
§ - 'Vossii' ♀H6	Widely available
* - 'Vossii Pendulum'	CCVT

Lachenalia (*Asparagaceae*)

§ ***aloides***	CMiW CPbh EAri SDeJ
- var. ***aurea***	see *L. flava*
- var. ***luteola***	see *L. flava*
- var. ***quadricolor***	see *L. quadricolor*
- 'Rainbow Bells'PBR **new**	LAma
- var. ***vanzyliae***	see *L. vanzyliae*
'Aqua Lady'PBR **new**	LAma
bachmanii	NRog
bifolia	see *L. bulbifera*
§ ***bulbifera*** ♀H2	CBor CBro WCot
'Cherise'PBR **new**	LAma
contaminata ♀H2	CPbh EAri NRog
§ ***corymbosa*** ♀H2	CBor
elegans var. ***suaveolens***	NRog
ensifolia	WCot
§ - subsp. ***maughanii***	NRog
§ ***flava*** ♀H2	CPbh SGro WCot
'Fransie' (African Beauty Series)	NRog
'Josephine'PBR **new**	LAma
kliprandensis	NRog
latimerae	NRog
§ ***longituba*** ♀H2	EDAr NRog SGro
mathewsii	NRog
maughanii	see *L. ensifolia* subsp. *maughanii*
mediana	NRog
'Namakwa' (African Beauty Series) ♀H2	GKev LAma NRog
namaquensis	NRog
'Nelsonii'	SGro
obscura	WCot
orchioides var. ***glaucina***	NRog
pallida	CBor NRog
I 'Pearsonii'	SPlb
pendula	see *L. bulbifera*
pusilla	CPla
pustulata ♀H2	NRog
§ ***quadricolor*** ♀H2	NRog WCot
reflexa	EAri NRog
'Robijn' (African Beauty Series)	NRog
'Romaud' (African Beauty Series)	GKev LAma NRog SDeJ
'Romelia' (African Beauty Series)	WCot
'Ronina' (African Beauty Series)	GKev LAma NRog
'Rosabeth' (African Beauty Series)	GKev LAma NRog WCot
rubida	CBor
'Rupert' (African Beauty Series) ♀H2	GKev NRog SDeJ WCot
tricolor	see *L. aloides*
unicolor	NRog
unifolia	NRog

§ ***vanzyliae*** ♀H2 NRog
viridiflora ♀H2 NRog
zeyheri EAri NRog

Lactuca (*Asteraceae*)

alpina see *Cicerbita alpina*
perennis EPPr GGro WHer

Lagarostrobos (*Podocarpaceae*)

§ ***franklinii*** IDee SMad WPGP

Lagenaria (*Cucurbitaceae*)

siceraria SVic
'Speckled Swan'

Lagerstroemia (*Lythraceae*)

BLACK DIAMOND BEST RED (Black Diamond Series) SGsty
ENDURING SUMMER WHITE ('Piilag B1'PBR) **new** CDoC
indica ♀H3 CBod CCCN EPfP ILea LMaj LPar MGil SCob SEND SEle SIvy SPlb SVen WFar
- B&SWJ 12660 WCru
- 'Berlingot Menthe' CBcs
- BERRY DAZZLE ('Gamad VI') LCro LRHS
- BLACK SOLITAIRE PURELY PURPLE ('18li'PBR) (Black Solitaire Series) **new** WHlf
- BURGUNDY COTTON ('Whit VI') **new** NLar
- 'Cedar Lane Red' see *L. indica* 'Cedar Red'
§ - 'Cedar Red' WPGP
- 'Coral Filli'PBR (Fleming Filigree Series) ELan
- 'Cordon Bleu' LRHS
- 'Lafayette' LRHS
- MIMIE FUCHSIA ('Dablage01'PBR) WHlf XSte
- 'Nivea' EBee
- PETITE PINKIE ('Monkie') CCCN EGrI ELan EShb
- 'Red Filli'PBR (Fleming Filigree Series) ELan
- 'Red Imperator' CBcs EShb
- RHAPSODY IN PINK ('Whit VIII') CBcs CDoC ELan LRHS NLar SGsty XSte
- 'Rosea' CBcs EBar IPap SEND
- 'Rubra' XSte
- 'Violet Filli'PBR (Fleming Filigree Series) ELan
- (With Love Series) WITH LOVE BABE ('Milaperl'PBR) SPoG
- - WITH LOVE CHERIE ('Cov') SPoG
- - WITH LOVE ETERNAL ('Milavio'PBR) **new** WHlf
- - WITH LOVE KISS ('Milarosso'PBR) **new** WHlf
- - WITH LOVE VIRGIN ('Milabla'PBR) LCro WHlf
- 'World's Fair' LRHS
'Natchez' **new** WPGP
subcostata WPGP
- CWJ 12352 WCru
'Tuscarora' WPGP
'Tuskegee' WPGP

Lagotis (*Plantaginaceae*)

glauca GEdr WFar
takedana GEdr

Lagunaria (*Malvaceae*)

patersonia LRHS WJur

Lagurus (*Poaceae*)

ovatus CTtf SAdn SPhx SRot WChS WWke

Lallemantia (*Lamiaceae*)

canescens 'Blue Snap' SPhx

Lamiastrum see *Lamium*

Lamium (*Lamiaceae*)

album CHab SMrm
- 'Friday' (v) NBir
§ ***galeobdolon*** CTri EShb LRHS LWaG MHer NAts SPhx SRms WHer WWtn XSen
- 'Emil Tramposch' LPla
§ - 'Florentinum' (v) CMac ECha GQue MMuc MRav SCob WCAu WFar WSFF
- 'Hermann's Pride' CBod EHyd ELan EPfP GKev GMaP LRHS LShi MHer MHol NBir NDov NMir NRHS SCob SMrm SPoG SRms SWvt WWke XLum
- 'Kirkcudbright Dwarf' EPPr EWes GBin WFar XLum
§ - 'Silberteppich' ECha MRav XLum
- 'Silver Angel' XLum
- SILVER CARPET see *L. galeobdolon* 'Silberteppich'
- 'Variegatum' see *L. galeobdolon* 'Florentinum'
garganicum subsp. ***garganicum*** EWes
- subsp. ***pictum*** see *L. garganicum* subsp. *striatum*
- subsp. ***reniforme*** see *L. garganicum* subsp. *striatum*
§ - subsp. ***striatum*** CDor WAbe
luteum see *L. galeobdolon*
maculatum GJos LWaG MMuc SRms WCot WHlf WWtn
- 'Album' EPfP SHar SPer SRms WWtn
- 'Anne Greenaway' (v) SCob SMrm
§ - 'Aureum' ECtt SWvt WFar XLum
- 'Beacon Silver' Widely available
- 'Brightstone Pearl' ELon EWes EWld SHar
- 'Cannon's Gold' EBee ECtt SWvt
- 'Chequers Board' GAbr
- 'Dingle Candy' MHCG
- 'Ghost' CKel ECtt EPPr EPfP LBuc LRHS NLar SCob SRms WWke
- 'Gold Leaf' see *L. maculatum* 'Aureum'
- GOLDEN ANNIVERSARY ('Dellam'PBR) (v) EHyd ELan GJos LRHS LSRN MBow NBro NRHS SWvt
- 'Golden Nuggets' see *L. maculatum* 'Aureum'
- 'Golden Wedding' EMor SRms
- 'James Boyd Parselle' WCot
- (Lami Series) LAMI DARK PURPLE EHyd LRHS NRHS
- - LAMI MEGA PURPLE EBee
- 'Margery Fish' SRms
- 'Orchid Frost' EBee ELon GQue
- PINK CHABLIS ('Checkin'PBR) ELon LRHS MRav NCou NLar SCoo SPer WWke
- 'Pink Nancy' SWvt
- 'Pink Pearls' CSBt NLar SHar SMrm
- 'Pink Pewter' CDor CRos EBee ECha ECtt EHyd ELan EMor EPfP GKev GMaP LRHS LShi MAvo MBel MPie NLar NRHS SCob SHar SMrm SPer SPlb SPoG SRms WGwG
- 'Purple Dragon' SCoo SPoG
- 'Red Nancy' CRos EHyd ELan EPfP LRHS NLar NRHS SCob SWvt XLum
§ - 'Roseum' EBee ELan EPfP MCot MRav SPer SPhx WCAu XLum

- 'Shell Pink' see *L. maculatum* 'Roseum'
- 'White Nancy' Widely available
- 'Wootton Pink' MHCG NBir SWvt
orvala Widely available
- 'Album' CCBP CDor CKel CMiW CTtf EBee EMor EPPr GBin LEdu LPla LRHS MAvo MBel MBriF NBir NLar SEND SMrm WCAu WHer
- pink-flowered LWaG
- 'Silva' EPfP LEdu LRHS WCot WMal
purpureum GJos WSFF
sandrasicum SGro WAbe

Lampranthus (*Aizoaceae*)

sp. CDoC EAri
aberdeenensis see *Delosperma aberdeenense*
apricot-flowered EHyd LRHS NRHS
aurantiacus CBcs
blandus CBcs CCCN
'Blousey Pink' SVen
§ ***brownii*** CBcs CCCN CRos EAri EHyd ELan EPfP LRHS NRHS SPlb
coccineus CPla
deltoides see *Oscularia deltoides*
edulis see *Carpobrotus edulis*
'Exposure' CCCN SSim
multiradiatus SEND
oscularis see *Oscularia deltoides*
'Pink' CBod CPbh CPla ELan SPlb SRms SSim
purple-flowered CBen SPlb
roseus CCCN CRos EHyd LRHS NRHS
'Salmon Pink' SPlb
'Shanklin' SPlb SVen
spectabilis CBcs CCCN CTri GLet SSut
- double lilac-flowered (d) **new** CPbh
- orange-flowered CBod CPbh SSim WFar
- purple-flowered CBod CPla ELon SPlb SSim
- 'Tresco Apricot' CCCN
- 'Tresco Brilliant' CCCN CKel CPbh ELon MBros SEND SRms SSim
- 'Tresco Fire' CBod CCCN CPbh SPlb SRms SVen
- 'Tresco Orange' CCCN CPbh
- 'Tresco Peach' CCCN CPbh
- 'Tresco Pearl' CPla WCav
- 'Tresco Purple' CPbh ELan
- 'Tresco Red' CCCN CPla SEND SEdd SSim
- white-flowered SPlb SSim SVen WFar
- yellow-flowered CBod CPbh CPla SSim SVen WFar
stipulaceus SPlb
'Ventnor Red' SChr

Lamprocapnos (*Papaveraceae*)

§ ***spectabilis*** ♀H6 Widely available
- 'Alba' ♀H6 Widely available
- 'Cupid' **new** GLet
- 'Gold Heart'PBR Widely available
- VALENTINE ('Hordival'PBR) ♀H6 Widely available
- WHITE GOLD ('Tndicwg'PBR) EMor ESwi GLet LBar LRHS NCth SPad SPeP WHil

Lamprothyrsus (*Poaceae*)

hieronymi CSde ECha
- RCB RA K2-2 CCht CKno EBee ELon LEdu MAvo MHol SMad WCot WPGP

Lancea (*Phrymaceae*)

tibetica GEdr

Lantana ✿ (*Verbenaceae*)

camara EShb SEle
- (Bandana Series) BANDANA CHERRY ('Bante Cheria') EMdy
- - BANDANA ORANGE SUNRISE ('Bante Oransun'PBR) EMdy
- - BANDANA RED 09 ('Bant Reda09'PBR) EMdy
- CALIPPO TUTTI FRUTTI ('Lan 519'PBR) CWal LSou SPad
- (Lucky Series) LUCKY PEACH ('Balucpea') SPoG
- - LUCKY PURE GOLD ('Balucpure'PBR) SPoG
- - LUCKY RED FLAME ('Balandimfla') SPoG
- - LUCKY SUNRISE ROSE ('Balandrise'PBR) SPoG
- - LUCKY WHITE ('Balucwite'PBR) SPoG
- orange-flowered CCCN
- pink-flowered CCCN
- red-flowered CCCN
- white-flowered CCCN
'Chapel Hill Gold' EMdy
'Dallas Red' EHyd ELan LRHS NRHS
'Miss Huff' EBee ELan EMdy EPfP
§ ***montevidensis*** EShb
- f. ***albifora*** EShb
'Pink Caprice' EPfP
'Radiation' ELan EPfP
sellowiana see *L. montevidensis*

Lapageria ✿ (*Philesiaceae*)

rosea ♀H3 CCCN CRHN CTsd SAdn SChF SWvt WPGP
- var. ***albiflora*** ♀H3 CRHN SChF
- - 'Hugletts Blush' SChF
- 'Beatrix Anderson' CRHN
- 'Flesh Pink' CRHN
- 'Pink Panther' CRHN

Lapeirousia (*Iridaceae*)

cruenta see *Freesia laxa*
laxa see *Freesia laxa*

Lardizabala (*Lardizabalaceae*)

biternata see *L. funaria*
§ ***funaria*** WCru

Larix ✿ (*Pinaceae*)

decidua CAco CCVT CMen CPer ELan EPfP EWTr GDam GMcL IPap LRHS MGos MMuc NWea SCob SEND SPlb SSha WHtc WTSh
- 'Bükk' CAco
- 'Corley' CKen
§ - var. ***decidua*** NBwr
- 'Globus' CAco
- 'Horstmann's Recurved' CAco NLar SLim
- 'Krejci' NLar SLim
- 'Little Bogle' CAco CKen LRHS MAsh MBlu NLar SLim
- 'Lucek' NLar SLim
- 'Oberförster Karsten' CAco CKen
- 'Pendula' CAco
- 'Puli' ♀H7 CAco LRHS MBlu MPri NHol NLar SPoG
× ***eurolepis*** see *L.* × *marschlinsii*
europaea DC. see *L. decidua* var. *decidua*
gmelinii var. ***olgensis*** CAco
- var. ***principis-rupprechtii*** CAco

	- 'Tharandt'	CAco CKen
§	***kaempferi***	CAco CCVT CMen EDir ELan EPfP IPap LBuc LIns LPal LPar SCob SCoo SEWo SSha WTSh
	- 'Bambino'	CKen SLim
	- 'Bingman'	CKen
	- 'Blue Ball'	CKen
	- 'Blue Dwarf' ♀H7	CAco EPfP MAsh NLar SLim
	- 'Blue Rabbit'	CAco CKen
	- 'Blue Rabbit Weeping'	CAco SLim
	- 'Cruwys Morchard'	CKen
	- 'Diana'	CAco CKen CMen MAsh NHol NLar SLim
	- 'Elizabeth Rehder'	CAco CKen
	- 'Grant Haddow'	CKen
	- 'Grey Green Dwarf'	MAsh
	- 'Grey Pearl'	CKen MAsh SLim
	- 'Hobbit'	CKen
	- 'Jakobsen'	LRHS NLar
	- 'Jakobsen's Pyramid'	MAsh WMat
	- 'Kaskade' **new**	CAco
	- 'Magic Gold'	NLar
I	- 'Nana'	CAco CKen CMen NHol
I	- 'Nana Prostrata'	CKen
	- 'Paper Lanterns'	CAco
	- 'Pendula'	CAco EPfP SPoG
	- 'Pulii'	CAco SLim
	- 'Stiff Weeper' ♀H7	CAco LRHS SLim
	- 'Varley'	CKen
	- 'Wehlen'	CKen NLar
	- 'Wolterdingen'	CAco CKen NLar
	laricina	CAco
	- 'Arethusa Bog'	CKen
	- 'Bear Swamp'	CKen
	- 'Bingman'	CKen
	- 'Blue Sparkler'	NLar
	- 'Greg Williams'	CKen
	- 'Hartwig Pine'	CKen
	- 'Iron Red'	NLar
	- 'Madie G.'	CAco
	- 'Michigan Tower'	NLar
	- 'Newport Beauty'	CKen
	- 'Stubby'	CKen
	leptolepis	see *L. kaempferi*
§	× ***marschlinsii***	NWea
	- 'Domino'	CKen
	- 'Gail'	CKen
	- 'Julie'	CKen
	- 'Orvelte'	CAco
	- 'Varied Directions'	CAco
	occidentalis	EBtc
	- 'Nowhere'	CAco

Laser (*Apiaceae*)

	trilobum	MAvo SPhx
	- PAB 3382	LEdu WPGP

Laserpitium (*Apiaceae*)

	gallicum	CKel EMor SPhx
	halleri	SPhx
	latifolium	EBee SPhx
§	***siler***	CSpe EBee EMor EShb LPla MNrw NDov SPhx SPlb WHil WSHC WSpi

Lasiagrostis see *Stipa*

Lasiospermum (*Asteraceae*)

	bipinnatum	SPlb

Latania (*Arecaceae*)

	loddigesii	LPal
	lontaroides **new**	NPlm

Lathraea (*Orobanchaceae*)

	clandestina	CAvo

Lathyrus ✿ (*Fabaceae*)

	annuus red	SPhx
§	***aureus***	CAby CBor CDor CSpe EPPr EWld GEdr LRHS MCot MHer MNrw NBid NBir SBrt SPhx WCAu WFar WKif
	bauhini **new**	SBrt
	chilensis	LShi WPav
	cyaneus misapplied	see *L. vernus*
	davidii	CSpe LEdu SBrt
	fremontii hort.	see *L. laxiflorus*
	gmelinii	SBrt
	grandiflorus ♀H6	CCBP CRHN NChi NHpl SMHy WCot
	× ***hammettii*** 'Erewhon'	CArg SPhx
	- 'Turquoise Lagoon'	CArg
	inermis	see *L. laxiflorus*
	japonicus	CEls EBee
	- subsp. ***maritimus***	SPhx WCot
	laetiflorus var. ***vestitus***	see *L. vestitus*
	laevigatus	SBrt
	latifolius ♀H7	CAgr CRHN CSde EPPr GMcL MHol NPer SCob SRms SVic WBrk WCot WFar WHer XLum
§	- 'Albus' ♀H7	CTri SRms WFar WHlf WKif XLum
	- deep pink-flowered	ETho
	- pale pink-flowered	ETho
	- PINK PEARL	see *L. latifolius* 'Rosa Perle'
	- 'Red Pearl'	CAby CBcs CBod CKel CRos CTsd CWGN EBee EHyd ELan EPfP GAbr LBar LBuc LCro LRHS LSRN MHer NLar NRHS SPer SPlb SPoG SRms SWvt WFar
§	- 'Rosa Perle' ♀H7	CAby CBcs CBod CEme CKel CRos CTri EBee EHyd ELan EPfP LCro LOPS LRHS LSRN LShi MRav NBir NLar NPer NRHS SCgs SNig SPer SPoG SWvt WBor WFar WHlf XLum
	- 'Rose Queen'	GJos
	- WEISSE PERLE	see *L. latifolius* 'White Pearl'
	- 'White Pearl' misapplied	see *L. latifolius* 'Albus'
§	- 'White Pearl' ♀H7	Widely available
§	***laxiflorus***	CBor WOut
	linifolius	SBrt
	montanus	GPoy
	nervosus	CSpe LShi SRms
	niger	CSpe EWld LEdu LShi MHer MMrt SBut SHar
	nissolia	SPhx WSFF
	odoratus 'Albutt Blue'	CArg CSpe
	- 'Almost Black'	CArg
	- 'America' ♀H3	CArg
	- 'Anniversary'	CArg MCot
	- 'Barry Dare'	CArg
	- 'Beaujolais'	LCro LOPS SPhx
	- 'Beth Chatto'	MCot
	- 'Betty Maiden'	MCot
	- 'Black Knight'	CArg
	- 'Blue Medley'	MCot
	- 'Blue Velvet'	CArg CSpe
	- 'Bobby's Girl' ♀H3	LCro
	- 'Bouquet Navy'	CArg
	- 'Bristol' ♀H3	CSpe
	- 'Burnished Bronze'	MCot
	- 'Cathy' ♀H3	CArg
	- 'Charlie's Angel' ♀H3	CArg LCro LOPS MCot
	- 'Cupani'	LCro LOPS SPhx
	- 'Daphne'	LCro
	- 'Dark Passion'	MCot

	- 'Dawn'	MCot
	- 'Ethel Grace'	MCot
	- 'Evening Glow' ℽH3	MCot
	- 'Flora Norton'	CArg
	- 'George Priestley'	MCot
I	- 'Gwendoline' ℽH3	CArg LCro LOPS
	- 'Heaven Scent'	CArg
	- 'Henry Eckford'	SPhx
	- 'High Scent' ℽH3	LCro LOPS
	- 'Honey Pink'	MCot
	- 'Honeymoon'	MCot
	- 'Jilly' ℽH3	CArg LCro LOPS MCot
	- 'Just Julia' ℽH3	CArg CSpe
	- 'Karen Louise'	LCro LOPS
	- 'King Edward VII' ℽH3	CArg LCro LOPS
	- 'Linda C'	LCro
	- 'Lord Nelson'	CArg
	- 'Magnificent Maroon'	CArg
	- 'Marion'	MCot
	- 'Marti Caine'	MCot
	- 'Matucana' ℽH3	CArg CSpe ELan LCro LOPS MNHC SPhx
	- 'Midnight'	LCro LOPS
	- 'Millennium'	CArg
	- 'Milly'	MCot
	- 'Misty Mountain'	MCot
	- 'Mollie Rilstone'	CArg LCro LOPS MCot
	- 'Mrs Bernard Jones' ℽH3	LCro LOPS MCot
	- 'Mrs Collier'	CArg CSpe SPhx
	- 'Noel Sutton' ℽH3	CArg
	- 'Old Spice'	SVic
	- 'Our Harry'	CArg
	- 'Oxford Blue'	LCro LOPS
	- 'Painted Lady'	LCro LOPS SPhx
	- 'Pink Pearl'	CArg LBar
	- 'Pluto'	LCro LOPS
	- 'Princess Elizabeth' **new**	LCro
	- 'Promise'	CArg MCot
	- 'Restormel'	CArg MCot
	- 'Richard and Judy'	MCot
	- 'Royal Wedding'	LCro LOPS
	- 'Solitude'	CArg
	- SPENCER MIXED	LCro SVic
	- 'Valerie Harrod' ℽH3	CArg
	- 'Wedding Day' ℽH3	MCot
	- 'White Frills'	CArg LCro LOPS
	palustris	EBee LLWG MMuc SPhx SPlb
	pannonicus	CPla
	pratensis	CHab EBee NMir SPhx WSFF
	pubescens	CRHN
	roseus	WSHC
	rotundifolius ℽH6	GLog SMHy SPhx WBor WSHC
	- 'Tillyperone' ℽH7	EBee SPhx WSHC
	sativus	CSpe SPhx
	subandinus	SPlb
	sylvestris	CBod LShi MMuc NAts WOut
	tingitanus	CSpe
	transsylvanicus	GBin SBrt SPhx
	tuberosus	CRHN EBee EPPr LEdu WCot WSHC
	'Tubro'	EBee
	venetus	EBee EWes MNrw SPhx WSHC
§	***vernus*** ℽH6	Widely available
	- 'Albiflorus'	MNrw
	- 'Alboroseus' ℽH6	Widely available
	- var. ***albus***	MNrw NChi SRms WCot
	- ***aurantiacus***	see *L. aureus*
	- 'Caeruleus'	WHoo
*	- 'Cyaneus'	CDor SBrt SHar WCot
	- 'Dama Duet'	SHar
	- 'Dama Emily'	SHar
I	- 'Filifolius'	CSpe
	- 'Flaccidus'	MAvo MNrw WCot WMal
*	- 'Gracilis'	EBee EWld LEdu SHar
I	- 'Gracilis Alboroseus'	SHar
	- 'Little Elf'	SHar
	- 'Madelaine'	WCot
	- narrow-leaved	CTtf
I	- 'Pendulus'	SHar
	- purple-flowered	CRos EHyd LRHS MMuc NRHS SEND
	- 'Rainbow'	CBor CRos EHyd EPfP LRHS NRHS
	- 'Rosenelfe'	EMor GEdr GJos LBar LEdu LSou MHer SBea SHar SPhx WCot WHil
	- 'Spring Melody'	EBee SHar WCot
	- 'Subtle Hints'	SHar WCot
§	***vestitus***	GDam

Latua (*Solanaceae*)

	pubiflora	WPav

Laurelia (*Atherospermataceae*)

§	***sempervirens***	CBcs
	serrata	see *L. sempervirens*

Laureliopsis (*Atherospermataceae*)

	philippiana	CMCN NLar

Laurentia see *Isotoma*

Laurus (*Lauraceae*)

	nobilis ℽH4	Widely available
	- f. ***angustifolia*** ℽH4	CDoC CKel CMac LRHS MBlu MHer MMuc MRav NLar SArc SEND SPoG
	- 'Aurea' ℽH4	CBcs CEme CMac ELan ELon EPfP LSto MHer MMuc NLar SEND SPoG SWvt
	- clipped pyramid	LSRN
	- 'Crispa'	MRav
	- variegated (v)	CMac SRms

Lavandula ✿ (*Lamiaceae*)

	'After Midnight'	see *L.* 'Avonview'
	'Alba'	see *L. angustifolia* 'Alba', *L. × intermedia* 'Alba'
	'Alba' ambig.	SPer
§	***angustifolia***	Widely available
	- 'Alba' misapplied	see *L. angustifolia* 'Blue Mountain White'
§	- 'Alba'	ELan EPfP EWoo GPoy LRHS MHer MHoo NBwr NGrs SCob SEdi SGsty SPlb SVen SVic WAvo WGwG WHlf WJek WLov WSpi XSen
	- 'Alba Nana'	see *L. angustifolia* 'Nana Alba'
	- 'Arctic Snow'	CBcs CRos CWal EHyd ENor EPfP EWhm LCro LOPS LRHS MAsh MHer MSwo NGrs NRHS SDow SFai SPoG SRms WLav WSpi
	- AROMATICO BLUE ('Lablusa'PBR)	EHyd LRHS NRHS
	- AROMATICO FORTE BLUE ('Laa20001')	EHyd LRHS NRHS SPoG
	- AROMATICO SILVER ('Lasila')	GMcL
	- 'Ashdown Forest'	EBee ENfk EWhm LSto MHoo SAdn SDow SFai SRGP SRms SSut WLav WSpi XSen
	- 'Backhouse Purple'	SDow
	- 'Beechwood Blue' ℽH5	SDow WLav
	- 'Betty's Blue'	SDow
	- BLUE CUSHION ('Schola')	ELan LCro MAsh SPoG SRms WLav
	- BLUE ICE ('Dow3'PBR)	NLar SDow WLav XSen
§	- 'Blue Mountain White'	WLav
	- 'Blue Rider'	NRHS WLav
	- BLUE SCENT ('Syngablusc')	LRHS
	- BLUE SPEAR ('Pas1213799')	LBar LBuc LRHS MBros MDon MPri SCgs WHil WWke

§	- 'Bowles's Early'	WGwG
	- 'Bowles's Grey'	see *L. angustifolia* 'Bowles's Early'
	- 'Bowles's Variety'	see *L. angustifolia* 'Bowles's Early'
	- 'Cedar Blue'	EWhm MHer MHoo SDow SRms WLav XSen
	- 'Coconut Ice'	ELan LRHS WLav WSpi
	- 'Compacta'	SDow WLav
	- 'Dursley White'	WLav
	- 'Dwarf Blue'	CBod CCBP LSRN MAsh MHed NWea SRms WFar WHlf XSen
	- ELIZABETH ('Fair 16'[PBR])	ENor LSRN NLar SDow SFai SPoG WLav WNPC XSen
	- (Ellagance Series) 'Ellagance Ice'	GMcL LSou SRms WOut
	- - 'Ellagance Purple'	LRHS MBros MNHC SRms XSen
	- - 'Ellagance Sky'	LSou SRms
	- - 'Ellagance Snow'	EWTr LRHS MDon
	- 'Essence Purple'	CBod LRHS WHlf
	- 'Folgate' ♀H5	EWhm MHer MHoo NGdn SDow SEdi SRms WHoo WLav WSpi
	- 'Forever Blue'	MNHC NLar SFai SGBe WTyc
	- GARDEN BEAUTY ('Lowmar'[PBR]) (v)	SGBe
	- GRANNY'S BOUQUET ('Lavang 38'[PBR])	WNPC WSpi XSen
	- HAVANA ('Arbelpaso'[PBR])	ELan LRHS MAsh MHol NGrs SGBe SPoG WNPC XSen
§	- 'Hidcote' ♀H5	Widely available
	- 'Hidcote Pink'	CBrac EWhm MHer MHoo MRav NGdn SCob SDow SEdi SRms
	- 'Hidcote Superior'	NGdn
	- IAN LAVENDER	see *L. angustifolia* 'Purple Treasure'
	- 'Imperial Gem' ♀H5	Widely available
	- 'Jean Davis'	see *L. angustifolia* 'Rosea'
	- 'Lady'	NPer WSpi
	- 'Lady Ann'	WLav
	- 'Lavenite Magic Blue Chip'	NLar XSen
	- 'Lavenite Petite'[PBR]	ENor WLav WSpi XSen
	- LITTLE LADY ('Batlad') ♀H5	ENor GMcL LCro LOPS LRHS LSRN MAsh MHed MHoo MNHC MSwo NLar NRHS SAko SCob SDow SFai SPoG SRms SWvt WHoo WLav WSpi XSen
	- LITTLE LOTTIE ('Clarmo') ♀H5	EWhm MHer MHoo SDow SEdi WLav XSen
	- 'Loddon Blue'	CRos EHyd ENor EPfP EWhm LRHS MAsh MHoo NGrs NRHS SDow SFai SRms WLav WNPC WSpi XSen
§	- 'Loddon Pink'	CBcs CRos EHyd ELan ENor EPfP EWhm GMaP LRHS MAsh MHoo MMuc MRav NBwr NGdn NGrs NRHS SEND SEdi SFai SRms WAvo WLav WLov WNPC XSen
	- 'Lullaby Blue'	SDow
	- 'Maillette'	SDow SRms WLav XSen
	- 'Melissa'	MHol XSen
	- MELISSA LILAC ('Dow4'[PBR])	CBcs CRos CSBt EHyd ENfk ENor LCro LOPS LRHS LSRN MAsh MGos MHer MHol MHoo MNHC NGrs NRHS SCob SDow SFai SGBe SRms WLav XSen
	- 'Middachten'	EHyd XSen
	- 'Miss Dawnderry'	SDow
	- 'Miss Donnington'	see *L. angustifolia* 'Bowles's Early'
	- 'Miss Katherine'[PBR] ♀H5	ENor LBar MAsh MHed NLar SDow SPoG WLav XSen
	- MISS MUFFET ('Scholmis') ♀H5	SDow SRms WLav XSen
	- 'Munstead'	Widely available
§	- 'Nana Alba' ♀H5	EHyd ELan ENfk EPfP EWhm GMaP GPoy MAsh MHer MHoo SEdi SRGP SRms SWvt WLov WSpi XSen
	- 'Nana Atropurpurea'	SDow XSen
	- 'No 9'	SDow
	- 'Pacific Blue'	LRHS SDow XSen
	- 'Peter Pan'	ELan MHer MHoo MNHC NLar SCob SDow WLav XSen
	- 'Princess Blue'	ELon EWhm MHoo SEdi WLav
	- 'Purity'	SDow
§	- 'Purple Treasure'	SDow
§	- 'Rosea'	Widely available
	- 'Royal Purple'	EWes MHoo NGdn SDow SSut SWvt WLav
	- 'Royal Velvet'	SDow
	- 'Saint Jean'	SDow
	- 'Siesta'	XSen
	- 'Silver Blue'	XSen
	- 'Silver Line'	EHyd LRHS NRHS
	- 'Silver Line Blue'	LRHS
	- 'Silver Mist'	CBod GMcL SRms WHer XSen
	- 'Thumbelina Leigh'[PBR]	ENor MHoo SFai SRms WSpi XSen
	- 'Twickel Purple'	CBar CBcs EBee EHyd ELan EPfP LRHS LSRN MAsh MHed MHol MHoo MNHC NGrs NRHS SCob SDow SEdi SFai SGbt SPer SRms SWvt WGwG WLav WSpi XSen
	- 'Walberton's Silver Edge'	see *L. × intermedia* WALBERTON'S SILVER EDGE
	- white-flowered	MBros
	aristibracteata	MHer WLav
	AROMATICO ROSEA	LRHS
§	'Avonview'	MHer WLav
	'Ballerina' ♀H4	SDow
§	'Bee Brilliant'[PBR]	ENfk EWhm WLav
§	'Bee Cool'[PBR]	ENfk WLav
§	'Bee Happy'	ENfk EWhm WLav
§	'Bee Pretty'	ENfk EWhm
	BIG TIME BLUE ('Armtipp01') **new**	ELan
	'Blue Star'	EWhm GMcL MNHC WGwG
	'Bouquet of Roses'	CRos EHyd LRHS NRHS SCoo
	buchii var. ***buchii***	SDow SVen WLav
	'Bulls Cross'	WLav
	× ***cadevallii*** (Fairy Wings Series) BLUSH	see *L.* × *cadevallii* (Fairy Wings Series) 'FW Whimsical'
§	- - 'FW Radiance' **new**	LCro SFai
§	- - 'FW Spellbound' **new**	LCro SFai
§	- - 'FW Whimsical' **new**	SFai
	- - PINK	see *L.* × *cadevallii* (Fairy Wings Series) 'FW Radiance'
	- - PURPLE	see *L.* × *cadevallii* (Fairy Wings Series) 'FW Spellbound'
	canariensis	MHer SDow SVen WLav
	× ***chaytoriae*** 'Bridehead Blue'	SDow
	- 'Gorgeous'	SDow
	- 'Joan Head'	SDow
	- MOLTEN SILVER ('Lavang 12')	XSen
	- 'Richard Gray' ♀H4	LRHS LSRN MHed MHer MNHC SDow SRms WAvo WLav XSen
§	- 'Sawyers' ♀H4	CRos EHyd EPau EPfP GMaP LRHS LSRN MCot MHed MHer MHoo MRav NBir NPer NRHS SEND SPer SPhx SPoG SRms WKif WMal XSen
	- SILVER SANDS ('Fair 14'[PBR])	CBcs ELan ENfk EPfP LRHS MNHC SFai SPoG XSen
	× ***christiana***	ENor LBar MHol SDow SFai SVen WJek WLav WNPC
	'Cornard Blue'	see *L.* × *chaytoriae* 'Sawyers'
	dentata	CBrac ENfk EShb SIvy SRms WJek
§	- var. ***candicans***	MHer SDow SRms WJek WLav
	- var. ***dentata*** 'Dusky Maiden'	SDow WLav

	- - 'Ploughman's Blue'	SVen WGwG
	- - f. ***rosea***	SDow
	- - 'Royal Crown' ♀^{H3}	WLav
	- silver-leaved	see *L. dentata* var. *candicans*
	'Devonshire Compact'	CPla CSBt MHol SRms
	'Fathead'	CBcs CBrac CChe EHyd ELan EPfP LRHS LSRN MAsh MGos MHer NBir NGdn NLar SCob SCoo SDow SFai SGBe SPoG WAvo WLav
	'Flaming Purple'	SDow
	× ***ginginsii*** 'Goodwin Creek Grey' ♀^{H4}	CGBo MHer MPri SRms WJek WLav
	'Hazel'	EHyd EPfP LRHS NRHS SGBe
	'Helmsdale'^{PBR}	CRos CSBt ELan ENor EPfP GMaP GMcL LRHS LSRN MAsh NLar SCoo SFai SGBe
	heterophylla misapplied	see *L.* × *heterophylla* Viv. Gaston Allard Group
§	× ***heterophylla*** Viv. Gaston Allard Group	WLav
	- 'African Pride'	SVen
	- 'Meerlo' (v)	CCht MHol SCgs SFai WCot
	'Hidcote Blue'	see *L. angustifolia* 'Hidcote'
	× ***intermedia*** 'Abrialii'	SDow
§	- 'Alba' ♀^{H5}	EHeP MHed MHer MHoo SEND SEdi SGbt SVen
	- ANNIVERSARY BOUQUET	SDow
	- 'Arabian Night'	see *L.* × *intermedia* 'Impress Purple', 'Sussex'
	- 'Arabian Night' ambig.	SRms
§	- Dutch Group	CGBo CSBt EHyd ENfk EPfP EWhm LRHS MAsh MNHC MRav MSwo SArc SCob SCoo SFai SPer SRms SVic XSen
	- 'Edelweiss'	CBcs CBod CSBt ECul EHyd ENfk EPfP EWhm LRHS LSto MACG MAsh MHoo MNHC NGrs NLar NRHS SDow SEdi SFai SPer SPoG SRms SWvt WHlf WLav WSpi XSen
	- 'Fragrant Memories'	MHoo SCoo SDow SRms WLav XSen
	- 'Fred Boutin'	WSpi
	- 'Grappenhall' misapplied	see *L.* × *intermedia* 'Pale Pretender'
	- 'Grappenhall' ambig.	CGBo CSBt EWhm LSto MHoo WSpi XSen
	- 'Grey Hedge'	EWhm MHoo SRms WLav
	- 'Gros Bleu'	LWaG SDow WLav
	- 'Grosse Séguret'	XSen
	- 'Grosso'	Widely available
	- (Heavenly Series) HEAVENLY ANGEL ('Dowphangel'^{PBR})	SDow SGBe XSen
	- - HEAVENLY NIGHT ('Dowphnight'^{PBR})	SDow XSen
	- - HEAVENLY SCENT ('Dowphscent')	ENor MHoo SDow XSen
	- 'Hidcote Giant' ♀^{H5}	CRos EHyd EPfP LRHS NPer NRHS SDow WKif WLav WSpi XSen
§	- 'Impress Purple'	SDow WLav XSen
	- 'Lullingstone Castle'	ENfk EWhm MHoo SIvy SRGP SRms SSut WAvo WLav
	- 'Magnum'	SDow
	- 'Old English' misapplied	see *L.* × *intermedia* 'Seal'
	- 'Old English'	CBrac ENfk SDow SRms SWeb
	- Old English Group	MMuc SEND WHoo WLav XSen
	- OLYMPIA ('Downoly'^{PBR})	MHol SDow SGBe SPoG XSen
§	- 'Pale Pretender'	GQue SPer SRms
	- PHENOMENAL ('Niko'^{PBR})	ENor LCro LOPS LRHS MNHC NDov SCoo SEdd SFai SPad SPoG WNPC XSen
	- PLATINUM BLONDE ('Momparler'^{PBR})	CCht CGBo CRos EHyd ENor LRHS LSou MAsh NRHS SCob SCoo SPoG
	- 'Provence'	CBcs CSBt MNHC SDow SFai SRms XSen
§	- 'Seal'	ENfk GMaP SDow SRms
§	- 'Sussex' ♀^{H5}	CFis CRos EHyd EPfP LRHS NRHS SDow WLav
	- 'Twickel Purple'	ELan EWes NLar
§	- WALBERTON'S SILVER EDGE ('Walvera') (v)	EHyd ELan EPfP LBuc LRHS MGos NBwr NRHS SCoo SDow SRms XSen
	- 'Woodhayes' **new**	CBee
	'Jamboree'	WLav
	'Jean Davis'	see *L. angustifolia* 'Rosea'
	lanata ♀^{H3}	ECha SRms WLav XSen
§	***latifolia***	XSen
	'Loddon Pink'	see *L. angustifolia* 'Loddon Pink'
	'Madrid Blue'	see *L.* 'Bee Happy'
	'Madrid Pink'	see *L.* 'Bee Pretty'
	'Madrid Purple'	see *L.* 'Bee Brilliant'
	'Madrid White'	see *L.* 'Bee Cool'
	minutolii	SDow
	multifida	CWal LDai WLav
	- 'Spanish Eyes'	CWal
	officinalis	see *L. angustifolia*
	PASSIONNÉ ('Lavsts 08'^{PBR}) ♀^{H4}	WLav
	pedunculata	CBod ENor SSha XSen
	- subsp. ***lusitanica***	EHyd EPfP LRHS NRHS SPoG
	- - LUSI PINK ('Wijs02'^{PBR})	CRos ENfk SFai SGBe
	- - LUSI PURPLE	CRos EHyd LRHS NRHS SFai SGBe SPoG
§	- subsp. ***pedunculata***	CAby CBar CBrac ECha EHyd ELan EPfP LCro LOPS LRHS LSRN MAsh MBow MGos MHoo MNHC MSwo NGdn NRHS SCob SFai SGbt SPer SRms WAvo WSpi
	- - 'James Compton' ♀^{H3}	CRos ECha EHyd LRHS NGdn
	- subsp. ***sampaiana*** 'Purple Emperor'	CRos EHyd LRHS NRHS WLav
	'Pink Panache' **new**	SDow
	pinnata	CCBP CCht ELan ENfk ENor LRHS MHol MHoo SAng SDow
	'Pretty Polly' ♀^{H4}	CBcs EHyd ELan EPfP LRHS MAsh NLar SDow SFai SGBe SRkn WLav
	'Pukehou'	EHyd EPfP LRHS MAsh NRHS SCoo WLav
	'Purple Panache' **new**	SDow
	'Regal Splendour'^{PBR}	CBcs CRos CSBt EHyd ELan ENor EPfP LBar LCro LRHS LSRN MAsh MGos MHer MNHC NRHS SCoo SFai SGBe SPoG SRms WLav
	ROCKY ROAD ('Fair09'^{PBR})	CSBt ENor SFai WLav
	'Rosea'	see *L. angustifolia* 'Rosea'
	rotundifolia	SDow
	'Silver Edge'	see *L.* × *intermedia* WALBERTON'S SILVER EDGE
	'Somerset Mist'	WLav
	spica	see *L. angustifolia*, *L. latifolia*
	- 'Hidcote Purple'	see *L. angustifolia* 'Hidcote'
	stoechas	CBcs CEme CRos CSBt ECha EHeP EHyd ELan EPfP GArf GMaP GPoy LPal LRHS LSRN MGil MSwo NRHS SCob SPer SPlb SWeb SWvt WCav
	- from Corsica	SGBe
	- var. ***albiflora***	see *L. stoechas* subsp. *stoechas* f. *leucantha*
	- 'Anouk'^{PBR} (Anouk Series)	EBee ELan EPfP SPoG
	- 'Antibes' (Provençal Series)	GJos SRms
	- 'Bandera'	MBros NBir
	- (Bella Series) BELLA LAVENDER ('Bellav')	CRos EHyd LRHS NRHS
	- - BELLA ROSE ('Belros')	EHyd EPfP LRHS NRHS
	- 'Blueberry Ruffles'^{PBR} (Ruffles Series)	ELan LRHS

- 'Boysenberry Ruffles'PBR (Ruffles Series) ELan ENfk
- CASTILLIANO VIOLET GMcL
- 'Dark Royalty'PBR ELan SCob
- 'Fancy Feathers' **new** CBor
- (Javelin Series) JAVELIN BLUE ('Jin Bulle') CRos EHyd GMcL LRHS NRHS
- - JAVELIN COMPACT ROSE ('Labz0001'PBR) GMcL
- - JAVELIN UPRIGHT WHITE BLUSH ('Labz0002'PBR) GMcL
- (Javelin Forte Series) JAVELIN FORTE DEEP PURPLE ('Labz0004'PBR) LRHS
- - JAVELIN FORTE DEEP ROSE ('Labz0006') LRHS
- LAVENDER LACE ('Colace') WLav
- LITTLE BEE DEEP PURPLE ('Florvendula Deep Purple') (Little Bee Series) GMcL
- 'Mulberry Ruffles'PBR (Ruffles Series) ELan LRHS SCob
- 'Night of Passion' SCoo SDow
- 'Papillon' see *L. pedunculata* subsp. *pedunculata*
- subsp. ***pedunculata*** see *L. pedunculata* subsp. *pedunculata*
- 'Purley' SRms
- Ruffles Series ENfk
- 'Sancho Panza'PBR EGrI
- 'Spring-break Princess' CRos EHyd LRHS NRHS
§ - subsp. ***stoechas*** f. ***leucantha*** EHeP EPfP MSwo
- - - 'Snowman' CBcs CSBt EHyd EPfP LRHS MAsh MHer NLar NRHS SCob SCoo SFai SGBe SPoG SWvt
- - LILAC WINGS ('Prolil'PBR) CRos EHyd ENor LCro LRHS MAsh NRHS SCoo SDow SFai SGBe WLav
- - 'Provençal' CRos EHyd LRHS NRHS SCoo
- - 'Purple Wings' EHyd ELan MAsh MGos
- - f. ***rosea*** ENor
- - - 'Kew Red' CTri ENfk LRHS MGos MHer SFai SRms SWvt WLav
- 'Sugarberry Ruffles'PBR (Ruffles Series) LRHS
- 'Victory' CRos EHyd LRHS NRHS SPoG
- 'With Love'PBR SDow
TIARA ('Fair 10'PBR) CBcs CRos CSBt EHyd ENor EPfP LRHS MGos NEoE NLar NRHS SCob SCoo SFai SPoG SRms WLav
vera misapplied see *L. × intermedia* Dutch Group
vera DC. see *L. angustifolia*
viridis CRos EHyd EPfP LRHS MHer MHoo NPer NRHS SDow SRms WJek WLav
'Willow Vale' ♀H3 EHyd ENor EPfP EWhm LRHS MAsh MHer NRHS SDow SWvt WAvo WJek

Lavatera (*Malvaceae*)

arborea CPla SChr
- 'Rosea' see *L. × clementii* 'Rosea'
- 'Variegata' (v) CPla ELan LBar NPer SEND WCot WHil WOut
bicolor see *L. maritima*
BLUE BIRD ('Renlav') LRHS MNrw WHlf
cachemiriana EPPr GGro NPer
CHAMALLOW ('Inovera'PBR) LSRN
× ***clementii*** 'Barnsley' Widely available
- 'Barnsley Baby' CBod CBrac CMac CRos EBee EHyd ELan EPfP GMcL LBuc LCro LRHS LSto MAsh MTin NLar NPer SCob SEle SGBe SGbt SPer SPoG SRkn SWvt WFar WHlf WNPC
- 'Blushing Bride' EPfP MGos NLar SCob SGBe SPer SWvt
- 'Bredon Springs' ♀H5 CBrac CSBt EBee ECha EDir EHyd ELon EPfP GMcL LCro LRHS LSRN LSto MAsh MGos MMuc NGdn NRHS SCob SEND SGBe SGbt SPer SWvt WAvo XLum
- 'Burgundy Wine' ♀H5 Widely available
- 'Candy Floss' ♀H5 CBrac GMcL NLar NPer SGBe
- 'Eye Catcher' CBrac EPPr LRHS MSwo NLar SGBe SPer WLov
- 'Kew Rose' CBod MHtn MMuc MNHC MSwo NLar NPer SEND SRms XLum
- 'Lavender Lady' EPPr NPer SEND
- 'Lisanne' MSwo
- 'Mary Hope' ♀H5 CDoC CRos EHyd EPfP LRHS MAsh NRHS SCoo SEle SWvt
§ - 'Pink Frills' CEme SWvt WCot WFar
- RED RUM ('Rigrum'PBR) ♀H5 CBod CDoC CEme CKel CMac CSBt EHyd EPfP GDam LSRN MAsh MGos MNrw MPri NLar NRHS SCob SPoG SWvt WFar WHlf
§ - 'Rosea' ♀H5 CBcs CBod CBrac CDoC CKel CMac CPla CRos EBee EHeP EHyd EPfP GMcL LCro LOPS LRHS LSRN LShi MAsh MGos MPri NHol NRHS SCob SGBe SGbt SPer SPoG SWvt WHlf
- RUBY STAR ('Jostar'PBR) CBod CKel EBee EHyd EMil LRHS MAsh NLar NRHS
- SONGBIRD ('Jobird'PBR) MAsh NRHS SPad
§ - 'Wembdon Variegated' (v) NPer
'Frederique' LRHS SWvt WKif WMal
'Grey Beauty' LRHS MPri SEND
'Magenta Magic'PBR MAsh MHol SEdd SPoG
§ ***maritima*** ♀H3 CBod CDoC CKel CMac CPla CSde MPri SEND SGBe SPer SRkn SRms SWvt WCFE WCot WFar WHlf
- 'Princesse de Lignes' XLum
olbia SDix SPlb SRms WFar
- 'Lilac Lady' CBod CKel ECha ELan ELon MGos MMuc WFar WKif
'Peppermint Ice' see *L. thuringiaca* 'Ice Cool'
phoenicea WMal
'Pink Frills' see *L. × clementii* 'Pink Frills'
'Rosea' see *L. × clementii* 'Rosea'
thuringiaca 'First Light' SPhx
§ - 'Ice Cool' SCob SWvt WKif
- 'Saalestrand' MNrw
trimestris 'Loveliness' GJos
- 'Mont Blanc' GJos
- 'Silver Cup' ♀H3 GJos LCro LOPS
'Variegata' see *L. × clementii* 'Wembdon Variegated'
'White Satin'PBR NHol

Lecanthus (*Urticaceae*)

peduncularis GGro SBrt

Ledebouria (*Asparagaceae*)

adlamii see *L. cooperi*
concolor misapplied see *L. socialis*
§ ***cooperi*** CBor EAJP ECha EDAr ELan EPri EShb GKev LEdu MPie SBrt SRot WBor WPGP WTor XLum
'Gary Hammer' SPtp
ovalifolia NWad
§ ***socialis*** EAri EShb GKev LEdu MCot MPie SGro SIvy WCot WFar

- green-leaved EShb
- 'Juda' (v) new EAri
violacea see *L. socialis*

Ledum see *Rhododendron*

leek see AGM Vegetables Section

Legousia (*Campanulaceae*)

speculum-veneris CSpe

Leibnitzia (*Asteraceae*)

anandria GGro SBls

Leiotulus (*Apiaceae*)

aureus new SPhx

Lembotropis see *Cytisus*

Lemna (*Araceae*)

gibba NPer
minor CWat NPer
trisulca CWat EWat NPer

lemon see *Citrus × limon*

lemon balm see *Melissa officinalis*

lemon grass see *Cymbopogon citratus*

lemon, rough see *Citrus × taitensis*

lemon verbena see *Aloysia citrodora*

lemonquat see *Citrus × taitensis × C. × limon*

Leonotis (*Lamiaceae*)

leonurus CBcs CCCN CDTJ CHll CPbh ECre EMdy EShb LRHS SGBe SMrm SPlb WJek XLum
- var. ***albiflora*** CCCN EShb
nepetifolia CCCN
var. ***nepetifolia*** 'Staircase'
§ ***ocymifolia*** CCCN CHll

Leontodon (*Asteraceae*)

hispidus CHab NMir
§ ***rigens*** ELan EPPr GEdr MMuc NBid NBir SMrm SPtp WFar
- B&SWJ 12527 GGro WCru WSHC
- 'Girandole' see *L. rigens*

Leontopodium (*Asteraceae*)

alpinum see *L. nivale* subsp. *alpinum*
discolor WAbe
haastioides WAbe
hayachinense GEdr
AJS/J 111 new
himalayanum GKev
kurilense GKev
nanum SPlb
§ ***nivale*** subsp. ***alpinum*** CTri EBou EDAr ELan EPfP MAsh MBel NHpl NSla SLee SPlb SPoG SRms XLum
- - BLOSSOM OF SNOW ('Berghman') LBar LRHS SCoo WHlf
- - 'Everest' LRHS
- - 'Matterhorn' GEdr GMaP NLar
- - 'Mignon' EPfP EWes GArf GMaP NLar WAbe
§ ***ochroleucum*** NLar XLum
var. ***campestre***
pusillum EDAr EPot SPlb WAbe WCot
souliei MMuc XLum
wilsonii GKev

Leonurus (*Lamiaceae*)

artemisia see *L. japonicus*
cardiaca CBee CBod CCBP EGrI GGro GPoy LRHS MHer MHoo MNHC NGrd SPhx SRms WFar
- 'Grobbebol' EPPr SBls WCot WHer
§ ***japonicus*** MHoo
sibiricus misapplied see *L. japonicus*
sibiricus L. CPla SPhx
turkestanicus EBee

Leopoldia (*Asparagaceae*)

comosa see *Muscari comosum*
spreitzenhoferi see *Muscari spreitzenhoferi*
tenuiflora see *Muscari tenuiflorum*

Lepechinia (*Lamiaceae*)

bella SDys
hastata CSpe ECha EWld LRHS SPlb WJek WOut
salviae WFar WHer

Lepidium (*Brassicaceae*)

campestre CHab
latifolium CAgr ENfk LEdu

Lepidothamnus (*Podocarpaceae*)

§ ***colensoi*** SMad

Lepismium (*Cactaceae*)

cruciforme new EAri NPlm
§ ***houlletianum*** new EAri

Leptinella (*Asteraceae*)

atrata subsp. ***luteola*** ELan
'County Park' EDAr
dendyi CBor ELan EWes GEdr NSla WIce
dioica GBin
- 'Minima' WFar
hispida see *Cotula hispida* (DC.) Harv.
§ ***pectinata*** ITim
§ ***potentillina*** CTri ECha GQue MBNS NBro NLar SRms XLum
§ ***pusilla*** XSte
§ ***pyrethrifolia*** GEdr
§ ***squalida*** ECha EDAr GBin NSti SLee
* - 'Minima' GQue WFar WSFF
§ - 'Platt's Black' Widely available
traillii NBro

Leptodermis (*Rubiaceae*)

oblonga 'Summer Stars' LRHS

Leptopus (*Phyllanthaceae*)

§ ***chinensis*** EWTr WCot

Leptospermum ✿ (*Myrtaceae*)

citratum see *L. petersonii*
'Copper Sheen' CTrC
'County Park Blush' ELon
cunninghamii see *L. myrtifolium*
'Electric Red' (Galaxy Series) CAbb CKel EPfP GMcL MGil SEle
ericoides see *Kunzea ericoides*
flavescens misapplied see *L. glaucescens*
flavescens Sm. see *L. polygalifolium*
§ ***glaucescens*** SPlb
§ ***grandiflorum*** CBcs CTrC EPfP SVen
grandifolium LRHS
'Havering Hardy' LSto SEle

humifusum	see *L. rupestre*
juniperinum	SPlb
'Karo Pearl Star'	CBcs CTrC CTsd MGil WLov
'Karo Spectrobay'	CBcs CKel CTsd MGil SEle
laevigatum	SVen
§ ***lanigerum***	CTri CTsd EPfP GAbr SPlb SPtp SVen
- 'Cunninghamii'	see *L. myrtifolium*
liversidgei	SPlb
§ ***myrtifolium***	CMac CTrC
nitidum	SPlb
§ ***petersonii***	GPoy
phylicoides	see *Kunzea ericoides*
'Pink Cascade'	CBcs CMac CTri EDir SEle XSte
§ ***polygalifolium***	SPlb
prostratum	see *L. rupestre*
pubescens	see *L. lanigerum*
'Red Cascade'	SWvt
rodwayanum	see *L. grandiflorum*
rotundifolium	CBcs SPlb
§ ***rupestre***	CTrC CTri SPlb SVen
scoparium	CBee CTrC CTsd EGrI GPoy MNHC SPlb SVen WJek WKor
- 'Adrianne'	EHyd EPfP LRHS NRHS
- 'Appleblossom' ♀H4	CBcs CBod CDoC CEnd CKel CTrC ELon EPfP GMcL MMuc SEle SSha
- 'Autumn Glory'	CBod WLov
- 'Blossom' (d)	CBcs CMac
- 'Burgundy Queen' (d)	CBcs CCCN CEme CMac CTrC CTsd
- 'Chapmanii'	CCCN
- 'Coral Candy'	CBcs CBod CCCN CEnd MGil SEle SGbt WFar WLov
- 'Crimson Glory' (d)	CBod CSBt SEle SSha
- 'Elizabeth Jane'	WFar
- 'Gaiety Girl' (d)	CKel CSBt
- var. ***incanum***	ESwi
- 'Jubilee' (d)	CBcs CCCN CCoa CMac
- 'Leonard Wilson' (d)	CTri
- 'Martini'	CAbb CBcs CCCN CDoC CKel CMac CSBt EHyd EPfP LCro LRHS MGil NRHS SEdd SGol SPoG WLov
- (Nanum Group) 'Huia'	SCob
- - 'Kea'	CBcs MHer
- - 'Kiwi' ♀H4	CBcs CBod CBrac CCCN CEme CKel CRos CSBt EBee EGrI EHyd ELan EPfP LRHS MAsh MMuc SEle SPoG WFar
- - 'Nanum'	CCCN
- - 'Tui'	CMac CSBt CTrC
- 'Nichollsii' ♀H4	CBcs SVen
- 'Nichollsii Nanum' ♀H4	WAbe WThu
- 'Pink Damask'	SWvt
- var. ***prostratum*** misapplied	see *L. rupestre*
- 'Red Damask' (d) ♀H4	Widely available
- 'Red Ensign'	LCro SPoG
* - 'Ruby Wedding'	EHyd ELan EPfP LRHS LSRN MAsh SPoG
- 'Snow Flurry'	CBcs CDoC CKel CRos EHyd EPfP LRHS NRHS SGol SVen WFar
- 'Winter Cheer' (d)	CBcs CKel CTrC EGrI SGol
- 'Wiri Donna'	CSde
- 'Wiri Kerry' (d)	XSte
- 'Wiri Linda'	CBcs CMac
'Silver Sheen' ♀H3	CAbb CBcs CCCN CDoC CEnd CKel CSde CTrC CTsd ELan EPfP LRHS MAsh NLar SPer SPoG SRHi SVen WPGP
squarrosum	CBee

Lespedeza (*Fabaceae*)

bicolor	CAgr CCCN EGrI EHed WFar
- 'Yakushima'	NLar
buergeri	CSpe MMrt NLar SHar
capitata	EBee NLar
japonica	SPlb
maximowiczii <u>**new**</u>	WSHC
thunbergii ♀H5	CBcs CDoC CEme CKel CRos CSde CSpe EBee EHyd ELan EPfP LRHS MAsh MBlu MGil NLar NRHS SEdd SMad SMrm SPer SPoG SSta WHil WHlf WSHC
- subsp. ***formosa***	EBee EGrI MGil WSHC
- 'Gibraltar'	EBee NLar WPGP
- 'Summer Beauty'	CBcs
- subsp. ***thunbergii*** 'Albiflora'	ELan
- - 'Edo-shibori'	CKel EBee EHed ELan EPfP LRHS MMrt NLar SEdd SPer WHil WPGP WSHC
- - 'White Fountain'	CRos EHyd EPfP LRHS MAsh NRHS SPoG WSHC
tiliifolia	see *Desmodium elegans*

Lesquerella (*Brassicaceae*)

arctica var. ***purshii***	GKev

lettuce see AGM Vegetables Section

Leucadendron (*Proteaceae*)

argenteum	CBcs CCCN CPbh SPlb
'Bell's Supreme'	CTrC
'Burgundy Sunset'PBR	CBcs CCCN
conicum	CPbh
'Cream Delight'	CCCN
daphnoides	SPlb
discolor	SPlb
eucalyptifolium	CPbh SPlb
galpinii	CPbh
gandogeri	CPbh
'Highlights'	CCCN
'Inca Gold' ♀H1c	CBcs CPbh
'Jack Harre'	LRHS
'Jester' (v)	CCCN CPbh
'Jolly Joker' (v) <u>**new**</u>	CCCN
'Jubilee Crown'	XSte
laureolum	CCCN CPbh
'Maui Sunset'	CTrC
modestum 'Strawberry Fair'	CCCN
'Mrs Stanley'	CTrC
'Pisa'	LRHS XSte
'Red Dwarf'	CPbh
'Safari Magic'	CCCN
'Safari Sunset' ♀H3	CBcs CCCN CPbh CTrC CTsd
salicifolium	SPlb
salignum	CCCN CPbh
- 'Fireglow'	CTrC LRHS
- 'Winter Red'	CBcs
'Sand Dollar'	CPbh
sessile	CPbh
'Sixteen Candles'	CBcs
strobilinum	CPbh
'Summer Sun'	XSte
'Sundance'	MPkF XSte
tinctum	CPbh

Leucaena (*Fabaceae*)

leucocephala	SPlb

Leucanthemella (*Asteraceae*)

§ ***serotina*** ♀H7	Widely available
- 'Herbststern'	NLar

Leucanthemopsis (*Asteraceae*)

hosmariensis	see *Rhodanthemum hosmariense*

Leucanthemum ✿ (*Asteraceae*)

'Angel' — CBod ELon MBros NCou NLar
atlanticum — see *Rhodanthemum atlanticum*
catananche — see *Rhodanthemum catananche*
graminifolium — EPPr
hosmariense — see *Rhodanthemum hosmariense*
mawii — see *Rhodanthemum gayanum*
maximum misapplied — see *L.* × *superbum*
§ ***maximum*** (Ramond) DC. — NBro NPer
- ***uliginosum*** — see *Leucanthemella serotina*
nipponicum — see *Nipponanthemum nipponicum*
'Osiris Neige' — ECtt MAvo XLum
paludosum 'Snowland' — LRHS
'Real Charmer'PBR (Realflor Series) — CRos EHyd LBar LRHS MAsh MBros NRHS SGBe SPeP SRms SWvt WHlf
'Sante' — EHyd ELan EMor EPfP LRHS MPri NRHS
'Sunshine Peach' — EHyd EPfP ILea SRms
§ × ***superbum*** — CMac CWal GAbr MBow MMuc SEND WBrk
- 'Aglaia' (d) — Widely available
- 'Alaska' — CRos EHyd ELan EWoo GAbr GBin GQue LRHS LSun MACG MCot NLar NRHS SCoo SEdd SOrN SPer SWvt XLum
- 'Amelia' — EBee EHyd LRHS NLar NRHS
- 'Anita Allen' (d) — ECtt WCot
- 'Antwerp Star' — NLar
- 'Banana Cream' — CAby CBcs CRos CWGN CWnw ECtt EHyd EMor EPfP EWTr LCro LEdu LRHS MACG MAsh MBriF MBros NGrs NHol NLar NRHS SCob SCoo SEle SPoG WFar WPnP WTor
- 'Barbara Bush' (d/v) — SWvt
§ - 'Beauté Nivelloise' — CElw ECtt EPfP LRHS LSou NBir SRms WFar WSpi WTor
- 'Becky' — CMac CRos EBlo ECha EHyd ELan ELon EPfP GBin ILea LRHS LSRN MBel MSpe NEoE NLar NRHS WCAu WCot WJam WSpi
- 'Belgian Lace' — NLar
- 'Bishopstone' — EBee ELan LEdu MSpe SMrm
- 'Bridal Bouquet'PBR — CRos EHyd LRHS NRHS
- 'Brightside' — EHyd ELan ELon EMor LRHS LSun NRHS SBls SBut WFar
- BROADWAY LIGHTS ('Leumayel'PBR) — CKel CRos CWnw EHyd EMor EPfP EWes GBin GDam GMcL LRHS MAsh MPri MRav NFav NGrs NRHS SCob SRms WAvo WCAu WFar WSpi WTor
- CHER (Sweet Daisy Series) **new** — LBar
- 'Christine Hagemann' — CElw ECtt ILea MNrw MRav SHar WBrk WCFE
- 'Cloud Cumulus' — SCoo
- 'Crazy Daisy' — CBod CChe CTri CWal ECtt EHyd EMor EPfP MACG NFav NGrs NRHS NWsh SCoo SWvt WFar WWke
- DARLING DAISY ('Kiemar') **new** — WCot
- 'Droitwich Beauty' — ECtt MAvo WAvo WCFE WCav WHoo
- 'Dwarf Snow Lady' — SGBe
- 'Edgebrook Giant' — WBrk
- 'Eisstern' — LEdu SHar
- 'Elworthy Sparkler' — CElw MAvo WBrk
- 'Engelina'PBR — EBee ECtt EPfP EShb LRHS MBriF NBir NCth WCAu
- 'Esther Read' (d) — EBee ECtt EHyd EPfP GBin GQue LRHS MACG NBPC NBro NChi NLar NRHS SRms SWvt WBrk WCot WFar
§ - 'Everest' — SRms
- 'Exhibition' — EHyd LRHS NRHS
- 'Fiona Coghill' (d) — CElw CWGN ECtt EHyd EPfP GBee GBin LRHS MHol MNrw NBPC NBir NFav NGdn NLar NRHS WCot WHoo
- 'Flore Pleno' (d) — MMuc SEND SPlb
- FREAK! ('Leuz0001'PBR) — CBcs CRos EHyd EPfP LRHS LSou MDon MHol NGrs NRHS SCoo SWvt
- 'Goldfinch'PBR — CWCL CWGN ECtt LBar MACG MHol MPri NCth NGBl NGdn NHpl NLar NWsh SCob SPoG SRms WCot WHil WHlf
- 'Goldrausch'PBR — EBee ECtt ELan LEdu LRHS MRav NBPC NBir NGdn NHol SCob SGbt SRms SWvt WFar
- 'Gruppenstolz' — GBin
- 'H. Seibert' — MArl
- 'Horace Read' (d) — CDor CElw ECtt NBir NHol SGro SWvt
- 'Ice Star' — EHyd ELan LRHS NBPC NRHS
- 'Jennifer Read' — NLar
§ - 'John Murray' (d) — NBir NWsh WFar
- 'King's Crown' — LBar
- 'LaCrosse' (Ooh La Series) — CRos EHyd ELon EPfP LRHS NLar NRHS SCob WFar
- 'LaSpider' (Ooh La Series) — EHyd GBee LRHS MPri NRHS
- 'Little Miss Muffet' — CSBt CWGN ECtt EHyd EPfP LRHS LSou MBNS NRHS
- 'Little Princess' — see *L.* × *superbum* 'Silberprinzesschen'
- 'Luna'PBR — CBod LBar LRHS MACG MPri SPeP
- 'Madonna' **new** — CBod LBar MDon MPri
- 'Manhattan' — CDor GBin SEdd
- 'Margaretchen' — MAvo
- 'Marion Bilsland' — MSpe NChi WBrk
- 'Mayfield Giant' — MACG
- 'Mount Everest' — see *L.* × *superbum* 'Everest'
- 'Old Court' — see *L.* × *superbum* 'Beauté Nivelloise'
- 'Paladin'PBR — ECtt
- 'Phyllis Smith' — EBee ECtt ELan ELon MHer MPie MRav MSpe NBPC NGdn SHar SMad SMrm WBrk WCAu WCot WFar WWke
- 'Polaris' — CRos EBlo LRHS NRHS XLum
- 'Rags and Tatters' — ECtt
- (Realflor Series) 'Real Dream'PBR — EBee EHyd ELan LRHS MDon MSCN NRHS SCob SWvt WFar WNPC
- - 'Real Galaxy'PBR — CRos EHyd ELan EPfP LBar LRHS MHol NRHS SGBe SPoG
- - 'Real Glory' — CRos ECtt EHyd ELan EPau LBar LRHS LSou MDon MMrt NGdn NHpl NRHS SCob SGBe SWvt WCAu WFar WHlf WNPC
- - 'Real Neat' — CRos EBee ECtt EHyd ELan EPfP GElm LBar LRHS MAsh NHpl NRHS SCob SGBe WNPC
- - 'Real Sunbeam'PBR — LBar LRHS
- 'Shaggy' — see *L.* × *superbum* 'Beauté Nivelloise'
- 'Shapcott Gossamer' — ECtt GElm NGBl SEdd SPoG SRms WBrk WChS WCot
- 'Shapcott Ruffles' — EBee ECtt WBrk WCot
- 'Shapcott Summer Clouds' — CDor CKno EBee ECtt GMaP SEdd SMad SPoG WBrk WCot
§ - 'Silberprinzesschen' — CSBt EBee EBou EHyd EPfP GMaP LRHS NRHS SPlb SRms XLum
- 'Silver Spoon' — EHyd EPfP SCoo
- 'Snehurka' — CBor WCot WFar WHoo
- 'Snow Lady' — EAJP EHyd EPfP GDam GMcL LRHS NPer SRms WFar
- 'Snowbound' — EHyd LRHS NEoE NRHS

- 'Snowcap'	EBlo ECha EHyd EPfP LCro LOPS LRHS MRav MTin NRHS SCoo SWvt WCAu WGwG
- 'Snowdrift'	CRos LRHS NLar NRHS WBrk WCot WFar WPnP
§ - 'Sonnenschein'	CBod CDor CRos EBee EBlo ECha ECtt ELan EPfP EWoo GMaP GQue LRHS MArl MRav MSpe NBPC NBir NGdn NRHS NWsh SMrm SRms WCAu WChS
- SPELLBOOK LUMOS ('Bl14007') new	MDon
- 'Starburst' (d)	CRos EBlo EHyd ELan LRHS LSun NRHS SRms WFar
- 'Stina'	EBee XLum
- 'Summer Snowball'	see *L.* × *superbum* 'John Murray'
- 'Sunny Side Up'PBR	CBod EBee ECtt EHyd EWes LBar LRHS LSou LSto NCth NLar NRHS SCob SEdd WFar
- SUNSHINE	see *L.* × *superbum* 'Sonnenschein'
- 'T.E. Killin' (d) ♀H4	CBod CRos ECha ECtt EHyd EPfP GMaP LCro LRHS MPri MRav NFav NRHS SCoo WCAu WFar
- 'Victorian Secret'PBR	ECtt EHyd EPfP LBuc LRHS LSou MAsh MNrw MPri NEoE NRHS SMad SPeP WCot
- WESTERN STAR TAURUS ('Leuz0003'PBR) new	NGrs
- 'White Magic' new	LBar
- WHITE MOUNTAIN ('Gfleuwhmtn'PBR)	EHyd LRHS NRHS
- 'Wirral Pride'	WBrk
- 'Wirral Supreme' (d) ♀H5	CBcs CBod CRos CSBt EBee EHyd ELan EPfP GJos GMaP ILea LCro LOPS LRHS MACG MNHC MNrw MRav NBir NCth NFav NLar NRHS SCob SEdd SRms SWvt WCAu WFar WSpi
'Tizi-n-Test'	see *Rhodanthemum catananche* 'Tizi-n-Test'
§ ***vulgare***	Widely available
- 'Filigran'	EHyd LRHS NRHS WFar
§ - 'Maikönigin'	CRos EBlo EHyd LRHS NRHS SCob XLum
- MAY QUEEN	see *L. vulgare* 'Maikönigin'
'White Knight'	CBod EHyd GMcL LRHS NRHS SCob

Leucocoryne (*Alliaceae*)

'Andes' ♀H3	CBor CCCN GKev LAma NRog SDeJ
'Dione'	SDeJ
* ***ixioides alba***	NRog
- 'Blue Ocean'	SDeJ
pauciflora	NRog
purpurea ♀H2	NRog
'Spotlight'	GKev LAma
'Sunny Stripe'	GKev
vittata	NRog
'White Dream'	NRog SDeJ

Leucogenes (*Asteraceae*)

grandiceps	WAbe
leontopodium	NSla WAbe

Leucogenes × *Raoulia* see × *Leucoraoulia*

Leucojum ✿ (*Amaryllidaceae*)

aestivum	CBcs CCBP CDor CTri EAJP EBee EWTr EWoo GKev LRHS LSto MCot NBir NChi NHol NLar NRHS NRog SDeJ SEND SMrm SRms WCot WFar WShi
- 'Gravetye Giant' ♀H7	Widely available
autumnale	see *Acis autumnalis*
roseum	see *Acis rosea*
tingitanum	see *Acis tingitana*
trichophyllum	see *Acis trichophylla*
valentinum	see *Acis valentina*
vernum ♀H5	CBor CWCL EBee EPfP EPot EWoo GKev LAma LCro LOPS MNrw NBir NHol NHpl NLar NPol NRHS NRog NRya SDeJ SRms WCot WHer WPnP WShi
- var. ***carpathicum***	EPri GRum
- var. ***vagneri***	ECha SDys WSHC
- var. ***vernum*** 'Green Lantern'	CElw

Leucophyllum (*Scrophulariaceae*)

frutescens	XSen
- 'Green Glory' new	XSen
langmaniae new	XSen

Leucophyta (*Asteraceae*)

§ ***brownii***	CDoC GMcL IDee MBros
- 'Silver Sand'	LRHS

Leucopogon (*Ericaceae*)

§ ***colensoi***	MGil WThu
ericoides	GKev
§ ***fraseri***	WThu

× *Leucoraoulia* (*Asteraceae*)

§ ***loganii***	WAbe

Leucosceptrum (*Lamiaceae*)

canum	SBrt
- GWJ 9424	WCru
japonicum B&SWJ 10804	WCru
- B&SWJ 10981	WCru
- 'Golden Angel'	SBls
- 'Silver Angel' (v)	MAvo
stellipilum	MHol
- var. ***formosanum*** B&SWJ 1926	WCru
- - RWJ 9907	SBrt WCru
- var. ***tosaense*** B&SWJ 8892	WCru

Leucospermum (*Proteaceae*)

(Carnival Series) 'Carnival Copper'	CBcs CCCN
- 'Carnival Red'	CCCN
- 'Carnival Yellow'	CCCN
conocarpodendron 'Mardi Gras Ribbons'	CCCN
cordifolium	CCCN CPbh
glabrum	SPlb
'Scarlet Ribbon'	CCCN
'Succession'	CCCN
'Tango'	CPbh
'Vulkano'	CCCN

Leucostegia (*Davalliaceae*)

immersa PAB 7836	LEdu
truncata	WPGP

Leucothoe (*Ericaceae*)

axillaris 'Curly Red'PBR	CDoC CKel CMac CRos EBee ELan EPfP LCro LPar LRHS MAsh MGos NLar NRHS SCob SCoo SPoG SWvt SavN WFar
- 'Royal Red'	SavN
- 'Tricolor' (v)	SavN
- TWISTING RED ('Opstal20'PBR)	MBlu
CARINELLA ('Zebekot')	CRos EPfP LRHS MRav NLar NRHS SPoG

davisiae	NLar
§ ***fontanesiana***	CMac
- 'Makijaz'PBR (v)	CBod EBee EPfP LRHS MAsh NLar SNig SPoG
- 'Rainbow' (v)	CBcs CBod CBrac CDoC CEme CKel CMac CRos EBee EGrI EHyd EPfP GMcL LPal LRHS MAsh MGos NLar SCob SGbt SGol SPer SPoG SRms SWvt WFar WHlf
- 'Rollissonii' ♀H6	SRms
- WHITEWATER ('Howw'PBR) (v)	CBod CBrac CMac LCro LRHS NLar SNig WFar
keiskei BURNING LOVE ('Opstal50'PBR)	LCro LRHS MAsh NLar SEdd XSte
- HALLOWEEN ('Opstal16'PBR)	EBee XSte
- 'Royal Ruby'	GMcL MAsh MGos NLar SGbt SPoG SavN WFar
'Little Flames'PBR	LRHS MAsh MPkF XSte
LOVITA ('Zebonard')	GMcL NLar SCoo
RED LIPS ('Lipsbolwi'PBR)	EPfP GMcL MAsh SCob
SCARLETTA ('Zeblid') ♀H6	Widely available
walteri	see *L. fontanesiana*
- 'Hokus Pokus' (v)	CBod NLar SPad

Leuzea (*Asteraceae*)

centaureoides	see *Rhaponticum centaureoides*

Levisticum (*Apiaceae*)

officinale	Widely available

Lewisia ✿ (*Portulacaceae*)

'Archangel'	EPot NRya
Ashwood Carousel hybrids	NHar
- orange shades	NHpl
- pink shades	NHpl NRya
- yellow shades	NHpl
Birch strain	CBcs
Brynhyfryd hybrids	GKev
columbiana	NHpl
- 'Alba'	EPot GKev NSla WAbe
- subsp. ***rupicola***	NSla WAbe
- subsp. ***wallowensis***	MAsh NSla
cotyledon ♀H4	CRos CWCL CWal EDAr EHyd EPfP EPot GArf GKev GMaP ITim LCro LOPS LRHS MPri NHpl NRHS NSla SRot SSim WIce
- f. ***alba***	CWCL
- 'Ashwood Ruby'	MAsh
- Ashwood strain	EPfP EWes MAsh NHpl SRms
- 'Brannan Bar'	MAsh
- BRIDAL BOUQUET (mixed) **new**	WAbe
- ELISE MIXED	CBod EAJP LRHS MACG MDon MHol SRot
- var. ***heckneri***	MAsh
- hybrid	EBee NRya SPoG
- magenta-flowered	CWCL
- orange-flowered	CWCL
§ - REGENBOGEN (mixed)	LRHS MHer
- rose-pink-flowered	CWCL
- (Safira Series) 'Safira Coral' **new**	LBar
- - 'Safira Pink'	EPfP
- - SAFIRA VIOLET ('Lore3509'PBR) **new**	LBar
- salmon-flowered	CWCL
- Sunset Group ♀H4	NHpl NLar
- 'White Splendour'	MAsh
'George Henley'	EWes NRya WAbe
glandulosa	GKev
leeana	MAsh
(Little Series) 'Little Mango'	EDAr GEdr NHar NRya NSla SSim
- 'Little Peach'	CWCL EDAr NHpl NRya NSla SEdd SSim
- 'Little Plum'	CPla CTsd EDAr EHyd EPfP GEdr MAsh NHpl NLar NRya NSla SSim WIce
- 'Little Raspberry'	EDAr NSla
- 'Little Snowberry'	EDAr
- LITTLE TUTTI FRUTTI (mixed)	NSla
longipetala 'Darcies Sunrise' **new**	EDAr
§ ***nevadensis***	CRos EBou EHyd LRHS NRHS NRya WAbe
I - 'Alba'	GKev NHpl
- ***bernardina***	see *L. nevadensis*
- 'Rosea'	NHpl NRya NSla
'Pinkie'	GArf NHpl
pygmaea	EHyd EWes GKev ITim LRHS MAsh MHer NBir NRHS NRya NSla SPlb XLum
Rainbow mixture	see *L. cotyledon* REGENBOGEN
rediviva	EDAr GKev ITim MAsh NHpl NSla WAbe
- pink-flowered **new**	WAbe
- white-flowered	WAbe
tweedyi	see *Lewisiopsis tweedyi*

Lewisiopsis (*Portulacaceae*)

§ ***tweedyi*** ♀H4	CRos EDAr EHyd EPot GKev ITim LRHS MAsh NHar NHpl NRHS SPlb WAbe
- 'Alba'	WAbe
- 'Rosea'	CRos EHyd EPot LRHS MAsh NHar NRHS WAbe

Leycesteria (*Caprifoliaceae*)

crocothyrsos	CBcs EBee NLar SPoG WFar
formosa	Widely available
- 'Gold Leaf'	CMac CPla LShi MGil MHer SHar WFar
- GOLDEN LANTERNS ('Notbruce'PBR) ♀H4	Widely available
- 'Purple Rain'	CDoC CRos EBee EHyd EPfP EWes LAlb LPar LRHS MAsh MGos NLar NRHS SGsty

Leymus (*Poaceae*)

from the Falkland Islands	ELon EPPr
§ ***arenarius***	CBod CElw CEme CKno EBee ECha EHeP ELan EShb GBin GMaP LRHS MMuc NBid NBro SCob SDix SEND SGbt SPlb SRms WFar WTre XLum XSen
- 'Blue Dune'	CAby EBee EPfP SEdd
cinereus	WCot
hispidus	see *Elymus hispidus*

Lhotzkya see *Calytrix*

Liatris (*Asteraceae*)

aspera	ECha
elegans	SPlb
ligulistylis	SPhx
microcephala	SBls
mucronata	NLar
pycnostachya	CSpe GBin GQue SAko SRms
scariosa	LRHS SPhx
- 'Alba'	CBcs CSpe EBee LSun SAko SPhx
- 'White Spire'	SBls
§ ***spicata***	Widely available
- 'Alba'	CBWd CBod CMac CSBt EAJP EBee ECha ELan EMor EPfP GBin LAma LBar LSRN LShi MBel MHoo MPri

	MSCN NBir NLar SCob SMrm SPer SPlb WCAu XLum
- ***callilepis***	see *L. spicata*
- 'Cobalus' **new**	LBar
- 'Floristan Violett'	CRos CSBt CTri EBee EHyd EPfP GMaP GMcL LRHS LSto MDon MHer MHol MSpe NLar NRHS SBls SCob SCoo SGbt SOrN SPlb SPoG SWvt WFar WGwG XLum
- 'Floristan Weiss'	CRos CTri EBee EHyd EPPr EPfP ERCP EShb GMaP GMcL LRHS LSto MACG MHer MRav NLar NRHS SBls SDeJ SGbt SOrN SPoG SRms STPC SWvt WFar WGwG
- GOBLIN	see *L. spicata* 'Kobold'
§ - 'Kobold'	Widely available
squarrosa	SPhx

Libanotis see *Seseli*

montana	see *Seseli libanotis*

Libertia ✿ (*Iridaceae*)

'Amazing Grace'	EBee
breunioides	see *L. cranwelliae*
§ ***chilensis*** ♀[H3]	Widely available
- Elegans Group	EBee EBlo WCru
§ - Formosa Group	CBcs CBro CEme CTri EBee EHyd ELan EPfP GKev LRHS NChi NRHS NSti SArc SCob SRms SSha SWvt WHer
- Procera Group	CAby CSpe CTsd EBee EPfP GBin LEdu LRHS SPlb WPGP
§ ***cranwelliae***	WPGP
formosa	see *L. chilensis* Formosa Group
grandiflora misapplied	see *L. chilensis*
grandiflora ambig.	CBod CCht CDoC CMac CTsd EAri EGrI EWTr EWoo GBin GKev MACG MBel MBow MMrt MSCN NBro SArc SCob SGBe SIvy WCAu
grandiflora (R. Br.) Sweet	CAby EHyd GMaP LRHS SDix SVen
'Grasshopper'	CAby GBin SGBe
ixioides	CBcs ECha EGrI LEdu SGBe SPtp WCFE WPGP
- 'Goldfinger' (v)	CBcs CBor CKno CMac EBee EHyd ELan EMor EPfP GMcL LEdu LLWG LPal LRHS NFav NHol NLar NRHS SBls SCob SEdd SPoG SWvt WFar WHer WWke XSte
- 'Highlander'	LRHS
- 'Taupo Blaze'	CBct CBor CMac ELan ELon EPfP LSRN MRav SCob SPoG
- 'Taupo Sunset'[PBR]	CBcs CBct CCCN EPfP LEdu LPal LRHS MBNS NSti SGBe SPeP SSha SWvt WPGP XSte
- 'Tricolor'	CSde EWld GEdr GKev LDai MRav
ixioides* × *peregrinans	CMac LPal
'Nelson Dwarf'	EBee ESwi EWes
paniculata	EBee
peregrinans	CAbb CBod CKno CSpe EAri EBee ECha EGrI EHyd ELan EPri EShb EWoo GElm GKev LEdu LRHS MACG MRav NBir NRHS SCob SEdd SGBe SPer SPtp SRkn SWvt WLov WPGP
- 'Gold Leaf'	CCCN CTri CTsd EBee ELan EPfP GMcL SWvt WFar
- 'Gold Stripe'	SWvt
pulchella misapplied	EHyd LRHS NRHS
pulchella ambig. blue-flowered	GKev
sessiliflora	NBir
- 'Ballyrogan Blue'	EBee GKev WMal
- 'Caerulescens'	CBcs CBod CCCN CCht CExl CMac CSde EGrI EPfP LRHS NBir NGBl SMad SPer SPtp WCAu WFar XSte
'Sunset Strain'	LRHS MHtn WFar

Libocedrus (*Cupressaceae*)

chilensis	see *Austrocedrus chilensis*
decurrens	see *Calocedrus decurrens*
plumosa	CBrP

Libonia see *Justicia*

Ligularia (*Asteraceae*)

aff. ***atkinsonii*** WJC 13663	WCru
'BBQ Banana'	CBod EPfP
'Bottle Rocket'[PBR]	CBor LBar NLar SMad
'Britt Marie Crawford'[PBR] ♀[H6]	Widely available
clivorum	see *L. dentata*
§ ***dentata***	ECtt NBro SRms
- 'Candlelight' **new**	LBar
- 'Dark Beauty'	EMor
- 'Desdemona'	Widely available
- 'Franz Feldweber'	EBee ELon
- 'Megamona'	EBee
- 'Midnight Lady'	EHyd ELan EMor EPfP GPSL MHol NCth NLar SBls
- 'Orange Princess'	NPer
- 'Osiris Café Dark'[PBR]	EMor SCob
- 'Osiris Fantaisie' (v)	CDor CExl ECtt EPfP EWes GBee GMcL MHol NLar NSti SPoG WFar WPnP
- 'Othello'	CBod CEme CRos ECtt EHyd EPfP GBee GElm GMcL LRHS MACG NGdn NLar NRHS NWad SCob SRms SWvt WCAu
- 'Pandora'	ECtt LBar MHol SMad SPad
- 'Sommergold'	WFar
- 'Twilight'	ECtt LBar MBNS
§ ***fischeri*** B&SWJ 2570	WCru
- B&SWJ 4381	WCru
- B&SWJ 4478	WCru
- B&SWJ 5653	WCru
- B&SWJ 8802	WCru
- var. ***megalorhiza*** 'Cheju Charmer'	ELon WCru
'Garden Confetti'	ECtt
'Gold Torch'	ECtt NLar
§ 'Gregynog Gold' ♀[H6]	ECha EHyd GBee GMaP LRHS MRav NBro NLar NRHS
× ***hessei***	EBlo GMaP MMuc
hodgsonii	EPPr MRav
- B&SWJ 10855	WCru
intermedia B&SWJ 606a	WSHC
japonica	CDor ECha LEdu NLar
- B&SWJ 2883	WCru
- 'Rising Sun'	CExl ESwi NLar WCot WCru
'Laternchen'[PBR]	ECtt LBar NLar SAko
'Little Rocket'[PBR]	CBod CBor CExl EBee ECtt EPfP GDam LBar MBNS NBro NGdn NLar NRHS SPoG WFar
'Osiris Café Noir'	ECtt MHol NLar WFar
'Osiris Pistache' (v)	ECtt
× ***palmatiloba***	see *L.* × *yoshizoeana* 'Palmatiloba'
pleurocaulis	GArf
§ ***przewalskii***	Widely available
- SSSE 176	WCot
- 'Dragon Wings'	GBin MAsh MHol NEoE NLar SCob
- 'Dragon's Breath'	ECtt GBin MAsh MHol SCob
sibirica	NLar
- B&SWJ 4383	WCru
- B&SWJ 5841	WCru
- var. ***speciosa***	see *L. fischeri*

	smithii	see *Senecio smithii*
	speciosa	see *L. fischeri*
	stenocephala	EBee EMor MBros NBro NLar XLum
I	- 'Globosa' **new**	EBlo
	'Sungold'	CMac CRos EBlo ECtt EHyd LRHS NGdn NRHS
	tangutica	see *Sinacalia tangutica*
	'The Rocket' ♀H6	Widely available
	tussilaginea	see *Farfugium japonicum*
	- 'Aureo-maculata'	see *Farfugium japonicum* 'Aureomaculatum'
	veitchiana	CBod CToG
	vorobievii	CElw EBee NLar
	wilsoniana	EBlo EHyd EMor LRHS MMuc MRav NRHS SEND WCAu WFar
	- B&SWJ 14195	WCru
§	× ***yoshizoeana*** 'Palmatiloba'	CRos EHyd EWTr EWes LRHS MRav NRHS SPhx WFar
	'Zepter' ♀H6	CAby CBWd CBod CFis CRos CToG EBlo ECtt EHyd ELan EPfP EShb GBee GElm GQue LRHS MMuc NHol NLar NRHS NWad SMad WCot

Ligusticum (*Apiaceae*)

	hultenii	WCot
	lucidum	CDor CMCN EPfP EWTr GBin LEdu LPla NSti SMHy SPhx SPtp WBor WCot WPGP WSHC
	- subsp. ***lucidum***	CSpe
§	***scoticum***	CBod ELan EShb EWes GBin GElm GJos GLog GPSL GPoy GQue LEdu LPla LRHS MBel MHer NAts SBut SDix SPhx SPtp SRms WFar WJek WPGP
	- variegated (v)	LEdu WCot

Ligustrum ✿ (*Oleaceae*)

	chenaultii	see *L. compactum*
§	***compactum***	NLar
	confusum **new**	CBcs
§	***delavayanum***	CBod ELan ERom EShb GKev MNHC MPri MVil SArc SCob SGsty SWeb WJur WPGP
	ibota	EBtc
	- MUSLI	see *L. ibota* 'Muster'
§	- 'Muster'PBR (v)	EBee LRHS MAsh MGos NLar SPoG WCot
	ionandrum	see *L. delavayanum*
	japonicum	CLnd EBar LIns LMaj LPar LSRN SArc SCob SEND SGol SGsty SPer SWeb
	- B&SWJ 14604	WCru
	- 'Coriaceum'	see *L. japonicum* 'Rotundifolium'
	- GREEN CENTURY ('Melgreen'PBR)	LRHS WMat
	- 'Korea Dwarf'	NLar
§	- 'Rotundifolium'	CBcs CBod CDoC CKel EBee EHyd ELan EPfP GBin LPar LRHS MAsh MRav NLar SDix SPer SPoG SPtp WCFE WCot WFar
§	- 'Silver Star' (v)	NLar SEND SGol
§	- 'Texanum'	CCVT CDoC EPfP LMaj LPar LRHS NLar SArc SGsty SavN WCFE WReH
	- 'Texanum Argenteum'	see *L. japonicum* 'Silver Star'
	- 'Variegatum' (v)	LPar SGol SWeb
	lucidum ♀H5	CBcs CCVT CSBt CSde CTri ELan IDee LRHS MHer MRav NBwr NWea SArc SCob SEND SGol SPer SWvt WFar WJur
	- Guiz 296	CExl
	- 'Curly Wurly'	EHyd LRHS NRHS
	- 'Excelsum Superbum' (v) ♀H5	CCVT CLnd CMac EBar EHyd ELan EPfP LMaj LRHS LSRN MGos SArc SGol SGsty SPoG SWeb WCot
	- 'Golden Wax'	CJun MRav
	- 'Tricolor' (v) ♀H5	EHyd ELan EPfP LRHS MAsh MGos NLar SPer SWvt
	obtusifolium var. ***regelianum***	MMuc NLar
	ovalifolium	Widely available
§	- 'Argenteum' (v)	CBcs CBod CCVT CMac CTri EHeP ELan EShb GArf GMcL LRHS LSto MMuc MRav NLar SCob SEND SLim SPer SPoG SWvt WFar WHtc
	- 'Aureomarginatum'	see *L. ovalifolium* 'Aureum'
§	- 'Aureum' (v) ♀H5	Widely available
	- 'Lemon and Lime' (v)	CBod CDoC CEme ELan LCro LSRN MAsh MThu SCoo SRms SWvt WCot WFar
	- 'Variegatum'	see *L. ovalifolium* 'Argenteum'
	- 'Vicaryi'	ELan LRHS MGos NWad SDix SGol WFar WHtc
	quihoui	CKel CTri EBee EHyd ELan EPfP IDee LRHS MBlu NLar SDix SEND SPer SPoG
	sinense	CMCN MRav
	- 'Fragrant Cloud' **new**	LCro
	- 'Multiflorum'	WFar
	- var. ***myrianthum***	SPtp
	- 'Sunshine'	CRos EHyd LRHS MAsh NRHS SPoG WHtc
	- 'Variegatum' (v)	MRav SPer
	- 'Wimbei'	WLov
	strongylophyllum	CExl
	texanum	see *L. japonicum* 'Texanum'
	tschonoskii	MBlu NLar
	undulatum 'Lemon Lime and Clippers'	EHyd EShb LRHS NLar SDix SGBe SPoG
	vulgare	CArg CBTr CCVT CHab CMac CPer CTri EHeP ELan EPfP LBuc LIns LPar LSto MDon MMuc MNic MSwo NWea SCob SEND SEWo SGsty SWvt WHtc WMat WMou WSFF WTSh XSen
	- 'Atrovirens'	EDir LIns
	- 'Aureovariegatum' (v)	MDon
	- 'Lodense'	EBtc

Lilaeopsis (*Apiaceae*)

brasiliensis	LPfP

Lilium ✿ (*Liliaceae*)

'Abbeville's Pride' (Ia/b)	GKev SDeJ
'Acapulco' (VII-/d)	SDeJ
'Adonis' (Ic/d)	GEdr
African Queen Group (VI-/a) ♀H6	CAvo ERCP GKev LAma LCro LHWs LOPS MACG SCoo SDir SRms
- 'African Queen' (VIb-c/a)	LAma SDeJ
African Queen Group × ***sulphureum*** (VI)	EGrl MBros
'After Eight' (VIIa/b)	LHWs
'Agostini' (VIIIa/b)	LHWs
'Altari' (VIIIa-b/b)	SDeJ
'Amarossi' (VIIIa-b/b-c)	LHWs
'Anastasia' (VIIIb-c/b-d)	EGrl GKev LAma LCro LHWs LOPS SDeJ SDir
'Angela North' (Ic/d)	GEdr
'Annemarie's Dream' (Ia/c)	LAma SDeJ SDir
'Apogee'PBR (VIIa/b)	LHWs
APOLLO (Ia/b)	see *L.* 'Blizzard'
'Apricot Fudge'PBR (VIIIa/b)	GKev LAma LCro SDir
'Arabian Knight' (IIc/d)	ERCP GKev LAma LCro LHWs SDeJ SDir WFar
'Arena' (VIIa/b)	SCoo
Asiatic hybrids (I)	EHyd LRHS MBros
'Atacama'PBR (VIIIa/b)	LHWs
auratum 'Gold Band'	see *L. auratum* var. *platyphyllum*

§	- var. ***platyphyllum*** (IXb/c)	CBod LAma SDeJ
	- - B&SWJ 4824	WCru
	- - B&SWJ 5041	WCru
	- var. ***virginale*** (IXb/c)	SDeJ
*	***aureum***	LHWs
	'Avalon Sunset' (VIIIa/b) **new**	GKev
	Backhouse hybrids	see *L.* × *dalhansonii* Backhouse Group
	'Baferrari' (VIIa/b)	GKev LAma SDeJ SDir
	'Bald Eagle' (Ia/b) **new**	LAma SDir
	'Bamako' (VIIa-b/b)	SDeJ
	'Bandiëra' (VIIa/b-d)	LHWs
	'Barbara North' (Ic/d)	GEdr
	'Barbaresco' (VIIa-b/b)	SCoo
	'Beijing Moon' (VIb-c/a)	GKev LAma LHWs SDeJ SDir
	'Belém' (Ia/b-c)	LRHS
	'Belgrado'^{PBR} (VIIa/b-c)	SDeJ
	'Belladonna'^{PBR} (VIIIb-a/b)	SDeJ
	'Belle Epoque' (VIIb/b-c)	SDeJ
	'Bergamo' (VIIb/b)	SCoo SDeJ
	'Beverly Hills'^{PBR} (VIIIa-b/b)	SDeJ
	'Black Beauty' (VIIIb-c/d)	CCBP EGrI GBin GKev IPot LAma LCro LHWs LOPS NHpl SDeJ SDir
§	'Blizzard'^{PBR} (Ia/b)	SCob SDeJ
	'Blushing Joy' (Ia/b)	LRHS
	'Boogie Woogie' (VIIIa-b/b)	SDeJ
	'Bracelet' (VIIIa-b/b)	SDeJ
	'Brasil'^{PBR} (Ia/b)	GKev
	BRASILIA ('Zora') (VIIa/b-c)	LAma SDeJ SDir
	'Bright Joy' (Ia/c)	LRHS
	BRIGHT PIXIE ('Ceb Bright') (Ia/b)	SDeJ
	'Broken Heart' (VIIb-a/c)	SDeJ
	'Buriano'^{PBR} (VIII a/b)	LHWs
	'Butter Pixie'^{PBR} (Ia/b)	GMcL SCob SDeJ
	'Cali'^{PBR} (VIII a-b/a)	LHWs
§	***canadense*** (IXc/a)	GEdr WCot
	- var. ***flavum***	see *L. canadense*
	'Cancun' (Ia/b-c)	SDeJ
	candidum (IXb/a)	CAvo CBcs CTri ECha ELan EPot ERCP GKev LAma LCro LHWs LOPS NRog SCob SDeJ SDir SRms WSpi
	'Candy Blossom' (Ia/b)	SDeJ
	'Candy Club' (VIIIa-b/b-c) **new**	CAvo
	'Carbonero' (VIIIa-b/b)	LHWs
	'Casa Blanca' (VIIb/b-c) 🏆^{H6}	CAvo CBro GKev LAma LCro LHWs LOPS NBir SCoo SDeJ SDir
	'Cavoli' (Ia-b/b)	GKev LCro
	'Cecil' (VIIIa/b)	SDeJ
	cernuum (IXc/d)	SDeJ
*	- 'Album'	SDeJ
	'Child in Time' (VIIIa-b/b)	LHWs
	'Chill Out' (VIIa/b)	LCro LOPS
§	'Chocolate Canary' (Ic/b-c)	SDeJ
	'Chocolate Event' (Ib-c/c-b)	LAma LHWs
	'Christopher'^{PBR} (VIIa/b)	LHWs
	Citronella Group (Ic/d)	NHpl SDeJ
	'Classic Joy' (Ia/b)	LRHS
	'Claude Shride' (IIc/d)	CAvo CBcs CBor EPot ERCP GKev IPot LAma LHWs LRHS NHpl SDeJ WCot WPnP
	'Clearwater' (VIIa/b)	LHWs
	'Cocktail Twins' (Ia/b)	SDeJ
	'Cogoleto'^{PBR} (VIIIa-b/b)	LAma SDir
	'Coldplay' (Colour Carpet Series) (VIIa-b/b-c)	EHyd LBuc LRHS NRHS
	'Collesium' (VIIa/b)	LHWs
	columbianum (IXc/d) B&SWJ 9564	WCru
	'Con Amore' (VIIb/b)	SCoo
	'Conca d'Or'^{PBR} (VIIIb/b)	LHWs SDeJ
	'Corsage' (Ib/b-c)	GKev LHWs
	'Creation' (VIa/b)	SDeJ
	'Crimson Pixie' (Ia/b)	GMcL LCro LOPS NRHS SDeJ
	'Crossover' (Ia/b-c)	GMcL
	'Curitiba' (Ia/b)	LAma LHWs
	'Curly Sue' (VIIa-b/b)	LAma LCro LOPS MHol
	× ***dalhansonii*** (IIc/d)	LRHS MBros SDeJ
§	- Backhouse Group (IIc/d)	WFar
	- 'Guinea Gold' (II)	GKev LAma LHWs SDir
	- 'Mrs R.O. Backhouse' (IIc/d)	GEdr SDeJ
	- 'Sutton Court' (IIc/c)	GEdr
	- Terrace City Group (IIc/d)	GKev LAma LHWs SDeJ
	'Dark Romance' (Romance Series) (VIIb/b)	CRos EHyd LHWs LRHS NRHS
	dauricum f. ***rebunense*** (IXa/b)	CBor
	davidii (IXc/d)	NHpl SDeJ WCru
§	- var. ***willmottiae*** (IXc/d)	WCru
	DAZZLER ('Maru') (Colour Carpet Series) (VIIa/b)	LRHS
	'Debby' (VIIIa-b/b-c)	GKev LHWs SDeJ
	'Delicate Joy' (Ia/b)	LHWs LRHS
	'Dimension' (Ia/b-c)	LCro LOPS
	'Disco' (Ia)	SDeJ
	distichum (IXb-c/d) B&SWJ 794	WCru
	- B&SWJ 4465	WCru
	'Dizzy' (VIIa-b/b-c)	SDeJ
	'Double Sensation' (Ia/b) (d)	LHWs
	duchartrei (IXc/d)	CBor CExl GEdr WCru
	'Easter Morn' (VIIIb-c/a)	LHWs SDir
	'Eastern Moon' (VIb-c/a) **new**	LAma
	'Easy Beat' (Ia/b) **new**	LAma SDir
	'Easy Dance' (Ia/b)	LAma LHWs
	'Easy Dream' (Ia/b) **new**	LAma SDir
	'Easy Samba' (Ia/c) **new**	LAma LCro
	'Easy Vanilla' (Ia/c) **new**	GKev LAma LCro SDir
	'Easy Waltz' (Ia/b)	LCro
	'Electric Yellow'	see *L.* 'Yellow Electric'
	'Elgrado' (Ia/b)	SDeJ
	'Ellen Willmott' (II)	WMal
	'Elodie'^{PBR} (Ia/b)	LAma LHWs SDeJ SDir
	'Elusive' (VIIIb/b-d)	GKev LAma LHWs MNrw SDeJ SDir
	'Emani'^{PBR} (VIIa/b)	LHWs
	'Enchantment' (Ia/b)	SDeJ
	'Entertainer' (VIIa/b)	LRHS
	'Eros' (Ic/d)	GEdr
	'Euskadi' (VIIa/b)	LHWs
	'Expression' (VII)	SDeJ
	'Eyeliner'^{PBR} (VIIIa/b)	LHWs
	'Fairy Morning' (IIc/c)	CAvo GKev LAma LHWs SDir WFar
	'Fangio' (VIIIa/b)	EGrI
	FANTASIATIC LIPGLOSS (mixed) (I)	MHol
	'Fata Morgana' (Ia/b) 🏆^{H6}	LAma SCoo SDeJ SDir
	'Fields of Gold' (VIIIb/b)	LHWs
	'Fire King' (Ib/d)	SCoo SDeJ SRms
	'Firebolt' (VIIa/b-c)	LHWs
	'Fopapo' (Ia-b/c)	SDeJ
	'Forever Linda' (Ia/c) **new**	LAma SDir
	'Forever Marjolein' (Ia/b)	LAma LCro SDir
	'Forever Susan' (Ia/b)	GKev LAma LHWs SDeJ SDir
	'Formia' (VIII a-b/b)	LHWs
	formosanum (IXb/a)	EBee MHol
	- short, from high altitude RWJ 10005 (IXb/a)	WCru
	- var. ***formosanum*** (IXb/a)	LRHS
	- - B&SWJ 1589	WCru

	- var. ***pricei*** (IXb/a)	CEme CKel CRos EBee EDAr EHyd ELan GBin GEdr LEdu LRHS MHer MTin NRHS SCoo SRms WIce WTyc
*	- - f. ***album***	GElm SBls
	- - 'Snow Queen' (Vb/a)	SDeJ
	'Foxtrot' (Ia/b)	LRHS SDeJ
	'Fredo'PBR (VIII a/a)	LHWs
	'Friso' (VIIIb/b)	LHWs SDeJ SDir
	'Frosty Wonder' (VIIIa/b-a)	LHWs
	'Fusion' (IVb-c/b-c)	LAma LHWs MHol NHpl SDir WCot
	'Garden Party' (VIIb/b) ♀H6	LAma SDeJ SDir
	'Gaybird' (IIc/c)	LAma LHWs
	'Gironde' (Ia/b)	SDeJ
	'Gizmo'PBR (VIIIb-a/b)	LHWs
	'Gold Class' (VIIIb-a/b-c)	LHWs SDeJ
	'Golden Matrix' (Ia/b)	CBod
	'Golden Morning' (IIc/d) **new**	GKev
	'Golden Romance' (Romance Series) (VIIa/b)	LHWs
	Golden Splendor Group (VIb-c/a) ♀H6	CAvo GKev LAma LCro LHWs SCoo SDeJ SDir
	'Golden Stone' (VIIIa-b/b)	SDeJ
	'Gran Tourismo' (VIIa/b-c)	LAma
	'Grand Cru' (Ia/b)	MACG SDeJ
	'Hachi' (VIIa/c) **new**	CBod LAma
	'Hannah North' (Ic/d)	GEdr
	hansonii (IXb-c/d)	CWCL GBin LAma LHWs NHpl SDeJ WPnP
	- B&SWJ 4309	WCru
	- B&SWJ 8506	WCru
	- B&SWJ 8528	WCru
	henryi (IXc/d) ♀H6	CAvo EWTr LAma LHWs SDeJ SDir WCru
	'Hit Parade' (VIa-b/b)	SDeJ
	'Honeymoon' (VIIIa-b/b)	EGrI SDeJ
	'Hotel California' (VIIIb/b)	LHWs
	humboldtii (IXc/d)	CBor CWCL
	'Ice Breaker' (VIIa/a)	LHWs
	'Ice Pixie' (Ia/b)	SDeJ
	'Indus' (VIIa-b/b) **new**	LAma
	'Inuvik' (Ia/b)	SDeJ
	'Island Joy' (Ia/b-c)	LRHS
	'Ivory Pixie' (Ia/b)	SDeJ
	'João Pessoa' (Ia/b-c)	SDeJ
	'Jo's Choice' (VIa-b/a)	SDeJ
	'Josephine' (VIIa/b)	LAma SDeJ SDir
	'Joy'	see *L.* 'Le Rêve'
	'Kamsberg'PBR (VIIIa/b)	LHWs
	'Karen North' (Ic/d)	GEdr
	'King Pete' (Ib/b-c)	SDeJ
	'Kingdom'PBR (VIIIa/b-c)	SDeJ
	'Kushi Maya'PBR (VIIIc/b-c)	LAma LHWs SDeJ SDir
	'Lady Alice' (VI-/d)	GKev LAma LHWs MAsh SDeJ SDir
	'Ladylike' (Ia/b)	GMcL
	'Lake Tulare' (IVc/c-d)	GEdr
§	***lancifolium*** (IXc/d)	EPot GBin LHWs XLum
	- B&SWJ 4352	WCru
*	- ***album***	WHlf
	- var. ***flaviflorum*** (IXc/d)	SDeJ WFar
	- 'Flore Pleno' (IXc/d)	EPPr GKev LHWs NBir SDeJ SMrm WCot WCru WHil XLum
	- var. ***fortunei*** (IXc/d)	EGrI EPPr SDix
	- - B&SWJ 539	WCru
	- pink-flowered	SDeJ
	- 'Splendens' (IXc/d)	GKev LAma NBid SDeJ SDir WCot
	'Landini'PBR (Ia/b)	SDeJ
	'Lankon' (VIIIc/a)	LHWs
	lankongense (IXc/d)	CBor CWCL EPot GEdr GGGa GKev LAma LCro LHWs MHol SDir WCru
	- BWJ 7554	WCru
	- BWJ 7691	WCru
	'Late Morning' (VIIIb/c)	SDeJ
	'Latvia' (Ia/b)	SDeJ
	'Lavon' (VIIIa-b/b-c) **new**	SDir
	'Lazy Lady'	see *L.* 'Chocolate Canary'
§	'Le Rêve' (VIIa-b/b)	SDeJ
	leichtlinii (IXc/d)	EPot GBin NHpl SDeJ
	'Lemon Pixie' (Ia/b)	NRHS SCob
	'Leslie Woodriff' (VIIIb-c/d)	GKev LHWs
	leucanthum	WCru
	var. ***centifolium*** (IXb-c/a)	
	- - BWJ 8130	WCru
	'Levi'PBR (Ia/c)	SDeJ
	lijiangense (IXc/d)	GEdr
	LILY ALLEN	see *L.* 'Popstar'
I	'Linda' (Ia/b)	SDeJ
	'Little John' (VIIa-b/b)	SDeJ
	'Little Kiss' (Ia/d)	SDeJ
	LOLLYPOP ('Holebibi') (Ia/b)	GMcL SCoo SDeJ
	'Londrina' (Ia/b)	SDeJ
	longiflorum (IXb/a)	LAma SCoo SDir XLum
	- B&SWJ 11376	WCru
	- 'Foliis Variegatis' (Vb/a/v)	MAvo
	- 'Rose' (V)	SDeJ
	- 'White Heaven'PBR (Vb/a)	LCro LHWs LOPS
	'Lotus Beauty' (VIIa/c)	LCro LHWs
	'Lotus Breeze' (VIIb/c)	LCro LHWs
	'Lotus Dream' (VIIa/c)	LHWs
	'Lotus Elegance' (VIIb/c)	LCro LHWs
	'Lotus Queen' (VIIa/c)	LHWs
	'Lotus Wonder' (VIIb-c/c)	LCro LHWs
	'Love Story' (VIIa-b/b)	LRHS
	'Lovely Girl' (VII-/b)	SDeJ
	'Luzia' (VIIa-b/c)	EHyd LRHS NRHS
	mackliniae (IXc/a) ♀H5	CWCL EWes GEdr GGGa ITim LAma NBir WPGP WTyc
	- PAB 9327	LEdu WPGP
	- PAB 9668	LEdu WPGP
	- from Nagaland, India	GGGa
	- deep pink-flowered	GGGa
	× ***maculatum***	CBor
	var. ***flavum*** **new**	
	'Magic Star'PBR (VIIa-b/b)	SDeJ
	'Magny Cours' (VIIa/b)	LRHS
	'Mandarin Star' (Ia/b) **new**	LAma
	'Manitoba Morning' (IIc/c)	GKev LAma LHWs LRHS MBros NHpl SDeJ SDir
	'Mansfield' (VIIa-b/b)	LHWs
	'Mapira' (VIIIb/b)	SDeJ
	'Marco Polo' ambig.	SCoo SDeJ
	'Marie North' (Ic/d)	GEdr
	'Maroon King' (IIc/d)	WFar
	martagon (IXc/d) ♀H6	CBro CTtf CWCL ECha EMor EPot ERCP GAbr GKev GPoy LAma LCro LHWs LOPS NBir NChi NGrd NHpl SDeJ SRms WCAu WPnP WShi WSpi
	- var. ***albiflorum*** (IXc/d)	CTtf LAma LHWs SDeJ
	- var. ***album*** (IXc/d)	CBor CBro CSpe EMor EPot GAbr GBin GKev LAma LHWs LRHS MCot NBir NChi NRHS SDeJ SRms WShi
	- var. ***cattaniae*** 'The Moor' (IXb/d)	LHWs
*	- var. ***rubrum***	EGrI MACG
	'Mascara' (Ia-b/b)	GKev LAma MHtn SDir
	'Matrix' (Ia-b/b)	SCoo
	medeoloides (IXc/d) B&SWJ 4184	WCru
	- B&SWJ 4363	WCru
	'Miss Feya' (VIIIb/c)	EGrI GKev LAma LHWs MHol MNrw SDeJ SDir
	'Miss France' (VIIb/b-c)	SDeJ
I	'Miss Lily' (VIIIb/b-c)	MNrw SDeJ
	'Miss Lucy'PBR (VIIa-b/b-c)	SDeJ
	'Miss Peculiar' (VIII b-c/a)	GKev LCro

	MISS RIO	see *L.* 'Rio'
	'Mister Cas' (VIIIb/b)	LHWs
	'Mister Job' (VIIIa/c)	LHWs SDeJ
	'Mister Pistache' (VIIIb-a/b-c)	LAma LHWs
	'Mona Lisa' (VIIb/b-c)	NGdn SCob SDeJ
	monadelphum (IXc/d)	CBor SDeJ
	'Mont Blanc' (Ia/b-c)	SCob SDeJ
	'Montezuma'PBR (VIIa-b/b)	SDeJ
	'Montreux' (Ia/b-c)	SDeJ
	'Morpho Pink' (VIIIa/b-c)	LHWs
	'Mount Cook' (VIIa/b)	LAma LRHS SDeJ SDir
	'Mountain Joy' (Ia/b)	LHWs LRHS
	'Muscadet' (VIIa-b/b)	GKev LAma LCro LHWs LOPS SDeJ SDir
	'Must See' (Ia/b)	GKev LAma LHWs SDir
	'Navona' (Ia/b)	GKev SDeJ
	nepalense (IXc/a)	CBcs CBro CWCL EPot ERCP GKev LAma LCro LOPS MCot SDeJ SDir WCru WPnP WTyc XLum
	- B&SWJ 2985	WCru
	'Netty's Pride' (Ia/b-c)	CAvo SDeJ SDir
	'New Wave' (Ia/b)	GKev GMcL SDeJ
	'Night Flyer' (Ib-c/b-c)	LHWs SDeJ
	'Nightrider' (VIIIa/b)	GKev LAma LHWs MBros
	'Nove Cento' (Ia/b)	SDeJ
	'November Rain' (VIIIa/b)	GKev LHWs
	'Nymph'PBR (VIIIa/b-d)	LHWs
	'Orange County' (Ia/b)	SDeJ
	'Orange Electric' (Ia/b)	SDeJ SDir
	'Orange Marmalade' (IIb/c-d)	ERCP GKev LAma LCro LHWs LRHS NHpl SDeJ SDir WPnP
	'Orange Matrix' (Ia/b)	CBod
	'Orange Pixie' (Ia/b)	GDam NRHS SCob SCoo
	'Orange Planet' (VIa/a)	SDeJ
	'Orange Twinkle' (Ib-c/b)	SDeJ
	'Orania'PBR (VIIIb/b)	EGrI SDeJ
	Oriental hybrids (VII)	MACG MBros
*	Oriental Superb Group	NGdn
	oxypetalum var. ***insigne*** (IXb-c/b)	GBin NHpl SDir
	'Pan' (Ic/d)	GEdr
	'Paposo'PBR (VIIIa-b/b)	LHWs
	pardalinum (IXc/d) 🏆H6	CWCL ECha LAma SBrt WCot WCru
	- var. ***giganteum*** (IXc/d)	MNrw
	- subsp. ***pardalinum*** (IXc/d)	SDeJ
§	- subsp. ***vollmeri*** (IXc/d)	WCru
§	- subsp. ***wigginsii*** (IXc/d)	WCru
	× ***parkmanii*** 'Rosy Dimple' (VIIa/b)	SDeJ
	'Passion Moon' (VIIb-c/a)	LAma SDeJ SDir
	'Patricia's Pride' (Ia-b/b-c)	GKev LAma SDeJ SDir
	'Peach Butterflies' (Ic/d)	SDeJ
	'Peach Dwarf' (Ia/b-c)	SDeJ
	'Peach Pixie' (Ia/b)	SCob SCoo
	'Pearl Jennifer' (Ib-a/c)	SDeJ
	'Pearl Jessica' (Ib-c/b-c)	SDeJ SDir
	'Pearl Justien' (Ia-b/c)	SDeJ
	'Pearl Loraine' (Ib-c/b-c)	LAma SDeJ SDir
	'Pearl Melanie' (Ib/c)	LAma SDeJ SDir
	'Pearl Sonja' (Ib/b)	SDeJ
	'Pearl Stacey' (Ib-c/c)	SDeJ
	'Pearl White' (Ib/b)	LHWs
	'Peggy North' (Ic/d)	GEdr
	'Peppard Gold' (IIc)	GKev LAma LHWs SDir
	philippinense (IXa-b/a)	LAma SBls SDir
	'Pieton' (Ia/b-c)	SDeJ
	'Pimento' (VIIa/b)	SDeJ
	'Pink Flavour' (Ic/c)	SDeJ
	'Pink Flight' (Ic/b-c)	GKev
	'Pink Flush' (Ic/d)	LHWs
	'Pink Giant' (Ic/-)	GKev
	'Pink Morning' (IIc/c)	ERCP LAma LRHS NHpl SDir
	Pink Perfection Group (VIb/a) 🏆H6	EGrI ERCP LAma LCro LHWs LOPS SCoo SDeJ SDir
	'Pink Pixie'PBR (Ia/b)	GMcL NRHS SDeJ
	'Pink Romance' (Romance Series) (VIIa/b)	LHWs
	'Pink Zsar' (VIIa/b)	LRHS
	poilanei misapplied	see *L. primulinum*
	poilanei Gagnep.	see *L. primulinum* var. *poilanei*
	'Polar Star' (VIIa-b/b)	SDeJ
	pomponium (IXc/d)	CBor
§	'Popstar' (Ia/c)	LHWs
	'Pretty Woman' (VIII a/b)	MNrw
§	***primulinum*** (IXc/a) HWJ 681	WCru
	- WWJ 11679	WCru
	- var. ***ochraceum*** (IXc/a)	WCru
	- aff. var. ***ochraceum*** KWJ 12064 (IXc/a)	WCru
§	- var. ***poilanei*** BWJ 15633 **new**	WCru
	'Proud Bride' (VIIa/b)	SDeJ
	'Prunotto'PBR (Iab/b)	SDeJ
§	***pumilum*** (IXc/d)	EPot GKev LAma LHWs MHol SDeJ SDir
	'Purple Dream' (Ia/b) **new**	LAma LCro SDir
	'Purple Eye' (Ia-b/b)	SDeJ
	'Purple Marble' (VIIIb) **new**	LAma SDir
	'Purple Prince' (VIIIa-b/a-b)	SDeJ
	pyrenaicum (IXc/d)	WShi
	'Red Carpet' (Ia/b)	SCob SDeJ
	'Red County' (Ia/c-b)	LAma SDeJ SDir
	'Red Electric' (Ia/b)	SDeJ
	'Red Flavour' (Ic/b-c)	SDeJ
	'Red Hot' (VIIIc-d/b)	SDeJ
	'Red Life' (Ib-a/c)	NHpl
	'Red Matrix' (Ia/b-c)	CBod
	'Red Twinkle' (Ib-c/b-c)	MHol SDeJ
	'Red Velvet' (Ic/d)	LHWs SDeJ SDir
	regale (IXb/a) 🏆H6	CAvo CBro ECha EGrI ELan EPfP ERCP GKev LAma LCro LHWs LOPS LRHS MCot SCob SDeJ SDir SPer SRms
	- 'Album' (IXb/a)	CAvo ERCP GKev LAma LCro LHWs LOPS LRHS SCoo SDeJ SDir
	- pink	NBwr
	'Reinesse' (Ia/b)	NRHS SDeJ
§	'Rio' (VIIb/b-c)	SCoo
	RIO NEGRO ('Corvara'PBR) (VIIa-b/b-c)	SDeJ
	'Robert Griesbach' (VIIIc/b-c)	SDir
	'Robert Swanson' (VIIIb-c/b)	GKev LHWs SDeJ
	'Robina' (VIIIa-b/b-c)	WCot
	'Rose Arch Fox' (IIc/c-d)	GKev
	ROSELILY AISHA ('Dl102085') (VIIa-c/b)	LHWs
	ROSELILY ANGELA ('Dl111421') (VIIa-b/b)	LHWs
	ROSELILY ANOUSKA ('Dl111067') (VIIa/b)	LHWs
	ROSELILY CAROLINA ('Dl044040'PBR) (VIIa-b)	LAma LHWs SDir
	ROSELILY CELINA ('Dl041121'PBR) (VIIa-b/b)	LHWs
	ROSELILY EDITHA ('Dl11356') (VIIa-b/b)	LHWs
	ROSELILY ELENA ('Dl04581'PBR) (VIIa-b)	LHWs
	ROSELILY FELICIA ('Dl04881'PBR) (VIIa-b)	LHWs

ROSELILY ISABELLA ('DI044033'PBR) (VIIa-b/-) LAma LHWs SDir
ROSELILY KENDRA ('DI112077') (VIIa-b/b) LHWs
ROSELILY LEONA ('DI112773') (VIIa-b/b) new LAma SDir
ROSELILY NATALIA ('DI04544'PBR) (VIIa-b/-) LAma LHWs SDir
ROSELILY ROBERTA ('DI112598') (VIIa-b/b) LHWs
ROSELILY SAMANTHA ('DI112317') (VIIa-b/b) LAma LHWs SDir
'Rosella's Dream' (Ia/b) SDeJ
'Rosemary North' (Ic/d) GEdr
'Rosselini' (VIIIa-b/b) SDeJ
rosthornii (IXc/d) WCru
'Royal Kiss' (VIIIa-b) new LAma
rubellum (IXb/a) GEdr
sachalinense (IXa/b) RBS 0235 EPPr
'Salinas' (VIIa/b) SDeJ
'Salmon Flavour' (Ic/b-c) LAma SDir
'Salmon Star'PBR (VIIa-b/b/c) LHWs
'Salmon Tiger' (Ib-c/b-c) SDeJ
'Salmon Twinkle' (Ib-c/c) SDeJ
'Satisfaction' (VIIIa-b/-) SDeJ SDir
'Scarlet Delight' (VIIb-c/c-d) SDeJ SDir
'Scheherazade' (VIIIc/d) GKev LAma LHWs SDeJ SDir
'Secret Kiss'PBR (Ia/b) LHWs
'Serene Angel' (VIIa/c) new WCot
'Set Point' (VIIb/b) SDeJ
'Showwinner' (VIIa/b-c) EHyd LRHS NRHS
'Silk Road' (VIIIb-c/b) LHWs
'Slate's Morning' (IIc/c) GKev LAma LHWs WCot
'Smoky Mountain' (VIIIc/d) SDeJ
'Snowy Morning' (IIc/d) new GKev
'Solution' (VIIa-b/b) LHWs
'Souvenir'PBR (VIIa-b/b) CBod SDeJ
'Space Star' (VIIa/b-c) LRHS
'Spark' (Ia-b/b) MHol
'Sparkling Joy' (Ia-b/c) LRHS
'Special News' (VIIa/b) LHWs LRHS
speciosum (IXb-c/d) LHWs
- B&SWJ 4847 WCru
- B&SWJ 4924 WCru
- var. ***album*** (IXb-c/d) LHWs NBir NHpl SDeJ WFar
- 'Ida Uchida' (IX) SDir
- var. ***rubrum*** (IXb-c/d) ECha LCro LOPS NBir SDeJ SRms
§ - - 'Uchida' (IXb-c/d) CAvo GKev LAma SDeJ
'Spring Pink' (Ia/-) LAma SDeJ SDir
'Spring Romance' (Romance Series) (VIIa/b) LHWs
'Stainless Steel' (Ia/b) SDeJ
'Star Gazer' (VIIa/c) CRos EGrl EHyd GKev LAma LCro LHWs LOPS LRHS NRHS SCoo SDeJ SDir
'Star Romance' (Romance Series) (VIIa-b/b) LHWs
'Starfighter' (VIIa-b/c) LRHS SDeJ
'Starlight Express' (VIIa-b/b-c) LRHS
'Stonehenge'PBR (VIIIa-b/b) LHWs
'Stracciatella Event' (Ic-d/b) LHWs
'Strawberry Event' (Ic-d/b) LAma LHWs
'Sun Ray' (Ia/b) SCob
'Sunny Bonaire'PBR (VIIa/b) LHWs LRHS
'Sunny Grenada' (VIIa-b/b) LRHS
'Sunny Keys' (VIIa/b) LHWs
'Sunny Martinique' (VIIa-b/b) LHWs
'Sunny Morning' (IIc/d) CAvo GKev LAma LHWs
'Sunny Okinawa'PBR (VIIa-b/b) LHWs
'Sunny Robyn' (VIIa-b/b) LHWs
'Sunset Boulevard' (VIIIb/b) GKev LHWs
superbum (IXc/d) GKev WCru
'Sweet Desire'PBR (VIIIa-b/b) LAma LHWs SDir
'Sweet Lord' (Ia/b) SDeJ
'Sweet Sugar'PBR (VIIIa/b) LHWs
'Sweet Surrender' (Ib-c/c-d) LHWs SDeJ SDir
'Sweet Talk'PBR (VIIIa-b/b) LHWs
'Sweet Zanica'PBR (VIIIa/b) LHWs
'Tailor Made' (Ia/b) SDeJ
taliense (IXc/d) WCru
'Tarragona'PBR (VIIIb/b) SDeJ
tenuifolium see *L. pumilum*
'Terrasol' (VIIIa/a) LHWs
'Terry' (IIc/c-d) LHWs
Tiger Babies Group (VIIIb-c/c-d) LHWs SDeJ SDir
'Tigermoon' (VIIa/b) LHWs
'Tigerwoods' (VIIa/c) LCro LOPS
tigrinum see *L. lancifolium*
'Tinilco' (Ia/b) new LAma
'Tiny Bee'PBR (Ia-b/b) LHWs
'Tiny Dino'PBR (Ia-b/b) LHWs
'Tiny Double You'PBR (Ia-b/b) LHWs
'Tiny Epic' (Ia/c) LHWs
'Tiny Ghost'PBR (Ia-b/b-c) SCob
'Tiny Nanny'PBR (Ia-b/b-c) SCob
'Tiny Nugget' (Ia-b/b) LHWs
'Tiny Orange Sensation'PBR (Ia/b) LHWs
'Tiny Padhye'PBR (Ia-b/b-c) LHWs
'Tiny Parrot' (Ia/b) LHWs
'Tiny Poems' (Ia-b/b) LHWs
'Tiny Rocket'PBR (Ia-b/b) LHWs
'Tom Pouce' (VIIa/b) SDeJ
'Top Draw' LHWs
'Toronto' (Ia-b/b) SDeJ
'Toscane' (Ia/b-c) SDeJ
'Tribal Dance' (Ia/b-c) GKev LAma
TRIUMPHATOR ('Zanlophator'PBR) (VIIIb/a-b) GKev MCot SDeJ
'True Romance' (Romance Series) (VIIa/b) LHWs
tsingtauense (IXa/c) SDeJ
- B&SWJ 519 WCru
- B&SWJ 4263 WCru
- B&SWJ 4698 WCru
'Twyford'PBR (VIIa/b) LHWs
'Uchida Kanoka' see *L. speciosum* var. *rubrum* 'Uchida'
'Urandi' (VIIIc/b) SDeJ
'Val di Sole'PBR (Ia/b) SDeJ
'Venezuela' (VIIa-b/b-c) SDeJ SDir
'Visaversa' (VIIIa-b/b) SDeJ
'Viva la Vida' (VIIIa-b/b) GKev LHWs
'Vivaldi' (Ia/b) SDeJ
vollmeri see *L. pardalinum* subsp. *vollmeri*
wallichianum (IXb/a) GKev SDeJ XLum
'Whistler' (Ia/c) LAma SDeJ SDir
'White Paradise' (V-/a) SCoo
'White Pixels' (Ia/b) SDeJ
'White Present' (Vb/a) SDeJ
'White Proud'PBR (VIIa/b-c) new LAma
'White Twinkle' (Ia-b/b) GKev LAma LCro LHWs SDeJ
wigginsii see *L. pardalinum* subsp. *wigginsii*
willmottiae see *L. davidii* var. *willmottiae*

'Wine Electric' (Ia/c)	SDeJ
'World Trade' (Vb-c/a)	LRHS
xanthellum var. ***luteum*** (IXb-c/d)	WCru
'Yang'PBR (VIIIb-c/a)	LHWs
'Yellow Bruse' (Ic/c)	LHWs SDeJ
'Yellow Cocotte' (Ia/c)	LAma SDir
'Yellow County' (Ia/b-c)	SDeJ
§ 'Yellow Electric' (Ia/b-c)	SDeJ
'Yellow Eye' (Ia/b)	SDeJ
'Yellow Planet' (VIb-a/a)	LCro
'Yellow Space' (VIIIc-b/b-c)	LHWs
'Yeti' (Ia/b)	SDeJ
'Yin'PBR (VIIIb/a)	LHWs
'Zambesi'PBR (VIIIa/b-c)	LHWs
'Zeba'PBR (VIIIa-b/c) **new**	GKev
'Zelmira' (VIIIa-b/b)	LHWs

lime see *Citrus* × *aurantiifolia*

lime, Philippine see *Citrus* × *microcarpa*

limequat see *Citrus* × *floridana*

Limnanthes (*Limnanthaceae*)

douglasii ♀H5	ELan LCro LOPS MNHC NBir
- subsp. ***nivea***	SPhx
- subsp. ***rosea***	CSpe

Limnobium (*Hydrocharitaceae*)

sp.	LPfP
spongia	LLWG

Limonium (*Plumbaginaceae*)

bellidifolium	CFis EBou EDAr SLee SWvt WHoo
binervosum	NAts
'Blauer Diamant'	EWoo
cosyrense	MHer
dumosum	see *Goniolimon tataricum* var. *angustifolium*
gmelinii	SPlb
* - subsp. ***hungaricum***	SBut XLum
latifolium	see *L. platyphyllum*
§ ***platyphyllum***	CBod CKel EPfP EWoo GJos GMaP LRHS LShi LSto LSun MHer MHol MMuc NFav SAng SCob SEdd SGbt SPer SRms SSut WCAu WCot XSen
- 'Blue Cloud'	SRms
- 'Robert Butler'	ECtt GPSL LRHS MRav WCot WGwG
- 'Violetta'	CBod CTri ECtt EHyd ELan EPfP GBin GMcL LRHS MPie NRHS SEdd SMrm SPer SPoG WHoo
'Salt Lake'	LRHS
§ ***sinuatum***	SVic
tataricum	see *Goniolimon tataricum*
vulgare	LSun SGBe XSen

Linanthastrum see *Linanthus*

Linanthus (*Polemoniaceae*)

nuttallii subsp. ***floribundus***	WAbe

Linaria (*Plantaginaceae*)

aeruginea	SBut
- 'Lindeza Violet'	CSpe
- 'Neon Lights'	CSpe CWal EDAr SPoG WFar WWke
- subsp. ***nevadensis*** 'Gemstones'	SGro
alpina	CSpe ECha LShi NRya NSla SRms WFar
- red-flowered	WFar
anticaria 'Antique Silver'	ECha LBar MMrt MRav
cymbalaria	see *Cymbalaria muralis*
§ ***dalmatica***	ECha MMuc NBid NGBl NSti SBut SPhx WCot WFar
dalmatica × ***purpurea***	WCot
'Dial Park'	CSpe ECha ECtt LBar MHol NDov NLar SPad WCot WMal WTor
× ***dominii*** 'Carnforth'	LPla SBut
'Florence Lily Sophia Brown'	WCot WFar
genistifolia	WCot
- W&B BGB-6	WCot WFar
- subsp. ***dalmatica***	see *L. dalmatica*
hepaticifolia	see *Cymbalaria hepaticifolia*
'Lemon Cream'	WCot
* ***lobata alba***	SPlb
* 'Lucy's Pink'	ECha
maroccana Fairy Bouquet Group ♀H6	LCro LOPS
- 'Licilia Red' (Licilia Series) **new**	CWCL
- NORTHERN LIGHTS (mixed) **new**	CWCL
origanifolia	see *Chaenorhinum origanifolium*
pallida	see *Cymbalaria pallida*
'Peachy'	CDor CSpe ECha ECtt GBin LBar LPla LSou MHol MNrw NDov NLar SBut SEdd SMHy SPad SPoG WCot WFar WTor
'Phillant Ruby'	WMal
pilosa	see *Cymbalaria pilosa*
'Pink Kisses'	ECha ECtt LBar LSou MHol MPie SPad SPoG WCot WFar WMal
purpurea	CBod CDor CKel CTri EBee EGrl ELan EPfP LBar LSto MBow MHer MNHC NBro NPer NPol SEND SPhx SRms WCot WFar WHlf WPnP WSFF
- 'Alba'	see *L. purpurea* 'Springside White'
- 'Brown's White Strain'	ECha EPPr WCot
- 'Canon Went'	Widely available
- FREEFOLK PICCOLO ('Harlinone')	SHar
- pink-flowered	CSpe LEdu
- 'Poached Egg'	ECha LEdu WGoo
- 'Radcliffe Innocence'	see *L. purpurea* 'Springside White'
§ - 'Springside White'	CAby CDor CSpe GJos LBar LRHS NBir NGdn SBut SGro SPhx SVic WFar WHlf WTor
repens	WCot WHer
× ***sepium***	WCot
triornithophora	SPlb WWFP
- 'Rosea'	CSpe
tristis	LShi
vulgaris	CHab EBou EDAr EPfP GQue LDai MBow MHer MHoo MMuc MNHC NAts NGrd NMir SRms WHer WShi WWild
- f. ***peloria***	WMal

Lindelofia (*Boraginaceae*)

anchusoides misapplied	see *L. longiflora*
anchusoides (Lindl.) Lehm.	NBid SBrt
§ ***longiflora***	GGro

Lindera (*Lauraceae*)

aggregata	CBcs WPGP
angustifolia	NLar WJur
- FMWJ 13156	WCru
assamica B&SWJ 13984	WCru
benzoin	CBcs CMCN LRHS MBlu NLar
erythrocarpa B&SWJ 6271	WCru

- B&SWJ 8730	WCru
glauca **new**	NLar WJur
metcalfiana	WCru
var. ***dictyophylla*** KWJ 12312	
neesiana B&SWJ 13984	WCru
obtusiloba ♀H5	MBlu WJur WLov
- B&SWJ 8723	WCru
- B&SWJ 11054	WCru
- B&SWJ 12555 from Korea	WCru
praecox	CBcs NLar
- B&SWJ 10802	WCru
- B&SWJ 10953 from north Japan	WCru
- B&SWJ 11125 from south Japan	WCru
praetermissa	WPGP
reflexa	NLar
sericea B&SWJ 11123	WCru
- B&SWJ 11141	WCru
- var. ***lancea***	NLar
- - B&SWJ 11071	WCru
- - B&SWJ 11118	WCru
tonkinensis FMWJ 13123	WCru
triloba	NLar
- B&SWJ 5570	WCru
- B&SWJ 11121	WCru
- B&SWJ 11466	WCru
umbellata B&SWJ 10881	WCru
- var. ***membranacea*** B&SWJ 10837	WCru

Lindernia (*Linderniaceae*)

grandiflora	LLWG SLee WTor

Linnaea (*Caprifoliaceae*)

borealis	GRum NSla WAbe

Linum (*Linaceae*)

alpinum	SBut
arboreum ♀H4	GKev WThu
austriacum	WAbe WThu
capitatum	EPot NSla
flavum	XSen
- 'Compactum'	CFis EDAr GAbr SRms
'Gemmell's Hybrid' ♀H4	EWes WAbe WThu
grandiflorum ♀H4	LCro LOPS
- 'Bright Eyes'	CSpe
- 'Charmer Salmon' **new**	CSpe
- 'Rubrum'	CSpe
hypericifolium	LPla
lewisii	EDAr SBls
narbonense	CKel CSpe ECha LDai SPhx
- 'Heavenly Blue'	LSun
§ ***perenne***	CBod EBee EBou ECha ENfk EPfP GKev MHer MNHC SPhx SPoG WJek
- 'Album'	EBee ECha EPfP SBut
- subsp. ***alpinum*** 'Alice Blue'	WAbe
§ - 'Blau Saphir'	NHol SBut
- BLUE SAPPHIRE	see *L. perenne* 'Blau Saphir'
I - 'Nanum'	NSla
- 'Nanum Sapphire'	see *L. perenne* 'Blau Saphir'
sibiricum	see *L. perenne*
uninerve	WAbe

Lippia (*Verbenaceae*)

sp.	SWvt
canescens	see *Phyla nodiflora* var. *canescens*
chamaedrifolia	see *Glandularia peruviana*
citriodora	see *Aloysia citrodora*
dulcis	ENfk MNHC SRms WFar WJek
nodiflora	see *Phyla nodiflora*
repens	see *Phyla nodiflora*

Liquidambar ✿ (*Hamamelidaceae*)

acalycina	CBcs EHed ELan EPfP NOra SCoo SLim SSta WLov WMat WPGP
- 'Burgundy Flush' ♀H5	NLar SSta
- 'Spinners'	CRos EHyd ELan EPfP LMil LRHS WPGP
formosana	CMCN CMac SGol SSta
- 'Afterglow'	MBlu NLar
- 'Ellen'	NLar
- Monticola Group	SLim SSta
orientalis	CJun CLnd CMCN EPfP SSta WPGP
poilanei B&SWJ 11756	WCru
styraciflua	Widely available
- 'Andrew Hewson'	CJun CLnd CRos EBee EHyd EPfP LRHS MAsh MBlu NRHS SSta WLov
- 'Anja'	CJun MBlu SSta
- 'Anneke'	CJun SSta
- 'Aurea'	see *L. styraciflua* 'Variegata' Overeynder
- 'Aurea Variegata'	see *L. styraciflua* 'Variegata' Overeynder
- 'Aurora'	CJun
- 'Burgundy'	CJun MAsh MBlu SSta
I - 'Corky'	EPfP LRHS MTrO SSta WMat
- 'Dark Autumn' **new**	NLar
- 'Emerald Sentinel'	CJun SSta
- 'Festeri'	CEnd SSta
- 'Festival'	CLnd MBlu
- 'Frosty' (v)	SSta
- 'Globe'	see *L. styraciflua* 'Gum Ball'
- 'Golden Sun' PBR	CBcs LSRN NLar
- 'Golden Treasure' (v)	CLnd CMCN LPar LSRN MGos SGol SSta
- 'Granary Sunset'	SSta
§ - 'Gum Ball'	CAco CCVT CEnd CMCN EBee ELan EPfP ERom EWes LPar LRHS MAsh NLar NOra SGsty SLim SPoG SSta SWvt WLov
- 'Jennifer Carol'	SSta
- 'Kia'	CEnd CJun
- 'Lane Roberts' ♀H6	Widely available
- 'Lynn'	SSta
- 'Manon' (v)	CJun
- 'Midwest Sunset'	CJun MBlu NLar
- 'Moonbeam' (v)	SLim SSta
- 'Moraine'	CAco CJun
- 'Naree'	NLar SSta WLov
- 'Nina'	SSta
- 'Oconee'	CEnd SLim SSta WLov
- 'Paarl' (v)	CAco CLnd
- 'Palo Alto' ♀H6	CAco CEnd EPfP LPar MBlu MTrO SCoo SLim SSta WLov WMat WMou WPGP
- 'Parasol'	CEnd CJun CLnd SSta
- 'Pasquali Fastigiata'	CRos ELan LRHS MAsh
- 'Pendula'	MBlu SSta
- 'Penwood' ♀H6	CJun NLar SSta WLov
- 'Red Sunset'	SSta
- 'Rotundiloba'	CJun CMCN EPfP MBlu MMrt NLar SGsty WLov WPGP
- 'Savill Torch'	CJun SSta
- 'Schock's Gold'	NLar SSta
§ - 'Silver King' (v)	CAco CJun CMCN CMac LPar LRHS MGos NOrn SCoo SGol SSta WHtc
- 'Simone'	CAco NLar SSta
- 'Slender Silhouette' ♀H6	Widely available
- 'Stared'	CAco CJun CLnd EBee EPfP MBlu MGos MTrO NOra NOrn SCoo SLim SSta WHtc WLov WMat WMou
- 'Teresa'	EBee LRHS

- 'Thea'	CAco CJun CRos EBee EHyd ELan EPfP LMil LRHS MAsh MBlu MTrO NRHS SSta
- 'Variegata' misapplied	see *L. styraciflua* 'Silver King'
§ - 'Variegata' Overeynder (v)	CJun CMac EBee ELan LPar LRHS SLim SSta WLov
- 'Wisley King'	LRHS WPGP
- 'Woorby Rose'	CJun
- 'Worplesdon' ♀H6	Widely available

Liriodendron (*Magnoliaceae*)

sp.	EFPl
chinense ♀H6	CMCN EPfP MBlu WPGP
× ***sinoamericanum***	CAco
- 'Chapel Hill'	MBlu
- 'Doc Deforce's Delight'	LRHS MBlu NLar
tulipifera ♀H6	Widely available
- 'Aureomarginatum' (v) ♀H6	CAco CBcs CCVT CEme CEnd CMCN CMac EBee ELan EPfP IPap LMaj LPar LSRN MAsh MBlu MGos MSwo MTrO NOrn NWea SGol SMad SPer SPoG SSta WHtc WLov WMat
- 'Edward Gursztyn' PBR **new**	CAco
- 'Fastigiatum'	CAco CEnd CMCN CPer ELan EPfP MAsh MBlu MGos MTrO NLar SGol SGsty SPer
- 'Glen Gold'	CEnd MBlu NLar
- 'Purgatory'	MBlu
- 'Roodhaan'	MBlu NLar
- 'Rotundiloba'	MBlu
- 'Snow Bird' (v)	EBee MAsh SPoG WMat

Liriope ✿ (*Asparagaceae*)

'Big Blue'	see *L. muscari* 'Big Blue'
§ ***exiliflora***	NLar
- 'Ariaka-janshige' (v)	EHyd NRHS
- SILVERY SUNPROOF misapplied	see *L. spicata* 'Gin-ryu', *L. muscari* 'Variegata'
§ ***gigantea***	EBee
graminifolia misapplied	see *L. muscari*
'Grassy' **new**	ESwi
hyacinthifolia	see *Reineckea carnea*
'Majestic'	CKel WHoo
minor	CMac
§ ***muscari*** ♀H5	Widely available
- 'Alba'	see *L. muscari* 'Monroe White'
- AMETHYST ('Liptp')	CBod CDor NRHS WNPC
§ - 'Big Blue'	Widely available
- 'Big Pink'	CBod
- 'Emerald Cascade' **new**	ESwi
- 'Evergreen Giant'	see *L. gigantea*
- 'Gold-banded' (v)	CBct CKel EHed EHyd LCro LRHS SBea SCob SEdd SMad WFar WHlf
- 'Goldfinger'	CExl EMor SMad
- 'Ingwersen'	CExl CKno EBee EPPr EPfP NRHS SCob XLum
- ISABELLA ('Lirf')	EPPr
- 'John Burch' (v)	CBct CExl CKel CMac SCob
- 'Kindi Pink'	EHed ELan WHlf
- 'Lilac Wonder'	EHyd EMor EPPr EPfP GBin LRHS
- 'Majestic' misapplied	see *L. exiliflora*
- 'Moneymaker'	CDor EBee EPPr EPfP GKev LCro LSRN MACG MNrw SCob SCoo SPoG WNPC
§ - 'Monroe White'	CBcs CBod CExl CMac EHed ELan EPfP EShb EWoo LCro LOPS MACG MBel MCot MRav NBid NLar SBea SCob SPer SWvt WHlf
- 'Okina' (v)	CBro CPla EBee ELon EMor LCro LOPS MBNS MBel MHol MNrw NLar NSti SEdd SMad SPoG WCot WHlf WMal
- 'Pee Dee Ingot'	SPoG
- 'Royal Purple'	CDor EBee ECtt EHyd EPfP LCro LRHS MAsh MBel NCth NLar NRHS SCob SPer WHoo WNPC
- 'Silver Ribbon'	CBro MGos
- 'Super Blue'	ESwi NLar
§ - 'Variegata' (v)	CExl CRos EBee EBlo EHyd ELan EPfP EWes LCro LPal LRHS LSto NBir NRHS SCob SCoo SPoG SWvt WHoo
- 'Webster Wideleaf'	EBee WCot
platyphylla	see *L. muscari*
'Samantha'	ECha EMor MACG SPer
spicata	CBod EBee WFar XLum
- 'Alba'	MRav
§ - 'Gin-ryu' (v)	CBct CExl EHed EMor EShb LPal MCot MRav NLar NSti SCob WBrk WJam XLum
- 'Silver Dragon'	see *L. spicata* 'Gin-ryu'

Litchi (*Sapindaceae*)

chinensis	CCCN WJur

Lithocarpus ✿ (*Fagaceae*)

densiflorus	CMCN
edulis	SArc
pachyphyllus	CBcs

Lithodora (*Boraginaceae*)

diffusa	see *Glandora diffusa*
× ***intermedia***	see *Moltkia* × *intermedia*
oleifolia	see *Glandora oleifolia*
rosmarinifolia	see *Glandora rosmarinifolia*
zahnii	EHyd LRHS SVen WFar
- 'Azure-ness'	SChF SGro WAbe

Lithophragma (*Saxifragaceae*)

parviflorum	CMiW CTtf EWes LPla

Lithops ✿ (*Aizoaceae*)

sp.	CDoC EAri
aucampiae ♀H2 **new**	EAri
hallii ♀H2	SSim

Lithospermum (*Boraginaceae*)

diffusum	see *Glandora diffusa*
doerfleri	see *Moltkia doerfleri*
'Heavenly Blue'	see *Glandora prostrata* 'Heavenly Blue'
officinale	GPoy
oleifolium	see *Glandora oleifolia*
purpureocaeruleum	see *Buglossoides purpurocaerulea*

Lithraea (*Anacardiaceae*)

caustica	WPav

Litsea (*Lauraceae*)

NJM 13.047	WPGP
glauca	see *Neolitsea sericea*
japonica	CMCN SVen

Livistona (*Arecaceae*)

chinensis ♀H2	CPHo LPal NPlm
decora	LPal
mariae	NPlm
rotundifolia	LWaG NHrt

Loasa (*Loasaceae*)

triphylla var. ***volcanica***	EWes WSHC

Lobelia ✿ (*Campanulaceae*)

angulata	see *Pratia angulata*
'Bordervale'	WBor
bridgesii	CDTJ EBee LBar LRHS SPlb WKif WPav

	'Bruce Wakefield'	WHil
§	***cardinalis***	CMac CPud CWal CWat EWld GMaP LCro LOPS LPfP NGBl NPer SPer SPlb SRms SWvt WFar
	- 'Bee's Flame'	CEme CNor CWGN ECtt EHyd EWoo LBar LRHS MArl MRav MSpe NCth NGdn NRHS SCoo SRkn WGwG
	- 'Black Truffle'	see *L. cardinalis* 'Chocolate Truffle'
§	- 'Chocolate Truffle'PBR	EBee SRms
§	- 'Elmfeuer'	CWCL EWoo NLar SPlb SPoG SWvt XLum
§	- 'Queen Victoria' ♀H3	Widely available
	- 'Russian Princess' misapplied	EHyd EPfP EWoo GElm LLWG LRHS MAsh NGdn NRHS SPoG SRkn SWvt WFar
	chinensis	LLWG
	'Cinnabar Deep Red'	see *L.* × *speciosa* (Fan Series) 'Fan Tiefrot'
	'Cinnabar Rose'	see *L.* × *speciosa* (Fan Series) 'Fan Zinnoberrosa'
	COMPLIMENT BLUE	see *L.* × *speciosa* (Kompliment Series) 'Kompliment Blau'
	COMPLIMENT DEEP RED	see *L.* × *speciosa* (Kompliment Series) 'Kompliment Tiefrot'
	COMPLIMENT PURPLE	see *L.* × *speciosa* (Kompliment Series) 'Kompliment Purpur'
	COMPLIMENT SCARLET	see *L.* × *speciosa* (Kompliment Series) 'Kompliment Scharlach'
	'Compton Pink'	CBcs CBod CNor CToG EAJP ECha ECtt ELon EMor EWTr EWes EWoo IPot LBar LBuc LCro LOPS LRHS LSou MPie MSpe NBPC NGBl NLar NRHS NSti SOrN WFar WGwG
	erinus **new**	MBros
	- 'Cambridge Blue' ♀H2	MBros
	- Cascade Series ♀H2	LCro LOPS
	- 'Crystal Palace' ♀H2	MBros MPri
	- (Fountain Series) 'Fountain Blue'	MBros MPri
	- - 'Fountain Rose'	MBros
	- - 'Fountain White'	MBros MPri
	- HOT TIGER ('Wesloti'PBR)	WWke
	- 'Mrs Clibran' ♀H2	LCro LOPS MBros
	- Riviera Series	MPri
	- 'Sapphire'	LCro LOPS MBros MPri
	- 'String of Pearls' ♀H2	LCro MBros
	- WATERFALL BLUE ICE (Waterfall Series)	LSou MPri
	- 'White Lady'	MBros
	- WONDERFALL (mixed) **new**	WWke
	excelsa	CSpe SEND WPav
	FAN DEEP RED	see *L.* × *speciosa* (Fan Series) 'Fan Tiefrot'
	FAN DEEP ROSE	see *L.* × *speciosa* (Fan Series) 'Fan Orchidrosa'
	FAN SALMON	see *L.* × *speciosa* (Fan Series) 'Fan Lachs'
	fistulosa **new**	CDTJ WCot
	'Flamingo'	see *L.* × *speciosa* 'Pink Flamingo'
	fulgens	see *L. cardinalis*
	- SAINT ELMO'S FIRE	see *L. cardinalis* 'Elmfeuer'
	× ***gerardii***	see *L.* × *speciosa*
	giberroa	CDTJ
	'Gladys Lindley'	LRHS
	'Grape Knee-Hi'	ECtt EHyd LRHS NRHS
	'Hadspen Purple'	see *L.* × *speciosa* 'Hadspen Purple'
	'Infinity Blue' **new**	MPri
	inflata	GPoy

	laxiflora	CFis SAdn WFar
	- var. ***angustifolia***	CDTJ CHll CPbh CPla CWCL EWld SBrt SRms SVen WCot
	linnaeoides	SPlb
§	***montana***	EWld
	- B&SWJ 8220	ESwi WCru
	pedunculata	see *Pratia pedunculata*
	'Queen Victoria'	see *L. cardinalis* 'Queen Victoria'
	sessilifolia	CExl EBee
	- B&SWJ 8875	WCru
	siphilitica	Widely available
	- f. ***albiflora***	EBee ECtt LEdu
	- - 'Alba'	CPud CToG CWat EMor EPfP LBar LShi NDov SBls SRms SWvt WFar
	- 'Rosea'	MNrw
	'Sombre Purple'	EBee
§	× ***speciosa***	EGrI LBar NCth SVic WFar XLum
	- 'Alba'	NCth
	- 'Butterfly Blue'	CNor SGbt
	- 'Cranberry Crush'	EHyd LRHS NRHS
	- CRIMSON PRINCESS ('Gencrim'PBR) (Princess Series)	EPfP LSou SPoG
	- 'Dark Crusader'	CToG EBee ECtt EHyd EPfP EWTr GElm LBar LRHS MHol MPie NRHS SGbt
	- Fan Series	MRav
	- - 'Fan Blau'	CKel EHyd ELan EMor LRHS MHol NLar SCob WFar
	- - 'Fan Burgundy'	EHyd ELan EMor LBar LRHS NGdn NLar
§	- - 'Fan Lachs'	EHyd SCob WFar
§	- - 'Fan Orchidrosa'	EMor
	- - 'Fan Scharlach'	EHyd ELan LBar LRHS NRHS SPoG SWvt WFar
§	- - 'Fan Tiefrot'	SRms SWvt WBor
§	- - 'Fan Zinnoberrosa'	SRms SWvt
§	- 'Hadspen Purple'PBR	Widely available
	- 'Kimbridge Beet'	CMac EBee LRHS
	- Kompliment Series	WFar
§	- - 'Kompliment Blau'	SWvt WFar
*	- - 'Kompliment Pale Pink'	WFar
§	- - 'Kompliment Purpur'	SWvt
§	- - 'Kompliment Scharlach' ♀H5	EHyd EPfP MNrw NPer NRHS SWvt
§	- - 'Kompliment Tiefrot'	EHyd MNrw SWvt
	- 'Monet Moment'	CWCL EBee ECtt EHyd ELon EWes LRHS NLar NRHS SWvt
	- 'Pauline'	ECtt
	- 'Pink Elephant' ♀H5	CPud CToG ECtt EHyd ELan EMor GBee LBar LRHS NCth NRHS NSti SGbt SHar
§	- 'Pink Flamingo'	CKel ELan EPfP LRHS
	- purple-flowered	NCth
	- ROSE PRINCESS ('Genross'PBR) (Princess Series)	SPoG
	- 'Royal Purple'	EMor
	- 'Ruby Slippers'	CMac EBee ELan EPfP
	- 'Russian Princess' purple-flowered	CRos CToG CWnw ECtt ELan ELon ILea LBar LSou MBel MHer MHol MPie MSpe NGBl NHol SCob SCoo SGbt SMrm SPoG WFar WKif
	- 'Sparkling Ruby'	CAby CBod EBee ECtt EMor EPfP EWTr EWoo LBar LRHS LShi NCth NDov NRHS SCoo SMrm SWvt
	- (Starship Series) 'Starship Blue' **new**	LBar
	- - 'Starship Burgundy' **new**	LBar
	- - 'Starship Deep Rose'	CBod CRos EHyd LBar LRHS MDon MHol NRHS SBls SCoo

- - 'Starship Scarlet'	CBod CRos EHyd EPfP LBar LRHS MBros MDon MHol MPie NRHS SBls SCob SCoo WHil
- 'Tania'	Widely available
- 'Tania's Sister'	ECtt WCot WFar
§ - 'Vedrariensis'	CMac CSpe CWat ECtt EPfP GElm LPfP LRHS MBel MNrw NGBl SRms SWvt WCFE WCav WFar WHoo XLum
telekii	LShi
treadwellii	see *Pratia angulata* 'Treadwellii'
tupa	Widely available
- Archibald's form	WPGP
valida	SWvt
- 'Delft Blue'	LBar LRHS
- 'True Blue'	SWvt
vedrariensis	see *L.* × *speciosa* 'Vedrariensis'

Lobivia see *Echinopsis*

Lobostemon (*Boraginaceae*)

belliformis	CPbh

Lobularia (*Brassicaceae*)

maritima 'Carpet of Snow'	LRHS
- GOLF BRIGHT MIXED (Golf Series)	LCro
- 'Snow Crystals'	MPri
- 'Violet Queen' ♀H3	LCro LOPS
PRINCESS IN PURPLE	CPla
SNOW PRINCESS ('Inlbusnopr'[PBR])	CPla MHol

loganberry see *Rubus* × *loganobaccus*

Lomandra (*Asparagaceae*)

'Arctic Frost' **new**	CBod
hystrix	SPlb
longifolia	LEdu SPlb
- PLATINUM BEAUTY ('Roma13'[PBR]) (v)	CBod SPad SPeP SPoG XSte
- TANIKA ('Lm300'[PBR])	GBin

Lomaria see *Blechnum*

Lomatia (*Proteaceae*)

dentata	MRav
ferruginea	CBcs CCCN CDTJ CDoC CExl CKel CSde CTsd EPfP LRHS MGil SArc SEdd SPoG WCru WPGP XSte
fraseri	CCCN CDoC CKel EHyd EPfP LRHS NLar SPoG WHlf WPGP
hirsuta	MGil
longifolia	see *L. myricoides*
§ ***myricoides***	CBcs CCCN CDoC CExl CTsd EPfP IDee NLar SArc SEdd SPoG WHlf
tinctoria	CBcs CExl CPbh LRHS SPlb WHlf XSte

Lomatium (*Apiaceae*)

columbianum	SPhx
grayi	LPla SPhx WHil

Lomatogonium (*Gentianaceae*)

perenne	GKev

Lonicera ✿ (*Caprifoliaceae*)

KR 10106	WPGP
KR 10608	CRHN
§ ***acuminata***	CMCN EBee
- B&SWJ 3480	WCru
- B&SWJ 6743	CRHN WCru
- B&SWJ 6815	WCru
- var. ***acuminata***	WCot
albertii	MBNS NLar
alseuosmoides	CBcs CBod CKel CRHN EPfP LRHS MACG NLar SEND SPoG WCru WPGP WSHC WSpi
× ***americana*** misapplied	see *L.* × *italica*
americana ambig.	ETho NBwr
§ ***americana*** (Mill.) K. Koch	CBcs CRHN EPfP LEdu MSwo NBwr SEND SRms
§ × ***brownii*** 'Dropmore Scarlet'	Widely available
- 'Fuchsioides' misapplied	see *L.* × *brownii* 'Dropmore Scarlet'
caerulea	CDoC EPom IDee LRHS MRav SBmr SEdi SPre SRms SVic WBor WKor WLov
- 'Atut'	NLar
- 'Duet'	NLar
- var. ***edulis***	CAgr LBuc LEdu MCoo NLar
- var. ***kamtschatica***	EPom LCro NLar SBmr WHlf WPGP
- - 'Balalaika' (F)	CAgr MCoo
- - 'Borealis' (F)	CAgr
- - 'Eisbar' (F)	CAgr
- - 'Erin' (F)	LEdu
- - 'Fialka'[PBR] (F)	EDir NLar
- - 'Honey Bee' (F)	CAgr XSte
- - 'Indigo Gem' (F)	CAgr
- - 'Indigo Yum' (F)	CAgr
- - 'Kalinka' (F)	CAgr
- - 'Larisa' (F)	LEdu WPGP
- - 'Maries' (F)	LEdu WFar WPGP
- - 'Morena'[PBR] (F)	EBee EDir EPom
- - 'Nimfa' (F)	IDee
- - 'Rebecca' (F)	LEdu WPGP
- - 'Ruth' (F)	LEdu WLov WPGP
- - 'Sinoglaska' (F)	EBtc NLar
- - 'Vicky' (F)	LEdu WFar WPGP
- - 'Wojtek' (F)	CAgr IDee NLar SPre
- - 'Zojka' (F)	CAgr NLar
- 'Kirke'	NLar SMad
* - var. ***longifolia***	NLar
§ ***caprifolium***	CKel CRHN EHyd EPfP LRHS NLar WCot
- 'Anna Fletcher'	CRHN WCFE
- f. ***pauciflora***	see *L.* × *italica*
caucasica **new**	WCot
'Celestial'[PBR]	CRos EPfP LCro LOPS LRHS
chaetocarpa	CEnd
ciliosa	CRHN WCFE WPGP
'Clavey's Dwarf'	EPPr
crassifolia	CBcs EWld GEdr GKev NLar SBrt WPGP
- 'Little Honey'	GKev LCro LRHS MBNS MBlu MGil MMrt MRav NLar SPoG XSte
deflexicalyx	CMCN NLar
dioica red-flowered	GGro
'Early Cream'	see *L. caprifolium*
'Elegant'	see *L. ligustrina* 'Elegant'
elisae	CBcs CMac CRos EHed EPfP GBin LRHS MMuc NCth NLar NRHS SMad SPoG SSta WCot WLov WPGP
etrusca	CRHN MRav SSha XSen
- 'Donald Waterer'	CRHN CRos EPfP LRHS NLar WFar
- 'Michael Rosse'	CKel ELan MBNS NLar SNig WLov
- 'Superba' ♀H5	CKel CRHN EBee ELan EPfP LEdu LRHS NLar SEND WSHC
'Fire Cracker'	NLar
flexuosa	see *L. japonica* var. *repens*
fragrantissima	Widely available
giraldii misapplied	see *L. acuminata*
giraldii Rehder	CRHN WSHC

	glabrata	SCoo
	- B&SWJ 2150	WCru
	- 'Damchin La'	WPGP
	'Golden Trumpet'	CWGN MGos SGsty
	grata	see *L.* × *americana* (Mill.) K. Koch
	harae **new**	WJur
	× ***heckrottii***	CRHN CSBt NLar
	- 'Gold Flame' ambig.	GKin NLar SCob
	- 'Gold Flame' hort. ♀H5	CArg CKel CMac CRos EBee EDir EHyd ELan EPfP ETho LBuc LCro LOPS LRHS MAsh MMuc NRHS SCoo SEND SNig SPer SPoG SRms SWvt WFar WHtc WLov WSHC
§	***henryi***	Widely available
	- B&SWJ 8109	WCru
	- NJM 11.033	WPGP
	- 'Copper Beauty'[PBR]	Widely available
	- var. ***subcoriacea***	see *L. henryi*
	hildebrandiana ♀H2	CCCN CExl CRHN IKel SSha WPGP
	hirsuta	EBee SBrt
	hispidula	SBrt
	'Honey Baby'[PBR]	ELon EPfP LCro NHol NLar
	implexa	CMCN CRHN
	insularis	see *L. morrowii*
	involucrata	CMCN EBee EPfP MBNS MBlu MMuc SEND
	- var. ***ledebourii***	EHyd EPPr EPfP LRHS MGil NLar WHlf
	- - 'Vian'	NLar
§	× ***italica***	CRHN CTri EBee MSwo NPer SCob SCoo SPer
§	- HARLEQUIN ('Sherlite') (v)	CMac EPfP GMcL SPlb SRms SWvt
	japonica	CMen WFar XSen
§	- 'Aureoreticulata' (v) ♀H5	CMac EHeP ELan EPfP EShb LCro MRav NPer SRms WFar WLov
	- var. ***chinensis***	SGsty XSen
	- 'Cream Cascade'	MSwo NLar SCoo
	- 'Dart's Acumen'	CRHN
	- 'Dart's World'	CArg CBod CSBt EBee EDir EHyd LCro LPar LRHS NLar NRHS SRms WLov
	- 'Halliana'	Widely available
	- 'Hall's Prolific' ♀H5	Widely available
§	- 'Horwood Gem' (v)	CDoC ECtt ETho LAlb LCro MGos NLar SCoo
	- 'Maskerade' (v)	NLar
	- 'Mint Crisp'[PBR] (v)	CBod CDoC CKel CMac CPla CRos CSBt CWGN EBee ECtt ELan EPfP EShb GMcL LCro LRHS MGos NLar SCoo SPad SPer SPoG SRms SWvt WHtc
	- 'Peter Adams'	see *L. japonica* 'Horwood Gem'
	- 'Princess Kate'	ELan ETho NLar SRms
	- 'Purpurea' **new**	ETho
	- 'Red World'	EDir EFPl WLov
§	- var. ***repens*** ♀H5	CMac CRos CSBt ECtt EDir EHeP EHyd ELan EPfP EShb ETho GGro LRHS MNHC MRav MSwo NLar NRHS SCoo SPad SPer SPoG SRms WFar
	- - PINK APERITIF ('Crowthlon'[PBR])	CKel LRHS
	- 'Variegata'	see *L. japonica* 'Aureoreticulata'
	korolkowii	EPPr MBNS NBir NLar WAvo WCot WHtc
	- 'Blue Velvet'	CAgr MCoo NLar
	- 'Mayberry Farm'	MCoo
	- var. ***zabelii*** misapplied	see *L. tatarica* 'Zabelii'
	lanceolata BWJ 7935	WCru
§	***ligustrina*** 'Elegant'	CKel LBuc MNic SArc
	- 'Lemon Beauty' (v)	CBcs CCoa CEme CKel CMac EHeP EHyd EShb GMcL LRHS LSRN LSto MBNS MDon MGos NBwr NLar NWad SCob SGbt SGol SPer SRHi SRms SWvt WAvo WFar WHtc
	- 'Lime Twist' (v)	CBod LSto
§	- var. ***pileata***	Widely available
	- - 'Loughall Evergreen'	CBod
	- - 'Moss Green'	CBod
§	- var. ***yunnanensis***	Widely available
	- - 'Baggesen's Gold' ♀H5	Widely available
*	- - 'Compacta'	SGsty
	- - EDMÉE GOLD ('Briloni')	WCot
	- - 'Ernest Wilson'	CKel EPPr
§	- - 'Fertilis'	CBrac
	- - 'Golden Glow'[PBR]	CBod NBwr NEoE
	- - 'Lemon Queen'	LSto MMuc MSwo SEND
§	- - 'Maigrün'	CBar CBcs CCVT CKel EHeP EHyd ELan GDam GMcL LPar LRHS MNHC MSwo NBwr NEoE SCob SPer SWvt WFar XSen
	- - MAYGREEN	see *L. ligustrina* var. *yunnanensis* 'Maigrün'
	- - 'Red Tips'	EShb NLar SCoo SRms
	- - 'Silver Beauty' (v)	CCoa CMac EHeP GMcL LRHS MGos MSwo NBwr SPer SPlb SPoG SRms SWvt WFar
	- - 'Silver Lining' (v)	WCFE
	- - TIDY TIPS ('Panmin')	CBcs CDoC LSto MTin NEoE SCob
	- - 'Twiggy' (v)	CSBt EDAr MDon MHer NBwr NHol NLar NWad SCob WAvo WFar WHtc
	maackii	CMCN CRos EHyd EPPr EPfP LRHS LShi MRav NLar NRHS WCFE
	macrantha B&SWJ 11687	WCru
	- WWJ 11606	WCru
	'Mandarin' ♀H5	CBcs CKel CRHN LCro LOPS MBlu NLar SCoo SWvt WHlf WLov
	maximowiczii var. ***sachalinensis***	NLar
§	***morrowii***	SBrt XSen
	- 'Ullung do'	CMCN
	myrtillus	NLar SBrt
	nitida	see *L. ligustrina* var. *yunnanensis*
	- MAYGREEN	see *L. ligustrina* var. *yunnanensis* 'Maigrün'
	olgae **new**	SBrt
	aff. ***pamirica***	WPGP
	periclymenum	CCVT CPer CRHN CTri GPoy MHer MRav NWea SCob SPlb WSFF XSen
	- 'Belgica' misapplied	see *L.* × *italica*
	- 'Belgica'	Widely available
	- 'Belgica Select'	SOrN
	- CAPRILIA CREAM ('Inov71'[PBR]) **new**	WHlf
	- CAPRILIA IMPERIAL ('Inov86'[PBR])	LAlb LCro LOPS
	- CHIC ET CHOC ('Inov205'[PBR])	CKel LCro NLar SCoo SPoG
§	- 'Chojnów'[PBR]	EBee
*	- 'Cream Cascade'	GMcL
	- 'Florida'	see *L. periclymenum* 'Serotina'
	- FRAGRANT CLOUD	see *L. periclymenum* 'Chojnów'
	- 'Graham Thomas' ♀H6	Widely available
	- 'Harlequin'	see *L.* × *italica* HARLEQUIN
	- 'Heaven Scent'	CDoC ETho LBuc LCro LOPS LSRN NLar WFar
	- 'Honeybush'	CWGN MAsh MGos NHol NWad WFar WNPC
	- 'La Gasnérie'	SCoo
	- 'Munster'	WSHC
	- 'Purple Queen'	CChe
	- 'Red Gables'	CBod CDoC CRHN ELon LSRN MGos MHtn NLar SCoo SEND SWvt WCot WKif WLov

- 'Rhubarb and Custard'	CBcs CDoC CEnd LAlb LCro LOPS LRHS MGos SCoo WHlf WNPC
- 'Scentsation' PBR	CEnd CMac CRos CSBt CWGN EBee EHyd ELan EPfP GBin LCro LOPS LRHS MAsh NCth NLar NRHS SCoo SPoG WHlf WNPC
§ - 'Serotina' ♀H6	Widely available
- 'Strawberries and Cream'	CDoC LCro LOPS LRHS MGos WHlf WNPC
- 'Sweet Sue'	CDoC CRHN CRos EBee EDir EHyd ELan ELon EPfP ETho LCro LRHS LSRN MAsh MGos MSwo NLar NRHS SCoo SNig SPoG SWvt WFar
- 'Winchester'	SRms
pileata	see *L. ligustrina* var. *pileata*
- var. ***yunnanensis*** misapplied	see *L. ligustrina* var. *yunnanensis* 'Fertilis'
pilosa Maxim.	see *L. strophiophora*
pilosa (Kunth) Willd. ex Kunth	CRHN EWld
- F&M 207	WPGP
- F&M 256	WPGP
prolifera	CRHN NLar
× ***purpusii***	CMac CRHN CTri EBee EPfP MBNS NBwr SCob SRms WCFE WFar
- 'Spring Romance'	CMac
- 'Winter Beauty' ♀H6	Widely available
quinquelocularis	CMCN
- f. ***translucens***	GKev
ramosissima	NLar
reticulata 'Silver'	NLar
sempervirens	CBcs CRHN CSBt
- 'Blanche Sandman'	EShb
- 'Cedar Lane'	EHyd LRHS SBrt
- 'Dropmore Scarlet'	see *L.* × *brownii* 'Dropmore Scarlet'
- 'Leo'	CWGN
- f. ***sulphurea***	CMCN
- - 'John Clayton'	EHyd EPfP LRHS
setifera 'Daphnis'	CJun EPfP IDee WPGP
similis var. ***delavayi*** ♀H5	CBod CRHN CWGN EDir EHyd ELan EPfP ETho GMcL LCro LPar MAsh MRav NLar SCoo SDix SEND SRms SSha SWvt WCot WCru WSHC
'Simonet'	EBee NLar
'Spring Purple'	NLar
standishii	CTri WFar
- var. ***lancifolia*** 'Budapest'	EHyd ELan EPfP LRHS MBlu NLar SBrt SMad SRms WFar
stenantha	SBrt
§ ***strophiophora***	WAvo
subaequalis Og 93.329	CExl WPGP WSHC
syringantha	CBcs CRHN EBee EHed ELan EPPr EPfP EWTr LSto MMuc MNrw MRav NLar SBut SDix SEND SIvy WCFE WFar WHlf
tatarica	CMCN MRav
- 'Arnold Red'	MBlu MGos SEND
- 'Hack's Red'	CMCN EHed ELan EPfP LRHS NLar SCoo SVen SWvt
§ - 'Zabelii'	MNrw
× ***tellmanniana*** ♀H5	Widely available
- 'Joan Sayers'	SCoo
thibetica	MBlu
tomentella B&SWJ 2654	WCru
tragophylla ♀H5	CKel ELan EPfP IDee LRHS MBNS NLar SCoo SWvt
- 'Maurice Foster'	CBcs CKel CRHN EBee EMil EWTr LAlb LEdu NLar SNig WLov WSpi
trichosantha var. ***deflexicalyx***	WHil
× ***xylosteoides***	NLar
xylosteum	EPPr LEdu MMuc XSen

Lophomyrtus ✿ (*Myrtaceae*)

§ ***bullata*** ♀H2	CDTJ GMcL SPer
§ ***obcordata***	CCht SSha
× ***ralphii*** BLACK PEARL ('Yanearl')	CDoC CMCN EHyd LRHS NCth SCoo SGBe SGbt WFar
- 'Gloriosa'	CCCN CTrC
- 'Kathryn'	CBcs CCCN CCoa CDoC CKel CTrC LRHS NLar
- 'Krinkly'	SVen
- 'Little Star' (v)	CBcs CBod CSde CTrC LCro SEle SGBe SSha XSte
- Logan's form (v)	CBcs CKel MGil NLar NRHS SGBe SIvy
- 'Magic Dragon' PBR (v)	CBod CDoC CKel CMac CRos CTsd EGrI EHyd ELan LCro LOPS LRHS NRHS SEle SGBe SGbt SPoG WFar XSte
- 'Multicolor' (v)	CBcs CCCN CCoa CDoC EBee LRHS MRav SSha SVen
- 'Pixie'	CBcs CBod CCCN CCoa CDoC CKel CTrC LRHS MAsh SEle SGBe SPoG SVen
- 'Purpurea'	CBod CTrC
- 'Purpurea Nana' **new**	CSBt
- 'Red Dragon'	CBcs CMac EHyd EPfP LCro LPar LRHS MAsh MGos NRHS SGBe SIvy WFar XSte
- 'Variegata' (v)	CMCN
- 'Wild Cherry'	CKel

Lophophora (*Cactaceae*)

williamsii **new**	EAri

Lophosoria (*Dicksoniaceae*)

quadripinnata	CBdn CDTJ CKel IKel LEdu WPGP

Lophospermum (*Plantaginaceae*)

'Cream Delight'	CCCN
§ ***erubescens*** ♀H2	CRHN CSpe SGro
- white-flowered	SGro
(Lofos Series) LOFOS COMPACT PINK ('Sunlorose' PBR)	LSou
- LOFOS WINE RED ('Sun-asaro')	EShb
§ 'Magic Dragon'	SEND SLim SPlb
§ 'Red Dragon'	CCCN CDoC SGro
§ ***scandens***	CCCN
- 'Joan Loraine'	SGro

loquat see *Eriobotrya japonica*

Loropetalum (*Hamamelidaceae*)

chinense	SEle
- BLACK PEARL	see *L. chinense* var. ***rubrum*** 'Pearl'
- CAROLINA MOONLIGHT ('Nci 002')	CBcs SEle WHlf
- EVER RED	see *L. chinense* var. ***rubrum*** 'Chang Nian Hong'
- HOT SPICE	EGrI SEle
- 'Ming Dynasty'	EGrI MAsh SEle SSta WFar
- var. ***rubrum***	SGsty
- - 'Blush'	CBcs GMcL SEle SSha
§ - - 'Chang Nian Hong' PBR	CDoC EGrI LCro LOPS LRHS SEle XSte
- - 'Daybreak's Flame'	CCCN CSde MGil SEle SIvy
- - 'Fire Dance'	Widely available
§ - - 'Pearl' PBR	EGrI SEdd SGsty WCot WHlf
- - 'Pipa's Red'	EGrI
- RUBY SNOW ('Iwai' PBR) **new**	LCro SEdd SOrN
- 'Tang Dynasty'	CDoC WFar

Lotononis (Fabaceae)

aff. ***lotononoides*** **new**	WCot

Lotus (Fabaceae)

berthelotii	CCCN CDTJ EShb MCot MPri
- deep red-flowered ♀H2	SWvt
berthelotii* × *maculatus ♀H2	CCCN MSCN
corniculatus	CHab EBou GJos LCro LOPS MBow MCoo MHer MMuc MNHC NAts NFav NGrd NMir SEND SPhx SRms WOut WSFF WWild
creticus	SPhx
dorycnium	CKel SPhx XSen
hirsutus ♀H4	CBod CPla EAJP ECha EGrI ELan EPfP LCro MAsh MRav SAdn SEND SPer SPhx SPlb SPoG SWvt WMal WOut WSHC XLum XSen
- 'Brimstone' (v)	EPPr EWTr SIvy SPer SPoG SWvt
* - var. ***italica***	LSun
- LITTLE BOY BLUE ('Lisbob'PBR)	CRos CSBt EHyd EPfP LRHS NRHS SGBe
- 'Lois'	SIvy SNig SPoG
jacobaeus	MCot
maritimus	CBor NFav XLum
mearnsii	SPlb
pedunculatus	CHab NAts NMir SPhx WSFF
tetragonolobus	EDAr SPhx SVic

lovage see *Levisticum officinale*

Loxostigma (Gesneriaceae)

kurzii GWJ 9342	WCru

Luculia (Rubiaceae)

gratissima ♀H1c	WPGP

Ludwigia (Onagraceae)

palustris	LLWG

Luetkea (Rosaceae)

pectinata	GArf GEdr

Luffa (Cucurbitaceae)

aegyptiaca	NRob

Luma ✿ (Myrtaceae)

§ ***apiculata*** ♀H4	Widely available
§ - 'Glanleam Gold' (v)	Widely available
- 'Nana'	LEdu WJek WPGP
- 'Penlee'	WJek
- 'Rainbow's Gold' (v)	EShb
- 'Saint Hilary' (v)	CEme CTrC WJek WPav
- 'Variegata' (v)	CTri WFar
§ ***chequen***	CCoa EShb LEdu WJek WPGP WPav

Lunaria (Brassicaceae)

§ ***annua***	CBod GJos LCro LOPS WCot WSFF
- var. ***albiflora*** ♀H6	CKel LCro LOPS NBir SCgs SEND WCot
I - - 'Alba Variegata' (v) ♀H6	CDor CSpe CTtf WBrk
- 'Chedglow'	CSpe GBin LCro LEdu LRHS MAvo MHer SGro SPhx WCot
- 'Corfu Blue' ♀H6	CDor CSpe EWes GBin SPhx SPtp WSFF
- 'Munstead Purple' ♀H6	CSpe
- 'Purple Emperor'	CTtf
- 'Variegata' (v)	CSpe CTtf GJos LBar NBir WCot
biennis	see *L. annua*
rediviva ♀H7	CDor CSpe CTtf EBee ECha EMor EPPr GAbr GBin GMaP LCro LEdu MBel MHer MMuc NBid NChi NPer NSti SBrt SEND SHor SPtp WCAu WCot WFar WPGP
- 'Partway White' (v)	CMil MAvo WCot

Lunathyrium (Woodsiaceae)

petersenii	LEdu SPlb WPGP

Lupinus ✿ (Fabaceae)

arboreus ♀H4	CBcs CEme CSBt CTri CWCL EHyd ELan EPfP LRHS LShi MCoo MGil MHer MNHC MNrw NBir NLar NRHS SBls SCob SEle SIvy SNig SPer SPlb SPoG SRms SVic WFar
- 'Barton-on-Sea'	CDoC SPad
- blue and white-flowered	CEme WFar
- 'Blue Boy'	ELan SWvt
- blue-flowered	CBcs CBod CWCL LShi NLar NRHS SPer SPlb SPoG SRms SWvt WFar
- 'Chelsea Blue'	EHyd EPfP LRHS NRHS
- 'Lavender Spires'	LCro LOPS
- 'Mauve Queen'	MNrw
- prostrate	WAvo
- 'Snow Queen'	CDoC CWCL LRHS SPer SPoG SWvt
- 'Sulphur Yellow'	SWvt
- white-flowered	CBcs CBod CEme ELan EMil EWTr LEdu LShi MNHC SPlb
- yellow and blue-flowered	EAri NBir SRkn WFar
- yellow-flowered	CBod CDoC CEme ELan GArf SPhx SWvt
arcticus	EBee
(Avalune Series) 'Avalune Blue' **new**	LCro
- 'Avalune Lilac-White' **new**	LCro
- 'Avalune Pink' **new**	LCro
- 'Avalune Red-White' **new**	LCro
- 'Avalune White' **new**	LCro
Band of Nobles Series	SBls
'Beefeater'	CRos CWCL EHyd ELan EPfP EWes GBee LBar LBuc LRHS LSou MHol MPri NLar NRHS SCoo SPoG SWvt
'Bishop's Tipple'	MPri
'Blacksmith'	CWCL EPfP LRHS LSou MPri
'Blossom'PBR	CRos CWCL CWGN EHyd ELan EPfP EWes LBar LRHS LSRN LSou MPri NRHS SOrN SPoG SWvt
caespitosus	see *L. lepidus* var. *utahensis*
(Camelot Series) 'Camelot Blue'	GMcL
- 'Camelot Rose'	GMcL
- 'Camelot White'	ECul GMcL
- 'Camelot Yellow'	ECul GDam GMcL
'Cashmere Cream'	CWCL CWGN NRHS WHlf
'Chameleon'	LRHS NRHS
chamissonis	CCCN EHyd LRHS NRHS SBut SPer
'Chandelier' (Band of Nobles Series)	Widely available
'Desert Sun'PBR	CBcs CRos CWCL EHyd ELan EPfP LRHS LSou MPri NLar NRHS SCoo SPoG SWvt WHlf
'Dwarf Lulu'	see *L.* 'Lulu'
Gallery Series	CSBt EPfP MBros MDon SCob SCoo SPlb WFar WHlf WWke
- 'Gallery Blue'	CBod CRos EAJP ECtt ECul EDAr EHyd ELan EPfP LBuc LCro LOPS LRHS LSRN MACG MBros MHol MPri NLar NRHS SCoo SPoG WFar WHlf
- 'Gallery Pink Bicolor'	CBod
- 'Gallery Pink'	CRos EAJP EDAr EHyd ELan EPfP LCro LRHS MACG MHol MPri NLar NRHS SCoo SPoG SRms WFar WHlf

- 'Gallery Pink White' EPfP LRHS
- 'Gallery Red' CBod CRos EAJP ECtt EDAr EHyd ELan EPfP EWTr GPSL LCro LOPS LRHS MACG MBow MBros MHol MPri NLar NRHS SCob SCoo SPoG WFar WHlf
- 'Gallery Rose' LSRN NRHS SPoG WFar
- 'Gallery White' CBod CRos EAJP ECul EHyd ELan EPfP LCro LRHS MACG MBros MHol MPri NLar NRHS SCoo SPoG WFar WHlf
- 'Gallery Yellow' CBod CRos EAJP ECtt EHyd ELan EPfP EWoo LCro LRHS MACG MBros MHol MPri NLar NRHS SCob SPoG WFar WHlf

'Gladiator'PBR CRos CWCL EHyd ELan EPfP EWes LRHS LSou MHol MPri NLar NRHS SCob SCoo SPoG SWvt
'Judy Harper' ECtt GBee
'Jupiter' LRHS
'King Canute' CWCL CWGN EHyd ELan EPfP GBee LRHS MPri NRHS
lepidus CPbh
§ - var. ***utahensis*** SPlb
§ 'Lulu' SGbt SPoG SWvt
'Magic Lantern' CWCL EHyd EPfP LRHS LSou MHol MPri NRHS SCoo SPoG WHlf
'Manhattan Lights'PBR CBcs CRos CWCL CWGN ELan EPfP EWes LRHS LSou MHol MPri NLar NRHS SCob SCoo SGBe SPoG SWvt WHlf
'Masterpiece'PBR CBcs CDoC CKel CRos CWCL EHyd ELan EPfP EWes GMaP LCro LOPS LRHS LSRN LSou MPri NLar NRHS SCoo SGBe SOrN SPoG SWvt WCAu WHlf WNPC WTyc
Minarette Group EHyd EPfP LRHS MNrw NRHS SRms
'My Castle' (Band of Nobles Series) CBcs CRos CSBt CTri ECtt EHyd ELan EPfP GAbr GMaP GMcL GQue LRHS LSRN MACG MAsh MCot MGos MPri NGBl NLar NRHS SCob SGbt SOrN SPer SPoG SWvt WFar
'Noble Maiden' (Band of Nobles Series) Widely available
nootkatensis GLog LDai
'Pam Ayres' GBee
perennis SPhx
'Persian Princess' LRHS
'Persian Slipper'PBR CBcs CKel CRos CWCL CWGN EBee EHyd ELan EPfP EWes LBuc LRHS LSRN LSou MPri NLar NRHS SCob SGBe SPoG SWvt WCAu WNPC
pilosus **new** SPhx
'Polar Princess' CBcs CKel CWCL CWGN ECtt EHyd ELan EPfP EWes GBee LRHS LSou MHol MPri NRHS SCob SPoG SWvt
'Purple Emperor' LBar
'Purple Swirl' EHyd EPfP GBee LRHS NRHS
'Rachel de Thame' CRos CWCL CWGN EBee EHyd EPfP EWes LRHS LSou MHol MPri NRHS SCoo SPoG SWvt WNPC
'Red Rum'PBR CBcs CWCL CWGN EHyd ELan EPfP LBuc LRHS LSRN MPri NLar NRHS SCob SCoo SPoG SWvt WHlf
§ × ***regalis*** Russell Group CPla CSBt EHeP EPfP MHer SCob SPlb SRms SVic SWvt WFar
'Rote Flamme' ELon EWes
Russell hybrids see *L.* × ***regalis*** Russell Group
'Saffron'PBR EHyd LRHS NRHS
'Salmon Star'PBR CRos CWCL CWGN EHyd LRHS LSou MPri NLar NRHS SCob
'Salmon Sultan' **new** LBar
'Silver Fleece' CCCN WFar
'Tequila Flame'PBR CRos CWCL ELan EPfP LBuc LRHS LSou MPri NLar NRHS SCob SCoo SPoG SWvt WHlf
'Terracotta' CWCL ELan EPfP LRHS MPri NRHS SPoG
texensis CSpe
'The Chatelaine' (Band of Nobles Series) Widely available
'The Governor' (Band of Nobles Series) Widely available
'The Page' (Band of Nobles Series) CAby CBcs CRos EHyd ELan ELon EPfP EWoo GBin GMaP GQue LCro LOPS LRHS LSRN LSun MACG MAsh MBel MNHC NLar NRHS SOrN SPer SPoG SWvt WBor WFar
'Thundercloud' EBee
'Towering Inferno' CRos CWCL EBee EHyd ELan EPfP EWes LBuc LRHS LSou MPri NLar NRHS SCoo SPoG
variicolor LDai
Woodfield hybrids LRHS

Luronium (*Alismataceae*)

natans **new** EWat LLWG LPfP

Luzula (*Juncaceae*)

alpinopilosa EPPr
× ***borreri*** 'Botany Bay' (v) GBin WCot
luzuloides CAby LPla
- 'Schneehäschen' NWsh WSHC
maxima see *L. sylvatica*
nivalis GAbr
nivea Widely available
pilosa 'Igel' CBod CKno ELan EShb LEdu LPla NBid NLar WSpi
purpureosplendens WCot
'Snowflake' CKno
§ ***sylvatica*** EBee EGrI EHeP ELan EPPr EPfP GBin GDam GMcL GQue LPal LRHS MMuc MRav NBro NLar NMir NPol NRHS SCob SCoo SEND SPer WPnP WShi XLum
- 'A. Rutherford' see *L. sylvatica* 'Taggart's Cream'
- from Tatra Mountains, Slovakia EPPr
- 'Aurea' CDoC CKel CKno CRos EBee EBlo ECha EHyd EMor EPPr EPfP EWoo LRHS MMuc NRHS NSti NWsh SEND WCot WFar
- 'Aureomarginata' see *L. sylvatica* 'Marginata'
I - 'Auslese' EPPr
- 'Bromel' EPPr
- 'Hohe Tatra' ♀H7 CSpe EPPr EWes GMaP GQue MBNS NFav NGdn SCob SPer SPoG
§ - 'Marginata' (v) ♀H7 CKno ECha ELan EMor EPPr EWoo GBin GMaP MAvo MBNS MMuc NBid NFav NGdn NLar NSti SArc SCob SEND WChS WCot WFar WHoo WPnP
- 'Mariusz' EPPr
* - f. ***nova*** EPPr
- 'Solar Flair' CKno EBee EMor GBin GJos NLar NRHS
§ - 'Taggart's Cream' (v) CRos EBee EBlo EHyd EPPr LRHS NHol NRHS NWad WFar
- 'Tauernpass' EPPr

	- 'Thierry's Cream' (v)	CAby EBee EPPr MHol MMuc SPoG WCot WFar
	- 'Wintergold'	EPPr
	ulophylla	GBin NFav SPlb

Luzuriaga (*Luzuriagaceae*)

	polyphylla HCM 98202	WCru
	radicans	CCCN CRHN GEdr WCru
	- RH 0602	ESwi WCru

Lychnis (*Caryophyllaceae*)

	alpina	EDAr LRHS NGdn WFar XLum
	- 'Rosea'	NBir
	- 'Snow Flurry'	EPPr GQue
§	× ***arkwrightii***	NRHS
	- 'Orange Zwerg'	SGbt
	- 'Vesuvius'	CBcs CMac EBee ECha NBPC SBls SCob SPer SRms
	chalcedonica ♀H7	Widely available
	- var. ***albiflora***	EMor EPPr EPfP NBro NLar WCAu WHrl
	- 'Carnea'	EBee ELan EMor EPPr EPfP EShb NBPC NGdn SBls SPhx WCAu
	- 'Dusky Salmon'	WHrl
	- 'Flore Pleno' (d)	EShb WCot
	- 'Pinkie'	GJos MMuc NFav NLar
	- 'Rauhreif'	NLar WHer
	- 'Rosea'	EGrl EMor EPfP NBir WHrl
*	- 'Salmonea'	EMor EPPr GPSL NBir SRms
	- salmon-pink-flowered	MBow
	cognata B&SWJ 4234	ESwi GGro WCru
§	***coronaria*** ♀H7	Widely available
	- 'Alba' ♀H7	Widely available
	- 'Angel's Blush'	LShi LSun NBPC NBir NGrd NLar SBut SRkn WMal
	- Atrosanguinea Group	CDoC CRos EBlo EHyd EPfP GMaP GMcL LBar LRHS MBel MRav NGdn NRHS NSti NWad SCob SGbt SPer WTor
	- 'Blood Red'	CSpe LEdu LRHS WBrk
	- 'Cerise'	MArl NBir
	- GARDENERS' WORLD ('Blych') (d)	CCBP CTtf EBee EBlo ECha ECtt EHyd ELan EPfP EWes LBar LRHS LSou MAsh MBNS MBel MHol NBPC NRHS NSti SAko SCoo SGBe SRkn WCot WHil WTyc
	- MESE 356	LRHS SPhx
	- Oculata Group	CSpe CTtf EBee ELan EPfP LEdu SBls SPlb WFar WKif
§	***coronata*** var. ***sieboldii***	NFav SPhx
	dioica	see *Silene dioica*
	flos-cuculi	Widely available
	- var. ***albiflora***	EWoo NLar WHer WSFF
	- JENNY ('Lychjen') (d)	CRos EBee ECtt EGrl EHyd EMor EPfP LBar LCro LEdu LRHS LSRN MAsh MBNS MNrw NRHS NSti SCob SRkn WCAu WCot WHlf
	- 'Little Robin'	EBou EMor SLee
	- 'Nana'	EAJP GJos LLWG NGdn NLar SPeP WGwG
	- PETIT HENRI ('Iflyph')	LBar LEdu LPla LRHS LSou MAsh MPri NSti SGBe SOrN WCot WNPC WTor WTyc XSte
	- 'Petite Jenny' (d)	CRos EBee ECtt EHyd ELan EPfP LRHS LSou MBNS MPri NRHS SCob SGBe SMad SOrN SPoG SRms WCAu WCot WHlf WNPC WTyc
	- 'White Robin'	Widely available
	flos-jovis ♀H6	CCBP ECha EHyd EMor GJos LRHS NBir NRHS SPhx SRms WMal XLum
	- 'Hort's Variety'	EBee EBlo EHyd LRHS NBir NRHS
	- 'Minor'	see *L. flos-jovis* 'Nana'
§	- 'Nana'	GEdr SCoo
	- 'Peggy'	EBee EBou EHyd EMor EPfP GEdr NGdn NLar SBut
	fulgens W&O 7151	GGro
	× ***haageana***	SRms
	- 'Lengai Red'	GMcL
	'Hill Grounds'	CElw EBee ECha ECtt ELon GBin LBar NLar SCoo WCot WGoo WSHC
	lagascae	see *Petrocoptis pyrenaica* subsp. *glaucifolia*
	'Molten Lava'	EDAr EHyd EPfP GEdr LBar LRHS MACG MHol NRHS SRms WHlf
	nutans	SPtp
	sieboldii 'Lipstick' **new**	LBar
I	- 'Plena' (d)	WFar
§	***viscaria***	ECha EMor EPPr GJos GPSL LDai
	- 'Alba'	ECha EGrl XLum
	- ***alpina***	see *L. viscaria*
§	- subsp. ***atropurpurea***	ELan EPPr EWes GJos MMuc MPie SBut SPhx SRms
	- 'Feuer'	EWes MHol NGBl
	- 'Firebird'	EWes SPeP
	- 'Plena' (d)	CBor EMor NBPC NBir SRkn
	- 'Schnee'	GJos NGBl NLar
	- 'Splendens'	CCBP EGrl EMor NGrd SCob WCav WFar XLum
	- 'Splendens Plena' (d) ♀H5	WSHC XLum
	wilfordii 'Karafuto'	GGro
§	***yunnanensis***	GKev NSti SPhx WBrk
	- ***alba***	see *L. yunnanensis*

Lycianthes (*Solanaceae*)

§	***rantonnetii*** ♀H3	CBcs CCCN CHll ELan EShb SEND SPoG SRkn SSha WAvo WJur WKif
*	- var. ***stenophylla*** 'Alba' **new**	EShb
	- 'Variegata' (v)	CHll EShb

Lycium (*Solanaceae*)

	afrum	SVen
	barbarum	CAgr CBcs CCCN CDoC CLau CSBt EPom LCro LEdu MAsh MGil MHoo MHtn NLar SBmr SEND SEdi SPre SVic SWvt WJur WKor WLov
	- 'Big Lifeberry'	CAgr
	- 'Number 1 Lifeberry'	CAgr
	- 'Sweet Lifeberry'	CAgr LEdu
	chinense	MGil NQui

Lycopodium (*Lycopodiaceae*)

	clavatum	GPoy

Lycopsis see *Anchusa*

Lycopus (*Lamiaceae*)

	europaeus	CHab CPud GPoy LPfP MMuc NAts NMir WSFF

Lycoris (*Amaryllidaceae*)

	albiflora	GKev NRog
	aurea	GKev LAma NRog SDeJ
	caldwellii	NRog
	chinensis	NRog
	haywardii	NRog
	houdyshelii	NRog
	longituba	NRog
	radiata	CCCN GKev LAma SDeJ
	sanguinea	NRog
	sprengeri	NRog
	straminea	NRog

Lygeum (*Poaceae*)

	spartum	XSen

Lygos see *Retama*

Lyonothamnus (*Rosaceae*)

floribundus subsp. ***aspleniifolius*** CCCN EBee SArc WPGP

Lysichiton (*Araceae*)

camtschatcensis ♀H7 CAby CBen CPud CWat ECha GBin LCro LLWG LOPS LPfP LRHS NPer SWvt WPnP WShi XLum
× ***hortensis*** ECha EGrI SPer

Lysiloma (*Fabaceae*)

watsonii SPlb

Lysimachia (*Primulaceae*)

albescens XLum
§ ***atropurpurea*** CBod CSpe EAJP EBee EHyd ELan GKev LRHS LShi NLar SCoo SPer
- 'Beaujolais' CChe CKel CRos GElm GGro LBar LCro LOPS LRHS LShi MGos NGBl NRHS SCoo SPeP SPoG WTor
- 'Geronimo' CSpe
barystachys ♀H6 MArl MBel MRav SHar WCot WFar WHoo XLum
- PAB 8755 LEdu
- 'Huntingbrook' LEdu MAvo WPGP
CANDELA ('Innlyscand') Widely available
candida WCot
christinae 'Sunburst' **new** LLWG
- 'Zixin' LEdu WPGP
ciliata CMac ECha GMaP MNrw NBir NFav NGdn NLar
§ - 'Firecracker' ♀H6 Widely available
- 'Purpurea' see *L. ciliata* 'Firecracker'
clethroides ♀H6 Widely available
- 'Geisha' (v) ECha WCot
- 'Lady Jane' CEme CPla CRos GJos MAvo MNrw SBls SRms
- 'Leigong Storm' WPGP
§ ***congestiflora*** NPer
- 'Midnight Sun' PBR CCCN ECtt MDon
- 'Outback Sunset' PBR (v) ECtt
- 'Persian Chocolate' LBar NLar WFar WMal
ephemerum ♀H6 Widely available
fordiana Og 454 SPtp WPGP
fortunei GGro MACG WFar XLum
japonica var. ***minutissima*** GRum ITim SLee SRot
lichiangensis EBlo GKev NBir
lyssii see *L. congestiflora*
minoricensis WSpi XLum
nemorum NAts
- 'Lola Playle' PBR WCot
nummularia CPud CWat ECha EPfP GPoy LLWG LPfP MBow NAts NBir SSha WBrk
- 'Aurea' ♀H5 Widely available
paridiformis from Roy Lancaster **new** ESwi
- var. ***paridiformis*** LEdu
- - NJM 11.067 WPGP
- var. ***stenophylla*** CDTJ CExl GBin GEdr SPtp WMal WPGP
punctata misapplied see *L. verticillaris*
punctata L. CBod CSBt EBou ECha EPfP LBar LSto MACG MHer MRav NBro NMir NPer SBls SCob SPer SRms WBrk WCAu WCav WFar WMAq
§ - 'Alexander' (v) Widely available
- 'Gaulthier Brousse' EBee MHCG WCot
- GOLDEN ALEXANDER ('Walgoldalex' PBR) (v) CChe CKel CTtf MBNS NHol NLar
- 'Golden Glory' (v) WCot
- 'Hometown Hero' EBee LBar NLar
- 'Ivy Maclean' (v) SWvt
- 'Variegata' see *L. punctata* 'Alexander'
- ***verticillata*** see *L. verticillaris*
'Purpurea' see *L. atropurpurea*
serpyllifolia GJos
SNOW CANDLES ('L9902') ELon EWes MNrw SIvy WFar
taliensis GGro
thyrsiflora EBee LPfP NPer WCot WMAq
§ ***verticillaris*** CTri WCot
vulgaris CBod CHab CPud EWat LLWG LPfP
- subsp. ***davurica*** WCot
- - B&SWJ 8632 WCru

Lysionotus (*Gesneriaceae*)

gamosepalus MVil
- B&SWJ 7241 WCru
kwangsiensis MVil
- HWJ 625 WCru
pauciflorus IArd MVil WAbe
- B&SWJ 303 WCru
- B&SWJ 335 WCru
- HWJ 643 from Vietnam WCru
- HWJ 811 from Vietnam WCru
- dwarf B&SWJ 189 WCru
- 'Lady Lavender' MVil WFar
serratus MVil
- HWJK 2426 WCru

Lythrum (*Lythraceae*)

anceps NLar
'Rose Dream' NWad
salicaria Widely available
- 'Augenweide' XLum
- 'Blush' ♀H7 Widely available
§ - 'Feuerkerze' ♀H7 CAby CBWd CRos EBee ECtt ELan ELon EPfP EShb GQue LBar LRHS MArl MBel MRav MSpe NBir NHol NRHS NSti SCob SGbt SMrm SOrN SPer WFar WWtn
- FIRECANDLE see *L. salicaria* 'Feuerkerze'
- 'JS Pink Tails' IPot
- 'Lady Sackville' EBee ECtt ELon GMaP IPot LSou MCot NDov NLar SMrm WSHC
- 'Little Robert' ECtt WFar
- 'Morden Pink' CTri EBee EHyd ELan ELon EMor MMuc NLar NRHS SCob SEND WFar XLum
- 'Prichard's Variety' ELon
- 'Red Beauty' LSun
- 'Robert' Widely available
- 'Robin' CBod CRos EBee ECtt EHyd GElm IPot LRHS MAsh MHol MPri NLar NRHS SGbt SWvt WBor
- 'Rose' NBir SWvt
- 'Stichflamme' ELon
- 'Swirl' CBWd ECha ECtt EHyd ELan ELon EMor EPfP ILea LCro LEdu LLWG LRHS MACG NDov NLar NRHS NSti SHar WHoo
- 'The Beacon' CPla CTtf EBee ELon GQue NLar SRms
- 'Zigeunerblut' ECtt ELon GQue MRav NLar SMHy WCAu XLum
virgatum SMHy SMrm SPhx WCFE
- 'Dropmore Purple' Widely available
- 'Helene' NDov
- pale-flowered NDov SMHy
- 'Rose Queen' ECtt EMor IPot MRav SPeP

- 'Rosy Gem'	EBee EMor GJos GMaP GQue LShi MACG NBPC NBro NRHS SCob SDix SRms SWvt WFar
- 'The Rocket'	CTri EHyd EMor EPfP LBar LRHS MBel MPie MRav NBro NDov NRHS SMrm SPer SWvt WFar WWtn

Lytocaryum (*Arecaceae*)

§ ***weddellianum*** ♀H1b	LPal

M

Maackia (*Fabaceae*)

amurensis	CBcs CMCN EPfP GBin LMaj LPar MVil
hupehensis	MBlu NLar WJur

Macadamia (*Proteaceae*)

integrifolia (F)	SVic
tetraphylla	CAco

mace, English see *Achillea ageratum*

Macfadyena see *Dolichandra*

unguis-cati	see *Dolichandra unguis-cati*

Machaeranthera (*Asteraceae*)

sp.	EBee
coloradoensis	WHil

Machaerina (*Cyperaceae*)

rubiginosa	LLWG

Machilus see *Persea*

Mackaya (*Acanthaceae*)

§ ***bella*** ♀H1b	EShb

Macleaya (*Papaveraceae*)

cordata misapplied	see *M.* × *kewensis*
§ ***cordata*** (Willd.) R. Br. ♀H6	CKel CRos CWal EBee EWoo LRHS LSun NBir NRHS SPer SPlb SRms WCAu XLum
- NJM 11.002	WPGP
§ × ***kewensis***	CBod EHeP EPfP SCob SMrm SPoG WFar
- 'Flamingo' ♀H6	EBee ECha MBNS NLar SPer SWvt WCot
§ ***microcarpa***	LSun SMrm
- 'Kelway's Coral Plume' ♀H6	Widely available
- 'Spetchley Ruby'	EBee ECha GBin LRHS MRav NLar SPhx WCot XLum

Maclura (*Moraceae*)

pomifera	CBcs CMCN EWTr IDee MBlu MVil SBrt SPlb WJur XSen
- 'Cannonball'	CDoC LRHS
- 'Naughty Boy'	NLar
- 'Pretty Woman'	NLar
tricuspidata	WJur
- B&SWJ 12755	WCru
- 'Parthenos' (F)	CAgr
- seedless (F)	CAgr

Macrodiervilla see *Weigela*

Macropiper (*Piperaceae*)

§ ***excelsum***	GPoy

Macrothelypteris (*Thelypteridaceae*)

torresiana	WPGP

Macrozamia (*Zamiaceae*)

communis	CBrP LPal NPlm
lucida	CBrP
miquelii	NPlm
moorei	CBrP NPlm

Maddenia (*Rosaceae*)

hypoleuca	IDee MBlu NLar

Maesa (*Primulaceae*)

japonica CWJ 12371	WCru

Magnolia ✿ (*Magnoliaceae*)

acuminata	CAco CMCN LMaj
- 'Blue Opal'	CBcs LAlb LPar LRHS MAsh NCth NLar SGsty
* - 'Kinju'	CJun
- 'Koban Dori'	CJun
- 'Patriot'	CMCN
- 'Patriot' × (× ***brooklynensis*** 'Yellow Bird')	MAsh
- 'Seiju'	CJun NLar
- var. ***subcordata*** 'Miss Honeybee'	CJun
- - 'Mister Yellowjacket'	CJun
'Advance'	CBcs CDoC
'Albatross'	CBcs CJun WPGP
'Alex'	CJun LMil
'Alixeed'	CJun
'Ambrosia'	CJun
'Amethyst Flame'	XSte
'Angelica'	CJun
'Anilou'	CJun
'Anna'	CJun
'Anticipation'	CBcs CEnd CJun LRHS WPGP
'Antje Zandee'	CBcs
'Aphrodite'	CAco NLar
'Apollo'	CBcs CDoC CJun LSRN WPGP XSte
'Archangel'	CJun
ashei	see *M. macrophylla* subsp. *ashei*
'Asian Artistry'	CDoC CJun LRHS
'Athene' ♀H5	CBcs CDoC CEnd CJun LMil SAko WPGP
'Atlas'	CBcs CDoC CEnd CJun WPGP
'Aurora'	CJun XSte
'Avocet'	LRHS
'Banana Split'	CDoC LMil LRHS MAsh
'Betty'	CAco CBcs CDoC CKel CMac EBee EDir ELon LRHS LSRN MBlu MGos MMuc NLar NTrD SGsty SLim SSta SWeb
'Big Dude'	CEnd CJun EPfP IDee LRHS MGos MTrO NLar NOra SLim WMat
'Binette'	CJun
biondii	MBlu
'Black Swan'	CBcs WPGP
BLACK TULIP ('Jurmag1'[PBR])	CAco CBcs CDoC CMac ELan EPfP GGGa IDee LCro LMil LOPS LPar LRHS LSRN MAsh MGos MPri MTrO NLar NOra NOrn SCoo SEWo SEdd SPoG WLea WMat WPGP WTSh XSte
BLACKBERRY ROSE ('Brombeer')	CBcs
'Blushing Belle'	CAco CJun
'Brenda'	CJun
'Brixton Belle'	CAco CBcs NCth WPGP XSte

× ***brooklynensis*** 'Amber'	CJun
- 'Black Beauty'	CAco CBcs CJun LRHS SEdd XSte
- 'Evamaria'	CAco XSte
- 'Golden Joy'	CJun
- 'Hattie Carthan'	CJun NLar
- 'Woodsman'	CAco CBcs EHed NLar NOra WMat
- 'Yellow Bird'	CAco CBcs CCVT CDoC CEnd CJun CMCN CMac EBar EPfP LMil LPar LSRN MAsh MBlu MGos MPri MThu MTrO NLar NOra NOrn SCob SEdd SLim SPoG SWeb WMat XSte
BURGUNDY STAR ('Jurmag4')	CBcs LCro MGos SWeb XSte
'Butterbowl'	CJun
'Butterflies'	CAco CBcs CCCN CDoC CJun CKel CWnw EHyd ELan EPfP LPar LRHS LSRN MBlu MGos NLar NOra NRHS SCob SGsty SLim SRms SSta WFar WMat WSpi
'Caerhays Belle' ♀^{H5}	CBcs CDoC CJun LMil LRHS NLar SAko SPoG WPGP XSte
'Caerhays Surprise' ♀^{H5}	CBcs CJun WPGP
campbellii	CMCN EPfP
- Alba Group	WPGP
- - 'Chyverton'	WPGP
- - 'Strybing White'	WPGP
- 'Ambrose Congreve'	WPGP
- 'Betty Jessel'	CBcs CJun IDee WPGP
- 'Darjeeling' ♀^{H4}	CBcs CJun LRHS WPGP XSte
- 'Lionel de Rothschild'	WPGP
- subsp. ***mollicomata***	LRHS
- - 'Lanarth'	CBcs WPGP
- - 'Peter Borlase'	WPGP
- - 'Werrington'	CBcs IDee
- 'Queen Caroline'	SBdl WPGP
- (Raffillii Group) 'Charles Raffill'	CDoC EPfP LRHS SPoG XSte
- - 'Kew's Surprise'	WPGP
- 'Sidbury'	CBcs
campbellii* × *sargentiana var. ***robusta***	LRHS
campbellii* × *sprengeri	WPGP
'Candy Cane'	CJun
'Carlos'	CJun NLar
cathcartii	WPGP
- B&SWJ 11802	WCru
- HWJ 874	WCru
'Cathryn' **new**	WPGP
caveana	LEdu
- NJM 13.037	WPGP
- NJM 13.044	EBee WPGP
'Cecil Nice'	CJun
CHAMELEON	see *M.* 'Chang Hua'
§ 'Chang Hua'	CJun NLar
changhungtana* × *insignis	WPGP
'Charles Coates'	CJun NLar WPGP
'Charming Lady'	CJun
chevalieri B&SWJ 11802	WCru
- DJHV 06037	WCru
- HWJ 621	WCru
CHINA TOWN ('Jing Ning')	CAco CJun
'Columnar Pink'	CAco LMil LRHS NLar
compressa	XSte
'Coral Lake'	CJun LMil LRHS
'Cornish Chough'	WPGP
crassifolia hort.	see *M. fansipanensis*
'Crescendo'	CJun
'Crystal Chalice'	CJun
'Cup Cake'	CJun
'Curlew'	WPGP
cylindrica misapplied	see *M.* 'Pegasus'
cylindrica ambig.	CBcs SPtp
cylindrica E.H.Wilson	WPGP
- 'Bjuv'	CJun
'Daphne' ♀^{H6}	CAco CBcs CDoC CJun ELan EPfP LMil LPar LRHS LSRN MAsh MGos MTrO NCth NLar SEWo SLim SPoG WMat WPGP WTSh XSte
'Darrell Dean'	CJun
'David Clulow' ♀^{H5}	CBcs CJun SSta WPGP XSte
dawsoniana	CAco CBcs CMCN IDee WSpi
- 'Barbara Cook'	CJun
- 'Chyverton Red'	CBcs WPGP
- 'Ruby Rose'	CJun
- 'Valley Splendour'	CJun
'Daybreak' ♀^{H6}	CAco CBcs CJun ELan EPfP LMil LPar LRHS MBlu MGos MRav MTrO NLar NOra SSta WMat WPGP XSte
'Deborah'	CJun
decidua	CBcs
delavayi	CAco CBcs CBrP CJun CMCN EPfP IDee LRHS SArc SEND WPGP XSte
'Delia Williams'	WPGP
§ ***denudata*** ♀^{H6}	CAco CBcs CMCN ELan EPfP LMaj LMil MBlu SSta
- 'Double Diamond'	CAco CJun
- FESTIROSE ('Minfor')	EHed EWes LRHS
- 'Forrest's Pink'	CBcs
- FRAGRANT CLOUD ('Dan Xin')	CAco CJun
- 'Gere'	CBcs CJun
- 'Ghost Ship'	CJun
- YELLOW RIVER ('Fei Huang')	CAco CDoC CEnd CJun LMaj LPar NLar NOra SCob SPoG WLea WMat
doltsopa	CBcs CCCN CExl EPfP SSta WPGP
- B&SWJ 13996	WCru
- NJM 12.028	WPGP
- NJM 12.047	WPGP
'Early Red'	LRHS
'Early Rose'	CJun
'Elegance'	CJun
'Elisa Odenwald'	CAco LMil LRHS XSte
'Elizabeth' ♀^{H6}	CBcs CDoC CJun CMCN EPfP LMil LRHS LSRN MAsh MBlu MGos MTrO NLar NOra NOrn NRHS SGsty SPer SPoG SRms SWvt WMat
'Emma Cook'	CJun
§ ***ernestii***	WPGP
'Eskimo'	CJun EPfP LRHS MTrO NOra WMat
'F.J. Williams'	CBcs WPGP
'Fairy'	MThu
FAIRY LIME **new**	XSte
FAIRY MAGNOLIA BLUSH ('Micjur01'^{PBR})	CAco CBcs CDoC CWnw EGrI LCro LOPS LRHS MGos XSte
FAIRY MAGNOLIA CREAM ('Micjur02'^{PBR})	CAco CBcs CCCN LCro LOPS LRHS NLar WHlf XSte
FAIRY MAGNOLIA WHITE ('Micjur05'^{PBR})	CBcs CCCN EDir LCro LOPS NLar SPoG WHlf XSte
§ ***fansipanensis*** FMWJ 13054	WCru
- FMWJ 13163	WCru
'Felicity'	CJun
FELIX JURY ('Jurmag2'^{PBR})	CAco CBcs ELan EPfP LCro LRHS MTrO NOra SEWo WMat XSte
figo	CBcs CCCN CExl CKel EBee EHed EHyd ELan EMil EPfP MGil NRHS SSta WPGP
'Fireglow'	CJun
'Flamingo'	CJun NLar
floribunda FMWJ 13384 from Tonkin, Vietnam	WCru
- NJM 09.179	WPGP
- WWJ 11874	WCru
- WWJ 11982 from Tonkin, Vietnam	WCru

– WWJ 11996	WCru
– WWJ 12003	WCru
– WWJ 12011	WCru
– 'Fansipan Furry'	WCru
– 'Furry Uok'	WPGP
× ***foggii*** 'Allspice'	CBcs LRHS XSte
– 'Jack Fogg'	CBcs
fordiana	CExl
'Foster's Late White'	WPGP
§ ***foveolata*** B&SWJ 11749	WCru
– DJHV 06105	WCru
– WWJ 11900	WCru
– WWJ 11929	WCru
– WWJ 11955	WCru
'Frank Gladney'	CJun
fraseri	CMCN
'Galaxy' ♀H6	CAco CBcs CBrac CDoC CEnd CJun CMac EBar ELon EPfP IPap LMaj LMil LPar MAsh MGos MMuc MTrO NLar NOrn SLim SPer SSta SavN WMat
'Genie'PBR	CAco CBcs CCVT CDoC CKel CWnw EHed ELan EMil LMaj LMil LPar LRHS LSRN MTrO NLar NOra NRHS SCob SGsty SWeb WMat WPGP XSte
'George Henry Kern' ♀H6	CAco CBrac CLnd EDir EPfP LMil LPar MGos MRav NBwr NLar SGsty WHlf XSte
'Ghislaine'	WPGP
'Gladys Carlson'	CJun
globosa	CExl LEdu NRHS WPGP
'Gold Crown'	CJun
'Gold Star' ♀H6	CAco CJun EHyd LMil LRHS MGos NLar NOra NRHS SPoG SSta WGob WMat WPGP XSte
'Golden Endeavour'	CJun
'Golden Gala'	CJun
'Golden Gift'	CJun LMil LRHS MAsh WPGP
'Golden Pond'	CJun LMil LRHS MAsh
'Golden Rain'	CJun
'Golden Sun'	CJun
'Goldfinch'	CBcs CJun
I × ***gotoburgensis*** Chollipo clone	WPGP
grandiflora	CAco CMCN CSBt CTsd EBee EDir EPfP ESwi LCro LEdu LIns LOPS LPar LSRN MGos MMuc MRav NBwr NLar NOrn SArc SEND SEWo SPlb SWeb WHlf WJur WTSh XSte
– ALTA ('Tmgh'PBR)	LMaj LRHS MGos MTrO NLar XSte
– 'Blanchard'	CJun LRHS NLar XSte
– 'Bracken's Brown Beauty'	LMil NLar NRHS
– 'Charles Dickens'	SVen
– 'Edith Bogue'	LRHS SSta
– 'Exmouth'	CBcs CDoC CEme CEnd CKel CLnd CMCN CMac CSBt CTri CWnw EHyd ELan EPfP LMil LSRN MAsh MBlu NLar NRHS SCob SPer SPoG SRms SSta SWvt
– 'Ferruginea'	CAco CBcs CBod CJun ELan LPar NLar SEdd SGsty WLov
– 'Foothills'	CMCN
– 'François Treyve'	CAco CDoC CKel CWnw EPfP EWTr LSRN NLar XSte
– 'Galissonnière'	CAco CBcs CCVT CDoC EHyd EPfP ERom LMaj LPal NPlm SCob SGol SGsty SWvt
I – 'Galissonnière Nana'	LPal
– 'Goliath'	ELan EPfP LMaj LPar SEWo SGsty SSta
– 'Harold Poole'	CJun
– 'Kay Parris' ♀H5	CBcs CJun EHed EHyd ELan EPfP LMil LRHS MAsh MGos NRHS SPoG XSte
– 'Little Gem'	CAco CBcs CBod CCCN CDoC CJun EBee EDir ELan ELon EPfP IDee LCro LMaj LOPS LPar LRHS LSRN NLar SPoG SSta WFar WHtc WLov XSte
– 'Mainstreet'	CJun LRHS XSte
– 'Nannetensis' (d)	EHed ELan MHtn NLar
– 'November Fox'	LRHS
– 'Pistoiese'	SGsty
– 'Praecox'	LMaj
– 'Purpan'	NLar
– 'Russet'	CJun
– 'Saint Mary'	CJun
– 'Samuel Sommer'	CJun
– 'Symmes Select'	CJun
– 'Treyvei'	CAco
– 'Victoria' ♀H5	CJun CTri ELan ELon EPfP LMil LSRN MAsh MBlu NLar SSta XSte
'Green Bee'	CJun
'Green Diamond'	CAco SGsty
'Hawk'	WPGP
'Heaven Scent' ♀H5	Widely available
'Helen Fogg'	CJun
heptapeta	see *M. denudata*
'Honey Belle'	CJun
'Honey Flower'	CJun
'Honey Liz'	LRHS MAsh
HONEY TULIP ('Jurmag5')	CBcs LCro LRHS MTrO NLar SWeb WMat XSte
§ 'Hong Yun'	CJun WHlf
'Hot Flash'	CJun
'Hot Lips'	CJun
hypoleuca	see *M. obovata* Thunb.
'Ian's Red'	CBcs CEnd CJun LMil LRHS MAsh WMat WPGP
§ ***insignis***	CBcs CExl EBee LEdu LRHS WPGP
– B&SWJ 11810	WCru
– NJM 12.040	WPGP
– WWJ 11854	WCru
insignis* × *yuyuanensis	WPGP
'Iolanthe'	CBcs CEnd CMCN EPfP LMil LRHS MAsh MGos WMat WPGP XSte
'Iufer'	CJun
'J.C. Williams'	CBcs CJun SSta WPGP
'Jane'	CAco CJun CMac EPfP LMil MAsh MGos NOrn
'Jersey Belle'	CJun
'Joe McDaniel'	CAco CBcs CJun IArd NLar
'John Bond'	LRHS
'John Congreve'	CJun WPGP
'Joli Pompom'	CBcs CJun ELan EPfP LMil LRHS MTrO NLar NOra SSta WMat
'Judy Zuk'	CBcs CJun LRHS MAsh
× ***kewensis*** 'Wada's Memory'	see *M. salicifolia* 'Wada's Memory'
'Kim Kunso'	SSta
kobus	CBcs CCCN CCVT CLnd CMCN CTsd EPfP EWTr GKin IPap LMaj LPar MBlu NLar NWea SEWo SGsty SPer WMou
– B&SWJ 12751	WCru WHlf WHtc
– 'Esveld Select'	CJun EHed
– 'Janaki Ammal'	CJun
– 'Maráczy'PBR	CAco LRHS
§ – 'Norman Gould'	CJun CMCN LMil
– 'Octopus'	CJun
– pink-flowered	CBcs CJun
– 'White Elegance'	CJun
– 'Wisley Star'	CJun SSta
kwangtungensis	WPGP

	laevifolia	CBcs CExl CJun CMCN LPar MGil SEdd WPGP XSte
	- arborescent	WPGP
	- 'Dali Velvet'	CExl
	- 'Gail's Favourite'	CAco EHyd EPfP LMil LRHS MAsh NRHS
	- 'Kh-Achteraan'	XSte
	- 'Mini Mouse'	EHyd EPfP LMil LRHS MAsh NRHS
	- 'Summer Snowflake'	CBcs NLar
	'Laura Saylor'	CJun
	'Leda'	CJun LMil SSta WPGP
	'Legacy'	WPGP
	'Lemon Star'	LRHS
	'Lennarth Jonsson'	CJun
	liliiflora 'Darkest Purple'	CJun
§	- 'Nigra' ♀H6	Widely available
	- 'Raven'	LMil MAsh WPGP
*	'Limelight'	CAco CJun NLar NOra NWea WMat WPGP
	'Livingstone'	CBcs
	× ***loebneri*** 'Ballerina'	CAco
	- 'Donna' ♀H6	CDoC CJun LMil LRHS SSta
	- 'Encore'	CJun XSte
	- 'Green Mist'	CJun NRHS
	- 'Leonard Messel' ♀H6	Widely available
	- 'Lesley Jane'	CJun
	- 'Mag's Pirouette' ♀H6	CBcs CJun EMil EPfP LMil LRHS NLar SPoG SSta XSte
	- 'Merrill' ♀H6	CAco CBcs CBod CDoC CJun CKel CLnd CMCN CMac CWnw EDir ELan EPfP LMaj LMil LPar LRHS MAsh MGos MMuc MRav NLar NOrn NRHS SPer SSta
	- 'Neil McEacharn'	CJun
	- 'Pink Cloud'	CJun
	- 'Powder Puff'	CJun
	- 'Raspberry Fun'	CAco CJun NLar
	- 'Raspberry Fun' seedling **new**	CAco
	- 'Snowdrift'	CAco CJun CKel EMil EPfP SLim
	- 'Spring Snow'	CJun
	- 'Star Bright'	CJun
	- 'Swansong'	WPGP
	- 'White Stardust'	CJun
	- 'Wildcat' ♀H6	CAco CBcs CJun EHed LMil NLar SLim SSta XSte
	- 'Willow Wood'	CJun
	'Lois' ♀H6	CAco CBcs CJun EGrl EPfP GGGa LMil LRHS MAsh NLar NRHS SSta WPGP
	lotungensis	WPGP
	'Lotus'	CJun WPGP
	'Lucy Carlson'	CJun
	'Luscious'	CJun
	macrophylla	CAco CBcs CBrP CMCN CMac EBee EPfP LRHS MBlu MPkF NLar WPGP XSte
§	- subsp. ***ashei***	CAco CJun CMCN WPGP
	- subsp. ***ashei*** × ***macrophylla*** subsp. ***dealbata***	WPGP
	- subsp. ***ashei*** × ***sieboldii***	CJun
	- subsp. ***ashei*** × ***virginiana***	CJun WPGP
	macrophylla × ***sieboldii***	CJun
	'Malin'	CJun
	'Manchu Fan'	CBcs CDoC CJun EPfP GBin IArd LMil LRHS LSRN MTrO SLim WMat WPGP
§	'March til Frost'	CAco CBcs EBee ELan LMil LRHS NLar WPGP
	'Margaret Helen'	CBcs CJun WPGP

	'Marillyn'	LRHS
	'Marj Gossler'	CJun
	'Marjorie Congreve'	WPGP
	'Mary Nell'	CJun
	'Maryland'	CJun GGGa NLar
	maudiae	CBcs CExl
	'Maxine Merrill'	CAco CBcs CJun
	'May to Frost'	see *M.* 'March til Frost'
	'Mighty Mouse' **new**	NLar
	'Milky Way' ♀H5	CJun EPfP LRHS MGos WPGP
	'Mister Yellowjacket'	CJun
	'Moondance'	CJun
	'Nimbus'	CJun WPGP
	nitida	CExl
	obovata Diels	see *M. officinalis*
§	***obovata*** Thunb.	CBcs CMCN EPfP IDee WPGP
	- B&SWJ 10821	WCru
	- B&SWJ 12626	WCru
	- pink-flowered	WPGP
	obovata × ***sargentiana*** var. ***robusta***	WPGP
§	***officinalis***	NLar
	- var. ***biloba***	CBcs CMCN MBlu NLar WPGP
	'Old Port'	NLar
	'Olivia'	CBcs CJun WPGP
	'Orchid'	CAco
	'Paul Cook'	CDoC CEnd LRHS
	'Peaches 'n' Cream'	CBcs CJun
	'Peachy'	CBcs CJun LMil LPar LRHS WMat
§	'Pegasus' ♀H6	CBcs CEnd CJun LMil LRHS SSta
	'Peppermint Stick'	NLar WMat
	'Peter Smithers'	CJun
	'Phelan Bright'	CJun LMil WPGP
	'Phillip Tregunna'	LMil WPGP
	'Phil's Masterpiece'	CJun
	'Pickard's Sundew'	see *M.* × *soulangeana* 'Sundew'
	'Piet van Veen'	CJun
	'Pink Beauty'	CAco SEdd
	'Pink Delight'	CJun
	'Pink Goblet'	CAco EWes
	'Pink Surprise'	CJun
	'Pinkie'	CAco CJun EDir XSte
	'Porcelain Dove'	CBcs CJun LMil MGos WPGP
	'Premier Cru'	CJun LMil LRHS
	'Princess Margaret'	CBcs CDoC CJun LMil LRHS NOra WMat
	'Pristine'	EPfP LMil LRHS
	× ***proctoriana***	LMil MBlu WPGP
	- 'Robert's Dream'	CJun SSta
	- 'Slavin's No 44'	CJun
	- 'Slavin's Snowy'	CTsd
	'Purple Breeze'	CJun LRHS MBlu NLar SLim
	'Purple Globe'	CBcs CEnd CJun
	'Purple Platter'	CBcs
	'Purple Sensation'	CBcs CJun SLim WPGP
	'Purple Star'	WPGP
	'Raspberry Ice'	CMac EPfP SRms
	'Raspberry Swirl'	SSta
	'Rebecca's Perfume'	CBcs CJun ELan LRHS MGos MTrO NLar WMat WSpi
	'Red as Red'	CAco CBcs CDoC CJun NLar
	'Red Baron'	CJun
	'Red Lion'	CBcs CJun LRHS NLar
	'Red Lucky'	see *M.* 'Hong Yun'
	'Ricki'	CEme CJun CKel CMac MBlu
	'Rose Marie'	NLar
	'Roseanne'	CJun
	rostrata	CExl NLar WPGP
	'Royal Crown'	EPfP IArd XSte
	'Royal Splendor' **new**	CAco CBcs NLar
	'Ruby'	CBcs CJun
	'Ruth'	CBcs NLar
	salicifolia	CBcs CMCN WJur WSpi

	- 'Aia'	WPGP
	- var. ***concolor***	CJun
	- 'Jermyns'	CJun
	- 'Louisa Fete'	CJun LMaj
	- 'Miss Jack'	CMCN
*	- 'Rosea'	CJun
	- 'Sandy Carlson' **new**	CJun
	- upright	WPGP
	- 'Van Veen'	CJun WPGP
§	- 'Wada's Memory' 𝕐H6	CExl CJun CMCN ELan EPfP LMaj LMil LRHS MAsh MBlu SSta WFar WMat
	- 'Windsor Beauty'	CJun SSta
	'Sangreal'	NLar
	sapaensis	IKel
	- FMWJ 13315	WCru
	- FMWJ 13330	WCru
	- HWJ 533	WCru
	- NJM 09.168	WPGP
	'Sara Koe'	CJun MTrO WMat
	sargentiana	SSta
	- var. ***robusta alba***	SavN
	- - 'Blood Moon'	CJun WPGP
	- - 'Multipetal'	WPGP
	'Satisfaction'	CDoC ELon LPar NLar SEdd WHlf WTSh
	'Sayonara' 𝕐H6	CBcs CDoC CJun EPfP LMil LRHS MTrO NOra WMat XSte
	'Scented Gem'	SSta
	'Schmetterling'	see *M.* × *soulangeana* 'Pickard's Schmetterling'
	'Sentinel'	CAco LMaj LRHS WMat
	'Serene'	CBcs CEnd CJun EPfP IArd IDee LMil NLar
	Shirazz ('Vulden')	CAco CBcs CDoC EBee EPfP IArd LMil LRHS MTrO NCth NLar NOra SLim SPoG WMat WPGP
	sieboldii	Widely available
	- B&SWJ 4127	WCru
	- 'Colossus' 𝕐H6	CJun LMil MBlu WPGP XSte
	- 'Genesis'	CJun NLar
	- 'Genesis' × ***tripetala***	CJun
	- 'Genesis' × ***virginiana***	CJun
	- 'Michiko Renge' (d)	CJun
	- 'Min Pyong-gal'	CJun
	- 'Pride of Norway'	CAco CJun
	- subsp. ***sieboldii*** B&SWJ 12553 from Korea	WCru
	- subsp. ***sinensis***	CAco CBcs CJun CMCN EPfP WPGP
I	- - 'Grandiflora'	CJun WPGP
	- 'White Flounces' (d)	CJun NLar
	'Sir Harold Hillier'	CBcs CJun WPGP
	'Solar Flair'	CAco CBcs CJun LPar NLar
	× ***soulangeana***	Widely available
	- 'Alba'	see *M.* × *soulangeana* 'Alba Superba'
§	- 'Alba Superba'	CAco CBcs CDoC CKel CTsd EPfP LCro LMaj LMil LOPS LPar MBlu MMuc MRav NLar NOra SPer SPoG SavN WFar WSpi
	- 'Alexandrina'	CBcs CLnd EPfP MBlu
	- 'André Leroy'	CKel CWnw LRHS
	- 'Beugnon'	IArd LRHS
	- 'Big Pink'	CAco
	- 'Brozzonii' 𝕐H6	CDoC CMac EPfP LMil SSta
	- 'Cleopatra' PBR	CAco CBcs LRHS NLar XSte
	- 'Just Jean'	CJun
	- 'Lennei'	CAco CBcs CBrac CKel CMCN CMac CSBt EHyd EPfP IArd IPap LPar MGos MRav NOrn SCob SPer SPoG SRms WFar WLov
	- 'Lennei Alba'	CBTr CMCN ELan MBlu NLar NOra WFar WMat WSpi XSte

	- 'Lombardy Rose'	CAco
	- 'Nigra'	see *M. liliiflora* 'Nigra'
§	- 'Pickard's Schmetterling' 𝕐H6	EPfP LMil MAsh
	- 'Pickard's Snow Queen'	CJun
	- 'Pickard's Sundew'	see *M.* × *soulangeana* 'Sundew'
	- 'Picture'	CBcs NOrn XSte
	- 'Purple Rocket'	LRHS
	- 'Rubra' misapplied	see *M.* × *soulangeana* 'Rustica Rubra'
§	- 'Rustica Rubra'	CAco CBcs CBod CEme CKel CMCN CTri CWnw LMil LPar LRHS LSRN MACG MAsh NLar NRHS SRms SavN WLov
	- 'San José'	CJun LMil MAsh WFar
	- 'Speciosa'	SSta SavN
§	- 'Sundew'	EPfP GMcL LMaj NLar
	- 'Superba'	CAco EBee LPar LRHS
	- 'Sweet Simplicity'	CBcs
	- 'Verbanica'	EPfP LMil MAsh
	'Spectrum' 𝕐H6	CAco CDoC CJun CKel CWnw EBar ELan EPfP EWes IArd IDee LMil LPar LRHS MBlu MGos MTrO NOra SSta WMat
	sprengeri	CAco
	- from Guizhou, China	WPGP
	- var. ***diva***	CBcs CExl LMil WPGP
	- - 'Burncoose' 𝕐H6	CBcs
	- - 'Copeland Court' 𝕐H6	CJun LMil LRHS MTrO NOra WMat WPGP
	- - 'Dark Diva'	CJun
	- - 'Diva'	CDoC LRHS WPGP
	- - 'Eric Savill' 𝕐H6	CJun WPGP
	- - 'Lanhydrock'	CBcs CDoC CJun LRHS WPGP
	- - 'Marwood Spring'	CBcs CJun LMil LRHS WPGP
	- - 'Westonbirt'	WPGP
	'Spring Rite'	CJun
	'Star Wars' 𝕐H5	CAco CBcs CCVT CDoC CEnd CExl CJun CMCN CMac ELan EPfP GGGa LMil LRHS MAsh MGos MTrO NOra NOrn NRHS SEWo SPoG SSta WMat WPGP XSte
	'Stellar Acclaim'	CBcs CJun LMil
	stellata	Widely available
	- 'Centennial' 𝕐H6	CJun LMil WHlf
	- 'Chrysanthemumiflora'	CJun EPfP LAlb MACG
	- 'Dawn'	CJun
	- 'Jane Platt' 𝕐H6	CBcs CJun CRos EGrI EHyd ELan EPfP LEdu LMil LRHS MGos NLar NRHS SSta WPGP
	- f. ***keiskei***	CBcs CJun MGos NHol SLim
	- 'Kikuzaki'	CJun
	- 'King Rose'	CBcs CJun CTsd EBee EPfP SPer
	- 'Massey'	CJun
	- 'Norman Gould'	see *M. kobus* 'Norman Gould'
	- 'Rosea'	CAco CBod CJun CKel CMCN CWnw EDir ELan ELon EPfP GMcL LMaj LMil MAsh MGos MPri MRav MSwo NLar NOrn NTrD NWea SCob SWeb WFar
	- 'Rosea Massey'	CJun
	- 'Royal Star' 𝕐H6	CAco CBcs CBrac CCVT CDoC CEnd CJun CKel CLnd CMCN CRos CTri CWnw ELon EPfP ILea LMil LRHS MBlu MGos MRav NLar NRHS SCob SGol SPer SSta WFar WHlf
	- 'Rubra'	LPar
	- 'Scented Silver'	CJun LMil
	- 'Shi-banchi Rosea'	CJun
	- 'Water Lily'	CAco CBcs CBod CDoC CJun CKel CMCN CMac CRos EBee EHyd ELan

		ELon EPfP LMil LRHS LSRN MAsh MBlu MGos NRHS SCob SPer SPoG SSta WPGP
	'String of Pearls'	CJun
	'Summer Solstice'	CBcs CJun EBee EPfP LMil LRHS SSta WPGP
	'Summer Sonnet'	WPGP
	'Sun Ray'	CJun
	'Sunburst'	CJun SRms
	'Sundance'	CBcs CJun LRHS MBlu
	'Sunrise'	CBcs LRHS SEdd
	'Sunsation'	CAco CDoC CJun ELan LPar LRHS NCth NLar SEdd SLim XSte
	'Sunset Swirl'	CJun LRHS
	'Sunspire'	CJun
	'Suntown'	CJun
	'Susan' ♀H6	Widely available
	'Susanna van Veen'	CBcs CDoC CJun LMil WPGP
	'Swedish Star'	CJun
	'Sweet Merlot'	CBcs CJun
	'Sweet Valentine'	CBcs CJun GMcL NLar WPGP
	'Sweetheart' ♀H5	CBcs CJun LMil
	'Sybille'	CMCN SLim WPGP
	tamaulipana	WPGP
	'Theodora'	CBcs LMil LRHS SSta
	× ***thompsoniana***	CBcs CMCN
	- 'Olmenhof'	IArd
	'Thousand Butterflies'	CJun
	'Tikitere'	CBcs LMil
	'Tina Durio'	CDoC NLar WMat
	'Tranquility'	CJun
	tripetala	CAco CBcs CExl CMCN ELan EPfP IDee LMaj LRHS MBlu NLar SSta XSte
	- 'Bloomfield'	CJun
	'Ultimate Yellow'	CJun
	× ***veitchii***	CBcs
	- 'Columbus'	CJun LRHS WPGP
	'Venus'	CBcs NLar
	virginiana	CBcs CJun CMCN EWTr LRHS NLar XSte
I	- 'Glauca'	CBcs
§	- 'Jim Wilson'	CJun MBlu
	- MOONGLOW	see *M. virginiana* 'Jim Wilson'
	'Vulcan'	CAco CBcs CDoC CEnd CJun EGrI ELan EPfP LMil LRHS NLar NOrn XSte
	× ***watsonii***	see *M.* × *wieseneri*
	'Wedding Vows'	CJun
	WHITE CAVIAR ('Micwc') **new**	CBcs SRHi
	'White Mystery'	CJun XSte
§	× ***wieseneri***	CBcs CJun CMCN EBee EPfP MBlu NLar NWea SHor WPGP
	- 'Aashild Kalleberg'	CBcs CJun WPGP
	- 'Swede Made'	CJun
	- 'William Watson'	SSta
	wilsonii ♀H6	CAco CBcs CCVT CDoC CExl CJun CMCN CTri EHed EHyd ELan EPfP EWTr GGro IArd LRHS MBlu MGos MMuc MNrw MTrO NLar NWea SEND SPlb SPtp SSta WGob WMat WPGP
	- 'Gwen Baker'	CJun
	'Yaeko'	CAco CDoC
	'Yellow Fever'	CBcs CJun WPGP
	'Yellow Garland'	CJun
	'Yellow Lantern' ♀H6	CAco CBcs CDoC CEnd CJun CKel EHed EHyd ELan EPfP GGGa LMil LSRN MAsh MBlu MPri NLar NRHS SPoG SSta WPGP
	'Yellow Sea'	CJun
	Yuchelia No. 1	CBcs WPGP
	yunnanensis	CCCN CDoC CTsd ELan ELon EPfP LRHS
	zenii	CAco CBcs CMCN IArd LRHS
	- 'Pink Parchment'	CBcs CJun XSte

× *Mahoberberis* (Berberidaceae)

	aquisargentii	CBcs CKel CMac EBee EHyd EPfP LRHS MMuc MRav NLar SEND WFar
	'Dart's Desire'	NLar
	miethkeana	SRms
§	***neubertii***	NLar

Mahonia ✿ (Berberidaceae)

§	***aquifolium***	CAgr CBcs CBrac CKel EHeP GMcL GPoy LPar MGos MMuc MRav NCth NWea SCob SEND SGbt SPer SPlb SWvt
	- 'Apollo' ♀H5	CBcs CDoC CKel CMac EBee EHeP EHyd ELan EPfP GMcL LCro LOPS LRHS LSRN MAsh MBlu MGos MRav NBwr NLar NWea SCob SCoo SPoG SRHi SRms SWvt WFar WSpi
	- 'Atropurpurea'	CMac CRos CSBt CTsd ELan EPfP LRHS MRav SPer
	- 'Fascicularis'	see *M.* × *wagneri* 'Pinnacle'
	- 'Magnifica' **new**	WPGP
	- 'Moseri'	WLov
	- 'Smaragd'	CMac EHeP ELan EPfP LRHS LSRN MBlu MGos MRav NLar SCob WSpi
	- 'Versicolor'	MBlu
	'Arthur Menzies'	EHyd LMil LRHS NRHS
§	***bealei***	CBcs CBod CBrac CDoC CKel CRos CSBt EHeP EHyd ELan ELon EPfP GMcL LRHS LSto MAsh MGos MRav MSwo NLar NPer SCob SCoo SGol SRHi SWvt
	- 'Cornish Silver'	EBee
	BLACKFOOT ('Bokrafoot'PBR)	EHyd ELan EPfP LRHS MAsh
	bodinieri	WPGP
	- Og 93.033	WPGP
	chochoco	CExl
	confusa × ***gracilipes***	see *M.* × *savilliana*
§	***duclouxiana***	SPtp
	- KR 7692	WPGP
	'Esme'	WPGP
	eurybracteata	CExl SPtp WCru WJur WPGP
	- subsp. ***ganpinensis***	SEND WPGP
	- - 'Soft Caress'	Widely available
	- 'Minganpi'PBR	LSRN
	- 'Narihira'	LPar SGsty
	- 'Sweet Winter'	CDoC CKel EMil EPfP IDee LMil MAsh MMrt NLar SWvt
	eurybracteata × ***nitens*** **new**	WPGP
	eutriphylla misapplied	see *M. trifolia*
	fargesii	see *M. sheridaniana*
	fortunei	CBcs
	- 'Curlyque'	WPGP
	gracilipes	CBcs CExl CMCN EBee EPfP ESwi EWes MBlu NLar WAvo WCru WPGP
	gracilis	EBee
	haematocarpa	WPGP
	hartwegii	WPGP
	japonica ♀H5	CAco CBar CBcs CDoC CEme CMac CRos CTri EBee EHyd EPfP LRHS MAsh MGos MMuc MRav MSwo NHol NLar NRHS SCob SEND SGbt SPer SPoG SRms SSta WCFE
	- 'Gold Dust'	MBlu
	- 'Hiemalis'	see *M. japonica* 'Hivernant'
§	- 'Hivernant'	NWea

lanceolata	EPfP MBlu
leschenaultii B&SWJ 9535	WCru
× ***lindsayae*** 'Cantab' ♀H4	EBee EPfP WPGP
lomariifolia	see *M. oiwakensis* subsp. *lomariifolia*
longibracteata	GKin
mairei	see *M. duclouxiana*
× ***media*** 'Buckland' ♀H5	CMac EPfP SRms WLov
- 'Charity'	Widely available
- 'Lionel Fortescue' ♀H5	CBcs CBod CKel CMac CRos CSBt EBee EHyd EPfP GKin LRHS MAsh NRHS SWvt
- 'Winter Sun' ♀H5	Widely available
moranensis	EBee
- T 292	WPGP
napaulensis	NLar
- 'Maharajah'	IArd
nervosa	CMac EPfP MBlu WPGP
- B&SWJ 9562	WCru
- B&SWJ 13580	WCru
neubertii	see × *Maboberberis neubertii*
nevinii	SBrt
nitens	EBee ELan SPtp WCru WPGP
- 'Cabaret'PBR ♀H4	CBcs CRos EBee EHyd EPfP LCro LOPS LRHS LSRN MAsh MBlu MDon MGos NLar NRHS SCob SPoG SSta SWvt WSpi
oiwakensis	LRHS WPGP
- B&SWJ 371	WCru
- B&SWJ 3660	WCru
- PBR 371 from Hong Kong	WCru
§ - subsp. ***lomariifolia*** ♀H4	CExl CRos ELan EPfP LRHS SArc SPtp
- - var. ***tenuifoliola*** Cox 6509 **new**	WPGP
pallida	EBee SPtp WJur WPGP
'Pan's Peculiar'	EBee WPGP
pinnata misapplied	see *M.* × *wagneri* 'Pinnacle'
pinnata (Lag.) Fedde 'Ken S. Howard'	WPGP
- 'Maurice Foster'	NLar
- subsp. ***insularis*** 'Schnilemoon'	EBee SMad WPGP
repens	NLar WKor WSpi
- 'Rotundifolia'	SPlb
§ × ***savilliana***	EBee IArd NLar WPGP WSpi
§ ***sheridaniana***	ESwi
- Og 93033	WPGP
- Og 93056	WPGP
* ***sinensis*** **new**	ESwi
SIOUX ('Bokrasio'PBR)	EHyd LRHS MAsh NRHS SPoG
subimbricata BWJ 16211 **new**	WCru
§ ***trifolia***	IArd
- EKB 4618	EBee WPGP
volcania B&SWJ 10400	WCru
× ***wagneri***	SWvt
- 'Hastings' Elegant'	NLar
§ - 'Pinnacle' ♀H5	CRos EHeP EHyd ELan EPfP LRHS MAsh MBlu NLar SPoG SWvt WFar
- 'Sunset'	MBlu
- 'Undulata'	MBlu SPer

Maianthemum (*Asparagaceae*)

atropurpureum	WCru
bicolor	LEdu
bifolium	CAvo CBct ESwi GLog GMaP LEdu MAvo MBel MNrw NBro SHar SRms WCru WHlf WShi WThu XLum
- from Yakushima, Japan	GRum WFar
§ - subsp. ***kamtschaticum***	CAvo EMor EPPr GKev LEdu MAvo NLar NRya WCot WPGP WSHC
- - B&SWJ 4360	ESwi WCru
- - CD&R 2300	WCru
- - var. ***pumilum***	EBee LEdu WCru
canadense	EBee EPPr EPot ESwi GKev LEdu MNrw NBid SIvy WCru
chasmanthum	see *M. bifolium* subsp. *kamtschaticum*
comaltepecense B&SWJ 10215	WCru
dilatatum	see *M. bifolium* subsp. *kamtschaticum*
flexuosum	LEdu
- B&SWJ 9069	WCru
- B&SWJ 9079	WCru
- B&SWJ 9150	WCru
aff. ***flexuosum*** B&SWJ 9026	WCru WFar
- B&SWJ 9055	WCru
formosanum B&SWJ 349	EPPr WCru WFar
forrestii	WCru
fuscum	LAma WCot WCru WPnP
- var. ***cordatum***	WCru
- 'Shirui Giant'	WPGP
- 'Tangkhul Giant'	LEdu
gigas B&SWJ 10470	WCru
henryi	LEdu WCru WPGP
- BWJ 7616	WCru WFar
japonicum	GKev LEdu
- B&SWJ 1179	WCru
- B&SWJ 4714	WCru
- B&SWJ 7306	LEdu WCru
- 'Ki-shiro-fukurin-fu' (v)	WCot
oleraceum	CExl GEdr GKev LAma LEdu SDir WFar WHil WPnP
- B&SWJ 2148	WCru
paniculatum	LEdu SHar
- B&SWJ 9137	WCru
- B&SWJ 9140	WCru
- purple-flowered B&SWJ 9139	WCru
pendent, B&SWJ 10305 from Guatemala	WCru
purpureum	GKev LEdu
- G-W&P 150	EPPr LEdu
racemosum ♀H6	Widely available
- subsp. ***amplexicaule***	SMHy
- - B&SWJ 13558 **new**	WCru
- - 'Emily Moody'	CBct CExl EPPr EPfP IPot WCot WPGP
aff. ***salvinii*** B&SWJ 9000	WCru
- B&SWJ 9030	ESwi
- B&SWJ 9088	WCru
- B&SWJ 10402	WCru
scilloideum B&SWJ 10407	WCru
* - var. ***roseum*** B&SWJ 10335	CBct WCru
stellatum	CBct EBlo ECha EHyd EMor EPPr EPfP GQue ILea LEdu LRHS NChi NLar NRHS NRya SMHy WCru WFar WKor XLum
szechuanicum	WCru
tatsienense	CDor CExl GEdr GKev LEdu WCot WCru WPGP
- dark-stemmed	WPGP

Maihuenia (*Cactaceae*)

poeppigii	EAri SPlb
- F&W 9670	WCot
- JCA 2.575.600	WCot

Maihueniopsis (*Cactaceae*)

§ ***darwinii***	EAri SPlb
fulvicoma	see *Cumulopuntia boliviana* subsp. *boliviana*

pentlandii	see *Cumulopuntia boliviana* subsp. *boliviana*

Malephora (*Aizoaceae*)

crocea new	EAri
- var. ***purpureocrocea***	EAri

Mallotus (*Euphorbiaceae*)

japonicus	WJur
- B&SWJ 14613	WCru
- B&SWJ 14679	WCru

Malope (*Malvaceae*)

trifida 'Alba'	CSpe

Malotigena (*Aizoaceae*)

§ ***frantiskae-niederlovae***	CCCN EBou EPot GEdr NHpl SSim WIce XLum
- 'Album'	see *M. frantiskae-niederlovae* 'White Nugget'
- 'Gold Nugget' 🏆^{H4}	EHyd LRHS NBwr SRms
§ - 'White Nugget'	CCCN EDAr ELan EPot GEdr LRHS NBwr NHpl SLee SSim WIce

Malus ✿ (*Rosaceae*)

'Adams'	LMaj
§ 'Adirondack' 🏆^{H6}	CLnd CSBt ELan EPfP EWTr LBuc LCro LOPS LRHS MPri MTrO NOra SCoo SPoG WMat WMou
'Admiration'	see *M.* 'Adirondack'
× ***adstringens*** 'Almey'	LMaj SBdl
- 'Hopa'	CAgr CLnd
- 'Purple Wave'	SBdl
- 'Simcoe'	EBee SBdl
'Aldenhamensis'	see *M.* × *purpurea* 'Aldenhamensis'
'Allow Super' (D)	WMat
'Amberina'	CLnd
'American Beauty'	SBdl
'Appletini' (D)	LCro LOPS
× ***atrosanguinea*** 'Gorgeous'	Widely available
baccata	CLnd CMCN CPer GKev NOra NWea SCoo SEND SPlb WMat
- var. ***mandshurica***	CPer
- 'Street Parade'	EWTr LMaj
aff. ***baccata***	MTrO
'Barbara'	NOra WMat
'Baskatong'	SBdl
§ ***bhutanica***	SBdl
- 'Mandarin'	SCoo
BRANDYWINE ('Branzam')	NOra SPer
brevipes	CLnd LRHS SCoo
- 'Wedding Bouquet' 🏆^{H6}	CBod EBee EPfP EWTr LCro LSRN MAsh MTrO NLar NOra NOrn SGol SOrN SPer SRHi WHtc WMat
'Butterball' 🏆^{H6}	CArg CBod CCVT CLnd CPer CSBt EBee EPfP EPom EWTr LMaj MNic MTrO NOra NOrn NWea SBmr SCoo SEdi SGol SLim SPoG SRms SVic WMat WMou WWct
'Candymint Sargent'	see *M. sargentii* 'Candymint'
'Cave Hill'	CLnd
'Cheal's Scarlet'	CHab NRog
* 'Cheal's Weeping'	CAco CLnd CMac SEdi SGsty SRms
CINDERELLA ('Cinzam')	LCro MTrO NOra WMat
COCCINELLA ('Courtarou')	SGol SMad WHlf
'Comtesse de Paris' 🏆^{H6}	CBcs CLnd EBee EPfP EWTr LRHS MBlu MTrO NLar NOra NOrn WMat
CORALBURST ('Coralcole')	LCro LOPS MTrO NOra NOrn SPoG WMat
coronaria	SPtp
- var. ***dasycalyx*** 'Charlottae' (d)	CCVT EWTr SPer
- 'Elk River'	CLnd NOra SBdl SCoo WMat
'Cowichan'	CLnd SBdl SSFr
'Crimson Brilliant'	CLnd
'Dartmouth'	CHab CLnd CSBt CTri NRog
'Directeur Moerlands'	CArg CCVT CDoC CLnd CSBt EHeP EPfP MTrO NOra SCoo SRHi SWvt WMat WMou
domestica 'A.D.W. Atkins' (C/D)	SBdl
- 'Acklam Russet' (D)	CHab NRog SBdl SKee
- 'Acme' (D)	SKee
- 'Adams's Pearmain' (D)	CArg CBTr CEnd CHab CLnd CPer CTri MTrO NOra NOrn NRog SKee WMat WWct
- 'Admiral'^{PBR} (D)	EFPl SBdl SKee
- 'Advance' (D)	SBdl
- 'Akane' (D)	NOra
- 'Akerö' (D)	SBdl SKee
- 'Aldenham Blenheim' (D)	SBdl
- 'Alderman' (C)	SBdl
§ - 'Alexander' (C)	NRog SBdl
- 'Alfriston' (C)	CAgr CHab NRog SBdl SKee WMat
§ - 'Alkmene' (D) 🏆^{H6}	CAgr LPar NOra NRog SBdl SKee
- 'All Doer' (C/D/Cider)	SEdi
- 'All Red Gravenstein' (D)	SBdl
- 'Allen's Everlasting' (D)	SKee
- 'Allington Pippin' (D)	CArg CHab CSBt CTri MGos NOra NRog SBdl SKee WMat
- AMBASSY ('Dalil'^{PBR}) (D)	SBdl SEdi SKee SSFr
- 'Amber' (D)	SBdl
- 'Ambro'^{PBR} (D)	SBdl
- 'American Golden Russet' (D)	SBdl
- 'American Mother'	see *M. domestica* 'Mother'
- 'Ames' (D)	SBdl
- 'Ananas Reinette' (D)	CHab LPar NRog SBdl SKee
- 'Anna Boelens' (D)	SBdl
- 'Annie Elizabeth' (C)	CAgr CArg CHab MGos MTrO NOra NRog SBdl SBmr SKee SSFr SVic WJas WMat WWct
- 'Antonovka' (C)	NOra SBdl SKee
- 'Apache' (F)	SSFr
- 'Apez Zagarra' (D)	SBdl
- 'Api' (D)	LSRN MTrO NOra NWea SBdl SKee WLov WMat
- 'Api Noir' (D)	LPar SBdl SKee
- 'Ard Cairn Russet' (D)	IArd SBdl SKee
- 'Ariwa'^{PBR} (D)	SBdl
- 'Arkansas' (D)	NOra SBdl SKee
- 'Aroma' (D)	SBdl
- 'Aromatic Russet' (D)	NRog SBdl SKee
- 'Arthur Turner' (C) 🏆^{H6}	CArg CBod CCVT CHab CTri EPom LBuc MLod MTrO NOra NRog NWea SBdl SBmr SKee SSFr WJas WMat
- 'Arthur W. Barnes' (C)	SKee
- 'Ascot' (D)	SBdl
- 'Ashmead's Kernel' (D) 🏆^{H6}	Widely available
- 'Ashton Bitter' (Cider)	CHab CTri SBdl
- 'Ashton Brown Jersey' (Cider)	CArg SBdl
- 'Astrachan Large Fruited' (D)	SBdl
- 'Auralia' (D)	NRog
- 'Autumn Harvest' (C/D)	NRog SBdl
- 'Autumn Pearmain' (D)	SBdl SKee
- 'Backwell Red' (Cider)	SBdl
- 'Baker's Delicious' (D)	NOra SBdl SKee SSFr WMat

– 'Baldwin' (D)	NOra SBdl
– 'Ballarat Seedling' (D)	SBdl
– Ballerina Series (D)	MLod
– – 'Ballerina Bolero' (D)	SKee WMat
– – 'Ballerina Polka' (D)	SKee WMat
– – 'Ballerina Samba' (D)	CArg LCro MTrO NLar NOra WMat
– 'Ball's Pippin' (D)	SBdl
– 'Ballyfatten' (C)	SBdl
– 'Ballyvaughan Seedling' (D)	IArd
– 'Balsam'	see *M. domestica* 'Green Balsam'
– 'Banana Pippin' (F)	CEnd
– 'Banns' (D)	SBdl SKee
– 'Barchard's Seedling' (D)	SBdl
– 'Bardsey' (D)	CAgr CArg CEnd CHab EPom MTrO NOra SKee WGwG WMat
– 'Barnack Beauty' (D)	CHab NOra NRog SBdl SKee
– 'Barnack Beauty' sport (D)	SBdl
– 'Barnack Orange' (D)	SBdl SKee
– 'Barnhill Pippin' (D)	SBdl
– 'Baron Ward' (C)	CHab NRog SBdl
– 'Baron Wood' (C)	SBdl SKee
– 'Bascombe's Mystery' (D)	SBdl SKee
– 'Baumann's Reinette' (D)	SBdl SKee
– 'Baxter's Pearmain' (D)	SBdl SKee
– 'Beauty of Bath' (D)	CAgr CArg CBod CCVT CEnd CHab CLnd CPer CTri CWnw ELan EPom LBuc LPar MDon MLod MRav MTrO NBwr NOra NRog SBdl SBmr SEdi SKee SPer SSFr WMat WWct
– 'Beauty of Bedford' (D)	SBdl SKee
– 'Beauty of Blackmoor' (D)	CLnd SBdl
– 'Beauty of Hants' (C/D)	SBdl SKee
– 'Beauty of Kent' (C)	SBdl SKee
– 'Beauty of Moray' (C)	SBdl SKee
– 'Beauty of Stoke' (C)	NRog SBdl SKee
– 'Bedfordshire Foundling' (C)	SBdl
– 'Bedwyn Beauty' (C)	SBdl
– 'Beeley Pippin' (D)	SBdl SKee
– 'Belgica'[PBR] (D)	SBdl
– 'Bell Apple' (Cider/C)	CPer
– 'Belle de Boskoop' (C/D) ♀H6	CAgr CEnd CHab LMaj NOra NPlm NRog NWea SBdl SKee
– 'Belle de Pontoise' (D)	SBdl
– 'Belle Flavoise' (F)	SBdl SKee
– 'Belledge Pippin' (C/D)	SBdl
– 'Belle-fille Normande' (C)	SBdl
– 'Belle-fleur de France' (C)	SBdl
– 'Bellefleur Kitika' (D)	SKee
– 'Bellida'[PBR] (D)	SBdl
– 'Belvoir Seedling' (C/D)	SBdl
– 'Bembridge Beauty' (F)	CHab
– 'Benenden Early' (D)	SBdl SKee
– 'Benoni' (D)	LPar SBdl
– 'Ben's Red' (D)	CAgr CBod CDoC CEnd CPer CTsd SKee WMat
– 'Bess Pool' (D)	CHab NRog SBdl
– 'Betty Geeson' (C)	SBdl
– 'Bewley Down Pippin'	see *M. domestica* 'Crimson King' (Cider/C)
– 'Bielaar'[PBR] (C/D)	SBdl
– 'Bismarck' (C)	NRog SBdl SKee
– 'Black Dabinett' (Cider)	CArg CEnd CPer MTrO SBdl WMat
– 'Black Tom Putt' (C/D)	MTrO
– 'Black Vallis' (Cider)	SBdl
– 'Blackwell Red' (F)	SBdl
– 'Blanc Sur' (C/D)	SKee
– 'Blaze' (D)	SBdl
– 'Blenheim Orange' (C/D) ♀H6	Widely available
– 'Blood of the Boyne' (D)	IArd
– 'Bloody Butcher' (C)	SBdl
– 'Bloody Ploughman' (D)	CArg CHab CLnd LBuc MLod MTrO NOra NRog SBdl SKee WMat
– 'Blue Moon' (D)	LRHS NOrn
– 'Blue Pearmain' (D)	SBdl SKee
– 'Bodil Neergaard' (D)	SBdl
– 'Boiken' (D)	SBdl
– BOLERO	see *M. domestica* 'Tuscan'
– 'Bonum' (D/C)	WMat
– 'Bosbury Pippin' (D)	SBdl
– 'Bossom' (D)	SBdl
– 'Boston Russet'	see *M. domestica* 'Roxbury Russet'
– 'Bountiful' (C)	CAgr CArg CBod CDoC CLnd CMac CSBt CTri EPom LCro LRHS LSRN MAsh MRav MTrO NLar NOra NRog SBdl SBmr SKee SSFT SSFr WMat WWct
– 'Bow Hill Pippin' (C)	SBdl SKee
– 'Box Apple' (D)	SBdl SKee
– 'Brabant Bellefleur' (C)	SBdl
– 'Braddick's Nonpareil' (D)	SBdl SKee
– 'Bradley's Beauty' (C/D)	NRog NWea
– 'Braeburn' (D)	Widely available
– 'Braeburn Hillwell' (D)	EPom NOra SKee
– 'Braintree Seedling' (D)	SBdl SKee
– 'Bramley 20' (C)	CSBt LCro LOPS MLod MTrO NOra NOrn NWea SBdl SCoo SGbt SOrN WMat
– 'Bramley's Seedling' (C) ♀H6	Widely available
– 'Bramley's Seedling' clone 20 (C)	CLnd CSBt CTsd EBee LBuc LSRN MAsh MNHC NLar NOra SCoo SKee SLim SPoG WWct
– 'Bramshott Rectory' (D/C)	CLnd SBdl SKee SSFr
– 'Bread Fruit' (C/D)	CEnd CTsd
– 'Breakwell's Seedling' (Cider)	SBdl
– 'Breitling' (D)	SBdl SKee
– 'Brenchley Pippin' (D)	SBdl SKee
– 'Bridgwater Pippin' (C)	SBdl
– 'Bright Future' (D)	CArg EPom NOra SKee WMat WWct
– 'Bringewood Pippin' (D)	CHab
– 'Brith Mawr' (C)	CHab WGwG
– 'Broad-eyed Pippin' (C)	SKee
– 'Broadholme Beauty' (C)	CArg EPom MTrO NOra WMat
– 'Brookes's' (D)	SBdl SKee
– 'Brown Crofton' (D)	IArd NRog SBdl
– 'Brown Snout' (Cider)	NRog SBdl
– 'Brown Thorn' (Cider)	SBdl
– 'Brownlee's Russet' (D)	CAgr CHab CTri EDir NOra NRog SBmr SKee SSFr WMat
– 'Brown's Apple' (Cider)	CAgr CArg CHab CTri MTrO NOra SBdl WMat
– 'Brown's Seedling' (D)	NRog
– 'Broxwood Foxwhelp' (Cider)	MTrO SBdl
– 'Budimka' (D)	SBdl SKee
– 'Bulmer's Norman' (Cider)	SBdl
– 'Burn's Seedling' (D)	SBdl SKee
– 'Burr Knot' (C)	SBdl SKee
– 'Burrowhill Early' (Cider)	SBdl WMat
– 'Bushey Grove' (C)	SKee
– 'Byeloborodovka' (C/D)	SBdl
– 'Byfleet Seedling' (C)	SBdl SKee
– 'Byford Wonder' (C)	SBdl
– 'Calville Blanc d'Hiver' (D)	NOra SBdl SKee
– 'Calville des Femmes' (C)	SBdl
– 'Calville Rouge d'Hiver' (C)	SBdl
– 'Cambusnethan Pippin' (D)	SBdl SKee
– 'Camelot' (Cider/C)	EDir SBdl SEdi
§ – 'Captain Broad' (Cider/D)	CDoC CEnd CTsd SBdl
– 'Captain Kidd' (D)	EPom NOra SBdl SKee
– 'Captain Tom' (C/D)	WMat

- 'Caravel' (D) SBdl
- 'Carlisle Codlin' (C) NOra SBdl WMat
- 'Caroline' (D) SBdl
- 'Carswell's Honeydew' (D) SBdl SKee
- 'Carswell's Orange' (D) SBdl SKee
- 'Carter's Pearmain' (D) SBdl
- 'Castle Major' (C) SBdl
- 'Catherine' (C) SBdl SKee
- 'Catshead' (C) CAgr CArg CDoC CHab CTri NOra NRog SBdl SKee WMat WWct
- 'Caudal Market' (F) SBdl
- 'Cellini' (C) NOra SBdl SKee
- 'Cevaal' (D) WWct
- 'Channel Beauty' (D) SBdl WGwG
- 'Charles Eyre' (C) SBdl
- 'Charles Ross' (C/D) ♀^{H6} Widely available
- 'Charlestown Pippin' (F) NRog
- 'Charlotte' (C) SBdl SKee
- 'Chaxhill Red' (Cider/D) SBdl
- 'Cheddar Cross' (D) CAgr CCVT CTri SBdl SKee
- 'Chehalis' (D) SBdl
- 'Chelmsford Wonder' (C) SBdl SKee
- 'Cherry Cox' (D) SBdl
- 'Chips' (F) SBdl SKee
- 'Chisel Jersey' (Cider) CAgr CTri NOra SBdl SKee
- 'Chivers Delight' (D) CAgr CArg CBod CLnd EBee EPom EWTr LBuc MCoo MTrO NOra NRog SBdl SBmr SKee SSFr
- 'Chorister Boy' (D) SBdl
- 'Christie Manson' (C) SBdl
- 'Christmas Pearmain' (D) CAgr CArg CLnd SBdl SKee SSFr WMat
- 'Christmas Pippin'^{PBR} (D) ♀^{H6} CArg CEnd CRos CTri EBee ELan EPfP EPom LBuc LCro LRHS MCoo MLod MPri MTrO NLar NOra NRHS SCoo SGbt SKee SOrN SPoG SSFr WMat
- 'Cider Lady's Finger' (Cider) SBdl SKee
- 'Cissy' (D) SBdl WGwG
- 'Cistecké' (D) SBdl SKee
- 'Claygate Pearmain' (D) CAgr CHab CTri NOra NRog SBdl SKee SVic WMat
- 'Cleeve' (D) SBdl SKee
- 'Climax' (D) SBdl
- 'Clopton Red' (D) SBdl SKee
- 'Close' (D) SBdl
- 'Clydeside' (C) SBdl
- 'Coat Jersey' (Cider) SBdl
- 'Cobra' (F) CAgr CArg NOra SKee SPoG SSFr WJas WMat
- 'Cockett's Red' (D) SBdl
- 'Cockle Pippin' (D) CAgr SBdl SKee
- 'Cockpit' (C) CHab SBdl SKee
- 'Coeur de Boeuf' (C/D) SBdl SKee
- 'Colapuy' (D) NRog
- 'Coleman's Seedling' (Cider) CPer
- 'Collogett Pippin' (C/Cider) CBod CDoC CEnd CTsd SBdl
- 'Colonel Vaughan' (C/D) SBdl SKee
- 'Colonel Yate' (D) SBdl SKee
- 'Comrade' (D) SBdl SKee
- 'Cooper's Seedling' (C) SBdl
- 'Coo's River Beauty' (D) SBdl
- 'Core Blimey' (D) EBee EPom LBuc MTrO SCoo SKee SPoG
- 'Cornish Aromatic' (D) CAgr CArg CBod CDoC CPer CTri CTsd MTrO NOra SBdl SBmr SKee WMat
- 'Cornish Gilliflower' (D) CAgr CBod CDoC CEnd CHab CPer CTsd MTrO NOra NRog SBdl SBmr SKee WMat
- 'Cornish Honeypin' (D) CDoC CEnd CTsd SBdl SKee SSFr
- 'Cornish Longstem' (D) CAgr CEnd
- 'Cornish Mother' (D) CEnd CPer
- 'Cornish Pine' (D) CBod CDoC CEnd CTsd SBdl SKee
- 'Cornish Queen' (C/D) CBod CTsd
- 'Coronation' (D) CHab NRog SBdl SKee
- 'Cortland' (D) NOra SBdl SKee
- 'Costard' (C) CHab SKee
- 'Cottenham Seedling' (C) SBdl SKee
- 'Coul Blush' (D) MTrO SBdl SKee WMat
- 'Court of Wick' (D) CAgr CArg CHab NOra NRog SBdl SKee SVic WMat
- 'Court Pendu Plat' (D) CAgr CArg CHab NOra NRog SBdl SKee SSFT WJas WMat WWct
- 'Court Royal' (Cider) SBdl SKee
- 'Cox Cymraeg' (D) WGwG
- 'Cox's Orange Pippin' (D) Widely available
- 'Cox's Pomona' (C) LPar NRog SBdl SKee
- 'Cox's Rouge de Flandres' (D) SKee
- 'Cox's Selfing' (D) CBTr CMac CSBt CTri EBee EPfP LBuc LRHS MAsh MDon MGos MNHC NLar SKee SPer SPoG WJas WMat WWct
- 'Crawley Beauty' (C) CAgr CArg CHab NRog SBdl SKee SSFT WMat
- 'Crawley Reinette' (D) CHab NRog SBdl SKee
- 'Crimson Beauty' (D) SBdl SKee
- 'Crimson Beauty of Bath' (D) CAgr SBdl
- 'Crimson Bramley' (C) EFPl SBdl SKee
- 'Crimson Cox' (D) SBdl
- 'Crimson Crisp' (D) **new** SKee

§ - 'Crimson King' (Cider/C) CAgr SBdl
- 'Crimson King' (D) CAgr CHab CTri SBdl
- 'Crimson Newton' (C) SBdl
- 'Crimson Peasgood' (C) SBdl SKee
- 'Crimson Queening' (D) SBdl SKee
- 'Crimson Superb' (D) SBdl
- 'Crimson Victoria' (Cider) SBdl

§ - 'Cripps Pink'^{PBR} (D) SGsty SSFr
- CRISPIN see *M. domestica* 'Mutsu'
- 'Croen Mochyn' (D) WGwG
- 'Croquella' (D) LRHS

§ - 'Crowngold' (D) EPom SBdl
- 'Cummy Norman' (Cider) SBdl
- 'Curl Tail' (D) SBdl
- 'Cutler Grieve' (D) SBdl
- CYBÈLE ('Delrouval') (D) SKee
- 'Dabinett' (Cider) CAgr CArg CHab CLnd CMac CPer CTri EPom LBuc MLod NOra NRog SBdl SKee WMat WWct
- 'D'Arcy Spice' (D) CAgr EPfP MTrO NOra SBdl SBmr SKee WMat WWct
- 'Dawn' (D) SBdl SKee
- 'Deacon's Blushing Beauty' (C/D) CLnd
- 'Decio' (D) SBdl SKee
- DELBARD JUBILÉ ('Delgollune') (D) NPlm SBdl
- DELBARESTIVALE ('Delcorf') (red) (D) LPar SBdl
- 'Delicious' (D) SBdl
- 'Delorgue'^{PBR} (F) SBdl
- 'Delprim' (D) SBdl SKee
- 'Delprivale'^{PBR} (F) SBdl
- 'Devonshire Buckland' (C) CEnd CPer SBdl
- 'Devonshire Crimson Queen' (D) CEnd SBdl
- 'Devonshire Quarrenden' (D) CAgr CBod CHab CPer NOra NRog SBdl SBmr SKee SVic WMat
- 'Diamond' (D) WGwG
- 'Diamond Jubilee' (D) SBdl SKee
- 'Discovery' (D) ♀^{H6} Widely available

	– 'Discovery NFT' (D)	CEnd
	– 'Doctor Clifford' (C)	SBdl SKee
	– 'Doctor Harvey' (C)	SBdl
	– 'Doctor Hogg' (C)	CLnd NRog SBdl
	– 'Doctor Kidd's Orange Red'	see *M. domestica* 'Kidd's Orange Red'
	– 'Doddin' (D)	WWct
	– 'Dog's Snout' (C/D)	NRog
	– 'Domino' (C)	SBdl SKee
	– 'Don's Delight' (C)	CPer WMat
	– 'Doux Normandie' (Cider)	SBdl
	– 'Dove' (Cider)	SBdl
	– 'Downton Pippin' (D)	CHab NRog SBdl SKee
	– 'Dredge's Fame' (D)	SBdl SKee
	– 'Duchess of Bedford' (D)	SBdl SKee
	– 'Duchess of Oldenburg' (C)	NOra SBdl SKee
	– 'Duchess's Favourite' (D)	SBdl SKee
	– 'Duck's Bill' (D)	SKee
	– 'Dufflin' (Cider)	CTsd SBdl
	– 'Duke of Cornwall' (C)	CBod
	– 'Duke of Devonshire' (D)	CSBt CTri NRog NWea SBdl SKee
	– 'Dumeller's Seedling'	see *M. domestica* 'Dummellor's Seedling'
§	– 'Dummellor's Seedling' (C) ♀H6	CHab NOra NRog SBdl SKee
	– 'Dunkerton Late Sweet' (Cider)	CArg CCVT CHab SBdl SEdi WMat
	– 'Dunn's Seedling' (D)	SBdl
§	– 'Dutch Codlin' (C)	SBdl
§	– 'Dutch Mignonne' (D)	SBdl SKee
	– 'Dymock Red' (Cider)	SBdl
	– 'Eady's Magnum' (C)	SKee
	– 'Early Blenheim' (D/C)	CEnd
	– 'Early Bower' (D)	CEnd
	– 'Early Julyan' (C)	SBdl SKee
	– 'Early McIntosh' (D)	SBdl
	– 'Early Strawberry' (D)	SBdl
	– 'Early Victoria'	see *M. domestica* 'Emneth Early'
	– EARLY WINDSOR	see *M. domestica* 'Alkmene'
	– 'Early Worcester'	see *M. domestica* 'Tydeman's Early Worcester'
	– 'East Lothian Pippin' (C)	SBdl SKee
	– 'Easter Orange' (D)	SBdl SKee
	– 'Eccleston Pippin' (D)	SBdl
	– 'Ecklinville' (C)	SBdl SKee
	– 'Edelborsdorfer' (D)	NRog
	– 'Eden' (D)	CBTr CDow LRHS MTrO NOra SBdl SBmr SCoo SPoG WMat
	– EDEN ('Sjca38r6a74') (D) **new**	LCro
	– 'Edith Hopwood' (D)	SBdl SKee
	– 'Edward VII' (C) ♀H6	CHab NOra NRog SBdl SKee WMat WWct
	– 'Egremont Russet' (D) ♀H6	Widely available
	– 'Elektra' (D)	NRog
	– 'Ellis' Bitter' (Cider)	SBdl SKee SVic
	– 'Ellison's Orange' (D) ♀H6	Widely available
	– 'Elmore Pippin' (D)	SBdl
	– 'Elstar' (D) ♀H6	CBod CCVT CLnd EDir EPom EWTr LPar MDon NOra SBdl SEdi SKee SSFr
	– 'Elton Beauty' (D)	SBdl SKee
§	– 'Emneth Early' (C) ♀H6	CAgr CArg CHab NOra NRog SBdl SEdi SKee WMat WWct
	– 'Emperor Alexander'	see *M. domestica* 'Alexander'
	– 'Empire' (D)	NOra SBdl SKee
	– 'Endsleigh Beauty' (D)	SBdl
	– 'English Codlin' (C)	CPer CTri
	– 'Epicure'	see *M. domestica* 'Laxton's Epicure'
	– 'Eros' (D)	SBdl
	– 'Esopus Spitzenburg' (D)	NOra SBdl SKee
	– 'Etlin's Reinette' (D)	NRog
	– 'Evagil' (C)	SBdl
	– 'Excelsior' (C)	SBdl SKee
	– 'Exeter Cross' (D)	CBod CSBt SBdl
	– 'Exquisite' (D)	SBdl SKee SRms SWeb
	– 'Eynsham Challenger' (F)	SBdl
	– 'Eynsham Dumpling' (C)	SBdl
	– 'Fair Maid of Devon' (Cider)	CAgr CArg CEnd WMat
	– 'Fairie Queen' (D)	SBdl SKee
	– 'Fall Pippin' (D)	SBdl
	– 'Fall Russet' (D)	SBdl
	– 'Falstaff' PBR (D) ♀H6	CAgr CBod CTri EPfP EPom LSRN MDon MGos NOra NTrD SBdl SBmr SCoo SEdi SKee SPer SSFr
	– 'Fameuse' (D)	NOra SBdl SKee
	– 'Farmer's Glory' (D)	CAgr CBod SEND WMat
	– 'Fearn's Pippin' (D)	SBdl SKee
	– 'Feltham Beauty' (D)	SBdl
	– 'Feuillemorte' (D)	SKee
	– 'Fiessers Erstling' (C)	SBdl
	– 'Fiesta' (D) ♀H6	Widely available
	– 'Filippa' (D)	SBdl
	– 'Fillbarrel' (Cider)	CHab NRog SBdl
	– 'Fillingham Pippin' (C)	CHab NRog SBdl SKee
	– 'Firedance' (D)	LRHS
	– 'Fireside' (D)	SBdl
	– 'Firmgold' (D)	SBdl
	– 'First and Last' (D)	NOra WMat
	– 'Flame' (D)	SBdl SKee
	– 'Flamenco'	see *M. domestica* 'Obelisk'
	– 'Florina' (F)	NOra SBdl
§	– 'Flower of Kent' (C)	CHab EPom MTrO NOra NRog NWea SBdl SKee SSFr WMat
	– 'Flower of the Town' (D)	CHab NRog SBdl SKee
	– 'Folkestone' (D)	SBdl
	– 'Forester' (C)	SBdl
	– 'Forfar'	see *M. domestica* 'Dutch Mignonne'
	– 'Forge' (D)	CAgr CHab NRog SBdl SKee
	– 'Forpear' (D)	SBdl
	– 'Fortosh' (D)	SBdl
	– 'Fortune'	see *M. domestica* 'Laxton's Fortune'
	– 'Forty Shilling' (D)	SBdl
	– 'Foster's Seedling' (D)	SBdl SKee
	– 'Four Square' (F)	SBdl
	– 'Foxwhelp' (Cider)	CArg CHab CLnd NRog NWea SKee
	– 'Francis' (D)	SBdl SKee
	– 'Frederick' (Cider)	CArg CLnd SBdl WMat
	– 'Freiherr von Berlepsch' (D)	SBdl SKee
	– 'French Codlin'	see *M. domestica* 'Dutch Codlin'
	– 'French Crab' (C)	SBdl
	– 'Freyberg' (D)	NOra SKee
	– 'Friandise' (D)	SBdl
	– 'Frogmore Prolific' (C)	SBdl
	– 'Fuji' (D)	LMaj NOra SBdl SKee
	– 'Gala' (D)	CLnd CSBt CTri EBee EDir EPom IPap MTrO NBwr NOra NOrn NRog SBdl SCoo SEdi SGbt SGsty SKee SSFr SVic WMat
	– 'Gala Mondial' (D)	MDon
	– 'Gala Musk' (D)	LPar
	– 'Galaxy' PBR (D)	NOra SBdl SEdi
	– 'Galloway Pippin' (C)	MTrO NLar NOra NWea SBdl SKee WMat
	– 'Galton' (D)	SBdl
	– 'Garden Fountain' (D)	LRHS
	– 'Garnet' (D)	SBdl SKee
	– 'Gascoyne's Scarlet' (C/D)	NRog SBdl SKee
	– 'Gavin' (D)	CAgr SBdl SKee
	– 'Genet Moyle' (C/Cider)	CTri SBdl WMat
	– 'George Carpenter' (D)	CTri NRog SBdl SKee
	– 'George Cave' (D)	MDon NOra NRog SBdl SEND SEdi SKee SSFr WJas

- 'George Fox' (D)	NRog
- 'George Neal' (C)	CAgr NRog SBdl SKee
- 'Gibbon's Russet' (D)	IArd SBdl
- 'Gilliflower of Gloucester' (D)	SBdl
- 'Gipsy King' (D)	NRog
- 'Gladstone' (D)	CAgr NOra SBdl SKee WMat WWct
- 'Glasbury' (C)	SBdl
§ - 'Glass Apple' (C/D)	CEnd SBdl
- 'Glockenapfel' (C)	SBdl SKee
- 'Gloria Mundi' (C)	SBdl SKee
- 'Gloster '69' (D)	CLnd LMaj LPar SBdl SKee
- 'Gloucester Cross' (D)	SBdl SKee
- 'Gloucester Royal' (D)	SBdl SKee
- 'Gold Medal' (D)	SBdl
- 'Golden Bittersweet' (D)	CAgr SBdl WMat
- 'Golden Delicious' (D)	CArg CMac EDir ELan EPom IPap LBuc LCro LMaj LPar LRHS MDon MPri MTrO NBwr NOra NOrn NRog NTrD SBdl SBmr SEWo SEdi SGsty SKee SSFr SVic WMat
- 'Golden Gate' (D)	LRHS NOrn
- 'Golden Harvey' (D)	CAgr SBdl SKee
- 'Golden Knob' (D)	CTri SBdl SKee
- 'Golden Noble' (C) ♀H6	CAgr CTri IArd NOra NRog SBdl SKee
- 'Golden Nugget' (D)	CAgr NRog SBdl SKee
- 'Golden Pearmain' (D)	LMaj LPar NRog
- 'Golden Pippin' (C)	CAgr NOra NRog SBdl SKee WMat
- 'Golden Reinette' (D)	SBdl SKee
- 'Golden Russet' (D)	CAgr NOra SKee
- 'Golden Spire' (C)	CHab NBwr NOra NRog SBdl SKee
- GOLDRUSH ('Coop 38'[PBR]) (F)	NOra
- 'Gooseberry' (C)	SBdl SKee
- 'Grandpa Ailes' (D)	CPer
- 'Grandpa Buxton' (C)	CHab NRog
- 'Grange's Pearmain' (C)	SBdl
- 'Granny Smith' (D)	CBcs CBod EDir IPap LMaj LPar LSRN MDon MTrO NOra NOrn NRog SBdl SEdi SGbt SKee SPer SVic WMat
- 'Grantonian' (C) **new**	SKee
- 'Gravenstein' (D)	CHab LMaj NOra NRog SBdl SEdi SKee
- 'Greasy Pippin' (D/C)	SBdl
§ - 'Green Balsam' (D)	CHab CTri NRog
- 'Green Chisel' (D)	IArd
- 'Green Harvey' (D/C)	SBdl SKee
- 'Green Roland' (C/D)	SBdl
- 'Green Sensation' (D) **new**	EDir
- 'Greenfinch' (D)	LRHS NOrn
- 'Greensleeves'[PBR] (D) ♀H6	CAgr CArg CBod CMac CTri ELan EPfP EPom LPar MAsh MGos MMuc MTrO NOra NRog NWea SBdl SBmr SEND SEdi SKee SLim SPer SSFT SSFr WJas WMat WWct
- GREENSTAR ('Nicogreen'[PBR]) (D)	SBdl
- 'Greenup's Pippin' (D)	CHab NRog SBdl
- 'Grenadier' (C) ♀H6	CAgr CArg CBod CHab CLnd CTri EDir EPom MDon MGos MMuc MTrO NOra NRog NWea SBdl SEND SEdi SKee SPer SSFT SSFr WMat
- 'Grimes Golden' (D)	NOra NRog SBdl
- 'Groninger Kroon' (D)	CLnd SBdl
- 'Grvena Lepogvetka' (D)	SBdl
- 'Guelph' (D)	SBdl
- 'Guillevic' (Cider)	CHab NRog
- 'Guldborg' (C)	SBdl
- 'Gwell Na Mil' (D)	WGwG
- 'Halstow Natural' (Cider)	CAgr
- 'Hambledon Deux Ans' (C)	CLnd SBdl SKee
- 'Hambling's Seedling' (C)	SKee
- 'Hangy Down' (Cider)	CArg WMat
- 'Hannan Seedling' (D)	SBdl
- 'Hanwell Souring' (C)	SBdl SKee
- 'Haralson' (D)	SBdl
- 'Harbert's Reinette' (D)	SBdl SKee
- 'Harling Hero' (D)	SBdl
- HARMONIE ('Delorina') (F)	SBdl
§ - 'Harry Master's Jersey' (Cider)	CAgr CArg CTri EPom MTrO NOra NRog SKee WMat WWct
- 'Harry Master's Red Streak' (Cider)	SEdi
- 'Harry Pring' (D)	SBdl SKee
- 'Harvey' (C)	SKee
- 'Hastings' (Cider)	MTrO NRog
- 'Hawthornden' (C)	CHab NRog SBdl SKee
- 'Hector MacDonald' (C)	SBdl
- 'Helen's Apple' (Cider)	NRog
- 'Hereford Cross' (D)	SBdl SKee
- 'Herefordshire Beefing' (C)	SBdl SKee
- 'Herefordshire Redstreak' (Cider)	CAgr CArg EPom LBuc MLod NOra WMat
- 'Herefordshire Russet'[PBR] (D)	CArg CDoC EBee EPom LBuc LCro LRHS MLod MPri MTrO NLar NOra NOrn NRHS SBdl SKee SSFr WMat WWct
- 'Herring's Pippin' (C/D)	CTri NRog SKee
- 'Heusgen's Golden Reinette' (D)	SKee
- 'Hibb's Seedling' (C)	SKee
- 'Hibernal' (C)	SBdl SKee
- 'Hidala'[PBR] (D)	SBdl
- 'Hidden Rose' (D) **new**	SKee
- 'High View Pippin' (D)	SBdl SKee
- 'Histon Favourite' (D/C)	SBdl SKee
- 'Hoary Morning' (C)	CBod CPer SBdl SKee
- 'Hocking's Green' (C/D)	CAgr CEnd CTsd
- 'Holiday' (D)	SBdl
- 'Holland Pippin' (C)	SBdl SKee
- 'Hollandbury' (C)	SBdl
- 'Hollow Core' (C)	CAgr
- 'Holstein' (D)	IPap NOra SBdl SEdi SKee
- 'Honey Pippin' (D)	SBdl SKee
- 'Honeycrisp'[PBR] (D)	MTrO NOra WMat
§ - 'Honeygold' (D)	SBdl
- 'Hormead Pearmain' (C)	SBdl SKee
- 'Horneburger Pfannkuchen' (C)	SBdl SKee
- 'Hornsea Herring' (D/C)	NRog
- 'Horsford Prolific' (D)	SBdl SKee
- 'Horsham Russet' (D)	SKee
- 'Houblon' (D)	SBdl SKee
- 'Hounslow Wonder' (C)	SBdl
- 'Howgate Wonder' (C) ♀H6	Widely available
- 'Hubbard's Pearmain' (D)	SKee
- 'Hubbardston Nonesuch' (D)	NOra SBdl
- 'Hume' (D)	SBdl
- 'Hunter's Majestic' (D/C)	SBdl
- 'Hunthouse' (D)	NRog
- 'Huntingdon Codlin' (D)	SBdl
- 'Hunt's Duke of Gloucester' (D)	SBdl SKee
- 'Hunt's Early' (D)	SKee
- 'Idared' (D)	EDir MDon NBwr NOra SBdl SEdi SKee SSFr SVic WMat
- 'Improved Ashmead's Kernel' (D)	SBdl
- 'Improved Cockpit' (C)	NRog SBdl
- 'Improved Dove' (Cider)	SBdl
- 'Improved Keswick' (C/D)	CEnd

	- 'Improved Lambrook Pippin' (Cider)	CArg CTri SBdl
	- 'Improved Redstreak' (Cider)	SBdl
	- 'Ingall's Pippin' (D)	SKee
	- 'Ingall's Red' (D)	NRog SKee
	- 'Ingrid Marie' (D)	EDir NRog SBdl SKee SSFr
	- 'Irish Peach' (D)	CAgr CArg CHab CTri IArd MTrO NOra NRog SBdl SKee SSFr WMat
	- 'Isaac Newton's Tree'	see *M. domestica* 'Flower of Kent'
	- 'Isle of Wight Pippin' (D)	CLnd SBmr SSFr
	- 'Jackson's'	see *M. domestica* 'Crimson King' (Cider/C)
	- 'Jacques Lebel' (C)	SBdl SKee
	- 'James Grieve' (D) ♀H6	Widely available
	- 'James Lawson' (D)	SBdl SKee
	- 'Jane' (Cider)	NRog
	- JAZZ ('Scifresh'PBR) (D)	SSFr
	- 'Jeanne Hardy' (C)	SBdl
	- 'Jefferies' (D)	SKee
	- 'Jersey Beauty' (C/D)	CLnd SBdl
	- 'Jersey Black' (D/Cider)	SBdl SKee
	- 'Jerseymac' (D)	SBdl
	- 'Jester' (D)	CLnd NRog SBdl SKee SSFr
	- 'Joaneting' (D)	CAgr CHab NRog SBdl
	- 'John Apple' (C)	SKee
	- 'John Broad'	see *M. domestica* 'Captain Broad'
	- 'John Divers' (C)	SBdl
	- 'John Standish' (D)	CAgr CTri NRog SBdl SKee
	- 'John Toucher's'	see *M. domestica* 'Crimson King' (Cider/C)
	- 'John Waterer' (C)	SBdl
	- 'Johnny Andrews' (Cider)	CAgr
	- 'Johnny Voun' (D)	CEnd CTsd
	- 'Jonagold' (D) ♀H6	CArg CBod CLnd CTri EDir ELan EPom IArd IPap LMaj LRHS NOra NRog SBdl SEdi SGsty SKee SPer SSFr WWct
	- 'Jonagold Crowngold'	see *M. domestica* 'Crowngold'
§	- 'Jonagored'PBR (D)	NOra NRog SBdl SEdi SKee WMat
	- 'Jonared' (D)	SBdl
	- 'Jonathan' (D)	NOra SBdl SKee
	- 'Jordan's Weeping' (C)	EFPl
	- 'Josephine' (D)	SBdl
	- 'Joybells' (D)	SBdl SKee
	- 'Joyce' (D)	SBdl
	- 'Jubilee'	see *M. domestica* 'Royal Jubilee'
	- 'Julgrans' (D)	SBdl
	- 'Julie's Late Golden' (F)	CTri
	- 'Jumbo' (C/D)	MTrO NOra SBdl SKee WJas WMat
	- 'Jupiter'PBR (D) ♀H6	CAgr CArg CBod CSBt CTri EDir EPfP LSRN MDon MRav MTrO NLar NOra NRog NWea SBdl SEdi SKee SRHi SSFr WJas WMat
	- 'Kandil Sinap' (D)	SBdl SKee
	- 'Karmijn de Sonnaville' (D)	NOra SBdl SKee
§	- 'Katja' (D)	Widely available
	- KATY	see *M. domestica* 'Katja'
	- 'Kemp' (D)	IArd SBdl
	- 'Kendall' (D)	SBdl
	- 'Kenneth' (D)	SBdl WGwG
	- 'Kent' (D) ♀H6	SKee
	- 'Kentish Fillbasket' (C)	SBdl SKee
	- 'Kentish Pippin' (C/Cider/D)	SKee
	- 'Kentish Quarrenden' (D)	SBdl
	- 'Kerry Pippin' (D)	IArd NRog SBdl SKee
	- 'Keswick Codlin' (C)	CArg CHab EBee MTrO NLar NOra NRog NWea SBdl SKee SSFr WJas WMat WWct
§	- 'Kidd's Orange Red' (D) ♀H6	CAgr CArg CBod CEnd CMac CRos CTri EBee EPfP EPom LBuc LRHS MLod MTrO NOra NRog NWea SBmr SKee SSFr WMat WWct
	- 'Kilkenny Pearmain' (D)	IArd SBdl
	- 'Kim' (C/D)	SBdl
	- 'King Albert' (C)	SBdl
	- 'King Byerd' (C/D)	CBod CDoC CEnd SBdl
	- 'King Charles' Pearmain' (D)	SBdl SKee
	- 'King Coffee' (D)	SBdl
	- 'King David' (C/D)	NOra SBdl
	- 'King George V' (D)	SBdl SKee
§	- 'King of the Pippins' (D) ♀H6	CArg CHab CLnd EPom MTrO NOra SBdl SKee SVic
	- 'King of Tompkins County' (D)	NOra SBdl
	- 'King Russet' (D) ♀H6	SBdl
	- 'King's Acre Bountiful' (C)	SKee
	- 'King's Acre Pippin' (D)	MTrO NOra NRog SKee WMat
	- 'Kingston Black' (Cider/C)	CAgr CArg CEnd CHab CLnd CMac CTri EPom LBuc MLod MTrO NOra NRog SBdl SKee WMat
	- 'Kirton Fair' (D)	CBod
	- 'Knobby Russet' (D)	SBdl SKee SSFr
	- 'Koningin Juliana' (D)	NRog
	- 'Korobovka' (D)	SBdl
	- 'Lady Henniker' (C)	CEnd CHab MTrO NOra NRog SBdl SKee
	- 'Lady Hollendale' (D)	SBdl SKee
	- 'Lady Isabel' (D)	SBdl SKee
	- 'Lady Lambourne' (C/D)	CHab NRog SBdl SKee
	- 'Lady of the Lake' (D)	SBdl
	- 'Lady of the Wemyss' (C)	SBdl SKee
	- 'Lady Sudeley' (D)	CEnd CHab NRog SKee
	- 'Lady Williams' (D)	SBdl
	- 'Lady's Finger' (C/D)	CEnd
	- 'Lady's Finger of Lancaster' (C/D)	CHab NRog SKee
	- 'Lady's Finger of Offaly' (D)	IArd
	- 'Lakeland' (D)	SBdl SKee
	- 'Lamb Abbey Pearmain' (D)	SBdl SKee
	- 'Lamb's Seedling' (D)	SKee
	- 'Landsberger Reinette' (D)	SBdl SKee
	- 'Lane's Prince Albert' (C) ♀H6	CAgr CArg CHab CLnd CSBt CTri EPfP LRHS MGos MRav MTrO NBwr NOra NRog NWea SBdl SCoo SEdi SKee SSFr SVic SWeb WMat
	- 'Langley Pippin' (D)	SBdl SKee
§	- 'Langworthy' (Cider)	SBdl SKee
	- 'Lass o' Gowrie' (C)	SBdl SKee
	- 'Lawfam' (D)	SBdl
	- 'Laxton's Early Crimson' (D)	SBdl
§	- 'Laxton's Epicure' (D) ♀H6	CAgr CEnd CHab CTri NRog SBdl SKee
	- 'Laxton's Favourite' (D)	SBdl SKee
§	- 'Laxton's Fortune' (D) ♀H6	CArg CHab CMac CSBt CTri IArd MTrO NBwr NOra NRog SBdl SEdi SKee SSFr WMat WWct
	- 'Laxton's Herald' (D)	SBdl
	- 'Laxton's Pearmain' (D)	SBdl
	- 'Laxton's Rearguard' (D)	SBdl SKee
	- 'Laxton's Reward' (D)	SBdl
	- 'Laxton's Royalty' (D)	SBdl
§	- 'Laxton's Superb' (D)	Widely available
	- 'Laxton's Triumph' (D)	SBdl SKee
	- 'Laxton's Victory' (D)	SBdl
	- 'Leatherjacket' (C)	SKee
	- 'Leicester Burton'	see *M. domestica* 'Dutch Codlin'
	- 'Lemon Pippin' (C)	ELan NOra SBdl SKee
	- 'Lemon Queen' (D)	SBdl
	- 'Lewis's Incomparable' (C)	SBdl SKee
	- 'Liberty' (D)	NOra SBdl

- 'Limberland' (C) CBod
- 'Limelight' (D) ♀H6 CArg CDoC EBee MAsh MCoo MLod MTrO NLar NOra NRog NWea SBdl SCoo SKee SSFT SSFr WMat
- 'Limoncella' (D) SBdl
- 'Linda' (D) SBdl SKee
- 'Link Wonder' (D) CEnd
- 'Little Pax' (D) EPom LRHS MLod MTrO NLar NOra SKee SSFT
- 'Llwyd Hanner Goch' (D) WGwG
- 'Lobo' (D) SBdl
§ - 'Loddington' (C) SBdl
- 'Lodgemore Nonpareil' (D) SBdl SKee
- 'Lodi' (C) SBdl
- 'London Pearmain' (D) SBdl SKee
- 'London Pippin' (C) CAgr SBdl SKee
- 'Long Bider' (C) SBdl
- 'Longkeeper' (D) CAgr CEnd
- 'Longney Russet' (Cider/D) SBdl
- 'Longstart' (F) SBdl
- 'Lord Burghley' (D) SBdl SKee
- 'Lord Derby' (C) CAgr CArg CBod CHab CMac EDir EPom EWTr MRav MTrO NLar NOra NRog SBdl SBmr SEND SEdi SKee SPer SSFT SVic WMat WWct
- 'Lord Grosvenor' (C) SBdl SKee
- 'Lord Hindlip' (D) CHab MLod NOra NRog SBdl SKee WMat WWct
- 'Lord Lambourne' (D) ♀H6 CAgr CArg CEnd CHab CLnd CMac CSBt CTri ELan EPom LSRN MGos MTrO NOra NRog SBdl SBmr SEdi SKee SPer SSFr WJas WMat WWct
- 'Lord Lennox' (D) SBdl
- 'Lord of the Isles' (Cider) CAgr
- 'Lord Peckover' (D) SBdl
- 'Lord Rosebery' (D) SBdl SKee
- 'Lord Stradbroke' (C) SBdl SKee
- 'Lord Suffield' (C) SBdl SKee
- 'Lough Tree of Wexford' (D) IArd
- 'Love Beauty' (D) SBdl
- 'Lucombe's Pine' (D) CAgr CDoC CEnd SVic
- 'Lucombe's Seedling' (D) SKee
- 'Lynn's Pippin' (D) SBdl SKee
- 'Mabbott's Pearmain' (D) SBdl SKee
- 'Machen' (D) WGwG
- 'Maclean's Favourite' (D) SBdl SKee
- 'Macoun' (D) NOra SBdl
- 'Macy' (C/D) SBdl
- 'Madresfield Court' (D) SBdl SKee WWct
- 'Magdalene' (D) SBdl
- 'Maggie Grieve' (D) SBdl
- 'Maggie Sinclair' (D) SBdl
- 'Maid of Kent' (F) SBdl
- 'Maidstone Favourite' (D) SBdl SKee
- 'Major' (Cider) CAgr SBdl WMat
- 'Maldon Wonder' (D) SBdl SKee
- 'Malling Kent' (D) SBdl
- 'Maltster' (D) SBdl SKee
- 'Manaccan Primrose' (C/D) CBod CDoC CEnd CTsd
- 'Mank's Codlin' (C) SBdl
- 'Mannington's Pearmain' (D) NRog SBdl SKee WMat
- 'Marged Nicolas' (D) WGwG
- 'Margil' (D) NOra NRog SBdl SKee
- 'Marriage-maker' (D) SBdl SKee
- 'Marston Scarlet Wonder' (C) SBdl
- 'Maxton' (D) SBdl
- 'May Beauty' (D) SBdl SKee
- 'May Queen' (D) SBdl SKee WWct
- 'Maypole' (D) MDon SBdl SEdi
- 'McIntosh' (D) NOra NRog SBdl SKee
- 'Mead's Broading' (C) SBdl SKee
- 'Measday's Favourite' (C) SBdl SKee
- 'Médaille d'Or' (Cider) CArg SBdl SKee WMat
- 'Medina' (D) SBdl
- 'Megabite' (C/D) EPom
- 'Melba' (D) SBdl SKee
- 'Melon' (D) SBdl
- 'Melrose' (D) LMaj LPar NRog SBdl SGsty SKee
- 'Merchant Apple' (D) SBdl
- 'Mère de Ménage' (C) NRog SKee
- 'Meridian' PBR (D) CAgr MTrO NOra NRog SBdl SEdi SSFr WMat
- 'Merlin's Apple' (D) NRog
- 'Merlyn' (F) SBdl
- 'Merton Beauty' (D) SBdl SKee
- 'Merton Charm' (D) SBdl SKee
- 'Merton Delight' (D) SBdl
- 'Merton Joy' (D) SBdl
- 'Merton Knave' (D) SBdl
- 'Merton Prolific' (D) SBdl
- 'Merton Russet' (D) SBdl SKee
- 'Merton Worcester' (D) SBdl SKee
- 'Meteor' (F) **new** SKee
- 'Michaelmas Red' (D) NRog SBdl SKee
- 'Michelin' (Cider) CAgr CArg CTri MTrO NOra SBdl SKee WMat WWct
- MIEL D'OR see *M. domestica* 'Honeygold'
- 'Miller's Seedling' (D) NOra SBdl SKee
- 'Millet' (D) SBdl
- 'Millicent Barnes' (D) SBdl SKee
- 'Minister von Hammerstein' (D) SBdl
- 'Minshull Crab' (C) SBdl SKee
- 'Missing Link' (D) SBdl
- 'Molleskov' (C/D) SBdl
- 'Mollie's Delicious' (D) SBdl SKee
- 'Monarch' (C) CAgr CBod CTri EPom NRog SBdl SKee SSFr
- 'Monmouthshire Green' (D) WGwG
- 'Montfort' (D) SBdl SKee
- 'Morgan's Sweet' (C/Cider) CArg CHab CPer CTri NOra NRog SBdl SKee WMat
- 'Morley's Seedling' (C) SBdl
- 'Moss's Seedling' (D) SBdl
§ - 'Mother' (D) ♀H6 CAgr CLnd SBdl SKee SSFr
- 'Mrs Barron' (D) SBdl
- 'Mrs Lakeman's Seedling' (C) SBdl
- 'Mrs Phillimore' (D) SBdl
- 'Munster Tulip' (D/C) IArd SBdl
- 'Murfitt's Seedling' (C) SBdl
- 'Muscadet de Dieppe' (Cider) SBdl
§ - 'Mutsu' (C/D) CArg MRav NOra NRog SBdl SEND SEdi SKee SPer SSFr WMat
- 'Mylor Pike' (D) CEnd
- 'Nancy Jackson' (C) CHab NRog SBdl SKee
- 'Nanny' (D) CLnd SBdl SKee
- 'Nant Gwrtheyrn' (D) WGwG
- 'Nasona' (D) SBdl SKee
- 'Nehou' (Cider) SBdl
- 'Neild's Drooper' (D/C) SBdl
- 'Nemes Szercsika Alma' (C) SBdl SKee
- 'New Bess Pool' (D) NRog SBdl
- 'New German' (D) SBdl
- 'New Hawthornden' (C) SBdl
- 'New Rock Pippin' (D) SBdl
- 'Newport Cross' (D) SBdl
- 'Newton Wonder' (C) CAgr CArg CEnd CHab CLnd CPer CSBt CTri EPom LMaj MGos MTrO NOra NRog NWea SBdl

	SBmr SEdi SKee SRms SSFr WJas WMat WWct
- 'Newtosh' (D)	SBdl
- 'Newtown Pippin' (D)	NOra SBdl
- 'Nigde' (D)	SBdl SKee
- 'Nine Square' (D)	CPer
- 'No Pip' (C)	SBdl
- 'Nolan Pippin' (D)	SBdl SKee
- 'Nonpareil' (D)	NRog SKee
- 'Norfolk Beauty' (C)	NRog SBdl SKee
- 'Norfolk Beefing' (C)	CArg CHab EFPl NOra NRog SBdl SKee WMat
- 'Norfolk Royal' (D)	CHab CLnd NOra NRog SBdl SBmr SKee
- 'Norfolk Royal Russet' (D)	MLod NOra NRog SBdl SKee WMat
- 'Norfolk Summer Broadend' (C)	SKee
- 'Norfolk Winter Coleman' (C)	SKee
- 'Norman's Pippin' (D)	SBdl
- 'Northern Greening' (C)	SBdl SKee
- 'Northern Spy' (D)	NOra SBdl SKee
- 'Northland Seedling' (D)	SBdl
§ - 'Northwood' (Cider)	SBdl SKee WMat
- 'Nottingham Pippin' (D)	NRog SBdl
- 'Nutmeg Pippin' (D)	SBdl
- NUVAR CHEERFULL GOLD (D)	SKee
- NUVAR FRECKLES (D)	SKee
- NUVAR GOLD (D)	SKee
- NUVAR GOLDEN ELF (D)	SKee
- NUVAR GOLDEN HILLS (D)	SKee
- NUVAR HOME FARM (D)	SKee
- NUVAR LONG HARVEST (D)	SKee
- NUVAR MELODY (D)	SKee
- 'Oaken Pin' (D)	CEnd CPer SBdl
§ - 'Obelisk'[PBR] (D)	CArg MGos MTrO NOra SKee WMat
- 'Old Fred' (D)	SBdl
- 'Old Pearmain' (D)	SBdl SKee
- 'Old Somerset Russet' (D)	SBdl
- 'Onibury Pippin' (D)	SBdl
- 'Ontario' (C)	LPar SBdl
- 'Opal'[PBR] (D)	SBdl
- 'Opalescent' (D)	CEnd SBdl SKee
- 'Orange Goff' (D)	SBdl SKee
- 'Orangenburg' (D)	SBdl SKee
- 'Orin' (D)	SBdl SKee
- 'Orkney Apple' (F)	SKee
- 'Orleans' (D)	SBdl
- 'Orleans Reinette' (D)	CAgr CArg CBod CEnd CTri EPom MTrO NOra NRog SBdl SBmr SKee SSFr WMat WWct
- 'Ortley' (D)	SBdl
- 'Osennee Desertnoe' (D) <u>**new**</u>	SKee
- 'Osier' (Cider)	SBdl
- 'Oslin' (D)	SBdl SKee WMat
- 'Osnabrucker Reinette' (D)	SBdl
- 'Otava'[PBR] (C/D)	SKee
- 'Owen Thomas' (D)	SBdl SKee
- 'Oxford Beauty' (D)	SBdl
- 'Oxford Conquest' (D)	SBdl SKee
- 'Oxford Sunrise' (D)	SBdl
- 'Oxford Yeoman' (C)	SBdl
- 'Ozark Gold' (D)	SBdl
- 'P.J. Bergius' (D)	SBdl
- 'Paignton Marigold' (Cider)	SBdl
- 'Palmer's Rosey' (D)	SBdl SKee
- PARADICE GOLD (D)	CRos EBee EPom LRHS MTrO SCoo SKee SPoG
- 'Park Farm Pippin' (D)	SKee
- 'Paroquet' (D)	SBdl SKee
- 'Patricia' (D)	SBdl
- 'Paulared' (D)	SBdl
- 'Payhembury' (C/Cider)	CAgr
- 'Peacemaker' (D)	SBdl SKee
- 'Pear Apple' (D)	CAgr CEnd
- 'Pearl' (D)	NOra SBdl WMat
- 'Peasgood's Nonsuch' (C) 🏆[H6]	CAgr CArg CHab EPom IArd LSRN MAsh MTrO NOra NRog SBdl SBmr SKee WMat
- 'Peck's Pleasant' (D)	SBdl SKee
- 'Pederstrup' (D)	SBdl
- 'Pedro' (D)	SBdl
- 'Pendragon' (D)	CEnd
- 'Pennard Bitter' (Cider)	SBdl
- 'Pépin Shafrannyi' (D)	SBdl SKee
- 'Peter Lock' (C/D)	CAgr CEnd SBdl SKee
- 'Pethyre' (Cider)	CCVT SBdl
- 'Petit Pippin' (D)	SBdl
- 'Pewaukee' (D)	SBdl
- 'Pickering's Seedling' (D)	NRog SBdl SKee
- 'Pig Aderyn' (C)	CHab WGwG
- 'Pigeonette de Rouen' (D)	SKee
- 'Pig's Nose Pippin' (D)	CEnd SBdl SKee
- 'Pig's Nose Pippin' Type III (D)	CAgr
- 'Pig's Snout' (Cider/C/D)	CEnd NRog SBdl
- 'Pine Apple Russet' (C/D)	CAgr SBdl
- 'Pine Apple Russet of Devon' (D)	CEnd
- 'Pine Golden Pippin' (D)	SBdl SKee
- PINK LADY	see *M. domestica* 'Cripps Pink'
- 'Pinova'[PBR] (D)	CAgr CBod EPom LPar MTrO NOra SBmr SSFr
- 'Pitmaston Pine Apple' (D)	CArg CHab CLnd CPer CTri EWTr MAsh MLod MTrO NOra NRog SBdl SKee SSFr WMat WWct
- 'Pitmaston Russet Nonpareil' (D)	SBdl SKee
- 'Pixie' (D) 🏆[H6]	CBod CDoC CSBt EPom LRHS MPri MTrO NOra NRog SBdl SKee SRHi WWct
- 'Plum Vite' (D)	CAgr CTri
- 'Plymouth Cross' (D)	SBdl SKee
- 'Plympton Pippin' (C)	CEnd CPer
- POLKA ('Trajan') (D)	NOra SBdl
- 'Polly' (C/D)	SBdl SKee
- 'Polly Prosser' (D)	SBdl SKee
- 'Pomeroy of Somerset' (D)	CHab CTri NRog SBdl SKee
- 'Ponsford' (C)	CAgr SBdl SKee WMat
- 'Pónyik Alma' (C)	SBdl
- 'Pope's Scarlet Costard' (D/C)	SBdl
- 'Port Allen Russet' (C/D)	SBdl
- 'Port Wine'	see *M. domestica* 'Harry Master's Jersey'
- 'Porter's Perfection' (Cider)	CTri NOra NRog SBdl
- 'Pott's Seedling' (C)	SBdl SKee
- 'Present van Holland' (D)	SBdl
- 'Prima' (D)	SBdl
- 'Prince Alfred' (C)	SBdl
- 'Prince Charles' (D)	SBdl SKee
- 'Prince Edward' (C)	SBdl
- 'Prince George' (C)	SBdl
- 'Princesse' (F)	CEnd SKee
- 'Priscilla' (D)	NOra SBdl
- 'Proctor's Seedling' (D)	SBdl
- 'Pumpkin Sunset' (F)	SBdl

- 'Purpurroter Cousinot' (D) SBdl SKee
- 'Queen' (C) CAgr NRog SBdl SKee
- 'Queen Alexandra' (C) SBdl
- 'Queen Caroline' (C) SKee
- 'Queen Cox' (D) CLnd CTri EPom LPar LSRN NOra NRog NTrD SBdl SBmr SEdi SKee SSFr SWvt WMat WTSh
- 'Radford Beauty' (F) NRog
- 'Rajka'PBR (D) NOra NRog SKee WWct
- 'Rambour Papeleu' (C) SBdl
- 'Rathe Ripe' (D) SBdl
- 'Red Alkmene' see *M. domestica* 'Red Windsor'
- 'Red Astrachan' (D) SBdl
- 'Red Belle de Boskoop' (D) CAgr CWnw NRog SBdl
- 'Red Blenheim' (C/D) SBdl
- 'Red Charles Ross' (C/D) SBdl
- 'Red Delicious' see *M. domestica* 'Starking'
- 'Red Devil' (D) Widely available
- 'Red Ellison' (D) CTri NRog SBdl
- 'Red Elstar' (D) SBdl
- 'Red Falstaff'PBR (D) ♀H6 Widely available
- 'Red Fortune' (D) SBdl
- 'Red Gravenstein' (D) NRog SBdl SEdi
- 'Red Ingestrie' (D) NRog
- 'Red James Grieve' (D) SKee
- 'Red Jersey' (Cider) SBdl
- 'Red Joaneting' (D) SBdl SKee
- 'Red Jonagold' see *M. domestica* 'Jonagored'
- § 'Red Jonaprince'PBR (D) SBdl WMat
- 'Red Jonaprince Wilton's' (F) MTrO
- 'Red Melba' (D) SBdl
- 'Red Newton Wonder' (C) SBdl
- 'Red Pixie' (D) CArg SBdl WMat
- 'Red Rattler' (D) CTri
- 'Red Roller' (D) CTsd
- 'Red Sauce' (C) SBdl SKee
- 'Red Victoria' (C) NRog SBdl
- § 'Red Windsor' (D) ♀H6 CArg CEnd CLnd CMac CRos CTri EBee ELan EPom LBuc LCro LOPS LRHS MAsh MLod MPri MTrO NLar NOra NOrn NRog SCoo SKee SLim SPoG SSFr WMat
- 'Redcoat Grieve' (D) SBdl
- 'Redfree' (D) NOra SBdl
- 'Redlane'PBR (F) **new** CWnw
- 'Redsleeves' (D) CAgr CBod CLnd NOra SBdl SKee
- 'Redwing' (D) SBdl
- REGALI ('Delkistar'PBR) (D) SBdl
- 'Reid's Seedling' (C/D) SBdl
- 'Reine de Pommes' (Cider) SBdl
- 'Reine des Reinettes' see *M. domestica* 'King of the Pippins'
- 'Reinette de Champagne' (C) SBdl
- 'Reinette de Mâcon' (D) NRog
- 'Reinette Descardre' (D) SBdl
- 'Reinette Dorée de Boediker' (D) SBdl
- 'Reinette du Canada' (D) LMaj SBdl SGsty SKee
- 'Reinette Grise' (D) **new** LMaj
- 'Reinette Rouge Etoilée' (D) SBdl
- 'Renora' (D) SBdl
- 'Renown' (D) SBdl
- 'Resi'PBR (C/D) WWct
- 'Reverend W. Wilks' (C) CAgr CArg CBod CEnd CHab CSBt CTri EBee EPom MLod MTrO NOra NRog SBdl SBmr SEdi SKee SSFr WJas WMat WWct
- 'Rhode Island Greening' (C/D) NOra SBdl SKee
- 'Ribston Pippin' (D) ♀H6 CArg CPer CTri LBuc MRav MTrO NOra NRog NWea SBdl SKee SSFr WJas WMat WWct
- 'Richardson' (F) SBdl
- 'Richared Delicious' (D) SBdl
- 'Ringstad' (D) SBdl
- 'Rival' (D) CAgr SBdl SKee
- 'Rivers' Early Peach' (D) SBdl
- 'Rivers' Nonsuch' (D) CHab SBdl
- 'Robert Blatchford' (C) SBdl
- 'Robin Pippin' (D) SBdl
- 'Rock' (C) SBdl
- 'Rogers McIntosh' (D) SBdl
- 'Rokewood' (D) SBdl
- 'Rome Beauty' (D) SBdl
- 'Rosemary Russet' (D) ♀H6 CAgr CArg CHab CPer ELan NOra NRog SBdl SBmr SKee SSFr WMat WWct
- 'Rosette' (D) CArg EPfP EPom LRHS MAsh MTrO NLar NOra SKee WMat
- 'Rosmarina Bianca' (D/C) SBdl
- 'Ross Nonpareil' (D) CAgr IArd NOra NRog SBdl SKee WMat
- 'Rossie Pippin' (C) SBdl
- 'Rosy Blenheim' (D) SBdl
- 'Roter Ananas' (D) SKee
- 'Roter Stettiner' (D) SBdl
- 'Rougemont' (D) SBdl
- 'Rough Pippin' (D) CBod CEnd SBdl SKee
- 'Roundway Magnum Bonum' (C/D) CAgr SBdl
- § 'Roxbury Russet' (D) NOra SBdl SKee
- 'Royal Blush'PBR (D) SBdl
- 'Royal Gala' (D) CMac EDir EPom LBuc LMaj LPar MRav NTrD SBdl SBmr
- § 'Royal Jubilee' (C) SBdl SKee
- 'Royal Russet' (C) CAgr CEnd SBdl SKee
- 'Royal Snow' (D) SKee
- 'Royal Somerset' (C/Cider) CPer SBdl WMat
- 'Rubens' (D) SBdl SKee
- RUBINETTE ('Rafzubin') (D) CBod NOra SKee
- RUBINETTE ROSSO ('Rafzubex'PBR) (D) MTrO NOra WMat
- 'Rubinola'PBR (D) SKee
- 'Ruby' Seabrook (D) SBdl SKee
- 'Ruby' Thorrington (D) SBdl SKee
- 'S.T. Wright' (C) NRog SBdl
- 'Sabaros' (C) SBdl
- 'Saint Ailred' (D) SBdl SKee
- 'Saint Albans Pippin' (D) SBdl SKee
- 'Saint Cecilia' (D) CHab SBdl SKee
- § 'Saint Edmund's Pippin' (D) ♀H6 CHab CPer ELan EPfP MTrO NOra NRog NWea SBmr SKee SSFr
- 'Saint Edmund's Russet' see *M. domestica* 'Saint Edmund's Pippin'
- 'Saint Everard' (D) SBdl SKee
- 'Saint Magdalen' (D) SKee
- 'Saint Martin's' (D) SBdl
- 'Saltcote Pippin' (D) SBdl SKee WMat
- 'Sam Young' (D) CAgr NRog SBdl SKee
- 'Samba' (C/D) LOPS
- 'Sandew' (C/D) SBdl
- 'Sandlin Duchess' (D) NOra WMat
- 'Sandringham' (C) SBdl SKee
- 'Sanspareil' (D) CAgr SBdl SKee
- 'Santana'PBR (D) ♀H6 LPar NOra SBdl WMat
- 'Saturn' (D) CAgr CArg CCVT MLod MTrO NOra NRog SBdl SKee SSFr WMat WWct
- 'Saw Pits' (D) CAgr CEnd SKee
- 'Scarlet Crofton' (D) IArd SBdl

- 'Scarlet Nonpareil' (D)	SBdl SKee
- 'Scarlet Pearmain' (D)	SBdl
- 'Scarlet Pimpernel' (D)	SBdl SKee
- 'Schoolmaster' (C)	NRog SBdl SKee
- 'Schweizer Orange' (F)	SBdl
- 'Scilly Pearl' (C)	SBdl
- 'Scotch Bridget' (C)	CArg CHab EBee MTrO NBid NOra NRog SBdl SKee WMat WWct
- 'Scotch Dumpling' (C)	GKin MTrO NOra SBdl SKee WMat
- 'Scotia' (C/D)	SBdl
- 'Scrumptious'PBR (D) ♀H6	Widely available
- 'Seabrook's Red' (D)	SBdl SKee
- 'Seaton House' (C)	SBdl
- 'September Beauty' (D)	SBdl
- 'Severn Bank' (C)	SBdl SKee
- 'Sharleston Pippin' (D)	NRog SBdl SKee
- 'Sharon' (D)	SBdl
- 'Sheep's Nose' (C)	CHab SKee
- 'Shenandoah' (C)	SKee
- 'Shoesmith' (C)	SBdl
- 'Siddington Russet' (C/D)	SBdl
- 'Sidney Strake' (C)	CAgr CEnd SBdl
- 'Signe Tillisch' (C/D)	SBdl
- 'Sikulai Alma' (D)	SBdl
- 'Sir Isaac Newton's'	see *M. domestica* 'Flower of Kent'
- 'Sir John Thornycroft' (D)	SBdl
- 'Sisson's Worksop Newtown' (D)	NRog SBdl SKee
- 'Skovfoged' (C)	SBdl
- 'Slack Ma Girdle' (Cider)	CArg CBod NOra SBdl SKee WMat
- 'Sleeping Beauty' (C)	SBdl
- 'Small's Admirable' (C)	SBdl
- 'Smart's Prince Arthur' (C)	CHab NRog SBdl
- 'Smiler' (D)	SBdl
- 'Smoothee' (D)	SBdl
- 'Snell's Glass Apple'	see *M. domestica* 'Glass Apple'
- 'Somerset Lasting' (C)	CTri
- 'Somerset Redstreak' (Cider)	CAgr CArg CHab CTri MTrO NOra NRog SBdl WMat
- 'Sops in Wine' (Cider/D)	CArg EDir NOra SBdl SKee SVic WMat
- 'Sour Bay' (Cider)	CAgr
- 'Sour Natural'	see *M. domestica* 'Langworthy'
- 'Sowman's Seedling' (C)	SBdl
- 'Spartan' (D)	Widely available
- 'Spätblühender Taffetapfel' (D)	SKee
- 'Spencer' (D)	SBdl SKee
- 'Splendour' (D)	SBdl
- 'Spotted Dick' (Cider)	CPer
- 'Stable Jersey' (Cider)	SBdl
- 'Stamford Pippin' (D)	NRog
- 'Stanway Seedling' (C)	SBdl SKee
- 'Star of Devon' (D)	CEnd SBdl SKee
§ - 'Starking' (D)	LMaj NOra SBdl SGsty SKee
- 'Starkrimson' (D)	SBdl SKee
- 'Stark's Earliest' (D)	SBdl SVic
- 'Starkspur Golden Delicious' (D)	SBdl SKee
- 'Stembridge Cluster' (Cider)	CTri SBdl
- 'Stembridge Jersey' (Cider)	SBdl
- 'Steyne Seedling' (D)	NRog
- 'Stibbert' (D)	SBdl
- 'Stirling Castle' (C)	CAgr MTrO NOra SBdl SKee WMat
- 'Stobo Castle' (C)	SBdl SKee
- 'Stoke Edith Pippin' (D)	SBdl
- 'Stoke Red' (Cider)	CArg NOra NRog SBdl SKee WMat
- 'Stone's'	see *M. domestica* 'Loddington'

- 'Stonetosh' (D)	SBdl
- 'Storey's Seedling' (D)	SBdl
- 'Strawberry Pippin' (D)	NRog SBdl
- 'Striped Beefing' (C)	NRog SBdl SKee
- 'Strippy' (C)	SBdl
- 'Stub Nose' (F)	SKee
- 'Sturmer Pippin' (D)	CSBt CTri EBee NOra NRog SBdl SKee SWeb WWct
- 'Summer Golden Pippin' (D)	NRog SBdl SKee
- 'Summerland' (D)	SBdl
- 'Sunburn' (D)	SBdl
- 'Sunrise'PBR (D)	CEnd NOra SKee
- 'Sunrise' (D)	CBod SBdl
- 'Sunset' (D) ♀H6	Widely available
- 'Suntan' (D)	NOra NRog SBdl SKee
- 'Superb'	see *M. domestica* 'Laxton's Superb'
- 'Sure Crop' (D)	SBdl
- 'Surprise' (D)	LRHS MTrO SBdl
- SURPRIZE (D)	EPom LBuc NOra
- 'Sussex Mother' (C/D)	CHab NRog SBdl
- 'Swaar' (D)	SBdl SKee
- 'Sweet Alford' (Cider)	CArg CPer SBdl WMat WWct
- 'Sweet Bay' (Cider)	CAgr
- 'Sweet Caroline' (D)	LPar SBdl
- 'Sweet Coppin' (Cider)	CArg CTri SBdl WMat
- 'Sweet Lilibet'	see *M. domestica* 'Red Windsor'
- 'Sweet Merlin' (D/Cider)	SBdl
- 'Sweet Pethyre' (C)	SEdi
- 'Sweet Sixteen' (D)	NOra SBdl
- 'Sweet Society' (D)	NOra SKee WMat
- 'Sylvia' (D)	SBdl
- 'Tale Sweet' (Cider)	SBdl
- 'Tamar Beauty' (D)	CEnd
- 'Tan Harvey' (Cider)	CEnd SBdl
- 'Tare de Ghinda' (F)	SBdl
- 'Tasman Pride' (D)	SBdl
- 'Taunton Cross' (D)	CAgr CArg SBdl WMat
- 'Taylor's' (Cider)	CAgr SBdl
- 'Taylor's Favourite' (F)	NWea
- 'Ten Commandments' (Cider/D)	SBdl SKee WWct
- 'Tenroy'PBR (D)	SBdl
- 'Téton de Demoiselle' (D)	NRog SBdl
- 'Tewkesbury Baron' (D)	SBdl
- 'The Rattler' (Cider)	CEnd
- 'Thoday's Quarrenden' (D)	SBdl
- 'Thomas Jeffrey' (D)	SBdl
- 'Thomas Rivers' (C)	SBdl
- 'Thompson's Apple' (D)	SBdl
- 'Thorle Pippin' (D)	SBdl SKee
- 'Thorpe's Peach' (D)	SBdl
- 'Thurso' (D)	SBdl
- TICKLED PINK ('Baya Marisa') (C/D)	CArg EPom LBuc LCro LRHS MGos MLod MTrO NOra SBmr SKee SPer SSFr WMat
- 'Tidicombe Seedling' (D)	CPer WMat
- 'Tiffen' (C)	SBdl
- 'Tillington Court' (C)	SBdl
- 'Tinsley Quince' (D)	SBdl WMat
- 'Tom Putt' (C)	CAgr CArg CCVT CHab CLnd CPer CSBt CTri LBuc NOra NRog SBdl SKee WJas WMat WWct
- 'Tommy Knight' (D)	CAgr CEnd SBdl
- 'Topaz'PBR (D) ♀H6	LPar MTrO NOra SBdl SKee SSFr
- 'Totnes Apple' (D)	CPer
- 'Tower of Glamis' (C)	CHab NRog SBdl SKee
- 'Transparente de Bois Guillaume' (D)	SBdl
- 'Transparente de Croncels' (C)	SBdl
- 'Trecarrell Mill No.1' (Cider) **new**	CBod

– 'Tregonna King' (C/D)	CBod CDoC CEnd CPer CTsd
– 'Tremlett's Bitter' (Cider)	CAgr CArg CHab CTsd MTrO NOra NRog SBdl SKee SVic WMat
– 'Trwyn Mochyn' (C)	WGwG
§ – 'Tuscan' (D)	SBdl SKee
– 'Twenty Ounce' (C)	SBdl SKee
§ – 'Tydeman's Early Worcester' (D)	CAgr CBod CHab CLnd EDir LPar MDon NRog SBdl SBmr SEdi SKee SRms SSFr WWct
– 'Tydeman's Harvest' (D)	SBdl
– 'Tydeman's Late Orange' (D)	CArg CHab CTri MLod NBwr NOra NRog SBdl SBmr SKee WMat
– 'Tyler's Kernel' (C)	SBdl
– 'Uland' (C)	SBdl
– 'Underleaf' (D)	SBdl
– 'Upton Pyne' (C/D)	CEnd CPer SBdl
– 'Vanda'[PBR] (F)	SBdl
– 'Veitch's Perfection' (C/D)	WMat
– 'Venus Pippin' (C/D)	CEnd SBdl
– 'Vernade' (F)	SBdl
– 'Vicar of Beighton' (D)	SBdl
– 'Vickie' (Cider)	NRog
– 'Victory' (C)	SBdl
– 'Vileberie' (Cider)	CTri NRog
– 'Violette' (C)	SBdl SKee
– 'Vista-bella' (D)	MDon SBdl SEdi SKee
– 'Vitgylling' (D/C)	SBdl
– 'Von Zuccalmaglio's Reinette' (D)	SBdl
– 'Wadey's Seedling' (D)	SBdl
– 'Wadhurst Pippin' (C/D)	NRog SBdl
– 'Wagener' (D)	NRog SBdl SKee
– WALTZ ('Telamon') (D)	SKee
– 'Wanstall Pippin' (D)	SKee
– 'Warden' (D)	SBdl
– 'Warner's King' (C) ♀H6	CTri MTrO NOra NRog SBdl SKee
– 'Warren's Seedling' (C)	SBdl
– 'Washington Strawberry' (D)	SBdl
– 'Wealthy' (D)	SBdl SKee
– 'Weight' (C)	SBdl
– 'Wellington' (Cider)	CAgr
– 'Wellington' (C)	see *M. domestica* 'Dummellor's Seedling'
– 'Wellington Bloomless' (D)	NRog
§ – 'Wellspur' (D)	SBdl
– 'Wellspur Red Delicious'	see *M. domestica* 'Wellspur'
– 'Werrington Wonder' (D)	CEnd
– 'West View Seedling' (D)	SBdl
– 'Weston's Seedling' (C)	SBdl
– 'Wheeler's Russet' (D)	NRog SBdl SKee
– 'White Jersey' (Cider)	SBdl
– 'White Melrose' (C)	NOra SKee WMat
– 'White Quarrenden' (D)	SBdl
– 'White Transparent' (C/D)	SBdl SKee
– 'White Winter Pearmain' (D)	SBdl
– 'Whitpot Sweet' (Cider)	CEnd
– 'William Crump' (D)	CEnd CHab CPer MTrO NOra NRog SBdl SKee WMat WWct
– 'William Peters' (D)	NRog
– 'Williams Favourite' (D)	SBdl
– 'Windsor Early' (D)	SSFr
– 'Winesap' (C/D)	NOra SBdl
– 'Winston' (D) ♀H6	CAgr CBod CCVT CMac CTri EDir LPar NRog SBdl SKee SRms SVic SWeb WWct
– 'Winter Banana' (D)	CArg CHab MLod NOra NRog SBdl SKee SVic WMat
– 'Winter Cockpit' (C)	NRog
– 'Winter Gem' (D)	CAgr CArg CBod CCVT CEnd CLnd EPom LBuc MLod MTrO NOra NRog SBdl SBmr SKee SSFr WJas WMat
– 'Winter Lemon' (C/D)	SBdl SKee
– 'Winter Majetin' (C)	SBdl
– 'Winter Peach' (D/C)	CAgr SBdl
– 'Winter Pearmain' (D)	SBdl SKee
– 'Winter Quarrenden' (D)	SBdl SKee
– 'Winter Stubbard' (C)	SBdl
– 'Withington Fillbasket' (C)	SBdl
– 'Wolf River' (D/C)	NOra NRog SBdl
– 'Woodbine'	see *M. domestica* 'Northwood'
– 'Woodford' (C)	SBdl
– 'Woolbrook Pippin' (D)	CAgr CEnd CPer SBdl WMat
– 'Woolbrook Russet' (C)	SBdl
– 'Worcester Cross' (D)	SBdl
– 'Worcester Pearmain' (D) ♀H6	Widely available
– 'Worcester Woodsil' (F)	SBdl
– 'Wyatt's Seedling'	see *M. domestica* 'Langworthy'
– 'Wyken Pippin' (D)	SBdl SKee WWct
– 'Yarlington Mill' (Cider)	CAgr CArg CHab CTri MTrO NOra NRog SBdl SKee SVic WMat WWct
– 'Ye Old Peasgood' (D)	SBdl
– 'Yellow Bellflower' (D/C)	SBdl
– 'Yellow Ingestrie' (D)	CArg CHab MTrO NOra NRog SBdl SKee WMat WWct
– 'Yorkshire Aromatic' (C)	NRog SBdl SKee
– 'Yorkshire Greening' (C)	CHab NOra NRog SBdl SKee
– 'Young America' (D)	SBdl
– 'Young's Pinello' (D)	SBdl
– 'Zabergäu Renette' (D)	NOra SBdl SKee
'Donald Wyman'	CLnd EBar EPfP MAsh MTrO NLar NOra SCoo WMat
§ 'Echtermeyer'	LMaj SBdl
'Elise Rathke'	CLnd SBdl
'Evelyn'	CBcs CLnd MTrO NOra NWea WMat
§ 'Evereste' ♀H6	Widely available
florentina	CPer
– 'Rosemoor'	CLnd
× ***floribunda*** ♀H6	Widely available
'Gardener's Gold'	CEnd CLnd SRms
'Gibbs' Golden Gage' (D)	SBdl
× ***gloriosa*** 'Oekonomierat Echtermeyer'	see *M.* 'Echtermeyer'
'Golden Gem'	CLnd MTrO NLar NOra NOrn SBdl SEWo SKee WMat
'Golden Hornet'	see *M.* × *zumi* 'Golden Hornet'
'Harry Baker'	CBod CCVT CDoC CEnd CLnd CMac CSBt EPfP EPom LRHS LSRN MBlu MRav MTrO NOra SCoo SLim SPer SPoG SRHi WMat WMou WWct
× ***hartwigii***	CLnd
'Hillieri'	see *M.* × *scheideckeri* 'Hillieri'
hupehensis ♀H6	CBcs CEnd CLnd CMCN CPer CSBt CTri EHeP EPfP LRHS MBlu MGos MRav MTrO NLar NOra NOrn NRog NWea SCob SDix SPer SPtp WJur WMat WMou WTSh
'Hyde Hall Spire'	SCoo
'Hyslop'	CLnd
'Indian Magic'	CBTr CSBt EBee EPfP EWTr LRHS MAsh MTrO NLar NOra SPer WHCr WHtc WMat
'Indian Summer'	CLnd
ioensis **new**	WJur
– 'Fimbriata' (d)	LCro LRHS MAsh MTrO NLar NOra
JELLY KING ('Mattfru') ♀H6	CBTr CLnd CPer EBee EPfP EPom EWTr LBuc LCro LOPS LRHS LSRN MAsh MPri MTrO NLar NOra NOrn NWea SEWo SGbt SOrN SPer SPoG WHCr WMat WMou

	'John Downie' (C)	Widely available
	'Kaido'	see *M.* × *micromalus*
	'Lady Northcliffe'	CLnd SBdl
	'Laura' ♀H6	CBod CLnd EBee ELan EPom LCro LOPS LRHS LSRN MAsh MGos MTrO NOra SCoo SKee SLim SPer SPoG WJas WMat
	'Louisa'	EBee EPfP LSRN MAsh MTrO NOra NWea SCoo SGbt SGol SLim WLov WMat
	× ***magdeburgensis***	CAco CCVT CLnd EHeP
	'Makamik'	SBdl
	'Mariri Red' (D)	WMat
	'Mary Potter'	CPer
§	× ***micromalus***	CLnd
	× ***moerlandsii*** 'Liset'	CEnd CLnd MRav NOra NRog SBdl SCob SCoo SEdi WFar
§	- 'Profusion'	CBcs CTri EBar EDir ELan EPfP IPap LCro LOPS LRHS MDon MGos MPri MRav MSwo MTrO NBwr NOra NRHS NRog NWea SGol SGsty SKee SPer SRms SWvt WHtc WSpi
	'Mokum'	EBar EDir EHeP EWTr LMaj LPar LSRN
	MOLTEN LAVA ('Molazam')	CLnd
	'Montreal Beauty'	CLnd EPom SBdl WJas
	niedzwetzkyana	CLnd SBdl
	NUVAR CARNIVAL	SKee
	NUVAR MARBLE (C)	EBee MTrO NOra NOrn SKee WMat
	'Oporto' (F)	SBdl
	orientalis	SBdl
	PERPETU	see *M.* 'Evereste'
	'Peter's Red'	CLnd LMaj SHor
	'Pink Perfection'	CEnd EPfP LCro LOPS MAsh MTrO NOra SGbt SPoG WMat
	× ***platycarpa***	SBdl
	'Pond Red'	CLnd
	'Prairifire'	CBod CLnd EBee EDir EGrI LRHS MAsh MTrO NOra SCoo SLim SPer SPoG WMat
	prattii	CLnd CPer GLog WLov
	- 'Pourpre Noir'	CLnd
	aff. ***prattii*** SICH 775 **new**	WPGP
	'Princeton Cardinal' ♀H6	CLnd CMac EBee EPfP MAsh SCoo SLim SPoG
	'Professor Sprenger'	see *M.* × *zumi* 'Professor Sprenger'
	'Profusion'	see *M.* × *moerlandsii* 'Profusion'
	prunifolia	MBlu
	- var. ***rinkii***	CLnd
	'Purple Prince'	CLnd
§	× ***purpurea*** 'Aldenhamensis'	CLnd NRog
	- 'Crimson Cascade' **new**	CBcs NOra NOrn
	- 'Eleyi'	CLnd EPfP LMaj NRog NWea SBdl SEdi
	- 'Neville Copeman'	CCVT CLnd EPom LRHS SBdl SEdi SSFr
	- 'Pendula'	see *M.* 'Echtermeyer'
	'Ralph Shay'	CLnd
	'Red Barron'	CLnd
	'Red Glow'	CAco CLnd NRog SBdl
	'Red Jade'	see *M.* × *scheideckeri* 'Red Jade'
	RED OBELISK ('Dvp Obel')	CBTr CCVT CLnd EBee LBuc LMaj MTrO NOra NOrn SCoo SPoG WLov WMat
	'Red Peacock'	CLnd
	'Red Prince'	see *M. domestica* 'Red Jonaprince'
	'Red Topaz' PBR	MTrO
	'Roberts Crab'	LCro MTrO NOra
	'Robinson'	CLnd
§	× ***robusta***	CLnd LSRN NRog NWea SBdl SRms
	- 'Dolgo'	CLnd CSBt EDir EPfP EPom EWTr LCro LRHS MBlu MTrO NLar NOra NWea SBdl SCoo SKee SPoG WMat
	- 'Red Sentinel' ♀H6	Widely available
	- 'Red Siberian'	EHeP
	- 'Yellow Siberian'	CLnd
	'Rosehip'	CBod CEnd CLnd EWTr LCro MTrO NLar NOra NOrn WMat WMou
	'Royal Beauty'	CBod CLnd EPfP IPap LMaj LRHS MAsh MBlu MDon MGos MPri MSwo MTrO NOra NOrn NWea SBdl SCoo SEdi SPer WHtc WMat WMou
	'Royal Burgundy'	NRog
	'Royalty'	Widely available
	'Rudolph'	CBTr CCVT CLnd EBar EBee EDir EHeP IPap LBuc LMaj LPar LSRN MAsh MGos MPri MTrO NOra NOrn SCob SCoo SEND SEWo SEdi SLim SPer SPoG WHtc WJas WMat WMou
	'Ruth Ann'	CLnd
	sargentii	CLnd NOra NRog NWea
§	- 'Candymint'	CLnd EWTr MAsh MTrO NOra SGol SLim SPoG WMat
	- 'Tina'	CKel CLnd CWnw LRHS MTrO NOra NOrn SPoG WMat
	'Satin Cloud'	CLnd
§	× ***scheideckeri*** 'Hillieri'	CLnd MBlu NOra WHtc
§	- 'Red Jade'	CDoC CTri EDir EHeP ELan LRHS MGos MRav MSwo NOrn NRog NWea SBdl SEND SEdi SPer SRms WJas
	Siberian crab	see *M.* × *robusta*
	sieboldii	see *M. toringo*
	sieversii	NOra
	sikkimensis	WJur
	- B&SWJ 2431	WCru
	'Silver Drift'	CLnd
	'Simon'	WMat
	'Snowcloud'	CBod CLnd MAsh NOrn SLim
	'Strathmore'	SBdl
	'Street Parade'	CLnd
	× ***sublobata***	CLnd
	SUGAR TYME ('Sutyzam')	CLnd SGol
	'Sun Rival' ♀H6	Widely available
	sylvestris	CArg CBTr CBrac CCVT CHab CKel CLnd CPer EHeP EPfP IPap LBuc LMaj LPar MMuc MNic MRav NBwr NRog NTrD NWea SCob SEND SEWo SEdi SPre WKor WMou WTSh
§	***toringo***	CLnd CPer EPfP LMaj NOra SBdl WJur
I	- var. ***arborescens***	CLnd
	- 'Aros' PBR	EBee ELan EPfP LBuc LCro LRHS MTrO NLar NOra NOrn SBmr SEWo WHtc WMat
	- 'Browers'	LPar
	- 'Freja' PBR **new**	CKel CWnw LMaj
	- 'Scarlett' ♀H6	CBTr CCVT CEnd CLnd CMac ELan EPfP EWTr IArd LCro LMaj LPar LRHS LSRN MAsh MTrO NOra NOrn NWea SCoo SEWo SLim SPer SPoG SRHi WMat
	- 'Wintergold'	SBdl
	- 'Wooster'	CLnd
	toringoides	see *M. bhutanica*
	transitoria ♀H6	CEnd CLnd CMac ELan EPfP GKin LRHS MAsh MBlu MRav MTrO NLar NOra NWea SCoo SLau SPer WHtc WMat WMou WPGP
	- 'Roundabarrow Ruby'	EBee WPGP
	- 'Thornhayes Tansy'	CPer NOra SLim SPoG WMat

trilobata	CPer EBee EHeP ELan EPfP LMaj LPar MBlu MGos SCoo
- 'Guardsman'	CLnd CMac EBee EPfP MPri NOra SBdl WMat WMou
tschonoskii	CAco CDoC CMCN CMac CTri EHeP ELan EWTr LMaj LPar LRHS MBlu MDon MGos MMuc NBwr NOrn NRog NWea SBdl SCob SEND SEdi SPer SRms SWvt WJas WJur WMou WTSh
- 'Belmonte'	MBlu
'Van Eseltine'	CAgr CBod CDoC CMac CSBt EPfP MAsh MDon MMuc SBdl SEdi SPer WJas
'Veitch's Scarlet'	CHab CLnd CSBt NRog SBdl
VELVET PILLAR ('Velvetcole')	SPer
'Virginia Crab'	SBdl
WEEPING CANDIED APPLE ('Weepcanzam')	CLnd SGol
'White Angel'	CLnd
'White Star'	CCVT CLnd CSBt EWTr LRHS NOra SBdl WMat
'Winter Gold'	LMaj SEdi SGol
'Wisley Crab'	CBod CLnd MDon SBdl SEdi SGol SKee SRms
yunnanensis	SBdl WJur
× ***zumi***	GLog
- var. ***calocarpa***	CPer
§ - 'Golden Hornet'	Widely available
§ - 'Professor Sprenger'	CLnd EPfP LIns LMaj LPar MTrO NOra SCoo WHtc

Malva (*Malvaceae*)

alcea	CAgr
- var. ***fastigiata***	CMac EPPr LRHS SRms
- 'Royal Flush'	NRHS
bicolor	see *Lavatera maritima*
crispa	see *M. verticillata*
'Gibbortello'	GJos NBPC
moschata	CAgr CBcs CBod CTtf EBee ECha ELan ENfk EPfP GJos GPoy GQue MHer MNHC NAts NLar NMir SPer SPlb SRms WFar WHer WShi WWild
§ - f. ***alba***	Widely available
- 'Appleblossom'	EShb GJos
- 'Romney Marsh'	see *Althaea officinalis* 'Romney Marsh'
- 'Rosea'	EHyd EPfP GMaP GMcL LRHS NPer NRHS SPoG SWvt
- 'Snow White'	see *M. moschata* f. *alba*
- 'White Perfection'	WFar
pusilla	CCCN
sylvestris	CBod GJos SRms
- 'Blue Fountain'PBR	EBee SRms WMal
- 'Brave Heart'	CTtf GJos SWvt
- MARINA ('Dema'PBR)	NLar
- var. ***mauritiana***	LCro MHoo NLar NPer
- - 'Bíbor Fehlő'	CSpe
- - 'Mystic Merlin'	GJos
- - 'Primley Blue'	EBee ELan EPfP GMaP LRHS MRav NLar NPer SGBe WKif WSpi XSen
- - 'Zebrina'	CTtf GJos LDai LShi MHoo NGBl NPer SBut SWvt WOut
- 'Perry's Blue'	NPer
- 'Poetry'PBR	LBar SGBe
- 'Windsor Castle'	LShi
§ ***verticillata***	CLau

Malvastrum (*Malvaceae*)

× ***hypomadarum***	see *Anisodontea* × *hypomadara* (Sprague) D.M. Bates

Malvaviscus (*Malvaceae*)

arboreus	CHll

Mammillaria ✿ (*Cactaceae*)

albicans subsp. ***fraileana*** new	NMen
baumii ♀H2 new	NMen
bocasana ♀H2 new	NMen
bombycina ♀H2 new	EAri
candida	see *Mammilloydia candida*
carmenae ♀H2 new	EAri
crinita new	NMen
decipiens subsp. ***camptotricha*** new	SPlb
elongata ♀H2 new	EAri NMen
erythrosperma new	SPlb
glassii new	SPlb
§ ***grahamii*** subsp. ***sheldonii*** new	NMen
hahniana ♀H2 new	EAri NPlm
- subsp. ***woodsii*** new	LCro
marksiana new	EAri
marnieriana	see *M. grahamii* subsp. *sheldonii*
matudae new	EAri
plumosa ♀H2 new	EAri
pringlei ♀H2 new	NMen
prolifera new	SPlb
scheinvariana new	SPlb
sphacelata new	SPlb
spinosissima ♀H2 new	EAri
- 'Un Pico' new	EAri
supertexta new	EAri
vetula new	SPlb
- subsp. ***gracilis*** new	SPlb
zeilmanniana NEW DAWN (mixed) new	NMen

Mammilloydia (*Cactaceae*)

§ ***candida*** ♀ new	EAri

mandarin see *Citrus reticulata* Mandarin Group

mandarin, Cleopatra see *Citrus reticulata*

Mandevilla ✿ (*Apocynaceae*)

§ × ***amabilis***	CCCN
- 'Alice du Pont' ♀H1c	CCCN EMdy SPre
× ***amoena***	see *M.* × *amabilis*
'Audrey'PBR (Vogue Series)	CWGN SPoG
boliviensis ♀H1c	CCCN CRHN
(Diamantina Series) DIAMANTINA OPALE FUCHSIA FLAMMÉ ('Lanmissouri'PBR)	LCro
- DIAMANTINA OPALE GRENAT ('Lanutah')	EMdy
'Ginger' (Vogue Series)	CWGN SPoG
§ ***laxa*** ♀H2	CBor CCCN CRHN CSpe ECre ELan EMdy EShb SVen
(Rio Series) RIO DEEP RED ('Fisrix Dered'PBR)	CCCN
- RIO PINK ('Fisrix Pinka'PBR)	CCCN
- RIO WHITE ('Fisrix Whit'PBR)	EMdy
'Ruby' (Vogue Series)	CWGN
sanderi	CCCN EShb SPre
- 'Pink of Hint'	EMdy
- 'Rosea'	CCCN
splendens ♀H1c	CCCN
suaveolens	see *M. laxa*

Sundaville Series CCCN
- SUNDAVILLE CREAM PINK ('Sunparapibra'PBR) EMdy
- SUNDAVILLE DARK RED ('Sunparabeni') CAbb EMdy
- SUNDAVILLE GRAND RED ('Sunpara15'PBR) EMdy
- SUNDAVILLE IMPROVED WHITE 16 ('Sunparamakuho') EMdy
- SUNDAVILLE PEARL ('Patmandewi') EMdy
- SUNDAVILLE PINK ('Sunmandecripi'PBR) EMdy
- SUNDAVILLE RED ('Sunmandecrim'PBR) EMdy

Mandragora (*Solanaceae*)

autumnalis GEdr SBrt SPhx
caulescens GEdr
- BO 15-123 GGro
§ ***officinarum*** EBee GEdr GGro GPoy SPhx

Manettia (*Rubiaceae*)

cordifolia SBrt
inflata see *M. luteorubra*
§ ***luteorubra*** CCCN

Manfreda see *Agave*

× *Mangave* see *Agave*

Mangifera (*Anacardiaceae*)

indica (F) CCCN SPre
- 'Osteen' (F) SVic
- 'Palmer' (F) SVic

Manglietia see *Magnolia*

yunnanensis see *Magnolia insignis*

mango see *Mangifera indica*

Manihot (*Euphorbiaceae*)

carthaginensis SPlb
esculenta EAri
- 'Variegata' EAri
grahamii SPlb

Manoao (*Podocarpaceae*)

colensoi see *Lepidothamnus colensoi*

Mantisia (*Zingiberaceae*)

saltatoria PAB 4208 LEdu WPGP

Maranta (*Marantaceae*)

leuconeura LCro NHrt
- var. ***erythroneura*** ♀H1a NHrt
- var. ***kerchoveana*** ♀H1a NHrt
- var. ***leuconeura*** 'Fascinator' **new** LCro

Margyricarpus (*Rosaceae*)

§ ***pinnatus*** EWld WAbe WPav
setosus see *M. pinnatus*

Mariscus see *Cyperus*

marjoram, pot see *Origanum onites*

marjoram, sweet see *Origanum majorana*

marjoram, wild, or oregano see *Origanum vulgare*

Marlothistella (*Aizoaceae*)

stenophylla **new** EAri

marrow see AGM Vegetables Section

Marrubium (*Lamiaceae*)

§ ***bourgaei*** var. ***bourgaei*** 'All Hallows Green' ECha SRms
candidissimum see *M. incanum*
* ***cylleneum*** 'Velvetissimum' WCot
§ ***incanum*** EPPr XSen
libanoticum ECha
supinum EBou ECha LRHS NFav SGro
vulgare CBee CBod CCBP ENfk GJos GPoy MHer MHoo MNHC SRms WJek

Marsdenia (*Apocynaceae*)

oreophila CBcs CKel CRHN LRHS SPoG WPGP WSHC

Marshallia (*Asteraceae*)

grandiflora EBee

Marsilea (*Marsileaceae*)

mutica EWat
quadrifolia LLWG LPfP

Mascarena see *Hyophorbe*

Massonia (*Asparagaceae*)

depressa ♀H2 SChF WAbe WCot
echinata SChF WCot
aff. ***echinata*** EAri
jasminiflora WHil
longipes EAri WCot
pseudoechinata WCot
pustulata ♀H2 SChF WAbe WCot
- purple-leaved WCot
thunbergiana WCot

Mathiasella (*Apiaceae*)

bupleuroides GElm
- 'Green Dream' CAvo CBcs CBod CSpe EBee EGrI ELan EMor EPfP EWoo GBin GMaP ILea LAlb LBar LCro LOPS LRHS MBel MHol MNrw MPnt SCob SMrm SPeP SPoG WCAu WCot WHIf

Matricaria (*Asteraceae*)

chamomilla see *M. recutita*
maritima see *Tripleurospermum maritimum*
parthenium see *Tanacetum parthenium*
§ ***recutita*** GPoy MBros MNHC
tchihatchewii XLum XSen

Matteuccia (*Onocleaceae*)

orientalis ♀H5 CAby CBod CDTJ CLAP CRos CSde CSta CWCL EFer EHyd EMor GArf GMaP ISha LEdu LLWG LPal LRHS NBid NBro NBwr NLar NRHS SCob SPlb WPGP WPnP XLum
pensylvanica EHyd LRHS LSto NRHS
struthiopteris ♀H5 Widely available
- 'Bedraggled Feathers' LEdu
* - 'Depauperata' CLAP
- 'Jumbo' CBdn CCCN EBee EHyd LRHS MAsh NRHS WPGP
- 'The King' ISha LRHS WCot

Matthiola (*Brassicaceae*)

fruticulosa 'Alba' CWal EPfP

- subsp. ***perennis***	CWal NSti
incana	CEls LCro SVic WKif
- 'Alba'	EBee ECha ELan LRHS MHol SMad SPhx
- Cinderella Series, mixed 🏆H4	LCro LOPS
- - 'Cinderella Appleblossom' **new**	CWCL
- - 'Cinderella Champagne' **new**	CWCL
- dwarf, mixed	MBros
- 'Low'	WCot
- 'Pillow Talk'	ECha LRHS WMal
scapifera	WAbe
sinuata	CEls
white-flowered perennial	CSpe NPer

Matucana ✿ (*Cactaceae*)

hoxeyi **new**	EAri
oreodoxa subsp. ***roseiflora*** **new**	EAri
weberbaueri **new**	NMen

Maurandya (*Plantaginaceae*)

§ ***barclayana*** 🏆H2	CSpe
erubescens	see *Lophospermum erubescens*
lophantha	see *Lophospermum scandens*
lophospermum	see *Lophospermum scandens*
'Magic Dragon'	see *Lophospermum* 'Magic Dragon'
'Red Dragon'	see *Lophospermum* 'Red Dragon'

Maytenus (*Celastraceae*)

boaria	LEdu SArc SBrt SEND
disticha (Hook.f.) Urb.	LEdu
magellanica	WPGP

Mazus (*Phrymaceae*)

radicans	ECha
reptans	CPud CWat EBee EBou ECtt ELan GEdr LPfP NLar NPer SPtp WFar WIce WWke XLum
- B&SWJ	CExl
- 'Albus'	CPud CWat EBee ECtt LBar LLWG LPfP LRHS NLar SPeP SPlb WFar WIce
- 'Blue'	LLWG

Mecardonia (*Plantaginaceae*)

'Goldflake'	CCCN

Meconopsis ✿ (*Papaveraceae*)

'Arley Hall' **new**	GEdr
§ ***baileyi*** 🏆H5	CBcs CTri EBee GDam GGGa GKev GMcL ITim LCro LOPS MBel NBir NChi SCob WFar
* - var. ***alba***	EBee EHyd GKev LBar NLar NRHS
- 'Hensol Violet'	EBee EWes GGGa GKev GMcL NRHS WTyc
- violet-flowered	ITim
balangensis	EDAr
- BO 16-072	GGro
Ballyrogan form	GEdr GKev
betonicifolia misapplied	see *M. baileyi*
'Biggar Park'	GEdr
cambrica	see *Papaver cambricum*
chelidoniifolia	see *Cathcartia chelidoniifolia*
'Cluny White' **new**	GEdr
'Clydeside Early Treasure'	GEdr GKev
× ***cookei***	GKev NHpl
- 'Old Rose'	GGGa GKev GMaP
'Edrom'	GEdr
§ Fertile Blue Group	ITim
- 'Blue Ice'	see *M.* (Fertile Blue Group) 'Lingholm'
- 'Harry Bush'	GEdr
§ - 'Lingholm'	Widely available
- 'Louise'	GEdr GKev GMaP
- 'Mop-head' 🏆H5	GEdr GKev GMaP
(George Sherriff Group) 'Ascreavie'	GEdr GKev GMaP
- 'Barney's Blue'	GEdr GKev GMaP
- 'Dalemain' 🏆H5	GEdr GMaP
- 'Dorothy Renton'	GEdr
- 'Branklyn' ambig.	CExl GEdr
- 'Huntfield'	GEdr GGGa GKev GMaP
- 'Jimmy Bayne'	GEdr GKev GMaP
- 'Spring Hill'	GKev
- 'Susan's Reward' 🏆H5	GEdr GMaP
grandis ambig.	ITim
- 'Himal Sky'	GEdr GKev
'Great Glen'	GEdr GKev
(Infertile Blue Group) 'Bobby Masterton' 🏆H5	GEdr GKev GMaP
- 'Bryan Conway'	GEdr
- 'Crarae'	GEdr GGGa GKev GMaP
- 'Crewdson Hybrid'	GEdr GKev GMaP
- 'Cruickshank'	GKev
- 'Dawyck'	see *M.* (Infertile Blue Group) 'Slieve Donard'
- 'Maggie Sharp'	GEdr
- 'Mrs Jebb' 🏆H5	GArf GEdr GMaP
- 'P.C. Abildgaard' 🏆H5	GEdr GKev GMaP
§ - 'Slieve Donard' 🏆H5	EHyd GArf GEdr GGGa GKev GMaP LRHS NRHS
integrifolia	CCCN GEdr
- subsp. ***integrifolia*** W&O 7158	GGro
'Inverewe' 🏆H5	GEdr GKev GMaP
'Keillour' 🏆H5	GEdr GMaP
'Keillour Violet'	GKev
'Kilbryde Castle White'	GEdr GMaP
'Lunanhead' **new**	GEdr
'Marit' 🏆H5	GEdr GKev GMaP
'Mervyn Kessell'	GEdr GKev
'Mildred'	GEdr GKev GMaP
'Moonglow' **new**	GEdr
napaulensis misapplied	EBee GAbr ITim
napaulensis DC. from Solukhumbu, Nepal	GDam
nudicaulis	see *Papaver nudicaule*
paniculata	GAbr GMaP
'Pride of Angus'	GEdr
punicea	GKev NHpl
- 'Sichuan Silk'	NHpl
quintuplinervia 🏆H5	GKev GRum NHpl
× ***sheldonii*** misapplied (fertile)	see *M.* Fertile Blue Group
× ***sheldonii*** misapplied (sterile)	see *M.* Infertile Blue Group
× ***sheldonii*** ambig.	CBcs EPfP EWoo GMcL LRHS NLar NPer NRHS
'Stewart Annand'	GEdr GKev GMaP
'Strathspey'	GEdr GKev GMaP NHpl
'Willie Duncan'	GEdr GMaP

Medeola (*Asparagaceae*)

virginiana	EBee

Medicago (*Fabaceae*)

arborea	SEND SPlb
lupulina	CHab NGrd SPhx
sativa	NGrd SPhx SVic WSFF

Medinilla (*Melastomataceae*)

'Bella' PBR (Florinilla Series)	CDoC
magnifica 🏆H1a	CCCN CDoC LCro

Mediolobivia see *Rebutia*

medlar see *Mespilus germanica*; see also AGM Fruit Section

Meehania (*Lamiaceae*)

cordata	EBee
urticifolia	EBee GEdr WPnP
- B&SWJ 1210	WCru

Megaskepasma (*Acanthaceae*)

erythrochlamys	SVen

Melaleuca (*Myrtaceae*)

acuminata	SPlb
alternifolia	CCCN CTsd EShb GPoy MHer MHoo NWad SEle SPlb SSha SVen
armillaris	CCCN CTsd SEND SPlb
cuticularis	SPlb
decussata	CCCN CSde SPlb
diosmifolia	CPbh
ericifolia	CTri CTsd SEND SPlb
fulgens	SPlb
gibbosa	CKel SEND SVen
hypericifolia	SPlb SVen
linariifolia	CCCN SPlb
nesophila	SPlb
pallida	GAbr
pungens	SPlb
pustulata	SVen
squamea	SPlb
squarrosa	CBcs SEle SPlb SVen
thymifolia	SPlb
trichophylla	SPlb
wilsonii	IDee

Melampodium (*Asteraceae*)

§ ***montanum*** AZTEC GOLD ('Starbini'PBR)	MBNS MBros MPri
- 'Gold Queen'	LSou
- 'Sunbini'PBR	CCCN LSou
- 'Sunlight'	LSou MPri

Melandrium see *Silene*

rubrum	see *Silene dioica*

Melanoselinum (*Apiaceae*)

§ ***decipiens***	CAbb CPla CSpe EAJP ELan EShb GBin LEdu LPla LRHS MHer MNrw NBPC SDix SPhx SPtp WOut WPGP WSHC

Melanoseris (*Asteraceae*)

atropurpurea BWJ 7891 new	GGro
aff. ***atropurpurea*** W&O 8108 new	GGro
aff. ***cyanea*** W&O 7169 new	GGro

Melanthium (*Melanthiaceae*)

virginicum	MNrw

Melasphaerula (*Iridaceae*)

graminea	see *M. ramosa*
§ ***ramosa***	CBor GKev NRog

Melia (*Meliaceae*)

§ ***azedarach***	CBcs CCCN SBrt SPlb WJur
- B&SWJ 14625	WCru
- 'Jade Snowflake'	SPtp
- var. ***japonica***	see *M. azedarach*

Melianthus (*Melianthaceae*)

comosus	CDTJ CPla ESwi NLar SBls SCoo SPlb
major ♀H3	Widely available
villosus	EBee SPad SPlb WPGP

Melica (*Poaceae*)

altissima	LSto
- 'Alba'	CBWd CWnw EHyd GKev LCro LRHS LSto MBel SHor SWvt
- 'Atropurpurea'	CBod CCBP ECha EPPr GQue LRHS MBel SBls SEND SPlb SPoG
ciliata	CBWd CBod ECha ELon EMor EPPr LSto MBel XLum XSen
- subsp. ***taurica***	SPhx
cupani	EPPr
nutans	EAJP EPPr GMaP GQue LRHS MAsh NWsh SMHy SPhx WCot
persica	EPPr
transsilvanica 'Red Spire'	LShi MACG SPeP XLum
uniflora	NWsh SPhx
- f. ***albida*** ♀H7	CKno ECha EGrI EPPr GKev GQue LPla MACG MAvo MRav SMHy SPhx WCot
- 'Variegata' (v)	EPPr LPla MAvo SMHy WCot

Melicytus (*Violaceae*)

alpinus	WThu
crassifolius	EBee
obovatus	EBtc NLar

Melilotus (*Fabaceae*)

albus	SPhx
officinalis	CHab SPhx WHer
- subsp. ***albus***	SPhx

Melinis (*Poaceae*)

nerviglumis	CBod

Meliosma (*Sabiaceae*)

alba	WPGP
dilleniifolia WJC 13819	WCru
- subsp. ***cuneifolia***	CBcs CExl SBrt WPGP
- subsp. ***dilleniifolia***	WPGP
- subsp. ***tenuis***	CExl
myriantha var. ***discolor*** MF 97132	WCru
pinnata var. ***oldhamii***	CExl
veitchiorum	CExl NLar

Melissa ✿ (*Lamiaceae*)

officinalis	CBod CCBP CHab CLau CWal EBou ENfk GJos GMaP GPoy GQue LCro LEdu LOPS MBow MBros MGil MHer MHoo MMuc MNHC NBir SEND SEdi SPlb SRms SVic WBor WFar XLum
- 'All Gold'	CLau ECha ENfk GQue MHoo NBid SPoG SRms SVic WFar WJek
- subsp. ***altissima***	MNHC
§ - 'Aurea' (v)	CBod CCBP CLau CTsd EBou ELan GPoy MBow MHer MHoo MMuc MNHC NBid NBir NBro NGrd SPoG SRms WFar
- 'Citronella'	CWal MGil
* - 'Compacta'	GPoy LEdu
- 'Lemona'	CAgr SPhx
- 'Lime Balm'	LEdu MHer MHoo NPol
- 'Variegata' misapplied	see *M. officinalis* 'Aurea'

Melittis (*Lamiaceae*)

melissophyllum	CAby CSpe CTtf LEdu LRHS MHol MNrw MPie MPnt MRav SGro SHar WCAu WCot

- subsp. ***albida***	EBee EMor LEdu LRHS NSti WCAu WCot WHil WTor
- pink-flowered	LEdu WCot
- 'Royal Velvet Distinction'PBR	CRos EBee EHyd ELan EMor EPfP ILea LBar LRHS MHol MPie MRav MSCN NBPC NCou NGBl NHpl NRHS SCoo SHar SPoG WCot WHil WHlf WTyc
- white-flowered **new**	LBar WCAu
- 'Wit Laag'	SHar

Melliodendron (*Styracaceae*)

xylocarpum	CExl SAko WPGP
- pink-flowered **new**	WPGP

Melocactus (*Cactaceae*)

broadwayi **new**	LCro
matanzanus **new**	LCro

melon see AGM Vegetables Section

Melothria (*Cucurbitaceae*)

scabra	LRHS SVic

Menispermum (*Menispermaceae*)

canadense	CTri
dauricum	NLar

Mentha ✿ (*Lamiaceae*)

	from Vietnam **new**	MMen
	angustifolia Corb.	see *M.* × *villosa*
	angustifolia Host	see *M. arvensis*
	aquatica	CBen CHab CPud CWal CWat GPoy LLWG LPfP MHer MMen MWts NAts NMir NPer NPol SPlb SRms SVic WHer WMAq WPnP WSFF XLum
§	***arvensis***	MHer MMen
	- 'Banana'	CBod ENfk LEdu MHer MHoo MMen MNHC SEdi SRms SVic WFar WJek
	- 'Lemon'	LEdu MHer MMen
	- var. ***piperascens***	CBod LEdu MHer MMen SRms WJek
§	- - 'Sayakaze'	CLau
	- 'Thai'	ENfk MMen SRms
	asiatica	MHer
	'Berries and Cream'	CBod CCBP CLau ENfk EWhm LCro LEdu MHer MMen MNHC SRms WJek
	'Blackcurrant'	MHer MHoo MMen
	Bowles's mint	see *M.* × *villosa* var. *alopecuroides* Bowles's mint
	cervina	CBen CPud CWat LEdu LLWG LPfP MHer MHoo MMen MWts SRms WJek XLum
*	- ***alba***	ENfk LLWG MHer MMen MWts WJek
I	'Chocolate Peppermint'	CBod CLau ENfk EWhm LEdu MHoo NBir NLar SPhx WCav
	citrata	see *M.* × *piperita* f. *citrata*
	cordifolia	see *M.* × *villosa*
	corsica	see *M. requienii*
	crispa L. (1753)	see *M. spicata* var. *crispa*
	cunninghamii **new**	MMen
	'Dionysus'	MMen
	'Eau de Cologne'	see *M.* × *piperita* f. *citrata*
	eucalyptus mint	MHer MMen
	× ***gentilis***	see *M.* × *gracilis*
§	× ***gracilis***	CBod CLau ENfk EWhm GJos MBow MBros MMen MPri NGrd NLar NSti SEdi SRms SVic WFar
	- 'Aurea'	see *M.* × *gracilis* 'Variegata'
§	- 'Variegata' (v)	CCBP ECha GAbr GPoy GQue LEdu MHer MHoo MMen MNHC MPri SPlb WHer WJek XLum
	'Grannie's Gloucester' **new**	MMen
	graveolens	MHoo
	haplocalyx	MMen
*	'Hillary's Sweet Lemon'	ECul ENfk MHer MMen SRms
	'Jessica's Sweet Pear'	ENfk EWhm MHer MMen
	'Julia's Sweet Citrus'	MHer MMen
	lavender mint	GPoy LEdu MHer MMen MNHC SRms
§	***longifolia***	ENfk GJos GQue LEdu MBow MHoo MMen MMuc SPlb SRms
	- from Crete **new**	MMen
	- from Lahij, Azerbaijan **new**	MMen
	- from Vaik, Armenia **new**	MMen
	- Buddleia Mint Group	CCBP ENfk EWhm LEdu MHer MMen NSti WFar WJek WWFP XLum
	- - variegated (v)	CBod MMen WJek
	- 'Habek'	MMen
	- 'Lake Van'	LEdu MMen
	- subsp. ***schimperi***	MHer MMen SRms WJek
	- silver-leaved	LEdu MHer MHoo MMen MNHC NBir SEND SRms SVic WFar WJek
	- 'Tajik Silver' **new**	MMen
*	- 'Variegata' (v)	MHoo SRms
	Nile Valley mint	CLau LEdu SRms
	'Orange Fresh'	CBod
	× ***piperita***	CBod CHby ECha GJos GPoy GQue LCro LOPS LWaG MBow MHer MHoo MMen MNHC MPri NGrd NPol SPlb SVic WFar
	- 'After Eight'	ECul ENfk WFar
	- 'Black Mitcham'	CLau MMen SPhx WFar WJek XSen
	- black peppermint	CAgr CBod CHby CLau ENfk EPfP LEdu LRHS MHoo MMen MMuc MNHC NBir NLar SRms SVic WFar
§	- f. ***citrata***	CBod CCBP CHby CLau CTri ECha ENfk EWhm GMaP GPoy GQue LEdu MBow MHer MHoo MMen MPri NBir NLar NPer SEdi SPlb SRms SVic WFar WGwG WJek
	- - 'Basil'	CBod CLau CTsd CWal ECul GJos GLog LCro LEdu LOPS MHer MHoo MMen MNHC SEdi SRms SVic WFar WJek
	- - 'Bergamot'	SRms
	- - 'Chocolate'	CCBP ECul EHyd ENfk EPfP EWhm GJos LCro LEdu LOPS MBros MHer MHoo MMen MNHC NGrd NPer NRHS SEdi SPlb SRms SVic WFar WGwG WJek XLum
	- - 'Grapefruit'	CBod EWhm LCro MHer MHoo MMen MNHC SRms SVic
	- - 'Kumin'	LEdu
	- - 'Lime'	CLau EMor ENfk EWhm MBow MHer MHoo MMen MNHC NBir SEdi SPlb SRms SVic WFar WJek
	- - 'Mandarin' **new**	MMen
	- - 'Nevis' **new**	MMen
	- - 'Orange'	EMor ENfk EWhm GJos LEdu MHer MMen MMuc MNHC NGrd NPer SEdi SRms WJek
	- - 'Swiss Ricola'	CLau MHer MMen WJek
	- 'Crispa'	NPol
	- 'Logee's' (v)	MMen WFar
§	- 'Multimentha'	SRms
	- f. ***officinalis*** 'Aurea' **new**	MMen
	- 'Strawberry'	CBod ENfk GJos LCro LOPS LWaG MBros MHoo SVic WFar
	- 'Swiss'	CBod ENfk GJos LCro LOPS MHoo MMen NGrd NLar SRms WHer
*	- var. ***vulgaris*** **new**	CWal
	pulegium	CBen CHby CPud ENfk EWhm GJos GPoy GQue LLWG LPfP MHer MHoo MMen MNHC SPlb SRms SVic WHer WSFF

- 'Cunningham Mint'	MMen WJek
- 'Upright'	ENfk GPoy MHer MHoo MMen SRms WJek
- upright, from Portugal **new**	MMen
§ ***requienii***	CCBP CKel EBou ENfk EPot GAbr GPoy LCro LEdu LLWG LOPS MHer MHoo MMen MNHC NBir NWad SDix SPlb SPtp SRms SVic WGwG WJek WNPC
rotundifolia misapplied	see *M. suaveolens*
rotundifolia (L.) Huds.	see *M.* × *villosa*
rubra var. ***raripila***	see *M.* × *smithiana*
'Russian' curled leaf	MHoo MMen
'Russian' plain leaf	MMen
sachalinensis	MMen SVic
'Sayakaze'	see *M. arvensis* var. *piperascens* 'Sayakaze'
§ × ***smithiana***	CLau GPoy LCro MHer MHoo MMen MNHC NBir NGrd SRms SVic WFar WJek
§ ***spicata***	Widely available
- from Cyprus **new**	MMen
- from the Berbers, Morocco **new**	MMen
- ALMIRA **new**	MMen
- 'Cretan'	MMen
* - var. ***crispa***	ECha ENfk MHer MMen SPlb SRms SVic WFar WGwG WJek
- - 'Moroccan'	CBod CCBP CLau ECul ENfk EWhm GAbr GJos GLog GPoy LCro LEdu LOPS MBow MHer MHoo MMen MNHC MPri NBir NGrd NLar SEdi SRms SVic
- 'Crispula'	XLum
- 'Erdbeere'	WFar
- 'Guernsey'	CLau MMen SRms
- 'Kentucky Colonel'	LEdu MMen
- 'Mexican'	CLau MMen
- 'Newbourne'	CLau MMen SRms
- 'Nile Valley'	MMen WJek
- 'Russian'	CAgr MHer SVic WFar
- 'Spanish'	ECul MMen NGrd NLar SRms WFar
- 'Spanish Furry'	MHer
- 'Stavordale' **new**	MMen
- 'Tashkent'	CHby CLau EHyd ENfk EWhm LCro LEdu LOPS LRHS LSto MHer MHoo MMen MNHC NGrd NRHS SRms WFar WGwG WHer WJek
- YAKIMA **new**	MMen
I 'Strawberry Mint'	CBod CCBP CLau ECul EWhm LEdu MHer MNHC SEdi SRms WCav WFar WJek
§ ***suaveolens***	CAgr CBod CCBP CHby ENfk GJos GMaP GPoy GQue LCro LOPS LWaG MBow MBros MHer MHoo MNHC NGrd SPlb SRms SVic WFar WSFF
* - var. ***crispa*** 'Mojito' **new**	EWhm MMen
* - 'Grapefruit'	CAgr CLau ECul GJos LEdu WFar
- 'Le Boues' **new**	MMen
* - 'Pineapple'	CBod CLau EBou ECul ENfk EWhm GLog LWaG MBow MHoo SVic WFar WJek
- subsp. ***timija***	LEdu MHer MHoo MMen SRms WJek
- 'Variegata' (v)	CCBP ECha GJos GMaP GPoy GQue LEdu LShi MCot MHer MMen MNHC MPri MRav NSti SPlb SRms WHer XLum
'Sweet Pear'	MHer SRms WJek
sylvestris L.	see *M. longifolia*
I 'Tangerine Mint'	LEdu MMen
Thüringer minze	see *M.* × *piperita* 'Multimentha'
'Turkish Green' **new**	MMen
§ × ***villosa***	MMen MMuc SEND
§ - var. ***alopecuroides*** Bowles's mint	CLau EWhm GPoy LCro LEdu LOPS MHer MHoo MMen MNHC NBir NLar NSti SRms WFar WHer WJek
- 'Jack Green'	CLau
viridis	see *M. spicata*

Mentzelia (*Loasaceae*)

decapetala	CSpe

Menyanthes (*Menyanthaceae*)

trifoliata	CBen CPud CToG CWat EWat GPoy LLWG LPfP MWts NPer WHlf WMAq WSFF XLum

Menziesia see *Rhododendron*

alba	see *Daboecia cantabrica* f. *alba*

Mercurialis (*Euphorbiaceae*)

perennis	GPoy WHer WSFF WShi

Merendera see *Colchicum*

eichleri	see *Colchicum trigynum*
hissarica	see *Colchicum robustum*

Merrilliopanax (*Araliaceae*)

alpinus B&SWJ 13906	WCru
- B&SWJ 13939	WCru
membranifolius	WPGP

Mertensia (*Boraginaceae*)

lanceolata	EBee GEdr
§ ***maritima***	CEls CLau CSpe CWCL EBee EWes GKev GPoy GRum SPlb SRms WHoo
- subsp. ***asiatica***	see *M. maritima*
pterocarpa	see *M. sibirica*
pulmonarioides	see *M. virginica*
§ ***sibirica***	CWCL SPlb SPtp
§ ***virginica*** ♀H4	CBor CMiW CWCL EBee EGrI ELan EPfP EPot GKev LAma LBar LCro LEdu MNrw NLar NSti SRms WFar
viridis	SPlb

Merwilla (*Asparagaceae*)

§ ***dracomontana*** **new**	WCot
§ ***plumbea***	WCot

Merxmuellera (*Poaceae*)

cincta	see *Capeochloa cincta*
macowanii **new**	WPGP

Mesembryanthemum (*Aizoaceae*)

sp.	MAsh
brownii	see *Lampranthus brownii*
crystallinum	MPri

Mespilus ✿ (*Rosaceae*)

germanica (F)	CHab CLnd CMCN CTri EDir EWTr IPap LIns LMaj LPar MGil NLar NRog NWea SGsty WFar WJur
- 'Boom en Vrucht' (F)	NRog
- 'Bredase Reus' (F)	ELan NRog SKee
- 'Dutch' (F)	SKee
- 'Flanders Giant' (F)	CAgr LRHS MTrO WMat
- 'Iranian' (F) ♀H6	CAgr SKee
- 'Large Russian' (F)	CAgr
- 'Macrocarpa' (F)	NRog SKee
- 'Nottingham' (F) ♀H6	Widely available
- 'Royal' (F)	CAgr LRHS MCoo NLar NOra NRog SCoo SKee WMat
- 'Westerveld' (F)	CAgr CBod CLnd EPom LMaj LPar MTrO NLar NRog SKee

Metapanax ✿ (*Araliaceae*)

davidii	SPtp WPGP
delavayi	WPGP

Metaplexis (*Apocynaceae*)

japonica	GGro

Metasequoia ✿ (*Cupressaceae*)

	glyptostroboides	Widely available
	- 'All Bronze'	CAco
	- AMBER GLOW ('Wah-08ag')	CBcs LRHS SRHi
	- 'Chubby'PBR	CAco
	- 'Daweswood Tawney Fleece' **new**	CAco
	- 'Emerald Feathers'	SLim
	- 'Fastigiata'	see *M. glyptostroboides* 'National'
	- GOLD RUSH	see *M. glyptostroboides* 'Golden Oji'
	- 'Golden Dawn'	NLar
	- GOLDEN MANTLE	see *M. glyptostroboides* 'Golden Oji'
§	- 'Golden Oji' ♀H7	CAco CBcs CCVT CEme CMac CTri ELan EPfP IArd LRHS LSRN MAsh MBlu MGos MTrO NLar NOra NOrn NPoe NWea SAko SCob SCoo SLim SPer SPoG SWvt WFar WHtc WMat
	- 'Hamlet's Broom'	NLar SLim
	- 'Little Creamy' (v)	CAco NLar
	- 'Little Giant'	MBlu
	- 'Matthaei'	CAco LIns MAsh MBlu SLim
	- 'McCracken's White'	see *M. glyptostroboides* 'Snow Flurry'
	- 'Miss Grace'	CAco SLim
§	- 'National'	MBlu
	- 'Schirrmann's Nordlicht'	LRHS MAsh NLar SLim
	- 'Sheridan Spire'	CEnd MBlu
§	- 'Snow Flurry' (v)	NLar
	- 'Waasland'	MBlu SLim
	- 'White Spot' (v)	MBlu

Metrosideros (*Myrtaceae*)

	carminea	CCCN CTsd
§	***excelsa***	CTrC ECre ESwi IKel WCFE
	- 'Maori Princess'	CBcs
	- 'Parnell'	CBcs CCCN
	- 'Vibrance'	CCCN
	kermadecensis 'Variegata' (v)	CBcs
	lucida	see *M. umbellata*
	robusta	CBcs CCCN SPlb
	- ***aureovariegata*** (v)	CCCN EShb
§	'Springfire'	CCCN
	× ***subtomentosa*** 'Mistral'	WPGP
	'Thomasii'	see *M.* 'Springfire'
	tomentosa	see *M. excelsa*
§	***umbellata***	CBcs CCCN EBee MVil
	- 'Gold Nugget'	CBcs CCCN SSta
	- MOONLIGHT ('Lowmoo')	CBcs CCCN CKel SEle SIvy

Meum (*Apiaceae*)

athamanticum	CSpe EBee EBlo EMor EPPr EPfP GPoy GQue LEdu LRHS MHol MRav SMHy SPhx SPtp WJek WSHC

Michauxia (*Campanulaceae*)

campanuloides	CSpe EDAr GJos SBls
tchihatchewii	CDTJ

Michelia see *Magnolia*

fulgens	see *Magnolia foveolata*
wilsonii	see *Magnolia ernestii*

Micranthocereus (*Cactaceae*)

polyanthus **new**	EAri

Microbiota (*Cupressaceae*)

	decussata ♀H7	CAco CBcs CSBt GMcL LBee LRHS MGos NHol SLim WFar WPav
	- CELTIC PRIDE	see *M. decussata* 'Prides'
	- 'Gold Spot' (v)	CAco CKen LRHS WFar
	- 'Jakobsen'	CKen
	- 'Lucas'PBR **new**	CAco
§	- 'Prides' **new**	CAco
	- 'Sibirteppe' **new**	CAco
	- 'Trompenburg'	CKen

Microcachrys (*Podocarpaceae*)

tetragona	IDee LRHS

Microcoelum see *Lytocaryum*

Microlepia (*Dennstaedtiaceae*)

strigosa	CCCN CLAP EHyd ISha LEdu LRHS NRHS WPGP
- 'MacFaddeniae' ♀H4	CLAP CRos EHyd ISha LEdu LRHS NRHS WPGP

Micromeria (*Lamiaceae*)

	sp.	SRms
	corsica	see *Clinopodium corsicum*
	fruticosa	WJek
	juliana	XLum
	rupestris	see *M. thymifolia*
§	***thymifolia***	SPlb XSen

Microseris (*Asteraceae*)

ringens hort.	see *Leontodon rigens*

Microsorum (*Polypodiaceae*)

§	***diversifolium***	CDoC EShb IKel LEdu SPlb WPGP
	musifolium 'Crocodyllus'PBR	CDoC
	punctatum **new**	LEdu
	pustulatum	IKel

Microtropis (*Celastraceae*)

petelotii HWJ 719	WCru

Milium (*Poaceae*)

effusum	CBor
- 'Aureum' ♀H7	Widely available
- 'Yaffle' (v)	CKno EBee EPPr EShb

Millettia (*Fabaceae*)

reticulata	see *Wisteriopsis reticulata*

Mimetes (*Proteaceae*)

chrysanthus	SPlb
cucullatus	CPbh
- 'Crackerjack Red'	CCCN

Mimosa (*Fabaceae*)

pudica ♀H1b	CCCN CDTJ CDoC EShb NGrs

Mimulus (*Phrymaceae*)

	'Andean Nymph'	see *M. naiandinus*
§	***aurantiacus*** ♀H2	CMac CSpe ECtt EShb MGil NPer SPlb SPoG SRms WFar WMal
	- 'Primrose'	MGil
	cardinalis ♀H4	EBee ELan EPfP EWes EWld GKev LPfP
	- gold-flowered	EBee
	- 'Red Dragon'	MHol
	cardinalis × ***lewisii***	EWes
	cupreus 'Red Emperor'	CWat GQue LCro LOPS LPfP
	- 'Whitecroft Scarlet' ♀H4	LShi
	eastwoodiae	GEdr

'Eleanor' ECtt EShb WMal
glutinosus see *M. aurantiacus*
– ***atrosanguineus*** see *M. puniceus*
– ***luteus*** see *M. aurantiacus*
§ ***guttatus*** LCro LOPS LPfP MBow NPer WMAq
'Highland Orange' EPfP MAsh SPlb SPoG WIce
'Highland Pink' MAsh NHpl SPlb SPoG
'Highland Red' ♀H4 EBou MAsh NHpl SPlb SPoG
'Highland Yellow' NHpl SPlb SPoG
hose-in-hose (d) NPer
× ***hybridus*** Mystic Series RHS
langsdorffii see *M. guttatus*
lewisii ♀H3 EWes MNrw SRms
luteus CWat GAbr LLWG NPer WBrk XLum
– 'Queen's Prize' CWat
– 'Variegatus' ambig. (v) NPer
Magic Series LRHS SVic
MAXIMUS MIXED LRHS
§ ***naiandinus*** ♀H4 EWes GKev LShi SPlb
'Orange Glow' LLWG LShi
§ 'Orkney Gold' (d) ECtt
'Popacatapetl' CSpe WMal
primuloides EDAr EWes SPlb
§ ***puniceus*** SChF SRkn WFar WMal
RED EMPEROR see *M.* 'Roter Kaiser'
ringens CBen CPla CPud CWat EBee LLWG LPfP NBir NPer SPlb SRms WMAq
§ 'Roter Kaiser' ELan
yellow hose-in-hose see *M.* 'Orkney Gold'

Mina see *Ipomoea*

mint, apple see *Mentha suaveolens*

mint, basil see *Mentha* × *gracilis*

mint, Bowles's see *Mentha* × *villosa* var. *alopecuroides*

mint, curly see *Mentha spicata* var. *crispa*

mint, eau-de-Cologne see *Mentha* × *piperita* f. *citrata*

mint, ginger see *Mentha* × *gracilis*

mint, horse or long-leaved see *Mentha longifolia*

mint (pennyroyal) see *Mentha pulegium*

mint (peppermint) see *Mentha* × *piperita*

mint, round-leaved see *Mentha suaveolens*

mint (spearmint) see *Mentha spicata*

Minthostachys (*Lamiaceae*)

andina new GPoy

Minuartia (*Caryophyllaceae*)

parnassica see *M. stellata*
§ ***stellata*** EPot GArf
verna subsp. ***caespitosa*** CTri
– – 'Aurea' see *Sagina subulata* var. *glabrata* 'Aurea'

Mirabilis (*Nyctaginaceae*)

dichotoma EShb
jalapa GKev LAma SDeJ SRms WHil
– 'Buttermilk' CCCN
longiflora EShb SBrt WHil
multiflora EBee

Miscanthus (*Poaceae*)

capensis SPlb
'Champagne' new EWes
chejuensis B&SWJ 8803 WCru
flavidus ESwi SRms XLum
– B&SWJ 6749 EPPr
floridulus misapplied see *M.* × *giganteus*
floridulus ambig. EHeP MMuc MNrw SPlb XLum
§ × ***giganteus*** CKno ELon EPPr GBin GElm GMcL MAsh MNrw MWht NWsh SCob SCoo SDix SDys SVic WCot XLum
– 'Aksel Olsen' SAko
– ALLIGATOR ('Lottum'PBR) (v) new CKno SPeP
– 'Gilt Edge' (v) CKno EPPr NWsh WCot
– 'Gotemba' (v) ELon EPPr
– 'Jubilar' (v) MWht
– 'Meidl' SAko
lutarioriparius WPGP
nepalensis Widely available
– NJM 09.141 WPGP
– 'Shikola' WCru
nudipes EPPr
oligostachyus SBls
§ – 'Afrika' EPPr GBin MNrw WPGP
I – 'Nanus Variegatus' (v) ELon LEdu WCot
'Purpurascens' CBod CKno ECha EHyd ELan EPPr EPfP LPar LRHS LSRN MAsh MNrw NRHS SCob XLum
§ 'Rosi' EPPr MAvo WPGP
sacchariflorus misapplied see *M.* × *giganteus*
sacchariflorus ambig. CBcs CKno EBee ECha EHyd ELan EPfP LRHS MBrN NRHS SPeP
sacchariflorus (Maxim.) Hack. LEdu SBls WPGP WSpi
– 'Robustus' SPeP
sinensis CTri GDam WFar XSen
– CL 1325 EPPr
– 'Abundance' CKel CKno CRos EHyd EPPr EPfP LRHS NRHS
– 'Adagio' ♀H6 CBod CDor CKel CKno CSde ECtt EHyd ELan ELon EPPr EShb EWhm GKev LPar LRHS MAsh MNrw NRHS NWad NWsh SCoo SMHy SPoG SRms WCot WHoo XLum XSen
– 'Afrika' see *M. oligostachyus* 'Afrika'
– 'Aldebaran' EPPr
– 'Andante' CKno
– 'Arabesque' EPPr XLum
– 'Augustfeder' EPPr MAvo XLum
– 'Autumn Light' EPPr XLum
– 'Barney Campbell' NWsh
– 'Beth Chatto' ECha EPPr LEdu WPGP
– 'Blütenwunder' EBee EPPr XLum
– 'Bogenlampe' EBee EPPr GBin
– 'Brazil'PBR new CBod
– 'China' ♀H6 CKno CPar CRos CTtf EHyd ELon EPPr EPfP EWes LEdu LRHS MAsh MAvo MNrw NRHS NWsh SDys SRms WHoo
– 'Cindy' CKno EPPr
– var. ***condensatus*** NJM 11.021 WPGP
– – 'Cabaret' (v) CKno EBee EBlo EHyd ELan EPPr EPfP EShb GElm GMaP GMcL LEdu LPar LRHS LSRN LSun MNrw NRHS NSti NWsh SBls SMad SPoG

		WCot WFar WPGP WSpi XLum XSen
	- - 'Central Park'	see *M. sinensis* var. *condensatus* 'Cosmo Revert'
§	- - 'Cosmo Revert'	EPPr NWsh WPGP
	- - 'Cosmopolitan' (v) ♀H6	Widely available
	- - 'Emerald Giant'	see *M. sinensis* var. *condensatus* 'Cosmo Revert'
	- - 'Laigong'	LEdu
	- 'Cute One'	CBct CKel ELan WPnP XSte
	- 'David'	ELon EPPr XLum
	- 'Digestif'	EBee
	- 'Dixieland' (v)	CKno ELan ELon EPPr EWes NLar
	- 'Dreadlocks'	EBee EPPr GBin MAvo MNrw NWsh
	- 'Dronning Ingrid'	CKno EPPr LPla LRHS MNrw NDov SBls WHil XLum
	- EARLY HYBRIDS	EBou
	- 'Elfin'	CKno EPPr
	- 'Emmanuel Lepage'	CKno EPPr LPla MAvo NWsh XLum
	- 'Etincelle'	CKno EPPr EWes
	- 'Federriese'	GBin
	- 'Ferner Osten' ♀H6	Widely available
	- 'Flamingo' ♀H6	Widely available
	- 'Flammenmeer'	EPPr SAko
	- 'Gearmella'	EPPr
	- 'Gewitterwolke' ♀H6	EWes NWsh SMHy XLum
	- 'Ghana' ♀H6	CDor CKel CSpe CWnw ECha ELon EPPr EPfP EWoo LEdu MAvo MMrt MNrw NLar SCoo SDys SEdd SMHy SPoG SRms SSut WPGP XLum
	- 'Giraffe'	CDTJ CKno ELon EWes LEdu XLum
	- 'Gnome'	CKno EHyd EPPr EPfP EShb LRHS MAsh MTin NRHS SRms
	- 'Gold Bar'[PBR] (v)	Widely available
	- 'Gold Breeze'[PBR]	CDoC EHyd LRHS NRHS
	- 'Gold und Silber' ♀H6	XLum
	- 'Goldfeder' (v)	EWes XLum
	- 'Goldglanz'	EBee
	- 'Goliath'	CKno ELon EPPr GElm GLog LEdu MACG NWsh WFar XLum
	- 'Gracillimus'	Widely available
	- 'Graziella'	CEnd CKno EHyd EPPr GBin LRHS MAsh NRHS SCoo SPer SRms WFar WHoo XSen
	- 'Grosse Fontäne' ♀H6	ELon EPPr LEdu LRHS LSRN NWsh SCob SEdd WCot XLum
	- 'Gutenberg Gold'	XLum
	- 'Haiku'	CKno EPPr LEdu XLum
	- 'Helga Reich'	EWes
	- 'Hercules'	EPPr MAvo XLum
	- 'Hermann Müssel'	CRos EBlo EHyd EPPr EWes LEdu LRHS NRHS WHlf XLum
§	- 'Hinjo' (v)	ECha ECtt EHyd ELon EPPr EPfP GKev LRHS MAsh NGdn NRHS NWsh WCot
	- 'Ibiza'[PBR]	CKno EBee SCoo
I	- 'Jubilaris' (v)	ELon EPPr
	- 'Juli'	EPPr WSpi
	- 'Kaskade' ♀H6	CKno EBlo EHyd EPPr LEdu LRHS NDov NLar NRHS WHlf
	- 'Kim'	NDov
	- 'Kirk Alexander' (v)	EPPr
	- 'Kleine Fontäne' ♀H6	Widely available
	- 'Kleine Silberspinne' ♀H6	Widely available
	- 'Korea'	EPPr
	- 'Krater'	EHyd EPPr LRHS MBrN NRHS NWsh SDys XLum
	- 'Kupferberg'	XLum
	- 'Kupferzwerg'	EBee EPPr
	- 'Little John' **new**	NWsh
§	- 'Little Kitten'	EPPr LEdu LRHS SCob SRms XLum
	- 'Little Miss'	CPla EPfP LRHS SPad SPeP
	- LITTLE NICKY	see *M. sinensis* 'Hinjo'
	- 'Little Zebra'[PBR] (v)	CDoC GMaP LRHS LSRN MGos MPnt NWsh SEdd SEle SRms
	- 'Lorelei'	GBin
	- 'Malepartus'	Widely available
	- 'Memory'	EPPr MAvo
	- 'Morning Light' (v) ♀H6	Widely available
	- 'Mrs Higgins'	NWsh
	- 'München'	EBee
	- 'Navajo'[PBR]	CBct CBod CKel CSpe MBNS SPeP WWke
	- 'Nippon'	EHyd EPPr EPfP GBin LEdu LRHS MAsh NGdn NRHS NWsh SCob SDys SPer WCAu WSpi XLum
	- 'Nishidake'	EPPr XLum
	- 'November Sunset'	EPPr XLum
	- 'Overdam'	ECtt NGdn
	- 'Poseidon'	ECha EPPr MAvo SDys SMad XLum
	- 'Positano'	EPPr XLum
	- 'Professor Richard Hansen'	CKno EPPr EWes NWsh SMHy XLum
	- 'Pünktchen' (v)	ECha ELon EPPr GBin SRms XLum
	- 'Purple Fall'	CDor CKno CSpe ECha ECtt EHyd EWes GMaP IPot LEdu LRHS MAvo MNrw SCoo
	- 'Red Chief'	CKno CMiW CRos ECha EHyd EPPr EPfP EWes GElm LRHS MACG MAvo MHtn MNrw NDov NLar NRHS SCob SCoo WCot WTor
	- RED CLOUD ('Empmis01'[PBR])	LCro LOPS LRHS NDov SCoo SMad
	- 'Red Meister'	CKno EHyd EPPr EPfP LRHS NRHS
	- 'Red Spear' **new**	CKno
	- 'Red Wine'	MNrw
	- 'Roland'	EPPr SMad XLum
	- 'Rosi'	see *M.* 'Rosi'
	- 'Roterpfeil'	EPPr
	- 'Rotfeder'	EPPr NLar
	- 'Rotfuchs'	CMac MAvo XLum
	- 'Rotsilber'	CKno ECha EHyd EPPr GMaP IArd LEdu LRHS MAsh MMuc NRHS SRms WHoo WOld WPGP XLum
	- 'Russia'	NWsh
	- 'Samurai'	EPPr GMaP MAvo MNrw SCob
	- 'Sarabande' ♀H6	EPPr NLar SMHy WSpi
	- 'Septemberrot' ♀H6	EPPr MMuc SEND
	- 'Serim'	EPPr
§	- 'Silberfeder' ♀H6	Widely available
	- 'Silberspinne'	EBee ELon EPPr SCob SMHy SPlb XLum
	- 'Silberturm'	EPPr XLum
	- SILVER FEATHER	see *M. sinensis* 'Silberfeder'
	- 'Silver Sceptre'	MAvo SMHy
	- 'Silver Stripe'	EPPr
	- 'Sioux'	ECtt EHyd EPPr EPfP GBin LRHS MAsh MBNS NRHS WCAu
	- 'Sirene'	EPPr MMuc NBir NWsh
	- 'Spätgrün'	EPPr
	- 'Starlight'	CKno CRos EPPr LRHS MAvo NWsh
	- 'Strictus' (v) ♀H6	Widely available
	- 'Strictus Compactus'	LRHS
	- 'Super Stripe' (v)	EPPr
	- 'Taiwan'	EBee EPPr
	- 'Tiger Cub' (v)	EPPr
	- 'Undine' ♀H6	CKel ECha EPPr EPfP MBel MBrN MMuc XLum
	- 'Vanilla Sky'	EBee EWes SCoo
	- 'Variegatus' (v)	CEme ECha ECtt EHyd ELan ELon EPPr EPfP EWoo GElm GMaP GMcL LPar LRHS LSRN LSun

	MMuc MRav NGdn NRHS NSti SDix SPer SPoG SRms WCot WOld WSpi XLum
- 'Vorläufer'	EPPr
- 'Westacre Wine'	EPPr EWes
- 'Wetterfahne'	EPPr
- 'Yaka Dance'PBR **new**	SSut
§ - 'Yaku-jima'	CBod CKel CWnw ECha ECtt EHyd ELan EPPr LRHS MMuc MWht NCth NRHS WFar
- 'Yakushima Dwarf'	CEnd CExl CKel CRos EHyd ELan ELon EPPr EPfP GBin GElm GMcL LRHS MBel NRHS NSti NWsh SBea SCob SCoo SDys SRms SSha SSut STPC WCot WHoo WOld XLum
- 'Zebrinus' (v) ♀H6	Widely available
- 'Zwergelefant'	MAvo SMHy XLum
tinctorius 'Nanus Variegatus' misapplied	see *M. oligostachyus* 'Nanus Variegatus'
transmorrisonensis	EHyd EPPr LEdu LPla LRHS MAvo MBel NDov NRHS NWsh WCot WPGP
- 'Sunset' **new**	CKno
yakushimensis	see *M. sinensis* 'Little Kitten', *M. sinensis* 'Yaku-jima'

Mitchella (*Rubiaceae*)

repens	CBcs CBod EBee EPot ESwi GEdr LEdu MNrw WCru
undulata B&SWJ 10928	WCru
* - f. ***quelpartensis*** B&SWJ 4402	WCru

Mitella (*Saxifragaceae*)

acerina B&SWJ 11029	EWld GGro WCru
breweri	CBod CBor CDor CMac EBee ECha EWld GLog MAvo MBriF MPnt MRav NSti WBor WFar WPnP
caulescens	ECha NBro
formosana B&SWJ 125	WCru
furusei var. ***subramosa*** B&SWJ 11097	GGro WCru
× ***inami*** B&SWJ 11122	GGro WCru
japonica B&SWJ 4971	WCru
- 'Variegata' (v)	GGro
kiusiana	WFar
- B&SWJ 5401	GGro WFar
- B&SWJ 5888	WCru
makinoi	EWld
- B&SWJ 4992	CExl GGro WCru WHoo
ovalis	CPla GGro
pauciflora B&SWJ 6361	WCru
- B&SWJ 11067	GGro
stylosa B&SWJ 5669	WCru
- PB 04-301	GGro
yoshinagae	WFar
- B&SWJ 4893	CExl EPPr GGro WCru

Mitraria (*Gesneriaceae*)

coccinea	CCCN CExl CMac CPbh CRHN CTsd GBin GEdr GKev IDee MBlu NLar SPlb
- Clark's form	LRHS NLar SIvy
- 'Lago Puyehue'	CAbb CBcs CCCN CDoC CExl CKel CSpe EBee EPfP LRHS MAsh MGil SEdd SIvy SPlb SVen SWvt WPav WSHC WThu
- 'Lake Caburgua'	CCCN ELon NLar WAbe WPav

Modiolastrum (*Malvaceae*)

lateritium	CBod CRHN CSpe CTri EBee EGrl ELan EPPr EShb MAvo NBir SIvy SPhx SPoG SRms WSHC XLum

Moehringia (*Caryophyllaceae*)

muscosa	WCot

Molinia ✿ (*Poaceae*)

altissima	see *M. caerulea* subsp. *arundinacea*
caerulea	CBod CKno EHyd EPPr LRHS MBlu NBwr NRHS SCoo
§ - subsp. ***arundinacea***	CFis CKno CSpe CWCL ECha EPPr SSut WChS XLum
- - 'Autumn Charm'	CKno
- - 'Bergfreund'	CKno EPPr GBin MAvo SMHy
- - 'Black Arrows'	EMor MAvo NDov
- - 'Breeze'	CKno EPPr NDov
- - 'Cordoba'	CBod EBee ECha ELan EPPr GQue MAvo NDov SMHy WFar XLum
- - 'Crystal Veil' **new**	NDov
- - 'Fontäne'	ECha EMor EPPr GQue MAsh MAvo
- - 'Golden Chimes'	EPPr
- - 'Intruder'	NWsh
- - 'JS Mostenveld' (v)	ECha ELon EPPr
- - 'JS Witches Broom'	EPPr GBin
- - 'JS Yellow Pipe'	GBin
- - 'Karl Foerster'	Widely available
- - 'Les Ponts de Cé'	EBee ECha EPPr
- - 'Liebreiz'	EPPr
- - 'Skyracer' ♀H7	CBod CKno CRos CSde EHyd ELan ELon EMor EPPr EWoo GBin GLog GMaP GQue LEdu LRHS MAsh MAvo MNrw NLar NRHS SCoo SMHy SPoG WCot WPGP WPnP
- - 'Staefa'	EPPr
- - 'Sunbeam'	EPPr
- - 'Tears of Joy'	EBee ECha EPPr
- - 'Transparent' ♀H7	Widely available
- - 'Windsaule'	CKno ECha EPPr MAvo MNrw NDov
- - 'Windspiel' ♀H7	CAby CBod CKno CSde CWCL EBou ECha EHyd ELon EPPr EPfP EShb GBin GElm GMcL GQue LRHS MAsh MAvo MNrw NDov NRHS NWsh SCoo SDix SPeP SPoG WCAu WCot XLum
- - 'Zuneigung'	ECha EPPr MAvo
- subsp. ***caerulea***	EPPr LRHS
- - 'Carmarthen' (v)	ELon
- - 'Claerwen' (v)	ECha ELon MAvo
- - 'Coneyhill Gold' (v)	EPPr
- - 'Dark Defender'	ECha EPPr LEdu MAvo NDov SPhx
- - 'Dauerstrahl'	CBWd CKno EPPr GMaP GQue LEdu MAsh MBel MNrw NBid NDov
- - 'Edith Dudszus' ♀H7	CBWd CBod CKno CWCL EAJP EBou ECha EHyd ELan ELon EMor EPPr EPfP GBin GQue LRHS MAsh MBel MBrN NDov NHol NRHS SCob WPnP
- - 'Heidebraut'	CAby CBWd CKel ECha EHyd ELon EMor EPPr EPfP EWoo GMaP GQue LCro LOPS LPar LRHS MBel MHtn MRav NDov NRHS NWsh SAko SCob WCot
- - 'Heidezwerg'	CKno ELon EMor EPPr GBin GQue
- - 'Heinrichs Dauerstrahl'	EPPr
- - 'Igel'	CKno EBee EPPr GBin
- - 'Moorflamme'	ELon EMor MAvo NDov
- - 'Moorhexe' ♀H7	Widely available
- - 'Overdam'	CKno EBee EPPr MNrw NDov
- - 'Poul Petersen' ♀H7	CKno EPPr LRHS MBel NDov SCob SHor SPhx WChS

- - 'Strahlenquelle'	CFis EHyd EPPr GQue LRHS LSto NDov NHol NRHS NWsh WCAu
- - 'Variegata' (v) ♀H7	Widely available
- 'Torch'PBR	CKno EMor NCth
- 'Winterfreude'	EPPr
litoralis	see *M. caerulea* subsp. *arundinacea*

Molopospermum (*Apiaceae*)

peloponnesiacum	CSpe EBee ELan EPPr GBin GElm LEdu LRHS MAvo MHer SBrt SMHy SPhx SPtp WCru WKif WPGP WSHC

Moltkia (*Boraginaceae*)

§ ***doerfleri***	CPla LEdu LPla NBir NChi SBrt WKif WSHC
§ × ***intermedia*** ♀H4	CRos EHyd LRHS NRHS WAbe
petraea	CRos EDAr EHyd GKev LRHS NRHS SBut

Moluccella (*Lamiaceae*)

laevis	CSpe LCro LOPS SPhx SVic

Monanthes (*Crassulaceae*)

laxiflora	WCot

Monarda ✿ (*Lamiaceae*)

'Adam'	ELon GBee LSRN MRav NGrd NLar WMon WSHC
'André Eve'	NDov WMon
'Aquarius'	CWCL EHyd ELon GQue LRHS LSto MAvo NLar NRHS WCAu WFar WMon XLum
'Baby Spice'	LBar LRHS MPie WFar WMon
§ 'Balance'	EBee ECtt EHyd EWoo LRHS MAvo MMrt MPie MRav NGdn NRHS SMrm WMon WSHC XLum
'Beauty of Cobham' ♀H4	Widely available
'Bergamo'	LCro LOPS
§ 'Blaustrumpf'	CBod ECtt EGrI EHyd EPfP EWes GQue LRHS MACG MNHC NGrd NLar SPer WFar WMon WSHC XLum
'Blue Moon' **new**	EBlo
BLUE STOCKING	see *M.* 'Blaustrumpf'
BOWMAN	see *M.* 'Sagittarius'
bradburyana	EBee EShb LRHS SAko SBrt SPhx
- 'Grey Summit'	NDov
- 'Maramek'	IPot NLar WMon
- 'Ozark'	ECha NDov SAko WMon
'Cambridge Scarlet'	Widely available
'Camilla'	WGoo WMon
'Capricorn'	WMon XLum
'Cherokee'	MSpe WFar WMon
citriodora	GJos GPoy MHoo NSti SRms
'Comanche'	EWes NLar WFar WMon
'Croftway Pink'	CAby CBcs CEme CRos CSBt ECha ECtt EGrI EHeP EHyd ELan EPfP GMaP LCro LOPS LRHS MAvo MHoo NRHS SCob SPeP SPer SWvt WCAu WFar WHlf WMon WSHC XLum
I 'Dark Ponticum'	WMon
'Desert Jewel' **new**	LShi
didyma	CBod CLau EBou ENfk EPfP MHoo MNHC NBro SRms SVic WFar
- 'Alba'	WMon
- (Balmy Series) BALMY LILAC ('Balbalmac'PBR)	EHyd LRHS MDon MHol NRHS SCob SPoG WMon
- - BALMY PINK ('Balbalmink'PBR)	LRHS MDon MHoo SPoG WHil WMon
- - BALMY PURPLE ('Balbalmurp'PBR)	EHyd LRHS MDon MHol MHoo NRHS SCob SPoG WFar WHil WMon
- - BALMY ROSE ('Balbalmose'PBR)	EPfP MDon SCob
- (Bee-You Series) BEE-BRIGHT ('Monbebr') **new**	CBod LBar WHil
- - BEE-FREE ('Mon0012bfr'PBR)	CBod CWGN EBee LBar LRHS NCth NLar SHeu SRkn WMon
- - BEE-HAPPY ('Mon0001bha'PBR)	CBod CWGN EBee LBar LEdu LRHS MNrw NLar SHeu SPeP SRkn WHil WMon WPGP
- - BEE-LIEVE ('Mon0004bli'PBR)	EBee LBar LRHS MNrw NLar NSti SHeu WMon
- - BEE-MERRY IMPROVED **new**	LBar WMon
- - BEE-PRETTY **new**	LBar
- - BEE-PURE ('Monard0039'PBR) **new**	LBar WMon
- - BEE-TRUE ('Mon0005btr'PBR)	CWGN EBee LBar LRHS MNrw NCth NLar SHeu SPeP SRkn WMon
- 'Bubblegum Blast' (Sugar Buzz Series) **new**	WMon
- 'Coral Reef'	WFar WMon
- 'Cranberry Lace'PBR	CRos ECtt EHyd EPfP LRHS MHol NRHS SPoG WCAu WMon
- DANCING BIRD ('Allmobird'PBR)	LBar NLar
- 'Grape Gumball'PBR (Sugar Buzz Series) **new**	EBlo WMon
- (Pardon My Series) 'Pardon My Cerise'	NCth WFar
- - 'Pardon My Lavender' **new**	WMon
- - 'Pardon My Pink'	EBee NCth NLar SPad WMon
- - 'Pardon My Purple'	EPfP MAvo NCth NLar SPoG WMon
- 'Pink Lace'PBR	CBod CPla CRos ECtt EHyd EPfP LRHS LSou MHol MNrw MThu NHol NLar NRHS NSti SCob SPoG WCAu WFar WMon
- 'Purple Lace'PBR	EBlo EHyd EPfP LRHS NRHS NSti WFar
- 'Sugar Lace'PBR	WMon
'Earl Grey'	ECtt NChi SCoo SEdi WFar WMon
'Elsie's Lavender'	EBee EHyd EPfP GMaP IPot LRHS NDov NLar NRHS WFar WMon WSHC
'Elworthy'	CElw WWFP
'Eugens Kirschrot'	WMon
'Eugens Purpursamt'	WMon
'Feckenham Danielle'	WHoo WMal WMon
'Feckenham Foundling' **new**	WHoo
§ 'Feuerschopf'	WMon
'Fireball'PBR	Widely available
FIRECROWN	see *M.* 'Feuerschopf'
§ 'Fishes'	CBod CMac EBee ECtt ELan EWes GQue LEdu LRHS LShi MACG MRav NDov NGdn NLar SGbt SMrm SWvt WFar WMon WTor WWke
fistulosa	CBod CHby CMac EBou LEdu MBow MHoo MNHC NDov SRms XLum
- 'Humdinger'	EBee WMon
- var. ***menthifolia*** 'Mohikaner'	NDov WGoo WMon
- - 'Pummel'	NDov WMon
- 'Wahpe Washtemna'	NDov WCot
'Gardenview Scarlet' ♀H4	Widely available
GEMINI	see *M.* 'Twins'
'Gewitterwolke'	ECtt EGrI ELon IPot NDov WFar WMon
'Hartswood Wine'	EWes LEdu SMrm WFar WMon WPGP

'Häuptling'	NDov WMon
'Heidelerche'	WFar WMon
'Huckleberry'	GBin NDov WMon
'Jacob Cline'	Widely available
'Kardinal'	GBin LRHS NDov WMon XLum
'Knight Rose'	MNHC WFar WMon
'Knight Violet'	WMon
'Leading Lady Lilac' **new**	LBar WHil
'Leading Lady Plum' PBR **new**	LBar
'Lederstrumpf'	WFar WMon
LIBRA	see *M.* 'Balance'
'Loddon Crown'	CAby ECtt MBNS MHer MHoo NHol NLar SHar WCAu WFar WMon WNPC WSHC
'Mahogany'	CRos EBee ECtt EHyd ELan EPfP EWoo GBee GMaP IPot LRHS LSto MHol NRHS NSti SMrm SPer SPoG WFar WMon XLum
'Marshall's Delight' ♀H4	CBod CDor CRos EBee ECtt EHyd EPfP EWes GQue LRHS MNHC MNrw MRav NRHS SMrm SWvt WCAu WFar WMon
'Melissa'	CRos EHyd EPfP LRHS NLar NRHS WMon WSHC
menthifolia	SRms
'Mohawk'	CBWd CBod ECtt EHyd EPfP EWoo GMcL GQue IPot LRHS MHol MPie NDov NGdn NGrd SGbt SMrm WCAu WFar WMon XLum
'Neon'	LRHS NDov WHoo WMon
'On Parade'	CWCL ECtt EHyd ELon GBee GPSL LEdu LPla LRHS MMrt NDov NGdn SMrm WFar WMon
'Othello'	EHyd LRHS NDov NRHS WGoo WMon
'Ou Charm'	EWes NLar SMrm WFar WMon
Panorama Series	LSun SPlb WMon
- 'Panorama Red Shades'	CCBP EPfP WFar WMon
'Pawnee'	GBin WGoo WMon
PETITE DELIGHT ('Acpetdel')	LBar WMon XLum
'Petite Wonder'	WFar WMon
'Pink Frosting' (Sugar Buzz Series) **new**	WMon
'Pink Supreme' PBR	ECtt EHyd ELan EPfP GMcL LEdu LRHS MAvo MBel MPie NLar SCoo WFar WHil WMon WTor WWke
'Pink Tourmaline'	SMrm WMon
PISCES	see *M.* 'Fishes'
'Poyntzfield Pink'	GPoy LEdu WMon
PRAIRIE NIGHT	see *M.* 'Prärienacht'
§ 'Prärienacht'	Widely available
punctata	CFis MACG MNHC WMon
- 'Bee Bop'	LCro LOPS
'Purple Acres'	ECtt
'Purple Ann'	XLum
'Purple Tower'	EWes
'Raspberry Wine'	CBod CDor CRos EBee ECtt EHyd EPPr EPfP EWes LEdu LRHS LSou MACG NRHS WFar WMon WPGP
'Rebecca'	NDov WMon
'Remie'	WMon
'Ruby Glow'	EHyd GDam GMcL NRHS WHoo WMon
§ 'Sagittarius'	EBee EHyd LRHS MAvo MSpe NGdn NRHS NSti SPoG WFar WMon
'Saxon Purple'	MBel NDov WHoo WMon XLum
§ 'Schneewittchen'	CAby EBee ECha ECtt ELan EPfP LRHS MRav NHol SCob SCoo SGbt SPer SPoG SRms SWvt WCAu WFar WHlf WMon WNPC XLum
'Scorpion'	CRos EBee ECtt EHyd ELan EPfP GBee GBin GMcL GQue LCro LOPS LRHS MRav NBir NGdn NRHS NSti SGbt SMrm SPoG SWvt WCAu WHlf WMon XLum
'Shelley'	ECha WFar WMon
'Snow Maiden'	see *M.* 'Schneewittchen'
'Snow Queen'	EBee ECtt EHyd EWhm LRHS MPie SMrm WMon
SNOW WHITE	see *M.* 'Schneewittchen'
'Squaw' ♀H4	Widely available
'Talud' ♀H4	IPot MNrw NDov WMon
'Tante Polly'	WMon
§ 'Twins'	NLar SWvt WFar WMon WSHC
'Vintage Wine'	CElw NDov WMon
'Violacea'	NHol WFar WMon
'Violet Queen'	CBod CRos CWCL EBee ECtt EHyd ELan EWes GQue LEdu LRHS MCot MPie MSpe NEoE NRHS SCoo SMrm WCAu WCot WFar WMon WPGP WWke
'Violette'	WFar WMon
'Westacre Purple'	ECha EGrl EPPr EWes WMon

Monardella (*Lamiaceae*)

odoratissima	MHer

Monochoria (*Pontederiaceae*)

§ ***hastata***	EWat LLWG

Monstera (*Araceae*)

adansonii	CDoC LWaG NHrt
deliciosa (F) ♀H1b	CDoC LCro LOPS LWaG NGrs NHrt NPlm NTrD WLea
obliqua **new**	NHrt
- 'Monkey Mask'	LCro LOPS LWaG NHrt WLea

Montbretia see *Crocosmia*

Montia (*Portulacaceae*)

perfoliata	see *Claytonia perfoliata*
sibirica	see *Claytonia sibirica*

Moraea (*Iridaceae*)

alticola	GAbr GKev SPlb
§ ***aristata***	CBor NRog
atropunctata	NRog
§ ***bellendenii***	NRog
bipartita	NRog WCot
britteniae	NRog
ciliata	NRog
§ ***collina***	CBor GKev NRog
flaccida	MBros
gigandra	NRog
glaucopsis	see *M. aristata*
huttonii	CBor CCCN CFis CPbh CSpe EPri EWoo GAbr GEdr GKev SBrt SMad WSHC
iridioides	see *Dietes iridioides*
loubseri	NRog
lugubris	NRog
macrocarpa	NRog
marlothii	NRog
ochroleuca	CBor GKev MBros NRog
pavonia var. ***lutea***	see *M. bellendenii*
pendula **new**	CBor
polystachya	NRog
robusta	GKev
setifolia	NRog
sisyrinchium	EWoo GKev NRog SDeJ
spathacea	see *M. spathulata*
§ ***spathulata***	CExl GKev SBrt WCot
thomsonii	NRog

tricuspidata	NRog
tripetala	NRog
tulbaghensis	NRog
vegeta	NRog SBrt
villosa	NRog

Morella (*Myricaceae*)

californica	CAgr
pensylvanica	CAgr NLar

Moricandia (*Brassicaceae*)

moricandioides	WCot

Morina (*Caprifoliaceae*)

longifolia	Widely available
persica	GElm
polyphylla	GPoy

Morinda (*Rubiaceae*)

umbellata WWJ 11688	WCru

Moringa (*Moringaceae*)

hildebrandtii **new**	EAri
oleifera **new**	EAri

Morisia (*Brassicaceae*)

	hypogaea	see *M. monanthos*
§	***monanthos***	CBor EPfP GEdr NBwr SRot WIce
	- 'Fred Hemingway'	ELan EPot GArf NSla WAbe

Morus ✿ (*Moraceae*)

§	***alba***	CBcs CCVT CHab CMCN EDir ELan IPap LBuc LEdu LIns LMaj LPar MRav MTrO NRog SPre SVic WFar WLov WMou WTSh
	- 'Agate' (F)	CAgr
	- fruitless	EHed LIns
	- 'Laciniata'	EBee ELan
§	- 'Macrophylla'	CMCN LIns MBlu SCob
	- 'Pakistan' (F)	CAgr NOra SPoG
	- 'Paradise' (F)	CAgr
	- 'Pendula'	CAco CEnd CMCN CMac ELan LPar MBlu MPri MTrO NOra SCoo SPoG SWeb SWvt WMat
	- 'Platanifolia'	see *M. alba* 'Macrophylla'
	- var. ***tatarica***	CAgr LEdu NLar
	'Black Tabor' (F)	CAgr
	'Capsrum' (F)	CAgr
	'Carman' (F)	CAgr ELan MTrO NLar NOra SKee
	cathayana	EBee WPGP
	CHARLOTTE RUSSE	see *M.* 'Waisei-kirishima-shikinari'
	'Illinois Everbearing' (F)	CAgr
	'Italian' (F)	CAgr
	'Ivory' (F)	CAgr
	kagayamae	see *M. alba*
	latifolia 'Spirata'	NLar
	macroura	EBee LCro MTrO SBmr
	'Matsunaga'	see *M.* 'Waisei-kirishima-shikinari'
	MOJO BERRY	see *M.* 'Waisei-kirishima-shikinari'
	nigra (F)	Widely available
§	- 'Chelsea' (F) ♀H6	CEnd CPer CSBt CTri EBee EPfP EPom LCro LRHS MGos MLod MTrO NLar NOra NWea SCoo SEWo SKee SLim SPer SPoG SSFT WMat
	- 'Izvor' (F)	CAgr
	- 'Jerusalem' (F) ♀H6	MTrO NOra WMat
	- 'King James'	see *M. nigra* 'Chelsea'
	- 'Large Black' (F)	EPom
	- 'Repsime' (F)	CAgr
	- 'Sham Dudu' (F)	CAgr
	rubra	EBtc
§	'Waisei-kirishima-shikinari' (F)	CBcs LCro LRHS MTrO NOra SSFT
	'Wellington' (F)	CCVT CEnd CLnd EBee ELan LEdu LRHS LSRN MPri MTrO NOra SSFT WMat WMou

Mosla (*Lamiaceae*)

dianthera	MAvo WCot

Muehlenbeckia ✿ (*Polygonaceae*)

	astonii	EBee ELan SIvy WPGP
	axillaris misapplied	see *M. complexa*
§	***axillaris*** (Hook. f.) Endl.	CBcs CTri EBee EShb GBin IDee MGil XLum
	- variegated (v) **new**	EBtc
§	***complexa***	Widely available
	- (f)	CDoC LPar
	- MAORI	see *M. complexa* 'Top Secret'
	- 'Nana'	see *M. axillaris* (Hook. f.) Endl.
	- 'Spotlight'PBR (v)	EShb
	- 'Texture Big Leaf'	EBee WPGP
§	- 'Top Secret' **new**	EBtc
	- var. ***trilobata***	CTrC EShb ESwi SSta WBor XLum
	platyclados	see *Homalocladium platycladum*
	volcanica B&SWJ 14913	WCru

Muhlenbergia (*Poaceae*)

capillaris	CBod CKel CSpe CWnw EBee ELan LPal LSRN MACG MBel NGBl SDix SEdd SMad SPeP WSpi XSen
dumosa	CKno SMad WCot WPGP
lindheimeri	CKno EBee WCot
mexicana	SRms
reverchonii UNDAUNTED ('Pund01s')	SBls
rigens	CKno WSpi XLum XSen

Mukdenia (*Saxifragaceae*)

	acanthifolia	GEdr LEdu WPGP
	rossii	CAby CTtf EBee ECha EWTr GBin LEdu LPla MBel MNrw NBid NLar SBut SIvy WCAu WFar WOld WPGP WPnP XLum
	- 'Crimson Fans'	see *M. rossii* 'Karasuba'
	- dwarf	MNrw
§	- 'Karasuba'	Widely available
	- 'Shishiba'	GEdr LEdu

× *Mukgenia* (*Saxifragaceae*)

§	'Flame'	CBcs CBct EBee EHed ELan EMor EWoo GBin GEdr IBal LEdu LSou MHol MNrw MPnt NHar SMad SPoG XSte
	NOVA	see × *M.* 'Flame'

mulberry see *Morus*

Murdannia (*Commelinaceae*)

loriformis BRIGHT STAR ('Ppimur004') (v) **new**	LCro

Murraya (*Rutaceae*)

koenigii	see *Bergera koenigii*

Musa ✿ (*Musaceae*)

§	***acuminata***	EAri NHrt
	- Cavendish Group (AAA Group) (F)	NHrt
§	- 'Dwarf Cavendish' (AAA Group) (F) ♀H1b	CAbb CBod CCht CDoC CDow ELan NHrt SIvy SPlb
	- 'Zebrina' ♀H1b	CDTJ LRHS
	balbisiana 'Black Thai'	EAri
	basjoo ♀H2	Widely available
I	- 'Rubra'	CCCN
	- 'Sakhalin'	LRHS

	– 'Tchetchenie' **new**	XVPe
	'Blue Java'	see *M.* 'Ice Cream'
	'Cavendish Super Dwarf'	NPlm
	cavendishii	see *M. acuminata* 'Dwarf Cavendish'
	ensete	see *Ensete ventricosum*
	hookeri	see *M. sikkimensis*
§	'Ice Cream' (ABB Group)	EAri
	itinerans	EAri
	lasiocarpa 🏆^{H2}	CDTJ EAri ETod IDee IKel LCro LOPS LRHS LWaG MGos MPkF NPlm SArc SPlb XSte
	nana misapplied	see *M. acuminata* 'Dwarf Cavendish'
	nana Lour.	see *M. acuminata*
	ornata 🏆^{H1b}	CCCN
	× ***paradisiaca*** 'Dwarf Orinoco' (ABB Group) (F)	XVPe
	– 'Ney Poovan' (AB Group) (F)	CCCN
§	***sikkimensis*** 🏆^{H2}	CDTJ CTsd LPal SGsty SPlb
	– 'Red Tiger'	CCCN CDTJ EAri EHed NPlm
	velutina 🏆^{H1b}	CCCN CTsd WTyc

Muscari ✿ (*Asparagaceae*)

	adilii	GKev NRog
	'Aleyna'	NRog
	ambrosiacum	see *M. muscarimi*
	anatolicum	NRog WCot
	– giant	GKev
	armeniacum 🏆^{H6}	CArg CRos CTri ECul ETay EWoo GKev LAma LCro LOPS LRHS NBwr NRHS NRog SPer SRms WCot WShi
	– PAB 6748	LEdu
	– 'Alida'	GKev
	– 'Argaei Album'	NRog
	– 'Artist'	GKev NRog SDeJ
	– 'Atlantic'	EHyd GKev LRHS NRHS NRog
	– 'Big Smile'	NRog
	– 'Blue Pearl'	NRog
	– 'Blue Spike' (d)	GKev LAma NBir NRog SDeJ
	– 'Cantab'	SDeJ XLum
	– 'Carola'	GKev
	– 'Cupido'	GKev LAma SPhx
	– 'Dark Eyes'	ELan GKev SDeJ
	– 'Early Giant'	SDeJ
	– 'Fantasy Creation'	GKev LAma NRog SDeJ WSHC
	– 'Gül'	WCot
	– 'Helena'	ERCP GKev LAma
	– 'Lady Blu'	LRHS
	– 'Manon'	LAma
	– 'Peppermint'	CBor CRos EHyd ETay GKev LAma LCro LRHS LSto NRHS SDeJ SPer
	– 'Saffier' 🏆^{H6}	WCot
	– 'Siberian Tiger'	CDoC CRos ECul EHyd EPfP EPot ERCP ETay GKev LAma LHWs LRHS NHpl NRHS SPer WHoo WTor
	– 'Touch of Snow'	ELan ETay GKev LAma LCro LOPS LRHS
	– 'Valerie Finnis'	CAby CAvo EPfP EPot EWoo GKev LAma MBNS NBwr NLar NRog SDeJ SPer WCot
	'Arthur Henry' **new**	WCot
	aucheri 🏆^{H6}	GKev NRya
*	– var. ***bicolor***	WCot
	– 'Blue Magic'	CAvo ECul EPot GKev LAma LRHS NRog SDeJ
	– 'Ocean Magic'	CAvo GKev LAma LCro LOPS MBriF NHpl NLar WBrk WHlf
	– 'White Magic'	CAvo EPot EWoo GKev LAma LCro LOPS LRHS NHpl SDeJ WBrk WFar
§	***azureum*** 🏆^{H6}	CAvo ELan EPfP ERCP GKev GMaP LAma NBir NRog WCot WFar
	– 'Album'	NRog WCot
	– 'Bling Bling'	LRHS SDeJ WCot
	'Baby's Breath'	see *M.* 'Jenny Robinson'
	'Big Smile'	CRos EHyd EPfP GKev LRHS NRHS WCot
	'Blue Eyes'	WCot
	botryoides	NRog WCot
	– 'Album'	CAvo CTri GKev LAma LCro LOPS NRog SDeJ SRms WCot WHlf WShi
	bourgaei	GKev NRog
	caucasicum	GKev WCot
	chalusicum	see *M. pseudomuscari*
	coeleste	GKev WCot
	commutatum	GKev NRog
	– white-flowered	GKev
§	***comosum***	CAby CKel EDAr ERCP GKev LAma NRog WCot WFar WHlf
	– 'Epirus Giant'	GKev
	– 'Monstrosum'	see *M. comosum* 'Plumosum'
	– 'Pinard'	GKev
§	– 'Plumosum'	ELan ETay GKev LAma NRog SDeJ WHlf
	cycladicum subsp. ***subsessile***	GKev
	dionysicum	NRog
	discolor	NRog
	inconstrictum	WCot
	'Ivor's Pink'	WCot WHlf
§	'Jenny Robinson' 🏆^{H5}	CAvo EPfP ERCP GKev LAma LHWs NBwr SDys SPhx WCot WHoo
	'Joyce Spirit'	ECul ERCP GKev LAma LRHS
	kerkis	GKev
	latifolium 🏆^{H6}	CAby CDoC CRos EHyd ELan ERCP GKev LAma LCro LOPS LRHS LSto MBNS MBow NBwr NLar NRHS NRog SDeJ WCot WHlf
*	– 'Blue Angels'	NBir
	– 'Grape Ice'	CRos ELan LRHS
§	***macrocarpum***	ECha GKev MACG NRog WAbe WShi
	– 'Golden Fragrance'[PBR]	CAvo CBor EPot ERCP GKev LAma MNrw NRog SDeJ WHlf
	'Marleen' **new**	GKev
	'Maxabel' **new**	LAma
	'Memory of Gary Fisher'	WCot
	mirum	NRog WCot
	'Morgenhimmel'	GKev
	moschatum	see *M. muscarimi*
	'Mount Hood'	NRog SDeJ
	'Mountain Lady'	GKev LAma
§	***muscarimi***	CAvo GKev LAma NRog SDeJ WCot
	– var. ***flavum***	see *M. macrocarpum*
§	***neglectum***	CKel GKev LAma NLar NRog SEND WCot WShi
	pallens	GKev NRog
	paradoxum	see *Bellevalia paradoxa*
	parviflorum	GKev WCot
	'Pink Sunrise'	CBor EPot ERCP ETay GKev NHpl NRog SDeJ WCot WHlf
	'Pink Surprise'	LAma
§	***pseudomuscari*** 🏆^{H5}	GKev WCot
	pulchellum subsp. ***clepsydroides***	GKev
	racemosum	see *M. neglectum*
	'Rosy Sunrise'	GKev WCot
	'Sky Blue'	WCot
§	***spreitzenhoferi***	NRog
	'Superstar'	GKev LAma NRog
§	***tenuiflorum***	WCot
	aff. ***tenuiflorum*** JCA 0.691.251	WCot

'Venus'	GBin GKev LAma SPhx WCot
weissii	GKev
'White Beauty'	GKev LRHS WCot
'Winter Amethyst'	WCot

Muscarimia see *Muscari*

ambrosiacum	see *Muscari muscarimi*

Musella see *Musa*

Mussaenda (*Rubiaceae*)

'Tropic Snow'	CCCN

Musschia (*Campanulaceae*)

wollastonii	CAbb EAri

Mutisia (*Asteraceae*)

decurrens	GKev

Myoporum (*Scrophulariaceae*)

acuminatum	see *M. tenuifolium*
laetum	SPlb SVen
§ ***tenuifolium***	SVen

Myosotidium (*Boraginaceae*)

§ ***hortensia***	CBcs CBct CPla CTsd ELan GBin GKev ITim LRHS NBid NRHS SEdd SIvy
nobile	see *M. hortensia*

Myosotis (*Boraginaceae*)

alpestris 'Alba'	LSto
arvensis	MBow
australis	WCot
glabrescens	EPot
MY OH MY ('Myomark'PBR)	CBod
palustris	see *M. scorpioides*
pulvinaris	EDAr GArf SPlb
rakiura	CPla EWes
§ ***scorpioides***	CHab CPud CWat GQue LCro LLWG LOPS LPfP MMuc MWts NAts SCoo SPlb SRms WBrk WMAq WPnP XLum
- 'Alba'	CPud LLWG MWts
- 'Ice Pearl'	ECha
- MAYTIME ('Blaqua') (v)	NBir
- 'Mermaid'	CBen ECha EWat LLWG SRms
- 'Pinkie'	LLWG
- 'Snowflakes'	CWat EWat LPfP
- variegated (v)	LPfP
sylvatica	LCro LOPS MMuc SCgs WWild
- 'Bluesylva' (Sylva Series) 🏆H6	SPhx
- 'Indigo'	ELan
- 'Mon Amie Blue' **new**	WHlf
- 'Rosylva' (Sylva Series) 🏆H6	GJos
- 'Ultramarine' 🏆H6	LCro LOPS
'Sylvia Blue'	LCro LOPS

Myrceugenia (*Myrtaceae*)

ovata var. ***nannophylla***	WPGP

Myrica (*Myricaceae*)

gale	CAgr GPoy LPar NLar WSpi

Myricaria (*Tamaricaceae*)

germanica	NLar

Myriophyllum (*Haloragaceae*)

crispatum **new**	LPfP
propinquum	LLWG
* 'Red Stem'	LPfP
spicatum	CBen EWat LPfP MWts WMAq
verticillatum	CWat LPfP SCoo

Myrrhis (*Apiaceae*)

odorata	Widely available
- 'Forncett Chevron'	LEdu SPhx

Myrsine (*Primulaceae*)

africana	CBod CCht EShb MHer
australis	SArc SVen
divaricata	GBin SVen
salicina	CTsd

Myrteola (*Myrtaceae*)

§ ***nummularia***	GArf GRum ITim WPav WThu
- from Falkland Islands	GRum

Myrtillocactus (*Cactaceae*)

geometrizans **new**	NPlm

Myrtus ✿ (*Myrtaceae*)

apiculata misapplied	see *Luma apiculata*
bullata	see *Lophomyrtus bullata*
chequen	see *Luma chequen*
communis 🏆H4	Widely available
- 'Flore Pleno' (d)	MHer
- 'Jekka's All Gold'	WJek
- 'Jenny Reitenbach'	see *M. communis* subsp. *tarentina*
- 'Lumi'	LRHS
- 'Merion'	WJek
- 'Microphylla'	see *M. communis* subsp. *tarentina*
- 'Nana'	see *M. communis* subsp. *tarentina*
- 'Pyewood Park'	SRms WJek
§ - subsp. ***tarentina*** 🏆H4	Widely available
- - 'Compacta'	SCoo SEdd
- - 'Microphylla Variegata' (v)	EShb MNHC SPer SRms WJek
I - - 'Variegata' (v)	CEme MHoo
- 'Tricolor'	see *M. communis* 'Variegata'
§ - 'Variegata' (v)	CBod CCoa CMac CSBt CTri EBee EHyd ELan ENfk EPfP EShb LEdu LRHS MDon MGil MHer MHoo MSwo NLar NRHS SCob SGBe SGbt SPer SPoG WAvo WFar WHer WJek
'Glanleam Gold'	see *Luma apiculata* 'Glanleam Gold'
lechleriana	see *Amomyrtus luma*
luma	see *Luma apiculata*
nummularia	see *Myrteola nummularia*
obcordata	see *Lophomyrtus obcordata*
* ***paraguayensis***	EBee
ugni	see *Ugni molinae*

N

Nabalus (*Asteraceae*)

albus	see *Prenanthes alba*

Nananthus (*Aizoaceae*)

aloides	EAri

Nandina (*Berberidaceae*)

BRIGHTLIGHT ('Selten004'PBR)	EBee LRHS SGol
domestica	Widely available
- B&SWJ 4923	WCru
- B&SWJ 11113	WCru
- BLUSH PINK ('Aka'PBR)	CDoC CMac EPfP LCro LRHS LSRN MAsh MPkF MThu SOrN SPoG SWvt
- 'Filamentosa'	EPfP LRHS MPkF NLar SGol XSte
- 'Fire Power'	Widely available
- FLIRT ('Murasaki'PBR)	MAsh MPkF SGol XSte

- 'Gulf Stream'	CRos EGrI EHyd ELan ELon EPfP ERom LAlb LPar LRHS LSRN MAsh MBNS MGos MPkF NLar NRHS SEdd SGsty SOrN SavN XSte
- 'Harbour Dwarf'	WFar
- var. ***leucocarpa***	NLar
- MAGICAL LEMON AND LIME ('Lemlim'^{PBR})	CBcs CBod CKel EBee ELan EWoo LAlb LCro LOPS LRHS MAsh MRav SEdd SGol SGsty SOrN SavN XSte
- 'Nana'	see *N. domestica* 'Pygmaea'
- OBSESSED	see *N. domestica* 'Seika'
- PLUM PASSION ('Monum')	EPfP MGos SavN
§ - 'Pygmaea'	CMen ELon SGol
- 'Red Dragon'	MPkF
- 'Richmond' $\mathbb{Y}^{H5}$	CBcs CBod CDoC CEme CKel CRos EBee EHeP EHyd ELan ELon EPfP LPar LRHS MAsh MGos MRav NLar NRHS SCob SJap SPer SPoG SWvt WCFE WFar WHlf
§ - 'Seika'^{PBR}	Widely available
- SIENNA SUNRISE ('Monfar')	CBod LRHS MPkF NLar SGol
- 'Sunset'^{PBR}	CAbb CBcs CBod EBee EHed GKev LRHS LSRN MMrt NLar SCob SPad
- 'Twilight'^{PBR} (v)	CBod CDoC CKel CMac CRos CSBt CWGN EBee EFPl EPfP LAlb LRHS MAsh MPkF SGsty SMad SWvt
- 'Wood's Dwarf'	CBcs EGrI WFar

Nannorrhops (*Arecaceae*)

arabica	see *N. ritchieana*
§ ***ritchieana***	LPal NPlm SPlb
- blue-leaved	LPal
- green-leaved	LPal

Napaea (*Malvaceae*)

dioica	LEdu SPhx WCot WPGP

Narcissus ✿ (*Amaryllidaceae*)

'Abba' (4) $\mathbb{Y}^{H6}$	CQua
'Aberfoyle' (2) $\mathbb{Y}^{H6}$	CQua
'Abstract' (11a)	CQua
'Accent' (2)	CQua ETay GKev
'Achentoul' (4)	CQua
'Achnasheen' (3)	CQua
'Acropolis' (4)	CQua ETay GKev LAma LHWs NRog SDeJ
'Actaea' (9) $\mathbb{Y}^{H6}$	CBro CQua ECul GBin GCro GKev LAma LCro LOPS NRog SDeJ
'Acumen' (2)	CQua
'Admiration' (8)	CQua
'Advocat' (3)	CQua
'Ahwahnee' (2)	CQua
'Ainley' (2)	CQua
'Aintree' (3)	CQua
'Aircastle' (3)	CQua
'Albatross' (3)	CQua WShi
'Albus Plenus Odoratus'	see *N. poeticus* 'Plenus' ambig.
'Alex Jones' (2)	CQua
'Alexis Beauty' (2) **new**	ETay
alpestris (13)	NDry
'Altruist' (3)	CQua ERCP NRog SDeJ
'Altun Ha' (2)	CQua ETay GKev
'Amabilis' (3)	CQua
'Amadeus Mozart' (2)	CQua
'Amazing Grace' (2)	CQua
'Amber Castle' (2)	CQua
'Ambergate' (2)	CQua ETay GKev LAma NRog SDeJ WPhe
'American Dream' (1)	CQua
'American Goldfinch' (7)	CQua
'American Heritage' (1)	CQua
'American Hero' (2) **new**	CQua
'Amico' (2) **new**	ETay
'Amstel' (4)	CQua
'Andrew's Choice' (7) $\mathbb{Y}^{H6}$	CQua
'Androcles' (4)	ETay WPhe
'Andy Blanchard' (5)	NDry
'Anfield' (7) **new**	ECul NBwr
'Angel' (3)	CQua
'Angel Face' (3)	CQua
'Angel of the North' (2) **new**	CQua
'Angelina' (6)	NDry
'Angel's Breath' (5) $\mathbb{Y}^{H6}$	CAvo EPot GKev
'Angel's Flight' (6)	NDry
Angel's tears	see *N. triandrus* subsp. *triandrus* var. *triandrus*
'Angel's Whisper' (5)	CQua EBee GKev LAma LHWs WShi
'Angel's Wings' (2)	CQua
'Angkor' (4)	CQua
'An-gof' (7)	CQua
'Annequin' (3)	CQua
'Apollo Gold' (10)	NHpl
'Apotheose' (4)	SDeJ
'Apple Pie' (11a)	LAma
'Applins' (2)	CQua
'Apricot' (1)	GCro
'Apricot Whirl' (11a)	CQua LAma LCro LRHS
'April Tears' (5)	WShi
'Ara' (6)	CQua GKev
'Arctic Gem' (3)	CQua
'Arctic Gold' (1) $\mathbb{Y}^{H6}$	CQua LAma
'Ard Righ' (1)	GCro
'Areley Kings' (2)	CQua
'Argent' (4)	CQua
'Argosy' (1)	CQua
'Ariel'^{PBR} (8)	GKev NRog
'Arkle' (1) $\mathbb{Y}^{H6}$	CQua ETay GKev SDeJ
'Arleston' (2)	CQua
'Armada' (2)	CQua
'Armidale' (3)	CQua
'Armoury' (4)	CQua
'Arndilly' (2)	CQua
'Arpege' (2)	CQua
'Art Design' (4) **new**	LAma
'Arthurian' (1)	CQua
'Articol' (11a)	CQua LAma NRog
'Arwenack' (11a)	CQua
'Ascot' (4)	GKev SDeJ
'Ashmore' (2)	CQua
'Aspasia' (8)	GKev
§ ***assoanus*** (13)	EPot LAma NRog WCot WShi
'Astrid's Memory' (3) **new**	CQua
'Astropink' (11a)	CQua
§ ***asturiensis*** (13)	GKev NDry NRog WShi
- giant	see *N. asturiensis* 'Wavertree'
§ - 'Wavertree' (1)	CQua MCor
asturiensis* × *cyclamineus	NDry
'Audubon' (2)	CQua SDeJ
'Auntie Eileen' (2)	CQua
'Aureolin' (7)	NDry
'Ava Grace' (2)	CQua
'Avalanche' (8) $\mathbb{Y}^{H4}$	CQua ELan ETay GKev LAma LCro LOPS NRog SDeJ WBrk
'Avalanche of Gold' (8)	CQua
'Avalon' (2)	CQua ETay GKev LCro SDeJ WPhe
'Bab's Hammer' (2) **new**	CQua
'Baby Boomer' (7)	CQua ERCP GKev LAma LCro LHWs WPhe
'Baby Moon' (7)	CCBP CQua EPot GKev LAma LRHS NBwr NRog SDeJ SDir
'Back Flash' (2)	CQua
'Badbury Rings' (3) $\mathbb{Y}^{H6}$	CQua
'Bahama Beach' (7)	CQua
'Bainden' (3) **new**	CQua
'Bala' (4)	CQua

'Balalaika' (2)	CQua
'Balanced Equation' (11a)	CQua
'Baldock' (4)	CQua
BALMACARA BEAUTY (2)	GCro
'Balvenie' (2)	CQua
'Banana Daiquiri' (11a)	WPhe
'Bandesara' (3)	CQua
'Bandit' (2)	CQua
'Bank Roll' (2) **new**	CQua
'Banker' (2)	CQua
'Banstead Village' (2)	CQua
'Bantam' (2) ♀H6	CQua ETay LRHS SDeJ
'Barbara Hunt' (7)	CQua
'Barbara's Passion' (1)	CQua
'Barbary Gold' (2)	CQua
'Barn Dance' (3)	CQua
'Barnham' (1)	CQua
'Barnsdale Wood' (2)	CQua
'Barrett Browning' (3)	GKev LAma MBros NRog SDeJ
'Barrii' (3)	CQua
'Bath's Flame' (3)	CAvo CQua GCro GKev WShi
'Battersby' (2) **new**	CQua
'Bear's Gold' (4)	CQua
'Beaulieu' (1)	CQua
'Beautiful Dream' (3)	CQua
'Beautiful Eyes' (7)	GKev
'Beauvallon' (4)	CQua ETay SDeJ
'Bebop' (7)	CBro
'Bedruthan' (2)	CQua
'Beersheba' (1)	CQua
'Beige Beauty' (3)	ETay
'Belcanto' (11a)	CQua NRog SDeJ
'Belisana' (2)	SDeJ
'Belize' (2)	CQua
'Bell Rock' (1) ♀H6	CQua
'Bell Song' (7)	CBro CQua LAma LCro LRHS NRog SDeJ WHlf WShi
'Bell Star' (5) **new**	MCor
'Bella Estrella' (11a)	ERCP
'Berceuse' (2)	CQua
'Bere Ferrers' (4)	CQua
'Bergerac' (11a)	CQua
'Berlin' (2)	GKev
'Bernardino' (2)	CQua GCro
'Beryl' (6)	CQua NRog WShi
'Best Friend' (3)	CQua
'Best Seller' (1)	CArg
'Bethal' (3)	CQua
'Bethan-Sîan' (2)	CQua
'Bideford Maid' (2) **new**	CQua
'Biffo' (4)	CQua
'Big Gun' (2)	WHlf
BIGGAR BOUNTIFUL (2)	GCro
'Bilbo' (6)	CBro
'Billy Graham' (2)	CQua
'Binkie' (2)	CQua ETay
'Biondina' (1)	NDry
'Bionic' (2)	CQua
'Birchwood' (3)	CQua
'Birma' (3)	ETay SDeJ
'Bittern' (12)	CBro CQua NRog SDeJ
'Black Prince' (9)	CQua
'Blackstone' (2)	CQua
'Blarney' (3)	CQua ETay
'Blessing' (2)	ETay
'Blisland' (9)	CQua
'Blossom Lady' (4)	CQua
'Bluntington' (3)	CQua
'Blushing Lady' (7)	GKev NBir
'Blushing Maiden' (4)	CQua
'Bobbysoxer' (7)	CBro CQua LEdu
'Bobolink' (2)	CQua
'Bodelva' (2)	CQua

	'Bolton' (7)	GCro
	'Bon Viveur' (11b)	CQua
	'Bonython' (1)	GCro
	'Bosbigal' (11a)	CQua
	'Boscastle' (7)	CQua
	'Boscoppa' (11a)	CQua
	'Boslowick' (11a) ♀H6	CQua
	'Bossa Nova' (3)	CQua
	'Bossiney' (11a)	CQua
	'Brackenhurst' (2)	ETay SDeJ WHlf
	'Bravoure' (1) ♀H6	GBin LAma SDeJ SDir
	'Breezand Tristar' (11a) ♀H6	CBro GKev
	'Brentswood' (8)	CQua
	'Bridal Crown' (4) ♀H6	CDoC ECul ETay GKev LAma LCro LOPS LRHS NRog SDeJ WHlf
	'Bright Flame' (2)	CQua
	'Bright Spangles' (8)	CQua
	'Bright Spot' (8)	CQua
	'Brilliancy' (3)	CQua
	'British Gamble' (1)	GKev LAma
	'Broadway Star' (11b)	SDeJ
	'Brodick' (3)	CQua
	'Brooke Ager' (2) ♀H6	CBro GKev
	'Broughshane' (1)	CQua
	broussonetii (13)	EPot GKev NRog
	- from Morocco	WPGP
	'Brunswick' (2)	SDeJ
	'Bryanston' (2) ♀H6	CQua
	'Buckshead' (4)	CQua
	'Budock Water' (2)	CQua
	'Bugle Major' (2)	CQua
	bulbocodium (13) ♀H4	CBro EHyd GKev LCro LOPS LRHS NRHS SRms WCot
	- 'Arctic Bells' (10)	EPfP ETay LHWs
§	- subsp. ***bulbocodium*** (13)	CBro
§	- - var. ***citrinus*** (13)	CRos EHyd LRHS NRHS SPlb
	- - var. ***conspicuus*** (13)	CBro CQua EGrI ERCP GKev LAma NHpl NRog SDeJ SDix WCot WShi XLum
*	- - var. ***filifolius*** (13)	CBro
§	- - var. ***graellsii*** (13)	NSla
	- - var. ***nivalis*** (13)	EPot GKev NDry NRog
§	- Golden Bells Group (10)	CAby CQua CRos CWCL EHyd EPfP EPot ETay GBin GKev GQue LAma LHWs LRHS NHol NRHS NRog SDeJ
	- subsp. ***obesus*** (13)	GKev NDry NRog
§	- - 'Diamond Ring' (10)	CQua CRos EHyd EPot GKev LAma LRHS MNrw NRHS
	- - 'Lee Martin' (10)	NDry
	- subsp. ***praecox*** (13)	EHyd NRHS
	- - var. ***paucinervis*** (13)	NRog
	- - - Rrw84.18	NDry
	- subsp. ***tananicus***	see *N. cantabricus* subsp. *tananicus*
	- subsp. ***vulgaris***	see *N. bulbocodium* subsp. *bulbocodium*
	'Bundle' (7)	NDry
	'Bunting' (7) ♀H6	CQua
	'Burntwood' (4)	CQua
	'Busbie' (12)	NDry
	'Bute Park' (4)	CQua
	'Butter and Eggs' (4)	GKev
	'Cadgwith' (2)	CQua
	'Cairngorm' (2)	NRog SDeJ WPhe
	'Cairntoul' (3)	CQua
	'Calamansack' (2)	CQua
	calcicola (13)	NDry
	'Calgary' (4)	CQua ETay GKev MBriF WCot
	'California Rose' (4)	CQua
	'Callisto' (10)	NDry
	'Camaraderie' (2)	CQua
	'Camborne' (1)	NDry
	'Camellia' (4)	CQua
	'Camelot' (2) ♀H6	CQua ETay SDeJ

'Cameo Angel' (2)	CQua
'Cameo Baron' (2)	CQua
'Cameo Fire' (2) **new**	CQua
'Cameo Frills' (2)	CQua
'Cameo Gem' (1)	CQua
'Cameo Honey' (2) **new**	CQua
'Cameo Jewel' (2) **new**	CQua
'Cameo Joy' (2)	CQua
'Cameo King' (2)	CQua
'Cameo Magic' (4)	CQua
'Cameo Marie' (3)	CQua
'Cameo Mist' (2)	CQua
'Campernelli' (7)	CQua NBwr
'Campernelli Plenus'	see *N.* 'Double Campernelle'
'Campion' (9)	CQua
'Can Can Girl' (2)	LHWs
'Canaliculatus' (8)	CArg CQua CTri ERCP GBin GKev LAma LCro LOPS NRog SDeJ SPer WHlf
canaliculatus Gussone	see *N. tazetta* subsp. *lacticolor*
canariensis (13)	CQua
'Canary' (7)	CQua
'Canarybird' (8)	CQua
'Canasta' (11a)	CQua
'Candlepower' (1)	CQua NDry
'Canoodle' (2)	CQua
'Cantabile' (9) ♀H6	CQua
cantabricus (13)	GKev LCro LOPS NDry
- subsp. ***cantabricus*** var. ***eu-albidus*** (13)	NDry
- - var. ***foliosus*** (13) ♀H4	GKev NDry
I - subsp. ***monophyllus*** var. ***laciniatus*** (13)	NDry
§ - subsp. ***tananicus*** (13)	LAma
cantabricus × ***romieuxii*** (13)	NDry
cantabricus × ***romieuxii*** subsp. ***albidus*** var. ***zaianicus*** f. ***lutescens*** (13)	NDry WCot
'Canterbury' (5)	CQua
'Capability Brown' (9)	CQua
'Capax Plenus'	see *N.* 'Eystettensis'
'Cape Cornwall' (2)	CQua
'Cape Helles' (3)	CQua
'Cape Point' (2)	CQua
'Capisco' (3)	CQua
'Carbineer' (2)	CQua GCro SDeJ
'Cargreen' (9)	CQua
'Carib Gipsy' (2) ♀H6	CQua
'Carlton' (2) ♀H6	CArg GCro GKev LAma LCro LOPS LSto NRog SDeJ
'Carn Brea' (3)	CQua
'Carnkief' (2)	CQua
'Carole Lombard' (3)	CQua
'Carrara' (3)	ETay
'Carra's Favorite' (8) **new**	CQua
'Carwinion' (2)	CQua
'Cassata' (11a)	GKev LAma LHWs NBir NRog SDeJ WHlf
'Castanets' (8)	CQua
'Castle Rings' (4)	CQua
'Casual Elegance' (10)	LAma LHWs
'Causeway Sunshine' (1)	CQua
'Cavalli King' (4)	CQua
'Caye Chapel' (3)	CQua
'Cazique' (6)	CQua
× ***cazorlanus*** (13)	NDry
'Cedar Hills' (3)	CQua
'Cedric Morris' (1)	ECha ECtt MCor WCot
'Celestial Fire' (2)	CQua
'Celtic Gold' (2)	CQua
'Centannées' (11a)	NRog

'Centenary Gold' (2)	CQua
'Cha-cha' (6)	CBro GKev
'Changing Colors' (11a)	ETay GKev NRog SDeJ
'Chanterelle' (11a)	NRog SDeJ
'Charity May' (6)	CQua
'Charleston' (2)	CQua
'Charlie Connor' (1)	CQua
'Charlotte Vreeburg' (11b) **new**	LAma
'Chat' (7)	CQua
'Cheeky Chappie' (6)	NDry
'Cheer Leader' (3)	CQua
'Cheerfulness' (4) ♀H6	CArg CQua ELan ETay GKev LAma LCro LOPS MBros NBwr NPer NRHS NRog SDeJ WHlf WPhe
'Cheetah' (1)	CQua
'Chelsea China' (2)	CQua
'Chelsea Girl' (2)	CQua
'Chemeketa' (2)	GKev
'Chérie' (7)	CQua
'Cherish' (2)	CQua
'Cherry Spot' (3)	CQua
'Cherrygardens' (2)	CQua
'Chesapeake Bay' (1)	CQua
'Chesterton' (9) ♀H6	CQua
'Chief Inspector' (1)	CQua
'Chiloquin' (1)	CQua
'Chinita' (8)	CQua GCro
'Chirp' (1)	NDry
'Chit Chat' (7) ♀H6	NRog SDeJ SPlb
'Chobe River' (1)	CQua
'Chortle' (3)	CQua
'Chorus Line' (8)	CQua
'Christelle' (4)	CQua
'Chromacolor' (2) ♀H6	ETay GKev LAma LHWs NRog WHlf WPhe
'Chuckar' (4) **new**	CQua
'Churchfield Bells' (5)	CQua
'Cisticola' (3)	CQua
citrinus	see *N. bulbocodium* subsp. *bulbocodium* var. *citrinus*
'Citron' (3)	CQua
'Citron Baby' (2) **new**	NDry
'Citronita' (3)	CQua
'Clare' (7)	CQua
'Classic Garden' (1)	LHWs
'Classic Gold' (10) ♀H6	CQua
'Claverley' (2)	CQua
'Cloneen' (2) **new**	CQua
'Cloud Nine' (2)	CBro CQua
'Clovelly Ayr' (9)	CQua
'Codlins and Cream'	see *N.* 'Sulphur Phoenix'
'Coker's Frome' (9)	CQua
'Colblanc' (11a)	GKev NRog
'Colin's Joy' (2)	CQua
'Colley Gate' (3)	CQua
'Color Run' (2) **new**	CQua LAma
'Colorama' (11a)	CQua
'Columba' (10) **new**	NDry
'Colville' (9)	CQua
'Come to Good' (2)	CQua
'Compressus'	see *N.* × *intermedius* 'Compressus'
'Conestoga' (2)	CQua
'Congress' (11a)	ETay LHWs
'Conowingo' (11a)	CQua
'Conspicuus' ambig. (3)	LAma
'Content' (1)	GCro
'Contravene' (2) **new**	CQua
'Coo' (12)	NDry
'Cool Crystal' (3)	CQua ETay
'Cool Evening' (11a)	CQua
'Cool Flame' (2)	ETay
'Cool Shades' (2)	CQua

'Copper Sheen' (2) **new**	CQua
'Corbiere' (1)	CQua
'Corbridge' (2)	CQua
'Corby Candle' (2)	CQua
'Corky's Song' (2)	CQua
'Cornish Chuckles' (12) 𝕐H6	CQua
'Cornish Couple' (4) **new**	CQua
'Cornish Gold' (1)	LCro LOPS
'Cornish King' (1)	CQua GKev LHWs WPhe
'Corofin' (3)	CQua
'Coromandel' (2)	CQua
'Cosette' (6)	NDry
'Cotchford' (1) **new**	CQua
'Cotinga' (6)	CBro CQua ETay NRog SDeJ
'Cottrell' (1)	CQua
'Countdown' (2)	CQua
'Coverack Glory' (2)	GCro
'Crackington' (4) 𝕐H6	CQua
'Cragford' (8)	CQua ETay GKev SDeJ
'Craig Stiel' (2)	CQua
'Craigton Chorister' (13)	NDry
'Craigton Clumper' (13)	NDry
'Creag Dubh' (2)	CQua
'Cream Satin' (2)	NDry
'Creation' (1)	ETay
Crème Fraîche Group (3)	NDry
'Crenver' (3)	CQua
'Crill' (7)	CQua
'Crimson Chalice' (3)	CQua
'Cristobal' (1)	CQua
'Croesus' (2)	CQua
'Crofty' (6)	CQua
'Croila' (2)	CQua
'Cromarty' (1) **new**	CQua
'Crowndale' (4)	CQua
'Crugmeer' (11a)	CQua
'Crystal Star' (2)	CQua
cuatrecasasii (13)	NDry
- var. ***segimonensis*** (13)	GKev
'Cudden Point' (2)	CQua
'Cul Beag' (3)	CQua
'Culmination' (2)	CQua
'Cum Laude' (11a)	SDeJ
'Curlew' (7) 𝕐H6	CQua ETay GKev LCro LOPS NRog SDeJ WShi
'Curly' (2)	NRog SDeJ
'Cuscarne' (8)	CQua
cyclamineus (13) 𝕐H6	CAvo CBor CBro CExl CRos CTtf EHyd EPot GKev LEdu LRHS NRHS NRog SRms
cypri (13)	CQua
'Cyros' (1)	CQua
'Dailmanach' (2)	CQua
'Dainty Miss' (7)	GKev
'Dalcharn' (2)	LRHS
'Dallas' (3)	CQua
'Dalmeny' (2)	CQua
'Damson' (2)	CQua
'Dan du Plessis' (8)	CQua
'Danehill' (1)	CQua
'Danger Zone' (2)	CQua
'Daphne' (4) **new**	GCro
'Daphnis' (10)	NDry
'Dateline' (3)	CQua
'Dawn Brooker' (2)	CQua
'Dawn Duel' (12)	NDry
'Daydream' (2)	ETay NRog
'Daymark' (8)	CQua
'Dayton Lake' (2)	CQua
'De Lacey' (11a)	CQua
'Dean' (2)	CQua
'Dear Love' (11a)	CQua
'Debutante' (2)	CQua
'December Bride' (11a)	CQua
'Del Rey' (1)	CQua
'Dell Chapel' (3)	CQua
'Delnashaugh' (4)	CQua GKev LAma NHol NRog SDeJ WHlf
'Delos' (3)	CQua
'Delta' (11a)	CQua
'Delta Flight' (6)	CQua
'Demand' (2)	CQua
'Demmo' (2)	CQua
'Denali' (1)	CQua
'Derek Buck' (5) **new**	CQua
'Derek Tangye' (2)	CQua
'Derringer' (7)	GKev
'Desdemona' (2) 𝕐H6	CQua GKev SDeJ
'Desert Bells' (7)	CAvo CQua GKev
'Desert Orchid' (2)	CQua
'Desert Storm' (2)	CQua
'Diamond Ring'	see *N. bulbocodium* subsp. *obesus* 'Diamond Ring'
'Diamond Wedding' (2) **new**	CQua
'Dick Wellband' (2)	GCro
'Dick Wilden' (4)	GKev NRog SDeJ
'Dickcissel' (7) 𝕐H6	CQua ERCP GKev NRog
'Dimple' (9)	CQua
'Dinkie' (3)	GCro
'Dispatch Box' (1) 𝕐H6	CQua
'Disquiet' (1)	CQua
'Diversity' (11a)	CQua
'Doctor Hugh' (3) 𝕐H6	CQua
'Doctor Jazz' (2)	CQua
'Doctor Who' (4)	CQua
'Dolcoath' (2)	CQua
'Doll Baby' (7)	GKev
'Dolly Mollinger' (11b)	NRog
'Don Stead' (10)	NDry
'Doombar' (1)	CQua
'Dorchester' (4)	CQua
'Dormouse' (1) **new**	NDry
'Dorothy Yorke' (2)	GCro
§ 'Double Campernelle' (4)	CQua GKev SDeJ WShi
'Double Fashion' (4)	NRog SDeJ
'Double Itzim' (4)	CQua
double pheasant eye	see *N. poeticus* 'Plenus' ambig.
- Roman	see *N.* 'Romanus'
'Double Smiles' (4)	GKev LAma WHlf
'Double White' (4)	CQua
'Doublet' (4)	CQua
'Dover Boy' (11a)	CQua
'Downlands' (3)	CQua
'Dragon Run' (2)	CQua
'Drama Queen' (11a)	CQua
'Dream Castle' (3)	CQua
'Dream Catcher' (2)	CQua
'Dream Team' (4) **new**	CQua
'Dreamlight' (3)	CQua GKev
dubius (13)	EPot NRog
'Dubloon' (4) **new**	CQua
'Duchess of Westminster' (2)	GCro
'Dunadry Inn' (4)	CQua
'Dunkery' (4)	CQua
'Dunley Hall' (3)	CQua
'Dunskey' (3)	CQua
'Dunstan's Fire' (1)	CQua
'Dutch Lemon Drops' (5) 𝕐H6	CQua EPot
'Dutch Master' (1) 𝕐H6	EPfP GKev LAma LCro LOPS NBwr NRog SDeJ SDir
'Early Bride' (2)	CQua
'Early Sensation' (1)	NRHS
'Early Splendour' (8)	CQua

	'Earthlight' (3)	CQua
	'Eastbrook Sunrise' (1)	CQua
	'Easter Moon' (2)	CQua GKev
	'Eastern Dawn' (2)	CQua SDeJ
	'Eastern Promise' (2)	CQua
	'Eaton Song' (12) ♀H6	CQua
	'Ebony' (1)	CQua
	'Edge Grove' (2)	CQua
	'Edinburgh' (11a)	GKev NRog
	'Edna Earl' (3)	ETay NRog SDeJ
	'Edward Buxton' (3)	CQua
	'Edward Hart' (2)	GCro
	'Egard' (11a)	CQua
	'Egmont King' (2)	CQua
	'Egmont Star' (2)	CQua
	'Eira Hibbert' (3)	CQua
	'El Camino' (6)	CQua
	'Eland' (7)	CQua
	'Elara' (10)	NDry
	'Elegance' (2)	CQua
	elegans (13)	NRog
	'Elf' (2)	CQua
	'Elfin Gold' (6)	CQua
	'Elite' (8)	GKev
	'Elizabeth Ann' (6)	CQua WShi
	'Elka' (1) ♀H6	CAby CAvo CBro CQua ECha EPot ERCP GKev LAma LHWs LRHS MCor WShi
	'Ellen' (2)	CArg
	'Elusive' (3)	CQua
	'Elven Lady' (2)	CQua
	'Elvin's Voice' (5)	LAma LHWs
	'Elvira' (8)	CQua WShi
	'Emcys' (6)	CQua ERCP
	'Emerald Green' (2)	SDir
	'Emerald Pink' (3)	CQua
	'Emily' (2)	CQua
	'Eminent' (3)	ETay
	'Empire' (2)	GCro
	'Empress of Ireland' (1)	CQua ETay
	'Englander' (6)	EPot LRHS
	'Epona' (3)	CQua
	'Erlicheer' (4)	CQua GKev LCro LOPS NRog SDeJ WCot WHlf
	'Estrella' (3)	CQua
	'Estremadura' (2)	CQua
§	***eugeniae*** (13)	WCot
	'Euryalus' (1)	CQua
	'Eve Robertson' (2)	CQua
	'Evelyn Roberts' (11a)	CQua
	'Evesham' (3)	CQua
	'Exemplar' (1)	ETay
	'Exotic Beauty' (4)	CQua ETay NRog
	'Exotic Mystery' (11a)	CAvo GKev LHWs WHlf
	'Extravaganza' (4)	LAma SDeJ
§	'Eystettensis' (4)	NDry WFar
	'Fair Head' (9)	CQua
	'Fair Prospect' (2)	CQua
	'Fairlawns' (3)	CQua
	'Fairmile' (3)	CQua
	'Fairy Chimes' (5)	CQua EPot
	'Fairy Island' (3)	CQua
I	'Faith' (1)	SDeJ
	'Falaise' (4)	CQua
	'Falconet' (8) ♀H6	CQua ETay GKev NRog SDeJ WHlf
	'Falmouth Bay' (3)	CQua
	'Falstaff' (2)	CQua
	'Far Country' (2)	CQua
I	'Fashion' (11b)	CQua
	'Fat Rascal' (12)	NDry
	'February Gold' (6) ♀H6	CArg CAvo CBro CQua CRos CTri EHyd ELan EPfP EPot ERCP ETay GKev LAma LCro LOPS LRHS NBir NBwr NRHS NRog SDeJ SRms WPhe WShi
	'February Silver' (1)	CBro EPot ERCP LAma NRog SDeJ
	'Feeling Lucky' (2)	CQua ETay
	'Felindre' (9)	EPot ETay
	'Feock' (3)	CQua
	fernandesii (13)	EPot ITim NRog WCot
	- from Spain	ITim
	- var. ***cordubensis*** (13)	CAvo CBro CQua EPot GKev ITim LAma NDry
	- var. ***cordubensis*** × ***jonquilla*** (13)	NRog
	'Fertile Crescent' (7)	CQua
	'Ffitch's Ffolly' (2)	CQua
	'Fiery Maiden' (2)	CQua
	'Filly' (2)	ETay
	'Filoli' (1)	CQua
	'Filskit' (2)	CQua
	'Finchcocks' (2)	CQua
	'Fine Gold' (1)	CQua
	'Fine Romance' (2)	CQua
	'Finland' (2)	LAma
	'Fiona MacKillop' (2)	CQua
	'Fire-Blade' (2)	CQua
	'Firebrand' (3)	CQua WShi
	'Firetail' (3)	CQua GKev
	'First Born' (6)	CQua
	'Five Ashes' (2)	CQua
	'Flambards Village' (4)	CQua
	'Fletching' (1)	CQua
	'Fling' (6)	NDry
	'Flintlock' (2) **new**	CQua
	'Flirt' (6)	CQua
	'Flor d'Luna' (2)	CQua
	'Flora Brava' (2)	CQua
	'Flower Drift' (4)	NRog SDeJ WHlf
	'Flurry' (1) **new**	NDry
	'Fly Half' (2)	ETay
	'Flying High' (3)	CQua
	'Foff's Way' (1)	CQua
	'Folkestone Girl' (11a)	CQua
	'Folly' (2) **new**	GCro
	'Foresight' (1)	CQua
	'Fortissimo' (2)	ETay GKev NRog SDeJ
	'Fortune' (2)	CArg CQua LAma SDeJ
	× ***fosteri*** (13)	NDry
	'Foxhunter' (2)	CQua
	'Fragrant Breeze' (2)	ETay NRog SDeJ
	'Fragrant Rose' (2)	CQua ETay GKev NRog WHlf
	'Frances Delight' (11a)	CQua
	'Frank Miles' (2)	CQua GCro
	'Freedom Rings' (2)	CQua
	'Fresco' (11a)	CQua
	'Fresh Breeze' (6) **new**	NDry
	'Frigid' (3)	CQua
	'Frileuse' (11a) **new**	LAma
	Fringella Group (6)	NDry
	'Frostkist' (6)	CBro CQua
	'Frosty Snow' (2)	GKev LAma
	'Fruit Cup' (7)	CQua NRog SDeJ
	'Full House' (4)	GKev SDeJ
	'Fulwell' (4)	CQua
	'Furbelow' (4)	CQua
	'Gabriella Rose' (4)	CQua
	gaditanus (13)	CBro
	gaditanus × ***rupicola*** subsp. ***watieri*** (13)	LAma
	Galantoquilla Group (12)	NDry
	'Gale Force' (6)	NDry
	'Gallipoli Dawn' (2)	CQua
	'Gamebird' (1)	CQua
	'Garden Princess' (2)	CQua
	'Gay Kybo' (4) ♀H6	CQua ETay

'Gay Swain' (4)	CQua
'Gay Time' (4)	SDeJ
gayi (13)	CQua WShi
'Geevor' (4)	CQua
'Gellymill' (2)	CQua
'Gentle Giant' (2)	LHWs SDeJ WHlf
'Gentleman at Arms' (2) **new**	ETay
'Georgie Boy' (2) **new**	ETay
'Georgie May' (2)	CQua
'Geranium' (8) ♀^{H6}	CBro CQua ERCP ETay GKev LAma LCro LOPS LRHS NRHS NRog SDeJ WHlf WShi
'Gianna' (6) **new**	NDry
'Gigantic Star' (2)	NRog SDeJ WHlf
'Gillan' (11a)	CQua
'Gilly Drummond' (1)	CQua
'Gipsy Moon' (2)	CQua
'Gipsy Queen' (1)	CBro ECha EPot GKev MCor NDry WCot WFar WShi
'Gipsy Vale' (1)	NDry
'Giselle' (10)	NDry
'Glapthorne' (2)	CQua
'Glasnevin' (2)	CQua
'Glasney' (3)	CQua
'Glen Cassley' (3)	CQua
'Glen Clova' (2)	CQua
'Glendurgan' (2)	CQua
'Glenfarclas' (1)	CQua
'Glenside' (2)	CQua
'Gloaming Hill' (1)	CQua
'Gloria Townsin' (4)	CQua
'Gloriana Fair' (2)	CQua
'Gloriosus' (8)	CQua
'Glorious' (8)	CQua
'Glory of Lisse' (9)	CQua WShi
'Glover's Reef' (1)	CQua
'Glowing Phoenix' (4)	CQua
'Goblet' (1)	LAma SDeJ
'Golant' (2)	CQua
'Gold Bond' (2)	CQua
'Gold Charm' (2)	CQua
'Gold Convention' (2) ♀^{H6}	CQua
'Gold Ingot' (2) ♀^{H6}	CQua
'Gold Medal' (1) ♀^{H6}	ETay
'Gold Medallion' (1)	CQua
'Gold Sails' (2)	CQua
'Gold Top' (2)	CQua
'Gold Velvet' (1) **new**	CQua
'Golden Amber' (2)	CQua
'Golden Anniversary' (2)	CQua
'Golden Aura' (2) ♀^{H6}	CQua ETay
'Golden Bear' (4)	CQua
'Golden Bells'	see *N. bulbocodium* Golden Bells Group
'Golden Dawn' (8) ♀^{H4}	CQua GKev LAma LRHS NRog SDeJ
'Golden Ducat' (4)	CArg LAma NBir NRog SDeJ WHlf
'Golden Echo' (7)	CQua ETay GKev SDeJ WPhe
'Golden Flute' (2)	CQua
'Golden Harvest' (1)	LAma NPer NRog
'Golden Incense' (7)	CQua
'Golden Jewel' (2) ♀^{H6}	CQua
'Golden Joy' (2)	CQua ETay
'Golden Mary' (3)	GCro
'Golden Orbit' (4)	CQua
'Golden Perfection' (7)	CQua
'Golden Phoenix' (4)	CQua WShi
'Golden Rain' (4)	GKev
'Golden Sheen' (2)	CQua
'Golden Spur' (1)	CQua GKev LAma
'Golden Torch' (2)	CQua
'Golden Trumpet' (1)	CQua
'Golden Twins' (7)	CQua

'Golden Vale' (1)	CQua
'Golden Years' (6)	CQua
'Goldfinger' (1) ♀^{H6}	CQua SDeJ
'Goldhanger' (2)	CQua
'Golitha Falls' (2)	CQua
'Good Fella' (2)	CQua
'Good Measure' (2)	CQua
'Good Success' (11a)	CQua
'Goonbell' (2)	CQua
'Gorran' (3)	CQua
'Gossamer' (3)	ETay GBin
'Gossmoor' (4)	CQua
graellsii	see *N. bulbocodium* subsp. *bulbocodium* var. *graellsii*
'Grand Monarque' (8)	CQua
'Grand Primo' (8)	ETay LCro LOPS
'Grand Primo Citronière' (8)	CQua
'Grand Prospect' (2)	CQua
'Grand Soleil d'Or' (8)	CQua ECul GKev LAma LCro LOPS NRog SDeJ SDir SPer
'Grandis' (1)	GCro
'Great Expectations' (2)	CQua
'Greatwood' (1)	CQua
'Greek Surprise' (4)	CQua
'Green Howard' (3)	CQua
'Green Island' (2)	ETay GKev SDeJ
'Green Lawns' (9)	CQua
'Greenodd' (3)	CQua
'Grenoble' (2)	CQua
'Gresham' (4)	CQua
'Gribben Head' (4)	CQua
'Guiding Spirit' (4)	CQua
'Gulliver' (3)	CQua GCro
'Gwendoline Rae' (3)	CQua
'Gwenllian' (3)	CQua
'Gwennap' (1)	CQua
'Gwinear' (2)	CQua
'Gylly Glow' (6)	CQua
'Hacienda' (1)	CQua
'Half Magic' (3) **new**	CQua
'Half Moon Caye' (2)	CQua
'Halley's Comet' (3)	CQua
'Halloon' (3)	CQua
'Hamish Wood' (2) **new**	CQua
'Hammoon' (3)	ETay
'Hampton Court' (2)	CQua
'Hannah Jesse' (7)	CQua
'Happy Fellow' (2)	CQua
'Happy Valley' (2)	CQua
'Harmony Bells' (5)	CQua
'Harpers Ferry' (1)	CQua
'Harpsicord' (11a)	ETay
HARTLAND'S IRVING (1)	GCro
'Hartlebury' (3)	CQua
'Harvard' (2)	CQua
'Havelock' (2)	GCro
'Hawera' (5) ♀^{H6}	CArg CAvo CBro CQua CTri EPfP EPot ERCP ETay GKev LAma LCro LOPS NBwr NRog SDeJ WShi
'Heamoor' (4) ♀^{H6}	CQua ETay GKev
hedraeanthus (13)	EPot NDry
- subsp. ***luteolentus*** (13)	NDry
'Helene' (10)	NDry
'Helford Dawn' (2)	CQua
'Helios' (2)	CQua GCro
hellenicus	see *N. poeticus* var. *hellenicus*
henriquesii	see *N. jonquilla* var. *henriquesii*
'Henry Irving' (1)	CQua GCro
'Hero' (1)	CQua
'Hesla' (7)	CQua
'Heslington' (3)	CQua
'Hexameter' (9)	CQua
'High Note' (7)	ETay

'High Society' (2) ♀H6	CQua ETay LCro LOPS NRog SDeJ
'Highfield Beauty' (8) ♀H6	CQua ETay
'Highgrove' (1)	CQua
'Highlite' (2)	CQua
'Hilda's Pink' (2)	CQua
'Hillstar' (7) ♀H6	CQua GKev LAma NRog SDeJ
'Hindenburg' (1)	CQua
hispanicus (13)	NRog
'Holme Fen' (2)	CQua
'Home Fires' (2)	CQua
'Honeybird' (1)	CQua
'Honeybourne' (2)	CQua
'Hoopoe' (8) ♀H6	CQua NRog
'Horace' (9)	CQua GCro
'Horn of Plenty' (5)	WPhe
'Hors d'Oeuvre' (1)	CBro
'Hospodar' (2)	CQua
'Hot Gossip' (2)	CQua
HOWICK BEAUTY (2)	GCro
HOWICK'S HALF NELSON (2)	GCro
'Hugh Town' (8)	CQua
'Hugus' (7)	CQua
humilis misapplied	see *N. pseudonarcissus* subsp. *pseudonarcissus* var. *humilis*
'Hummingbird' (6)	EPot
'Hungarian Rhapsody' (11a) ♀H6	LHWs WPhe
'Hunting Caye' (2)	CQua
'Huntley Down' (1)	CQua
'I Love You' (2) **new**	CQua
'Ian's Gift' (9) **new**	CQua
'Ice Baby'PBR (1)	CBro CRos EPfP ERCP GKev LHWs LRHS WShi
'Ice Dancer' (2)	CQua
'Ice Diamond' (4)	CQua
'Ice Follies' (2) ♀H6	CArg CQua EPfP ETay GBin GKev LAma LCro LOPS LRHS NBir NRog SDeJ WHlf
'Ice King' (4)	LCro MBros NBir NRog SDeJ SPer WHlf
'Ice Wings' (5) ♀H6	CQua EPot ETay GKev NRog SDeJ
'Immaculate' (2)	CQua
'Impeccable' (2)	CQua
'Inara' (4)	CQua
'Inbal'PBR (8)	GKev
'Inca' (6)	CQua
'Inchbonnie' (2)	CQua
§ × ***incurvicervicus*** (13)	NDry
'Indian Maid' (7) ♀H6	CQua
'Indora' (4)	CQua
'Inglescombe' (4)	CQua NRog
'Innovator' (4)	CQua
'Insulinde' (4)	CQua
'Interim' (2)	CQua SDeJ
× ***intermedius*** (13)	CBro CQua
§ - 'Compressus' (8)	CBro CQua NPoe WShi
'Intrigue' (7) ♀H6	CQua ETay GKev WShi
'Invercassley' (3)	CQua
'Inverpolly' (2)	CQua
'Iola' (4) **new**	CQua
'Ireland's Eye' (9)	CQua
'Irene Copeland' (4)	CQua GKev WHlf
'Irish Cream' (3)	CQua
'Irish Fire' (2)	CQua
'Irish Light' (2)	CQua
'Irish Linen' (3)	CQua
'Irish Luck' (1)	CArg
'Irish Minstrel' (2) ♀H6	CQua
'Irish Wedding' (2)	CQua
'Iroquois' (2) **new**	CQua
'Isambard' (4)	CQua
'Isenhurst' (2)	CQua
'Island Pride' (8)	CQua

'Isobel Salt' (8)	CQua
italicus (13)	GKev
'Itzim' (6) ♀H6	CBro CQua GKev LAma NRog SDeJ
'Iwona' (6) **new**	LAma
'Jabberwocky' (11a)	CQua
jacetanus (13)	GKev
'Jack Snipe' (6) ♀H6	CBro CQua ELan EPot ERCP ETay GKev LAma LCro LOPS NHol NRog SDeJ WCot WShi
'Jack the Lad' (4)	ETay
'Jack Wood' (11a)	CQua
'Jake' (3)	CQua
'Jamage' (8)	CQua
'Jambo' (2)	CQua
'Jamboree' (2)	CQua
'Jammin' (3)	CQua
'Janelle' (3)	CQua
'Jazz' (11b)	CQua
'Jenna' (3)	CQua
'Jenny' (6) ♀H6	CBro CQua EMor EPot ERCP ETay GKev LAma LCro LOPS NBir NRog SDeJ SPhx WShi
'Jersey Lace' (2)	CQua GKev LHWs WPhe
'Jersey Roundabout' (4)	CQua
'Jersey Star' (4)	CQua LHWs
'Jersey Torch' (4)	CQua
'Jessie Jane' (8)	CQua
'Jetfire' (6) ♀H6	CArg CQua CRos EHyd EPfP EPot ERCP EShb ETay GKev LAma LCro LOPS LRHS NBwr NHol NRHS NRog SDeJ SPer WHlf WShi
'Jim Lad' (2)	NDry
'Jimmy Noone' (1)	CQua
'Johann Strauss' (2)	ETay
'Johanna' (5)	CBro CQua
'John Daniel' (4)	CQua
'John Evelyn' (2)	CQua GCro
'John Lanyon' (3)	CQua
'John's Delight' (3)	CQua
jonquilla (13)	CBro CQua EPot LAma NRog WShi
- subsp. ***cerrolazae*** (13) **new**	GKev
§ - var. ***henriquesii*** (13)	CQua EPot GKev NRog
'Joy Bishop'	see *N. romieuxii* 'Joy Bishop'
'Juanita' (2)	LCro LOPS NBwr NPer SDeJ
'Julia Jane'	see *N. romieuxii* 'Julia Jane'
'Jumblie' (12) ♀H6	CBro CQua CRos EHyd EPfP EPot GKev LRHS NRHS SDeJ
'Jump Start' (1)	CQua
juncifolius Req. ex Lag.	see *N. assoanus*
'June Christy' (2)	CQua
'June Lake' (2)	CQua
'Justin's Star' (11a) **new**	CQua
'Kabani' (9)	CQua
'Kalyke' (10)	NDry
'Kamms' (1)	CQua
'Kapiti Talisman' (8)	CQua
'Karamudli' (1)	CQua
'Kari' (10)	NDry
'Kate Davies' (2)	CQua
'Katherine Jenkins' (7) ♀H6	CQua
'Kathy's Clown' (6)	CQua
'Katie Heath' (5)	ERCP GKev LAma NRog SDeJ SDir WBrk WPhe
'Katrina Rea' (6)	CQua
'Kaydee' (6) ♀H6	CQua EMor GKev LAma NRog SDeJ SDir WShi
'Kea' (6)	CQua
'Keats' (4)	CQua
'Kebaya' (2)	CQua
'Kedron' (7)	ERCP GKev SDeJ
'Kelly Bray' (1)	CQua
'Kerryteuila' (8)	CQua

'Kidling' (7)	CQua
'Killara' (8)	CQua
'Killearnan' (9)	CQua
'Killigrew' (2)	CQua
'Killivose' (3)	CQua
'Kilndown' (2)	CQua
'Kilworth' (2)	CQua
'Kimmeridge' (3)	CQua
'King Alfred' (1)	CArg CQua GCro LCro LOPS NBwr SDeJ SPer
'Kingham' (1)	CQua
'Kinglet' (7)	CQua
'King's Grove' (1)	CQua
'Kings Pipe' (2)	CQua
'Kingscourt' (1)	CQua
'Kingsleigh' (1)	CQua
'Kingsmill Lake' (2)	CQua
'Kissproof' (2)	NRog SDeJ
'Kit Hill' (7)	CQua
'Kiwi Magic' (4)	CQua
'Kiwi Sunset' (4)	CQua
'Knightsbridge' (1)	CQua
'Knocklayde' (3)	CQua
'Kokopelli' (7) 🏆H6	CBro CQua GKev LCro NRog SDeJ
'Kuantan' (3)	CQua
'La Belle' (7)	SDeJ
'La Fiancée' (8)	CQua
'La Riante' (3)	CQua
'Lady Be Good' (2)	CQua
'Lady Hilaria' (2)	CQua
'Lady Margaret Boscawen' (2)	CQua GCro
'Lady Moore' (3)	GCro
'Lady Serena' (9)	CQua
'Ladymeads' (2)	CQua
'Lake Alabaster' (2)	CQua
'Lake District' (2)	CQua
'Lakeland Fair' (2)	CQua
'Lalique' (3)	CQua
'Lamanva' (2)	CQua
'Lanarth' (7)	CQua
'Lancaster' (3)	CQua ETay GKev
'Landewednack Lady' (4)	CQua
'Lara Lovely' (1)	NDry
'Larkwhistle' (6)	NRog SDeJ
'Las Vegas' (1)	GKev NRog SDeJ
'Latchley Meadows' (2)	CQua
'Laurens Koster' (8)	CQua
'Lavender Lass' (6)	CQua
'Lavender Mist' (2)	CQua
'Leedsii' (3)	CQua
'Lemnos' (2) **new**	ETay
'Lemon Beauty' (11b)	CQua ETay GKev LAma NRog SDeJ
'Lemon Breeze' (6) **new**	NDry
'Lemon Brook' (2)	CQua
'Lemon Drizzle' (2)	CQua
'Lemon Drops' (5)	CQua EPot ERCP GKev LAma LCro NRog SDeJ WShi
'Lemon Haze' (2)	CQua
'Lemon Heart' (5)	CQua
'Lemon Silk' (6)	CBro CQua ELan ETay
'Lemon Spice' (3)	CQua
'Lemonade' (3)	CQua
'Lennymore' (2)	CQua
'Letsee' (2)	CQua
'Lezant' (3)	CQua
'Liberty Bells' (5)	CQua GQue
'Liebeslied' (3)	CQua
'Lieke' (7)	EPot ERCP GKev LCro LOPS SDeJ
'Lighthouse' (3)	CQua
'Lilac Mist' (2)	CQua
'Limbo' (2)	ETay
'Lincolnshire Lady' (3)	CQua
'Lindsay Joy' (2)	CQua
'Lingerie' (4) 🏆H6	CQua ETay WHlf
'Little Beauty' (1)	CQua
'Little Becky' (12)	WShi
'Little Dancer' (1)	CBro
'Little Dryad' (6) **new**	NDry
'Little Emma' (12)	LAma LHWs
'Little Finn' (6) **new**	NDry
'Little Jen' (5) **new**	NDry
'Little Jewel' (3)	CQua
'Little Meg' (7)	CQua
'Little Oliver' (7)	GKev LRHS SDeJ
'Little Racer' (6)	NDry
'Little Rusky' (7)	CBro
'Little Sentry' (7)	CBro
'Little Soldier' (10)	EPot
'Little Spell' (1)	NDry
'Little Sunray' (5)	GKev LHWs
'Little Tyke' (2)	CQua
'Little Witch' (6)	CQua GKev LAma NRog SDeJ WShi
'Littlefield' (7)	CQua
'Liverpool Festival' (2)	CQua
'Living Colour' (3)	CQua
'Lizard Beacon' (2)	CQua
'Lobularis'	see *N. lobularis* (Haw.) Schult. & Schult. f.
lobularis misapplied	see *N. nanus*
§ ***lobularis*** (Haw.) Schult. & Schult. f. (13)	CAby CAvo CBro CQua CTri EHyd EPot ERCP ETay GKev LAma LCro LHWs LOPS LRHS NRHS NRog SDeJ SPer
'Loch Brora' (2)	CQua
'Loch Coire' (3)	CQua
'Loch Fada' (2)	CQua
'Loch Hope' (2)	CQua
'Loch Leven' (2)	CQua
'Loch Loyal' (2)	CQua
'Loch Lundie' (2)	CQua
'Loch Maberry' (2)	CQua
'Loch Naver' (2)	CQua
'Logan Rock' (7)	CQua
'Lord Kitchener' (2)	GCro
'Lordship' (1)	CQua
'Lorikeet' (1)	CQua
'Lough Gowna' (1)	CQua
'Louise de Coligny' (2)	ERCP
'Love Call' (11a)	CQua
'Lucie Nottingham' (4)	CQua
'Lucifer' (2)	CQua GCro GKev WShi
'Ludo' (1)	NDry
'Lundy Light' (2)	CQua
'Lynher' (2)	CQua
'Lyric' (9)	CQua
'Lysander' (2)	CQua
'M.J. Berkeley' (1)	GCro
'Ma Belle' (1)	ETay LAma
'Madam Speaker' (4)	CQua
'Madame Plemp' (1)	GCro
'Madison' (4)	CQua GKev
'Magic Moment' (3)	CQua
'Magician' (2)	CQua
'Magnificence' (1)	CQua
'Maker's Mark' (1)	CQua
'Mallee' (11a) 🏆H6	CQua
'Malvern City' (1)	ETay
'Mangaweka' (6)	CQua
'Manly' (4) 🏆H6	CQua NRog SDeJ
'Manon Lescaut' (2)	NRog
'March Sunshine' (6)	CQua
'Margaret Herbert' (7)	CQua
'Marguerite Patten' (8)	CQua
'Marie Curie Diamond' (7) 🏆H6	CQua

'Marieke' (1)	SDeJ
'Marilyn Anne' (2)	CQua
'Marjorie Treveal' (4)	CQua
'Market Merry' (3)	GCro
'Marlborough' (2)	CQua
'Marshfire' (2)	CQua
'Martha Washington' (8)	CQua
'Martinette' (8)	CAvo CQua ETay GKev LAma LCro NBwr NRog SDeJ
marvieri	see *N. rupicola* subsp. *marvieri*
'Mary Bohannon' (2)	NRog SDeJ
'Mary Copeland' (4)	CQua
'Mary Jose' (2)	CQua
'Mary Moore' (2)	CQua
'Mary Poppins' (10)	LAma WShi
'Mary Rosina' (4)	CQua
'Mary Veronica' (3)	CQua
'Matador' (8)	CQua
'Mawla' (1)	CQua
'Max' (11a)	CQua
'Maximus Superbus' (1)	CQua
'Maya Dynasty' (2)	CQua
'Mazzard' (4)	CQua
× ***medioluteus*** (13)	CBro CQua GCro
'Medway Gold' (7)	CQua
'Mega' (9)	CQua
'Meldrum' (1)	CQua
'Memento' (1)	CQua
'Mên-an-Tol' (2)	CQua
'Menehay' (11a) ♀H6	CQua
'Merlin' (3) ♀H6	CQua SDeJ SDir
'Mersing' (3)	CQua
'Merthan' (9)	CQua
'Midas Touch' (1)	CQua ETay
'Midget'	see *N. nanus* 'Midget'
MIDTOWN AEROLITE (2)	GCro
MIDTOWN ALFIE (1)	GCro
MIDTOWN AMBER (2)	GCro
MIDTOWN BEAUTY (2)	GCro
MIDTOWN BRIGADIER (2)	GCro
MIDTOWN LAURIE (1)	GCro
MIDTOWN MEPHISTOPHELES (2) **new**	GCro
MIDTOWN NOBLE (1)	GCro
MIDTOWN SPARKLER (2)	GCro
'Mike Pollock' (8)	CQua
'Milan' (9)	CQua
'Millennium Gold' (1)	CQua
'Millennium Sunrise' (2)	CQua
'Millennium Sunset' (2)	CQua
Minicycla Group (6)	MCor NDry
minimus misapplied	see *N. asturiensis*
'Minionette' (6)	NDry
'Minnow' (8) ♀H6	CArg CAvo CBro CQua CRos EHyd ELan EPfP ERCP EShb ETay GKev LAma LCro LOPS LRHS NBir NBwr NRHS NRog SDeJ WHlf
'Minnowlet' (11a)	CQua
minor (13) ♀H5	CQua ECha MCor NRog WFar WShi
- 'Little Gem' (1) ♀H6	CBro CQua CTri GKev LAma NRog SDeJ SDir
- var. ***pumilus*** 'Plenus'	see *N.* 'Rip van Winkle'
'Mint Julep' (3) ♀H6	ETay GKev SDeJ
'Mirar' (2)	CQua ETay
'Miss Diddles' (7)	CQua
'Miss Mabel' (6)	CQua
'Miss Muffit' (1)	CQua
'Mission Bells' (5) ♀H6	CQua
'Mission Impossible' (11a)	CQua
'Mist of Avalon' (4)	CQua
'Mistress Mine' (2)	CQua
'Misty Glen' (2) ♀H6	CQua ETay GKev LAma LCro SDeJ
'Misty Moon' (3)	CQua
'Mite' (6) ♀H6	CAvo CBor CBro CQua EPot GKev NDry NHpl NRog WShi
'Mitimoto' (10)	NDry
'Mitzy' (6)	NDry
'Modern Art' (2)	CQua ETay NRog SDeJ
'Modulation' (2)	SDeJ
'Mogley's Favorite' (7) **new**	CQua
'Mona Lisa' (2)	ETay
'Mondragon' (11a)	ETay GKev NRog
'Mongleath' (2)	CQua
'Monksilver' (3)	CQua
'Montego' (3)	CQua
'Moon Ranger' (3)	CQua
'Moon Shadow' (3)	CQua
'Moonlight Sensation' (5)	GKev LAma LHWs
'Morab' (1)	CQua
'Moralee' (4)	CQua
'More and More' (7)	CAvo EPot ERCP GKev LAma LHWs LRHS NHpl SDir WTor
'Morning View' (1) **new**	CQua
'Mortie' (6)	NDry
moschatus (13) ♀H6	CAvo CBro CQua EPot LAma NRog WShi
'Mother Duck' (6)	GKev LAma WOld
'Motmot' (8)	CQua
'Mount Hood' (1) ♀H6	CArg ETay GKev LAma NBir NRog SDeJ SDir
'Mountain Poet' (9)	CQua
'Mousehole' (3)	CQua
'Mowser' (7)	CQua
'Mrs Ernst H. Krelage' (1)	GCro
'Mrs Iwasa Masako' (2) ♀H6	GKev
'Mrs Langtry' (2)	CQua GCro GKev WShi
'Mrs R.O. Backhouse' (2)	CQua WShi
'Mullion' (3)	CQua
'Mulroy Bay' (1)	CQua
'Murlough' (9)	CQua
'My Story' (4) ♀H6	ETay GKev LAma LHWs SDeJ SDir WPhe
'My Sweetheart' (3)	CQua
'Mystic' ambig. (3)	CQua
'Namraj' (2)	CQua
'Nancegollan' (7)	CQua
'Nangiles' (4)	CQua
'Nanpee' (7)	CQua
'Nansidwell' (2)	CQua
'Nanstallon' (1)	CQua
§ ***nanus*** (13)	CQua
§ - 'Midget' (1)	CQua EPot NHpl WShi
'Neahkahnie' (1)	CQua
× ***neocarpetanus*** var. ***romanensis*** (13)	NDry
'Nessa' (7)	CQua
nevadensis (13)	NDry
'New Life' (3)	CQua
'New Penny' (3)	CQua
'New World' (2)	CQua ETay
'New-Baby' (7)	CQua GKev LRHS MMrt NRog SDeJ SDir
'Newcomer' (3)	CQua
'Nickelodeon' (8)	CQua
'Night Life' (2)	CQua
'Night Music' (4)	CQua
'Nightcap' (1)	CQua
'Nightflight' (1)	CQua
'Niphetos' (2)	GCro
'Nirvana' (7)	CQua
'Niveth' (5)	CAvo CQua GCro WShi
§ ***nobilis*** (13)	EPot GCro GKev NDry
- var. ***leonensis*** (13)	NRog
'Norma Jean' (2)	CQua
'North Rim' (2)	CQua
'Notre Dame' (2) ♀H6	CQua

Nylon Group (10)	EPot EPri GKev
'Nynja' (2)	CQua
'Oadby' (1)	CQua
'Oakwood' (3)	ETay
'Obdam' (4)	GBin LCro NRog SDeJ
obsoletus (13)	GKev WCot
obvallaris (13) $\mathbb{Y}^{H6}$	CAvo CBro CQua EPot ERCP ETay GCro GKev LAma LCro LHWs SDeJ WShi
'Odd Job' (12)	CQua
× ***odorus*** (13)	CQua NRog WShi
- 'Plenus' (4)	CQua ERCP WPhe WShi
old pheasant's eye	see *N. poeticus* var. *recurvus*
'Oliver Carne' (4)	CQua
'Oliver Cromwell' (1)	CQua
'Ombersley' (1)	CQua
'Omri' (8)	GKev LAma
'Orange Comet' (6)	CQua
'Orange Phoenix' (4)	CQua WShi
'Orange Progress' (2)	NRog SDeJ
'Orange Queen' (3)	GKev
'Orange Queen' (7)	NRog
'Orange Supreme' (2)	CQua
'Orangery' (11a)	GKev LAma LHWs NRog SDeJ
'Oregon Cedar' (2)	CQua
'Orkney' (2)	CQua
'Ornatus' (9)	GCro
'Oryx' (7) $\mathbb{Y}^{H6}$	CQua
'Otaki Lights' (1)	CQua
'Ouma' (1)	CQua
'Oundle' (2)	CQua
'Oxford Gold' (10) $\mathbb{Y}^{H6}$	CAvo CQua GKev LAma LHWs LRHS MNrw
'Ozan' (2)	CQua
pachybolbus (13)	CQua NRog
'Pacific Coast' (8) $\mathbb{Y}^{H6}$	CQua LCro
'Pacific Mist' (11a)	CQua
'Pacific Rim' (2)	CQua ETay
'Pacific Waves' (3)	CQua
'Paean' (1)	CQua
'Pageboy' (12) **new**	NDry
'Painted Desert' (3)	CQua
pallidiflorus (13)	ECha
- var. ***pallidiflorus*** (13)	GKev
'Palmares' (11a)	SDeJ
'Pamela Hubble' (2)	CQua
'Pampaluna' (11a)	CQua
'Panache' (1)	CQua
panizzianus (13)	CQua
'Paper White'	see *N. papyraceus*
'Paper White Grandiflorus' (8)	CQua ECul EPfP NRHS SDeJ SPer
'Papillon Blanc' (11b)	GKev LAma LCro NRog
'Papua' (4)	CQua
§ ***papyraceus*** (13)	CQua ETay GKev MHtn NRog WHlf
- subsp. ***polyanthos*** (13)	GKev
- 'Ziva' (8)	CAvo ELan GKev LAma LCro LOPS NRog SDeJ
'Parcpat' (7)	CQua
'Paricutin' (2)	ETay
'Parisienne' (11a)	GKev NRog SDeJ
'Park Springs' (3)	CQua
'Parkdene' (2)	CQua
'Parterre' (2)	ETay
'Passionale' (2) $\mathbb{Y}^{H6}$	CQua GKev NBir NRog
'Pastorale' (2)	ETay
'Pat Redman' (3)	CQua
'Patois' (9)	CBro
'Paujen Gold' (7)	CQua
'Pawating' (4)	CQua
'Pay Day' (1)	CQua
'Peach Prince' (4)	CQua
'Pearl Wedding' (3)	CQua
'Peeping Jenny' (6)	ERCP LAma SDeJ
'Peeping Tom' (6) $\mathbb{Y}^{H6}$	CBro ERCP ETay GKev LAma NRog SDeJ SRms
'Peggy Irene' (3)	CQua
'Pemboa' (1)	CQua
'Pencrebar' (4)	CQua EPot GKev NHol NRog SDeJ WShi
'Penjerrick' (9)	CQua
'Penkivel' (2) $\mathbb{Y}^{H6}$	CQua
'Pennine Way' (1)	CQua
'Penny Perowne' (7)	CQua
'Pennyfield' (2)	CQua
'Penpol' (7)	CQua
'Penril' (6)	CQua
'Penselwood' (2)	CQua
'Pensioner' (2)	LHWs
'Penstraze' (7)	CQua
'Pentewan' (2)	GCro
'Pentire' (11a)	CQua
'Penvale' (7)	CQua
'Percuil' (6)	CQua
'Perdredda' (3)	CQua
'Perfect Peace' (2)	CQua
'Perpetuation' (7)	CQua
'Personable' (2)	CQua
'Petit Four' (4)	LAma NRog SDeJ
'Petrel' (5)	CQua ERCP GKev LAma LCro NRog SDeJ WShi
'Phantom' (11a)	CQua
'Philomath' (7)	CQua
'Phil's Gift' (1)	CQua
'Phoenician' (2)	CQua
'Picoblanco' (2)	CBro CQua
'Pimpernel' (2) $\mathbb{Y}^{H6}$	GKev WPhe
'Pina Colada' (4) **new**	CQua
'Pinafore' (2)	WFar
'Pink Angel' (7)	CQua
'Pink Champagne' (4)	CQua
'Pink Charm' (2)	CQua ETay GKev LHWs LRHS NBir NRog SDeJ WPhe
'Pink Chimes' (5)	CQua
'Pink China' (2)	CQua
'Pink Glacier' (11a)	CQua
'Pink Ice' (2)	CQua
'Pink Pageant' (4)	CQua
'Pink Paradise' (4)	NRog
'Pink Parasol' (1)	SDeJ
'Pink Pride' (2)	CArg
'Pink Silk' (1)	CQua ETay SDeJ
'Pink Smiles' (2)	CQua LAma
'Pink Surprise' (2)	CQua
'Pink Tango' (11a)	CQua
'Pinza' (2) $\mathbb{Y}^{H6}$	CQua SDeJ
'Pipe Major' (2)	CQua ETay NRog
'Pipers Barn' (7)	CQua
'Piper's Gold' (1)	CQua
'Pipestone' (2)	CQua
'Pipit' (7)	CAvo CBro CQua EPot ERCP EShb ETay GBin GKev LAma NBir NBwr NRog SDeJ SPhx WHlf WPhe WShi
'Pistachio' (1) $\mathbb{Y}^{H6}$	ETay GKev LHWs NRog
'Pitchroy' (2)	CQua
'Pitt's Diamond' (3)	CQua
'Pixie's Sister' (7) $\mathbb{Y}^{H6}$	CQua
'Pledge' (1)	CQua LRHS
'Plenipo' (4) **new**	GCro
'Plymouth Hoe' (1)	CQua
§ ***poeticus*** var. ***hellenicus*** (13)	CBro CQua ETay
- old pheasant's eye	see *N. poeticus* var. *recurvus*
- var. ***physaloides*** (13)	CQua GKev NRog

	– 'Plenus' misapplied	see *N. poeticus* 'Spalding Double White', *N.* 'Tamar Double White'
§	– 'Plenus' ambig. (4)	CBro CQua ERCP GKev LAma LHWs SDeJ WShi
§	– var. ***recurvus*** (13) ♀H6	CAvo CBro CQua ELan EPfP ERCP EShb ETay GKev LAma LCro LHWs LOPS MBros NBir NPoe NRog SDeJ SDir SPer WHlf WPhe WShi
§	– 'Spalding Double White' (4)	CQua GCro
	– white-flowered (13)	SDeJ
	'Poet's Way' (9)	CQua
	'Pol Crocan' (2)	CQua
	'Pol Voulin' (2)	CQua
	'Polar Ice' (3)	CQua ERCP GKev LAma NRog SDeJ
	'Polglase' (8)	CQua
	'Polgooth' (2)	CQua
	'Polindra' (2)	GCro
	'Polly's Pearl' (8)	CQua
	'Polmenor' (2)	CQua
	'Polnesk' (7)	GCro
	'Polonaise' (2)	CQua
	'Polruan' (7)	CQua
	'Polyphant' (2)	CQua
	'Pomona' (3)	GCro
	'Pompiere' (2) **new**	CQua
	'Pooka' (3)	CQua
	POOLEWE PINTUCK (2)	GCro
	'Popeye' (4)	ETay
	'Poppy's Choice' (4)	CQua
	'Port Noo' (3)	CQua
	'Porthchapel' (7)	CQua
	'Portloe Bay' (3)	CQua
	'Portrush' (3)	CQua
	'Posai' (2)	CQua
	'Praecox' (9)	CBro CQua
	'Prairie Fire' (3)	CQua
	'Preamble' (1)	CQua
I	'Precocious' (2) ♀H6	CQua ETay GKev LAma SDeJ
	'President Lebrun' (1) **new**	CQua
	'Presidential Pink' (2)	CQua
	'Pretty in Yellow' (11a)	SDeJ
	'Pride of Cornwall' (8)	CQua
	'Primrose Beauty' (4)	CQua
	'Princeps' (1)	CQua GCro GKev
	'Princess Zaide' (3)	ETay LAma
	'Printal' (11a)	GKev NRog SDeJ
	'Prism' (2)	CQua
	'Probus' (1)	CQua
	'Professor Einstein' (2)	CQua ETay NRog SDeJ
	'Prologue' (1)	CQua
	'Prom Dance' (11a) ♀H6	CQua ETay GKev LAma
	'Proska' (2)	CQua
	'Prototype' (6)	EBee GKev LAma
	pseudonarcissus (13)	CArg CHab CQua LCro MMuc NPoe WShi
	– subsp. ***eugeniae***	see *N. eugeniae*
	– subsp. ***nobilis***	see *N. nobilis*
	– var. ***porrigens*** (13)	GCro
	– subsp. ***pseudonarcissus*** double-flowered (4)	CQua
§	– – var. ***humilis*** (13)	NRog
	'Ptolemy' (1)	GCro
	'Pueblo' (7)	CQua ETay GKev LAma LRHS NBwr NRog SDeJ
	'Pukenui' (4)	CQua
	pumilus ambig. (13)	CQua SDeJ
	'Punchline' (7) ♀H6	CQua
	'Punk' (1)	NDry
	'Puppet' (5)	CQua SDeJ
	'Purbeck' (3) ♀H6	CQua
	'Pyjama Party' (2) **new**	LAma

	'Quail' (7) ♀H6	CQua ETay GKev LAma NBwr NRog SDeJ WHlf
	'Quasar' (2) ♀H6	CQua
	Queen Anne's double daffodil	see *N.* 'Eystettensis'
	'Queen Bess' (2)	CQua
	'Queen of Bicolors' (1) **new**	CQua
	'Queen of the North' (3)	CQua GCro LRHS WShi
	'Quetta' (3)	GCro
	'Quick Step' (7)	CQua
	'Radiant Gem' (8)	CQua
	radiiflorus (13)	EPot NRog
	– var. ***poetarum*** (13)	CQua GCro
	– var. ***radiiflorus*** (13)	GCro
	'Radjel' (4)	CQua
	'Raffles' (4)	CQua
	'Rager' (4)	CQua
	'Rainbow' (2) ♀H6	CQua ETay NRog
	'Rainbow of Colors' (11a)	LCro LOPS
	'Raj' (2)	CQua
	'Rameses' (2)	CQua
	'Raoul Wallenberg' (2)	SDeJ
	'Rapture' (6) ♀H6	CQua ERCP ETay GKev LAma NRog WOld
	'Rashee' (1)	CQua
	'Raspberry Ring' (2)	CQua WPhe
	'Rathowen Gold' (1)	CQua
	'Ravenhill' (3)	CQua
	'Rebekah' (4)	CQua
	'Red Beacon' (3)	GCro
	'Red Coat' (2)	CQua
	'Red Devon' (2)	CArg LAma LCro LOPS LRHS NRog SDeJ
	'Red Ember' (3)	CQua
	'Red Era' (3)	CQua
	'Red Mantle' (2)	CQua
	'Red Reed' (1)	CQua
	'Redstart' (3)	ETay
	'Refrain' (2)	CQua
	'Regeneration' (7)	LHWs
	'Reggae' (6) ♀H6	LAma LRHS NRog SDeJ
	'Rembrandt' (1)	CQua
	'Replete' (4)	CQua GKev NRog SDeJ WHlf
	requienii	see *N. assoanus*
	'Resolute' (2)	GCro
	'Reverse Image' (11a)	CQua
	rifanus	see *N. romieuxii* subsp. *romieuxii* var. *rifanus*
	'Rijnveld's Early Sensation' (1) ♀H6	CAvo CBro CQua ECha ERCP ETay GKev LAma LCro LOPS NRog SDeJ WShi
	'Rikki' (7)	CAvo CBro
	'Rimmon' (3)	CQua
	'Rimski' (2)	CQua
	'Ring Fence' (3)	CQua
	'Ringing Bells' (5)	CQua
	'Ringleader' (2)	CQua
§	'Rip van Winkle' (4)	CAby CBro CQua CRos EHyd EPfP EPot ERCP ETay GKev LAma LRHS NBir NBwr NHol NHpl NRHS NRog SDeJ WBrk WHlf WShi
	'Rippling Waters' (5)	CQua
	'Rival' (6)	CQua
	'River Queen' (2)	CQua
	'Rockall' (3)	CQua
	'Roger' (6)	CQua
	'Rogue' (2)	CBro
	'Romance' (2) ♀H6	ERCP LAma
§	'Romanus' (4)	CAvo CQua
	'Romeo' (8)	CQua
	romieuxii (13) ♀H4	CBor EHyd EPri GArf NDry NRHS WCot
	– SF 370	WCot WMal
	– subsp. ***albidus*** (13)	CBor EPot GKev LAma

- - SF 110	NDry WCot
§ - - var. ***zaianicus*** (13)	NRog
- - - SB&L 82 from Morocco	WCot
- - - M168 from Morocco (13)	NDry
§ - 'Joy Bishop' (10)	NDry WCot
§ - 'Julia Jane' (10)	CAvo CBor ERCP GKev LAma LCro LHWs LOPS LRHS NRog SDir WCot
- 'Mrs McGee' (10)	NDry
* - subsp. ***pallidus*** (13) SB&L 237	WCot
- subsp. ***romieuxii*** (13)	NRog
§ - - var. ***rifanus*** (13)	NRog
- - - B 8929	WCot
'Rongoiti Gem' (4)	CQua
'Rosannor Gold' (11a)	CQua
'Rose Lake' (2)	CQua
'Rose of May' (4)	CQua WShi
'Rose Royale' (2)	CQua
'Rose Villa' (2)	CQua
'Rosemary Pearson' (2)	CQua
'Rosemerryn' (2)	CQua
'Rosemoor Gold' (7) 🏆H6	CQua ETay
'Rosemullion' (4)	CQua
'Roulette' (2)	ETay GKev SDeJ
'Round Oak' (1)	CQua
'Roundita' (1)	CQua LRHS
'Royal Connection' (8)	CQua
'Royal Marine' (2)	CQua
'Royal Princess' (3)	CQua
'Royal Regiment' (2)	CQua
'Rubilina' (2)	NDry
'Ruby Red' (2)	CQua
'Rubythroat' (2)	CQua
'Ruddynosey' (1)	CQua
rupicola (13)	CBro GKev LAma NDry NRog NSla
§ - subsp. ***marvieri*** (13)	NDry
§ - subsp. ***watieri*** (13)	CBro ERCP GKev NDry SDir
'Rushlake Green' (2)	CQua
'Rustom Pasha' (2)	CQua GCro
'Sabine Hay' (3)	EPot ETay GKev
'Sabrosa' (7) 🏆H6	CBro CQua GKev LCro LHWs LOPS WShi
'Sailboat' (7) 🏆H6	CAvo CBro CQua ETay GKev LAma LCro LOPS LRHS NRog SDeJ SPhx
'Saint Agnes' (8)	CQua
'Saint Budock' (1)	CQua
'Saint David's Day' (2) **new**	ETay
'Saint Day' (5)	CQua
'Saint Keverne' (2) 🏆H6	CQua ETay SDeJ
'Saint Keyne' (8)	CQua
'Saint Mary Immaculata' (8) **new**	CQua
'Saint Olaf' (3)	GCro
'Saint Patrick's Day' (2)	CQua GBin NBir SDeJ
'Saint Peter' (4)	CQua
'Saint Petroc' (9)	CQua
'Saint Piran' (7)	CQua
'Salcey Forest' (1)	CQua
'Salome' (2) 🏆H6	CQua ETay GKev LAma LCro LOPS MBros NBir NPer NRog SDeJ
'Salou' (4) **new**	LCro
'Salute' (2)	CQua
'Sandra's Diamond' (3)	CQua
'Sandycove' (2)	CQua
'Sarchedon' (9)	GCro
'Satchmo' (1)	CQua
'Saturn' (3)	CQua
'Saxby' (11a)	CQua
'Scarlet Chord' (2)	CQua
'Scarlet Elegance' (2)	CQua
'Scarlet Gem' (8)	SDeJ
'Scilly White' (8)	CQua WShi
'Scorrier' (2)	CQua
'Scrumpy' (2)	CQua
'Sea Dream' (3)	CQua
'Sea Green' (9)	CQua
'Sea Princess' (3)	GKev SDeJ
'Seagrave' (4)	CQua
'Seagull' (3)	CQua LAma
'Sealing Wax' (2)	CQua ETay
'Sedna' (10) **new**	NDry
'Segovia' (3) 🏆H6	CAvo CBor CBro CQua ELan ERCP ETay GKev LAma NRHS NRog SDeJ WOld
'Sempre Avanti' (2)	CArg LAma NRog SDeJ
'Senara' (2) **new**	CQua
'Sentinel' (2)	GKev SDeJ
'Seraglio' (3)	CQua
'Serena Lodge' (4) 🏆H6	CQua
serotinus (13)	NRog
'Sharnden' (1)	CQua
'Sharon's Champagne' (3)	CQua
'Shepherd's Hey' (7)	CQua SDeJ
'Sherborne' (4) 🏆H6	CQua
'Shining Light' (2)	CQua
'Shrike' (11a) 🏆H6	CQua ETay GKev LAma
'Shurdington' (3)	CQua
'Shykowski' (4)	CQua
'Sidley' (3)	CQua
'Sidora' (1)	NDry
'Silver Chimes' (8)	CAvo CBro CQua ECul EPfP ETay LAma LCro LOPS NBir NRog SDeJ
'Silver Smiles' (7)	GKev LAma LHWs NRog
'Silverwood' (3)	CQua
'Sinopel' (3)	ETay GKev LAma LHWs NRog SDeJ WHlf
'Sir Watkin' (2)	CQua GCro
'Sir Winston Churchill' (4) 🏆H6	CAvo CQua ECul ETay GKev LAma LCro LOPS LRHS MPie NRog SDeJ SPer WHlf
'Sirius' (2)	GCro
'Sissy' (6)	CQua
'Skerry' (2)	CQua
'Skilliwidden' (2) 🏆H6	CQua
'Skookum' (3)	CQua
'Sleek' (6)	NDry
'Small Fry' (1)	CQua
'Small Talk' (1) 🏆H6	CQua
'Smiling Sun' (2)	GKev
'Smiling Twin' (11a)	CQua SDeJ
'Smokey Bear' (4)	CQua
'Smooth Sails' (3)	CQua
'Snipe' (6)	CQua WShi
'Snook' (6)	NDry
'Snowball' (4)	CQua GKev NRog
'Snowboard' (2) **new**	ETay
'Soldier Brave' (2)	ETay
'Soleil d'Or' (8)	CQua ETay NBwr
'Solferique' (2)	CQua
'Solveig's Song' (12)	EPot WCot
'Sonata' (9)	CQua
'Songket' (2)	CQua
'Sorbet' (11b)	CQua NRog SDeJ
'Sorcerer' (3)	CQua
'Southease' (2)	CQua
'Southern Gem' (2)	CQua GCro
'Spaniards Inn' (4)	CQua
'Sparkling Tarts' (8)	CQua
'Special Envoy' (2)	CQua
'Speedie' (6)	NDry
'Spellbinder' (1)	CQua SDeJ
'Spindletop' (3)	CQua
'Spirit of Rame' (3)	CQua
'Split Vote' (11a)	CQua

	'Spoirot' (10) ♀H6	ERCP GBin GKev LAma LRHS MNrw MPie NHpl SDeJ WTor
	'Sportsman' (2)	CQua
	'Spring Dawn' (2)	ETay LCro LOPS SPer WBrk
	'Stainless' (2)	GKev LAma NRog SDir WHlf WPhe
	'Standard Value' (1)	NRog
	'Stann Creek' (1)	CQua
	'Stanway' (3)	CQua
	'Star Glow' (2)	CQua
	'Star War' (2)	ETay
	'Starfire' (7)	CQua
	'Starlight Sensation' (5)	ERCP LAma LCro LHWs
	'Starlit' (1)	NDry
	'State Express' (2)	CQua
	'Stella' (2)	ERCP GCro
	'Stella Corscadden' (6)	CQua
	'Step Child' (6)	CQua
	'Step Forward' (7)	CQua
	'Steren' (7)	CQua
	'Stilton' (9)	CQua
	'Stint' (5) ♀H6	CQua ERCP GKev LAma SDeJ SDir
	'Stoke Doyle' (2)	CQua
	'Stratosphere' (7) ♀H6	CQua SDeJ
	'Strines' (2) ♀H6	CQua
	'Suave' (3)	ETay SDeJ
	'Suda' (2)	GCro
	'Sugar Cups' (8)	CQua
	'Sugar Loaf' (4)	CQua
	'Sugar Rose' (6)	CQua
	'Suisgill' (4)	CQua
§	'Sulphur Phoenix' (4)	CQua WShi
	SULPHUR STAR (2)	GCro
	'Sun Disc' (7) ♀H6	CBro CTri ETay GKev LAma LCro LOPS MBros NBwr NRog SDeJ WPhe WShi
	'Sundial' (7)	CBro NRog
	'Sunlight Sensation' (5)	LAma LHWs
	'Sunny Girlfriend' (11a)	SDeJ WHlf WPhe
	'Sunnyside Up' (11a) ♀H6	SDeJ
	'Sunrise' (3)	CQua
	'Sunstroke' (2)	CQua
	'Suntory' (3)	CQua
	'Surfside' (6) ♀H6	GKev NRog SDeJ
	'Suzy' (7)	CQua SDeJ
	'Swallow' (6)	SDeJ
	'Swedish Sea' (2)	CQua
	'Sweet Blanche' (7)	CQua
	'Sweet Lorraine' (2)	CQua
	'Sweet Memory' (2)	CQua
	'Sweet Pomponette' (4)	ETay GKev SDeJ
	'Sweet Smiles' (7)	GKev LHWs
	'Sweetness' (7) ♀H6	CAvo CQua EShb ETay GCro GKev LAma LCro LOPS NRog SDeJ WShi
	'Swift Arrow' (6) ♀H6	CQua
	'Swoop' (6)	SDeJ
	'Sydling' (5)	CQua
	'Taffeta' (10)	EPri
	'Tahiti' (4) ♀H6	CQua ELan ETay GKev LAma LCro LOPS NBwr NRog SDeJ
	× ***taitii*** (13)	GKev WShi
	'Talgarth' (2)	CQua
§	'Tamar Double White' (4)	CBro CQua
	'Tamar Fire' (4) ♀H6	CQua
	'Tamar Lad' (2)	CQua
	'Tamar Snow' (2)	CQua
	'Tamara' (2)	CArg NBwr
	'Tangent' (2)	CQua
	'Tasgem' (4)	CQua
	'Taslass' (4)	CQua
	tazetta (13)	CQua GKev WHlf
§	- subsp. ***lacticolor*** (13)	CQua ERCP LAma NRog SDeJ SDir
	- subsp. ***ochroleucus*** (13)	CQua
*	- var. ***odoratus*** (13)	CQua LHWs WShi
	- subsp. ***tazetta*** (13)	CQua
	'Teal' (1)	CQua
§	'Telamonius Plenus' (4)	CQua GBin GCro GKev NRog SEND WShi
	× ***tenuior*** (13)	GKev WShi
	'Terracotta' (2)	CQua
	'Tête Bouclé' PBR (4)	CBro CQua ERCP GKev LAma SDir WPhe
	'Tête Deluxe' (4)	ETay LRHS
	'Tête Rosette'	LAma LCro
	'Tête-à-tête' (12) ♀H6	CArg CAvo CBro CQua CRos EGrI EHyd EPfP EPot ERCP ETay GAbr GKev LAma LCro LOPS LRHS LSto MBow MBros NBwr NHpl NRHS NRog SDeJ SDir SPer WPhe WShi
	'Tethys' (10)	NDry
I	'Thalia' (5)	CArg CAvo CBro CQua ELan EPfP ERCP ETay GKev LAma LCro LOPS MBriF NBir NHol NRog SDeJ SPer SPhx WHlf WShi
	'The Alliance' (6) ♀H6	CQua
	'The Caley' (2)	CQua
	'The Little Gentleman' (6)	CQua
	'Themisto' (10)	NDry
	'Thistledome' (3) **new**	CQua
	'Thomas Kinkade' (2)	CQua
	'Three Oaks' (1)	CQua
	'Thriplow Gold' (1)	CQua
	'Tickled Pinkeen' (2)	ETay WPhe
	'Tideford' (2)	CQua
	'Tiercel' (1)	CQua
	'Tiffany Jade' (3)	CQua
	'Tino Pai' (9)	CQua
	'Tintagel Lady' (4)	CQua
	'Tiny Bubbles' (12)	CBro CQua ERCP ETay GKev LAma LHWs LRHS
	'Tiritomba' (11a)	CQua
	'Tittle-tattle' (7)	CQua
	'Tiwi' (2)	CQua
	'Toby' (2)	SDeJ
	'Tommy White' (2)	NRog
	'Top Hit' (11a)	CQua
	'Topolino' (1) ♀H6	CBro CQua CRos EHyd EPfP EPot ERCP GKev LAma LCro LOPS LRHS LSto NRHS NRog WHlf
	'Topsy Turvy' (4)	CQua
	'Torianne' (2) ♀H6	CQua
	'Torridon' (2)	CQua
	'Toru' (8) **new**	CQua
	'Toto' (12) ♀H6	CAvo CBro EBee ERCP GKev LAma LCro LHWs LOPS LRHS MBriF SDeJ SDir
	'Tracey' (6)	LAma
	'Tranquil Morn' (3)	ETay
	'Transmitter' (4)	CQua
	'Trebah' (2) ♀H6	CQua
	'Treble Two' (7)	CQua
	'Trecara' (3)	CQua
	'Trelawney Gold' (2)	CQua
	'Trelissick' (7)	CQua
	'Trembroath Belle' (2) **new**	CQua
	'Trena' (6) ♀H6	CQua ERCP GKev LAma NRog SDeJ
	'Trenwith' (1)	CQua
	'Trepolo' (11b)	LAma SDeJ
	'Tresamble' (5)	CBro CQua ETay GCro GKev LAma LCro LOPS NBir NRog SDeJ
	'Tresserve' (1)	GCro
	'Trevarrack' (4) **new**	CQua
	'Treviddo' (2)	CQua

'Trevithian' (7)	CQua GCro GKev NRog SDeJ
triandrus var. ***albus***	see *N. triandrus* subsp. *triandrus* var. *triandrus*
- subsp. ***triandrus*** (13)	NDry
§ - - var. ***triandrus*** (13)	CBor GBin NRog
'Tricollet' (11a)	ETay NRog SDeJ
'Trigonometry' (11a) ♀H6	CQua
'Tripartite' (11a) ♀H6	CQua ETay GKev NRog SDeJ
'Triple Crown' (3) ♀H6	CQua
'Tristar' (11a)	CQua
'Tristram' (2)	CQua
'Tropic Isle' (4)	CQua
'Trousseau' (1)	CQua
'Tru' (3)	CQua
'Truculent' (3)	CQua
'Trumpet Voluntary' (1)	NDry
'Trumpet Warrior' (1) ♀H6	CQua
'Tudor Minstrel' (2)	CQua
'Tuesday's Child' (5) ♀H6	CQua
'Tullybeg' (3)	ETay
'Tunis' (2)	GCro
'Turncoat' (6)	CQua ETay
'Twicer' (2)	CQua
'Twin Cam' (12)	NDry
'Twink' (4)	CQua GCro
'Twinkling Yellow' (7) ♀H6	CBro CQua GKev LHWs
'Tyrone Gold' (1) ♀H6	CQua
× ***ubriquensis*** hort.	see *N.* × *incurvicervicus*
'Ulster Bank' (3)	CQua
'Ultimus' (2)	CQua
'Unique' (4) ♀H6	ETay NRog SDeJ
'Unsurpassable' (1)	GCro LAma
'Upalong' (12)	CQua
'Upshot' (3)	CQua
'Utiku' (6)	CQua
'Val d'Incles' (3)	CQua
'Valdrome' (11a)	CQua
'Valinor' (2)	CQua
'Van Sion'	see *N.* 'Telamonius Plenus'
'Vanilla Peach' (11a)	LAma LRHS SDeJ WPhe
'Vanya Noeletta' (2)	CQua
'Vaticaan' (1)	SDeJ
'Velocity' (6)	ETay LAma LRHS
'Verdin' (7)	CQua
'Verger' (3)	EPfP GCro LAma SDeJ
'Vernal Prince' (3) ♀H6	ETay
'Verona' (3) ♀H6	CQua
'Vers Libre' (9)	CQua
'Victoria' (1)	GCro
'Victory' (2)	ETay
'Viking' (1) ♀H6	CQua
'Virginia Sunrise' (2) **new**	ETay
'Vitrina' (5)	NDry
'W.P. Milner' (1)	CAvo CBro CQua EMor EPfP ERCP GKev LAma LCro LOPS LRHS NRog SDeJ SPer WBrk WShi
'Walden Pond' (3)	CQua
'Waldorf Astoria' (4)	CQua
'Walton' (7)	CQua
'Waltz' (11a)	LAma LHWs
'War Dance' (3)	CQua
'Warbler' (6) ♀H6	CQua ETay GKev NRog SDeJ
'Watership Down' (2)	CQua
'Watersmeet' (4)	CQua
watieri	see *N. rupicola* subsp. *watieri*
'Wave' (4)	CQua ETay LHWs NRog SDeJ
'Wavertree'	see *N. asturiensis* 'Wavertree'
'Wee Dote' (1)	NDry
'Welsh Rugby Union' (1)	CQua
'Welsh Warrior' (1)	CQua
'Westward' (4)	NRog WPhe
'Wheal Bush' (4)	CQua
'Wheal Coates' (7) ♀H6	CQua
'Wheal Jane' (2)	CQua
'Wheal Kitty' (7)	CQua
'Whipcord' (7) ♀H6	CQua
'Whippet' (6)	NDry
'White Empress' (1)	CQua
'White Lady' (3)	CAvo CQua ERCP GCro GKev LAma WShi
'White Lion' (4) ♀H6	LAma NBir NRog SDeJ SDir WHlf
'White Marvel' (4)	CQua GKev NBwr NRog SDeJ
'White Medal' (4)	GKev NRog SDeJ
'White Nile' (2)	CQua GCro
'White Petticoat' (10)	CQua ERCP NHpl
'White Plume' (2)	CQua
'White Tea' (2)	CQua
'Whitewell' (2)	GCro
'Wicklow Hills' (3)	CQua
'Widgeon' (2)	CQua
'Wild Carnival' (2)	LHWs WPhe
willkommii (13)	CBro CQua EPot EPri GKev NRog
'Windy City' (2)	CQua
'Winholm Jenni' (3)	CQua
'Winning Shot' (2)	NDry
'Winter Waltz' (6)	CQua GKev LAma LHWs
'Wisley' (6) ♀H6	LCro LRHS
'Witch Doctor' (3)	CQua
WOODCROFT GOLD (2)	GCro
'Woodland Prince' (3)	CQua
'Woodland Star' (3)	CQua
'Woodley Vale' (2)	CQua
'Woodstar' (5)	CQua EPot
'Worcester' (2)	ETay
'World Class' (5)	CQua
'Xit' (3)	CBro CQua EPot LAma
'Xunantunich' (2)	CQua
'Yellow Cheerfulness' (4) ♀H6	CArg CQua ELan ETay GKev LAma LCro LOPS NBwr NRHS NRog SDeJ WPhe
'Yellow River' (1) ♀H6	NRog
'Yellow Sailboat' (7) **new**	EPfP
'Yellow Xit' (3)	CQua
'York Minster' (1)	CQua
'Young Blood' (2)	CQua
'Your Grace' (2)	CQua
zaianicus	see *N. romieuxii* subsp. *albidus* var. *zaianicus*
'Zeekie' (2)	NDry
'Zekiah' (1)	CQua
'Zion Canyon' (2)	CQua
'Zoë's Pink' (3)	CQua
'Zonk' (11a)	CQua

Nardostachys (*Caprifoliaceae*)

grandiflora	see *N. jatamansi* 'Grandiflora'
§ ***jatamansi*** 'Grandiflora'	GPoy

Nardus (*Poaceae*)

stricta	LPla

Nassauvia (*Asteraceae*)

darwinii	WAbe
digitata	SPlb
gaudichaudii	GArf SPlb
lagascae	WAbe

Nassella (*Poaceae*)

cernua	EPPr
tenuissima	see *Stipa tenuissima*
trichotoma	LDai
- 'Palomino'	EPPr

Nastanthus (*Calyceraceae*)

caespitosus	SPlb

Nasturtium (*Brassicaceae*)

	officinale	CBod CPud CWat LPfP MHoo MWts SVic WMAq

Natal plum see *Carissa macrocarpa*

nectarine see *Prunus persica* var. *nectarina*

Nectaroscordum see *Allium*

Neillia (*Rosaceae*)

	affinis	CExl CKel EHyd EPfP EWTr IDee LRHS MGil NBid NLar SNig SPoG SWvt WLov
	longiracemosa	see *N. thibetica*
	sinensis	NLar
§	***thibetica***	CBcs CBod CDoC CExl CMCN CMac EGrI EHyd ELan EPfP GBin GKin LEdu LRHS MAsh MBlu MGil MMuc NLar SCob SPer SRms SSta SWvt WAvo WBor WFar WLov
	thyrsiflora	EBee
	- PAB 3267	LEdu
	- var. ***tunkinensis*** HWJ 505	WCru

Nelumbo (*Nelumbonaceae*)

	'Pink 'n' Yellow'	EWat
	'Yu Ta Jiugui'	CBen

Nematanthus (*Gesneriaceae*)

	'Apres'	WDib
	'Black Magic'	WDib
	'Christmas Holly'	WDib
	'Freckles'	WDib
§	***gregarius*** ♀H1b	WDib
§	- 'Golden West' (v)	WDib
	- 'Variegatus'	see *N. gregarius* 'Golden West'
	'Lemon and Lime'	WDib
	radicans	see *N. gregarius*
	'Tropicana' ♀H1b	WDib

Nemesia (*Scrophulariaceae*)

§	AMELIE ('Fleurame'PBR)	CRos LBuc SPoG WHlf
	(Aroma Series) AROMA BANANA SPLIT	CRos
	- AROMA HEART OF GOLD **new**	WWke
	- AROMA PLUMS AND CUSTARD	MPri SCob
	- AROMA RHUBARB AND CUSTARD	CRos LCro LSou MBros MPri SCob
	(Aromatica Series) AROMATICA ROSE PINK ('Balarropi'PBR)	WHlf
	- AROMATICA ROYAL ('Balaroyal'PBR)	WHlf
	BERRIE WHITE ('Fleurbw'PBR)	LSou
	BERRIES AND CREAM ('Fleurbac'PBR)	CRos ECtt LBuc LCro LSou SPoG WHlf
	BLUE LAGOON ('Pengoon'PBR) (Maritana Series)	SCoo
	'Bluebird'	see *N.* BLUEBIRD ('Hubbird')
§	BLUEBIRD ('Hubbird'PBR)	CHll
	'Bordeaux'	CRos SPoG
	caerulea 'Joan Wilder' (clonal)	WAvo
	CANDY GIRL ('Pencand') (Maritana Series)	SCoo
	'Cream Surprise'	CRos
§	***denticulata*** ♀H3	CKel EWoo MHer SCoo WHlf
	- 'Confetti'	see *N. denticulata*
	'Easter Bonnet'PBR (French Connection Series)	CRos LCro MPri SCob SPoG WHlf
	'Evening Dusk'	CRos
	'Fleurie Blue'	LBuc SPoG
	FRAMBOISE ('Fleurfram'PBR)	CRos LBuc LCro
	HONEY GIRL ('Penhon') (Maritana Series)	SCoo
	'Innocence' ♀H3	SCoo
	(Karoo Series) KAROO BLUE ('Innkablue'PBR)	SCoo
	- KAROO DARK BLUE ('Innemkadab'PBR)	WHlf
	- KAROO PINK ('Innkapink'PBR)	EPfP LRHS WHlf
	- KAROO SOFT BLUE ('Innkarsofb'PBR)	LRHS WHlf
	- KAROO WHITE ('Innkarwhi'PBR)	WHlf
	'Lady Penelope'	CRos
	'Lyric Copper' (Lyric Series)	LSou MCot
	MARITANA SKY LAGOON ('Pensky') (Maritana Series)	SCoo
	'Mirabelle'	LBuc SPoG
	MYRTILLE ('Fleurmyr'PBR)	CRos LBuc LCro SPoG
	(Nesia Series) NESIA BURGUNDY	LCro
	- NESIA SNOW ANGEL	LRHS
	OPAL INNOCENCE	see *N.* AMELIE
	PINK CITRINE (Fairy Kisses Series) **new**	LSou
	PINK LEMONADE ('Innempinle') (Fairy Kisses Series)	LSou
	RASPBERRIES AND CREAM ('Fleurras'PBR)	LBuc SPoG
	'Sugar Almond'	CMac
	'Sundrops'	MBros MPri
	(Sunsatia Series) SUNSATIA BANANA ('Intraibana')	SPoG
	- SUNSATIA BLACKBERRY ('Inuppink'PBR)	SCoo
	- SUNSATIA CRANBERRY ('Intraired'PBR)	SCoo
	- SUNSATIA LEMON ('Intraigold'PBR)	SCoo
	- SUNSATIA PEACH ('Inupcream')	SCoo
	(Sunsatia Plus Series) SUNSATIA PLUS CHERRY ON ICE ('Innemcheoi'PBR)	CPla LRHS SPoG
	- SUNSATIA PLUS LYCHEE ('Innemlyche'PBR)	CRos EPfP LRHS
	- SUNSATIA PLUS PAPAYA ('Innemnewpa')	MPri
	- SUNSATIA PLUS POMELO ('Innemsunpo'PBR)	CRos EPfP LRHS
	VANILLA BERRY ('Innemvanbe') (Fairy Kisses Series) **new**	LSou
	'Vanilla Lady'	ECtt
	'Wisley Vanilla'	CRos EHyd LBuc LCro LRHS LSou MBros MPri NRHS SCob SPoG

Nemophila (*Boraginaceae*)

	menziesii var. ***menziesii***	SPhx
	- 'Penny Black'	CSpe WWke

Neobuxbaumia (*Cactaceae*)

polylopha **new** EAri NPlm
scoparia hybrid **new** NMen

Neocardenasia see *Neoraimondia*

Neodypsis (*Arecaceae*)

decaryi see *Dypsis decaryi*
leptocheilos see *Dypsis leptocheilos*

Neolepisorus (*Polypodiaceae*)

lancifolius CExl

Neolitsea (*Lauraceae*)

glauca see *N. sericea*
polycarpa B&SWJ 11705 WCru
- KWJ 12309 WCru
§ ***sericea*** CBcs CCCN EBee LRHS NLar WPGP XSte
- B&SWJ 12738 WCru
- CWJ 12800 WCru
- yellow-fruited CWJ 12830 WCru

Neomarica (*Iridaceae*)

caerulea CPla EAri WCot

Neopanax (*Araliaceae*)

§ ***arboreus*** CAbb CDTJ CTrC CTsd EBee LEdu SArc
colensoi CTsd
§ ***laetus*** [H3] CTrC CTsd EBee IDee IKel SArc WPGP XSte

Neoporteria see *Eriosyce*

Neoraimondia (*Cactaceae*)

herzogiana **new** NPlm

Neoregelia ✿ (*Bromeliaceae*)

'Adonis' **new** NCft
'Albomarginata' NPic
ampullacea NPic
'Atlantis' NCft
carolinae NPic
- 'Blush'[PBR] NPic
- 'Marachelle' [H1b] NPic
- f. ***tricolor*** (v) NPic
'Chiquita Linda' NPic
chlorosticta **new** NPic
concentrica NPic
- 'Big Blue' NPic
'Donger' (v) NPic
'Fancy Free' NPic
farinosa NPic
'Fireball' [H1b] NCft
'Fruit Salad' NPic
'Grace' NCft
'Iphigenie' (v) **new** NPic
lilliputiana NCft
'Luca' NPic
'Magali' NCft
marmorata NPic
- 'Variegata' (v) NPic
'Matilde' (v) **new** NPic
'Mo Peppa Please' NPic
'Narciss' NCft
nivea **new** NPic
pauciflora NCft NPic
I 'Paulinae' NCft
'Pink Sensation' NCft
'Red of Rio' NPic
'Red Waif' (v) **new** NCft NPic
'Royal Burgundy' NCft
rubrifolia NPic
'Sarah Head' NPic
I ***schultesiana*** NCft
I - 'Variegata' (v) NCft
'Sherlock' **new** NPic
smithii **new** NPic
spectabilis NPic
'Tiger Cub' (v) **new** NPic
tigrina **new** NPic
'Tossed Salad' **new** NPic
'Zoë'[PBR] NPic

Neoshirakia (*Euphorbiaceae*)

japonica MBlu WJur WPGP

Neotinea (*Orchidaceae*)

ustulata LAma

Nepenthes ✿ (*Nepenthaceae*)

alata* × *ventricosa [H1a] SHmp
'Bloody Mary'[PBR] CDoC LCro SHmp
bongso SHmp
burbidgeae* × *robcantleyi SHmp
× *burkei* × *hamata* SHmp
× *burkei* × *singalana* SHmp
(*copelandii* × *truncata*) × *spathulata* SHmp
densiflora SHmp
diatas SHmp
dubia* × *singalana SHmp
dubia* × *spathulata SHmp
fusca SHmp
fusca* × *maxima SHmp
glabrata* × *spathulata SHmp
× *hookeriana* [H1a] SHmp
jacquelineae* × *spectabilis SHmp
'Linda'[PBR] SHmp
'Louisa' SHmp
lowii SHmp
macfarlanei SHmp
***maxima* × (× *mixta*)** SHmp
maxima* × *talangensis SHmp
mira* × *spathulata SHmp
ovata SHmp
ovata* × *ventricosa SHmp
petiolata* × *veitchii SHmp
platychila* × *spathulata SHmp
ramispina SHmp
'Rebecca Soper' [H1a] SHmp
robcantleyi SHmp
robcantleyi* × *spathulata SHmp
robcantleyi* × *talangensis SHmp
sanguinea SHmp
sibuyanensis SHmp
singalana SHmp
spectabilis SHmp
talangensis SHmp
talangensis* × *veitchii SHmp
truncata highland form SHmp
- 'King of Spades' × ***truncata*** 'Queen of Hearts' SHmp
ventricosa LCro SHmp

Nepeta ✿ (*Lamiaceae*)

badachschanica LEdu
'Blue Beauty' see *N. sibirica* 'Souvenir d'André Chaudron'

'Blue Dragon'	CBWd CCBP CKel CKno CNor CSde ECha ECtt EHyd GBin GPSL GQue LBar LRHS LSou MACG MAsh MHol MPie MSpe NLar NRHS SGBe SPoG SRms WCot WFar
bucharica	WMal
* ***buddlejifolium***	NLar
* - 'Gold Splash'	NLar
camphorata	WSpi
cataria	CBee CBod CLau CTsd CWal EBou ENfk GJos GPoy GQue LCro LOPS MHer MHoo MNHC NBro NGrd SRms SVic WSpi
§ - 'Citriodora'	CBod CLau ENfk MHoo NGrd SRms SVic XSen
'Cat's Pajamas' **new**	LBar MHtn WNPC
'Chettle Blue'	CDor ECha MAvo WHoo
citriodora Dum.	see *N. cataria* 'Citriodora'
clarkei	GMaP GQue MRav WSpi
curviflora	SPhx SPtp
'Dropmore'	EBee ECha EHyd LPla LRHS NLar NRHS WSpi
'Early Bird'	LBar MAvo
§ × ***faassenii*** ♀H7	Widely available
- 'Alba'	EBee EHyd ELan EPfP EWhm LRHS MHoo NLar SRms WSpi
- 'Blauknirps'	NLar
- 'Blue Wonder'	CRos EBee EBlo EHyd ELan ELon EPfP LRHS LSou NDov NLar NRHS SPhx WCAu WFar WSpi
- 'Crystal Cloud'	CKno CRos ECtt EHyd EPfP LBar LRHS LSou MBriF MHol NCth NLar NRHS SHar WCAu
- 'Gletschereis'	ECha NDov NLar WCAu
- JUNIOR WALKER ('Novanepjun'PBR)	CBod CRos EBee EBlo EHyd EPfP GMaP LBar LCro LOPS LRHS LSRN MMrt MPri NDov NLar NRHS SCob SCoo SEdd SWvt WCot XSen
- 'Kit Cat'	CBod CKel CRos EBee EBlo ECtt EHyd ELon EPfP GBin LBar LRHS MAsh MBel MHer MHoo NRHS SCob SEdd SWvt WAvo WCAu XSen
- 'Purrsian Blue'PBR	CKno CRos ECha ECtt EHeP ELon EPfP LBar LBuc LRHS LSRN MHtn MPri NCou NCth NLar SGbt SPad SPoG WCav WNPC WTor
- 'Senior'	ELon XLum
'Florina' **new**	SMHy
glechoma 'Variegata'	see *Glechoma hederacea* 'Variegata'
govaniana	Widely available
grandiflora	CDor MRav
- 'Blue Danube'	EBee ECha GBee GBin GQue NDov NLar SDix XLum
- 'Blue Elf'	LPla MAvo NDov
- 'Bramdean' ♀H6	CBWd CCBP CDor CMac CRos CSde EBee ECtt EHyd EPfP EWes GBin LBar LRHS LSou LSto MCot MHol MRav NRHS SPhx SRms WCAu WCot WKif XLum
- 'Dawn to Dusk'	Widely available
- 'Pool Bank'	CElw EBee ECtt EWes NLar SMrm XLum
- 'Summer Magic'PBR	CKno CRos EBee EBlo ECha EHyd EPfP LBar LRHS LSou MBel MHol NCth NLar NRHS SCob SHar SOrN SPhx SPoG SRkn SWvt WCAu WFar WNPC WTor
- 'Wild Cat'	MAvo WCAu
- 'Zinser's Giant'	EBee LPla SAko
hederacea 'Variegata'	see *Glechoma hederacea* 'Variegata'
'Hill Grounds'	CKno EBee ECha GBin LBar LPla MAvo MHol SPhx SRkn WCot
italica	EBee LRHS SHar SPhx
'Joanna Reed'	ECha GBin NLar WSpi
kubanica	CSpe EBee EHyd GBin LRHS MBel MRav NRHS SAng SDix SHor SPhx SPtp WCAu WCot WMal WSHC
'Lamendi'	NDov
§ 'Leeds Castle'	CBod CCBP EBee ECtt EHyd EPfP LBar LRHS MAsh MHol NGdn NLar NRHS NSti SCoo SHar SPoG WAvo WCAu
'Limelight'	NLar
LITTLE TRUDY ('Psfike')	EPfP LRHS
longipes hort.	see *N.* 'Leeds Castle'
macrantha	see *N. sibirica*
'Maurice'	LPla NLar
mussinii misapplied	see *N.* × *faassenii*
mussinii Spreng.	see *N. racemosa*
NEPTUNE ('Bokratune')	CBod CKno LBar LCro LOPS LSou MBel MPri SHor SMad WNPC
nervosa	CAby CDor CSpe ECha ELan EPfP GQue LRHS NBro NLar NSti SHar
- 'Blue Carpet'	CSpe
- 'Blue Moon'	EBee EHyd EPfP EWes GBee GJos LBar LRHS LShi LSun MACG MBNS MHol MMrt MPnt NBPC NDov NGdn NLar NRHS SRms WFar WSpi
- 'Forncett Select'	MRav
- 'Pink Cat'	CDor CRos EHyd EPfP GBee GJos LBar LRHS MACG NRHS WFar
- 'Schneehäschen'	SAko WSpi
§ ***nuda***	ECha EMor EWes GQue LPla LShi MAvo MRav SBut SHar SMHy WGoo
- 'Accent'	IPot
- 'Alba'	LEdu MAvo SBut
- subsp. ***albiflora***	ECha
- 'Anne's Choice'	IPot SMHy
- 'Lake Sevan'	LEdu WFar
- 'Purple Cat'	EBee EPfP IPot
- 'Romany Dusk'	CKno ECha LEdu LPla MAvo SMHy SMrm SWvt WPGP
pannonica	see *N. nuda*
parnassica	EPPr GLog GQue MCot MHol MMuc SMrm
'Pink Candy'	SPhx SRms
'Porzellan'	LPla
'Poseidon'	CKno MAvo MHol
§ ***prattii***	NLar
'Purple Haze'PBR	CBod ECtt EHyd ELan EPfP LBar LRHS LSou MHol NRHS
§ ***racemosa*** ♀H7	CEme CHby CMac EBou EPfP EWhm GJos MCot MHoo MNHC
- RCB AM 3	WCot
- 'Alba'	CDor ECha LBar MHoo SBut XLum
- 'Amelia'	CBWd CCBP CElw CKel CKno ECha EPfP LBar LPla MBriF MHer WAvo WCAu WCav WGoo WTor
- 'Felix'	ELan ELon EPfP LRHS WFar
- 'Grog'	EBee ECha EWTr LRHS NCth NLar SBut SEdd SPoG
- 'Little Titch'	CBod ECha ECtt EHyd EPfP LBar LRHS LShi MTin NBPC NCth NGdn NLar SCob SCoo SMrm WHlf WHoo
- 'Senior'	CBod ELon
- 'Snowflake'	Widely available
- 'Superba'	XSen
- 'Toria'	NDov
- 'Walker's Low' ♀H7	Widely available
'Rae Crug'	EWes
reichenbachiana	see *N. racemosa*

§ ***sibirica***	CCBP ECha EHyd ELan EPfP LRHS NBid NBro NRHS SRkn WCAu WCot XLum
§ - 'Souvenir d'André Chaudron' 🏆H6	CDor CRos CWCL EBee ELan EPfP GMaP LBar LRHS LSto MCot MHol MRav NLar NRHS SCob SMHy SPer SPoG WCAu WSpi
'Six Hills Giant'	Widely available
'Six Hills Gold' (v)	CDor EBee ELon LBar LBuc LShi NBPC NCth WCAu WCot WFar WSpi
stenantha	WCot
stewartiana	ECha EPPr LDai MRav
aff. ***stewartiana*** W&O 7173	GGro WFar
subsessilis	CAby CBcs CBod CKel CRos CSpe ECtt EHyd ELan EPfP GJos GLog GMaP LRHS LSou MRav MSpe NBid NBir NGdn NLar NRHS NSti SPhx SPoG SRms WCAu WCru
- 'Blue Dreams'	GQue LRHS MACG MHol NLar SBut SHar SPhx SRkn WSpi XLum
- 'Candy Cat'	MCot NLar
- 'Cool Cat'	EBee EMor
- 'Pink Dreams'	CBod ECha EHyd ELan EMor EPfP GJos LRHS SHar SMrm XLum
- pink-flowered	SPhx
- 'Sweet Dreams'	EHyd EMor EPfP EShb LRHS MRav NBPC NLar NRHS XLum
- 'Washfield'	EBee NLar SAko
transcaucasica	SDix
- 'Blue Infinity'	GMaP NGrd WFar
tuberosa	CTsd ECha EPPr LShi WFar XSen
'Veluws Blauwtje'	ECha MAvo NLar WSpi
'Weinheim Big Blue'	CKno ECha MAvo MHol NCth
'Weinheim Summer Blues'	EBee GBin
* ***yunnanensis***	EPPr NBid SMrm SPhx WPGP

Nephrolepis (*Lomariopsidaceae*)

'Boston' **new**	LWaG NHrt
cordifolia	CDTJ
duffii	EShb
exaltata 🏆H1b	LCro LWaG SEND
- 'Bostoniensis' 🏆H1b	EShb NHrt
- 'Green Lady' **new**	LCro NHrt
- 'Marisa'	EShb
- 'Smithii'	EShb
- 'Verona'	WCot

Nephrophyllidium (*Menyanthaceae*)

crista-galli	GGro

Nerine ✿ (*Amaryllidaceae*)

'Afterglow'	LAma WCot
'Alexandra'	WCot
alta	see *N. undulata* Alta Group
angustifolia	SPtp WAbe
'Aurora'	WCot
'Baghdad'	SChr WCot
'Belladonna'	CWCL WCot
'Bennett-Poë'	WCot
'Berlioz'	SGro WCot
'Blanchefleur'	WCot
bowdenii 🏆H5	Widely available
- 'Alba' misapplied	see *N.* 'Pallida'
- 'Alba' ambig.	CBor CBro CTsd CWCL EPfP EPri EPot ERCP GBin GKev LAma MNrw NHoy SCoo SDir SGBe SPeP WCot WFar
- 'Albivetta'	CBor EAri ELon EPri GKev LAma MNrw NHoy NRog
- 'Bianca Perla' 🏆H5	CAvo CBro ELan EPri EShb GKev LAma LRHS NHoy WHil
- 'Bicolor'	GKev SMad
- 'Bionce' **new**	LAma
- 'Codora'	see *N.* 'Codora'
- 'Edelweiss'	LAma LEdu NHoy WHil
- 'Ella K'	CBor EPfP EPot EPri LAma LCro LOPS NHoy SPer WFar
- 'Emma'	WCot
- 'Eric Smith'	WCot
- 'Gletsjer'	NHoy WCot
- Irish clone	WCot
- 'Isabel' 🏆H4	CAby CAvo CBor CBro CMac CTsd CWCL ECha ELan EPot EPri ERCP EShb EWes GKev LAma LSou NHoy NWad SDeJ SPeP WBor WCot WHlf WHoo
- 'John Crisp' 🏆H5	WCot
- 'Kathleen Pollock'	WCot
- 'Lady Cerise' **new**	LAma
- 'Like a Virgin' **new**	GKev LAma
- 'Linda Vista'	WCot
- 'Lipstick'	EBee LAma LRHS NHoy WMal
- 'Marjorie' 🏆H5	EHyd EMal EPfP LRHS NRHS
- 'Mark Fenwick'	CBro MWht WCot
- 'Marney Rogerson'	CBro WCot
§ - 'Mollie Cowie' (v)	WCot WCru
- 'Mount Stewart' 🏆H5	WCot
- 'Nikita'	EPri ERCP GKev LRHS MNrw NHoy NWad SDeJ WCot
- 'Ostara'	EBee ELan EPfP EPot EPri GKev LAma LCro LOPS NHoy NWad SPer WCot WFar WHil
§ - 'Pallida'	EBee LRHS SDeJ
- 'Patricia'	EGrl EPot EPri GKev LAma LRHS MNrw NHoy
- 'Pink Frostwork'	EPri WCot
- 'Pink Surprise' 🏆H5	EPri WCot WMal
§ - 'Quinton Wells' 🏆H5	WCot
- 'Quinton Wells' pale yellow-leaved	WCot
- 'Richard Blakeway-Phillips'	WCot WHil
- 'Robert Smith'	WCot
- 'Rowie'	EPri
- 'Sheila Owen'	WCot WMal
- 'Sofie'	EBee
- 'Stam 63' 🏆H5	CWCL EPot ERCP LRHS NWad WCot WHil
- 'Stefanie' 🏆H5	EAri EBee ELan EPri EShb EWTr GKev LAma NHoy SDeJ SDir SPeP
- 'Stewart Gilkison'	SHar
- Ted Allen No 2	WCot
- 'Tess Allen'	WCot WHil
- 'Variegata'	see *N. bowdenii* 'Mollie Cowie'
- 'Vesta K'	EPot EPri GKev LAma LRHS NHoy WHlf
- 'Wellsii'	see *N. bowdenii* 'Quinton Wells'
- Wellsii pale form	SHar
bowdenii* × *sarniensis	WFar
'Canasta'	WCot
'Cardinal'	EAri
'Caryatid'	WCot WFar
'Catkin'	WCot
'Clent Charm'	WCot
§ 'Codora'	CCCN EAri EPfP LCro WCot WFar
'Corlette'	WCot
'Countess of Mulgrave'	WCot
'Cranfield'	WCot
crispa	see *N. undulata* Crispa Group
'Cynthia Chance'	WCot
'Diana Oliver'	WCot
'Doris Vos'	WCot
Elegance Series	LRHS NHoy WCot
- 'Elegance Red'	CBro

	'Elspeth'	WCot
	'Exbury Red'	WCot
	'Falaise'	WCot
	filamentosa misapplied	see *N. filifolia* Baker
	filamentosa ambig.	CBro
§	***filifolia*** Baker	WAbe
	'Firelight'	WCot
	flexuosa	see *N. undulata* Flexuosa Group
	gaberonensis	WAbe
	'Giraffe'	WCot
	'Glensavage Gem'	CBro
	gracilis	WCot
	'Harlequin'	WCot
	'Helena'	WCot
	'Hera'	CBro ELon
	'Hertha Berg'	WCot
*	***hirsuta***	WCot
	humilis ♀H2	CBro WAbe
	- from Bredasdorp, South Africa	WCot
	- Breachiae Group	SAng
	'Iman'	WCot
	'Isobel'	EGrI LEdu LRHS SHar WFar
	'Janet'	WCot
	'Jenny Wren'	WCot
	'Judith'	SChr
	'King Leopold'	WCot WFar
	'King of the Belgians'	LAma
	'Kinn McIntosh'	EPri WCot
	krigei	WCot
	'Kyle'	WCot
	'Lady Cynthia Colville'	WCot
	'Lady Downe'	WCot
	'Lady Eleanor Keane'	WCot
	'Lady Havelock-Allen'	WCot
	'Lady Llewellyn'	WCot
	'Lady St Aldwyn'	WCot
	'Lambourne'	WCot
	laticoma	WCot
	'Lawlord'	WCot
	'Leila Hughes'	WCot
	'Long Island Beauty'	WCot
	'Lucinda'	WCot
	'Lyndhurst Salmon'	WCot
	'Malvern'	WCot
	'Maria'	WCot
	masoniorum ♀H2	CBor EPot WAbe
	'Meadowbankii'	WCot
	'Miss E. Cator'	WCot
	'Miss Florence Brown'	WCot
	'Miss Frances Clarke'	WCot
	'Mr John'	CBro CWCL EBee EGrI ELan EPri ERCP EShb GKev LAma LRHS LSou NHoy SDir SMad WCot WHil
	'Mrs Cooper'	WCot
	'Mrs Dent Brocklehurst'	WCot
	'Natasha'	WCot
	'Nena'	WCot
	'November Cheer'	LAma
	'Oberon'	WCot
	'Ophelia'	WCot
	'Owslebury'	WCot
	'Pamela'	LAma
	'Pink Triumph'	CBcs CMac CWCL EAri EHyd ELan EPot ERCP GKev NHoy NRHS NWad SDeJ SGBe SPeP WCot WHoo
	'Plymouth'	EAri SChr
	'Prince of Orange' **new**	LAma
	pudica pink-flowered	WCot
	'Quivotina'	WCot
	'Red Pimpernel'	LAma NHoy
	'Regina' ♀H5	WCot
	'Rembrandt'	WCot
	'Rose Princess'	WCot
	'Rushmere Star'	SChr WCot
	'Ruth'	WCot WFar
	sarniensis	CBro CWCL ECha EPot EPri EShb LAma SDeJ SDir WCot WFar
*	- 'Alba'	NHoy
*	- 'Borde Hill White'	WCot
	- var. ***corusca*** 'Major'	EGrI LAma WCot
	- var. ***curvifolia***	CBro
	- - f. ***fothergillii***	WCot
	- 'Hanley Castle'	WCot
	- 'Lydia'	NHoy
	- 'Mother of Pearl'	WCot
	- 'Mottistone'	WCot
	- red-flowered	GKev NHoy
	- rose-pink-flowered	CBor NHoy
	- var. ***sarniensis***	CBor
	- 'Twyford' **new**	EAri
	'Snowflake'	WCot
	'Stephanie'	CCCN CTca LEdu LRHS MBros MNrw WCot WHlf WHoo
	'Susan Norris'	WCot
	'Sweet Sixteen'	SGro
	'Tweedledee'	WCot
	undulata	CBor CCCN CWCL ECha EGrI EPri GKev LAma MPie NHoy NRog SDeJ SDir SPer WMal
§	- Alta Group	WCot
§	- Crispa Group	EPfP WFar
§	- Flexuosa Group	MRav
	- - 'Alba' ♀H3	CAvo CBro ECha EPri EWTr GKev MRav NRog WCot
	× ***versicolor*** 'Mansellii'	CBro
	'Vestal'	SDir
	'Vicky'	WCot
	'White Supreme' **new**	LAma
	'Winter Sun'	SRms
	'Yealm King' **new**	WCot
	'Yealm Queen' **new**	WCot WMal
	'Zeal Giant' ♀H3	CAvo CBro EPri LPla WCot WFar
	'Zeal Grilse'	WCot
	'Zennor'	WCot

Nerium (*Apocynaceae*)

§	***odoratum*** 'Miss Agnes Campbell'	SEND
	oleander misapplied	see *N. oleander* 'Soeur Agnès'
	oleander L.	CAbb EShb SArc SPlb SPoG
	- from Morocco	WPGP
	- 'Agnes Campbell'	see *N. odoratum* 'Miss Agnes Campbell'
	- 'Album'	SEND
	- 'Album Plenum' (d)	EAri
	- 'Alsace'	SEND
	- 'Angiolo Pucci'	EAri
*	- 'Atlas'	XSen
*	- 'Barcelona'	SEND
	- 'Cavalaire' (d)	XSen
*	- 'Claudia'	SEND
	- 'Commandant Barthélemy' (d)	XSen
	- double apricot (d)	SEND
	- 'Flavescens Plenum' (d)	EAri XSen
	- 'Hardy Red'	XSen
*	- 'Harriet Newding'	XSen
	- 'Jannoch'	XSen
	- 'Madame Allen' (d)	EShb
	- 'Magaly'	SEND
	- 'Margaritha'	SEND
	- 'Minouche'	SEND
	- 'Oasis' (d)	EAri
	- 'Petite Red'	XSen

- 'Professeur Granel' (d) EShb
- 'Provence' (d) EAri XSen
- 'Red Beauty' XSen
- red-flowered SPad
- 'Roseum Plenum' (d) CRHN SEND
* - 'Rubis' (d) EAri
§ - 'Soeur Agnès' XSen
- 'Soleil Levant' XSen
- 'Splendens Giganteum' (d) EShb
- 'Tito Poggi' EAri XSen
- 'Variegatum' (v) ♀H2 EShb
- 'Villa Romaine' XSen

Neviusia (*Rosaceae*)

alabamensis NLar

Nicandra (*Solanaceae*)

physalodes CHby ELan ENfk NBir SMrm
- ***alba*** CSpe
- 'Splash of Cream' (v) CCCN GJos
- 'Violacea' CSpe GJos GLog SRms SWvt

Nicotiana ✿ (*Solanaceae*)

alata CSpe LCro LOPS SPhx WHlf
- 'Grandiflora' LCro LOPS
glauca CCCN CDTJ EWld LDai NGKo SPlb
knightiana CDTJ CSpe
langsdorffii ♀H2 CSpe LCro LOPS SPhx
- 'Cream Splash' (v) CTtf WHil
- 'Hot Chocolate' CSpe
'Lime Green' ♀H2 CSpe LCro LOPS SPhx
mutabilis CSpe LCro LDai LOPS SDys SPhx WBor
'Perfume Antique Lime' (Perfume Series) SPhx
quadrivalvis SPhx
rustica CSpe SPhx
× ***sanderae*** Avalon Series MBros
- Cuba Series MPri
- 'Perfume Deep Purple' (Perfume Series) CSpe SPhx
solanifolia SPlb
suaveolens CSpe SPhx
sylvestris ♀H2 CDTJ CRos CSpe ELan EPfP EWoo LCro LOPS MPri NFav SEND SPhx SPoG SWvt
tabacum 'Tobaco Rosa' **new** WHil
'Tinkerbell' CSpe
WHISPER MIXED SPhx

Nidularium (*Bromeliaceae*)

amazonicum **new** NPic
billbergioides NCft

Nierembergia (*Solanaceae*)

§ ***repens*** NLar WCot XLum
rivularis see *N. repens*

Nigella (*Ranunculaceae*)

damascena CKel
- 'Albion Green Pod' LCro
- 'Miss Jekyll' ♀H3 LCro LOPS LSto MNHC SPhx
- 'Miss Jekyll Alba' ♀H3 CSpe LCro LOPS
- 'Mulberry Rose' **new** LSto
- 'Oxford Blue' LCro LOPS
- Persian Jewels Group SVic
hispanica L. CKel LCro SPhx
orientalis CBod
'Transformer' **new**
papillosa 'African Bride' CSpe CWCL SPhx
- 'Delft Blue' LCro SPhx
- 'Midnight' CSpe SPhx
sativa CBod

Nigritella see *Gymnadenia*

Niphidium (*Polypodiaceae*)

crassifolium EShb LEdu WCot

Nipponanthemum (*Asteraceae*)

§ ***nipponicum*** EBee ELon GBin NLar NSti SAko SPoG SRms XLum
- 'Hama-giku' NWad

Nitella (*Characeae*)

flexilis **new** LPfP

Noccaea see *Thlaspi*

Nolina (*Asparagaceae*)

§ ***hibernica*** EBee NPlm WPGP
'La Siberica' see *N. hibernica*
lindheimeriana WCot
longifolia NPlm
microcarpa XSen
nelsonii CBod CCht CDoC LPal LRHS NPlm SArc SPlb WPGP XSen XSte
parviflora XSen
texana WCot

Nomocharis (*Liliaceae*)

sp. LAma SDir
aperta CExl EBee EPot GGGa GKev NHpl WTyc
farreri EBee
mairei see *N. pardanthina*
meleagrina GEdr NHpl
§ ***pardanthina*** NHpl

Nonea (*Boraginaceae*)

lutea EPPr MMrt NSti

Nothaphoebe (*Lauraceae*)

cavaleriei CExl

Nothochelone see *Penstemon*

Nothofagus ✿ (*Nothofagaceae*)

§ ***alpina*** ELan NWea SCob WJur
antarctica CAco CMCN EBee ELan EPfP GKin LMaj LPal LPar MAsh MBlu MMuc MTrO NOra NOrn NWea SAko WMat
betuloides GBin IArd SAko SPlb WPGP
cunninghamii CBrP EPfP IArd IDee SAko SPlb
dombeyi ♀H5 CBrP EPfP IArd IDee MBlu SArc WPGP WSpi
fusca IDee SAko WPGP
menziesii WPGP
moorei WPGP
nervosa see *N. alpina*
obliqua GAbr IPap WPav
procera Oerst. see *N. alpina*

Notholaena see *Cheilanthes*

Notholirion (*Liliaceae*)

bulbuliferum EBee
campanulatum EBee GKev MNrw
macrophyllum CBor GArf GBin GKev
thomsonianum CBor GKev

Nothopanax see *Polyscias*

Nothoscordum (*Alliaceae*)

bivalve var. ***bivalve*** **new** CBor

	dialystemon	CBor EDAr EPot NHpl NRog WAbe
§	***hirtellum***	NRog
	montevidense	GKev WCot
	neriniflorum	see *Allium neriniflorum*
	ostenii	WCot

Notocactus see *Parodia*

	roseoluteus	see *Parodia mammulosa*

Nuphar (*Nymphaeaceae*)

	japonica	CToG LLWG
	lutea	CBen CHab LCro LLWG LOPS LPfP
	– subsp. ***advena***	LLWG
	pumila	CToG LLWG

Nuytsia (*Loranthaceae*)

	floribunda	SPlb

Nylandtia (*Polygalaceae*)

	spinosa	SPlb

Nymphaea ✿ (*Nymphaeaceae*)

	alba (H)	CBen CHab CPud CWat LCro LOPS LPfP MWts NBir SVic WCAu WMAq
	'Albatros' misapplied	see *N.* 'Hermine'
§	'Albatros' Latour-Marliac (H)	LLWG LPfP NPer WMAq
	'Albatross'	see *N.* 'Albatros' Latour-Marliac, *N.* 'Hermine'
*	'Albida'	CWat LLWG WMAq
	'Almost Black' (H)	CBen CPud EWat LCro LLWG LOPS LPfP
	'Amabilis' (H)	CBen EWat WMAq
	'Andreaa Berthold' (H)	LLWG
	'Andreana' (H)	EWat LLWG
	'Angelique' (H)	LLWG
	'Anna Epple' (H)	LLWG
	'Arc-en-ciel' (H)	CBen LLWG LPfP WMAq
	'Atropurpurea' (H)	CBen EWat LLWG NPer WMAq
	'Attorney Elrod' (H)	LLWG
	'Attraction' (H)	CBen CPud EWat LLWG LPfP MWts NPer SVic WMAq XLum
	'Aurora' (H)	CBen CPud LCro LLWG LOPS LPfP MWts SVic WMAq
	'Barbara Davies' (H)	LLWG
	'Barbara Dobbins' (H)	CBen EWat LCro LLWG LOPS LPfP
	'Bateau' (H)	LLWG
	'Bernice Ikins' (H)	LLWG
	'Betsy Sakata' (H)	LLWG
	'Black Cherry' (H)	LLWG
	'Black Princess' (H)	CBen CPud CWat EWat LLWG LPfP MWts
	'Blushing Bride' (H)	LLWG
	'Bua Rapee' (H)	LLWG
	'Burgundy Princess' (H)	CBen CWat EWat LLWG NPer
	candida (H)	CBen CPud MWts NPer WMAq
	'Candidissima' (H)	CBen
	'Carolina Sunset' (H)	LLWG
	'Caroliniana Nivea' (H)	CBen
	'Caroliniana Perfecta' (H)	CBen
	'Celebration' (H)	LLWG
	'Charlene Strawn' (H)	EWat LLWG WMAq
	'Charles de Meurville' (H)	CBen LCro LLWG LOPS LPfP NPer SVic WMAq
	'Chompoo Pairat' (H)	LLWG
	'Chrysantha' (H)	LLWG
	'Château le Rouge' (H)	CBen LLWG
	'Chubby' (H)	LLWG
	'Citrus Twist' (H)	LLWG
	'Cliff Tiffany' (H)	CBen LLWG
	'Clyde Ikins' (H)	EWat LLWG
	'Colonel A.J. Welch' (H)	CBen LPfP NPer WMAq
	'Colorado' (H)	CBen CWat EWat LLWG LPfP NPer
	'Colossea' (H)	CBen CPud NPer
	'Comanche' (H)	CBen LLWG LPfP NPer WMAq
	'Concordia' (H)	LLWG
	'Conqueror' (H)	CBen CWat LLWG LPfP NPer SVic
	'Cranberry Cup'	LLWG
	'Crazy Pom Pom' (H)	LLWG
	'Curly Purple' (H)	LLWG
	'Cynthia Ann' (H)	LLWG
§	'Darwin' (H)	CBen CWat LLWG LPfP MWts NPer WMAq
	'David' (H)	CBen EWat LLWG
	'Debbie June' (H)	LLWG
	'Denver' (H)	CPud EWat LLWG
	'Dwarf Beauty' (H)	LLWG
	'Ellisiana' (H)	CPud LLWG NPer
	'Erhard Van Oldehoff' (H)	LLWG
	'Escarboucle' (H) 🏆H5	CBen CPud CWat EWat LLWG NPer SVic WMAq
§	'Fabiola' (H)	LPfP NPer WMAq
	'Fairy Skirt' (H) **new**	LLWG
	'Fiesta' (H)	CBen
	'Fire Cracker' (H)	LLWG
	'Fire Crest' (H)	CBen CPud LLWG NPer SVic WMAq
	'Fireball' (H)	LLWG
	'Flore de Cologne' (H)	LLWG
	'Frezzby' (H)	LLWG
	'Fritz Junge' (H)	CBen
	'Froebelii' (H)	CBen CPud CWat EWat LLWG LPfP NPer WMAq
	'Frosted Pink' (H)	LLWG
	'Fuchsia Pom-pom' (H)	LLWG
	'Galatée' (H)	CBen
	'Georgia Peach' (H)	LLWG
	'Gladstoniana' (H) 🏆H5	CBen CPud CWat LPfP MWts NPer WMAq
	'Gloire du Temple-sur-Lot' (H)	CBen LLWG LPfP NPer WMAq
	'Gloriosa' (H)	CBen EWat LLWG MWts NPer
	'Gold Medal' (H)	CBen LLWG
	'Golden Goblet' (H)	LLWG
	'Golden Star' (H)	LLWG
	'Gonnère' (H) 🏆H5	CBen CPud CWat EWat LLWG LPfP MWts NPer WMAq
	'Graziella' (H)	WMAq
	'Gregg's Orange Sunset' (H)	LLWG
	'Guava Chiffron' (H)	LLWG
	'Gypsy' (H)	LLWG
	'Hal Miller' (H)	LLWG
	'Hassell' (H)	LLWG
	'Haunting Beauty' (H)	LLWG
	'Hawaiian Gold' (H)	LLWG
	'Hazorea Dagan White' (H)	LLWG
	'Heart Beat' (H)	LLWG
	'Helen Fowler' (H)	WMAq
	'Helen Hariot' (H)	LLWG
	× ***helvola***	see *N.* 'Pygmaea Helvola'
§	'Hermine' (H)	CBen NPer WMAq
	'Hidden Violet' (H)	LLWG
§	'Highlight' (H)	LLWG
	'Hilite'	see *N.* 'Highlight'
	'Hollandia' misapplied	see *N.* 'Darwin'
	'Honeycup' (H)	LLWG
	'Indiana' (H)	CBen LLWG NPer WMAq
	'Inner Light' (H)	EWat LLWG
	'Irene Heritage' (H)	CBen
	'J.C.N. Forestier' (H)	CBen
	'Jakkaphan' (H) **new**	LLWG
	'Jakkaphong' (H) **new**	LLWG
	'James Brydon' (H) 🏆H5	CBen CPud CWat EWat LLWG LPfP MWts NPer SVic WMAq
	'Jean de Lamarsalle' (H)	LLWG
§	'Joanne Pring' (H)	CBen

	'Joey Tomocik' (H)	CBen CWat EWat LLWG LPfP MWts WMAq
	'Kiss the Sky' (H)	LLWG
	'Lactea' (H)	CBen LLWG
	'Laydekeri Fulgens' (H)	CBen CPud EWat LLWG MWts WMAq
	'Laydekeri Lilacea' (H)	CBen LLWG LPfP WMAq
	'Laydekeri Purpurata' (H)	WMAq
	'Laydekeri Rosea' misapplied	see *N.* 'Laydekeri Rosea Prolifera'
§	'Laydekeri Rosea Prolifera' (H)	CBen EWat
	'Lemon Cup' (H)	LLWG
	'Lemon Drop' (H)	LLWG
	'Lemon Meringue' (H)	LLWG
	'Lemon Mist' (H)	LLWG LPfP
	'Lily Pons' (H)	CBen LLWG
	'Liou' (H)	CBen LLWG
	'Little Champion' (H)	LLWG
	'Little Sue' (H)	CPud LLWG
	'Lucida' (H)	LLWG WMAq
	'Lucky Red' (H)	LLWG
	'Madame Bory Latour-Marliac' (H)	CBen
	'Madame Wilfon Gonnère' (H)	CBen CWat EWat LLWG LPfP MWts NPer SVic WMAq
	'Manee Red' (H)	LLWG
	'Manee Siam' (H)	LLWG
	'Mangkala Ubol' (H)	CBen
	'Marliacea Albida' (H)	CBen CPud EWat LCro LLWG LOPS LPfP MWts NPer WMAq XLum
	'Marliacea Carnea' (H)	CBen CPud LCro LOPS LPfP MWts NPer WMAq
§	'Marliacea Chromatella' (H) 𝕐H5	CBen CPud CWat EWat LPfP SVic WMAq XLum
	'Marliacea Rosea' (H)	CBen LPfP WMAq XLum
	'Martha' (H)	EWat
	'Mary' (H)	LLWG
	'Masaniello' (H)	CBen LPfP WMAq
	'Maurice Laydeker' (H)	CBen LLWG
	'Maxima'	see *N.* 'Odorata Maxima'
	'Mayla' (H)	CBen CWat LLWG LPfP NPer
§	'Météor' (H)	CBen EWat WMAq
	mexicana (H)	CBen LLWG
	'Millennium Pink' (H)	CBen
	'Miss Siam' (H)	LLWG
	'Moon Dance' (H)	LLWG
	'Moorei' (H)	CBen WMAq
	'Mrs Richmond' misapplied	see *N.* 'Fabiola'
	'Mrs Richmond' Latour-Marliac (H)	CBen LPfP MWts
	'Munkala Ubon' (H)	LLWG
	'Myra' (H)	LLWG
	'Neptune' (H)	LLWG
	'Newchapel Beauty'	WMAq
	'Newton' (H)	CBen CWat LLWG WMAq
	'Nigel' (H)	LLWG
	'Norma Gedye' (H)	CBen WMAq
§	***odorata*** (H)	CBen LLWG WMAq
§	- var. ***minor*** (H)	CBen CPud WMAq
	- 'Pumila'	see *N. odorata* var. *minor*
	- f. ***rubra*** (H)	LPfP
	- subsp. ***tuberosa*** (H)	CBen
	'Odorata Alba'	see *N. odorata*
	'Odorata Juliana' (H)	CBen
§	'Odorata Maxima' (H)	WMAq
	'Odorata Sulphurea' (H)	LLWG LPfP
	'Odorata Sulphurea Grandiflora' (H)	LLWG
	'Odorata William B. Shaw'	see *N.* 'W.B. Shaw'
	'Ori Flame' (H)	LLWG
	'Ori Oruba' (H)	LLWG
	'Pam Bennett' (H)	CBen
	'Patio Joe' (H)	LLWG
	'Pattern Ruby' (H) **new**	LLWG
	'Paul Hariot' (H)	CPud EWat LLWG LPfP MWts NPer WMAq
	'Peace Lily' (H)	LLWG
	'Peach Glow' (H)	EWat LLWG
	'Peach Sunrise' (H)	LLWG
	'Peaches and Cream' (H)	LLWG
	'Perry's Baby Red' (H)	CBen CPud CWat EWat LLWG LPfP MWts NPer WMAq
	'Perry's Crinkled Pink' (H)	CBen
	'Perry's Deepest Red' (H)	LLWG
	'Perry's Double White' (H)	LLWG LPfP NPer
	'Perry's Double Yellow' (H)	LLWG
	'Perry's Dwarf Red' (H)	LLWG
	'Perry's Fire Opal' (H)	CPud EWat LLWG LPfP NPer
	'Perry's Orange Sunset' (H)	LLWG
	'Perry's Pink' (H)	WMAq
	'Perry's Pink Bicolor' (H)	CBen
	'Perry's Red Bicolor' (H)	CBen
	'Perry's Red Glow' (H)	LLWG
	'Perry's Red Wonder' (H)	CBen
	'Perry's Viviparous Pink' (H)	CBen
	'Perry's White Star' (H)	LLWG
	'Perry's Yellow Sensation'	see *N.* 'Yellow Sensation'
	'Peter Slocum' (H)	CBen
	'Phoebus' (H)	CBen
	'Pia Stella Berthold' (H)	LLWG
	'Picciola' (H)	LLWG
	'Piksy Skirt' (H) **new**	LLWG
	'Pink Beauty' (H)	LLWG
	'Pink Dawn' (H)	LLWG
	'Pink Grapefruit' (H)	LLWG
	'Pink Lemonade' (H)	LLWG
	'Pink Opal' (H)	CBen LLWG
	'Pink Peony' (H)	CWat LPfP
	'Pink Pom-pom' (H)	LLWG
	'Pink Pumpkin' (H)	LLWG
	'Pink Ribbon' (H)	LLWG
	'Pink Sensation' (H)	CBen CWat EWat LLWG NPer WMAq
	'Pink Silk' **new**	LLWG
	'Pink Sparkle' (H)	LLWG
	'Pink Sunrise' (H)	LLWG
	'Pink Tulip' (H)	LLWG
	'Pinwaree' (H)	LLWG
	'Pinwheel' (H) **new**	LLWG
	'Pöstlingberg' (H)	LLWG
	'Prakeisap' (H)	LLWG
	'Princess Elizabeth' (H)	LLWG
	'Purple Fantasy' (H)	LLWG
	'Purple Star' (H) **new**	LLWG
	'Pygmaea Alba'	see *N. tetragona*
§	'Pygmaea Helvola' (H) 𝕐H5	CBen CPud CWat EWat LCro LLWG LOPS LPfP MWts NPer SVic WMAq
	'Pygmaea Rubis' (H)	WMAq
	'Pygmaea Rubra' (H)	CPud CWat EWat LCro LLWG LOPS LPfP MWts NPer SVic WMAq
	'Queen of the Whites' (H)	CBen LLWG
	'Rattana Ubol' (H)	LLWG
	'Ray Davies' (H)	CBen LLWG
	'Razzberry' (H)	LLWG
	'Red Paradise' (H)	LLWG
	'Red Queen' (H)	LLWG
	'Red Spider' (H)	LLWG NPer SVic
	'Reflected Flame' (H)	LLWG
	'Rembrandt' misapplied	see *N.* 'Météor'
	'René Gérard' (H)	CBen CPud CWat LLWG LPfP MWts NPer WMAq
	'Rosanna Supreme' (H)	LLWG
	'Rose Arey' (H)	CBen CPud LCro LOPS LPfP NPer SVic WMAq

'Rose Magnolia' (H)	CWat
'Rosennymphe' (H)	CBen NPer WMAq
'Rosy Morn' (H)	CBen LLWG
'Ruby Star' (H)	LLWG
'Savanlamp' (H)	LLWG
'Seignoureti' (H)	LLWG
'Shady Lady' (H)	CPud LLWG
'Siam Angel' (H)	LLWG
'Siam Beauty' (H)	LLWG
'Siam Dahlia' (H) **new**	LLWG
'Siam Jasmine' (H)	LLWG
'Siam Marble' (H) **new**	LLWG
'Siam Purple 1' (H)	LLWG
'Siam Purple 2' (H)	LLWG
'Siam Rose' (H)	LLWG
'Siam Sunset' (H)	LLWG
'Sioux' (H)	CBen CPud LLWG LPfP NPer SVic WMAq
'Sirius' (H)	LLWG LPfP
'Snow Princess' (H)	CPud CWat EWat LPfP MWts
'Snowflake' (H)	LLWG
'Solfatare' (H)	EWat LLWG
'Splendida' (H)	WMAq
'Starbright' (H)	LLWG
'Steven Strawn' (H)	LLWG
'Strawberry Milkshake' (H)	LLWG
'Sunfire' (H)	LLWG
'Sunny Pink' (H)	CBen LLWG LPfP
'Sunrise' (H)	LCro LOPS LPfP
'Sunset Dawn' (H)	LLWG
'Superba' (H)	CBen
'Sweet Pea' (H)	LLWG
'Tangerine Pink' (H)	LLWG
'Tan-khwan' (H)	LLWG
§ ***tetragona*** (H)	EWat LCro LLWG LOPS LPfP NPer WMAq
- 'Alba'	see *N. tetragona*
- 'Johann Pring'	see *N.* 'Joanne Pring'
'Texas Dawn' (H)	CBen CWat LLWG WMAq
'Thomas O'Brian' (H)	LLWG
'Thongsup' (H)	LLWG
'Tony's Starlike'	LLWG
'Tuberosa Flavescens'	see *N.* 'Marliacea Chromatella'
'Tuberosa Richardsonii' (H)	CBen NPer
'Turtle Island Tropic Star' (H × T)	LLWG
'Turtle Island Violicious' (H × T)	LLWG
'Venusta' (H)	EWat
'Vésuve' (H)	CWat LLWG LPfP
'Virginalis' (H)	CBen CWat LLWG LPfP NPer WMAq
'Virginia' (H)	LLWG
§ 'W.B. Shaw' (H)	CBen CPud NPer
'Walter Pagels' (H)	CBen EWat LLWG WMAq
'Wanvisa' (H)	CBen CPud LCro LLWG LOPS LPfP
'Weymouth Red' (H)	CBen
'White 1000 Petals' (H)	LLWG
'White Star' (H)	LLWG
'White Sultan' (H)	LCro LLWG
'William Falconer' (H)	CBen LLWG NPer
'Wow' (H)	LLWG
'Yellow Princess' (H)	CWat EWat
'Yellow Queen' (H)	LLWG
§ 'Yellow Sensation' (H)	CBen LPfP
'Yellow Watermelon' (H)	LLWG
'Yul Ling' (H)	EWat LLWG

Nymphoides (*Menyanthaceae*)

peltata	CBen CHab CPud CWat EWat LCro LLWG LOPS LPfP NPer SVic WMAq WPnP XLum

Nyssa ✿ (*Nyssaceae*)

aquatica	MBlu SMad SSta
ogeche	CJun
shweliensis FMWJ 13122	WCru
sinensis	CBcs CEme CMCN CRos EGrI EHyd ELan EPfP LRHS MAsh MBlu MPkF NLar SPer WFar WPGP
- 'Inferno'	CPer CRos EPfP LRHS MTrO NWea SPoG WMat
- 'Jim Russell' ♀^{H5}	EBee LRHS WPGP
- 'Volcano'	LRHS
sylvatica	Widely available
- 'Autumn Cascades'	CJun EHyd EPfP LRHS MAsh MBlu
- var. ***biflora***	CMCN SSta
- 'Haymen's Red'	see *N. sylvatica* RED RAGE
- 'Isabel Grace'	CRos EHyd EPfP LRHS MAsh
- 'Jermyns Flame'	CRos EHyd EPfP LRHS MAsh NLar
- JOLLY ('Yiping') (v)	MPkF
- 'Lakeside Weeper'	CRos ELan LRHS MAsh
- 'Miss Scarlet' (f)	NLar WPGP
§ - RED RAGE ('Haymanred')	ELan EPfP LMil LRHS MAsh MBlu MPkF
- 'Sheffield Park'	MAsh SLim
§ - 'Valley Scorcher'	EHyd LRHS MAsh NLar
- 'Wildfire'	LRHS NLar
- 'Windsor'	see *N. sylvatica* 'Valley Scorcher'
- 'Wisley Bonfire' (m) ♀^{H6}	CBcs CJun CRos EBee EHyd ELan EPfP LMil LRHS MAsh MTrO NLar NRHS SPoG SSta WMat WPGP

O

Oakesiella see *Uvularia*

Ochagavia (*Bromeliaceae*)

carnea	NCft
elegans	WCot
§ ***litoralis***	EAri SArc SMad
* ***rosea***	SPlb

Ochna (*Ochnaceae*)

serrulata	CCCN

Ocimum (*Lamiaceae*)

'African Blue'	CBod CSpe ENfk EWhm GPoy LCro LOPS MBros MHer MHol SCoo SPoG SRms
§ × ***africanum***	ENfk MHoo MNHC SCoo SPoG
- 'Lesbos'	MHer
- 'Lime'	ENfk MHoo MNHC
§ - 'Perpetuo'^{PBR} (v)	ENfk
- PESTO PERPETUO	see *O.* × *africanum* 'Perpetuo'
- 'Siam Queen'	CBod MHer MHoo SRms
basilicum	EWhm GPoy LCro MHoo MPri SCoo SPoG SRms
- 'Anise'	see *O. basilicum* 'Horapha'
- 'Ararat'	SRms
- 'Aristotle'	MHer SRms
- 'Aroma 2' ♀^{H1c}	LCro LOPS MCtn
- 'Blue Spice'	SEdi
I - 'British Basil'	MBros SRms
- ***camphorata***	see *O. kilimandscharicum*
- 'Christmas'	SEdi SRms
- 'Cinnamon'	CBod ENfk MNHC SEdi SRms WJek
- 'Crimson King'^{PBR}	SRms
- 'Dark Opal'	ENfk SEdi SRms
- 'Genovese'	CLau MHer MNHC SEdi
- 'Glycyrrhiza'	see *O. basilicum* 'Horapha'

- 'Green Globe'	SRms
- 'Green Ruffles'	SCoo SPoG SRms
- 'Holy'	see *O. tenuiflorum*
- 'Holy Tulsi'	see *O. tenuiflorum*
§ - 'Horapha'	ENfk LCro MNHC SCoo SEdi SPoG WJek
* - 'Horapha Nanum'	ENfk SRms
- 'Lemonade' ♀H1c	SRms
- lettuce leaf	SEdi
- 'Magic Mountain'	SPoG
- 'Magic White'	SPoG
- 'Marseillais' **new**	CBod
- 'Mrs Burns' Lemon' ♀H1c	CBod EKin MCtn SRms WJek
- 'Napoletano'	ENfk LCro LOPS SRms
- 'Pluto' ♀H1c	LCro LOPS
- 'Puck'	SRms
- var. ***purpurascens***	MHoo
- - 'Purple Ruffles'	LCro LOPS SRms
- - 'Red Rubin'	MHer NRHS SRms WJek
- var. ***purpurascens*** × ***kilimandscharicum***	CSpe GPoy WJek
- 'Sweet Genovese'	CBod SVic
- 'Thai'	see *O. basilicum* 'Horapha'
× ***citriodorum***	see *O.* × *africanum*
gratissimum	SEdi
§ ***kilimandscharicum***	CBod CLau GPoy MHoo
minimum	ENfk LCro LRHS MHoo MNHC SRms
sanctum	see *O. tenuiflorum*
'Spice'	ENfk
§ ***tenuiflorum***	GPoy MHoo MNHC SPre SVic WJek

Odontonema (*Acanthaceae*)

schomburgkianum	CCCN
tubaeforme	CCCN

Oemleria (*Rosaceae*)

cerasiformis	CBcs CJun CTri ELan ELon EPfP EWes IDee LEdu MGil MMuc WBor WCot WGwG

Oenanthe (*Apiaceae*)

fistulosa	LLWG
javanica	LEdu
- 'Flamingo' (v)	CBen CToG CWat EBee ELan LEdu LLWG LPfP MWts SRms WMAq XLum
pimpinelloides	CHab SPhx

Oenothera ✿ (*Onagraceae*)

§ ***acaulis***	CSpe MNrw WCot
§ - 'Aurea'	XLum
- 'Lutea'	see *O. acaulis* 'Aurea'
'Apricot Delight'	MACG SGbt
§ ***biennis***	CBod ELan ENfk GAbr GJos GPoy GQue LCro LOPS MBow MHer MHoo MNHC NBro SPhx SRms WBrk WHer WSFF
'Blood Orange'	GEdr GJos
caespitosa	GArf
childsii	see *O. speciosa*
cinaeus	see *O. fruticosa* subsp. *glauca*
'Cold Crick'	LBar
'Crown Imperial'	CChe CMac MACG MArl NHol
§ ***elata*** subsp. ***hookeri***	EWes GJos
erythrosepala	see *O. glazioviana*
§ ***filiformis*** (G)	SPhx
'Flamingo White' (G)	MBNS SEdd SGBe
§ ***fruticosa***	NLar SPlb
- 'African Sun'	LBar MMrt SGBe SHar
- 'Camel' (v)	LDai XLum
- FIREWORKS	see *O. fruticosa* 'Fyrverkeri'
§ - 'Fyrverkeri'	CBcs EHyd GJos GMaP GMcL LRHS MRav NBPC NRHS SCob SPer SWvt WCAu XLum
§ - subsp. ***glauca***	CAby CElw MHer NLar SMrm SRms
- - 'Erica Robin' (v)	CChe CDor ECtt GBin MNrw MRav NGdn SCob SMad SWvt WCav WCot WHoo
- - 'Longest Day'	EHeP MBrN
- - SOLSTICE	see *O. fruticosa* subsp. *glauca* 'Sonnenwende'
§ - - 'Sonnenwende'	CElw MACG MMrt NEoE NLar XLum
- HIGHLIGHT	see *O. fruticosa* 'Hoheslicht'
§ - 'Hoheslicht'	EBee NLar
- 'Lady Brookeborough'	MRav
- 'Yellow River'	CElw EBee LBar
glabra Miller	see *O. biennis*
glabra misapplied	ECha
§ ***glazioviana***	NBir
hookeri	see *O. elata* subsp. *hookeri*
ICE COOL ROSY ('Harcool') (G)	EBee LBar SHar
kunthiana	EBou ECha GJos
- 'Glowing Magenta'	LBar SPoG
lamarckiana	see *O. glazioviana*
'Lemon Sunset'	ECha EGrI
LILLIPOP PINK ('Redgapi'PBR) (G)	CAby CWCL EPfP MBrN NLar SGBe SMrm SPoG
* 'Lime Green' (G)	LRHS
§ ***lindheimeri*** (G) ♀H4	CBar CBcs CKel CSBt CSpe EBee ECha EHyd ELan EPau EPfP EWoo LCro LOPS LRHS MBow MGos MHer NRHS SBut SDix SPer SPoG SRot SWvt WCAu WHoo XLum XSen
- Belleza Series (G)	CKel EHyd EPfP LRHS NRHS SSha
- - BELLEZA DARK PINK ('Kleau04263') (G)	MPri
- 'Blaze'PBR (G)	WCot
- CHERRY BRANDY ('Gauchebra'PBR) (G)	EBee ECtt ELan EPfP LRHS MNrw SWvt WHlf
- 'Chiffon' (G)	SHar
- compact pink-flowered (G)	SRot XLum
- - red-flowered (G)	XSen
- 'Cool Breeze' (G)	CDor EAJP EWTr LSun MAvo MNrw SPhx WHoo
- 'Corrie's Gold' (G/v)	EBee ECha ECtt EHyd ELan EPfP LBar LRHS MHer NRHS
- 'Crimson Butterflies'PBR (G)	CWGN ECtt EHyd ELan EPfP LRHS
- 'Dwarf White' (G)	LRHS
- 'Elurra' (G)	CSpe LRHS
- 'Elurra White' (G)	LRHS
- FREEFOLK ROSY ('Harrfolk') (G/v)	CAby CDor CRos ECtt EHyd EPfP LCro LOPS LRHS LSou MPri MSCN NRHS SGBe SHar SIvy SMrm XLum
- 'Gambit Rose Bicolor' (G)	EAJP
- 'Gambit White' (G)	MNHC
- GAUDI PINK ('Florgaucompi'PBR) (G)	CRos EHyd EPfP LRHS NRHS
- GAUDI RED ('Florgaured') (G)	CRos EHyd EPfP LBar LRHS NRHS
- GAUDI ROSE ('Florgaucomro'PBR) (G)	EHyd EPfP LRHS NRHS SCob
- (Geyser Series) GEYSER PINK ('Gaudros') (G)	EBee EPfP LSou
- - GEYSER WHITE ('Gaudwwhi'PBR) (G)	EBee EPfP EWTr LSou
- 'Graceful Light Pink' (Graceful Series) (G) **new**	LBar
- 'Jo Adela' (G/v)	ECha

	– KARALEE PETITE ('Gauka') (G)	CWCL EPfP SEle
	– KARALEE WHITE ('Nugauwhite'[PBR]) (G)	CAby CBod CKel CWnw EHyd ELan EPfP EWoo LRHS NRHS SCoo SEdd SPoG WTor
	– 'My Melody'[PBR] (G/v)	CWCL
	– PAPILLON ('Nugaupapil'[PBR]) (G)	CRos CWCL CWnw EHyd LRHS MPri NRHS SEdd SPoG
	– 'Passionate Blush'[PBR] (G)	CBcs CChe CWCL ECtt EHyd EPfP LBar LRHS MGos NRHS SCoo SGBe SOrN SPoG SRms
	– 'Passionate Rainbow'[PBR] (G/v)	CWCL EHyd EPfP LRHS NRHS SCob SCoo SGBe SPeP SRms
	– 'Pink Dwarf' (G)	EBee
	– PINK FOUNTAIN ('Walgaupf') (G)	EHyd LRHS NRHS
	– 'Pink Gin' (G)	SPoG
	– ROSYJANE ('Harrosy'[PBR]) (G)	Widely available
	– RUBY RUBY ('Harruby'[PBR]) (G)	LBar SHar
	– short (G)	XLum
	– 'Siskiyou Pink' (G)	Widely available
	– SNOW FOUNTAIN ('Walsnofou') (G)	EHyd EPfP LRHS MNrw NRHS SMrm WNPC
	– SNOWBIRD ('Flogausnb'[PBR]) (G)	EWTr MNrw
	– 'Sparkle White' (G)	CBod EAJP EBee EHyd ELon EPfP LRHS LSou LSun MACG MDon NWsh SBea SSha WFar XSen
	– STRATOSPHERE PINK PICOTEE	see *O. lindheimeri* GAUDI PINK
	– 'Summer Breeze' (G)	CDor EAJP EHyd EPPr EPfP GPSL LRHS NGBl NRHS SPhx WHil XSen
	– 'Summer Emotions' (G)	LSou
	– 'The Bride' (G)	CBcs CBod CKel CTri CWCL EBee EHyd ELan EPfP GQue LBar LRHS LSRN LShi LSto MACG MPie MRav NRHS SAdn SGbt SMrm SOrN SWvt WCav WGwG WJam
	– 'Val's Pink' (G)	WAvo
	– 'Vanilla' (G)	LSou
I	– 'Variegata' (G/v)	CWCL SRms
	– 'Whirling Butterflies' (G)	CBcs CKel CKno CSpe CWCL ECtt ELan EPfP EWoo LBuc LCro LOPS LRHS MNrw SCob SCoo SGBe SMrm SOrN SPer SPhx SPoG SSha SWvt WCAu WTor
	– 'Whiskers Deep Rose' (G)	MDon WFar
	– 'White Dove' (G)	LBar WHlf
	– 'White Heron' (G)	MNrw
	linearis	see *O. fruticosa*
§	***macrocarpa*** ♀H5	CAby CBod CHab CSBt EBee EBou ECha EHeP EHyd ELan EPfP EShb GJos GMcL LBar LRHS MBel MHer SEND SPer SPlb SPoG SRms SVic SWvt WCAu XLum XSen
	– subsp. ***fremontii*** 'Silver Wings'	ELan GEdr
	– subsp. ***incana***	WHoo
	missouriensis	see *O. macrocarpa*
	oakesiana	SPhx
	odorata misapplied	see *O. stricta*
	odorata Hook. & Arn.	see *O. biennis*
	odorata Jacquin	XLum
	– cream-flowered	CSpe
	organensis	EBee MNrw
	pallida 'Innocence'	LCro
§	***perennis***	MPie SRms XLum
	pilosella 'Mella Yella'	EBee
	– 'Yella Fella'	ELan NWad
	pumila	see *O. perennis*
	rosea	XLum
	ROSY SHIMMERS ('Harshim') (G)	EWTr LBar SHar
§	***sinuosa*** (G)	CAby SHar WMal
§	***speciosa***	SRms XLum
*	– 'Alba'	CBod EBee ELon SCob
	– var. ***childsii***	see *O. speciosa*
	– 'Pink Petticoats'	ECha GJos LSun NPer SBut
	– 'Rosea'	SPlb
	– 'Siskiyou'	CAby CBcs CBod EBee ECha ECtt EHyd ELan EPfP LBar LEdu LRHS MAvo MNrw NRHS SCob SCoo SGBe SMad SPer SPoG SSut WGwG WMal WWke XLum
	– TWILIGHT ('Turner01'[PBR]) (v)	EBee EHyd ELan EPfP LRHS LSou NEoE NHol NLar SHar WNPC
	– 'Woodside White'	SMrm
§	***stricta***	EPPr MNrw
	– 'Sulphurea'	CBWd CDor CFis EAJP EHyd ELan EPPr EPfP LCro LRHS NPer SPhx
§	***suffrutescens*** (G) **new**	SBrt
	'Summer Sun'	EHyd GMcL LBar LRHS MPie NRHS SGbt WCAu
	'Sunny Delight'	CBod
	taraxacifolia	see *O. acaulis*
	tetragona	see *O. fruticosa* subsp. *glauca*
	– var. ***fraseri***	see *O. fruticosa* subsp. *glauca*
	versicolor	CKel LDai
	– 'Sunset Boulevard'	CSpe CWal GJos LDai XLum

Olea (*Oleaceae*)

	europaea (F)	Widely available
	– 'Arbequina' (F)	EOli
§	– 'Cipressino' (F)	IDee LPal
	– 'El Greco' (F)	CBcs
	– 'Frantoio' (F)	EOli
	– 'Leccino' (F)	LMaj SWeb
	– 'Picual' (F)	EOli
	'Pyramidalis'	see *O. europaea* 'Cipressino'

Olearia ✿ (*Asteraceae*)

	algida	GBin
	arborescens 'Moondance' (v)	CBcs CWnw LRHS SGBe
	argophylla	CExl
	avicenniifolia	CMac CTrC
§	***cheesemanii***	CExl CTrC GMcL IDee NLar SVen
	erubescens × ***ilicifolia***	SVen
	fragrantissima	GBin
	gunniana	see *O. phlogopappa*
	× ***haastii***	Widely available
	– FAIRLIE FRAGRANT ('Hutfair')	GBin
	– 'McKenzie'	ELon
§	'Henry Travers'	CCCN CExl EPfP WPGP
	ilicifolia	EPfP WPGP
	insignis	see *Pachystegia insignis*
	lacunosa	IDee WPGP
	macrodonta ♀H4	Widely available
	– 'Major'	CCCN CTrC EBee LSto SCob
	– 'Minor'	CCCN CDoC CKel CMac CTrC EBee ELan EPfP SPlb SRms WPGP WSpi
	× ***mollis*** (Kirk) Cockayne	CMac
	– 'Zennorensis' ♀H4	CCCN EBee IDee SEdd
	nummularifolia	CBcs CCCN CDoC CKel CTrC CTri ELan EPfP GBin LRHS NLar SEND SPer SVen SWvt
	odorata	SSha
	× ***oleifolia*** 'Waikariensis'	CCCN EHyd SEND
	paniculata	CCCN CCoa CDoC CTri EHyd EPfP LRHS SEND SEdd SRms SVen

§	***phlogopappa***	CTri SVen
	- 'Comber's Blue'	CBcs CCCN CKel EHyd ELan EPfP LRHS SAko SPer
§	- 'Comber's Pink'	CBcs CCCN CExl CKel ELan EPfP EWld LRHS NPer SAko SEle SGBe SNig SPer SPoG
	- 'Rosea'	see *O. phlogopappa* 'Comber's Pink'
I	- var. ***subrepanda*** (DC.) J.H.Willis	CTrC
	ramulosa	CCCN CSde
	- 'Blue Stars'	CMac SRms
	rani misapplied	see *O. cheesemanii*
	× ***scilloniensis*** misapplied	see *O. stellulata* DC.
	× ***scilloniensis*** ambig.	CBcs CBod CCoa CDoC CKel CTrC EWld GMcL LRHS NBwr SGBe SPoG WKif WLov
	× ***scilloniensis*** Dorrien-Smith 🏆H4	CCCN
	- 'Master Michael' 🏆H4	CBcs CCCN CTri EHyd ELon EPfP EWld LRHS SEdd SGBe SPer SPoG WLov
	semidentata misapplied	see *O.* 'Henry Travers'
	solandri	CBod CCCN CCht CCoa CMac CTrC EPPr NLar SDix SEND
	- 'Aurea'	CBcs
	'Stardust'	SPlb SVen
	stellulata misapplied	see *O. phlogopappa*
§	***stellulata*** DC.	CMac CSBt EPfP SEdd SPer
	- 'Michael's Pride'	CExl
	traversii	CBcs CBod CCCN CCht CCoa CDoC CSBt CTrC CTsd EHyd EPfP LRHS SArc SEND SRms WHer
	- 'Compacta'	CCCN CTrC
	- dwarf	CBod
	- 'Tweedledee' (v)	SEND
	- 'Tweedledum' (v)	CBcs CBod CCCN CCoa
	virgata	CCCN IDee SSha
	- var. ***laxiflora***	WHer
	- var. ***lineata***	CCoa MMuc NLar SEND WHer
	- - 'Dartonii'	CBcs CBod GBin NLar SPlb SSta SVen

Oligoneuron see *Solidago*

Oligostachyum (*Poaceae*)

	lubricum	see *Semiarundinaria lubrica*
§	***oedogonatum***	MWht

olive see *Olea europaea*

Olsynium (*Iridaceae*)

	biflorum	GEdr
§	***douglasii*** 🏆H5	CBor CBro EBee GArf GEdr NBwr NHar NHpl NRya NSla
	- 'Album'	CBor EBee EPot EWes MNrw NHar NRya NSla WFar
	- var. ***inflatum***	EWes
§	***junceum***	CBor EDAr SPlb WKif

Omphalodes ✿ (*Boraginaceae*)

	'Blue Eyes'	NLar WCot
	cappadocica 🏆H5	CDor CMac EPfP EPot EWld GKev LEdu LRHS MRav NBro NPer NSla SRms WMal WPGP
	- 'Alba'	SPoG
	- 'All Summer Blues'	CSpe LBar NLar
	- 'Cherry Ingram' 🏆H5	Widely available
	- 'Lilac Mist'	EBee SRms SWvt
	- 'Starry Eyes'	Widely available
	kuzinskyanae	MAsh
§	***linifolia*** 🏆H3	CSpe ELan LCro LOPS MCot SPhx
	- ***alba***	see *O. linifolia*
	nitida	EWes EWld MMuc MNrw NQui WMal
	verna	Widely available
	- 'Alba'	Widely available
	- 'Elfenauge'	EBee EPPr GMaP NBir NLar WCot
I	- 'Grandiflora'	WCot

Omphalogramma (*Primulaceae*)

delavayi	GEdr
tibeticum	GKev

Oncostema see *Scilla*

onion see *Allium cepa*; also AGM Vegetables Section

Onixotis (*Colchicaceae*)

stricta	see *Wurmbea stricta*

Onobrychis (*Fabaceae*)

viciifolia	NGrd SPhx

Onoclea (*Onocleaceae*)

	sensibilis 🏆H6	Widely available
	- copper-leaved	EBee EPfP EWes WPGP
	- var. ***interrupta***	LEdu WPGP
*	- var. ***minima***	LEdu WPGP
	- 'Rotstiel'	EBee

Ononis (*Fabaceae*)

repens	NAts
spinosa	CDor GEdr MHer WSpi

Onopordum (*Asteraceae*)

	acanthium	CDor CRos CTtf EBee ECha EHyd ELan ENfk EPfP GAbr GGro GPoy LRHS LSun NGBl NRHS SCob SEND SHar SPhx SPtp WSpi
	arabicum	see *O. nervosum*
§	***nervosum*** 🏆H7	CSpe

Onosma (*Boraginaceae*)

alborosea	ECha ECre ELan GKev SEND WKif
conferta W&O 208636	GGro
nana	EDAr EPot WAbe
rigida	GKev SPhx
taurica 🏆H4	EDAr

Onychium (*Pteridaceae*)

contiguum	LEdu WCot
japonicum	CExl CLAP CRos EFer EHyd LEdu LRHS MRav NRHS SPlb WAbe WCot
- 'Dali'	CLAP WSHC

Operculicarya (*Anacardiaceae*)

decaryi new	SPlb

Ophiopogon ✿ (*Asparagaceae*)

	BWJ 8244 from Vietnam	WCru
	NJM 11.018	WPGP
	'Black Dragon'	see *O. planiscapus* 'Kokuryū'
	bodinieri	EShb EWes LEdu SEND
	- B&L 12505	EBee EPPr
	caulescens B&SWJ 8230	WCru
	- B&SWJ 11813	WCru
	aff. ***caulescens*** B&SWJ 11287	WCru
	- HWJ 590	WCru
	chingii	EBee EPPr EPfP EWes LEdu NLar WCot
*	- 'Crispum'	EBee ESwi
	clavatus KWJ 12267	WCru
	formosanus B&SWJ 3659	ESwi WCru
	'Gin-ryu'	see *Liriope spicata* 'Gin-ryu'

	graminifolius	see *Liriope muscari*
	'Hosoba Kokuryu'	CBod EShb GGro LRHS MAsh MPie MPkF NEoE XSte
	intermedius	CSpe EPPr EShb ESwi LPla WCot
	- GWJ 9387	WCru
§	- 'Argenteomarginatus' (v)	EWes
	- 'Variegatus'	see *O. intermedius* 'Argenteomarginatus'
§	***jaburan***	CMac EBee LEdu
	- 'Variegatus'	see *O. jaburan* 'Vittatus'
§	- 'Vittatus' (v)	EBee EWes LEdu WCot
	japonicus	CMac EBee EShb LEdu LPal SCob XLum
	- B&SWJ 1871	ESwi WCru
	- 'Albus'	EPri
	- 'Comet' (v)	EPPr
	- 'Compactus'	WPGP
	- 'Gyoku-Ryu'	EBee
	- 'Kigimafukiduma'	CExl CMac MRav NGdn
	- 'Kyoto'	ESwi
	- 'Lengteng Giant'	LEdu
	- 'Minor'	CBod CKel CKno EBee ELon EPPr GMaP LPal LRHS NLar NWsh SCob WAbe WLea WPGP XLum
	- 'Nanus'	CBod CKel
	- 'Nanus Variegatus' (v)	EBee ESwi
	- 'Nippon'	EPPr NGdn
	- 'Silver Dragon' (v)	EMor EPPr
	- 'Tama-ryu'	WAbe
	- 'Tama-ryu Number Two'	ESwi
*	- 'Variegatus' (v)	CDTJ CMac CPla SRms
	aff. ***latifolius*** KWJ 12031	WCru
	longifolius FMWJ 13278	WCru
	malcolmsonii B&SWJ 7271	WCru
	megalanthus FMWJ 13118	WCru
	parviflorus GWJ 9387	WCru
	- HWJK 2093	WCru
	planiscapus	CCBP CExl CKno CSde CSpe ECha EGrI EPPr GArf NBro NWsh SPtp
*	- 'Albovariegatus' (v)	WFar
	- BLACK BEARD ('Yapard'PBR)	CBod CKno EMor MAsh NBir NRHS SCob SHar SPoG WFar
	- 'Black Needle'	EBee
	- 'Black Smaragd'	EBee
	- green-leaved **new**	SSha
	- 'Kansu'	ESwi
§	- 'Kokuryū' 🏆H5	Widely available
	- f. ***leucanthus***	CDor EPPr WCot
	- 'Little Tabby' (v)	CBen CMil EBee EBlo EShb ESwi MAsh WCot WHoo WSHC
	- 'Nigrescens'	see *O. planiscapus* 'Kokuryū'
	scaber B&SWJ 1842	ESwi WCru
	- B&SWJ 3655	EPPr WCru
	'Sparkler' **new**	ESwi
	'Spring Gold'	EShb ESwi LEdu

Ophrys (*Orchidaceae*)

apifera	CHab

Oplopanax (*Araliaceae*)

horridus	GGro
- B&SWJ 9551	WCru
japonicus	WCru

Opopanax (*Apiaceae*)

chironium	SPhx
- PAB 845	LEdu WPGP
- PAB 872	WPGP
hispidus	SPhx WCot

Opuntia (*Cactaceae*)

	aciculata **new**	NPlm
	angustata	see *O. phaeacantha*
	articulata	see *Tephrocactus articulatus*
	basilaris	SPlb
	brasiliensis	see *Brasiliopuntia brasiliensis*
	camanchica	see *O. phaeacantha*
*	***camptotricha*** **new**	NPlm
	cantabrigiensis	EAri
	compressa	see *O. humifusa*
	cymochila	see *O. tortispina*
	darwinii	see *Maihueniopsis darwinii*
	elata	SChr
§	***engelmannii***	EAri SChr
	erinacea var. ***utahensis***	see *O. polyacantha* var. *erinacea*
§	***ficus-indica***	EAri SPlb WKor
	- 'Dar 1-27-24 Orange' (F) **new**	EAri
	fragilis	EAri SPlb XSen
	fulgida	see *Cylindropuntia fulgida*
	galapageia **new**	SPlb
§	***humifusa***	CDTJ EAri SChr WKor XLum XSen
*	- subsp. ***littoica***	SPlb
	inermis	see *O. stricta*
	invicta	see *Corynopuntia invicta*
	joconostle	see *O. ficus-indica*
	leucotricha **new**	NCft NPlm
	lindheimeri	see *O. engelmannii*
	linguiformis	see *O. engelmannii*
	littoralis **new**	SEND
	mackensenii	see *O. macrorhiza*
	macrocentra	EAri NPlm
§	***macrorhiza***	EAri
	microdasys 🏆H2	CBen EAri NMen WHlf
§	- 'Albata' 🏆H2 **new**	SPlb
	- 'Albispina'	EAri NPlm
	- 'Angel's Wings'	see *O. microdasys* 'Albata'
	- 'La Vila' **new**	NPlm
	- var. ***pallida*** **new**	NPlm
	- - f. ***cristata*** **new**	NPlm
	molinensis	see *Tephrocactus molinensis*
	monacantha	EAri SPlb
§	***phaeacantha***	SChr
	- NNS 99-264	WCot
	- var. ***major*** NNS 95-285	WCot
	pollardii	see *O. humifusa*
	polyacantha	EAri SChr SEND SPlb
	- 'Carmin'	XSen
§	- var. ***erinacea***	SChr WCot
§	- var. ***hystricina***	NPlm
	pycnantha **new**	EAri
	rhodantha	see *O. polyacantha* var. *hystricina*
	robusta	EAri NPlm
	robusta × ***scheeri*** **new**	SChr
	rufida **new**	EAri
	salmiana	SEND
	scheeri	SChr
	'Semi Inermis' **new**	NPlm
	sphaerica	see *Cumulopuntia sphaerica*
	spinosior	see *Cylindropuntia spinosior*
§	***stricta***	NPlm
	syringacantha	see *Tephrocactus articulatus*
	tardospina	see *O. engelmannii*
	'Titania' **new**	NPlm
§	***tortispina***	EAri
	verschaffeltii	see *Austrocylindropuntia verschaffeltii*

orange, sour or Seville see *Citrus* × *aurantium* Sour Orange Group

orange, sweet see *Citrus* × *aurantium* Sweet Orange Group

Orbea (*Apocynaceae*)

§	***variegata*** 🏆H2	CBen EWoo

Orbexilum (*Fabaceae*)

pedunculatum var. ***psoralioides***	SPhx

Orchis (*Orchidaceae*)

foliosa	see *Dactylorhiza foliosa*
fuchsii	see *Dactylorhiza fuchsii*
laxiflora	see *Anacamptis laxiflora*
maculata	see *Dactylorhiza maculata*
maderensis	see *Dactylorhiza foliosa*
majalis	see *Dactylorhiza majalis*
§ ***mascula***	LAma NLAp WHer
militaris	LAma NLAp
morio	see *Anacamptis morio*

oregano see *Origanum vulgare*

Oreocereus (*Cactaceae*)

leucotrichus new	NPlm
trollii ♀^{H2} new	NMen

Oreocharis (*Gesneriaceae*)

aurea B&SWJ 11718	WCru
§ 'Calliantha'	NHar
§ ***convexa*** B&SWJ 6624	WCru
- B&SWJ 7182	WCru

Oreopanax ✿ (*Araliaceae*)

bogotensis B&SWJ 14900 new	WCru
cecropifolius B&SWJ 14761	WCru
dactylifolius	WCot
echinops B&SWJ 10302 new	WCru
floribundus	see *O. incisus*
hypargyreus B&SWJ 14870	WCru
§ ***incisus*** B&SWJ 10669	WCru
mutisianus B&SWJ 14912	WCru
sectifolius B&SWJ 14805	WCru
xalapensis B&SWJ 10444	WCru

Oreostemma (*Compositae*)

§ ***alpigenum***	GEdr NWad

Oresitrophe (*Saxifragaceae*)

rupifraga	CTtf GEdr LEdu WCot

Origanum ✿ (*Lamiaceae*)

from Kalamata, Greece	SEND
amanum ♀^{H4}	EWes NBir NSla WAbe
- var. ***album***	WAbe
'Amethyst Falls'	ECtt LCro SPeP XSte
'Barbara Tingey'	ELan EWes SRms WIce
BELLISSIMO	see *O.* 'Solferino'
'Bristol Cross'	CAby EBee ECha ECtt EPot MHer SBut SMHy WFar WGoo WMal WTor
'Buckland'	WSHC
caespitosum	see *O. vulgare* 'Nanum'
§ ***calcaratum***	WMal
creticum	see *O. vulgare* subsp. *hirtum*
dictamnus	EPot GPoy MHer MHoo SPlb WAbe WJek
'Dingle Fairy'	EBee ECha ECtt EWTr EWes GJos MCot MHer NBir SCoo SGro SPoG SWvt WIce WSpi XSen
'Emma Stanley'	EPot WAbe WMal
'Frank Tingey'	ELan
'French'	CLau SRms WJek
'Gold Splash'	CBod MHoo
heracleoticum L.	see *O. vulgare* subsp. *hirtum*
'Hot and Spicy'	CLau ENfk EWhm MHoo SPhx SRms WFar WJek XSen
'Jekka's Beauty'	WJek
'Kent Beauty' ♀^{H4}	Widely available
laevigatum ♀^{H6}	EWhm NBro NPer WCot WKif WSHC XSen
- 'Dingle'	NLar
- 'Herrenhausen' ♀^{H6}	Widely available
- 'Hopleys' ♀^{H6}	CBod CCBP CDor CRos CTri EBee ECha EHyd EPfP LEdu LRHS MBow MCot MHer MHol MHoo MRav NBir NDov NLar NRHS SCob SEND SPer SPhx SPoG WSHC XSen
- 'Purple Charm'	SRms
majorana	CBod CHab ENfk GQue MHer MHoo MNHC SRms SVic WJek
I - 'Aureum'	GKev
- Italian	SEdi
- var. ***tenuifolium***	WJek
× ***majoricum***	WJek
'Marchants Seedling'	SMHy
'Norton Gold'	ECtt NPer
'Nymphenburg'	XSen
onites	CBod CCBP CHby CLau CTsd EBou ENfk GQue LEdu MHer MHoo MNHC SPlb SRms
- 'Limelight'	NWad
'Pilgrim'	WCAu XSen
'Rosenkuppel' ♀^{H7}	CAby CBWd CBar CDor CKel EBee ECha ECtt EPPr EWhm GQue LCro LOPS LRHS MHer MHol MHoo NDov SCob SMHy SPhx SPlb SRms SWvt WCAu XSen
'Rotkugel'	WCFE
rotundifolium ♀^{H4}	LEdu MHer MHoo NBir
- 'Jan's Pink'	ECha
scabrum subsp. ***pulchrum*** 'Newleaze'	SGro
§ 'Solferino'^{PBR}	WNPC
syriacum	WJek
'Teddy'	EBee
tournefortii	see *O. calcaratum*
vulgare	Widely available
- 'Acorn Bank'	EBou ECtt ENfk EWes EWhm LEdu MHer MHoo MNHC SPoG SRms WFar WJek
- 'Aureum' ♀^{H6}	Widely available
- 'Aureum Crispum'	ECha ENfk GBin GQue MHoo NBid SRms WFar
- 'Compactum'	CBar CBod CCBP CKel CLau EBee EBou ECha ECtt ENfk EWhm GBin GPoy LEdu MHer MHoo MNHC NBir NPol NRHS NSla SPlb SRms WJek XLum
- 'Corinne Tremaine' (v)	WHer
- 'Country Cream' (v)	Widely available
- 'Curly Gold'	CLau CTsd MBow
- GENTLE BREEZE ('All120506'^{PBR})	LPla
§ - 'Gold Tip' (v)	CBod EBou ENfk EWhm GJos MHer MHoo MNHC SCob SPlb SRms WFar WHer
- 'Golden Shine'	EWes EWhm MHoo SEdi
- 'Greensleeves'	WFar
- 'Himal'	GPoy
§ - subsp. ***hirtum***	CHby EBou GPoy LCro LOPS MHoo SPlb XSen
- - 'Greek'	CArg CBod CCBP CLau ECul ENfk EWhm MHer MNHC SEdi SRms SVic WJek
§ - 'Nanum'	SRms WJek
- 'Pink Mist'	MNrw NWad SRms WHoo

- 'Pink Thumbles'	ECha
- 'Polyphant' (v)	MHoo SRms
- 'Thumble's Variety'	CRos EBee ECha ECtt EHyd ELan EPfP LRHS MHer MRav NRHS NWad SRms SWvt WCFE WFar XLum XSen
- 'Tomintoul'	GPoy
- 'Variegatum'	see *O. vulgare* 'Gold Tip'
- 'Waddow Delight'	NWad
- 'White Charm'	EBee MHoo NWad SEdi

Orixa (*Rutaceae*)

japonica	EBee NLar WPGP
- 'Variegata' (v)	NLar

Orlaya (*Apiaceae*)

grandiflora ♀H7	CAvo CKel CMiW CSpe EDAr ELan EPfP LBar LCro LEdu LOPS LRHS LSto MAvo MCot SPhx WHlf

Ornithogalum (*Asparagaceae*)

arabicum	CBro CCCN GKev LAma MBros NRog SDeJ SRms
arcuatum	WCot
baeticum	GKev
balansae	see *O. oligophyllum*
caudatum	see *O. longibracteatum*
creticum	GKev
I ***dictaeum***	GKev
dubium ♀H2	CBor CPla SDeJ
- hybrids	GKev
- yellow-flowered	CBor GKev
fimbriatum	GKev NRog
lanceolatum	GKev WCot
§ ***longibracteatum***	GKev NGKo SChr WHer
magnum	CBro CKel CWCL GBin MCot MNrw NRog SDeJ WCot
- 'Moskou'	CAvo ERCP
- 'Saguramo'	NRog
montanum	GKev
'Mount Fuji'	GKev LAma
'Namib Gold'	SDeJ
nanum	see *O. sigmoideum*
narbonense	GKev NRog WCot
nutans ♀H5	CAby CAvo CBod CWCL EAJP ECha EHyd ELan EPfP EPot EWoo GKev LAma LRHS LShi MNrw NBir NRog SDeJ SEND SPer WFar WShi
§ ***oligophyllum***	EBee EPot ERCP GKev LAma MNrw NRog SDeJ
ponticum	WCot
- 'Sochi'	GKev MBow
pyramidale	EBee LAma NRog
pyrenaicum	CAvo CSpe ECha EPPr GKev WCot WShi
reverchonii	EBee ERCP GKev LAma SBrt WShi
saundersiae	GKev LAma MPtr NGKo
sibthorpii	see *O. sigmoideum*
§ ***sigmoideum***	GKev
sintenisii	GKev NRog
thyrsoides ♀H2	CCCN GKev LAma LCro LOPS SDeJ WHlf
umbellatum	CAvo CHab CRos CTri EGrl EHyd ELan GKev GPoy LAma LRHS MBow MCot MNrw NRHS NRog SDeJ SEND SRms WShi
'White Trophy'	GKev

Orontium (*Araceae*)

aquaticum	CBen CPud CToG CWat EWat GQue LCro LLWG LOPS LPfP NPer WMAq

Orostachys (*Crassulaceae*)

furusei	WFar
iwarenge	SPlb SSim
§ ***spinosa***	CRos EDAr EHyd EWes LRHS NFav NRHS SPlb WAbe WFar

Orthophytum (*Bromeliaceae*)

gurkenii	WCot

Orthrosanthus (*Iridaceae*)

chimboracensis JCA 13743	EBee
laxus	CAbb CWCL EGrl MACG NBir SBrt SMHy SMad WCAu
multiflorus	CBor CPbh CSde EBee EPri
polystachyus	CTsd LPla MHer SIvy WSHC

Orychophragmus (*Brassicaceae*)

violaceus	CCCN CSpe

Oryzopsis (*Poaceae*)

hymenoides	LDai
lessoniana	see *Anemanthele lessoniana*
miliacea	CAby CSpe EPPr LDai NSti SDix SEND WCot WPGP
paradoxa	EPPr

Oscularia (*Aizoaceae*)

copiosa	SEdd
§ ***deltoides*** ♀H2	CCCN CPbh EShb SVen WFar WOld

Osmanthus (*Oleaceae*)

armatus	CBcs CJun CKel CMac EBee EPfP LMaj LSRN NLar SGol
× ***burkwoodii*** ♀H5	Widely available
§ ***decorus***	CBcs CBrac CJun CMac CTri EBee EPfP MGos MRav NLar SGol SPer WPav
- 'Angustifolius'	NLar
delavayi ♀H5	Widely available
- 'Frank Knight'	EPfP LRHS MAsh
- 'George Gardner'	CMac SRms
- 'Heaven Scent'	SPoG XVPe
- 'Latifolius'	CExl CJun CRos EHyd ELon LRHS MAsh SWvt
forrestii	see *O. yunnanensis*
× ***fortunei***	CBcs CCVT CKel EBee EHyd EPfP LMaj LPar LRHS
fragrans	LPar SWeb SWvt XVPe
- f. ***aurantiacus***	XSte XVPe
§ ***heterophyllus***	CBcs CDoC CMac EBee EHeP ELan EPfP ERom GDam GMcL LIns LMaj LPar MDon MGos MRav NLar SArc SCob SGol SPer SRms SWeb WCFE WFar
§ - all gold	CKel EBee ELan EMil EPfP LRHS SPer SPoG
- 'Argenteomarginatus'	see *O. heterophyllus* 'Variegatus'
§ - 'Aureomarginatus' (v)	CBcs CMac CTsd ELon MDon MHtn SRms WHtc
- 'Aureus' misapplied	see *O. heterophyllus* all gold
- 'Aureus' Rehder	see *O. heterophyllus* 'Aureomarginatus'
§ - 'Goshiki' (v) ♀H5	Widely available
- 'Gulftide'	CRos EGrl EHeP EHyd EPfP LRHS MAsh MGos NLar NRHS
- 'Kembu' (v)	NLar
- 'Myrtifolius'	CMac NLar
- 'Ōgon'	NLar
- 'Purple Shaft' ♀H5	CRos EHyd ELan EPfP LRHS NRHS
- 'Purpureus'	CBcs CBod CKel CMac CTsd EBee EGrl ELon EPfP EShb LPar LSto

	MGos MRav MSwo NLar SCoo SEND SGol SNig SPer SSha WLov
- 'Rotundifolius'	CMac NLar
- 'Sasaba'	NLar SMad
- TRICOLOR	see *O. heterophyllus* 'Goshiki'
§ - 'Variegatus' (v) 🏆H5	Widely available
ilicifolius	see *O. heterophyllus*
'Perfume of Nature' **new**	LCro
serrulatus	LRHS NLar WPGP
suavis	CJun NLar
§ ***yunnanensis*** 🏆H5	CBcs CMCN EBee ELon EPfP LSRN MBlu MRav NLar SArc WKif WPGP

× *Osmarea* see *Osmanthus*

Osmaronia see *Oemleria*

Osmorhiza (*Apiaceae*)

aristata B&SWJ 1607	WCru
claytonii	SPhx

Osmunda ✿ (*Osmundaceae*)

sp.	CCCN
asiatica	EBee WCru
cinnamomea 🏆H6	CBod CCCN CLAP CRos CSde EFer EHyd ELan EMor EWes ISha LEdu LRHS NBro NLar NRHS SPlb SRot
claytoniana	CBdn CEme CLAP CRos CSta EFer EHyd ELon EMor ISha LEdu LRHS NBro NLar NRHS WCot XLum
japonica	CLAP CSta EBee ISha NBro
regalis 🏆H6	Widely available
- from southern USA	CLAP ISha
- 'Cristata' 🏆H6	EHyd NRHS SWvt WFib
- 'Purpurascens'	Widely available
- var. ***spectabilis***	CCCN CLAP EHyd ISha NRHS
- 'Undulata'	WFib

Osteomeles (*Rosaceae*)

subrotunda	WPGP

Osteospermum (*Asteraceae*)

3D Series	MDon SPoG
- 3D PURPLE ('Kleoe12198'PBR)	MBros
- 3D VIOLET ICE ('Kleoe14223')	MBros
'African Queen'	see *O.* 'Nairobi Purple'
(Akila Series) AKILA GRAND CANYON MIX	WHil
- AKILA SUNSET SHADES (mixed) **new**	WHil
BANANA SYMPHONY ('Sekiin47') (Symphony Series)	CCCN
barberae misapplied	see *O. jucundum*
barberae (Harv.) Norl. 'Compactum'	GArf WFar
BLUE EYED BEAUTY ('Balostlueye'PBR)	LCro LOPS MBros MPri
'Blue Streak'	CCCN CMac
'Buttermilk' 🏆H3	CCCN ELan
'Cannington John'	CCCN CWal LShi
'Cannington Joyce'	CCCN
'Cannington Kira'	CWal
'Cannington Roy'	CBcs CCCN CEnd CMac EBee ECtt ELan ELon EPfP EWoo GAbr GBee LRHS MACG NRHS SGBe WFar WHlf WMal
caulescens misapplied	see *O.* 'White Pim'
'Dwarf Pink'	CTtf
ecklonis	CBcs CCCN CDTJ CTri GBee MBros NBro
- var. ***prostratum***	see *O.* 'White Pim'
(Erato Series) 'Erato Lemon Pink'	LRHS
- 'Erato Pink Eye'	LRHS
- 'Erato Purple'	LRHS WHlf
- 'Erato Purple Stripe'	LRHS
- 'Erato Yellow'	LRHS
(Flowerpower Series) FLOWERPOWER ICE WHITE ('Kleo06123')	LCro LOPS
- FLOWERPOWER LAVENDER PINK ('Kleoe14235') **new**	LCro
Flowerpower Double Series (d)	MDon
'Giles Gilbey' (v)	CCCN
'Gweek Variegated' (v)	CCCN
'Hopleys' 🏆H3	SEND
'In the Pink'	CBod LBar LCro LOPS LRHS MHol SCoo SGBe WHil
'Irish'	CTtf ECtt EPPr EPot SMrm WIce
§ ***jucundum*** 🏆H3	CCht CTri CWCL ECha EHyd EPPr EPfP GAbr LCro LOPS LRHS LSRN LShi NBir NPer NRHS SGBe SRms WIce
- 'Blackthorn Seedling' 🏆H3	CBor CCCN CWGN ECha
- var. ***compactum***	CBod CMac CRos CTsd CWnw EHyd ELan EPfP GBee GLog GMaP LRHS LSRN MBow MPri NPer NRHS SCoo SIvy SWvt WFar WHil WHoo WTor
- 'Elliott's Form'	WHoo
- 'Langtrees' 🏆H3	SMrm
- 'Nanum'	EDAr
§ 'Lady Leitrim' 🏆H3	Widely available
'Lisa Traxler'	SVen
§ 'Nairobi Purple'	CBcs CBod CCCN CCht CDoC EBee ECtt EHyd ELan EPfP EShb LRHS MPri NRHS SGBe SWvt WFar WHil WHlf
NASINGA CREAM ('Aknam'PBR) (Cape Daisy Series)	CCCN
ORANGE SYMPHONY ('Seimora'PBR) (Symphony Series)	CBcs CCCN WTyc
'Pale Face'	see *O.* 'Lady Leitrim'
'Peggyi'	see *O.* 'Nairobi Purple'
'Pink Gem'	MHer WFar
'Pink Whirls' 🏆H3	CCCN
'Port Wine'	see *O.* 'Nairobi Purple'
PURPLE SUN ('Kleoe19396') **new**	LCro MDon MPri WHil WWke
'Sennen Sunrise' **new**	CBod LBar WHil
(Serenity Series) SERENITY BLUSHING BEAUTY ('Balostush')	MBros
- SERENITY PINK EYED BEAUTY ('Balostroseye') **new**	LCro
- SERENITY RED ('Balsered')	MBros WBor
- SERENITY ROSE MAGIC ('Balseroma')	WHlf
- SERENITY WHITE ('Balserwhit') **new**	WHlf
'Shire Pink' **new**	LShi
'Silver Sparkler' (v) 🏆H3	CCCN CDTJ MHer SVen
'Snow Pixie'	CBod CWGN ECtt ELan LBar LCro LOPS LRHS MPri SPoG SWvt WFar WHil WHlf WIce

	SONJA	see *O.* 'Sunny Sonja'
	'Sparkler'	CCCN
	'Stardust'	CRos ECtt EHyd LRHS NPer NRHS SCoo
	(Sunny Series) 'Sunny Bronze'	CSpe
	- 'Sunny Carlos' PBR	SPoG
	- 'Sunny Cherry'	SPoG
	- 'Sunny Mary' PBR	LCro LOPS SPoG
§	- 'Sunny Sonja' PBR	SPoG
	- 'Sunny Victoria' PBR	SPoG
	- 'Sunny Xena' PBR	SPoG
I	'Superbum'	MACG WFar
	'Tauranga'	see *O.* 'Whirlygig'
	'Tresco Peggy'	see *O.* 'Nairobi Purple'
	'Tresco Pink'	CCCN
	'Tresco Purple'	see *O.* 'Nairobi Purple'
	'Upright Purple'	CDoC
	VOLTAGE YELLOW ('Balvoyelo') (Voltage Series)	MBros WHlf
	'Weetwood' ♀H3	CCCN CEnd ECtt ELan EPPr EPot EWoo GLog LRHS MHer SPoG SWvt WFar WMal
	'Westwood White'	EDAr
§	'Whirlygig' ♀H3	CCCN CWal
§	'White Pim' ♀H3	CDTJ NPer SEND SMrm
	'Wine Purple'	see *O.* 'Nairobi Purple'
	'Zaurak' (Springstar Series)	CCCN
	'Zulu' (Cape Daisy Series)	CCCN

Ostrowskia (*Campanulaceae*)

	magnifica	EPot GKev

Ostrya (*Betulaceae*)

	carpinifolia	CCVT CMCN EBee EHeP ELan EPfP IPap LIns LMaj LPar MBlu MMuc MTrO NOra NWea SCob SEND SGol SWvt WHtc WJur WMat WTSh
	japonica	MVil
	virginiana	SBrt

Otacanthus (*Plantaginaceae*)

	caeruleus 'Atlantis'	CDoC

Otatea (*Poaceae*)

	acuminata **new**	WCot

Otholobium (*Fabaceae*)

	glandulosum	EBee

Othonna (*Asteraceae*)

	cheirifolia	see *Hertia cheirifolia*
	coronopifolia	SVen

Othonnopsis see *Hertia*

Ourisia (*Plantaginaceae*)

	× ***bitternensis*** 'Cliftonville Canary'	WAbe
	- 'Cliftonville Pink'	WAbe
	- 'Cliftonville Roset'	WAbe
	caespitosa	GAbr GArf
	- var. ***gracilis***	EPot GKev
	coccinea	CBor EBee EWes GArf GBin GKev GQue NHpl WAbe
	'Loch Ewe'	CExl EBee GKev NFav
	macrophylla	GKev
	microphylla	WAbe
	- f. ***alba***	WAbe
	- 'Hollowcliffe'	WAbe
	polyantha 'Cliftonville Scarlet'	WAbe
	'Snowflake' ♀H4	GAbr GArf NHpl

Ovidia (*Thymelaeaceae*)

	andina	MGil

Oxalis (*Oxalidaceae*)

	acetosella	GPoy GQue MHer NQui SPhx WHer WShi
	- var. ***rosea***	GRum
	- var. ***subpurpurascens***	MMrt WCot
	adenodes	NRog
	adenophylla ♀H4	CMiW CRos EHyd ELan EPfP GAbr GBin GKev GMaP LAma LRHS NFav NHol NHpl NLar NRHS NRog SDeJ SPoG SRms WBrk WCav
	adenophylla × ***enneaphylla***	see *O.* 'Matthew Forrest'
	'Anne Christie'	NRya NSla
	arenaria F&W 10584	WCot
§	***articulata***	ELan GElm NPer SEND WCav WSHC XLum
	- 'Alba'	ELan WCot XLum
	- f. ***crassipes*** 'Alba'	WCot
	- 'Festival'	GKev
§	- subsp. ***rubra***	GKev SDeJ
	'Autumn Pink'	GKev
	'Black Velvet' (Xalis Series)	WWke
	bowiei	WCot
*	- ***purpurea***	CBor
	brasiliensis	CBor EPPr GKev LShi
	compressa	NRog
	convexula	NRog
	'Dark Eye'	EPot
	dentata 'Pot of Gold'	GKev
	deppei	see *O. tetraphylla*
§	***depressa***	EPot EWes GKev LShi NBir NRya NSla SDeJ SGro
	'Double Trouble' (d)	CBor GKev
	dregei	NRog
	eckloniana var. ***sonderi***	NRog
	enneaphylla ♀H4	CElw CRos EHyd GBin GEdr GMaP LRHS MNrw NRHS NRya SGro SPlb
	- 'Alba'	CElw CMiW GArf NRya
	- subsp. ***ibari***	EPPr GEdr NRya WFar
	- 'Minutifolia'	GEdr GQue NRya NWad
	- 'Rosea'	CBor EPot GKev ITim LAma NLar NRog NRya NSla SGro
	- 'Sheffield Swan'	GEdr NSla NWad
	- 'Ute'	EPPr GEdr NRya NWad
	'Fanny'	GKev LAma
	flava	CPla NRog SChr
	- white-flowered	EPot GKev
	floribunda misapplied	see *O. articulata*
	foveolata	NRog
	gracilis	CBor EPot GKev
	griffithii double-flowered (d)	CMiW GGro WFar
	- 'Pink Charm'	GEdr
	- 'Snowflake'	CMiW GEdr
	'Gwen McBride'	GArf GEdr
	hedysaroides misapplied	see *O. spiralis* subsp. *vulcanicola*
	'Hemswell Knight'	EPPr
§	***herrerae*** **new**	WOld
	hirta	SGro
	- 'Gothenburg'	EPPr EPri EShb GKev ITim LAma NRog
	inops	see *O. depressa*
	'Ione Hecker' ♀H4	CBor CMiW EPot GArf GKev GMaP ITim NHpl NLar NRog NRya
	'Jay'	NSla
*	***karroica***	CBor NHpl WCot
	laciniata hybrid	GEdr

	lactea double-flowered	see *O. magellanica* 'Nelson'
	lasiandra	CCCN GKev
	magellanica	GAbr SPlb WCot
	- 'Flore Pleno'	see *O. magellanica* 'Nelson'
§	- 'Nelson' (d)	GBin NBir NPer SMad
	magnifica	CBor GKev
	massoniana ♀H2	ECha EPot WAbe WCot
§	'Matthew Forrest'	NBwr
§	***megalorrhiza***	NWad SChr
	melanosticta	EPot GEdr SDeJ WCot
§	- 'Ken Aslet' ♀H3	CBor GKev ITim LAma NBir NBwr NHpl SDeJ
	obtusa	ECha EPot GKev
	- amber-flowered **new**	NBwr
	- apricot-flowered	SDeJ
	oregana	CMac ECha EPPr EWld MNrw WCot WCru
	- 'Bob Haszeldine'	GEdr
	- 'Klamath Ruby'	EWld WSHC
	- f. ***smalliana***	CMiW EWld GEdr GElm MNrw NBro NLar WCot WCru
	- white-flowered	WCot
	perdicaria	CBor EHyd EPot GKev LRHS NRHS NRog WAbe WIce
	- 'Citrino'	WAbe WCot
	polyphylla var. ***heptaphylla***	GEdr
	'Pom Pom' (d) **new**	CBor
§	***purpurea***	NRog
*	- 'Alba'	GKev
	- 'Ken Aslet'	see *O. melanosticta* 'Ken Aslet'
	regnellii	see *O. triangularis* subsp. *papilionacea*
	rosea misapplied	see *O. articulata* subsp. *rubra*
	semiloba	EPPr LShi NCth
	Slack Top hybrids	NSla
	'Slack's Hummingbird'	WFar
	'Slack's Peacock'	CBor NSla WFar
	'Snipe'	NSla
	speciosa	see *O. purpurea*
§	***spiralis***	CCCN
	subsp. ***vulcanicola***	
	- - 'Sunset Velvet'	WCot
	squamata	SPlb
	stricta	SPhx
	succulenta misapplied	see *O. herrerae*
	succulenta Barnéoud	see *O. megalorrhiza*
	'Sunny'	GKev
§	***tetraphylla***	CPla NPer
	- 'Iron Cross'	ELan EPPr GKev LAma LCro NLar SDeJ SPlb WHil
	triangularis	CCCN EWld LAma MHer NPer WBrk
	- 'Birgit'	GKev SDeJ
	- BURGUNDY WINE ('JR Oxburwi') (Xalis Series)	CWGN NPer SBls
	- 'Mijke'	GKev LAma
§	- subsp. ***papilionacea*** ♀H3	GKev LAma WCot
	- - 'Atropurpurea'	CSpe SDeJ
	- subsp. ***triangularis***	GKev LAma LDai MBow
	tuberosa	CLau EPfP GPoy LEdu SPoG WKor
	'Ute'	NSla
	valdiviensis	NWad
	versicolor ♀H3	CBor EPot ETay GKev ITim LAma NBir NRog SDeJ
	- 'Golden Cape'	CBor EPot GKev NBwr
	virginea	NRog
I	'Waverley Hybrid'	GKev GRum NBwr
	zeekoevleyensis	NRog

Oxycoccus see *Vaccinium*

Oxydendrum ✿ (*Ericaceae*)

	arboreum	CBcs CEme CEnd CMCN EBee EGrI EHyd EPfP LPar LRHS MAsh MBlu MGil MPkF SCob SPoG SSta XSte

Oxypetalum (*Apocynaceae*)

	caeruleum	see *Tweedia coerulea*

Oxyria (*Polygonaceae*)

	digyna	CAgr GGro WKor

Oxytropis (*Fabaceae*)

	campestris var. ***gracilis***	GKev WSHC

Ozothamnus (*Asteraceae*)

§	***coralloides***	EPot SPlb WAbe
§	'County Park Silver'	GEdr LShi
§	***hookeri***	CDoC SPer SVen WCFE WJek WPGP
§	***ledifolius***	CBcs CBod CCoa CDoC ELan EPfP GMcL LRHS MGil SPer
§	***rosmarinifolius***	CBcs CDoC CRos EHyd ELan EPfP GBin GMcL LRHS MAsh MSwo SEdd SGBe SPer SVen
	- 'Silver Jubilee'	CBcs CBod CCht CKel CRos CSBt CWnw ECre ELan EPfP GMcL LRHS MAsh MHtn MRav MSwo SPer SPlb
§	***selago***	ELan EPot WCot
	- 'Major'	EDAr SPlb
§	- var. ***tumidus***	ITim WAbe WThu
	'Threave Seedling'	CBod CCht CDoC CKel EHyd ELan GQue LRHS MAsh SPer SRHi

P

Pachira (*Malvaceae*)

	aquatica **new**	LCro NHrt NPlm SPre
	insignis	XSte

Pachycereus (*Cactaceae*)

§	***marginatus*** **new**	NPlm
	pecten-aboriginum **new**	NPlm
	pringlei **new**	EAri LCro NPlm

Pachyphragma (*Brassicaceae*)

§	***macrophyllum***	EBee ECha ELon EWld LEdu MBel MMuc MRav NLar NSti SDix WCAu WCot WCru WPGP WPnP WSHC

Pachyphytum (*Crassulaceae*)

	bracteosum	CDoC CSBt EAri SCoo SEdd SIvy SPoG
	compactum	EAri SEdd
	glutinicaule	EAri
	hookeri	EAri
	oviferum ♀H2	EAri SEdd

Pachypodium (*Apocynaceae*)

	geayi ♀H1a	EAri NPlm
	lamerei ♀H1a	EAri NPlm SPad SPlb
	lealii subsp. ***saundersii***	EAri

Pachysandra (*Buxaceae*)

	axillaris	SGBe WCot WPGP
	- BWJ 8032	WCru
	- 'Crûg's Cover'	ESwi EWld GBin SMad WCru WFar
	- var. ***stylosa***	MRav

procumbens	EBee GKev MNrw NLar WCot
- 'Angola' (v)	WCot
terminalis	Widely available
- 'Green Carpet'	Widely available
- 'Green Sheen' 🏆H5	ECha ELan EPPr EPfP GQue LPal LPar LRHS LWaG NRHS SCob WCAu
- 'Green Spire' new	SRHi
- 'Silver Edge' (v)	EBee
- 'Variegata' (v) 🏆H5	Widely available

Pachystachys (*Acanthaceae*)

lutea 🏆H1b	CCCN EShb

Pachystegia (*Asteraceae*)

§ ***insignis***	CTsd LRHS SGBe WMal

× *Pachyveria* (*Crassulaceae*)

sp.	CDTJ CSBt NCft SEdd SIvy SSim
'Elaine Reinelt' new	SEdd
'Mrs Coombes'	SEdd
'Pinko' new	SEdd
scheideckeri	CDoC EAri
'Thunderbird' new	SEdd
'Yvonne' new	SEdd

Paederia (*Rubiaceae*)

scandens	SBrt

Paederota (*Plantaginaceae*)

§ ***bonarota***	GEdr GKev WAbe
lutea	GEdr GKev WCot

Paeonia ✿ (*Paeoniaceae*)

'All That Jazz' (d) new	LPmr
'America'	GBin LPmr NCth NLar WCAu
'Anna Marie' (S)	GBin
§ ***anomala*** subsp. ***anomala***	EPot ILea LPmr MPhe NLar SPtp
§ - subsp. ***veitchii***	CExl CJun CKel CMiW GAbr GBin GKev GMaP LPla NBid NLar WCAu WCot WSpi WThu
- subsp. ***veitchii*** × ***tenuifolia***	CJun
'Apricot Queen'	LPmr
arietina W&B BG A-4	WCot
'Armani'	EPfP LRHS
'Athena'	EHyd GBin LPmr LRHS WCAu
'Auten's Red'	WCAu
'Avant Garde'	GBin WCAu
'Bai Xue Ta' (S)	NTPC
'Ballarena de Saval'	GBin ILea LPmr WKif
banatica	see *P. officinalis* subsp. *banatica*
§ 'Bartzella' (d) 🏆H6	CKel CRos EHed EHyd ELan EPfP GBin GMaP ILea LCro LOPS LPla LPmr LRHS MACG MMrt MNrw NLar NRHS SEdd SHar SPeP SPoG WCAu WCot
beresowskii	see *P. anomala* subsp. *veitchii*
'Berry Berry Fine' new	LPmr
'Berry Garcia'	GBin LRHS
'Blaze'	CKel EHyd GMaP ILea LPmr LRHS MACG NLar NRHS SPeP WCAu WCot
'Blushing Princess' (d)	GBin
'Border Charm'	CKel GBin GEdr ILea LAma LPmr SDir
'Bridal Icing'	CKel GBin LPmr NCth WCAu
'Bride's Dream'	GBin
'Buckeye Belle' (d)	CBod CKel EBee EGrI ELan EPfP EWoo GBin GMaP GMcL ILea LCro LOPS LPmr LRHS LSRN MBel NCth NLar SCob SPoG WCAu WCot WTor
'Burma Joy'	WCAu
'Burma Midnight'	GBin WCAu WKif
'Callie's Memory'	CKel EGrI EPfP GBin ILea LPmr LRHS WCAu
cambessedesii 🏆H3	CBro CRos CSpe EHyd EPot ESwi GEdr GKev LRHS NBir NRHS NSla WAbe WCot
cambessedesii × ***daurica*** subsp. ***mlokosewitschii***	CRos EHyd LRHS NRHS
'Canary Brilliant' PBR	CKel GBin LPmr MThu WCAu WKif
'Carina'	GBin
'Carol'	ILea LPmr LSRN WCAu
caucasica	see *P. daurica* subsp. *coriifolia*
× ***chamaeleon***	GKev WCAu
'Cherry Ruffles'	WCAu
'Chocolate Soldier'	NCth WCAu
'Christmas Velvet' (d)	GBin LPmr WCAu
'Claire de Lune'	CBWd CKel EWoo GBin GMaP ILea IPot LAma LPmr LRHS MGil NLar SMad WCAu WCot WKif
'Claudia'	GBin
'Clouds of Colour' new	LPmr
'Color Magnet'	GBin WCAu
'Command Performance'	GBin ILea LPmr SHar WCAu
'Convoy' (d)	WCAu
'Copper Kettle' (d)	CKel ELan GBin ILea LPmr WCAu
'Cora Louise'	CKel EHed ELan GBin ILea LPmr LRHS MBros MHol NLar SMad SPeP WCAu WKif
'Coral Beach'	LRHS MPri
'Coral Charm' 🏆H6	CKel EBee EGrI EPfP GBin GMaP ILea LAma LCro LOPS LPmr LRHS LSRN MHol MMrt MPri NCth NLar SDeJ SPeP WCAu WCot WHoo XSen
'Coral Fay'	GBin MPri WCAu
'Coral 'n' Gold'	LRHS MPri WCAu
'Coral Sunset'	CKel CWnw EGrI GBin ILea LAma LCro LPmr LRHS MACG MPri NCth NLar SCob SDeJ SPer WCAu WCot WTyc
'Coral Supreme'	GBin LPmr MPri
corallina	see *P. mascula* subsp. *mascula*
'Court Jester'	CKel ELan GBin ILea LPmr
'Cutie'	WCAu
'Cytherea'	GBin LPmr LRHS WCAu
'Dancing Butterflies'	see *P. lactiflora* 'Zi Yu Nu'
'Dark Eyes' new	GBin WCAu
§ ***daurica***	EPot GKev WCot
§ - subsp. ***coriifolia***	GKev
- - RCB UA 12	WCot
§ - subsp. ***mlokosewitschii*** 🏆H6	CBro CExl CKel CRos CSpe EBee ECha EHyd ELan EPot GBin GEdr GKev LEdu LPmr LRHS MBel MNrw NBir NRHS SWvt WAbe WCAu WCot WHoo WKif WSpi
- - hybrids	GKev
§ - subsp. ***wittmanniana***	ECha GEdr MBel WCAu
- - PAB 3673	LEdu
- - 'Rosea'	GBin WCAu
'Dearest'	GBin
decora	see *P. peregrina*
delavayi (S)	CBor CEme CPla CRos CTsd EHyd ELan EPfP GEdr GKev GMaP LCro LRHS MAsh MGil MGos NBir SCob SDix SPer SPoG SRms WCot WJur
- BWJ 7775	WCru
- from China (S)	MPhe
- var. ***angustiloba*** f. ***alba*** (S)	CExl
§ - - f. ***angustiloba*** (S)	GKev SEND
§ - - f. ***trollioides*** (S)	CExl SPtp
- cf. var. ***angustiloba*** BO 15-142	GGro

§ – var. ***delavayi*** f. ***lutea*** (S) CCVT CDoC CRos EHyd EPfP GLog LEdu LRHS MAsh MGos NBir SCob SIvy SPoG SRms WLov
– var. ***lutea*** see *P. delavayi* var. *delavayi* f. *lutea*
– Potaninii Group see *P. delavayi* var. *angustiloba* f. *angustiloba*
– 'Tapestry' (S) CSpe
– Trollioides Group see *P. delavayi* var. *angustiloba* f. *trollioides*
'Diana Parks' GBin ILea LPmr NLar WCAu
'Don Richardson' WCAu
'Early Glow' GBin WCAu
'Early Scout' GBin NLar WCAu
'Early Windflower' CKel ELan GBin ILea LPmr WCAu
'Eden's Perfume' CKel LPmr NCth SPer
'Eliza Lundy' (d) GBin WCAu
'Ellen Cowley' NCth WCAu
emodi CKel GKev ILea LPmr LRHS MCot SHar WCAu WCot WMal
'Etched Salmon' CKel GBin LPmr WCAu
'Eventide' WCAu
'Fairy Princess' GBin WCAu
§ × ***festiva*** 'Alba Plena' (d) CKel EHyd ELan EPfP ILea LPmr LRHS MRav NLar NRHS SCob SPer SWvt WFar
§ – 'Mutabilis Plena' (d) LPmr
§ – 'Rosea Plena' (d) 🏆^{H6} ECtt ELan EPfP LPmr LRHS SCob SPer SWvt WCAu WCot WFar
– 'Rosea Superba Plena' (d) LPmr
§ – 'Rubra Plena' (d) 🏆^{H6} CKel CTri EBee ECtt EGrI ELan EPfP GMaP ILea LPmr LRHS MBel MRav NGdn NLar SCob SPer SRms SWvt WBor WCAu WCot
'Firelight' GBin WCAu
'First Arrival' CKel GBin ILea LPmr LRHS MHol WCAu
'First Dutch Yellow' see *P.* 'Garden Treasure'
'Flame' CKel EHyd EPfP GBin GMaP ILea LPmr LRHS MBNS MBel MNrw NCth NRHS NSti SDeJ SPeP WCAu WCot
'Fuso-no-tsukasa' (S) CKel
§ Gansu Group (S) MPhe NTPC
– 'Bai Bi Lan Xia' (S) MPhe
– 'Bai Zhang Bing' (S) NTPC
– 'Bing Xin Zi' (S) NTPC
– 'Dan Feng Ling Kong' (S) NTPC
– 'Er Long Nao Hai' (S) MPhe
– 'Fen Guan Yu Zhu' (S) NTPC
– 'Fen He' (S) MPhe NTPC
– 'Fen Jin Yu' (S) NTPC
– 'Fen Yu Sheng Hui' (S) **new** NTPC
– 'Gan Lan Yu' (S) NTPC
– 'He Ping Er Qiao' (S) **new** NTPC
– 'Hei Feng Die' (S) MPhe
– 'Hei Xuan Feng' (S) MPhe
– 'Hei Yuan Shuai' (S) MPhe
– 'Hui He' (S) MPhe
– 'Jiao Rong' (S) MPhe
– 'Lan He' (S) MPhe
– 'Lan He Qi Ming' (S) NTPC
– 'Lan Tian Meng' (S) MPhe
– 'Lan Yu San Cai' (S) NTPC
– 'Long Yu Er Qiao' (S) NTPC
– 'Long Yuan Hong' (S) MPhe
– 'Mo Hai Yin Bo' (S) MPhe
– 'Pan Deng' (S) **new** NTPC
– 'Ri Yue Tong Hui' (S) MPhe
– 'San Hua Nu' (S) MPhe
– 'Shu Sheng Peng Mo' (S) MPhe
– 'Tie Mian Wu Si' (S) MPhe
– 'Wu Kong Xiu Xing' (S) NTPC
– 'Xiong Mao' (S) MPhe
– 'Xue Hai Bing Xin' (S) MPhe NTPC
– 'Xue Lian' (S) NTPC
– 'Ye Guang Bei' (S) MPhe NTPC
– 'Yin Yang Shan' (S) MPhe
– 'Yuan Yang Pu' (S) MPhe
– 'Yun Zhong He' (S) **new** NTPC
– 'Zi Ban Bai' (S) NTPC
– 'Zi Die Ying Feng' (S) MPhe NTPC
– 'Zi Yan' (S) NTPC
– 'Zong Ban Bai' (S) MPhe NTPC
Gansu Mudan Group see *P.* Gansu Group
'Garden Peace' GBin WCAu
§ 'Garden Treasure' CKel EHyd EPfP GBin LPmr LRHS MHol NLar NRHS SDeJ SPoG WCAu
'Going Bananas' CKel LPmr LRHS NLar
'Golden Dream' see *P.* 'Bartzella'
'Golden Fairy' **new** LPmr
'Golden Thunder' CKel
'Goldenball' (S) CKel
'Hei Hua Kui' see *P.* × *suffruticosa* 'Hei Hua Kui'
'Hélène Martin' GBin LPmr
'Henry Bockstoce' (d) CBod EHed GBin GMaP ILea LPmr LRHS MGil NCth NLar WCAu
'Hillary' CKel EHed GBin GMaP ILea LPmr MCot MThu WCAu
'Ho-gioku' NCth
'Hoki' NRHS WCAu
'Hong Bao Shi' (S) NTPC
'Honor' WCAu
humilis see *P. officinalis* subsp. *microcarpa*
'Huo Lian Jin Dan' (S) NTPC
'Illini Belle' EBlo
'Illini Warrior' CKel GBin ILea WCAu
'Impossible Dream' (d) LPmr
japonica ambig. GEdr
japonica (Makino) Miyabe & Takeda see *P. obovata*
'Jay Cee' WCAu
'Jin Ge' (S) NTPC
'Joanna Marlene' GBin ILea LPmr WCAu
'John Harvard' WCAu
'Joyce Ellen' LPmr NCth WCAu
'Julia Rose' CKel EHyd EPfP GBin ILea LPmr LRHS NRHS SHar SPoG WCAu
'Kasagayama' CKel
kavachensis EGrI ESwi GEdr
'Kinkaku' see *P.* × *lemoinei* 'Souvenir de Maxime Cornu'
'Kinko' see *P.* × *lemoinei* 'Alice Harding'
'La Donna' (d) GBin WCAu
lactiflora 'Abalone Pearl' GBin
– 'Adolphe Rousseau' LCro LOPS LRHS WCAu
– 'Agida' EBlo ECtt EHyd LRHS MRav NRHS
– 'Albert Crousse' CBcs CKel LPmr MRav NBir WCAu
– 'Albert Niva' WCAu
– 'Alertie' CKel GBin LPmr LRHS
– 'Alice Harding' CKel LPmr NLar WCAu
– 'Allan Rogers' WCAu
– 'Amabilis' LPmr WCAu
– 'Amalia Olson' WCAu
– 'Angel Cheeks' CKel GBin LCro LOPS LPmr WCAu
– 'Ann Cousins' CKel GMcL LPmr MGil WCAu
– 'Antwerpen' CRos EHyd LRHS NRHS
– 'Argentine' WCAu
– 'Armistice' WCAu
– 'Auguste Dessert' CKel WCAu
§ – 'Augustin d'Hour' CKel LPmr LRHS NLar SHar
– 'Aureole' MRav
– 'Avalanche' CKel EPfP ILea LPmr LRHS NLar NRHS
– 'Avalon' WCAu

- 'Ballerina'	MRav
- 'Barbara'	WCAu
- 'Baroness Schröder'	CKel EBee GBin LPmr MGil WCAu
- 'Barrington Belle'	CKel ECtt EHyd EPfP GBin LPmr LRHS MBros NRHS WCAu WFar
- 'Bella Donna' **new**	LPmr
- 'Belle Center'	WCAu
- 'Bess Bockstoce'	WCAu
- 'Best Man'	LPmr WCAu
- 'Better Times'	WCAu
- 'Big Ben'	CBod CKel EPfP LPmr LRHS NLar SMrm
- 'Black Beauty'	EHyd LPmr LRHS NRHS SCob SDeJ SPeP
- 'Blush Queen'	CKel GBin LPmr WCAu
- 'Border Gem'	CRos EHyd LRHS MRav NRHS WCAu
- 'Bouchela'	LPmr NSti
- 'Boule de Neige'	CKel ILea LPmr
- 'Bouquet Perfect'	EHyd LRHS NRHS WCAu
- 'Bowl of Beauty' ♀H6	Widely available
- 'Bowl of Cream'	CKel GBin ILea LPmr LRHS SCob SHar SWvt WCAu
- 'Bridal Gown'	CKel GBin LPmr WCAu
- 'Bridal Shower'	GBin
- 'Bright Knight'	WCAu
- 'Bunker Hill'	CKel CRos ECtt EHyd EWTr GBin LPmr LRHS LSto NRHS SPer SWvt WCAu WGwG
- 'Bu-te'	LAma NLar
- 'Butter Bowl'	GBin WCAu
- 'Candy Stripe'	GBin LBar LPmr
- 'Catharina Fontijn'	CBod CKel CWnw EHyd GBin ILea LPmr LRHS NCth NRHS WCAu WTor
- 'Celebrity'	CKel LPmr SMad
- 'Charles Burgess'	EPfP GBin ILea LPmr NCth WCAu
- 'Charlie's White'	GBin LPmr LRHS NCth NLar SDeJ SPer WCAu
- 'Charm'	EGrI WCAu
- 'Cheddar Cheese'	CKel LPmr NCth WCAu
- 'Cheddar Gold'	WCAu
- 'Cherry Hill'	GBin SMad WCAu
- 'Chiffon Clouds'	WCAu
- 'Claire Dubois'	EHyd LRHS NRHS
- 'Class Act'	GBin
- 'Cora Stubbs'	CKel GBin WCAu
- 'Cornelia Shaylor'	WCAu
- 'Couronne d'Or'	GBin LPmr WCAu
- 'Cream Puff'	WCAu
- 'Cringley White'	SRms
- 'Dawn Pink'	WCAu
- 'Day Dream' **new**	LBar
- 'Daystar'	MRav
- 'Dayton'	WCAu
- 'Dinner Plate'	CKel GBin LPmr MGil NCth WCAu
- 'Do Tell'	CKel EHed EPfP ILea LPmr NCth NLar SMad SPer WCAu WHlf
- 'Doctor Alexander Fleming'	CEme CKel EGrI EHyd EPfP EWoo GBin ILea LPmr LRHS MACG MBNS MGil MNrw MPri NBir NRHS SDeJ SOrN SWvt WCAu WFar
- 'Doreen'	CKel EHyd EPfP GBin LPmr LRHS NRHS SHar WCAu
- 'Doris Cooper'	WCAu
- 'Dresden'	WCAu
- 'Drumline'	SDeJ
- 'Dublin'	LPmr NCth
- 'Duchesse de Nemours' ♀H6	Widely available
- 'Edulis Superba'	CRos EBee ECtt EHyd GBin LEdu LPmr LRHS MBNS MRav NPer NRHS SPer WCAu WGwG

- 'Elaine'	MRav
- 'Elsa Sass'	CKel GBin ILea LPmr WCAu
- 'Emma Klehm'	CKel GBin SHar WCAu
- 'Evelyn Tibbets'	GBin
- 'Evening World'	ECha
- 'Fairy's Petticoat'	CKel GBin LPmr NCth WCAu
- 'Félix Crousse' ♀H6	CBcs CKel CTri EBee EGrI ELan EPfP GBin GMaP ILea LPmr LRHS LSRN MBNS MPri MRav NBir NLar SDeJ SPer WCAu WFar XSen
- 'Felix Supreme'	GBin
- 'Festiva Maxima' ♀H6	Widely available
- 'Festiva Supreme'	NCth
- 'Festivity' (d) **new**	LPmr
- 'Fiesta Posey'	WCAu
- 'Fiona'	WCAu
- 'Firebelle'	WCAu
- 'Florence Ellis'	WCAu
- 'Florence Nicholls'	CKel ELan EPfP ILea LPmr NCth WCAu
- 'Foxtrot'	GBin
- 'François Ortegat'	EPfP LRHS
- 'Fuji-no-mine'	NCth
- 'Garden Lace'	SDeJ WCAu
- 'Gardenia'	CKel CRos EHyd EPfP GBin ILea LPmr LRHS NLar NRHS SDeJ WCAu WCot
- 'Gay Paree'	CKel GBin ILea LPmr MGil MHol MRav NCth WCAu
- 'Gayborder June'	EBlo GMcL WCAu
- 'Général Joffre'	MRav
- 'Général MacMahon'	see *P. lactiflora* 'Augustin d'Hour'
- 'Germaine Bigot'	CKel MRav WCAu
- 'Gilbert Barthelot'	WCAu
- 'Glory Hallelujah'	WCAu
- 'Golden Fleece'	WCAu
- 'Golden Frolic'	GBin WCAu
- 'Goldilocks'	CKel WCAu
- 'Goldmine'	NCth SMrm SPeP
- 'Great Sport'	MRav
- 'Green Halo'	GBin LPmr WCot
- 'Green Lotus'	LPmr NLar
- 'Guidon'	WCAu
- 'Hakodate'	NCth
- 'Hansina Brand'	GBin
- 'Happy Days'	WCAu
- 'Hari-ai-nin'	ILea
- 'Helen Hayes'	CKel WCAu
- 'Henri Potin'	NCth
- 'Henry Sass'	CKel WCAu
- 'Hermione'	GBin LPmr WCAu
- 'Highlight'	LPmr
- 'Hit Parade'	WCAu
- 'Honey Gold'	CKel EHed EWoo GBin ILea LPmr SMad SPoG WCAu WSpi
- 'Hot Chocolate'	GBin WCAu
- 'Immaculée'	CKel CWnw EHyd EPfP EWoo GBin ILea LCro LPmr LRHS MRav NCth SCob SPer SPoG
- 'Inspecteur Lavergne'	CKel ECtt EHyd EPfP ILea LPmr LRHS MACG NGdn NRHS SMrm SPer WCAu WCot
- 'Instituteur Doriat'	WCAu
- 'Jacorma'	GBin ILea LPmr NLar
- 'James Kelway'	CKel
- 'Jan van Leeuwen'	CKel CWnw EPfP GBin GMaP LCro LOPS LPmr LRHS NCth SEdd SPer WCAu WCot WKif WTor
- 'Jean Ericksen'	WCAu
- 'Joker'	GBin LPmr WCAu
- 'Jubilee'	LPmr LRHS
- 'Judith Eileen'	WCAu
- 'June Rose'	WCAu

- 'Kansas' CKel EBee EHyd ELan EPfP GBin GMcL ILea LPmr LRHS MPri NBir NCth NGdn NLar NRHS SCob SPoG WCAu WCot WFar WTor
- 'Karen Gray' GBin WCAu
- 'Karl Rosenfield' Widely available
- 'Kelway's Glorious' CKel ECtt EHyd EPfP EWTr LPmr LRHS MBNS MHol MRav NLar NRHS WCAu WGwG WHoo
- KIEV EHyd LPmr LRHS NRHS
§ - 'Koningin Wilhelmina' GBin MNrw
- 'Krekler's Red' WCAu
- 'Krinkled White' CBod CKel CRos EBee EHyd EPfP EWTr EWoo GBin GMaP ILea LPmr LRHS MPri MRav NCth NLar NRHS SDeJ SPeP SPoG WCAu
- 'Lady Alexandra Duff' 🏆H6 CKel GBin GMaP ILea LPmr LRHS MRav NBir NGdn SWvt WCAu WKif
- 'Lady Anna' LPmr
- 'Lady in Red' MHol
- 'Lady Liberty' LPmr NCth
- 'Lady Orchid' WCAu
- 'Lancaster Imp' GBin WCAu
- 'Largo' WCAu
- 'Laura Dessert' 🏆H6 CKel GBin ILea LCro LPmr LRHS WCAu
- 'Laura Shaylor' WCAu
- 'Lavender Whisper' GBin
- 'Le Cygne' CKel NCth WCAu
- 'L'Éclatante' LRHS
- 'Lemon Queen' NCth
- 'Leslie Peck' **new** WCAu
- 'Liebchen' WCAu
- 'Lilac Times' WCAu
- 'Lillian Wild' WCAu
- 'Little Pink Lullaby' GBin
- 'Lois Kelsey' WCAu
- LONDON EHyd LPmr LRHS NRHS
- 'Lord Kitchener' CRos ECtt EHyd EPfP GBin LPmr LRHS NRHS WCAu WGwG
- 'Lotus Queen' ECtt WCAu
- 'Louis van Houtte' EGrI
- 'Love's Touch' GBin
- 'Lowell Thomas' GBin LPmr WCAu
- 'Ma Petite Cherie' GBin
- 'Madame Calot' CKel EHyd LPmr LRHS NCth NRHS WCAu
- 'Madame Claude Tain' GBin LPmr WCot WKif
- 'Madame de Verneville' CKel
- 'Madame Edouard Doriat' WCAu
- 'Madame Emile Debatène' MBNS MHol WCAu WFar
- 'Madame Gaudichau' WCot
- MADRID EHyd LPmr LRHS NRHS SPeP
- 'Magenta Moon' WCAu
- 'Margaret Truman' LPmr WCAu
- 'Marie Crousse' WCAu
- 'Marie Lemoine' CKel CWnw LPmr LRHS MACG NCth WCAu WCot
- 'Martha Reed' WCAu
- 'Midnight Sun' WCAu
- 'Minnie Shaylor' WCAu
- 'Mischief' MRav WCAu
- 'Miss America' 🏆H6 CKel EPfP GBin LPmr NCth NLar WCAu WKif
- 'Miss Eckhart' WCAu
- 'Mister Ed' WCAu
- 'Monsieur Jules Elie' 🏆H6 CKel ELan EPfP EWTr EWoo GBin ILea LCro LPmr LRHS MHol NGdn NLar SPer WCAu
- 'Monsieur Martin Cahuzac' GBin LRHS
- 'Moon of Nippon' GMcL ILea LPmr LRHS MBel NCth NLar WCAu
- 'Moon River' CKel EPfP GBin LPmr NLar WCAu
- 'Morning Kiss' EPfP LPmr NCth
- 'Moscow' (d) LPmr NCth
- 'Mother's Choice' CKel EWoo GBin LCro LOPS LPmr LSRN NGdn NLar WCAu WCot
- 'Mr G.F. Hemerik' CKel EGrI GBin NCth WBor WCAu WCot
- 'Mrs Edward Harding' WCAu
- 'Mrs F.J. Hemerik' MHtn
- 'Mrs Livingston Farrand' GBin
- 'My Pal Rudy' GBin WCAu
- 'Myrtle Gentry' GBin WCAu
- 'Nancy Nicholls' WCAu
- 'Nancy Nora' ILea NCth SPer WCAu
- 'Nellie Shaylor' GBin ILea WCAu
- 'Neon' LPmr LRHS NLar WCAu
- 'Nice Gal' GBin LPmr WCAu
- 'Nick Shaylor' GBin WCAu
- 'Nippon Beauty' EGrI GMcL ILea LPmr LRHS NCth NLar SCob SDeJ WCAu WCot WFar WHlf
- 'Noémie Demay' CKel LPmr LRHS
- 'Norma Volz' WCAu
- 'Nymphe' CKel LPmr MBel MRav NCth NLar SDeJ WCAu
- OSLO LPmr LRHS NCth
- 'Paul M. Wild' CKel ELan ILea LPmr NLar WCAu WHlf
I - 'Peaches and Cream' LPmr
* - 'Pecher' EHyd EPfP LRHS NCth NLar NPer NRHS SDeJ
- 'Peppermint Patti' **new** EHed
- 'Peter Brand' CKel ECtt ELan GBin ILea LPmr LRHS LSRN NCth NLar
- 'Petite Elegance' GBin WCAu
- 'Petite Porcelain' WCAu
- 'Philippe Rivoire' CKel LPmr WCAu
- 'Philomèle' CKel NCth WCAu
- 'Pietertje Vriend Wagenaar' GBin
- 'Pillow Cases' WCAu
- 'Pillow Talk' ELan GBin ILea LPmr LRHS NLar SPoG WCAu
- 'Pink Cameo' WCAu WCot WFar
- 'Pink Dawn' Kelways WCAu
- 'Pink Delight' GBin
- 'Pink Giant' WCAu
- 'Pink Parfait' CKel GBin ILea LPmr SCob SPer WCAu
- 'Pink Princess' GBin WCAu
- 'President Franklin D. Roosevelt' ECtt EHyd LRHS NRHS
- 'President Lincoln' WCAu
- 'Président Poincaré' MRav
- 'President Taft' see *P. lactiflora* 'Reine Hortense'
- 'Primevère' CKel CWnw ECtt GMcL LPmr NBir NCth NLar SPer WFar
- 'Princess Bride' GBin
- 'Princess Margaret' WCAu
§ - 'Purple Spider' LPmr NCth NLar SPeP
- 'Queen of Hearts' **new** LPmr
- 'Queen of Sheba' WCAu
- 'Queen Wilhelmina' see *P. lactiflora* 'Koningin Wilhelmina'
- 'Raoul Dessert' WCAu
- 'Raspberry Sundae' CKel EHed EHyd ELan EPfP ILea LAma LPmr LRHS MRav NLar NRHS SPer SPoG WCAu WCot
- 'Red Emperor' WCAu
- 'Red Queen' CKel GBin NCth
- RED SARAH BERNHARDT EPfP GBin ILea LPmr SDeJ SPer
- 'Red Satin' WCAu
- 'Red Spider' see *P. lactiflora* 'Purple Spider'

§	– 'Reine Hortense'	CKel ECtt GBin LPmr LRHS MRav WCAu
	– 'Renato'	MHol
	– 'Riches and Fame'	LPmr
	– 'Roland'	WCAu
	– ROME	EHyd EPfP LPmr LRHS NRHS SCoo
	– 'Ruth Cobb'	WCAu
	– 'Salmon Dream'	GBin WCAu
	– 'Santa Fe'	CKel EHyd EPfP LRHS NRHS WCAu
	– 'Sarah Bernhardt' ♀H6	Widely available
	– 'Sea Shell'	CKel GBin GMaP ILea SPeP WCAu
	– 'Sebastiaan Maas'	ILea LPmr
	– 'Serene Pastel'	CKel GBin WCAu
	– 'Shawnee Chief'	GBin
	– 'Shirley Temple'	CEme CKel CRos EBee EHyd EPfP EWoo GBin ILea LAma LCro LOPS LPmr LRHS MGos MPri MRav NBir NGdn NRHS SCob SCoo SDeJ SEdd SPoG WCAu WCot WFar WTor
	– 'Silver Rose'	GBin
	– 'Sir Ernest Shackleton'	MRav
	– 'Snow Mountain'	CKel LPmr
	– 'Soft Salmon Joy'	EGrI GBin WCAu
	– 'Solange'	CKel ILea LPmr LRHS WCAu
	– 'Sorbet'	CKel EPfP LPmr LRHS MHol MHtn NBir NLar NPer SDeJ SMad WCAu WFar WTor
	– 'Super Gal'	WCAu
	– 'Surugu'	WCAu
	– 'Suzanne Krekler'	WCAu
	– 'Sweet Sixteen'	GBin LPmr WCAu
	– 'Sword Dance'	CKel CRos EGrI EHyd EPfP GDam GMcL ILea LPmr LRHS NCth NLar NRHS SDeJ WCAu WSpi
	– 'Tamate-boko'	NCth
	– 'The Fawn'	CKel EPfP ILea LPmr WCAu WTor
	– 'The Mighty Mo'	NCth WCAu
	– 'The Nymph'	LRHS NBir
	– 'Theatrical'	WCAu
	– 'Thérèse'	WCAu
	– 'Tom Eckhardt'	CKel GBin WCAu
	– 'Top Brass'	CKel ECtt GBin LPmr MHtn MRav NCth SDeJ WCAu
	– 'Topeka Garnet'	WCAu
	– 'Unique'	WCAu
	– 'Ursa Minor'	WCAu
	– 'Victoire de la Marne'	CKel LPmr
	– 'Victoria Blush'	WCAu
	– 'Vivid Rose'	WCAu
	– 'Vogue'	CKel EPfP LPmr LRHS MRav NCth NRHS SWvt WCAu
	– 'West Elkton'	GBin
	– 'Westerner'	GBin WCAu
	– 'White Angel'	LPmr SPer
	– 'White Cap'	CKel GBin ILea LPmr MMrt NCth NLar WCAu
	– 'White Grace'	GBin WCAu
	– 'White Sands'	GBin
	– WHITE SARAH BERNHARDT	WCot
	– 'White Wings'	CBcs CKel CRos CTri ECtt EHyd ELan EPfP GBin GMaP ILea LPmr LRHS MBel MNrw NCth NLar NRHS NSti SWvt WCAu WCot
	– 'Whitleyi Major' ♀H6	WCot
	– 'Wilbur Wright'	CKel WCAu
	– 'Wine Red'	GBin
	– 'Władysława'	CKel GBin LPmr LRHS MPri NCth NLar SMad SOrN SPer WCot WTor
§	– 'Zi Yu Nu'	MACG NRHS WCAu
	– 'Zuzu'	GBin WCAu
	× ***lagodechiana***	see *P. daurica* subsp. *mlokosewitschii*
	'Late Windflower'	GBin GKev LPla LPmr NLar WCAu WMal
	'Lavender Baby'	GBin
	'Le Printemps'	GBin
§	× ***lemoinei*** 'Alice Harding' (S)	CKel
	– 'High Noon' (S) ♀H5	CKel GMaP LBar LPmr LRHS MPhe WCAu
§	– 'Souvenir de Maxime Cornu' (S)	CKel LBar NRHS
	'Lemon Chiffon'	CBod CKel GBin LPmr NCth WCAu WCot
	'Lemon Dream'PBR	CKel ELan GBin ILea LPmr WCAu
	lobata 'Fire King'	see *P. peregrina*
	'Lollipop' (d)	CKel ELan GBin GMaP ILea LPmr LRHS WCAu
	'Lorelei' (d)	GBin
	'Love Affair'	ELan LPmr WCAu
	'Lovebirds'	WCAu
	'Lovely Rose'	GBin WCAu
	ludlowii (S)	Widely available
	lutea	see *P. delavayi* var. *delavayi* f. *lutea*
	'Mackinac Grand'	GBin WCAu WCot
	'Magenta Gem'	GBin
	'Magical Mystery Tour'	GBin LPmr LRHS WCAu
	'Mahogany'	GBin
	'Mai Fleuri'	GBin WCAu
	mairei	CExl GGGa GGro SPtp WMal
	'Many Happy Returns'	CKel GBin ILea LPmr WCAu
	'Martha Bulloch'	CKel
	mascula	CBro ECha EGrI GEdr GLog NBir WCot
§	– subsp. ***mascula***	GKev
§	– subsp. ***russoi***	WCot
	– – 'Reverchoni'	EPot WAbe
	– subsp. ***triternata***	see *P. daurica*
	'May Apple'	WCAu
	'Merry Mayshine'	GBin GKev
	'Mikuhino-akebono'	CKel SDeJ
	mlokosewitschii	see *P. daurica* subsp. *mlokosewitschii*
	mollis	see *P. officinalis* subsp. *officinalis*
	'Montezuma'	WCAu
	'Moonrise'	CKel GBin LPmr NCth NLar WCAu
	'Morning Lilac'	CKel GBin ILea LPmr LRHS SMad SPeP WCAu
	'Muramatsu-no-yuki'	LPmr
	'My Love'	CKel GBin LPmr WCAu
	'Norwegian Blush'	CKel GBin ILea LPmr WCAu
	'Nosegay'	GBin WCAu
	'Nova'	GBin
§	***obovata***	GKev
	– subsp. ***obovata***	SPtp
	– – 'Alba' ♀H5	CExl GEdr GKev WSHC WSpi
	– subsp. ***willmottiae***	CExl GGro
	officinalis	GKev MCot WCot
	– WM 9821 from Slovenia	MPhe
	– from NW Croatia	LEdu
	– 'Alba Plena'	see *P.* × *festiva* 'Alba Plena'
	– 'Anemoniflora Rosea' ♀H6	EHyd EPfP ILea LPmr LRHS NRHS SWvt WCAu
§	– subsp. ***banatica***	GKev MPhe WCAu
	– subsp. ***humilis***	see *P. officinalis* subsp. *microcarpa*
§	– subsp. ***huthii***	LPmr LRHS SEND WCAu
	– 'James Crawford Weguelin'	WCot
§	– subsp. ***microcarpa***	LPmr WCot
	– 'Mutabilis Plena'	see *P.* × *festiva* 'Mutabilis Plena'
§	– subsp. ***officinalis***	GKev LPmr NLar
	– 'Rosea Plena'	see *P.* × *festiva* 'Rosea Plena'
	– 'Rubra Plena'	see *P.* × *festiva* 'Rubra Plena'
	– subsp. ***villosa***	see *P. officinalis* subsp. *huthii*
	'Old Faithful'	GBin LPmr WCAu
	'Old Rose Dandy'	CKel ELan GBin ILea LPmr

	ostii (S)	CExl GKev
	'Oukan' (S)	CKel
	'Paladin'	GBin
	papaveracea	see *P.* × *suffruticosa*
	paradoxa	see *P. officinalis* subsp. *microcarpa*
	'Paris'	EHyd LRHS
	'Pastel Splendor'	CKel CRos EHyd ELan GBin ILea LPmr LRHS MCot NLar NRHS WCAu
	'Patio Moscow Deep' (Patio Series)	LRHS
	'Paula Fay'	EPfP GBin GMaP ILea LPmr MGil MRav NCth NLar SDeJ WCAu WCot
	'Pehrson's Violet Frisbee'	GBin
§	***peregrina***	CBro CSpe GEdr GKev LEdu MPhe WCAu
	- 'Fire King'	LPmr WCAu
§	- 'Otto Froebel' ♀H6	CKel CWnw LPmr WCAu WCot WKif
	- 'Rosabella'	EHyd LRHS NRHS
	- 'Sunshine'	see *P. peregrina* 'Otto Froebel'
	'Picotee'	GBin WCAu
	'Pink Ardour'	GBin
	'Pink Double Dandy' (d)	GBin LPmr
	'Pink Hawaiian Coral'	CKel EHed GBin ILea LPmr MPri NCth NLar WCAu WCot WTor
	'Pink Pom Pom'	WCAu
	'Pink Vanguard'	WCAu
	'Postilion'	GBin
	potaninii	see *P. delavayi* var. *angustiloba* f. *angustiloba*
	'Prairie Charm'	CKel EPfP ILea LPmr LRHS
	'Prairie Moon'	CKel GBin WCAu
	'Raggedy Ann'	CKel ELan GBin LPmr
	'Raspberry Charm'	SDir
	'Red Charm'	CKel EPfP EWTr GBin ILea LAma LPmr LRHS NCth SPer WCAu WFar WSpi
	'Red Glory'	WCAu
	'Red Grace' (d)	GBin LPmr WCAu
	'Red Magic'	EPfP WFar WSpi
	'Red Red Rose'	GBin WCAu
	'Requiem'	GBin WCAu
§	***rockii*** (S)	GKev LRHS MPhe SMDa SPtp WSpi
	- from Tai Bai Shan, China **new**	MPhe
	- subsp. ***linyanshanii*** (S)	CJun
	'Roman Gold'	CKel
	romanica	see *P. peregrina*
	'Rose Flame' (S)	WCAu
	'Rose Garland'	GBin
	'Rosedale'	GBin WCAu
	'Roselette'	GBin NCth WCAu
	'Roselette's Child'	GBin
	'Roy Pehrson's Best Yellow'	GBin
	russoi	see *P. mascula* subsp. *russoi*
	'Salmon Beauty' (d)	WCAu
	'Salmon Chiffon'	GBin
	'Scarlet Heaven'	CKel ELan GBin ILea LPmr LRHS MNrw NLar WCAu
	'Scarlet O'Hara'	CKel EWoo LPmr NLar SPer WCAu WCot
	'Scrumdidleumptious' (d)	GBin LPmr WHlf
	'Sebastian Maas' (d)	LPmr
	'Sequestered Sunshine'	CKel ILea LPmr LRHS WCAu
	'Serebrenyi Velvet'	GBin
	'Serenade'	WCAu
	'Shikoh' (S)	CKel
	'Shimano-fuji' (S)	CKel WCAu
	'Shining Light'	LPmr
	'Show Girl'	LPmr WCAu
	'Silver Dawn'	GBin
	'Simply Red'	LPmr
	'Singing in the Rain'	CKel GBin ILea LBar LPmr WCAu
	sinjianensis	see *P. anomala* subsp. *anomala*
	'Smith Family Yellow'	LPmr
	× ***smouthii***	EHyd GEdr LRHS NRHS
	'Soft Salmon Saucer'	GBin WCAu
	'Sonoma Amethyst'	CKel ELan GBin LPmr
	'Sonoma Apricot'	LPmr WCAu
	'Sonoma Blessing' **new**	LPmr
	'Sonoma By the Bay' **new**	GBin LPmr
	'Sonoma Floozy' **new**	LPmr
	'Sonoma Halo' (d) **new**	LPmr
	'Sonoma Kaleidoscope'	CKel GBin ILea LPmr
	'Sonoma Opal' **new**	LPmr
	'Sonoma Rosy Future' **new**	LPmr WCAu
	'Sonoma Sun'	CKel LPmr
	'Sonoma Velvet Ruby'	GBin LPmr LRHS
	'Sonoma Welcome' **new**	LPmr
	'Sonoma YeDo' **new**	LPmr
	'Soshi'	GBin LRHS
	'Stardust'	WCAu
	'Starlight'	LCro LPmr LRHS NCth SHar WCAu WCot WTor
§	× ***suffruticosa*** (S)	CDoC MGil MGos
	- 'Akashigata' (S)	CKel
	- 'Akisato-no-hamare' (S) **new**	LBar
	- 'Alice Palmer' (S)	CKel
	- BIRD OF RIMPO	see *P.* × *suffruticosa* 'Rimpo'
	- BLACK DRAGON BROCADE	see *P.* × *suffruticosa* 'Kokuryū-nishiki'
	- BLACK FLOWER CHIEF	see *P.* × *suffruticosa* 'Hei Hua Kui'
	- 'Cardinal Vaughan' (S)	CKel
	- dark lavender-flowered (S)	EWTr
	- dark pink-flowered (S)	EWTr
	- 'Dou Lu' (S)	NTPC
	- DOUBLE CHERRY	see *P.* × *suffruticosa* 'Yae-zakura'
	- 'Duchess of Kent' (S)	CKel
	- 'Duchess of Marlborough' (S)	CKel
	- ETERNAL CAMELLIAS	see *P.* × *suffruticosa* 'Yachiyo-tsubaki'
	- FLIGHT OF CRANES	see *P.* × *suffruticosa* 'Renkaku'
	- FLORAL RIVALRY	see *P.* × *suffruticosa* 'Hana-kisoi'
	- 'Gekkyu-den' (S)	LPmr LRHS
	- 'Hai Huang' (S)	NTPC
§	- 'Hakuo-jisi' (S/d)	LRHS WCAu
	- 'Hakushin' (S)	LPmr
	- 'Hana-asobi' (S)	LRHS
§	- 'Hana-daijin' (S)	LRHS WCAu
§	- 'Hana-kisoi' (S)	LPmr LRHS NRHS WCAu
§	- 'Hei Hua Kui' (S)	NTPC
	- JEWEL IN THE LOTUS	see *P.* × *suffruticosa* 'Tama-fuyo'
	- 'Jitsugetsu-nishiki' (S)	LPmr
§	- 'Kamada-fuji' (S)	CKel LPmr
§	- 'Kaow' (S)	LPmr NRHS WCAu
	- KING OF FLOWERS	see *P.* × *suffruticosa* 'Kaow'
	- KING OF WHITE LIONS	see *P.* × *suffruticosa* 'Hakuo-jisi'
	- 'Kinkaku'	see *P.* × *lemoinei* 'Souvenir de Maxime Cornu'
	- 'Kinshi'	see *P.* × *lemoinei* 'Alice Harding'
§	- 'Kokuryū-nishiki' (S)	LPmr
	- 'Koshi-no-maihime' (S) **new**	LPmr
	- 'Koshino-yuki' (S)	LRHS
	- 'Kuro-ageha' (S) **new**	LPmr
	- 'Lan Bao Shi' (S)	NTPC
	- MAGNIFICENT FLOWER	see *P.* × *suffruticosa* 'Hana-daijin'
	- 'Mikasayama' (S)	LBar
	- 'Mrs William Kelway' (S)	CKel
	- 'Nigata Akashigata' (S)	CKel
	- 'Ofuji-nishiki' (S)	LBar
	- 'Okan' (S) **new**	LPmr
	- purple-flowered (S)	EWTr

§ - 'Renkaku' (S) CKel LBar LPmr LRHS
§ - 'Rimpo' (S) CKel WSpi
- subsp. ***rockii*** see *P. rockii*
- 'Rou Fu Rong' (S) WSpi
- 'Sakurajishi' (S) CKel
- 'Seidai' (S) LRHS
- 'Shichi-fukujin' (S) **new** LPmr
- 'Shikōden' (S) LRHS
- 'Shimadaijin' LBar LPmr LRHS NRHS WCAu
- 'Shimafuji' (S) **new** LBar
- 'Shimane-chōjuraku' (S) CKel LPmr
- 'Shimane-hakugan' (S) CKel
- 'Shimane-seidai' (S) CKel LPmr
- 'Shimanishiki' (S) CKel LPmr
- 'Shimazu-kurenai' (S) **new** LPmr
- 'Shunkoju' (S/d) **new** LPmr
- SNOWY PAGODA see *P.* × *suffruticosa* 'Xue Ta'
- 'Superb' (S) CKel
§ - 'Taiyo' (S) LPmr LRHS NRHS
§ - 'Tama-fuyo' (S) CKel
- 'Teikan' (S/d) **new** LPmr
- THE SUN see *P.* × *suffruticosa* 'Taiyo'
- white-flowered (S) EWTr
- WISTERIA AT KAMADA see *P.* × *suffruticosa* 'Kamada-fuji'
- 'Wu Long Peng Sheng' (S) LPar WSpi
§ - 'Xue Ta' (S) LPar
§ - 'Yachiyo-tsubaki' (S) CKel LPmr WCAu
§ - 'Yae-zakura' (S) LRHS
- yellow-flowered (S) GMcL
- 'Yin Hong Qiao Dui' (S) NTPC
- 'Yu Ban Bai' (S) EGrl
- 'Zhao Fen' (S) NPer NTPC SRms
'Sugar 'n' Spice' GBin
'Summer Glow' (d) LPmr WCAu
'Sunny Girl' GBin WCAu
'Sunshine' see *P. peregrina* 'Otto Froebel'
'Syukiden' CKel
'Tama-usagi' CKel
'Tango' WCAu
'Ten' i' LBar
tenuifolia CBro CJun CPla EPot EWes GBin GEdr GKev LPmr MBel SMad WCAu WSpi
- 'Rosea' GBin WCAu
'Terrific Gal' GBin
'Tolomeo No 59' **new** GBin LPmr
'Unique' ILea LPmr
veitchii see *P. anomala* subsp. *veitchii*
- var. ***woodwardii*** see *P. anomala* subsp. *veitchii*
'Viking Full Moon' CKel ILea LPmr NLar WCAu
'Walter Mains' WCAu
'Watermelon Wine' CKel GBin ILea LPmr WCAu
'White Charm' GBin
'White Emperor' CKel ELan GBin ILea LPmr LRHS WCAu
'White Imperial' **new** WCAu
'White Innocence' GBin
'White Towers' NCth NLar WFar
'Whopper' GBin
wittmanniana see *P. daurica* subsp. *wittmanniana*
'Yankee Doodle Dandy' (d) GBin LPmr LRHS WCAu
'Yellow Crown' GBin LAma LPmr LRHS MHol SCob SDir WCAu
'Yellow Dream' LPmr
'Yellow Gem' LPmr
'Yellow Waterlily' CKel GBin LPmr

Paesia (*Dennstaedtiaceae*)

scaberula CBrP EHed LEdu NBir WCot WPGP

pak choi see AGM Vegetables Section

Paliurus (*Rhamnaceae*)

spina-christi WJur XSen

Pallenis (*Asteraceae*)

§ ***maritima*** CCCN

Pamianthe (*Amaryllidaceae*)

peruviana WMal

Panax (*Araliaceae*)

ginseng GPoy
japonicus WCru
- BWJ 7932 WCru

Pancratium (*Amaryllidaceae*)

canariense NRog
illyricum SBrt
maritimum CBor GKev LAma SDeJ WCot WJur

Pandanus (*Pandanaceae*)

utilis NPlm

Pandorea (*Bignoniaceae*)

jasminoides ♀H1c CCCN CDoC CHll CRHN EAri EShb
- 'Alba' CHll CRHN EShb
§ - 'Charisma' (v) CBcs CCCN CHll CKel EAri ECre EPfP EShb SEND WAvo
- 'Lady Di' CCCN
- 'Rosea' CCCN WAvo
- 'Rosea Superba' ♀H1c CBcs CRHN SEND WLov
- 'Variegata' see *P. jasminoides* 'Charisma'
lindleyana see *Clytostoma calystegioides*
pandorana CHll CRHN MGil WAvo
- 'Golden Showers' CBcs CCCN CKel CRHN MRav WLov
- 'Snowbells' IArd IDee

Panicum (*Poaceae*)

amarum EPPr
- 'Dewey Blue' EWes SMHy
bulbosum EBee EPPr
clandestinum EPPr EWes
'Frosted Explosion' CSpe LRHS
miliaceum SVic
- 'Violaceum' SPhx
virgatum CKno EPPr LRHS XLum
- 'Black and Blue' MNrw SMHy
- 'Black and Light' MNrw
- 'Blue Tower' CKno ELon EPPr XLum
- 'Cardinal' CKno ECha EPPr EWes MNrw WFar WHoo
- 'Carthage' EPPr
- 'Cave-in-Rock' EPPr
- 'Cheyenne Sky' ECha EPPr SMHy
- 'Cloud Nine' ♀H5 CBWd CKno EBee EPPr LRHS MAvo
- 'Dallas Blues' ♀H5 CBod CKel CKno EBee ECha EHyd ELan ELon EPPr EPfP EShb EWes GBee LRHS MAvo NLar NRHS SCob SGbt SMHy SPeP SPer SPoG WFar XLum XSte
- 'Emerald Chief' EPPr LSun SBls
- 'Farbende Auslese' EPPr
- 'Hänse Herms' ♀H5 CBod CKno EAJP EBlo EHyd ELon EMor EPPr LRHS NLar NRHS WFar
- 'Heavy Metal' ♀H5 Widely available
- 'Heiliger Hain' CBWd ECha EHyd ELon EPPr GElm LRHS NRHS NWsh WCot WFar WHoo
- 'Hot Rod' CBod IPot NDov
- 'JS Blue Darkness'PBR IPot LRHS MAvo SCoo SPoG WFar
- 'JS Dark Night'PBR MAvo
I - 'Kupferhirse' ECha EPPr MAvo WFar
- 'Kurt Bluemel' EBee ECha EPPr

- 'Külsenmoor' EBee ECha IPot WCot
- 'Nican' EPPr
- 'Northwind' ♀H5 CBWd CKno CRos CSde EBlo EHyd ELon EPPr EPfP LRHS MACG MAvo NRHS SCob SCoo SEdd SMHy SMad SPeP SPoG SRms WFar
- 'Prairie Fire' ECtt
- 'Prairie Sky' CBod CKel CKno CRos CWnw EAJP EBee EHyd ELon EPPr EPfP EWTr EWhm EWoo GMaP LEdu LRHS MACG MAsh MAvo NBro NLar NRHS NWsh SCob SCoo SEdd SGbt SMHy SRms
- PURPLE BREEZE ('Joz276'PBR) CBod CKno CPar LCro LOPS LRHS SPad SPeP
- 'Purple Haze' EBlo ECha EPPr
- 'Red Cloud' CKno ELon MAvo
- 'Rehbraun' CSde EHyd ELan EPPr EPfP GElm LCro LOPS LRHS LSRN MBel NRHS SCob SRms WCAu WChS XLum
- 'Rotstrahlbusch' CKno EHeP ELan EPPr GMaP LRHS LSun MAvo SPer SRms WCot XLum
- 'Rubrum' EPfP LRHS MAvo SRms
- 'Sangria'PBR CBod CSpe LEdu SPoG
- 'Shenandoah' ♀H5 Widely available
- 'Squaw' Widely available
- 'Straight Cloud' EPPr WFar
- 'Strictum' CBod EPPr EWes GQue LRHS SCob SMHy SPer SPhx
- 'Sunburst' EPPr
- 'Thundercloud' CKno SPeP
- 'Warrior' CAby CBWd CKno CRos CTri EAJP ECtt EHyd ELan ELon EPPr EPfP EWhm LRHS MAsh MAvo MCot NFav NLar NRHS NWsh SBls SCob SCoo SPer WCAu WFar WHoo WTor
- 'Wood's Variegated' (v) WCot

Papaver (*Papaveraceae*)

alboroseum EHyd GArf LRHS NRHS
alpinum EHyd GQue MAsh NRHS
atlanticum LDai NBro SPlb
- 'Flore Pleno' (d) CSpe NBro
bracteatum see *P. orientale* var. ***bracteatum***
burseri SRot
§ ***cambricum*** CCCN CDor CMac CTri CTtf ECha EHyd ELan EMor EPfP LEdu LRHS NAts NRHS SPer WBrk WCot WFar WHer
- var. ***aurantiacum*** CDor WCot
§ - 'Frances Perry' CSpe EPPr
- 'Rubrum' see *P. cambricum* 'Frances Perry'
'Cherry Glow' SPhx
commutatum ♀H5 CSpe LCro LOPS SPhx
- 'Ladybird' ♀H5 GAbr LBar SPoG SVic
dubium GPoy SPhx
- subsp. ***lecoqii*** 'Albiflorum' CSpe ECha LCro LRHS SDix SPhx
'Faucett Moon' LRHS
glaucum CSpe SPhx
guerlekense W&B BG-K-5 WCot
'Heartbeat' (Super Poppy Series) EPfP MHol NBPC WFar
heldreichii see *P. pilosum* subsp. *spicatum*
lateritium SRms
'Matador'PBR ♀H6 NRHS
'Medallion' (Super Poppy Series) MPie
§ ***miyabeanum*** CSpe EHyd LRHS NRHS
'Moondance' CBcs CFis CRos EHyd LRHS MACG NRHS SVic
§ ***nudicaule*** EHeP LCro SVic
- Champagne Bubbles Group CBod EHyd LRHS NRHS WFar WWke
- - 'Champagne Bubbles Scarlet' LBar
- DELUXE MIXED CSpe
- Garden Gnome Group see *P. nudicaule* Gartenzwerg Group
§ - Gartenzwerg Group ♀H7 EHyd EPfP LBar LRHS NRHS SPoG SRot SWvt
- 'Kelmscott Giant' SVic
- 'Pacino' LRHS
- (Wonderland Series) 'Wonderland Orange' LBar
- - 'Wonderland Pink' LBar
- - 'Wonderland White' LBar
- - 'Wonderland Yellow' LBar
Oriental Group EHeP
- 'Aglaja' ♀H7 CBcs CDor LRHS NGdn WCAu WCot WSpi
- 'Allegro' CSBt EHyd GMaP LRHS LSun MPri NGdn SCob SCoo SPlb SPoG SVic SWvt WFar
- 'Baby Kiss'PBR WFar
- 'Beauty of Livermere' CBod CDor EAJP ECha EHyd ELan EWoo LBar LCro LOPS LRHS MACG MAvo MCot MNHC MPri NGdn NLar SBls SCoo SGbt SPer SPoG SRms WCAu WFar WPnP
§ - 'Beauty of Livermere' clonal WCot
- 'Beauty Queen' CDor NGdn
- 'Bolero' EPri MACG MHol
- 'Bonfire Red' SCob
- 'Brilliant' CTsd CWal EHyd GQue LBar LRHS MPri NGdn NRHS SCoo WFar
- 'Brooklyn' (New York Series) EGrI LRHS
- 'Burning Heart' CWGN
- 'Carneum' EHyd EPfP LRHS NRHS SPoG SRms
- 'Cedric Morris' ♀H7 ECha EPPr
- 'Central Park' (New York Series) CBod EHyd LRHS NLar WFar
- 'Coral Reef' CBod GJos MSCN SCgs
- 'Curlilocks' EHyd GMcL SRms SWvt WFar
- Double Red Shades (d) NGdn
- 'Doubloon' (d) WFar
- 'Dwarf Allegro' LRHS MPri
- 'Dwarf Allegro Vivace' EHyd
- 'Eyecatcher' NLar
- 'Fiesta' ELon
- 'Flamenco' WFar
- 'Forncett Summer' EPfP NLar SPer SPoG WCAu WCot WHlf
- 'Fruit Punch' EPfP
- 'Garden Glory' MAvo
- 'Goliath' ELan NBro SRms WFar
- HAREMSTRAUM (mixed) WFar
- 'Harlem' (New York Series) CBcs CElw CRos EHyd EPfP LRHS MNrw NLar WHlf
- 'Harvest Moon' (d) CBod EHyd EPfP LRHS NPer NRHS SPeP WHlf
- 'Indian Chief' NPer SCob WFar
- 'Karine' ♀H7 SCob
- 'King Kong' MBel WFar
- 'Kleine Tänzerin' CBod SEND WFar
- 'Ladybird' EHyd LRHS
- 'Little Patty Plum'PBR MHol NLar WTyc
- 'Louvre' (Parisienne Series) WFar
- 'Manhattan' (New York Series) CElw EHyd EPfP LRHS MNrw NRHS NSti SGbt SPeP WFar
- 'Marlene' LRHS NLar WCAu WHlf
- 'May Queen' (d) EWes WCot WFar
- 'Miss Piggy'PBR SGbt WFar
- 'Mrs Perry' EHyd LRHS NLar NPer SGbt SRms WCAu WFar

- 'Orange Glow' NBPC
- 'Papillon'PBR CBcs NRHS
§ - 'Patty's Plum' Widely available
- 'Perry's White' CBcs EHeP EHyd GMcL NChi SCob SRkn SWvt WCAu WPnP WSpi
- 'Picotée' ECtt GMcL LRHS SCob SWvt WFar WPnP
- 'Pink Ruffles'PBR SGbt WFar
- 'Pinnacle' WFar
- 'Pizzicato' CBod CRos EAJP EHyd LRHS NPer WFar
- 'Place Pigalle' (Parisienne Series) NBPC WPnP
- 'Plum Pudding' EHyd ELan EPfP LRHS
- 'Prince of Orange' SWvt
- 'Prinz Eugen' WFar
§ - 'Prinzessin Victoria Louise' CDor CKel CRos EAJP EHyd ELan EPfP EWoo GJos GMaP LBar LRHS MPri NGdn NRHS SEND SPoG SRms WBrk
- 'Queen Alexandra' CDor EHyd EPfP LRHS NChi SCoo
- 'Raspberry Brûlée' EHyd LRHS NRHS
- 'Raspberry Queen' CDor MAvo NChi
- 'Rembrandt' EWoo LPal WCot
- 'Royal Chocolate Distinction' CBod ECtt ELan EPfP LRHS MHol NBPC WFar
- 'Royal Wedding' Widely available
- 'Ruffled Patty'PBR ECtt ELan SGbt WCot WPnP
- 'Salmon Glow' (d) WFar
- 'Scarlett O'Hara'PBR (d) ECtt WFar
- 'Snow Goose' CDor CWGN ECtt EHyd EPfP GAbr LRHS NBPC NLar NRHS SCob SPoG WCot WTor WTyc
- 'Springtime' WCav
- 'Staten Island' (New York Series) MNrw
- 'Sweet Sensation' MHol
- 'Tiffany' ECtt
- 'Türkenlouis' CBcs CBod ECtt NLar NQui SPoG WBrk WCAu WFar
- 'Turkish Delight' EWoo MBel NBir SWvt WCAu
- 'Walking Fire' MNrw
- 'Waltzing Elisabeth'PBR MNHC
- 'Watermelon' SCob SPoG
- 'White Ruffles'PBR CBod EPfP SGbt

orientale CBcs EGrI GArf LPal SRms SVic
§ - var. ***bracteatum*** GGro
- 'Guardsman' see *P.* (Oriental Group) 'Beauty of Livermere' clonal
- 'Mrs Marrow's Plum' see *P.* (Oriental Group) 'Patty's Plum'
- PRINCESS VICTORIA LOUISE see *P.* (Oriental Group) 'Prinzessin Victoria Louise'

§ ***pilosum*** subsp. ***spicatum*** CSpe ECha LPla NBir WCot
popovii GGro
- from Tajikistan **new** GGro
rhoeas CBod CHab LCro LOPS LRHS MBow MHoo MNHC SPhx SVic
- 'Amazing Grey' **new** CSpe
- 'Bridal Silk' CSpe LCro
- 'Bridal White' LOPS SPhx
- Mother of Pearl Group CSpe LCro LRHS SPhx
- 'Pandora' **new** CSpe LCro SPhx
- 'Paradise' CSpe
rupifragum CBod CKel ECha LShi SPhx WCot
- 'Double Tangerine Gem' see *P. rupifragum* 'Flore Pleno'
§ - 'Flore Pleno' (d) CBcs CDor CSpe CWal EPPr GBin MAsh MBNS SVic WBrk
'Shasta' (Super Poppy Series) LRHS WFar
somniferum ENfk GPoy SVic
- var. ***album*** LRHS
- 'Blackcurrant Fizz' (d) LCro LOPS SPhx
- 'Boudoir Babe' (d) CSpe
- 'Hungarian Blue' **new** LCro
- (Laciniatum Group) 'Black Swan' **new** LCro
- 'Lauren's Grape' CSpe LCro LOPS LRHS SPhx
- 'Lilac Pompom' (d) LCro LOPS
- (Paeoniiflorum Group) 'Black Beauty' (d) CSpe SDeJ SPhx SVic
- - 'Black Paeony' (d) CKel LCro LRHS
- - 'Scarlet Paeony' (d) **new** WCot
- - 'Schwarzer Drachen' (d) LRHS
- 'Persian White' CSpe SPhx
- single black-flowered CSpe SPhx
- - white-flowered CSpe
- 'Sissinghurst White' **new** SPhx
- 'White Cloud' (d) CSpe
'Spring Fever Red' LRHS MPri
triniifolium GGro SPhx WCot

papaya (pawpaw) see *Carica papaya*

Parabenzoin see *Lindera*

Parachampionella see *Strobilanthes*

Paradisea (*Asparagaceae*)

liliastrum misapplied see *P. lusitanica*
liliastrum (L.) Bertol. ♀H5 EBee EPfP EPri LRHS NBid NChi NSla
§ ***lusitanica*** CAvo CBor CNor CSpe EBee EGrI EHed EPri GBin GKev LEdu MHol SPhx WCot WKif

Parahebe (*Plantaginaceae*)

× ***bidwillii*** EDAr GJos SRms
- 'Kea' SRot
§ ***catarractae*** CExl ECha EHyd ELan EPfP EWld ITim LRHS MSCN NBir NRHS SLee SRms WCav WKif
- 'Avalanche'PBR CBod CWGN EHyd EPfP GDam GMaP LRHS MAsh MMrt MSCN NRHS SGBe SGbt SPoG SSha WHer WHlf WHtc WNPC WWke XSte
- 'Baby Blue' EHyd LRHS NRHS
- blue-flowered GJos SGbt SPer
§ - 'Delight' ♀H4 CExl EHyd GMaP GQue LRHS MHer MMrt NPer NRHS SCob WLov
- subsp. ***diffusa*** NPer SRot
- 'Miss Willmott' ECtt SPer SPlb
- 'Pink Avalanche' **new** WNPC
- 'Porlock' CBod CDoC CWnw EPfP GDam GKev SBut SDix SGBe SRms SRot SSha SWvt WCav WHoo
- 'Porlock Purple' see *P. catarractae* 'Delight'
- 'Rosea' MAsh SRms WTyc
- white-flowered EGrI GAbr SRms
- 'Whittallii' GBin
decora GKev
densifolia see *Chionohebe densifolia*
§ ***formosa*** SPlb
'Greencourt' see *P. catarractae* 'Delight'
§ ***hookeriana*** GKev
'Jean' GBin
'Kenty Pink' CWnw MMuc WHlf
linifolia 'Blue Skies' ECtt EPot GBin
§ ***lyallii*** EBee ELan EPfP GDam GMaP MHer MMuc MRav MSwo NQui SLee SPlb SRms WIce WKif
- 'Julie-Anne' ♀H4 LRHS SGBe SLee
- 'Snowcap' EBee LCro LRHS MRav SGBe SPlb SRms
'Mervyn' CNor CTri

§ ***perfoliata*** CDor CExl CSde EBee ECha EGrI GMaP LEdu MAsh MMrt MNrw MRav SBrt SBut SDix SEND SPer SPlb SRms WHlf WOld WSHC WTor WWFP XLum
'Snow Clouds' CBar CBod CElw CKel CSpe CTsd CWnw ECtt EHyd ELan EPfP EWoo GKev LRHS NEoE NHpl NRHS SBut SDix SEdd SGBe SGro SPad SRot SSha WFar WHoo WTor

Parajubaea (*Arecaceae*)

torallyi LRHS NPlm

Parakmeria see *Magnolia*

Paramongaia (*Amaryllidaceae*)

weberbaueri WMal

Paranomus (*Proteaceae*)

reflexus SPlb

Paraquilegia (*Ranunculaceae*)

adoxoides see *Semiaquilegia adoxoides*
§ ***anemonoides*** CExl EDAr GKev WAbe
grandiflora see *P. anemonoides*

Parasenecio (*Asteraceae*)

delphiniifolius B&SWJ 5789 WCru
- B&SWJ 10885 WCru
- B&SWJ 11189 WCru
- B&SWJ 11415 WCru
farfarifolius WCru
- var. ***acerinus*** B&SWJ 11549 WCru
- - B&SWJ 11554 WCru
- var. ***bulbifer*** WCru
hastatus var. ***farfarifolius*** see *P. maximowiczianus*
- subsp. ***orientalis*** variegated (v) GGro
§ ***maximowiczianus*** B&SWJ 11468 WCru
mortonii GWJ 9419 WCru
- HWJK 2214 WCru
tebakoensis B&SWJ 11167 WCru
- B&SWJ 11536 WCru

Paraserianthes (*Fabaceae*)

distachya see *P. lophantha*
§ ***lophantha*** ♀H2 CExl CTsd EAri EShb MVil SPlb

Parastyrax (*Styracaceae*)

BWJ 15185 from Northern Vietnam WCru

Parasyringa see *Ligustrum*

Parathelypteris (*Thelypteridaceae*)

beddomei LEdu WCot WPGP
- crested LEdu

× *Pardancanda* (*Iridaceae*)

norrisii see *Iris* × *norrisii*

Parietaria (*Urticaceae*)

judaica GPoy WHer WSFF

Paris (*Melanthiaceae*)

chinensis WCru
forrestii WCru
incompleta CTtf ESwi GEdr GKev LEdu MAvo WCru
japonica GEdr
lancifolia B&SWJ 3044 from Taiwan WCru
polyphylla CMiW ECha EGrI GKev LAma MNrw NBid NFav NHpl NLar SDir SDix WCru WPnP
- B&SWJ 2125 WCru
- HWJCM 475 WCru
- var. ***alba*** GEdr
- var. ***polyphylla*** GKev
- var. ***stenophylla*** WCru
quadrifolia CSpe CTtf EBee EMor EPfP GEdr GKev GPoy LEdu MNrw MVil NGrd NLar WCru WFar WHer WShi
thibetica EBee GKev LAma
- var. ***thibetica*** SDir

Parkinsonia (*Fabaceae*)

aculeata SPlb WJur

Parnassia (*Celastraceae*)

asarifolia GKev
cabulica GKev
foliosa NHar
gansuensis NHar
- SDR 5128 GKev
nubicola GKev
palustris EMor GKev
- var. ***yakushimensis*** NHar

Parochetus (*Fabaceae*)

communis ambig. CExl EWld MSCN NPer WFar
communis Buch.-Ham. ex D. Don subsp. ***africanus*** ♀H2 CPla
* - 'Blue Gem' CCCN

Parodia (*Cactaceae*)

comarapana new NMen
§ ***concinna*** ♀H2 new NMen
haselbergii new NMen
§ ***hausteiniana*** new NMen
laui see *P. hausteiniana*
leninghausii ♀H2 new EAri
magnifica ♀H2 new NMen
§ ***mammulosa*** new NMen
§ ***microsperma*** new NMen
mutabilis see *P. microsperma*
ottonis ♀H2 new NMen
* ***peruviana*** new NMen
scopa see *P. scopa* subsp. *scopa*
§ - subsp. ***scopa*** ♀H2 new EAri
tabularis see *P. concinna*
warasii new EAri

Parolinia (*Brassicaceae*)

ornata WCot

Paronychia (*Caryophyllaceae*)

argentea EDAr
§ ***capitata*** CTri SRms
kapela SPlb XSen
§ - subsp. ***serpyllifolia*** XLum
- - 'Binsted Gold' (v) XLum
nivea see *P. capitata*
serpyllifolia see *P. kapela* subsp. *serpyllifolia*

Parrotia ✿ (*Hamamelidaceae*)

persica Widely available
- PAB 13.046 LEdu

- 'Bella'	CJun EBee LMaj MBlu MTrO NLar WHtc WMat WMou
- 'Biltmore'	CJun SSta
- 'Burgundy'	CJun EPfP MAsh NLar
- 'Cobhay Upright'	CJun
- fastigiate	CJun SSta
- 'Felicie'	CJun EPfP IArd IDee NLar
- 'Het Plantsoen'	NLar
- 'Horizontalis'	CJun
- 'Jodrell Bank'	CJun LIns MBlu NLar
- 'Pendula'	CJun CMCN EPfP MBlu SSta
- 'Persian Carpet'	NLar
- PERSIAN SPIRE ('Jlpn01'PBR)	CBcs EBee LCro LMil LOPS LPar LRHS MAsh SGol SGsty SMad WHtc
- 'Summer Bronze'	CJun EHyd ELan EPfP LRHS MAsh
- 'Vanessa' ♀H6	CBcs CCVT CJun CMCN CWnw EBee EGrl EHyd ELan EPfP EWTr EWes IArd IPap LMaj LMil LPar LRHS LSRN MAsh MBlu MPkF MTrO NLar NRHS SCob SGol SSta WMat WMou
subaequalis	CBcs CJun MBlu NLar SGol WPGP

Parrotia × *Sycopsis* see × *Sycoparrotia*

Parrotiopsis (*Hamamelidaceae*)

jacquemontiana	CBcs GBin LMaj LPar MBlu NLar

Parrya (*Brassicaceae*)

pulvinata	GKev

parsley see *Petroselinum crispum*

parsnip see AGM Vegetables Section

Parsonsia (*Apocynaceae*)

heterophylla	CTsd

Parthenium (*Asteraceae*)

integrifolium	CBWd GPoy LPla SPhx

Parthenocissus (*Vitaceae*)

§ ***henryana*** ♀H4	Widely available
- 'Malene'	EShb
himalayana	WJur
- 'Purpurea'	see *P. himalayana* var. *rubrifolia*
§ - var. ***rubrifolia***	CMac ELan GBin MAsh MRav SPtp WCru
inserta misapplied	see *P. quinquefolia*
inserta ambig.	CMac NLar
laetevirens	NLar
§ ***quinquefolia***	Widely available
- var. ***engelmannii***	CBcs EPfP EShb LBuc LPar NBwr SEND WCFE
- 'Guy's Garnet'	WCru
- 'Kirigami' **new**	CKel CWnw
- RED WALL ('Troki')	CRos EHyd EPfP LPar LRHS NRHS
- STAR SHOWERS ('Monham') (v)	NLar
- 'Yellow Wall'PBR	CBar CKel EHyd LRHS NRHS
semicordata B&SWJ 6551	WCru
striata	see *Cissus striata*
thomsonii	see *Cayratia thomsonii*
§ ***tricuspidata***	CCVT CMCN EPfP LSto MAsh MGos NBwr SArc SNig SOrN SPer
- 'Beverley Brook'	CRHN ELon ETho LCro LSRN MGos NLar SNig SPer SRms
- 'Crûg Compact'	WCru
- 'Fenway Park'	EBee ELan MRav
- 'Green Spring'	CBcs ELan ETho IArd MGos NLar
- 'Lowii'	CDoC CMac ELan EPfP MBlu MRav NLar SPoG
- 'Robusta'	GMcL
§ - 'Veitchii' ♀H5	Widely available

Pasithea (*Hemerocallidaceae*)

caerulea	MHol WCot WGob WPGP WSHC

Paspalum (*Poaceae*)

glaucifolium	MNrw
quadrifarium	LDai
- RCB RA S-5	WCot

Passiflora ✿ (*Passifloraceae*)

actinia	CCCN SPlb
'Adularia'	CCCN
alata (F) ♀H1c	CCCN LCro
× ***alatocaerulea***	see *P.* × *belotii*
× ***allardii***	CCCN
ambigua	CCCN
§ 'Amethyst' ♀H3	CBcs CCCN CDoC CHll CKel CRHN CSBt ETho LCro LSRN MAsh SPoG WHlf
amethystina misapplied	see *P.* 'Amethyst'
§ ***amethystina*** Mikan	ECre LRHS
'Anastasia'	CCCN
'Andy'	CCCN
'Anemona'	CCCN
'Annika'	CCCN
antioquiensis misapplied	see *P.* × *exoniensis*
antioquiensis ambig.	CBcs CCCN CHll SEND
antioquiensis H. Karst. × ***parritae***	CRHN
'Ariane'	CCCN
× ***atropurpurea***	CCCN
§ ***aurantia***	CCCN
banksii	see *P. aurantia*
§ × ***belotii***	CCCN NPlm
- 'Impératrice Eugénie'	see *P.* × *belotii*
- 'Perfume Passion'PBR	CCCN
'Betty Myles Young'	CBcs CCCN CRHN ECre ELan ELon EPfP LPar LRHS
'Blue Bouquet'	CCCN
'Blue Crown'	CCCN
'Blue Moon'	CCCN
'Blue Stripper'	CCCN
'Blue Velvet'	CCCN
bogatensis B&SWJ 14951	WCru
'Byron Beauty'	CCCN
'Byte'	CCCN
§ ***caerulea*** ♀H4	Widely available
- 'Chinensis'	CCCN
- 'Clear Sky'PBR	CBod CCCN CKel ELan EPfP LPar LRHS MNHC SNig SOrN SRms
- 'Constance Eliott' ♀H4	CAgr CBcs CBod CBrac CCCN CHll CKel CMac CRHN CRos EBee EHyd ELan EPfP ETho LCro LOPS LPar LRHS LSto MAsh MGos NLar NRHS SCob SNig SPer SWvt
- 'Duuk' **new**	CCCN
- 'Pierre Pomié'	CCCN
I - 'Rubra'	CBod CCCN CDoC CSBt ETho LCro
- WHITE LIGHTNING ('Yanpas'PBR)	CCCN EDir EHyd ELan EPfP EShb ETho LRHS NRHS SCoo SPoG SWvt
× ***caeruleoracemosa***	see *P.* × *violacea*
× ***caponii***	CCCN CHll
- 'John Innes'	CCCN
chinensis	see *P. caerulea*
citrifolia	CCCN
citrina	CCCN
* ***classica*** × ***coccinea***	CCCN
× ***colvillii***	CCCN
'Coral Glow'	CCCN

	'Crimson Tears'	CCCN
	cuatrecasasii B&SWJ 14834	WCru
§	'Damsel's Delight'	CCCN CPla CWGN ECre EDir EHyd ELan ELon LRHS NRHS SCoo SGsty SPeP SPoG
	'Daylight'	CCCN
	'Debby'	CCCN
	EDEN ('Hil Pas Eden') ♀H3	CCCN
	edulis (F)	CBcs CBod CCCN CHll LCro SPre SVic
	- 'Byte' (F)	CCCN
§	- f. ***edulis*** (F)	CCCN
	- f. ***flavicarpa*** (F)	CCCN
	- 'Frederick' (F)	WHlf
	- 'Lilikoi' (F)	CAgr
	- 'Norfolk' (F)	CCCN
	- 'Purple Giant' (F) **new**	EDir
	'Elizabeth' (F)	CCCN
	'Empress Eugenie'	see *P.* × *belotii*
§	× ***exoniensis*** ♀H2	CBod CCCN CHll CRHN CSBt EAri ECre
	'Fantasma'	CCCN
	'Fata Confetto'	CCCN
	'Fledermouse'	CCCN
	'Flying V'	CCCN
	'Grand Duchess'	CCCN
	gritensis	CCCN
	'Hetty Nicolaas'	CCCN
	incarnata (F)	CAgr CCCN GPoy SPlb
	'Incense' (F) ♀H2	CCCN SPlb
	'Inspiration'	CCCN
	'Jara'	CCCN
	'Jelly Joker'	CCCN
	'Justine Lyons'	CCCN SNig
	× ***kewensis***	CCCN
	'Lady Margaret'	CCCN
	'Lambiekins'	CCCN
	'Lavender Lady'	see *P.* 'Amethyst'
§	***ligularis*** (F)	CCCN SVic WJur
	'Lilac Lady'	see *P.* × *violacea* 'Tresederi'
	lowei	see *P. ligularis*
	'Manapany'	CCCN
	manicata (F)	CCCN
	- - B&SWJ 14284	WCru
	- - B&SWJ 14868	WCru
	'Maria'	CCCN
	'Marijke'	CCCN
I	***matthewsii*** 'Alba'	CRHN
	'Mavis Mastics'	see *P.* × *violacea* 'Tresederi'
	mayana	see *P. caerulea*
	membranacea (F)	CCCN
	'Michael'	CCCN
	'Mini Lamb'	CCCN
	mixta (F)	CCCN SEND
	- B&SWJ 14832	WCru
	- clone 2	CCCN
	- red-flowered	CCCN
	aff. ***mixta*** B&SWJ 14302	WCru
	mollissima misapplied	see *P. tarminiana*
	mollissima ambig. (F)	CBcs CCCN CSBt EShb SPlb
	mollissima (Kunth) L.H. Bailey (F) ♀H2	CAgr CRHN
	- B&SWJ 14876	WCru
	'Monika Fischer'	CCCN
	mucronata	CCCN
	murucuja	CCCN
	'New Incense'	CCCN
	'Nightshift'	CCCN
	onychina	see *P. amethystina* Mikan
	'Panda'	CCCN
	'Party Animal'	CCCN ECre EDir ELan
	'Pink Passion'PBR	CCCN
	'Pinky'	CCCN
	× ***piresiae***	CCCN
	'Polaris' **new**	CCCN
	'Poppet'	CCCN
	'Precioso'	CCCN
	'Pura Vida'	CCCN
	'Pura Vida 2'	CCCN
	'Purple Companion'	CCCN
	'Purple Haze'	CBod CCCN CDoC EDir EHyd ELan ETho LCro LOPS LRHS NRHS SCoo WFar
	'Purple Passion'	see *P. edulis* f. *edulis*
	'Purple Pendulum'	CCCN
	'Purple Rain'	CCCN
	quadrangularis (F) ♀H1a	CCCN CHll
	quinquangularis	CCCN
	racemosa ♀H1a	CCCN LCro
	- 'Blushing Bride'	CCCN
	- 'Buzios'	CCCN
	- 'Diva'	CCCN
	- pink-flowered	CCCN
	'Red Inca'	CCCN
	semiciliosa B&SWJ 14824	WCru
	'Silly Cow'	see *P.* 'Damsel's Delight'
	'Silvie'	CCCN
	'Simply Red'	CCCN
	'Snow Queen'PBR	CBcs CBod CCCN CHll CRos CSBt CWGN ELan EPfP ETho LCro LRHS SCoo SGsty SNig SPeP WHlf
	'Star of Bristol' ♀H2	CCCN
	'Star of Kingston'	CCCN
	'Star of Surbiton'	CCCN ELan LRHS
	'Sunburst'	CCCN
	'Surprise'	CCCN
§	***tarminiana*** (F)	CCCN CRHN CSBt
	- B&SWJ 14960	WCru
	- white-flowered	CCCN
	'Temptation'	CCCN
	tetrandra	CExl
	× ***tresederi***	see *P.* × *violacea* 'Tresederi'
	trifasciata	CCCN
	tripartita B&SWJ 14768	WCru
	- B&SWJ 14807	WCru
	tulae	CCCN
§	× ***violacea*** ♀H2	CCCN CRHN CRos LCro
	- 'Eynsford Gem'	CCCN
	- 'Lilac Lady'	see *P.* × *violacea* 'Tresederi'
§	- 'Tresederi'	CCCN
	- 'Twin Star'	CCCN
	- 'Victoria'	CCCN CSBt EDir WHlf
	'Violetta'	CCCN
	vitifolia (F)	CCCN
	- 'Innocentiae' (F)	CCCN
	'White Queen'	CCCN
	'White Surprise'	CCCN
	'White Wedding'	CCCN
	'Wilgen Heintje'	CCCN
	'Wilgen K Verhoeff'	CCCN
	'Wilgen Marieke'	CCCN
	'Winterland'	CCCN

passion fruit see *Passiflora*

passion fruit, banana see *Passiflora mollissima* (Kunth) L.H. Bailey

Pastinaca (*Apiaceae*)

sativa	CHab CKel SPhx SVic WCot
- subsp. ***sylvestris***	NGrd

Patersonia (*Iridaceae*)

occidentalis	SGBe SPlb

Patrinia (*Caprifoliaceae*)

gibbosa	CSpe EBee EMor GGro GKev MMrt NLar SBut WFar WPnP
- B&SWJ 874	ESwi WCru
heterophylla	GGro GKev
cf. ***monandra***	EBee ESwi
punctiflora	CAby CSpe EShb GGro SDix WPGP
aff. ***punctiflora***	ECha GBee NDov SPhx WGoo
rupestris B&SWJ 12654	WCru
scabiosifolia	CAby CKno CMiW CSpe ECha ECtt EMor EShb ESwi GGro GKev GQue LRHS MAvo MHol NBir NLar SBls SBut SDix SMrm SPhx SPtp WFar WHoo
- B&SWJ 8740	WCru
- 'Nagoya'	MNrw
triloba	CBod CMiW CSpe EMor GEdr MMrt NLar SBut WFar WPnP
- var. ***palmata***	EBee
villosa	CExl EMor GGro SBut

Paulownia (*Paulowniaceae*)

catalpifolia	EBee NLar
elongata	IDee NLar
fargesii misapplied	see *P. tomentosa* 'Lilacina'
fargesii ambig.	WCot
fortunei	CBcs MBlu SPlb
- NMWJ 14533	WCru
- FAST BLUE ('Minfast') 🏆H5	CExl LRHS LSRN
kawakamii	CBct CMCN EBee EPfP ESwi MVil SChF WJur WPGP
- NMWJ 14552	WCru
- RWJ 9909	WCru
'Purple Spendour'	EPfP SPer
taiwaniana NMWJ 14529	WCru
tomentosa 🏆H5	Widely available
- W 769	WPGP
- 'Coreana'	ESwi WCru
§ - 'Lilacina'	CBcs EPfP ESwi

Pauridia (*Hypoxidaceae*)

aquatica **new**	CBor
canaliculata	NRog
serrata subsp. ***serrata***	NRog

Pavonia (*Malvaceae*)

multiflora ambig.	CCCN
praemorsa	CCCN
strictiflora	CCCN
* ***volubilis***	CCCN

pawpaw (false banana) see *Asimina triloba*

pawpaw (papaya) see *Carica papaya*

pea see AGM Vegetables Section

peach see *Prunus persica*

pear see *Pyrus communis*; see also AGM Fruit Section

pear, Asian see *Pyrus pyrifolia*

pecan see *Carya illinoinensis*

Pelargonium ✿ (*Geraniaceae*)

'A.M. Mayne' (Z/d)	WFib
'Aaron West' (St)	WFib
'Abba' (Z/d)	WFib
'Abbie Hillier' (R)	WFib
'Abel Carrière' (I/d)	WFib
abrotanifolium (Sc)	CSpe ENfk EPPr EWoo MHer SPet SVen WFib WGwG
acetosum	EPPr EWoo MHer SMrm WFib
acraeum	EWoo
'Ada Green' (R)	WFib
'Ada Sutterby' (Dw/d)	WFib
'Ade's Elf' (Z/St)	WFib
'Ainsdale Beauty' (Z)	WFib
alchemilloides	EWoo WFib
'Aldwyck' (R) 🏆H1c	WFib
'Alex Kitson' (Z)	WFib
'Algenon' (Min/d)	WFib
I 'Alice' (Min)	MHer WFib
'Alison March' (Z/Dw/d/v)	WFib
'Allesley Shadow' (Dw/d)	WFib
'Alma' (Dw/C)	SSea
alpinum	MHer
'Amari' (R)	WFib
'Ambrose' (Min/d)	WFib
AMELIT ('Pacameli' PBR) (I/d)	SSea
'American Prince of Orange' (Sc)	SPet
'Amethyst' (R)	SCoo WFib
I 'Amy' (Dw)	WFib
ANGELEYES RANDY ('Pacra') (Angeleyes Series) (A)	SSea
'Angelique' (Dw/d)	WFib
'Ann Hoystead' (R) 🏆H1c	WFib
'Annabelle Stephenson' (Dw/d)	WFib
'Annsbrook Beauty' (A/C)	MHer SPet WFib
'Annsbrook Jupitor' (Z/St)	WFib
(Antik Series) ANTIK ORANGE ('Tikorg' PBR) (Z) 🏆H1c	SPoG
- ANTIK PINK ('Tikpink' PBR) (Z)	SPoG
- ANTIK SCARLET ('Tikscarl' PBR) (Z)	SPoG
- ANTIK VIOLET ('Tikvio' PBR) (Z)	SPoG
'Antoine Crozy' (I × Z/d)	WFib
'Apache' (Z/d)	WFib
appendiculatum	EWoo MHer
'Apple Betty' (Sc)	EPPr EWoo NWsh WFib
'Apple Blossom Rosebud' (Z/d) 🏆H1c	CBod CWal ECre ECtt EShb EWoo MHer SMrm WFib
'Apricot Fool' (U/Sc)	WFib
'Apricot Glace' (U/Sc)	MHer WFib
'April Hamilton' (I)	LCro WFib
'April Showers' (A)	WFib
AQUARELLO ('Fisaqua') (Z) **new**	MPri
'Arctic Frost' (I)	WFib
§ 'Arctic Star' (St) 🏆H1c	CSpe WBrk WFib
'Arcturus' (Min)	MHer
'Ardens' 🏆H1c	CDow CNor CPbh CSpe CTsd EAri EBee ELan EWoo LCro LOPS MCot MHer NCou SEND SMrm SWvt WCAu WCot WFib WWFP
'Ardwick Cinnamon' (Sc)	ENfk EWoo MHer NWsh SPet SRms WFib
'Arnside Fringed Aztec' (R)	MHer WFib
'Ashby' (Dec/Sc) 🏆H1c	ECtt ENfk EPPr EWoo MHer SGro SPet WFib
'Ashfield Jubilee' (Z/C)	WFib
'Ashfield Serenade' (Z) 🏆H1c	WFib
'Askham Fringed Aztec' (R) 🏆H1c	WFib
asperum Ehr. ex Willd.	see *P.* 'Graveolens'
§ 'Atomic Snowflake' (Sc/v)	ECtt ENfk EWoo MNHC NWsh SPet SRms WFib
'Atrium' (U)	MHer NWsh WFib

'Attar of Roses' (Sc) ♀H1c	CCBP CCht CLau CSpe ECtt ENfk EPPr EWoo LCro LOPS MCot MHer MHoo MNHC MPri NCou NWsh SAng SEdi SGro SMrm SPet SPoG SRms WBrk WFib WGwG
australe	EWoo MCot MHer NWsh SPhx WFib
- pink-flowered	EPPr
'Australian Mystery' (R/Dec) ♀H1c	CSpe ECtt WFib
'Aztec' (R) ♀H1c	MHer WFib
'Baby Bird's Egg' (Min)	WFib
'Baby Harry' (Dw/v)	WFib
'Ballerina' (R)	see *P.* 'Carisbrooke'
I 'Ballerina' (Min)	WFib
'Barbara Eldridge' (Z)	WFib
§ 'Barbe Bleu' (I/d) ♀H1c	LCro WFib
barklyi	WFib
'Baronne A. de Rothschild' (Z/d)	WFib
'Bath Beauty' (Dw)	CSpe EPri
'Beatrice Cottington' (I/d)	WFib
'Beauty of Calderdale' (Z/C)	WFib
'Beauty of Eastbourne' misapplied	see *P.* 'Lachskönigin', *P.* 'Eastbourne Beauty'
BELLADONNA ('Fisopa') (I/d)	SCoo
'Bembridge' (Z/St/d)	CDow WFib
'Ben Matt' (R)	WFib
§ 'Bergpalais' (Z/d)	SSea
'Berkswell Bolero' (A)	WFib
'Berkswell Bonanza' (A)	WFib
'Berkswell Carnival' (A)	ELan WFib
'Berkswell Dainty' (A)	WFib
'Berkswell Debonair' (A)	WFib
'Berkswell Golden Anniversary' (A) **new**	MHer WFib
'Berkswell Harmony' (A) **new**	WFib
'Berkswell Lace' (A)	MHer
'Berkswell Pixie' (A)	SPet WFib
'Beromünster' (Dec)	ECtt EWoo MHer WFib
'Bert Pearce' (R)	WFib
'Beryl Gibbons' (Z/d)	WFib
'Beryl Reid' (R)	WFib
'Betty Catchpole' (Z)	EWoo
betulinum	CPbh EWoo WFib WOld
'Betwixt' (Z/v)	WFib
'Big Apple' (Sc)	EWoo SRms
'Bird Dancer' (Dw/St) ♀H1c	CSpe EPPr EWoo MHer MNHC SIvy WBrk WFib
(Birdbush Series) 'Birdbush Bobby' (Sc)	SRms
- 'Birdbush Bold and Beautiful' (Sc)	SRms
- 'Birdbush Eleanor' (Z)	WFib
- 'Birdbush Nutty' (Sc)	SRms
'Birthday Girl' (R) ♀H1c	ECtt WFib
'Bitter Lemon' (Sc)	EWoo WFib
'Black Butterfly'	see *P.* 'Brown's Butterfly'
'Black Country Bugle' (Z/d)	WFib
'Black Knight' (A)	SMrm SPet
'Black Knight' (R)	ECtt MHer
'Black Prince' (R/Dec)	CSpe EWoo WFib
'Black Velvet' (R)	EWoo
'Black Vesuvius'	see *P.* 'Red Black Vesuvius'
'Blackman Beauty'	NWsh
BLANCHE ROCHE ('Guitoblanc') (I/d)	MBros MHer SCoo
§ 'Blandfordianum' (Sc)	EWoo MHer NWsh
I 'Blandfordianum Album' (Sc)	EAri WFib
'Blandfordianum Roseum' (Sc)	EAri EWoo MHer WFib
'Blazonry' (Z/v)	WFib
(Blizzard Series) BLIZZARD BLUE ('Fisrain'PBR) (I)	SCoo
- BLIZZARD DARK RED ('Fisblizdark') (I)	EWoo
- BLIZZARD RED ('Fizzard') (I)	SCoo
- BLIZZARD WHITE ('Fisbliz'PBR) (I)	SCoo
'Blue Beard'	see *P.* 'Barbe Bleu'
BLUE WONDER ('Pacbla'PBR) (Z/d)	SSea
'Bob Newing' (Min/St)	WFib
'Bobberstone' (Z/St)	WFib
'Bold Ann' (Z/Dw/d)	WFib
'Bold Appleblossom' (Z)	WFib
'Bold Bridesmaid' (Dw/d)	WFib
'Bold Carousel' (Z/d)	WFib
'Bold Cherie' (Dw/d)	WFib
'Bold Cherub' (Z/d)	WFib
'Bold Cyclamen' (Dw/d)	WFib
'Bold Debonair' (Dw/d)	WFib
'Bold Dove' (Dw)	WFib
'Bold Flame' (Z/d)	WFib
'Bold Gem' (Z/d)	WFib
'Bold Limelight' (Z/d)	WFib
'Bold Minstrel' (Z/d)	WFib
'Bold Moonlight' (Dw)	WFib
'Bold Pixie' (Dw/d)	WFib
'Bold Princess' (Z/d)	WFib
'Bold Special' (Z)	WFib
'Bold Spirit' (Z)	WFib
'Bold Sunset' (Z/d) ♀H1c	WFib
'Bolero' (U) ♀H1c	WFib
'Bon Bon' (Min/St)	WFib
'Bontrosai'PBR (Sc)	MCot MHer WCot
'Bosham' (R)	WFib
'Both's Snowflake' (Sc/v)	WFib
'Bourbon Rose' (Sc)	MHer
bowkeri	WFib
BRAVO ('Fisbravo') (Z/d)	WFib
'Brenda' (Min/d)	WFib
'Brenda Hyatt' (Dw/d)	WFib
'Brian West' (Min/St/C)	WFib
'Brian West Butterfly' (Z/St) ♀H1c	WFib
'Bright Eyes' ambig. (Dw)	WFib
'Brightstone' (Z/d)	ECtt WFib
'Brilliant' (Dec)	ENfk WFib
'Brilliantine' (Sc)	ENfk EPri EWoo MHer NWsh SRms WFib
'Britannia' (R)	WFib
'Brixworth Pearl' (Z)	WFib
'Broadway Scarlet'	CWCL
(Brocade Series) BROCADE FIRE (Z/C/d) **new**	MPri
- BROCADE SALMON NIGHT (Z/C/d) **new**	MPri
'Brook's Purple'	see *P.* 'Royal Purple'
'Brookside Flamenco' (Dw/d)	WFib
'Brookside Primrose' (Min/C/d)	WFib
'Brookside Serenade' (Dw)	WFib
§ 'Brown's Butterfly' (R)	EWoo WFib
'Brunswick' (Sc)	EWoo MHer SMrm WFib
'Bushfire' (R) ♀H1c	EWoo WFib
BUTTERFLY ('Fisam'PBR) (I)	SCoo
caespitosum	MHer
caffrum	EWoo WFib
- 'Diana'	MHer

'Cal'	see *P.* 'Salmon Irene'
'California Brilliant' (U)	MHer
'Calignon' (Z/St)	WFib
'Cameo' (Dw/d)	WFib
'Camphor Rose' (Sc) 🏆H1c	SRms
'Can-can' (I/d)	WFib
CANDY FLOWERS VIOLET ('Camvio'[PBR]) (Candy Flowers Series) (R)	EWoo
canescens	see *P.* 'Blandfordianum'
'Cape Town' (Z/Dw/v)	WFib
capitatum	ENfk EWoo WFib
'Capri' (Sc)	SMHy WFib
'Captain Starlight' (A) 🏆H1c	EShb EWoo MHer SPet WFib
'Cara Mia' (Za) **new**	WFib
'Cara Nonna' (Za) **new**	WFib
'Cara Regina' (Za) **new**	WFib
'Carefree' (U) 🏆H1c	ECtt WFib
§ 'Carisbrooke' (R) 🏆H1c	WFib
'Carmel' (Z)	WFib
carnosum	EAri MHer
'Carole Munroe' (Z/d)	WFib
'Caroline' (Dec)	WFib
'Caroline Schmidt' (Z/d/v)	ECtt MCot WBrk WFib
'Carolyn Hardy' (Z/d)	WFib
'Catford Belle' (A)	MHer
caucalifolium subsp. ***caucalifolium***	EWoo MHer
- subsp. ***convolvulifolium***	WFib
'Cedric Morris Corvette' (Z)	WFib
'Celebration' (Z/d)	WFib
'Celestial Rose' (Z/d)	WFib
'Cézanne' (R)	MCot
'Charity' (Sc) 🏆H1c	ENfk MHer MHoo MNHC NWsh SPet SRms WFib
'Charlotte Bronte' (Dw/v)	WFib
'Charmay Cocky' (Z/d)	WFib
'Charmay Hampshire' (Z/d)	WFib
'Charmay Marjorie' (A)	MHer
'Charmay Snowflake' (Sc/v)	SRms
'Charmay Snowflurry' (Sc/v)	WFib
'Chavarri Hermanos' (Z/d)	WFib
'Chelsea Gem' (Z/d/v) 🏆H1c	WFib
'Chelsea Morning' (Z/d)	WFib
'Cherry' (Min)	WFib
'Cherry Baby' (Dec) 🏆H1c	ECtt WFib
'Cherry Orchard' (R)	WFib
'Chew Magna' (R)	WFib
'Chieko' (Min/d)	WFib
'Chinese Cactus' (Z/St)	WFib
§ 'Chocolate Peppermint' (Sc)	ECtt ELan ENfk EWoo MCot MHer NWsh SPet SRms WFib
'Chocolate Tomentosum'	see *P.* 'Chocolate Peppermint'
'Choun Cho' (I)	LCro LOPS WFib
'Chrissie' (R)	WFib
'Cindy' (Dw/d)	WFib
'Citriodorum' (Sc) 🏆H1c	ELan MCot MHer WFib
'Citronella' (Sc)	SRms WFib
'Claret Rock Unique' (U)	EWoo WFib
CLASSIC CALYPSO IMPROVED ('Pecz0007') (Z) **new**	MPri
'Clorinda' (U/Sc)	ENfk EShb EWoo MCot MHer MNHC NWad SRms WFib
'Clown' (R)	WFib
'Coddenham' (Dw/d)	WFib
'Cola Bottles'	CCht CDow ELan NPer NWsh SPet SPoG WFib
§ 'Colonel Baden-Powell' (I/d)	WFib
COLUMBIA (St)	WFib
'Colwell' (Min/d)	WFib

'Concolor Lace'	see *P.* 'Shottesham Pet'
'Conron' (Sc)	NWsh
'Contrast' (Z/C/v)	SCoo SPoG WFib
'Cook's Peachblossom' (Z/d)	WFib
'Copthorne' (U/Sc) 🏆H1c	CDow EWoo MCot MHer NWsh SPet SRms WFib
cordifolium	EPPr WFib
- var. ***rubrocinctum***	EShb EWoo MHer NWsh SPet
coriandrifolium	see *P. myrrhifolium* var. *coriandrifolium*
'Cornell' (I/d)	WFib
cortusifolium	MHer
'Cotta Lilac Queen' (I/d)	ECtt
'Cottenham Bliss' (A)	WFib
'Cottenham Cynthia Haird' (A)	SPet WFib
'Cottenham Delight' (A)	WFib
'Cottenham Glamour' (A) 🏆H1c	MHer
'Cottenham Harmony' (A)	SPet WFib
'Cottenham Jubilee' (A)	MHer
'Cottenham Surprise' (A) 🏆H1c	SPet
'Cottenham Wonder' (A) 🏆H1c	MHer SPet WFib
cotyledonis	EWoo WFib
'Countess of Scarborough'	see *P.* 'Lady Scarborough'
'Cover Girl' (Z/d)	WFib
'Covina' (R)	WFib
'Cramdon Red' (Dw)	WFib
'Crampel's Master' (Z)	WFib
'Creamery' (d)	WFib
'Creamy Nutmeg' (Sc/v)	ENfk EShb EWoo MHer NWad SRms
'Credo' (Z)	WFib
'Crimson Unique' (U) 🏆H1c	CSpe ELan ENfk EWoo MCot MHer WFib
§ ***crispum*** (Sc)	GPoy WOld
- 'Cy's Sunburst' (v) 🏆H1c	CLau ECtt MHer NWsh SPet WFib
§ - 'Golden Well Sweep' (Sc/v)	WFib
- 'Major' (Sc)	WFib
- 'Peach Cream' (Sc/v)	ENfk WFib
- 'Prince Rupert' (Sc)	NWsh
- 'Variegatum' (Sc/v) 🏆H1c	ECtt ENfk EWoo GPoy MHer SPet SRms WCot WFib WOld
crithmifolium	EWoo MHer
'Crock O Day' (I/d)	ECtt
'Crocodile' (I/C/d) 🏆H1c	CDow ECtt ELan EWoo MHer MNHC NWad WCot WFib
'Crowfoot Rose' (Sc)	WFib
'Crystal Palace Gem' (Z/v)	CDow ECtt WFib
cucullatum	WFib
- 'Flore Pleno' (d)	EWoo WFib
- subsp. ***strigifolium***	EWoo
'Cupid' (Min/Dw/d)	WFib
'Cynthia'[PBR] (R)	LCro
§ 'Czar' (Z/C)	SCoo
'Dainty Maid' (Sc)	ECtt ENfk SPet
'Dale Queen' (Z)	WFib
'Dark Red Irene' (Z/d)	WFib
'Dark Secret' (R)	CSpe SMrm WFib
'Dark Venus' (R)	WFib
'Davina' (Min/d)	WFib
'Deacon Avalon' (Dw/d)	WFib
'Deacon Barbecue' (Z/d)	WFib
'Deacon Bonanza' (Z/d)	WFib
'Deacon Clarion' (Z/d)	WFib
'Deacon Coral Reef' (Z/d)	WFib
'Deacon Fireball' (Z/d)	WFib
'Deacon Gala' (Z/d)	WFib
'Deacon Golden Bonanza' (Z/C/d)	WFib

	'Deacon Golden Lilac Mist' (Z/C/d)	WFib
	'Deacon Lilac Mist' (Z/d)	WFib
	'Deacon Mandarin' (Z/d)	WFib
	'Deacon Minuet' (Z/d)	WFib
	'Deacon Peacock' (Z/C/d)	WFib
	'Deacon Picotee' (Z/d)	WFib
§	'Deacon Summertime' (Z/d)	WFib
	'Deborah Miliken' (Z/d) 🏆H1c	WFib
	'Decora Lavender'	see *P.* 'Decora Lilas'
§	'Decora Lilas' (I)	ECtt
	'Decora Mauve'	see *P.* 'Decora Lilas'
	'Decora Pink'	see *P.* 'Decora Rouge'
	'Decora Red'	see *P.* 'Decora Rouge'
§	'Decora Rose' (I)	ECtt
§	'Decora Rouge' (I)	ECtt
	'Deerwood Angel Wings' (A)	EWoo WFib
	'Deerwood Darling' (Min/d/v)	WFib
	'Deerwood Lavender Lad' (Sc)	ENfk EWoo MHer SAng SPet WFib
	'Deerwood Lavender Lass' (Sc)	EWoo MCot MHer SMHy SRms
	'Deerwood Pink Puff' (St/d)	WFib
	'Delightful' (R)	WFib
	'Delli' (R) 🏆H1c	MHer NPer SMrm WFib
	denticulatum	EWoo MHer
§	- 'Filicifolium' (Sc)	ELan ENfk EPPr EPri EWoo MCot MHer NWsh SPet WFib
	'Designer Hot Pink'PBR	MBros
	'Designer White' (Z) **new**	MBros
	DIABOLO ('Fiscrid') (Z/d)	MPri
	'Diana Louise' (Z/d)	WFib
	'Diana Palmer' (Z/d)	WFib
	dichondrifolium (Sc)	EWoo MHer WFib
	'Dick Key' (Z/d)	WFib
	'Display' ambig. (Dw/v)	WFib
	'Distinction' (Z)	CSpe EWoo SPoG WFib WMal
	'Dodd's Super Double' (Z/d)	SMrm WFib
	'Dolce Vita'	SSea
	'Dolly' (R)	WFib
	'Dolly Varden' (Z/v) 🏆H1c	ECtt WFib
	'Don Franco'PBR (R)	LCro
	'Don Mila' (R) **new**	LCro
	'Don Palido'PBR (R)	LCro LOPS
	'Don Valentino'PBR (R)	LCro
	'Don's Helen Bainbridge' (Z/C)	WFib
	'Don's Richard A. Costain' (Z/C)	WFib
	'Don's Stokesley Gem' (Z/C)	WFib
	'Doris Hancock' (R)	WFib
	'Doris Shaw' (R)	WFib
	'Dorothy Baker' (R)	WFib
	'Double New Life' (Z/d)	WFib
	'Double Pink' (R/d)	WFib
	'Dovedale' (Dw/C)	WFib
	'Downlands' (Z/d)	WFib
	'Dresden Pink' (Dw)	MHer
	'Dresden White' (Dw)	MHer WFib
	drummondii **new**	SPet
	'Dubonnet' (R)	WFib
	'Duchess of Devonshire' (U)	WFib WMal
	'Duke of Buckingham' (Z/d)	WFib
	'Duke of Edinburgh'	see *P.* 'Hederinum Variegatum'
	'Dunkery Beacon' (R)	WFib
	'E. Dabner' (Z/d)	WFib
§	'Eastbourne Beauty' (I/d)	WFib
	echinatum	MHer WFar
	- 'Album'	EAri EWoo NWsh SIvy WFib
	'Eden Gem' (Min/d)	WFib
	'Edmond Lachenal' (Z/d)	WFib
	'Edward Hockey' (Z)	WFib
	'Eileen Postle' (R) 🏆H1c	WFib
	'Elaine Ward' (R)	WFib
	(Elegance Series) ELEGANCE IMPERIAL (R) **new**	LCro
	- ELEGANCE JEANETTE ('Rg8036'PBR) (R) **new**	LCro
	'Elizabeth Taylor' (Z)	WFib
	'Ella' (Sc)	NWsh
	'Ella Jane' (Z/d)	WFib
	'Elmsett' (Dw/C/d)	ECtt WFib
	elongatum	EWoo SChr SPet
	'Els' (Dw/St)	WBrk
	'Elsi' (I × Z/d/v)	WFib
	'Elsie Gillam' (St)	WFib
	'Elsie Taylor' (R)	WFib
	'Embassy' (Min)	WFib
	EMILIA ('Pactina'PBR) (Z)	SSea
	'Emma Hössle'	see *P.* 'Frau Emma Hössle'
	'Emma Jane Read' (Dw/d)	WFib
	'Emma Louise' (Z)	WFib
	'Emperor Nicholas' (Z/d)	WFib
	endlicherianum	EDAr MHer WAbe WCot
	'Endsleigh' (Sc)	WFib
	englerianum	EWoo
	'Eskay Gold' (A)	WFib
	'Eskay Jewel' (A)	WFib
	'Eskay Sugar Candy' (A)	WFib
	'Eskay Verglo' (A)	WFib
	EVENING GLOW	see *P.* 'Bergpalais'
	'Evka'PBR (I/v)	ECtt SCoo
	exstipulatum	EPPr EWoo MHer SMHy
	'Fair Ellen' (Sc)	MHer WFib
	'Fairlee' (Dw)	WFib
	'Fairy Orchid' (A)	SPet WFib
	'Fandango' (Z/St)	SMrm WFib
	'Fanny Eden' (R)	EWoo WFib
	'Fantasia' white-flowered (Dw/d) 🏆H1c	WFib
	'Fareham' (R) 🏆H1c	WFib
	'Fern Mint' (Sc)	MHer SRms
	'Fiat Queen' (Z/d)	WFib
	'Fieldings Unique' (U)	EWoo
	'Fiery Sunrise' (R)	WFib
	'Fifth Avenue' (R)	SGro WFib
	'Filicifolium'	see *P. denticulatum* 'Filicifolium'
	'Fir Trees Catkins' (A)	MHer
	'Fir Trees Echoes of Pink' (A)	EWoo
	'Fir Trees Eileen' (St)	SMrm
	'Fir Trees Flamingo' (Dw)	EWoo
	'Fir Trees Hayley' (R)	WFib
	'Fir Trees Pearl Anniversary' (Z/C)	WFib
	'Fir Trees Silver Wedding' (Z/C/d)	WFib
	'First Blush' (R)	WFib
	FIRST YELLOW ('Pacyell'PBR) (Z/d)	WFib
	'Fleur d'Amour' (R)	WFib
	'Fleurisse' (Z)	WFib
	'Floria Moore' (Dec)	EWoo
	(Flower Fairy Series) FLOWER FAIRY BERRY ('Sweberry'PBR) (Z)	SSea
	- FLOWER FAIRY ROSE ('Swero'PBR) (Z)	SSea
	- FLOWER FAIRY VELVET ('Swevel'PBR) (Z)	SSea
	- FLOWER FAIRY WHITE SPLASH ('Swewhi'PBR) (Z)	SSea
	fragrans	CDow ENfk EWoo MBow SPet SRms

	Fragrans Group (Sc)	CDow GPoy MCot MHer NWsh WFib WGwG
§	- 'Fragrans Variegatum' (Sc/v) ♀H1c	MCot MHoo NWsh SGro SPet SPoG WFib WHlf
	- 'Snowy Nutmeg'	see *P.* (Fragrans Group) 'Fragrans Variegatum'
	'Fragrant Frosty' (Sc/v)	CDow
	'Fraiche Beauté' (Z/d)	WFib
	'Francis Gibbon' (Z/d)	WFib
	'Francis Parmenter' (I/Min/v)	CDow
	'Francis Parrett' (Min/d) ♀H1c	WFib
	'Frank Headley' (Z/v) ♀H1c	ECtt EShb MCot NPer SCoo SMrm SPoG WFib
§	'Frau Emma Hössle' (Dw/d)	WFib
	'Freak of Nature' (Z/v)	MHer WFib
	'Frensham' (Sc)	ENfk MHer NWsh WFib
	'Freshwater' (St/C)	WFib
	'Friary Wood' (Z/C/d)	WFib
	'Friesdorf' (Fr/Dw)	MCot MHer WBrk WFib WMal
	'Fringed Apple' (Sc)	WFib
	'Fringed Aztec' (R) ♀H1c	MHer WFib
	'Frosty' misapplied	see *P.* 'Variegated Kleine Liebling'
	'Frosty Petit Pierre'	see *P.* 'Variegated Kleine Liebling'
	'Fruity' (Sc)	SRms
	fruticosum	CDow EAri EPPr EWoo WFib
	fulgidum	EWoo MCot MHer WFib
	fumariifolium	NWsh
	'Gabriel' (A)	EWoo WFib
	'Galway Star' (Sc/v) ♀H1c	MHer WFib
	'Ganther' (Dec)	WFib
	'Gareth Mark Pratt' (Z/C)	WFib
	'Garland' (R)	WFib
	'Garnet Rosebud' (Min/d)	WFib
	'Garnet Wings' (R)	WFib
	'Gartendirektor Herman' (Dec) ♀H1c	ELan EWoo MHer WFib
	'Gaudy' (Z)	WFib
	'Gemini' (Z/St/d) ♀H1c	WFib
	'Gemstone' (Sc) ♀H1c	ENfk MHer SPet WFib
	'Genie' (Z/d)	WFib
	'Gentle Georgia' (R)	WFib
	'Georgia' (R)	WFib
	'Georgia Peach' (R)	WFib
	'Georgina Blythe' (R) ♀H1c	WFib
	'Georgina Forever' (A)	WFib
	'Giant Butterfly' (R)	WFib
	gibbosum	CSpe EAri EWoo MHer WFib
	'Gillian Shaw' (R)	WFib
	'Giroflée' (I/d)	MHer
	'Glacis' (Quality Series) (Z/d)	SSea
	'Gladys Evelyn' (Z/d)	WFib
	'Gladys Weller' (Z/d) ♀H1c	WFib
	glaucum	see *P. lanceolatum*
§	***glutinosum***	EWoo WFib
	'Goblin' (Min/d)	MHer
	'Goesta' (Z/d)	SSea
	GOLDEN ANGEL	see *P.* 'Sarah Don'
	'Golden Brilliantissimum' (Z/v)	WFib
	'Golden Chalice' (Min/v)	WFib
	'Golden Clorinda' (U/Sc/C)	NWsh WFib
	'Golden Ears' (Dw/St/C) ♀H1c	NPer WFib
	'Golden Edinburgh' (I/v)	WFib
	'Golden Lilac Gem' (I/d)	WFib
	'Golden Princess' (Min/C)	WFib
	'Golden Square' (Dw/St)	WFib
	'Golden Staphs' (Z/C/St)	MHer
	'Golden Warwick'	MHer
	'Golden Well Sweep'	see *P. crispum* 'Golden Well Sweep'
	'Gooseberry Leaf'	see *P. grossularioides*
	'Gosport' (Z/v)	WFib
	'Grace Thomas' (Sc) ♀H1c	MHer WFib
	'Grace Wells' (Min)	WFib
	'Grainger's Antique Rose' (Z/d)	WFib
	'Grand Slam' (R) ♀H1c	WFib
	'Grandad Mac' (Dw/St) ♀H1c	MHer
	GRANDEUR BUTTERFLY BICOLOUR RED (I)	LSou
	GRANDEUR BUTTERFLY IVY WHITE (I)	LSou
	GRANDEUR BUTTERFLY NEON (I)	LSou
	GRANDEUR BUTTERFLY PINK (I)	LSou
	GRANDEUR BUTTERFLY PURPLE (I)	LSou
	grandiflorum	EShb EWoo MCot MHer SPet WFib
	graveolens L'Hér.	see *P.* 'Graveolens'
	graveolens ambig.	SEND SGro SMHy
	graveolens *sensu* J.J.A. van der Walt	CBod WFib
§	'Graveolens' (Sc)	ENfk GPoy LWaG MHer SPet SVen WBrk WFib
	'Graveolens Minor' (Sc)	EWoo
	'Great Glemham Lemon' (Sc)	EWoo
	'Green Eyes' (I/d)	MHer
	'Greetings' (Min/v)	WFib
	GRETA ('Pacgret') (Darkline Series) (Z)	SSea
	'Grey Lady Plymouth' (Sc/v)	CPbh EWoo LCro MCot MHer MHoo NWsh WFib
	'Grey Sprite' (Min/v)	WFib
§	***grossularioides***	EWoo MHer
	'Gustav Emich' (Z/d)	WFib
§	'Hannaford Star' (Z/St)	WFib
	'Hansen's Pinkie' (Dec)	WFib
	'Hansen's Wild Spice' (Sc)	NWsh WFib
	'Happy Thought' (Z/v) ♀H1c	ECtt MCot SCoo WFib
	'Harbour Lights' (R)	WFib
	'Harewood Slam' (R)	WFib
	'Harlequin Liverbird' (I)	MHer
	'Harlequin Pretty Girl' (I × Z/d)	WFib
	'Harlequin Rosie O'Day' (I)	ECtt WFib
	'Harvard' (I/d)	WFib
	'Hazel' (R)	WFib
	'Hazel Cherry' (R)	WFib
	'Hazel Dean' (R)	ECtt
	'Hazel Glory' (R)	WFib
	'Hazel Gypsy' (R)	WFib
	'Hazel Peach' (R)	WFib
	'Hazel Star' (R)	WFib
	'Hazel's Finale' (Dec)	WFib
§	'Hederinum Variegatum' (I/v)	WFib
	'Helen Christine' (Z/St) ♀H1c	MHer WFib
	'Henry Weller' (A) ♀H1c	WFib
	'Hermanus Show' (Sc)	WFib
	'Hermione' (Z/d)	WFib
	'Highfields Attracta' (Z/d)	WFib
	'Highfields Candy Floss' (Z/d)	ECtt WFib
	'Highfields Choice' (Z) ♀H1c	WFib
	'Highfields Delight' (Z)	WFib
	'Highfields Festival' (Z/d) ♀H1c	ECtt WFib
	'Highfields Flair' (Z/d)	WFib
	'Highfields Melody' (Z/d)	WFib

'Highfields Pink' (Z)	WFib
'Highfields Pride' (Z)	WFib
'Highfields Snowdrift' (Z)	WFib
'Highfields Symphony' (Z)	WFib
'Highfields Vogue' (Z)	WFib
'Hilda's Memory' (Z/Dw/d)	WFib
'Hills of Snow' (Z/v)	MHer WFib
'Hindoo' (R × U) ♀H1c	EWoo WFib
hirtum	EWoo
hispidum	EWoo MHer
'Hit Parade' (I/d)	WFib
'Hitcham' (Min/d)	WFib
'Holbrook' (Dw/C/d)	WFib
'Holt Beauty'	EWoo
'Honeywood Lindy' (R)	WFib
Horizon Series (Z)	MBros
- 'Horizon Deep Salmon Improved' (Z)	MBros
- 'Horizon Deep Scarlet' (Z)	MBros
- 'Horizon Lilac Rose' (Z)	MBros
'House and Garden' (R)	ECtt
'Hula' (R × U)	EWoo WFib
'Icing Sugar' (I/d)	WFib
ignescens	EAri EWoo WFib
'Immaculatum' (Z)	WFib
'Imperial Butterfly' (A/Sc) ♀H1c	ENfk MHer SPet SRms WFib
iocastum	EWoo
ionidiflorum	CSpe EDAr EShb EWoo MCot MHer MNHC SRms WAvo
'Irene' (Z/d)	WFib
'Irene Cal' (Z/d)	WFib
'Irene Toyon' (Z)	WFib
'Islington Peppermint' (Sc)	SPet SRms WFib
'Ivalo' (Z/d)	WFib
'Ivory Snow' (Z/d/v)	WFib
'Jack of Hearts' (I × Z/d)	WFib
'Jack Phillips' (Z/d)	WFib
§ 'Jackie' (I/d) ♀H1c	WFib
'Jackie Davies' (R)	EWoo
'Jackie Gall'	see *P.* 'Jackie'
'Jackie Totlis' (Z/St)	WFib
'Jackpot Wild Rose' (Z/d)	WFib
'Jane Innes' (I/d)	WFib
'Janet Hofman' (Z/d)	WFib
'Janet Kerrigan' (Min/d)	WFib
'Jayne Eyre' (Min/d)	WFib
§ 'Jeanne d'Arc' (I/d)	MHer WFib
'Jer'Rey' (A)	EWoo WFib
'Jip's Bishops Wood' (Dw/d)	WFib
'Jip's Desert Poppy' (Z/Min)	WFib
'Jip's Eleanor Renton' (Dw/d)	WFib
'Jip's Little Lady' (Dw)	WFib
'Jip's Megan' (Z/C/d)	ECtt
'Jip's Pippin' (Dw)	WFib
'Jip's Proud Sentinel' (Dw/d)	WFib
'Jip's Sky Gipsy' (Dw)	WFib
'Jip's Twilight' (Dw)	WFib
'Joan Fontaine' (Z)	WFib
'Joan Morf' (R) ♀H1c	EWoo WFib
'Joan of Arc'	see *P.* 'Jeanne d'Arc'
'Joy' (R) ♀H1c	CSpe WFib
'Joy Lucille' (Sc)	NWsh
'Julie Smith' (R)	WFib
'Juniper' (Sc)	WFib
'Just Beth' (Z/C/d)	WFib
'Just Jip' (Z/Dw)	WFib
'Just Joss' (Dw/d)	WFib
'Just William' (Min/C/d)	WFib
'Kamahl' (R)	WFib
'Karl Hagele' (Z/d)	WFib
'Karmin Ball'	WFib
karooicum	EWoo
'Karrooense'	see *P. quercifolium*
'Katie Hillier' (R)	WFib
'Kaufman's Bonfire' (R)	WFib
'Keepsake' (Min/d)	WFib
'Kenny's Double' (Z/d)	ECtt WFib
'Kerensa' (Min/d)	WFib
'Kesgrave' (Min/d)	WFib
'Kewensis' (Z)	EAri EShb WFib
'Key's Unique' (U)	SEND WFib
'Kimono' (R) ♀H1c	ECtt
'King Edmund' (R) ♀H1c	WFib
'King of Denmark' (Z/d)	WFib
'King Solomon' (R)	WFib
'King's Ransom' (R)	WFib
§ 'Kleine Liebling' (Min)	WFib
'La France' (I/d) ♀H1c	ECtt LCro MHer WFib
'La Jolla' (Z/d)	WFib
'La Paloma' (R)	WFib
§ 'Lachskönigin' (I/d)	WFib
'Lady Ilchester' (Z/d)	WFib
'Lady Love Song' (R)	WFib
'Lady Mary' (Sc)	MHer SRms WFib
'Lady Mavis Pilkington' (Z/d)	WFib
'Lady Plymouth' (Sc/v) ♀H1c	CPbh ECtt ELan ENfk EPPr EWoo GLog MCot MHer MHoo NWad NWsh SEND SMrm SPet SRms WFib WGwG
§ 'Lady Scarborough' (Sc)	ENfk MHer SPet SRms WFib
laevigatum	MHer
'Lancastrian' (Z/d)	ECtt WFib
§ ***lanceolatum***	EWoo MHer
'Land of Song' (A)	ENfk NWsh
'Lara Ballerina' (Sc/d) ♀H1c	SPet SRms
'Lara Beacon'	CSpe EWoo
'Lara Candy Dancer' (Sc) ♀H1c	MAsh NWsh SPet WFib
'Lara Dora Price' (Za)	WFib
'Lara Happy' (Za/d) **new**	WFib
'Lara Jester' (Sc)	ECtt ENfk EWoo NWsh WFib
'Lara Largo' (Za)	WFib
'Lara Mandarin' (Za/d)	WFib
'Lara Marjorie' (Za)	WFib
'Lara Rajah' (R)	EWoo
'Lara Starshine' (Sc) ♀H1c	ENfk EPPr EWoo MHer SPet SRms WFib
'Lara Susanne' (Za)	WFib
'Lara Waltz' (R/d)	WFib
'Laurel Hayward' (R)	WFib
'Lauren Alexandra' (Z/d)	WFib
'Lavender Grand Slam' (R) ♀H1c	WFib
'Lavender Lindy' (Sc)	CDow EWoo MHer NWsh SPet WFib
'Lavender Mini Cascade'	see *P.* LILAC MINI CASCADE
'Lavender Sensation' (R)	WFib
'Lawrenceanum'	EWoo LCro WFib
laxum	WFib
'Le Lutin' (Z/d)	WFib
'L'Élégante' (I/v) ♀H1c	CDow MCot MHer SIvy SMrm WFib
'Lemon Air' (Sc)	WFib
'Lemon Crisp'	see *P. crispum*
'Lemon Fancy' (Sc) ♀H1c	MHer NWad NWsh SPet WFib
'Lemon Fizz'	MHoo
'Lemon Kiss' (Sc)	CSpe EWoo NWsh SPet WFib
'Lemon Meringue' (Sc)	WFib
'Leslie William Burrows'	EWoo
'Letitia' (A)	ENfk MHer
LILA COMPAKT-CASCADE	see *P.* 'Decora Lilas'
LILAC ('Paclilac'[PBR]) (I)	SSea
'Lilac Gem' (I/Min/d)	ENfk

§	LILAC MINI CASCADE ('Lilamica'[PBR]) (I) 🏆H1c	CDow
	'Lilian Pottinger' (Sc) 🏆H1c	ENfk EPPr EWoo MHer NWsh WFib
	'Lilian Woodberry' (Z)	WFib
	'Lily Diggle' **new**	WFib
	'Limoneum' (Sc)	ENfk EWoo MHer NWsh SPet WFib
	'Lincolnshire Lady' (R)	ECtt
	'Lipstick' (St)	WFib
	'Lisa' (Min/C)	WFib
	'Lisa Jo' (St/v/Dw/d)	WFib
	'Little Alice' (Dw/d) 🏆H1c	WFib
	'Little Gem' (Sc)	ENfk MHer WFib
	'Little Jip' (Z/d/v) 🏆H1c	WFib
	'Little Spikey' (St/Min/d)	MHer WFib
	'Lizzie Hillier' (R)	WFib
	lobatum	EWoo
	'Lollipop' (Z/d)	WFib
	longicaule	EWoo
	'Lord Baden-Powell'	see *P.* 'Colonel Baden-Powell'
	'Lord Bute' (R) 🏆H1c	CSpe ECtt ELan EWoo LCro LOPS MCot MHer NPer SMrm SPet SVen WFib WGwG
	'Lord de Ramsey'	see *P.* 'Tip Top Duet'
	'Lord Roberts' (Z)	WFib
	'Lottie Lungburgh' (Z/St)	WFib
	'Lotusland' (Dw/St/C) 🏆H1c	ECtt SPoG WFib
I	'Louise' (R) 🏆H1c	WFib
	'Love Song' (R/v)	WFib
	'Lovely Greta' (Za)	WFib
	'Lovely Wera' (Za/d)	WFib
	'Lucy Gunnett' (Z/d/v) 🏆H1c	WFib
	'Lyewood Bonanza' (R)	WFib
	'Lyric' (Min/d)	WFib
	'Mabel Grey' (Sc) 🏆H1c	CSpe ECtt ENfk EWoo MHer MNHC NPer NWsh SPet WFib
	madagascariense	EWoo
§	'Madame Auguste Nonin' (U/Sc)	ENfk MHer NWsh WFib
	'Madame Crousse' (I/d) 🏆H1c	EWoo WFib
	'Madame Layal' (A) 🏆H1c	WFib
	'Madame Margot'	see *P.* 'Hederinum Variegatum'
	'Madame Recamier' (Z/d)	ECtt
	'Madame Salleron' (Min/v)	EShb WFib
	'Madcap' **new**	WFib
	magenteum	MHer
	'Magnum' (R)	WFib
	'Majestic' (Z/d)	WFib
	'Mangles' Variegated' (Z/v)	WFib
	'Maple Leaf' (Sc)	EWoo NWsh
	'Mårbacka Harald' (Z/d) **new**	WFib
	'Maréchal MacMahon' (Z/C)	ENfk
	'Margaret Soley' (R) 🏆H1c	WFib
	'Margaret Waite' (R)	WFib
	'Margery Stimpson' (Min/d)	WFib
	'Marie Thomas' (Sc)	SGro
	MARIMBA ('Fisrimba'[PBR])	SCoo
	'Marion Saunders' (Dec)	WFib
	'Mariquita' (R)	WFib
	'Mark' (Dw/d)	WFib
	'Marmalade' (Min/d)	WFar
	'Marquis of Bute' (R/v)	MHer
	'Martin Parrett' (Min/d)	WFib
	'Mary Harrison' (Z/d)	WFib
I	'Maureen' Hoddinott (Z/d)	MHer
	'Mauve Beauty' (I/d)	WFib
	'Maxime Kovalevski' (Z)	WFib
	'May Day' (R)	WFib
	'May Magic' (R)	WFib
	'Meadowside Dark and Dainty' (St)	WFib
	'Meadowside Midnight' (St/C)	WFib
	'Medley' (Min/d)	WFib
	MELOCHERRY ('Pacmel'[PBR]) (Tempo Series) (Z/d)	SSea
	'Memento' (Min/d)	WFib
	'Mendip' (R)	WFib
	'Mendip Candy Floss' (R)	WFib
	'Mendip Royale' (R)	WFib
	'Meon Maid' (R)	SMrm WFib
	'Mere Casino' (Z)	WFib
	'Mexican Beauty' (I)	WFib
	'Mexicana'	see *P.* 'Rouletta'
	'Mexicanerin'	see *P.* 'Rouletta'
	'Michael' (A) 🏆H1c	EWoo MHer SPet
	'Michelle West' (Min)	WFib
	'Mike West' (St)	WFib
	'Millfield Gem' (I/d)	WFib
	'Millfield Rose' (I/d)	EWoo
	'Mini Czech' (Z/Ca/Min)	ECtt WBrk
	'Minnie' (Z/St/d)	WBrk WFib
	'Minstrel Boy' (R)	EWoo WFib
	'Minx' (Min/d)	WFib
	'Miss Burdett Coutts' (Z/v)	MHer WFib
	'Miss Muffett' (Min/d)	WFib
§	'Miss Stapleton'	EWoo LCro MHer WFib
	'Misterioso' (R)	WFib
	'Misty Morning' (R)	EWoo WFib
	'Modesty' (Z/d)	WFib
	'Mohawk' (R)	WFib
	'Mole'	see *P.* 'The Mole'
	mollicomum	EWoo
	'Molly' (A)	ENfk
	'Monique McEwan' (Z/St)	WFib
	'Monsieur Ninon' misapplied	see *P.* 'Madame Auguste Nonin'
§	'Monsieur Ninon' (U)	WFib
	'Mont Blanc' (Z/v)	CDow WFib
	'Montague Garabaldi Smith' (R)	WFib
	'Monty's Magic' (R)	ECtt
	'Moon Maiden' (A)	WFib
	'More's Victory' (U/Sc)	WFib
	'Morlens Bella Mi' (Za) **new**	WFib
	'Morlens Stella' (Za/d) **new**	WFib
	'Morval' (Dw/C/d) 🏆H1c	WFib
	'Morwenna' (R)	MHer WCot WFib
	'Mosaic Gay Baby' (I/d/v)	WFib
	MOSQUITAWAY EVA (Mosquitaway Series) (A)	LCro
	– MOSQUITAWAY LIZZY ('Floang01'[PBR]) (A)	LCro
	'Mr Henry Cox' (Z/v) 🏆H1c	MHer WFib
	'Mr Wren' (Z)	ECtt ELan EPri EShb SIvy WFar WFib
	'Mrs Cannell' (Z)	WFib
	'Mrs Farren' (Z/v)	MCot
	'Mrs G.H. Smith' (A) 🏆H1c	ECtt SPet WFib
	'Mrs J.C. Mappin' (Z/v) 🏆H1c	ECtt
	'Mrs Kingsbury' (U)	WFib
	'Mrs Martin' (I/d)	WFib
	'Mrs McKenzie' (Z/St)	WFib
	'Mrs Morf' (R)	ECtt
	'Mrs Parker' (Z/d/v)	ECtt WFib
	'Mrs Pollock' (Z/v)	ECtt ELan EShb MBow MBros MCot SCoo SMrm WBrk WFib
	'Mrs Quilter' (Z/C) 🏆H1c	ECtt SMrm WBrk WFib
	'Mrs W.A.R. Clifton' (I/d)	WFib
	multibracteatum	EWoo WFib
	multiradiatum	WFib
	mutans	WFib
	'My Chance' (Dec)	WFib
	myrrhifolium	EWoo SPet
§	– var. ***coriandrifolium***	MHer WFib
	'Mystery' (U) 🏆H1c	CWCL ECtt LCro WFib
	'Narina' (I)	SCoo

	'Needham Market' (A)	ENfk SPet
	'Nellie Nuttall' (Z)	WFib
	'Nervosum' (Sc)	ENfk
	'Nervous Mabel' (Sc) ♀H1c	MHer WFib
	'New Gypsy' (R)	ELan MHer
	'Newchurch' (Z/St)	WFib
	'Nicor Star' (Min)	WFib
	'Night' (I)	EWoo
	'Noblesse'	MPri
	'Noche' (R)	SMrm
	'Noele Gordon' (Z/d)	WFib
	'Occold Shield' (Dw/C/d) ♀H1c	ECtt SMrm WBrk WFib
	'Occold Tangerine' (Z)	WFib
	'Occold Volcano' (Dw/C/d)	WFib
	ochroleucum new	EWoo
	odoratissimum (Sc) ♀H1c	ENfk EWoo GPoy MHer SPet SRms WFib
	'Odyssey' (Min)	WFib
	'Old Spice' (Sc/v)	ENfk SPet WFib
	'Oldbury Duet' (A/v) ♀H1c	MHer NWad SPet
	'Olivia' (R)	WFib
	'Opera House' (R)	WFib
	'Orange Fizz' (Sc) ♀H1c	CCht EWoo MHer NWsh SPet SRms WFib WGwG
	'Orange Parfait' (R)	WFib
	'Orange Ricard' (Z/d)	WFib
	'Orangeade' (Dw/d)	WFib
	'Orchid Clorinda' (Sc)	WFib
	'Orchid Paloma' (Dw/d)	WFib
	'Orion' (Min/d)	WFib
	'Orsett' (Sc) ♀H1c	GLog MHer WFib
	otaviense	WFib
	'Our Flynn' (Z/St)	WFib
	'Our Gynette' (Dec)	EWoo
	'Our Henry' (Dw/d)	WFib
	PAC cultivars	see under selling name
	'Pagoda' (Z/St/d)	MHer WFib
	'Paisley Red' (Z/d)	WFib
	Palladium Series	MBros MDon
	'Pamela Vaughan' (Z/St)	WFib
	'Pampered Lady' (A)	SPet
	panduriforme	EWoo WFib
	papilionaceum	ELan EPri EShb EWoo MCot MHer WFib
	'Parisienne' (R) ♀H1c	EWoo WFib
	'Party Dress' (Z/d)	WFib
	'Pat Hannam' (St)	WFib
	'Paton's Unique' (U/Sc) ♀H1c	CDow ECtt ELan ENfk EWoo MCot MHer SVen WCot WFib
*	'Patricia' (I)	LCro
	'Patricia Andrea' (Z/T) ♀H1c	NPer WFib
	patulum	WFib
	'Paul Crampel' (Z) ♀H1c	EShb EWoo MCot MHer WFib
	'Paul West' (Min/d)	NWad SGro
	'Pauline Harris' (R)	WFib
	'Peace' (Min/C)	WFib
	PELFI cultivars	see under selling name
	peltatum	EWoo WFib
	'Penny' (Z/d)	WFib
	'Penny Lane' (Z)	WFib
	'Pensby' (Dw)	WFib
	'Peppermint Lace' (Sc)	EWoo NWsh SPet
	'Perfect' (Z)	WFib
	'Pershore Princess'	WAvo WBrk
	'Petals' (Z/v)	SPoG
	'Peter Godwin' (R)	WFib
	'Peter's Choice' (R)	WFib
	'Petit Pierre'	see *P.* 'Kleine Liebling'
	'Phyllis Richardson' (R/d)	WFib
	'Phyllis Variegated' (U/v)	ECtt ENfk EWoo MHer NWsh SPet WCot WFib
	'Pink Aurore' (U)	WFib
	'Pink Bonanza' (R)	WFib
	'Pink Capitatum'	see *P.* 'Pink Capricorn'
§	'Pink Capricorn' (Sc)	CCBP ENfk EPPr EPri EWoo LCro MBow MHoo NWsh SAng SMrm SRms WFib
	'Pink Champagne' (Sc)	MHer
	'Pink Dolly Varden' (Z/v)	ECtt WFib
	'Pink Fondant' (Min/d)	WFib
	'Pink Gay Baby'	see *P.* 'Sugar Baby'
	'Pink Happy Thought' (Z/v)	ECtt WFib
	'Pink Hindoo' (Dec)	EWoo
	'Pink Needles' (Min/St)	MHer WFib
	'Pink Pandora' (Z/T)	WFib
	'Pink Pet' (U)	ECtt
	'Pink Rambler' (Z/d)	WFib
	'Pink Raspail' (Z/d)	WFib
	'Pink Rosebud' (Z/d)	WFib
	'Playmate' (Min/St)	WFib
	'Plenty' (Z/d)	WFib
	'Plum Rambler' (Z/d)	ECtt EShb WBrk WFib
	'Polka' (U) ♀H1c	EWoo WFib
	'Pompeii' (R)	WFib
	'Poquita' (Sc)	SRms
	'Porchfield' (Min/St)	WBrk
	praemorsum	WFib
	(Precision Series) PRECISION AMETHYST	MDon
	- PRECISION BICOLOUR (I)	MDon
	- PRECISION BRIGHT LILAC	MDon
	- PRECISION BRIGHT RED	MDon
	- PRECISION BURGUNDY RED (I)	MDon
	- PRECISION DARK RED	MDon
	- PRECISION LIGHT PINK ('Klep02060'PBR) (I)	MDon
	- PRECISION RED ICE ('Sil Chris')	MDon
	- PRECISION ROSE LILAC	MDon
	'Preseli Lottie' (Z/d)	WFib
	'Preston Park' (Z/C)	WFib
	'Pretty Polly' (Sc)	WFib
	'Pride of Exmouth'	CWCL
	'Prim' (Dw/St/d)	WFib
	'Prince of Orange' (Sc) ♀H1c	CCBP CCht ECtt ENfk EWoo GPoy MCot MHer MHoo NWsh SEND SPet SRms WFib
	'Princeanum' (Sc) ♀H1c	WFib
	'Princess Abigail' (Dw/d)	ECtt WFib
	'Princess Josephine' (R)	WFib
	'Princess of Wales' (R)	WFib
	'Princess Virginia' (R/v)	WFib
	'Priory Salmon' (St/d)	EShb
	'Priory Star' (St/Min/d)	WFib
	pseudoglutinosum	EWoo MHer WFib
	'Pungent Peppermint' (Sc)	SRms
	'Purple Rogue' (R)	WFib
	'Purple Unique' (U/Sc)	ECtt ENfk EShb EWoo MCot MHer SVen WFib
	'Pygmalion' (Z/d/v)	WFib
	'Quantock' (R)	WFib
	'Quantock Angelique' (A)	SPet
	'Quantock Butterfly' (A)	SPet
	'Quantock Candy' (A) ♀H1c	ELan SPet WFib
	'Quantock Clare' (A)	SPet WFib
	'Quantock Classic' (A)	EWoo WFib
	'Quantock Double Dymond' (A/d) ♀H1c	MHer WFib
	'Quantock Kirsty' (A) ♀H1c	EWoo SPet
	'Quantock Louise' (A)	SPet
	'Quantock Marjorie' (A) ♀H1c	SPet WFib
	'Quantock May' (A)	SPet WFib

	'Quantock Perfection' (A) ♀H1c	MHer SPet WFib
	'Quantock Plume' (A)	WFib
	'Quantock Sally' (A/d)	ENfk SPet
	'Queen of Denmark' (Z/d)	WFib
	'Queen of Hearts' (I × Z/d)	WFib
	'Queen of the Lemons' (Sc)	EWoo
§	***quercifolium*** (Sc)	ECtt ELan EWoo GPoy WFib
	quinquelobatum	CSpe EWoo WFib
	radens (Sc)	ENfk EWoo WFib
	'Radula' (Sc) ♀H1c	CCBP ELan MHer SPet SRms WFib
	'Radula Roseum' (Sc)	EWoo WFib
	'Rager's Star' (Dw)	MHer
	'Ray Bidwell' (Min)	WFib
§	'Red Black Vesuvius' (Min/C)	WFib
	'Red Capri' (Sc)	EWoo
	'Red Cascade' (I) ♀H1c	WFib
	'Red Gables'	WAvo WCot
	'Red Pandora' (Z/T) ♀H1c	WFib
	'Red Pimpernel' (Z/T)	WFib
	'Red Rambler' (Z/d)	WBrk WFib
	'Red Robin' (R)	ENfk EPPr WCot
	'Red Spider' (Dw/Ca)	MHer WFib
	'Red Startel' (Z/St/d)	WFib
	'Red Susan Pearce' (R)	WFib
	'Red Witch' (Dw/St/d)	EWoo MHer WBrk WFib
§	RED-MINI-CASCADE ('Rotemica') (I)	CDow
	'Reflections' (Z/d)	WFib
	'Regina' (Z/d) ♀H1c	WFib
	'Rembrandt' (R)	WFib
	'Renate Parsley' ♀H1c	EWoo LCro MHer WFib
	reniforme	EAri EWoo MHer WFib
	'Retah's Crystal' (Z/v)	MHer
	'Reunion Rose' (Sc)	WFib
	ribifolium	SPet
	'Richard Gibbs' (Sc)	ENfk MHer SPet
	'Richard Key' (Z/C/d)	WFib
	'Rietje van der Lee' (A)	ENfk WFib
	'Rimfire' (R) ♀H1c	ELan EWoo LCro MHer NWad WFib
	'Rio Grande' (I/d)	MHer WFib
	'Rober's Lemon Rose' (Sc)	ENfk EWoo MHer SPet SRms WBrk WFib
	'Robert Fish' (Z/C)	SCoo
	'Robert McElwain' (Z/d)	WFib
	'Robin' (R)	ECtt
	'Robin's Unique' (U)	MHer WFib
	'Rogue' (R)	WFib
	'Roller's Echo' (A)	SPet WFib
	'Roller's Pioneer' (I/v)	ENfk EWoo
	'Roller's Satinique' (U)	MHer WFib
	'Rollison's Unique' (U)	MHer WFib
	'Romeo' (R)	EWoo
	'Rose Bengal' (A)	ENfk
	'Rose Eye' (Dw)	WFib
	'Rose of Amsterdam' (Min/d)	WFib
	'Rose Paton's Unique' (U/Sc)	SMrm
	'Rose Silver Cascade' (I)	ECtt MCot MHer
	'Rosebud Supreme' (Z/d)	WFib
	'Rosmaroy' (R)	WFib
	'Rosy Dawn' (Min/d)	WFib
	'Rote Mini-cascade'	see *P.* RED-MINI-CASCADE
§	'Rouletta' (I/d)	WFib
	'Royal Ascot' (R)	EWoo SMrm
	'Royal Banner' (R) **new**	WFib
	'Royal Beauty' (R) **new**	WFib
	'Royal Celebration' (R)	WFib
	'Royal Court' (R)	WFib
	'Royal Dream' (R) **new**	WFib
	'Royal Escort' (R) **new**	WFib
I	'Royal Flush' (R) **new**	WFib
	'Royal Lady' (R) **new**	WFib
	ROYAL LAVENDER ('Klepp07196'PBR) (I)	SSea
	'Royal Oak' (Sc) ♀H1c	CPbh ECtt ENfk EPPr EWoo MCot MHer MHoo MNHC NWad NWsh SEND SPet SPoG SRms SVen WFib
	'Royal Park' (R) **new**	WFib
	'Royal Picotee' (R) **new**	WFib
	'Royal Prince' (R)	WFib
	'Royal Princess' (R)	WFib
§	'Royal Purple' (Z/d)	WFib
	'Royal Regiment' (R) **new**	WFib
	'Royal Sovereign' (R)	WFib
	'Royal Star' (R)	WFib
	'Royal Surprise' (R) ♀H1c	EWoo
	'Ruby' (Min/d)	WFib
	'Rushmere' (Dw/d)	WFib
	'Rushmoor Beautiful' (d/Za)	WFib
	'Rushmoor Bondi Blue' (Z/St/Min/d)	MHer
	'Rushmoor Golden Rosebud' (Za)	WFib
	'Rushmoor Golden Ruffles' (Z/C/St/Min/d)	MHer
	'Rushmoor Mrs Eve Scott' (Za/d)	WFib
	(Rushmoor River Series) 'Rushmoor Amazon' (Za/d)	WFib
	- 'Rushmoor Amur' (Za)	WFib
	- 'Rushmoor Avon' (d/Za)	WFib
	- 'Rushmoor Colorado' (d/Za)	WFib
	- 'Rushmoor Congo' (Za/d)	WFib
	- 'Rushmoor Danube' (Za)	WFib
	- 'Rushmoor Euphrates' (Za)	WFib
	- 'Rushmoor Ganges' (Za)	WFib
	- 'Rushmoor Indus' (Za)	WFib
	- 'Rushmoor Irtysh' (Za)	WFib
	- 'Rushmoor Krishna' (Za)	WFib
	- 'Rushmoor Main' (Za)	WFib
	- 'Rushmoor Mekong' (Za/d)	WFib
	- 'Rushmoor Mississippi' (Za)	WFib
	- 'Rushmoor Missouri' (Za)	WFib
	- 'Rushmoor Morava' (Za)	WFib
	- 'Rushmoor Mosman' (Za)	WFib
	- 'Rushmoor Murray' (Za)	WFib
	- 'Rushmoor Niger' (Za)	WFib
	- 'Rushmoor Nile' (Za/d)	WFib
	- 'Rushmoor Orinoco' (Za/d)	WFib
	- 'Rushmoor Paraná' (Za)	WFib
	- 'Rushmoor Rhine' (Za/d)	WFib
	- 'Rushmoor Rhone' (Za/d)	WFib
	- 'Rushmoor Ribble' (Za/d)	WFib
	- 'Rushmoor Rio Grande' (Za)	WFib
	- 'Rushmoor Saint Lawrence' (Za/d)	WFib
	- 'Rushmoor Salween' (Za/d)	WFib
	- 'Rushmoor Sava' (Za)	WFib
	- 'Rushmoor Severn' (Za/d)	WFib
	- 'Rushmoor Thames' (Za/d)	WFib
	- 'Rushmoor Tiber' (Za/d)	WFib
	- 'Rushmoor Vistula' (Za/d)	WFib
	- 'Rushmoor Wheaton' (Za)	WFib
	- 'Rushmoor Yamuna' (Za/d)	WFib
	- 'Rushmoor Yangtze' (Za/d)	WFib

	- 'Rushmoor Yarra' (Za/d)	WFib
	- 'Rushmoor Yenisei' (Za/d)	WFib
	- 'Rushmoor Zambezi' (Za/d)	WFib
	'Saint Elmo's Fire' (St/Min/d)	MHer WFar WFib
	SAINT MALO ('Guisaint') (I)	ECtt
	'Salmon Angel'	CSpe
	'Salmon Beauty' (Dw/d)	WFib
§	'Salmon Irene' (Z/d)	WFib
	'Salmon Queen'	see *P.* 'Lachskönigin'
	SALMON QUEEN ('Pacsalque'PBR) (Z)	SSea
	salmoneum	WFib
	'Samantha' (R)	WFib
	'Samantha Stamp' (Dw/C/d)	WFib
	SAMELIA ('Pensam'PBR) (Dark Line Series) (Z/d)	SSea
	'Sammi Brougham' (Z/Dw)	WFib
	'Sancho Panza' (Dec)	CSpe WFib
	'Sandra Lorraine' (I/d)	WFib
	'Sanguineum'	CSpe
§	'Sarah Don' (A/v)	WFib
	'Sarah Jane' (Sc)	WFib
	'Saxifragoides'	WFib
	scabrum	EWoo
	'Scarlet Gem' (Z/St)	WBrk WFib
	'Scarlet Pet' (U) 🏆H1c	CDow ECtt ENfk SMrm
	'Scarlet Rambler' (Z/d)	ECtt EShb SMrm WFib
	'Scarlet Unique' (U)	CSpe EPri EWoo MCot MNHC WFib
	schizopetalum	MHer WFib
	'Schottii' 🏆H1c	CPbh EWoo MHer WFib
	'Scottow Star' (Z/C)	WFib
	'Seaview Silver' (Min/St)	WFib
	'Seaview Sparkler' (Z/St)	WFib
	'Secret Love' (Sc)	SRms
	'Seeley's Pansy' (A)	EWoo MHer
	'Sefton' (R) 🏆H1c	WFib
	'Shannon'	EWoo WFib
	'Shelley' (Dw)	WFar
§	'Shottesham Pet' (Sc)	CCBP CCht ENfk EWoo MHer NWad SMrm SPet SRms WGwG
	sidoides 🏆H1c	CDow CPbh CSpe CTtf CWCL EAJP EAri ECtt EGrI ELan ENfk EWoo LCro LOPS MCot MHer NWsh SBrt SGro SMrm SPhx SPlb SVen WAvo WFib WHer WKif
	'Silver Blazon' (Z/Dw/C/v)	WFib
	'Silver Dawn' (Min/St)	MHer
	'Silver Delight' (Z/v/d)	WFib
	'Silver Kewense' (Dw/v)	WFib
	'Silver Snow' (Min/St/d)	WFib
	'Skelly's Pride' (Z)	WFib
	'Skies of Italy' (Z/C/d)	WFib
	'Snow Flurry' (Sc)	WFib
	'Snowbaby' (Min/d)	WFib
	'Snowdrift' (I/d)	WFib
	'Snowflake' (Min)	see *P.* 'Atomic Snowflake'
	'Snowstorm' (Z)	WFib
	'Sofie'	see *P.* 'Decora Rose'
	'Solferino' (A)	ENfk
	'Something Special' (Z/d) 🏆H1c	WFib
	'Sophia' (Z)	WGwG
	SOPHIE CASADE	see *P.* 'Decora Rose'
	'Sophie Dumaresque' (Z/v) 🏆H1c	WFib
	'Sophie Emma' (Z)	WFib
	'Sophie Marion' (Z/Dw)	WFib
	'South American Bronze' (R) 🏆H1c	SMrm WFib
	'Southern Rosina' (Dw)	WFib
	'Southern Sundae' (Dw/d)	MHer
	'Souvenir de Prue' (Sc)	EWoo
	'Spanish Angel' (A) 🏆H1c	MHer SPet WFib
	'Spellbound' (R)	WFib
	'Spital Dam' (Dw/d)	WFib
	'Spitfire' (Z/Ca/d/v)	CDow WFib
§	'Splendide' 🏆H1c	CPbh CSpe CTtf EWoo MHer SWvt WFib
	'Spot-on-bonanza' (R) 🏆H1c	ECtt WFib
	'Springfield Black' (R)	MCot
	'Springtime' (Z/d)	WFib
	'Stadt Bern' (Z/C) 🏆H1c	CSpe
	× ***stapletoniae***	see *P.* 'Miss Stapleton'
	'Startel Salmon' (Z/St)	MHer
	'Stella Ballerina'	SMrm
	'Stellar Arctic Star'	see *P.* 'Arctic Star'
	'Stellar Hannaford Star'	see *P.* 'Hannaford Star'
	'Stewart Meehan' (R)	WFib
	'Strawberry Fayre' (Dw/St)	WFib
§	'Sugar Baby' (I/Dw)	MHer WFib
	'Summer Cloud' (Z/d)	WFib
	SUMMER RAIN (mixed) (I)	MBros
	SUMMER TWIST RED/WHITE ('Gentwiststar') (Summer Twist Series) (Z/St) **new**	MBros
	'Summertime' (Z/d)	see *P.* 'Deacon Summertime'
	'Sun Rocket' (Dw/d)	WFib
	'Sundridge Moonlight' (Z/C)	WFib
	'Sundridge Surprise' (Z)	WFib
	'Sunraysia' (Z/St)	WFib
	'Sunset Snow' (R)	WFib
	'Sunspot Petit Pierre' (Min/v)	WFib
	'Sunstar' (Min/d)	WFib
	'Supernova' (Z/St/d)	WFib
	'Supreme Red' (I)	MDon
	'Surcouf' (I)	WFib
	'Susan Hillier' (R)	WFib
	'Susan Payne' (Dw/d)	MHer
	'Susie' (Z/C)	WFib
	'Sussex Gem' (Min/d)	WFib
	'Sussex Lace'	see *P.* 'White Mesh'
	'Swanland Lace' (I/d/v)	WFib
	'Swedish Angel' (A)	WFib
	'Sweet Mimosa' (Sc) 🏆H1c	CCBP CCht CPbh ECtt ELan ENfk EWoo MCot MHer NWsh SEND SPet SRms WFib
	'Sweet Sixteen' (R)	WFib
	'Sybil Holmes' (I/d)	ECtt WFib
	'Tammy' (Dw/d)	WFib
	TANGO NEON PURPLE ('Fistaneon'PBR) (Z/d)	SSea
	'Tara Caws' (Z)	WFib
	'Ted Dutton' (R)	WFib
	tetragonum	EShb EWoo MHer SIvy WFib
	'The Boar' (Fr) 🏆H1c	EShb EWoo MCot WFib
	'The Culm' (A)	MHer WFib
	'The Czar'	see *P.* 'Czar'
	'The Joker' (I/d)	WFib
	'The Kenn-Lad' (A)	EWoo
	'The Marchioness of Bute' (R)	MHer WFib
§	'The Mole' (A)	WFib
	'The Tamar' (A)	EWoo MHer
	'The Yar' (Z/St)	WFib
	'Thomas Earle' (Z)	WFib
	'Tinker West' (Z/St/Dw)	WFib
§	'Tip Top Duet' (A) 🏆H1c	LCro MHer SMrm SPet WFib
	'Tirley Garth' (A)	WFib
	tomentosum (Sc) 🏆H1c	CPbh CSpe EAri ENfk EPPr EShb EWoo GLog GPoy LCro LWaG

	MCot MHer MHoo NWsh SEND SIvy SPet WFib
- 'Chocolate'	see *P.* 'Chocolate Peppermint'
TOMMY ('Pactommy') (I)	ELan SSea
tongaense	EWoo WFib
'Topscore' (Z/d)	WFib
'Tornado' (R) 🏆H1c	LCro WFib
'Torrento' (Sc)	EWoo MHer NWsh SEND SPet SRms WFib
'Tortoiseshell' (R)	WFib
transvaalense	CPbh EWoo
tricolor misapplied	see *P.* 'Splendide'
tricolor Curt.	CPbh
tricuspidatum	EShb EWoo MHer WFib
trifidum	EAri EWoo WFib
'Triomphe de Nancy' (Z/d)	WFib
triste	EAri EWoo MHer WFib
'Trudie' (Fr/Dw)	MHer SGro WFib
'Turkish Coffee' (R)	WFib
'Turkish Delight' (Dw/C)	WFib
'Turtle's Surprise' (Z/d/v)	WBrk
'Two Dees' (Dw/d)	WFib
'Tyabb Princess' (R)	EWoo
'Unicorn Bride' (Za/d)	WFib
'Unicorn Diva' (Za)	WFib
'Unicorn Frills' (Za)	WFib
'Unicorn Gold' (Za)	WFib
'Unicorn Hot Butter' (Za/d)	WFib
'Unicorn Hot Pepper' (Za/d)	WFib
'Unicorn Linea' (Za) **new**	WFib
'Unicorn Rose' (Za/d)	WFib
'Unicorn Shy' (Za) **new**	WFib
'Unicorn Spring' (Za) **new**	WFib
'Unique Aurore' (U)	CSpe MHer
'Unique Mons Ninon'	see *P.* 'Monsieur Ninon'
urbanum	EWoo
'Urchin' (Min/St)	WFib
'Ursula Key' (Z/C)	WFib
'Ursula's Choice' (A)	SPet WFib
'Val Merrick' (Dw/St)	WFib
'Valentine' (Z/C)	WFib
'Vancouver Centennial' (Dw/St/C) 🏆H1c	ECtt MHer SCoo SPoG SSea WFib
'Vandersea' (Sc)	EWoo MCot MHer NWsh
'Variegated Clorinda' (Sc/v)	WFib
'Variegated Fragrans'	see *P.* (Fragrans Group) 'Fragrans Variegatum'
§ 'Variegated Kleine Liebling' (Min/v)	WFib
'Variegated Petit Pierre' (Min/v)	MHer WFib
'Vectis Cascade' (I)	EWoo
'Vectis Glitter' (Z/St) 🏆H1c	WBrk WCot WFib
'Vectis Pink' (Dw/St)	WFib
'Vectis Purple' (Z/d)	WFib
'Vectis Starbright' (Dw/St)	WFib
'Vectis Volcano' (Z/St)	WFib
'Vicki' (R)	EWoo MHer
'Vicki Town' (R)	WFib
'Vicky Claire' (R)	SMrm WFib
VICKY ('Pacvicky'[PBR]) (I)	SSea
VILLE DE DRESDEN ('Pendresd') (I)	EWoo
'Vina' (Dw/C/d)	WFib
violareum misapplied	see *P.* 'Splendide'
'Viscossisimum' (Sc)	MHer
viscosum	see *P. glutinosum*
'Vivat Regina' (Z/d)	WFib
'Voodoo' (U) 🏆H1c	CPbh CSpe ECtt ENfk EWoo MCot MHer WCot WFib
'Wallis Friesdorf' (Dw/C/d)	WFib
'Wantirna' (Z/v) 🏆H1c	ECtt
'Warrenorth Coral' (Z/C/d)	WFib
'Warrenorth Emerald' (Z)	MHer
'Wayward Angel' (A)	ENfk SPet
'Wedding Royale' (Dw/d)	WFib
'Welling' (Sc)	ENfk SPet WFib
'Wendy Jane' (Dw/d)	WFib
'Wendy Read' (Dw/d)	WFib
'Westdale Appleblossom' (Z/C/d)	ECtt MHer WFib
'Westside' (Z/d)	MHer WFib
'Westwood' (Z/St)	WFib
'Whisper' (R)	EWoo WFib
'White Bird's Egg' (Z)	WFib
'White Boar' (Fr)	CSpe EAri ECtt EShb WFib
'White Bonanza' (R)	WFib
'White Eggshell' (Min)	WFib
'White Feather' (Z/St)	MHer
§ 'White Mesh' (I/v)	CDow
'White Unique' (U)	WFib
'Wilhelm Kolle' (Z)	WFib
'Wilhelm Langath' (Z/v)	ECtt EShb SCoo WBrk
'Willa' (Dec)	WFib
'Wirral Moonlight' (Z/C/d)	WFib
'Wolverton' (Z)	WFib
'Wootton's Unique' (U)	EWoo
'Wychwood' (A/Sc)	EWoo
'Yale' (I/d) 🏆H1c	MHer WFib
'Yan le Grounch' (Z/C)	WFib
'Yhu' (R)	SMrm WFib
'York Florist' (Z/d/v)	ECtt
'Yvonne' (Z)	WFib
'Zinc' (Z/d)	WFib
zonale	EWoo WFib
'Zulu King' (R)	WFib
'Zulu Warrior' (R)	WFib

Peliosanthes (*Asparagaceae*)

caesia B&SWJ 5183	WCru
macrostegia B&SWJ 3639	WCru
teta subsp. ***humilis*** RWJ 10044	WCru

Pellaea (*Pteridaceae*)

atropurpurea	GBin
falcata 🏆H4	EShb
ovata	Plb
paradoxa 'Glowstar'	ISha
rotundifolia 🏆H2	CLAP CRos CTsd EHyd EShb ISha LEdu LLWG LPal LRHS MAsh NBro NRHS SMrm WCot
viridis	EShb LEdu WCot WPGP

Pellionia see *Elatostema*

Peltandra (*Araceae*)

undulata	see *P. virginica* (L.) Schott
§ ***virginica*** (L.) Schott	LLWG LPfP NPer

Peltaria (*Brassicaceae*)

alliacea	CCBP CSpe LEdu WCot

Peltiphyllum see *Darmera*

Peltoboykinia (*Saxifragaceae*)

§ ***tellimoides***	EMor ESwi LShi NBir WFar
watanabei	CElw CPla EBee EMor GEdr GPSL LEdu LShi MACG MBriF MMrt NFav NLar SBls WCru WPnP

Pennellianthus see *Penstemon*

Pennisetum ✿ (*Poaceae*)

	advena 'Fireworks'PBR (v)	CBcs CBod CKel EBee EHyd EPfP LPar LRHS MAsh NRHS SRHi SWvt WHil
§	- 'Rubrum' ♀H3	CBcs CBod CExl CKno EBee EHyd EShb LCro LOPS LPal LRHS MAsh MBros NRHS NWsh SCoo SMad SWvt WHlf
§	***alopecuroides***	CBcs CBod CWCL EHeP EHyd EPfP EWhm GMcL LRHS NBwr NGdn NRHS SCob SPer SPlb SWvt WCot XLum XSen
	- AUTUMN WIZARD	see *P. alopecuroides* 'Herbstzauber'
	- 'Black Beauty'	CKno EBlo ECha ELon IPot LShi NLar SMHy SSut WHoo
	- 'Cassian's Choice' ♀H3	CKno EWes SHar WBor
	- 'Caudatum'	CKno
	- 'Dark Desire'	CKno CRos CSde EHyd EPfP LEdu LRHS NRHS
	- 'Foxtrot'	EPPr
	- 'Gelbstiel'	CKno EBee EHyd ELon EPfP LRHS NRHS
	- 'Goldstrich'	ELon SAko XSen
	- 'Hameln' ♀H3	Widely available
	- 'Hameln Gold'PBR	CBod CKel CKno ELon EWes LRHS LSou NLar SPeP XSen
§	- 'Herbstzauber'	CKno ELon NLar SMHy XLum XSen
	- 'JS Jommenik'PBR	EBee ELon
	- 'Lady U' **new**	IPot
	- 'Little Bunny'	CBod CKel CMac CSde CWnw EBee EHeP EHyd ELan ELon EPfP GMcL LPal LRHS LSRN MAsh MHol NGdn NLar NRHS SCob SMrm SWvt XSen
	- 'Little Honey' (v)	ELan ELon WPnP XLum XSen
	- 'Magic'	CBod EBee ELon IPot SMHy
	- 'Moudry'	CDor CExl CSde EBee ELon EPPr EPfP IPot LPal LRHS MACG NLar XLum XSen
	- 'Red Head' ♀H3	CBWd CBod CKno CMac CRos EBee EHyd ELan ELon EPfP EWes LEdu LRHS LSou LSun MAvo MHol MNrw NLar NRHS NSti SEdd SMad SPeP SPoG WChS WCot WHlf WPGP WTor
	- f. ***viridescens***	CBod EAJP EHyd ELon EPPr EShb LEdu LRHS LSun NRHS SBls SCob SMad SMrm SPtp XLum XSen
	- 'Weserbergland'	CKno EBlo ELon EPPr SAko
	- 'Woodside'	CKno XLum
	clandestinum	EShb
	compressum	see *P. alopecuroides*
	'Fairy Tails' ♀H3	CBWd CKno CRos ECha EHyd ELon EPPr EPfP LCro LOPS LPla LRHS MAsh MAvo NDov NRHS NWsh SMHy SPoG WCot WHoo
	flaccidum	EPPr
	glaucum 'Purple Majesty'	CSpe MPri SWvt
	incomptum	XLum
	longistylum misapplied	see *P. villosum*
	macrourum ♀H3	CAby CBWd CBod CKno CSde CSpe EAJP EBlo ECha EHyd EMor EPPr EPfP LEdu LRHS MACG MAvo MNrw NDov NRHS NWsh SDix SMHy SMad SPlb SPtp WBor WPGP XSte
	- blue-leaved **new**	WCot
	- 'Short Stuff'	CKno ECha LEdu WPGP
	- 'Tail Feathers'	SBls
	massaicum 'Red Bunny Tails'	CChe NLar NRHS SRms WHlf
	- 'Red Buttons'	see *P. thunbergii* 'Red Buttons'
	orientale ♀H3	CBod CKno CRos CSde CSpe EBlo ECha EGrI EHyd EPfP EWoo LPal LRHS LSun MRav NBir NRHS SEND SMHy SPer SRkn SWvt WKif XLum XSen
	- 'Flamingo'	EHyd IPot NRHS
	- 'Karley Rose'PBR	CKno CPar CSpe EWes EWoo LRHS MAvo MBNS NDov NRHS SCob SMad SWvt WFar WPGP WTor
I	- 'Robustum'	EPPr WPGP
	- 'Shogun'	CKno CRos ECha EHyd EPPr EPfP LRHS NRHS SMHy
	- 'Tall Tails'	CSde EBee EPPr EWes GMaP LRHS NDov SMHy XLum
	'Paul's Giant'	EBee ELon XLum
	purpureum	SRms
	setaceum 'Rubrum'	see *P. advena* 'Rubrum'
	thunbergii	CAby CBod
§	- 'Red Buttons'	CKno CRos CSde EHyd ELon EPPr EPfP LEdu LRHS LSun MACG MAsh MAvo MGos MNrw NRHS SBls SCob SMHy SPoG SSut WAvo WHoo WPGP
	VERTIGO ('Tift-8'PBR)	WCot
§	***villosum*** ♀H3	Widely available
	- 'Cream Falls'	SBls

pennyroyal see *Mentha pulegium*

Penstemon ✿ (*Plantaginaceae*)

	'Abbotsmerry'	EGrI ELon MBNS MCot MGil SGBe
§	'Alice Hindley'	CMac CSpe CTri CWCL EAJP EHyd ELan EPfP LRHS LSRN MCot MGil MRav NBir NRHS SGBe SPer SRms SWvt WAvo WCAu WCot WFar WHlf WHoo WJam WKif WMal WPnP XLum
	'Amy Gray'	WAvo WJam
§	'Andenken an Friedrich Hahn' ♀H5	Widely available
§	***angustifolius***	CSpe EDAr
	'Apple Blossom' misapplied	see *P.* 'Thorn'
	'Apple Blossom'	Widely available
	'Arabesque Appleblossom'	CBod EHyd LBar LRHS MBros MDon NRHS
	'Arabesque Orchid'	CBod LBar LRHS MDon SCoo
	'Arabesque Pink'	EHyd LBar LRHS MBros MDon MHol NRHS
	'Arabesque Red'	CBod EHyd LBar LRHS MBros MDon NRHS SCoo
	'Arabesque Violet'	EHyd LBar LRHS MDon MHol NRHS SCoo
	arizonicus	see *P. whippleanus*
	'Ashton'	WAvo WJam
	attenuatus var. ***attenuatus***	GKev
	- subsp. ***militaris***	SPlb
	'Audrey Cooper'	CMac WAvo WJam
	'Avon Belle'	WHlf
	azureus	GKev LShi
	'Barbara Barker'	see *P.* 'Beech Park'
§	***barbatus***	ECha GElm SPer SRms SSut XSen
	- 'Cambridge Mixed'	WPnP
	- 'Coccineus'	CSpe GBin LEdu SBut WJam XLum
	- 'Iron Maiden'	LRHS
	- 'Jingle Bells'	CBod EPfP GArf MACG SBls SPeP
	- orange-flowered	SPlb
	- Pinacolada Series	EHyd LRHS NRHS
	- - 'Pinacolada Blue'	CRos LRHS
	- - 'Pinacolada Dark Rose'	EHyd LRHS NRHS
	- - 'Pinacolada Rosy Red'	EHyd LRHS NRHS
	- - 'Pinacolada White'	EHyd LRHS NRHS SRms

	- var. ***praecox*** f. ***nanus*** 'Rondo'	EAJP
	- - (Pristine Series) 'Pristine Deep Rose' **new**	LBar
	- - - 'Pristine Lila Purple'	LBar
	- - - 'Pristine Pink' **new**	LBar
	- - - 'Pristine Scarlet' **new**	LBar
	- 'Roseus'	SHar
	'Beckford'	CWCL EWes LRHS MBNS MGil SGBe
§	'Beech Park' 🏆^{H4}	EBee EHyd ELan EMor EPfP LRHS SRms WAvo WJam
	'Bisham Seedling'	see *P.* 'White Bedder'
	'Blackberry'	NCth WHlf
	'Blackbird' (Bird Series)	Widely available
	'Blue Riding Hood'^{PBR} (Riding Hood Series)	SPoG
	'Blue Spring' misapplied	see *P. heterophyllus* 'Blue Spring'
	'Blueberry Taffy'^{PBR}	ECtt EHyd LRHS NRHS
	'Bodnant' 🏆^{H4}	WAvo WHoo WMal
	'Boysenberry Taffy'^{PBR}	EHyd LRHS NRHS
	bradburii	see *P. grandiflorus*
	'Bredon'	WAvo WJam
	brevisepalus	LPla
	'Bubblegum' (Ice Cream Series)	SCoo
	'Burford Purple'	see *P.* 'Burgundy'
	'Burford Seedling'	see *P.* 'Burgundy'
	'Burford White'	see *P.* 'White Bedder'
§	'Burgundy'	CBod CGBo CMac CWnw ECtt GMaP NBir NPer SMrm SRms WAvo WJam XLum
	caeruleus	see *P. angustifolius*
	californicus	EDAr
§	***campanulatus***	CRos EHyd EPot EWes LRHS NRHS SGro SRms
	- 'Roseus' misapplied	see *P. kunthii*
	'Candy Pink'	see *P.* 'Old Candy Pink'
	cardwellii	EWes
	'Castle Forbes'	EBee GMaP SRms WAvo WJam
	'Cathedral Rose'	EBee EHyd ELan EPfP LRHS
	'Catherine de la Mare'	see *P. heterophyllus* 'Catherine de la Mare'
	'Centra'	WAvo WJam
	'Cha Cha Lavender'^{PBR}	EWTr
	'Charles Rudd'	CGBo ECtt ELan ELon LSRN MBNS MGil MHer NLar SGBe SOrN SRms SWvt WAvo WJam
§	'Cherry'	ECtt SHar SMrm WAvo WJam
	'Cherry Ripe' misapplied	see *P.* 'Cherry'
§	'Chester Scarlet'	ECtt EGrI WAvo WJam WKif
	'Choirboy'	EWes
	cinicola	GArf
	cobaea	CSpe
	'Comberton'	SRms WAvo WHoo WJam
	confertus	CTri EBee EPot GKev LShi
	- RCB/MO A-7	WCot
	'Connie's Pink' 🏆^{H4}	SRms WAvo
	'Coral Sea'	WFar
	'Cottage Garden Red'	see *P.* 'Windsor Red'
§	'Countess of Dalkeith'	ECtt GBin MCot MRav SHar SRms SWvt WAvo WBor WJam
	'Craigieburn Taffeta'	WAvo WJam
	cristatus	see *P. eriantherus*
*	***cyananthus*** var. ***utahensis***	WCot
	'Dark Towers'^{PBR}	Widely available
	davidsonii	EWes GEdr
	- var. ***menziesii*** 'Microphyllus'	GEdr NBwr WAbe
	- var. ***praeteritus***	GEdr
	- 'Silverwells'	EPot GEdr
	'Dazzler'	SWvt WAvo WJam
	'Delfts Blue Riding Hood'^{PBR} (Riding Hood Series)	LCro LOPS
	'Devonshire Cream'	WAvo WJam
	diffusus	see *P. serrulatus*
	digitalis	CWal EGrI SRms
	- 'Gold Foil'	LBar LShi
	- 'Goldfinger'	EPfP LBar LRHS
§	- 'Husker Red'	Widely available
	- 'Isa'	WCot
	- 'Joke'	NCth
	- 'Mystica'	EHyd EPfP LBar LRHS MACG NRHS SPeP SRms
	- 'Purpureus'	see *P. digitalis* 'Husker Red'
§	'Drinkstone Red'	SDix SRms WAvo WJam
	'Drinkwater Red'	see *P.* 'Drinkstone Red'
	(Elgar Series) 'Elgar Crown of India'	WCot
	- 'Elgar Firefly'	WCot
	- 'Elgar Light of Life'	WCot
	- 'Elgar Nimrod'	WCot
	'Ellenbank Amethyst'	SDys
	'Ellenbank Cardinal'	WKif
	'Ellwood Red Phoenix'	WAvo
	'Elmley'	WAvo WJam
§	***eriantherus***	GKev SPlb
	ETNA ('Yatna') (Volcano Series)	ECtt EPfP GMcL LRHS NRHS SCoo SPad SRms WHlf WJam
	euglaucus	GKev
§	'Evelyn' 🏆^{H4}	CMac CSBt ECha ELan ELon EPfP EShb LRHS LSRN MBNS MCot MGil MHer MRav SPoG SRms SWvt WAvo WBrk WHoo WJam WKif WSHC XLum
	'Fanny's Blush'	SWvt
	'Firebird'	see *P.* 'Schoenholzeri'
	'Flame'	WAvo WBrk WJam
	'Flamingo'	EAJP EBee ECtt ELon EMor EPfP EWes MBNS NLar SCoo SGbt SHar SRms SWvt WAvo WHlf WJam
	fruticosus	GEdr
§	- var. ***scouleri*** 🏆^{H4}	EDAr MAsh
	- - 'Amethyst'	WAbe
	FUJIYAMA ('Yayama'^{PBR}) (Volcano Series)	CPla ECtt EPfP LRHS MBow SCoo SPad SRms SWvt WHlf WJam
	'Garden Red'	see *P.* 'Windsor Red'
	'Garnet'	see *P.* 'Andenken an Friedrich Hahn'
	gentianoides B&SWJ 10271	WCru
	'Geoff Hamilton'	CElw ECtt ELon MBNS MGil SGBe SPoG WAvo WJam WPnP
§	'George Home' 🏆^{H3}	EWes GBin MBNS SMrm SRms WAvo WJam
	'George Moon'	SPad
	'Gilchrist'	SAng
	glaber	ECha EWld LShi MBow SPlb WHlf
	- 'Roundway Snowflake'	SHar SRms
	'Gloire des Quatre Rues'	XLum
§	***grandiflorus***	WMal
	'Grape Taffy'^{PBR}	EHyd LRHS NRHS
	hallii	EWes GEdr SPlb
	hartwegii 'Albus'	SHar SRms WJam
	- 'Picotee Red'	CBod EHyd NRHS
§	***heterophyllus***	LRHS SIvy SRms
	- 'Blue Gem'	CElw
§	- 'Blue Spring'	CFis CSpe EPfP MRav WAbe
§	- 'Catherine de la Mare'	EBee EGrI EHyd EShb EWTr GBin LSRN MGil NLar NRHS SCob SHar SIvy SOrN SWvt WHlf WKif WPnP WSpi XLum
	- 'Electric Blue'	CBod CRos EHyd LBar LRHS LSou MBNS MDon NRHS SCoo WFar
	- 'Heavenly Blue'	Widely available
	- 'Jeanette'	WTor
	- 'Margarita Bop'	SSha

	– 'True Blue'	see *P. heterophyllus*
	– 'Züriblau'	SPlb
§	'Hewell Pink Bedder' ♀H4	CBar CKel CRos EHyd EPfP LRHS MBNS MRav NCou NCth NRHS SCoo SHar SIvy SRms SWvt WAvo WHlf
	'Hidcote Pink' ♀H3	Widely available
	'Hidcote Purple'	SHar WHoo XLum
	'Hidcote White'	MHer SWvt
	'Hillview Pink'	XLum
§	***hirsutus***	EBee SBut WJam XLum
	– f. ***albiflorus***	WAbe
	– var. ***pygmaeus***	EDAr EPfP EPot EWTr NHpl NRya SBut SPlb SRms WHoo
*	– – f. ***albus***	GArf
	– – 'Purpureus'	WAbe
	'Hopleys Variegated' (v)	SWvt
	'Hot Pink Riding Hood'PBR (Riding Hood Series)	EHyd LCro LRHS NRHS
	JEAN GRACE ('Penbow')	ECtt
	'John Nash' misapplied	see *P.* 'Alice Hindley'
	'John Nash'	CDor SRms
	'Juicy Grape' (Ice Cream Series)	WCot
	'June'	see *P.* 'Pennington Gem'
	'Jupiter'	XLum
	KILIMANJARO ('Yajaro') (Volcano Series)	EPfP LRHS SCoo SRms WFar WHlf
	'King George V'	Widely available
§	***kunthii***	MAsh
§	***laetus*** subsp. ***roezlii***	EPot MAsh NBwr
§	'Le Phare'	WAvo WJam XLum
	'Lilac and Burgundy'	SHar SRms SWvt WAvo
	linarioides 'Marilyn Ross'	ECtt
	– subsp. ***sileri***	WJam
	'Lord Home'	see *P.* 'George Home'
	lyallii	GAbr SRms
	'Lynette'	WAvo WBrk
	'Macpenny's Pink'	CMac MBNS WAvo WJam XLum
	'Madame Golding'	XLum
	'Margery Fish' ♀H3	CFis ECtt EWes
	'Maurice Gibbs' ♀H3	CBcs CGBo CMac CWCL EGrl ELon EWes LSRN MBNS MGil NGBl SRms WHlf WJam
	'Melting Candy' (Ice Cream Series)	WCot
	mensarum	CPla EPfP GLog MACG SHor XSen
	Mexicali hybrids	LSun SBut
	– (Carillo Series) 'Carillo Purple'	EHyd LRHS NRHS
	– – 'Carillo Red'	EHyd LRHS NRHS
	– PIKE'S PEAK PURPLE ('P007s')	GArf
	× ***mexicanus*** 'Sunburst Amethyst'	ELan SRms XLum
	– 'Sunburst Ruby'	EDAr ELan LSun
	'Midnight'	EAJP ECtt EGrl ELan LRHS MGil MRav MSwo NCth SEND SHar SWvt WAvo WHlf WJam XLum
	'Miniature Bells'	EPfP
	'Modesty'	SRms
	'Mother of Pearl'	CBcs CTri EHyd ELan EMor EPfP GMaP LRHS LSRN MCot MSwo SHar SRms SSha SWvt WAvo WHlf WJam
	'Mrs Miller'	WJam
	'Mrs Morse'	see *P.* 'Chester Scarlet'
	'Mrs Oliver'	EWes
	multiflorus	EBee
§	'Myddelton Gem'	SRms WJam
	'Myddelton Red'	see *P.* 'Myddelton Gem'
	newberryi f. ***humilior***	LShi NBwr
§	– subsp. ***sonomensis***	SRms WAbe
	'Newbury Gem'	SHar SWvt WJam
	'Oaklea Red'	WAvo WJam
§	'Old Candy Pink'	LRHS SWvt WAvo WJam
	'Osprey' (Bird Series) ♀H3	CWGN EAJP EBee ECtt EHyd EMor EPfP EWes LRHS NBir SGBe SHar SRms SWvt WAvo WHlf WMal
	ovatus	CMac SPhx SRms WJam WKif
	'Overbury'	SRms WAvo WBrk WJam
	'Papal Purple'	MBNS SBut SHar SRms WAvo WJam XLum
	'Patio Wine'	WAvo WPnP
	'Peace'	GBin
§	'Pennington Gem'	CTri MHer NBir SHar SRms SWvt WAvo
	(Pensham Series) 'Pensham Amelia Jane'	CAby CRos CWGN CWnw ECtt EGrl EHyd ELon EPfP GMcL LRHS NCth NLar NRHS SCoo SPer SRms SWvt WCav WJam
	– 'Pensham Anniversary'	WJam
	– 'Pensham Arctic Fox'	CSpe ECtt EPfP LRHS MGil SBut SPoG WSpi
	– 'Pensham Arctic Sunset'	WJam
	– 'Pensham Avonbelle' ♀H4	SRms
	– 'Pensham Bilberry Ice'	EGrl SWvt
	– 'Pensham Blackberry Ice'	ECtt SRms
	– 'Pensham Blueberry Ice'	ECtt SWvt
	– 'Pensham Charlotte Louise'	ECtt SRms
	– 'Pensham Czar'	Widely available
	– 'Pensham Dorothy Wilson'	EGrl
	– 'Pensham Eleanor Young'	CRos ECtt EPfP SEdd SWvt WJam
	– 'Pensham Freshwater Pearl'	SRms WHoo
	– 'Pensham Jessica Mai'	ECtt SCob SPer SRms SWvt WJam
	– 'Pensham Just Jayne' ♀H4	ECtt EGrl ELon SCoo SPoG SRms SWvt WBrk WHoo WSpi XLum
	– 'Pensham Laura'	Widely available
	– 'Pensham Miss Wilson'	SRms
	– 'Pensham Plum Jerkum'	CDor CRos CWGN CWnw ECtt EGrl EHyd ELon EPfP GMcL LCro LOPS LRHS MBNS MBel MHer MPie NDov NLar NRHS SCob SEdd SPer SRms SSha SWvt WCav WFar
	– 'Pensham Skies'	SRms
	– 'Pensham Son of Raven'	CGBo WAvo WJam
	– 'Pensham Tayberry Ice'	ECtt SRms WJam
	– 'Pensham Victoria Plum' ♀H4	CElw SGro SHar SRms WHoo
	– 'Pensham Wedding Bells'	SRms
	– 'Pensham Wedding Day'	CBod CGBo CKel EHyd EPfP GMcL LSRN NCth NGdn NLar NRHS SCoo SEdd SPer SPoG WFar WJam WMal
	– 'Pensham Westminster Belle'	ECtt SCob SRms
	(Pentastic Series) PENTASTIC PINK ('Yapmine')	LCro LSou MHol WHlf
	– PENTASTIC RED ('Yapruby')	CAby CWGN LCro LSou MHol WFar WHlf
	– PENTASTIC ROSE ('Yaprose')	CWGN LCro LSou MHol WHlf WPnP
	(PepTalk Series) 'Pep Talk Cerise'	LBar
	– 'Pep Talk Hot Pink'	LBar
	– 'Pep Talk Purple'	LBar SPad
	– 'Pep Talk Red' **new**	LBar
	'Pershore Anniversary'	WAvo
	'Pershore Carnival'	SRms WAvo WJam
	'Pershore Fanfare'	WAvo WJam
	'Pershore Festival'	WAvo WJam
	'Pershore Pink Lady' **new**	WBrk
	'Pershore Pink Necklace'	EGrl SRms SWvt WAvo WHlf WJam
	'Phare'	see *P.* 'Le Phare'
	(Phoenix Series) PHOENIX APPLEBLOSSOM ('Pheni Ablos') **new**	EPfP

- PHOENIX APPLEBLOSSOM 09 ('Peni Ablos09')	CRos EHyd LRHS NCth NRHS
- PHOENIX MAGENTA 09 ('Peni Mag09')	CRos EHyd LRHS NRHS
- PHOENIX MAGENTA ('Pheni Magna')	EPfP
- PHOENIX PINK ('Pheni Pinka')	EHyd LRHS NRHS
- PHOENIX RED ('Pheni Reeda'ᴾᴮᴿ)	CRos EHyd EPfP LRHS NRHS SRms
- PHOENIX VIOLET 09 ('Peni Vio09'ᴾᴮᴿ)	CRos EHyd EPfP LRHS NRHS
- PHOENIX VIOLET ('Pheni Vio')	SRms
'Phyllis'	see *P.* 'Evelyn'
pinifolius ♀H4	CRos CTri EDAr EHyd EPot GArf GKev LRHS LShi MAsh NBwr NRHS SRms SRot WFar WHoo WIce WJam XSen
- 'Compactum'	GKev
- 'Mersea Yellow'	EBee EDAr EHyd ELan EPfP EPot GKev LRHS LShi MAsh MHer NBwr NRHS SLee SPlb SRms WHoo WIce WJam XLum
- 'Wisley Flame' ♀H4	EPfP EPot EWes GEdr MBNS MHer NHpl WMal
'Pink Bedder'	see *P.* 'Hewell Pink Bedder', 'Sutton's Pink Bedder'
'Pink Endurance'	WJam
'Pocahontas'	LBar LRHS NLar
'Port Wine' ♀H3	CGBo CTri ELon GMaP LRHS MGil NBir SEND SPoG SWvt WAvo WHlf WJam WKif
'Powis Castle'	ECtt WAvo WBrk WJam
§ ***procerus*** var. ***formosus***	EPot NBwr SRms WAbe
§ - 'Roy Davidson' ♀H5	EPot MHol MMrt NBwr SGro WAbe
- var. ***tolmiei***	CPla EPot GEdr GKev
pseudospectabilis	XSen
pubescens	see *P. hirsutus*
pulchellus Greene	see *P. procerus* var. *formosus*
pulchellus Lindl.	see *P. campanulatus*
'Purple and White'	see *P.* 'Countess of Dalkeith'
'Purple Bedder'	CMac CRos EGrI EHyd ELan EPfP LRHS LSRN NRHS SCoo SGBe SPoG SRkn SRms SWvt WJam XLum
'Purple Passion'	CRos EBee EBlo EHyd ELan ELon EPfP LRHS NRHS SCob WHlf
PURPLE PERFECTION ('Pmoore14'ᴾᴮᴿ) **new**	WHlf
'Purple Riding Hood'ᴾᴮᴿ (Riding Hood Series)	EHyd LCro LOPS LRHS NRHS
'Purple Sea'	WFar
'Purpureus Albus'	see *P.* 'Countess of Dalkeith'
'Raven' (Bird Series) ♀H3	Widely available
'Razzle Dazzle'	SPlb SRms WAvo WCot WJam
'Red Ace'	WJam
'Red Emperor'	WAvo WJam
'Red Knight'	WAvo
'Red Riding Hood'ᴾᴮᴿ (Riding Hood Series)	EHyd EPfP LCro LOPS LRHS NRHS SPoG WPnP
RED ROCKS ('P008s')	EWTr GQue SSha WCot
'Red Sea'	WFar
'Rich Purple'	MBNS SPlb XLum
'Rich Ruby' ♀H3	CAby CFis CRos EAJP EHyd ELan EPfP EWes GBin LRHS MBel NBir NRHS SHar SPlb SWvt WAvo WHlf WJam XLum
'Ridgeway Red'	WAvo WJam
(Rock Candy Series) ROCK CANDY LIGHT PINK ('Novapenlig')	LRHS
- ROCK CANDY RUBY ('Novapenrub')	LRHS

roezlii Regel	see *P. laetus* subsp. *roezlii*
'Roger Skipper'	ECtt
'Ron Sidwell'	WAvo WJam
'Rosy Blush'	SPlb WAvo
'Roy Davidson'	see *P. procerus* 'Roy Davidson'
'Royal White'	see *P.* 'White Bedder'
'Rubicundus' ♀H4	CBod CRos CWCL EHyd ELan ELon EPfP LRHS LSRN MGil NCth SRms SWvt WHlf WJam
'Ruby' misapplied	see *P.* 'Schoenholzeri'
'Ruby Candle'	ECtt
rupicola ♀H5	GArf GKev NSla
- 'Conwy Lilac'	WAbe
- 'Conwy Rose'	WAbe
'Russian River'	ECtt LRHS SPlb SWvt XLum
rydbergii	SPlb
§ 'Schoenholzeri' ♀H4	Widely available
scouleri	see *P. fruticosus* var. *scouleri*
§ ***serrulatus***	EWes XLum
'Sherbourne Blue'	WAvo WJam
'Sissinghurst Pink'	see *P.* 'Evelyn'
'Six Hills'	EPot GBin SDys WAbe
smallii	EBee EHyd EMor EPfP ESgI EWes LSRN MHer SPhx
'Snow Storm'	see *P.* 'White Bedder'
'Snowflake'	see *P.* 'White Bedder'
sonomensis	see *P. newberryi* subsp. *sonomensis*
'Sour Grapes' misapplied	see *P.* 'Stapleford Gem'
'Sour Grapes' ambig.	CAby CBcs CDor CTri EHeP EMor LShi MBow NGdn SCob SGBe SPoG SRHi WCAu WHlf
§ 'Sour Grapes' M. Fish ♀H4	Widely available
'Southcombe Pink'	WAvo
'Southgate Gem'	GMcL MHCG SRms SWvt WAvo
'Souvenir d'Adrian Regnier'	MHCG
'Souvenir d'André Torres' misapplied	see *P.* 'Chester Scarlet'
spatulatus	EPot
'Species RLB'	EGrI
spectabilis	CSpe
§ 'Stapleford Gem' ♀H4	CFis CMac LRHS LShi MRav SBut SHar SRms SWvt WAvo WFar WHlf WHoo WMal WPnP
aff. 'Stapleford Gem'	NCth
'Strawberries and Cream' (Ice Cream Series)	CGBo NLar SCoo SPoG WCot WHlf
'Strawberry Fancy'	SRms
'Strawberry Fizz'	SRms
'Strawberry Taffy'ᴾᴮᴿ (Taffy Series)	LRHS
strictus	EBee EPfP WJam XSen
STROMBOLI ('Yaboli') (Volcano Series)	CTri WHoo
§ 'Sutton's Pink Bedder'	WAvo
'Sweet Cherry' (Ice Cream Series)	SCob WCot
tall, pink-flowered	see *P.* 'Welsh Dawn'
'The Juggler'	ECtt SWvt
§ 'Thorn'	ECtt LRHS MRav SRms SWvt WAvo WHlf WJam
'Threave Pink'	ECtt SHar SMrm SRms SWvt WAvo WJam
'Thundercloud'	WAvo WJam
'Tiger Bell Coral'	NChi
'Torquay Gem'	WAvo WJam
'True Sour Grapes'	see *P.* 'Sour Grapes' M. Fish
tubaeflorus	CPla
'Tubular Bells Red'	WBrk
'Vanilla Plum' (Ice Cream Series)	EGrI SCob
venustus purple-flowered	SBrt
VESUVIUS ('Yasius') (Volcano Series)	CKel CRos CWnw EPfP LRHS NRHS SCoo SRms WFar WHlf WJam

	virgatus 'Blue Buckle'	EPfP SPlb WFar
	'Watermelon Taffy'PBR (Taffy Series)	ECtt EHyd LRHS NRHS
	watsonii	EDAr
§	'Welsh Dawn'	MBNS
§	***whippleanus***	LRHS MMuc MNHC SBut SMad SPlb
	- 'Chocolate Drop'	EDAr SBls
§	'White Bedder'	Widely available
	'Whitethroat' Sidwell	MBNS WHoo WJam WMal
	'Willy's Purple'	CDor ECtt
§	'Windsor Red'	CTri ECtt EPfP LRHS SGBe SRms SWvt WAvo WBrk WCot WHlf WJam
	'Woodpecker'	ECtt ELon EMor IPot LPla SRms WAvo WHlf WHoo

Pentaglottis (*Boraginaceae*)

§	***sempervirens***	EPfP SRms WSFF

Pentapanax see *Aralia*

Pentapterygium see *Agapetes*

Pentas (*Rubiaceae*)

	lanceolata	CCCN EShb

Peperomia ✿ (*Piperaceae*)

	albovittata 'Piccolo Banda'PBR **new**	CDoC NHrt
§	***argyreia*** ♀H1b	CDoC
	arifolia	CDoC
	caperata	CWal NHrt
	- 'Emerald Ripple' ♀H1b **new**	CWal
	clusiifolia	NHrt
	- 'Jellie' **new**	NHrt
	'Eden Rosso'PBR **new**	CWal
	ferreyrae	CDoC EShb LCro
	graveolens	NHrt
	incana **new**	CDoC
	obtusifolia ♀H1b **new**	NHrt
	- 'Variegata' (v)	NHrt
	polybotrya 'Raindrop'	CDoC LCro LOPS
	prostrata	CDoC LCro LWaG
	pulchella	see *P. verticillata*
	quadrangularis	CDoC LCro LWaG NHrt
	sandersii	see *P. argyreia*
	scandens 'Variegata' (v)	CDoC NHrt
§	***verticillata***	EShb

pepino see *Solanum muricatum*

peppermint see *Mentha* × *piperita*

Pericallis (*Asteraceae*)

	× ***hybrida*** Senetti Series	MDon MPri NPer SPoG
	- - SENETTI BLUE ('Sunsenebu')	SPoG
	- - SENETTI BLUE BICOLOR ('Sunseneribuba'PBR) ('Sunsenereba'PBR)	MGos SPoG
	- - SENETTI MAGENTA ('Sunsenere'PBR)	SPoG
	- - SENETTI MAGENTA BICOLOR	MGos SPoG

Perilla (*Lamiaceae*)

	frutescens	CBod WJek
§	- var. ***crispa*** ♀H3	CBod CLau CSpe
	- var. ***nankinensis***	see *P. frutescens* var. *crispa*
	- var. ***purpurascens***	CLau WJek

Periploca (*Apocynaceae*)

	graeca	CBcs CCCN EAri EBee MGil MHtn WJur
	sepium	CExl GEdr
	- W&O 7191	GGro

Perkinsiodendron (*Styracaceae*)

§	***macgregorii***	MBlu

Pernettya see *Gaultheria*

Perovskia see *Salvia* (Pe)

	atriplicifolia	see *Salvia yangii*

Persea (*Lauraceae*)

	americana	CCCN SVic
	indica	CCCN
	- B&SWJ 12535	WCru
	japonica	CBcs
	- B&SWJ 12789	WCru
	thunbergii	CBcs
	- B&SWJ 12747	WCru

Persicaria ✿ (*Polygonaceae*)

	B&SWJ 11268 from Sumatra	WCru
	from Myanmar **new**	EPPr
§	***affinis***	CBcs CSBt GAbr NBro SCob WFar
	- 'Darjeeling Red' ♀H7	Widely available
	- 'Dimity'	see *P. affinis* 'Superba'
	- 'Donald Lowndes' ♀H7	Widely available
	- 'Kabouter'	EBee GBin NLar WBor
§	- 'Superba' ♀H7	Widely available
	alata	see *P. nepalensis*
	ALBA JUNIOR ('Ifperaj') **new**	LBar SHar
	alpina ♀H6	Widely available
	amphibia	CPud EWat LLWG LPfP XLum
§	***amplexicaulis***	CCBP CKno CWal EHeP EWes GMaP MBel MCot NChi WBor WBrk WFar XLum
	- 'Alba'	Widely available
	- 'Amethyst'	CKno WCAu
	- 'Ample Pink'	MAvo
	- 'Arends Pride'	SDix
	- 'Arends Stolz'	ECha
	- 'Atrosanguinea'	CBod CMac CTri EBee EBlo ECha EHyd ELan ELon EPfP GLog GQue LRHS MMuc MRav MSpe NBir NLar NRHS SEND SPer SRms SWvt WFar XLum
	- 'Black Adder'	ELon
	- 'Blackfield'PBR	Widely available
	- 'Blush Clent'	WBor WCot
	- 'Clent Charm'	MBriF MHCG MSpe NChi WCot
	- 'Cottesbrooke Gold'	ECtt EWhm MAvo
	- dark red-flowered **new**	ESwi
	- 'Dikke Floskes'	CBWd CBct CBod CKno ECtt ELon EPPr GBin LEdu LRHS MHol MSpe SRms WBrk WCot WHoo
	- 'Early Pink Lady'	ELon EPPr
	- 'Fascination'	CBWd ELon MAvo WCot
	- 'Fat Domino'PBR	CBct CBod CKno CRos EBee ECtt EHyd EMor EPfP EWoo ILea LPla LRHS LSun MAvo MBel MCot MHol MNrw MSCN NCou NDov NLar NRHS SDix SHeu SPoG WCAu WCot WNPC
	- 'Fat White'	ELon GBin
	- 'Fine Pink' **new**	LSto
	- 'Firedance'	CAby CKno ECtt ELon EPPr GQue MSpe NDov SPhx SRms WCot WFar
	- 'Firetail'	Widely available
	- 'Golden Arrow' (v)	CAby CBct CBod CTtf EBee ECtt ELon EMor GBin LBar MACG NEoE NSti SCob SPeP SPoG SRms WCAu WCot WFar WHil WPnP WTor WWke
	- 'High Society'	CKno SPoG SRms WCAu

- 'Inverleith'	CBct CBod CKno EBee ECha ECtt EHyd ELon GBin GMaP GMcL GQue LRHS MAvo MMuc NBPC NBid NBir NGrd NRHS SGbt SPoG WCAu WPnP
I - 'Jo and Guido's Form'	CBWd ELon EPPr MSpe NLar WCAu WFar
- 'JS Caliente'PBR	CBod ECtt ELon EMor LRHS LSun MACG MHol MNrw SAko SCob SHar SHeu SRms WCot WPnP WSpi
- 'JS Calor'PBR	EBee
- 'JS Delgado Macho'PBR	CKno EBee ELon ESwi MNrw SHeu SRms
- JS SEVEN OAKS VILLAGE ('JS Pesovi')	EBee
- 'Lisan'	CBod EPPr MNrw WCAu
- 'Marchant's Red Devil'	SMHy
- 'October Pink'	EPPr SMHy
- ORANGE FIELD ('Orangofield'PBR)	Widely available
- var. ***pendula***	ELon GBin MBel NBir SMHy WFar
- - HWJK 2255	GGro WCru
- 'Pink Elephant'	see *P.* 'Pink Elephant'
- 'Pink Knot'	CRos EBlo EHyd LRHS NRHS
- 'Pink Lady'	MPie
- 'Pink Mist'	WCAu WGoo
- 'Red Baron'	CBod ECtt ELon EPPr WFar
- 'Rosea'	Widely available
- 'Rosy Clent'	WCot
- 'Rowden Gem'	CBWd ECha ELon GBin MSpe WCAu
- 'Rubie's Pink'	ECha
- 'September Spires'	CKno NDov WGoo
- 'Spotted Eastfield' (v)	EPPr WCot WFar
- 'Summer Dance'	CKno ECtt ELon EPPr WCAu
- TAURUS ('Blotau')	CDor CRos EBlo ECha ECtt EHyd ELon EPPr ESwi EWoo GBin LRHS MCot NLar NRHS NSti SMHy SRkn SRms WCAu WFar
- 'White Eastfield'	CBod CDor CKno ECha ELan GElm GPSL NDov NLar SAko WCAu
§ ***bistorta***	GPoy LPfP LSun MHer MMuc NBir NGrd NLar SRms WFar WSFF WShi
- subsp. ***carnea***	CBWd CRos CTtf EBee ECha EHyd ELon EMor EPPr EWhm GPSL LRHS MBNS MMuc MPie NBir NBro NRHS WCot
- dwarf, shell-pink-flowered **new**	WCot
- 'Hohe Tatra'	CBWd CDor CRos EBlo ECtt EHyd EPPr GMaP LBar LRHS LSun MBel MCot MHol NCou NDov NRHS SDix SPoG WBrk WCot WFar
- 'Superba' ♀H7	Widely available
campanulata	CBod CElw EBee ECha ECtt EGrl GAbr LBar LShi MACG MAvo MMuc MRav NSti SMad SPer WFar
- Alba Group	CElw MPie
- 'Madame Jigard'	ECha GBin GGro WFar WMal
- 'Rosenrot'	WOld
- 'Southcombe White'	ECha
§ ***capitata***	XLum
- 'Pink Bubbles'	CExl SWvt
chinensis B&SWJ 11268	WCru
dshawachischwilii	MAvo SMHy
* ***hydropiper*** var. ***rubra***	WJek
'Indian Summer'	ECha EPPr GGro LPla SBrt WCot WFar WMal
§ ***macrophylla***	GArf LDai WCot
- 'Ellie's Pink'	WCot
microcephala	LWaG MHer
- 'Dragon's Eye'PBR	EBee LBar
- 'Night Dragon' **new**	LBar
- 'Red Dragon'PBR	Widely available
- 'Silver Brown'	GBin
milletii	CBor EBee ECha EHyd LRHS NDov NRHS NSti WCru
nakaii	GBin NLar WCot
neofiliformis	EMor EShb GGro
§ ***nepalensis***	CExl EMor EPPr EShb GGro
§ ***odorata***	CBod CLau ENfk GPoy LLWG LWaG MHer MHoo MNHC NGrd SEdi SPre SRms WHer WJek
orientalis	CSpe SMrm SPhx
§ 'Pink Elephant'	CBWd CDor ECha ELon EMor EPPr GBin ILea LBar MNrw NDov NLar SAko SCob SEdd SHeu SRms WBrk WCAu WFar WHoo WMal WNPC WSpi
polystachya	see *P. wallichii*
regeliana	EBlo
§ ***runcinata***	EBee WFar
- Needham's form	EMor GGro
- 'Purple Fantasy'	CDTJ CEnd CPla CSde CSpe ELan EMor EPPr EShb GGro LBar LPla LRHS LWaG MAvo MBel MBriF MNrw MSpe NSti SCob SDix SEdd SPtp WFar WHil WMal WNPC WWke
scoparia	see *Polygonum scoparium*
'Silver Dragon'PBR	CBcs CBct CBod CSpe EBee EMor EShb LPla NSti SMad SPeP SPoG WCot WPnP
sphaerostachya Meisn.	see *P. macrophylla*
tenuicaulis	CMiW GBin SBrt SGro WCru
§ ***tinctoria***	WSFF
§ ***vacciniifolia*** ♀H7	CBcs CSBt CTri ECha ECtt GAbr GEdr GKev GMaP MCot MHer NBid NBir NFav NLar SCob SDix SLee SPlb SRms SWvt WAbe WBor WFar WHoo WIce WSpi
- 'Harran'	GArf
§ ***virginiana***	LEdu LSun
- 'Alba'	EMor EPPr LPla
- 'Brushstrokes'	EShb SDix WCot
- var. ***filiformis***	CAby CBod CSpe EMor LEdu MBel MPie NChi SBrt SPoG SPtp SRkn SWvt WCot
- - 'Ballet'	WCot
- - 'Batwings'	LWaG SPtp
- - 'Compton's Red'	CBod ECha ECtt EMor EPPr EShb LDai MAvo WCot WFar
- - 'Guizhou Bronze'	LEdu LPla SBrt
- - 'Lance Corporal'	CMac EMor EPPr EShb GBee GBin GElm MAvo MHol NLar
- Variegated Group (v)	ECha EShb MBNS WCot WFar
- - 'Painter's Palette' (v)	CBod CDTJ CMac EBee ECha ECtt EMor EShb GMcL LBar LRHS LShi MHol MPie MRav NRHS NSti SPer SRms SWvt WCot WFar WMal XLum
§ ***wallichii***	LSto MMuc NLar SEND WCot XLum
§ ***weyrichii***	EShb NBir NBro NLar WFar XLum

persimmon see *Diospyros virginiana*

persimmon, Japanese see *Diospyros kaki*

Petalostemon see *Dalea*

Petamenes see *Gladiolus*

Petasites (*Asteraceae*)

albus	GPoy MHer NSti

	fragrans	ELan SRms WHer XLum
§	***frigidus*** var. ***palmatus***	NLar WCot
	- - 'Golden Palms'	MHer
	hybridus	LPfP
	- 'Variegatus' (v)	XLum
	japonicus	CAgr CBcs GPoy
	- var. ***giganteus***	ECha EPfP GGro LEdu MBel WCru
§	- - 'Nishiki-buki' (v)	CMac EBee ECha GGro GQue LEdu MHer NBir NSti SMad SRms WFar XLum
	- - 'Variegatus'	see *P. japonicus* var. *giganteus* 'Nishiki-buki'
	palmatus	see *P. frigidus* var. *palmatus*
	paradoxus	EWld LEdu MBel SBrt WCot WFar

× *Petchoa* (*Solanaceae*)

	BeautiCal Series **new**	MDon
	- BEAUTICAL CARAMEL YELLOW ('Sakpxc024') **new**	MPri
	- BEAUTICAL CINNAMON ('Sakpxc021') **new**	MPri

Petrea (*Verbenaceae*)

	volubilis	CCCN

Petrocallis (*Brassicaceae*)

	lagascae	see *P. pyrenaica*
§	***pyrenaica***	WAbe
	- white-flowered	WAbe

Petrocoptis (*Caryophyllaceae*)

	pyrenaica	EWes SRms
§	- subsp. ***glaucifolia***	CBor

Petrocosmea ✿ (*Gesneriaceae*)

	barbata 'Marion King' **new**	WDib
	begoniifolia misapplied	see *P. chrysotricha*
§	***chrysotricha***	SPlb WDib
§	***cryptica***	WAbe WDib
	- 'Yumebutai'	WDib
	flaccida	WDib
	'Fluffer Nutter'	WDib
§	***formosa*** 'Crûg's Capricious'	WAbe
	forrestii	WAbe WDib
	grandiflora misapplied	see *P. thermopuncta*
	'Ht-2'	WDib
	iodioides ♀H1c	WDib
	kerrii	WAbe
	- 'Crème de Crûg'	WCru
	- var. ***crinita*** **new**	WDib
	'Keystone's Angora'	WDib
	'Keystone's Bantam'	WDib
	'Keystone's Barnswallow'	WDib
	'Keystone's Belmont'	WDib
	'Keystone's Blue Jay'	WDib
	'Keystone's Lafayette'	WDib
	'Keystone's Magic'	WDib
	× ***longianthera*** **new**	WDib
	aff. ***martini*** 'Crûg's Capricious'	see *P. formosa* 'Crûg's Capricious'
	minor	WDib
	'Morning Mr Magpie' **new**	WDib
	parryorum	WDib
	'Paul Kroll'	WDib
	'Rosemary Platz'	WDib
	rosettifolia misapplied	see *P. cryptica*
	sericea	WDib
§	***thermopuncta*** **new**	WAbe WDib
	'Yuki-no-sei'	WDib

Petrophytum (*Rosaceae*)

	caespitosum	WAbe
	cinerascens	WFar
§	***hendersonii***	GArf WAbe

Petrorhagia (*Caryophyllaceae*)

	saxifraga ♀H4	CSpe EPPr EPfP EShb GLog MACG MBel NLar NSla SBls SBut SRms XLum

Petroselinum (*Apiaceae*)

§	***crispum***	CArg CBod CLau ENfk GPoy LCro LOPS MHoo MNHC MPri NPol SPoG SRms
	- 'Bravour' ♀H6	CBod MHer
	- 'Champion Moss Curled'	MBros SVic
	- 'Curlina' ♀H4	LCro
	- 'Extra Moss Curled'	LCro LOPS
	- French	CCBP CLau ENfk LCro LOPS LRHS MBros MHer MHoo MNHC MPri SPoG SRms
	- 'Italian'	see *P. crispum* var. *neapolitanum*
	- 'Laura'PBR	CLau
	- 'Moss Curled' ♀H6	CHby EHyd EKin LRHS MCtn MHoo NRHS NRob SRms
§	- var. ***neapolitanum***	CBod CLau ENfk LCro LOPS MHoo SPoG SRms SVic
§	- var. ***tuberosum***	CBod CLau SRms SVic
	hortense	see *P. crispum*
	tuberosum	see *P. crispum* var. *tuberosum*

Petteria (*Fabaceae*)

	ramentacea	EBtc

Petunia (*Solanaceae*)

	AMORE QUEEN OF HEARTS ('Damorqueen'PBR) (Amore Series)	MBros MDon MPri
	× ***atkinsiana*** 'Storm Lavender' ♀H2	LCro
	axillaris 'Hualco' **new**	CSpe
	BABYDOLL ('Kleph17342')	SCob WHlf
	BALCONY MIX	LCro
	BEDDING STRIPED MIX	LCro
	BLACK VELVET ('Balpevac'PBR)	MBros WHlf
	BLACK VELVET IMPROVED	MDon MPri
	CASCADIAS RIM MAGENTA ('Dcas298'PBR) (Cascadias Series) ♀H2	LSou MPri
	CRAZYTUNIA MANDEVILLE ('Wespecramand') (Crazytunia Series)	MBros
	DESIGNER BUZZ PURPLE ('Kerbuzzby') (Designer Series) ♀H2	LSou MBros MPri
	Double Pirouette Series (d)	LCro LOPS
	- 'Double Pirouette Rose' (d)	LCro LOPS
	Duo Series	MBros
	EASY WAVE BERRY VELOUR ('Pas982903') (Easy Wave Series)	MBros
	exserta	CSpe EDAr WCot
	FANFARE APPLEBLOSSOM ('Kerappfan'PBR) (Fanfare Series)	MBros
	FANTASIA MIX	LCro LOPS
	Frenzy Series	MBros
	- FRENZY REFLECTION MIX	LCro LOPS
	GLACIERSKY ('Kleph18370') **new**	MDon MPri

LAVENDER SKY ('Kleph20411') **new**	MDon
'Lightning Sky'	LSou MDon WHlf
MARGARITA ('Kermar') (Tumbelina Series)	MBros
NIGHTSKY ('Kleph15313') ΨH2	LSou MBros MDon MPri SCob WHlf
OVATION DARK HEART (Ovation Series)	MDon MPri
patagonica	SPlb WAbe
PHANTOM ('Balpephan'[PBR])	MBros MDon WHlf
PINSTRIPE ('Balpepin'[PBR])	MBros
'Prism Sunshine' (Prism Series)	MBros
SHOCK WAVE DEEP PURPLE ('Pas933531') **new**	LCro
(Surfinia Series) SURFINIA BLUE OCEAN ('Keipeblocnul') **new**	MDon
- SURFINIA BLUE ('Sunblu')	LSou MDon MPri
- SURFINIA BLUE TOPAZ ('Sunsurfbupa')	MBros MDon
- SURFINIA BLUE VEIN ('Sunsolos'[PBR])	MBros
- SURFINIA BURGUNDY ('Keiburtel'[PBR])	MBros
- SURFINIA CORAL MORN ('Surf Gonitomi') **new**	MDon
- SURFINIA DEEP RED ('Sunsurf Akatora'[PBR]) ΨH2 **new**	MDon
- SURFINIA DOUBLE LILAC ('Keidopinul'[PBR]) (d)	MDon
- SURFINIA GIANT PURPLE ('Sunlapur'[PBR])	MBros MDon
- SURFINIA HEAVENLY BLUE ('Sunsurf Skytatsu'[PBR])	LSou MDon
- SURFINIA HOT PINK ('Sunrovein'[PBR]) ΨH2	LSou MBros MDon MPri
- SURFINIA HOT RED ('Sunhore'[PBR])	LSou MBros
- SURFINIA IMPULZ SNOW ('Sunsurfkuri'[PBR]) ΨH2	MBros MPri
- SURFINIA LIME ('Keiyeul'[PBR])	MBros MDon
- SURFINIA PINK VEIN ('Suntosol') ΨH2	MBros
- SURFINIA PURPLE ('Sunpurple'[PBR]) ΨH2	LSou MPri
- SURFINIA ROSE VEIN ('Sunrove'[PBR])	MBros MDon
- SURFINIA SWEET PINK ('Sunsurfmomo'[PBR])	MBros MDon
- SURFINIA VARIEGATED PURPLE MINI ('Sunpapuhu'[PBR]) (v)	LSou
- SURFINIA WHITE ('Kesupite')	LSou MDon
- SURFINIA YELLOW DREAM	MBros MDon
SUZIE STORM ('Dueswesustor') (Sweetunia Series) **new**	MDon
TIDAL WAVE RED VELOUR ('Pas1085269') (Tidal Wave Series) **new**	LCro
Tumbelina Series	MDon
- TUMBELINA BELINDA (d)	MBros WHlf
- TUMBELINA BELLA ('Kerbella') (d)	MBros
- TUMBELINA CANDYFLOSS ('Kercan'[PBR]) (d)	MBros
- TUMBELINA CHERRY RIPPLE ('Kerripcherry'[PBR]) (d)	LSou
- TUMBELINA CRAZY RIPPLE	LSou MBros
- TUMBELINA INGA (d)	MBros
- TUMBELINA JOANNA	WHlf
- TUMBELINA MARIA (d)	MBros
- TUMBELINA MELISSA ('Kermelis'[PBR]) (d)	WHlf
- TUMBELINA PRISCILLA ('Kerpril'[PBR]) (d) ΨH1c	LSou MBros
- TUMBELINA QUEEN	WHlf

Peucedanum (*Apiaceae*)

japonicum	GGro
officinale	CSpe GBin LRHS SPhx SPlb
ostruthium	GPoy LEdu
- 'Daphnis' (v)	EBee ECha EWhm GGro LEdu MAvo MBriF MNrw NChi NGrd NLar SPtp WAvo WCot WHil WHrl WSHC XLum
rablense	ECha EPPr GBin LEdu SPhx
verticillare	CBWd CRos CSpe EBee EHyd GBin GGro LEdu LPla LRHS MAvo MBel MBriF NDov NRHS SBrt SDix SPhx WCot

Pfeiffera (*Cactaceae*)

boliviana **new**	LCro

Phacelia (*Boraginaceae*)

bolanderi	CPla GEdr GKev LDai
sericea	EDAr LShi
tanacetifolia	LCro WSFF

Phaedranassa (*Amaryllidaceae*)

viridiflora	WCot

Phaenocoma (*Asteraceae*)

prolifera	SPlb

Phaenosperma (*Poaceae*)

globosa	CBod CSpe ECha EPPr GBin LRHS MACG SPlb WCot WPGP XLum

Phaiophleps see *Olsynium*

nigricans	see *Sisyrinchium striatum*

Phalaris (*Poaceae*)

arundinacea	CPud LPfP MBNS SPlb SVic
- 'Elegantissima'	see *P. arundinacea* var. *picta* 'Picta'
- var. ***picta***	CBen CTri EHeP LPfP MHol NBir NPer WCAu WFar XLum
- - 'Arctic Sun' (v)	EBee EShb GBin LBuc LLWG MAsh MHol MMuc NEoE SEND SPoG
- - 'Aureovariegata' (v)	MRav NPer XLum
- - 'Feesey' (v)	Widely available
- - 'Luteopicta' (v)	EPPr MMuc XLum
§ - - 'Picta' (v)	CBod EHyd ELan EPfP LRHS MMuc NRHS SCob SEND SPer
- - 'Streamlined' (v)	EPPr NWsh

Phanerophlebia (*Dryopteridaceae*)

caryotidea	see *Cyrtomium caryotideum*
falcata	see *Cyrtomium falcatum*
fortunei	see *Cyrtomium fortunei*

Pharbitis see *Ipomoea*

Phaseolus (*Fabaceae*)

caracalla	see *Cochliasanthus caracalla*

Phedimus see *Sedum*

Phegopteris (*Thelypteridaceae*)

§ ***connectilis***	CLAP EFer LEdu NHar
decursive-pinnata	CBod CRos EHyd LEdu LPal LRHS MMuc NRHS SEND WFib WPnP
hexagonoptera	LEdu SPlb
§ ***levingei***	LEdu

Phellodendron (*Rutaceae*)

amurense	CBcs CCCN CMCN EBee EPfP GBin IPap LRHS MBlu SEND WBor
- B&SWJ 11000	WCru
japonicum B&SWJ 11175	WCru

Phemeranthus (*Portulacaceae*)

sediformis	GKev
- 'Zoe'	GKev

Pherosphaera (*Podocarpaceae*)

fitzgeraldii	CKen WPav WThu

Philadelphus ✿ (*Hydrangeaceae*)

'Atlas' (v)	NLar
'Avalanche'	CExl MMuc NBwr NLar SRms
'Beauclerk' ♀H6	CBod CBrac CCCN CDoC CEme CKel CTri EBee EPfP LRHS MGos MRav NLar NWea SCob SPer SRms SWvt WLov WSpi
'Belle Étoile' ♀H6	Widely available
'Bialy Karzel'	WHlf
'Bialy Sopel'	CCCN WAvo
'Bicolore'	NLar WAvo WSpi
'Bouquet Blanc'	MRav NLar SGol SRms WLov
brachybotrys	MRav
'Buckley's Quill' (d)	EBee MRav SWvt
'Burfordensis'	MMuc MRav SEND WSpi
'Casa Azul'	EBee WPGP
coronarius	CBcs EDir EPfP LBuc LIns LPar LRHS MRav NWea WSpi
- 'Aureus' ♀H6	Widely available
- 'Bowles's Variety'	see *P. coronarius* 'Variegatus'
- 'Bridal Showers' **new**	SRHi
§ - 'Variegatus' (v) ♀H6	CMac CRos EFPl ELan ELon EPfP GBin GMcL LRHS MAsh MGil MGos MRav MSwo NLar SCob SPer SPoG SRms WAvo WCFE WFar WHtc WKif WLov WSpi
coulteri	EBee EPfP SBrt WPGP
'Coupe d'Argent'	MRav
'Dainty Lady'[PBR]	GBin LCro LOPS LRHS SGBe
'Dame Blanche' (d)	EPfP MRav NLar WFar
delavayi	CKel EPPr EPfP GBin LEdu NLar SPer WLov WPGP WSpi
- var. ***calvescens***	MRav SPtp
- - BWJ 8005	WCru
- f. ***melanocalyx***	EPfP MRav SChF WLov WPGP
- - B&L 12168	EBee WPGP
- - 'Nyman's Variety' ♀H5	CExl EPfP WKif WLov WPGP
aff. ***delavayi***	SBrt
'Enchantement' (d)	MRav SDix
'Erectus'	CBod CKel CSBt EBee ELan ELon EPfP LIns LRHS MRav NBwr NLar SBrt SPer SPoG WAvo WHlf WHtc WLov WSpi
'Étoile Rose'	WAvo
'Falconeri'	MRav
'Favorite' **new**	WHtc
'Frosty Morn' (d)	CBcs CBod EShb LEdu MACG MBlu MRav SPer SPoG WLov
'Girandole' (d) **new**	WHtc
incanus B&SWJ 8616	WCru
§ 'Innocence' (v) ♀H6	CAgr CExl CMac CRos CTsd CWGN EDir EHyd ELan EPfP LRHS MAsh MDon MGos MMuc MRav MSwo NEoE NLar NRHS SPad SPer SPoG SRms WFar WHlf WLov
'Innocence Variegatus'	see *P.* 'Innocence'
§ ***insignis***	MRav NLar
'Kalina' **new**	NLar
'Karolinka'	NLar
karwinskianus F&M 152	WPGP
'Lemoinei'	CBcs CCCN CTri EHeP GDam GMcL LPar NBwr NLar NWea SCob SOrN WFar WHtc WSpi
lewisii	SPhx
- 'Waterton'	ELon WAvo WHtc WLov WSpi
'Limestone'	EBtc MRav
'Little White Love'	SGol WHlf
maculatus 'Mexican Jewel'	CBcs CBod CExl CKel EBee EHed ELan ELon EMil EPfP GBin LEdu LRHS MNHC NLar SChF SMad SPad WGob WKif WLov WPGP
- 'Sweet Clare' ♀H5	CRos EHyd EPfP LCro LOPS LRHS MMrt NRHS SPoG WSpi
madrensis	EBee MRav
- F&M 326	WPGP
'Manteau d'Hermine' (d) ♀H6	Widely available
'Marjorie'	EBtc NLar
mexicanus	SDix
- B&SWJ 10253	WCru
- 'Rose Syringa'	CExl SBrt WLov WPGP
mexicanus* × *palmeri	EBee
microphyllus	CBrac CKel CMCN CTri EBee ELan ELon EPfP GBin LRHS MGos MRav NLar SMad SPer SPoG WFar WKif
'Minnesota Snowflake' (d)	CBcs EHeP EHyd ELon EPfP LRHS LSRN MMuc MRav NLar NRHS SGol SRHi WFar
'Mont Blanc'	CBcs GKin MRav NLar
'Mrs E.L. Robinson' (d)	CMac CRos EHyd EPfP GLog LRHS MGos NLar WAvo WCFE WHtc WLov
myrtoides B&SWJ 10436	WCru
'Natchez' (d)	CBod CMac LEdu NLar SChF WHtc WLov
'Norma'	WLov
palmeri	EBee LRHS WPGP
'Patricia'	WAvo WHtc WLov
pekinensis	CExl NLar
'Perryhill'	MRav
'Polar Star'	NLar
purpurascens	CExl EBee EPfP EWes GLog LEdu MBlu MGos MRav NLar SChF WCFE WJur WLov WPGP
- BWJ 7540	ESwi WCru
'Purpureomaculatus'	MRav NLar WPGP
'Pyramidal' (d)	CBrac
'Rachel'	CMac
satsumi	NLar
- B&SWJ 10811	WCru
- B&SWJ 11004	WCru
schrenkii	NLar
- B&SWJ 8465	ESwi WCru
- var. ***jackii*** **new**	WPGP
sericanthus	NLar
§ 'Silberregen' ♀H6	CKel CMac EBee EHeP EHed ELan ELon EPfP LEdu LRHS MDon MGos MMuc MRav NBwr NLar SCob SPoG SRms SWvt WFar WHlf WHtc
SILVER SHOWERS	see *P.* 'Silberregen'
'Snowbelle' (d)	CCCN CDoC CEnd CKel CWnw EBee EDir EPfP LCro LOPS LRHS MAsh MDon MPri NLar SCob SPoG SRms SSha SWvt SavN WHlf WHtc WLov

'Snowgoose'	SGol
'Souvenir de Billiard'	see *P. insignis*
'Starbright'PBR	CBcs CBod CCCN CKel EBee ELan EPfP LPar LRHS NLar SCob SPoG SRHi WLov
subcanus	SPtp
- L 524	CExl
'Sybille' ♀H5	CKel CMac EHyd EPfP LRHS MRav MSwo SDix SPer SRms WAvo WKif WLov WSpi
tomentosus	WPGP
- B&SWJ 2707	WCru
- GWJ 9215	WCru
'Velléda'	WAvo WHtc
'Virginal' (d)	Widely available
× ***virginalis***	EPau
'Voie Lactée'	MRav NLar WSpi
WHITE ROCK ('Pekphil') ♀H6	CMac LSRN MRav NLar
'Yellow Cab'	MAsh SSha
'Yellow Hill'	CKel CMac EPfP LRHS

Philesia (*Philesiaceae*)

buxifolia	see *P. magellanica*
§ ***magellanica***	CExl CRHN MGil WCru
- 'Rosea'	CRHN

Philibertia (*Apocynaceae*)

§ ***stipitata*** **new**	EAri

Phillyrea (*Oleaceae*)

sp.	LTop
angustifolia	CBcs CBod CKel CMCN CWnw EBee EHyd ELan EPfP ERom EShb LPar LRHS LTop MGos MRav NLar SArc SEND SRHi SSha SWeb WLov WPGP WReH XSen
- f. ***rosmarinifolia***	CCCN CCoa
- - 'French Fries'	EBee EPfP WPGP
decora	see *Osmanthus decorus*
§ ***latifolia***	CBcs CBod CCCN CDoC CKel EBee EHyd ELan EPfP LRHS LTop SArc SEND SHor SSha WPGP XSen
media	see *P. latifolia*

Philodendron (*Araceae*)

'Atom'	LCro
bipennifolium	SPlb
bipinnatifidum ♀H2	SEND
- GOLDEN XANADU ('Twyph0007'PBR) **new**	LCro
* 'Cobra' (v) **new**	LCro
erubescens 'Red Emerald'	LCro
hastatum **new**	CDoC LCro
§ ***hederaceum*** 'Brasil' (v) **new**	LCro
- var. ***hederaceum*** **new**	CDoC
'Imperial Green'	NHrt
'Imperial Red'	LCro NHrt WLea
pedatum	CDoC
scandens ♀H1b	CDoC LCro LOPS LWaG NHrt
- 'Brasil'	see *P. hederaceum* 'Brasil'
xanadu	LCro LOPS LPal LWaG NGBl NHrt SPlb WLea

Philotheca (*Rutaceae*)

§ ***myoporoides***	CBod EGrl ILea LRHS WHlf XSte
- 'Flower Girl Pink' **new**	LCro
- 'Flower Girl White' **new**	LCro

Phlebodium (*Polypodiaceae*)

§ ***aureum*** ♀H1b	CSpe SPlb WCot
- var. ***areolatum***	EShb WCot
- 'Blue Star'	ISha LCro NHrt
- DAVANA ('Raadphle01') **new**	LCro
- 'Glaucum'	CSpe WCot
pseudoaureum ♀H3	LEdu MAsh SEND WCot
- 'Virginia Blue'	LEdu

Phlebosia (*Polypodiaceae*)

'Nicolas Diamond' **new**	WCot

Phleum (*Poaceae*)

hirsutum	WCot
phleoides	EHyd LRHS NRHS
pratense	WSFF

Phlomis ✿ (*Lamiaceae*)

alpina	SPlb
* ***anatolica***	EHyd LRHS
- 'Lloyd's Variety'	see *P. grandiflora* 'Lloyd's Silver'
anisodonta white-flowered	XSen
armeniaca	XSen
atropurpurea BWJ 7922	GGro SBrt WCru
bourgaei	CKel CWnw XSen
- NJM 12.008	WPGP
bovei subsp. ***maroccana***	SEND XLum
capitata	XSen
cashmeriana	CBod CDor CPla CRos EBee ECha EHyd EPfP LDai LRHS MCot MHoo NQui NRHS WAvo WCFE WSpi XSen
chrysophylla ♀H5	ECha EHyd ELan EPfP LRHS MAsh MRav NLar WCFE WSpi XSen
cretica	SVen WMal
× ***cytherea***	XSen
'Edward Bowles'	CKel EBee ECha EHyd EPfP EWTr GBin LRHS MRav NBid NLar SEND SWvt WAvo WCFE WSpi XSen
* 'Elliot's Variety'	CExl
fruticosa ♀H5	Widely available
- white-flowered	CBcs
aff. ***fruticosa***	LBar MDon WSpi
grandiflora	EBee EPfP MNrw SEND XSen
- NJM 10.014	WPGP
§ - 'Lloyd's Silver' ♀H5	CRos EHyd ELan LRHS MAsh NLar
herba-venti	XSen
italica	Widely available
lanata	CRos CSde EHyd EPfP LRHS SBrt SPer WCFE XSen
- 'Pygmy'	XSen
'Le Chat'	WMal XSen
'Le Sud'	LRHS WCot XSen
leucophracta	SVen
longifolia	CBod CDoC CKel EHyd EPfP LRHS MNrw SDix SEND SPer WPGP XSen
- var. ***bailanica*** ♀H4	EHyd EPfP LRHS NRHS XLum
- var. ***longifolia***	WSpi
lychnitis	XSen
lycia	LRHS XSen
macrophylla	LPla SPhx
× ***margaritae***	XSen
'Marina'	WMal XSen
monocephala	XSen
purpurea	CBod CKel CRos CWnw EHyd ELan EPfP LRHS MAsh NBir NRHS SEND WCot XSen
I - 'Alba'	CBod EAri ELan GBin LRHS MMrt
- subsp. ***almeriensis***	XSen
§ ***russeliana*** ♀H6	Widely available
- PAB 7444	LEdu
- 'Dappled Shade' (v)	WCot
samia Boiss.	see *P. russeliana*

samia L.	CMac EHyd EWTr EWoo LDai LRHS MNrw NBir NGdn NLar NRHS SBrt SEND SPtp WMal XSen
- - JMT	EPPr
- 'Green Glory'	WCot
× ***termessi***	XSen
'Toob'	SBrt WPGP
'Tramuntana'	XSen
tuberosa	CBcs CBod ELan EPfP EWTr LEdu LRHS LSRN MPnt SPhx WCAu WMal XLum XSen
- 'Amazone' 🏆H5	Widely available
- 'Bronze Flamingo'	CMac EPfP GBin ILea LRHS MHol MNrw MPie MPnt MRav NLar SBls SPoG SRms WSpi
- 'Prima Donna'PBR **new**	LBar
viscosa misapplied	see *P. russeliana*

Phlox ✿ (*Polemoniaceae*)

adsurgens 'Alba'	WFar
- 'Wagon Wheel'	CBor ECtt EHyd EMor EPot LRHS NHpl NRHS SPlb SRms WFar
amplifolia	WCot XLum
- 'Apanatschi'	WCot
- 'Augenstern'	WFar
- 'Hercules' **new**	LBar
- 'Minnehaha'	NDov
- 'Winnetou'	NDov
× ***arendsii*** 'Andrew'	WCot
- 'Autumn's Pink Explosion'	WCot
- 'Babyface'	NGdn
- 'Casablanca'	NDov
- 'Dylan'	WCot
- 'Eyecatcher'	NBro
- 'Gary'	WCot
- 'Hesperis'	CMiW CSpe ECha ELon GBee LEdu LRHS MAvo MCot MNrw NDov NLar SPhx WCAu WHil WSHC
- 'Luc's Lilac' 🏆H7	CBWd ECtt EPPr LPla LRHS NBro NDov NSti SGbt SPhx WCot
§ - 'Miss Jill' (Spring Pearl Series)	ELan EPfP WCot
§ - 'Miss Karen' (Spring Pearl Series)	EBee NBro
§ - 'Miss Margie' (Spring Pearl Series)	EGrI
§ - 'Miss Mary' (Spring Pearl Series) 🏆H7	EBee ELan EPfP ILea NLar SRkn WHlf
§ - 'Miss Wilma' (Spring Pearl Series)	EBee ELan EPfP
- 'Paul'	MNrw WCot WSHC
- 'Ping Pong'	LDai SGbt
- 'Pink Attraction'	LRHS NBro
- 'Sweet William'	ECha
- 'Utopia' 🏆H7	CSpe ELon GBin LPla MCot NDov WCAu WCot
austromontana	EPot NWad
bifida 'Alba'	EPot
- 'Ralph Haywood'	ECtt EPot
borealis	see *P. sibirica* subsp. *borealis*
caespitosa	EDAr EWes
- subsp. ***pulvinata***	see *P. pulvinata*
- 'Zigeunerblut'	ECtt EPot NSla NWad WAbe
canadensis	see *P. divaricata*
carolina subsp. ***angusta***	LPla
- 'Bill Baker'	see *P. glaberrima* 'Bill Baker'
- 'Magnificence'	EWes SMad SPlb WCot
- 'Miss Lingard' 🏆H6	CBod CDor CKel ECtt EHyd GBee LRHS LSou LSto MRav NBir NGdn NLar NRHS NSti SGbt SMrm WCAu WCot
'Chattahoochee'	see *P. divaricata* subsp. *laphamii* 'Chattahoochee'
'Daniel's Cushion'	see *P. subulata* 'McDaniel's Cushion'
diffusa	EPot WAbe
§ ***divaricata*** 🏆H5	SPlb
- f. ***albiflora***	EMor
- 'Blue Dreams'	ECtt EMor LSou MNrw WFar
- 'Blue Moon'	CWCL EAJP EWes GKev MACG NCth NLar
- 'Blue Perfume'	EBee ECtt LCro
- 'Charles'	XLum
- 'Clouds of Perfume'	Widely available
- 'Dirigo Ice'	EHyd LRHS NRHS WSHC
- 'Fuller's White'	CWCL
- subsp. ***laphamii***	EBee EWes MACG WFar
§ - - 'Chattahoochee' 🏆H5	Widely available
- 'May Breeze'	CWCL EAJP ECtt EHyd GKev GMaP LRHS MACG MNrw MPnt NRHS SCoo SHar SPoG WAvo
- 'Plum Perfect'	ECtt
- 'White Perfume'	CWCL EAJP EBee EHyd EPfP EWes LRHS MACG MBel MMrt NDov NLar SBut SHar SPoG WFar XLum
douglasii	SRms
- 'Apollo'	CBor CTri ECtt
- 'Boothman's Variety' 🏆H6	ECha ECtt ELan EPot SRms
- 'Crackerjack' 🏆H6	CTri ECtt EHyd ELan ELon EPot GKev GMaP LCro LRHS MAsh MBow NBir NHol NHpl NRHS NSla SLee SPoG SRot WIce
- 'Eva'	CBor EBou ECtt EDAr EHyd ELon EPot GArf GMaP GQue LCro LRHS LSRN MAsh NBir NHpl NLar NRHS NWad SLee WFar
- 'Georg Arends'	CBor ECtt WFar
- 'Ice Mountain'	CBor ECtt EDAr ELan EPot MACG NHol NWad SPoG SRot WFar
- 'J.A. Hibberson'	EPot EWes NWad
- 'Lilac Cloud'	ECtt
- LILAC QUEEN	see *P. douglasii* 'Lilakönigin'
§ - 'Lilakönigin'	CTri
- 'Napoleon'	ECtt GArf NWad
- 'Ochsenblut'	CBor ECtt EHyd EPot GArf LRHS NLar NRHS NSla NWad SRms WIce
- 'Red Admiral' 🏆H5	ECtt ELan EPfP EWes GMaP LRHS NWad WFar
- 'Rose Cushion'	EWes
- 'Rosea'	ECha EGrI ELan LCro MAsh MMuc NHpl SLee SRot WIce
- 'Sprite'	SRms
- 'Tycoon'	see *P. subulata* 'Tamaongalei'
- 'Violet Queen'	GArf
- 'Waterloo'	CBor EBou ECtt EHyd EPot LRHS NRHS
I - 'White Admiral'	CRos CTri ECtt EHyd ELan EPfP GBin LRHS LSRN NRHS
drummondii 'Crème Brûlée'	CKel
- POPSTARS (mixed)	LSou MBros
(Fashionably Early Series) 'Fashionably Early Crystal'	LCro WHil
- 'Fashionably Early Flamingo'	NCth SMad WHil
- 'Fashionably Early Princess'	LCro NCth WHil
- 'Fashionably Lavender Ice'	LCro NCth SMad WHil
'Flare'	see *P. paniculata* 'Neon Flare'
§ ***glaberrima*** 'Bill Baker' 🏆H6	CKel ECha ECtt EGrI ELon GElm GMaP LEdu MAsh MBow MNrw NBir NGdn NSti SBut SWvt WCAu WFar WMal XLum
- 'Morris Berd'	MAvo WFar WSHC
'Goliath'	CBod LBar NCth WHlf
hendersonii	WAbe
hoodii	WAbe

'Jeff's Pink'	ECtt NCth NLar
'Kelly's Eye' ♀H5	CBor EBou ECtt EHyd EPot LRHS LShi NBir NRHS SPoG
kelseyi 'Lemhi Purple'	EPot WAbe
- 'Rosette'	NWad
LIGHT PINK FLAME ('Bareleven'PBR)	ECtt SPoG
LILAC FLAME ('Barten'PBR)	EHyd LBar LRHS NRHS SCob
maculata	EGrl
- 'Alba'	EGrl SAko
- 'Alpha' ♀H6	CWCL EBee ECha ECtt EHyd ELon EMor EWoo GMaP LEdu LRHS NLar NRHS SCoo SGbt SPer SPoG SWvt WCAu WFar WSHC WTyc XLum
- AVALANCHE	see *P. maculata* 'Schneelawine'
- 'Delta'	ELon EMor LRHS NLar SAko SGbt SRkn SWvt
- 'Natascha' ♀H6	CMac CWCL EBee ECtt EHyd ELon EMor EPfP EWes EWoo GMaP GMcL LRHS LSRN NCth NGdn NHol NLar NRHS SAko SGbt SMad SPer SRkn SWvt WCAu WFar WHil WTyc
- 'Omega' ♀H6	CBod CMac ECha ECtt EMor EWoo GBee GMcL LEdu LRHS LShi NCth NGdn NLar SGbt SWvt WCAu WFar WSpi WTyc
- 'Princess Sturdza' ♀H6	NDov SDix
- 'Reine du Jour'	LPla MAvo MHol NDov SPhx
- 'Rosalinde'	CBod ECtt ELon EMor LRHS MCot NLar SAko SCoo SPoG SWvt WSHC
§ - 'Schneelawine'	ELon NCth SPer SPlb WCAu WSpi
'Millstream'	see *P.* × *procumbens* 'Millstream'
'Minnie Pearl'	EWes LPla NDov WCot
nivalis 'Nivea'	EPot WAbe
paniculata	CWal ELon EPPr LEdu NBid NDov SDix WCot WPGP
- 'A.E. Amos'	ELon
- (Adessa Series) ADESSA ORANGE	NLar WHil
- - ADESSA PINK STAR	LRHS NLar NRHS
- - ADESSA RED	NLar
- - ADESSA ROSE EYE	NLar WHil
- - ADESSA SPECIAL DEEP PURPLE	WHil
- - ADESSA SPECIAL FIRE	NLar
- - ADESSA SPECIAL PURPLE STAR	NRHS
- - ADESSA WHITE	NLar
- var. ***alba***	ECha SDix WCot WSHC
- 'Alba Grandiflora' ♀H7	MAvo MNrw NChi WCot WHoo
- 'Alexandra'PBR	LCro LOPS WHlf
- 'Aljonuschka'	GBin
- 'All in One'	MAvo
- 'Amethyst' misapplied	see *P. paniculata* 'Lilac Time'
- 'Amethyst' ambig.	EGrl WHlf
- 'Amethyst' Foerster	ELon LRHS MRav NBir NLar WBor WCAu
- 'Anastasia'PBR **new**	WHlf
- 'Anne'	ELon MSpe
- 'Balmoral'	CMac ECtt ELon NCou NSti SWvt
- BAMBINI CANDY CRUSH ('Verscan'PBR)	CWGN
- BAMBINI DESIRE ('Versde'PBR)	CWGN
- 'Becky Towe'PBR (v) ♀H7	ECtt MHol MNrw NHol SPoG WCot
- 'Blauer Morgen'	XLum
- 'Blue Boy'	CRos EBee ECtt EHyd ELan ELon EMor EPfP GMaP LRHS NBir NRHS SWvt WBor WCAu WFar
- 'Blue Evening'	EBee ELon LCro MSpe NLar
- BLUE FLAME	MNrw
- 'Blue Ice'	NCth
- 'Blue Moon'	ELon
- 'Blue Paradise'	Widely available
- 'Blushing Bride'	SRms
- 'Bold and Beautiful' (Neon Series)	SPad
- 'Bonny Maid'	MAvo
- 'Border Gem'	CBcs CBod CMac ECtt ELon EShb LRHS MRav SDix SPeP SWvt WBrk WCot
- 'Bosvigo Pink'	ELon MAvo SAko SHar
- 'Brigadier'	CBod CTri EBee ECtt ELan LRHS MNrw MSpe SPer SRms WWke
- 'Bright Eyes'	Widely available
- 'Burgi'	SDix
- 'Butonik'	ELon
- 'Cardinal'	NDov
- 'Caroline van den Berg'	SAko SRms
- 'Charlotte'	MSpe WGoo
- 'Cheriton'	EBlo EHyd LRHS NRHS
- 'Chintz'	EHyd LRHS MRav NRHS SRms
- 'Cinderella'	ECtt
- 'Cleopatra'PBR	NLar SPad WHlf
- COMPACT LILAC	see *P. paniculata* (Sweet Summer Series) SWEET SUMMER FAVOURITE
- COMPACT ROSE WHITE	see *P. paniculata* (Sweet Summer Series) SWEET SUMMER CANDY
- 'Cool Best'	NCth NDov
- 'Cool Water'	NLar WHlf
- CORAL FLAME ('Barsixtytwo'PBR) (Flame Series)	CMac LBar LSou NLar SCob SCoo SPoG SRkn WHil
- 'Coral Queen'	SRms
- 'Cosmopolitan'PBR	EPfP MHol MNrw NLar
- COUNT ZEPPELIN	see *P. paniculata* 'Graf Zeppelin'
- 'Crème de Menthe' (v)	EMor
- 'Danielle' ♀H7	LRHS NRHS SHar
- 'Darwin's Choice'	see *P. paniculata* 'Norah Leigh'
- 'David' ♀H7	Widely available
- 'David's Lavender' ♀H7	EBlo EHyd ELon LBar LRHS MAvo NLar NRHS WSpi
- 'Delilah'PBR	CWGN ECtt NHpl
- 'Discovery'	EShb EWes LCro LPla MRav MSpe SHar
- 'Dodo Hanbury-Forbes'	MNrw
- 'Doghouse Pink'	SAko SDix
- 'Dresden China'	SHar
- 'Duchess of York'	MAvo MNrw MSpe SDix
§ - 'Düsterlohe'	EBee ECtt EHyd ELon GBin ILea LRHS MACG MCot MHer MRav NBir NDov NGdn NRHS NSti SPer SRkn SRms WCAu WCot WSpi XLum
- (Early Series) EARLY CERISE	LBar SPad WHil
- - EARLY MAGENTA **new**	WHil
- - EARLY PINK ('Barsixtyfive') **new**	WHil
- - EARLY PINK CANDY ('Dophlearpica')	LBar WHil
- - EARLY PURPLE EYE ('Barphlearpur'PBR) **new**	LBar WHil
- - EARLY PURPLE PINK EYE **new**	WHil
- - EARLY RED	WHil
- - EARLY WHITE	WHil
- 'Eclaireur' misapplied	see *P. paniculata* 'Düsterlohe'
- 'Eden's Flash'	CElw
- 'Eden's Glory'	MAvo
- 'Elisabeth' (v)	NWad

- 'Elizabeth Arden'	ELon LPla MACG
- 'Elizabeth Campbell'	EPPr
- 'Ending Blue'	MAvo
- 'Etoile de Paris'	see *P. paniculata* 'Toits de Paris' Symons-Jeune
- 'Europa'	EBee ECtt ELan ELon EWoo LRHS NBir NGdn NLar SPer WCAu WHlf WSHC
- 'Eva Cullum' ♀H7	CBod CRos EBee ECtt EHyd ELan ELon EPfP EWoo GMaP LRHS MHer NHpl NRHS SAko SDix SPer WCAu WCot WFar
- 'Eva Foerster' ♀H7	EHyd LRHS NRHS XLum
- 'Eventide'	CMac EBee ECtt EHyd EPfP LRHS MArl MAvo MBel MNrw MRav NRHS SPer WFar
- 'Fairy's Petticoat'	ELon
- (Famous Series) FAMOUS CERISE	ELan EPfP LRHS MPri
- - FAMOUS LIGHT PURPLE ('Appofalp'PBR)	LRHS MPri
- - FAMOUS PINK DARK EYE ('Appofapide')	ELan LRHS MPri
- - FAMOUS PURPLE ('Appotwpu'PBR)	ELan EPfP LRHS MPri
- - FAMOUS WHITE	ELan LRHS MPri
- - FAMOUS WHITE EYE ('Appofamwe'PBR)	ELan LRHS MPri
- 'Ferris Wheel'	WHlf
- (Flame Series) FLAME LIGHT BLUE	WHil WPnP
- - FLAME MARINE **new**	LBar
- 'Flamingo' ♀H7	ECtt ELon MSpe NLar SWvt XLum
- 'Fondant Fancy'PBR	NLar SMrm
- 'Franz Schubert' ♀H7	CDor CRos ECtt EHyd ELan ELon EPfP EWTr EWoo GBin ILea LCro LRHS LSto MCot MSpe NBir NChi NGdn NLar NRHS NSti SMrm SPer SWvt WCot WFar
- 'Fujiyama'	see *P. paniculata* 'Mount Fuji'
- 'Gamlingay Purple'	MAvo
- 'Geisha's Blush'	SMHy
- 'Geisha's Glance'	SMHy
- 'Glamour Girl'PBR (Garden Girls Series) **new**	NCth
- 'Goldmine'PBR (v)	ELon MNrw MSCN SMad SPoG SRms WCot
§ - 'Graf Zeppelin'	ECtt ELon MSpe NHol NLar SRms XLum
- 'Green Lady'PBR	EMor
- 'Grenadine Dream'PBR	CWGN EGrI MNrw WHlf
- 'Grey Lady' ♀H7	EBlo EHyd LRHS MNrw NRHS SHar WGoo
- 'Harlequin' (v)	CWGN ECha GBee WCot
- 'Herbstwalzer'	ELon WCot
- 'Ice Cream'	CWGN ELon WHlf
- 'Iris'	MNrw SRms WCot
- 'Jade' (Neon Series)	ELon EMor GQue LEdu LRHS MBros MNrw NCth NLar WCot
- 'Jeana'	ELon MNrw
- 'Jeff's Blue'	NLar WCot
- 'Judy'	MAvo
- 'Jules Sandeau'	LRHS
- 'Julia' **new**	LBar
§ - 'Juliglut'	EHyd ELon LRHS NRHS WCot
- JULY GLOW	see *P. paniculata* 'Juliglut'
- 'Junior Dance'	GBee
- 'Katherine'	EHyd ELon EMor LRHS MSpe NRHS
- 'Katja'	EGrI NLar WPnP
- 'Kirchenfürst'	CElw CRos EHyd GElm LCro LRHS MACG NBir NLar NRHS SAko WCAu WFar
- 'Kirmesländler'	ECtt MAvo MSpe NLar SAko
- 'Königin der Nacht' (Zauberflöte Series) ♀H7	SMHy
- 'Ksenija'	ELon
- 'Lads Pink'	SDix
- 'Lady Clare'	SRms
- 'Landhochzeit'	WFar
- 'Larissa'PBR	LBar LCro MNrw NCth
- 'Laura'	see *P. paniculata* 'Uspekh'
§ - 'Lavendelwolke'	EPPr LRHS MSpe NBir NLar WCot
- LAVENDER CLOUD	see *P. paniculata* 'Lavendelwolke'
- 'Lavender Lady' **new**	WCot
- 'Le Mahdi' ♀H7	NLar SRms
- 'Lichtspel'	ELon LPla NDov SPhx
§ - 'Lilac Time'	CElw CRos ECtt EHyd EPfP GKev GMaP LRHS NLar NRHS SCob SWvt WSpi
- 'Little Boy'	CElw ELon LRHS MNrw NLar SGbt
- 'Little Laura'	CFis ECtt LRHS LSRN MNrw NGdn NLar SMrm WCot WHoo
- 'Little Princess'	ELon NLar
- 'Little Sara'	NDov
- 'Logan Black'	SHar WOld WSHC
- MAGICAL DREAM	see *P. paniculata* (Sweet Summer Series) SWEET SUMMER DREAM
- MAGICAL FAVORITE	see *P. paniculata* (Sweet Summer Series) SWEET SUMMER FAVOURITE
- MAGICAL SURPRISE	see *P. paniculata* (Sweet Summer Series) SWEET SUMMER SURPRISE
- 'Manoir d'Hézèques'	WCot
- 'Marchant's Darkest'	SMHy
- 'Mardi Gras'	ELan EPfP
- 'Mary Christine' (v)	LRHS NBid NRHS
- 'Maude Stella Dagley'	MSpe WCot
- 'Mike's Favourite'	MBros
- 'Milly van Hoboken'	WKif
- 'Miss Holland'	NGdn SGbt XLum
- 'Miss Jill'	see *P.* × *arendsii* 'Miss Jill'
- 'Miss Karen'	see *P.* × *arendsii* 'Miss Karen'
- 'Miss Kelly'	EShb
- 'Miss Margie'	see *P.* × *arendsii* 'Miss Margie'
- 'Miss Mary'	see *P.* × *arendsii* 'Miss Mary'
- 'Miss Pepper' ♀H7	ECtt EHyd ELon EWoo LRHS MBel MMuc NGdn NLar NRHS WBor
- 'Miss Universe'	ELon
- 'Miss Wilma'	see *P.* × *arendsii* 'Miss Wilma'
- 'Modern Art'	MNrw
- 'Monica Lynden-Bell' ♀H7	CBWd CCBP CDor CWGN EBee ECha ELon EWTr EWoo GMaP LRHS LSun MAvo MBel MBriF MCot MNrw MRav NBid NChi NDov NLar NSti SGbt WCot WKif WSHC
- 'Monte Cristallo'	MSpe
- 'Mother of Pearl' ♀H7	LRHS WSpi
§ - 'Mount Fuji'	Widely available
- 'Mount Fujiyama'	see *P. paniculata* 'Mount Fuji'
- 'Mrs A.E. Jeans'	SRms
- 'Natural Feelings'PBR (Feelings Series)	NLar
§ - 'Neon Flare' (Neon Series)	CWGN MHol WHil
- 'Newbird'	EBee ECtt SRms
- 'Nicky'	see *P. paniculata* 'Düsterlohe'
§ - 'Norah Leigh' (v) ♀H7	CElw CMac CWGN EBee ECha ECtt ELan EMor EPfP EWes GMcL LRHS MHer MPie NPer NRHS NSti SDix SPoG SRms SWvt WCAu WCFE WCot WFar WOld
- 'Oljenka'	ELon
- 'Orange Perfection'	see *P. paniculata* 'Prince of Orange'

- 'Othello' ECtt ELon LRHS MSpe NGdn SMrm WHoo
- 'Otley Choice' ECtt EGrl MRav NCou NLar NSti
- 'Otley Purple' MAvo MHer NCou
- 'P.D. Williams' WCot
- 'Pastorale' WCot
- 'Pat Coleman' MAvo
- (Peacock Series) PEACOCK CHERRY RED 🏆H7 CRos EHyd GMcL LRHS NRHS WTor
- - PEACOCK LILAC 🏆H7 CRos EHyd GMcL LRHS NRHS
- - PEACOCK NEON PURPLE 🏆H7 CRos EHyd LRHS NRHS
- - PEACOCK PURPLE BICOLOR CRos EHyd GMcL LRHS NRHS SCoo SPoG
- - PEACOCK WHITE 🏆H7 CRos EHyd GDam GMcL LRHS NRHS WTor
- 'Peppermint Twist' CWGN ELon LBar MNrw NCth SPad SWvt WFar WHlf
- 'Picasso' CWGN ECtt NLar WHil WTyc
- 'Pina Colada'PBR CWGN LRHS MPri WCAu WFar
- PINK EYE FLAME ('Barthirtyfive'PBR) 🏆H7 EHyd EPfP LBar LRHS NRHS SPoG SRkn SRms
- PINK FLAME ('Bartwelve'PBR) (Flame Series) EPfP LBar LSou NLar SCob SRkn SRms WHil
- 'Pink Lady'PBR EBee NCth WFar
- 'Pink Posie' (v) WCot
- PINK RED EYE FLAME ('Barthirtyfour') SPoG
- 'Popeye' LBar LPla WCot
- 'Prime Minister' ELon
- § - 'Prince of Orange' 🏆H7 CBcs CBod CRos CSBt EAJP EBee ECtt EHyd ELon EPfP GMcL LRHS MAvo MHol MRav NCth SCob SGbt SMrm SPeP SPer SRms SWvt WCot WHlf XLum
- 'Prospero' 🏆H7 CElw CSpe EBlo LRHS MRav NBid
- PURPLE EYE FLAME ('Barthirtythree'PBR) 🏆H7 EHyd LBar LRHS NRHS SPad SRkn SWvt WCAu WFar
- 'Purple Kiss'PBR CWGN ECtt LRHS MHol MPri WFar WHil WHlf WWke
- 'Purple Paradise' LRHS
- 'Rainbow' ELon NLar
- 'Rainbow Dancer' ELon
- 'Raving Beauty' LRHS
- 'Red Caribbean' ECtt LRHS MPri NLar
- 'Red Feelings' (Feelings Series) CBod LRHS LSto SGbt
- 'Red Flame' CWGN ECtt EPfP LBar MNrw SAko SRkn WFar WHil
- 'Red Riding Hood' see *P.* × *arendsii* 'Miss Mary'
- I - 'Reddish Hesperis' MAvo
- 'Rembrandt' EHyd ELon EPfP LCro LOPS LRHS MAvo NRHS WCAu WHlf XLum
- 'Rijnstroom' CBcs ECha ELon GMcL MArl NLar SCob WBrk WCAu
- 'Robert Poore' ECtt ELon
- 'Roberta' LCro LOPS
- 'Rosa Pastell' 🏆H7 CDor CSpe ECtt ELon GBin LRHS MAvo NLar SHor WCot
- 'Rowie' NBid
- 'Roze Casablanca' **new** NDov
- 'Sandringham' ECtt LRHS MArl MRav NBir NCou NRHS SMrm SPer SWvt
- § - 'Schneerausch' LPla SPhx
- 'Septemberglut' CRos EHyd ELon EPfP LRHS NRHS
- 'Shockwave' (v) WCot
- SNOWDRIFT see *P. paniculata* 'Schneerausch'
- 'Speed Limit 45' WCot
- 'Starfire' 🏆H7 Widely available
- I - 'Stars and Stripes' LRHS
- 'Steeple Bumpstead' MAvo WCot
- 'Sterling Brocade' (v) WCot
- 'Sternhimmel' LPla MSpe
- 'Strawberry Daiquiri'PBR WFar
- § - (Sweet Summer Series) SWEET SUMMER CANDY ('Ditosdre'PBR) NCth WHlf
- § - - SWEET SUMMER DREAM ('Ditomdre'PBR) MAvo MPri NLar WCAu WHlf
- - SWEET SUMMER FANTASY ('Ditopur'PBR) MAvo MPri WCAu WHlf
- § - - SWEET SUMMER FAVOURITE ('Ditomfav'PBR) 🏆H7 NLar WCAu
- - SWEET SUMMER FIREBALL MPri
- - SWEET SUMMER OCEAN ('Ditoocean'PBR) WHlf
- - SWEET SUMMER PURPLE WHITE see *P. paniculata* (Sweet Summer Series) SWEET SUMMER TEMPTATION
- - SWEET SUMMER QUEEN ('Ditoran'PBR) MPri NLar
- - SWEET SUMMER SENSATION ('Ditosse'PBR) MPri WCAu
- - SWEET SUMMER SNOW ('Ditosnow'PBR) WHlf
- § - - SWEET SUMMER SURPRISE ('Ditomsur'PBR) ECtt MPri WCAu
- § - - SWEET SUMMER TEMPTATION ('Ditostem'PBR) LBar
- - SWEET SUMMER WINE ('Ditowine'PBR) ECtt MAvo NLar
- 'Swizzle' CWGN WFar WWke
- 'Tatjana' EBee ELon
- 'Tenor' CTri ECtt ELon EPfP LEdu LRHS SGbt SRms SWvt WCAu WSHC
- 'Tequila Sunrise'PBR ECtt LRHS MNrw
- 'The King' 🏆H7 ECtt EGrl MAvo WHlf WSHC WSpi
- 'Tiara'PBR (d) ECtt LRHS NCth NGdn SWvt WCot
- 'Toits de Paris' ambig. MAvo
- § - 'Toits de Paris' Symons-Jeune WSHC
- TWINKLE LIGHT PINK **new** MPri
- 'Twister' EBee LBar MAsh MBros MNrw NCth WFar
- § - 'Uspekh' 🏆H7 Widely available
- 'Velvet Flame' 🏆H7 EHyd LRHS NRHS
- 'Vintage Wine' MNrw
- 'Violetta Gloriosa' ELon SAko WFar
- 'Visions' 🏆H7 EBlo
- 'Volcano Betty' MNrw
- 'Watermelon Punch' ECtt LRHS MAsh NLar WFar
- 'Wendy House' LEdu MAvo MNrw NHol SMDa
- 'White Admiral' 🏆H7 CBcs CElw CRos EBee ECtt EHyd ELan ELon EPfP EWoo GArf GMaP LRHS MNrw MSpe NGrd NLar NRHS SCob SCoo SGbt SPer SPhx SRms SWvt WCAu WFar WJam XLum
- WHITE FLAME ('Bartwentynine'PBR) 🏆H7 CDor CWGN EHyd EPfP LBuc LRHS LSou NRHS SCob SWvt WCot
- 'White Pepper' MAvo
- 'Wilhelm Kesselring' ECtt ELon NChi WBor
- 'Willow Lodge' SHar
- 'Windsor' CFis EBee ECtt ELon EMor EPfP LRHS NCou NHol SRms SWvt WCAu WHlf
- (Younique Series) YOUNIQUE BICOLOR ('Versbicolor') LBar WFar WHlf
- - YOUNIQUE MAUVE ('Versmauve') LBar LCro

	- - YOUNIQUE OLD BLUE ('Versoldblue')	CDor CWGN LBar LRHS MBros WFar WHlf
	- - YOUNIQUE OLD CERISE ('Verscerise')	LBar MBros WFar WHlf
	- - YOUNIQUE OLD PINK ('Versoldpink')	LBar MBros WFar WHlf
	- - YOUNIQUE OLD PURPLE	LBar WFar
	- - YOUNIQUE ORANGE ('Versorange') **new**	LBar
	- - YOUNIQUE TRENDY **new**	LBar
	- - YOUNIQUE WHITE ('Verswhite')	LBar LEdu MBros MNrw WFar
	- 'Zauberspiel' **new**	ELon
	'Peppermint Candy'	WFar
	'Petticoat'	ECtt EPot WIce
	'Pride of Rochester'	CBor EBou ECtt EHyd LRHS NRHS
§	× ***procumbens*** 'Millstream' 🏆H5	ECtt
	- 'Variegata' (v)	EBou ECha ECtt NBwr SLee SRot WCav
§	***pulvinata***	SPlb WAbe
	PURPLE FLAME ('Barfourteen'^{PBR}) (Flame Series)	EHyd EPfP LRHS LSou NRHS SCob SRkn SRms WFar WHil
	'Sherbet Cocktail'^{PBR}	CWGN NCth NHol WPnP
§	***sibirica*** subsp. ***borealis***	WAbe
	'Sileniflora'	EPot WAbe
	'Smokey'	LBar
	'Spätsommer'	NDov
	stolonifera	MNrw
I	- 'Alba'	EPfP LBar NLar WFar WKif
	- 'Ariane'	ECha ECtt MNrw
I	- 'Atropurpurea'	CBod
	- 'Blue Ridge' 🏆H6	CExl EBee ECha ECtt EPfP EWld MRav SRms WFar
	- 'Fran's Purple'	ECtt EWld MNrw WAvo WBrk WFar WKif
	- 'Home Fires'	ECtt EPfP LEdu SMrm SPlb
	- 'Pink Ridge'	WFar XLum
	- 'Purpurea'	EPfP
	- 'Violet Vere'	EAJP
	subulata	LPar
	- 'Alexander's Surprise'	ECtt EHyd EPfP EPot LRHS MAsh NBir NRHS
	- 'Amazing Grace'	CBor CTri CWCL ECtt EHyd EPfP EPot EWes LCro LRHS NBir NBwr NDov NRHS NSla NWad SCoo SPoG SRms WCav WFar WHoo WIce
	- 'Apple Blossom'	GKev NHol SCoo SPoG SRms
	- 'Atropurpurea'	SPoG XLum
	- 'Bavaria'	CBod CBor CRos EHyd EPfP EPot LBar LCro LOPS LRHS MACG MDon NRHS SRms WFar WHlf WWke
	- 'Blue Eyes'	see *P. subulata* 'Oakington Blue Eyes'
	- 'Bonita'	ECtt EHyd EPot MAsh NBwr NRHS WIce
	- 'Bressingham Blue Eyes'	see *P. subulata* 'Oakington Blue Eyes'
	- 'Candy Stripe'	see *P. subulata* 'Tamaongalei'
	- 'Coral Eye'	CBod LBar
	- 'Daisy Hill'	XLum
	- 'Drumm'	see *P. subulata* 'Tamaongalei'
	- 'Drummons Pink' **new**	LBar
	- (Early Spring Series) EARLY SPRING PURPLE ('Barseventyfour'^{PBR})	CRos EHyd EPfP LRHS NRHS
	- - EARLY SPRING WHITE ('Barseventythree'^{PBR})	SGBe
	- 'Emerald Cushion'	CBod CBor CTri EBou ECtt EGrI ELon EPfP LRHS LSto NHol NHpl NSla SGBe SGbt WTor XLum
	- 'Emerald Cushion Blue'	CExl CTri EAJP EBou ECtt EHyd ELan EPfP LBar LRHS MAsh MHCG MHol NBir NBwr NRHS SPlb SPoG SRot WCAu WFar WWke
	- FABULOUS BLUE VIOLET ('Florphfabv') (Fabulous Series)	CBod EPfP LRHS
	- 'Fort Hill'	ECtt
	- 'G.F. Wilson'	see *P. subulata* 'Lilacina'
	- 'Holly'	EPot NHol NWad
	- 'Kimono'	see *P. subulata* 'Tamaongalei'
§	- 'Lilacina'	ECha EPfP MAsh MBel
§	- 'Maischnee'	CTri ECtt MAsh NBwr SPlb
	- 'Marjorie'	EBou ECtt EGrI GArf GKev MBow MHer NBir SPoG
	- MAY SNOW	see *P. subulata* 'Maischnee'
§	- 'McDaniel's Cushion' 🏆H6	Widely available
	- 'Mikado'	see *P. subulata* 'Tamaongalei'
	- 'Nettleton Variation' (v)	CRos EHyd EPot EWes LRHS MMuc NRHS SPoG SRms SRot WFar WHoo
§	- 'Oakington Blue Eyes'	CTri SRms
	- 'Purple Beauty'	ECtt EHyd EPfP GMaP LRHS NRHS NWad SPoG WFar WHoo XLum
	- 'Red Wings' 🏆H6	ECtt EPfP MACG SRms
	- 'Samson'	EPot NBwr SRot
	- 'Scarlet Flame'	EBou ECtt EGrI EPfP LBar LCro MACG MAsh NHol NHpl SLee SMrm WCAu
	- 'Snow Queen'	see *P. subulata* 'Maischnee'
	- 'Snowflake'	LCro LShi NSla
§	- 'Tamaongalei'	CBod CGBo CPla CRos CTri EBou EHyd ELan ELon EWes LBar LRHS MAsh MMuc NGrs NRHS NWad SCoo SLee SPoG SRot WCav WFar WHlf WHoo WIce XLum
	- 'Temiskaming'	CTri EHyd EWes LRHS NRHS NSla SRms WSHC
	- 'White Delight'	ECtt EHyd ELan ELon EPfP LBar MACG SPoG WCAu
	- white-flowered	NSla
	VIOLET FLAME ('Barsixtyone'^{PBR})	CBod CDor EPfP MAvo MHol NLar SPoG WCot WHil
	'Violet Pinwheels'	CBor WFar WHlf
	WHITE EYE FLAME ('Barsixty'^{PBR})	CBod CDor CWGN EPfP LBar LSou NLar SCoo SPoG WHil
	'White Kimono'	CRos EHyd LRHS NRHS
	'Zwergenteppich'	CBor CRos EHyd EPfP LRHS NRHS SPoG WFar

Phoenix (*Arecaceae*)

	canariensis 🏆H2	CBod CDoC EBee EDir EPfP ERom LPal LPar MPri NHrt NPlm SArc SChr SEND SPlb SPoG SWeb
	dactylifera (F)	NPlm
	loureiroi	NPlm
	roebelenii 🏆H1b	CDTJ CTsd EDir LCro LPal NPlm
	rupicola	NPlm
	theophrasti	CPHo LPal NPlm

Phormium ✿ (*Hemerocallidaceae*)

§	'Alison Blackman'^{PBR}	CBcs CWnw EBee EPfP LPal LSRN MAsh MGos SCob SCoo SEND SPoG SWvt XSte
	'Amazing Red'	LPal
	'Apricot Queen' (v)	CAbb CBcs CBrac CCCN CDoC CSBt EBee EHeP EHyd EPfP GMcL LCro LPal LRHS LSRN MGos NBPC NLar NRHS SCob SEND SGbt SPer SPoG
	BACK IN BLACK ('Seilack'^{PBR})	CBcs CBrac CCht CMac CSBt MTin NPlm SCob SWvt WFar XSte
	'Black Adder'^{PBR}	EBee EHyd EPfP ILea LPal LRHS LSRN MAsh NRHS SCob SEND SGbt SPoG

	'Black Rage'	CBcs
	BLACK VELVET ('Seivel'PBR)	CBcs CCht CSpe CTsd EHyd ELan EPfP LRHS MSwo WCot
	'Blondie'PBR (v)	LCro LRHS
	'Bronze Baby'	CBcs CBod CCCN CDoC CKel CSBt EBee EHeP EHyd ELan EPfP LRHS LSRN MAsh MGos MSwo NBPC NBwr NRHS SCob SGBe SPer SPoG SWvt
	'Brown Sugar'	CTsd
	'Buckland Ruby'	EBee
	'Chocomint'PBR	CDoC ELan LCro SCob
	colensoi	see *P. cookianum*
§	***cookianum***	GAbr SArc
	- 'Alpinum Purpureum'	see *P. tenax* 'Nanum Purpureum'
	- subsp. ***hookeri*** 'Cream Delight' (v) ♀H4	CAbb CBcs CCCN CCht CDoC CMac CSBt EBee EGrI EHyd EPfP GMcL LPal LRHS LSRN MAsh MGos MSwo NRHS SCob SCoo SPeP SPer SWvt WFar
	- - 'Tricolor' (v) ♀H4	CBcs CBrac CChe CDTJ CDoC CMac CSBt CWnw EBee EHyd ELan EPfP GMcL LCro LOPS LRHS MGos NBPC NBwr NRHS SArc SCob SEND SPer SPoG SRms SWvt WFar XSte
	'Crimson Devil'	CBcs EHyd EPfP LRHS
	'Dark Delight'	CBcs XSte
	'Dazzler' (v)	MAsh
	'Duet' (v) ♀H3	CBcs CCCN NBPC NLar SEND SWvt
	'Dusky Chief'	CSBt CWal EBee LPal
	'Evening Glow' (v)	CBcs CCCN CDoC CKel EHeP EHyd EPfP GMcL LPal LRHS LSRN MAsh MGos NBPC NRHS SPoG SRms SWvt
	'Firebird'	LSRN SWvt
	'Flamingo' (v)	CBcs CCCN CDTJ CDoC EHeP EPfP GMcL MGos NPlm SCob SGbt SPer SPoG
	'Gold Ray' (v)	CBcs CBod CBrac CKel CTsd CWnw EHyd EPfP GMcL LRHS MAsh MDon NRHS SCoo SWvt WFar WLov
	'Gold Sword' (v)	CBcs CCCN CMac CSBt EPfP GMcL SCob SGbt
	'Golden Alison'	see *P.* 'Alison Blackman'
	'Green Sword'	CCCN EHeP
	'Jack Spratt' (v)	SWvt
	'Jester' (v)	Widely available
	'Limelight'	SEND SWvt
§	'Maori Chief' (v)	CSBt MAsh SWvt WFar
	'Maori Eclipse' (v)	GMcL
§	'Maori Maiden' (v)	CCCN CDoC CTri CWnw EBee EHeP GMcL MSwo NBPC SGBe SRms SWvt WFar
§	'Maori Queen' (v)	CBcs CBod CCCN CDTJ CDoC CMac EBee EHeP EHyd EPfP LCro LPal LRHS MACG MAsh MGos MSwo NBPC NRHS SCoo SEND SGBe SGbt SPer SWvt WFar
§	'Maori Sunrise' (v)	CBcs CBrac CCCN CDoC CMac EGrI EHeP GMcL IArd LCro LOPS LPal LSRN MGos NBPC SCoo SRms SWvt
	'Margaret Jones'PBR	CCCN LSRN XSte
	'Moonraker'PBR	SCob
	'Pink Jester' (v)	GMcL
	'Pink Panther' (v)	CAbb CBcs CBod CCCN CKel CWnw EHeP EPfP LSRN MGos NBPC SPoG SRms XSte
	'Pink Stripe' (v)	CBcs CKel CSBt CWnw EGrI EHyd EPfP GMcL LCro LPal LRHS MAsh MGos NBwr NPlm NRHS SCob SGbt SGsty SPoG SWvt XSte
	'Platt's Black'	CBod CCCN CKel CWnw EBee EPfP GMcL LCro LOPS LPar LSRN MACG MAsh MGos MSwo NBir NPlm SCob SPer SPoG SWvt WFar WLov
	'Rainbow Chief'	see *P.* 'Maori Chief'
	'Rainbow Maiden'	see *P.* 'Maori Maiden'
	'Rainbow Queen'	see *P.* 'Maori Queen'
	'Rainbow Sunrise'	see *P.* 'Maori Sunrise'
	'Red Sensation'	CDoC CEme CKel CWnw LSRN NBPC SPeP
	'Sundowner' (v) ♀H3	Widely available
	'Sunset' (v)	CBcs CCCN CSBt SWvt
	'Surfer' (v)	CDoC
	'Surfer Bronze'	CCCN NBwr
	'Surfer Green'	CCCN
	'Sussex Velvet'	SCoo
	tenax	CAgr CBcs CBrac CMac EHeP EPfP GArf GDam GMcL LCro LOPS LPal LPar LSto MGos MPri MSwo NGdn SArc SCob SEND SGsty SPer SPlb SPoG SWeb SWvt
	- 'All Black'	MGos SCoo XSte
	- 'Bronze'	SWvt
	- 'Co-ordination' (v)	CCCN NBPC
	- 'Croce di Malta'	SArc
	- 'Joker' (v)	CBcs CDoC EBee EHeP LPal NLar SCob
*	- ***lineatum***	SEND
§	- 'Nanum Purpureum'	SArc
	- Purpureum Group ♀H5	CBod CBrac CDoC CKel CMac EBee EGrI EHeP ELan EPfP ERom GAbr GArf GDam GMcL LPal LPar LSto MPri MSwo NBwr NLar SCob SEND SGsty SPlb SWeb WFar XLum
	- 'Thumbelina'	CCCN
	- 'Tiny Tiger' (v)	EPfP
	- 'Tom Thumb'	LRHS NLar
	- 'Variegatum' (v) ♀H5	CDTJ CDoC CKel CWnw EBee EPfP GMcL LPal LPar MGos MPri NBwr NPlm SArc SCob SEND SGsty SRms SWeb
	- 'Veitchii' **new**	NBwr
	- 'Yellow Queen' (v)	LPal WFar
	'Yellow Wave' (v) ♀H4	Widely available

Photinia ✿ (*Rosaceae*)

	arbutifolia	see *Heteromeles salicifolia*
	arguta var. ***arguta***	SMad
	- - KR 10738	WPGP
	beauverdiana	WJur
	- var. ***notabilis***	CBcs IDee
	CORALLINA ('Bourfrits'PBR)	CBod
	davidiana	CMac CTri ELan GMcL MGil MRav NLar SPer SPtp SRms SVen WPav
	- PAB 8097	LEdu
	- 'Dwarf Ness'	GKev
	- 'Palette' (v)	CBcs CBod CBrac CMac ELan EPfP GMcL MGos MSwo NLar SChF SGol SPer SPoG SRms SSha SWvt WFar WMat
	- Salicifolia Group	WPav
	- var. ***undulata*** 'Fructu Luteo'	CMac MRav NLar
	- - 'Prostrata'	CMac CTri MRav NLar WCFE
	'Diamond Red'	CDoC
	× ***fraseri***	CBTr LPar WTSh
I	- 'Atropurpurea Nana'	CBcs CDoC EPfP MGos
	- 'Birmingham'	CMac SRms

	- 'Canivily' 🏆H5	CEnd CKel CRos CWnw EFPl EHyd EShb LRHS LSto MGos NLar SGol SWvt
	- 'Carré Rouge'	CBod CWnw MThu SGsty SOrN SRHi WReH
	- CHICO ('Br2011')	LCro LRHS
	- CRACKLIN' RED ('Parred'PBR)	LPar
	- 'Devil's Dream'	LRHS
	- 'Dicker Tony'	NLar
	- 'Little Red Robin'	Widely available
	- LOUISE ('Mclarlou'PBR) (v)	CBod CRos CSBt EBee EFPl EHyd GMcL LBuc LPar LRHS MAsh MDon MGos MHed MPri NLar NOrn SCob SGBe SWvt WFar
	- MAGICAL VOLCANO ('Kolmavoca'PBR)	LRHS MAsh NLar SGol SGsty SPoG
	- PINK MARBLE ('Cassini') (v) 🏆H5	Widely available
	- 'Red Robin' 🏆H5	Widely available
	- 'Red Robin Variegated' (v)	ERom SavN
	- 'Red Select'	WFar
	- 'Robusta'	CMac EPfP LRHS SRms SWvt WReH
I	- 'Robusta Compacta'	LSRN SGsty
	glabra	GKev SArc
§	- 'Parfait' (v)	CMac
	- 'Pink Lady'	see *P. glabra* 'Parfait'
	- 'Rubens'	EHyd EPfP LRHS MAsh MRav
	- 'Variegata'	see *P. glabra* 'Parfait'
	glomerata ambig. **new**	WPGP
	integrifolia	SPtp
	lasiogyna	CMCN
	lucida	WCru
	microphylla B&SWJ 11837	WCru
	- HWJ 564	WCru
	niitakayamensis	MVil SPtp
	- CWJ 12435	WCru
	'Redstart'	CMac ELan LRHS MMuc NLar SPer SWvt WFar
§	***serratifolia***	CBcs CMCN EPfP NLar SArc SEND SPer WFar WPGP
	- var. ***ardisiifolia*** NMWJ 14513	WCru
I	- 'Compacta'	LPar
	- CRUNCHY ('Rev100'PBR)	EPfP LBuc LRHS MDon SCob
	- CURLY FANTASY ('Kolcurl'PBR)	LRHS MAsh MRav NLar SavN
	- 'Jenny'	NLar SavN WFar
	- PINK CRISPY ('Oploo5'PBR)	CAco CKel CWnw ELan LCro LPar LRHS LSRN MDon NLar SMad SPoG SavN
	serrulata	see *P. serratifolia*
	SUPER HEDGE ('Branpara'PBR)	MSwo WFar
	SUPER RED ('Parsur')	CSBt NLar
	villosa	WPav
	- B&SWJ 8665	WCru
	- var. ***coreana***	CBcs
	- - B&SWJ 8789	WCru
	- var. ***laevis***	WPGP
	- - B&SWJ 8877	WCru
	- f. ***maximowicziana***	CDoC NLar
*	- var. ***zollingeri*** B&SWJ 8903	WCru

Phragmites (*Poaceae*)

	sp.	CHab
	from Sichuan, China	EPPr
§	***australis***	CBen CHab CPud CWat LPfP NMir NWea SVic WMAq XLum
	- subsp. ***australis*** var. ***striatopictus***	EPPr
	- - 'Variegatus' (v)	CBen CWat EPPr LLWG LPfP MMuc NBir SEND XLum
	- subsp. ***humilis***	CHab
	- subsp. ***pseudodonax***	EPPr
	communis	see *P. australis*

Phuopsis (*Rubiaceae*)

§	***stylosa***	Widely available
	- 'Purpurea'	EBee ECha ELon MNrw MRav NChi

Phycella (*Amaryllidaceae*)

	cyrtanthoides	WCot

Phygelius (*Scrophulariaceae*)

	aequalis	MRav
	- ***albus***	see *P. aequalis* 'Yellow Trumpet'
	- 'Aureus'	see *P. aequalis* 'Yellow Trumpet'
	- 'Cream Trumpet'	see *P. aequalis* 'Yellow Trumpet'
	- 'Indian Chief'	see *P.* × *rectus* 'African Queen'
	- 'Sani Pass'	CKel MHer SIvy SPer SPlb
	- 'Trewidden Pink' 🏆H5	EHyd ELan GBin LRHS MHer MHtn NLar NRHS SNig SWvt XLum
§	- 'Yellow Trumpet' 🏆H5	CSBt EHeP ELan GMaP GMcL LSRN MAsh MGil SDix SEND SGbt SMrm SWvt WAvo
	(Candy Drops Series) CANDY DROPS RED ('Kerphyrouge'PBR)	GMcL
	- CANDY DROPS SALMON ORANGE ('Kerphysalm'PBR)	SRms
	capensis	CTri GMcL MHer SRms
	- 'Coccineus' **new**	EHeP
	'Golden Gate'	see *P. aequalis* 'Yellow Trumpet'
	Logan form	GBin
	'Passionate'PBR	NLar
§	× ***rectus*** 'African Queen' 🏆H5	CTri EBee EHyd ELan EPfP LRHS MGil MNHC MRav MSwo NBir NGdn SCob SDix SEND SPlb SWvt WAvo WHlf WKif XLum
	- 'Devil's Tears' 🏆H5	CBcs CPla GArf MBNS SCob SEND SWvt WPnP
	- 'Ivory Twist'	CKel MHtn NLar SPer
	- 'Jodie Southon'	LSou SDys WCot
	- 'Moonraker'	CAby CBcs CTri EBee ELan ELon EPfP GBin MAsh MGil MHer MRav NGdn NLar SCob SEND SMrm SNig SPer SPlb SRms WKif XLum
	- NEW SENSATION ('Blaphy'PBR)	GMcL MRav SRms SWvt
	- 'Rory'PBR	SRms
	- 'Salmon Leap' 🏆H5	CBcs CKel CTri EHyd ELan EPfP LRHS LSRN MGos MRav NLar NRHS SBut SCob SMrm SPlb SRms SWvt
	- (Somerford Funfair Series) SOMERFORD FUNFAIR APRICOT ('Yapapr')	SWvt
	- - SOMERFORD FUNFAIR CORAL ('Yapcor')	EGrI EHyd EPfP MAsh NLar SRkn SWvt
	- - SOMERFORD FUNFAIR CREAM ('Yapcre')	CBod EPfP LBar MBros SPoG SWvt
	- - SOMERFORD FUNFAIR ORANGE ('Yapor')	CPla EBou EPfP LBar MAsh SCob SRms SWvt
	- - SOMERFORD FUNFAIR WINE ('Yapwin')	CAby CBod CChe EGrI EHyd ELan EPfP LBar LRHS MAsh NRHS SCob SPoG SWvt
	- - SOMERFORD FUNFAIR YELLOW ('Yapyel')	EPfP MAsh SWvt
§	- 'Winchester Fanfare'	CSBt GMcL MGos MRav NLar SMrm SPer SWvt

- 'Winton Fanfare'	see *P.* × *rectus* 'Winchester Fanfare'
YELLOW SOVEREIGN ('Croyelsov'PBR) (Croftway Series)	LRHS

Phyla (*Verbenaceae*)

lanceolata	LLWG
§ ***nodiflora***	ECha MHer SLee SRms WJek XSen
- 'Alba'	SEND
§ - var. ***canescens***	CKel XLum

Phylica (*Rhamnaceae*)

arborea	LRHS
pubescens	CPbh

Phyllanthus (*Phyllanthaceae*)

fluitans new	LPfP

× *Phylliopsis* (*Ericaceae*)

'Coppelia' 🏆H5	EPot
hillieri 'Askival'	EPot GKev WThu
- 'Pinocchio'	EPot WThu
- 'Sugar Plum'	CCCN SWvt
'Mermaid'	GRum
'Puck'	EPot
'Sprite'	EPot

Phyllitis see *Asplenium*

Phyllocladus (*Podocarpaceae*)

trichomanoides	IDee
- var. ***alpinus***	CBcs
- - 'Blue Blades'	MGil SLim
- - 'Highland Lass'	MGil SLim
- - 'Highlander'	MGil SLim

Phyllodoce (*Ericaceae*)

aleutica	WThu
§ - subsp. ***glanduliflora***	EPot
§ - - 'Flora Slack'	WThu
- - white-flowered	see *P. aleutica* subsp. *glanduliflora* 'Flora Slack'
× ***alpina***	GRum
caerulea 🏆H7	GArf
- ***japonica***	see *P. nipponica*
- 'Murray Lyon'	GArf
- 'W.M. Buchanan's Peach Seedling'	GRum
empetriformis	GRum WThu
glanduliflora	see *P. aleutica* subsp. *glanduliflora*
× ***intermedia*** 'Drummondii'	GArf
- 'Fred Stoker'	GRum
§ ***nipponica***	WThu

× *Phyllosasa* (*Poaceae*)

tranquillans	MMuc MWht SEND
- 'Shiroshima'	CAbb CDTJ CDoC EPfP LPal LPar MBrN MMuc MWht SEND

Phyllostachys ✿ (*Poaceae*)

angusta	MWht
arcana 'Luteosulcata'	MMuc MWht
§ ***atrovaginata***	CBdn LPar MWht SGol
aurea 🏆H5	Widely available
- 'Albovariegata' (v)	EPfP MWht SPoG
- 'Flavescens Inversa'	LPal
- 'Holochrysa'	CDTJ CJun LPal LPar MWht NLar
- 'Koi'	CDTJ LPar MWht SGol
aureocaulis	see *P. aureosulcata* f. *aureocaulis*, *P. vivax* f. *aureocaulis*
aureosulcata	CAco EDir LPar
§ - f. ***aureocaulis***	CAbb CBcs CBdn CJun CKel CSBt EDir ELon EPfP GMcL LCro LOPS LPal LRHS LSRN MGos MSwo MWht NRHS SArc SBGi SCob SCoo SEWo SEdd SGol SGsty SPoG SWvt
- 'Lama Tempel'	CDTJ CJun
- f. ***spectabilis*** 🏆H5	Widely available
bambusoides 'Allgold'	see *P. bambusoides* 'Holochrysa'
- 'Castillonii' 🏆H5	EWes LEdu LPal LPar
- 'Castillonii Inversa'	LEdu MWht
§ - 'Holochrysa' 🏆H5	CDTJ LPal MMuc MWht NPlm SEND WPGP
- f. ***lacrima-deae***	CDTJ
- 'Marliacea'	CBdn
- 'Sulphurea'	see *P. bambusoides* 'Holochrysa'
- 'Tanakae'	CDTJ
bissetii 🏆H5	Widely available
congesta misapplied	see *P. atrovaginata*
decora	MMuc MWht
dulcis	CBdn EPfP LPal MWht SBGi
§ ***edulis***	CAgr SBGi SPlb
- 'Bicolor'	LPar
- f. ***pubescens***	see *P. edulis*
flexuosa	CBcs LPal MWht SBGi SGol
glauca	EPfP LPar MWht
- f. ***yunzhu***	MWht
heteroclada 'Solid Stem' misapplied	see *P. purpurata* 'Straight Stem'
heterocycla var. ***pubescens***	see *P. edulis*
humilis	CBdn LPal LPar MMuc MWht SEND
iridescens 🏆H5	MWht
kwangsiensis	MWht
mannii	MWht
nigra 🏆H5	Widely available
- 'Boryana'	CBdn CCVT CEnd EPfP MGos MMuc MWht NLar SBGi SEND SWvt
- 'Hale'	MWht
- f. ***henonis*** 🏆H5	CBdn MMuc MWht NLar SEND SGol WPGP
- 'Megurochiku'	MWht
- f. ***nigra***	SBGi
- f. ***punctata***	MAvo MMuc SEND
nuda	MWht
- f. ***localis***	MWht
parvifolia	MWht
praecox	MWht SBGi
propinqua	LPal MWht
§ ***purpurata*** 'Straight Stem'	MWht
rubromarginata	MWht
stimulosa	MWht
sulphurea 'Houzeau'	MMuc SEND
§ - f. ***viridis***	LPar
violascens	CAgr MWht
viridiglaucescens	CAgr CDTJ LPar MMuc MWht SBGi SEND WCot
viridis	see *P. sulphurea* f. *viridis*
vivax	EPfP MWht NLar SBGi
§ - f. ***aureocaulis*** 🏆H5	CAbb CAgr CCVT CDoC CEnd CKel EPfP LEdu LMaj LPal LPar LSRN MGos MMuc MWht NLar SCob SEND SGol SWeb WPGP
- - 'Huangwenzhu'	CDTJ MWht
* - 'Katrin'	LEdu

Phymatosorus (*Polypodiaceae*)

diversifolius	see *Microsorum diversifolium*

Phymosia (*Malvaceae*)

§ ***umbellata***	LEdu LRHS WFib WOld WPGP XSte
- 'Blood of Pan' new	WPGP

Phyodina see *Callisia*

Physalis (Solanaceae)

	alkekengi ♀H7	CTri EPfP NBir SBls SMrm SWvt WMal WWke
	- var. ***franchetii***	CBcs CMac CSBt CTri CWal EBee ECha EHyd ELan EPfP GQue LCro LOPS LRHS MNrw NBir NBro NRHS SCob SPer SPoG SRms WFar WOld
	- - dwarf	NLar
	- - 'Gigantea'	CAby CBod CRos EHyd LBar LRHS NLar NRHS SPlb WFar
	- - 'Gnome'	see *P. alkekengi* var. *franchetii* 'Zwerg'
	- - 'Variegata' (v)	EWes LEdu SEND WPGP
§	- - 'Zwerg'	CDor EBou EDAr GMcL LSun SEdi WPnP
	- 'Halloween King'	EBee NLar
	- 'Halloween Queen'	NLar
	edulis	see *P. peruviana*
§	***peruviana*** (F)	CBod CCCN CSpe SPlb SVic

Physaria (Brassicaceae)

	alpina	GEdr SPlb

Physocarpus (Rosaceae)

	capitatus 'Tilden Park'	EBee
	opulifolius	MTrO
	- ALL BLACK ('Minall2'PBR)	EHed LRHS MPkF NCth SRHi WCot XSte
	- ALL RED ('Minalco')	NEoE NLar WLov WNPC
	- AMBER JUBILEE ('Jefam'PBR)	CDoC EHed LCro LOPS LPar LRHS MMrt NEoE SCob SRms XSte
	- 'Amber Queen' **new**	SRHi
	- ANGEL GOLD ('Minange'PBR)	CCCN CDoC CRos EHyd LRHS MAsh NRHS SPoG XSte
	- 'Anny's Gold'PBR	EBee NLar SRms WFar
	- 'Brown Sugar'	CBod WLov WNPC
	- 'Burning Embers'	CBod CDoC EGrI SRms
	- 'Chameleon'	CKel NEoE SCob SGol
	- COPPERTINA	see *P. opulifolius* DIABLE D'OR
	- 'Dart's Gold' ♀H7	Widely available
§	- DIABLE D'OR ('Mindia'PBR)	CBar CBod CCCN CDoC CEnd CKel CRos EBee EHyd EPfP LCro LOPS LRHS LSRN MAsh MBlu MGos NOra NRHS SGbt SGol WLov
	- 'Diabolo'PBR ♀H7	Widely available
§	- 'Donna May'PBR	CBod CKel LPar LSou MAsh MGos NEoE SCob WFar
	- FIREBRAND ('Hyfbrand')	NEoE
§	- LADY IN RED ('Tuilad'PBR) ♀H7	Widely available
	- LITTLE ANGEL ('Hoogi016'PBR)	CBod CKel CWGN EMil EPfP LCro LOPS MThu SCob SPoG
	- LITTLE DEVIL	see *P. opulifolius* 'Donna May'
	- LITTLE JOKER ('Hoogi021')	NLar
§	- 'Luteus'	EHeP WFar
	- MIDNIGHT ('Jonight'PBR)	CBcs CBod EHed MAsh MGil NLar SCob SGBe WFar WHlf XSte
	- 'Red Baron'	GMcL MACG WFar
	- RUBY SPICE	see *P. opulifolius* LADY IN RED
	- SUMMER MOON ('Tuimon')	CBcs NEoE NLar SGol WFar
	- SUMMER WINE ('Seward'PBR)	CDoC CKel EBee ELan EPfP EWTr EWes MAsh NLar WSpi
	- TINY WINE ('Smpotw'PBR)	EPfP LPar MAsh NLar SGsty
	ribesifolius 'Aureus'	see *P. opulifolius* 'Luteus'

Physochlaina (Solanaceae)

	orientalis	CSpe GEdr WCot

Physoplexis (Campanulaceae)

§	***comosa*** ♀H6	EPot

Physostegia (Lamiaceae)

I	'Aquatica'	LLWG
§	***virginiana***	CSBt CTri CWal GMaP LPfP LShi MBel SBut SRms WJam
	- 'Alba'	CMac CSBt EBee ECha ELon EMor EPfP GAbr GMaP LEdu MBel NBir SPlb WCav XLum
	- 'Autumn Carnival'PBR	LBar NLar
§	- 'Crown of Snow'	CWal EHyd EPfP GMcL LRHS MHer MRav NRHS SBea SMrm SPeP SWvt WJam WTre
	- 'Crystal Peak White'	LBar LRHS MACG NLar WFar
	- 'Grandiflora'	WTre
	- 'Miss Manners'	EBee ECtt EHyd LBar LRHS MCot MPie NBPC NGdn NLar NRHS SCoo SGbt
	- 'Pink Manners'	NLar
	- 'Red Beauty'	NLar
	- 'Rose Crown'	CWal SPer
	- 'Rose Queen'	EMor LBar SBls WFar
	- 'Rosea'	EHyd EPfP GJos LRHS NChi NCou NGdn NRHS SHar SPoG SWvt WFar WHrl WWke
	- SCHNEEKRONE	see *P. virginiana* 'Crown of Snow'
	- 'Snow Queen'	see *P. virginiana* 'Summer Snow'
§	- var. ***speciosa*** 'Bouquet Rose'	CRos EBee ECha EPfP EShb EWoo LBar LEdu LRHS LSto MHol MPie MRav NBir NLar NRHS SGbt SPeP SPer SRms SWvt WCAu WFar XLum
	- - ROSE BOUQUET	see *P. virginiana* var. *speciosa* 'Bouquet Rose'
	- - 'Variegata' (v)	CMac EBee ECtt ELan EPfP GLog LBar LRHS MRav NBPC NBir NGdn NHol SBea SPeP SPer SPoG SRms WCAu WCot WFar XLum
§	- 'Summer Snow' ♀H7	CBcs CCBP ELan EPfP EWTr EWoo LRHS MHol NGBl NLar SBls SPer SRms WCAu WCot
	- 'Summer Spire'	LRHS
	- 'Vivid' ♀H7	Widely available
	- 'Wassenhove'	SMrm

Phyteuma (Campanulaceae)

	balbisii	see *P. cordatum*
	betonicifolium	GJos
	comosum	see *Physoplexis comosa*
	confusum	GJos
§	***cordatum***	GJos
	halleri	see *P. ovatum*
	hemisphaericum	NSla
	humile	GArf WThu
	nigrum	GEdr NBid SBrt WBor
	orbiculare	GEdr GJos
§	***ovatum***	SPlb
	scheuchzeri	CAby CBor EBee EBou ECha EDAr ELan EPfP GEdr GJos MMrt SPad SRms WIce XLum
	spicatum	GJos NBro
	- subsp. ***coeruleum***	GJos

Phytolacca (Phytolaccaceae)

	acinosa	EWld WHil
	- HWJ 647	WCru
§	***americana***	CAby CBcs CCBP EBee EGrI ELan EPfP ESwi GPoy LShi MBNS MHer MPie NChi SPlb SRms
	- B&SWJ 8817A	WCru
	- B&SWJ 12743	ESwi
	- 'Silberstein' (v)	EBee LDai
	bogotensis B&SWJ 14221	ESwi WCru
	clavigera	see *P. polyandra*
	decandra	see *P. americana*

dioica	SPlb
esculenta	LEdu SEND
icosandra Purpurascens Group	EBtc WFar
- - B&SWJ 11251	WCru WFar
japonica B&SWJ 3005	NBid WCru
- B&SWJ 3522	WCru
§ ***polyandra***	EGrl GGro NBid NBro SRms

Picea ✿ (*Pinaceae*)

§ ***abies***	CAco CBTr CBod CCVT CKel CLnd CMac CPer CTri EDir EHeP EPfP GBin GMcL GQue IPap LBuc LMaj NBwr NWea SCoo SPoG WHtc WMou WTSh
- 'Aarburgh'	CAco
- 'Acrocona' ♀H7	CAco LPar NLar
- 'Archer'	CKen
- 'Archer's Pygmy'	NLar
- 'Argenteospica' (v)	CAco
- 'Aurea'	CAco
- 'Aurea Magnifica'	CAco
- 'Bago'	CKen
- 'Bally'	CKen
- 'Capitata'	CKen LRHS MGil
- 'Chub' **new**	CAco
- 'Cincinnata' **new**	CAco
- 'Clanbrassiliana' ♀H7	ELan EPfP NWad
- 'Cobra'	CAco
- Compacta Group	CAco
I - 'Congesta'	CKen
- 'Cranstonii'	CAco
- 'Crippsii'	CKen
I - 'Cruenta'	CAco CKen
- 'Cupressina'	CAco CKen
- 'Dáblice'	CAco
- 'Diedorfiana'	CAco
- 'Diffusa'	CKen MGil
- 'Dumpy'	CKen NHol
- 'Dundaga'	CAco
- 'Echiniformis'	CAco CKen
- 'Elegantissima'	CAco
- 'Emsland'	LRHS
- 'Excelsa'	see *P. abies*
- 'Fahndrich'	CKen
- 'Finedonensis'	CAco
- 'Formanek'	CAco
- 'Four Winds'	CKen
- 'Frohburg'	CAco CKen NLar
- 'Glimra'	CAco
- 'Globosa'	CAco
- 'Gold Drift'	CAco NLar
- 'Gold Finch'	NLar
- 'Gold Nugget' **new**	CKen
- 'Gregoryana'	CKen
- 'Hasin'	SAko
- 'Heartland Gem'	CKen
- 'Horace Wilson'	CKen
- 'Humilis'	CKen
- 'Humphrey's Gem'	CKen
- 'Inversa' ♀H7	CAco CKen MBlu NLar SLim
- 'J.W. Daisy's White'	see *P. glauca* var. *albertiana* 'J.W. Daisy's White'
- 'Jana'	CKen NLar
- 'Jermyns Broom No. 1'	CKen
- 'Kámon'	CAco
- 'Kral'	CKen
- 'Krenek'	NLar
- 'Lemon Drop'	NLar
- 'Lithuanian Snake'	CAco
- 'Little Gem' ♀H7	CKen ELan EPfP EPot LRHS MAsh MGil MGos NHol NLar NWad NWea SCoo
- 'Little Santa'	LRHS
- 'Loreley'	CKen
- 'Lubecensis' **new**	CAco
- 'Lucky Strike'	CAco NLar
- 'Marcel'	CKen
- 'Maxwellii'	CAco
- 'Mini Kalous'	CKen
- 'Nana Compacta'	CKen MAsh SCoo
- 'Nidiformis' ♀H7	CAco CKen CMac CMen GMcL LPar LRHS MGos SRms
- 'Norrköping'	CKen
- 'Ohlendorffii'	CAco CKen GMcL
- 'Pachyphylla'	CAco CKen
- 'Parviformis'	CAco
- 'Pendula'	CAco
- 'Perry's Gold'	LRHS
- 'Pumila'	WCFE
- 'Pumila Nigra'	CAco
- 'Pusch'	CAco CKen NLar
- 'Pygmaea'	CKen LPar
- 'Reflexa'	CAco
- 'Remontii'	NLar
- 'Repens'	CAco
- 'Ripley Broom'	CKen
- 'Roseospicata'	CAco NLar
- 'Rothenhausii'	CAco NLar
- 'Rubra Spicata'	CAco
- 'Rydal' ♀H7	CAco CBcs CKen ELan MAsh NLar
- 'Sargentii'	MGil
- 'Spring Fire'	CKen
- 'Tompa'	CAco
- 'Tuka Puka'	CAco
- 'Typner'	CKen NLar
- 'Vermont Gold'	CKen LRHS NLar
- 'Virgata'	CAco
I - 'Virgata Aurea'	CAco
I - 'Virgata Glauca' **new**	CAco
- 'Wagner'	NLar
- 'Weeping Blue'	CAco
- 'Wichtel'	CKen
- WILL'S DWARF	see *P. abies* 'Wills Zwerg'
§ - 'Wills Zwerg'	CAco ELan LRHS NLar
- 'Ylivska Snake'	CAco
alcoquiana	CAco
§ - var. ***alcoquiana***	CAco SLim
asperata	CAco
- glaucous-leaved	CAco
bicolor	see *P. alcoquiana* var. *alcoquiana*
brachytyla	CAco
- var. ***brachytyla***	CAco
breweriana ♀H6	CAco EPfP GKin IPap LEdu MBlu MGos NLar NWea SLim SSta WCFE WTSh
- 'Emerald Midget'	CAco
- 'Frühlingsgold'	CKen NLar
- 'Kohout's Dwarf'	CKen NLar
chihuahuana	CAco
crassifolia	CAco SPtp
engelmannii	CAco LMaj NWea
- 'Blue Magoo'	CAco
- 'Bush's Lace'	CAco
- 'Cienega'	CKen
- 'Compact'	SLim
- subsp. ***engelmannii***	CKen
- Glauca Group	CAco LMaj
- 'Jasper'	CAco CKen
- 'Lace'	NLar
- subsp. ***mexicana***	CAco
- - 'Pervana'	CAco
- 'Snake' **new**	NLar
- 'Tomschke' **new**	NLar
farreri	CAco WPGP
glauca	CAco NBwr SWvt

	- var. ***albertiana***	CAco
	- - ALBERTA BLUE ('Haal'^{PBR})	CAco CKen LRHS
	- - 'Alberta Globe' ♀^{H7}	CAco CBrac ELan EPot GKin GMcL LCro LRHS MAsh MGos NHol NWad SCoo SPoG
	- - 'Conica' ♀^{H7}	Widely available
	- - 'Gnome'	CKen
§	- - 'J.W. Daisy's White' ♀^{H7}	CBcs CKen ELan EPfP GKin LCro LRHS LSta MGos NHol NLar NOrn NWea SCoo SLim SMad SPoG SSha
	- - 'Laurin' ♀^{H7}	CAco CKen NWad SCoo SLim
	- - 'Lilliput'	CKen EPfP NWad NWea SPoG
	- - 'Piccolo'	CKen NWad
	- - 'Sander's Blue'	CAco CKen EPfP GKin LRHS MAsh SAko SCoo SPoG SVic
	- - 'Tiny'	CKen MGil NWad
	- 'Arneson's Blue Variegated' (v)	CKen
	- 'Baby'	NWea
	- 'Biesenthaler Frühling'	CKen SLim
	- 'Blue Planet'	CKen
	- 'Cecilia' **new**	CAco
	- 'Cy's Wonder'	CKen
	- 'December'^{PBR}	CAco
	- 'Dendroforma Gold'	CKen
	- 'Eagle Rock'	NLar
	- 'Echiniformis' ♀^{H7}	CAco CKen GMcL LRHS MGil
	- 'Goldilocks'	CAco CKen
	- 'Jalako Gold'	CAco NLar NWea
I	- 'Julian Potts Monstrosa'	NLar
	- 'Milford'	CKen
§	- 'Nana'	CKen
	- 'Pendula'	CAco CKen
	- PERFECTA ('Hb07'^{PBR})	CAco
	- 'Pixie'	CKen
	- 'Pixie Dust'	CKen
	- 'Rainbow's End' (v)	CAco CKen LRHS SCoo
	- 'Speedy' **new**	CAco
	- 'Spring Surprise'	CKen NLar
	- 'Sun on the Sky'^{PBR} **new**	CAco
	- 'Super Green' **new**	CAco
	- 'Zuckerhut'	CAco LRHS LSta
	glehnii	CAco
	- 'Shimezusei'	CKen
	jezoensis	CAco CKen CMen NWea
	- subsp. ***hondoensis***	CMen
	- 'Landis'	CAco
	- 'Marianbad'	CKen
	- 'Pygmy'	CKen
	- 'Yatsabusa'	CKen CMen
	koraiensis	CAco EDir
	kosteri 'Glauca'	see *P. pungens* (Glauca Group) 'Koster'
	koyamae	CAco
	- 'Bedgebury Cascade'	CAco SLim
	likiangensis	CAco EPfP
	- var. ***balfouriana***	see *P. likiangensis* var. *rubescens*
§	- var. ***rubescens***	CAco SLim
	× ***lutzii***	LPar
	mariana	CAco MAsh
	- 'Austria Broom'	CKen
	- 'Bill Archer'	NWad
	- 'Blue Teardrop'	CKen
	- 'Fastigiata'	CKen
	- 'Nana' ♀^{H7}	CAco CKen CMac CMen EPfP GMcL MGos MMuc NHol NWad NWea SCoo SLim SPoG SSha
I	- 'Pygmaea'	CKen NWad SLim
	× ***mariorika*** 'Machala'	CAco
	meyeri	EPfP SSha
	morrisonicola	CKen
	obovata	CAco
I	- 'Glauca'	CAco
	omorika ♀^{H7}	CAco CBcs CBrac CCVT CMCN CPer EDir EHeP EPfP EWTr EWhm IPap LBuc LIns LPar MMuc NWea SCob SEND WCFE WMou
	- 'Cinderella'	NLar
	- 'Frohnleiten'	CKen
	- 'Frondenberg'	CKen
	- 'Karel'	CAco CKel CKen LRHS SLim
	- 'Linda'	NLar
	- 'Minimax'	CKen
	- 'Nana' ♀^{H7}	CAco LPar SLim WCFE
	- 'Pendula' ♀^{H7}	CAco LRHS MBlu SSta
	- 'Pendula Bruns'	CAco MBlu NLar SAko SLim
	- 'Pévé Tijn'	NLar SLim
	- 'Pimoko'	CKen NLar SLim
	- 'Pygmy'	CKen
	- 'Schneverdingen'	CKen SAko
	- 'Tijn'	CKen SLim
	- 'Treblitsch'	CKen NLar SLim
	- 'Virgata'	CAco
	orientalis ♀^{H7}	CAco NWea
	- 'Aurea' (v) ♀^{H7}	CAco
	- 'Aureospicata'	CAco LPar LRHS MAsh MBlu SLim
	- 'Bergman's Gem'	CKen
	- 'Early Gold' (v)	CAco
	- 'Golden Start'	CAco SLim
	- 'Gowdy Gold'	NLar
	- 'Gracilis'	CAco
	- 'Horstmann'	CAco
	- 'Juwel'	CKen NLar
	- 'Kenwith'	CKen
	- 'Little Kya'	NLar
	- 'Mount Vernon'	CAco CKen
	- Nana Group	CAco GKin
	- 'Pévé Tiny Gold'	CKen NLar
	- 'Professor Langner'	CKen
	- 'Shadow's Broom'	CKen CMen
§	- 'Silver Seedling'	NLar
	- 'Skylands' ♀^{H7}	CAco MAsh NLar SLim
	- 'Sulphur Flush'	see *P. orientalis* 'Silver Seedling'
	- 'Tom Thumb'	CKen
	- 'Wittboldt'	CKen LRHS NLar
	pungens	CAco CCVT EWhm LMaj NWea
	- 'Anton'	NLar
	- 'Baby Blueeyes'	NLar
	- 'Białobok' **new**	CAco
	- 'Blaukissen'	CKen NLar
	- 'Blue Diamond'	CAco EPfP LPar LRHS SPoG
	- 'Blue Pearl'	CKen NLar
	- 'Blue Waters'	CKen
	- 'Brexit Blue' **new**	MDon
	- 'Donna's Rainbow'	NLar
	- 'Edith' ♀^{H7}	CAco CKen GMcL LRHS MDon NLar NOrn SCoo SGsty WMat
	- 'Erich Frahm'	CAco CCVT EDir GMcL MAsh MTrO NLar SCoo SPoG WMat
	- 'Fat Albert' ♀^{H7}	CAco CCVT EDir LMaj LPar LRHS LSta MAsh SCoo SGsty SPoG
	- 'Glauca Globosa'	see *P. pungens* (Glauca Group) 'Globosa'
	- Glauca Group	CAco CBrac CCVT EHeP EWTr IPap NWea SCoo SPoG SSha WMou WTSh
	- - 'Barabits' Blue'	CAco
	- - 'Bizon Blue'	CAco
	- - 'Blue Totem'	CAco
	- - 'Glauca Pendula'	CAco
	- - 'Glauca Procumbens'	CKen
§	- - 'Glauca Prostrata'	SLim
I	- - 'Globosa' ♀^{H7}	CAco CBcs CCVT CKen CSBt EDir GMcL LPar LRHS MAsh NHol NLar SCoo SGsty SLim SPoG SWeb

- - 'Hoopsii' ♀H7	CAco EPfP GKin GMcL LCro LMaj MAsh MGos NLar NOrn NWea SCoo SPoG SWvt WHlf WMat
- - 'Iseli Fastigiate'	CAco CCVT GKin GMcL LRHS LSta MAsh SCoo SLim SPoG
- - 'Khaibab'	CAco
§ - - 'Koster'	CAco EDir EPfP NWea SPoG
- - 'Misty Blue'	CAco
- - 'Oldenburg'	CAco NWea SLim
- - 'Thomsen'	CAco
- - 'Virgata'	CAco
- 'Globe'	CKen CMen
- 'Gloria'	CKen SLim
- 'Hermann Naue'	CKen
- 'Horizontalis Glauca'	CAco
- 'Iseli Foxtail'	CAco
- 'Koster Fastigiata'	GMcL LPar
- 'Koster Prostrate'	NBwr
- 'Maigold' (v)	CAco CKen NLar SLim
- 'Montgomery'	CKen
- 'Mrs Cesarini'	CKen
- 'Niemitz'	NLar
- 'Nimetz'	CKen
- 'Novák'	CAco
- 'Ökrös'	CAco
- 'Omega'	CAco
- 'Pali'	CAco
- 'Porcupine'	NLar
- 'Prostrata'	see *P. pungens* (Glauca Group) 'Glauca Prostrata'
- 'Royal Blue' **new**	CAco
- 'Saint Mary's Broom'	CKen
- 'Silvanus Conica'	CAco
- 'Super Blue Seedling' **new**	CAco
- 'The Blues'	CAco CKen NLar
- 'Thuem'	SCoo
- 'Waldbrunn'	CAco CKen
- 'Waterfall'	CAco
purpurea	EPfP
retroflexa	CAco
rubens	NWea
× ***saaghii***	CAco
schrenkiana	CAco CMCN
sitchensis	CAco CPer IPap MAsh NWea SSha WTSh
- 'Foxtail'	CAco
- 'Foxy Lady'	CAco
- 'Glenmasson' **new**	NLar
- 'Nana'	CAco NLar
- 'Papoose'	CAco EPfP GMcL SLim
- 'Pévé Wiesje'	NLar
- 'Silberzwerg'	CAco CKen SAko SLim
- 'Strypemonde'	CKen
- 'Tenas'	CAco CKen SLim SPoG
smithiana	CAco
I - 'Aurea'	CAco
- 'Sunray'	NLar SLim
torano	CAco
wilsonii	CAco CKen
'Wodan'	NLar

Picrasma (*Simaroubaceae*)

ailanthoides	see *P. quassioides*
§ ***quassioides***	CMCN EBee EPfP WJur WPGP

Picris (*Asteraceae*)

echioides	see *Helminthotheca echioides*

Picrorhiza (*Plantaginaceae*)

kurrooa	GPoy LEdu

Pieris (*Ericaceae*)

'Balls of Fire'	CMac
'Bert Chandler'	CBod CMac WSpi
'Brouwer's Beauty'	LRHS NLar SPoG
'Firecrest' ♀H5	SCob
'Flaming Silver' (v) ♀H5	Widely available
floribunda	CBrac
'Forest Flame' ♀H5	Widely available
formosa B&SWJ 2257	WCru
- var. ***forrestii***	CDoC NWea SCob XSte
- - 'Charles Michael'	CExl
- - 'Jermyns'	CMac MRav
- - 'Wakehurst' ♀H5	CBod CCCN CDoC CExl CMac EHyd EPfP GKin LMil LRHS MAsh MGos MRav NWea SAko SCob WSpi
HAVILA ('Mouwsvila') (v)	CCCN CMac MAsh SCob
japonica	CMac SavN
- 'Bonfire' ♀H5	CCCN CRos EHyd ELan EPfP GMcL ILea LCro LRHS MAsh MGos NLar SCob SGbt SGsty SPoG WHtc XSte
- 'Carnaval' (v) ♀H5	CCCN CDoC CKel CMac CRos CSBt CTsd CWnw EHyd ELan EPfP EShb GMcL LBuc LMil LRHS LSRN LSto MAsh MGos MPri NLar NRHS SCoo SPoG SWvt WFar
§ - 'Christmas Cheer'	CMac SCob
- 'Cupido'	MAsh SLim WFar
- 'Debutante' ♀H5	CDoC GKin GMcL MAsh MGos NBwr NLar SCob SCoo SGsty SWvt WFar
- 'Don'	see *P. japonica* 'Pygmaea'
- 'Dorothy Wyckoff'	CMCN MDon NLar SCob SGbt SSta
- 'Erik'	GKev SAko
- 'Flaming Star'	SGbt SWvt
- 'Flamingo'	CMac
- 'Hino Crimson'	SWeb
I - 'Katsura' PBR	CBcs CDoC CMac CRos EHyd ELan EPfP GKin LBuc LCro LMil LPar LRHS LSRN MAsh MBlu MGos NHol NLar NRHS SCoo SPer SPoG SWvt WFar
- 'Little Heath' (v)	Widely available
- 'Little Heath Green'	CBod CBrac CCCN CMac GKin LPar MGos MTin SCob SPer SPoG SWvt WFar XSte
- 'Minor'	GKev WFar WThu
- 'Mountain Fire' ♀H5	Widely available
- 'Passion' PBR	CBcs CBod CDoC CEnd CKel CRos CSBt EBee EGrl EHyd EPfP GMcL LCro LMil LOPS LRHS LSRN MAsh MMrt NLar NRHS SPer XSte
- 'Pink Delight' ♀H5	CDoC CRos LMil LRHS LSRN MAsh MGos MRav SCob SRms
- 'Prelude' ♀H5	CRos CSBt EHyd EPfP LMil LRHS MAsh SRHi WAbe
- 'Purity' ♀H5	CBcs CBod CCCN CMac MAsh MGos SArc SCob SWvt WFar
§ - 'Pygmaea'	EGrl GKev
- 'Ralto' PBR	CRos EHyd LCro LMil LOPS LRHS MAsh MGos MRav NRHS SCob SPoG XSte
- RED MILL ('Zebris')	CEnd SPer
- 'Sarabande' ♀H5	ILea MAsh SCob XSte
- 'Scarlett O'Hara'	CSBt
- Taiwanensis Group	CMac GKin NLar SRms WFar
- - 'Snowdrift'	LRHS
- 'Temple Bells'	CSBt
- 'Valley Rose'	CSBt GKin MAsh NLar
- 'Valley Valentine' ♀H5	CBcs CDoC CMac CRos EGrl EHyd EPfP GMcL LCro LMil LOPS LRHS LSRN MAsh MGos NHpl NLar SCob SCoo SPer SPoG SRHi SRkn SWvt WFar XSte
- 'Variegata' misapplied	see *P. japonica* 'White Rim'
- 'Variegata' ambig.	CBcs CBrac EHeP GMcL SPer

- 'Variegata' (Carrière) Bean (v)	CRos EHyd LRHS NRHS
- 'Wada's Pink'	see *P. japonica* 'Christmas Cheer'
- 'White Cascade'	SCob
- 'White Pearl'	CMac SCob
§ - 'White Rim' (v)	CMac EPfP MAsh SCob SPlb
- 'William Buchanan'	NWad WThu
- var. ***yakushimensis***	NLar
nana	WThu
'Tilford'	CMac

Pilea (*Urticaceae*)

angulata subsp. ***petiolaris*** PB 96-1074	GGro
cadierei ♀H1c	EShb
insolens	GGro
involucrata ♀H1a **new**	WFar
kiotensis PB 08-880	GGro
libanensis	EShb
matsudai 'Taiwan Silver'	GGro WPGP
peperomioides ♀H1c	CCBP CDoC ELan EShb LCro LOPS LWaG NHrt
plataniflora CMBTW 1485 **new**	GGro
- 'Glossy'	GGro
- 'Pelling'	GGro MHid SBrt
scripta PB 02-520	GGro
umbrosa PB 02522 **new**	GGro

Pileostegia (*Hydrangeaceae*)

viburnoides	Widely available
- B&SWJ 3565	WCru
- B&SWJ 3570 from Taiwan	WCru
- B&SWJ 7132	CKel SNig WCru
- from Taiwan	XSte

Pilgerodendron (*Cupressaceae*)

uviferum	CAco LRHS

Pilosella (*Asteraceae*)

§ ***aurantiaca***	CBor CWCL EBou ELan EPPr EPfP GJos IRos LCro LEdu LRHS LShi MBow MHer MNHC NBid NBir SPhx SRms WCot WHer WSFF WShi
§ - subsp. ***carpathicola***	MMuc SEND
§ ***officinarum***	NRya XSen
rubra	CSpe

Pilosocereus (*Cactaceae*)

glaucochrous **new**	EAri
gounellei **new**	NHrt
pachycladus **new**	EAri

Pilularia (*Marsileaceae*)

globulifera	CPud LPfP

Pimelea (*Thymelaeaceae*)

coarctata	see *P. prostrata*
drupacea	IDee
ferruginea	SVen
oreophila	GArf WAbe WThu
§ ***prostrata***	EPot EWes GEdr GRum

Pimpinella (*Apiaceae*)

anisum	CBod SPhx SVic
major	LEdu
- 'Rosea'	Widely available
saxifraga	CHab EBou NAts SPhx WSFF
- 'Rosea' **new**	NAts
siifolia	WHil
tripartita	ECha SPhx
- PAB 6112	LEdu

pineapple see *Ananas comosus*

pineapple guava see *Acca sellowiana*

Pinellia (*Araceae*)

cordata	LEdu WCot WCru XLum
pedatisecta	GKev LAma MRav WCot
peltata	GKev
pinnatisecta	see *P. tripartita*
ternata	EBee GEdr GKev NLar
§ ***tripartita***	CExl GKev
- 'Gold Dragon' **new**	GKev

Pinguicula (*Lentibulariaceae*)

grandiflora ♀H4	EWld NRya NWac WAbe
'Tina'	NWac
'Weser' ♀H1c	NWac

pinkcurrant see *Ribes rubrum* (P)

Pinus ✿ (*Pinaceae*)

albicaulis	CAco
- 'Falling Rock'	CAco
- 'Flinck'	CKen
- 'Lake Sabrina'	CAco
- 'Nana'	see *P. albicaulis* 'Noble's Dwarf'
- 'No 3'	CKen
§ - 'Noble's Dwarf'	CAco CKen
aristata ambig.	CAco EPfP
aristata Engelm.	CMCN
- 'Bashful'	CKen
- 'Cecilia'	CKen
- 'Elko' **new**	CAco
- 'Elko Run' **new**	CAco
- 'Kohout's Mini'	CKen
- 'Lemon Frost'	CAco
- 'Sherwood Compact'	CAco CKen MAsh SLim
- 'Silver Day'	CAco
- 'Silver Doll'	CAco
arizonica var. ***ornelasii***	CAco
armandi	CAco CMCN EPfP MGil NLar SArc SPtp
- 'Vanc Gold' **new**	CAco
attenuata	CAco
austriaca	see *P. nigra* subsp. *nigra*
ayacahuite	CAco CKen
- 'Maya'	CAco
balfouriana	CAco
- dwarf	CKen
'Bambino'	see *P.* 'Gaëlle Brégeon'
banksiana	CAco LPar
- 'Chippewa'	CKen
I - 'Compacta'	CKen
- 'Manomet'	CAco
- 'Neponset'	CKen
- 'Schoodic'	SLim
'Bayo'	CAco
bhutanica	CAco WPGP
- KR 10358	WPGP
'Brepo'	see *P.* 'Pierrick Bregéon'
brutia	CAco
- var. ***brutia***	CAco
- var. ***eldarica***	CAco
- var. ***pityusa***	CAco
bungeana	CAco CTsd EPfP MBlu MGil
- 'Diamant'	CKen
- 'June's Broom'	CKen
- 'Silver Ghost' **new**	CAco
- white bark	CAco
canariensis	CAco WPGP
cembra	CAgr EPfP LRHS MCoo WLea
- 'Aurea'	see *P. cembra* 'Aureovariegata'

	Name	Suppliers
§	- 'Aureovariegata' (v)	CAco
	- 'Barnhourie'	CKen
	- 'Blue Mound'	CKen
	- 'Compacta Glauca'	CAco
	- Glauca Group	CAco
	- 'Inverleith'	CKen
	- 'Jermyns'	CKen
	- 'King's Dwarf'	CKen
	- 'Ortler'	CKen
	- 'Stricta'	CAco CKen LRHS NLar
	- witches' broom	CKen
	cembroides	CAco
	- 'Fancy Nancy'	CKen
	- subsp. ***orizabensis***	CAco
	clausa	CAco
	contorta	CAco CBcs CPer GJos IPap SPlb
	- 'Anna'	CAco
	- 'Asher'	CAco CKen NLar
	- 'Chief Joseph' 🏆H6	CAco CKen MAsh NLar SLim
	- var. ***contorta***	CAco
	- 'Fordham's Dwarf Rug'	CKen
	- 'Frisian Gold'	CAco
	- var. ***latifolia***	CAco EBtc
	- var. ***murrayana***	CAco
	- 'Spaan's Dwarf'	CAco CKen NLar SLim
	- 'Taylor's Sunburst'	CAco CKen NLar
	coulteri	CAco EPfP WPGP
	densata	CAco
	densiflora	CAco EBtc SSha
	- 'Alice Verkade' 🏆H7	CAco LIns LPar MAsh SArc WFar
	- 'Aurea'	CAco
I	- 'Bedgebury Sport Broom'	CKen
	- 'Burke's Red Variegated' (v)	CAco
	- erect **new**	CAco
	- 'Glitzer's Weeping'	CAco
	- 'Golden Ghost'	CAco NLar
	- 'Haybud'	CAco
	- 'Heavy Bud' **new**	CAco
	- 'Jim Cross'	CKen
	- 'Kim'	CAco NLar
	- 'Low Glow'	CAco CKen LRHS NLar SCoo SLim SPoG
	- 'Oculus-draconis' (v)	CAco SLim
	- 'Pendula'	CAco CKen MBlu MGil SLim
	- 'Rainbow' (v) **new**	CAco
	- 'Rata'	CAco
	- 'Umbraculifera'	CAco MAsh
	× ***densithunbergii*** 'Beni-kujaku'	CAco CKen CMen
	- 'Jane Kluis' 🏆H7	CAco LPar SLim SPoG WLea
§	***devoniana***	CAco
	durangensis	CAco
	echinata	CAco
	edulis	CAco CMCN
	- 'Juno'	CKen
	elliottii	CAco
	- var. ***densa***	CKen
	engelmannii	CAco WPGP
	fenzeliana	CAco CKen
	flexilis	CAco
	- 'Blackfoot'	CAco
	- 'Cesarini Blue'	CAco NLar
	- 'Cow Creek'	NLar
	- 'Damfino'	CAco
	- 'Extra Blue'	CAco
	- 'Firmament'	SLim WMat
	- 'Glenmore Dwarf'	CKen
	- 'Lil Wolf'	NLar
	- 'Nana'	CKen
	- 'Navajo'	CAco
I	- 'Pygmaea'	CAco
	- var. ***reflexa***	CAco
	- 'Ririe'	CKen
	- 'Tarryall'	CKen
	- 'Tiny Temple'	CAco MGil
	- 'Vanderwolf's Pyramid'	CAco CCVT CWnw LPar MGos MTrO NLar SLim WLea WMat
	- WB No 1	CKen
	- WB No 2	CKen
	'Fulda'	CAco
§	'Gaëlle Brégeon'PBR	CAco CKen
	gerardiana	CAco
	glabra	CAco
	greggii	CAco EBtc
	griffithii McClell.	see *P. wallichiana*
	× ***hakkodensis***	CAco
	halepensis	CAco SEND
§	***heldreichii***	CAco EPfP LPar LRHS SLim WMat
	- 'Atze Saule'	CAco
	- 'Aureospicata'	CAco
	- 'Barabits' Compact'	CAco
	- 'Beran Conical'	CAco
§	- 'Biała Chmura' **new**	CAco
	- 'Compact Gem' 🏆H6	CAco CKen GMcL LRHS NLar SEWo SLim
	- 'Den Ouden' **new**	CAco
	- 'Dolce Dorme'	CAco CKen
	- 'Emerald Arrow'	CAco NLar
	- 'Green Bun'	CAco
	- 'Green Giant'	CAco NLar WLea
	- 'Green Pyramid'	WLea
	- 'Groen'	CKen
	- 'Grüne Lagune' **new**	CAco
	- 'Honorio Fastigiata' **new**	CAco
	- 'Indigo Eyes'	CAco
	- 'Irish Bell'	CAco CKen
	- var. ***leucodermis***	see *P. heldreichii*
	- 'Lindenhof' **new**	CAco
	- 'Little Dracula'	CAco LRHS NLar SCoo
	- 'Malink'	CAco CKen
	- 'Mint Truffle'	CAco
I	- 'Nana' **new**	CAco
	- 'Pirin No 3'	CAco SAko
	- 'Pygmy'	CKen
	- 'Satellit' 🏆H6	CAco CKen GMcL MAsh SLim
	- 'Schmidtii'	see *P. heldreichii* 'Smidtii'
§	- 'Smidtii' 🏆H6	CAco CKen CMen MAsh NLar NPoe SCoo SLim SPoG
	- WHITE CLOUD	see *P. heldreichii* 'Biala Chmura'
	- 'Zwerg Schneverdingen'	CKen SLim
	× ***holfordiana***	CAco EPfP WPGP
	hwangshanensis	CAco
	jeffreyi	CAco CMCN EBtc
	- 'Joppi'	CAco CKen LSta NLar SLim
	- 'Misty Lemon'	CAco
	- 'Paula' **new**	CAco
	kesiya	CAco
	koraiensis	CAco
	- 'Anna'	NLar
	- 'Baishan'	NLar
	- 'Bergman'	CKen NLar
	- 'Blue Ball'	CAco CKen NLar
	- 'China Boy'	NLar
	- 'Compacta Glauca'	CAco
	- 'Dragon Eye'	CKen SLim
	- 'Jack Corbit'	CAco CKen NLar WFar
	- 'Morris Blue' **new**	CAco
	- 'Shibamichi' (v)	CAco CKen
	- 'Silver Lining'	CAco
	- 'Silveray'	CAco CKen CWnw NLar
	- 'Silvergrey'	CKen
	- 'Spring Grove'	CKen NLar
	- 'Tong Hua'	NLar
	- 'Tsingtao'	NLar
	- 'Variegata' (v) **new**	CAco

- 'Verkade's Select' **new**	CAco
- 'Winton'	CAco CKen NLar
lambertiana	CAco
latteri	CAco
lawsonii	CAco
leiophylla	CAco
leucodermis	see *P. heldreichii*
longaeva	CAco
luchuensis	CAco
magnifica	see *P. devoniana*
'Marie Bregéon' PBR	CAco LRHS
massoniana	CAco WBor
maximartinezii	CAco
maximinoi	CAco WPGP
monophylla	CAco
- 'Oregon'	CAco
montezumae ambig.	CAco
montezumae Lamb.	CAco SArc WPGP
- NJM 09.016	WPGP
- 'Forde Abbey'	CAco
- glaucous-leaved, from Mexico	CAco
- 'Grahame Oakey Pendula'	CAco
- var. ***montezumae***	CAco
- 'Nymans'	CAco
- 'Sheffield Park'	CAco SLim
monticola	CAco
- 'Ammerland'	CAco
- 'Crawford'	NLar
- 'Ondulata'	CAco
- 'Pendula'	CAco CKen
- 'Pygmy'	see *P. monticola* 'Raraflora'
§ - 'Raraflora'	CKen
- 'Snow White' **new**	CAco
- 'Strobicola'	CAco EPfP
- 'Windsor Dwarf'	CKen
mugo	CAco CBcs CTsd EHeP EPfP GDam MAsh MGos MNHC NGrs SCob SGsty SSha SWeb WLea
- 'Agnieszka'	CAco
- 'Allgäu'	CAco CKen NLar
- 'Árpád'	NLar
- 'Benjamin'	CAco CKen CWnw LPar LSta WLea
- 'Big Tuna'	CAco
- 'Bisley Green'	NLar
- 'Boži Dar'	CAco
- 'Brownie'	CKen
- 'Carsten' ♀H7	CAco CKen EPfP GMcL LRHS MAsh NLar SCoo SJap SLim SPoG
- 'Columbo'	CAco CWnw
- 'Corley's Mat'	CKen LRHS NLar SLim
- 'Cristata Contorta'	CAco
- 'Dezember Gold'	SLim
- 'Elemér'	CAco
- 'Filigran'	CAco
- 'Fischleinboden'	CAco
- 'Flanders Belle'	SLim
- 'Frohlings Gold'	CAco
- 'Fructata'	CAco
- 'Gnom'	CAco EPfP GKin LRHS MAsh MGos SCoo SJap SLim
- 'Gold Star'	CAco NLar
- 'Golden Glow'	CAco LRHS NLar SLim SPoG
- 'Grüne Kugel'	CAco
- 'Heinis Triumph'	CAco
- 'Hesse'	GMcL SCoo
- 'Hoersholm'	CKen
- 'Hulk'	CKen
- 'Humpy' ♀H7	CAco CKen LPar LRHS MAsh SCoo SLim
- 'Ironsides'	CKen
- 'Jacobsen'	CAco CKen NLar SLim
- 'Jalubi'	CKen
- 'Janovsky'	CKen
- 'Kissen' ♀H7	CAco EPfP NHol NLar SLim
- KLOSTERGRUN	see *P. mugo* 'Klosterkötter'
§ - 'Klosterkötter'	CAco SCoo
- 'Kobold'	CAco LPar
- 'Krauskopf'	CAco CKen
- 'Laarheide'	CAco LRHS SPoG
- 'Laurin'	CAco CKen LPar
- 'Lemon'	CAco NLar
- 'Little Gold Star'	CKen
- 'March'	CAco CKen NLar
- 'Mini Mini'	CKen
- 'Mini Mops'	CKen SLim
- 'Minikin'	CKen
- 'Minima Kalous'	CAco
- 'Misty Lemon'	CAco
- 'Mitsch Mini'	CKen
- 'Mops' ♀H7	CKel CMen CWnw ELan EPfP GMcL IPap LPar LRHS MAsh MBlu MGos SCob SCoo SGsty SJap SLim SPoG
- 'Mops Gold'	CAco NLar
- 'Mops Midget'	CAco MAsh
- var. ***mughus***	see *P. mugo* subsp. *mugo*
§ - subsp. ***mugo***	CKel CSBt CWnw EHeP GMcL SCob WHtc
- - 'Milky Way'	CAco CKen
- 'Mumpitz'	CAco CKen LRHS WLea
- 'Northern Lights'	CKen
- 'Ophir' ♀H7	CAco CBcs ELan EPfP LRHS MAsh MGos SCoo SLim SPoG WLea
- 'Pal Maleter' (v)	CAco SCoo SLim SPoG
- 'Pici'	CAco
- 'Picobello'	CAco LRHS MAsh NHol NLar SCoo SLim SPoG
- 'Piggelmee'	CKen NLar
- Pumilio Group	CAco ELan EPfP IPap LPar LRHS MGos MMuc NBwr SCob SEND SJap SPad SSha
- 'Rigi'	CAco NLar
- 'Rock Garden'	NLar
- var. ***rostrata***	see *P. mugo* subsp. *uncinata*
- subsp. ***rotundata*** 'Ježek'	CKen MAsh
- 'Sherwood Compact'	CAco LRHS SLim WLea
- 'Spaan'	CKen
- 'Starkl'	CAco
- 'Sunshine' (v)	CAco NLar
- 'Suzi'	CKen NLar
- 'Tuffet'	CAco CKen NHol SLim
- 'Uelzen'	CKen
§ - subsp. ***uncinata***	CAco IDee LIns LPal
- - 'Etschtal'	CKen
- - 'Grüne Welle'	CAco CKen NLar SLim
- - 'Heideperle'	CAco NLar
- - 'Kostelnicek'	CAco CKen NLar
- - 'Leuco-like'	CKen
- - 'Litomysl'	NLar
- - 'Offenpass'	CKen
- - 'Paradekissen'	CAco CKen NLar
- - 'Süsse Perle'	CKen
- 'Varella'	CAco LPal LPar LRHS LSta NLar SCoo SLim
- 'White Tip'	CKen
- 'Winter Gold'	CWnw EPfP LPal LPar LRHS MGos NHol
- 'Winter Sun'	CAco LRHS NLar
- 'Winzig'	CKen
- 'Yellow Marble'	CAco
- 'Yellow Tip' (v)	CAco NHol SLim
- 'Zundert'	CKen SPoG
- 'Zwergkugel'	CKen SAko
muricata	CAco EBtc
× ***murraybanksiana***	CAco

	nigra	CAco CBcs CLnd CMac CTri EHeP EPfP LPal MGos NLar SArc WHtc
	- var. ***austriaca***	see *P. nigra* subsp. *nigra*
	- 'Black Prince' ♀H7	CAco CKen SLim WMat
	- 'Bobo'	CAco CKen
	- 'Buda' **new**	CAco
	- var. ***calabrica***	see *P. nigra* subsp. *laricio*
	- 'Caperci's Golden Cream'	CAco
	- var. ***caramanica***	see *P. nigra* subsp. *pallasiana*
	- var. ***cebennensis***	see *P. nigra* subsp. *salzmannii*
	- 'Cebennensis Nana'	CKen
	- 'Cobra'	CAco
	- var. ***corsicana***	see *P. nigra* subsp. *laricio*
	- subsp. ***dalmatica***	CAco
*	- 'Fastigiata'	CAco
	- 'Frank'	CKen
	- 'Globosa'	CAco
	- 'Globosa Viridis'	LPar
	- 'Green Tower'	CAco CKel LPar LRHS NLar SLim
	- 'Helga'	CAco LPar
	- 'Hornibrookiana'	CAco CKen CWnw LPar NLar
	- 'Hubert'	CAco
	- 'Karaca Ball'	CAco
	- 'Keightley Broom'	SLim
	- 'Komet'	CAco NLar SAko SLim
§	- subsp. ***laricio***	CAco CCVT CMac EHeP MMuc SArc SCob SEND SLim WPGP
	- - 'Aurea'	CAco MBlu
	- - 'Bobby McGregor'	CKen
	- - 'Goldfinger'	NLar
	- - 'Wurstle'	CAco CKen LPar
	- subsp. ***maritima***	see *P. nigra* subsp. *laricio*
	- 'Molette'	CAco
	- 'Moseri'	CAco CKen
	- 'Nana'	CAco LPar LRHS
§	- subsp. ***nigra***	CAco CBrac CCVT CLnd CMac CPer EWTr GMcL IPap LIns LMaj LPar LRHS MMuc SCob SEND SEWo SGsty SSha WLea
	- - 'Birte'	CKen
	- - 'Bright Eyes'	MAsh
	- - 'Schovenhorst'	CKen
	- - 'Skyborn'	CKen
	- - 'Strypemonde'	CKen
	- - 'Yaffle Hill'	CKen
	- 'Obelisk'	CKen NLar
	- 'Ola'	CKen
	- 'Oregon Green'	CAco NLar
§	- subsp. ***pallasiana***	CAco
	- - 'Pyramidalis'	CAco CWnw
	- 'Pirin'	CAco
	- 'Richard'	CAco CKen LSta NLar SLim
	- 'Rondello'	CAco NLar
§	- subsp. ***salzmannii***	CAco
	- 'Smaragd'	CAco
	- 'Spielberg'	CAco LPar LRHS NLar
	- 'Wabito' **new**	CAco
	oocarpa	CAco
	palustris	CAco
	parviflora	CAco SPlb WLea
	- 'Aaba-jo'	CKen
	- 'Acto Goyo' **new**	NLar
	- 'Adcock's Dwarf' ♀H7	CAco CKen SLim
	- 'Al Fordham'	CAco CKen
	- 'Ama-no-gawa'	CAco
	- 'Aoi'	CAco CKen
	- 'Ara-kawa'	CKen CMen
	- 'Atco-goyo'	CKen
	- Azuma-goyo Group	CAco CKen CMen
I	- 'Baasch's Form'	CAco CKen LRHS MGil NLar
	- 'Beran'	SLim
	- 'Bergman'	CAco MAsh NLar SLim
	- 'Blue Angel'	CAco MBlu NLar
	- 'Blue Giant'	CAco MBlu WLea
	- 'Blue Lou'	CAco NLar
	- 'Bonnie Bergman' ♀H7	CAco CKen EPfP LRHS NHol NLar
	- 'Brevifolia'	CAco SEWo
	- 'Bunty'	CKen LRHS MGil NLar
	- 'Catherine Elizabeth'	CKen NLar
	- 'Chikusa Goten'	CAco
	- 'Cuddles'	CKen
	- 'Dai-ho'	CKen
	- 'Daisetsusan'	CKen
	- 'Daisy Sunset'	NLar
	- 'Dougal'	CKen
	- 'Fatsumo'	CAco
	- 'Frankenhof' **new**	CAco
	- 'Frick Estate'	LRHS NLar
	- 'Fukai' (v)	CAco CKen NHol SLim
	- 'Fukiju'	CKen
	- Fukushima-goyo Group	CKen CMen
	- 'Fuku-zu-mi'	CAco CKen
	- 'Fu-shiro'	CAco CKen
	- 'Gemstar'	CKen
	- 'Gin-sho-chuba'	CKen
	- Glauca Group	CAco LMaj LRHS MAsh MBlu
	- - 'Glauca' ♀H7	CAco GMcL
I	- - 'Glauca Nana'	CKen
	- 'Goykuri'	CAco CKen
	- 'Green Monkey'	CAco
	- 'Gyok-kan'	LRHS
	- 'Gyok-kasen'	CKen
	- 'Gyo-ko-haku'	CKen
	- 'Gyokusen Sämling'	CKen
	- 'Gyo-ku-sui'	CKen CMen
	- 'Hagaromo Seedling'	CAco CKen CMen NLar
	- 'Hakko'	CKen
	- 'Hatchichi'	CKen
	- 'Ha-tzumari'	CAco MGil NLar SLim
	- 'Himburgii' **new**	CAco
	- 'Hobbit'	CKen NLar
	- 'Ibo-can'	CKen CMen
	- 'Ichi-no-se'	CAco CKen
	- 'Iona'	CKen
	- 'Iri-fune'	CAco CKen
	- Ishizuchi-goyo Group	CKen
	- 'Jim's Mini Curls'	CKen NLar
	- 'Jyu-roko-ra-kan'	CAco
	- 'Ka-ho'	CKen
	- 'Kanrico'	CKen NLar
	- 'Kanzan'	CKen
	- 'Kenwith'	CAco NLar
	- 'Kin-po'	CAco CKen
	- 'Kiyomatsu'	CAco CKen
	- 'Kobe'	CAco CKen
	- 'Kokonoe'	CAco CKen CMen
	- 'Kokuho'	CAco CKen
	- 'Kusu-dama'	CKen
	- 'Little Hedgehog'	CKen
	- 'Lorraine'	CKen
	- 'Mai-tsuzumi'	CAco
	- 'Mano-jama'	CAco
	- 'Masami'	CKen
	- 'Meiko'	CKen
	- 'Michinoku'	CKen
	- 'Momo-yama'	CKen
	- 'Myo-jo'	CKen
	- Nasu-goyo Group	CKen
	- 'Negishi' ♀H7	CAco CKen CMen LIns LRHS LSta MAsh MTrO NLar SLim WMat
	- 'Nellie D.'	CAco
	- 'Ōgon-goyo'	CKen
	- 'Ōgon-janome'	CAco CKen MAsh SLim
	- 'Ooh la la'	CAco NLar
	- 'Ossorio Dwarf'	CKen
I	- var. ***pentaphylla*** 'Glauca'	NLar

	- 'Perido'	NLar
	- 'Primorge'	CKen
	- 'Regenhold Broom'	CKen
	- 'Richard Lee'	CKen
	- 'Ryo-ku-ho'	CKen
	- 'Ryu-ju'	CAco CKen
	- 'Sa-dai-jin'	CKen
	- 'San-bo'	CKen
§	- 'Saphir'	CAco CKen NLar
	- 'Schoon's Bonsai'	CAco CWnw LRHS NHol NLar
	- 'Setsugekka'	CKen SAko
	- 'Shika-shima'	CKen NLar
	- Shikoku-goyo Group	CAco
	- 'Shimada'	CKen
	- 'Shinbacu' **new**	CAco
	- Shiobara-goyo Group	CKen
	- 'Shiro-Janome' (v)	CKen
	- 'Shizukagoten'	CAco CKen SLim
	- 'Shu-re'	CKen NLar
	- 'Sieryoden'	CKen
	- 'Smout'	CKen
	- 'Tani-mano-uki'	CAco CKen NLar
	- 'Tayo-nishiki'	CAco
	- 'Tempelhof'	CAco LPar NOrn
	- 'Tenysu-kazu'	CAco CKen EPfP LRHS MAsh NLar SLim
	- 'Tokyo Dwarf'	CKen
	- 'Tribune'	EPfP NLar
	- 'Walker's Dwarf'	CKen
	- 'Watnong'	CKen
	- 'Zelkova'	CMen
	- 'Zui-sho'	CAco CKen
	patula 🏆H4	CAco CBcs CBod CCCN CMCN ECre EPfP IDee SArc SCoo SIvy SLim SPlb SPoG SSha WMat WPGP
	peuce	CAco EPfP GMcL NLar
	- 'Arnold Dwarf'	CAco CKen
	- 'Cesarini'	CKen NLar
	- 'Daniel'	CKen
	- 'Harlekin'	NLar
	- 'Thessaloniki Broom'	CKen
	- 'Wageningen'	CAco
	'Pichounet'	CAco
§	'Pierrick Bregéon'PBR	CAco LPar LRHS SArc
	pinaster	CAco CBcs CBod CPer EPfP IPap MMuc SEND SSha
	pinea 🏆H4	CAco CAgr CCVT EPfP IPap LPal LPar MGil MGos MMuc SArc SCob SCoo SEND SEWo SGsty SPlb SWeb WJur WPGP
	- 'Gold Crest' **new**	CAco
	- 'Queensway'	CKen
	ponderosa	CAco EPfP IPap MMuc NLar SSha
	- 'Mary Ann Heacock' **new**	CAco
	- 'Penaz'	CAco
	- var. ***ponderosa***	CAco
	- SDL2	NLar
	pseudostrobus	CAco
	- var. ***apulcensis***	CAco
	pumila	CAco
	- 'Blue Mops'	NLar
	- 'Blue Note'	NLar
	- 'Buchanan'	CKen
	- 'Draijer's Dwarf'	CAco NLar SLim
	- 'Dwarf Blue'	CAco NHol
	- 'Glauca' 🏆H7	CAco CKen MAsh
	- 'Globe'	CAco MAsh NLar SLim
	- 'Jeddeloh'	CAco CKen
	- 'Pinocchio'	CKen
	- 'Säntis'	CAco CKen MAsh NLar
	- 'Saphir'	see *P. parviflora* 'Saphir'
	pungens	CAco
	- 'Johnny's Goldstrike' **new**	CAco

	radiata	CAco CBcs CBod CBrac CCCN CCVT CCoa CDoC CMCN CMac CPer CSBt CSde ELan EPfP IPap LMaj LRHS MMuc NLar NOrn SArc SCoo SPtp SSha WHtc WMat
	- Aurea Group	SCoo SLim SPoG WMat
	- - 'Aurea' 🏆H5	CAco CKen MAsh
	- 'Bodnant'	CKen
	- 'Marshwood' (v)	CKen SLim
	resinosa	CAco
	- 'Don Smith'	CAco CKen
	- 'Joel's Broom'	CKen
	- 'Nana'	CAco LPar
	- 'Pillnitz'	CAco LRHS
	- 'Quinobequin'	CKen
	- 'State Trooper'	CAco
	rigida	CAco
	roxburghii	CAco EBtc
	sabineana	CAco CMCN
	× ***schwerinii***	CAco CKen
	- 'Wiethorst' 🏆H7	CAco CKen CWnw LRHS NLar SLim WMat
	serotina	CAco
	sibirica 'Blue Smoke'	CKen
	- 'Mariko'	CKen
	strobiformis	CAco
	- 'Coronado'	CKen
	- 'Fox Tail'	CAco
	- 'Loma Linda'	SLim
	strobus	CAco CBcs CCVT EPfP IPap LIns LPar MGos MMuc NLar SCob SEND
§	- 'Alba'	NLar SLim
	- 'Angel Falls'	CAco CKen NLar
	- 'Anna Fiele'	CAco CKen
	- 'Aurea'	CAco
	- 'Beal's Starry Night'	NLar
	- 'Bergman's Mini'	CAco CKen LRHS NLar SLim
	- 'Bergman's Pendula Broom'	CKen
I	- 'Bergman's Sport of Prostrata'	CKen
	- 'Beth'	CKen
	- 'Bloomer's Dark Globe'	CKen
	- 'Blue Shag' 🏆H7	CAco LPar LRHS NLar SCoo SLim
	- 'Bob's Wishes'	CAco
	- 'Brevifolia'	CAco CKen SArc
	- 'Cedar Ridge Broom'	SLim
	- 'Cesarini'	CAco CKen
	- var. ***chiapensis***	CAco
	- 'Connecticut Slate' **new**	NLar
	- 'Contorta'	CAco NLar
	- 'Densa'	CKen LRHS
	- 'Densa Hill'	CAco SLim
	- 'Diggy'	NLar
	- 'Ed's Broom'	CKen
	- 'Elf'	NLar
	- 'Elkins Dwarf'	CKen NLar
	- 'Fastigiata'	CAco CKen MBlu WLea
	- 'Fastigiata Devine'	NLar
	- 'Golden Candles'	CAco
	- 'Green Curls'	CKen NLar
	- 'Green Twist'	CAco CKen NLar SLim
	- 'Greg'	CKen LRHS NLar
	- 'Ground Hugger'	CAco NLar
	- 'Hershey'	CKen
	- 'Hillside Gem'	CKen NLar
	- 'Horsford'	CKen NLar SLim
	- 'Horsford Sister'	CKen NLar
	- 'Jamaican Curls'	CKen
	- 'Julian Pott'	CKen
	- 'Julian's Dwarf'	CKen
	- 'Krügers Lilliput'	CAco NLar SLim
	- 'Louie'	CAco CKen MAsh NLar SLim
	- 'Macopin'	CAco WFar

	- 'Mary Butler'	CKen NLar
	- 'Mary Sweeny'	NLar
	- 'Merrimack'	CAco CKen
	- 'Minima' ♀H7	CAco CKen LSRN MBlu NLar SLim SPoG
	- 'Minuta'	CAco CKen EPfP LRHS NLar SLim
	- 'Nana'	see *P. strobus* Nana Group
§	- Nana Group	SEWo
	- 'Niagara Falls'	CAco CKen NLar
	- 'Nivea'	see *P. strobus* 'Alba'
	- 'North Star Gold'	NLar
	- 'Northway Broom'	CKen
	- 'Ontario'	NLar
	- 'Pacific Sunrise'	NLar
	- 'Paul Waxman'	NLar
	- 'Pendula'	CAco CKen MBlu MGil
I	- 'Pendula Broom'	CKen
	- 'Pygmaea'	MGil NLar
	- 'Radiata'	CAco GMcL NLar
	- 'Reinshaus'	CAco
	- 'Sayville'	CKen
	- 'Sea Urchin'	CAco CKen EPfP MAsh SLim
	- 'Secrest'	CAco LRHS
	- 'Smokey Hollow'	NLar
	- 'Soft Touch'	SLim
	- 'Squiggles'	CAco LRHS NLar
	- 'Stowe Pillar'	CAco NLar SLim
	- 'Tiny Kurls'	CAco CKen LCro LRHS MAsh MGos MTrO NLar SLim
	- 'Torulosa'	CAco MBlu
	- 'Uncatena'	CKen
	- 'Verkade's Broom'	CKen
	- 'White Mountain'	CAco MBlu MGil NLar
	sylvestris	Widely available
	- from the Casadéen Massif, Auvergne	CAco
	- 'Abergeldie'	CKen
	- 'Andorra'	CKen
	- 'Anny's Wintersun'	NLar
	- Aurea Group	CKen LRHS MBlu NLar SLim WMat
	- - 'Aurea' ♀H7	CAco MAsh
	- 'Avondene'	CKen
	- 'Beuvronensis' ♀H7	CAco CMen LPar MGil NLar SLim WHtc
	- 'Bialogon'	CAco
	- 'Brentmoor Blonde'	CAco
	- 'Buchanan's Gold'	CKen
	- 'Candlelight'	CAco
	- 'Chantry Blue'	CAco CCVT EPfP GMcL LPar LRHS MAsh MGos NLar SCoo SLim SPoG WMat
	- 'Clumber Blue'	CKen
	- 'Dereham'	CKen
	- 'Doone Valley'	CAco CKen
	- 'Edwin Hillier'	SLim WMat WPGP
	- Fastigiata Group	CAco CEnd CKen CLnd SCoo SLim WHtc
	- 'Filip's Silver Surprise'	CAco
	- 'Frensham' ♀H7	CAco CKen MAsh
	- 'Frosty' **new**	CAco
I	- 'Glauca' **new**	CAco
	- 'Globosa'	CAco
	- 'Gold Coin' ♀H7	CAco CKen SPoG
	- 'Gold Medal'	CAco CKen LRHS
	- 'Grand Rapids'	CKen
	- 'Green Penguin'	CAco NLar
	- 'Greg's Variegated' (v)	CAco
	- 'Gwydyr Castle'	CKen
	- var. ***hamata***	CAco
	- 'Hillside Creeper'	CAco CKen SLim
	- 'Humble Pie'	CKen
	- 'Irchester Park'	CKen
	- 'Isaszeg'	CAco
	- 'Jeremy'	CKen
	- 'John Boy'	CKen
	- 'Kelpie'	CAco SLim
	- 'Kenwith'	CKen
	- 'Lodge Hill'	CMen MAsh SLim
	- 'Longmoor'	CKen
	- 'Martham'	CKen
	- 'Martulka' **new**	CAco
	- 'Meffen Gold'	CAco NLar
	- 'Mitsch Weeping'	CKen
	- var. ***mongolica***	CAco
	- 'Mosaic'	CAco
	- 'Nana' misapplied	see *P. sylvestris* 'Watereri'
	- Nana Group	CAco SWeb WLea
I	- - 'Nana Arguta' **new**	CAco
	- - 'Nana Compacta'	CMen
§	- 'Nisbet's Gem'	CKen
	- 'Norska' **new**	CAco
	- 'Ødegård'	CAco
	- 'Padworth'	CMen
	- 'Piskowitz'	CKen
	- 'Pixie'	CKen MAsh
I	- 'Prostrata'	SLim
	- 'Pulham'	CKen
I	- 'Repandens' **new**	CAco
	- 'Repens'	CAco CKen
	- 'Rita'	CAco
	- 'Saint George'	CKen
	- 'Sandringham'	CAco NLar
	- 'Saxatilis'	CAco CKen CMen NLar
	- subsp. ***scotica***	CAco NTrD
	- 'Scott's Dwarf'	see *P. sylvestris* 'Nisbet's Gem'
	- 'Sé'	CAco
	- 'Sentinel'	CKen
	- 'Skjak I'	CKen
	- 'Skjak II'	CKen SLim
	- 'Spaan's Slow Column'	CKen SLim
	- 'Tabuliformis'	CAco
	- 'Tage'	CKen
	- 'Tanya'	CKen
	- 'Tilhead'	CKen
	- 'Treasure'	CKen MAsh
	- 'Trefrew Quarry'	CKen
	- 'Trollguld'	CAco CKen
	- 'Vinney Ridge' **new**	CKen
§	- 'Watereri'	CAco CCVT CWnw GMcL LMaj LPar SCoo SLim
	- 'Westonbirt'	CKen CMen MAsh
	- 'Wintergold'	CAco
	- 'Wittichenau'	CKen
	- 'Xavery'	CAco NLar
	tabuliformis	CAco SLim
	- 'Jiuzhaigou Valley'	CAco
	- var. ***mukdensis***	CAco
	- 'Shenyang'	CAco NLar
	taeda	CAco
	taiwanensis	CAco
	- var. ***taiwanensis***	CAco
	tecunumanii	CAco SLim
	teocote	CAco
	thunbergii	CAco CBod CMen MMuc SEND SSha
	- 'Akame'	CKen CMen
	- 'Akame Yatsabusa'	CMen
	- 'Aocha-matsu' (v)	CKen
	- 'Arakawa-sho'	CKen CMen
	- 'Banshosho'	CAco CKen CMen NLar SLim
	- 'Compacta'	CKen CMen
	- var. ***corticosa*** 'Fuji'	CMen
	- - 'Iihara'	CMen
	- 'Dainagon'	CKen CMen
	- 'Frosty Patches' (v) **new**	CAco
	- 'Hayabusa'	CMen

- 'Iwai' CMen
- 'Janome' (v) CMen
- 'Katsuga' CMen
- 'Kotobuki' CAco CKen CMen NLar
- 'Koyosho' CMen
- 'Kyokko' CKen CMen
- 'Kyushu' CKen CMen
- 'Maijima' CAco
- 'Mikawa' CMen MBlu
- 'Miyajuna' CKen CMen
- 'Nishiki-ne' CKen
- 'Nishiki-tsusaka' CMen
- 'Ogi-matsu' CKen
- 'Ōgon' CAco CMen NLar SLim
- 'Porky' CKen

§ - 'Sayonara' ♀H7 CAco CMen MAsh SLim
- 'Senryu' CKen CMen
- 'Shinsho' CKen CMen
- 'Shio-guro' CKen CMen
- 'Suchiro' CAco
- 'Suchiro Yatabusa' CKen CMen
- 'Sunsho' CKen CMen
- 'Taihei' CMen

I - 'Thunderhead' ♀H7 CAco CKen NLar SLim
- 'Torafu' CAco
- witches' broom CKen
- 'Yatsubusa' see *P. thunbergii* 'Sayonara'
- 'Ye-i-kan' CKen
- 'Yoshimura' CMen
- 'Yumaki' CAco CKen

torreyana CAco CBcs
uncinata see *P. mugo* subsp. *uncinata*
virginiana 'Driscoll' NLar
- 'Wate's Golden' CKen

§ ***wallichiana*** ♀H6 Widely available
- 'Densa Hill' CAco LMaj LRHS
- 'Frosty' CAco CKen
- 'Glauca' CAco
- 'Kenwith Cascade' CKen
- 'Nana' ♀H6 CAco CKen LRHS MBlu MGil NLar SCoo SLim
- 'Umbraculifera' CWnw
- 'Winter Light' CAco NLar
- 'Zebrina' (v) CAco LRHS MBlu NHol

yunnanensis CAco WPGP
- var. ***yunnanensis*** SLim

Piper (*Piperaceae*)

auritum GPoy LEdu
betle GPoy
excelsum see *Macropiper excelsum*
heydei B&SWJ 10445 WCru

Piptanthus (*Fabaceae*)

forrestii see *P. nepalensis*
laburnifolius see *P. nepalensis*

§ ***nepalensis*** CBcs CSpe EBee EHed EHyd EPfP IDee LAlb LRHS MGil MGos MMrt NBid NLar SBrt SPer SRms WAvo WJur

aff. ***nepalensis*** SWvt

Pistacia (*Anacardiaceae*)

chinensis CBcs CMCN EBee EPfP IDee XSen
lentiscus CBcs CCCN CKel SEND SVen WJur WPGP XSen
terebinthus WJur XSen
- NJM 11.004 WPGP
vera EBee

Pistia (*Araceae*)

stratiotes LCro LLWG LOPS LPfP NPer SCoo SVic

Pitavia (*Rutaceae*)

punctata IArd

Pitcairnia (*Bromeliaceae*)

bergii CHll
heterophylla WCot
pungens WCot
punicea WCot
ringens WCot

Pittosporum (*Pittosporaceae*)

adaphniphylloides CBcs
anomalum CCCN CTrC CTsd GBin SEle SIvy
'Arundel Green' (f) ♀H4 CDoC CRos EHyd ELon EPfP LRHS MAsh MGos NGrs NRHS SCob SLim SPer SWvt
bicolor CTsd WPGP
'Bicton Silver' (m/v) CCCN
brevicalyx **new** WPGP
buchananii SVen
'Collaig Silver' EHyd EPfP LRHS MAsh MHed NRHS SLim SWvt
crassifolium CBcs CCCN CCoa CSde CTsd IDee SPlb
- 'Variegatum' (v) CBcs CCCN CCoa CKel MGil SEdd WAvo
'Crinkles' (f) SVen
dallii CCCN SPlb
daphniphylloides EBee IDee SArc WPGP
- B&SWJ 6789 WCru
- CWJ 12404 WCru
- RWJ 9913 WCru
eugenioides CCht CMCN CSde ELan ELon SEND
- 'Platinum' (v) CCCN
- 'Variegatum' (v) ♀H3 CBcs CCCN CCoa CDoC CKel CMac EBee EHyd EPfP LRHS MGos MPri NLar NRHS SAko SNig SSha SVen WAvo WHlf WHtc
'Garnettii' (v) ♀H3 Widely available
glabratum EBee WPGP
- var. ***neriifolium*** B&SWJ 11685 WCru
heterophyllum CKel EGrI EPfP EWes LRHS MHtn MMrt SEND SMad
- 'La Blanca' (v) EHed
- variegated (v) CCCN CKel EBee EHyd EPfP LRHS
illicioides WPGP
var. ***angustifolium***
- - B&SWJ 14560 WCru
- - RWJ 9846 WCru
- var. ***illicioides*** B&SWJ 6712 WCru
- - PAB 9004 LEdu WPGP
× ***intermedium*** SWvt
- 'Craxten' (f) CCCN
'Nanum Variegatum' see *P. tobira* 'Variegatum'
napaulense WCru
oblongilimbum DJHV 06137 WCru
omeiense EWes
- VdL 80626 WPGP
parvilimbum WPGP
patulum WPGP
phillyreoides CTsd
ralphii CCCN CTsd
- 'Green Globe' CBod
- 'Variegatum' (v) CCCN WPGP
'Saundersii' (v) ELon SCoo
tenuifolium Widely available
- 'Abbotsbury Gold' (f/v) Widely available
- 'Atropurpureum' CBcs ELan SRHi WHtc
- 'Bannow Bay' **new** CBod NLar SPad

- 'Brockhill Compact'	CCCN LRHS SAko SWvt
- 'County Park'	CBrac CCCN SRms
- 'County Park Dwarf'	MAsh NGrs
- 'County Park Green'	ELon
- 'Cratus'	ELan LSRN SArc SEdd
- 'Elizabeth' (m/v)	Widely available
- EMERALD DOME ('Minpitto'PBR)	SGsty
- 'Emerald Star'	MSwo
- 'French Lace'	CCCN CCoa CDoC CSde ELan GMcL NLar SCob WFar WHtc
- 'Gloria Robinson'	see *P. tenuifolium* 'Rotundifolium'
- 'Godsmark Green' **new**	NLar
- 'Gold Star'	Widely available
- 'Golden Ball'	CCCN CDoC CKel ELan LRHS MAsh MPri SGsty
- 'Golden King'	CBrac CCCN CKel CMac CSBt EPfP LRHS MAsh MGos NRHS SLim SRms WHtc
- 'Golf Ball'PBR	Widely available
- 'Green Elf'	XSte
- 'Green Thumb'	CCCN CMac EBee EPfP
- 'Irene Paterson' (m/v) 🏆H4	Widely available
- 'Irish Luck' **new**	CBod
- 'James Stirling'	CCCN
- 'John Flanagan'	see *P. tenuifolium* 'Margaret Turnbull'
- 'Limelight' (v)	CBcs CBod CBrac CCCN CKel CSBt CWal EBee EPfP LRHS LSRN SPoG SSha
- 'Loxhill Gold'	CCCN CCoa EPfP NLar SGol SGsty
§ - 'Margaret Turnbull' (v)	CTrC EWes MGos NLar SGsty
- 'Marjory Channon' (v)	CKel EHyd EPfP LRHS NRHS
- 'Moonlight' (v)	MRav
- 'Mountain Green'	CMac
- 'Nutty's Leprechaun'	CBod CCCN CTrC SSta
- 'Oliver Twist'	CTrC EHyd EPfP LRHS MAsh NRHS SCoo SSta
- 'Petite Plum' **new**	NLar WCot
- 'Pompom'	CCCN EHyd ELan LRHS LSRN MGos NBwr NRHS
- 'Purpureum' (m)	CBod CBrac CCCN CDoC CMac CSBt CTri EHyd ELon GBin LRHS LSRN MAsh MGil NRHS SCob SEND SNig SPer SPoG SRms SSha WAvo WCot WFar
§ - 'Rotundifolium' (v) **new**	CWal
- 'Silver Ball' (v)	CBcs CBod CDoC CKel CWnw ELan EPfP LRHS LSRN MAsh MMrt MSwo NGrs SGsty SPer XSte
* - 'Silver Dollar'	NBwr
- 'Silver Magic' (v)	CBcs CBod GMcL SEle SRkn SSha
- 'Silver Queen' (f/v) 🏆H4	Widely available
- 'Silver Sheen' (m)	CBcs CBod CKel CMac CWnw EBee EHyd LRHS NRHS SCob SWvt
- 'Stevens Island'	CCoa CDoC CTrC LRHS
- 'Tandara Gold' (v)	CBcs CBod CCCN CCoa CDoC CKel CMac CSBt CTrC CWnw EHyd ELan ELon EPfP GMcL LCro LRHS MAsh MGil MGos MSwo NRHS SCoo SGBe SRms SSha WAvo WHtc
- 'Tiki' (m)	CCCN
- 'Tom Thumb' 🏆H4	Widely available
- 'Tresederi' (f/m)	CCCN
- 'Variegatum' (m/v)	CBcs CBod CKel CSBt CWnw EBee EHyd ELon EPfP GMcL LCro LOPS LPar LRHS LSRN MGos MHed MSwo NRHS SArc SCob SEND SGbt SGsty SLim SPer SSha SWeb SWvt WFar
- 'Victoria' (v)	CBcs CCCN EBee LSRN SEdd SPer WFar XSte
- 'Warnham Gold' (m) 🏆H4	CBcs CBrac CCCN CDoC CKel CMac CRos EBee EHyd ELan EPfP LRHS MAsh MGos NLar NRHS SCob SEdd SLim SPoG SRms SVen
- 'Wendle Channon' (m/v)	CCCN CMac EPfP GMcL LRHS
- 'Wrinkled Blue'	CBcs CBod CBrac CDoC CKel CRos EBee EHyd EPfP LRHS MAsh MRav MSwo NRHS SPoG SWvt XSte
tobira 🏆H3	Widely available
* - 'Nanum'	CBcs CCCN CCoa CKel CMac CSde CWnw EGrl EHyd ELan EPfP ETod LCro LOPS LPal LPar LRHS LSRN MGos SCob SGsty SHor SPer SPoG SWeb XSen
- 'Tall 'n' Tough'	SMad
§ - 'Variegatum' (v) 🏆H2	CBcs CCCN CCoa CKel CMac CSde EHyd ELan EPfP LRHS LSRN MGos SArc SCob SEND SPer SPoG
- 'West Acre Gold'	CKel LRHS
'Trim's Hedger'	CBod ELan LSto SSta
truncatum	CCCN CExl XSen
undulatum	WAvo WJur WLov
viridiflorum	EShb

Plagianthus (*Malvaceae*)

betulinus	see *P. regius*
lyallii	see *Hoheria lyallii*
§ ***regius***	CBcs

Plagiorhegma see *Jeffersonia*

Planera (*Ulmaceae*)

aquatica	IDee

Plantago (*Plantaginaceae*)

coronopus	CAgr GGro WFar WKor
holosteum	GKev
lanceolata	CAgr CHab NMir SPhx WSFF
major	GPoy SPhx WSFF
- 'Atropurpurea'	see *P. major* 'Rubrifolia'
- 'Bowles's Variety'	see *P. major* 'Rosularis'
- 'Frills'	GGro NPoe
- 'Purple Perversion'	CSpe GGro
- 'Rosenstolz'	CTtf NChi
§ - 'Rosularis'	CSpe CTtf GGro LEdu NBro NPoe SRms WFar WHer
§ - 'Rubrifolia'	CSpe EShb GGro LDai NBid NPoe SRms WFar XLum
- 'Variegata' (v)	GGro
maritima	SSut
media	CHab MHer NMir WOut
nivalis	GEdr
rosea	see *P. major* 'Rosularis'

Platanthera (*Orchidaceae*)

bifolia	NLAp
chlorantha	NLAp

Platanus ✿ (*Platanaceae*)

× ***acerifolia***	see *P.* × *hispanica*
§ × ***hispanica*** 🏆H6	CAco CBTr CCVT CDoC CLnd CMCN EHeP ELan EPfP IPap LIns LMaj LPar MGos MMuc NBwr NRog NWea SArc SCob SEND SEWo SPer WHtc WMat WMou WTSh
- 'Alphen's Globe'	LPar
- 'Malburg'	LMaj
- 'Pyramidalis'	IPap LMaj
orientalis	CAco CCVT CMCN EBee EPfP ESwi IPap WPGP
- PAB 346	LEdu
§ - f. ***digitata*** 🏆H6	CCVT CLnd CMCN EHeP EPfP WMou
- var. ***insularis***	WPGP

	– 'Laciniata'	see *P. orientalis* f. *digitata*
	– 'Mirkovec'	IArd

Platycarya (*Juglandaceae*)

	strobilacea	SPtp WJur

Platycerium (*Polypodiaceae*)

	sp.	LWaG
	alcicorne misapplied	see *P. bifurcatum*
§	***bifurcatum*** ♀H1b	CCCN CDoC LCro LWaG NCft NHrt SPlb
	grande hort.	see *P. superbum*
§	***superbum*** ♀H1a	CCCN EShb NCft

Platycladus (*Cupressaceae*)

§	***orientalis***	CAco LEdu MAsh
§	– 'Aurea Nana' ♀H7	CBod CBrac CMac CSBt EPfP GMcL LBee LCro LPar LRHS LSta MAsh MGos SCoo SGsty SLim SPoG SSha
	– 'Autumn Glow'	CKen
	– 'Conspicua'	CKen CSBt
	– 'Elegantissima'	NLar
	– 'Franky Boy' ♀H7	SPoG
	– 'Golden Pygmy'	CKen MAsh
	– 'Kenwith'	CKen
	– 'Little Susie'	LRHS
	– 'Meldensis'	CTri
	– 'Miller's Gold'	see *P. orientalis* 'Aurea Nana'
	– 'Minima Glauca'	CKen
I	– 'Pyramidalis Aurea'	LBee SCoo
	– 'Rosedalis'	CSBt EPfP LBee MAsh SCoo SLim
	– 'Sanderi'	WCFE
	– 'Shirley Chilcott'	MAsh
	– 'Southport'	LBee LRHS
	– 'Summer Cream'	CKen

Platycodon (*Campanulaceae*)

	grandiflorus ♀H5	CTri ECha EPfP GKev MHoo SRms
	– W&O 7195	GGro
	– 'Albus'	EPfP GKev SPer SWvt
	– (Astra Series) 'Astra Blue'	CRos EHyd EPfP LRHS NRHS SPoG
	– – 'Astra Pink'	CRos LRHS SPoG
	– – 'Astra White'	CRos EPfP SPoG
	– 'Fuji Blue'	SBls SPeP WHoo XLum
	– 'Fuji Pink'	GKev MRav SPeP SPer SWvt WHoo XLum
	– 'Hakone'	MRav
	– 'Hakone Blue'	CPla
	– 'Hakone Double Blue' (d)	SRms
	– 'Hakone White'	GGro LSun MRav
	– 'Mariesii' ♀H5	CAby CSBt EBee EPfP MRav NBir SPer SPlb SRms SWvt WSHC
	– MOTHER OF PEARL	see *P. grandiflorus* 'Perlmutterschale'
§	– 'Perlmutterschale'	MRav
	– pink-flowered	GKev WHil WSHC
	– 'Sentimental Blue'	XLum
	– 'Shell Pink'	see *P. grandiflorus* 'Perlmutterschale'
	– 'Willy'	XLum
	– 'Zwerg'	CSpe

Platycrater (*Hydrangeaceae*)

	arguta	EBee EBtc EWld WCru WPGP
	– B&SWJ 6266	WCru

Plecostachys (*Asteraceae*)

§	***serpyllifolia***	LSou

Plectranthus ✿ (*Lamiaceae*)

	ambiguus 'Nico'	CBct SDix
	amboinicus	CCBP MNHC WJek
	argentatus ♀H1c	CBct CDTJ CSpe MCot SEND SMHy SRkn WKif WOld
	– 'Hill House' (v)	CHll EShb MPie
	– 'Silver Shield'	EShb MCot MPie WFar
	australis misapplied	see *P. verticillatus*
	behrii	see *P. fruticosus*
	caninus	CRos SPoG
	ciliatus	CPbh CWal EShb SRkn WFar
	– 'Easy Gold' (v) ♀H1c	MPie WDib
	– 'Nico'	CKel
	– 'Sasha' (v)	CCCN CHll ECtt EShb MPie
	coleoides 'Variegatus'	see *P. madagascariensis* 'Variegated Mintleaf'
	Cuban oregano	ENfk
	'Dzoukou Choc'	SBrt
	ernstii	WCot WFar
	– blue-flowered	WCot
	'Franklin's Olive'	CWal
§	***fruticosus***	CPbh
	– 'James' ♀H2	CWCL WKif
I	***hadiensis*** 'Variegata' (v)	CWal
	madagascariensis	EShb
	– 'Lynne' (v)	WDib
§	– 'Variegated Mintleaf' (v) ♀H1c	MNHC SRms
	MONA LAVENDER ('Plepalila'PBR) ♀H1b	CCht CPla MHol WKif WWFP
	neochilus	CCBP CSpe
§	***oertendahlii*** ♀H1c	CBct CPbh WDib
	ornatus	CBct
	saccatus	WKif
	subsp. ***pondoensis***	
	Swedish ivy	see *P. oertendahlii*, *P. verticillatus*
	'Velvet Elvis'PBR	CBct WHlf
§	***verticillatus***	EPri EShb WFar
	zuluensis	CKel CPbh EAri EPri SDix SRkn WBor WOld

Pleioblastus (*Poaceae*)

§	***argenteostriatus*** f. ***pumilus***	GMaP MWht NLar NWad SCob SPlb
	auricomus	see *P. viridistriatus*
	– 'Vagans'	see *Sasaella ramosa*
	chino f. ***elegantissimus***	CBcs EPfP EShb MMuc SEND
	– var. ***hisauchii***	MWht
	fortunei	see *P. variegatus* 'Fortunei'
	'Gauntlettii'	see *P. argenteostriatus* f. *pumilus*
	glaber 'Albostriatus'	see *Sasaella masamuneana* 'Albostriata'
	humilis var. ***pumilus***	see *P. argenteostriatus* f. *pumilus*
	kongosanensis 'Aureostriatus' (v)	MWht
	linearis	EShb MWht
§	***pygmaeus***	CTri ELan GMaP GMcL MBrN NBwr SCob SGol SPer SRms
§	– 'Distichus'	NBwr
§	– 'Mirrezuzume'	CExl
*	– var. ***pygmaeus*** 'Mini'	MMuc WCot
§	***simonii***	CAgr CRos EHyd LRHS MMuc MWht NRHS SEND SPoG
	– 'Variegatus' (v)	CBcs CRos EHyd LRHS NRHS SPer SPoG
§	***variegatus*** (v) ♀H5	CBcs CBod ELan EPfP GMaP MBrN MWht SCob SDix SPlb SRms SWvt WFar
§	– 'Fortunei' (v)	GMcL MMuc SEND SGol
	– 'Tsuboii' (v)	CAbb CDTJ GMcL MBrN NPlm SGol
§	***viridistriatus*** ♀H5	CKel ECha ELon EPfP GMaP GMcL LRHS MMuc MRav MWht NWsh SCob SDix SEND SGol SPer SRms WFar
	– f. ***variegatus*** (v)	SWvt

Pleione (*Orchidaceae*)

	Alishan gx 'Mother's Day'	GEdr

Asama gx 'Red Grouse'	GEdr
Askia gx	GEdr
aurita	GEdr GKev LAma SDir
Berapi gx 'Purple Sandpiper'	LEdu WPGP
Brigadoon gx 'Stonechat'	LEdu WPGP
Britannia gx 'Doreen'	GEdr LEdu WPGP
§ ***bulbocodioides***	GEdr GKev
- 'Ginzanko' new	GKev
- 'New Forest'	GEdr
§ - 'Yunnan'	GEdr GKev
Burnsall gx	GEdr
chunii	GEdr
Eiger gx	GEdr
Erebus gx 'Redpoll'	GEdr
formosana ♀H3	EPot GKev LAma LCro LEdu LOPS MAvo MHer NHpl SDeJ SDir WFar WPGP
- Alba Group	GKev WFar
- - 'Claire'	LEdu WPGP
- - 'Snow Bunting'	LEdu WPGP
- 'Blush of Dawn'	NHpl
- 'Snow White'	LEdu WPGP
forrestii	EPot LAma NHpl SDir
Gerry Mundey gx	GEdr
§ ***grandiflora***	GKev LAma
Hekla gx 'Locking Stumps'	GEdr
- 'Partridge'	GEdr
- 'Partridge' × **Zeus Weinstein gx**	GEdr
humilis orange-red-flowered	GKev
Irazu gx 'Cheryl'	GEdr
Jorullo gx 'Long-tailed Tit'	GEdr
limprichtii ♀H2	GKev
Myojin gx	GEdr
Orinoco gx 'Gemini'	GEdr
Orizaba gx	GEdr
pinkepankii	see *P. grandiflora*
Piton gx	EPot
pogonioides (Rolfe) Rolfe	see *P. bulbocodioides*
Rakata gx 'Blackbird'	MHer
- 'Locking Stumps'	GEdr
- 'Shot Silk'	GEdr
- 'Skylark'	LEdu WPGP
'Rossini'	GEdr GKev LAma SDir
Shantung gx	NHpl
- 'Muriel Harberd' ♀H2	GEdr
Sorea gx	GEdr
Soufrière gx	GEdr
Stromboli gx 'Fireball'	EPot LEdu WPGP
- 'Robin'	GEdr
Tolima gx 'Moorhen'	LEdu WPGP
Tongariro gx	CBor EPot GEdr GKev LAma LCro LEdu LOPS LRHS MHer MNrw WPGP
'Verdi'	GEdr GKev LAma
Versailles gx	NHpl
- 'Bucklebury'	GEdr LEdu WPGP
- 'Muriel Turner'	GEdr
Vesuvius gx	GEdr
- 'Tawny Owl'	GEdr
'Vivaldi'	LAma
Volcanello gx 'Honey Buzzard'	GEdr
yunnanensis misapplied	see *P. bulbocodioides* 'Yunnan'
yunnanensis ambig.	GEdr LAma SDir

Pleiospilos (*Aizoaceae*)

bolusii ♀H2	EAri
nelii ♀H2	EAri

Pleomele see *Dracaena*

Pleurospermum (*Apiaceae*)

benthamii B&SWJ 2988	WCru
brunonis	GKev
camtschaticum B&SWJ 12627	WCru

plum see *Prunus domestica*

Plumbago (*Plumbaginaceae*)

§ ***auriculata*** ♀H2	CBcs CCCN CHll CSBt CWCL EAri ELan EPfP EShb LRHS MGil MRav SEND SPer SPoG SRms WAvo WFib
- f. ***alba*** ♀H2	CBcs CCCN CHll CRHN ELan EShb IDee SEND WFib
- 'Crystal Waters'	CCCN CHll EShb
- dark blue-flowered	CRHN WFib
- (Escapade Series) 'Escapade Blue'	CWGN EShb SPre
- - 'Escapade White'	EShb
capensis	see *P. auriculata*
larpentiae	see *Ceratostigma plumbaginoides*

Plumeria (*Apocynaceae*)

sp.	EAri SPre
'Divine'	CCCN
pudica new	EAri
rubra ♀H1b	CCCN WSFF
- HAWAIIAN OPAL PINK ('Php2016'PBR) new	LCro
'Thumbelina'	CCCN

Poa (*Poaceae*)

alpina	XLum
chaixii	EPPr
cita	SBls SPlb
glauca 'Blue Hills'	LPla
labillardierei	CKno CWCL EBee ECha EHyd ELan ELon EPPr EPfP EShb LRHS SEND XLum
pratensis	CHab

Podalyria (*Fabaceae*)

calyptrata	SPlb
sericea	SPlb

Podanthus (*Asteraceae*)

ovatifolius	SVen

Podocarpus ✿ (*Podocarpaceae*)

acutifolius	CBcs
andinus	see *Prumnopitys andina*
'Autumn Shades' (m)	NLar
'Blaze' (f)	LEdu MMuc
chilinus	see *P. salignus*
'Chocolate Box' (f)	ELan LRHS MAsh NLar SLim
'County Park Fire'PBR (f) ♀H6	CBcs EPfP LRHS MAsh MGos NHol NLar SCoo SLim SRms SWvt WFar
dacrydioides	see *Dacrycarpus dacrydioides*
elatus new	WJur
elongatus	CTrC
- 'Blue Chip'	CBcs
'Flame' (m)	GKev NFav NLar SLim
'Guardsman'	LRHS SLim
henkelii	CBcs CTrC
laetus 'Roro' (m)	CBcs
lawrencei 'Blue Gem' (f)	CAco CBod CJun GKev LRHS MAsh MMuc NFav SCoo SLim WFar
- 'Purple King'	NLar
- 'Red Kiss' new	CAco
- 'Red Tip'	CAco CBod GKev SCoo SPad SSha

	macrophyllus	CAco IDee SArc WJur WPGP
	- (m)	CMCN
	'Maori Prince' (m)	NFav
	matudae	WPGP
	nivalis	CBcs CTrC CWal NGKo SRms SSha WThu
	- 'Cover Girl' (f)	CWal
	- 'Jack's Pass' (m)	LRHS
	- 'Kilworth Cream' (m/v) ♀H6	CBcs LCro LRHS NFav NHol SCoo SLim SWvt WCot
	- 'Livingstone' (f)	CBcs
	- 'Otari' (m)	MAsh
	- 'Ruapehu' (m)	CBcs MGil
	'Red Embers' (f)	CBcs LCro LRHS SCoo SLim
§	***salignus*** ♀H4	CBcs CExl EPfP IDee LRHS MGil SArc SLim WPGP WPav WThu
	'Spring Sunshine' (f)	CBcs NLar
	totara	CBrP CTrC LEdu
	- 'Albany Gold'	CTrC LRHS
	- 'Aureus'	MMuc
	- 'Pendulus'	LRHS MGil SMad WFar
	'Young Rusty' (f)	CBcs EPfP LRHS MAsh SLim WFar

Podophyllum (*Berberidaceae*)

	aurantiocaule	CExl GGGa GKev
	- subsp. ***aurantiocaule***	GEdr
§	***delavayi***	CDTJ CExl EBlo EMor WCot WSHC
	difforme	LEdu
	- 'Hunan'	WFar
	emodi	see *Sinopodophyllum hexandrum* var. *emodi*
	- var. ***chinense***	see *Sinopodophyllum hexandrum* var. *chinense*
	guangxiensis	WFar
	hexandrum	see *Sinopodophyllum hexandrum*
	'Kaleidoscope' (v)	CBcs CBct CMiW CWCL EBee ECtt ELan EMor GBin LEdu MPnt NHpl NLar WCot WFar WPGP WSHC
	peltatum	CBct CBro CMiW CTtf CWCL EBee EGrI EMor EPfP EWld GBin GGro GKev GMcL GPoy ILea LAma LEdu MACG MBel NLar NSti SPtp WCru WHlf WPGP WPnP
	pleianthum ♀H4	CMiW GEdr LEdu WCot WCru WPGP
	- B&SWJ 282 from Taiwan	WCru
	- var. ***album***	GEdr
	- short	WCru
	veitchii	see *P. delavayi*
	versipelle	LEdu MACG WCru WSHC
	- 'Spotty Dotty'PBR (v) ♀H4	Widely available

Podranea (*Bignoniaceae*)

	brycei	SPlb
§	***ricasoliana*** ♀H1c	EShb SPoG WBor

Pogonatherum (*Poaceae*)

§	***paniceum***	EShb
	saccharoideum	see *P. paniceum*

Pogonia (*Orchidaceae*)

	sp.	NDav
	ophioglossoides	GArf NLAp

Pogostemon (*Lamiaceae*)

§	***cablin***	GPoy
	patchouly	see *P. cablin*

Polaskia (*Cactaceae*)

	chichipe new	EAri NPlm

Polemonium ✿ (*Polemoniaceae*)

	ambervicsii	see *P. pauciflorum* subsp. *hinckleyi*
	'Apricot Beauty'	see *P. carneum* 'Apricot Delight'
§	***archibaldiae*** ♀H5	NBir SRms
	'Blue Pearl'	CGBo EHyd EPfP GJos GMcL LBar LRHS MBel NBro NGdn NLar SPer WFar WSpi
§	***boreale***	CPla EPot GJos NPol SWvt
	- 'Heavenly Habit'	EHyd EMor GJos
	brandegeei misapplied	see *P. pauciflorum*
§	***brandegeei*** Greene	GJos GKev
	- subsp. ***mellitum***	see *P. brandegeei* Greene
§	***caeruleum***	CBod CTri ECha ELan ENfk EPfP GKev GMaP GPoy LCro LOPS LRHS MBow MHer MNHC NAts NBro NGrd NLar NPol NRHS SPer SPlb SPoG SRms SWvt WBrk WCAu WSpi
	- subsp. ***amygdalinum***	see *P. occidentale*
	- - 'Album'	see *P. caeruleum* subsp. *caeruleum* f. *album*
	- 'Bambino Blue'	EPfP MPri SRms SWvt
	- BRISE D'ANJOU ('Blanjou'PBR) (v)	CMac CRos ECtt EHyd ELan EPfP EWes GMcL LRHS MAsh MBel MHol MHoo MPri NBir NRHS SCob SPeP SPer SPoG SWvt
	- subsp. ***caeruleum***	GKev
§	- - f. ***album***	CRos CWCL EBee ECha EHyd ELan EPfP EWoo GKev GMcL GQue LBar LRHS LSto MBel MHer MHoo MRav NBro NRHS SCob SGbt SPer SPoG SRms WBrk WCAu WSpi
	- - - 'White Pearl'	CBod
	- 'Days of Thunder'	EBee
I	- f. ***dissectum***	NPol
	- 'Filigree Skies'	NGdn
§	- subsp. ***himalayanum***	EPot
	- - CC 7325	GGro
	- 'Humile'	see *P.* 'Northern Lights'
	- 'Snow and Sapphires' (v)	CWGN MPnt NPer SWvt
	- 'Southern Skies'	NPol
	- subsp. ***vulgare***	NPol
	- white-flowered	GJos
	carneum	CElw CTri EAJP ECha EHyd EWTr LBar NPol
§	- 'Apricot Delight'	CTtf EMor GJos GMaP LShi MNrw NGdn NPol NQui SBut SGbt SIvy SRms WSpi
	cashmerianum	see *P. caeruleum* subsp. *himalayanum*
	'Churchills'	NPol WSHC
	'Dawn Flight'	NPol
	'Eastbury Purple'	CElw NPol
	'Elworthy Amethyst'	CElw EBee NPol
	flavum	see *P. foliosissimum* var. *flavum*
	foliosissimum misapplied	see *P. archibaldiae*
	foliosissimum A. Gray	NPol
	- var. ***albiflorum***	see *P. foliosissimum* var. *alpinum*
§	- var. ***alpinum***	NPol
	- 'Bressingham'	SCoo
	- 'Cottage Cream'	LEdu NPol WFar
§	- var. ***flavum***	NPol
	- var. ***foliosissimum***	NPol WSpi
	- 'Scottish Garden'	NPol
	- 'White Spirit'	NPol
	'Glebe Cottage Lilac'	CDor NBir NPol
	'Glebe Cottage Violet'	NPol
	'Hannah Billcliffe'	LPla MBrN NChi NPol SWvt WFar
	'Heaven Scent'PBR	CRos EBee ECtt EHyd ELan EMor EPfP LBar LRHS LSou MBNS MPnt MPri NDov NLar NRHS SCoo SGBe SMDa SPad WCAu WCav WTor
§	'Hopleys'	MNrw NChi

	× ***jacobaea***	EPPr WCot
	'Katie Daley'	see *P.* 'Hopleys'
	kiushianum	GGro
	'Lambrook Mauve'	Widely available
	'Mary Mottram'	NPol
	mellitum	see *P. brandegeei* Greene
	'North Tyne'	NChi NPol
§	'Northern Lights' ♀H7	Widely available
	'Norwell Mauve'	MNrw NPol WFar
§	***occidentale***	NPol
§	***pauciflorum***	CTtf GJos NBir
§	- subsp. ***hinckleyi***	NPol
§	- subsp. ***pauciflorum***	NPol
	- silver-leaved	see *P. pauciflorum* subsp. *pauciflorum*
	- 'Sulphur Trumpets'	GBin GJos SWvt
	- subsp. ***typicum***	see *P. pauciflorum* subsp. *pauciflorum*
	'Pink Beauty'	EBee EHyd ELan EMor EPfP LBar NGdn NPol
	pulchellum Salisb.	see *P. reptans*
	pulchellum Turcz.	see *P. caeruleum*
	pulcherrimum misapplied	see *P. boreale*
	pulcherrimum Hook.	LBar
§	***reptans***	EPfP GPoy MHer NBro NPol SRms
	- 'Album'	see *P. reptans* 'Virginia White'
	- 'Blue Ice'	NPol
	- 'Jacob's Gold' (v)	EBee EHyd ELan EPfP LBar LRHS NPol NRHS SCob
*	- 'Sky Blue'	NBro
	- 'Stairway to Heaven'PBR (v)	Widely available
	- 'Touch of Class'PBR (v)	CWGN EMor MHoo MPri NLar SCob SPoG
§	- 'Virginia White'	EWes MAvo NChi NPol NQui
	- 'White Pearl'	WPnP
	'Ribby'	NPol
	× ***richardsonii*** misapplied	see *P.* 'Northern Lights'
	× ***richardsonii*** Graham	see *P. boreale*
	'Sonia's Bluebell'	CWCL ECtt EPPr EWes GBin LBar MCot MNrw NDov NPol NSti WFar
	'Sunnyside Storm'	NPol
	'Theddingworth'	NPol
	'Triffids' Lilac'	CTtf
	viscosum	NPol SPlb
	- f. ***leucanthum***	NPol
	yezoense	NPol WFar
	- var. ***hidakanum***	EMor GAbr NPol
	- - BRESSINGHAM PURPLE ('Polbress')	Widely available
	- - 'Halfway to Paradise'	CNor EMor EPfP LBar SCob SPad WNPC
	- - 'Purple Rain'	Widely available
	- 'Kaleidoscope' (v)	LRHS MPri NPol SCoo WNPC

Polianthes (*Asparagaceae*)

	elongata	WCot
	tuberosa	CBcs CCCN GKev LCro XLum
	- 'Pink Sapphire'	GKev LAma WCot
	- 'Sensation'	GKev LAma LCro SDeJ
	- 'Super Gold'	GKev SDeJ
	- 'The Pearl' (d)	CBor GKev LAma LCro LOPS SDeJ WHlf XLum
	- 'Yellow Baby'	WCot

Poliomintha (*Lamiaceae*)

	bustamanta	NBir WSHC

Poliothyrsis (*Salicaceae*)

	sinensis	CBcs CMCN EBtc

Pollia (*Commelinaceae*)

	japonica	ESwi WCot

Polygala (*Polygalaceae*)

	'Africana'PBR	CPbh
	africana 'Nana'	SGBe
	arillata	LEdu
	calcarea	WAbe
	- Bulley's form	EPot WFar
	- 'Lillet' ♀H7	EHyd EPot GEdr LRHS NRHS WAbe
	chamaebuxus	see *Polygaloides chamaebuxus*
§	× ***dalmaisiana*** ♀H1c	CAbb CBod CCCN CDoC CKel CSde CSpe CTsd ECre EGrl EHed ELan SEND SIvy WCFE
	'Dolomite'	EPot GEdr
	myrtifolia ♀H1c	CCCN CPbh CTrC SAdn SGBe SPlb
	- BIBI PINK ('Polylap')	CTrC
	- 'Grandiflora'	see *P.* × *dalmaisiana*
	'Purple Passion'	CCCN SRms WFar WHlf
	virgata	CCCN ELan SIvy

Polygaloides (*Polygalaceae*)

§	***chamaebuxus*** ♀H7	GKev MAsh MGos NSla NWad SRms WThu
I	- ***alba***	WAbe
§	- 'Grandiflora' ♀H7	CBcs EPfP EPot GAbr GEdr GKev GMcL MAsh MGos NBir NHpl NSla SPlb SPoG WAbe WFar
	- 'Kamniski'	EPot
	- 'Loibl'	EPot WFar
	- 'Purpurea'	see *P. chamaebuxus* 'Grandiflora'
	- 'Rhodoptera'	see *P. chamaebuxus* 'Grandiflora'

Polygonatum (*Asparagaceae*)

	Og 944047 **new**	GEdr
	SBQE 310	LEdu
	altelobatum B&SWJ 286	WCru
	- B&SWJ 1886	WCru
	annamense B&SWJ 9752	WCru
	arisanense B&SWJ 271	WCru
	- B&SWJ 3839	WCru
§	***biflorum***	CRos CWCL EBee ECtt EHyd ELan ELon EMor EPfP GBin GElm GKev GMaP ILea LPal LRHS MACG MNHC NLar NRHS SPoG SWvt WCru WFar WJam WPnP XLum
	brevistylum B&SWJ 2421	WCru
	canaliculatum	see *P. biflorum*
	cathcartii B&SWJ 2429	WCru
	- yellow-flowered B&SWJ 2412	WCru
	cirrhifolium	CBor EBee EPot GAbr GEdr GKev LEdu MAvo MNrw NHpl SBrt SBut WCru WPGP
	- ARGS 320	EPPr
	- from China	WCru
	- red-flowered	NLar
	commutatum	see *P. biflorum*
	costatum B&SWJ 6599	WCru
	cryptanthum	WCru
	curvistylum	CAvo CBct CDor ECha EHed EPPr ESwi EWld GEdr GKev LEdu MAvo NBPC NLar NRya WCru WFar WSHC
	cyrtonema misapplied	see *Disporopsis pernyi*
	cyrtonema Hua	WCru
	- B&SWJ 271	GKev LEdu MAvo
*	***desoulavyi*** var. ***yezoense*** B&SWJ 764	WCru
	falcatum misapplied	see *P. humile*
	falcatum A. Gray	EBee GEdr NHpl NRya
	- B&SWJ 1077	CBct WCru
	- B&SWJ 5054	WCru
	- NJM 11.012	WPGP
	- 'Shikoku Silver'	CBct EPPr LEdu WCru

	- 'Silver Mist'	LEdu
	- 'Variegatum'	see *P. odoratum* var. *pluriflorum* 'Variegatum'
	'Falcon'	see *P. humile*
	filipes	EBee EPPr LEdu WCru
	fuscum	WCru
	geminiflorum	CBct LEdu LPla WCru WFar
	giganteum	see *P. biflorum*
	glaberrimum	WCot WPGP
	'Golden Gift'	LPla
§	***graminifolium***	CBct EBlo GEdr WCru WThu
	hirtum	see *P. latifolium*
	hookeri	CBct CBor CExl CSpe CTtf EBee EDAr EHed EMor EPPr EPot EWld GBin GEdr GKev GQue LEdu NBid NHpl NLar NRya NSla SPtp WCru WFar
§	***humile***	CBct CWCL EBee EBlo ELan EMor EPPr EPfP EPot EWTr GKev ITim LEdu LRHS MAvo NGdn NLar SPtp SWvt WCav WCru WHil WPGP WTor XLum
	- 'Shiro-shima-fu' (v)	WFar
I	- 'Variegatum' (v)	CMac EMor WCot
§	× ***hybridum*** 🏆H7	Widely available
	- 'Bere'	LEdu WPGP
	- 'Betberg'	CTtf ECha EHed ELon EMor EPPr GKev IPot LEdu LPla MBriF NBir WCot WFar
	- 'Flore Pleno' (d)	WHer
	- 'Nanum'	CBct MRav WCot
	- 'Purple Katie'	ESwi MAvo MMrt
§	- 'Striatum' (v)	Widely available
	- 'Variegatum'	see *P.* × *hybridum* 'Striatum'
	- 'Wakehurst'	LEdu
	- 'Weihenstephan'	EBee EPPr ILea LBar LEdu MAvo
	- 'Welsh Gold' (v)	CAvo EBee ESwi
	inflatum	WCru
	- B&SWJ 922	WCru
	involucratum	WCru
	- B&SWJ 4285	WCru
	japonicum	see *P. odoratum*
	kingianum	EHed GGro LEdu WMal
	- red-flowered	GKev
	- yellow-flowered B&SWJ 6545	WCru
	- - B&SWJ 6562	WCru
	'Langthorn's Variegated' (v)	ELan
	lasianthum	MAvo SMHy WCru
	- B&SWJ 671	WCru
§	***latifolium***	ECha EHyd EPPr LEdu WCru
	- W&B BG C-2	WCot
	- 'Robustum'	WCru
	macranthum	GGro
	maximowiczii	EPPr LEdu LPla WCru WPGP
§	***mengtzense*** HWJ 861 **new**	GGro
	- f. ***mengtzense*** HWJ 588	WCru
	- - HWJ 861	LEdu WCru
	- f. ***tonkinense*** B&SWJ 8246	LEdu WCru
	- - HWJ 551	WCru
	- - HWJ 567	WCru
	- - HWJ 573	CBct WCru
	- - HWJ 861	LEdu
	'Multifide'	EBee GKev
	multiflorum misapplied	see *P.* × *hybridum*
	multiflorum L.	Widely available
	- CC 4572	WCot
	- 'Flore Pleno' (d)	WFar
	- ***giganteum*** hort.	see *P. biflorum*
	- 'Ramosissima'	LEdu MAvo WCru
	- var. ***ramosum***	LEdu
*	***nanum*** 'Variegatum' (v)	CBcs
	nodosum	GKev WCru

§	***odoratum***	CAvo CBct CBro EBee ECha EMor EPfP GKev GMaP LEdu MBriF MPnt NBid NLar NRya WCru WJam WShi
	- 'Amanogawa' (v) **new**	LAma
	- 'Byakko' (v)	GKev
	- 'Dai Koga' (v)	GEdr WFar
	- 'Dusky Bere'	ESwi WPGP
§	- dwarf	LEdu
	- 'Echigo-nishiki' (v) **new**	LAma
	- 'Flatmate'	ESwi LEdu MAvo WCru
	- 'Flore Pleno' (d)	CAvo CDor EPri GKev LEdu MBriF MHer WCot WHoo
	- 'Georgia'	WPGP
	- 'Goldilocks' (v)	WCot
	- 'Grace Barker'	see *P.* × *hybridum* 'Striatum'
	- 'Kouda-nishiki' (v) **new**	LAma
	- 'Kouga' (v) **new**	LAma
	- var. ***odoratum***	GKev
	- 'Pangolin' **new**	WPGP
§	- var. ***pluriflorum*** 'Variegatum' (v)	Widely available
	- 'Pruhonice'	ECha
	- 'Red Legs' **new**	GEdr
	- 'Red Stem'	ECha EHed GKev LEdu MAvo SMHy WCru
	- 'Shiro-kujaku' (v) **new**	LAma
	- 'Silver Wings' (v)	CBct ECha IPot LEdu NBPC NBir NLar WFar WSHC
	- var. ***thunbergii***	WCru
	- 'Tora-fu' (v) **new**	LAma
	- 'Triglav'	MAvo
	- 'Ussuriland'	EPPr LEdu LPla MAvo
	- 'Ussuriland Roundleaf'	ESwi LEdu MAvo
	officinale	see *P. odoratum*
	oppositifolium	EBee
	- B&SWJ 2537	WCru
§	***orientale***	CAvo EBee EPfP ESwi GKev
	- S&F 364	WCot
	pluriflorum	see *P. graminifolium*
	polyanthemum	see *P. orientale*
	prattii	EBee EPot GKev WCru WHil
	- CLD 325	GEdr LEdu
	pubescens	WCru WThu
	pumilum	see *P. odoratum* dwarf
	punctatum misapplied	see *P. mengtzense*
	punctatum ambig.	NBid WPGP
	punctatum Royle ex Kunth	WCot
	- B&SWJ 2395	WCru
	roseum	EBee EHed EPPr ESwi GKev MAvo MMrt SMHy WCru
	sewerzowii	EMor EPPr
	sibiricum	CAvo CBct ESwi GKev WCru WFar
	- DJHC 600	EBee LEdu MAvo WPGP
	singalilense	LEdu WCru
	stenanthum B&SWJ 5727	LEdu WCru
	- B&SWJ 11425	WCru
	stenophyllum	WCru
	stewartianum	EBee EHed EPPr EPri ESwi NRya
	tessellatum PAB 8336	LEdu WPGP
	verticillatum	CBct CBro EBee EBlo ECha EHed EHyd EPPr EPfP ESwi GEdr LEdu LRHS MACG MBriF MNrw MRav SHor SMad WCru WFar WPGP WShi
	- B&SWJ 2147	WCru
	- CLD 1308	EPPr
	- PAB 2455	LEdu
	- 'Himalayan Giant'	CSpe EBlo EHed EMor EPPr GKev MAvo
	- 'Krynica'	LEdu WPGP
*	- 'Roseum'	CAvo CBor EBlo EPri LRHS
	- 'Rubrum'	CAby CBct EHed EMor EPPr GEdr GGro LEdu MAvo MBel MHid NBPC

	NBid NChi NLar WCot WCru WFar WHoo
- 'Serbian Dwarf'	CBct ESwi GKev WPGP
aff. ***verticillatum***	CTtf
yunnanense	CBct EBee ESwi LEdu WPGP
zanlanscianense	EBee EHed ESwi EWld LEdu MVil WCru
aff. ***zanlanscianense***	EPri SPlb

Polygonum (*Polygonaceae*)

affine	see *Persicaria affinis*
amplexicaule	see *Persicaria amplexicaulis*
aubertii	see *Fallopia baldschuanica*
baldschuanicum	see *Fallopia baldschuanica*
bistorta	see *Persicaria bistorta*
capitatum	see *Persicaria capitata*
equisetiforme misapplied	see *P. scoparium*
filiforme	see *Persicaria virginiana*
forrestii	GKev
multiflorum	see *Reynoutria multiflora*
odoratum	see *Persicaria odorata*
polystachyum	see *Persicaria wallichii*
runciforme	see *Persicaria runcinata*
§ ***scoparium***	EPPr ESwi EWes LRHS SDys SVen WFar WOld XLum
tinctorium	see *Persicaria tinctoria*
vacciniifolium	see *Persicaria vacciniifolia*
weyrichii	see *Persicaria weyrichii*

Polylepis (*Rosaceae*)

australis	CBcs IDee SMad
- tall	WPGP

Polymnia (*Asteraceae*)

sonchifolia 'Red China'	WPGP

Polypodiodes (*Polypodiaceae*)

formosana ♀^{H3}	GBin IKel WCot

Polypodium ✿ (*Polypodiaceae*)

aureum	see *Phlebodium aureum*
australe	see *P. cambricum*
azoricum	WCot
californicum	LEdu WPGP
calirhiza 'Sarah Lyman'	LEdu WFib
§ ***cambricum***	CLAP EFer WCot WFib
- GG 20131	SMHy
- 'Barrowii'	CLAP LEdu WAbe WFib WGwG
I - 'Cambricum' ♀^{H7}	WAbe
- 'Conwy'	WFib
- (Cristatum Group) 'Cristatum'	EBee LEdu WCot WFib WHoo
- - 'Diadem'	WFib
- - 'Grandiceps Fox' ♀^{H7}	MRav WFib
- - 'Herbert Whitley'	LEdu
- - old form	SMHy
- - 'Trippitt's Crested' **new**	WFib
- 'Hornet'	WCot WFib
- 'Macrostachyon'	LEdu NBid WFib
- 'Oakleyae'	CDor LEdu SMHy WCot
- 'Omnilacerum Oxford'	LEdu
- 'Prestonii'	CDor CLAP WCot WFib
- Pulcherrimum Group	SDys WAbe WCot
- - bifid	EBee
- - 'Pulcherrimum Addison'	EBee LEdu WCot WFib
- - 'Pulchritudine'	LLWG WCot
- 'Richard Kayse' ♀^{H7}	CLAP EShb EWes MPie SGro SMHy WAbe WBrk WCot WFib WPGP
- Semilacerum Group	EFer
- - 'Carew Lane'	LEdu WFib
- - 'Falcatum O'Kelly'	WCot
- - 'Robustum'	EBee WFib
- 'Whilharris' ♀^{H7}	CDor SMHy WCot
I × ***coughlinii*** bifid	WFib
'Dancing Girls' **new**	WCot
glycyrrhiza	EMor GPoy LEdu NBro SMHy WFib
- bifid	see *P.* × *coughlinii* bifid
- 'Lawrence Crocker'	LEdu WCot
- 'Longicaudatum' ♀^{H7}	EFer LEdu SMHy WAbe WBrk WCot WFib
- 'Malahatense'	CLAP GBin SMHy
- 'Malahatense' (sterile)	WAbe WCot
glycyrrhiza × ***scouleri***	WPGP
guttatum	SPlb
interjectum	EFer EShb MRav WCot
- 'Glomeratum Mullins'	WFib
- 'Ramosum Hillman'	WCot
macaronesicum	LEdu WCot
× ***mantoniae***	CLAP LEdu WFib
- 'Bifidograndiceps'	GQue NBid WFib
- 'Cornubiense' ♀^{H7}	CDor CLAP EShb EWld LEdu NBid NBir NHar SMHy
pseudoaureum 'Virginia Blue'	EHyd LRHS NRHS
scouleri	CLAP EBee EFer EHyd EMor ESwi ISha LEdu LRHS MAsh MRav NBro NRHS WAbe WCot WPGP
vulgare	Widely available
- 'Bifidocristatum'	CBod CLAP CTsd ELon EMor EPfP GBin GEdr ISha LEdu LLWG MAsh MGos MRav NLar WBrk
- 'Bifidomulticeps'	WCot
* - 'Congestum Cristatum'	SRms
- 'Cornubiense Grandiceps'	SRms
* - 'Cornubiense Multifidum'	WCot
- 'Elegantissimum'	LEdu NBid WAbe WFib
- 'Parsley'	LEdu WCot
- 'Ramosum Hillman'	GBin WCot
- 'Trichomanoides Backhouse'	CLAP WAbe WFib
'Whitley Giant'	CTsd EBee ECtt EMor EShb ESwi GBin GEdr ISha ITim LEdu LLWG LPla LSun MHol MPie NBid NLar WCot WPnP

Polypompholyx see *Utricularia*

Polyscias (*Araliaceae*)

'Fabian' **new**	NHrt
filicifolia **new**	WHlf
fruticosa	LCro
'Roble' **new**	NHrt
scutellaria 'Marginata' (v) ♀^{H1c} **new**	LCro WHlf

Polyspora (*Theaceae*)

§ ***axillaris***	CBcs CCCN CTsd EBee LRHS XSte
longicarpa B&SWJ 11704	WCru
- WWJ 11604	WCru
- WWJ 11894	WCru
speciosa	WPGP
- B&SWJ 11708 from Vietnam	WCru
- B&SWJ 11750	WCru
- WWJ 11934	WCru

Polystichum ✿ (*Dryopteridaceae*)

acrostichoides	CDTJ CLAP EHed EHyd EMor ISha LEdu LRHS NBro NLar NRHS SPlb WCot WFib WPGP XLum
aculeatum ♀^{H7}	CBod CKel CLAP CRos CSde EAJP ECha EFer EHyd ELan EMor GMaP GMcL ISha LCro LEdu LRHS MGos MMuc NBid NLar NRHS SCob SCoo SPoG SRms SWvt WBrk WFib XLum
- 'Cristatum Wollaston'	EMor

I - Densum Group	EFer GMcL
- 'Portia'	WFib
andersonii	CLAP NBro
biaristatum	WPGP
bissectum	CExl
braunii	CBcs CDoC CDor CLAP CMac CRos CWCL EHyd EMor EPfP GMaP ISha LEdu LRHS MAsh NBid NBro NLar NRHS SPoG WFib WPnP XLum
caryotideum	see *Cyrtomium caryotideum*
× ***dycei*** ♀H5	CLAP EHyd LEdu LRHS MAsh NRHS WCot WPGP
falcatum	see *Cyrtomium falcatum*
falcinellum	EBee
fortunei	see *Cyrtomium fortunei*
imbricans	CLAP
interjectum	MRav
makinoi	CBdn CCCN CLAP CRos EHyd EMor LEdu LLWG LRHS MAsh NBid NBro NLar NRHS SPlb SRot WCot WFib
mayebarae	CLAP EBee ISha
munitum ♀H7	Widely available
aff. ***munitum***	LPal
neolobatum	CLAP EBee EHed ISha LEdu LLWG NBro NLar WCot WFib WPGP
- BWJ 8182	WCru
ovatopaleaceum	LEdu
polyblepharum ♀H7	Widely available
proliferum misapplied	see *P. setiferum* Acutilobum Group
proliferum ambig.	CBod EMor GMcL
proliferum (R. Br.) C. Presl	CLAP LBuc WAbe WFib WPGP
* - ***plumosum***	LPal SWvt
retrorsopaleaceum	ISha
rigens	CAby CBod CLAP CSta CWCL EFer EHyd ELon EPau LEdu LPal LRHS NBro NLar NRHS SEdd SRms SRot WFib
setiferum ♀H7	Widely available
§ - Acutilobum Group	CKel EAJP ECha EHyd EMor GMaP ISha LEdu LLWG LPal LRHS NHar NRHS SCob SDix SMrm SPad SRms WBor WCAu WPGP XLum
- Congestum Group	CDor CLAP ELon EMor EShb NBro NHol NLar SPer SRms SRot WBrk WFib
- - 'Congestum'	CSta CWCL EHyd ELan EPfP ISha LEdu LRHS MAsh MCot MRav NBir NGdn NHol NRHS SCoo SMHy SPad SPoG XLum
- 'Cristatopinnulum'	CLAP EBee LEdu NHar WPGP
- Cristatum Group	CLAP SRms
- - 'Multifidum Polydactylum'	LEdu
- (Decompositum Group) 'Proliferum'	CWCL ISha
- Divisilobum Group ♀H7	CLAP EBee EFer ELan MCot MGos SRms WAbe WFar WFib WHoo WPGP
- - 'Dahlem'	CBdn CKel CMac CRos EBee ECha ECtt EFer EHyd ELan ELon EMor EPfP GMaP LEdu LRHS LSRN NBid NLar NRHS SMrm SPer WBrk WFib XLum
- - 'Divisilobum Densum' ♀H7	CMac MRav NBir
- - 'Divisilobum Grandiceps'	CLAP
- - 'Divisilobum Iveryanum' ♀H7	CLAP EFer SRms WFib
- - 'Divisilobum Laxum'	EBee
§ - - 'Divisilobum Wollaston'	CBod CDTJ CLAP CRos CSta CWCL ECtt EHyd EMor GBin ISha LRHS MAsh MGos MRav NBid NLar NRHS SCob WBrk WCot
- - 'Herrenhausen'	Widely available
- - 'Proliferum'	EMor LEdu NLar
- 'Falcatum' **new**	EMor
- Foliosum Group	EFer
- 'Gracile'	MRav NBir
§ - 'Gracillimum'	CLAP
- 'Grandiceps'	EFer
- GREEN LACE	see *P. setiferum* 'Gracillimum'
- 'Hamlet'	WFib
- 'Helena'	WFib
- 'Hirondelle'	SRms
- Lineare Group	WFib
- Multilobum Group	SRms WFib
- 'Othello'	WFib
- Perserratum Group	NBid WFib
- 'Plumosodensum'	see *P. setiferum* Plumosomultilobum Group
- Plumosodivisilobum Group	EBee ECha EHed EMor EWoo LPal MPnt NBid NBro WAbe WFib
- - 'Baldwinii'	WFib
- - 'Bland'	WFib
§ - Plumosomultilobum Group	CDor CWCL EMor EPfP GBin GQue LCro LOPS LRHS MCot MGos NBir NLar SEdd WCot WFib WHoo WPnP
I - - 'Plumosomultilobum Densum'	CAby CBod CKel CLAP CRos CSta ECtt EHyd EMor LLWG LRHS LSun MBel NRHS SEdd WBrk WCot WFar
- Plumosum Group	CMac CSpe EFer EHyd ELon EMor EPfP LLWG LRHS MAsh NHar NRHS SArc
- - dwarf	CSBt
* - ***plumosum grande*** 'Moly'	SRms
- Proliferum Group	see *P. setiferum* Acutilobum Group
- 'Proliferum Wollaston'	see *P. setiferum* (Divisilobum Group) 'Divisilobum Wollaston'
- 'Pulcherrimum Bevis' ♀H7	CBdn CLAP EFer EHed EHyd ELon EShb ESwi LEdu LPal LRHS MPie NRHS SArc SMHy SWvt WFib WLov WPGP
- (Rotundatum Group) 'Cristatum'	CLAP
- 'Smith's Cruciate'	MRav WFib WPGP
- 'Wakeleyanum'	EFer SRms
'Spiny Holly'	CLAP
tsussimense ♀H6	Widely available
- 'K Rex'	CRos EHyd LEdu LRHS NRHS
wawranum	LEdu WPGP
xiphophyllum	CLAP EBee LEdu NBro SPlb WPGP
yunnanense	CBct CBdn CTsd EHed LEdu NLar

Polyxena (*Asparagaceae*)

corymbosa	see *Lachenalia corymbosa*

pomegranate see *Punica granatum*

Poncirus see *Citrus*

Ponerorchis (*Orchidaceae*)

graminifolia	see *Hemipilia graminifolia*

Pontederia (*Pontederiaceae*)

cordata ♀H5	CBen CPud CToG CWat ECha EPfP EWat LCro LLWG LOPS LPfP MWts NPer SPlb WHlf WMAq WPnP XLum
- f. ***albiflora***	CPud CToG CWat EWat LLWG WPnP XLum
§ - var. ***lancifolia***	CBen CToG CWat ECha LLWG LPfP MNrw MWts NPer
- pink-flowered	LLWG
- 'Sunsplash' (v)	LLWG

dilatata	see *Monochoria hastata*
lanceolata	see *P. cordata* var. *lancifolia*

Populus ✿ (*Salicaceae*)

× ***acuminata***	WMou
alba	CBTr CBcs CCVT CLnd CMac CPer CTri EHeP IPap LBuc LPar MMuc NBwr NRog NWea SCob SEWo SPer WMou WTSh
- 'Bolleana'	see *P. alba* 'Pyramidalis'
§ - 'Pyramidalis'	CPer EHeP WMou
§ - 'Raket'	CCVT ELan NRog
- 'Richardii'	EBtc SDix WCot WMou
- ROCKET	see *P. alba* 'Raket'
§ 'Balsam Spire' (f)	NWea WMou
§ ***balsamifera***	CCVT CLnd CSBt CTri EHeP SPer WCot
- 'Vita Sackville West'	MBlu
× ***canadensis***	CBTr
§ - 'Aurea' ♀H7	WMat WMou
- 'Aurea' × ***jackii*** 'Aurora'	CCCN ELan WFar
- 'Columbia'	WMou
- 'Eugenei' (m)	WMou
- 'Gaver' **new**	CBTr
- 'Ghoy' (m) **new**	CBTr
- 'Robusta' (m)	CCVT CLnd EHeP NRog NWea WHtc WMou
- 'Serotina' (m)	NRog WMou
× ***canescens***	CLnd NWea WMou
- 'Tower'	WMat
ciliata	WPGP
deltoides 'Fuego'	SGol
- 'Purple Tower' PBR	CBTr CBcs EBee ELan EPfP MBlu MMuc MTrO NOra SDix SLim WMat
× ***generosa*** 'Beaupré'	CBTr WMou
glauca	WPGP
× ***jackii*** 'Aurora' (f/v)	CBcs CCVT CMac CSBt CTsd GMcL IPap NRog NWea SPer WFar WMou
lasiocarpa	CBcs CMCN IDee MBlu SPtp WMou WPGP
- (m/f)	WPGP
maximowiczii	SPtp WMou
nigra	CHab CTri NOrn NWea
- (f)	CPer MMuc
- (m)	MMuc
- subsp. ***betulifolia***	CBTr CCVT CHab CLnd EHeP NWea WMou
- - (f)	EBtc WMou
- - (m)	EBtc WMou
- 'Hanging Tree'	CBTr MTrO
§ - 'Italica' (m) ♀H7	CBTr CBod CCVT CLnd CMac CPer CSBt EHeP ELan IPap LBuc LPar MGos MMuc NRog NWea SCob SEWo SPer WHtc WMou
- 'Italica Aurea'	see *P. nigra* 'Lombardy Gold'
§ - 'Lombardy Gold' (m)	SMad
- 'Pyramidalis'	see *P. nigra* 'Italica'
purdomii	SPtp WPGP
'Serotina Aurea'	see *P.* × *canadensis* 'Aurea'
simonii 'Fastigiata'	WMou
- 'Obtusata'	NRog
szechuanica	WMou
§ - var. ***tibetica***	WMou WPGP
tacamahaca	see *P. balsamifera*
'Tacatricho 32'	see *P.* 'Balsam Spire'
tomentosa	WMou
tremula	CBTr CCVT CHab CLnd CMac CPer CTri EHeP ELan GAbr IPap LBuc LPar NBwr NRog NWea SCob SEWo WHtc WMou WSFF WTSh
§ - 'Erecta' ♀H7	CEnd LPar LRHS MBlu MMuc NOrn WMat WMou
- 'Fastigiata'	see *P. tremula* 'Erecta'
- 'Pendula' (m)	CEnd WMou
trichocarpa	CBTr EHeP NRog
- 'Columbia River' (m)	CBTr
- 'Fritzi Pauley' (f)	CBTr WMou
- 'Scott Pauley' (m) **new**	CBTr
- 'Trichobel'	CBTr
violascens	see *P. szechuanica* var. *tibetica*
× ***wilsocarpa*** 'Beloni'	WPGP
wilsonii	WPGP
- KR 3993	WPGP
- MF 20088	WPGP
yunnanensis	WMou

Porophyllum (*Asteraceae*)

ruderale	WJek

Portulaca (*Portulacaceae*)

sp.	MBros
gilliesii	NFav
oleracea	ENfk SSim SVic
- var. ***aurea***	MNHC

Portulacaria (*Didiereaceae*)

afra	CDoC EAri EShb LWaG NCft
- 'Mediopicta' (v) **new**	NCft
- 'Variegata' (v)	CDoC EAri EShb NCft SIvy SSim

Potamogeton (*Potamogetonaceae*)

crispus	CBen CWat LLWG LPfP MWts WMAq
lucens	LLWG LPfP
malainus	LLWG
natans	LLWG LPfP XLum
pectinatus	LPfP
perfoliatus	LLWG LPfP

potato see AGM Vegetables Section

Potentilla ✿ (*Rosaceae*)

alba	CTri ECha ELan GKev LShi MRav NChi NWad SHar SPer WSHC
alchemilloides	CMac
alpina (Willk.) Zimmeter	see *P. aurea*
ancistrifolia var. ***dickinsii***	GEdr GKev
anserina	CAgr MHer SPhx WHer XLum
- 'Golden Treasure' (v)	NSti
arbuscula misapplied	see *P. fruticosa* 'Elizabeth'
- 'Beesii'	see *P. fruticosa* 'Beesii'
'Arc-en-ciel'	Widely available
argentea	SPlb WFar XLum
argyrophylla	see *P. atrosanguinea* var. *argyrophylla*
atrosanguinea	Widely available
- CC 7167	GGro
§ - var. ***argyrophylla***	CDor CWCL EAJP EBee EBou ECha ELan GKev GPSL MRav NBPC NBir NBro NChi NLar SRms XLum
- - 'Golden Starlit'	CChe MACG SVic
- - 'Orange Starlit'	SBls
§ - - 'Scarlet Starlit'	CAby CChe CDor EDAr GElm GJos LLWG MACG NCou NEoE SVic
- 'Chadwell's Tibetan Velvet'	GGro
- var. ***leucochroa***	see *P. atrosanguinea* var. *argyrophylla*
§ ***aurea***	ECtt GArf GBin
- 'Plena' (d)	NBwr NRya
'Blazeaway'	CBod CFis EBee ECtt EHyd EPfP LRHS LSto MArl MBel NEoE NGdn NRHS SRms
calabra	ECha EWes MMuc SPhx
§ ***cinerea***	CTri

'Congo'	EBlo LRHS
§ ***crantzii***	EBou SRms
- 'Nana'	see *P. crantzii* 'Pygmaea'
§ - 'Pygmaea'	ECtt
davurica 'Abbotswood'	see *P. fruticosa* 'Abbotswood'
delphinensis new	GQue
'Emilie' (d)	CWCL ECtt GMcL LRHS MBel MNrw NBPC NLar SWvt WBor WFar
§ ***erecta***	GPoy MBow MNHC SPhx SRms
eriocarpa	EPot GArf GEdr NBwr NSla WAbe WIce
'Esta Ann'	CMac EBee ECtt LRHS LShi MArl MAvo MBel MNrw MTin NBPC NLar NRHS NSti WCAu
'Etna'	CWCL ECtt EHyd ELan GAbr GArf GElm GJos LRHS LShi MACG MNrw MPie MTin NBir NLar NRHS WCAu WFar WHrl
'Everest'	see *P. fruticosa* 'Mount Everest'
'Fireflame'	NBPC NLar
fissa	MNrw NBir NLar SPhx
'Flambeau' (d)	EBee ECtt EMor EPfP EShb LDai MArl MRav MSpe NChi NGdn NLar NRHS NSti WCAu
'Flamboyant' (d)	NCth
'Flamenco'	CRos CTri ECtt EHyd LRHS MArl MAvo MRav NBir NCth NRHS WFar
fragariiformis	see *P. megalantha*
fruticosa	LBuc NWea
§ - 'Abbotswood' 𝕐H7	Widely available
- 'Annette'	NLar
- var. ***arbuscula*** hort.	see *P. fruticosa* 'Elizabeth'
- var. ***arbuscula***	EHeP
- 'Argentea Nana'	see *P. fruticosa* 'Beesii'
§ - 'Beesii'	EHyd LRHS MAsh NRHS
- BELLA BIANCA ('Hachbianca' PBR)	CBod LCro LRHS WLov
- BELLA LINDSEY ('Hendlin') new	NLar
- BELLA SOL ('Hachdon')	CBod CWGN EBee LCro LRHS NLar SPad WLov
- BELLISSIMA ('Hachliss' PBR)	CBod CKel CWGN EMil LCro LRHS SEdd
- 'Bewerley Surprise'	MGil WFar
- 'Bo-Peep'	CEnd WFar
- 'Chelsea Star' 𝕐H7	CDoC CKel CMac CRos EBee EHyd EPfP LRHS LSRN MAsh SPoG SRGP
- 'Clotted Cream'	SGbt
- var. ***dahurica*** 'Hersii'	see *P. fruticosa* 'Snowflake'
- 'Dakota Sunrise'	WFar
- DANNY BOY ('Lissdan' PBR)	CKel CRos EBee EHyd EMil EPfP LCro LOPS LRHS MAsh NEoE NLar NRHS SCob SPad SPoG
- 'Daphne'	NWad
- 'Dart's Golddigger'	CTri
- 'Daydawn'	CBcs CBrac CGBo CMac CTri EHeP EHyd ELan EPfP GMcL LRHS MAsh MGil MMuc MRav MSwo NBwr NLar NWad SCob SGol SPer SRms SWvt WFar
- 'Farreri'	see *P. fruticosa* 'Gold Drop'
- 'Friedrichsenii'	CBrac
- 'Glenroy Pinkie'	MRav
§ - 'Gold Drop'	CMac NHol
- 'Goldfinger'	CAgr CBod CBrac CChe CDoC CKel CRos CSBt EBee EHeP EHyd EPfP GMcL LRHS MAsh MGos MMuc MRav MSwo NBwr NRHS SCob SCoo SPer SPlb SPoG WFar XSen
- GOLDKUGEL	see *P. fruticosa* 'Gold Drop'
- 'Goldstar'	CGBo IArd MMuc SCob SEND SRms WFar
- 'Goldteppich'	LBuc
- 'Grace Darling'	MGil NLar SRGP SWvt
- 'Groneland' 𝕐H7	CRos EHyd ELan EPfP LRHS MAsh NRHS SCoo SPoG
- 'Hopleys Orange' 𝕐H7	CBrac CDoC CGBo CKel CRos EBee EHyd EPfP EWes LRHS MGil NHol NLar SEdd SGbt SGol SRHi SRms WFar
- 'Jackman's Variety' 𝕐H7	EHyd EPfP LRHS MAsh SRms
- 'Katherine Dykes'	CTri EBee EHeP EHyd EPfP GDam GKin GMcL LRHS LSRN MAsh NBwr NRHS NWea SCob SCoo SGbt SPer SRms WBor WFar WHtc
- 'King Cup' 𝕐H7	CRos EHyd EPfP LRHS MAsh
§ - 'Klondike'	CBcs CBrac NWea
- 'Kobold'	CDoC EHeP GMcL NLar
- 'Lemon and Lime'	see *P. fruticosa* 'Limelight'
§ - 'Limelight' 𝕐H7	CKel CRos CSBt EBee EHyd EPfP GKin LRHS MAsh MGil MMuc MRav MSwo NEoE NRHS NWad SRms WFar WHtc WLov
- 'Lovely Pink'	see *P. fruticosa* 'Pink Beauty'
§ - 'Maanelys'	CBrac CSBt NLar NWea SPer
- 'Macpenny's Cream'	CMac SRms
§ - 'Manchu'	CKel CMac MRav SPer SRms WCFE
- MANGO TANGO ('Uman' PBR)	CBod CKel CSBt EDir EHyd EPfP LRHS LSRN MAsh NEoE NLar NRHS SCob SPad SPoG WFar
§ - MARIAN RED ROBIN ('Marrob' PBR) 𝕐H7	CBod CDoC CRos EHeP EHyd ELan EPfP GKin GMcL LCro LOPS LRHS MAsh MRav MSwo NRHS NWea SCoo SNig SPer SRms SWvt WFar WLov
- 'Medicine Wheel Mountain' 𝕐H7	CBod CKel CRos EHyd ELan EPfP EWes IArd LRHS MAsh MRav NEoE NRHS SCoo SPer SPoG WFar WHtc
- MOONLIGHT	see *P. fruticosa* 'Maanelys'
§ - 'Mount Everest'	CMac CTri GMcL MMuc NBwr NWea
- 'Nana Argentea'	see *P. fruticosa* 'Beesii'
- 'New Dawn'	CBcs GKin
- 'Orange Star'	NBwr
- 'Orangeade'	CRos EHyd EPfP LRHS MAsh SCoo SPoG
§ - 'Pink Beauty' PBR 𝕐H7	CBar CDoC CKel CRos CSBt EBee EDir EHyd ELan EPau EPfP GKin GMcL LCro LRHS LSRN LSto MAsh MRav NHol NRHS SCob SCoo SPer SPoG SRkn SRms SWvt WFar
- PINK PARADISE ('Kupinpa' PBR)	MAsh SCob
- 'Pink Pearl'	NBwr WFar
- 'Pink Queen'	SRGP
- 'Pink Whisper'	NBwr SRms
- 'Pretty Polly'	CGBo EHeP EHyd ELan EPfP LRHS MSwo NHol NLar NWad SRHi WFar
- 'Primrose Beauty' 𝕐H7	Widely available
§ - PRINCESS ('Blink')	CBcs CBrac CDoC CKel EBee EHyd ELan EPfP GMcL LRHS LSto MAsh MRav NLar NRHS SCob SCoo SRms SSut WFar
- var. ***pumila***	WAbe
- 'Red Ace'	Widely available
- 'Red Joker'	LRHS NLar SRHi
- 'Red Lady' PBR	CRos EBee EHyd ELan EPfP LRHS MAsh NEoE NHol NRHS SPoG
- RED ROBIN	see *P. fruticosa* MARIAN RED ROBIN
- 'Red Surprise'	WFar
- 'Royal Flush'	NWad
- SILVER 'N' GOLD ('Lisstreas')	LRHS
- 'Snowbird'	NEoE WFar

§ - 'Snowflake' — CBcs
- 'Sommerflor' ♀H7 — CRos EHyd EPfP LRHS MAsh NRHS
- 'Sophie's Blush' — MGil MRav NWea
§ - (Sulphurascens Group) 'Elizabeth' — CBcs CBod CMac EHeP LSRN MGos MMuc MSwo NBwr NHol NLar NWea SCob SGbt SGol SPer SRms SWvt WFar WHtc
- - 'Longacre Variety' — CMac CTri IArd MSwo NLar NWea
- 'Sunset' — CBcs CBrac CMac GKin LSRN NBwr NLar NWea SCoo SPer SRms WFar
- 'Tangerine' — Widely available
- 'Tilford Cream' — CBod CDoC CKel CRos CSBt CTri EBee EHeP EHyd ELan EPfP GKin LRHS LSRN MRav MSwo NHol NRHS SCob SGbt SPer SRms WCFE WFar
- 'Tom Conway' — CMac SRms
- var. ***veitchii*** — CSBt NBwr
- 'Vilmoriniana' — CKel CMac CTri EHyd ELan EPfP GBin LRHS MAsh MRav NLar NWea SPer SPoG SSha SWvt WSpi
- 'Whirligig' — CMac
- 'White Lady' PBR — CBod NEoE
- 'Yellow Bird' ♀H7 — CRos EHyd LRHS MAsh
gelida — EWes
'Gibson's Scarlet' ♀H7 — Widely available
§ ***glandulosa*** subsp. ***nevadensis*** — CTri MAsh
'Gloire de Nancy' (d) — LRHS MRav NBir NChi NLar
'Herzblut' — NLar
hippiana — EBee
× ***hopwoodiana*** — CSpe CTtf EBee ECha ELan EPPr GMaP ILea LEdu MCot MNrw MPnt MRav NBir NChi NDov NLar WCAu WFar
× ***hybrida*** 'Jean Jabber' — GLog MAvo MBow MRav NEoE NLar WFar
hyparctica — CPla GJos
kurdica — XLum
'Light My Fire' — MAsh MHol MNrw NBPC
'Mandshurica' — see *P. fruticosa* 'Manchu'
§ ***megalantha*** — CBcs CBod CBro CRos EBou ECha ECtt EDAr EHyd ELan EPfP EPri GGro GQue LRHS MBNS MPie MRav NBir NBro NRHS NSti SCoo SGbt SPer SRms XLum
- 'Gold Sovereign' — WMal
'Melton Fire' — GElm GKin GPSL MNrw NBPC NBir
micrantha 'Purple Haze' — LEdu
- 'Purple Heart' — WPGP
'Monarch's Velvet' — see *P. thurberi* 'Monarch's Velvet'
'Monsieur Rouillard' (d) — CBod CElw CMac CRos EBee ECtt EHyd GElm GPSL LRHS MACG MArl MNrw MRav NBPC NGdn NLar NRHS WHoo WKif
'Mont d'Or' — EBee GKev MAvo MRav NLar
nepalensis — CPla EHyd LRHS NBro NChi NRHS XLum
- 'Craigieburn' — NChi
- 'Helen Jane' — CDor EBee GBin GJos GQue LEdu NBir NHol NLar WFar WHrl
§ - 'Miss Willmott' — Widely available
- 'Ron McBeath' — CDor CRos CWCL EHyd ELan EPfP EWoo GAbr GBin GJos LRHS MAvo MRav NFav NHol NLar NSti SRkn SRms SWvt WGwG WHoo WPnP
- 'Roxana' — EBee ELan MRav NBro SBut
- 'Shogran' — CRos EBee EBou EDAr EHyd GElm GJos GQue LRHS NChi NHol NLar NRHS WPnP
§ ***neumanniana*** — MAsh NBir NPoe WCav
- 'Goldrausch' — XLum
§ - 'Nana' — EBou EPot GArf MAsh NRya NWad SLee SPlb SRms WFar WHoo WIce XLum
nevadensis — see *P. glandulosa* subsp. *nevadensis*
nitida — EPot GKev MAsh WAbe
- 'Alba' — EPot GArf GEdr
- 'Rubra' — GEdr NBir NBwr WAbe
palustris — CPud CWat EWat LLWG LPfP MWts NAts NLar XLum
parvifolia 'Klondike' — see *P. fruticosa* 'Klondike'
pedata — NChi XLum
'Pink Panther' — see *P. fruticosa* PRINCESS
porphyrantha — GEdr GJos
recta — CKel SRms XLum
- 'Alba' — GMaP LDai
- 'Citrina' — see *P. recta* var. *sulphurea*
- 'Macrantha' — see *P. recta* 'Warrenii'
§ - var. ***sulphurea*** — CAby CBWd EAJP EGrI EPPr EWTr GElm LSun MNrw NBir NLar NSti NWad SPhx SRkn WBrk WCAu WHrl WJam XLum
§ - 'Warrenii' — CSBt GMaP MRav NBir SHar SRms WHrl XLum
'Red Giant' — LBar
reptans 'Pleniflora' (d) — WCot
I × ***rosea*** 'Pleniflora' (d) — LRHS
'Roxanne' (d) — MHer
rupestris — CAby CFis ECha EPPr GJos GQue LSun MACG MHer NSti SBut WCAu WFar WOut
salesoviana — GKev
SCARLET DREAMS **new** — LBar
'Scarlet Starlet' — see *P. atrosanguinea* var. *argyrophylla* 'Scarlet Starlit'
speciosa — EWes
sterilis — WHer WSFF
* ***sundermanii*** — WHrl
tabernaemontani — see *P. neumanniana*
thurberi — LRHS NLar NRHS SPhx XLum
§ - 'Monarch's Velvet' — Widely available
tommasiniana — see *P. cinerea*
× ***tonguei*** ♀H5 — Widely available
tormentilla — see *P. erecta*
tridentata — see *Sibbaldiopsis tridentata*
'Twinkling Star' — LBar MHol NEoE
verna misapplied — see *P. neumanniana*
- 'Pygmaea' — see *P. neumanniana* 'Nana'
'Versicolor Plena' (d) — NLar
villosa — see *P. crantzii*
'Vogue' — EBee
'Volcan' — CWCL EWes LBar NChi WCAu WFar
'White Queen' — GElm GLog MRav SBut SHar SRms
'William Rollisson' ♀H7 — Widely available
willmottiae — see *P. nepalensis* 'Miss Willmott'
'Yellow Queen' — CMac CTri EHyd GKin GMaP LRHS MRav NLar NRHS SPer SRms WCAu

Poterium see *Sanguisorba*

sanguisorba — see *Sanguisorba minor*

Pothos (*Araceae*)

scandens **new** — NHrt

Prangos (*Apiaceae*)

ferulacea — WCot

Pratia (*Campanulaceae*)

§ ***angulata*** — GArf
§ - 'Treadwellii' — ECha ECtt ELan EWTr NBro SPlb SRms WFar
'Fairy Footsteps' **new** — EDAr

	montana	see *Lobelia montana*
§	***pedunculata***	CTri EBee EBou ECha ECtt EDAr EPfP GQue LLWG LRHS LSun MAsh NFav NHpl SLee SPlb SRms SRot WFar WIce
I	- 'Alba'	EWes GAbr LRHS MACG NHpl SLee SRms SRot WFar WIce
	- 'County Park'	CTri EBou ECha EDAr ELan EPfP EWoo LLWG LRHS MACG MAsh NBwr NGrs NHpl SCoo SLee SPlb SPoG SRms SRot WCav WFar WIce XLum
	- 'White Stars'	LLWG

Prenanthes (*Asteraceae*)

§	***alba***	GGro

Preslia see *Mentha*

Primula ✿ (*Primulaceae*)

	(Si)	MAsh
	acaulis	see *P. vulgaris*
	'Adrian Jones' (Au)	NSum
	'Alexina' (*allionii* hybrid) (Au)	NHar XBar
	algida (Al)	XBar
	'Alice Collins'	NSum
§	***allionii*** (Au)	GKev WAbe
	- 'Aire Waves'	see *P.* × *loiseleurii* 'Aire Waves'
	- 'Allen Charm' (Au)	ITim
	- 'Allen Moonbeam' (Au)	GAbr ITim NHar
	- 'Anna Griffith' (Au)	WAbe
	- 'Anne' (Au)	NSum
	- 'Apple Blossom' (Au)	NHpl
	- 'Archer' (Au)	ITim
	- 'Ares' (Au)	NHar
	- 'Aries Violet' (Au)	ITim NHar
	- 'Bill Martin' (Au)	ITim NSum NWad
	- 'Cherry' (Au)	WAbe
	- 'Chivalry' (Au)	WAbe
	- 'Circe's Flute' (Au)	NHar
	- 'Cissie' (Au)	ITim NHar
	- 'Crystal' (Au)	NSum
	- 'Edrom' (Au)	NSum
	- 'Eureka' (Au)	NSum WAbe
	- 'Fanfare' (Au)	NHar
I	- 'Forma' (Au)	XBar
	- 'Frank Barker' (Au)	NWad
	- 'Gilderdale Glow' (Au)	NHar
	- 'Grandiflora-alp' (Au) **new**	GKev
	- 'Hartside 6' (Au)	ITim
	- 'Hemswell' (Au)	NHpl
	- 'Henry Burrow' (Au)	WAbe
	- 'Herald' (Au)	ITim
	- 'Hocker Edge' (Au)	GKev
	- 'Horwood' (Au)	ITim
	- 'Joyce Bacon' (Au) **new**	GKev
	- 'Lee Mayers' (Au)	WFar
	- 'Lepus' (Au)	WAbe
	- 'Lucy' (Au)	NHar
	- 'Malcolm' (Au)	ITim
	- 'Marion' (Au)	XBar
	- 'Marjorie Wooster' (Au)	XBar
	- 'Neptune's Wave' (Au)	NHar
	- 'New Dawn' (Au)	ITim
	- 'Peace' (Au)	NHar
	- 'Pennine Pink' (Au)	GArf
	- 'Phoebe's Moon' (Au)	NHar
	- 'Pinkie' (Au)	WAbe
	- 'Raymond Wooster' (Au)	GKev
	- 'Tranquility' (Au)	ITim
	- 'William Earle' (Au)	XBar
	allionii × ***allionii*** 'Apple Blossom' (Au)	GArf
	allionii × ***auricula*** misapplied 'Old Red Dusty Miller' (Au)	NWad WFar
	allionii × ***auricula*** misapplied 'Blairside Yellow' (Au)	GArf NBwr NSum
	allionii × ***hirsuta*** (Au)	GArf
	allionii × 'Lismore Treasure' (Au)	ITim NHpl
	allionii × ***pubescens*** (Au)	NHpl
	allionii × ***pubescens*** 'Harlow Car' (Au)	WFar
	allionii × 'White Linda Pope' (Au)	NHpl
	alpicola (Si) $♀^{H6}$	CAby GAbr GKev GQue LShi NBid NGdn WTyc XBar
	- var. ***alba*** (Si)	CPla GAbr GRum NBid NChi
§	- var. ***alpicola*** (Si)	GRum LShi
	- hybrids (Si)	MACG NHpl
	- var. ***luna***	see *P. alpicola* var. *alpicola*
	- mixed (Si)	GEdr
	- var. ***violacea*** (Si)	CPla GAbr GGro GRum MNrw NBid
	'Altaica'	see *P. elatior* subsp. *meyeri*
	altaica grandiflora	see *P. elatior* subsp. *meyeri*
	amoena	see *P. elatior* subsp. *meyeri*
	'Amy Smith' (Pr/Prim)	GAbr
	anisodora	see *P. wilsonii* var. *anisodora*
	× ***anisodoxa*** 'Kevock Surprise' (Pf)	GKev
	'Annemijne' (Pr/Poly)	WCot
	apoclita (Mu)	XBar
I	'Appleblossom' (Pr/Prim/d)	GEdr
	× ***arctotis***	see *P.* × *pubescens*
	'Arduaine' (Pe)	NHar
	aurantiaca (Pf)	GAbr GKev GRum NHpl XBar
	- 'Harperley Pink' (Pf)	MPnt NHpl
	aurantiaca × ***pulverulenta*** (Pf)	GRum NFav
	aureata (Pe)	NHar
	auricula L. (Au) $♀^{H5}$	CRos EHyd EWld GKev GRum LRHS MAsh NRHS NSla SPer SPlb SPoG
	- subsp. ***bauhinii*** (Au)	GKev
	auricula misapplied (Au)	EBou EHyd LRHS LSto MBow NRHS WCav WWke
	- A74 (Au)	MMuc SEND
	- 'A.C. Hadfield' (Au)	XBar
	- 'Abdor' (Au/St)	EWoo NDro
	- 'Abundance' (Au/A)	EWoo NDro
	- 'Achates' (Au/A)	EWoo
	- 'Admiral' (Au/A)	NDro
	- 'Adrian' (Au/A)	GAbr ITim NDro NSum WHil XBar
	- 'Adrian's Cross' (Au/A)	EWoo
	- 'Adrienne' (Au/A)	EGrI EWoo GKev WHil
	- 'Adrienne Ruan' (Au/A)	NDro NSum
	- 'After Glow' (Au/St)	NDro
	- 'Aga Khan' (Au/A)	NDro WAln
	- 'Agamemnon' (Au/A)	EWoo NDro NSum XBar
	- 'Airy Fairy' (Au/S)	NDro
	- 'Alamo' (Au/A)	NDro
	- 'Albert Bailey' (Au/d)	NDro WFar WHil XBar
	- 'Alexandra Georgina' (Au/A)	WAln XBar
	- 'Alf' (Au/A)	NDro NSum WHil XBar
	- 'Alice' (Au/d)	NDro
	- 'Alice Haysom' (Au/S)	EDAr ELan EWoo ITim NDro WHil XBar
	- 'Alicia' (Au/A)	NDro NSum XBar
	- 'Alien' (Au/S)	NDro
	- 'Alison' (Au/S)	NDro
	- 'Alison Jane' (Au/A)	NDro NSum WHil XBar
	- 'Alison Rose' (Au/B)	NDro
	- 'Alison Telford' (Au/A)	NWad WHil

– 'Allard' (Au/A)	WAln WHil
– 'Alloway' (Au/d)	WAln
– 'Amicable' (Au/A)	NDro NSum WHil XBar
– 'Amie Rosalind' (Au/B)	NDro
– 'Amore' (Au/St)	NDro
– 'Ancient Society' (Au/A)	EWTr EWoo NDro NSum NWad WHil XBar
– 'Andrea Julie' (Au/A)	NDro WHil XBar
– 'Andrew Hunter' (Au/A)	NDro NSum WHil XBar
– 'Andy Cole' (Au/A)	NDro WAln
– 'Angel Eyes' (Au/St)	EWoo NDro
– 'Angel Islington' (Au/S)	EGrI NDro
– 'Angela Gould' (Au/B)	EWoo NDro
– 'Angostura' (Au/d)	EBee EWoo WHil
– 'Ann Brookes' (Au/d)	WAln
– 'Ann Taylor' (Au/A)	WAln
– 'Anna' (Au/B)	NDro
– 'Anne Hyatt' (Au/d)	NDro
– 'Annette' (Au/B)	NDro
– 'Ansells' (Au/S)	EGrI WAln
– 'Antoc' (Au/S)	EWoo
– 'Anwar Sadat' (Au/A)	EWoo NDro NSum WHil XBar
– 'Apple Blossom' (Au/B)	NDro
– 'Applecross' (Au/A)	NDro NHpl NSum WHil XBar
– 'April Moon' (Au/S)	NDro
– 'Arab Prince' (Au/A)	WAln
– 'Arab Queen' (Au/A)	WAln
– 'Arabian Night' (Au/A)	NDro
– 'Arctic Fox' (Au/A)	WAln WHil XBar
– 'Argentine' (Au/S)	XBar
– 'Argus' (Au/A)	EGrI ITim LSun NDro NWad WHil XBar
– 'Arras' (Au/d)	WHil
– 'Art Deco' (Au/B)	NDro
– 'Arthur Delbridge' (Au/A)	NDro NSum WHil XBar
– 'Artwork' (Au/S)	NDro
– 'Arundell' (Au/S/St)	EBee ITim NDro NSum WFar WHil XBar
– 'Arwen' (Au/A)	XBar
– 'Ascot Gavotte' (Au/S)	NDro
– 'Ashcliffe Gem' (Au/A)	NDro
– 'Ashcliffe Royal' (Au/A) **new**	WHil
– Ashwood strain (Au)	MAsh
– 'Astolat' (Au/S)	EBee NDro NHpl WHil XBar
– 'Athene' (Au/S)	ITim NDro
– 'Atlantic' (Au/S)	NDro
– 'Aubergine' (Au/B)	NDro
– 'Audacity' (Au/d)	NDro WAln
– 'Audrey' (Au/S)	NDro
– 'Aurora' (Au/A)	NSum WAln
– 'Austin' (Au/A)	NSum
– 'Autumn Fire' (Au/A)	EWoo GAbr WHil
– 'Autumn Glow' (Au/d)	NDro
– 'Avon Citronella' (Au/d)	XBar
– 'Avon Tan' (Au/d)	GAbr
– 'Avon Twist' (Au/d)	EWoo
– 'Avondale' (Au/B)	LRHS
– 'Avonwick' (Au/B)	NDro
– 'Avril' (Au/A)	NDro WAln WHil XBar
– 'Avril Hunter' (Au/A)	EWoo ITim NDro NSum WHil XBar
– 'Awesome' (Au/St)	WHil
– 'Baby Blue' (Au)	LRHS NDro
– 'Bacchus' (Au/A)	NDro WHil XBar
– 'Baggage' (Au/St)	ITim NDro WHil
– 'Bailey Boy' (Au/B)	NDro
– 'Bakerloo Line' (Au/S)	NDro
– 'Balbithan' (Au/B)	NDro
– 'Ballynahinch' (Au)	ITim
– 'Baltic Amber' (Au/d)	GAbr NDro WAln WHil XBar
– 'Bank Error' (Au/S)	NDro WAln
– 'Barbara Mason' (Au)	NDro
– 'Barbarella' (Au/S)	NDro
– 'Barbe à Papa' (Au/B)	XBar
– 'Barber's Pole' (Au/St)	NDro
– Barnhaven Border hybrids (Au/B)	XBar
– Barnhaven doubles (Au/d)	GAbr XBar
– 'Barr Beacon' (Au/A)	ITim NDro NSum
– 'Bartl' (Au/A)	EBee ELan MAvo
– 'Basilio' (Au/S)	NDro
– 'Basuto' (Au/A)	EWoo ITim NSum WHil XBar
– 'Beatrice' (Au/A)	EWoo NDro NHpl WFar WHil XBar
– 'Beauty of Bath' (Au/S)	WAln
– 'Beckminster' (Au/A)	WAln
– 'Bedford Lad' (Au/A)	NDro
– 'Beechen Green' (Au/S)	ITim NDro
– 'Beeches Variegated' (Au/A/v)	EBee MAvo WFar
– 'Beervelde' (Au/B)	WHil
– 'Belgravia Gold' (Au/B)	NDro WHil
– 'Bellamy Pride' (Au/B)	NDro NSum WHil
– 'Belle Zana' (Au/S)	NDro
– 'Bellini' (Au/d)	XBar
– 'Ben' (Au/A) **new**	WHil
– 'Ben Wyves' (Au/S)	NDro
– 'Bendigo' (Au/S)	EWoo NDro
– 'Benny Green' (Au/S)	NDro WHil XBar
– 'Beppi' (Au/B)	NDro WHil
– 'Best Wishes' (Au/F)	NDro
– 'Bethan McSparron' (Au/B)	NDro
– 'Betty Sherriff' (Au/B)	GAbr
– 'Betty Stewart' (Au/A)	WAln
– 'Bewitched' (Au/A)	NDro WHil XBar
– 'Bielfeld' (Au/B)	NDro
– 'Big Thrill' (Au)	WFar
– 'Bilbao' (Au/A)	WAln
– 'Bilbo Baggins' (Au/A)	NDro WAln
– 'Bill Bailey' (Au/d)	EWoo GAbr NDro WHil
– 'Bingley Folk' (Au/B)	NDro
– 'Bingley Snowflake' (Au/B)	NDro
– 'Bisto' (Au/S)	WAln
– 'Bitter Lemon' (Au/d) **new**	XBar
– 'Bitterne Primrose' (Au/d)	EWoo
– 'Bizarre' (Au)	NDro
– 'Black Diamond' (Au/d)	WHil XBar
– 'Black Jack'^PBR (Au/d)	CWCL ECtt ELan LBar LCro NHpl SEdd
– 'Blackhill' (Au/S)	EWoo ITim NHpl
– 'Blackpool Rock' (Au/St)	NDro WHil
– 'Blairside Yellow' (Au/B)	NDro NSla WAbe
– 'Blakeney' (Au/d)	NDro XBar
– 'Blossom' (Au/A)	EWoo WHil XBar
– 'Blue Bella' (Au/B)	NDro
– 'Blue Belle' (Au/B)	NDro
– 'Blue Bonnet' (Au/A/d)	EWoo GAbr NDro XBar
– 'Blue Boy' (Au/S)	NDro
– 'Blue Chip' (Au/S)	NDro NSum XBar
– 'Blue Cliff' (Au/S)	NDro
– 'Blue Fire' (Au/S)	XBar
– 'Blue Frills' (Au/d)	NDro WAln
– 'Blue Heaven' (Au/A)	EWoo NDro XBar
– 'Blue Jay' (Au/A)	WHil
– 'Blue Lace' (Au/A)	WAln
– 'Blue Merle' (Au/B)	NDro
– 'Blue Mist' (Au/B)	NDro
– 'Blue Night' (Au/B)	ITim NDro
– 'Blue Ridge' (Au/A)	NDro
– 'Blue Velvet' (Au/B)	EWoo GQue NDro NHpl NSum XBar
– 'Blue Wave' (Au/d)	CBor
– 'Blue Waves' (Au/B)	EGrI NDro
– 'Blue Yodeler' (Au/A)	EGrI NDro NSum WFar WHil XBar
– 'Blue Yonder' (Au/S)	ITim
– 'Blush Baby' (Au/St)	EBee EWoo NDro NSum NWad WHil XBar
– 'Blyth Spirit' (Au/A)	NDro WAln XBar
– 'Bob Lancashire' (Au/S)	GAbr ITim NDro WHil XBar

- 'Bokay' (Au/d) WAln
- 'Bold Tartan' (Au/St) NDro
- 'Bolero' (Au/A) WAln
- 'Bonafide' (Au/d) EWoo WAln
- 'Bonnie the Cat' (Au) WHil
- 'Bookham Firefly' (Au/A) NDro WHil XBar
- 'Border Bandit' (Au/B) EWoo NDro WHil XBar
- 'Border Beauty' (Au/St) NDro
- 'Border Blue' (Au/B) NDro
- 'Border Patrol' (Au/B) ITim NDro
- 'Border Tawny' (Au/B) NDro
- 'Boromir' (Au/A) EWoo NDro NSum WAln
- 'Bowen's Blue' (Au/B) EWoo NDro
- 'Bradford City' (Au/A) CFis EBee LCro MAvo NDro WFar
- 'Bradmore Bluebell' (Au/B) GAbr NDro
- 'Bramshill' (Au/S) NDro
- 'Bran' (Au/B) NDro
- 'Brandaris' (Au/A) WAln
- 'Branston' (Au/d) XBar
- 'Brasso' (Au/S) NDro WAln XBar
- 'Brazen Hussy' (Au/d) CRos WAln
- 'Brazil' (Au/S) EBee GAbr NDro WHil
- 'Brazos River' (Au/A) NDro
- 'Breckland Joy' (Au/A) NDro WAln WHil
- 'Brenda's Choice' (Au/A) EWoo NDro NSum XBar
- 'Brenda's Dilemma' (Au/S) NDro
- 'Brick Lane' (Au/S) NDro
- 'Bright Eyes' (Au/A) XBar
- 'Bright Ginger' (Au/S) EWoo NDro WAln
- 'Brigitte' (Au/A) XBar
- 'Brimstone and Treacle' (Au/d) WAln XBar
- 'Brixton' (Au/S) NDro
- 'Broad Gold' (Au/A) NDro NSum XBar
- 'Broadwell Gold' (Au/B) GAbr NDro NSum WHil
- 'Brocade' (Au/St) NDro
- 'Brookfield' (Au/S) GAbr NDro NHpl XBar
- 'Broughton' (Au/S) NDro
- 'Brown Ben' (Au/A) EWoo WFar WHil
- 'Brown Bess' (Au/A) GAbr ITim WHil
- 'Brownie' (Au/B) EWoo NBir NDro NSum WHil XBar
- 'Brownie Point' (Au/B) NDro
- 'Brunhilde' (Au/B) NDro
- 'Bucks Green' (Au/S) NDro
- 'Buffy' (Au/St) NDro
- 'Buildwas' (Au/A) **new** WHil
- 'Bunny Black' (Au) GKev
- 'Bunty' (Au/A) XBar
- 'Burnished Gold' (Au/d) WAln
- 'Bush Baby' (Au/B) NDro
- 'Buttermere' (Au/d) WAln
- 'Butterwick' (Au/A) ITim NDro NSum WHil
- 'C.G. Haysom' (Au/S) NDro
- 'C.W. Needham' (Au/A) ITim NDro
- 'Cadiz Bay' (Au/d) EWoo WAln
- 'Café au Lait' (Au/A) XBar
- 'Calypso' (Au/d) EWoo NDro WAln
- 'Cambodunum' (Au/A) NDro NSum WFar WHil XBar
- 'Cambrai' (Au/d) WHil
- 'Camelot' (Au/d) EWoo GKev NDro WFar XBar
- 'Cameo' (Au/A) NHpl
- 'Cameo Beauty' (Au/d) NDro
- 'Candy Stripe' (Au/St) NDro
- 'Cannelle' (Au/d) XBar
- 'Caramel' (Au/A) GAbr WAln
- 'Cardinal Red' (Au/d) NDro
- 'Cardington' (Au/A) WAln
- 'Carmel' (Au/d) EWoo NDro WAln
- 'Carnaval' (Au/B) WHil XBar
- 'Carne' (Au/d) NDro
- 'Carnival' (Au/A) WAln
- 'Carole' (Au/A) NSum WHil
- 'Carousel' (Au/B) EWoo NDro NSum WHil
- 'Carreras' (Au) NDro
- 'Carsa Wakes' (Au/d) NDro WAln
- 'Carzon' (Au/A) NDro
- 'Catta Ha' (Au/d) NDro
- 'Celtic One' (Au/St) NDro
- 'Ceri Nicolle' (Au/B) NDro
- 'Chaffinch' (Au/S) EGrI EWoo GAbr NDro NSum
- 'Chamois' (Au/B) NDro NSum NWad WHil XBar
- 'Chamomile' (Au/B) NDro
- 'Chanel' (Au/S) WAln
- 'Charisma' (Au/St) NDro
- 'Charles Bronson' (Au/d) GAbr NDro XBar
- 'Charles Rennie' (Au/B) EWoo NDro NSum WHil XBar
- 'Charlie's Aunt' (Au/A) NDro
- 'Charlotte' (Au/B) NDro
- 'Charlotte Brookes' (Au/d) WAln
- 'Checkmate' (Au/d) EWoo WAln XBar
- 'Cheeky' (Au/d) EWoo
- 'Chelsea Bridge' (Au/A) EGrI EWoo NDro
- 'Chelsea Girl' (Au/d) NDro
- 'Cheops' (Au/A) EGrI NDro NSum WHil
- 'Cherille' (Au/S) NDro
- 'Cherry' (Au/S) GAbr NDro
- 'Cherry Picker' (Au/A) EGrI NDro NSum
- 'Chestnut' (Au/B) NDro
- 'Cheyenne' (Au/S) EWoo GAbr NDro
- 'Chiffon' (Au/S) EWoo NDro NSum XBar
- 'Chigwell' (Au/S) **new** NDro
- 'Chiquita' (Au/d) EWoo NDro
- 'Chirichua' (Au/S) WAln
- 'Chloë' (Au/S) GRum NDro NHpl
- 'Choir Boy' (Au/A) WAln
- 'Chorister' (Au/S) EBee ITim NDro NSum WHil
- 'Chyne' (Au) NDro
- 'Cindy' (Au/A) NDro
- 'Cinnamon' (Au/d) NDro WFar WHil XBar
- 'Ciribiribin' (Au/A) WAln
- 'Citron-Ella' (Au/d) XBar
- 'Clara' (Au/d) WFar
- 'Clare' (Au/S) NDro
- 'Classy Stripe' (Au/St) ITim
- 'Clatter-Ha' (Au/d) NSum WHil
- 'Claud Wilson' (Au/St) NDro
- 'Claudia Taylor' (Au) NSum
- 'Cleft Stick' (Au) NDro
- 'Cloth of Gold' (Au/A) NDro
- 'Clotted Cream' (Au/B) NDro
- 'Clouded Yellow' (Au/S) NDro
- 'Cloudscape' (Au/S) NDro
- 'Cloudy Bay' (Au/B) NDro WCot
- 'Clunie' (Au/S) NDro XBar
- 'Clyde the Cat' (Au/B) **new** WHil
- 'Cobbydale Orange' (Au/B) NDro
- 'Cocoa' (Au/d) XBar
- 'Coffee' (Au/S) NDro WFar
- 'Colbury' (Au/S) NDro
- 'Colonel Champney' (Au/S) NDro
- 'Colonel Mustard' (Au/d) XBar
- 'Comet' (Au/S) NDro WHil
- 'Connaught Court' (Au/A) CBor EWoo NDro NSum
- 'Conquistador' (Au/A) NDro WAln
- 'Conservative' (Au/S) NDro
- 'Consett' (Au/S) WHil
- 'Cooper's Gold' (Au/B) NDro
- 'Copper Knight' (Au) **new** NDro
- 'Coppi' (Au/A) EWoo NDro
- 'Cornish Cream' (Au/B) NDro
- 'Cornmeal' (Au/S) NDro WHil XBar
- 'Corntime' (Au/S) EWoo WAln
- 'Corrie Files' (Au/d) XBar

- 'Cortina' (Au/S) EGrI EWoo ITim NDro WHil
- 'County Park Red' (Au/B) NDro
- 'Coventry Street' (Au/S) NDro NSum
- 'Crackling Rosie' (Au/A/d) WAln
- 'Craig Nordie' (Au/B) NDro
- 'Craig Vaughan' (Au/A) NDro NSum WHil
- 'Cranborne' (Au/A) WAln
- 'Crimple' (Au/S) NDro
- 'Crimson Glow' (Au/d) EWTr GAbr ITim LCro MAvo NDro NSum WHil XBar
- 'Crinoline' (Au/S) NDro WHil
- 'Cuckoo Fair' (Au/S) ECtt EWoo NDro NSum WFar
- 'Cuddles' (Au/A) EWoo NDro WAln
- 'Curry Blend' (Au/B) EDAr EWoo NDro NWad WHil
- 'D.S.J.' (Au/S) NDro
- 'Daftie Green' (Au/S) NDro
- 'Dakota' (Au/S) EWoo
- 'Dales Red' (Au/B) EWoo NDro NHpl NSum WHil
- 'Dan Tiger' (Au/St) EWoo NDro WHil
- 'Dangerous Moonlight' (Au) **new** MAvo
I - 'Daniel' (Au/d) XBar
- 'Daniel' (Au/A) NDro WAln
- 'Daphnis' (Au/S) NDro
- 'Darent Tiger' (Au/St) NDro XBar
- 'Dark Eyes' (Au/d) EWoo NDro NSum WHil
- 'Dark Lady' (Au/A) WAln
- 'D'Artagnan' (Au/B) NDro
- 'Darth Vader' (Au/d) XBar
- 'David Beckham' (Au/d) WAln
- 'David McSparron' (Au/B) NDro
- 'Day by Day' (Au/St) NDro
- 'Deal' (Au/S) NDro
- 'Deckchair' (Au/St) NDro
- 'Dedham' (Au/d) WAln WHil
- 'Del Boy' (Au/A) WAln
- 'Delilah' (Au/d) NDro NSum WFar WHil
- 'Denise' (Au/S) WAln
- 'Denna Snuffer' (Au/d) EWoo GAbr NDro
- 'Derrill' (Au/B) NDro
- 'Derwent Water' (Au/S) NDro
- 'Deuce of Hearts' (Au/St) NDro
- 'Devon Cream' (Au/d) NDro XBar
- 'Devon's Road' (Au/S) NDro
- 'Diamond Dust' (Au/B) NDro
- 'Diane' (Au/A) NDro
- 'Dick Rogers' (Au/B) NDro
- 'Dido' (Au/B) XBar
- 'Digby' (Au/d) NDro WAln
- 'Digit' (Au/d) NDro WAln
- 'Dill' (Au/A) NDro NSum WHil
- 'Dilly Dilly' (Au/A) NDro XBar
- 'Divint Dunch' (Au/A) NDro WHil XBar
- 'Doctor Duthie' (Au/S) NDro
- 'Doctor Lennon's White' (Au/B) EWoo GAbr NDro NWad WHil XBar
- 'Dolly' (Au/B) NDro
- 'Don Carlos' (Au/d) XBar
- 'Donhead' (Au/A) ITim NDro WHil
- 'Donna Clancy' (Au/S) NDro XBar
- 'Doreen Stephens' (Au/A) NDro
- 'Doris Jean' (Au/A) NDro
- 'Dorothy' (Au/S) WHil
- 'Doublet' (Au/d) EGrI NDro NSum WHil XBar
- 'Doubloon' (Au/d) XBar
- 'Doublure' (Au/d) EWoo GAbr NDro WHil
- 'Douglas Bader' (Au/A) ITim NDro NSum
- 'Douglas Black' (Au/S) EGrI EWoo GAbr NDro WHil
- 'Douglas Green' (Au/S) NDro
- 'Dovedale' (Au/S) NDro
- 'Doyen' (Au/d) EWoo ITim NDro NHpl WAln WHil XBar
- 'Dragon's Hoard' (Au/A) WAln
- 'Dubarii' (Au/A) NDro WAln
- 'Duke of Edinburgh' (Au/B) NDro
- 'Dusky Girl' (Au/A) NDro WAln WHil
- 'Dusky Maiden' (Au/A) EWoo NDro NSum WHil
- 'Dusky Yellow' (Au/B) NDro
- 'Eastern Promise' (Au/A) EWoo NDro NSum WHil
- 'Ed Spivey' (Au/A) NDro
- 'Eden Alexander' (Au/B) EWoo NDro WHil XBar
- 'Eden Amethyst' (Au/B) NDro
- 'Eden Aramis' (Au/B) NDro
- 'Eden Blue Star' (Au/B) EWoo NDro NSum WFar WHil
- 'Eden Bramley' (Au/B) NDro
- 'Eden Carmine' (Au/B) EWoo NDro NWad WHil XBar
- 'Eden Dark Eyes' (Au/B) NDro
- 'Eden David' (Au/B) NDro WFar WHil
- 'Eden Emma' (Au) **new** NDro
- 'Eden Ensign' (Au/B) NDro WFar WHil
- 'Eden Fanfare' (Au/B) NDro WFar
- 'Eden Glow' (Au/B) NDro
- 'Eden Goldfinch' (Au/B) EWoo GAbr NDro WFar WHil
- 'Eden Greenfinch' (Au/B) EWoo NDro NSum WHil XBar
- 'Eden Lilactime' (Au/B) NDro WFar WHil
- 'Eden Moonlight' (Au/B) NDro WHil XBar
- 'Eden Porthos' (Au/B) NDro
- 'Eden Rhiann' (Au/B) NDro WHil
- 'Eden Royalty' (Au/B) WFar WHil
- 'Eden Ruby Star' (Au/B) NDro
- 'Eden Simon' (Au/B) NDro XBar
- 'Eden Sunrise' (Au/B) NDro NSum WHil
- 'Eden Surprise' (Au/B) NDro
- 'Eden Wendy' (Au/B) NDro
- 'Edinburgh' (Au/A) WAln
- 'Edith Major' (Au/d) NSum
- 'Eglinton' (Au) NDro NSum
- 'Eileen K' (Au/S) NDro
- 'Elegance' (Au/S) WFar
- 'Elf Star' (Au/A) NSum
- 'Eli Jenkins' (Au) WAln
- 'Elizabeth Ann' (Au/A) NDro
- 'Ellen Thompson' (Au/A) EGrI NDro WHil
- 'Ellie May' (Au/S) XBar
- 'Eloise' (Au/d) XBar
- 'Elsie May' (Au/A) EWoo ITim NDro
- 'Embley' (Au/S) NDro NHpl
- 'Emery Down' (Au/S) NDro
- 'Emily Mary' (Au/B) NDro
- 'Emmett Smith' (Au/A) NDro NSum
- 'Ems Blue' (Au/B) NDro
- 'Ems Funny Face' (Au/B) NDro
- 'Enlightened' (Au/A) NDro
- 'Erica' (Au/A) EWoo NDro NSum WHil
- 'Erjon' (Au/S) NDro
- 'Error' (Au/S) NDro
- 'Eschman Starflower' (Au/S) WHil
- 'Ethel' (Au) CBor NDro
- 'Ethel Wild' (Au/d) XBar
- 'Ethel Wilkes' (Au/d) WAln
- 'Etna' (Au/S) NDro
- 'Euston Road' (Au/S) NDro
- 'Eve Guest' (Au/A) NDro NSum
- 'Everest Blue' (Au/S) EWoo GAbr NDro XBar
- 'Everso Lovely Blue' (Au/B) NDro
- 'Excalibur' (Au/d) GAbr NDro NSum
- (Exhibition Series) 'Exhibition Blau' (Au/B) WHil
- - 'Exhibition Rot' (Au/B) GKev
- 'Exotic Booze' (Au/St) **new** NDro
- 'Eye Candy' (Au/St) NDro
- 'Eyeopener' (Au/A) NDro NSum WHil XBar
- 'Fabuloso' (Au/St) EWoo NDro
- 'Fairy' (Au/A) WAln
- 'Fairy Dust' (Au/D) XBar

- 'Fairy Light' (Au/S) NDro
- 'Fairy Queen' (Au/S) NDro
- 'Faliraki Fanciful' (Au/A) NDro WHil
- 'Falstaff' (Au/d) WAln
- 'Fanciful' (Au/S) NDro WHil XBar
- 'Fancy Free' (Au) EWoo
- 'Fancy Pants' (Au/S) NDro
- 'Fandango' (Au/St) NDro WFar
- 'Fanfare' (Au/S) NDro WHil XBar
- 'Fanny Meerbeck' (Au/S) EPfP GAbr NDro WHil
- 'Fantasia' (Au/d) NDro
- 'Faro' (Au/S) NDro
- 'Favourite' (Au/S) EWoo ITim NDro NSum WHil XBar
- 'Femme Fatale' (Au/St) NDro
- 'Fenby' (Au/S) EWoo
- 'Fennay' (Au/S) EWoo NSum
- 'Ferrybridge' (Au/A) NDro
- 'Festubert' (Au/d) WHil
- 'Fiddler's Green' (Au/d) GAbr NDro NWad WCot XBar
- 'Figaro' (Au/S) NDro XBar
- 'Figurine' (Au/d) WAln WHil
- 'Finchfield' (Au/A) EWoo NDro WAln
- 'Fine Art' (Au/S) NDro
- 'Finley' (Au/B) NDro
- 'Firsby' (Au/d) NDro WHil XBar
- 'First Lady' (Au/A) NDro WAln WFar WHil
- 'First Light' (Au/B) NDro NSum WHil
- 'Fleet Street' (Au/S) NDro NSum WFar WHil XBar
- 'Fleminghouse' (Au/S) GAbr NDro
- 'Flirty' (Au/St) NDro
- 'Florence Brown' (Au/S) NDro
- 'Fluffy Duckling' (Au/S) NDro
- 'For You' (Au/St) NDro
- 'Forest Autumn Glow' (Au/d) WHil
- 'Forest Beech' (Au/d) WHil
- 'Forest Blue Angel' (Au) **new** WHil
- 'Forest Blush' (Au/d) WHil
- 'Forest Bordeaux' (Au/d) WHil XBar
- 'Forest Bracken' (Au/d) EWoo GAbr WHil
- 'Forest Bronze' (Au/d) **new** WHil
- 'Forest Brown Sugar' (Au/d) WHil
- 'Forest Burgundy' (Au/d) WHil
- 'Forest Burnt Gold' (Au/d) WHil
- 'Forest Buttercup' (Au/d) WHil
- 'Forest Canary' (Au/d) WHil
- 'Forest Cappuccino' (Au/d) EWoo WHil XBar
- 'Forest Chocolate Teapot' (Au/d) WHil
- 'Forest Coffee' (Au/d) NDro WHil
- 'Forest Dawn' (Au/d) WHil
- 'Forest Dazzler' (Au/St/d) **new** WHil
- 'Forest Delight' (Au/d) WHil
- 'Forest Devon Dream' (Au/d) **new** WHil
- 'Forest Diamond' (Au/d) WHil
- 'Forest Disco Dancer' (Au/d) WHil
- 'Forest Duet' (Au/d) EWoo NDro WFar WHil
- 'Forest Dusk' (Au/d) WHil
- 'Forest Emperor' (Au/d) WHil
- 'Forest Evermore' (Au/d) WHil
- 'Forest Fall' (Au/d) WHil
- 'Forest Fancy That' (Au/d) WHil
- 'Forest Fire' (Au/d) EWoo NSum WHil XBar
- 'Forest Forever' (Au/d) **new** WHil
- 'Forest Foxy Girl' (Au/d) WHil
- 'Forest Garnet' (Au/d) WHil
- 'Forest Gingernut' (Au/d) WHil
- 'Forest Glade' (Au/d) WHil
- 'Forest Gold' (Au/d) **new** WHil
- 'Forest Golden Crown' (Au/d) WHil
- 'Forest Goldfinch' (Au/d) **new** WHil
- 'Forest Gorge' (Au/d) **new** WHil
- 'Forest Heartbreaker' (Au/d) WHil
- 'Forest Hint of Pink' (Au/d) WHil
- 'Forest Hot Stuff' (Au/d) WHil
- 'Forest Kingcup' (Au/d) WHil
- 'Forest Lemon' (Au/d) EWoo WHil XBar
- 'Forest Lemon Sorbet' (Au/d) WHil
- 'Forest Lime' (Au/d) WHil
- 'Forest Love' (Au/d) WHil
- 'Forest Mayday' (Au/d) WHil
- 'Forest Old Gold' (Au/d) **new** WHil
- 'Forest Old Thumper' (Au/d) WHil
- 'Forest Peach' (Au/d) WHil
- 'Forest Pecan' (Au/d) WHil
- 'Forest Pink Frills' (Au/d) **new** WHil
- 'Forest Pink Lustre' (Au/d) WHil
- 'Forest Pink Sensation' (Au/d) WHil
- 'Forest Pink Surprise' (Au/d) WHil
- 'Forest Plum' (Au/d) WHil
- 'Forest Prince' (Au/d) WHil
- 'Forest Purple Penny' (Au/d) WHil
- 'Forest Raspberry' (Au/d) **new** WHil
- 'Forest Raspberry Delight' (Au) WHil
- 'Forest Red Beret' (Au/d) WHil
- 'Forest Red Mist' (Au/d) WHil
- 'Forest Red 'n' Fred' (Au/d) WHil
- 'Forest Redstart' (Au/St) WHil
- 'Forest Rocket' (Au/d) WHil
- 'Forest Rose' (Au/d) EWoo
- 'Forest Scarlet Woman' (Au/d) WHil
- 'Forest Sensation' (Au/d) **new** WHil
- 'Forest Shade' (Au/d) WHil
- 'Forest Sorcerer' (Au/d) WHil
- 'Forest Splendid' (Au/d) WHil
- 'Forest Starlet' (Au/d) WHil
- 'Forest Stormcloud' (Au) **new** WHil
- 'Forest Sunbeam' (Au/d) WHil
- 'Forest Sunburst' (Au/d) WHil
- 'Forest Sunfire' (Au/d) WHil
- 'Forest Sunlight' (Au/d) WHil
- 'Forest Sunshade' (Au/d) WHil
- 'Forest Sunshine' (Au/d) WHil
- 'Forest Thatch' (Au/d) WHil
- 'Forest Twilight' (Au/d) EWoo WHil XBar
- 'Forest Way' (Au/d) WHil
- 'Foundling' (Au) ITim
- 'Foxfire' (Au/A) WAln
- 'Foxy' (Au/B) NDro
- 'Fradley' (Au/A) NDro WFar WHil
- 'Françoise' (Au/d) XBar
- 'Frank Bailey' (Au/d) EWoo WAln
- 'Frank Crosland' (Au/A) NDro NSum WHil
- 'Frank Faulkner' (Au/A) WAln

- 'Frank Hemmingway' (Au/B) NDro
- 'Frank Jenning' (Au/A) NDro WAln
- 'Fred Booley' (Au/d) EWoo NDro NSum WFar WHil XBar
- 'Fred Livesley' (Au/A) WAln
- 'Freya' (Au/S) NDro
- 'Fridl' (Au) EBee ELan
- 'Friends of Ashwood' (Au/S) NDro
- 'Friskney' (Au/d) EWoo WAln
- 'Frittenden Yellow' (Au/B) NDro
- 'Fromelles' (Au/d) WHil
- 'Frosty' (Au/S) NDro
- 'Fuller's Red' (Au/S) NDro WHil XBar
- 'Funny Valentine' (Au/d) EWoo NDro NSum WHil XBar
- 'G.L.Taylor' (Au/A) NDro
- 'Gaia' (Au/d) WHil XBar
- 'Gail Atkinson' (Au/A) NSum WAln
- 'Galator' (Au/A) WAln
- 'Ganymede' (Au/d) WAln
- 'Gary Pallister' (Au/A) WHil
- 'Gas Lane' (Au/A) WHil
- 'Gay Crusader' (Au/A) NDro WFar WHil
- 'Gee Cross' (Au/A) NDro NSum
- 'Geldersome Green' (Au/S) GKev GRum NDro
- 'Geldersome Green No. 2' (Au/S) ITim
- 'Gemini' (Au/S) NDro
- 'Generosity' (Au/A) NDro NSum WHil
- 'Geordie' (Au/A) WAln
- 'George Edge' (Au/B) NDro
- 'George Harrison' (Au/B) NDro
- 'George Jennings' (Au/A) NDro
- 'George Swinford's Leathercoat' (Au/B) NDro WHil
- 'Geronimo' (Au/S) GAbr NDro
- 'Gerry Thompson' (Au/A) WAln
- 'Ghost Ridge' (Au/B) NDro
- 'Gild Green' (Au/S) NDro
- 'Gimli' (Au/A) WAln WHil
- 'Ginger Spice' (Au/B) NDro WHil
- 'Girl Guide' (Au/S) WHil
- 'Gizabroon' (Au/S) CBor EBee GAbr GKev NDro NLar WHil XBar
- 'Gleam' (Au/S) EDAr NDro NSum WHil XBar
- 'Gleneagles' (Au/S) GKev GRum NDro
- 'Glenelg' (Au/S) GAbr ITim NDro WHil XBar
- 'Glenluce' (Au/S) EWoo NDro
- 'Gnome' (Au/B) GAbr GArf NDro WHil
- 'Goeblii' (Au/B) EWoo NDro WHil XBar
- 'Gold Seam' (Au/A) WAln WHil XBar
- 'Golden Boy' (Au/A) NDro NSum WAln
- 'Golden Chartreuse' (Au/d) EWoo NDro
- 'Golden Fleece' (Au/S) EWoo NDro
- 'Golden Galator' (Au/A) WAln
- 'Golden Glory' (Au/A) NDro
- 'Golden Hind' (Au/d) EWoo NDro NSum WHil XBar
- 'Golden Splendour' (Au/d) EWoo GKev NDro NSum WFar WHil XBar
- 'Golden Wedding' (Au/A) NDro WAln WHil XBar
- 'Goldie' (Au/S) NDro
- 'Goldwin' (Au/A) NDro NSum
- 'Gollum' (Au/A) NDro WAln WFar WHil XBar
- 'Good Report' (Au/A) NDro NSum WFar WHil
- 'Goody Goody' (Au/St) NDro
- 'Googie' (Au/d) NDro WHil
- 'Gorey' (Au/A) EWoo NDro WHil
- 'Grabley' (Au/S) NDro
- 'Grace Ellen' (Au/S) NDro
- 'Gracie Lou' (Au/B) NDro
- 'Grand Slam' (Au/D) XBar
- 'Grandad's Favourite' (Au/B) EWoo NDro WHil
- 'Grasmere' (Au/d) NDro
- 'Green Abundance' (Au/B) EWoo
- 'Green Finger' (Au/S) EWoo
- 'Green Frill' (Au) NSum
- 'Green Goddess' (Au/St) EWoo NDro
- 'Green Isle' (Au/S) GAbr NDro XBar
- 'Green Jacket' (Au/S) NDro
- 'Green Lane' (Au/S) XBar
- 'Green Parrot' (Au/S) NDro WHil
- 'Green Shank' (Au/S) NDro WHil XBar
- 'Greenfinger' (Au/S) NSum
- 'Greenpeace' (Au/S) GAbr NDro
- 'Grenville' (Au) EGrl
- 'Greswolde' (Au/d) EWoo
- 'Greta' (Au/S) GAbr NDro WHil XBar
- 'Grey Cloud' (Au/B) NDro
- 'Grey Day' (Au/S) NDro
- 'Grey Hawk' (Au/S) NDro
- 'Grey Lag' (Au/S) NSum
- 'Grey Monarch' (Au/S) EWoo
- 'Grey Owl' (Au/S) NDro
- 'Grüner Veltliner' (Au/S) NDro
- 'Guinea' (Au/S) EWoo GAbr NDro
- 'Gwai Loh' (Au/B) NDro
- 'Gwen' (Au/A) NDro WAln XBar
- 'Gwen Baker' (Au/d) NDro
- 'Gwenda' (Au/A) WAln WHil
- 'Gypsy Boy' (Au/A) WAln
- 'H Old Gold' (Au/S) NDro
- 'Habanera' (Au/A) NDro NSum WFar
- 'Haffner' (Au/S) NDro
- 'Hallmark' (Au/A) NDro NSum WAln WHil XBar
- 'Handsome Lass' (Au/St) EWoo NDro WFar
- 'Hannah' (Au/A) WAln WHil
- 'Harlequin' (Au/B) NDro
- 'Harmony' (Au/B) EWoo NDro NSum WHil XBar
- 'Harry' (Au/A) **new** WHil
- 'Harry Armitage' (Au/B) NDro WHil
- 'Harry Hotspur' (Au/A) NDro NSum WFar WHil XBar
- 'Harry 'O'' (Au/S) NDro
- 'Harthorpeburn' (Au/B) NDro
- 'Harvest Glow' (Au/S) NDro WFar WHil
- 'Hawkwood' (Au/S) EBee GAbr GKev NDro WHil XBar
- 'Hazel' (Au/B) NDro XBar
- 'Hazel' (Au/A) NDro WHil
- 'Headdress' (Au/S) EWoo GAbr
- 'Heady' (Au/A) EWoo NDro WHil XBar
- 'Heart of Gold' (Au/A) NDro NSum WAln WHil
- 'Hearts of Oak' (Au/A) WAln WHil
- 'Heaven Scent' (Au) NDro
- 'Hebers' (Au) NDro
- 'Helen' (Au/S) NDro WHil
- 'Helen Barter' (Au/S) NDro NSum WHil
- 'Helen Ruan' (Au) NSum
- 'Helen Ruane' (Au/d) GKev GQue NDro WFar
- 'Helena' (Au/S) NDro WAln WHil
- 'Helena Dean' (Au/d) WAln
- 'Hello Gorgeous' (Au) **new** NDro
- 'Henry's Bane' (Au/St) NDro
- 'Her Nibs' (Au/St) NDro
- 'Hermes the Cat' (Au/B) WHil
- 'Hermia' (Au/A) WHil XBar
- 'Hetty Woolf' (Au/S) GAbr NDro
- 'Hew Dalrymple' (Au/S) NDro
- 'Highland Park' (Au/A) NDro NSum WHil XBar
- 'Hillhook' (Au/A) NSum WAln WHil
- 'Hillview Hermes' (Au/S) NDro
- 'Hinton Admiral' (Au/S) NDro NSum WHil XBar
- 'Hinton Fields' (Au/S) LCro MAvo NDro WFar XBar
- 'Hit Parade' (Au) WAln
- 'Hobby Horse' (Au/St) ITim NSum

- 'Holyrood' (Au/S) ITim NDro NHpl
- 'Honey' (Au/d) EWoo GAbr NDro NSum
- 'Honeydawn' (Au/B) NDro
- 'Hopleys Coffee' (Au/d) EWoo GAbr NDro
- 'Hopton Gem' (Au/B) NDro
- 'Hortense' (Au/d) XBar
- 'Hurstwood Midnight' (Au) XBar
- * – 'Hyacinth' (Au/S) EBee NDro WCAu
- 'Iago' (Au/S) NDro
- 'Ian Greville' (Au/A) NDro NSum XBar
- 'Ice Cap' (Au/d) XBar
- 'Ice Maiden' (Au/A) NDro NSum WHil XBar
- 'Idgy' (Au/d) WHil
- 'Idmiston' (Au/S) GAbr NDro WHil XBar
- 'Imari Stripe' (Au/St) WHil
- 'Immaculate' (Au/A) NDro NSum WHil XBar
- 'Impassioned' (Au/A) NDro
- 'Impeccable' (Au/A) XBar
- 'Imperturbable' (Au/A) NDro
- 'Indian Love Call' (Au/A) EGrl GAbr ITim NDro NSum WHil
- I – 'Innominata' (Au/S) NDro
- 'Innsworth' (Au/A) WAln
- 'Iris Scott' (Au/A) ITim NDro
- 'Isabel' (Au/S) WAln
- 'Isabella' (Au/A) NDro
- 'Jack Dean' (Au/A) WFar WHil XBar
- 'Jack Horner' (Au) NDro
- 'Jack Redfern' (Au/A) NDro
- 'Jaffa' (Au/A) NDro NSum
- 'James Arnot' (Au/S) NDro
- 'James Wattam' (Au/S) NDro
- 'Jane' (Au/S) WAln
- 'Jane Myers' (Au/d) WAln WHil
- 'Janet Watts' (Au/B) EWoo NDro
- 'Janie Hill' (Au/A) XBar
- 'Jb' (Au) GAbr
- 'Je t'Adore' (Au/St) NDro
- 'Jean Fielder' (Au/A) NDro
- 'Jean Jacques' (Au/A) NDro
- I – 'Jean Jacques' (Au/d) XBar
- 'Jean-Claude' (Au/d) XBar
- 'Jeanne' (Au/A) EWoo
- 'Jeannie Jingles II' (Au/St) NDro
- 'Jeannie Telford' (Au/A) NDro XBar
- 'Jeff Scruton' (Au/A) WAln
- 'Jenny' (Au/A) EWoo NDro NSum WFar XBar
- 'Jersey Bounce' (Au/A) EWoo ITim NDro WHil
- 'Jessie' (Au/d) NDro
- 'Jessy' (Au/A) **new** WHil
- 'Jilting Jessie' (Au/St) NDro NSum
- 'Joanna Shayler' (Au/A) **new** XBar
- 'Joanne' (Au/A) EWoo GAbr NDro
- 'Joanne' (Au/d) NDro XBar
- 'Joe Perks' (Au/A) EWoo ITim NDro WHil XBar
- 'Joel' (Au/S) EGrl EWoo ITim NDro NSum WHil XBar
- 'Johann Bach' (Au/B) EWoo NDro NSum
- 'John Hart' (Au/A) NDro WHil
- 'John Wayne' (Au/A) EWoo NDro WHil XBar
- 'John Woolf' (Au/S) NDro
- 'Jonathon' (Au/A) NDro WAln
- 'Joy' (Au/A) EWoo NDro NSum NWad WHil XBar
- 'Joyce' (Au/A) GAbr NDro NSum WFar WHil XBar
- 'Judith Borman' (Au/d) GKev NDro
- 'Judy' (Au/A) **new** WHil
- 'Julia Jane' (Au/B) NDro
- 'Julie Nuttall' (Au/B) EWoo GAbr NDro NSum NWad WHil
- 'June' (Au/A) NDro NSum
- 'Jungfrau' (Au/d) EWoo NDro XBar
- 'Jupp' (Au/d) EBee
- 'Jura' (Au/A) WAln
- 'Just Steven' (Au/A) WAln
- 'Justin Case' (Au/B) NDro
- 'K S' (Au/S) NDro
- KALEIDOSCOPE (mixed) (Au) ELan
- 'Karen Cordrey' (Au/S) EBee EWoo NDro NSum WHil
- 'Karen McDonald' (Au/A) NDro NSum XBar
- 'Kate Haywood' (Au/B) NDro
- 'Ken Chilton' (Au/A) EWoo NDro WHil XBar
- 'Kentucky Blues' (Au/d) EWoo NDro WAln XBar
- 'Kercup' (Au/A) EWoo WHil XBar
- 'Kersey' (Au/S) NDro
- 'Kevin' (Au/A) WAln
- 'Kevin Keegan' (Au/A) NDro NSum WHil XBar
- 'Key West' (Au/A) NDro WAln
- 'Khachaturian' (Au/A) NDro WAln
- 'Khaki' (Au/d) WHil
- 'Kidderminster' (Au/A) **new** WHil
- 'Kilby' (Au/A) NDro NSum
- 'Kim' (Au/A) NDro WHil
- 'Kimberworth Boy' (Au/A) NDro WAln
- 'Kingcup' (Au/A) GAbr NDro WHil XBar
- 'Kingfisher' (Au/A) EWoo NDro NSum WHil
- 'Kingpin' (Au/St) NDro
- 'Kirklands' (Au/d) ITim NDro WHil
- 'Kitterford Cross' (Au/B) NDro
- 'Kiwi' (Au/B) NDro
- 'Kohinoor' (Au/A) NDro NSum WHil
- 'Königin der Nacht' (Au/St) NDro WHil
- 'Krithia' (Au/d) WHil
- 'Lady Daresbury' (Au/A) NDro WHil XBar
- 'Lady Day' (Au/d) EWoo WAln
- 'Lady Diana' (Au/S) EWoo NDro
- 'Lady Emma Monson' (Au/S) NDro
- 'Lady Joyful' (Au/S) NDro
- 'Lady of the Vale' (Au/A) NDro WAln WHil
- 'Lady Penelope Sitwell' (Au/St) NDro
- 'Lady Zoë' (Au/S) EWoo NDro
- 'Lambert's Gold' (Au/B) EWoo GAbr WHil
- 'Lambrook Gold' (Au/B) NDro
- 'Lamplugh' (Au/d) EWoo NSum WHil
- 'Lancelot' (Au/d) EWoo
- 'Landy' (Au/A) NDro XBar
- 'Langley Park' (Au/A) NDro WHil XBar
- 'Laptop' (Au/St) NDro
- 'Lara' (Au/A) NDro NSum XBar
- 'Laredo' (Au/A) EWoo
- 'Larry' (Au/A) EWoo NDro WFar WHil XBar
- 'Late Romantic' (Au/d) CDor ECtt GAbr GRum MHol NHpl NLar WHil
- 'Lavender Hill' (Au/St) NDro
- 'Lavender Lady' (Au/B) EWoo NDro
- 'Lavender Ridge' (Au/B) NDro
- 'Laverock' (Au/S) NBir WHil
- 'Laverock Fancy' (Au/S) GAbr NDro XBar
- 'Lazy River' (Au/A) EWoo NDro WAln
- 'Le Cateau' (Au/d) WHil
- 'Leather Jacket' (Au/B) GAbr WHil
- 'Leathercoat' (Au/B) EWoo
- 'Lechistan' (Au/S) NDro NSum
- 'Lee' (Au/A) NDro WAln XBar
- 'Lee Clark' (Au/A) NDro NSum WAln XBar
- 'Lee Paul' (Au/A) EWoo GAbr NDro NSum WHil XBar
- 'Lee Sharpe' (Au/A) EWoo NDro NSum WAln XBar
- 'Legolas' (Au/A) WAln XBar
- 'Leicester Square' (Au/S) NDro
- 'Lemon Drop' (Au/S) ITim NDro
- 'Lemon Sherbet' (Au/B) EWoo GAbr GQue GRum NDro WHil

- 'Lepton Jubilee' (Au/S) GAbr NDro
- 'Lester' (Au/d) WAln WHil
- 'Leverton' (Au/d) NSum
- 'Light Fantastic' (Au/S) NDro
- 'Light Hearted' (Au/A) NDro WHil XBar
- 'Light Music' (Au/d) WAln
- 'Likely Lad' (Au/St) EWoo
- 'Lila' (Au/A) NDro WAln WHil XBar
- 'Lilac Domino' (Au/S) NDro WHil XBar
- 'Lilac Ladywood' (Au/d) EWoo WFar XBar
- 'Lilian Hill' (Au/A) EWoo XBar
- 'Lillibet' (Au/A) NDro
- 'Lime 'n' Lemon' (Au/d) ITim NDro WHil
- 'Lime Ridge' (Au) NDro WAln
- 'Limelight' (Au/A) NDro
- 'Limelight' (Au/S) NDro
- 'Lincoln Bullion' (Au/d) EWoo NDro WHil XBar
- 'Lincoln Chestnut' (Au/d) EWoo NDro XBar
- 'Lincoln Cuckoo' (Au/d) NDro XBar
- 'Lincoln Fair' (Au) XBar
- 'Lincoln Imp' (Au/d) NDro
- 'Lincoln Imperial' (Au/d) NDro
- 'Lincoln Melody' (Au/St/d) NDro XBar
- 'Lincoln Poacher' (Au/d) NDro
- 'Lincoln Whisper' (Au/d) NDro
- 'Linda' (Au/A) WHil
- 'Lindley' (Au/S) NDro
- 'Ling' (Au/A) GAbr NDro XBar
- 'Linnet' (Au/B) NDro
- 'Lintz' (Au/B) EWoo NDro WHil XBar
- 'Linze 2' (Au/S) NDro
- 'Lisa' (Au/A) EWoo NDro WFar WHil XBar
- 'Lisa Clara' (Au/S) EWoo NDro NHpl WFar XBar
- 'Lisa's Smile' (Au/S) EWoo NDro WHil XBar
- 'Little Bo Peep' (Au) NDro
- 'Little Rosetta' (Au/d) NDro NSum WHil
- 'Lizzie Files' (Au/A) WAln
- 'Lockyer's Gem' (Au/B/St) NDro
- 'Lockyer's Green' (Au/B) EWoo WHil
- 'Lofty' (Au/St) NDro
- 'Lolita' (Au/St) EWoo NDro NSum WHil XBar
- 'Lord Saye and Sele' (Au/St) EWoo GAbr NDro NSum NWad XBar
- 'Lottie Files' (Au/A) **new** WHil
- 'Loudhailer' (Au/B) NDro
- 'Louis' (Au/d) ELan XBar
- 'Louise Jordan' (Au/A) NDro
- 'Lovebird' (Au/S) GAbr NDro NHpl
- 'Lowther Show' (Au/St) NDro
- 'Luca' (Au/d) WHil
- 'Lucia' (Au/B) XBar
- 'Lucy Locket' (Au/B) GAbr LCro LRHS MAvo MPnt NDro WHil
- 'Ludlow' (Au/S) NDro
- 'Lunar Eclipse' (Au/d) CWCL GRum LBar MHol NLar WTor
- 'Lupy Minstrel' (Au/S) NDro
- 'Lyn' (Au/A) NDro
- 'Lynn' (Au/A) WAln
- 'Lynn Cooper' (Au/S) EWoo
- 'MacWatt's Blue' (Au/B) EWoo GAbr GArf NDro NWad WHil XBar
- 'Maggie' (Au/S) GAbr
- 'Mametz' (Au/d) WHil
- 'Mamm-Gozh' (Au/d) XBar
- 'Mandarin' (Au/A) NDro NSum WFar WHil XBar
- 'Mandy' (Au/S) NDro
- 'Marble Arch' (Au/S) NDro
- 'Mardi Gras' (Au/d) WAln
- 'Margaret' (Au/S) GAbr NDro NSum
- 'Margaret Faulkner' (Au/A) GAbr XBar
- 'Margaret Merril' (Au) GAbr
- 'Margot Fonteyn' (Au/A) EWoo GAbr WHil XBar
- 'Mariandl' (Au/A) WHIf
- 'Marie Crousse' (Au/d) ITim NDro WCot WFar
- 'Marie Pierre' (Au/d) XBar
- 'Marie-Jeanne' (Au/d) **new** XBar
- 'Marion Tiger' (Au/St) NDro
- 'Mark' (Au/A) GAbr NDro XBar
- 'Marmion' (Au/S) NDro WHil XBar
- 'Mars Bars' (Au/St) NDro
- 'Martha's Choice' (Au/A) WAln
- 'Martin Luther King' (Au/S) EWoo NDro XBar
- 'Mary' (Au/d) GAbr NDro NSum
- 'Mary Poppins' (Au/S) NDro
- 'Mary Taylor' (Au/S) NDro
- 'Mary Zach' (Au/S) EWoo NDro WHil
- 'Matthew' (Au) GKev
- 'Matthew Yates' (Au/d) GAbr ITim NDro NHpl WCot
- 'Maureen Millward' (Au/A) NDro
- 'May' (Au/A) EWoo NDro NSum
- 'Mazetta Stripe' (Au/S/St) GAbr NDro WHil
- 'Meadowlark' (Au/A) EWoo ITim NDro NSum WHil XBar
- 'Mehta' (Au/A) NDro
- 'Mellifluous' (Au/A) WHil
- 'Melody' (Au/S) NDro
- 'Merlin' (Au/S) NSum WFar
- 'Merlin Stripe' (Au/St) NDro WHil XBar
- 'Mermaid' (Au/d) GAbr
- 'Merridale' (Au/A) GAbr WHil
- 'Mersey Tiger' (Au/S) GAbr ITim NDro NSum WHil XBar
- 'Mexicano' (Au/A) NDro WAln
- 'Michael Wattam' (Au/S) NDro
- 'Michelle' (Au/B) **new** XBar
- 'Mick' (Au/A) WHil XBar
- 'Midland Marvel' (Au/St) NDro
- 'Mikado' (Au/S) NSum XBar
- 'Milkmaid' (Au/A) WMAq
- 'Millicent' (Au/A) NDro NSum WHil XBar
- 'Millwood's Lemon and Lime' (Au/d) CBor CFis
- 'Mink' (Au/A) NDro WHil XBar
- 'Minley' (Au/S) GAbr NBir NDro
- 'Minstrel' (Au/S) ITim NDro
- 'Minty' (Au/St) NDro
- 'Mipsie Miranda' (Au/d) EWoo NDro
- 'Mirabella Bay' (Au/A) WAln
- 'Mirandinha' (Au/A) NDro
- 'Mish Mish' (Au/d) GAbr NDro WHil
- 'Miss Bluey' (Au/d) EWoo NDro XBar
- 'Miss Jones' (Au/St) NDro
- 'Miss Muffet' (Au/S) NDro
- 'Miss Newman' (Au/A) NDro NSum
- 'Miss Pinky' (Au/d) EWoo NDro
- 'Miss Teak' (Au/S) NDro
- 'Mistral' (Au) **new** GAbr
- 'Misty' (Au/d) NDro
- 'Mojave' (Au/S) GAbr GArf GEdr GRum ITim NDro NHpl NSum WHil XBar
- 'Mollie Langford' (Au/A) NDro WHil XBar
- 'Mondeo' (Au/A) WAln
- 'Monet' (Au/S) NDro
- 'Moneymoon' (Au/S) EWoo GAbr NDro WHil
- 'Monica' (Au/A) XBar
- 'Monk' (Au/S) NDro XBar
- 'Monmouth Star' (Au/St) WHil
- 'Moon Fairy' (Au/S) NDro WHil XBar
- 'Moondance' (Au/d) WAln
- 'Moonglow' (Au/S) GAbr NDro
- 'Moonlight' (Au/S) EWoo WAln
- 'Moonrise' (Au/S) EWoo NDro
- 'Moonriver' (Au/A) EWoo NDro WHil XBar
- 'Moonshine' (Au/d) WAln
- 'Moonshot' (Au/d) NDro
- 'Morello' (Au/d) XBar
- 'Morning Glory' (Au/B) NDro
- 'Morven' (Au) GAbr

- 'Moselle' (Au/S) NDro
- 'Mr A' (Au/S) EWoo NDro WHil
- 'Mr Bojangles' (Au/d) NDro WAln
- 'Mr Hollis' (Au/St) NDro
- 'Mrs Cairn's Blue' (Au/B) NDro
- 'Mrs Dargan' (Au/d) NDro
- 'Mrs Harris' (Au/B) NDro
- 'Mrs L. Hearn' (Au/A) EWoo GAbr ITim NDro NSum WHil XBar
- 'Mrs R. Bolton' (Au/A) WHil XBar
- 'Mrs Wilson' (Au) GAbr
- 'Muriel James' (Au/A) WHil
- 'Murray Lakes' (Au/A) EGrI EWoo NDro NSum WAln
- 'Mustard Sauce' (Au/B) NDro
- 'My Fair Lady' (Au/A) NDro
- 'My Friend' (Au/B) GAbr NDro
- 'Mystery' (Au) GAbr
- 'Nancy Dalgetty' (Au/B) NDro
- 'Nantenan' (Au/S) GAbr NDro NSum
- 'Neat and Tidy' (Au/S) EWoo ITim NDro NWad
- 'Nefertiti' (Au/A) EWoo NDro NSum WHil
- 'Nessun Dorma' (Au/A) EWoo NDro
- 'Neville Telford' (Au/S) EWoo NDro WFar
- 'Newsboy' (Au/A) WAln
- 'Newton Harcourt' (Au/A) NDro WHil
- 'Nicholas van Zanten' (Au/B) NDro
- 'Nick Drake' (Au/d) NDro
- 'Nickity' (Au/A) EWoo GAbr ITim NDro NSum WHil XBar
- 'Nicola Jane' (Au/A) EWoo MAvo WAln
- 'Nigel' (Au/d) GAbr NDro
- 'Nightwink' (Au/S) WAln
- 'Nina' (Au/A) NDro
- 'Nita' (Au/d) WAln
- 'No 21' (Au/S) NDro
- 'Nocturne' (Au/S) NDro NSum
- 'Noelle' (Au/S) NDro NSum
- 'Nona' (Au/d) EWoo NDro NSum WHil
- 'Nonchalance' (Au/A) NDro NSum WHil
- 'Norma' (Au/A) EWoo NDro XBar
- 'Northern Blue' (Au/S) NDro
- 'Northern Lights' (Au/S) GAbr NDro
- 'Nymph' (Au/d) EWoo GAbr GRum NDro WHil
- 'Oakie Dokie' (Au/St) NDro
- 'Oban' (Au/S) NDro
- 'Odette' (Au/d) WHil XBar
- 'O'er the Moon' (Au/S) WAln
- 'Oikos' (Au/B) NDro
- 'Old Black Isle Dusty Miller' (Au/B) NDro WHil
- 'Old Buffer' (Au/St) NDro
- 'Old Clove Red' (Au/B) EWoo GAbr NDro NSum NWad WHil
- 'Old Cottage Blue' (Au/B) EWoo GAbr NDro WFar WHil
- 'Old Dublin Blue' (Au/B) NDro
- 'Old England' (Au/S) GAbr NDro
- 'Old Fashioned Sally' (Au/B) NDro
- 'Old Gold' (Au/S) EGrI GAbr NDro WFar
- 'Old Gold Double' (Au/d) EWoo
- 'Old Gold Dusty Miller' (Au/B) NDro
- 'Old Irish Blue' (Au/B) NDro WCot
- 'Old Irish Green' (Au/B) GAbr NDro NSum
- 'Old Irish Scented' (Au/B) EWoo GAbr NDro NWad WHil XBar
- 'Old Irish Yellow' (Au/B) NDro NHpl
- 'Old Kent Road' (Au/S) NDro
- 'Old Mustard' (Au/B) EGrI GAbr NDro
- 'Old Pink Dusty Miller' (Au/B) EWoo GAbr

§ - 'Old Purple Dusty Miller' (Au/B) GAbr

- 'Old Red' (Au) GArf
- 'Old Red Dusty Miller' (Au/B) EWoo NDro NSum WFar WHil
- 'Old Red Elvet' (Au/S) GAbr
- 'Old Smokey' (Au/A) EWoo NDro WHil XBar
- 'Old Suffolk Bronze' (Au/B) EWoo GAbr NDro WHil
- 'Old Tall Purple Dusty Miller' (Au/B) EWoo
- 'Old Yellow Dusty Miller' (Au/B) EWes EWoo GAbr NDro NLar NWad WHil
- 'Old-Fashioned' (Au/B) NDro
- 'Olton' (Au/A) NDro WFar
- 'Optimist' (Au/St) EWoo GAbr NDro
- 'Opus One' (Au/A) EWoo
- 'Orb' (Au/S) GRum XBar
- 'Ordvic' (Au/S) NDro
- 'Orlando' (Au/S) NDro
- 'Orwell Tiger' (Au/St) EWoo NDro NSum XBar
- 'Osborne Green' (Au/B) EWoo GArf GQue WHil
- 'Ossett Sapphire' (Au/A) NDro XBar
- 'Otto Dix' (Au/A) WAln
- 'Our Sophie' (Au/B) NDro
- 'Overdale' (Au/A) NDro NSum WAln
- 'Oyster' (Au/B) NDro
- 'Paddlin' Madeleine' (Au/A) EWoo NDro XBar
- 'Pageboy' (Au/A) WAln
- 'Pale Blue' (Au/B) WHil
- 'Paleface' (Au/A) NDro NSum
- 'Pall Mall' (Au/St) NDro WHil
- 'Palpatine' (Au/D) XBar
- 'Panache' (Au/S) WAln
- 'Pang Tiger' (Au/St) EWoo NDro
- 'Paradise Yellow' (Au/B) EWoo GEdr NDro
- 'Paragon' (Au/A) WHil
- 'Parakeet' (Au/S) EWoo NDro
- 'Party Animal' (Au/St) NDro XBar
- 'Passchendaele' (Au/d) EWoo WHil
- 'Pastures New' (Au) NDro
- 'Pat Barnard' (Au) NSum
- 'Pat Mooney' (Au/d) NDro
- 'Patience' (Au/S) NDro WHil
- 'Pauline' (Au/A) NDro XBar
- 'Pavarotti' (Au/A) ITim NDro NSum
- 'Paxton's Blue Eden' (Au/B) NDro
- 'Pearl the Cat' (Au/B) WHil
- 'Pegasus' (Au/d) EWoo NDro
- 'Peggy' (Au/A) GAbr ITim
- 'Pen Pink Stripe' (Au/St) WHil
- 'Pendeford Yellow' (Au/B) NDro
- 'Pendle Promise' (Au/A) NDro WHil
- 'Penelope' (Au/d) WHil
- 'Pequod' (Au/A) NSum
- 'Perirot' (Au) ITim
- 'Persephone' (Au/B) NDro
- 'Phantom' (Au/d) NSum
- 'Pharaoh' (Au/A) EGrI EWoo GAbr NDro XBar
- 'Phyllis Douglas' (Au/A) NDro WHil XBar
- 'Piccadilly' (Au/S) NDro
- 'Piccalilli' (Au/d) XBar
- 'Pierot' (Au/A) EGrI NDro NSum WHil XBar
- 'Piers Telford' (Au/A) GAbr LCro MAvo NDro NSum WFar WHil XBar
- 'Piglet' (Au/d) EWoo GAbr NDro NSum XBar
- 'Pikey' (Au/S) NDro
- 'Pimroagh' (Au/A) GAbr
- 'Pink Floyd' (Au/A) XBar
- 'Pink Fondant' (Au/d) GAbr NDro XBar
- 'Pink Hint' (Au/B) EWoo NDro
- 'Pink Lady' (Au/A) GAbr NSum WHil XBar
- 'Pink Lilac' (Au/A/S) NDro
- 'Pink Panther' (Au/S) EWoo

- 'Pink Triumph' (Au/B) NDro WHil
- 'Pinkerton' (Au/d) EWoo
- 'Pinkie' (Au/A) WHil
- 'Pinkie Dawn' (Au/B) EWoo NDro NWad
- 'Pinstripe' (Au/St) GAbr NDro NSum WHil
- 'Pioneer Stripe' (Au/S) EWoo GAbr
- 'Pippin' (Au/A) EGrl EWoo GAbr NDro WHil XBar
- 'Pixie' (Au/A) EWoo NDro XBar
- 'Playboy' (Au/A) NDro WAln
- 'Plum Pudding' (Au/d) EWoo WAln
- 'Poacher's Lady' (Au/d) NDro
- 'Poacher's Sky' (Au/d) XBar
- 'Poacher's Starlight' (Au/d) NDro XBar
- 'Polar Sight' (Au/B) NDro
- 'Polestar' (Au/A) NDro NSum WHil XBar
- 'Polly' (Au/B) GKev NDro NSum WHil
- 'Pop's Blue' (Au/S/d) EWoo
- 'Portree' (Au/S) GAbr
- 'Pot o' Gold' (Au/S) EBee EWoo NDro WHil
- 'Powder Puff' (Au/B) EWoo NDro WHil
- 'Powys' (Au/St) NDro
- 'Prague' (Au/S) NBir NDro
- 'Pretender' (Au/A) WHil
- 'Pretty Purple' (Au/d) NDro WAln
- 'Pride of Poland' (Au/S) EWoo
- 'Prima' (Au/d) NDro
- 'Prince Bishops' (Au/S) NDro
- 'Prince Charming' (Au/S) NDro
- 'Prince John' (Au/A) EWoo NDro WHil
- 'Proctor's Yellow' (Au/B) GAbr NDro NWad WHil
- 'Prometheus' (Au/d) EWoo GAbr ITim NDro NSum WHil XBar
- 'Prosperine' (Au/S) NDro
- 'Psyche' (Au/S) NDro
- 'Pumpkin' (Au) NHpl
- 'Purple Dusty Miller' see *P. auricula* 'Old Purple Dusty Miller'
- 'Purple Glow' (Au/d) WAln
- 'Purple Pip' (Au/d) CBod CWCL ELan GRum NLar SEdd WTor
- 'Purple Prolific' (Au/B) NDro
- 'Purple Promise' (Au/B) GAbr ITim NDro
- 'Purple Prose' (Au/St) WHil
- 'Purple Rose' (Au/d) ITim WAln
- 'Purple Royale' (Au/B) GAbr NDro
- 'Purple Sage' (Au/S) ITim NDro NSum WHil
- 'Purple Velvet' (Au/S) NDro
- 'Quality Street' (Au/d) XBar
- 'Quarry Lane' (Au/A) **new** NDro XBar
- 'Quatro' (Au/d) EWoo
- 'Queen Alexandra' (Au/B) EWoo GAbr NDro WHil
- 'Queen Bee' (Au/S) EWoo GAbr NDro
- 'Quintessence' (Au/A) EWoo NDro WHil
- 'R.L. Bowes' (Au/A) WHil
- 'Rabley Heath' (Au/A) GAbr ITim NDro NSum WHil
- 'Rachel' (Au/A) NDro WAln

I - 'Rachel' (Au/d) XBar
- 'Rag Doll' (Au/S) NDro
- 'Rainy Days' (Au/B) NDro
- 'Rajah' (Au/S) EWoo NHpl WHil XBar
- 'Raleigh Stripe' (Au/St) EWoo GAbr NWad
- 'Rameses' (Au/A) NDro NSum
- 'Randall's White' (Au/B) NDro
- 'Rebecca Baker' (Au/d) WHil
- 'Red Admiral' (Au/S) EWoo NDro WAln
- 'Red Arrows' (Au/S) NDro WAln
- 'Red Bordeaux' (Au/S) NDro
- 'Red Embers' (Au/S) WAln WHil
- 'Red Ensign' (Au/B) NDro
- 'Red Gauntlet' (Au/S) EGrl EWoo GAbr NDro NSum
- 'Red King' (Au/S) WAln
- 'Red Mark' (Au/A) WHil XBar
- 'Red Rum' (Au/S) GAbr
- 'Red Sonata' (Au/S) EWoo
- 'Red Wire' (Au/St) NDro NSum
- 'Red Wrekin' (Au/S) NDro
- 'Redcar' (Au/A) GAbr NDro WHil XBar
- 'Reddown Apricot' (Au/B) NDro
- 'Reddown Barley Meal' (Au/B) NDro
- 'Reddown Bat' (Au/d) NDro
- 'Reddown Dark Pink' (Au/B) NDro
- 'Reddown First Swallow' (Au/B) NDro NSum
- 'Reddown Rainman' (Au/B) NDro
- 'Reddown Tickled Pink' (Au/B) NDro
- 'Redstart' (Au/S) EWoo GKev NDro WHil
- 'Regency' (Au/A) NDro WHil
- 'Regency Carousel' (Au/St) NDro
- 'Regency Emperor' (Au/St) EWoo NDro WHil XBar
- 'Regency Paperchase' (Au/St) NDro
- 'Regency Saint Clements' (Au/St) NDro
- 'Reilly' (Au) WAln
- 'Remus' (Au/S) GAbr ITim NDro WHil XBar
- 'Rene' (Au/A) GAbr NDro WHil
- 'Renishaw Hall' (Au/S) WHil
- 'Renown' (Au/A) NDro WAln
- 'Resi' (Au/A) WHil
- 'Respectable' (Au/A) WAln
- 'Reverie' (Au/d) WAln
- 'Reynardine' (Au/d) WAln
- 'Rhinegold' (Au/d) XBar
- 'Rhubarb Rock' (Au/B) WHil
- 'Riatty' (Au/d) EWoo GAbr NDro
- 'Richard Shaw' (Au/A) EWoo NDro
- 'Ring of Bells' (Au/S) EWoo
- 'Ring of Fire' (Au/A) WAln
- 'Rintein' (Au/B) NDro
- 'Rivendell' (Au/A) WAln
- 'Robbo' (Au/B) EWoo GAbr NDro
- 'Robert Green' (Au/S) NDro
- 'Roberto' (Au/S) NDro
- 'Robin Hood Stripe' (Au/St) EWoo NDro NSum
- 'Robinette' (Au/d) EWoo GAbr XBar
- 'Rock Sand' (Au/S) EWoo GAbr ITim NDro WHil
- 'Rodeo' (Au/A) EWoo GAbr
- 'Rolts' (Au/S) GAbr GKev NDro XBar
- 'Rondy' (Au/S) ITim
- 'Rosalie Edwards' (Au/S) NDro
- 'Rose Conjou' (Au/d) EWoo GAbr NDro WHil XBar
- 'Rose Kaye' (Au/A) GAbr
- 'Rose Petal' (Au/d) XBar
- 'Rosebud' (Au/S) EWoo GAbr NDro
- 'Rosemarket Rackler' (Au/B) NDro
- 'Rosemary' (Au/S) EWoo GAbr NDro WHil
- 'Rosewood' (Au/d) EWoo WAln
- 'Rosie' (Au/S) NDro
- 'Rostock' (Au/B) NDro
- 'Rouge Gorge' (Au/B) XBar
- 'Rowena' (Au/A) NDro NSum XBar
- 'Roxborough' (Au/A) EWoo
- 'Roxburgh' (Au/A) NDro XBar
- 'Roxie' (Au/d) WHil
- 'Roy Keane' (Au/A) NSum WAln
- 'Royal Mail' (Au/S) EGrl EWoo NDro NSum XBar
- 'Royal Velvet' (Au/S) GAbr NDro WFar WHil
- 'Ruby Hyde' (Au/B) EWoo GAbr NDro NSum WHil
- 'Ruddy Duck' (Au/S) EWoo NDro
- 'Runwell' (Au/B) NDro

- 'Rusty Dusty' (Au) EWoo GAbr NDro
- 'Rusty Red' (Au/B) NDro
- 'Sabrina' (Au/A) WAln
- 'Sailor Boy' (Au/S) NDro
- 'Saint Elmo' (Au/A) GAbr
- 'Saint-Émilion' (Au/d) XBar
- 'Salad' (Au/S) GAbr
- 'Sale Green' (Au/S) EWoo NDro
- 'Sally' (Au/A) NDro NSum XBar
- 'Sam Brown' (Au/S) WAln
- 'Sam Gamgee' (Au/A) NDro WAln
- 'Sam Hunter' (Au/A) NDro
- 'Samantha' (Au/A) NDro WAln
- 'Samantha' (Au/d) NDro WFar XBar
- 'San Antonio' (Au/A) NDro
- 'San Gabriel' (Au/A) WAln WHil
- 'Sanctuary Wood' (Au/d) WHil
- 'Sandhills' (Au/A) WHil XBar
- 'Sandra' (Au/A) GAbr NDro WHil XBar
- 'Sandra's Lass' (Au/A) EWoo
- 'Sandwood Bay' (Au/A) EWoo GAbr NDro WHil
- 'Sappho' (Au/S) NDro
- 'Sarah Gisby' (Au/d) NDro
- 'Sarah Lodge' (Au/d) GAbr NDro WHil
- 'Sarah Suzanne' (Au/B) NDro
- 'Saruman' (Au/A) WAln
- 'Sasha Files' (Au/A) NDro WAln
- 'Satsuma' (Au/d) WAln
- 'Scaraben' (Au) GAbr
- 'Schaumburg' (Au/B) NDro
- 'Schicchi' (Au/d) XBar
- 'Scipio' (Au/S) NDro
- 'Scorcher' (Au/S) EWoo GAbr NSum XBar
- 'Second Victory' (Au/S) NDro XBar
- 'Seen-a-Ghost' (Au/S) NDro
- 'Serenity' (Au/S) XBar
- 'Sergeant Wilson' (Au/S) NDro
- 'Shadow Boxer' (Au/St) NDro
- 'Shalford' (Au/d) GAbr WCot WHil
- 'Sharon Louise' (Au/S) NDro
- 'Shaun' (Au/d) ECtt NHpl NLar
- 'Sheila' (Au/S) GAbr NDro WHil
- 'Shere' (Au/S) EWoo NDro NSum
- 'Shergold' (Au/A) XBar
- 'Sherwood' (Au/S) GAbr NDro NHpl XBar
- 'Shirley' (Au/S) NDro
- 'Show Bandit' (Au/St) NDro
- 'Showtime' (Au/S) NDro
- 'Sibsey' (Au/d) EWoo NDro WFar
- 'Silas' (Au/B) NDro
- 'Silbermond' (Au/B) NDro
- 'Silmaril' (Au/d) WAln
- 'Silverway' (Au/S) GKev NDro
- 'Simply Red' (Au/S) EWoo NDro NSum XBar
- 'Sir John' (Au/A) NDro
- 'Sir John Hall' (Au) NDro XBar
- 'Sir Robert' (Au/d) GAbr
- 'Sirbol' (Au/A) EWoo GAbr NDro
- 'Sirius' (Au/A) EWoo GAbr NDro NSum WHil XBar
- 'Skylark' (Au/A) GAbr ITim NDro WHil XBar
- 'Skyliner' (Au/A) NDro
- 'Slack Top Red' (Au/B) NDro WHil
- 'Slim Whitman' (Au/A) NDro NSum WHil XBar
- 'Slioch' (Au/S) EWoo GAbr NSum WFar
- 'Slip Anchor' (Au/A) WAln
- 'Smoothy' (Au/St) NDro
- 'Snips' (Au/St) NDro
- 'Snooty Fox' (Au/A) GAbr
- 'Snooty Fox II' (Au/A) NDro
- 'Snowstorm' (Au/S) NDro
- 'Snowy Owl' (Au/S) NDro
- 'Snowy Ridge' (Au/B) NDro
- 'Soliloquy' (Au/B) NDro
- 'Somme' (Au/d) WHil
- 'Soncy Face' (Au/A) WHil
- 'Sonia Nicolle' (Au/B) NDro
- 'Sonja' (Au/S) NDro
- 'Sonny Boy' (Au/A) NDro WAln
- 'Sooty' (Au/d) EWoo NDro XBar
- 'Sophie' (Au/d) WAln
- 'Sophie' (Au/A) NDro WHil
- 'South Barrow' (Au/d) GAbr WHil
- 'Southport' (Au/B) EWoo GAbr NDro
- 'Sparky' (Au/A) NDro
- 'Spider' (Au/S) NDro
- 'Splendide' (Au/d) XBar
- 'Split Ends' (Au/St) NDro
- 'Spring Meadows' (Au/S) GAbr NDro NSum
- 'Stafford Blue' (Au/B) NDro
- 'Standish' (Au/d) GAbr
- 'Stant's Blue' (Au/S) NDro NSum
- 'Star Spangle' (Au/St) NDro
- 'Star Wars' (Au/S) GAbr NDro XBar
- 'Starburst' (Au/S) WHil
- 'Stardust' (Au/S) NDro
- 'Starling' (Au/B) EWoo GAbr NDro NSum WHil XBar
- 'Steiff' (Au/S) NDro
- 'Stella Coop' (Au/d) NDro
- 'Stella North' (Au/A) NDro WAln
- 'Stella South' (Au/A) NDro WFar
- 'Stepney Green' (Au/S) NDro
- 'Stirling Castle' (Au/St) NDro
- 'Stoke Poges' (Au/A) NDro
- 'Stoney Cross' (Au/S) WAln
- 'Stonnal' (Au/A) NDro WHil
- 'Stormin' Norman' (Au/A) NDro XBar
- 'Stowe Pool' (Au) WAln
- 'Strand' (Au/St) NDro
- 'Strawberry Fields' (Au/S) EGrI NDro
- 'Stripe Tease' (Au/St) EWoo
- 'Stripe U Like' (Au/St) NDro
- 'Striped Ace' (Au/St) EWoo NDro WHil
- 'Stripey' (Au/d) NDro
- 'Stromboli' (Au/d) EGrI EWoo GAbr ITim NDro NSum WCot XBar
- 'Subliminal' (Au/A) NDro
- 'Sue Ritchie' (Au/d) NSum
- 'Suede Shoes' (Au/S) NDro
- 'Sugar Plum Fairy' (Au/S) EWoo GAbr NDro NSum
- 'Summer Sky' (Au/A) NDro
- 'Summer Wine' (Au/A) EWoo NDro WHil XBar
- 'Sumo' (Au/A) EWoo GAbr NDro NSum XBar
- 'Sunflower' (Au/A/S) EWoo GAbr ITim NDro WHil
- 'Sunlit Tiger' (Au/S) EWoo GAbr
- 'Sunshine' (Au/d) XBar
- 'Sunspot' (Au/A) WAln
- 'Sunstar' (Au/S) NDro NSum
- 'Super Para' (Au/S) GAbr WHil
- 'Superb' (Au/S) XBar
- 'Surething' (Au/A) WAln
- 'Susan' (Au/A) GAbr NDro NSum
- 'Susannah' (Au/d) EWoo GAbr NDro NSum WFar WHil XBar
- 'Sweet Caramel' (Au/d) XBar
- 'Sweet Chestnut' (Au/S) CArg
- 'Sweet Georgia Brown' (Au/A) NDro
- 'Sweet Lorraine' (Au/S) NDro
- 'Sweet Pastures' (Au/S) GAbr NDro
- 'Swiss Royal Velvet' (Au/B) NDro
- 'Sword' (Au/d) EWoo GAbr NDro NSum WFar WHil XBar
- 'Symphony' (Au/A) ITim NDro WHil XBar
- 'T.A. Hadfield' (Au/A) EWoo NDro NSum WHil XBar

- 'Taffeta' (Au/S)	EWoo GAbr LCro LOPS MAvo NDro NSum WFar WHil
- 'Tamino' (Au/S)	NDro
- 'Tango' (Au/d)	NDro WAln
- 'Tarantella' (Au/A)	GAbr NDro NSum
- 'Tawny Owl' (Au/B)	GAbr
- 'Tay Tiger' (Au/St)	EWoo GAbr NDro WHil XBar
- 'Taylor's Grey' (Au/S)	NDro
- 'Teawell Pride' (Au/d)	EWoo ITim NHpl WHil
- 'Ted Gibbs' (Au/A)	NDro NSum WHil XBar
- 'Ted Roberts' (Au/A)	CBor ITim NDro WHil XBar
- 'Teem' (Au/S)	GAbr NDro
- 'Temeraire' (Au/A)	XBar
- 'Tenderly' (Au/St)	NDro
- 'Terpo' (Au/A)	NDro WAln WHil XBar
- 'Tess' (Au/A)	XBar
- 'The Argylls' (Au/St)	NDro
- 'The Baron' (Au/S)	EWoo GAbr WHil XBar
- 'The Bishop' (Au/S)	ITim WAln XBar
- 'The Blues' (Au/B) **new**	WHil
- 'The Bride' (Au/S)	NDro
- 'The Cardinal' (Au/d)	EWoo WAln
- 'The Czar' (Au/A)	GAbr NDro XBar
- 'The Egyptian' (Au/A)	EWoo NDro WHil XBar
- 'The Hobbit' (Au/A)	WAln
- 'The Lady Galadriel' (Au/A)	NDro WHil
- 'The Raven' (Au/S)	EWoo GAbr ITim WHil
- 'The Sneep' (Au/A)	EWoo GAbr NDro NSum WHil XBar
- 'The Snods' (Au/S)	EWoo NDro
- 'Thea' (Au/B)	XBar
I - 'Theodora' (Au/S)	GAbr XBar
- 'Thetis' (Au/A)	XBar
- 'Thisbe' (Au/A)	NDro WHil
- 'Three Way Stripe' (Au/St)	EWoo GAbr WFar WHil
- 'Thutmoses' (Au/A)	NDro WAln
- 'Tim' (Au/d)	GAbr ITim NDro NSum
- 'Timpany Blues' (Au/B)	NDro
- 'Timpany Dawn' (Au/B)	NDro
- 'Tim's Fancy' (Au/S)	NDro
- 'Tinker' (Au/S)	NDro
- 'Tinkerbell' (Au/S)	NDro
- 'Tiptoe' (Au/St)	EWoo NDro
- 'Toffee Apple' (Au/d)	NDro
- 'Toffee Crisp' (Au/A)	EWoo GAbr NDro NSum WHil XBar
- 'Tomboy' (Au/S)	EWoo NDro
- 'Toolyn' (Au/S)	EWoo NDro
- 'Topaz' (Au/B)	NDro
- 'Tosca' (Au/S)	GAbr NDro NSum WHil XBar
- 'Trafalgar' (Au/S)	NDro
- 'Trafalgar Square' (Au/S)	EWoo GAbr NDro XBar
- 'Tregor Orange' (Au/d)	WCot
- 'Tregor Stripe' (Au/St)	XBar
- 'Trish' (Au)	GAbr
- 'Trouble' (Au/d)	EWoo GAbr GQue NDro NSum
- 'Troy Aykman' (Au/A)	NDro NSum WAln XBar
- 'Trudy' (Au/S)	EWoo GAbr ITim NDro WHil
- 'True Briton' (Au/S)	NDro
- 'Truman' (Au/B)	NDro
- 'Trumpet Blue' (Au/S)	NDro
- 'Tudor Rose' (Au/S)	XBar
- 'Tumbledown' (Au/A)	EWoo NDro XBar
- 'Tummel' (Au/A)	EWoo GAbr NDro WHil
- 'Tupelo Honey' (Au/d)	WAln
- 'Tutmoses' (Au/A)	XBar
- 'Twiggy' (Au/S)	EWoo GAbr NDro NSum WFar XBar
- 'Typhoon' (Au/A)	EWoo WHil
- 'Uncle Arthur' (Au/A)	WAln WHil XBar
- 'Upperfields' (Au/B)	NDro
- 'Ursula' (Au/d)	WAln
- 'Ushba' (Au/d)	NDro
- 'Valerie' (Au/A)	ITim XBar
- 'Valerie Clare' (Au/S)	WAln WHil
- 'Vee Too' (Au/A)	GAbr NDro WHil
- 'Vega' (Au/A)	WAln
- 'Velvet Moon' (Au/A)	NSum
- 'Venetian' (Au/A)	EWoo ITim NDro WHil XBar
- 'Venus' (Au/A)	WAln
- 'Vera' (Au/A)	NDro WAln
- 'Vera Hill' (Au/A)	NSum
- 'Veronique' (Au/A)	XBar
- 'Vesuvius' (Au/d)	EGrl EWoo GAbr NDro NSum
- 'Victoria de Wemyss' (Au/A)	NDro WHil XBar
- 'Victoria Jane' (Au/A)	WAln
- 'Victoria Park' (Au/A)	WAln XBar
- 'Vienna' (Au/B)	NDro
- 'Vimy Ridge' (Au/d) **new**	WHil
- 'Violet Surprise' (Au/St)	EWoo NDro
- 'Voodoo Mama' (Au/St)	NDro
- 'Vulcan' (Au/A)	NDro XBar
- 'Walhampton' (Au/S)	NDro
- 'Walton' (Au/A)	EWoo GAbr NDro WHil XBar
- 'Walton Heath' (Au/d)	EWoo GAbr NDro NWad WCot WFar WHil
- 'Wanda's Moonlight' (Au/d)	WAln
- 'Warpaint' (Au/St)	EWoo NDro NSum
- 'Warwick' (Au/S)	NDro
- 'Watchett' (Au/S)	NDro
- 'Wedding Day' (Au/S)	EWoo
- 'Weirdo' (Au)	NDro
- 'Werner Müller' (Au/B)	NDro
- 'West Harrow' (Au/S)	NDro
- 'Westbourne Park' (Au/S)	NDro
- 'Wheal' (Au/S)	NDro
- 'Whistlejacket' (Au/S)	NDro
- 'White Cliffs' (Au/d) **new**	XBar
- 'White Ensign' (Au/S)	GAbr NDro NWad
- 'White Pyne' (Au/B)	NDro WHil
- 'White Satin' (Au/S)	NDro
- 'White Water' (Au/A)	EWoo NDro WHil XBar
- 'White Wings' (Au/S)	ITim NDro NHpl NSum
- 'Whoopee' (Au/A)	EWoo NDro WAln
- 'Wide Awake' (Au/A)	NDro
- 'Wild and Grey' (Au/S)	NDro
- 'Wilf Booth' (Au/A)	XBar
- 'William Gunn' (Au/d)	EWoo NDro NSum WAln XBar
- 'Willslock' (Au/A) **new**	WHil
- 'Wincha' (Au/S)	ITim NDro NSum XBar
- 'Windward Blue' (Au)	NDro
- 'Windways Mystery' (Au/B)	GAbr NDro NSum
- 'Windy Border' (Au/B)	NDro
- 'Windy Goldtop' (Au/A)	WAln
- 'Winifred' (Au/B)	see *P.* × *pubescens* 'Winnifred'
- 'Winifrid' (Au/A)	NDro NWad
- 'Wonderous One' (Au/St)	NDro
- 'Wong' (Au)	WAln
- 'Woodlands Lilac' (Au/B)	NDro
- 'Woodmill' (Au/A)	EWoo NDro NSum WHil XBar
- 'Wookey Hole' (Au/A)	NDro
- 'Wootens Advent' (Au/B) **new**	EWoo
- 'Wootens Bloody Warrior' (Au/S) **new**	EWoo
- 'Wootens Cranberry' (Au/B) **new**	EWoo
- 'Wootens Crimson Border' (Au/B) **new**	EWoo
- 'Wootens Easter Chick' (Au/B) **new**	EWoo
- 'Wootens Egg Custard' (Au/B) **new**	EWoo

- 'Wootttens Glory' (Au/S)	EWoo
- 'Woottens Rich Cherry' (Au/B) **new**	EWoo
- 'Woottens Shepherd's Delight' (Au/B) **new**	EWoo
- 'Woottens Straw Boater' (Au/B) **new**	EWoo
- 'Wycliffe Harmony' (Au/B)	NDro
- 'Wycliffe Midnight' (Au/B)	EWoo ITim NDro WHil
- 'Wye Hen' (Au/St)	NDro
- 'Xavier' (Au/d)	EBee
- 'Yellow Ace' (Au)	GAbr
- 'Yellow Muff' (Au/S)	NDro
- 'Yellow Ribbon' (Au)	WAln
- 'Yitzhak Rabin' (Au/A)	NDro WHil
- 'Yorkshire Grey' (Au/S)	NDro
- 'Young Ian' (Au/B)	NDro
- 'Young Love' (Au/B)	NDro
- 'Zambia' (Au/d)	GAbr ITim
- 'Zephyr' (Au/St)	NDro
- 'Ziggy' (Au/St)	NDro
- 'Zircon' (Au/S)	NDro
- 'Zoe' (Au/A)	WAln
- 'Zoe Ann' (Au/S)	WAln
I - 'Zona' (Au/A)	NDro
- 'Zorro' (Au/St)	NDro
- 'Zus' (Au/A) **new**	WHil
auriculata (Or)	CTsd GKev SVic
- subsp. ***olgae*** (Or)	GKev
'Balmoral' (Royal Oakleaf Series) (Pr/Poly)	MMrt
'Barbara Barker' (Au)	NWad
'Barbara Midwinter' (Pr)	EBee GAbr MMrt NSum SHar WAbe WCot
Barnhaven Blues Group (Pr/Prim)	XBar
Barnhaven doubles (Pr/Prim/d)	XBar
Barnhaven Gold Group (Pr/Prim)	XBar
Barnhaven Gold-laced Group	see *P.* Gold-laced Group Barnhaven
Barnhaven hybrids (Pr)	WHlf
Barnhaven Pixies Group (Pr/Prim)	XBar
'Beatrice Wooster' (Au)	EHyd GAbr GArf NRHS NWad WFar XBar
'Beeches' Pink' (Prim/Poly)	GAbr LShi
beesiana (Pf) ♀^{H6}	Widely available
Belarina Series (Pr/Prim/d)	LRHS
- BELARINA AMETHYST ICE ('Kerbelpicotee'^{PBR}) (Pr/Prim/d)	CDor LRHS LSou WHil WHlf WTor
- BELARINA BUTTER YELLOW ('Kerbelbut'^{PBR}) (Pr/Prim/d)	CDor EPfP LRHS LSou NCth WHil
- BELARINA BUTTERMILK ('Kerbelmilk'^{PBR}) (Pr/Prim/d)	LSou NLar
- BELARINA CANDY FROST (Pr/Prim/d) **new**	LBar
- BELARINA COBALT BLUE ('Kerbelcob'^{PBR}) (Pr/Prim/d)	CWCL LRHS LSou NHpl WHil
- BELARINA CREAM ('Kerbelcrem'^{PBR}) (Pr/Prim/d)	CDor LBar LRHS NCth NHpl WHil
- BELARINA GOLDIE ('Kerbelgoldie') (Pr/Prim/d)	LBar LRHS WHil
- BELARINA LIVELY LILAC (Pr/Prim/d)	LBar LRHS WHil
- BELARINA PINK CHAMPAGNE ('Kerbelchamp'^{PBR}) (Pr/Prim/d)	LRHS LSou NCth WFar WHil
- BELARINA PINK ICE ('Kerbelpice'^{PBR}) (Pr/Prim/d)	CDor CWCL LBar LSou MAvo MHol NCth NHpl NLar WTor
- BELARINA ROSETTE NECTARINE ('Kerbelnec'^{PBR}) (Pr/Prim/d)	CDor CWCL ECtt LBar LRHS
- BELARINA ROSETTE VALENTINE ('Kerbelred'^{PBR}) (Pr/Prim/d)	CAby CDor CWCL LBar LRHS LSou NCth NLar WHil WTor
- BELARINA VANILLA ('Kerbelvan'^{PBR}) (Pr/Prim/d)	LRHS
- BELARINA YELLOW RUFFLES (Pr/Prim/d)	LRHS
bellidifolia (Mu)	GKev NGdn
beluensis	see *P.* × *pubescens* 'Freedom'
× ***berninae*** (Au)	GArf
'Berries and Cream Shades' (Pr/Prim/d)	LRHS
'Bewerley White'	see *P.* × *pubescens* 'Bewerley White'
bhutanica	see *P. whitei* 'Sherriff's Variety'
× ***biflora*** (Au)	GArf GRum
bileckii	see *P.* × *forsteri* 'Bileckii'
'Blindsee' (Au)	NHar NRya NSum
'Blue Ice' (Pr/Prim/d)	XBar
Blue Julians Group (Pr/Prim)	XBar
'Blue Riband' (Pr/Prim)	WFar
'Blue Sapphire' (Pr/Prim/d)	XBar
'Bon Accord Cerise' (Pr/Poly/d)	GAbr LShi
'Bonheur' (Pr/Prim/d)	XBar
boothii subsp. ***repens*** (Pe)	GKev
'Boothman's Ruby'	see *P.* × *pubescens* 'Boothman's Variety'
bracteata (Bu)	WAbe
'Brittany Blue' (Pr/Prim/d)	XBar
'Broadwell Chameleon' (Au)	ITim NHar NRya
'Broadwell Milkmaid' (Au) ♀^{H5}	NSum NWad WAbe WMal
'Broadwell Ruby' (Au)	ITim WAbe
'Broadwell Snowstorm' (Au)	ITim NSum
'Broxbourne' (Au) ♀^{H5}	ITim XBar
'Buckland Wine' (Pr/Prim)	CElw EBee ECtt GEdr XBar
bullata (Bu)	GKev
× ***bulleesiana*** (Pf)	CAby CBod CDor CPud CTsd EHyd EPfP EShb EWTr GAbr GKev GMaP LRHS MCot NChi NGdn NHol NRHS SAko SCob WFar XBar
bulleyana (Pf) ♀^{H7}	Widely available
- hybrids (Pf)	CWat
'Burgundy Ice' (Pr/Prim/d)	XBar
burmanica (Pf)	GKev WHoo XBar
Butterscotch Group (Pr/Prim)	XBar
'Caerulea Plena' (Pr/Prim)	NBid
calderiana subsp. ***calderiana*** (Pe)	GKev
- purple-flowered (Pe)	GKev
- subsp. ***strumosa*** (Pe)	GKev
'Camaieu' (Pr/Prim/d)	XBar
Candelabra hybrids (Pf)	EGrI GAbr ITim MBriF NBir NGdn NHpl SMrm WCav
CANDY MIX (Pr/Prim) **new**	MPri
Candy Pinks Group (Pr/Prim)	XBar
capitata (Ca)	CBcs CPla EPfP GArf GKev GRum NHpl SPer SRot WCAu WCot WFar

	- CC 3843	SRms
	- subsp. ***capitata*** (Ca)	WWke
	- subsp. ***mooreana*** (Ca)	CAby CAvo CExl CSpe CTsd EDAr EPfP GKev LBar LRHS NChi NGdn NHpl NLar SPlb WHlf XBar
	- 'Noverna Deep Blue' (Ca)	LRHS SRms
	'Captain Blood' (Pr/Prim/d)	NHpl
	Carnation Victorians Group (Pr/Poly)	XBar
	carniolica (Au)	WCot
	'Cassis' (Alaska Series) (Pr/Prim) **new**	MPri
	cernua (Mu)	XBar
	Chartreuse Group (Pr/Poly)	XBar
	'Cherry' (Pr/Prim)	GAbr
	'Cherry Ripple' (Pr/Prim/d)	XBar
§	***chionantha*** (Cy) ♀H6	CPla GArf GEdr GKev GRum NBir NGdn WFar WHil XBar
	- subsp. ***chionantha*** (Cy)	GKev NCth
§	- subsp. ***sinopurpurea*** (Cy)	GKev NBir
	chungensis (Pf)	CBod CDor CTsd ELan EPfP GArf GBin GKev GLog GQue MPri NBir NGdn NHol NLar SPtp SWvt WFar WHil WMAq XBar
§	***chungensis* × *pulverulenta*** (Pf)	GBin GKev MPnt SAko WSpi
	× ***chunglenta***	see *P. chungensis* × *pulverulenta*
	'Cisca' (Pr)	WCot
	'Clarence Elliott' (Au) ♀H5	GArf GKev MPnt NRya NSum NWad WFar WIce
	'Clarissa White' (Pr/Poly)	XBar
	clusiana (Au)	GKev WAbe
	- 'Murray-Lyon' (Au)	NDro NHar
	cockburniana (Pf) ♀H6	CSpe CTsd NWad XBar
	- SDR 1967	GKev
	- 'Kevock Sunshine' (Pf)	GKev NWad XBar
	- orange-flowered (Pf)	GKev
	concholoba (Mu)	GKev XBar
	'Corporal Baxter' (Pr/Prim/d)	ECtt GMaP LShi MBel XBar
	cortusoides (Co)	EPfP GRum NLar XBar
	'Cottage Cream' (Pr)	LSou MBros SVic
	Cowichan Amethyst Group (Pr/Poly)	XBar
	Cowichan Blue Group (Pr/Poly)	XBar
	Cowichan Garnet Group (Pr/Poly)	MBriF XBar
	Cowichan strain (Pr/Poly)	CElw
	Cowichan Venetian Group (Pr/Poly)	XBar
	Cowichan Yellow Group (Pr/Poly)	XBar
	'Craddock White' (Pr/Prim)	CFis
	'Craven Gem' (Pr/Poly)	LEdu
	'Crème du Tregor' (Pr/Prim/d)	XBar
	Crescendo Series (Pr/Poly)	WHil
	'Crimson Velvet' (Au)	NSum XBar
	crispa	see *P. glomerata*
	cuneifolia (Cu)	GKev
	- subsp. ***heterodonta*** (Cu)	GKev
	'Custard the Cat' (Au/D)	WHil
	daonensis (Au)	GKev
	darialica (Al)	GKev
	'Dark Rosaleen' (Pr/Poly)	CExl CRos ECtt EHyd EMor EPfP LRHS LShi MBNS MBriF MMuc MNrw MPie NCth NHpl NLar NRHS NWad SAko SPoG WBrk WCot WFar WHlf
	'David Valentine' (Pr/Poly)	CFis NSum WCot XBar
	'Dawn Ansell' (Pr/Prim/d)	CDor ECtt EPfP MBNS MBow NBir NHpl WCAu WHer XBar
	Daybreak Group (Pr/Poly)	XBar
	'Dentelle' (Pr/Prim/d)	XBar
	denticulata (De) ♀H6	Widely available
	- var. ***alba*** (De)	Widely available
	- blue-flowered (De)	EMor EPfP GAbr GBin MPri NLar
	- 'Bressingham Beauty' (De)	EBee EBlo
	- var. ***cachemiriana*** hort. (De)	GRum
	- hybrids (De)	EGrI WFar XBar
	- lavender-flowered (De)	CAby EMor
	- lilac-flowered (De)	CRos EHyd EPfP EShb LRHS NHol NRHS SCob WTor
	- 'Miss Esther' (De)	NSum
	- red-flowered (De)	CAby CAvo EPfP NBir SCob
	- 'Ronsdorf' (De)	WGwG
	- rose-flowered (De)	EMor
	- 'Rubin' (De)	CRos CTsd CWCL CWat EBee EBou EHyd EPfP GAbr GMaP LRHS MBel NChi NLar NRHS SPer SPoG SRms WFar XLum
	- 'Rubinball' (De)	GRum NHol
	deorum (Au)	GKev
	× ***deschmannii***	see *P.* × *vochinensis*
	Desert Sunset Group (Pr/Poly)	XBar
	dickieana (Am)	GAbr GKev
	× ***digenea*** (Pr)	XBar
	'Don Keefe' (Pr/Poly)	CBcs ECtt GMcL MBNS MBriF MNrw NGBl NHpl NLar WCot WFar
	'Double Lilac'	see *P. vulgaris* 'Lilacina Plena'
	'Duchess of York' (Pr/Poly)	ECtt GAbr LShi MHCG NLar
	'Early Bird' (*allionii* hybrid) (Au)	XBar
	'Easter Bonnet' (Pr/Prim)	LRHS MMuc SEND
	edgeworthii	see *P. nana*
§	***elatior*** (Pr) ♀H6	CAby CBod CDor EMor EPfP EWoo GAbr GJos GKev GMaP LCro LOPS LRHS MBel MBow MHer MNHC MNrw NAts NChi NLar SPer SPoG SRms SWvt WBrk WHoo XBar
	- hose-in-hose (Pr/d)	NBid
	- hybrids (Pr)	SPlb WHil
I	- 'Jessica' (Pr)	WHil
	- 'Magnifica' (Pr)	GKev
§	- subsp. ***meyeri*** (Pr)	GKev NSla
I	- - 'Alba' (Pr)	GRum
	- subsp. ***pallasii*** (Pr)	GKev SPhx
	- subsp. ***pseudoelatior*** (Pr)	GKev WAbe
	'Elizabeth Browning' (Pr/Poly)	ECtt GAbr WCot
	'Elizabeth Killelay' PBR (Pr/Poly/d)	CBor CDor CExl ECtt EMor LDai MNrw NBir NHpl NLar SPer WCot WFar
	'Ellen Page' (Au)	XBar
	'Ethel Barker' (Au)	NWad
	'Eugénie' (Pr/Prim/d)	ECtt MRav
	euprepes	see *P. melanantha*
	'Everlast' (Pr/Prim) **new**	NGrs
	'Fairy Rose' (Au)	NWad
	fangii (Pu) BO 16-118	GGro
	farinosa (Al)	GArf GKev NGdn XBar
	fasciculata (Ar)	SPlb
	- CLD 345	WAbe
	'Feuerkönig' (Au)	NDro
	'Fire Opal' (Pr/Poly)	CRos EBlo EHyd LRHS NRHS
	'Firecracker' (Au)	NSla NSum
	Firefly Group (Pr/Poly)	LShi WCot XBar
§	***firmipes*** (Si)	GArf GKev
§	***flaccida*** (Mu)	GEdr GKev GRum NHpl

Flamingo Group (Pr/Poly)	XBar
× ***floerkeana*** f. ***biflora*** 'Alba' (Au)	GRum
florindae (Si) ♀H7	Widely available
- bronze-flowered (Si)	NBir
- 'Dave's Red' (Si)	LEdu
- hybrids (Si)	CMac LBar NCth WFar WHil WWtn XBar
- Keillour hybrids (Si)	NGdn SBls SWvt
- orange-flowered (Si)	GArf GPSL LLWG MNrw SRms WPnP
- peach-flowered (Si)	CSpe
- 'Ray's Ruby' (Si)	CTsd MBow MNrw NBir NChi WCot
- red and copper hybrids (Si)	MWts SWvt WHoo
- 'Red Shades' (Si)	GRum SPtp
- red-flowered (Si)	CSpe GKev GPSL LLWG NBid NLar WFar
- terracotta-flowered (Si)	NGdn
Footlight Parade Group (Pr/Prim)	XBar
forbesii (Mo)	WCot
- CC 4084	CExl
forrestii (Bu)	GKev XBar
- SDR 4304	CExl
§ × ***forsteri*** (Au)	NHpl NLar
§ - 'Bileckii' (Au)	GMaP NBir NHar NSla NSum
- 'Dianne' (Au)	GAbr GKev NRya NSum WAbe
'Francisca' (Pr/Poly) ♀H7	CExl CWCL CWGN EBee ECtt EMor EPfP GBin MBNS MBel MCot NChi NHpl NLar SPad WBrk WCAu WCFE WFar WHlf XLum
'Fred Salter' (Au)	NRya
frondosa (Al) ♀H5	EWTr GAbr MPnt WAbe
'Frou-frou' (Pr/Prim/d)	XBar
Fuchsia Victorians Group (Pr/Poly)	XBar
'Garnet' (*allionii* hybrid) (Au)	XBar
'Garryarde Guinevere'	see *P.* 'Guinevere'
geraniifolia (Co)	GKev
'Gigha' (Pr/Prim)	EBee GKev MNrw WFar
'Gilded Garnet' (Pr/Poly/d)	LRHS NHpl
Gilded Ginger (Pr/Poly)	XBar
'Ginger Spice' (Au)	NDro
§ ***glomerata*** (Ca)	GKev XBar
'Gloriosa' (Pr/Prim)	WHlf
'Glowing Embers' (Pf)	NBir
glutinosa All.	see *P. allionii*
Gold-laced Group (Pr/Poly)	CDor CSpe CTsd ECtt EDAr EHyd ELan EMor EPfP GQue LRHS LShi MMuc MNHC NCth NGdn NHpl NLar NRHS SEND SPer SPlb SPoG WCAu WFar WHil
§ - Barnhaven (Pr/Poly)	NBir WHlf XBar
- - 'Gold-laced Jack in the Green' (Pr/Poly)	LShi XBar
- Beeches strain (Pr/Poly)	XBar
- hose-in-hose (Pr/Poly)	XBar
- red-flowered (Pr/Poly)	CRos ELan
gracilipes (Pe)	NHar WFar
- 'Minor'	see *P. petiolaris* Wall.
graminifolia	see *P. chionantha*
Grand Canyon Group (Pr/Poly)	XBar
grandis (Sr)	GKev XBar
'Green Lace' (Pr/Poly)	ECtt
'Groenekan's Glorie' (Pr/Prim)	EBee ECtt NBir NSum WCot WFar WHil
'Guernsey Cream' (Pr/Prim/d)	XBar
§ 'Guinevere' (Pr/Poly) ♀H6	CExl CRos CSpe EBee ECtt EHyd EMor EWTr GArf GMaP LRHS LShi MBow MBriF MMuc MNrw NBid NBir NGrd NHpl NLar NRHS NRya SEND SPlb WCot WFar XBar
'Hall Barn Blue' (Pr/Prim)	CSpe EBee ELan EPfP EWhm GAbr GArf GMaP GRum MHCG MMuc NSum SEND WCot WTor
§ ***halleri*** (Al)	GKev XBar
- 'Longiflora'	see *P. halleri*
Harbinger Group (Pr/Prim)	XBar
Harbour Lights Group (Pr/Poly)	XBar
Harlow Car hybrids (Pf)	CRos EHyd EPfP LRHS NCth NRHS NSla NWad WHil XBar
Harvest Yellows Group (Pr/Poly)	XBar
helodoxa	see *P. prolifera*
'Hemswell Blush' (Au)	GKev NHpl NSum WFar
'Hemswell Ember' (Au)	ECtt
heucherifolia (Co)	CPla
- SDR 3224	GKev
hidakana (R)	GEdr
hirsuta (Au)	MMuc SEND
- white-flowered (Au)	NRya
hirsuta* × *minima	see *P.* × *forsteri*
hoffmanniana	GKev NHar SPlb
hose-in-hose (Pr/Poly/d)	EWes
- Barnhaven (Pr/Poly/d)	XBar
HUSKY RASPBERRY PUNCH (Husky Series) (Pr/Prim) **new**	MPri
ianthina	see *P. prolifera*
Indian Reds Group (Pr/Poly)	XBar
'Ingram's Blue' (Pr/Poly)	CFis EBee EPfP
'Innisfree Pink' (Pr/Prim)	XBar
Inshriach hybrids (Pf)	GBin WWke
integrifolia (Au)	GKev
§ 'Inverewe' (Pf)	EBee GBin GEdr GKev MPnt NBir NFav NHar NHpl XBar
involucrata	see *P. munroi*
'Iris Mainwaring' (Pr/Prim)	CFis EBee ECtt ELan GKev WMal
irregularis hybrid (Pe)	NHar
'Jackie Richards' (Au)	NWad
Jack-in-the-Green Group (Pr/Poly)	MNrw NWad
- Barnhaven (Pr/Poly)	XBar
- red-flowered (Pr/Poly)	MMuc
'Jack-the-Lad' (Pr/Prim/d)	XBar
japonica (Pf)	CPud ECha GAbr LPfP MSCN MWts NBro NGdn
- 'Alba' (Pf)	CBod CTri CTsd EMor EPfP EShb EWoo GMcL LBar LLWG MBel MCot MHol MPri NChi NGdn NLar SHar SPer WCAu WFar WHlf
- 'Apple Blossom' (Pf)	Widely available
* - 'Carminea' (Pf)	CDor EDAr LShi NBro NGdn SPer WFar
- 'Fuji' (Pf)	GAbr NBro
- hybrids (Pf)	CMac WFar
- 'Miller's Crimson' (Pf) ♀H6	Widely available
- 'Oriental Sunrise' (Pf)	XBar
- pale pink-flowered (Pf)	ITim
- 'Postford White' (Pf) ♀H6	CAby CBcs CCBP CDor CPla CPud CRos CToG EBee ECha EHyd ELan EPfP GAbr GKev GMaP ITim LRHS LSRN LShi NBir NRHS SCob SPer SPoG SRms SWvt WBor WBrk XBar
- 'Valley Red' (Pf)	GKev
- Violet Oriental Group (Pf)	XBar
'Jay-Jay' (Pr)	XBar
'Jenny' ambig.	GArf
jesoana (Co)	GKev

- var. ***pubescens*** (Co)	GKev
'Jewel' (Pr)	GAbr
'Joan Hughes' (*allionii* hybrid) (Au)	WAbe
'Joanna' (Pr/Poly)	ECtt MPnt WPGP
'Johanna' (Pu)	GArf GKev LEdu NGdn NSum SGro WAbe
'John Fielding' (Pr)	CBro CElw GKev
'Jo-Jo' (Au)	ITim NSum WAbe XBar
'Jubilee' (Pr/Prim/d)	XBar
juliae (Pr)	CBor EHyd EWld GKev GRum LRHS NBid NHpl NRHS SPlb WAbe
'Ken Dearman' (Pr/Prim/d)	ECtt EShb NBir NHpl XBar
× ***kewensis*** (Sp) ♀H3	GAbr GKev XBar
'Kingscote' (Au)	NDro
'Kinlough Beauty' (Pr/Poly)	EBee ECtt GKev GMaP SRot XBar
§ ***kisoana*** (Co)	CExl GKev
- var. ***alba*** (Co)	XBar
- 'Barnhaven Blush' (Co)	XBar
- 'Iyo-beni' (Co)	NHar XBar
- 'Noushoku' (Co)	XBar
- var. ***shikokiana***	see *P. kisoana*
kitaibeliana (Au)	GKev
'Koblenz' (Au)	NSum
komarovii (Pr)	SPlb
'Kusum Krishna' (Au)	GEdr GRum MHol MPie NHpl NLar NRya WCot WFar
'Lady Greer' (Pr/Poly) ♀H5	CMac EBee ECtt ELan EPPr EPfP GKev GMaP LShi MTin NChi NGdn NHar NLar NSum SBrt WCAu WFar XBar
'Lady Rosalind' (Pr/Poly) **new**	XBar
'Lambrook Mauve' (Pr/Poly)	CElw CFis GAbr
§ ***latifolia*** (Au)	GArf
latisecta (Co)	GEdr GKev
§ ***laurentiana*** (Al)	EWes
'Lavender Shades' (Primlet Series) (Pr/Prim)	MPri
'Lee Myers' (*allionii* hybrid) (Au)	WFar XBar
'Lemon' (Primlet Series) (Pr/Prim)	MPri
leucophylla	see *P. elatior*
'Lilac Lace' (Pr/Poly)	CRos WHil WWke
'Lilian Foster' (Pr/Prim)	WCot
limbata (Cy)	GKev
'Lindum Angelic' (Au)	NHar
'Lindum Aria' (Au)	NHar
'Lindum Celebration' (Au)	NHar
'Lindum Countess' (Au)	NHar
'Lindum Crepes Suzette' (Au)	ITim NHar
'Lindum Dove' (Au)	NHar
'Lindum Finale' (Au)	NHar
'Lindum First Kiss' (Au)	ITim
'Lindum Flirtatious' (Au)	NHar
'Lindum Frosty Moon' (Au)	ITim
'Lindum Gecko' (Au)	NHar
'Lindum Golden Orb' (Au)	NHar
'Lindum Heavenly' (Au)	XBar
'Lindum Ibis' (Au) **new**	NHar
'Lindum Lancelot' (Au)	WMal
'Lindum Lavender Mist' (Au)	NSum XBar
'Lindum Limelight' (Au)	ITim
'Lindum Lyric' (Au)	NHar
'Lindum Memories' (Au)	NHar
'Lindum Moonlight' (Au)	WMal XBar
'Lindum Morning Flight' (Au)	NHar
'Lindum Rapture' (Au)	NHar
'Lindum Storm Cloud' (Au)	NHar
'Lindum Wedgwood' (Au)	GEdr ITim NHar NSum XBar
'Lingwood Beauty' (Pr/Prim)	CAby CElw CFis

'Lismore' (Au)	NWad
'Lismore Peardrop' (Au)	NSum
'Lismore Pink Ice' (Au)	NWad
Little Egypt Group (Pr/Poly)	XBar
littoniana	see *P. vialii*
'Lizzie Green' (Pr/Prim)	NLar
× ***loiseleurii*** 'Aire Mist' (Au) ♀H5	ITim NHpl NRya NSla NSum NWad WFar XBar
§ - 'Aire Waves' (Au)	ITim NHar NRya
- 'Lismore Yellow' (Au)	XBar
longiflora	see *P. halleri*
'Lopen Red' (Pr/Prim)	CFis GKev WSHC XBar
luteola (Or)	NGdn NHpl XBar
* ***lutescens***	CBor
macrocalyx	see *P. veris*
macrophylla (Cy)	EWes
'MacWatt's Claret' (Pr/Poly)	ECtt GAbr
'MacWatt's Cream' (Pr/Poly)	CTtf EHyd GAbr LEdu LRHS NLar NRHS NSum SGro
'Mademoiselle Zia' (Pr/Poly)	XBar
magellanica (Al)	GKev SPlb WAbe
mairei (Al)	GKev
'Maisie Michael' (Pr/Prim)	NHpl WAbe
malacoides (Mo) ♀H2	XBar
marginata (Au) ♀H5	EHyd EWoo LRHS LShi MMuc NRHS NSla SEND WAbe XBar
- 'Adrian Evans' (Au)	GEdr WIce
- 'Adrian Jones' (Au)	XBar
- 'Alba' (Au)	EHyd GEdr GKev NBro NRHS NRya NWad XBar
- 'Ardfearn' (Au)	GEdr
- 'Baldock's Purple' (Au)	NRya XBar
- 'Barbara Clough' (Au)	GEdr NRya NSum NWad XBar
- 'Beamish' (Au) ♀H5	GEdr NBro NRya NSla NWad
- 'Beatrice Lascaris' (Au)	EHyd GEdr NRHS NRya WAbe
- 'Bill Crow' (Au)	GEdr NRya
- 'Caerulea' (Au)	GArf GEdr GKev NRya NWad XBar
- 'Casterino' (Au)	NRya WAbe
- 'Clear's Variety' (Au)	GKev XBar
- 'Crookes Variety' (Au)	NRya
- 'Doctor Jenkins' (Au)	NRya NWad
- 'Dolomites' (Au)	NWad
- 'Drake's Form' (Au)	NRya XBar
- dwarf (Au)	EHyd LRHS NRHS NRya
- 'Earl L. Bolton'	see *P. marginata* 'El Bolton'
§ - 'El Bolton' (Au)	NRya NSum NWad
- 'Elizabeth Fry' (Au)	GEdr
- 'Grandiflora' (Au)	NWad
- 'Herb Dickson' (Au)	GEdr NRya
- 'Highland Twilight' (Au)	NSla
- 'Hilary' (Au) **new**	GEdr
- 'Holden Variety' (Au)	NRya NWad XBar
- 'Holly Leaf' (Au)	GEdr
- 'Ivy Agee' (Au)	NRya
- 'Janet' (Au)	GEdr NWad XBar
- 'Johannes Holler' (Au)	NRya
- 'Kesselring's Variety' (Au)	GEdr NSum NWad WFar WIce XBar
- 'Laciniata' (Au)	EHyd GKev GRum LRHS NRHS XBar
- 'Lemon Sorbet' (Au)	NSum
- 'Linda Pope' (Au) ♀H5	GArf GEdr NBir WThu XBar
- 'Manfield' (Au)	NRya
- maritime form (Au)	GArf NSum XBar
- 'Millard's Variety' (Au)	NWad
- 'Mrs Carter Walmsley' (Au)	NRya NWad
- 'Mylene' (Au)	NRya NSum
- 'Napoleon' (Au)	GEdr NRya NWad
- 'Peggy Fell' (Au)	NWad WHil
- 'Pixie' (Au) **new**	GEdr
- 'Prichard's Variety' (Au) ♀H5	GEdr GPSL NRya WAbe
- 'Sheila Denby' (Au)	NRya NWad

- 'Sugar Icing' (Au) **new**	XBar
- 'The President' (Au)	NWad
- 'Viv' (Au) **new**	GEdr
- 'Waithman's Variety' (Au)	NRya NSum NWad
- wild-collected (Au)	GArf
'Maria Talbot' (*allionii* hybrid) (Au)	NSum XBar
Marine Blues Group (Pr/Poly)	XBar
MARLI ROSE SHADES (Marli Series)	LRHS
'Mars' (*allionii* hybrid) (Au)	XBar
'Marven' (Au)	GEdr
'Mary Anne' (Pr)	GAbr LShi
matthioli	see *Cortusa matthioli*
'Mauve Mist' (Poly)	WCot
Mauve Victorians Group (Pr/Poly)	XBar
maximowiczii (Cy)	GEdr NGdn
§ - var. ***maximowiczii*** (Cy)	GKev NHpl
- Red-flowered Group	see *P. maximowiczii* var. *maximowiczii*
maximowiczii* × *tangutica (Cy)	GKev
megaseifolia (Pr)	GKev
§ ***melanantha*** (Cy)	GKev
'Melenoc'h' (Pr/Prim/d)	MBow XBar
§ × ***meridiana*** 'Miniera' (Au)	GKev
Midnight Group (Pr/Prim)	XBar
'Miel' (Pr/Prim/d)	XBar
'Millstream Cream' (Au)	NLar
'Millwood Blush' (Pr/Prim)	WMal
'Miniera'	see *P.* × *meridiana* 'Miniera'
minima (Au)	NBro WAbe
minima* × *wulfeniana	see *P.* × *vochinensis*
'Miss Doris' (Pr/Prim/d)	XBar
'Miss Indigo' (Pr/Prim/d)	CDor CTsd ECtt MBNS MBow NHpl WCAu XBar
mistassinica (Al)	XBar
- var. ***macropoda***	see *P. laurentiana*
miyabeana (Pf)	GKev
modesta (Al)	GAbr XBar
- var. ***faurieae*** (Al)	GKev
- - f. ***leucantha*** (Al)	GKev
- var. ***samanimontana*** (Al)	GKev
'Moerheimii' (Pr/Prim)	EPot GAbr GEdr
moupinensis (Pe)	CExl NHar
- subsp. ***barkamensis*** (Pe)	GKev
'Mrs Frank Neave' (Pr/Prim)	GAbr WFar
'Mrs Marjorie Banks' (Pr)	GKev
§ ***munroi*** (Ar)	GKev WAbe XBar
- subsp. ***munroi*** (Ar) CC 5311	GKev
- white-flowered (Ar)	WAbe
§ - subsp. ***yargongensis*** (Ar)	GArf GKev XBar
muscarioides (Mu)	GKev
Muted Victorians Group (Pr/Poly)	XBar
'Myline'	WThu
§ ***nana*** (Pe)	GEdr NHar
- 'Alba' (Pe)	GEdr NHar
'Netta Dennis' (Pe)	NHar
New Pinks Group (Pr/Poly)	XBar
'Nightingale' (Au)	ITim XBar
nivalis Pallas	see *P. chionantha*
nutans Delavay ex Franch.	see *P. flaccida*
'Oak Leaf Yellow Picotee' (Pr)	LRHS MPri
obconica subsp. ***werringtonensis*** (Ob)	GKev
odontocalyx (Da)	GKev
- 'Snow Flurry' (Da)	GKev

'Old Port' (Pr/Poly)	GKev GQue LShi NSum
Old Rose Victorians Group (Pr/Poly)	XBar
(Ooh La La Series) 'Ooh La La Blood Orange' (Ag × Pi)	WHlf
- 'Ooh La La Pastel Pink' (Ag × Pi)	LBar LCro LRHS MPri WHlf
'Orange Flame' (Pf)	GKev
orbicularis (Cy)	GKev NHpl
Osiered Amber Group (Pr/Prim)	XBar
palinuri (Au)	WMal
palmata (Co)	GEdr GKev
Paris '90 Group (Pr/Poly)	XBar
parryi (Pa)	GEdr GKev WHil
pedemontana 'Alba' (Au)	GEdr WThu XBar
'Perle von Bottrop' (Pr/Prim)	ECtt NSum WCot
petelotii (Ch)	GEdr
'Peter Klein' (Or)	ECtt EPot GKev
petiolaris misapplied	see *P.* 'Redpoll'
§ ***petiolaris*** Wall. (Pe)	NHar
- Sherriff's form	see *P.* 'Redpoll'
'Petticoat' (Pr/Prim/d)	ECtt WCot XBar
'Pink' (Primlet Series) (Pr/Prim)	EHyd LRHS MPri NRHS
'Pink Aire' (Au)	NSum NWad XBar
'Pink Fairy' (Au)	ITim
'Pink Grapefruit' (Pr/Prim/d)	XBar
'Pink Ice' (*allionii* hybrid) (Au)	LRHS NSum NWad XBar
'Pink Star' (Pr/Prim/d)	XBar
poissonii (Pf)	CDoC CDor CTri EDAr EHyd EPfP GAbr GKev GRum LRHS NGdn NHpl NRHS WShi WWtn
polyanthus (Pr/Poly)	SVic
polyneura (Co)	CTsd EBee EGrI GArf GKev GRum MHol NGdn WCot
'Powdery Pink' (Pf)	EHyd LRHS NRHS
PRIMA BELARINA CARMEN ('Kerbelcarmen') (Prima Belarina Series) (Pr/Prim/d)	LBar LRHS
Primlet Series (Pr/Prim)	MPri
§ ***prolifera*** (Pf) $♀^{H4}$	CToG ELan GKev LRHS MNrw NGdn NHpl SPtp XBar
§ × ***pubescens*** (Au) $♀^{H5}$	CDor ECha EHyd LRHS MHer NGdn NRHS
- 'Balfouriana' (Au)	NWad
§ - 'Bewerley White' (Au)	EBee EWoo NDro
§ - 'Boothman's Variety' (Au)	EWoo NLar NSla WHoo
- 'Carmen'	see *P.* × *pubescens* 'Boothman's Variety'
- 'Christine' (Au)	NBir NSum WCot
- 'Cream Viscosa' (Au)	EWoo NSum SPlb WFar
- 'Faldonside' (Au)	NSla NSum
§ - 'Freedom' (Au)	EWoo GKev NBir NSla NSum XBar
- 'George Harrison' (Au)	GArf
- 'Harlow Car' (Au)	MPnt NSum
- 'Hazel's White' (Au)	GAbr
- 'Henry Hall' (Au)	NSum
- 'Joan Danger' (Au)	NDro
- 'Joan Gibbs' (Au)	NHpl XBar
- 'Lilac Fairy' (Au)	GKev ITim NWad
- 'Moonlight' (Au)	NDro
- 'Mrs J.H. Wilson' (Au)	NRya XBar
- 'Pat Barwick' (Au)	NDro NSum
- 'Rufus' (Au) $♀^{H5}$	EWoo GAbr GEdr NDro NHar XBar
- 'Rumbling Bridge' (Au)	GRum
- 'Sid Skelton' (Au)	NRya
- 'Slack Top Violet' (Au)	NSla
- 'Snowcap' (Au)	ITim XBar
- 'Sonya' (Au)	NSum

	– 'The General' (Au)	GEdr NSum
§	– 'Wedgwood' (Au)	GAbr NDro NSla NSum WHil XBar
	– white (Au)	EWoo
§	– 'Winnifred' (Au)	EGrl EWoo GAbr NDro
	× ***pubescens*** × 'White Linda Pope' (Au)	GArf
	pulchella (Pu)	GKev
	pulverulenta (Pf) 🏆H6	Widely available
	– Bartley hybrids (Pf) 🏆H6	GEdr GRum NHpl
	'Purple' (Primlet Series) (Pr/Prim)	EHyd LRHS MPri NRHS
	'Purple Storm' (Pr/Prim/d)	WFar XBar
	'Quaker's Bonnet'	see *P. vulgaris* 'Lilacina Plena'
	'Rachel Kinnen' (Au)	EDAr GAbr WFar XBar
	Ramona Group (Pr/Poly)	XBar
	'Raspberry Ripple' (Pr/Prim/d)	MBow XBar
	'Ravenglass Vermilion'	see *P.* 'Inverewe'
	'Red' (Primlet Series) (Pr/Prim)	CRos EHyd LRHS MPri NRHS
	'Red Hugh' (Pf)	NHpl
	'Red Ruffles' (Pr/Poly/d)	ECtt
§	'Redpoll' (Pe)	GArf NHar
	reidii (So)	GEdr GKev
	– var. ***williamsii*** (So)	GEdr GKev
*	– – ***alba*** (So)	GEdr
	Reverie Group (Pr/Poly)	XBar
	'Rheniana' (Au)	NRya
	'Romance' (Pr/Prim/d)	LRHS
	'Romeo' (Pr/Prim)	NSum NWad WCot
	'Rose' (Primlet Series) (Pr/Prim)	CRos EHyd LRHS MPri NRHS
	'Rose Edge' (Primlet Series) (Pr/Prim)	MPri
	rosea (Or) 🏆H5	CAby EPfP GKev GLog GMaP MMuc NBid NBir NBwr NRya SCob SPlb WPnP XBar
	– 'Gigas' (Or)	GAbr WMAq
	– 'Grandiflora' (Or)	CMac EMor EPfP GKev GMcL GPSL LRHS MBel SPoG SRms XLum
	'Rosemary Cottage' (Pr/Poly)	GAbr WCot
I	'Rowena' (Pr/Prim)	CFis WCot
	Rubens Series (Pr/Prim/d)	MPri
	rubra	see *P. firmipes*
	'Ruby Tuesday' (Au)	NDro
	rusbyi (Pa)	GKev
	– subsp. ***ellisiae*** (Pa)	GKev
	'Sapphire' (Au)	XBar
	scapigera (Pe)	WFar
§	'Schneekissen' (Pr/Prim)	CWCL EBee EHyd LRHS NBro NChi NRHS NSum SRot WFar WTor
	'Scirocco Red'	CRos
	scotica (Al)	GKev GPoy GRum NSla WAbe
	secundiflora (Pf)	CTsd ELan EWes GArf GKev LLWG NBir NChi SPlb XBar
	× ***serrata***	see *P.* × ***vochinensis***
	'Sheryl Louise' (Pr/Prim)	NHar
	sibthorpii	see *P. vulgaris* subsp. *sibthorpii*
	sieboldii (Co) 🏆H5	EHyd EWld GKev MACG MAsh MNrw NHpl NRHS NSla SGro SRms
	– 'Aiaigasa' (Co)	CSta
	– 'Aka-tonbo' (Co)	CSta WFar XBar
	– 'Akedori' (Co) **new**	CSta
	– 'Akenotama' (Co) **new**	WFar
	– 'Aki-no-yosooi' (Co)	CSta
	– 'Alba' (Co)	CSta EBlo
	– 'Amaenbou' (Co) **new**	CSta
	– 'Amaendo' (Co)	CSta
	– 'Andromeda' (Co)	EBee
	– 'Aoba-no-fue' (Co)	CSta WFar
	– 'Aoi-no-ue' (Co)	CSta
	– 'Aoyagi-zome' (Co)	CSta XBar

	– 'Appare' (Co)	CSta
	– 'Apple Blossom' (Co)	XBar
	– 'Ariake' (Co)	CSta
	– 'Arimayama' (Co)	CSta WFar
	– 'Asahi' (Co)	CSta WFar
	– 'Asahigata' (Co)	CSta WFar
	– 'Ayanami' (Co)	WFar
	– 'Ayasegawa' (Co)	CSta WFar
	– 'Banshun' (Co) **new**	WFar
	– 'Beeches Star' (Co)	EBee
	– 'Benjamin' (Co)	CSta WFar
	– 'Bide-a-Wee Blue' (Co)	NBid
	– 'Bide-a-Wee Lace' (Co)	NBid
	– 'Bijyonomai' (Co)	WFar
I	– 'Blue Lagoon' (Co)	CBor CRos CSta EBee EHyd EPfP LRHS NLar NRHS WFar
	– 'Blue Shades' (Co)	CWCL
	– blue-flowered (Co)	CSta
	– 'Blush' (Co)	CSta WFar
	– 'Bonbori' (Co)	CSta WFar
	– 'Bureikou' (Co)	CSta WFar
	– 'Carefree' (Co)	CSta ECtt NBro NLar WFar XBar
	– 'Cherubim' (Co)	CSta EBee EBlo EHyd LRHS WFar
	– 'Chidoriasobi' (Co)	CSta
	– 'Chononemuri' (Co) **new**	WFar
	– 'Daikoshi' (Co)	CSta WFar
	– 'Daiminnishiki' (Co)	CSta WFar
	– 'Dancing Ladies' (Co)	ECtt NBro WFar XBar
	– 'Dart Rapids' (Co)	CSta WFar
	– 'Doushi-bai' (Co) **new**	WFar
	– 'Duane's Choice' (Co)	CSta
	– 'Edasango' (Co)	WFar
	– 'Edomurasaki' (Co)	CSta NPnk WFar
	– 'Ekiji-no-suzu' (Co) **new**	CSta
	– 'Ekiro-no-suzu' (Co)	CSta WFar
	– 'Elegance' (Co)	CSta WFar
	– 'Emerald Sun' (Co)	WFar
	– 'Essie' (Co)	CSta WFar
	– 'Flamenco' (Co/d)	WFar XBar
	– 'Frilly Blue' (Co)	CBor CRos CSta EBee EHyd LRHS NRHS WFar
	– 'Frilly White' (Co)	WFar
	– 'Fuji Shishi' (Co/d)	WFar XBar
	– 'Fuji-no-mai' (Co)	CSta
	– 'Fukiagezakura' (Co)	CSta
	– 'Fukuju' (Co)	CSta
	– 'Futami-gauri' (Co) **new**	WFar
	– 'Galactic' (Co)	CSta WFar
	– 'Galaxy' (Co)	NBro
	– 'Geisha Girl' (Co)	CDor CRos CSpe CSta EBee ECtt EHyd LRHS NLar NRHS WFar
	– 'George' (Co)	CSta
	– 'Ginfukurin' (Co)	CSta WFar
	– 'Gin-kaji-oku' (Co)	WFar
	– 'Gin-pukurin' (Co)	CSta WFar
	– 'Ginsekai' (Co) **new**	WFar
	– 'Girl of the Limberlost' (Co)	CSta WFar XBar
	– 'Gloaming' (Co)	WFar XBar
	– 'Gunma' (Co)	WFar
	– 'Gunma Niizatia' (Co)	CSta
	– 'Gyokk-bai' (Co)	CSta
	– 'Hakutaka' (Co)	CSta
	– 'Hana-angya' (Co/d)	CSta WFar XBar
	– 'Hanachirusato' (Co) **new**	WFar
	– 'Hana-fubuki' (Co) **new**	WFar
	– 'Hanaguruma' (Co)	CSta WFar
	– 'Hana-kamachi' (Co) **new**	CSta
	– 'Hanako' (Co) **new**	WFar
	– 'Hana-monyo' (Co)	CSta XBar
	– 'Hana-nishiki' (Co)	CSta WFar
	– 'Haru-no-yoi' (Co)	CSta WFar
	– 'Harutugedoric' (Co)	WFar

- 'Hatu-garasu' (Co) CSta WFar
- 'Hatu-goromo' (Co) CSta WFar
- 'Hazel' (Co) **new** CSta
- 'Heart's Desire' (Co) EBee WFar
- 'Hidamari' (Co) CSta
- 'Higurasi' (Co) WFar
- 'Hi-no-hakama' (Co) **new** CSta
- 'Hinomaru' (Co) CSta
- 'Hitome' (Co) **new** WFar
- 'Hokutosei' (Co) CSta
- 'Ikoko-no-e-beni' (Co) WFar
- 'Inukima Mincura' (Co) CSta WFar
- 'Inukine White' (Co) CSta
- 'Irino-no-miyako' (Co) CSta
- 'Isamijishi' (Co) CSta
- 'Iso-botan' (Co) CSta WFar XBar
- 'Izutu' (Co) CSta
- 'Janomegasa' (Co) CSta XBar
- 'Jessica' (Co) CSta WFar
- 'Jintsūriki' (Co) CSta
- 'Jisshū-no-sora' (Co) CSta
- 'Kafajin' (Co) CSta
- 'Kafka on the Shore' (Co) CSta
- 'Kakako-asobi' (Co) **new** WFar
- 'Kakuremino' (Co) CSta
- 'Kamiyo-no-kanmuri' (Co) CSta
- 'Kansenden' (Co) WFar
- 'Kara-chirimen' (Co) CSta
- 'Karafune' (Co) CSta WFar
- 'Karakoromo' (Co) CSta
- 'Kashima' (Co) CSta WFar
- 'Kassai' (Co) WFar
- 'Keepsake' (Co) CSta
- 'Kenkou' (Co) CSta WFar
- 'Kiaryodai' (Co) **new** WFar
- 'Kicchou' (Co) **new** CSta
- 'Kihi-no-yume' (Co) CSta
- 'Kiraboshi' (Co) WFar XBar
- 'Koenji' (Co) CSta
- 'Kohara-biyori' (Co) CSta
- 'Kokonoe-beni' (Co/d) CSta WFar
- 'Kokoroiki' (Co) CSta WFar
- 'Komodo-ne' (Co) WFar
- 'Ko-odori' (Co) **new** XBar
- 'Kotobuki' (Co) CSta WFar
- 'Kotonoshirabe' (Co) CSta WFar
- 'Kotyou-no-mail' (Co) CSta WFar
- 'Kourohou' (Co) WFar
- 'Kozakura-genji' (Co) CSta
- 'Kumoizuru' (Co) CSta
- 'Kurama' (Co) WFar
- 'Ky-kanoko' (Co) CSta
- 'Laced Lady' (Co) WFar
- 'Lacewing' (Co) CSta
- f. ***lactiflora*** (Co) CSta EHyd LRHS NBro
- 'Lacy Lady' (Co) **new** XBar
- 'Lilac Blue' (Co) CSta
- 'Lilac Crinoline' (Co) WFar XBar
- 'Lilac Sunbonnet' (Co) MACG WFar
- 'Mai-momiji' (Co/d) CSta WFar
- 'Mai-ōgi' (Co) CSta WFar
- 'Makazebeni' (Co) WFar
- 'Maki-no-o' (Co) CSta
- 'Managuruma' (Co) WFar
- 'Manakoora' (Co) ECtt EGrI NBro WFar XBar
- 'Mangeto' (Co) CSta WFar
- 'Martin Nest Blue' (Co) CSta WFar
- 'Martin Nest Pink' (Co) CSta WFar
- 'Masquerado' (Co) **new** WFar
- 'Matu-no-yuki' (Co) CSta WFar
- 'Mejirodai' (Co) CSta
- 'Miho-no-koji' (Co) CSta WFar
- 'Mikado' (Co) CSta EBee ECtt WFar WOld
- 'Mikini-no-mare' (Co) CSta WFar
- 'Mikuni-beni' (Co) CSta
- Minuet Group (Co) XBar
- 'Mitajiman' (Co) CSta WFar
- 'Miyakowakare' (Co) WFar
- 'Miyuki' (Co) WFar
- 'Molly' (Co) CSta WFar
- 'Momijbashi' (Co) CSta WFar
- 'Momo-kagari' (Co) WFar
- 'Momozono' (Co) **new** WFar
- 'Mukashi-no-ume' (Co) WFar
- 'Murasaki-koume' (Co) **new** WFar
- 'Musashino' (Co) CSta WFar
- 'Musasi' (Co) CSta
- 'Naka-fu' (Co) WFar
- 'Nami-no-ue' (Co) CSta
- 'Nankin-kozakura' (Co) CSta WFar XBar
- 'Nirvana' (Co) WFar XBar
- 'Noboruko' (Co) CSta WFar
- 'Nuretubame' (Co) CSta WFar XBar
- 'Ochibagoromo' (Co) CSta
- 'Ohseki' (Co) **new** WFar
- 'Okinanotomo' (Co) WFar
- 'Okinosabi' (Co) WFar
- 'Old Vienna' (Co) WFar XBar
- 'Oni-gokko' (Co) CSta WFar XBar
- 'Oriental Beauty' (Co) EBee
- 'Oshibori' (Co) CSta GKev MNrw NLar WFar
- 'Otomenosode' (Co) **new** WFar
- 'Ouchikazri' (Co) **new** WFar
- 'Our White' (Co) WFar
- 'Pago-Pago' (Co) CSta ECtt NBro WFar XBar
- 'Pale Moon' (Co) WFar XBar
- 'Pink Laced' (Co) WFar
- pink-flowered (Co) NBir NRya
- 'Purity' (Co) WFar
- 'Purple Dusk' (Co) WFar XBar
- 'Raspberry Buttons' (Co) WFar
- 'Rasyoumon' (Co) WFar
- 'Rock Candy' (Co) CSta WFar
- 'Romance' (Co) XBar
- 'Ryokuryū' (Co) CSta
- 'Saiun' (Co) CSta WFar
- 'Sakuragawa' (Co) CSta WFar
- 'Sakura-no-miya' (Co) WFar
- 'Sangoguko' (Co) GKev MNrw
- 'Sasanake' (Co) **new** WFar
- 'Sato-zakura' (Co) CSta WFar XBar
- 'Sekidaiko' (Co) CSta
- 'Senshō' (Co) CSta WFar
- 'Sen-yū' (Co) CSta
- 'Seraphim' (Co) CRos CSta EBee EBlo EHyd LRHS NLar NRHS WFar
- 'Seto-no-ume' (Co) CSta
- 'Shibori Gasane' (Co/d) XBar
- 'Shibori-tatuta' (Co) CSta
- 'Shiokemuri' (Co) CSta
- 'Shiratama' (Co) **new** WFar
- 'Shira-tonbo' (Co) CSta
- 'Shira-washi' (Co) CSta WFar
- 'Shiro-tombo' (Co) XBar
- 'Shirousagi' (Co) WFar
- 'Shishi-funjin' (Co) CSta WFar
- 'Sikoubai' (Co) WFar
- 'Sinakatonba' (Co) WFar
- 'Sinipukurn' (Co) CFis CSta WFar
- 'Sinnkirou' (Co) WFar
- 'Sinseto' (Co) CSta WFar
- 'Siritonbo' (Co) WFar
- 'Sitikenjin' (Co) WFar
- 'Smudge' (Co) **new** CSta
- 'Snow Flakes' (Co) CSta

- 'Snowbird' (Co)	CSta XBar
- 'Snowdrop' (Co)	CDor CSta ECtt GKev LSou MACG MBel MNrw WCot WFar
- 'Snowflake' (Co)	CSta EBee EHyd EPfP GKev LRHS NLar SBut WFar
- 'Sorcha's Pink' (Co)	CSta WFar
- 'Sōshiari' (Co)	CSta WFar
- 'Sotodorihime' (Co)	WFar
- 'Spring Blush' (Co)	CSta WFar
- 'Spring Song' (Co)	CSta WFar
- 'Suibijin' (Co)	WFar
- 'Sumida-no-hatu' (Co)	WFar
- 'Sumisonegawa' (Co)	CSta WFar
- 'Sumizomegenji' (Co)	CSta WFar XBar
- 'Sweetie' (Co)	CSta WFar
- 'Syosin' (Co)	CSta
- 'Syutyuka' (Co)	CSta WFar
- 'Tagonoura' (Co)	CSta WFar
- 'Tah-ni' (Co)	NBro XBar
- 'Tairou-no-tsuki' (Co)	CSta
- 'Takane-no-yuki' (Co)	CSta
- 'Tamagawa-zome' (Co)	CSta WFar XBar
- 'Tamashiki-no-miya' (Co)	CSta
- 'Tanuki-bayashi' (Co)	CSta
- 'Taoyami' (Co)	CSta WFar
- 'Tatsuta-no-yū' (Co)	CSta
- 'Tatuta-no-yūbe' (Co)	CSta WFar
- 'Tobitake' (Co)	CSta
- 'Tochirimen' (Co) **new**	WFar
- 'Tokasamesi' (Co)	WFar
- 'Tokiji-gata' (Co) **new**	WFar
- 'Tokimeki' (Co/d)	CSta WFar XBar
- 'Toyonoharu' (Co)	WFar
- 'Trade Winds' (Co)	CSta WFar XBar
- 'Tsuki-no-miyake' (Co)	CSta
- 'Tsukumo-jishi' (Co)	CSta
- 'Tukasamesi' (Co)	CSta
- 'Turu-no-kegoromo' (Co)	CSta
- 'Ue-no-ume' (Co)	CSta
- 'Ukima Aka' (Co)	CSta WFar
- 'Ukimashiro' (Co)	CSta WFar
- 'Usujanome' (Co)	CSta
- 'Utyū' (Co)	CSta
- 'Vilia' (Co)	XBar
- 'Vivid Pink' (Co)	CSta WFar
- 'White Buttons' (Co)	WFar
- 'Winter Dreams' (Co)	CWCL ECtt GKev MBel NBid NBro WFar
- 'Yodai-no-yume' (Co) **new**	WFar
- 'Yousei' (Co)	CSta
- 'Yugeshiki' (Co)	CSta WFar
- 'Yūhi-beni' (Co)	CSta WFar
- 'Yukiguruma' (Co)	WFar
- 'Yuki-meimaki' **new**	WFar
- 'Yukizakura' (Co)	CSta
sikkimensis (Si) ♀H6	CAby EBee EPfP GKev LEdu MBel NGdn SPoG
- CC	GGro
- var. ***pseudosikkimensis*** (Si)	GKev
- var. ***pudibunda*** (Si)	GArf GKev
- red-flowered (Si)	GKev
aff. ***sikkimensis*** (Si)	NGdn XBar
Silver-laced Group (Pr/Poly)	EPfP SEND SPoG SWvt WFar XBar
- black-flowered (Pr/Poly)	EMor WCAu
simensis (Sp)	GKev XBar
sinopurpurea	see *P. chionantha* subsp. *sinopurpurea*
'Sir Bedivere' (Pr/Prim)	WCot
smithiana	see *P. prolifera*
I 'Sneeuwwitje' (Pr) **new**	LEdu
'Snow Carpet'	see *P.* 'Schneekissen'
'Snow Ruffles' (Au)	ITim NSum XBar
'Snow White' (Pr/Poly)	MRav
SNOWCUSHION	see *P.* 'Schneekissen'
'Snowgoose' (Pr/Prim/d)	XBar
sonchifolia (Pe)	GKev
- subsp. ***emeiensis*** (Pe)	GKev
sorachiana	see *P. yuparensis*
Sorbet Group (Pr/Poly)	XBar
'Soup Plate' (Pe)	NHar
spectabilis (Au)	GKev
Spice Shades Group (Pr/Poly)	XBar
STAR FEVER WHITE (Pr/Prim) **new**	MPri
× ***steinii***	see *P. × forsteri*
Stella Series (Pr/Poly)	LCro
'Stella Scarlet Pimpernell' (Pr/Poly)	WHil
stenodonta (Pf)	GKev
'Stradbrook Charm' (Au)	NRya XBar
'Stradbrook Dainty' (Au)	NWad WFar XBar
'Stradbrook Dream' (Au)	ITim WFar XBar
'Stradbrook Lilac Lustre' (Au)	XBar
'Stradbrook Lucy' (Au)	GEdr ITim NWad
'Strawberries and Cream' (Pr/Prim)	XBar
stricta (Al)	GKev
Striped Victorians Group (Pr/Poly)	XBar
'Strong Beer' (Pr/Prim/d)	EBee ECtt EPfP NHpl SAko SGro WBrk WCot WFar XBar
'Sue Jervis' (Pr/Prim/d)	EMor EShb EWTr LShi NBir NGrd NHpl WHil XBar
suffrutescens (Su)	WAbe
'Sundae' (Pr/Prim/d)	MBow XBar
'Sunrise' (Au)	CRos EHyd LRHS NRHS
'Sunrise' (Primlet Series) (Pr/Prim)	MPri
'Sunshine Susie' (Pr/Prim/d)	EPfP GArf GMaP MAvo XBar
SWEETHEART (mixed) (Pr/Prim)	LCro LOPS LRHS
takedana (Bu)	GEdr
Tango Group (Pr/Poly)	XBar
tangutica (Cy)	GKev
- BO 16-123	GGro
'Tantallon' (Pe)	NHar
Tartan Reds Group (Pr/Prim)	XBar
'Tawny Port' (Pr/Poly)	CElw CFis ELan
'Theodora' (Pr)	EBee ELan GAbr WFar
'Tie Dye' (Pr/Prim)	MMrt MNrw NLar SAko WCot WFar
'Tinney's Moonlight' (Pe)	NHar NSum SGro
'Tipperary Purple' (Pr/Prim)	ECtt NHpl NWad
'Tomato Red' (Pr/Prim)	NHpl WCAu WCot WFar
'Tony' (Au) ♀H5	XBar
'Tortoiseshell' (Pr/d)	ECtt
tosaensis (R)	GArf
Traditional Yellows Group (Pr/Prim)	CWCL XBar
'Tregor Truffle' (Pr/Prim/d)	XBar
'Val Horncastle' (Pr/Prim/d)	ECtt EWTr GMaP NHpl WHil XBar
Valentine Victorians Group (Pr/Poly)	XBar
× ***venusta*** (Au)	GKev
'Vera Maud' (Pr)	MBriF XBar
§ ***veris*** (Pr) ♀H5	Widely available
- PAB 3777	LEdu NRHS
- subsp. ***columnae*** (Pr)	GKev
- Coronation Cowslips Group (Pr)	XBar
- hose-in-hose (Pr/d)	CElw EWes WHil WHoo
- hybrids (Pr)	GDam GMcL MACG

– 'Katy McSparron' (Pr/d)	CBor CDor CExl ECtt LRHS MNrw NHpl NLar SPer WCot WFar WHlf
– 'Lady Agatha' (Pr)	XBar
– 'Lime with Orange' (Pr)	LRHS MPri NCth
– Lord Alfred Group hose-in-hose (Pr)	XBar
– subsp. ***macrocalyx*** (Pr)	CPla EPPr
– orange-flowered (Pr)	MPri
– red-flowered (Pr)	NBid NGdn
– 'Sunset Shades' (Pr)	CDor EMor EPfP LShi NGdn NLar SWvt WCAu
– subsp. ***veris*** (Pr)	CPla LSou WHlf
'Veristar Yellow' (Pr)	CRos
vernalis	see *P. vulgaris*
verticillata (Sp)	CPla GAbr GKev
§ ***vialii*** (So) ♀^{H5}	Widely available
– 'Alison Holland' (So)	CBod EWld GBin GEdr LBar LCro LLWG LRHS MBel MPnt NHpl NLar SPad WTyc
'Vintage' (Pr/Prim/d)	XBar
Violet Victorians Group (Pr/Poly)	XBar
viscosa All.	see *P. latifolia*
§ × ***vochinensis*** (Au)	GEdr
§ ***vulgaris*** (Pr/Prim) ♀^{H7}	Widely available
– var. ***alba*** (Pr/Prim)	WBrk
– 'Alba Plena' (Pr/Prim/d)	GAbr LShi
– 'Avoca' (Pr/Prim)	WFar
– 'Avondale' (Kennedy Irish Series) (Pr/Prim)	CBod CDor CElw EBee GAbr MAvo MBriF MNrw WCot WHil XBar
– 'Blarney Castle Blush' (Pr/Prim)	NHar WFar
– 'Blarney Castle Pink' (Pr/Prim)	NHpl
– 'Blarney Castle Red' (Pr/Prim)	NHpl XBar
– 'Carrigdale' (Pr/Prim)	CBod CDor MBriF WCot WFar XBar
– 'Catherine Thompson' (Pr/Prim)	NBir
– 'Claddagh' (Pr/Prim)	MBriF NHpl WCot
– Cornish pink (Pr/Prim)	GKev
– DRUMCLIFFE ('K74'PBR) (Pr/Prim)	ECtt EMor EWTr GBin LRHS MNrw NHpl NLar WCot WFar WHil XBar
– 'Dunbeg' (Kennedy Irish Series) (Pr/Prim)	CDor ELan GBin LRHS MBel MBriF NLar WCot XBar
– 'Glengarriff' (Kennedy Irish Series) (Pr/Prim)	EMor LRHS MBriF NHpl WCot XBar
– 'Golden Gem' (Pr/Prim/d)	WCot
– green-flowered	see *P. vulgaris* 'Viridis'
– hybrids (Pr/Prim)	CTsd
– INNISFREE ('K72'PBR) (Pr/Prim)	CDor ECtt EMor EPfP GBin LRHS MMuc MNrw NHpl WCot WFar
§ – 'Lilacina Plena' (Pr/Prim/d)	GArf LShi NHpl XBar
– 'Moneygall' (Kennedy Irish Series) (Pr/Poly/d)	LRHS NHpl WFar XBar
– 'Raspberry Rose' (Pr/Prim) **new**	MPri
§ – subsp. ***sibthorpii*** (Pr/Prim) ♀^{H5}	CAby CDor CRos EBee EHyd ELan EMor EPfP GAbr GBin GKev LRHS MBriF MCot MNrw NBro NChi NRHS SPtp SRms WFar
– 'Taigetos' (Pr/Prim) ♀^{H7}	CBro CExl
– 'Tara' (Pr/Prim)	NCth NHpl XBar
– 'Tarragem Sparkling Ruby' (Pr/Prim/d)	CWCL LRHS MBriF NHpl WCot XBar
– 'Vanilla Cream' (Pr/Prim)	MBriF WCot WOld
§ – 'Viridis' (Pr/Prim/d)	MNrw
– subsp. ***vulgaris*** (Pr/Prim) ♀^{H7}	CPud GMcL MBriF WCav WMAq
waltonii (Si)	GEdr GJos GRum MNrw
– butter-yellow-flowered (Si)	GRum
– hybrids (Si)	WHil

'Wanda' (Pr/Prim) ♀^{H7}	CBcs CPud CRos CToG CTri EBee EHyd ELan GBin GKev GMcL GQue LRHS LShi LSto MBel MHer MMuc NBid SRms WCFE WCot WGwG XBar
Wanda Group (Pr/Prim)	NBro
– 'Wanda Hose-in-hose' (Pr/Prim/d)	NBir
– 'Wanda Jack-in-the-Green' (Pr/Prim)	WCot
– 'Wanda Tomato Red' (Pr/Prim)	LShi MBriF NHpl
wardii	see *P. munroi*
warshenewskiana (Or)	EWes GKev NBwr NSum WAbe WGwG
watsonii (Mu)	GKev XBar
– maroon-flowered (Mu)	GKev
'Wedgwood'	see *P.* × *pubescens* 'Wedgwood'
'Wharfedale Bluebell' (Au)	NBir NHar NSum WHil
'Wharfedale Buttercup' (Au)	ITim NSum
'Wharfedale Gem' (*allionii* hybrid) (Au)	NSum NWad WIce XBar
'Wharfedale Ling' (*allionii* hybrid) (Au)	XBar
'Wharfedale Sunshine' (Au)	GKev WFar
'Wharfedale Superb' (*allionii* hybrid) (Au)	CBor XBar
'Wharfedale Village' (Au)	MPnt NHar
'White Linda Pope' (Au)	GArf GEdr NSum
'White Valentine'	GAbr
'White Wanda' (Pr/Prim)	XBar
'White Waves' (*allionii* hybrid) (Au)	ITim
§ ***whitei*** 'Sherriff's Variety' (Pe)	NHar
'William Genders' (Pr/Poly)	ECtt
wilsonii (Pf)	CTri GAbr LDai LLWG NBir NGdn WTyc XBar
– SDR 7824	GKev
§ – var. ***anisodora*** (Pf)	GKev GLog GRum LBar NGdn NHpl XBar
– var. ***wilsonii*** (Pf)	GKev
Winter White Group (Pr/Prim)	CWCL XBar
'Wisley Crimson'	see *P.* 'Wisley Red'
§ 'Wisley Red' (Pr/Prim)	CElw
'Woodland Walk' (Pr/Prim)	EPfP SRms
yargongensis	see *P. munroi* subsp. *yargongensis*
'Yellow' (Primlet Series) (Pr/Prim)	CRos EHyd LRHS MPri NRHS
yunnanensis (Y)	GKev
§ ***yuparensis*** (Al)	GArf GKev
zambalensis (Ar)	GKev
'Zebra Blue' (Pr/Prim)	EPfP

Primulina (*Gesneriaceae*)

'Aiko'	WDib
'Candy'	WDib
'Chastity'	WDib
'Diane Marie'	WDib
§ ***dryas*** ♀^{H1c}	WDib
– 'Hisako'	WCot WDib
dryas × ***linearifolia***	WDib
'Erika'	WDib
flavimaculata	WDib
heterotricha	WDib
'Keiko'	WDib
linearifolia	WDib
longgangensis	WDib
'New York'	WDib
'Periwinkle'	WDib
'Stardust'	WDib
'Sweet Dreams'	WDib
tabacum 'Deco'	WDib

Prinsepia (*Rosaceae*)

	sinensis	MBlu NLar

Prionosciadium (*Apiaceae*)

	thapsoides	SDix

Pritchardia (*Arecaceae*)

	hillebrandii	LPal
	pacifica	NPlm

Pritzelago see *Hornungia*

Proboscidea (*Pedaliaceae*)

	louisianica	SBls

Prosartes (*Liliaceae*)

§	***hookeri***	CMiW EBee EHed MNrw
§	- var. ***oregana***	EBee WCru
§	***lanuginosa***	EPPr ESwi LEdu WCru WFar WPGP
§	***maculata***	LEdu MNrw NLar WCru
§	***smithii***	EBee ESwi EWld GAbr GKev GLog LEdu LRHS MNrw NHar NLar SMHy WCru WPGP WSHC

Prostanthera (*Lamiaceae*)

	aspalathoides	CCCN
	'Badja Peak'	CCCN CCht CTrC CTsd MHtn
	baxteri	CTrC
	- 'Silver Ghost'	SGBe
	calycinia	CTsd
	cuneata ♀^{H4}	Widely available
	- 'Alpine Gold' (v)	MAsh
	- 'Blushing Bride'	CMac CTrC MHtn
*	***digitiformis***	CTsd
	incana	CTsd
	incisa	EGrI
	lasianthos	CBcs CCCN CTsd SPlb SVen
	latifolia	CTsd
	melissifolia	CTsd
§	- var. ***parvifolia***	CCCN
	'Mint Royale'	CCCN LEdu SGBe
	'Mint-Ice'	SGBe
	ovalifolia ♀^{H3}	CCCN SEle WAvo
I	- 'Variegata' (v)	CBcs CBod CCCN CKel CMac CTrC CTsd ELan EPot LRHS LSou MAsh MGil MHoo SEle SIvy WAvo WKif XSte
	phylicifolia	CBcs CTrC CTsd MGil
	'Poorinda Ballerina'	CBod CCCN CKel ELan LRHS SEle SGBe SPer SRkn SSha
	'Poorinda Petite'	CBod CCCN CKel CTsd ELan LRHS
	rotundifolia ♀^{H2}	CAbb CBod CCCN CCht CTri CTsd EBee EGrI EPfP EWTr IDee MGil MHoo SEle SIvy SPer SVen WCFE
	- 'Chelsea Girl'	see *P. rotundifolia* 'Rosea'
§	- 'Rosea' ♀^{H2}	CCCN CTrC CTsd EPfP
	rugosa	CTsd
	sieberi misapplied	see *P. melissifolia* var. *parvifolia*
	sieberi Benth.	CTsd
	spinosa	CTrC CTsd
	'Starlight' (v)	CTsd
	walteri	CBcs CCCN EGrI EHed MGil SIvy SPhx

Protea (*Proteaceae*)

	aurea	CTrC SPlb
	- subsp. ***aurea***	CPbh
	burchellii	SPlb
	'Clark's Red'	LRHS XSte
	coronata	CPbh SPlb
	cryophila	SPlb
	cynaroides	CCCN CPbh CTrC SPlb XSte
	- 'King Pine'	CCCN
	- 'King White'	CCCN
	- 'Little Prince'^{PBR}	CBcs CCCN
	- 'Madiba'	CCCN
	- 'Mini King'	CCCN
	- 'White Crown'^{PBR}	CCCN
	effusa	SPlb
	eximia	CCCN CPbh SPlb
	grandiceps	CCCN CPbh SPlb
	'Juliet'	CCCN
	lacticolor	CPbh SPlb
	laurifolia	SPlb
	lepidocarpodendron	CPbh
	longifolia	CPbh
	nana	SPlb
	neriifolia	CCCN CPbh CTrC SPlb
	- 'Snowcrest'	CPbh
	obtusifolia	SPlb
	'Pink Crown'	XSte
	'Pink Ice'	LRHS
	repens	CPbh LRHS SPlb
	- 'Ruby Blush'	CCCN
	scolymocephala	LRHS SPlb
	'Southern Cross'	CCCN
	'Special Pink Ice'	CCCN
	subvestita	CPbh SPlb
	susannae	CPbh CTrC SPlb
	'Susara'	CCCN LRHS
	'Sylvia'	CCCN

Prumnopitys (*Podocarpaceae*)

§	***andina***	CBcs IDee LRHS WFar
	elegans	see *P. andina*

Prunella (*Lamiaceae*)

	'Blue Pearl'	MHol MHoo
§	***grandiflora***	CHby ECha NFav SBut SCob SPhx SRms
	- 'Alba'	EBee ECha ELan GMaP NBid NLar SRms WCAu
	- 'Altenberg Rosa'	WCAu
	- 'Bella Blue'	LRHS MACG
	- 'Blue Loveliness'	EBee SWvt
	- 'Carminea'	EBee MRav SPer
	- 'Gruss aus Isernhagen'	GBee
	- 'Loveliness'	CMac ECha ELan GMaP MACG MRav NBro NGdn NSti SPer SPlb WCAu WFar
	- 'Pagoda'	NLar
	- 'Pink Loveliness'	CRos EBee SRms WCAu WFar
	- 'Rosea'	SBut WFar
	- 'Rubra'	NLar
	- violet-flowered	NSti
	- 'White Loveliness'	CMac SRms
	'Icing Sugar'	WFar
	incisa	see *P. vulgaris*
	laciniata white-flowered	MHoo
	'Rose Pearl'	CBod EBou EPfP MACG MHol MHoo NHpl SPeP SRms WCav
	SUMMER DAZE ('Binsumdaz'^{PBR})	GMcL LSou STPC
§	***vulgaris***	CBod CCBP CHab CTri ENfk GPoy LCro MBow MHoo MNHC NMir SPhx SRms WHer WWild
	- f. ***leucantha***	WHer
	× ***webbiana***	see *P. grandiflora*

Prunus ✿ (*Rosaceae*)

	'Accolade' (d) ♀^{H6}	Widely available
§	'Amanogawa' ♀^{H6}	Widely available
	amygdalus	see *P. dulcis*
	angustifolia	MNic

'Aprimira' (miracot) (F)	EBee LCro MTrO
APRISALI (aprium)	EBee ELan NOra
armeniaca	MPri SGsty
- 'Alfred' (F)	CMac NRog SKee SPer
- 'Bergecot' (F)	SKee
- 'Bergeron' (F)	MTrO NOra SKee SSFr WMat
- 'Bergeval' (F)	CAgr ELan MTrO
- COMPACTA (F)	MTrO NOra SBmr SCoo
- 'Delicot'[PBR] (F)	SSFr
- 'Early Moorpark' (F)	CAgr CBod CMac LEdu NOra NRog SBmr SEND SSFr SWeb WMat
- FLAVORCOT ('Bayoto'[PBR]) (F)	CAgr CBod EPfP EPom MCoo NOra SBmr SKee SPer SSFr SWeb WMat
- 'Garden Aprigold' (F)	EPom LCro MTrO SBmr SSFr WMat
- 'Goldcot' (F)	CAgr CPer LRHS MGos MTrO NLar NOra SKee SPoG SSFr WMat
- 'Golden Glow' (F)	CAgr CBod CPer CTri EPfP EPom LRHS MGos MTrO NOra SGbt SKee SSFT WMat
- 'Goldrich' (F)	CAgr
- 'Hargrand' (F)	CAgr SVic
- 'Harogem' (F)	CAgr
- 'Helena de Roussilon' (F)	CAgr MTrO NOra
- 'Hemskirke' (F)	NRog SKee
- 'Hungarian Best' (F)	SVic
- 'Isabella' (F)	NRog
- 'Kioto'[PBR] (F)	CAgr LRHS MTrO NOra
- 'Luizet' (F)	SGsty
- 'Moorpark' (F)	CHab CMac CSBt CTri CWnw EDir ELan LBuc MPri MRav NRog SBdl SEdi SKee
- 'New Large Early' (F)	NRog SBdl SEND SEdi
- ORANGE SUMMER ('Zaitorde'[PBR]) (F)	EPom
- 'Petit Muscat' (F)	EPom SBmr SKee
- 'Pink Marry' (F) **new**	LCro
- 'Robada'[PBR] (F)	CAgr ELan MTrO NOra
- 'Tomcot' (F)	CAgr CBod CTri ELan EPfP EPom LBuc LCro LSRN MTrO NOra SBmr SKee SPer SPoG SSFr WMat
- 'Tross Orange' (F)	MDon NRog
- 'Vigama' (F)	NOra WMat
'Asano'	CLnd
'Athos' (F) **new**	CDow MGos
avium	Widely available
- 'Alfheim' (F)	SBdl
- 'Amber Heart' (F)	CArg MTrO NOra NRog SKee WMat
- 'Archduke' (F)	SBdl
- 'Belgian Rivers' (F)	SBdl
- 'Bigarreau Burlat' (D)	LMaj
- 'Bigarreau de Schrecken' (F)	SBdl SKee
- 'Bigarreau Gaucher' (F)	NRog SBdl SKee WMat
§ - 'Bigarreau Napoléon' (F)	CArg EDir EPom LMaj LPar MTrO NOra NRog SBdl SBmr SEdi SGsty SKee SSFr SVic WMat
- 'Bing' (F)	SBmr
- 'Birchenhayes'	see *P. avium* 'Early Birchenhayes'
- 'Black Eagle' (F)	SBdl
- 'Black Elton' (F)	SBdl SKee
- 'Black Glory' (F)	SBdl
- 'Black Heart' (F)	EDir
- 'Black Oliver' (F)	CTsd MTrO NOra NRog SBdl WWct
- 'Black Tartarian' (F)	SBdl SKee
- 'Black Varik' (F)	SBdl
- 'Bradbourne Black' (F)	SBdl SKee
- 'Bullion' (F)	CEnd SBdl
- 'Burcombe' (F)	CEnd CPer SBdl
- CELESTE ('Sumpaca'[PBR]) (D)	CAgr CArg CMac CTri EDir LCro MTrO NLar NOra NWea SBmr SCoo SGbt SLim SPoG SSFT WMat
- 'Cherokee'	see *P. avium* 'Lapins'
- 'Circassian' (F)	SBdl
- 'Colney' (F)	CArg EPom NOra NRog SBdl SBmr SKee SSFr WMat
- 'Cooper's Black' (F)	SBdl
- 'Coroon' (F)	SBdl SKee
- CRISTALINA ('Sumnue'[PBR]) (F)	SBdl
- 'Crown Morello' (F)	SBdl
- 'Danelia' (D)	WMat
- 'Dun' (F)	CHab CPer NRog WMat
§ - 'Early Birchenhayes' (F)	CEnd SBdl
- 'Early Rivers' (F)	CSBt EDir IArd LPar LSRN MTrO NOra NRog SBdl SBmr SEdi SKee SSFr SVic WMat
- 'Elton Heart' (F)	SBdl
- 'Emperor Francis' (F)	SBdl SKee
- 'Erianne' (F)	SBdl
- 'Fice' (F)	CEnd SBdl
- 'Florence' (F)	SBdl SKee
- 'Frogmore Early' (F)	SBdl
- 'Früheste der Mark' (D)	SBdl
- 'Garden Bing' (F)	EPom
- 'Giorgia' (D)	WMat
- 'Goodnestone Black' (D)	SBdl SKee
- 'Governor Wood' (F)	SBdl SKee
- 'Grandiflora'	see *P. avium* 'Plena'
- 'Guigne d'Annonay' (D)	SBdl
- 'Hannaford' (D/C)	CHab NRog
- 'Hertford' (F)	LPar MTrO NOra SBdl SBmr SEdi SKee SSFr WMat
- 'Inga' (F)	SBdl SKee
- 'Karina' (D)	WMat
- 'Kent Bigarreau' (F)	SBdl
- 'Kentish Red' (F)	SBdl SKee
- 'Knauff's Riesen' (F)	SBdl
- 'Knauff's Schwarze' (F)	SBdl
- 'Knight's Early Black' (D)	CArg MTrO NOra NRog SBdl WMat
- 'Kordia' (D) ♀H6	CArg CBod EDir EPom LPar MTrO NOra SBdl SBmr SKee SSFr WMat WWct
- 'Kozerska' (F)	WMat
§ - 'Lapins' (F) ♀H6	CAgr CArg CBod CLnd EDir EPfP EPom LMaj LPar MRav NLar NOra NWea SBmr SCoo SEdi SGsty SKee SPoG SSFT SSFr WJas WMat WWct
- 'Mansfield Black' (F)	SBdl SKee
- 'May Duke'	see *P.* × *gondouinii* 'May Duke'
- 'Merchant' (F) ♀H6	ELan MTrO NOra NRog SBdl SEdi SKee SSFT SSFr WMat WWct
- 'Mermat' (F)	SBdl
- 'Merpet' (F)	SBdl
- 'Merton Bigarreau' (F)	CArg CTsd NOra NRog SBdl SBmr SKee SSFr WMat
- 'Merton Crane' (F)	SBdl SKee
- 'Merton Favourite' (F)	SBdl SKee
- 'Merton Glory' (F)	CAgr CArg CBod CSBt EDir ELan EPfP MTrO NOra NRog SBdl SBmr SCoo SEWo SEdi SKee SLim SPoG SSFr WMat WWct
- 'Merton Late' (F)	SBdl
- 'Merton Marvel' (F)	SBdl
- 'Merton Premier' (F)	EDir LPar NRog SBdl SVic
- 'Merton Reward'	see *P.* × *gondouinii* 'Merton Reward'
- 'Mizia' (D)	WMat
- 'Moserkirsche' (F)	SBdl
- 'Nabella' (F)	MAsh SBdl
- 'Napoléon'	see *P. avium* 'Bigarreau Napoléon'
- 'Newstar' (F)	SBdl
- 'Noble' (F)	SBdl SKee
- 'Noir Boccard' (F)	SBdl
- 'Noir de Guben' (F)	NRog SBdl SKee WMat

- 'Noir de Meched' (D) SKee
- 'Nutberry Black' (F) SBdl
- 'Octavia' (D) WMat
- 'Old Black Heart' (F) SKee
- 'Penny'PBR (F) ♀H6 CAgr CArg CTri EPom MTrO NOra NRog SKee WMat WWct
- 'Petit Noir' (F) CArg MTrO NOra WMat
§ - 'Plena' (d) ♀H6 Widely available
- 'Polstead Black' (F) SKee
- 'Regina' (F) EDir EPom LPar MTrO NOra SBdl SKee WMat
- 'Ronald's Heart' (F) SBdl SKee
- 'Roundel Heart' (F) NRog SKee WMat
- 'Sandra Rose' (F) SBdl
- 'Santina'PBR (F) SBdl
- 'Sasha' (F) CBod SBdl
- 'Schauenburger' (F) SBdl
- 'Schneiders Späte Knorpel' (D) SBdl
- 'Skeena'PBR (F) CArg MTrO NOra WMat
- 'Small Black' (F) CHab NRog
- 'Smoky Dun' (F) SBdl
- STARBLUSH ('Spc 207'PBR) (F) NOra
- STARDUST ('13-7-70') (F) LCro LOPS MTrO NOra SCoo
- 'Starkrimson' (F) SBdl
- 'Stella' (F) ♀H6 Widely available
- 'Stella Compact' (F) LSRN MDon SBdl SEdi
- 'Strawberry Heart' (F) SBdl
- 'Summer Sun' (D) ♀H6 CAgr CArg CBod CLnd CMac CTri EDir EPom LBuc MAsh MGos MLod MTrO NLar NOra NOrn NRog SBdl SCoo SKee SLim SPoG SSFT SSFr WMat WWct
- 'Summit' (F) CLnd SBdl SBmr SEdi SKee SSFr WMat
- 'Sunburst' (D) Widely available
- 'Sweetheart' (F) ♀H6 CAgr CArg CLnd CTri EPom LCro LMaj LOPS LPar LRHS LSRN MAsh MDon MLod MTrO NOra NRHS NRog NWea SCoo SEWo SKee SLim SPoG SVic WMat
- 'Sylvia' (F) CAgr CBod NOra WMat
- 'Turkish Black' (F) SBdl
- 'Van' (F) CAgr CArg CSBt EDir EPom LMaj NLar NOra NRog SBdl SEdi SKee WMat
- 'Vanda'PBR (F) NOra WMat
- 'Vega' (F) CAgr CArg NOra NRog SBdl SBmr SEdi SKee SSFr WMat
- 'Vera'PBR (F) SBdl
- 'Vroege van Werder' (F) SBdl
- 'Waterloo' (F) MTrO NOra NRog SBdl SKee WWct
- 'Wellington A' (F) SBdl
- 'Werder's Early Black' (F) SBdl
- 'Werdersche Braune' (F) SBdl
- 'White Heart' (F) CHab NRog SBdl SKee
- 'Zoe' (F) NRog
- 'Zweitfrühe' (F) SBdl

§ 'Beni-tamanishiki' ♀H6 CBcs MTrO NOra WMat
'Beni-yutaka' ♀H6 CBcs CBod CCVT CPer EHeP EPfP MAsh MDon MRav MSwo MTrO NOra NOrn NRHS SCoo SLim WMat
besseyi WKor
'Blaze' see *P. cerasifera* 'Nigra'
× ***blireana*** (d) ♀H5 CAco CEnd CLnd CTri EDir EHeP EPfP LCro LMaj LRHS MDon MGos MRav MSwo NBwr SCob SCoo SPer SPoG WMou
- 'Moseri' (d) WTSh
BLUSHING BRIDE see *P.* 'Shōgetsu'
campanulata 'Felix Jury' EBee NOra WMat WPGP
canadensis MTrO
CANDY FLOSS see *P.* 'Matsumae-beni-murasaki'
'Carmine Jewel' (F) CAgr
caroliniana SArc
'Catherine' MTrO
cerasifera (F) CAco CAgr CBrac CHab CPer CTri EPom LBuc MNic NRog NWea SCob SKee SPer WKor
- 'Countess' (F) EPom NOra
- CRIMSON POINTE ('Cripoizam') EBee MAsh MTrO NOra SGsty SPoG
- 'Golden Sphere' (F) CAgr CArg CPer CTri EPom MLod MTrO NOra SKee SSFr WMat
- 'Gypsy' (F) CAgr MLod MTrO NOra SKee SSFr WHtc WMat
- 'Hessei' (v) MRav NOrn
§ - Myrobalan Group (F) MRav SPre SVic WMat
§ - 'Nigra' ♀H6 Widely available
- 'Pendula' SWvt
§ - 'Pissardii' CDoC EPfP ERom LCro LMaj LSRN NOrn NRog NWea SCoo SGsty SWvt WFar WHtc WJas
- 'Rosea' NLar
- 'Ruby' (F) CAgr EPom MTrO SKee
- 'Woodii' CSBt
cerasus 'Maynard' (F) SSFr
- 'Meteor Korai' (F) CAgr NOra NRHS WMat
- 'Montmorency' (F) NOra SBdl SKee
- 'Morello' (C) ♀H6 Widely available
- 'Nabella' (F) SKee
- 'Semperflorens' CLnd
'Cheal's Weeping' CKel CWnw EBar NTrD SBdl SBmr
CHOCOLATE ICE see *P.* 'Matsumae-fuki'
§ × ***cistena*** ♀H6 CBcs CDoC CRos EBee EDir EHeP EHyd ELan EPfP LRHS MAsh MGos MSwo NRHS SCob SCoo SGol SPoG SWvt WFar
- 'Crimson Dwarf' see *P.* × *cistena*
'Collingwood Ingram' ♀H6 ELan EPfP LRHS MBlu MTrO NOra NOrn SLim WHtc WMat
'Cot-N-Candy' (Aprium Series) CAgr EPom
'Daikoku' CBcs EBee LRHS MTrO NOra WMat
davidiana SPlb
'Delma'PBR (F) CSBt NOra WMat
domestica (D/C) SPre
- 'Angelina Burdett' (D) CHab NRog SKee
- 'Anna Späth' (C/D) NRog SKee
- 'Ariel' (C/D) SKee
- 'Avalon' (D) CAgr CBTr CCVT CLnd LBuc MDon MLod MTrO NLar NOra SBdl SBmr SEdi SKee SSFr WMat
- 'Belgian Greengage' (F) CHab SKee
- 'Belgian Purple' (C) NRog
- 'Belle de Louvain' (C) CArg CHab CLnd CTri MTrO NOra NRog SBdl SEdi SKee WMat WWct
- 'Birchenhayes' (F) CEnd
- 'Blaisdon Red' (C) NOra SKee WMat
- 'Blaisdon Red' misapplied (C) MTrO
- 'Blue Rock' (C/D) ♀H5 SKee
- 'Blue Tit' (C/D) ♀H5 CAgr CBod EDir EPom MMuc NOra NRog SEND SKee SSFr WMat WWct
- 'Bohemian' (C) SKee
- 'Bonne de Bry' (D) SKee
§ - 'Bountiful' (C) SEdi
- 'Brandy Gage' (C/D) SKee
- 'Bryanston Gage' (D) SKee WMat
- 'Bühler Frühzwetschge' (C) NRog
- 'Burbank's Giant' see *P. domestica* 'Giant Prune'
- 'Burcombe' (F) CEnd MTrO
- 'Cambridge Gage' (D) ♀H5 Widely available
- 'Coe's Golden Drop' (D) CAgr CArg CHab CLnd EPom MGos MLod MRav MTrO NOra NRog

NWea SBdl SEdi SKee SPer WMat WWct
- 'Conwy Castle' (F) WMat
- 'Cropper' see *P. domestica* 'Laxton's Cropper'
- 'Czar' (C) ♀H6 Widely available
- 'Delicious' see *P. domestica* 'Laxton's Delicious'
- 'Denbigh' (C) CHab WGwG
- 'Denniston's Superb' see *P. domestica* 'Imperial Gage'
- 'Des Bejonnieres' (D) SKee
- 'Dittisham Ploughman' (C) CBod SKee WMat
- 'Dunster Plum' (F) CPer CTri WMat
- 'Early Green Gage' (D) MDon MTrO
- 'Early Laxton' (C/D) CHab CPer EDir LPar MMuc NRog SBdl SEND SEdi SKee
- 'Early Orleans' see *P. domestica* 'Monsieur Hâtiff'
- 'Early Prolific' see *P. domestica* 'Early Rivers'
§ - 'Early Rivers' (C) CAgr CArg CHab CPer CSBt CTri EBee EDir EPom EWTr LPar LSRN MLod MTrO NOra NRog SBdl SCoo SEdi SKee SPer SSFr WMat WWct
- 'Early Transparent Gage' (C/D) CAgr CBTr CBod CEnd CMac CPer CSBt LBuc LRHS MLod MTrO NOra NRog SBdl SCoo SKee SSFr WMat
- 'Early Victoria' (C/D) MDon SGbt
- 'Edda' (D) NOra WMat
- 'Edwards' (C/D) CTri NRog SBdl SEdi SKee SSFr
- 'Excalibur' (D) CAgr EPom IArd LBuc LMaj LPar LSRN NOra SBdl SBmr SEdi SKee WMat
- 'Finger Plum' (F) WMat
§ - German Prune Group (C) NOra NRog SKee WMat WWct
§ - 'Giant Prune' (C) MDon MMuc NRog SEND SEdi SKee SSFr
- 'Gold Dust' (F) WMat
- 'Golden Transparent' (D) NRog SKee
- 'Goldfinch' (D) EDir NRog SEND SKee
- 'Gordon Castle' (D) MTrO NLar SKee SSFr WMat
- Green Gage Group see *P. domestica* Reine-Claude Group
- 'Grove's Late Victoria' (D) WWct
- 'Guinevere' (C) CAgr CEnd EPom LRHS MAsh MTrO NLar NOra SKee SSFT WMat
- 'Guthrie's Late Green' (D) SKee
- 'Haganta'PBR (F) ♀H5 CAgr MLod MTrO NOra WMat
- 'Hauszwetsche' (C/D) LMaj
- 'Herman' (D) CAgr CBTr CEnd CMac EPom LRHS MAsh MTrO NOra NRog SBmr SKee WMat
- 'Heron' (C) NOra SKee WMat WWct
§ - 'Imperial Gage' (D) ♀H5 CAgr CArg CLnd CMac CPer CSBt CTri EDir EPom EWTr LRHS MDon MMuc MTrO NOra NRog SEND SKee SPer SSFT SSFr WMat
- 'Italian Prune' (F) NRog
- 'Jan James' (F) CEnd
- 'Jefferson' (D) ♀H5 CAgr CArg CHab CLnd MTrO NOra NRog SKee SSFr SVic WMat
* - 'Jubilaeum' (D) CAgr CLnd CMac EPom LBuc MTrO NOra SBmr SCoo SEWo SKee SSFr
- 'Kea' (C) CLnd CPer SKee WMat
- 'Kirke's' (D) CHab ELan NOra NRog SKee SSFr WMat
§ - 'Kulinaria' (D) LRHS MTrO NLar SPoG
- 'Lancelot' (F) MTrO
- 'Landkey Yellow' (F) WMat
- 'Langley Gage' (D) CAgr
- 'Late Muscatelle' (D) SKee
- 'Late Transparent Gage' (D) SKee
- 'Laxton's Bountiful' see *P. domestica* 'Bountiful'
§ - 'Laxton's Cropper' (C) CHab NRog SEdi SKee
§ - 'Laxton's Delicious' (D) CHab NRog
- 'Laxton's Jubilee' (C/D) CSBt MTrO NRog SCoo SGbt SPoG SSFr WMat
- 'Mallard' (D) ♀H6 NOra SKee WMat
- 'Manaccan' (C) CPer WMat
- 'Manns No. 1' (C/D) SKee WMat
- 'Marjorie's Seedling' (C) ♀H5 Widely available
- 'Meritare' (F) MTrO NOra WMat
- 'Merton Gage' (D) SKee
- 'Merton Gem' (D) SKee
- 'Miraclaude' (F) EPom
- 'Monarch' (C) SKee
§ - 'Monsieur Hâtiff' (D) NRog
- (Myrobalan Group) 'Myrobalan B' (F) WTSh
- Old English gage (F) CLnd EBee EPom SBdl SEdi
- 'Ontario' (D) LPar NRog
- 'Opal' (D) ♀H6 Widely available
- 'Oullins Gage' (C/D) ♀H5 Widely available
- 'Pershore' (C) CAgr CHab MLod MTrO NOra NRog SBdl SCoo SEdi SKee SPoG WMat WWct
- 'Pershore Emblem' (F) WWct
- 'Pozegaca' (D) SKee
- 'President' (C) CHab LMaj MMuc NOra NRog SEND SSFr
- 'Purple Pershore' (C) ♀H5 CAgr CHab CTri IArd MLod NOra NRog SKee SSFr WMat WWct
- 'Queen's Crown' (C/D) MTrO WMat
- 'Quetsche d'Alsace' see *P. domestica* German Prune Group
- 'Red Magnum Bonum' (C) NRog
- 'Reeves' (C) NLar NOra NRog SKee
- 'Regina Claudia' (D) LMaj
- 'Reine Claude van Schouwen' (F) NRog
§ - Reine-Claude Group (D) CAgr ELan LRHS MPri MTrO NOra NRog NWea SEND SKee SLim SPer WMat
- - 'Count Althann's Gage' (D) CHab EDir NOra NRog SSFr WWct
- - 'Ingall's Grimoldby Green Gage' (D) SKee
- - 'Lindsey Gage' (F) MTrO NOra SKee
- - 'Old Green Gage' see *P. domestica* (Reine-Claude Group) 'Reine-Claude Vraie'
- - 'Reine-Claude de Bavais' (D) CArg CLnd CTri NOra NRog SSFr WMat
- - 'Reine-Claude de Vars' (D) SVic
- - 'Reine-Claude Dorée' see *P. domestica* Reine-Claude Group
- - 'Reine-Claude Noire' (F) NRog
- - 'Reine-Claude Violette' (D) CAgr NOra NRog SKee SSFr
§ - - 'Reine-Claude Vraie' (C/D) CAgr CArg CBod CDoC CSBt EPom LBuc LCro LPar LRHS LSRN MPri MTrO NOra NRog SEWo SGbt SSFr WMat
§ - - 'Willingham Gage' (C/D) EBee LSRN MTrO NOra NRog SKee WMat
- 'Sanctus Hubertus' (D) CTri NRog SKee WWct
- 'Seneca' (D) EPom NOra SBmr SKee SSFr WMat
- 'Severn Cross' (D) SSFr
- 'Stanley' (C/D) LMaj SGsty SVic
- 'Stella' (F) CCVT GDam LOPS LSRN MPri MTrO SLim
- 'Stella's Star' (D) CAgr CBTr MTrO NOra WMat
- 'Swan' (C) NOra SKee WMat WWct
- 'Syston White' (F) MGos
- 'Thames Cross' (D) NOra
- TOPTASTE see *P. domestica* 'Kulinaria'
- 'Transparent Gage' (D) SKee
- 'Valor' (D) ♀H5 LMaj LPar NOra NRog SKee

	Name	Suppliers
	- 'Verity' (C/D)	SKee WMat
	- 'Victoria' (D) 🏆H5	Widely available
	- 'Victory' (D)	NOra SBdl
	- 'Violet' (F)	MTrO
	- 'Violetta'PBR (D)	CAgr MTrO
	- 'Voyageur' (F)	NRog
	- 'Warwickshire Drooper' (C)	CAgr CHab CPer MAsh MLod MTrO NOra NRog SKee SSFr WMat WWct
	- 'Wheat Plum' (F)	NRog
	- 'Willingham'	see *P. domestica* (Reine-Claude Group) 'Willingham Gage'
§	***dulcis***	CAco CHab CLnd CTri EDir EPom LMaj LRHS MDon MGos MMuc NWea SCob SCoo SEND SWvt WJur WMou
	- 'Ai' (F)	CAgr
	- 'Ardéchoise' (F)	CAgr
	- 'Ferraduel' (F)	CAgr
	- 'Ferragnès' (F)	CAgr
*	- 'Phoebe' (F)	CAgr
	- 'Praecox' (F)	MTrO
	- 'Princesse' (F)	SKee
	- 'Sultane' (F)	SKee
	- 'Supernova' (F)	CCCN
	- 'Sweetheart' (F)	SBdl
	- 'Tuono' (F)	CCCN
	EASTER BONNET ('Comet'PBR)	CTri EPfP NLar
	× ***eminens*** 'Umbraculifera'	LPar SGsty
	'Flavor King' (Pluot Series) (D)	CAgr EBee LCro MTrO WMat
	'Flavour Supreme' (F)	EPom
	FRAGRANT CLOUD	see *P.* 'Shizuka'
	FRILLY FROCK ('Fpmspl') (v)	EBee ELan EPfP LCro LRHS MDon MGos MPri MTrO NLar NOra SGbt SGsty SPoG WHtc WMat
	fruticosa	WFar
	- 'Globosa'	SGsty
	'Fugenzō' misapplied	see *P.* 'Kofugen'
§	'Fugenzō' 🏆H6	Widely available
	glandulosa 'Alba Plena' (d)	CEnd CMac CSBt SDix SGol SPlb SRms SWvt WCFE
	- 'Rosea Plena'	see *P. glandulosa* 'Sinensis'
§	- 'Sinensis' (d)	CEnd CMac CSBt SGol SRms WHlf
§	× ***gondouinii*** 'May Duke' (F)	CBod NRog SKee
§	- 'Merton Reward' (F)	SBdl SEdi SKee
	grayana B&SWJ 10903	WCru
	'Gyoikō'	CBcs CEnd CLnd EBee LRHS MTrO NOra WMat
	'Hally Jolivette'	CEnd EBee LRHS MAsh MTrO NOra NOrn SPoG WMat
§	'Hanagasa' 🏆H6	CBcs CEnd EDir EPfP EWTr MTrO NOra NWea SGbt WMat WMou
	'Hillieri Spire'	see *P.* 'Spire'
	'Hilling's Weeping'	LCro LOPS
	himalaica	NOra WHtc WMat WPGP
	'Hokusai' 🏆H6	CBcs CBrac EBee EPfP LRHS MTrO NLar NOra SGol WHtc WMat
	HOLLYWOOD	see *P.* 'Trailblazer'
	'Horinji'	CBcs LRHS MTrO NLar NOra SCoo WHtc WMat
	'Howard No. 3'	WMat
	'Ichiyo' (d) 🏆H6	CBcs EPfP MTrO NLar NOra SBdl SCoo SPer WMat
	ilicifolia subsp. ***lyonii***	WPGP
	× ***incam*** 'Okamé' 🏆H6	Widely available
	- 'Shosar'	see *P.* 'Shosar'
	incisa	CTri NRog
	- 'Beniomi'	MRav
	- 'February Pink'	LIns NLar SGol
	- 'Fujimae' 🏆H6	LIns NLar
	- 'Kojo-no-mai' 🏆H6	Widely available
	- 'Lotte'	NLar
	- 'Mikinori'	CEnd CMac CSBt ELan ELon EPfP EWTr MBlu MTrO NLar NOra NOrn SCoo SEWo WMat
	- 'Oshidori' (d) 🏆H6	CMac CSBt ELon EPfP LRHS MRav MTrO NLar NOra NQui SRms WMat WSpi
	- 'Paean'	ELon WFar
	- 'Pendula' 🏆H6	ELan EWTr LRHS MTrO NOra SCoo WMat
	- 'Praecox'	CSBt EPfP NOra SCoo WMat
§	- f. ***yamadei*** 🏆H6	ELan MTrO NLar NOra WSpi
	incisa × ***sargentii*** **new**	CPer
	insititia (F)	MLod MWht
	- 'Abergwyngregin' (C)	WMat
	- 'Aylesbury Prune' (C)	CAgr MTrO NOra SKee WMat
	- 'Blue Violet Damson' (C)	CAgr MTrO NOra NWea SKee SSFr WMat
§	- 'Bradley's King Damson' (C)	CArg CLnd NOra NOrn SKee WMat
	- bullace (C)	LEdu SEdi
	- 'Countess' (C)	CTri
	- 'Dittisham Damson' (C)	WMat
	- 'Farleigh Damson' (C) 🏆H6	CAgr CArg CBod CDoC CHab EPfP EPom EWTr LBuc LEdu MDon MTrO NBwr NLar NOra NRog NWea SEdi SKee SPer SVic WMat WWct
	- 'King of Damsons'	see *P. insititia* 'Bradley's King Damson'
	- 'Langley Bullace' (C)	CAgr CTri LEdu NOra NRog SKee SSFr WMat
	- 'Lisna' (C)	WMat
	- 'Merryweather Damson' (C)	Widely available
	- 'Michaelmas Damson' (C)	WWct
	- 'Mirabelle Countess' (C)	EPom LRHS MTrO WMat
	- 'Mirabelle de Metz' (C)	SKee
	- 'Mirabelle de Nancy' (C)	CAgr CBTr EDir EPom LMaj MTrO NOra NRog SBmr SEWo SKee WMat
	- 'Mirabelle Ruby' (C)	CArg LRHS NOra SPoG WMat
§	- 'Prune Damson' (C) 🏆H6	Widely available
	- 'Shepherd's Bullace' (C)	EBee MCoo MTrO NLar SKee
	- 'Shropshire Damson'	see *P. insititia* 'Prune Damson'
	- 'Small Bullace' (C)	SKee
	- 'Westmorland Prune' (C)	CHab NLar NRog NWea
	- 'Yellow Apricot' (C)	SKee
	'Jacqueline' 🏆H6	EBee LRHS MTrO NLar NOra SRHi WHtc
§	***jamasakura***	LRHS
	'Jō-nioi'	CEnd CPer LRHS
§	'Kanzan' (d) 🏆H6	Widely available
§	'Kiku-shidare-zakura'	Widely available
	'Kobuku-zakura'	NOra NOrn WMat
§	'Kofugen'	NOra WMat
	Korean hill cherry	see *P. verecunda*
	'Kursar'	CBcs CDoC CLnd CSBt CTri EPfP GKin LRHS LSRN MDon MTrO NLar NOrn NRog NWea SBdl SCoo SGbt SLim SPer SSFr SWvt WHtc WMat WSpi
	laurocerasus	Widely available
	- 'Angustifolia'	CDoC CKel CWnw SCob
	- 'Camelliifolia'	CMac MBlu WCFE
§	- 'Castlewellan' (v)	CBrac CDoC CMCN CTri ELon EPfP EShb LPar LRHS MDon MGos MRav MSwo NBwr NLar NWad SCob SDix SPer SPoG WFar WHtc
	- 'Caucasica'	CEnd LIns LMaj MNic NBwr NLar SEND SGol SGsty
	- ETNA ('Anbri'PBR) 🏆H5	CBod CMac EDir EHeP GMcL LBuc LPar SArc SCob SWvt WReH
	- 'Gajo'PBR	CBod
	- GENOLIA ('Mariblon'PBR)	LPar SGol
	- 'Green Marble' (v)	CTri EBee
	- 'Greentorch'PBR	LIns

- 'Ivory' PBR	CBod
§ - 'Latifolia'	LRHS WCFE WMou
- 'Magnoliifolia'	see *P. laurocerasus* 'Latifolia'
- 'Mano'	LMaj
- 'Marbled White'	see *P. laurocerasus* 'Castlewellan'
- 'Mount Vernon'	CTri LBuc LPar MBlu WCot
- 'Novita'	CBod CDoC EDir EPfP GDam GMcL LMaj LPar LSRN MNic MPri NLar NOrn SCob SGsty SWeb WHtc WReH
- 'Otto Luyken' ♀H5	CBcs CBod CBrac CCVT CMCN CMac CTri EBee EHeP ELan EPfP GMcL LBuc LPar MDon MGos MSwo NBir NBwr NWea SArc SCob SPer SPlb WCFE WFar
- 'Piranha' PBR	NEoE
- 'Rotundifolia' ♀H5	Widely available
- 'Schipkaensis'	GMcL
- 'Variegata' misapplied	see *P. laurocerasus* 'Castlewellan'
- 'Variegata' ambig. (v)	SRms
- 'Zabeliana'	CMac CTri GDam GMcL LPar MSwo NBwr NWea SCob SRms WCFE
litigiosa	EBee EWTr MTrO NLar NOra WMat
'Little Pink Perfection'	EPom LCro LOPS MTrO NLar NOra NOrn NTrD SCoo SPoG WMat
* ***longipedunculata***	LRHS
lusitanica ♀H5	Widely available
- subsp. ***azorica***	EBee WMou WPGP
- - TICO ('Ybrazo01' PBR) **new**	LCro
- 'Brenelia' PBR	CBod CKel CWnw LIns LMaj
- 'Myrtifolia' ♀H5	CBar CBod CDoC CPer CRos CTri EHyd EPfP ERom GMcL LMaj LPar LRHS LSRN MTrO NBwr NLar NOra SArc SCob SGol SGsty SPoG SWvt WCFE WMat WReH
- 'Variegata' (v)	CBar CBrac CMac ELan ELon LPar MGos MRav MSwo SCob SGol SGsty SPer SPoG SSta SWvt WFar
maackii	LMaj NOrn WHtc
- 'Amber Beauty'	CBcs EDir EPfP EWTr IPap LMaj LPar MGos MMuc MRav MTrO NOra SEND WMat WMou
maritima	WKor
§ 'Matsumae-beni-murasaki'	CBcs LRHS MAsh MTrO NLar NOra WMat WMou
'Matsumae-beni-tamanishiki'	see *P.* 'Beni-tamanishiki'
§ 'Matsumae-fuki' ♀H6	CBcs EBee LRHS LSRN MTrO NLar NOra NOrn NRHS NWea SLim WHtc WMat
'Matsumae-hanagasa'	see *P.* 'Hanagasa'
maximowiczii B&SWJ 10967	WCru
Miracot Series (F)	MTrO
'Mount Fuji'	see *P.* 'Shirotae'
mume	CMen LPar MMrt WJur
- 'Beni-chidori' ♀H5	CEnd CMac CPer CSBt EHed ELon EPfP EWTr LCro LOPS LRHS MBlu MTrO NLar NOra NOrn SCoo SPoG WCot WMat
§ - 'Omoi-no-mama' (d)	CBcs CEnd CMen NOrn SAko WHtc WMal
- 'Omoi-no-wac'	see *P. mume* 'Omoi-no-mama'
myrobalana	see *P. cerasifera* Myrobalan Group
nigra	WMat
nipponica var. ***kurilensis*** 'Brillant'	CBcs CBod CDoC CRos CSBt EDir EHyd EPfP LPar LRHS MMrt NHol NLar NOrn NRHS SMad SPoG
- - 'Ruby'	EWTr LSRN
'Oku-miyako' misapplied	see *P.* 'Shōgetsu'
padus	CArg CBTr CCVT CHab CLnd CMac CPer CSBt EHeP LBuc LIns LPar MGos MSwo NBwr NLar NRog NWea SCob SEND SEWo SGsty SavN WKor WMou WTSh
- 'Albertii'	CCVT LPar MMuc NOra WHtc WMat
- 'Colorata' ♀H6	CArg CMac EDir EHeP ELan EWTr IPap LPar MGos MMrt MMuc MRav NLar SBdl SEND SGol SPer SWvt WHtc WMou
- 'Grandiflora'	see *P. padus* 'Watereri'
- 'Le Thoureil'	LRHS MMrt MTrO NOra WHtc
- 'Purple Queen'	SGol
§ - 'Watereri' ♀H6	CArg CBod CCVT CLnd CMCN CMac CPer EHeP ELan EPfP LMaj LPar SCob SEND SEWo SGol SPer WHtc WMat WMou
'Pandora' ♀H6	Widely available
pendula	MTrO
§ - f. ***ascendens*** 'Rosea' ♀H6	LRHS MRav MTrO NOra WMat
- 'Pendula Plena Rosea' (d)	MTrO NOra WMat
§ - 'Pendula Rosea'	CAco CLnd CTri EHeP EPfP LPar MTrO NRog NWea SGsty SPer
§ - 'Pendula Rubra' ♀H6	CBod CCVT CLnd CMac CSBt EHeP ELan EPfP EPom LMaj LRHS MDon MTrO NOra NOrn SBdl SCob SCoo SGbt SLim SPer SPoG WMat
§ - 'Stellata' ♀H6	EPfP MTrO NOra SGbt SPer WMat
persica	SGsty SPre
- 'Advance' (F)	NRog
- 'Amber' (F)	SBdl
- 'Amsden June' (F)	CLnd EDir MTrO NOra NRog SEdi SKee WMat
- 'Avalon Pride' (F)	CAgr CBod EPom LCro MTrO NOra SBmr SCoo SKee SPoG SSFr
- 'Bellegarde' (F)	LRHS MTrO NOra SKee WMat
- 'Bonanza' (F)	EPom LSRN SSFr
- 'Cal Red' (F)	SGsty
- 'Carman' (F)	WMat
- 'Champion' (F)	EDir
- 'Crimson Bonfire' (F)	EPom SBmr SGsty
- 'Crimson Cascade' (F)	ELan
- 'Darling' (F)	SVic
- 'Diamond' (F)	EPom
- 'Dixi Red' (F)	CAgr SGsty
- 'Doctor Hogg' (F)	NRog
- 'Duke of York' (F)	SBdl SBmr SKee SSFr
- 'Early Alexander' (F)	NRog
- 'Fayette' (F)	SGsty
- 'Foliis Rubris' (F)	WHtc
- 'Francis' (F)	SKee
- 'Frost' (F)	WMat
- 'Garden Lady' (F)	EPom MTrO NOra NOrn SEWo SLim WMat
- 'Gorgeous' (F)	MTrO NOra SKee WMat
- 'Hale's Early' (F)	CAgr MMuc MRav MTrO NOra SEdi SKee SLim WMat
- 'Hylands' (F)	NRog
- 'Jalousia' (F)	EPom NRog SVic
- 'Johnny Brack' (F)	EDir
- 'Kestrel' (F)	SKee
- 'Lacrima' (F)	EPom SBmr
- 'Madison' (F)	NRog
- 'Melred' (F)	EGrl LRHS
- 'Mesembrine' PBR (F)	EPom LRHS MTrO NOra
- var. ***nectarina*** (F)	EDir
- - 'Earliglo' (F)	NOra WMat
- - 'Early Gem' (F)	NRog
- - 'Early Rivers' (F)	LSRN MTrO NRog WMat
- - 'Fantasia' (F)	NRog SSFr
- - 'Fire Gold' (F)	NRog
- - 'Flavortop' (F)	SSFr
- - 'Garden Beauty' (F/d)	EBee MTrO NOrn WMat
- - 'Honey Kist' PBR (F)	EPom
- - 'Humboldt' (F)	CAgr SBdl SEdi SKee WMat

- - 'Lord Napier' (F)	CAgr CBod CSBt CTri EDir EPfP EPom IPap LCro LRHS MDon MGos MTrO NOra SBdl SBmr SEND SEdi SGbt SKee SLim SPer SSFT SSFr SVic WMat
- - 'Madame Blanchet' (F)	CBod CWnw NRog SVic
- - 'Nana Red Prolific' (F)	SGsty
- - 'Nectared' (F)	EDir SGsty
- - 'Nectarella' (F)	EPom LCro LSRN MTrO NOra NRog SLim WMat
- - 'Pineapple' (F)	CAgr CTri LRHS MTrO NOra SKee WMat
- - RUBIS ('Necta Zee'PBR) (F)	EPom
- - 'Sauzee Bel' (F)	EPom
- - 'Sauzee King' (F)	EPom
- - 'Snow Baby' (F)	EPom
- - 'Snow Queen' (F)	SSFr
- - 'Terrace Ruby' (F)	WMat
- 'Peregrine' (F)	Widely available
- 'Red Peachy' (F) **new**	MDon
- 'Redhaven' (F)	CAgr NOra NRog SKee SVic WMat
- 'Redlate Necta'PBR (F)	SEdi
- 'Redwing' (F)	CAgr NRog
- 'Robin Redbreast' (F)	CAgr NRog
- 'Rochester' (F)	CAgr CBod CLnd CMac CSBt EDir ELan EPom LRHS LSRN MGos MLod MTrO NLar NOra NRog SBdl SBmr SEdi SKee SLim SSFT SSFr SWeb WMat
- 'Royal George' (F)	NRog
- 'Sanguine de Savoie' (F)	EPom NOra WMat
- 'Saturne' (F)	CAgr CBod CLnd CMac EDir EPom LRHS MLod NOra SKee SSFr WMat
§ - 'Spring Snow'PBR (F)	NLar
- 'Springtime' (F)	NRog
- 'Terrace Amber' (F)	SEWo SSFr WMat
- 'Terrace Diamond' (F)	WMat
- 'Terrace Garnet' (F)	WMat
- 'Victor' (F)	SBdl
- 'White Peachy' (F)	MDon
× ***persicoides***	EHeP NWea SBdl
- 'Ingrid' (F)	CAgr CEnd LRHS MGos NOra SCoo SKee SSFr WMat
- 'Robijn' (F)	CAgr CBod EDir ELan EPom LEdu NOra SKee SVic
- 'Spring Glow'	CBod CCVT CEnd CLnd EDir EMil LRHS MDon MTrO NOra NRog SCoo SEND SLim WJas WMat
phaeosticta NJM 10.072	WPGP
'Pink Candy' (F)	EPom
PINK PARASOL	see *P.* 'Hanagasa'
'Pink Perfection' ♀H6	Widely available
'Pink Shell'	CLnd EPfP EPom MDon MTrO NOra NRog SBdl SPer SSFr WMat
PINK SNOW SHOWERS ('Pisnshzam')	EPom
pissardii	see *P. cerasifera* 'Pissardii'
'Pissardii Nigra'	see *P. cerasifera* 'Nigra'
prostrata	WCot
pumila var. ***depressa***	MRav SAko
'Royal Burgundy' (d) ♀H6	Widely available
ROYAL FLAME ('Mieke')	EBee EWTr MTrO
rufa	CBcs MTrO NOra WMat
salicina 'Burbank' (D) **new**	NBwr
- 'Lizzie' (F)	CBod EPom
- 'Methley' (D)	CAgr NOra WMat
sargentii	Widely available
- 'Charles Sargent' ♀H6	CMCN LMaj LPar LSRN MBlu MTrO
- 'Columnaris'	EBee LRHS MTrO NOra WMat
- 'Rancho'	CLnd LMaj LPar NOrn SCoo SLim SPer SPoG WHtc WMat

× ***schmittii***	CCVT EBee EHeP LMaj LPar NOra SBdl SCob WMat
'Sekiyama'	see *P.* 'Kanzan'
serotina	EDir
§ ***serrula***	Widely available
- 'Branklyn' ♀H6	EBee EPfP LRHS MGos NOra WHtc
- 'Dorothy Clive' ♀H6	EBee
- 'Princesse Sturdza'	MBlu
- var. ***tibetica***	see *P. serrula*
serrula × ***serrulata***	WPGP
serrulata (d)	NRog
- 'Erecta'	see *P.* 'Amanogawa'
- 'Grandiflora'	see *P.* 'Ukon'
- 'Longipes'	see *P.* 'Shogetsu'
- 'Miyako' misapplied	see *P.* 'Shogetsu'
- var. ***pubescens***	see *P. verecunda*
- 'Rosea'	see *P.* 'Kiku-shidare-zakura'
- var. ***spontanea***	see *P. jamasakura*
'Shidare-zakura'	see *P.* 'Kiku-shidare-zakura'
'Shimizu-zakura'	see *P.* 'Shogetsu'
'Shirofugen'	see *P.* 'Fugenzo'
§ 'Shirotae' ♀H6	Widely available
§ 'Shizuka' ♀H6	CAco CBcs IPap LBuc LRHS MSwo MTrO NLar NOra NOrn NWea SCob SCoo SGbt SLim SPer SRHi WHtc WMat WMou
§ 'Shōgetsu' ♀H6	Widely available
'Shogun'	MTrO
§ 'Shosar' ♀H6	CBcs CEnd NOra SCoo SPer
simonii	SPre
SNOW FOUNTAINS ('Snofozam')	LRHS SGsty SPer
'Snow Goose'	CMac CPer EBee EDir ELan EPfP EPom LCro LOPS LRHS MBlu MDon MMuc MTrO NBwr NLar NOra NOrn SCoo SGol SPoG WHtc WMat
'Snow Showers'	CBod CCVT CDoC CEnd CMac EBee EDir ELan EPfP EPom LCro LRHS LSRN MAsh MDon MGos MPri MTrO NLar NOra NOrn NWea SEND SLim SPer SPoG SRHi WMat
spinosa	Widely available
- 'Plena' (d)	MBlu
- 'Purpurea'	MBlu WMou
§ 'Spire' ♀H6	Widely available
SPRING SNOW	see *P.* 'Beni-tamanishiki'
'Spring Snow'	see *P. persica* 'Spring Snow'
'Stefania'	WMat
× ***subhirtella*** var. ***ascendens***	see *P. pendula* f. *ascendens*
- 'Autumnalis'	Widely available
- 'Autumnalis Rosea'	Widely available
§ - 'Dahlem'	MTrO
- 'Fukubana'	CLnd CMac EPfP LPar MAsh NLar SGsty WMat
- 'Pendula' misapplied	see *P. pendula* 'Pendula Rosea'
- 'Pendula Rosea'	see *P. pendula* 'Pendula Rosea'
- 'Pendula Rubra'	see *P. pendula* 'Pendula Rubra'
- 'Plena'	see *P.* × *subhirtella* 'Dahlem'
- 'Rosea'	see *P. pendula* f. *ascendens* 'Rosea'
- 'Stellata'	see *P. pendula* 'Stellata'
'Sunset Boulevard' ♀H6	CCVT CLnd EBee EHeP ELan EMil LMaj LRHS LSRN MGos MTrO NLar NOra SCob WMat
'Tai-haku' ♀H6	Widely available
TAOFLORA RED ('Mintao13')	LRHS
'Taoyame' ♀H6	CLnd
§ ***tenella***	ECha WCot WJur
- 'Alba'	WFar
- 'Fire Hill'	CBcs ELan EPfP MGos MMrt SPer WCot WJas WSpi
'The Bride' ♀H6	CAco CBcs CBrac CEnd CPer EBee EPfP EPom EWTr LCro LOPS LRHS

		MAsh MTrO NOra NOrn SChF SCoo SEWo SGbt SPer WMat
	tibetica	see *P. serrula*
	'Tiltstone Hellfire'	CCVT EBee EWTr GBin LRHS MTrO NLar NOra NOrn WMat
	tomentosa	CAgr WJur WKor XVPe
§	'Trailblazer' (C/D)	CEnd CLnd CMac EDir EHeP EMil EPfP MDon MRav MSwo MTrO SCob SKee
	triloba	CBcs CPer EDir LCro LOPS MBlu MDon
	- 'Multiplex' (d)	SRms WAvo
§	'Ukon' 🏆H6	CBcs CLnd CMCN CMac CTri EHeP ELan EPfP LCro LOPS LRHS MAsh MGos MRav MTrO NLar NOra NOrn NRog NWea SBdl SCob SGol SLim SPer SRHi WFar WHtc WMat
	'Umineko'	CBod CCVT CLnd EDir EHeP EMil LMaj LPar MGos MMuc SCob SEND SEWo SPer
§	***verecunda***	CLnd NRog SBdl WJas
	'Victoria Willis'	WMat
	virginiana	WKor
	- 'Canada Red'	CCVT
	- 'Schubert'	CBod EDir EHeP ELan LPar NWea
	'White Cloud'	CAco
	'Woodfield Cluster'	IArd
	yamadae	see *P. incisa* f. *yamadei*
	× ***yedoensis***	CCVT CKel CLnd CSBt CWnw EBar EDir EHeP ELan EPfP EWTr LCro LMaj LPar MRav MTrO NOra NWea SCob SGsty SPer WHtc WMat WMou
	- 'Ivensii'	CAco CKel CSBt CWnw EPom NRog NWea SCoo SPer WHtc
	- 'Pendula'	see *P. × yedoensis* 'Shidare-Yoshino'
	- 'Perpendens'	see *P. × yedoensis* 'Shidare-Yoshino'
§	- 'Shidare-Yoshino'	CAco CCVT CMac CPer CSBt IPap LBuc LRHS MGos MRav MTrO NLar NOrn NWea SGsty SLim SPer WHtc WMat
§	- 'Somei-Yoshino' 🏆H6	CCVT CMCN CPer CTri EDir MTrO SBdl SLim SSFr WJas
	'Yoshino'	see *P. × yedoensis* 'Somei-Yoshino'
	'Yoshino Pendula'	see *P. × yedoensis* 'Shidare-Yoshino'

Psammophiliella (*Caryophyllaceae*)

§	***muralis*** 'Garden Bride'	SWvt
	- 'Gypsy Deep Rose'	EHyd ELan EPfP LRHS NRHS
	- 'Gypsy Pink' (d)	SWvt

Pseuderanthemum (*Acanthaceae*)

	laxiflorum	EShb

Pseudocydonia (*Rosaceae*)

§	***sinensis***	CBcs CHab CMen LPar NRog SEND WJur WKor

Pseudofumaria see *Corydalis*

	alba	see *Corydalis ochroleuca*

Pseudogynoxys (*Asteraceae*)

§	***chenopodioides***	CCCN CSpe EAri ECre EShb SVen

Pseudolarix (*Pinaceae*)

	amabilis 🏆H7	CAco CMen EPfP LPar MBlu MPkF SLim WJur
	kaempferi (Lamb.) Gordon	see *Larix kaempferi*

Pseudomuscari see *Muscari*

Pseudopanax ✿ (*Araliaceae*)

	(Adiantifolius Group) 'Adiantifolius'	CAbb CBcs CCCN CTrC EBee SVen
	- 'Cyril Watson' 🏆H3	CBcs CBod EBee EPfP SEND SVen WPGP
	arboreus	see *Neopanax arboreus*
	'Bronze Eagle'	LRHS XSte
	'Chainsaw'	WPGP
	chathamicus	SArc
	crassifolius	CBrP CCCN CDTJ ELon GBin SArc WPGP XSte
	- var. ***trifoliolatus***	CBcs CDTJ WPGP
	'Dark Star'	CBcs CTrC LRHS XSte
	ferox	CBrP CDTJ CTrC CTsd GBin IDee LCro LRHS SArc SVen XSte
	'Gecko Gold' (v)	LRHS XSte
	laetus	see *Neopanax laetus*
	lessonii	CBcs CBrP
	- 'Gold Splash' (v) 🏆H3	CBcs CBod CCCN CTrC EBee ELon EPfP SEND SVen XSte
	- 'Goldfinger'	EAri LRHS XSte
	- 'Nigra'	CTrC
	- 'Rangitira'	CTrC LRHS XSte
	'Linearifolius'	CTrC LEdu
	'Moa's Toes'	CBcs CBct CCht CTrC CTsd EAri ELon MHtn SCob SEND WCot WLov
	'Purpureus' 🏆H3	CBod CCCN CDTJ CTrC CTsd ELon EPfP IDee SEND SEdd SVen
	'Sabre'	CAbb CBcs CCCN CDTJ CTrC EBee ELon EPfP LRHS SEND SEdd
	'Trident' 🏆H3	CTrC IDee SEND SVen
	'Tuatara'	CAbb CTrC GBin IDee LRHS MHtn SCob

Pseudophegopteris (*Thelypteridaceae*)

	levingei	see *Phegopteris levingei*

Pseudophoenix (*Arecaceae*)

	sargentii	NPlm

Pseudosasa (*Poaceae*)

	sp.	CAco
§	***japonica*** 🏆H5	CAbb CAco CAgr CBcs CBod CSBt EHyd EPfP ERom GArf GBin GMcL LCro LOPS LPal LPar LRHS MMuc MWht NBwr NLar NPlm SArc SBGi SCob SEND SGsty SPoG SWeb WFar
§	- 'Akebonosuji' (v)	SWeb
I	- var. ***pleioblastoides***	MWht
	- 'Tsutsumiana'	ELon GMcL MWht NLar
	- 'Variegata'	see *P. japonica* 'Akebonosuji'
	viridula	MWht

Pseudotaxus (*Taxaceae*)

	chienii	CBcs LRHS WPGP

Pseudotsuga (*Pinaceae*)

§	***menziesii***	CAco CBTr CBcs CLnd EDir EPfP LPar MBlu MMuc NWea SCob WHtc WTSh
	- 'Bhiela Lhota'	CAco CKen
	- 'Blue Wonder'	CKen
	- 'Densa'	CKen
	- 'Fastigiata'	CAco CKen
	- 'Fletcheri'	CAco CKen SLim
	- 'Foxy Fir'	SLim
	- var. ***glauca***	CAco
	- 'Glauca Pendula'	CAco LRHS MBlu
	- 'Gollen'	SLim
I	- 'Gotelli's Pendula'	CKen
	- 'Graceful Grace'	CKen
	- 'Hillside Pride'	NLar
	- 'Holata'	CAco
	- 'Holmstrup'	CAco

- 'Julie' CKen
- 'Les Barres' SLim
- 'Little Jamie' CKen
- 'Little Jon' CAco
- 'Lohbrunner' CKen SLim
- 'Maruška' CAco
- 'Misty First' CAco
- 'Moerheimii' CAco NLar
- 'Nana' CKen
- 'Nýřany' SLim
- 'Pannenhoef' SLim
- 'Pannonia' CAco
- 'Seattle Mountain' SLim
- 'Serpentine' CAco MBlu SLim
- 'Skryje' CAco
- 'Stairii' CKen
- 'Tidal Wave' CAco
- 'Uwes Golden' SLim

taxifolia see *P. menziesii*

Pseudowintera (*Winteraceae*)

§ ***colorata*** CBcs CCCN CDoC CMac CPla CTrC EBee GAbr GKin MHtn MRav NLar SEle WFar XSte
- 'Marjorie Congreve' CBcs CDoC GKin IArd
- 'Moulin Rouge' CBcs CTrC SEle
- 'Red Glow' CBcs
- 'Red Leopard' CTrC LRHS SEle WFar

Psidium (*Myrtaceae*)

cattleyanum see *P. littorale* var. *longipes*
guajava (F) CCCN CMCN SPlb SVic
littorale var. ***littorale*** (F) WKor
§ - var. ***longipes*** (F) CCCN WJur WKor

Psophocarpus (*Fabaceae*)

tetragonolobus LOPS SPhx

Psoralea (*Fabaceae*)

aphylla SVen
* ***fleta*** SPlb
glabra SPlb
glandulosa SPlb
oligophylla SPlb
pinnata IArd IDee WCot

Psylliostachys (*Plumbaginaceae*)

suworowii LRHS SPhx

Ptelea (*Rutaceae*)

trifoliata CBcs CLnd ELan EPfP LPar MBlu MVil SPer SRms WJur WPGP
- 'Aurea' ♀H6 CLnd ELan EPfP EWTr MBlu MMuc SPer

Pteracanthus see *Strobilanthes*

Pteridium (*Dennstaedtiaceae*)

aquilinum XLum

Pteridophyllum (*Papaveraceae*)

racemosum CMiW EWld GEdr GGro LEdu NHpl WCru WFar WSHC

Pteris (*Pteridaceae*)

§ ***actiniopteroides*** CDTJ
cretica var. ***albolineata*** see *P. nipponica*
- 'Mayi' (v) CBdn CRos EHyd LRHS NRHS WCot
- 'Ouvradii' SPlb
- 'Parkeri' LPal
- 'Rivertoniana' EHyd LRHS NRHS
- 'Roweri' CBdn CRos EHyd LPal LRHS NRHS
- 'Wimsettii' ♀H4 CBdn CRos EHyd LEdu LRHS MAsh NRHS WCot

ensiformis 'Evergemiensis' (v) CTsd EShb
henryi see *P. actiniopteroides*
incompleta LEdu
§ ***nipponica*** ♀H1c CBct CBdn EHed EHyd EShb GGro LLWG LPal LRHS SEND SMrm WCot
tremula EShb NBro WCot
umbrosa CBct CBdn CCht CDTJ CLAP CRos CTsd EHyd LLWG LRHS MAsh MHol NBro NRHS SEND SMrm SPlb WCot WPGP
wallichiana CDTJ WCot WPGP

Pterocactus (*Cactaceae*)

hickenii F&W 10240 WCot
kuntzei see *P. tuberosus*
reticulatus new SPlb
§ ***tuberosus*** ♀H2 new SPlb

Pterocarya ✿ (*Juglandaceae*)

fraxinifolia CBcs CCVT CMCN EBee EHeP EPfP IPap LMaj LRHS MBlu MCoo MMuc MRav MVil WTSh
- NJM 13.007 WPGP
- PAB 13.052 LEdu
- 'Abbotsbury Giant' WPGP

macroptera var. ***insignis*** CExl IArd SMad WPGP
× ***rehderiana*** MBlu
rhoifolia CMCN EPfP LAlb
stenoptera CBcs CDTJ CDoC NLar WJur
- 'Fern Leaf' ♀H6 CDoC CExl MBlu WPGP

tonkinensis CBcs WPGP

Pterocephalus (*Caprifoliaceae*)

depressus EDAr
parnassi see *P. perennis*
§ ***perennis*** MHer SRms WIce

Pterostylis (*Orchidaceae*)

curta ♀H2 CBro SGro
fischii SPlb

Pterostyrax ✿ (*Styracaceae*)

corymbosa CBcs CMCN GBin LPar LRHS MBlu MVil WJur XSte
- CWJ 12838 WCru

hispida ♀H5 CBcs CMCN EPfP ESwi MBlu MRav MVil NLar WFar WJur
psilophyllus CMCN MBlu
- var. ***leveillei*** MBlu WPGP
- trilobed WPGP

Pteroxygonum (*Polygonaceae*)

giraldii new GGro

Ptilostemon (*Asteraceae*)

§ ***diacantha*** EBee
echinocephalus GJos

Ptilotrichum see *Alyssum*

Ptilotus (*Amaranthaceae*)

exaltatus SPlb

Ptychosperma (*Arecaceae*)

elegans new EAri
macarthurii new EAri

Pulicaria (*Asteraceae*)

§ ***dysenterica*** CHab NGrd NMir WHer WSFF

Pulmonaria (*Boraginaceae*)

	angustifolia	CTri GKev GMaP MNrw NWad SHeu SRms
	- 'Azurea'	CElw EBee EGrI ELan EPPr EPfP GAbr GMaP MCot MMuc MRav NBro NGrd SRms WCAu WSpi
	- 'Blaues Meer'	EBee ECtt EHyd LRHS MNrw NRHS NSti SGbt SHeu WSpi
	- 'Munstead Blue'	MCot NRya SRms
	'Apple Frost'	SHeu
	'Ballyrogan Blue' ♀H6	EBlo EHyd LRHS
	'Barfield Regalia'	NChi NSti
	'Benediction'	MBriF MNrw NSti WBrk WCot WMal
	'Beth Chatto'	CElw
	'Beth's Pink'	GAbr
	'Blake's Silver'	CDor CSpe GElm LPla MHol MNrw SCob SMrm WBrk WCot WHoo
	'Blauer Hügel'	NSti
	'Blue Crown'	CElw WBrk
	'Blue Ensign' ♀H6	Widely available
	'Blue Moon'	see *P. officinalis* 'Blue Mist'
	'Blue Pearl'	EHyd LRHS NRHS
	'Bubble Gum'PBR	EMor LBar SCob SHeu
	Cally hybrid	EPPr
	'Cleeton Red'	MNrw WMal
	'Coral Springs'	MAvo NLar
	'Cotton Cool' ♀H6	EBee ECha ECtt EHyd EShb EWoo GBin GQue LRHS MAvo MBNS MBel MBriF MCot MRav MTin NHol NRHS NSti NWad SGbt SHeu SPer SSut WCAu WGwG WOld WWke
	'Dark Vader'	NCth SHeu SPoG
	'Diana Clare' ♀H6	Widely available
	'Elworth Sentinel'	MBriF
	'Excalibur'	ECtt NLar SHeu SRms
	'Fiona'	MNrw
	'Gavin Compton' (v)	MNrw
	'Glacier'	NChi WCot
	'High Contrast'	SHeu
	'Highdown'	see *P.* 'Lewis Palmer'
	'Ice Ballet' (Classic Series)	CDor EBee EPfP LBar LRHS MBriF MNrw SCob SHar SHeu WCAu
	'Joan Curtis'	MNrw
§	'Lewis Palmer' ♀H6	CBro CDor GMaP LRHS MAvo MNrw NBir SRms WAvo WBrk WHoo
	'Little Star' ♀H6	CElw CRos EBee EBlo EHyd GKev LRHS MAvo NRHS NSti SHeu WFar
	longifolia	EHyd ELan EPfP GBin GKev LRHS LSou LSto NBir NLar NRHS NSti SBls SRms WCav
§	- 'Ankum'	CElw NBir WCot
	- 'Bertram Anderson'	EBee ECtt EMor GMaP NBir SHeu SPer SRms SWvt WCAu
	- subsp. ***cevennensis***	EHyd EMor LRHS NLar NRHS SHeu WBrk WFar WSpi
	- 'Coen Jansen'	see *P. longifolia* 'Ankum'
	- 'Dordogne'	NBir NLar
	- 'Howard Eggins'	WAvo WBrk
	'Mado'	ECha
	'Majesté'	CDor CMiW CRos EAJP EBee ECha EHyd ELan EMor EPfP GMaP LBar LRHS MBel MPri MRav NBir NLar NRHS NSti SCob SHeu SMad SPer SPoG SRms WCAu WCot WFar
	'Margery Fish'	CDor LRHS NChi SHeu WBrk
	'Mary Mottram'	NBir NSti SHeu WCot
	'Mawson's Blue'	NBir NChi SWvt
	'Milky Way'	ECtt EPfP SHeu SPoG
	'Miss Elly'	MAvo NSti
	mollis	CBod EPPr GBin MNrw NSti WCAu
	- 'Royal Blue'	MRav
	'Monksilver'	CElw
	'Moonshine'PBR	CRos EBee ECtt EHyd EPfP GKev LRHS MAsh MBel NRHS NSti SHeu WCAu
	'Moonstone'	CElw
	'Mrs Kittle'	EHyd GPSL LRHS MBel MBriF MRav NBir NHol NLar NRHS NSti SHeu
	'Nürnberg'	CDor
	officinalis	CHby MHer MHoo NChi NGrd WBrk WCFE
	- 'Alba'	EBtc WBrk
§	- 'Blue Mist'	GMaP NBir WAvo WCot
	- 'Bowles's Blue'	see *P. officinalis* 'Blue Mist'
	- Cambridge Blue Group	MRav NBir NGdn WCot
	- 'White Wings'	NLar
	OPAL ('Ocupol') ♀H6	Widely available
	'Open Skies' (v)	WCot
	'Patric's Early Dawn'	ECha
	'Pierre's Pure Pink'	EBee SHeu
	'Pink Haze'PBR	NLar SWvt
	'Purple Haze'	NSti SCob
	'Raspberry Coulis' **new**	WCot
	'Raspberry Splash'PBR	CKel CRos ECtt ECul EMor EPfP GKev LCro LLWG LPla LRHS MNrw NBir NLar NSti SCob SDix SHeu SWvt WCAu WCot WPnP WWke
	'Richard Nutt'	WCot
*	'Rowlatt Choules'	MNrw
	'Roy Davidson'	CAby CDor ECtt EHyd EPPr EPfP MBow NBir NChi NHol SRms SWvt
	rubra	CBcs CElw ECha ELan GAbr LCro LOPS LShi MMuc MNrw NBid NChi NLar NSti SHeu SRms WCAu
	- var. ***alba***	see *P. rubra* var. *albocorollata*
§	- var. ***albocorollata***	EBee EBlo ECha EHyd EPfP GBin LRHS NBid
	- 'Ann'	GBin GQue
	- 'Barfield Pink'	MNrw NBir NLar SHeu
	- 'Bowles's Red'	CBod MNrw NBir NLar WCAu WFar WGwG
	- 'David Ward' (v)	ECha EHyd ELan EMor LRHS NBir NSti SCob SHeu SPoG SRms WCAu WCFE WCot
	- 'Rachel Vernie' (v)	NQui WAvo
	- 'Redstart'	CDor ECtt GKev GMaP LBar LRHS MNrw NBir NGrd NLar SCob SHeu SPer SRms SWvt WBrk WCAu WFar
§	***saccharata***	ECha EHeP GMaP MMuc SRms
	- 'Alba'	CElw SRms
	- Argentea Group ♀H6	CTri GMaP MRav NGdn
	- 'Clent Skysilver'	WAvo WBrk
	- 'Dora Bielefeld'	CBod ECha EGrI EPfP EWes GKev GMaP LSto MBriF MNrw MRav NBir NChi NGdn NHol NRHS NSti SHeu SPer SWvt WCAu WFar WHlf WOld
	- 'Frühlingshimmel'	CDor ECha LPla MRav
	- 'Glebe Cottage Blue'	CElw
	- 'Leopard'	CAby CDor CRos CWCL ECtt EHyd EMor EPfP LRHS MNrw NBir NGdn NLar SHeu SWvt WCAu WCot WGwG WHoo WSpi
	- 'Mrs Moon'	CBod CTri EBee EBlo ECtt EHeP EHyd EPfP GMaP LCro LOPS LRHS MBriF NLar SCob SHeu SPer SWvt WCAu
	- 'Old Rectory Silver'	NBir
	- 'Picta'	see *P. saccharata*
	- 'Pink Dawn'	EBee
	- 'Reginald Kaye'	ECha
	- 'Silverado'PBR	ECtt NGdn NLar SCob SHeu SWvt
	- 'Stanhoe'	EWes
	'Saint Ann's'	EBee EHyd LRHS NRHS NSti

'Samurai' ♀H6	CWCL EMor LRHS MAvo MNrw NCth NLar NSti SHeu WFar
'Shrimps on the Barbie'	CBod LBar SRHi WPnP
'Silver Bouquet'PBR	ECtt ECul EPfP LBar LCro LLWG LOPS LPla LRHS LSou NHpl NSti SHeu WCAu
'Silver Lance'	SHeu
'Silver Shimmers'PBR	SHeu
'Sissinghurst White' ♀H6	Widely available
'Smoky Blue'	MRav SCob SHeu
'Spilled Milk'	SHeu
'Spring Awakening' **new**	WCAu
'Stillingfleet Meg'	CDor CRos ECtt EHyd LBar LRHS MBNS MBriF MTin NGdn NLar NRHS NSti NWad SCoo SHeu WBrk WCAu WGwG WOld
'Trevi Fountain' ♀H6	Widely available
'Vera May' ♀H6	MBriF MNrw
'Victorian Brooch'PBR	CBod CRos CWCL ECtt EHyd EPfP GMaP LPla LRHS MBel MHol MNrw NCou NRHS NSti SHeu SPoG WCAu WSpi
'Weetwood Blue'	EBee EBlo EHyd LRHS MNrw NRHS WMal
'Wendy Perry'	EBlo EHyd LRHS

Pulsatilla (*Ranunculaceae*)

albana	EDAr EHyd GKev LRHS NRHS
- 'Lutea'	NSla
alpina	GKev SPlb SRms
- subsp. ***alpina***	GKev
§ - subsp. ***apiifolia***	EDAr EPot
- subsp. ***sulphurea*** misapplied	see *P. alpina* subsp. *apiifolia*
ambigua	GEdr
aurea	EDAr
bungeana	GKev
campanella	GArf GEdr GKev
- W&O 7223	GGro
caucasica	EHyd LRHS NRHS
halleri ♀H5	EBee GBin GKev
- subsp. ***slavica*** ♀H5	GJos
- subsp. ***taurica***	GEdr
lutea	see *P. alpina* subsp. *apiifolia*
montana	GEdr SPlb
occidentalis	GEdr
§ ***patens***	NGdn
- subsp. ***flavescens***	GEdr
pratensis	GPoy SRms
- subsp. ***nigricans***	EDAr GEdr WAbe
red-flowered	CTri
rubra	CAvo CRos EAJP EBou EGrl EHyd ELan EMor EPfP GJos GKev GMaP LRHS MHer NBir NGdn NLar NRHS SPeP SPer SPoG SRms SRot WAbe WHoo WIce WSHC WWke
* ***serotina***	EBee
subslavica	GKev WAbe
sugawarae	GEdr
tatewakii	EDAr GEdr
turczaninovii	EDAr GEdr GJos NSla WFar
§ ***vernalis***	EPot GEdr NLar NSla WAbe
violacea	CBcs
§ ***vulgaris*** ♀H5	Widely available
- 'Alba'	Widely available
- 'Barton's Pink'	CRos EHyd LRHS NRHS
- 'Blaue Glocke'	CAby CRos EHyd GEdr LRHS NRHS SHar SWvt
- blue-flowered	CTri
- double, fringed (d)	EDAr
- 'Eva Constance'	CRos EHyd LRHS NRHS
- subsp. ***grandis***	EHyd GEdr LRHS NLar NRHS NSla
- - 'Alba' **new**	CAby
- - 'Papageno'	CAby CDor CSpe EAJP EBee ELon EPfP EPot GAbr GEdr LRHS MAvo MBel MHol NHol NHpl NLar NSla
- Heiler hybrids	EShb LRHS LSou MArl MBel MPie MRav NDov NGdn SGbt SVic WGwG
- lilac-flowered **new**	WHlf
- 'Perlen Glocke'	EDAr EHyd EPot EWTr GEdr LRHS NLar NRHS SEdd
- pink-flowered	EAJP WFar
- (Pinwheel Series) PINWHEEL BLUE VIOLET SHADES	CBod EHyd LBar LCro LRHS MACG MHol NRHS
- - PINWHEEL DARK RED SHADES	LBar LCro LRHS MACG MHol
- - PINWHEEL WHITE	LBar LCro LRHS MHol WFar
- RED CLOCK	see *P. vulgaris* 'Röde Klokke'
- red-flowered	CTsd EBee EDAr EMor GAbr SGbt WFar WHlf
§ - 'Röde Klokke'	CAby CRos ECtt EHyd EPfP GEdr LRHS LSun MBel NRHS NSla SEdd SHar SMrm SWvt XLum
- ROTE GLOCKE	see *P. vulgaris* 'Röde Klokke'
- 'Violet Bells'	EBou GKev NSla
- violet-blue-flowered	EBee EHyd LRHS NRHS
§ - 'Weisse Schwan'	GEdr GMaP
- 'White Bells'	NHol WFar WHlf
- WHITE SWAN	see *P. vulgaris* 'Weisse Schwan'

Pultenaea (*Fabaceae*)

daphnoides	SVen
juniperina	SPlb SVen

pummelo see *Citrus maxima*

Punica (*Lythraceae*)

granatum	CBcs CCCN CMCN CMen EDir ELan EPfP ETod LPal LPar MGil SEND SGsty SIvy SPre SVic SWeb SWvt WJur WLov
- 'Acco' (F) **new**	WJur
- 'Chico' (d)	CBcs SEND WJur
- dwarf violet **new**	WJur
- 'Fina Tendral' (F)	CCCN XSen
- 'Flore Pleno'	see *P. granatum* f. *plena* 'Albescens Flore Pleno'
- 'Legrelleae' (F/d)	SEND
- 'Mollar de Elche'	WJur XSen
- var. ***nana*** ♀H3	CCCN CMen CTsd EPfP EShb LEdu MHer SMrm SPad SPre SRms SVen SVic SWeb WJur WKor WLov WPGP
- f. ***plena*** (d)	CBcs EPfP LRHS MRav SPer WCFE
§ - - 'Albescens Flore Pleno' (d)	EHed ETod WJur
- 'Provence' (F)	EPom IDee XSen
- 'Wonderful' (F)	CAgr LRHS WJur XSen

Puschkinia (*Asparagaceae*)

peshmenii white-flowered	NRog
scilloides	NBir NRog
- 'Alaverdi'	NRog
- 'Aragat's Gem'	GKev NRog
- blue-flowered	GKev
- var. ***libanotica*** ♀H6	CRos EHyd EPfP EPot ERCP GKev LAma LCro LOPS LRHS MPie NBir NBwr NRHS SDeJ SEND SPer WShi
- - 'Alba'	EPot GKev LAma NRog SDeJ
- 'Piatigorsk'	NRog
- 'Sky Vision'	NRog
- 'Snowdrift'	NRog
- 'Zanzegur'	NRog

Puya ✿ (*Bromeliaceae*)

RH 1809	WCot

alpestris CCCN CPla EAri SArc SPlb
§ - subsp. ***zoellneri*** CCCN CDTJ SPlb SVen WCot XSte
assurgens LRHS NPlm XSte
berteroana misapplied see *P. alpestris* subsp. *zoellneri*
bicolor B&SWJ 14869 WCru
castellanosii EAri NPlm SPlb
chilensis CAbb CBcs CCCN CDTJ CPla SPlb SVen WCot XSte
coerulea CCCN CDTJ CPla CTsd SPlb
§ - var. ***violacea*** LRHS NPlm XSte
dyckioides EAri LRHS WCot
ferruginea LRHS SPlb
grantii B&SWJ 14819 WCru
harmsii EAri
hromadnikii SPlb
killipii B&SWJ 14801 WCru
laxa SPlb WCot
lineata B&SWJ 14878 WCru
mirabilis CAbb CDTJ CSpe GBin SPlb
- B&SWJ 14825 WCru
- B&SWJ 14827 WCru
aff. ***nitida*** B&SWJ 14396 WCru
- B&SWJ 14887 WCru
ochroleuca B&SWJ 14716 WCru
santosii B&SWJ 14783 WCru
trianae B&SWJ 14818 WCru
- B&SWJ 14921 WCru
venusta CBcs CCCN CDTJ CPla EAri LRHS NPlm SPlb SVen WCot
violacea see *P. coerulea* var. *violacea*
yakespala LRHS

Pycnanthemum (*Lamiaceae*)

albescens ECha
curvipes EBee
muticum CSpe EBee LEdu MHol SBrt SPhx WPGP
pilosum CBod CLau EBee EBou MHer SPhx WFar WJek XLum
tenuifolium NLar SPhx
virginianum EBee SPhx

Pycnostachys (*Lamiaceae*)

urticifolia EWes

Pygmaeocereus (*Cactaceae*)

bieblii **new** EAri

Pygmea see *Chionohebe*

Pyracantha (*Rosaceae*)

ALEXANDER PENDULA ('Renolex') MRav SRms
angustifolia WCFE
- KR 2481 WPGP
§ ***atalantioides*** SPlb WCFE
- 'Aurea' EHeP
coccinea 'Lalandei' CMac
- 'Red Column' Widely available
- 'Red Cushion' EHeP ELan GDam GMcL SArc SRms
- 'Red Star'PBR **new** LCro
crenulata WCFE
DART'S RED ('Interrada') CSBt
'Fiery Cascade' EHeP EHyd LRHS NRHS SPoG WFar
gibbsii see *P. atalantioides*
'Golden Charmer' CDoC CMac EDir EFPl EHeP EPfP LBuc LRHS MGos MSwo NLar NWea SCoo SGol SNig SPer SPoG SRms SSha SWvt WFar
'Golden Glow' EDir LPar LRHS SGol
'Golden Paradise'PBR EBee NEoE WHlf
'Golden Sun' see *P.* 'Soleil d'Or'
'Harlequin' (v) CMac SGol WFar
'Knap Hill Lemon' MBlu
koidzumii 'Victory' WAvo
'Mohave' CBod CRos CTri EHyd ELan GMcL ILea LRHS MAsh NRHS SCob SRms SWvt WFar
'Mohave Silver' (v) CMac EHyd LRHS LSto MAsh NHol NRHS
'Navaho' LMaj SGsty
'Orange Charmer' CBrac CMac CTri EDir EHeP ELan LPar MGos NHol NWea SCob SCoo SGol SPer SPlb WFar
'Orange Glow' 🏆H6 Widely available
'Red Charmer' NHol
* 'Red Pillar' GDam SGbt
'Red Star'PBR LRHS NRHS
rogersiana EHeP NWea
- 'Flava' 🏆H5 CRos CSBt EHeP EHyd EPfP LRHS NRHS SPoG SWvt WAvo WHtc
'Rosedale' EHyd WAvo
SAPHYR JAUNE ('Cadaune') CBcs CBod CBrac CCVT CDoC CEnd CKel EBee EPfP ILea LCro LOPS LPar LRHS MAsh MGos MRav NHol SCob SGbt SGol SGsty SPer SSha SWeb
SAPHYR ORANGE ('Cadange') 🏆H6 Widely available
SAPHYR ROUGE ('Cadrou') 🏆H6 Widely available
'Shawnee' CMac MSwo NBwr
§ 'Soleil d'Or' CBrac CTri EBee EDir EFPl EHeP ELan EPfP GDam GMcL ILea LIns LSto MAsh MRav NLar NWea SCob SCoo SEND SEWo SGol SPer SPlb SRms SWvt WAvo WFar WHlf
'Sparkler' (v) CMac EBee ELan MAsh SPoG SSha
'Teton' 🏆H6 CMac EDir EHeP EHyd ELan EPfP GMcL LRHS LSto MAsh MGos MSwo NBwr SCoo SGol SPoG SRms WFar
'Watereri' EHeP WSpi
'Yellow Sun' see *P.* 'Soleil d'Or'

Pyrethropsis see *Rhodanthemum*

Pyrethrum see *Tanacetum*

Pyrola (*Ericaceae*)

rotundifolia WHer

Pyrrocoma (*Asteraceae*)

clementis EBee

Pyrrosia (*Polypodiaceae*)

hastata CMen WCot
- 'Harima Jishi' CMen
- 'Ryujin' CMen
- 'Sekaiichi' CMen
- 'Shikoku Jishi' CMen
- 'World Champion' CMen
linearifolia 'Urakoryu Jishi' CMen
lingua CMen LEdu
- 'Hiryu' CMen
- 'Ōgon Nishiki' (v) GGro WCot
- 'Tachiba Koryu' CMen
polydactyla CMen WCot
sheareri WCot

Pyrus ✿ (*Rosaceae*)

amygdaliformis CMCN WJur
- W&B B-10 WCot
betulifolia SBdl
calleryana CPer WJur

- 'Bradford'	CLnd
- 'Capital'	EBee LPar
- 'Chanticleer'	Widely available
- 'Chanticleer' variegated (v)	MAsh
- 'Redspire'	CCVT CLnd EHeP NWea SCob SPer
caucasica	WMat
communis (F)	CCVT CTri LBuc NBwr NRog NWea SPer SPlb SPre WMou WTSh
- 'Admiral Gervais' (D)	SBdl
- 'Alexandrina Bivort' (D)	SBdl
- 'André Desportes' (D)	SBdl
- 'Autumn Bergamot' (D)	SBdl
- 'Ayrshire Lass' (D)	SBdl
- 'Bambinella' (D)	SBdl SKee
- 'Barland' (Perry)	CHab NRog SBdl SKee
- 'Barnet' (Perry)	CHab NRog SBdl
- 'Baronne de Mello' (D)	NOra SBdl SKee WMat
- 'Beech Hill' (F)	CBod CLnd EBee EHeP LMaj LPar SCob
- 'Belle de Jumet' (D)	SBdl
- 'Belle de Soignies' (D)	SBdl
- 'Belle Guérandaise' (D)	SBdl SKee
- 'Belle Julie' (D)	SBdl SKee
- 'Bellissime d'Hiver' (C)	SBdl
- BENITA ('Rafzas') (F)	CWnw LCro LRHS MTrO WMat
- 'Bergamotte Esperen' (D)	SBdl SKee
- 'Beth' (D) ♀H6	Widely available
- 'Beurré Alexandre Lucas' (D)	NRog SBdl SKee
- 'Beurré Bedford' (D)	SBdl SKee
- 'Beurré Brown' (F)	SBdl
- 'Beurré Clairgeau' (C)	SBdl SKee
- 'Beurré d'Amanlis' (D)	SBdl SKee
- 'Beurré d'Anjou' (F)	SBdl
- 'Beurré d'Arenberg' (D)	SBdl
- 'Beurré d'Avalon' (D)	SBdl SKee
- 'Beurré de Beugny' (D)	SBdl SKee
- 'Beurré de Jonghe' (D)	SBdl
- 'Beurré de l'Assomption' (D)	SBdl
- 'Beurré de Naghin' (C/D)	SBdl
- 'Beurré Diel' (D)	SBdl
- 'Beurré Dubuisson' (D)	SBdl
- 'Beurré Dumont' (D)	CAgr SBdl
- 'Beurré Fouqueray' (D)	SBdl
- 'Beurré Giffard' (D)	CAgr SBdl
- 'Beurré Hardy' (D) ♀H6	Widely available
- 'Beurré Henri Courcelle' (D)	SBdl
- 'Beurré Jean van Geert' (D)	SBdl
- 'Beurré Mortillet' (D)	SBdl
§ - 'Beurré Précoce Morettini' (D)	SBdl WWct
- 'Beurré Rance' (C/D)	SBdl SKee
- 'Beurré Six' (D)	SBdl
- 'Beurré Sterckmans' (D)	SBdl
- 'Beurré Superfin' (D) ♀H6	MTrO SBdl SKee SSFr
- 'Bianchettone' (D)	SBdl
- 'Bishop's Thumb' (D)	SBdl SKee
- 'Black Worcester' (C)	CHab MTrO NOra NRog SBdl SKee WJas WMat WWct
- 'Blakeney Red' (Perry)	CHab MTrO NOra NRog SBdl SKee WMat
- 'Blickling' (D)	SBdl SKee
- 'Bon Chrétien d'Hiver' (D)	SBdl
- 'Brandy' (Perry)	CAgr CArg CHab MTrO NOra NRog SBdl SKee SVic WMat
- 'Bristol Cross' (D)	CAgr CHab NRog NWea SBdl
- 'Brown Bess' (Perry)	NRog
- 'Butt' (Perry)	CHab NRog SBdl
- 'Calebasse Bosc' (D)	NOra SBdl SKee
- 'Canal Red' (D)	SBdl
- 'Cannock' (F)	CArg WMat
- 'Cascade' (D)	SBdl
- 'Catillac' (C)	CAgr CHab LMaj MTrO NOra NRog SBdl SKee WMat
- 'Chalk'	see *P. communis* 'Crawford'
- 'Charles Ernest' (D)	SBdl
- 'Charneaux' (F)	LMaj
- 'Chaumontel' (D)	SBdl SKee
- 'Citron des Carmes' (C)	SBdl SKee
- 'Citron des Carmes Panaché' (D)	SBdl
- 'Clapp's Favourite' (D)	CHab CPer EDir NOra NRog SBdl SEdi SKee SVic WMat
- 'Colette' (D)	SBdl
- 'Colmar d'Eté' (D)	SBdl
- 'Comte de Lamy' (D)	SBdl
- 'Comte de Paris' (F)	SBdl
- 'Concorde' (D) ♀H6	Widely available
- 'Conference' (D) ♀H6	Widely available
- 'Constance Mary'PBR (F)	SBdl
- 'Coscia' (C/D)	SBdl
- 'Craig's Favourite' (D)	SBdl
- 'Crassane' (D)	SBdl
§ - 'Crawford' (D)	SBdl
- 'Dana's Hovey' (F)	SBdl
- 'Docteur Jules Guyot' (D)	CAgr NRog SBdl
- 'Double de Guerre' (C/D)	SBdl
- 'Doyenné Blanc' (F)	SBdl
- 'Doyenné Boussoch' (D)	SBdl SKee
- 'Doyenné d'Alençon' (D)	SBdl
- 'Doyenné d'Été' (D)	MCoo SBdl SKee
- 'Doyenné du Comice' (D) ♀H6	Widely available
- 'Doyenné Georges Boucher' (D)	SBdl
- 'Duchesse d'Angoulême' (D)	SBdl
- 'Duchesse de Bordeaux' (D)	SBdl
- 'Durondeau' (D)	NOra NRog SBdl SKee WMat WWct
- 'Easter Beurré' (D)	SBdl
- 'Emile d'Heyst' (D)	SBdl SKee WMat
- 'Enfant Nantais' (D)	SBdl
- 'English Caillot Rosat' (D)	SBdl
- 'Eva Baltet' (D)	SBdl
- 'Fair Maid' (D)	SBdl
- 'Fertility' (D)	SBdl SBmr
- 'Fertility Improved'	see *P. communis* 'Improved Fertility'
- 'Flemish Beauty' (F)	NOra
- 'Fondante d'Automne' (D)	CAgr CPer MTrO NOra SBdl SKee WMat
- 'Fondante de Bailly Maître' (D)	SBdl
- 'Forelle' (D)	SBdl SKee
- 'Gansel's Bergamot' (D)	SBdl SKee
- 'Garden Gem' (F)	SGsty WMat
- 'General Leclerc' (D)	SBdl
- 'General Tottleben' (C/D)	SBdl
- 'Gieser Wildeman' (F)	NRog SBdl
- 'Gin' (Perry)	CHab MTrO NRog SBdl WMat
- 'Glou Morceau' (D)	CAgr CArg MTrO NOra NRog SBdl SKee SSFT SSFr WMat WWct
- 'Gorham' (D) ♀H6	CAgr CPer MTrO NOra SBdl SKee SSFT SSFr WMat
- 'Green Horse' (Perry)	CHab MTrO NRog SBdl WMat
- 'Green Pear of Yair' (D)	SBdl SKee
- 'Gregoire Bordillon' (D)	SBdl
- 'Gros Blanquet' (D)	SBdl
- 'Hacon's Incomparable' (D)	SBdl SKee
- 'Harvest Queen' (D/C)	CAgr SBdl
- 'Harvester' (C)	SBdl
- 'Hellen's Early' (Perry)	CArg CHab NRog SBdl SKee WMat

- 'Hendre Huffcap' (Perry)	CAgr CHab EPom MTrO NOra NRog SBdl SKee WMat
- 'Hessle' (D)	CAgr CHab NRog NWea SBdl SEdi SKee
- 'Highland' (D)	SBdl
- HUMBUG ('Pysanka') (D)	CArg EPom MLod MTrO NOra SKee SSFT WMat
- 'Huyshe's Victoria' (C/D)	SBdl
§ - 'Improved Fertility' (D)	CAgr SBdl SBmr SKee
- INVINCIBLE ('Delwinor') (D/C)	CAgr CArg CDoC EPom LBuc MGos MLod MTrO NOra NRog SCoo SLim SPoG SSFT SSFr WMat
- 'Jargonelle' (D)	CAgr CHab MTrO NRog SBdl SKee WMat
- 'Jeanne d'Arc' (D)	SBdl
- 'Joséphine de Malines' (D) ♀H6	CAgr IArd MLod MTrO NOra SBdl SKee
- 'Judge Amphlett' (Perry)	EPom MTrO NOra NRog SBdl WMat
- 'Jules d'Airolles' (D)	SBdl
- 'Kieffer' (C)	SBdl
- 'Lady Naomi' (F)	LPar
- 'Laird Lang' (D)	SBdl
- 'Laxton's Early Market' (C/D)	SBdl
- 'Laxton's Foremost' (D)	CAgr SBdl
- 'Laxton's Satisfaction' (D)	SBdl
- 'Le Brun' (D)	SBdl
- 'Le Lectier' (D)	SBdl SKee
- 'Légipont' (D)	CAgr NRog SBdl
- 'Louise Bonne of Jersey' (D)	CAgr CArg CBod CLnd CMac CTri EDir EPfP EPom IArd MGos MLod MTrO NOra NRog SBdl SBmr SEdi SKee SSFr WMat WWct
- 'Luisa' (D)	LRHS
- 'Madame Treyve' (D)	SBdl
- 'Madernassa' (D)	SBdl
- 'Maggie' (D)	SBdl
- 'Magnate' (D)	SBdl
- 'Magness' (D)	SBdl
- 'Magyar Kobak' (C)	SBdl SKee
- 'Maréchal de Cour' (D)	SBdl
- 'Marguérite Marillat' (D)	SBdl
- 'Marie Benoist' (D)	SBdl
- 'Marie-Louise' (D)	SBdl SKee
- 'Marquise' (D)	SBdl
- 'Martin Sec' (C/D)	SBdl SKee
- 'Max Red Bartlett' (F)	SBdl
- 'Merrylegs' (Perry)	CHab
- 'Merton Pride' (D)	CAgr CArg CLnd EPom NOra SBdl SKee SSFr WMat WWct
- 'Merton Star' (D)	SBdl SKee
- 'Messire Jean' (D)	SBdl
- 'Michaelmas Nelis' (D)	SBdl
- 'Monarch' (D)	SBdl
- 'Monsieur le Curé'	see *P. communis* 'Vicar of Winkfield'
- 'Moonglow' (F)	CAgr NOra SBdl SKee WMat
- 'Moorcroft' (Perry)	NRog SBdl SKee
- 'Morettini'	see *P. communis* 'Beurré Précoce Morettini'
- 'Mrs Seden' (D)	SBdl
- 'Nec Plus Meuris' (F)	SBdl
- 'Nouveau Poiteau' (C/D)	CAgr SBdl SKee
- 'Nouvelle Fulvie' (D)	SBdl
- NUVAR ANNIVERSARY (D)	SKee
- NUVAR CELEBRATION (F)	MTrO SKee WMat
- 'Nye Russet Bartlett' (F)	CAgr SBdl
- 'Obelisk' (D)	EBee ELan EPom LCro LOPS LRHS MTrO NOra SPoG
- 'Old Home' (Perry)	SBdl WMat
- 'Oldfield' (Perry)	CHab NRog SBdl
- 'Olivier de Serres' (D)	SBdl
- 'Onward' (D)	CAgr CArg CBod CHab CTri EBee ELan EPom IArd MLod MTrO NOra NRog NWea SBdl SKee SSFT SSFr WMat WWct
- 'Ovid' (D)	CAgr SBdl
§ - 'Packham's Triumph' (D)	CAgr CTri EPom MTrO NOra NRog SBdl SBmr SEdi SKee SSFr WMat
- 'Parsonage' (Perry)	CHab SBdl
- 'Passe Colmar' (D)	SBdl
- 'Passe Crassane' (D)	SBdl SKee
- 'Pear Apple' (D)	CHab
- 'Penrhyn' (D)	WMat
- 'Pero Nobile' (D)	SBdl
- 'Petit Muscat' (D)	SBdl
I - 'Petite Poire' (D)	EPom
- 'Pierre Corneille' (D)	SBdl WWct
- 'Pitmaston Duchess' (C/D)	NRog NWea SBdl SKee WMat WWct
- 'Précoce de Trévoux' (D)	SBdl SKee
- 'Président Barabé' (D)	SBdl
- 'Président Héron' (D)	SBdl
- 'Red Comice' (D/C)	SBdl SKee
- 'Red Pear' (Perry)	CHab NRog WMat
- 'Red Sensation Bartlett' (D/C)	CArg EPom LBuc LRHS MLod MTrO NOra NRog NWea SKee SSFT SSFr WMat
- 'Redbald' (D)	SBdl SKee
- 'Reimer Red' (C)	SBdl
- 'Robin' (C/D)	EFPl SBdl SEdi SKee WMat
- 'Rogue Red' (D)	SBdl
- 'Roosevelt' (D)	SBdl
- 'Saels'PBR (F)	SBdl
- 'Saint-Rémy' (D)	NRog
- 'Santa Claus' (D)	SBdl SKee
- 'Seckel' (D)	NOra SBdl SKee
- 'Shipova'	see × *Sorbopyrus auricularis* 'Shipova'
- 'Sierra' (D)	CAgr SBdl
- 'Sirrine' (C)	SBdl
- 'Snowdon Queen' (D)	CHab WGwG
- 'Souvenir du Congrès' (D)	SBdl
- 'Starkrimson' (D)	SBdl
- 'Sucrée de Montluçon' (D)	SBdl
- 'Summer Bergamot' (F)	SBdl
- 'Swan's Egg' (D)	SBdl SKee
- 'Taynton Squash' (Perry)	NOra SBdl WMat
- 'Terrace Pearl' (D)	WMat
- 'Tettenhall Dick' (C/D)	NRog SBdl
- 'Thompson's' (D)	SBdl
- 'Thorn' (Perry)	CAgr CHab EPom MTrO SBdl SKee WMat
- 'Triomphe de Jodoigne' (D)	SBdl
- 'Triomphe de Vienne' (D)	NRog SBdl
- 'Triumph'	see *P. communis* 'Packham's Triumph'
- 'Turners Barn' (Perry)	NRog
- 'Uvedale's St Germain' (C)	SBdl SKee
- 'Van Mons Léon Leclerc' (D)	SBdl
- 'Verbelu' (C)	SBdl SKee
- 'Verdi' (F)	EPom
§ - 'Vicar of Winkfield' (C)	SBdl SKee
- 'Virgouleuse' (D)	SBdl
- 'Williams' Bon Chrétien' (D/C)	Widely available
- 'Williams' Red' (D/C)	NRog SBdl SEdi SGsty SKee
- 'Williams' Rouge Delbard' (F)	EPom
- 'Windsor' (D)	SBdl SKee
- 'Winnal's Longdon' (Perry)	EPom MTrO NRog WMat
- 'Winter Christie' (F)	MTrO
- 'Winter Nelis' (D)	CAgr CArg CHab CTri MTrO NLar NOra NRog SBdl SKee WMat WWct
- 'Winter Orange' (C/D)	SBdl
- 'Woodhall' (F)	WMat

- 'Zéphirin Grégoire' (D)	SBdl
elaeagrifolia	LMaj MAsh WJur
- subsp. ***kotschyana***	NOrn SLim
- 'Silver Sails'	CLnd CMac EBee LRHS MTrO NOra NOrn SCoo WMat WPGP
× ***michauxii***	SVen
nivalis	CLnd CPer EBee EHeP LEdu LMaj NWea SPer
- 'Catalia'	CLnd MAsh WHtc WMat
pashia	EBee LEdu LRHS NLar WMat
pyraster	CHab SBdl WJur
pyrifolia	WJur
- '20th Century'	see *P. pyrifolia* 'Nijisseiki'
- 'Chojuro' (F)	CAgr NRog
- 'Hayatama' (D)	NRog
- 'Hosui' (F)	CAgr NRog SVic
- 'Kosui' (F)	NRog SVic
- 'Kumoi' (F)	CAgr CSBt EPom LRHS MAsh MGos MTrO NOra NRog SKee SSFr WMat
- 'Niitaka' (D)	NRog
§ - 'Nijisseiki' (F)	CBod NRog SKee SVic
- 'Olympic' (D)	NRog
- 'Shinko' (F)	CAgr NRog SVic
- 'Shinseiki' (F)	CAgr CSBt CTri MGos MTrO NOra NRog SBmr SKee SVic WMat
- 'Shinsui' (F)	NRog SKee
- 'Tama' (D)	NRog
salicifolia 'Pendula' ♀H6	Widely available
ussuriensis	WJur

Pyrus × *Sorbus* see × *Sorbopyrus*

Q

Qiongzhuea see *Chimonobambusa*

Quercus ✿ (*Fagaceae*)

acerifolia	CMCN EPfP
acherdophylla	WJur
§ ***acuta***	CMCN
acutissima	CAco CLnd CMCN EPfP IPap
- subsp. ***kingii*** NJM 13.077	WPGP
aegilops	see *Q. ithaburensis* subsp. *macrolepis*
affinis ♀H5	CMCN
agrifolia	CMCN EBtc LMaj
ajudaghiensis	see *Q. hartwissiana*
alba	CAco CMCN EBtc IPap WPGP
× ***alentejana***	CMCN
aliena	CMCN
alnifolia	CBrP CMCN SBrt
anatolica	see *Q. pubescens* subsp. *crispata*
austrina	CMCN
× ***beadlei***	see *Q.* × *saulii*
'Bear Creek Ranch'	MBlu
benthamii	CMCN
berberidifolia	CMCN
bicolor	CAco CLnd CMCN EPfP IArd IDee IPap MBlu
§ × ***bimundorum*** 'Crimschmidt'	CAco CLnd EPfP EWTr MBlu SGol
borealis	see *Q. rubra*
brantii	CMCN
breweri	see *Q. garryana* var. *breweri*
buckleyi	CBcs CMCN EPfP IPap
- 'Dazzling Red'	EPfP MBlu
× ***bushii***	CMCN EPfP MBlu
- 'Seattle Trident'	EPfP MBlu WPGP
calophylla	CMCN
canariensis ♀H5	CLnd CMCN EPfP IDee IPap SPtp WPGP
canbyi	CMCN
castaneifolia	CMCN EBtc WMou
- 'Green Spire' ♀H6	CAco CLnd CMCN EBee EPfP MBlu MMuc SEND
cerris	CAco CArg CBcs CCVT CMCN CPer EHeP EPfP IPap LMaj LPar MGos NRog NWea SCob SEND SPer
- 'Afyon Lace'	MBlu
§ - 'Argenteovariegata' (v)	CEnd CMCN ELan EPfP MBlu NWea
- 'Athena'	MBlu
- 'Bolte's Obelisk'	MBlu
- 'Variegata'	see *Q. cerris* 'Argenteovariegata'
- 'Wodan'	MBlu
chenii	CMCN
chrysolepis	CMCN
coccifera	CMCN EPfP SVen WJur WPGP XSen
- NJM 12.006	WPGP
- subsp. ***calliprinos***	CMCN
coccinea	CAco CBcs CLnd CMCN EBee EPfP IArd IPap LMaj LPar MBlu MMuc MWht NRog SCob SEWo WJur WTSh
- 'Splendens' ♀H6	CAco CEnd CLnd CMCN EBee ELan EPfP MBlu SPer SPoG
crassifolia	CMCN WPGP
× ***crenata*** 'Diversifolia'	CMCN MBlu
- 'Fulhamensis'	CAco CMCN MBlu MMuc SEND SGol
§ - 'Lucombeana' ♀H6	CAco CMCN CPer CSBt EPfP MBlu MMuc
- 'Waasland Select'	LPar MMuc NLar NOrn SEND SGol WMou
- 'Wageningen'	CMCN IPap MMuc SEND
CRIMSON SPIRE	see *Q.* × *bimundorum* 'Crimschmidt'
dentata	CMCN IDee WJur
- 'Carl Ferris Miller'	CAco CBcs CMCN EPfP MBlu MMuc WLov WPGP
- 'Pinnatifida'	CMCN EPfP MBlu MPkF NLar WLov
- 'Sir Harold Hillier'	CBcs CMCN MBlu
- subsp. ***yunnanensis***	CMCN MBlu
douglasii	CMCN EBtc
durata	CMCN
× ***egglestonii***	CMCN
ellipsoidalis	CMCN NLar
- 'Hemelrijk' ♀H6	CMCN EPfP EWTr IDee MBlu
engleriana	CMCN
fabrei	CMCN
faginea	WPGP
falcata	CMCN EBtc WPGP
- var. ***pagodifolia***	see *Q. pagoda*
× ***fernaldii*** misapplied	see *Q. rubra* 'Cyrille'
'Fire Water'	EPfP MBlu
frainetto	CAco CMCN EPfP IPap LMaj LPar NWea SPer WMou
- 'Hungarian Crown' ♀H6	CMCN EPfP MBlu MMuc
- 'Trump'	CAco CMCN MMuc SEND
franchetii	WPGP
gambelii	CMCN EBtc
garryana	CMCN
§ - var. ***breweri***	CMCN
- var. ***fruticosa***	see *Q. garryana* var. *breweri*
georgiana	CMCN EBtc
germana	WPGP
gilva	CMCN
glabrescens	CMCN WPGP
glandulifera	see *Q. serrata* Thunb.
glauca	CMCN IPap MMuc NLar WJur

	- from Korea	WPGP
	gravesii	CMCN
	greggii	WPGP
	griffithii new	LEdu WPGP
	grisea	CMCN
§	***hartwissiana***	CMCN EPfP
	× ***hastingsii***	CMCN
	hemisphaerica	CMCN
	× ***heterophylla***	CLnd CMCN
	× ***hickelii***	CMCN
	× ***humidicola***	CMCN
	hypoleucoides	CMCN EPfP
	ilex	Widely available
	ilicifolia	CMCN
	imbricaria	CAco CBcs CLnd CMCN IArd WPGP
	incana Roxb.	see *Q. leucotrichophora*
§	***incana*** Bartram	CMCN
§	***ithaburensis*** subsp. ***macrolepis***	CMCN LEdu
	- - 'Hemelrijk Silver'	EPfP MBlu WPGP
	kelloggii	CMCN
	× ***kewensis*** ♀H6	CMCN SEND WMou
	laevigata	see *Q. acuta*
	laevis	CMCN
§	***laurifolia***	CMCN EPfP
	laurina	CMCN WPGP
	- NJM 05.013A	WPGP
	× ***leana***	CMCN
§	***leucotrichophora***	LEdu
	liaotungensis	see *Q. wutaishanica*
	× ***libanerris***	IPap
	- 'Rotterdam'	CMCN
	libani	CMCN WJur
	lobata	CMCN
	× ***lucombeana***	see *Q.* × *crenata* 'Lucombeana'
	- 'William Lucombe'	see *Q.* × *crenata* 'Lucombeana'
	lyrata	CMCN
	- 'Arnold'	MBlu
	macranthera	CMCN EPfP
	- PAB 13.002	LEdu
	macrocarpa	CAco CMCN EPfP IPap WPGP
	macrolepis	see *Q. ithaburensis* subsp. *macrolepis*
	marilandica	CMCN EPfP MBlu
	'Mauri'	MBlu
	'Maya' ♀H5	CBcs EPfP LPar WMat WPGP
	× ***megaleia***	CMCN
	mexicana	CMCN
§	***michauxii***	CMCN EPfP MBlu
	mongolica	EPfP MBlu
	- subsp. ***crispula***	CMCN EBtc
	'Monument'	WCot
	muehlenbergii	CMCN MBlu WPGP
	myrsinifolia	CBcs CMCN ELan IArd IPap LMaj MMuc NLar SArc
	myrtifolia	IDee WPGP
	nigra	CAco CMCN EBtc EPfP IPap WMou
	- 'Beethoven'	MBlu
	- 'Thierry'	MBlu
	nuttallii	see *Q. texana*
	obtusa	see *Q. laurifolia*
	oglethorpensis	CMCN
§	***pagoda***	CMCN IPap WPGP
	palustris ♀H6	CAco CArg CCVT CDoC CLnd CMCN CPer EHeP ELan EPfP IArd IPap LMaj LPar MBlu MMuc NLar NOrn NRog NWea SCob SEWo SGol SPer WJur WMou WTSh
	- 'Flaming Suzy'	EPfP MBlu
	- 'Green Dwarf'	CAco CMCN LCro LMaj LOPS MBlu NLar

	- GREEN PILLAR ('Pringreen')	CAco CDoC CPer EBee EPfP IArd LCro LMaj MAsh MBlu MTrO NLar NOra NOrn SGol SGsty WHtc WMat
	- 'Isabel'	CAco EPfP MPkF NLar WMat
	- 'Pendula'	CEnd CMCN
	- 'Swamp Pygmy'	CMCN MBlu
	- 'Windischleuba'	MBlu
	pedunculata	see *Q. robur*
	pedunculiflora	see *Q. robur* subsp. *pedunculiflora*
§	***petraea***	CArg CBTr CDoC CHab CLnd CPer CTri EHeP GAbr IPap LMaj LSto MBlu MMuc NBwr NRog NWea SCob WFar WMou WTSh
	- 'Laciniata'	see *Q. petraea* 'Laciniata Crispa'
§	- 'Laciniata Crispa'	CEnd CMCN MBlu
	- subsp. ***polycarpa*** NJM 13.025	WPGP
§	- 'Purpurea'	CMCN MBlu
	- 'Rubicunda'	see *Q. petraea* 'Purpurea'
§	***phellos***	CAco CLnd CMCN EPfP IArd IPap LMaj MBlu NLar
	- var. ***latifolia***	see *Q. incana* Bartram
	phillyreoides	CBcs CLnd CMCN IPap MMuc
	polymorpha	CMCN WPGP
	Pondaim Group	CMCN NOra NWea WPGP
	- 'Pondaim Giant'	MBlu
	pontica	CMCN EPfP EWTr IArd LMaj MBlu SEND
	prinoides	CMCN
	prinus misapplied	see *Q. michauxii*
§	***prinus*** L.	CMCN
	pubescens	CMCN IPap LMaj MMuc SEND
§	- subsp. ***crispata*** NJM 12.016	WPGP
	- - NJM 12.017	WPGP
	pungens	CMCN
	pyrenaica	CMCN MMuc SEND WJur
	- 'Pendula' ♀H6	CMCN EPfP
	rhysophylla	see *Q. rysophylla*
§	***robur***	Widely available
	- 'Argenteomarginata' (v)	CMCN MBlu
	- 'Atropurpurea'	EBtc NWea
	- 'Blue Gnome'	MBlu
	- 'Compacta'	MBlu
	- 'Concordia'	CEnd CMCN ELan EPfP MBlu
	- Cristata Group	CMCN
	- 'Dissecta'	CMCN EBtc
	- Fastigiata Group	CLnd EBee IArd LPar MGos NWea SGol
	- - 'Koster' ♀H6	CAco CMCN CMac EPfP IPap LMaj MBlu MRav NRog NWea SCob SGsty WMat
§	- - 'Salfast'	MBlu
	- 'Filicifolia' misapplied	see *Q. robur* 'Pectinata'
	- 'Filicifolia' Hort. ex Loud.	CEnd
	- var. ***haas***	CAco
	- 'Irtha'	EPfP MBlu
	- 'Menhir'	MBlu WLov
§	- 'Pectinata'	EPfP MBlu
§	- subsp. ***pedunculiflora***	CMCN
	- 'Pendula'	CEnd CMCN MBlu
	- 'Purpurascens'	CAco CEnd CMCN
	- 'Purpurea'	MBlu
	- 'Raba'	CMCN
	- 'Salicifolia Fastigiata'	see *Q. robur* (Fastigiata Group) 'Salfast'
	- 'Strypemonde'	CMCN
	- 'Timuki'	CAco LPar MBlu
	- 'Tromp Dwarf'	MBlu
	- (Variegata Group) 'Fürst Schwarzenburg' (v)	MBlu
	rotundifolia	CAgr CMCN WPGP
§	***rubra***	Widely available

	- 'Aurea'	CBcs CEnd CMCN EPfP MBlu
	- 'Bolte's Gold'	MBlu NOra WMat
§	- 'Cyrille'	CMCN MBlu
	- 'Haaren'	NLar
	- 'Magic Fire' ♀H6	CMCN EPfP MBlu
	- 'Red Queen'	EPfP MBlu
*	- 'Sunshine'	CMCN MBlu WCot
	× ***runcinata***	CMCN
§	***rysophylla***	CMCN IArd MBlu WPGP
	sadleriana	CMCN WPGP
	salicina	WPGP
	× ***sargentii*** 'Thomas'	EPfP MBlu
	sartorii	CMCN
§	× ***saulii***	CMCN EBtc
	× ***schochiana***	MBlu
	schottkyana	WPGP
	seemanii	CMCN
	semecarpifolia	CMCN MBlu WPGP
§	***serrata*** Thunb.	CAco CMCN
	- 'Herkenrode'	MBlu
	sessiliflora	see *Q. petraea*
	shumardii	CAco CMCN EPfP IPap LMaj MBlu NLar
	- 'Del Rio'	MBlu
	stellata	CMCN EPfP IDee
	suber	CAgr CBod CMCN CTsd EBee ELan EPfP IArd IPap LEdu LMaj LPar MBlu MGos SArc SCob SEND SPer SWeb WCot WJur WLov WMou WPGP
	- 'Sopron'	CAco MBlu
	× ***substellata***	CMCN
§	***texana***	CAco CMCN IArd IPap NOra
	- 'New Madrid'	CAco CPer EPfP ESwi IDee MAsh MBlu WMat WMou WPGP
	trojana	CMCN WPGP
	turbinella	CMCN
	× ***turneri***	CLnd CMCN EPfP WSpi
	- 'Pseudoturneri' ♀H5	CAco EBee ELan LPar MBlu MMuc SEND
	vacciniifolia	CMCN
	variabilis	CMCN EPfP IArd
	velutina	CBcs CMCN NLar NWea
	- 'Albertsii'	MBlu
	- 'Golden Dragon'	MBlu
	- 'Oakridge Walker'	MBlu
	- 'Rubrifolia'	CMCN EPfP
	'Vilmoriana'	CMCN
	virginiana	CBcs CMCN IArd
	× ***warei***	CMCN
	- 'Chimney Fire'	CBcs EPfP MBlu
§	- 'Long'	CAco EBee ELan EPfP EWTr IDee MBlu MTrO NOra WMat
	- REGAL PRINCE	see *Q.* × *warei* 'Long'
	- 'Windcandle'	CDoC LMaj MBlu
	wislizeni	CMCN NLar
§	***wutaishanica***	CBcs CMCN

Quillaja (*Quillajaceae*)

saponaria	CCCN EBee EPfP GBin IDee SPlb

quince see *Cydonia oblonga*

Quisqualis see *Combretum*

R

Racosperma see *Acacia*

Radermachera (*Bignoniaceae*)

sinica ♀H1b	EShb

radish see AGM Vegetables Section

Raffenaldia (*Brassicaceae*)

primuloides	GKev

× *Ramberlea* (*Gesneriaceae*)

'Inchgarth'	NHar

Ramonda (*Gesneriaceae*)

§	***myconi*** ♀H5	EMor EWes GEdr NSla NWad SRms
	- var. ***alba***	WAbe WThu
	- 'Jim's Shadow'	WAbe
	- 'Rosea'	EMor WAbe
	nathaliae ♀H5	WAbe WThu
	- 'Alba'	NSla
	pyrenaica	see *R. myconi*
	serbica	WThu

Ranunculus (*Ranunculaceae*)

	abnormis	CBor
	aconitifolius	CMiW CTtf EBee ECha EMor GJos GMaP NLar SHar WFar WSHC
	- Cally form	MNrw
	- 'Flore Pleno' (d) ♀H7	Widely available
	acris	CHab CToG NBir NMir NPer SPhx SRms SVic WSFF
	- subsp. ***acris***	SBut
	- - 'Stevenii'	LPla SDix
	- 'Citrinus'	CElw CMiW CTtf EAJP ECha EMor GEdr GQue LLWG LSun SRot WChS WCot WHrl WMal
	- 'Flore Pleno' (d) ♀H7	CDor CWCL EBee ECha ELan EPfP GMaP LEdu LLWG LPfP MACG MCot MRav NBid NBro NGdn NRya NSti SPoG SRms WCAu WFar WSHC XLum
	- 'Hedgehog'	MMrt MNrw
	- 'Sulphureus'	EBee WCAu
	alpestris	GEdr NSla SBrt WFar
	- 'Flore Pleno' (d)	GEdr
	amplexicaulis	EBee GEdr GJos GMaP WCot
	aquatilis	CPud CWat EWat LLWG LPfP MWts WMAq WSFF
	asiaticus	ERCP
	- Aviv Series	LAma WHlf
	- - 'Aviv Orange'	ERCP LAma SDeJ
	- - 'Aviv Picotee Café' **new**	ERCP LAma
	- - 'Aviv Picotee Orange' **new**	ERCP LAma
	- - 'Aviv Picotee Roze' **new**	ERCP LAma
	- - 'Aviv Purple' **new**	ERCP
	- - 'Aviv Red'	LAma LCro LOPS
	- - 'Aviv Rose'	ERCP LAma LCro LOPS
	- - 'Aviv White'	ERCP LAma LCro LOPS
	- - 'Aviv Yellow' **new**	ERCP LAma
	- 'Bloomingdale Pink Shades' (Bloomingdale Series)	SDeJ
	- peony-flowered	GKev
	bilobus	GArf GEdr
	bulbosus	SPhx SVic
§	- 'F.M. Burton'	CElw WCot
	- ***farreri***	see *R. bulbosus* 'F.M. Burton'
	- 'Speciosus Plenus'	see *R. constantinopolitanus* 'Plenus'
	calandrinioides ♀H5	NBir SBrt SGro WAbe WMal
	circinatus	LLWG
§	***constantinopolitanus*** 'Plenus' (d)	CMiW EBee GAbr GMaP MNrw MRav NBid NBro NLar WCot WMal WSHC
	cortusifolius	CPla ECre SBrt

crenatus GEdr
dongrergensis **new** GKev
ficaria see *Ficaria verna* subsp. *verna*
× ***flahaultii*** GArf
flammula CBen CHab CPud CWat LLWG LPfP MWts
- subsp. ***minimus*** EWat
gouanii NRya
'Gowrie' GEdr
gramineus ♀^{H7} CBor EBee EHyd GMaP LRHS NFav NRHS NRya SHar SRms
- 'Pardal' SMHy WCot WSHC
hederaceus LPfP
lanuginosus EPPr NGrd
lingua CPud NMir SPlb WSFF
- 'Grandiflorus' LLWG LPfP NPer WMAq
lyallii GKev
millefoliatus WAbe
montanus double-flowered (d) SHar WCot WSHC
- 'Miss Austria' (d) GEdr NHpl
- 'Molten Gold' ♀^{H5} GEdr GMaP MMrt MRav WFar
nivicola WCot
parnassiifolius GEdr GKev WAbe WCot
platanifolius EHyd LRHS NRHS SBrt
× ***prietoi*** 'Moonlight' LEdu MMrt WCot WSHC
'Purple Heart' (d) EPfP LCro LOPS SDeJ
repens 'Buttered Popcorn' (v) EBee
- var. ***pleniflorus*** (d) EWoo LLWG NGrd
- 'Timothy Clark' (d) WMal
seguieri EHyd GEdr NRHS WAbe
speciosus 'Flore Pleno' see *R. constantinopolitanus* 'Plenus'
traunfellneri WAbe
uniflorus GKev

Ranzania (*Berberidaceae*)

japonica EWld GEdr GKev WCru WFar

Raoulia (*Asteraceae*)

australis misapplied see *R. hookeri*
australis ambig. EDAr EPot GAbr GKev GMaP GQue NGrs NHpl WTor
australis Hook.f. ex Raoul ITim MAsh
§ - Lutescens Group ECha SPlb WIce
glabra EPot
§ ***hookeri*** ECha EDAr EPot EWes MAsh SPlb SRms SRot WAbe XSte
× ***loganii*** see × *Leucoraoulia loganii*
lutescens see *R. australis* Lutescens Group
petriensis EPot SPlb WAbe
× ***petrimia*** 'Margaret Pringle' WAbe
subsericea ECha
tenuicaulis ECha GArf SPlb

Raphiocarpus (*Gesneriaceae*)

petelotii 'Finale' **new** SBrt

raspberry see *Rubus idaeus*; see also AGM Fruit Section

Ratibida (*Asteraceae*)

columnifera CRos CWal EHyd EPfP LRHS LShi MACG NRHS SBut
- f. ***pulcherrima*** EHyd LRHS NRHS SBut XLum
- - 'Red Midget' CSpe ELan MACG NGBl
mexicana EBee EHyd ELan EPfP LRHS NRHS
pinnata CDor CSpe EPfP NBir NGBl SIvy SPhx SPlb WCot

Rauhocereus (*Cactaceae*)

riosaniensis **new** EAri

Raukaua (*Araliaceae*)

laetevirens WPGP

Ravenala (*Strelitziaceae*)

madagascariensis NPlm SPlb
- 'Ambanja' **new** NPlm

Ravenea (*Arecaceae*)

rivularis CCCN

Rebutia ✿ (*Cactaceae*)

'Burnt Orange' **new** SPlb
§ ***canigueralii*** ♀^{H2} **new** EAri SPlb
- 'Violacidermis' **new** LCro
CARNIVAL (mixed) **new** NMen
'Celebration' **new** NMen
'Coffee Cream' **new** SPlb
fabrisii var. ***aureiflora*** **new** EAri SPlb
fiebrigii **new** NMen
- 'Donaldiana' ♀^{H2} **new** NMen
'Flame' **new** SPlb
heliosa × ***pulvinosa*** subsp. ***albiflora*** **new** EAri
krugerae **new** SPlb
minuscula **new** NMen
- 'Marsoneri' ♀^{H2} **new** NMen
- orange-flowered **new** NMen
neocumingii subsp. ***lanata*** **new** NMen
'Orange Ice' **new** NMen
'Parma Violet' **new** SPlb
pulchra see *R. canigueralii*
pulvinosa subsp. ***albiflora*** ♀^{H2} **new** NMen
§ ***pygmaea*** ♀^{H2} **new** NMen

Rechsteineria see *Sinningia*

redcurrant see *Ribes rubrum* (R); see also AGM Fruit Section

Regelia (*Myrtaceae*)

velutina SPlb

Rehderodendron (*Styracaceae*)

indochinense B&SWJ 12115 WCru
- NJM 09.116 WPGP
- WWJ 11869 WCru
kwangtungense WWJ 11940 WCru
kweichowense WWJ 12019 WCru
macrocarpum CBcs CJun EBee IDee LEdu MBlu WPGP
- B&SWJ 11841 WCru
- KWJ 12310 WCru
- WWJ 11952 WCru

Rehmannia (*Plantaginaceae*)

angulata misapplied see *R. elata*
§ ***elata*** ♀^{H3} CBcs CBod CDor CPla CSpe CTsd EBee EHyd ELan EPfP EShb GGro LBar LRHS LShi LSun MHol MNHC MPie SAdn SBls SDys SRms WBor WHil WHlf WKif XLum
henryi EAri EBee WHlf XSte
piasezkii LBar LShi
'Polina'[PBR] LBar WHlf XSte
WALBERTON'S MAGIC DRAGON ('Walremadra'[PBR]) CRos EHyd EPfP LBuc LRHS LSRN NRHS SCoo SHar SPoG SRms

Reineckea (*Asparagaceae*)

§ ***carnea***	CDor CExl EBee ECha ELan EPPr GEdr GKev LEdu MPie NSti SBls SDys SEND SPlb WCot WPGP XLum
- B&SWJ 4808	WCru
- 'Baoxing Booty'	WCru
- 'Crûg's Broadleaf'	WCru
- 'Crûg's Linearleaf'	LEdu
- 'Jinfo Jewel'	WCru
- RBGE form	GGro
- 'Variegata' (v)	WCot
aff. ***carnea*** from Sichuan	WCot
incurva RKN 3605	EBee
- 'Crug's Linearleaf'	ESwi WCru
yunnanense	see *R. carnea*

Reinwardtia (*Linaceae*)

§ ***indica***	CCCN CExl CHll SAdn SEle
trigyna	see *R. indica*

Remusatia (*Araceae*)

hookeriana	EAri LAma
- B&SWJ 2529	WCru
pumila	EAri LAma
vivipara	EAri LAma SPlb

Reseda (*Resedaceae*)

alba	SPhx
lutea	SPhx SRms
luteola	CBod CHab CHby GPoy MHer MNHC WSFF
odorata	SPhx
- Crown Mixed **new**	CBod

Restio (*Restionaceae*)

festuciformis	CPbh LRHS
multiflorus	LRHS XSte
paniculatus	CBod CCCN CDTJ LRHS XSte
similis	XSte
subverticillatus 🏆H2	CPbh LRHS XSte
tetraphyllus	see *Baloskion tetraphyllum*
- 'Cornish Gold'	see *Baloskion tetraphyllum* 'Cornish Gold'

Retama (*Fabaceae*)

sphaerocarpa	SBrt

Reynoutria (*Polygonaceae*)

§ ***multiflora***	LEdu
- var. ***hypoleuca***	CSde SCoo SPoG
- - B&SWJ 120	WCru

Rhamnus (*Rhamnaceae*)

alaternus	XSen
§ - 'Argenteovariegata' (v) 🏆H5	CBcs CBod CDoC CTri CTsd CWal EBee EHyd ELan EPfP EShb LRHS MBlu MGil MGos MRav NLar NRHS SCob SEND SGbt SMad SPoG SSha SSta SWvt WAvo WCot WHtc WLov
- 'Variegata'	see *R. alaternus* 'Argenteovariegata'
cathartica	CCVT CHab CLnd CMac CPer CTri ELan LBuc MCoo NBwr NLar NWea SCob SEWo WMou WSFF WTSh
frangula	see *Frangula alnus*
imeretina	WCot WPGP
ludovici-salvatoris	SBrt
lycioides	SBrt
- subsp. ***oleoides***	XSen
microcarpa	GKev
schneideri var. ***manshurica*** **new**	WJur
taquetii	NLar

× *Rhaphiobotrya* (*Rosaceae*)

§ 'Coppertone'	CDoC CKel CWnw ELan IPap LPal LPar SArc SEND SGsty WPGP XSte XVPe

Rhaphiolepis (*Rosaceae*)

× ***delacourii***	EPfP SEND
- 'Coates' Crimson'	CDoC ELan EPfP LRHS MAsh MGil SMad WLov
- ENCHANTRESS ('Moness')	CCCN ELan EPfP LRHS MAsh MRav
- 'Pink Cloud'	EPfP MHtn
indica	SEND SMad
- B&SWJ 8405	WCru
- 'Coppertone'	see × *Rhaphiobotrya* 'Coppertone'
- SPRINGTIME ('Monme')	CBcs EGrI EPfP LCro LOPS LPar
integerrima	CMCN
minor B&SWJ 14669	WCru
umbellata	CBcs CBod CTri CTsd EGrI ELan EPfP GBin LEdu LSto MACG MAsh MGil MHtn MRav SEND SNig SRHi SVen SavN WLov WPGP
- f. ***ovata*** B&SWJ 4706	WCru

Rhaphithamnus (*Verbenaceae*)

cyanocarpus	see *R. spinosus*
§ ***spinosus***	CBcs EBee EPfP LEdu MGil SPoG WJur WPGP WPav

Rhapidophyllum (*Arecaceae*)

hystrix	CBrP CPHo LPal NPlm

Rhapis ✿ (*Arecaceae*)

§ ***excelsa*** 🏆H1b	CCCN LCro LOPS LPal NHrt NPlm SEND SPlb
humilis	LPal
multifida	LPal

Rhaponticum (*Asteraceae*)

carthamoides	GGro
§ ***centaureoides***	CCBP CDor ECha ELon EWTr GQue MAvo MSpe NBid NSti SPeP WCAu WCot WMal WSpi
coniferum	GGro

Rhazya (*Apocynaceae*)

orientalis	see *Amsonia orientalis*

Rheum ✿ (*Polygonaceae*)

CC	GGro
Chen Yi	WCot
GWJ 9329 from Sikkim	WCru
§ 'Ace of Hearts' 🏆H6	CDor CRos ECha ECtt EHyd ELan ELon EMor EPfP EWhm GBin GMaP LBar LRHS MGos MRav NBid NGdn NLar NRHS NSti NWad SCob SPer SPoG SRms SWvt WCot WFar
'Ace of Spades'	see *R.* 'Ace of Hearts'
acuminatum	WPGP
- HWJCM 252	WCru
- HWJK 2354	WCru
- PAB 2487	LEdu
alexandrae	CBct EWes GBin GEdr GGro GKev LBar MMrt MSCN NLar SBls SGBe SPlb WFar WHil WPGP
- SDR 2924	EBee
§ ***australe***	CRos EHyd GEdr LRHS NLar NRHS WCot WFar
- 'Pink Marble' (v)	WCot
aff. ***australe*** HPA 1385	GGro
'Cally Giant'	EWes GBin
cordatum	GGro
× ***cultorum***	see *R.* × *hybridum*

	delavayi	GKev NBPC NLar
	- BWJ 7592	WFar
	emodi	see *R. australe*
	'Great Bere'	LEdu WPGP
§	× ***hybridum***	SBmr
	- from Isle of Ely Horticultural Institute	NRog
	- 'Amerikiane Kampfe'	NRog
	- 'Apple Delight'	EBee EPfP LCro
	- 'Brandy Carr Scarlet'	CTri LEdu MRav
	- 'Champagne'	CAgr CBod CDoC EPfP EPom LCro LEdu LOPS LRHS NLar NRHS SBmr SCoo SGbt SPer SPoG SRms SVic WMat
	- 'Collis's Ruby'	NRog
	- 'Donkere Bloedrede Zoet'	NRog
	- 'Early Albert'	SBmr
	- 'Early Red Victoria'	NRog
	- 'Early Victoria'	SRms
	- 'Exhibition Red'	NRog
	- 'Fenton's Special'	CTri MRav SBmr
	- 'Fulton's Strawberry Surprise' 🏆H5	CDoC
	- 'Glaskin's Perpetual'	CAgr CRos CTsd EDir EHyd LBuc LRHS MAsh NRHS SCoo SRms SVic
	- 'Goliath'	CBod EBee NRog
	- 'Grandad's Favorite' 🏆H5	CRos EBlo EHyd LRHS NRHS
	- 'Hawke's Champagne' 🏆H5	WCot
	- 'Holsteiner Blut'	CBod EBee NLar SPoG
	- 'Livingstone'PBR	CDoC EPom LCro LRHS
	- 'Merton's Broadleaf'	NRog
	- 'Pink Champagne'	EBee EPfP
	- 'Prince Albert'	SBmr
	- 'Raspberry Red' 🏆H5	CBod CDoC CMac CRos EPfP EPom LCro LOPS NRHS SPoG
	- 'Red Champagne'	ELan EMor EPfP LBuc WSpi
	- 'Red Prolific'	NRog
	- 'Royal Albert'	NRog
	- 'Seedling Piggot'	NRog
	- 'Seedling Streeter'	NRog
	- 'Stein's Champagne'	NRob
	- 'Stockbridge Arrow'	CArg CTri NRog
	- 'Stockbridge Cropper'	NRog
	- 'Stockbridge Harbinger'	NRog
	- 'Strawberry'	LCro LOPS NBir NRog
	- 'Sutton's Seedless 29' **new**	NLar
	- 'The Sutton'	CBod
	- 'Thompson's Terrifically Tasty'	EPom
	- 'Timperley Early' 🏆H5	Widely available
	- 'Timperley Early 1'	SBmr SRms
	- 'Victoria'	Widely available
	- 'Vinrabarber Svenborg'	NRog
	- 'Vroege Engelse'	LEdu
	kialense	EBee GGro LEdu NBid NSti
	moorcroftianum	GEdr
	nobile	EDAr GJos
	officinale	CBct
	palmatum	CBcs CRos EBee ECha ELan EPfP GElm LPfP LRHS MGos MRav NGdn NRHS SCob SHar SRms
	- 'Atropurpureum'	see *R. palmatum* 'Atrosanguineum'
§	- 'Atrosanguineum'	CBct CDor CRos ECha EHyd ELan EPfP EShb EWoo LEdu LRHS MBel MGos MRav NBid NBro NChi NRHS NSti SCob SPer SPlb SPoG WCru WFar WSpi
	- 'Bowles's Crimson' 🏆H7	MRav NBid WCot
	- 'Ferguson's Red'	WCot
	- 'Hadspen Crimson' 🏆H6	ECtt MNrw NBid WCot
	- 'Red Herald'	WCot
	- 'Rubrum'	CFis EHyd LRHS NBir NRHS
	- 'Savill' 🏆H7	MRav
§	- var. ***tanguticum***	CAgr CBct CBod CDoC CDor EBee ECha EHeP ELan ELon EMor EPfP EWoo GElm GKev GMaP GMcL LSun MACG MPie MRav NBid NLar SBls SCob SGBe SPeP SPoG SRms SWvt WFar WPnP
	rhaponticum	NLar
	ribes	WCot WCru
	tanguticum	see *R. palmatum* var. *tanguticum*
	tataricum	LEdu

Rhinanthus (*Orobanchaceae*)

	minor	CHab LCro LOPS SVic WSFF

Rhipsalis (*Cactaceae*)

	sp.	NHrt
	baccifera **new**	LCro
	- subsp. ***horrida*** **new**	LCro
	- subsp. ***shaferi*** **new**	NPlm
	houlletiana	see *Lepismium houlletianum*
	teres **new**	NPlm
	- f. ***capilliformis*** red **new**	NPlm
	- f. ***heteroclada*** **new**	NPlm

Rhodanthe (*Asteraceae*)

	chlorocephala subsp. ***rosea*** 'Pierrot'	CSpe

Rhodanthemum (*Asteraceae*)

	'African Eyes'	ELan EPfP MBrN MGos SCoo SVen WMal
	'African Rose'	LBar MHol
	'African Spring'	CDoC LBar
	AGADIR (Atlas Daisy Series)	see *R.* MOONDANCE
§	***atlanticum***	EWes
	'Casablanca'PBR (Atlas Daisy Series)	CBod CDoC CRos EPfP LRHS MPri NRHS SCoo SIvy SPoG WTor
§	***catananche***	CCCN EWes
§	- 'Tizi-n-Test'	WAbe
	- 'Tizi-n-Tichka'	CRos EDAr EHyd EWes LRHS NRHS WAbe
§	***gayanum***	CCCN
	- 'Flamingo'	see *R. gayanum*
	- 'Pretty in Pink'	CBcs LBar MBNS MHol SPoG
§	***hosmariense*** 🏆H4	CCCN CRos EBou ECha EDAr EHyd ELan EPfP EPot GMaP LRHS MCot MHol NRHS SEND SGBe SPer SRms WIce WMal
	'Marrakech' (Atlas Daisy Series)	CDoC EPfP MPri SCoo SPoG SRms
§	MOONDANCE ('Usrhod0701')	LRHS
	'Tangier' (Atlas Daisy Series)	LRHS MPri

Rhodiola (*Crassulaceae*)

	SSSE 10	NWad
	bupleuroides HWJK 2326	WCru
	chrysanthemifolia WJC 13669	WCru
	crassipes	see *R. wallichiana*
	cretinii	NRya
	- HWJK 2283	WCru
	- subsp. ***cretinii*** **new**	NWad
§	***fastigiata***	GGro
	- BWJ 7544	WCru
§	***heterodonta***	ECha MRav WCot
	himalensis misapplied	see *R.* 'Keston'
	himalensis (D. Don) Fu	CTri
	- WJC 13723	WCru
§	***integrifolia***	SPlb
§	'Keston'	CTri
	kirilowii var. ***rubra***	EBee EGrl EHyd LRHS NRHS
	macrocarpa **new**	SBrt

§ ***pachyclados***	CPla CRos ECtt EGrI EHyd EPPr GBin GKev GMaP LRHS LShi MHer MMuc NBir NHpl NRHS NRya NSla NWad SEND SLee SPlb SRot SSim SWvt WAbe WCot WFar XLum
rhodantha	NLar
§ ***rosea***	Widely available
§ ***saxifragoides***	EDAr EHyd EPot LRHS NRHS SLee SPlb SRms
semenovii	GKev NLar
sinuata HWJK 2318	WCru
tibetica	GKev
trollii	see *R. saxifragoides*
§ ***wallichiana***	NBid
- GWJ 9263	WCru
- HWJK 2352	WCru
§ ***yunnanensis*** BWJ 7941	WCru

Rhodochiton (*Plantaginaceae*)

§ ***atrosanguineus*** ♀H2	CCCN CPla CRos CSpe EPfP GBee IDee LCro LOPS MBow MPri SPoG
volubilis	see *R. atrosanguineus*

Rhodocoma (*Restionaceae*)

arida	CCCN
capensis ♀H4	CAbb CBod CCCN CPbh CTrC SArc
foliosa	LRHS
gigantea	CCCN CTrC LRHS SPlb XSte

Rhododendron ✿ (*Ericaceae*)

'A.J. Ivens'	see *R.* 'Arthur J. Ivens'
aberconwayi	LMil MHid SLdr
- 'His Lordship'	GGGa IDee LMil LRHS
'Actress'	LMil
adenogynum	GKev LMil
adenosum	GGGa LMil
'Admiral Piet Hein'	SSta
'Adonis' (EA/d) ♀H5	CBcs CMac
'Advance' (EA)	SLdr
aeruginosum	see *R. campanulatum* subsp. *aeruginosum*
aganniphum var. ***aganniphum***	MHid
'Agayon'	LMil LRHS XSte
AIKO ROSE ('Ilvoaiko04'PBR) (EA) new	LCro
'Airy Fairy'	LMil
'Aksel Olsen'	CTri EGrI
'Aladdin' (EA)	SLdr
(Aladdin Group) 'Aladdin'	XSte
'Aladdin' (*auriculatum* hybrid)	SSta
'Alan Leslie' (Vs) new	LMil
(Albatross Group) 'Albatross'	SSta
- 'Albatross Townhill Pink'	LMil
'Albert Schweitzer' ♀H5	CAco CDoC LMil LPar LRHS LSRN NLar SCob SLdr SLim SPer XSte
albrechtii (A)	GGGa LMil
- Whitney form (A)	LMil
'Album Grandiflorum' (G)	LRHS XSte
'Alexander' (EA) ♀H4	LMil LSRN
'Alfred'	CAco WFar
'Alice' ♀H5	LMil SLdr
Alison Johnstone Group	SLdr
- 'Alison Johnstone'	CAco WThu
'All Gold'	GGGa
'Al's Picotee' (EA/d)	MPkF XSte
alutaceum var. ***alutaceum***	LMil
- var. ***iodes*** 'White Plains'	MHid
amagianum (A)	LMil
ambiguum	LMil MHid
- 'Jane Banks'	LMil
- 'Sunningdale' new	LMil
'Ambrosia' (EA)	CSBt
'Amity'	LMil
'Anah Kruschke'	CAco LCro MAsh SGsty SPoG
'Analin'	see *R.* 'Anuschka'
'Anchorite' (EA)	SLdr
Angelo Group	GGGa LMil
- 'Angelo'	CBcs LMil SSta
'Ann Lindsay'	NLar SPer
'Anna Baldsiefen'	CAco SPoG
'Anna Rose Whitney'	CAco CBcs CKel CTri EPfP LRHS LSRN MAsh MPri SLim WFar XSte
'Annabella' (K)	SSta
annae	IDee LMil LRHS
'Anne Frank' (EA)	CDoC WFar
'Anne Teese'	IDee LMil
'Anneke' (A)	CDoC EGrI GMcL LMil LRHS MGos MMuc MPkF NHol NLar SCob SCoo SPoG SSta XSte
'Anouk' (EA)	CDoC CEnd SCoo SPoG
anthopogon	LMil
- subsp. ***hypenanthum***	LRHS
- - 'Annapurna'	GGGa LMil WAbe WThu
'Antilope' (Vs) ♀H6	LMil MMuc SSta
§ 'Anuschka'	LMil MAsh
anwheiense	GGGa LMil
apodectum	see *R. dichroanthum* subsp. *apodectum*
'Apple Blossom' ambig.	CMac GKin
'Appleblossom' (EA)	see *R.* 'Ho-o'
'Apricot Blaze' (A)	SSta
'Apricot Fantasy'	LMil LRHS SSta
'Apricot Surprise'	CTri EGrI MAsh
'April Showers' (A)	LMil
'Arabesk' (EA)	CDoC GKin ILea MAsh MGos MPkF NLar SGsty SWeb XSte
arborescens (A) ♀H6	GGGa LMil
arboreum	GGGa IKel LMil LRHS NLar SLdr
- B&SWJ 2244	WCru
- subsp. ***albotomentosum*** KW 21976	LMil
- subsp. ***arboreum***	MHid
- subsp. ***cinnamomeum*** ♀H4	GGGa LMil
- - Sch 2049	LMil
- - WJC 13821	WCru
- - 'Everest Reunion'	IDee LMil
- - var. ***roseum***	GGGa
- - - 'Tony Schilling'	GKin LMil SSta
- subsp. ***delavayi***	GGGa LMil
§ - subsp. ***nilagiricum***	MHid
- 'Rubaiyat'	GKin LMil NLar
'Arctic Fox' (EA)	LMil
'Arctic Tern' ♀H5	CAco CDoC CTri EPot LCro LMil LOPS MGos NLar NWad WFar WThu
§ ***argipeplum***	GGGa LMil MHid
- 'Fleurie'	LMil
(Argosy Group) 'Argosy'	LMil
argyrophyllum subsp. ***argyrophyllum***	GGGa
- subsp. ***nankingense***	GGGa
- - 'Chinese Silver' ♀H5	LMil MHid
arizelum	GGGa LMil MHid WPGP
aff. ***arizelum*** KR 10420	WPGP
'Arneson Gem' (A) ♀H6	CBcs CDoC GGGa GKin LMil LRHS MPkF NLar SCoo SPoG XSte
§ (Aronense Group) 'Fumiko' (EA)	CBcs CDoC CKel CSBt CWnw EDir GMcL LCro LMil NLar SCob SLdr WFar
§ - 'Hanako' (EA)	LMil WFar
- 'Haruko' (EA)	LMil

§	- 'Hisako' (EA)	GMcL
§	- 'Kazuko' (EA)	CDoC CKel CWnw GMcL NLar SCoo
	- 'Michiko' (EA)	SAko
§	- 'Momoko' (EA)	CKel CWnw EGrI GMcL LRHS WFar
	- 'Noriko' (EA)	SLdr
§	- 'Satschiko' (EA) 🏆H6	CBcs CDoC CKel EDir GGGa GMcL LMil LRHS MPri NLar NRHS SPer
	'Arpège' (Vs)	LMil
	'Arthur Bedford'	CSBt
§	'Arthur J. Ivens'	SLdr
	'Arthur Stevens'	SLdr
	asterochnoum	GGGa MHid
	atlanticum (A)	GGGa LMil WFar XSte
	- 'Seaboard' (A)	LMil
	'August Lamken'	LMaj
	'August Rose' (A)	LRHS
	augustinii	CBcs GGGa LMil SLdr SSha SSta
	- subsp. ***augustinii***	MHid
	- 'Bowood Blue'	LMil NLar
	- 'Carolles'	XSte
§	- subsp. ***chasmanthum***	GGGa
	- Electra Group	LMil LRHS SLdr
§	- - 'Electra' 🏆H4	GGGa XSte
	- Exbury form	GGGa LMil
§	- subsp. ***hardyi***	GGGa
§	- subsp. ***rubrum***	MHid
*	- 'Trewithen'	LMil
I	- 'Werrington'	CExl SSta
	auriculatum	GGGa LMil MHid SLdr SSta
	austrinum (A)	IDee LMil
	'Autumn Gold'	SLdr
	(Avalanche Group) 'Avalanche'	LMil
	Avocet Group	LMil
	'Award'	LMil
	(Azor Group) 'Azor'	XSte
	Azrie Group	SLdr
§	'Azuma-kagami' (Kurume) (EA)	CAco LMil SCob SLdr
	'Azurika'	CAco NLar XSte
	'Azurro'	CAco LMil NLar SPer
	BABUSCHKA ('Hachbabu') (A)	LMil
	'Baden-Baden' 🏆H6	CMac CTri EGrI GKin GMcL LCro LMil MAsh SLdr WFar
	balangense	LMil
	balfourianum	MHid
	'Baltic Amber' (A)	CDoC
	'Balzac' (K)	GKin
	'Barbara Reuthe'	SSta
	'Barbarella'	IDee LMil LRHS NLar
	barbatum	GGGa GKev LMil MHid
	- WJC 13686	WCru
	'Barbecue' (K)	EGrI LMil
	'Barnaby Sunset'	LRHS MAsh
§	***basilicum***	LMil MHid
	'Bastion'	LMil
	bauhiniiflorum	see *R. triflorum* var. *bauhiniiflorum*
	beanianum	LMil
	- compact	see *R. piercei*
	'Beatrice Keir'	LMil SSta
	(Beau Brummell Group) 'Beau Brummell'	LMil
	beesianum	MHid
	'Beethoven' (Vuykiana) (EA)	SLdr XSte
	BELAMI ('Hachbela')	CAco IDee LMil NLar
	'Belkanto'	CAco GKin NLar
	'Bellini'	CAco LMil
	'Ben Cruachan' (K)	GGGa
	'Ben Lawers' (K)	GGGa
	'Ben Lomond' (K)	GGGa
	'Ben Morrison' (EA)	LMil XSte
	'Bengal'	CDoC CRos EGrI LRHS LSRN MAsh NLar SLim WFar
	'Bengal Beauty' (EA)	SLdr
	'Bengal Fire' (EA)	CMac SLdr
	benhallii 'Honshu Blue'	GGGa
	- 'Plum Drops'	GGGa
	- 'Slieve Donard'	CMac
	- 'Ylva'	GGGa
	'Beni-giri' (Kurume) (EA)	CMac
	'Beni-kirishima' (A)	SWeb
	'Benny Gery' (EA)	NLar
	'Bergensiana'	SSta
	'Bergie Larson' 🏆H4	LMil
	bergii	see *R. augustinii* subsp. *rubrum*
	'Berg's Queen Bee'	LMil
	'Berg's Yellow'	MAsh
	'Bernard Shaw'	SSta
	'Bernstein'	CAco
	'Berryrose' (K) 🏆H6	CBcs CDoC CMac CSBt CTri EGrI EPfP GKin GMcL LMil LRHS MAsh MGos SCob WFar XSte
	'Bert's Own'	CBcs
	'Betty Anne Voss' (EA)	CEnd LMil MAsh SCoo SLdr
	'Beverley Lear' **new**	LMil
	bhutanense	GGGa
	Bibiani Group	LMil
	'Big Point' (EA)	LMil
	'Bijou de Ledeberg' (Indian) (EA/v)	CMac
	'Birthday Girl'	LMil LSRN MAsh
	(Biskra Group) 'Biskra'	GGGa LMil
	'Blaauw's Pink' (Kurume) (EA) 🏆H4	CMac CSBt EGrI GKin GMcL LCro LMil LOPS SCob SGsty SLdr SPer SPlb SPoG XSte
	'Black Knight' (EA)	SLdr
	'Black Magic'	CAco CBcs GKin GMcL LMil MAsh WTyc
	'Black Widow'	SSta
	'Blaney's Blue'	XSte
	'Blattgold' (v)	CAco LMil LRHS
	BLAUE DONAU	see *R.* 'Blue Danube'
	'Blaue Jungs'	GGGa
	'Blewbury' 🏆H5	IDee LMil NLar
	BLOOMBUX ('Microhirs3'PBR) (Inkarho)	LCro LMil LOPS SJap WHlf XSte
	BLOOMCHAMPION PINK (EA)	LCro LMil
	BLOOMCHAMPION PURPLE (EA)	LCro LMil
	BLOOMCHAMPION RED ('Rlh1 9p7') (EA) **new**	LCro LMil
	BLOOMCHAMPION WHITE (EA)	LMil
	'Blue Boy'	LMil
§	'Blue Danube' (EA) 🏆H3	CBcs CDoC CMac CRos CSBt CTri CTsd EGrI EPfP GKin GMcL LCro LMil LOPS LRHS MAsh MGos MPri NLar SCob SCoo SGsty SLdr SLim SPer SPoG SSta WFar
	Blue Diamond Group	CBcs GMcL
	- 'Blue Diamond'	CAco EGrI LRHS LSRN MAsh NRHS SLdr
	'Blue Jay'	CAco XSte
	'Blue Monday' (EA)	SLdr
	'Blue Peter' 🏆H6	CAco CBcs CKel CSBt LCro LOPS MAsh NHol SCob SSta
	'Blue Pool'	IDee LMil NLar
	'Blue Silver'	CAco GGGa LMil MAsh WFar XSte
	'Blue Star'	EGrI GEdr GMcL
	'Blue Steel'	see *R. fastigiatum* 'Blue Steel'
	Blue Tit Group	CBcs CDoC CMac EPfP GGGa LRHS MAsh MGos NLar NRHS SLim SPer
	'Blueshine Girl'	SLdr

'Blutopia'	LMil MGos NLar
'Boddaertianum'	LMil LRHS XSte
BOHLKEN'S LUPINENBERG	LMil
BOHLKEN'S LUPINENBERG LAGUNA	IDee LMil LRHS NLar
BOHLKEN'S SNOW FIRE	LMil
BOLLYWOOD	see *R.* 'Farrow'
Bo-peep Group	CBcs
- 'Bo-peep'	LMil SLdr
'Bouquet de Flore' (G) 𝕐H6	LMil XSte
Bow Bells Group	SCob
- 'Bow Bells' 𝕐H4	EGrI EPfP GEdr GMcL LMil LRHS MAsh MGos NHol NLar SLdr
brachycarpum	GKev
§ - subsp. ***fauriei*** B&SWJ 4326	WCru
'Bremen'	LMil
'Brigitte'	CAco MAsh
'Brisanz' **new**	MGos
'Britannia'	CSBt NHol SCob SSta
'Bronze Fire' (A)	NHol SSta
'Broughtonii'	XSte
'Brown Eyes'	CAco MAsh
'Bruce Brechtbill'	GKin MAsh NLar
§ 'Bruns Gloria'	LMil NLar
'Bruns Schneewitchen'	SSta
'Buccaneer' (Glenn Dale) (EA)	SLdr
bullatum	see *R. edgeworthii*
'Bungo-nishiki' (Wada) (EA/d)	CMac
bureavii 𝕐H6	CBcs GGGa IDee LMil LRHS MHid SSta
bureavioides	GKev MHid
'Burletta'	LRHS
burmanicum	CBcs
Bustard Group	LMil
calendulaceum (A)	GGGa LMil
- red-flowered (A)	LMil
- yellow-flowered (A)	LMil
(Calfort Group) 'Calfort'	GGGa
callimorphum	GKev
calophytum 𝕐H5	GGGa LMil
calostrotum 'Gigha' 𝕐H6	CBcs GGGa IDee LMil
§ - subsp. ***keleticum*** 𝕐H6	GEdr IDee LCro WThu
- - R 58	GGGa LMil
§ - - Radicans Group	GEdr GGGa NWad WAbe WThu
§ - subsp. ***riparium*** Nitens Group	CBcs GGGa MAsh WThu XSte
'Calsap'	XSte
Calstocker Group	LMil
camelliiflorum	MHid
campanulatum	GKev LMil
- B&SWJ 13934	WCru
- HWJCM 195	WCru
- HWJCM 409	WCru
§ - subsp. ***aeruginosum***	LMil MHid
- subsp. ***campanulatum***	MHid
'Campfire' J.B. Gable (EA)	SLdr
campylocarpum	CBcs LMil LRHS
- subsp. ***campylocarpum***	MHid
campylogynum	GKev LCro LMil
- SBEC 0519	GGGa
- 'Album'	see *R.* 'Leucanthum'
- Charopoeum Group	WThu
- 'Patricia'	EGrI EPot GEdr
- Myrtilloides Group 𝕐H5	GGGa LMil WAbe WThu
camtschaticum	GGGa GKev LMil LRHS WAbe
- var. ***albiflorum***	GKev
- red-flowered	GGGa
canadense (A)	GGGa GKev
- f. ***albiflorum*** (A)	GGGa LMil
- dark-flowered (A)	LMil

CANDY LIGHTS ('UMinn's Candy Lights') (A)	CBcs LRHS MPkF XSte
§ ***canescens*** (A)	LMil LRHS MPkF
'Cannon's Double' (K/d) 𝕐H6	CBcs CDoC GKin LMil LRHS MGos SCoo SPoG
'Canzonetta' (EA/d) 𝕐H5	CEnd CRos EPfP GGGa LMil LRHS MAsh MGos NLar NRHS SAko SPer
'Captain Jack'	GGGa
cardiobasis	see *R. orbiculare* subsp. *cardiobasis*
(Carita Group) 'Golden Dream'	LMil
(Carmen Group) 'Carmen' 𝕐H6	CRos EGrI GEdr GGGa GKin LMil MAsh SLdr
'Caroline Allbrook'	MAsh NLar WFar
'Caroline de Rothschild' (A)	LMil
'Cary Ann'	CAco CTri LRHS MAsh
'Cassata'	CAco
catawbiense	CMCN SLdr
'Catawbiense Album'	CAco CTri MAsh
'Catawbiense Boursault'	CAco LMil
'Catawbiense Grandiflorum'	CAco LMil MAsh
'Catharine van Tol'	LMaj
'Caucasicum Pictum'	LMil LRHS SLdr
'Cavalier'	XSte
'Cayenne' (EA)	SLdr
'Cecile' (K)	CBcs CMac CTri EGrI GKin GMcL LMil LSRN MMuc
'Celestial' (EA)	CMac
cephalanthum	LMil
- subsp. ***cephalanthum*** SBEC 0751	WThu
- - Crebreflorum Group	GGGa LMil WAbe WThu
cerasinum	LMil MHid
- COALS OF FIRE	GGGa
chaetomallum	see *R. haematodes* subsp. *chaetomallum*
'Chanel' (Vs)	LMil NLar SSta
'Chanticleer' (Glenn Dale) (EA)	SLdr
chapaense	see *R. maddenii* subsp. *crassum*
'Chariots of Fire' (EA)	IDee LMil
charitopes	LMil
- F 25570	LMil
- subsp. ***charitopes***	MHid
* 'Charlotte de Rothschild' (EA)	SLdr
'Charlotte Megan' (A)	LMil
chasmanthum	see *R. augustinii* subsp. *chasmanthum*
'Cheer'	CAco MAsh
'Chelsea Reach' (K/d) 𝕐H6	LMil
'Chelsea Seventy'	SLdr
'Cherokee' (EA)	SLdr
'Cherries and Merlot'	LRHS
'Cherry Cheesecake'	LRHS
'Cherry Drops' (EA)	EPfP LRHS MAsh SPoG
CHERRY KISS ('Hachcher'PBR)	CAco GGGa IDee LMil LRHS NLar SAko
'Chetco' (A)	LMil
'Chevalier Félix de Sauvage'	WFar
'Chikor'	CDoC EGrI GKin MGos
'Chipmunk' (EA/d)	LRHS MAsh NRHS
'Chippewa' (Indian) (EA)	CTri LMil SAko
'Chocolate Dane'	LMil
Choptank River Group (A)	GKev
(Choremia Group) 'Choremia' 𝕐H5	LMil
'Christina' (Vuykiana) (EA/d)	SLdr
'Christmas Cheer' (EA/d)	see *R.* 'Ima-shojo'
'Christmas Cheer' (*caucasicum* hybrid) 𝕐H5	CAco CBcs CDoC CRos CSBt EPfP GGGa GKin LCro LMil MAsh MGos MPri NLar SLdr

	'Chromatella'	LMil
	chryseum	see *R. rupicola* var. *chryseum*
	ciliatum	CBcs SLdr
	- deep rose-flowered	SLdr
	- white-flowered	SLdr
	ciliipes	GMcL
	Cilpinense Group	CBcs
	- 'Cilpinense' 🏆H5	CMac EPfP LMil LRHS MAsh MMuc MPri SLdr XSte
	cinnabarinum	GKev LMil LRHS SLdr XSte
	- subsp. ***cinnabarinum***	MHid
	- - BL&M 234	LMil
	- - 'Nepal'	LMil
	- - Roylei Group	GGGa LMil
	- - - B&SWJ 13972	WCru
	- - - 'Vin Rosé'	LMil
	- Cinzan Group	LMil
§	- (Conroy Group) 'Conroy'	LMil
§	- subsp. ***xanthocodon***	GGGa GKev LMil WPGP
	- - 'Apricot Belle'	LMil
§	- - Concatenans Group	GGGa LMil
	- - - KW 5874	LMil
	- - Purpurellum Group	GGGa
	citriniflorum	LMil
	- R 108	LMil
	- var. ***citriniflorum***	LMil
	- var. ***horaeum*** F21850	LMil
	clementinae F 25705	LMil
	'Cliff Garland'	LMil
	'Coccineum Speciosum' (G) 🏆H6	CBcs CMac LMil LRHS XSte
	'Cockatoo' (K)	LMil
	coeloneurum	LMil MHid
	- EGM 334	LMil
	'Colin Kenrick' (K/d)	LMil
	Comely Group	SLdr
	concatenans	see *R. cinnabarinum* subsp. *xanthocodon* Concatenans Group
	concinnum	MHid
	- Pseudoyanthinum Group 🏆H5	GGGa
	'Concorde'	CMac
	'Connie' (Kaempferi) (EA)	CKel SSta
	'Conroy'	see *R. cinnabarinum* (Conroy Group) 'Conroy'
	'Contina'	LMil
	'Conversation Piece' (EA)	CEnd SLdr
	'Corany' (A)	CDoC LMil NLar SCoo
	coriaceum	LMil
	'Corneille' (G/d)	CBcs LMil LRHS XSte
	Cornish Early Red Group	see *R.* Smithii Group
	'Cornish Red'	see *R.* Smithii Group
	'Coronation Day'	LMil
	'Cosmopolitan'	CDoC CKel GMcL LCro LOPS MGos NLar SCob SPer SPoG XSte
	'Cotton Candy'	LMil
	'Countess of Athlone'	CMac
	'Countess of Haddington'	CBcs LMil LRHS
	Cowslip Group	CTri LMil MAsh MGos
	- 'Cowslip' 🏆H4	CDoC CRos EGrI EPfP IDee LRHS
	'Crane' 🏆H5	EPfP GGGa GKev LMil LRHS MAsh
	crassum	see *R. maddenii* subsp. *crassum*
	'Cream Crest'	CDoC CRos GKin NLar SLim XSte
	'Creamy Chiffon'	CAco NLar
	crinigerum	GKev LMil
	'Croceum Tricolor' (G)	LMil
	'Crosswater Belle'	LMil
	'Crosswater Red' (A) 🏆H6	LMil
	cubittii	see *R. veitchianum* Cubittii Group
	cumberlandense (A)	LMil
	- 'Sunlight'	LMil
	cuneatum	LRHS

	'Cunningham's White'	CAco CBcs CDoC CTri ELan EPfP GGGa GMcL LCro LMaj LMil LOPS LPar LRHS MAsh MGos MPri NHol NLar NWea SArc SCob SGsty SLdr SLim SPer SPoG SSta WHlf XSte
	'Curlew' 🏆H5	CMac GEdr GKin GMcL MAsh NHol SCob SLdr
	cyanocarpum	GKev
	'Cynthia' 🏆H6	CMac CSBt GGGa LMil LSRN SCob SLdr SSta
	'Daisetsuzan' (EA)	MPkF XSte
	dalhousieae	LRHS
	(Damozel Group) 'Damozel'	LMil
	'Darkness' (EA)	SWeb
	dasycladum	see *R. selense* subsp. *dasycladum*
	dauricum 'Album'	see *R. dauricum* 'Hokkaido'
§	- 'Hokkaido'	LMil
	- 'Mid-winter' 🏆H6	GGGa LMil
	davidii	LMil
	davidsonianum 🏆H5	CMac LMil MHid
	- Bodnant form	LMil
	- 'Caerhays Blotched'	GGGa
	- 'Ruth Lyons'	LMil
	'Daviesii' (G) 🏆H6	CBcs CDoC CEnd CRos CSBt CTri ELan EPfP GKin IDee LCro LMil LOPS LRHS MAsh MMuc MPkF MPri NLar SCob SCoo SPoG SSta XSte
	'Daybreak' (EA/d)	see *R.* 'Kirin'
	'Dear Barbara'	LSRN
	'Dear Grandad' (EA)	CTri LMil LSRN
	'Dear Grandma' (EA)	LMil LSRN
	'Dearest' (EA)	LMil LRHS MAsh MPri NRHS SCoo
	'Debutante'	SSta
	decorum 🏆H6	CBcs GGGa IDee LMil LRHS SLdr
	- subsp. ***cordatum***	MHid
	- - C&H 7132	GGGa
	- subsp. ***decorum***	MHid
§	- subsp. ***diaprepes***	MHid
	- pink-flowered	GGGa
§	***degronianum*** subsp. ***degronianum***	LMil
	- subsp. ***heptamerum*** 'Ho Emma'	LMil
	- - 'Oki Koki'	LMil
	- 'Rae's Delight'	LMil
	'Delicatissimum' (O) 🏆H5	CBcs CTsd GGGa GKin LRHS MPkF XSte
	'Delta'	CDoC MGos NLar SLim WFar
	dendrocharis	LMil
	- GLENDOICK GEM ('Gle002')	GGGa
*	'Denny's Rose' (A)	SSta
	'Denny's Scarlet'	NHol SSta
	'Denny's White' (A)	LMil NHol SSta
	denudatum	LMil MHid
	- EGM 294	LMil
	'Devisiperbile' (EA)	SLdr
	Diamant Group lilac-flowered (EA)	LMil
§	- red-flowered (EA)	EGrI SLdr
	'Diamant Rot'	see *R.* Diamant Group red-flowered
I	'Diana'	SLdr SWeb
	diaprepes	see *R. decorum* subsp. *diaprepes*
	dichroanthum	LMil
§	- subsp. ***apodectum***	LMil
§	- subsp. ***scyphocalyx***	LMil
	didymum	see *R. sanguineum* subsp. *didymum*
	'Diorama' (Vs)	SSta
	discolor	see *R. fortunei* subsp. *discolor*
	'Doc'	CBcs SLdr SSta XSte
	'Doctor Arnold W. Endtz'	SSta
	'Doctor H.C. Dresselhuys'	CKel CWnw

	'Doctor M. Oosthoek' (M)	GKin
	'Doctor Reiger'	CDoC NLar SPer
	'Dolores' (EA)	NLar
	'Doloroso' (A) **new**	LMil
	'Don Quixote' (K)	GMcL
	'Dopey' ♀H5	CAco CBcs CDoC CRos EDir ELan EPfP GGGa LMil LPar LRHS MAsh MGos NHol SCob SGsty SLdr SLim SSta
	'Dora Amateis' ♀H6	CBcs GGGa GKev LMil LRHS MAsh MGos MPri NRHS SCob SLdr SLim XSte
	Dormouse Group	LMil MAsh
	'Dorothy Hayden' (EA)	SGsty SLdr SWeb
	'Dotella'	SSta
	'Double Beauty' (Vuykiana) (EA/d)	SSta
	'Douggie Betteridge'	LMil
	'Dracula' (K)	LMil
	Dragonfly Group	SSta
	'Drake's Mountain'	GMcL
	DRAMATIC DARK ('Hachdram'PBR) **new**	IDee LMil
	'Dreamland' ♀H5	CBcs CDoC CRos EPfP LCro LMil LOPS LPar LRHS MAsh MGos NLar NRHS SCob SLdr SLim SPoG SSta WFar XSte
	'Dufthecke'	see *R.* WHITE DUFTHECKE
	DUFTHECKE ROSA ('Rhodunter 151') (Inkarho) **new**	LMil
	'Dusty Miller'	MAsh SLdr WFar
	'E.J.P. Magor'	LMil
	'Earl of Donoughmore'	SSta
	eclecteum	GGGa LMil MHid
§	***edgeworthii*** ♀H3	CBcs GGGa GKev LMil LRHS MPkF WPGP
	'Edith Bosley'	CDoC LRHS
	'Edna Bee' (EA)	LMil SLdr
	'Egret' ♀H4	GEdr GGGa GMcL LMil MAsh
	'Ehrengold'	CAco
	(Eleanore Group) 'Eleanore'	SLdr
	'Electra'	see *R. augustinii* (Electra Group) 'Electra'
	elegantulum	LMil MHid
	'Elfin Gold'	LMil
	(Elisabeth Hobbie Group) 'Elisabeth Hobbie' ♀H5	CDoC LMil NLar
	'Elizabeth' (EA)	CMac SCob SLdr
	Elizabeth Group	LMil MAsh SLdr
§	- 'Creeping Jenny'	GGGa
	- 'Elizabeth'	CBcs CTri LRHS LSRN NHol NRHS XSte
	'Elizabeth Jenny'	see *R.* (Elizabeth Group) 'Creeping Jenny'
	'Elizabeth Red Foliage'	CKel CTri CWnw IDee LMil MAsh MPkF NLar SLdr XSte
	'Elsie Lee' (EA/d) ♀H5	CEnd CSBt EPfP LMil MAsh SCob SLdr WFar
	'Emanuela'	XSte
	'Emasculum'	SLdr
	(Encore Series) ENCORE AUTUMN EMPRESS ('Conles'PBR) (EA)	EGrI
	- ENCORE AUTUMN FIRE ('Roblez') (EA) **new**	LCro
	- ENCORE AUTUMN SUNSET ('Roblen') (EA)	EGrI
	- ENCORE PURE WHITE JULIA ('Homlea') (EA) **new**	LCro
	- ENCORE SUNBURST ('Roblet') (EA) **new**	LCro

	'Endsleigh Pink'	LMil
	eriocarpum 'Gumpō' (EA)	CMac SLdr
	eriogynum	see *R. facetum*
	'Esmeralda'	CMac
	'Etna' (EA)	SLdr
	'Etoile de Sleidinge'	CRos MGos
	'Etta Burrows'	GGGa SLdr
	'Eucharis' (Glenn Dale) (EA)	MPkF
	'Eucharitis'	LCro XSte
	'Eunice Ann' (A)	SSta
	'Europa'	LMil SSta
	'Eurydice'	LMil
	'Evelyn Hyde' (EA)	SLdr
	'Everbloom' (EA)	SLdr
	'Everitt Hershey' (A)	SLdr
	EVERRED ('851C'PBR)	GGGa
	exasperatum KW 6855	LMil
	Exburiense Group	MMuc
	'Exbury Calstocker'	LMil
	excellens	LMil
I	'Excelsior' **new**	NLar
	eximium	see *R. falconeri* subsp. *eximium*
	'Exquisitum' (O) ♀H5	EGrI GGGa GKin LMil
	'Extraordinaire'	CBcs LMil MPkF SSta XSte
	(Fabia Group) 'Fabia' ♀H4	CMac GGGa GKin LMil SLdr
§	- 'Fabia Tangerine'	CMac
	- 'Fabia Waterer'	IDee LMil NLar
§	***facetum***	GGGa LMil
	'Faggetter's Favourite' ♀H5	LMil LRHS SSta
	Fairy Light Group	LMil SLdr
	faithae CGG 14142	GGGa
	falconeri ♀H4	GGGa IKel LMil LRHS
	- WJC 13825	WCru
§	- subsp. ***eximium***	GGGa GKev LMil MHid
	- subsp. ***falconeri***	MHid
	'Fanny'	see *R.* 'Pucella'
	'Fantasia'	LRHS
	'Fantastica' ♀H6	CAco CDoC CRos ELan EPfP GGGa LMil MAsh MGos MPri NLar SCob SGsty SLim SPoG XSte
	fargesii	see *R. oreodoxa* var. *fargesii*
	farinosum	LMil
§	'Farrow' (EA) **new**	LCro
	fastigiatum	EGrI GEdr LMil WAbe
	- SBEC 0804	WThu
	- SDR 7990	GKev
§	- 'Blue Steel' ♀H6	CTri GKin IDee LMil LRHS MAsh MPri NRHS SPlb WAbe
	- 'Indigo Steel'	GGGa
	'Fastuosum Flore Pleno' (d) ♀H6	CBcs CMac CSBt GGGa IDee LMil SCob SLdr SSta
	faucium	LMil
	fauriei	see *R. brachycarpum* subsp. *fauriei*
	'Favorite' ambig. (EA)	SLdr
	'Fawley' (K)	SLdr
	'Fay Norman'	LMil
	ferrugineum	LMil LRHS
	'Feuerwerk' (K)	GMcL NLar
	fictolacteum	see *R. rex* subsp. *fictolacteum*
	Fine Feathers Group	CMac
	'Fire Bird'	SLdr
	'Fire Rim'	LRHS MAsh
	'Fireball' (K) ♀H6	CBcs CDoC CTri EGrI EPfP GBin GGGa GKin GMcL IDee LMil LRHS MAsh MGos MMuc MPri SCob SPer SPoG XSte
	'Fireball' (hybrid)	MPkF
	'Firecracker' (A)	LRHS MAsh
	'Fireglow' (EA)	GKin LMil
	'Firelight' (EA)	CDoC CRos LPar
	'Firelight' (hybrid)	GKin LMil NLar SPer
§	'Firestorm'	MPri
	'First Light' (V)	LRHS XSte

	'Flaming Gold'	LMil LRHS LSRN MAsh SLdr
§	***flammeum*** (A)	LMil LRHS
	'Flanagan's Daughter'	LMil
	Flava Group	see *R.* Volker Group
	fletcherianum 'Yellow Bunting'	GGGa
	floccigerum	LMil
	'Floriade'	GMcL
	floribundum	LMil
	'Florida' (EA/d) ♀H4	CDoC CMac LMil NLar SCob SCoo SLdr
	'Flower Arranger' (EA)	LMil MAsh SCoo
	formosum	CBcs
§	- var. ***formosum*** Iteaphyllum Group	GGGa
	forrestii subsp. ***forrestii***	LMil
	- - Repens Group	LMil
	- - - 'Seinghku'	GGGa
	Fortune Group	SLdr
	fortunei ♀H5	GGGa LMil NLar
§	- subsp. ***discolor*** ♀H5	CBcs LMil MHid NLar
	- - (Houlstonii Group) 'John R. Elcock'	LMil
	- - var. ***kwangfuense*** AC 5208	LMil
	- subsp. ***discolor*** × 'Lodauric Iceberg'	GKin
	- subsp. ***fortunei***	MHid
	- 'Mrs Butler'	see *R.* 'Sir Charles Butler'
	'Fragrant Memories'	LMil
	'Fragrant Star' (A)	CBcs LRHS MPkF XSte
	'Fragrantissimum' ♀H3	CBcs CDoC CEnd CSBt CTsd GGGa IDee LMil LRHS MPkF MRav NLar SLdr XSte
	'Frank Galsworthy'	SCob
	(Fraseri Group) 'Fraseri' (M)	LMil
	'Fred Peste' ♀H4	LMil MGos SCob SLdr SLim
	(Fred Wynniatt Group) 'Fred Wynniatt'	LMil
	'Fred Wynniatt Stanway'	see *R.* 'Stanway'
	'Freya' (R/d)	LMil LSRN
	'Fridoline' (EA)	SAko
	'Frilly Lemon' (Ad)	ELan EPfP LRHS MPkF XSte
	'Frosted Orange' (EA)	LMil
	'Frosthexe'	WAbe
	'Fulbrook'	LMil
	fulgens	LMil MHid
	fulvum ♀H5	GGGa IDee LMil SSta
	'Furious Fujiori'PBR (EA)	NLar
	'Furnivall's Daughter' ♀H5	CAco CBcs CMac CSBt LMaj LMil NHol SLdr SSta
	fuyuanense	GGGa
	'Gabrielle Hill' (EA)	SLdr
	'Gaiety' (Glenn Dale) (EA)	LMil SLdr
	galactinum	GGGa LMil
	- 'Galacticus' **new**	LMil
	'Gandy Dancer'	CAco SLdr
	'Garden State Glow' (EA/d)	SLdr
	'Gartendirektor Glocker'	CDoC EGrI LMil MGos SCob SLim
	'Gartendirektor Rieger' ♀H5	CBcs GGGa IDee LMil XSte
	'Geisha Lilac'	see *R.* (Aronense Group) 'Hanako'
	'Geisha Orange'	see *R.* (Aronense Group) 'Satschiko'
	'Geisha Pink'	see *R.* (Aronense Group) 'Momoko'
	'Geisha Purple'	see *R.* (Aronense Group) 'Fumiko'
	'Geisha Red'	see *R.* (Aronense Group) 'Kazuko'
	'Geisha White'	see *R.* (Aronense Group) 'Hisako'
	GELB DUFTHECKE ('Rhodunter 150'PBR) (Inkarho)	LMil NLar
	'Gena Mae' (A/d) ♀H6	SLdr
	'General Practitioner'	SLdr
	'General Wavell' (EA)	CMac LMil
	'Gene's Favourite'	SSta
	'Geoffroy Millais'	LMil
	'Georg Arends' (A)	CDoC CRos EPfP LMil LRHS MAsh SCoo SPoG
	'George Hyde' (EA)	EPfP LRHS LSRN MAsh SCoo
	'Germania'	CBcs CDoC CKel CRos CWnw GMcL LCro LPar LRHS MAsh MGos MPri NLar SCob SGsty SPoG SSta
	Gertrud Schäle Group	CDoC CTri EGrI GMcL NLar
	'Gibraltar' (K) ♀H6	CBcs CDoC CSBt CTri CWnw EGrI EPfP GGGa GKin LMil LRHS MAsh MGos MPkF MPri NGrs NHol NLar SCob SLim SPer SSta XSte
	Gibraltar Group	LMil WFar
	'Gilbert Mullie' (EA)	CDoC LMil NLar SCoo SLim SPoG SSta
	'Gillian Bramley'	SLdr
	'Ginger' (K)	LMil
	'Ginny Gee' ♀H5	CAco CBcs CDoC EGrI EPfP EPot GEdr GGGa GKin GMcL IDee LMil LRHS MAsh MGos NLar NRHS NWad SSta WFar XSte
§	'Girard's Hot Shot' (EA)	GMcL LRHS MPkF NRHS SCoo SSta
§	'Girard's Variegated Hot Shot' (EA/v) ♀H4	CKel GGGa MAsh SLdr SPoG XSte
	'Gislinde' (A)	SAko
	'Glacier' (EA)	SLdr
	glanduliferum	GGGa MHid NLar
	- 'Peter the Great'	LMil
§	***glaucophyllum***	GGGa LMil MHid
	- Borde Hill form	LMil
	- 'Deer Dell'	LMil
	GLENDOICK CANDYFLOSS ('Gle033') (EA/d)	GGGa
	GLENDOICK CHIFFON ('Gle034') (EA/d)	GGGa
	GLENDOICK FLAMINGO ('Gle026')	GGGa
	GLENDOICK FRANGIPANI ('Gle035') (EA/d)	GGGa
	GLENDOICK GARDENIA ('Gle036') (EA/d)	GGGa
	GLENDOICK GEORGETTE ('Gle037') (EA/d)	GGGa
	GLENDOICK GLACIER ('Gle009') (EA)	GGGa
	GLENDOICK GLAMOUR ('Gle039') (EA)	GGGa
	GLENDOICK GOBLIN ('Gle010') (EA)	GGGa
	GLENDOICK GOLD ('Gle011')	GGGa
	GLENDOICK MYSTIQUE ('Gle014')	GGGa
	GLENDOICK PETTICOATS ('Gle015')	GGGa
	GLENDOICK PRINCESS ('Gle040') (EA/d)	GGGa
	GLENDOICK ROSEBUD ('Gle022') (EA)	GGGa
	GLENDOICK SHERBET ('Gle029')	GGGa
	GLENDOICK SNOWFLAKES ('Gle001') (EA)	GGGa
	GLENDOICK SORBET ('Gle028')	GGGa
	GLENDOICK VANILLA ('Gle017')	GGGa
	GLENDOICK VELVET ('Gle018')	GGGa
	glischrum	GGGa
	- subsp. ***glischroides***	LMil
§	- subsp. ***rude***	LMil MHid

'Gloria'	see *R.* 'Bruns Gloria'
'Gloria Mundi' (G)	XSte
'Glory of Littleworth' (Ad)	LMil
'Glowing Embers' (K)	CDoC CTri EGrI GKin GMcL LMil LRHS MAsh MGos MMuc NHol NLar SCob SGsty SLim SPer SSta
'Goblin'	SLdr
'Gog' (K)	CSBt
'Golden Coach'	CAco
'Golden Eagle' (K) ♀H6	CBcs CDoC CRos EGrI GKin GMcL LMil LRHS MGos NGrs NLar SCoo SLdr SPer SPoG WFar
GOLDEN EVEREST ('Hachgold'PBR)	GGGa LMil LRHS
'Golden Flame' (A)	EGrI
'Golden Flare' (A)	CBcs EGrI GKin GMcL
'Golden Fleece'	LMil
'Golden Gate'	CDoC CRos CSBt MGos NLar SCob SLdr SPer
'Golden Lights' (A)	EGrI GKin NLar
'Golden Princess'	LMil
'Golden Splendour'	LMil
'Golden Sunset' (K) ♀H6	EPfP LMil LRHS MAsh MPkF WFar XSte
'Golden Torch' ♀H5	CBcs CDoC CRos CSBt ELan EPfP LCro LMil LPar LRHS MAsh MGos MPri NLar SCob SLdr SLim SPoG WFar
'Golden Wedding'	CBcs LMil LSRN MAsh
'Golden Wit'	MAsh
'Golden Wonder'	MAsh
'Goldflimmer' (v)	CDoC EPfP LCro LPar LRHS MAsh MGos MPri SCob SLim SPer SPoG WFar WHlf
'Goldika'	LMil
GOLDINETTA ('Hachinetta')	IDee LMil
'Goldkrone' ♀H5	MAsh NLar SCob SPoG
'Goldsworth Orange'	CAco CMac SLdr
'Goldsworth Yellow'	CSBt
'Goldtopas' (K)	CTri EPfP GGGa GKin LRHS
'Gomer Waterer' ♀H6	CBcs CKel CSBt CWnw ELan EPfP GGGa GMcL IDee LCro LMil LRHS MAsh MGos NLar SCob SPoG SSta
'Gorbella'	CDoC
Gowenianum Group (Ad)	LMil LRHS MGos
'Grace Seabrook' ♀H5	CBcs CSBt CTri GGGa SLdr
GRAFFITO ('Hachgraf')	CBcs GGGa IDee LMil LRHS NLar
'Graham Thomas'	LMil
grande	IDee LMil MHid NLar
- WJC 13804	WCru
'Grandeur Triomphante' (G)	XSte
gratum	see *R. basilicum*
'Graziella'	CAco CBcs CKel CWnw GGGa LCro LOPS LRHS MGos MPkF NLar SArc SPoG SSta WFar XSte
'Greensleeves'	LMil
'Greenway' (Kurume) (EA)	CBcs SLdr XSte
griersonianum	GGGa LMil
- F 30392	LMil
griffithianum	MHid
- B&SWJ 2425	WCru
'Gristede' ♀H5	CDoC CRos LMil LRHS NLar SSta
groenlandicum	LMil NLar WAbe
- 'Compactum'	LRHS NLar
- 'Helma'	LMil NLar
- 'Lenie'	NLar
(Grosclaude Group) 'Grosclaude'	LMil
'Grumpy'	EPfP LMil LRHS MAsh XSte
'Gwenda' (EA)	CTri SLdr
habrotrichum	LMil
'Hachmann's Brasilia'	SSta
'Hachmann's Charmant'	CBcs GGGa XSte
'Hachmann's Constanze'	LMil
'Hachmann's Eskimo'	CAco CRos LMil LRHS SLdr
'Hachmann's Juanita' (K)	CRos CSBt LMil NLar
'Hachmann's Junifeuer'	NLar SSta
HACHMANN'S KABARETT ('Hachkaba')	CDoC LMil LPar LRHS NLar XSte
'Hachmann's Marlis' ♀H6	LMil LRHS
§ 'Hachmann's Metallica'	CBcs LMil LRHS NLar
§ 'Hachmann's Orakel'	LMil LRHS NLar SSta
'Hachmann's Pinguin'	CBcs SSta XSte
§ 'Hachmann's Polaris' ♀H7	CDoC LCro LMil
'Hachmann's Porzellan' ♀H6	LMil LRHS SGsty XSte
§ 'Hachmann's Rokoko' (EA)	CEnd LMil SSta
'Hachmann's Sunny Boy'	LMil
haematodes	GGGa LMil
§ - subsp. ***chaetomallum***	LMil
- subsp. ***haematodes***	LMil
'Halfdan Lem' ♀H5	CBcs CDoC GKin LMil LPar LRHS MGos NLar SLim SPoG SSta XSte
'Hallelujah'	CBcs
'Halopeanum'	GGGa LMil XSte
'Hamlet' (M)	LMil
'Hammondii'	LMil
'Hampshire Belle'	LMil LRHS SSta
'Hanger's Flame' (A)	LMil
'Hansel'	MAsh
HAPPYDENDRON PUSHY PURPLE ('Hachmagic'PBR) **new**	LMil
'Hardijzer Beauty' (Ad)	SLdr
'Hardy Gardenia' (EA/d)	SSta
hardyi	see *R. augustinii* subsp. *hardyi*
'Harkwood Red' (EA)	SLdr
Harmony Group	SLdr
'Harry Tagg'	CBcs
'Haru-no-sono' (EA)	MPkF SWeb XSte
'Harvest Moon' (K)	GMcL LMil NLar
'Hatsu-giri' (EA)	CMac LCro LMil LOPS SLdr SSta
(Hawk Group) 'Crest' ♀H5	CBcs LMil SSta
'Heather Macleod' (EA)	SLdr
'Heidi'PBR (EA)	SLdr
'Helen Close' (Glenn Dale) (EA)	SLdr
'Helena Evelyn' (A)	LMil
'Helene Schiffner'	SSta
heliolepis	LMil
hemsleyanum	LMil MHid
'Hendrik's Kers' (V)	LRHS XSte
'Herbert' (EA)	CDoC CMac CRos LMil MGos NLar SCoo SLdr SLim
'High Summer'	LMil LRHS NLar
'Hilda Margaret'	SSta
'Hinamayo'	see *R.* (Obtusum Group) 'Hinomayo'
'Hino-crimson' (Kurume) (EA) ♀H5	CBcs CDoC CMac CSBt CTri EGrI GKin GMcL LMil MAsh MGos MPkF NHol NLar SCob SLdr SPer SPoG SSta XSte
'Hinode-giri' (EA)	CBcs CMac CSBt SLdr
'Hino-scarlet' (EA)	CBcs
hippophaeoides	CBcs GKev LMil WFar
- 'Bei-ma-shan'	see *R. hippophaeoides* 'Haba Shan'
§ - 'Haba Shan' ♀H6	LMil LRHS WThu
hirsutum	LMil WAbe
hirtipes	GGGa MHid
hodgsonii	LMil MHid
- B&SWJ 2195A	WCru
'Holden'	MAsh NLar
'Homebush' (K/d) ♀H6	CBcs CDoC CMac CTri EGrI EPfP GMcL LMil LRHS MAsh MGos MMuc NLar SCob SPer SPoG SSta WHlf XSte
'Honeysuckle' (K)	NHol SSta

§ 'Ho-o' (Kurume) (EA) — EGrI SLdr
'Ho-oden' (EA) — XSte
'Hoppy' — CBcs CDoC CRos LMil MAsh MGos NLar SCob SLdr SLim
'Horizon Lakeside' — GGGa
'Horizon Monarch' ♀H4 — CAco CBcs CDoC CRos EGrI ELan GGGa GKin LMil LPar LRHS MGos NLar SCob SGsty SLdr SLim SPer SSta WFar XSte
'Hortulanus H. Witte' (M) — SSta XSte
'Hot Flush' — LRHS
'Hot Shot' — see *R.* 'Girard's Hot Shot'
'Hot Shot Variegated' — see *R.* 'Girard's Variegated Hot Shot' (EA/v)
'Hotei' — CAco CSBt EGrI GKin LMil MAsh NHol SSta
(Hotspur Group) 'Hotspur' (K) — MMuc
- 'Hotspur Red' (K) ♀H6 — EGrI EPfP GKin GMcL LMil MAsh MMuc XSte
huanum — LMil
- EGM 316 — LMil
'Hugh Koster' — SLdr
'Huisman's Sun Star' (A/d) — LMil LRHS
Humming Bird Group — EGrI GEdr LMil LRHS SLdr
hunnewellianum — MHid
'Hussar' — LMil LRHS
'Hydon Dawn' ♀H5 — LMil LRHS SSta
'Hydon Hunter' ♀H5 — CSBt SSta
'Hydon Velvet' — CBcs CTsd LMil LRHS NLar XSte
hyperythrum — GGGa LMil
- 'Ariel' — LMil
'Ice Cube' — MMuc SLdr
'Iceberg' — see *R.* (Lodauric Group) 'Lodauric Iceberg'
(Idealist Group) 'Idealist' — LMil
§ 'Ilam Melford Lemon' (A) — LMil
§ 'Ilam Ming' (A) — LMil
'Ilam Violet' — CMac LMil
'Imago' (K/d) — LMil
§ 'Ima-shojo' (Kurume) (EA/d) — CMac LRHS SLdr
impeditum — CBcs EGrI GEdr GKev LCro LOPS MGos SLdr SSta
- 'Blue Steel' — see *R. fastigiatum* 'Blue Steel'
- 'Indigo' — GKin
- 'Pygmaeum' — WAbe WThu
- 'Select' — XSte
- white-flowered **new** — CAco
(Impi Group) 'Impi' — LMil
§ ***indicum*** 'Macranthum' (EA) — SLdr SRms
insigne ♀H6 — GGGa LMil MHid
Intrifast Group — GGGa
'Irene Koster' (O) ♀H5 — CBcs CDoC EGrI ELan GGGa GKin LMil MGos MPkF SCob SLim XSte
'Irohayama' (Kurume) (EA) ♀H5 — CBcs CEnd CMac EPfP LMil LRHS MAsh MPri NRHS SCoo XSte
irroratum — LMil
- subsp. ***irroratum*** — MHid
- 'Polka Dot' — GGGa LMil
- subsp. ***yiliangense*** — MHid
- - EGM 339 — LMil
'Isabel' (EA) — GMcL MAsh
'Isabel' (hybrid) — MPri
iteaphyllum — see *R. formosum* var. *formosum* Iteaphyllum Group
'Ivette' (Kaempferi) (EA) — CMac
'Izumi-no-mai' (EA) — SLdr
'J.C. Williams' — CBcs
'J.M. de Montague' — see *R.* 'The Honourable Jean Marie de Montague'
'Jackwill' — SAko
(Jalisco Group) 'Jalisco Janet' — SLdr
- 'Jubilant' — LMil
'James Barto' — LMil
'James Burchett' ♀H6 — LMil LRHS SSta
'James Gable' (EA) — SLdr
Janet Group — LMil
'Janet Rhea' (EA) — SLdr
'Janet Ward' — LMil
japonicum (A. Gray) J.V. Suringar — see *R. molle* subsp. *japonicum*
- var. ***pentamerum*** — see *R. degronianum* subsp. *degronianum*
'Jason' — LMil
'Jean Marie Montague' — see *R.* 'The Honourable Jean Marie de Montague'
'Jeanne Church' **new** — LMil
'Jeff Hill' (EA) — SLdr
'Jenny' — see *R.* 'Creeping Jenny'
'Jens Jörgen Sörensen' **new** — NLar
'Jeritsa' — LMil
'Jessica de Rothschild' — LMil
'Jessica Rose' (A) — LMil
'Jingle Bells' — XSte
'Joanna' — CBcs
'Jock' — SLdr
'Jock Brydon' (O) ♀H6 — GGGa LMil LRHS
'Johann Sebastian Bach' (EA) — SLdr
'Johanna' (EA) ♀H5 — CDoC CEnd CTri EGrI EPfP GMcL LMil LRHS MAsh MGos MPkF MPri NHol NLar NRHS SCob SGsty SLdr SPer SWeb XSte
'John Cairns' (Kaempferi) (EA) — CMac SLdr
johnstoneanum — CBcs GGGa SLdr
- NJM 12.068 — WPGP
- 'Double Diamond' (d) — LMil
'Jolie Madame' (Vs) ♀H6 — CBcs CDoC CRos EGrI ELan EPfP GKin LMil LRHS MAsh MGos MPkF MPri NLar SGsty SPer WFar XSte
'Joseph Hill' (EA) — CEnd
'Jubilee' — SLdr
'June Fire' (A) — SSta
'Juniduft' (A) — GGGa
kaempferi (EA) — LMil SLdr
§ - 'Mikado' (EA) — LMil SLdr
- orange-flowered (EA) — CMac
'Kali' — NLar SPer
'Kalinka' — CDoC CRos EPfP LMil MAsh MGos MHtn NLar SPoG WFar
'Karen Triplett' — LMil
'Karl Naue' — GGGa
'Karminduft' (A) **new** — LMil
KARMINKISSEN ('Hachkarmin') — LMil LRHS
'Kasane-kagaribi' (EA) — SLdr
'Kathleen' van Nes (EA) — SLdr
'Katisha' (EA) — SLdr
'Katy Watson' — SSta
'Keija' (EA) — SLdr
keiskei var. ***ozawae*** 'Yaku Fairy' ♀H5 — LMil
keleticum — see *R. calostrotum* subsp. *keleticum*
'Kentucky Minstrel' (K) — MPkF
'Kermesinum' (EA) — CDoC CTri MAsh MGos NWad SCob SLdr SLim
I 'Kermesinum Album' (EA) — LMil
I 'Kermesinum Rosé' (EA) ♀H6 — CDoC CRos CWnw LMil NLar SLim
kesangiae — GGGa LMil
- var. ***album*** — GGGa
Kewense Group — LMil
keysii — GKev LMil
'Kilian' (A) — XSte

	(Kilimanjaro Group) 'Kilimanjaro'	LMil
	'King George' Loder	see *R.* 'Loderi King George'
	'Kings Ride'	LMil
§	'Kirin' (Kurume) (EA/d)	CBcs LMil SLdr SRms XSte
	kiusianum (EA)	LMil WAbe
I	- 'Album' (EA)	LMil WAbe
	- 'Hillier's Pink' (EA)	LMil
	- var. ***kiusianum*** (EA)	SLdr
	'Kleiner Prinz' (EA)	SAko
	'Klondyke' (K) ♀H6	CBcs CDoC CRos CSBt CTri CWnw EGrI EPfP GGGa GKin LCro LMil LOPS LRHS MAsh MGos MPkF MPri NLar SCob SCoo SLdr SPer SPoG XSte
	'Kluis Sensation' ♀H5	CAco CBcs CMac CSBt LMil SLdr SSta
	'Kluis Triumph'	SSta
	'Knap Hill Apricot' (K)	LMil
	'Knap Hill Red' (K)	LMil
	'Knap Hill Salmon' (K)	EGrI
	'Koichiro Wada'	see *R. yakushimanum* 'Koichiro Wada'
	'Kokardia'	LMil SAko WFar
	'Königstein' (EA)	LMil MGos SSta
§	'Koningin Emma' (M)	LMil
§	'Koningin Wilhelmina' (M)	LMil
	'Koningin Wilhelmina' (Vuykiana) (EA)	SLdr
	'Koran-yuki' (EA)	SRms
	'Koromo-shikibu' (EA)	MPkF XSte
	'Koster's Brilliant Red' (M)	CSBt LCro SSta
	'Kromlauer Parkperle'	SAko
§	'Kure-no-yuki' (Kurume) (EA/d)	CEnd LMil
	kyawii	LMil
	lacteum	GGGa LMil
	'Lady Alice Fitzwilliam' ♀H3	CBcs CTsd GKin IDee LMil
	(Lady Chamberlain Group) 'Salmon Trout'	LMil LSRN
	'Lady Clementine Mitford' ♀H6	CBcs CSBt LMil LRHS
	'Lady Dark' (EA)	LMil SAko
	'Lady Eleanor Cathcart'	SLdr
	'Lady Elphinstone' (Kurume) (EA)	SLdr
	LADY LASA ('Bouti0150') **new**	MPkF
	'Lady Louise' (EA)	SLdr
	Lamellen Group	LMil
	lanatoides	GGGa
	lanatum	LMil
	lanigerum	LMil
	lapponicum	GKev
	- Parviflorum Group	GGGa
	'Lapwing' (K)	SLdr
	'Laramie'	LMil
	'Late Love' (EA)	CBcs
	'Lavender Girl' ♀H6	IDee LMil NLar SLdr SSta
	'Lavendula'	LMil
	'Ledifolium'	see *R.* × *mucronatum*
	'Ledifolium Album'	see *R.* × *mucronatum*
	'Lee's Dark Purple'	CAco SCob
	'Lee's Scarlet'	LMil
	'Lemon Dream'	CDoC EPfP LRHS MAsh MGos MPri NRHS SLim
	'Lemon Lights' (A)	MPkF
	'Lemonora' (M)	CBcs GKin
	'Lem's Cameo' ♀H5	GGGa LMil SSta
	'Lem's Monarch' ♀H4	CBcs GGGa IDee LMil LRHS SLdr SSta XSte
	'Lem's Tangerine'	LMil
	'Lemur' (EA)	EGrI GEdr GGGa LMil
	'Leni'	LRHS MAsh NRHS

	'Leo' (EA)	WFar
	'Leonore'	LMil
	lepidostylum	CMac GGGa LMil MHid WFar
	lepidotum yellow-flowered McB 110	WThu
§	'Leucanthum'	WThu
	'Libretto'	CRos SPer
	'Lila Pedigo'	SLdr
	LILAC DUFTHECKE ('Rhodunter 149'PBR) (Inkarho)	LMaj LMil
	'Lilac Time' (EA)	SLdr
	'Lilactina'	SLdr
	'Liliatum' (EA) **new**	LMil
	'Lily Marleen' (EA)	CTri
	'Linda' ♀H5	CMac EPfP GGGa LMil LSRN MAsh
	lindleyi	CBcs LRHS MPkF XSte
	- 'Dame Edith Sitwell'	LMil
	'Linearifolium'	see *R. stenopetalum* 'Linearifolium'
	'Lingot d'Or' (A)	MPkF SGsty XSte
	Lionel's Triumph Group	LMil
	'Little Beauty' (EA)	SLdr
	'Little Ben'	EGrI
	'Little Favourite' (EA)	EGrI
	'Loch Awe'	GGGa LMil
	'Loch Earn'	GGGa
	'Loch Faskally'	GGGa
§	(Lodauric Group) 'Lodauric Iceberg'	LMil
	'Lodbrit'	LMil
	Loderi Group	SLdr
	- 'Loderi Fairy Queen'	SLdr
	- 'Loderi Game Chick'	LMil SLdr
	- 'Loderi Georgette'	SLdr
	- 'Loderi Helen'	LMil SLdr
	- 'Loderi Julie'	LMil
§	- 'Loderi King George' ♀H5	CAco CBcs GGGa GKin LMil LRHS SLdr SSta XSte
	- 'Loderi Patience'	SLdr
	- 'Loderi Pink Coral'	LMil SLdr
	- 'Loderi Pink Diamond' ♀H5	CBcs LMil SLdr XSte
	- 'Loderi Pink Topaz'	LMil SLdr
	- 'Loderi Pretty Polly'	SLdr
	- 'Loderi Princess Marina'	SLdr
	- 'Loderi Sir Edmund'	LMil SLdr
	- 'Loderi Sir Joseph Hooker'	SLdr
	- 'Loderi Titan'	SLdr SSta
	- 'Loderi Venus' ♀H5	LMil SLdr SSta
	- 'Loderi White Diamond'	SLdr
	'Loder's White' ♀H5	CMac LMil SSta
	longipes	LMil MHid
	- EGM 336	LMil
	- var. ***chienianum***	LMil MHid
	'Lord Roberts' ♀H6	CAco CBcs CDoC CMac CSBt CTri EGrI ELan LCro LMil MAsh MGos NHol NLar SCob SLdr SLim SPer SSta
	'Louisa' (EA)	MAsh
	'Louise Dowdle' (Glenn Dale) (EA)	LMil SLdr
	'Lovely William'	CMac LMil LRHS SLdr
	'Lucinda'	LMil
	'Lucy Lou'	GGGa
	ludlowii	GGGa
	'Lugano'	MGos
	'Lumina'	CRos NLar
	luteiflorum	MHid
	lutescens	CBcs CMac GKev LMil SEdd SLdr
	- 'Bagshot Sands' ♀H4	GGGa LMil
	- 'Exbury'	CExl LMil
	luteum (A)	Widely available
	- 'Golden Comet' (A)	GGGa
*	'Mac Ovata'	CMac

	macabeanum ♀H4	CBcs GGGa GKev GKin IDee IKel LMil LRHS MHid NLar SSta
	- NAPE 052	GGGa
	macabeanum × wardii	GGGa
	macranthum	see *R. indicum* 'Macranthum'
	macrophyllum B&SWJ 9561	WCru
	macrosmithii	see *R. argipeplum*
	'Macrostemon' (EA)	XSte
	'Madame Ad. van Hecke' (EA)	CTri GKin LMil MAsh SLim
	'Madame Albert van Hecke' (EA)	CDoC LCro NLar SLdr
	'Madame de Bruin'	SLdr
	'Madame Galle'	CDoC NLar
	'Madame Masson' ♀H6	CAco CDoC CTri ELan EPfP IDee LCro LMil LRHS LSRN MAsh MGos MPri NLar SCob SGsty SPer SSta WFar XSte
	maddenii	CBcs LMil SAko
§	- subsp. ***crassum***	CBcs CExl GGGa LMil LRHS WPGP
§	- subsp. ***maddenii*** Polyandrum Group	CBcs
	'Magic Flute' (EA)	LRHS MAsh NRHS SCoo
I	'Magic Flute' (V)	LMil SCoo
	'Mai-ogi' (EA)	SAko
	'Maischnee' (EA)	GGGa
	'Maja' (G)	SSta
§	***makinoi*** ♀H5	LMil SSta XSte
	- 'Fuju-kaku-no-matsu'	NLar
	'Makiyak'	NLar
	mallotum	GGGa LMil
	'Manda Sue'	NLar
	'Mandarin Lights' (A)	MPkF NLar
	'Manderley'	LMil
	'Maraschino' (EA)	SAko
	'Marcus Agius' **new**	LMil
	'Mardi Gras'	MGos NLar
	'Maria Elena' (EA/d)	CDoC CRos MGos
	'Maricee'	LMil
	'Marie Curie'	LMil
	'Marie Fortie'	CDoC CKel CWnw LRHS MGos NLar
	'Marie Hoffman'	LMil
	'Marie-Louise Agius' **new**	LMil
	'Marilee' (EA)	EPfP LRHS MAsh SLdr
	'Marinja' (EA)	LMil
	'Marinus Koster'	SSta
	'Markeeta's Prize' ♀H4	CAco CDoC CTsd ELan EPfP GGGa LMil LRHS MAsh MGos MPri NLar SGsty SLdr SLim XSte
	'Marmot' (EA)	GEdr
	'Maroon Sappho' **new**	LMil
	'Marsalla'	SAko
	'Martha Isaacson' (Ad)	LMil SLdr
	'Martha Wright'	CDoC GGGa MAsh MPri XSte
	'Maruschka' (EA) ♀H5	CDoC EPfP GGGa LMil LRHS MAsh MGos NLar SAko SCoo
	'Mary Desby' (EA)	CEnd
	'Mary Helen' (Glenn Dale) (EA)	CDoC LMil LRHS MAsh MGos NLar NRHS SCoo SLdr SLim SPer
	'Mary Poppins' (A)	CSBt EGrI GKin LMil LSRN MGos MPkF SCoo SLim XSte
	(Matador Group) 'Matador'	LMil SLdr
	'Mathie' (A)	SSta
	maximum	GKev MHid
	'Maxine Childers'	LRHS
§	'Maxwellii' (EA)	CMac SLdr
	May Day Group	CBcs
	- 'May Day' ♀H5	CMac SLdr
	'Mayor Johnstone'	CTri EPfP MAsh MPri
	'Mécène' (R)	XSte
	meddianum	LMil
	var. ***atrokermesinum*** F 2649	
	'Megan' (EA)	LSRN SLdr
	megaphyllum	see *R. basilicum*
	megeratum KR 9426	LMil
	- 'Bodnant'	NWad WAbe
	mekongense var. ***mekongense*** Rubroluteum Group	see *R. viridescens* Rubroluteum Group
	- - Viridescens Group	see *R. viridescens*
	'Melford Lemon'	see *R.* 'Ilam Melford Lemon'
	'Melle'PBR	MPkF
	'Melville'	XSte
	'Merganser' ♀H4	GGGa LMil SLdr
	'Merlin' (Glenn Dale) (EA)	LMil
	METALLICA	see *R.* 'Hachmann's Metallica'
	metternichii var. ***pentamerum***	see *R. degronianum* subsp. *degronianum*
	'Mi Amor'	LMil
	'Michael's Pride'	CBcs
	micranthum	LMil LRHS
	microgynum	GGGa MHid
	'Midnight Beauty'	CBcs EPfP LMil LRHS MAsh SAko
	'Midnight Mystique'	SSta
	'Midsummer'	SLdr
	'Midsummer Coral' (A)	LMil LRHS
	'Midsummer Girl' (A)	LMil
	'Midsummer Mermaid' (A)	LMil
	'Midsummer Moon' (A)	LMil LRHS
	'Midsummer Rose' (A)	LMil
	'Midsummer Star' (A)	LMil
	'Midsummer Wedding' (A)	LMil
	'Mikado' (EA)	see *R. kaempferi* 'Mikado'
	'Millennium' (A)	LRHS
	'Millennium Gold'PBR	IDee LMil NLar
	'Milton' (R)	LMil LRHS
	'Mimi' (Kaempferi) (EA)	CMac
	'Ming'	see *R.* 'Ilam Ming'
	'Minnetonka'	CDoC
	minus	CBcs GKev
	- var. ***chapmanii***	CBcs
	- var. ***minus*** (Carolinianum Group) 'Epoch'	LMil
§	- - Punctatum Group	MAsh
	'Moerheim' ♀H5	CBcs LRHS MAsh MPri SCgs SEdd SLim
§	'Moerheim's Pink'	SLdr
	(Mohamet Group) 'Mohamet'	LMil
	'Moidart' (Vs)	LMil
	'Moira Salmon' (EA)	SLdr
	molle 'Arctic Flush'PBR (A)	EGrI
§	- subsp. ***japonicum*** (A)	LMil
	Mollis, orange-flowered (M)	GKin SGsty SRms
	- pink-flowered (M)	GKin SGsty SRms
	- red-flowered (M)	GKin SGsty
	- yellow-flowered (M)	GKin SRms
	'Molly Ann'	EGrI LSRN
	'Molten Gold' (v)	GGGa LMil LRHS MAsh
	'Monsieur Marcel Ménard' ♀H6	CBcs CDoC CKel EPfP IDee LCro LMil LRHS MAsh MGos MPri NLar SCgs SCob SLdr SSta WFar WHlf XSte
	montroseanum	GGGa LMil MHid
	Moonstone Group	CMac LMil
	- 'Moonstone Pink'	SLdr
	- 'Moonstone Yellow'	SLdr
	'Moonwood Ivory' (V)	LRHS XSte
§	'Morgenrot'	CDoC WFar
	morii	GGGa MHid
	'Morning Cloud'	CDoC EPfP LPar LRHS MAsh MGos NHol SCob SLim SSta
	MORNING RED	see *R.* 'Morgenrot'
	'Moser's Maroon'	CBcs CDoC GGGa LSRN SGsty SLdr WFar XSte
	'Mother of Pearl'	SLdr

	Name	Suppliers
	'Mother's Day' (Kurume) (EA) ♀H4	CDoC CKel CMac CRos CSBt CTri CWnw EGrI EPfP GKin LCro LMil LOPS LRHS LSRN MAsh MGos MPri NHol NLar NRHS SCob SLdr SLim SPer SPoG SRms SSta WFar
§	***moulmainense***	CMCN
	'Mount Everest'	LMil SSta
	'Mount Rainier' (A)	LRHS MPkF XSte
	'Mount Saint Helens' (A)	CDoC LMil SLim
	'Mount Seven Star'	see *R. nakaharae* 'Mount Seven Star'
	moupinense	GGGa SLdr
	'Mrs A.T. de la Mare' ♀H6	LMil SSta
	'Mrs Betty Robertson'	CMac GBin
	'Mrs Charles E. Pearson' ♀H6	CBcs CSBt LMil SLdr SSta XSte
	'Mrs Davies Evans'	SSta
	'Mrs Emil Hager' (EA)	SLdr
	'Mrs G.W. Leak'	CSBt XSte
	'Mrs J.G. Millais'	LMil
	'Mrs James Horlick'	CAco
	'Mrs T.H. Lowinsky' ♀H6	CBcs CDoC CMac GGGa GKin LMil LRHS MGos NLar SCob SLdr SLim
§	× ***mucronatum*** (EA)	LRHS
	mucronulatum B&SWJ 786	WCru
	- B&SWJ 8657	WCru
	- var. ***albiflorum***	LMil SLdr
	'Muffet' (EA)	SLdr
	'Mulroy Cream'	LMil
	'Mum'	LMil
	'Muncaster Mist'	LMil
	'Nabucco' (A)	CBcs CRos EGrI LRHS MGos MMuc MPkF NLar SPer
	nakaharae (EA) ♀H5	SLdr
	- 'Mariko' (EA)	EPot WThu
§	- 'Mount Seven Star' (EA) ♀H5	LMil SLdr WThu
§	- orange-flowered (EA)	LMil LRHS MAsh NRHS SLdr XSte
	- pink-flowered (EA)	SLdr XSte
	'Nakahari Orange'	see *R. nakaharae* orange-flowered
	nakotiltum	MHid
	'Nancy Evans' ♀H5	CDoC CKel CRos CWnw EPfP GGGa GKin LMil LPar LRHS LSRN MAsh MGos MPri NLar SCob SLdr SLim SSta
	'Nani-wagata' (EA)	CSBt CTsd EGrI
	'Nanki Poo' (EA)	SLdr
	(Naomi Group) 'Exbury Naomi'	LMil
	- 'Naomi Nautilus'	LMil
	- 'Naomi Stella Maris'	LMil
	'Narcissiflorum' (G/d) ♀H6	CBcs EGrI GKin LMil LRHS MPkF XSte
	'Naselle'	LMil
	NEGLIGÉ ('Hachneg'[PBR]) (EA)	MPkF XSte
	neriiflorum	LMil
	- CN&W 906	LMil
	- subsp. ***neriiflorum***	MHid
§	- subsp. ***phaedropum***	LMil MHid
	- - KR 9308	LMil
	'Newcomb's Sweetheart'	LMil
	'Niagara' (Glenn Dale) (EA) ♀H5	CMac LMil SLdr
	'Niamh' (A)	LMil
	'Nicholas de Rothschild' (A/d)	LMil
	'Nico' (EA)	CMac LMil LRHS MAsh SCoo
	'Night Sky' ♀H5	CDoC CRos EPfP GGGa GKev LMil LRHS MAsh MGos NLar SLdr
	nilagiricum	see *R. arboreum* subsp. *nilagiricum*
	'Nishiki' (EA)	CMac
	nitens	see *R. calostrotum* subsp. *riparium* Nitens Group

	Name	Suppliers
	nitidulum var. ***omeiense***	WThu
§	***nivale*** subsp. ***nivale***	ITim NWad
	niveum ♀H5	GGGa LMil LRHS MHid
	- B&SWJ 2611	WCru
	- B&SWJ 2659	WCru
	- B&SWJ 2675	WCru
	Nobleanum Group	GGGa LMil SSta
	- 'Nobleanum Coccineum'	CMac LMil
	- 'Nobleanum Venustum'	LMil SSta
	Nobleanum Album Group	CMac GGGa LMil
	'Nofretete'	LMil
	(Norderney Group) 'Oudijk's Sensation'	MAsh
	'Nordlicht' (EA)	SLdr
	'Northern Hi-Lights' (A)	CBcs CDoC CRos GKin LMil LRHS MGos MPkF NLar SCob SLim SPer XSte
	'Nova Zembla'	CAco CBcs CDoC CTri EGrI EPfP IDee LCro LMil LOPS LPar LRHS MAsh MGos SCob SGsty SLim SPer SSta XSte
	'Nuccio's Blue Moon' (EA)	LMil SLdr
	'Nuccio's Wild Cherry' (EA)	SWeb
	nudiflorum	see *R. periclymenoides*
	nuttallii	LMil
	'Oban'	EPot GEdr ITim
	Obtusum Group (EA)	SLdr
	- 'Amoenum' (EA/d)	CBcs CMac CSBt EGrI LMil SLdr XSte
	- 'Amoenum Coccineum' (EA/d)	SLdr SSta
§	- 'Hinomayo' (EA) ♀H5	CBcs CMac CTri EPfP GKin LMil SCob SLdr XSte
	occidentale (A)	GKin LMil LRHS SLdr
	- SIN 1830	GGGa
	ochraceum ♀H5	GGGa LMil
	- C&H 7042	LMil
	'Odee Wright'	CAco EPfP MAsh
	'Oi-no-mezame' (Kurume) (EA)	SLdr
	'Old Port'	LMil SCob
	oldhamii B&SWJ 3742 (EA)	WCru
	'Olga' ♀H5	LMil SSta XSte
	'Olivia'	LMil
	'Opossum' (EA)	GGGa
	ORAKEL	see *R.* 'Hachmann's Orakel'
	'Orange Beauty' (Kaempferi) (EA)	CBcs EGrI ILea MAsh SLdr SRms
	'Orange Flirt'	LMil
	'Orange King' (EA) ♀H5	CDoC EPfP LMil LRHS MGos NLar SLdr SPoG
	'Orangeade' (K)	LRHS MPkF XSte
	orbiculare ♀H5	GGGa LMil
§	- subsp. ***cardiobasis***	LMil
	- subsp. ***orbiculare***	MHid
	'Orchid Lights'	MAsh
	'Oregon' (EA)	SLdr
	Oregonia Group	LMil
	oreodoxa	LMil
§	- var. ***fargesii*** ♀H5	GGGa LMil MHid
	- var. ***oreodoxa***	LMil MHid
	oreotrephes ♀H5	LMil MHid
	- 'Pentland'	GGGa IDee LMil NLar
	'Orpheus' (EA)	XSte
	'Osaraku Seedling' (EA)	LRHS
	'Osmar' ♀H5	GGGa
	'Ostara'	CBcs
	pachysanthum ♀H5	GGGa GKin LMil SLdr
	- 'Crosswater'	IDee LMil LRHS NLar
	- 'Little White Dane'	LMil
	pachytrichum	GGGa
	- var. ***pachytrichum***	MHid
	- - 'Sesame'	LMil

	'Palestrina' (Vuykiana) (EA) ♀H5	CBcs CMac CSBt EPfP GKin MPkF SCob SGsty SLdr SPer SSta
	paludosum	see *R. nivale* subsp. *nivale*
	'Pancake'	CMac
	'Panda' (EA) ♀H5	CSBt EDir EPfP EPot GEdr GGGa LMil LRHS MAsh SSta
	'Parkfeuer' (A) ♀H6	GGGa SGsty
	parmulatum	LMil
	- KW 5876	LMil
	- 'Ocelot'	GGGa LMil
	'Patricia's Day'	LMil
	'Patty Bee' ♀H5	CBcs CDoC CTri EGrI EPfP EPot GEdr GGGa IDee LMil LRHS MAsh MGos MPri NLar SCob SLim SSta XSte
	'Pavlova' (A)	LMil
	'Pearce's American Beauty'	CAco
	'Peep-bo' (EA)	SLdr
	'Peeping Tom'	NHol SSta
	'Peggy'	LMil
	'Pemakofairy'	WThu
	pendulum	GGGa MHid
	'Penheale Blue' ♀H5	GKev GKin LMil MAsh
	'Penjerrick'	GGGa
	pennivenium	see *R. tanastylum* var. *pennivenium*
	'Pennsylvania' (Vs)	LRHS
	'Penny Tomlin'	SSta
	'Peppermint Candy'	LMil
	'Peppina'	LMil
	'Percy Wiseman' ♀H5	CBcs CDoC CSBt EPfP GGGa GKin LCro LMil LOPS LPar LRHS MAsh MGos NLar SCob SEdd SGsty SLdr SLim SSta WFar XSte
§	***periclymenoides*** (A)	LMil
	'Persil' (K) ♀H6	CBcs CSBt CTri CWnw EGrI ELan EPfP GGGa GKin IDee LCro LMil LRHS MAsh MPri NHol NLar SCob SCoo SLdr SSta WFar
	'Peter Alan'	NLar
	'Peter Bee'	LMil LRHS
	'Peter Gable' (EA)	SLdr
	'Peter John Mezitt'	see *R.* (PJM Group) 'Peter John Mezitt'
	'Peter Koster' (M)	MPkF XSte
	'Peter Koster' (hybrid)	GKin
	petrocharis	GGGa
	PETTICOAT ('Hachpett') (EA)	LMil
	'Pfauenauge'	GGGa NLar
	phaedropum	see *R. neriiflorum* subsp. *phaedropum*
	phaeochrysum	GKev
	- var. ***agglutinatum***	GKev
	- 'Glossy Dane'	LMil
	- var. ***phaeochrysum***	MHid
	'Phalarope'	EGrI GEdr
	'Phyllis Korn'	LMil LRHS NLar
	'Picotee' (EA)	SCgs
§	***piercei***	GGGa LMil
	pingianum	EPfP GGGa
	- EGM 304	LMil
	'Pink and Sweet' (A)	LRHS
	'Pink Bride'	SLdr
	'Pink Cameo'	CAco
	'Pink Cherub' ♀H6	LMil MAsh NLar
I	'Pink Delight' (K)	GKin
	'Pink Drift'	GEdr LMil
	'Pink Gin'	LMil
	'Pink Pancake' (EA) ♀H4	CBcs EPfP LMil LRHS MAsh MPri SLdr
	'Pink Pearl' (EA)	see *R.* 'Azuma-kagami'
	'Pink Pearl' (hybrid) ♀H4	CBcs CSBt CTri GGGa LMil MAsh SLdr SSta
	'Pink Pebble' ♀H5	CExl MAsh
	'Pink Perfection'	CMac SLdr
	'Pink Polar Bear'	LMil
	'Pink Purple Dream'	LRHS
	'Pink Spider'PBR (EA)	LCro LMil LRHS SCoo
	'Pintail'	LMil LRHS MAsh
	'Pippa' (EA)	CMac
§	(PJM Group) 'Peter John Mezitt'	NLar
	platypodum	LMil
	- CGG 14005	GGGa
	'Pleasant White' (EA)	CDoC CKel CWnw LCro LMil LOPS NLar SCob
	'Plover'	LRHS XSte
	pocophorum var. ***pocophorum***	MHid
	'Polar Bear' (EA)	CAco CSBt SLdr
	Polar Bear Group	LMil
	- 'Polar Bear'	GKin LMil
	'Polaris'	see *R.* 'Hachmann's Polaris'
	'Polaris' (EA)	LRHS
	'Polarnacht'	CBcs CRos LCro LMil MAsh NLar
	poluninii KR 8231	LMil
	polyandrum	see *R. maddenii* subsp. *maddenii* Polyandrum Group
	polylepis	MHid
	'Polyroy'	GGGa
	ponticum	CAco CKel CMac CTri NHol WFar XSte
	- 'Filigran'	LMil
§	- 'Variegatum' (v)	CAco CMac EPfP IDee MAsh MGos MPri NLar SLdr SPer SPoG SRms XSte
	'Praecox' ♀H6	CBcs CDoC GBin GGGa GKin LCro LMil LOPS LRHS MAsh MGos MPri NLar SCgs SLdr SLim SPoG
	praestans	GKin LMil
	prattii	GGGa MHid
	'President Roosevelt' (v)	CMac CSBt EPfP GKin LMil MAsh MPri SCob SLdr SPoG SSta
	'Pridenjoy'	LMil
	primuliflorum 'Doker-La'	GGGa LMil WAbe
	'Princess Alice'	CBcs SLdr
	'Princess Anne' ♀H6	CBcs CDoC CMac CRos LCro LMil LOPS MAsh MGos NHpl NLar SCob SEdd SLdr SLim SPer SPoG SSta
	'Princess Margaret of Windsor' (K)	LMil
	principis	LMil
	- 'Lost Horizon'	LMil
§	- Vellereum Group	MHid
	prinophyllum (A)	GGGa LMil
	- 'Philip Holmes'	LMil
	'Prins Bernhard' (EA)	SLdr
	'Prinses Juliana' (Vuykiana) (EA)	SLdr
	'Prinses Máxima'	IDee LMil
	pronum R.B. Cooke form	GGGa
	- Towercourt form	GGGa
	proteoides	GGGa LMil
	prunifolium (A)	LMil
	- 'August Fire' (A)	LMil
	- 'Ted's Red' (A)	LMil
	pseudochrysanthum ♀H6	GGGa LMil
	- dwarf RWJ 9807	WCru
	'Ptarmigan' ♀H6	GGGa GKev IDee LMil MAsh WThu
	pubescens	GKev
§	'Pucella' (G)	XSte
	'Pulchrum Maxwellii'	see *R.* 'Maxwellii'
	pumilum	WAbe WThu
	punctatum	see *R. minus* var. *minus* Punctatum Group
	'Purple Cushion' (EA)	EPfP LMil LRHS MAsh MPri NRHS

'Purple Gem'	CDoC CRos MGos NLar SCob
'Purple Passion'PBR	CDoC LMil LRHS LSRN SLdr
'Purple Queen' (EA/d)	MAsh
'Purple Splendor' (Gable) (EA)	CMac SGsty SLdr
'Purple Splendour'	CBcs CSBt IDee LMil MGos SCob SSta
'Purple Triumph' (Vuykiana) (EA) ♀H5	LMil
'Purpureum Grandiflorum'	LMil
'Purpurtraum' (EA) ♀H5	LMil
qiaojiaense NN 0903	LMil
'Quail'	GGGa
'Queen Alice'	CDoC
'Queen Elizabeth II'	LMil LRHS
QUEEN EMMA	see *R.* 'Koningin Emma'
'Queen Mary'	SSta
QUEEN WILHELMINA	see *R.* 'Koningin Wilhelmina'
'Quiet Thoughts'	LRHS
quinquefolium (A)	LMil LRHS MHid SLdr
RABATZ ('Hachraba')	GGGa SAko
racemosum ♀H6	CBcs GKev LMil MHid
- BWJ 7811	WCru
- 'Rock Rose' ♀H5	IDee LMil SLdr
'Racoon' (EA)	GGGa LMil
radicans	see *R. calostrotum* subsp. *keleticum* Radicans Group
'Ramapo' ♀H6	CDoC GGGa IDee LMil LRHS MAsh MGos NRHS SCob SLdr SLim SPer
ramsdenianum	MHid
'Razorbill' ♀H5	CDoC GGGa GKin LMil NLar SLim
recurvoides	IDee LMil LRHS NLar SLdr
recurvum	see *R. roxieanum* var. *roxieanum*
Red Admiral Group	LMil
'Red and Gold'	EPfP GGGa LMil LRHS MAsh MPri
'Red Dawn'	LRHS NRHS
'Red Delicious'	LMil SLdr
RED DEVIL ('Hort18'PBR) **new**	LCro
'Red Diamond'	see *R.* Diamant Group red-flowered
'Red Heart'	LMil
'Red Jack'	CKel CWnw LCro MAsh SPoG SSta WFar
'Red Pimpernel' (EA)	SLdr
'Red Wood'	GGGa
'Redwing'	see *R.* 'Redwings'
'Redwings' (EA)	SLdr
'Reich's Schneewittchen'	CKel
Remo Group	CMac
'Rennie' (A)	MMuc
'Renoir' ♀H5	CSBt LMil
reticulatum (A)	CBcs IDee LMil LRHS
'Reuthe's Purple'	WThu
'Rêve d'Amour' (Vs)	SSta
'Rex' (EA)	MAsh SGsty
rex ♀H5	GGGa GKev GKin IDee LMil
- EGM 295	LMil
§ - subsp. ***fictolacteum*** ♀H5	GGGa GKin LMil LRHS MHid SLdr
- subsp. ***rex*** ♀H5	MHid
'Rexima'	LMil
'Ria Hardijzer' (Ad)	LMil
'Ribbon Candy' (A)	LRHS MPkF
rigidum	GGGa
- 'Album'	LMil
'Ring of Fire'	LMil LRHS MPkF XSte
riparioides	LMil
ririei	GGGa LMil
'Robert Croux'	SLdr
'Robert Seleger'	EPfP GKin IDee LMil MAsh NLar
'Robin Hill Gillie' (EA)	SLdr
'Rocket'	CAco CDoC LPar LRHS MAsh MGos NLar SLim SPoG
'Roehr's Peggy Ann' (EA)	MPkF XSte
'Rokoko'	see *R.* 'Hachmann's Rokoko'
(Romany Chai Group) 'Romany Chai'	XSte
'Rosa' (EA)	CDoC
Rosalind Group	CMac
- 'Rosalind'	LMil WFar
'Rosalinda' (EA)	SLdr
'Rosata' (Vs) ♀H5	SSta
'Rose Bud'	CBcs CSBt CTri WThu
'Rose Glow' (A)	SSta
'Rose Greely' (Gable) (EA) ♀H5	CRos SCoo SLim SPer
'Rose Haze' (Vs)	SSta
'Rose Marie'	XSte
'Rosebud' (EA/d)	CMac SLdr SSta SWeb
'Rosemary Hyde' (EA)	SLdr
roseum	see *R. canescens*
'Roseum Elegans'	CAco CDoC LCro LMaj LOPS LPar LRHS MAsh SCob SGsty SLim
'Rosevallon'	LMil MHid
ROSINETTA ('Hachrosi') (EA)	LMil
'Rosy Fire' (A)	LMil
rothschildii	GGGa LMil MHid
roxieanum	GGGa LMil
- var. ***oreonastes*** ♀H5	GGGa LMil
§ - var. ***roxieanum***	MHid
'Royal Command' (K)	CTri EPfP GKin LMil LRHS
'Royal Lodge' (K)	LRHS MPkF XSte
'Royal Windsor'	LMil
'Roza Stevenson'	SLdr
'Rubicon'	SLdr
rubiginosum ♀H6	GGGa LMil
- var. ***rubiginosum***	MHid
rubroluteum	see *R. viridescens* Rubroluteum Group
RUBY WEDDING	see *R.* 'Firestorm'
rude	see *R. glischrum* subsp. *rude*
§ ***rupicola*** var. ***chryseum***	GKev
russatum ♀H6	LMil SLdr
- blue-black-flowered	LMil
- 'Purple Pillow'	SCob
Russautinii Group	SLdr
'Rusty Dane'	LMil
'Rwain'	NLar XSte
'Ryde Heron' (EA)	SLdr
'Sabina' (EA)	SLdr
'Sacko'	CDoC LMil MAsh NLar SLim
'Saffron Queen'	CBcs CTsd LMil LRHS XSte
'Saint Kew'	SLdr
'Saint Merryn' ♀H5	CBcs EGrI
'Saint Minver'	LMil
'Saint Tudy'	SLdr
'Salmon Sander' (EA)	SLdr
'Salmon's Leap' (EA/v)	CMac CSBt LMil LRHS MAsh MPri SCoo SSta
saluenense	LMil SLdr WThu
'Samuel Taylor Coleridge' (M)	GKin
sanguineum	LMil
§ - subsp. ***didymum***	GGGa SLdr
- subsp. ***sanguineum*** var. ***cloiophorum***	LMil
- - - R 10922 **new**	LMil
- - var. ***didymoides*** **new**	LMil
- - - R 10903 **new**	LMil
- - - R 15638 **new**	LMil
- - var. ***haemaleum***	GGGa LMil
- - var. ***sanguineum*** F 25521	LMil
'Santa Maria' (EA) ♀H5	CDoC CRos GMcL LMil NLar SCob SCoo SPoG SSta
'Sapphire'	GMcL

'Sappho'	CAco CMac GGGa GKin LMil SCob SLdr SSta
sargentianum	WAbe WThu
(Sarled Group) 'Sarled' 🏆H5	LMil
'Sasonade'	LMil
'Satan' (K) 🏆H6	IDee LMil LRHS MGos MPri NLar SCob SSta WFar
Satsuki Group (EA)	SRms SWeb
- 'Gumpo Pink' (EA)	SLdr
- 'Gumpo Pink & White' (EA)	SLdr
- 'Gumpo White' (EA)	LRHS MAsh NRHS SPoG
'Saturnus' (M)	EGrl GKin
saxifragoides (V)	LRHS
'Saxon Blush' PBR (v)	LRHS XSte
§ ***scabrifolium*** var. ***spiciferum***	CMac SLdr
'Scarlet Wonder' 🏆H6	CBcs CDoC CRos EGrl EPfP GKev GKin LCro LMil LRHS MAsh MGos MPri NHpl NLar SCob SEdd WFar
Scarlett O'Hara Group	LMil
schistocalyx	LMil
- F 17637 **new**	LMil
schlippenbachii (A) 🏆H6	CBcs CMCN GGGa IDee LMil LRHS SLdr
'Schneekrone' 🏆H6	LMil
SCHNEEPERLE ('Hachschnee') (EA) 🏆H6	LMil LRHS NRHS
'Scintillation' 🏆H6	CDoC CRos ELan LMil LPar MAsh MGos MMuc NLar SCob SLdr SPer
scopulorum	SLdr
'Scout' (EA)	LMil MAsh
scyphocalyx	see *R. dichroanthum* subsp. *scyphocalyx*
'Seaview Sunset'	GGGa MGos
seinghkuense	GGGa LMil
- CCH&H 8106	LMil
§ ***selense*** subsp. ***dasycladum***	MHid
semnoides	LMil
'Sennocke'	LMil LRHS
'September Red'	LMil LRHS
'September Song' 🏆H4	GGGa LMil NHol
'Septembercharm'	WHlf
serotinum	GGGa LMil MHid
serpyllifolium var. ***albiflorum*** (A)	LMil
'Shamrock' 🏆H6	CDoC CTsd EGrl EPfP GEdr GKev LCro LRHS MAsh MGos NLar SCob SLim SPoG WFar
'Sheila' (EA)	CSBt MAsh MPri
'Shelley' (EA)	LMil
'Shiko' (EA)	MAsh
'Shiko Lavender' (A)	LMil SPoG
Shilsonii Group	LMil
'Shin-sekai' (Kurume) (EA/d)	SLdr
sikangense var. ***exquisitum***	MHid
- var. ***sikangense***	MHid
'Silbervelours'	LMil
§ 'Silberwolke' 🏆H6	EPfP LMil LRHS MAsh WFar XSte
SILVER CLOUD	see *R.* 'Silberwolke'
'Silver Edge'	see *R. ponticum* 'Variegatum'
'Silver Glow' (EA)	CMac
'Silver Jubilee' 🏆H4	IDee LMil
'Silver Queen' (EA)	CKel SPoG XSte
'Silver Sixpence'	EPfP LRHS LSRN SLdr
'Silver Skies'	LMil
'Silver Slipper' (K) 🏆H5	CBcs GKin LCro LMil NHol SSta WFar
'Silver Sword' (EA/v)	CKel SPoG WHlf
'Silvester' (Kurume) (EA)	CTri GMcL LMil LRHS MAsh SCoo SLdr
simsii (EA)	CMac SLdr
sinofalconeri	GGGa GKev LMil MHid
- KR 7342	LMil
- SEH 229	LMil
sinogrande 🏆H4	GGGa GKin IDee LMil LRHS NLar
- KR 4027	LMil
§ 'Sir Charles Butler'	LMil
'Sir Charles Lemon' 🏆H4	CBcs GGGa LMil LRHS MAsh XSte
'Sir Robert' (EA)	CKel EPfP LRHS MAsh
'Sleeping Beauty'	WAbe
'Sleepy'	CBcs MAsh NHol
smirnowii	LMil LRHS MHid
§ Smithii Group	CBcs XSte
smithii	see *R. argipeplum*
'Sneezy' 🏆H5	CBcs CRos EPfP LMaj LMil LRHS MAsh MGos SGsty SLdr SLim SSta XSte
'Snipe'	CDoC CTri CTsd LMil LRHS MAsh MGos NLar NRHS SLdr SLim SPer WThu
'Snow Crown' (*lindleyi* hybrid)	MAsh
'Snow Hill' (EA) 🏆H5	CEnd LMil
'Snow Lady'	CBcs CDoC EGrl EPfP GEdr GKin MAsh SLdr
'Snow Pearl'	CRos EPfP MAsh MPri SCoo
Snow Queen Group	LMil
- 'Snow Queen'	LMil
'Snowbird' (A)	CBcs ELan
'Snowflake' (EA/d)	see *R.* 'Kure-no-yuki'
'Snowwhite' (EA)	CDoC MGos
'Soft Lights' (A/d)	LMil
'Soir de Paris' (Vs) 🏆H6	CBcs CEnd CSBt GGGa GKin LMil NHol SSta WFar
'Solidarity'	CAco CBcs SLdr SSta
'Sonata'	GGGa
'Sonatine'	LMil
'Songbird'	LMil SLdr
sororium (V)	LMil
- KR 3085	LMil
souliei	LMil LRHS
'Souvenir de D.A. Koster'	SLdr
'Souvenir of Anthony Waterer'	SSta
'Souvenir of W.C. Slocock'	MAsh NLar
'Sparkler' (A)	LRHS
'Special Dane'	LMil LRHS
speciosum	see *R. flammeum*
'Spek's Orange' (M)	GKin SPer
sphaeranthum	see *R. trichostomum*
sphaeroblastum	MHid
- 'Super Dane'	LMil
spiciferum	see *R. scabrifolium* var. *spiciferum*
spilotum	MHid
'Spitfire'	NHol SSta
'Spring Pearl'	see *R.* 'Moerheim's Pink'
'Spring Rose'	SLdr
'Spring Sunshine'	LMil
'Squirrel' (EA) 🏆H5	CDoC GEdr GGGa GKin GMcL LMil MAsh NLar SCoo SLdr SLim SPoG
'Stadt Essen'	LMil SLdr
§ 'Stanway'	LMil
'Starbright Champagne'	MAsh SSta
'Statuette'	SAko
stenaulum	see *R. moulmainense*
§ ***stenopetalum***	CBcs CMac IDee LMil LRHS SLdr
'Linearifolium' (EA)	SMad XSte
stenophyllum	see *R. makinoi*
'Sternzauber' **new**	MGos
stewartianum	LMil MHid
'Stewartstonian' (EA)	CMac LCro LOPS
'Stoat' (EA)	NLar
'Stopham Girl' (A)	LMil
'Stopham Joy' (A)	LMil LRHS
'Stopham Lad' (A)	LMil

'Strategist'	SLdr
'Strawberry Cream'	EPfP LMil LRHS
'Strawberry Ice' (K) ♀H6	CBcs CSBt EGrI ELan GGGa GKin MMrt SCob SPer
'Strawberry Sundae'	SLdr
strigillosum	GGGa
suberosum	see *R. yunnanense* Suberosum Group
'Suga-no-ito' (Kurume) (EA)	SLdr
sulfureum	MHid
'Summer Blaze' (A)	SLdr
'Summer Dawn'	LMil
'Summer Fragrance' (A) ♀H6	LMil MPkF SSta
'Summer Sorbet'	LMil
'Summer Sunshine' (A)	LMil
'Sun Fire'	EGrI LMil LRHS MHtn NLar SCgs
'Sun Star' (EA)	GGGa LMil
'Sunte Nectarine' (K) ♀H6	CRos GKin NLar
suoilenhense	CMCN GGGa LMil MHid
'Surprise' ambig. (EA)	CTri EGrI SLdr
'Surrey Heath'	CBcs CDoC EPfP LMil LPar LRHS MGos SCob SLdr SLim SPer
'Susan' (EA)	IDee NLar SSta
'Susan' J.C.Williams	LMil
'Susannah Hill' (EA)	SLdr
sutchuenense	GGGa LMil
'Swansong' (EA)	CMac
'Swift' ♀H4	EPfP GEdr GGGa IDee LMil LRHS MAsh NRHS SLdr
'T.S. Black' (EA)	SLdr
'Tahitian Dawn'	LRHS XSte
'Talavera'	LMil
taliense	LMil
- SBEC 0350	GGGa
- 'Honigduft'	LMil LRHS
- 'Woolly Dane'	LMil
Tally Ho Group	LMil
'Tamanini' (EA)	XSte
'Tama-no-utena' (EA)	SLdr
§ ***tanastylum*** var. ***pennivenium***	LMil
'Tangerine'	see *R.* (Fabia Group) 'Fabia Tangerine'
'Tapestry' PBR	LMil
'Taragona'	MGos XSte
tatsienense	GKev
'Taurus' ♀H5	CBcs EPfP GKin IDee LMil LRHS MAsh NLar SAko SLdr
'Ted Millais'	LMil
'Teddy Bear'	EPfP SSta
Temple Belle Group	EGrI SLdr
'Tequila Sunrise'	LRHS
'Terracotta'	LMil LRHS
'Terra-cotta Beauty' (EA)	WThu
(Tessa Group) 'Tessa'	CMac
'Thai Gold' (V)	LRHS
§ 'The Honourable Jean Marie de Montague' ♀H4	CDoC GGGa GKin LMil MAsh MGos SSta
'The Marquis of Lansdowne'	LRHS
'Thomas David' (A)	LMil
thomsonii	GGGa LMil MHid
- B&SWJ 2638	WCru
- WJC 13737	WCru
'Thor'	GGGa
'Tibet'	LMil LRHS
'Tidbit' ♀H3	CMac IDee LMil SLdr
'Tina' (EA)	MPkF
'Tinkerbird'	CBcs CDoC EPfP GGGa IDee LMil LRHS MAsh MGos MPri NLar XSte
'Tinner's Blush'	CBcs
titapuriense	GGGa
'Titian Beauty'	CBcs CDoC CRos CSBt EPfP GGGa LMil LRHS MAsh MGos NRHS SLdr SLim SPer SPoG WFar
'Tit-Willow' (EA)	LMil LRHS MAsh MPri NRHS SCoo SLdr
tomentosum	MGil WThu
'Too Bee'	EGrI GEdr
'Torchlight' (EA) ♀H5	CDoC CRos LMil MGos SCoo SPoG
'Toreador' (EA)	SLdr
'Tornado'	EGrI
(Tortoiseshell Group) 'Champagne' ♀H3	CDoC CSBt LMil MAsh MPri
- 'Tortoiseshell Orange' ♀H3	CBcs CSBt IDee LMil LRHS MGos NLar SCob SGsty SLim SPer SSta XSte
- 'Tortoiseshell Wonder' ♀H3	EPfP LRHS MAsh
'Toucan' (K)	LMil LRHS MPkF XSte
'Tower Beauty' (A)	LMil
'Tower Dainty' (A)	LMil
'Tower Daring' (A)	LMil
'Tower Dexter' (A)	LMil
'Tower Dragon' (A)	LMil
traillianum	LMil
- var. ***dictyotum*** 'Kathmandu'	LMil
- var. ***traillianum***	MHid
'Treasure' (AE)	SGsty
'Tree Creeper'	GGGa GKev LMil
'Trewithen Orange'	SLdr
trichanthum 'Honey Wood'	LMil SLdr
trichocladum	GKev
§ ***trichostomum***	GGGa WAbe
- Ledoides Group	LMil
triflorum	LMil
§ - var. ***bauhiniiflorum***	CMac
- var. ***triflorum***	MHid
'Tri-Lights' (A)	MPkF
'Tromba'	LMil LRHS
'Tropic Glow' (V)	LRHS
'Tropical Salad' (A)	LRHS
'True Blue'	XSte
tsariense	LMil XSte
- var. ***trimoense***	LMil
- - KW 8288	LMil
- var. ***tsariense***	MHid
tubiforme	see *R. glaucophyllum*
'Tuffet' (EA)	LMil SLdr
'Tunis' (K)	EGrI MAsh MPri
'Turnstone'	GGGa
'Umpqua Queen' (K)	XSte
'Unique' (G)	CBcs
'Unique' (*campylocarpum* hybrid)	MAsh SLdr
uvariifolium var. ***griseum***	MHid
- 'Reginald Childs'	LMil
valentinianum	SLdr
'Van'	CDoC LMil LPar LRHS MGos SLim
'Van Nes Sensation'	LMil
Vanessa Group	LMil
- 'Vanessa Pastel' ♀H4	CMac GGGa LMil SLdr SSta
vaseyi (A) ♀H5	GGGa LMil
- 'White Find'	GGGa
- white-flowered (A)	LMil
'Vayo' (EA)	SLdr
§ ***veitchianum*** Cubittii Group	CBcs
vellereum	see *R. principis* Vellereum Group
venator	GGGa
'Venetia' (K)	SSta
vernicosum × ***wardii*** SDR 5026	GKev
§ 'Vernum'	LRHS
'Vernus'	see *R.* 'Vernum'
'Veryan Bay'	LMil

'Victoria Hallett'	LMil
'Vida Brown' (Kurume) (EA/d)	CMac SLdr
'Vinecourt Dream' (M)	GKin NLar SLdr
'Vinecourt Duke' (A/d)	GKin MMuc
'Vineland Dream' (K/d)	GKin
'Vintage Rosé' ♀H5	LMil MMuc SSta
'Violetta' (Glenn Dale) (EA)	SLdr
'Virginia Richards'	LPar LRHS MAsh SLdr
§ ***viridescens***	MHid
- 'Doshong La'	IDee LMil NLar
§ - Rubroluteum Group	SLdr
viscosum (Vs) ♀H6	CBcs CDoC CMac CRos GGGa LMil LRHS MGos NGrs NLar SLdr SPer
- 'Framingham' (A)	LRHS
- 'Grey Leaf' (Vs)	LMil
- f. ***rhodanthum*** (Vs)	LMil
- 'Roseum' (Vs)	LMil
- 'Sea of Stars' (A)	LMil
- 'Weston's Lemon Drop' (A)	LRHS
- 'White Ness' (Vs)	LMil
'Viscount Powerscourt'	SLdr
'Viscy' ♀H5	GKin LMil
'Viscy' (Inkarho)	NLar
'Vladimir Bukovski' (V)	LRHS XSte
§ Volker Group	LMil LRHS NRHS SGsty
'Vollblut'	SSta
'Vulcan' ♀H4	EPfP IDee LMil LRHS MAsh
'Vuyk's Rosyred' (Vuykiana) (EA) ♀H6	CBcs CMac CTri EGrI GKin LMil MAsh NHol NWad SLdr SPoG SRms SWeb WFar
'Vuyk's Scarlet' (Vuykiana) (EA) ♀H6	CBcs CMac CSBt CTri EGrI GKin LRHS MAsh MPri NHol NRHS NWad SCob SGsty SLdr SPer SPlb SSta
W.F.H. Group ♀H3	LMil SLdr
WALKÜRE ('Hachwalk')	LMil LRHS
wallichii	GKev MHid
'Wallowa Red' (A)	CBcs EGrI MMuc XSte
'Wally Miller'	MAsh
'Wanna Bee'	LMil LRHS
wardii	LMil
- L&S 5679	GGGa
- var. ***wardii***	MHid
'Ward's Ruby' (EA)	SLdr
wasonii	LMil LRHS
- f. ***rhododactylum***	LMil
- yellow-flowered	GGGa
'Water Baby' (A)	LMil
'Water Girl' (A)	LMil LRHS
'Water Pixie'	LMil
'Waterfall'	SLdr
'Wee Bee' ♀H5	CBcs CDoC CRos EGrI EPot GEdr GKin GMcL LMil MAsh MGos NLar SLim SSta WThu
'Weinlese'	SAko
'Wendy'	MAsh
'Western Lights' (A)	LRHS MPkF
'Westminster' (O)	LMil
'Weston's Innocence' (A)	MPkF
'Weston's Lollipop' (A)	LRHS MPkF
'What a Dane'	GGGa
'Whidbey Island'	LMil
'Whisperingrose'	EGrI GMcL LMil
'White Brocade'	SSta
§ WHITE DUFTHECKE ('Rhodunter 48'PBR) (Inkarho)	LMil NLar
'White Frills' (EA)	LRHS MPkF
'White Gold'	GGGa
'White Lights' (A) ♀H7	CTri
'White Moon' (EA)	XSte
'White Perfume' (A)	SSta
'White Prince' (EA/d)	MPkF XSte

'White Rosebud' (EA)	MHtn
'White Swan' (hybrid)	LMil
'White Swan' (K)	LRHS
'Whitestone'	SSta
'Whitethroat' (K/d) ♀H6	CBcs LMil LRHS SSta
'Whitney's Orange'	SLdr
'Wigeon'	LMil
wightii	CPla MHid
'Wilgen's Ruby'	CDoC CRos CSBt MGos SCob SLdr SLim SPer XSte
'Willbrit'	CBcs MAsh SLdr
williamsianum ♀H5	EGrI GGGa GMcL LMil
- Caerhays form	CExl
'Willy' (Kaempferi) (EA)	LMil
wiltonii ♀H5	GGGa LMil
'Wine and Roses'PBR	CBcs GGGa IDee LCro LMil LPar LRHS XSte
Winsome Group	CMac MAsh
- 'Winsome' ♀H5	CBcs CDoC EPfP GKin LCro MGos MPri NLar SLdr SSta XSte
'Witchery'	GGGa
'Wombat' (EA) ♀H5	CDoC CTri EPfP GGGa LMil LRHS MAsh MGos MPri NLar SCoo SLdr SPoG
wongii	CMac
'Woodcock'	SLdr
'Wren' ♀H5	EGrI EPot GEdr GGGa GMcL IDee LMil MAsh WThu
xanthocodon	see *R. cinnabarinum* subsp. *xanthocodon*
XXL ('Hort02'PBR)	LCro LRHS MAsh SSta
'Yaku Angel'	LMil SAko
'Yaku Incense'	LMil MAsh
yakushimanum ♀H5	GKin LMil MAsh NHol SCob SSta
- from Exbury	CMac
- FCC form	see *R. yakushimanum* 'Koichiro Wada'
§ - 'Koichiro Wada' ♀H6	CBcs CExl CMac GGGa IDee LMil LRHS SAko SLdr
- 'Mist Maiden'	LMil
'Yamato-no-hikari'	IDee
Yellow Hammer Group	SPer SSta
- 'Yellow Hammer' ♀H5	CAco CBcs CMac GGGa GKin SLdr
'Yellow Petticoats'	SSta
'Yellow Rolls Royce'	LMil
yuefengense	GGGa LMil
yunnanense	GGGa GKev LMil MHid
- 'Openwood' ♀H4	LMil
- pink-flowered	GGGa
- 'Red Throat'	SLdr
- red-blotched	LMil
§ - Suberosum Group	SLdr
- white-flowered	GGGa
zaleucum	LMil SLdr

Rhodohypoxis ✿ (*Hypoxidaceae*)

'1000 Cranes'	WPGP
'Alice'	WFar
'Andromeda'	EWes
'Ann Brazier'	NWad
baurii ♀H3	CAvo CCCN ECha LRHS MAsh NSla SEdd SPoG WAbe WAvo WCav WIce WWke
- 'Alba'	CRos EHyd EWes LRHS NRHS SEdd WFar
- 'Albrighton'	CTri EAri EWes GEdr NHol NHpl NWad WAbe
- 'Apple Blossom'	EWes GKev ITim LBee LEdu NHol NWad WFar WPGP
- 'Badger'	ITim NWad WAbe
- var. ***baurii***	CBor EWes
- 'Bridal Bouquet' (d)	EWes GEdr NHol WFar
- 'Caro'	EWes

- 'Charlotte'	EWes
- 'Coconut Ice'	EWes LEdu WPGP
- var. ***confecta***	CBor CElw EWes GEdr NHol NWad WFar WTyc
- 'Daphne Mary'	EWes
- 'David Scott'	EWes
- 'Dawn'	CPla EAri EWes GEdr GKev WAbe
- 'Douglas'	EWes GEdr GKev LBar LEdu NHol NHpl NWad SEdd WAvo WPGP
- 'Dulcie'	EWes GEdr WAbe
- 'Emily Peel'	EWes GEdr
- 'Eva-Kate'	EWes GEdr
- 'Fred Broome'	CRos EAri EWes GEdr LEdu LRHS NHol NWad WFar
- 'Goliath'	EWes GEdr MNrw WIce
- 'Harlequin'	EWes GEdr NHol NWad
§ - 'Helen'	CBor EPot EWes GEdr GKev LEdu NBwr NHol NHpl NWad WPGP
- 'Jeanette'	EWes
- 'Kitty'	EWes WFar
- 'Lily Jean' (d)	CBor CPla CTri EAri EWes GEdr GKev ITim NHpl NWad SEdd WFar WIce WTyc
- 'Luna'	EWes
- 'Margaret Rose'	EWes NHol
- 'Mars'	CBor CRos EHyd EWes GEdr LEdu LRHS NHol NRHS WFar WPGP
- 'Monique'	EWes
- 'Pearl'	CBor
- 'Perle'	CBor EWes GEdr LRHS NHol NWad
- 'Picta' (v)	EWes LEdu NHol NHpl NWad WAbe
- 'Pink Pearl'	EWes NHol
- pink-flowered	WLov
- var. ***platypetala***	EWes GEdr GKev NHol NHpl NWad WAvo
- var. ***platypetala*** × ***milloides***	NHol NWad
- - - Burtt 6981	EWes
- 'Rebecca'	EWes
- 'Red King'	EWes
- red-flowered	LRHS SPlb WLov
- 'Ruth'	EWes GEdr GKev NHol NWad SDeJ WFar
- 'Susan Garnett-Botfield'	EWes GEdr NHpl
- 'Tetra Pink'	CAby EWes GEdr GKev LBar LRHS NHol NWad WTyc
- 'Tetra Red'	EAri EGrl EWes GEdr NHol NWad SDeJ WFar
- 'The Bride'	EWes GEdr
- white-flowered	WLov
'Bernadette' **new**	GEdr
'Betsy' **new**	CBor
'Betsy Carmine'	CCCN GEdr NWad WFar
'Beverly'^PBR	LCro LOPS
'Bright Eyes' (d)	EWes
'Butterfly Wings'	NWad
'Candy Stripe'	EWes GEdr NWad
'Carina'	EWes
'Caroline'	EWes WFar
'Cathy'	EWes
'Confusion'	EWes LEdu NHol NHpl NWad
'Dainty Dee' (d)	EWes
'Damson'	CBor
deflexa	CBor CRos EAri EWes ITim LEdu LRHS MNrw NHol NHpl NRHS NWad SIvy WAbe WFar WPGP
'Donald Mann'	EShb EWes GEdr GKev LRHS NHol
'Dusky'	EWes GEdr NWad
'E.A. Bowles'	EAri EWes LBar NHpl NSla WFar
'Fire Wings' **new**	GEdr
'Flashing Ruby'	GEdr WFar
'Forge Robies'	EAri EWes

'Garnett'	EWes WFar
'Gemma'	EWes
'Giant Pink'	CBor
'Goya' (d)	NHpl
'Great Scot'	EWes GEdr NHpl NWad WAbe
'Hebron Farm Biscuit'	see *Hypoxis parvula* var. *albiflora* 'Hebron Farm Biscuit'
'Hebron Farm Cerise'	see × *Rhodoxis* 'Hebron Farm Cerise'
'Hebron Farm Pink'	see × *Rhodoxis hybrida* 'Hebron Farm Pink'
'Hinky Pinky'	GEdr NWad
'Holden Rose' (d)	NHol NWad WFar
'Hope' (d)	LBar
'Janey' **new**	GEdr
'Jap Double'	CBor
'Jeffrey' **new**	GEdr
'Jupiter'	CBor GEdr NWad WFar
'Kiwi Joy' (d)	EGrl EWes GEdr NHol NHpl NWad SDeJ WTyc
'Knockdolian Red'	GEdr NHol NWad WFar
'Lisette'	EWes
'Midori'	EPfP EWes GEdr NWad SDys WFar
milloides	CAby CBor CPla CRos EAri EWes GEdr ITim LBee LEdu LRHS NHol NHpl NRHS NWad WFar WIce WPGP
- 'Claret'	CElw CRos EAri ELon EPot EWes GEdr ITim LRHS NHol SDys SEdd SIvy WAbe WFar WTyc
- 'Claudia'	CRos EHyd EPfP LRHS NRHS WFar
- 'Damask'	CRos EWes LRHS SDys
- 'Drakensberg Snow'	EWes GEdr
- giant	WFar
- 'Susan'	EWes
'Mini Garnett' **new**	NWad
'Monty'	EAri EWes GEdr NWad WAbe WFar
'Mystery'	CBor EWes NHol
'Naomi'	EWes
'New Look'	EWes GEdr NHpl NWad SEdd
'Ori Zuru'	GEdr NWad
'Origami'	LEdu
'Pat Lacey'	EWes GEdr
'Pink Glow' **new**	GEdr
'Pink Ice'	GEdr NWad
'Pink Star'	LRHS
'Pinkeen'	CBor EWes WFar
'Pinkie'	SDys WFar
'Pintado'	CBor CRos EAri EHyd EWes GEdr LEdu LRHS NRHS NWad SDys WFar WPGP WTyc
'Pretty in Pink'	LBar
'Raspberry Ice'	GKev NHol NWad WFar
'Rosie Lee'	CBor EWes
'Ruby Giant'	EAri GEdr LRHS WFar
'Shell Pink'	EWes LBar NHol NWad
'Shirazz'	CBor
Slack Top hybrids	NSla
'Snow'	EWes
'Snow White'	EWes NHol
'Starlett'	EWes NHol
'Starry Eyes' (d)	EWes WFar
'Stella'	CCCN EPot EWes GEdr NBwr NHol NHpl NWad SDys WFar
'Summer Pink' **new**	GEdr
'Sunburst'	GEdr NWad
'Tetra Rose'	GEdr
'Tetra White'	see *R. baurii* 'Helen'
thodiana	CBor EWes GEdr LBar NHol NHpl NWad WAbe WFar
TWINKLE STAR MIXED	LRHS
'Two Tone'	EWes
'Venetian'	CBor LBar NHol NWad WFar
'Westacre Picotee'	EWes GEdr

'White Prince'	WFar
'Wild Cherry Blossom'	EWes

Rhodoleia (*Hamamelidaceae*)

championii B&SWJ 11603	WCru
- FMWJ 13155	WCru
- WWJ 11858	WCru
aff. ***henryi*** B&SWJ 11782	WCru
- DJHV 0640	WCru
parvipetala FMWJ 13422	WCru
- WWJ 11866	WCru
- WWJ 11943	WCru

Rhodophiala (*Amaryllidaceae*)

rosea	GKev LAma

Rhodora see *Rhododendron*

Rhodotypos (*Rosaceae*)

kerrioides	see *R. scandens*
§ ***scandens***	CBcs CBod CEme CExl EBee EHyd ELan EPfP ESwi GBin GKev LEdu LRHS MGil MMuc MNrw NHol NLar NQui SBrt SEND SPoG WAvo WCru WJur

× *Rhodoxis* ✿ (*Hypoxidaceae*)

'Abigail'	EWes GEdr WFar WTyc
'Anne Crock'	EWes NWad
'Aurora'	EWes LRHS WFar
'Betsy'	EWes NWad
'Bloodstone'	EWes NHol NWad
FAIRYTALE ('Hil200802'PBR)	IBal MPkF WTyc XSte
'Fanny'	EWes
'Hebron Farm Biscuit'	see *Hypoxis parvula* var. *albiflora* 'Hebron Farm Biscuit'
§ 'Hebron Farm Cerise'	CBor CCCN CElw CRos EHyd EWes GEdr GKev LEdu LRHS NRHS SDys WFar
§ ***hybrida***	EWes
- 'Aya San'	EWes GKev LRHS WFar
- FAIRY KISSES ('Im201208'PBR)	MPkF XSte
§ - 'Hebron Farm Pink'	CBor CElw CPla CRos EWes GEdr GKev LRHS NHol WFar WIce
- 'Hebron Farm Red Eye'	CCCN EWes NHpl WFar WIce
- 'Ruby Giant'	EWes GEdr
- 'White Stars'	EWes
'Irene'	GKev
'Jenny'	EWes GKev
'Little Pink Pet'	EWes GKev WFar
'Otterlo Ruby'	CBor EWes GKev WFar
'Red Flyer'	EWes
'Ria'	EWes
'Sandra'	EWes
'Sandy'	CBor EWes GKev
'Sonja'	CBor GKev
'Sue'	EWes WFar
(Summer Stars Series) 'Summer Stars Candy'	EDAr
- 'Summer Stars Peppermint'	EDAr WFar
- 'Summer Stars Pink Blush'	EDAr WFar
- 'Summer Stars Pinky'	CDoC EDAr WFar
- 'Summer Stars Ruby'	EDAr

Rhoeo see *Tradescantia*

Rhoicissus (*Vitaceae*)

digitata	EShb

Rhombophyllum (*Aizoaceae*)

dolabriforme	SSim

Rhopalostylis (*Arecaceae*)

sapida	CBrP LRHS

rhubarb see *Rheum* × *hybridum*; also AGM Vegetables Section

Rhus ✿ (*Anacardiaceae*)

ambigua	see *Toxicodendron orientale*
aromatica	CAgr NLar WKor
chinensis	CBcs CMCN WFar
copallinum	EBtc
cotinus	see *Cotinus coggygria*
glabra	CBcs EPfP
- 'Laciniata' ambig.	EGrI NLar WFar
hirta	see *R. typhina*
incisa	see *Searsia incisa*
potaninii	EBee EPfP NLar WPGP
× ***pulvinata*** (Autumn Lace Group) 'Red Autumn Lace' ♀H6	MBlu SPer
punjabensis	WJur
radicans	see *Toxicodendron radicans*
succedanea	see *Toxicodendron succedaneum*
toxicodendron	see *Toxicodendron radicans*
trilobata	WKor
§ ***typhina***	Widely available
§ - 'Dissecta' ♀H6	CBar CBcs CBod CDoC CKel CMac EDir EHeP ELan EPfP GMcL LMaj LPar MGos MPri MRav NLar NWea SArc SCob SEND SGol SGsty SLim SPer WFar
- 'Laciniata' hort.	see *R. typhina* 'Dissecta'
- RADIANCE ('Sinrus') ♀H6	EHyd LRHS MBlu NLar SPoG
- TIGER EYES ('Bailtiger'PBR) ♀H6	CBcs CWal ELan EPfP GMcL LCro MGos SCob SGol SMad SWvt XVPe
verniciflua	see *Toxicodendron vernicifluum*

Rhynchelytrum see *Melinis*

Rhynchospora (*Cyperaceae*)

colorata	LLWG LRHS MPkF NPer SBrt XSte
latifolia	SDix SMad

Ribes ✿ (*Grossulariaceae*)

alpinum	LPar LSto NWea SPer SRms WKor WSpi
- 'Schmidt'	LIns
americanum 'Variegatum' (v)	NLar NWad
aureum misapplied	see *R. odoratum*
aureum ambig.	CAgr NWea WKor
aureum Pursh	EGrI
- subsp. ***gracillimum***	SBrt
§ × ***beatonii***	CKel CSBt EBee EGrI EHyd EPfP EShb GBin LEdu LRHS MMuc NLar SGol SPer SPoG SRms WAvo WCot WFar WMal WSpi
'Ben Hope'PBR (B)	CAgr CDoC CSBt EPom MAsh MPri SCoo SWvt
'Black Velvet' (D)	CAgr
bracteosum B&SWJ 14159	WCru
californicum	SBrt
cereum	SBrt
× ***culverwellii*** (F)	CAgr CCCN CTri EPom LBuc LCro LEdu LOPS NLar SBmr SVic SWvt
divaricatum	CAgr LEdu WKor
gayanum	LEdu NLar WKor
glaciale PAB 3004	LEdu
× ***gordonianum***	see *R.* × *beatonii*
griffithii	WCot
- GWJ 9331	WCru

- PAB 4871	LEdu
jostaberry	see *R. × nidigrolaria*
laurifolium	CBcs CEnd CTri EBee ELan EWes IDee LRHS LSto MAsh MRav NLar SCob SGBe SMad SPer WCFE WFar WHlf WSpi
- (f)	EPfP SBrt SRms
- (m)	EPfP
- 'Mrs Amy Doncaster'	CBcs CRos EBee EHed EHyd EPfP LEdu LRHS MAsh NLar NRHS SBrt SMad SPoG SRms WBor WCot WGob WHtc WLov WMal WPGP WSpi
- Rosemoor form	CDoC CKel CRos EBee EHed EPfP LRHS NLar SPoG WCot WLov
longeracemosum	GGGa
menziesii	EWes NQui WCot
nevadense	SBrt
§ ***× nidigrolaria*** (F)	CDoC CMac GDam MAsh NBwr NWea SCoo SEdi
nigrum PAB 3755 (B)	LEdu
- 'Baldwin' (B)	EPfP LEdu MAsh MTrO NLar SCoo SEdi SSFr WMat
- 'Barchatnaja' (B)	CAgr
- 'Ben Alder' (B)	CAgr EPom GDam MAsh SCoo SRms
- 'Ben Connan' (B) ♀^{H6}	Widely available
- 'Ben Gairn'^{PBR} (B)	CAgr MCoo MMuc
- 'Ben Lomond'^{PBR} (B)	CAgr CDoC CSBt CTri EPfP LBuc LSRN MAsh MGos MNHC MRav MTrO NLar NRog NWea SBdl SBmr SCoo SEdi SKee SPer SPoG SRms SSFr SVic WMat
- 'Ben More' (B)	CAgr MPri NLar SOrN
- 'Ben Nevis' (B)	CAgr EBee EDir LPar NBwr SEdi SKee SPer
- 'Ben Sarek' (B)	Widely available
- 'Ben Tirran' (B)	CAgr CDoC CPer CSBt EHyd EPom LBuc LRHS LSRN MAsh MGos NBwr NLar SBdl SCoo SRms SWvt WMat
- 'Ben Tron' (B)	LRHS
- 'Big Ben'^{PBR} (B) ♀^{H6}	CArg CRos EBee EHyd EPfP EPom LBuc LCro LOPS LRHS LSRN MTrO NRHS SBdl SBmr SGbt SKee SPer SPoG WMat
- 'Black Reward' (B)	CAgr
- 'Boskoop Giant' (B)	CAgr ELan NRog
- 'Byelorussian Sweet' (B)	CAgr
- 'Cassis Blanc' (B)	CAgr
- CASSISSIMA NOIROMA (B)	LRHS
- 'Ebony' (B)	CArg CMac EPom NBwr NRog SVic
- 'Goliath' (B)	MPri
- 'Hystawneznaya' (B)	CAgr
- 'Jet' (B)	CAgr NBwr NRog
- 'Kosmicheskaya' (B)	CAgr
- 'Pilot Alexander Mamkin' (B)	CAgr
- 'Polar' (B)	CAgr
- 'Seabrook's' (B)	CAgr
- 'Titania' (B)	EDir LRHS MCoo MTrO NLar SEdi WMat
- 'Vertti' (B)	CAgr
- 'Wellington XXX' (B)	CAgr LBuc LEdu NBwr NRog NWea SEdi SSFr
§ ***odoratum***	CBcs CKel CMac CSBt EBee EHeP EHed EHyd ELan ELon EPfP LRHS LSto MGos MMuc MNrw NLar NWea SCob SPer SPoG SRms WCot WLov WSpi
- 'Crandall'	CAgr LEdu
orientale PAB 7066	LEdu
'Pink Perfection'	CMCN
praecox	MMuc SEND
rubrum	EDir
- 'Bar-le-Duc' (W)	NRog
- 'Blanka' (W) ♀^{H6}	CAgr CArg CMac CPer EHyd LRHS NRog SVic
- 'Cascade' (R)	CAgr
- 'Cherry' (R)	CAgr
- 'Fay's New Prolific' (R)	NRog
- 'Gloire de Sablons' (P)	EPom LCro LEdu SRms
- 'Jonkheer van Tets' (R) ♀^{H6}	CAgr CDoC CRos CSBt EDir EHyd EPom GQue IArd LPar LRHS LSRN MAsh MCoo MPri NBwr NLar NRHS NWea SBdl SBmr SCoo SEND SEdi SGbt SKee SPer SRms SSFr WMat
- 'Junifer' (R)	CAgr CMac EHyd EPom LEdu LRHS NLar NRHS NRog SKee
- 'Laxton's Number One' (R)	CAgr CDoC CTri EPfP EPom LCro LEdu LOPS LRHS LSRN NLar NRog NWea SBmr SCoo SGbt SPer SPoG SRms SSFr WMat
- 'Lisette' (R)	LRHS
- 'Red Lake' (R) ♀^{H6}	CAgr CTri EDir ELan EPfP EPom LBuc LEdu MGos MPri NBwr NLar NRog SBmr SEdi SPer SPoG SRms SSFr WMat
- 'Redstart' (R)	CAgr LBuc MAsh MMuc WMat
- RIBEST SONETTE (R)	LRHS
- 'Rolan' (R)	CAgr NRog
- 'Rondom' (R)	CAgr NRog SVic
- ROSA SPORT (P)	LRHS
- 'Rosetta' (R)	CAgr CDoC CPer NRog SBdl SCoo SRms
- 'Rotet' (R)	LEdu NRog
- 'Rovada' (R) ♀^{H6}	CAgr CArg CMac CPer CRos CSBt EHyd EPfP EPom LBuc LEdu LRHS LSRN MAsh NBwr NLar NRHS SBdl SBmr SCoo SEdi SKee SPoG SRms SVic WMat
- 'Roxby Red' (R)	NBwr NRog
- 'Stanza' (R) ♀^{H6}	CAgr NRog SEND
- 'Versailles' (R)	CPer MAsh SBmr
§ - 'Versailles Blanche' (W/C)	CAgr CRos CSBt CTri EDir EHyd EPfP EPom GQue LBuc LCro LOPS LPar LRHS LSRN MGos MMuc MPri NRHS NRog SBdl SBmr SCoo SEdi SKee SPer SRms SSFr
- 'Weisse Langtraubige' (W)	CAgr
- 'White Dutch' (W)	NRog
- 'White Grape' (W) ♀^{H6}	CTri LEdu NRog
- 'White Pearl' (W)	ELan NRog SEdi SVic
- WHITE VERSAILLES	see *R. rubrum* 'Versailles Blanche'
sachalinense	WKor
sanguineum	CBod EHeP GDam LPar NBwr SavN
- AMORE ('Annys2003'^{PBR})	EPfP LCro LRHS
- 'Brianjou'	SRms
- 'Brocklebankii'	CMac EPfP LRHS MRav NLar SRms WCFE
- 'Carneum'	EHyd LRHS NRHS
- 'Elkington's White'	CBod CRos EHyd EPfP LAlb LCro LOPS LRHS LSRN MAsh MGos NLar NSti SCoo SRms WBor WCot WSpi
- 'King Edward VII'	Widely available
- 'Koja' ♀^{H6}	CBod CRos EHyd EPfP GBin LRHS LSRN MAsh MGos MMuc NLar SCoo SGol SPoG SRms WCot WFar WLov WSpi
- 'Lombartsii' ♀^{H6}	CRos EHyd EPfP ILea LRHS MRav NRHS
- 'Poky's Pink' ♀^{H6}	CRos EHyd EWTr LRHS MAsh MRav SPoG SRms
- 'Pulborough Scarlet'	Widely available
- 'Red Bross'	CRos EPfP LRHS MAsh SWvt
- 'Red Pimpernel'	CSBt EHyd LRHS MAsh SRms SWvt WFar

- 'Somerset White'	LRHS MAsh SRHi
- 'Tydeman's White'	CSBt NLar NWea WSpi
- var. ***variegata***	CMac
- WHITE ICICLE ('Ubric') 🏆H6	CBcs CBod CDoC CTri EBee EHyd ELan EPfP EShb GBin GMcL LRHS LSto MAsh MBlu MHer MRav MSwo NBir NLar NRHS SCob SPer SPoG SRms SWvt WFar WLov
speciosum 🏆H4	Widely available
uva-crispa 'Achilles' (D)	NBwr
- 'Admiral Beattie' (F)	NRog
- 'Alma' (F)	NRog
- 'Annelii' (F)	CAgr
- 'Australia' (D)	NRog
- 'Bellona' (D)	NRog
- 'Broom Girl' (D)	NRog
- 'Captivator' (C)	CDoC CMac CRos CSBt EDir EPom LBuc LCro LRHS MAsh MCoo MNHC MTrO NBwr NLar NRHS SBdl SCoo SKee SPoG SRms WMat
- 'Careless' (C/D) 🏆H6	CSBt CTri EDir EPom LSRN MAsh MGos NBwr NRog SCoo SEdi SPer
- 'Cousen's Seedling' (D)	NRog
- CRISPA FLAVIA (D)	LRHS
- 'Criterion' (D)	NRog
- 'Early Sulphur' (D)	CTri ELan NBwr NRog NWea
- EASYCRISP LADY SUN (D)	LRHS
- 'Freedom' (C)	NRog
- 'Green Gem' (C/D)	NRog
- 'Greenfinch' (C) 🏆H6	CAgr
- 'Greengage' (D)	NBwr
- 'Heart of Oak' (D)	NRog
- 'Hero of the Nile' (D)	NRog
- 'Hinnonmäki' (D)	CAgr SPer
- 'Hinnonmäki Grön' (D)	CAgr CDoC CMac CPer CSBt EBee EPom LCro LRHS LSRN MAsh MRav MTrO NRog SBdl SBmr SCoo SEdi SKee SRms
- 'Hinnonmäki Gul' (D)	CAgr CDoC CMac EBee EPfP EPom LBuc LCro LEdu LRHS MAsh MGos MTrO NBwr NRHS SBmr SEdi SKee SPer SRms SSFr SVic WMat
- 'Hinnonmäki Röd' (C/D)	Widely available
- 'Invicta' (C/D) 🏆H6	Widely available
- 'Ironmonger' (D)	NRog
- 'Jubilee' (C/D)	NRog
- 'Jubilee Careless' (C/D)	EPom
- 'King of Trumps' (D)	NRog
- 'Lancashire Lad' (C/D)	NRog
- 'Langley Gage' (D)	MCoo NRog
- 'Larell' (C/D)	CAgr NBwr
- 'Leveller' (D) 🏆H6	MCoo NBwr NRog NWea SEdi SPer
- 'London' (C/D)	CTri NRog NWea
- 'Lord Derby' (C/D)	NRog
- 'Lord Kitchener' (D)	NRog
- 'Marigold' (F)	NRog
- 'Martlet' (D)	NBwr NRog
- 'Matchless' (D)	NBwr NRog
- 'May Duke' (C/D)	NBwr
- 'Mucurines' (D)	CAgr
- 'Pax'PBR (D)	CAgr SBmr SSFr SVic
- 'Peru' (D)	NRog
- 'Pitmaston Green Gage' (D)	NRog
- 'Redeva'PBR (D)	CAgr
- 'Rokula' (C/D)	ELan MCoo WMat
- 'Speedwell' (F)	NRog
- 'Spinefree' (C)	CAgr
- 'Talfourd' (D)	NRog
- 'Trumpeter' (D)	NRog
- 'Victoria' (C/D)	NRog
- 'Whinham's Industry' (C/D) 🏆H6	ELan LBuc LSRN MGos MMuc NBwr NRog SCgs SEND SEdi SPer SRms
- 'White Eagle' (C/D)	NRog
- 'Whitesmith' (C/D)	CTri LSRN MCoo NBwr NRog
- 'Woodpecker' (D)	NRog
- 'Xenia' (D)	CArg CRos EHyd EPfP EPom LCro LEdu MCoo NRHS NRog SPoG WMat
- 'Yellow Champagne' (D)	NRog
valdivianum	WCot WFar
viburnifolium	NLar SBrt SEND
'Worcesterberry' (C)	CHab IDee NBwr NRog

Ricinus (*Euphorbiaceae*)

communis	CDTJ CSpe CWal SPlb
- 'Bolivian Red' **new**	CSpe
- 'Carmencita' 🏆H2	NGBl
- 'Carmencita Pink'	CDTJ
- 'Carmencita Red'	CDTJ
- 'Dominican Republic'	CDTJ
- 'Gibsonii'	CDTJ
- 'Impala'	CDTJ
- 'New Zealand Black'	CDTJ CSpe EShb SBls
- 'Zanzibariensis' 🏆H2	CDTJ

Ridolfia (*Apiaceae*)

segetum	CKel LCro LOPS SPhx

Rigidella see *Tigridia*

Riocreuxia (*Apocynaceae*)

torulosa	CCCN SPlb

Robinia (*Fabaceae*)

§ ***hispida***	CEnd CLnd EPfP MBlu SPer WJur
- var. ***fertilis***	SBrt
- var. ***kelseyi***	WSpi
- 'Macrophylla'	CEnd
§ - var. ***rosea***	LSRN
- 'Rosea' misapplied	see *R. hispida*, *R. hispida* var. *rosea*
- 'Rosea' ambig.	CBcs
× ***margaretta*** CASQUE ROUGE	see *R.* × *margaretta* 'Pink Cascade'
§ - 'Pink Cascade'	CEnd EBee EDir EHeP ELan EPfP IPap LRHS MAsh MGos MTrO NBwr NOrn SCob SCoo SEND SGbt SGol WMat
pseudoacacia	CAgr CCVT CPer EDir EHeP ELan IPap LBuc MCoo MMuc NRog SEND SGol SPlb WJur
- 'Bessoniana'	EHeP ELan LPar
- 'Frisia'	Widely available
- 'Inermis' hort.	see *R. pseudoacacia* 'Umbraculifera'
§ - 'Lace Lady'PBR	CSBt ELan EPfP LBuc LRHS MAsh MGos MTrO NLar SCoo SPer SPoG WHtc WMat
- 'Tortuosa'	CEnd SPer
- 'Twisty Baby'	see *R. pseudoacacia* 'Lace Lady'
§ - 'Umbraculifera'	CLnd LPar LSRN NBwr SArc SCob SGsty
× ***slavinii*** 'Hillieri' 🏆H6	CBcs CEnd ELan EPfP LRHS LSRN MAsh MBlu NLar NOrn WSpi

Rochea see *Crassula*

Rodgersia ✿ (*Saxifragaceae*)

CLD 1432	CExl
from Castlewellan	EBlo
from Tibet	EBlo
aesculifolia 🏆H6	Widely available
- SSSE 36	SMHy
- var. ***henrici***	CRos EHyd EPfP GElm GLog LRHS MRav NBro NRHS SGbt WBor WHoo
- - KW 21015	WCru

- - 'Cherry Blush'	CBod EHed EPfP NLar SPad WFar
- - hybrid	NLar XLum
- large-leaved	LRHS
- 'Red Leaf'	EWoo
'Badenweiler'	EBlo ECha EHyd LRHS NRHS
'Blickfang' 🏆H6	EBlo EHyd LRHS MMrt NRHS
'Bloody Mary'	ECtt SCob WFar
'Borodin'	EBee
'Bronze Peacock'	Widely available
'Dark Pokers'	CBod ECtt LBar LRHS MCot MHol NLar SHar SHor SRms WFar
'Die Schöne'	NLar
'Die Stolze'	EBee GBin LEdu
'Grande Blanche'	EBlo
'Herkules'	ECha ECtt ELon EMor GDam GElm GMaP GMcL LEdu MBNS MMuc NLar NQui WCot WPnP
'Irish Bronze' 🏆H6	CRos ECtt EHyd EMor EPfP EShb GElm GPSL GQue LEdu LRHS LSRN LSto MBel MHer NChi NRHS NSti SMad WCAu WCot WFar WPnP
'Kupfermond'	NBir
'La Blanche'	ECtt EHed ELon LEdu LRHS MHol NLar
nepalensis	LEdu LRHS WPGP
- HWJK 2140	WCru
- 'High Flier'	WCru
'Parasol'	CBro CDor CMac NBir NHol NWad
pinnata	CPud CTri EHeP EPau EWTr GMaP LEdu LPal LPfP LRHS LSRN MGos MRav NHol NRHS SCob SPeP SRms WPnP WWtn XLum
- B&SWJ 7741A	CBcs WCru
- L 1670	CExl ELan
- 'Alba'	EMor
- 'Buckland Beauty' 🏆H6	CDor CRos EBlo EHyd EPfP LRHS NRHS WFar
- 'Cally Salmon'	EWes SMHy
- 'Candy Clouds' (d)	EBee NLar
- 'Chocolate Wing'	Widely available
- 'Crûg Cardinal'	CRos EBee EHyd ELon EPfP GBin LRHS NLar NRHS SHeu WCru WPnP
- 'Elegans' 🏆H7	CDor CPud CRos EBee EPfP GKev GMaP LEdu LPal LRHS MRav NChi NHol NRHS NWad SCob SPoG SRms SWvt WCAu
- 'Fireworks'PBR	EBee GMcL LBar NLar
- 'Hanna'	GBin SHeu
- hybrids	EHyd LRHS
- 'Jade Dragon Mountain'	LEdu
- 'Maurice Mason' 🏆H6	CExl EBlo GKev LRHS NLar SDix SMHy
- 'Pink Beauty'	EBee
- pink-flowered	WCru
- 'Shangri-La'	WCru
- 'Snow Clouds'	EBee LBar
- 'Superba' 🏆H6	CMac EBee ECha ECtt EHyd EMor EPfP GAbr GKev GMaP GMcL LCro LOPS LRHS MAvo MBel MCot MRav NBir NPer NRHS SCob SDix SPer SWvt WFar WKif WPnP WSHC
- white-flowered	WCru
podophylla	CAby CExl CMac ECha ELon EMor EPPr GAbr GKev GMaP GMcL GQue LCro LEdu MMuc NBid NBir NChi NCth NHol NLar NRya NSti NWad SCob SDix WCru WFar WHoo WWtn
- B&SWJ 10818	WCru
- B&SWJ 10823	WCru
- 'Braunlaub'	EMor ILea LCro MCot NBro SMad WPnP
- 'Crûg's Colossus'	WCru
- 'Rotlaub' 🏆H6	EBee
- 'Smaragd'	CRos CToG EBee EHyd EMor EShb LRHS MRav NBir NLar NRHS
purdomii hort.	CMac EHyd LRHS NRHS WCot WPGP
sambucifolia	CBcs CMac CRos EHyd EMor EWTr LEdu LRHS MMuc NBir NLar NRHS SCob SEND WCAu WFar WPnP XLum
- B&SWJ 7899	WCru
- large, red-stemmed	NBir
- 'Mountain Select'	EBee
tabularis	see *Astilboides tabularis*

Rohdea (*Asparagaceae*)

delavayi	WCot
japonica	CMac WCot WPGP
- B&SWJ 4853	WCru
- B&SWJ 5091	WCru
- 'Godaishu' (v)	WCot
- 'Gunjaku' (v)	EPPr WCot
- 'Lance Leaf'	LEdu WPGP
- long-leaved	WCot
- 'Miyakonojo' (v)	WCot
- 'Talbot Manor' (v)	CBct WCot WPGP
- 'Tama-jishi' (v)	WCot
- 'Tuneshige Rokujo' (v)	WCot
tonkinensis HWJ 562	WCru
watanabei B&SWJ 1911	WCru
wattii	WCot

Roldana (*Asteraceae*)

§ ***cristobalensis***	WCot
§ ***petasitis***	CAbb CHll WCot

Romanzoffia (*Boraginaceae*)

californica	EBee
§ ***sitchensis***	CTri
suksdorfii Greene	see *R. sitchensis*
unalaschcensis	SRms

Romneya (*Papaveraceae*)

coulteri 🏆H5	Widely available
§ - 'White Cloud' 🏆H5	CExl EBee EPfP MGil MRav SChF WPGP WSpi
× ***hybrida***	see *R. coulteri* 'White Cloud'

Romulea (*Iridaceae*)

atrandra	CBor
bulbocodium	CBor
- var. ***clusiana***	GKev NRog
- var. ***crocea***	GKev
- var. ***leichtliniana***	CBor GKev
columnae subsp. ***columnae***	NRog
- subsp. ***grandiscapa***	NRog
hallii	NRog
komsbergensis	NRog
linaresii	NRog
macowanii var. ***alticola***	CBor GArf
ramiflora	CExl GKev
requienii	EDAr
rosea	NRog
sabulosa	CBor
saldanhensis	CBor
setifolia new	CBor
tempskyana	CBor
tetragona	CBor

Rosa ✿ (*Rosaceae*)

NJM 11.048 from Guizhou, China	WPGP

	Name	Suppliers
	90TH CELEBRATION ('Tan10558') (HT)	MFry
	'A Faithful Friend' (F) **new**	NTrD
	'A. Mackenzie' (S)	EBls
	A ROSE FOR HEATHER ('Kirhiam') (Cl) **new**	MJon
	A ROSE FOR RYEDALE ('Websunshine') (F)	NRog
	A SHROPSHIRE LAD ('Ausled'^{PBR}) (S) 🏆^{H6}	CArg CRos EBee EPfP LBuc LRHS MJon MSwo NLar NRHS SCob SPer SPoG SSea
	A WHITER SHADE OF PALE ('Peafanfare'^{PBR}) (HT) 🏆^{H6}	CDoC CSBt EBls ECnt ESty LCro LOPS LSRN MAsh MFry MGos MJon MRav SApu SPer SSea
	ABBIE'S ROSE (F)	LSRN
	ABIGAILE ('Tanelaigib') (F)	LSRN MJon
	ABRACADABRA ('Korhocsel') (HT)	ESty
	ABRAHAM DARBY ('Auscot') (S)	EPfP LSRN
	ABSENT FRIENDS ('Dicemblem'^{PBR}) (F)	ESty WBor
	ABSOLUTELY FABULOUS ('Wekvossutono'^{PBR}) (F) 🏆^{H6}	CArg CBod CDoC CGro CSBt EBls ECnt EPfP ESty LRHS LSRN MAsh MFry MGos MJon MPri MRav NRog SApu SCoo SPad SPer SPoG SRGP SWCr
	abyssinica	EBtc LEdu
	ACAPULCO ('Dicblender') (HT)	NRog
	acicularis var. ***nipponensis***	EBls
	'Adam' (ClT)	EBls LSRN
	'Adam Messerich' (Bb)	EBls ETWh
	ADAM'S ROSE ('Wekromico') (F)	LSRN MJon
	'Adélaïde d'Orléans' (Ra) 🏆^{H6}	CArg CRHN EBls ETWh SEND
	'Admiral Rodney' (HT)	NRog
	'Agatha' (G)	EBls
	AGATHA CHRISTIE ('Kormeita') (ClF)	EBls EPfP LRHS LSRN
	'Aglaia' (Ra)	EBls ETWh
	'Agnes' (Ru)	CBcs CDoC EBls EPfP ETWh IArd MRav NLar NRog SPer
	'Aimée Vibert' (N)	EBee EBls ETWh NLar SPer
	'Alain Blanchard' (G)	EBls ETWh NLar
	ALAN TITCHMARSH ('Ausjive'^{PBR}) (S)	LCro LSRN
	ALASKA ('Korjoslio'^{PBR}) (ClHT)	ESty LPar
	× ***alba*** (A)	EBls NRog
§	- 'Alba Maxima' (A) 🏆^{H6}	EBls ETWh GBin MAsh NLar NRog SEND SPer WFar WHer
§	- 'Alba Semiplena' (A) 🏆^{H6}	EBls ETWh GBin LRHS NLar SPer WHer
	- CELESTIAL	see *R.* 'Céleste'
	- 'Maxima'	see *R.* × *alba* 'Alba Maxima'
	'Albéric Barbier' (Ra) 🏆^{H5}	CArg CDoC CEnd CRHN CSBt CTri EBee EBls ECnt EPfP ETWh LCro LOPS MFry MJon MRav MSwo NLar NRog NWea SApu SCob SCoo SEND SPer SSea SWCr WHer
	'Albertine' (Ra) 🏆^{H6}	Widely available
	'Alchymist' (ClS)	CBod CRHN EBls EPfP ESty ETWh LRHS MRav SPer SWCr
	ALDEN BIESEN ('Lengrati') (HM)	WKif
	ALDERLEY PARK ('Frygladiator') (F)	MFry
	ALEC'S RED ('Cored') (HT)	CArg CBcs CTri EBls EDir LSRN MFry MRav NRog SCob SPer SPoG SRGP SWCr
	ALEXANDER ('Harlex') (HT) 🏆^{H6}	EBls LHkn LSRN MJon NRog SApu
	'Alexander Hill Gray' (T)	EBls
	ALEXANDER'S ISSIE ('Dicland'^{PBR}) (F)	IDic
	'Alexandre Girault' (Ra) 🏆^{H6}	CRHN EBee EBls ETWh LRHS NRHS SPer WHer
	'Alfred Colomb' (HP)	EBls
	'Alfred de Dalmas' misapplied	see *R.* 'Mousseline'
	ALFRED SISLEY ('Delstrijor'^{PBR}) (S)	ESty ETWh LRHS
	'Alfresco'^{PBR} (ClHT)	MSwo
§	'Alibaba'^{PBR} (ClHT) 🏆^{H6}	CBod CDoC CSBt ECnt ELon EPfP ESty LBuc LRHS LSRN MFry MPri MRav SApu SPer SPoG SWCr
	'Alice Bracegirdle' (HT)	NRog
	'Alida Lovett' (Ra)	CRHN
	ALISON ('Coclibee'^{PBR}) (F)	LSRN
	ALISSAR, PRINCESS OF PHOENICIA ('Harsidon'^{PBR}) (S)	ETWh LHkn NLar
	'Alister Clark' (F)	EBls
§	'Alister Stella Gray' (N) 🏆^{H5}	EBls EPfP ESty ETWh MMuc NLar NRog SEND SSea
	ALL AMERICAN MAGIC ('Meiroylear'^{PBR}) (HT)	ESty
	ALL MY LOVING ('Fryrisky') (HT)	LRHS MFry SWCr
	ALL YOURS ('Wekwestypla') (HT)	MJon
	'Allen Chandler' (ClHT)	EBls
	ALNWICK CASTLE	see *R.* THE ALNWICK ROSE
	'Aloha' (ClHT) 🏆^{H6}	CArg CBcs CTri EBee EBls EDir ELon EPfP ESty ETWh LPar LRHS MRav NLar NRog SPer SPoG SRGP SWCr
	alpina	see *R.* ***pendulina***
	'Alpine Sunset' (HT)	CGro CTri EBls EDir ELon MGos MRav SCob SPer SPoG
	altaica misapplied	see *R.* ***spinosissima*** 'Grandiflora'
	altaica Willd.	see *R.* ***spinosissima***
	ALTISSIMO ('Delmur') (Cl)	CEnd EBls ETWh SSea
	ALWAYS REMEMBER ME ('Macpadspo') (HT)	LSRN MJon
	ALWAYS REMEMBERED ('Raw1114') (HT) **new**	ESty
	ALWAYS YOU ('Webalways') (HT)	ESty
	AMADEUS ('Korlabriax') (Cl) **new**	LPar
	'Amadis' (Bs)	ETWh
	AMANDA ('Beesian') (F)	EBls ESty LSRN MJon
	'Amanda Paternotte' (D)	ETWh
	AMAZING DAY ('Raw1113') (S)	ESty
	'Ambassador Nogami' (S)	EBls
	AMBER ABUNDANCE ('Harfizz'^{PBR}) (Abundance Series) (F)	LHkn
	AMBER QUEEN ('Harroony') (F) 🏆^{H6}	CArg CSBt CTri EBls ELan IArd LCro LHkn MFry MRav NRog SApu SPer SWCr
	AMBER STAR ('Manstar') (Min)	NRog
	AMBER SUN	see *R.* COUNTY OF STAFFORDSHIRE
	AMBER SUNSET ('Manamsun') (Min)	NRog
	AMBER SWEET DREAM ('Fryritz') (Patio)	CDoC CSBt MFry MRav
	AMBIANCE ('Bensiete') (Patio)	NRog
	'Amélia'	see *R.* 'Celsiana'
	AMELIA ('Poulen011'^{PBR}) (Renaissance Series) (S)	ECnt ETWh LSRN

	AMÉLIE NOTHOMB ('Delathom') (HT)	EBls
	'American Pillar' (Ra)	Widely available
	AMETHYST QUEEN ('Raw1074') (F)	ESty
	AMNESTY INTERNATIONAL ('Delcreja') (Cl)	ESty SSea
	AMPLEFORTH ('Rawforth') (F)	NRog
	'Amy Robsart' (RH)	EBls
	ANABELL ('Korbell') (F)	LSRN NRog
	ANDREA STELZER ('Korfachrit') (HT)	NRog
§	'Anemone' (Cl)	EBls ETWh
	anemonoides	see *R.* 'Anemone'
	ANGEL EYES ('Albravo') (HT)	LRHS MAsh
	ANGELA ('Grifgela') (S)	LSRN NRog
	ANGELA RIPPON ('Ocaru') (Min)	CSBt
	'Angela's Choice' (F)	LSRN
	ANGUS HAMILTON ('Dicfrapp') (F) **new**	MJon
	ANIS PERFUMELLA	see *R.* MONICA BELLUCCI
	ANISLEY DICKSON ('Dickimono') (F)	NRog SPer
	ANN ('Ausfete'[PBR]) (S)	LSRN
	ANN ('Raw1144') (F) **new**	ESty
	ANN GLANVILLE ('Cocbonanza') (HT) **new**	MJon
	ANN HENDERSON ('Fryhoncho') (F)	LSRN MFry
	ANNA ANCHER	see *R.* TRENCIN
	ANNA FORD ('Harpiccolo') (Min/Patio) ♀H5	SCob
	'Anna Olivier' (T)	EBls
	'Anna Pavlova' (HT)	EBls
	ANNAKARINA! ('Scherendee'[PBR]) (HT)	CPla
	ANNE BOLEYN ('Ausecret'[PBR]) (S)	EHyd EPfP LRHS MAsh NRHS SCoo
	ANNE HARKNESS ('Harkaramel') (F)	LHkn
	'Anne of Geierstein' (RH)	EBls
	'Anne Watkins' (HT)	EBls
	ANNE'S ROSE ('Frynippy'[PBR]) (F)	LSRN MAsh
	ANNIVERSARY WALTZ ('Raw237') (HT)	ESty
	ANNIVERSARY WISHES ('Noa140721') (F)	EBls MAsh SWCr
	'Anthony' (S)	EBls
	ANTIQUE '89 ('Kordalen') (ClF)	EBls ETWh
	APERITIF ('Macwaira'[PBR]) (HT)	MJon
	APHRODITE ('Tan00847'[PBR]) (S) ♀H6	CBod CEnd ESty ETWh LSRN MRav SApu
	APHRODITE ('Tanetidor') (HT)	CArg
	apothecary's rose	see *R. gallica* var. *officinalis*
	'Apple Blossom' (Ra)	EBls SHar
	APPLE JACK ('Kenendure'[PBR]) (F) **new**	MJon
	'Applejack' (S)	EBls
	'Apricot Ingrid' (Patio)	NRog
	'Apricot Silk' (HT)	CTri SPer
	APRICOT SUNBLAZE ('Savamark') (Min)	CSBt
	ARC ANGEL ('Fryorst') (HT)	MFry
	ARCANUM ('Tuckarc') (Min)	NRog
§	ARCHBISHOP DESMOND TUTU ('Kortutu'[PBR]) (F) **new**	MJon
	'Archduke Charles' (Ch)	EBls
	'Archiduc Joseph' misapplied	see *R.* 'Général Schablikine'
	'Archiduchesse Elisabeth d'Autriche' (HP)	EBls
	ARCHIE MOSS ('Dickumon') (S)	IDic
	ARCTIC BLUE ('Wekblufytirar') (F) **new**	MJon
	'Arctic Circle' (HT)	ESty NRog
	'Ardoisée de Lyon' (HP)	EBls
	'Ards Rover' (ClHP)	EBls
	'Arethusa' (Ch)	EBls ETWh
	'Arizona Sunset' (Min)	NRog
§	***arkansana* var. *suffulta***	EBls ETWh
	ARMADA ('Haruseful') (S)	EBls
	'Arthur Bell' (F) ♀H6	Widely available
	'Arthur de Sansal' (DPo)	ETWh NLar
	arvensis	CCVT CHab CLnd CPer EBls ETWh LBuc NWea WTSh
	'As Good As It Gets' (F) **new**	ECnt
§	'Aschermittwoch' (ClHR)	EBls
	ASCOT ('Tan01757'[PBR]) (HT)	CBod ESty MFry
	ASH WEDNESDAY	see *R.* 'Aschermittwoch'
	'Astra Desmond' (Ra)	EBls ETWh MNrw
I	'At Peace Rose' (HT)	LSRN NTrD
	ATLANTIC STAR ('Fryworld'[PBR]) (F)	MFry
	ATTLEBOROUGH ('Beaat') (ClHT)	EBls
	AUDIENZ	see *R.* TIMELESS CREAM
	AUDREY WILCOX ('Frywilrey') (HT)	ELon ESty MFry
	'Auguste Gervais' (Ra)	EBls
	Austrian copper rose	see *R. foetida* 'Bicolor'
	Austrian yellow	see *R. foetida*
	'Autumn' (HT)	LSRN NRog
	'Autumn Delight' (HM)	EBls ETWh NRog
	AUTUMN FIRE	see *R.* 'Herbstfeuer'
	AUTUMN SONG	see *R.* PURE POETRY ('Jacment') (F)
	'Autumn Sunset' (ClS)	EBls MCot
	'Autumnalis'	see *R.* 'Princesse de Nassau'
	AVEC AMOUR ('Tan04341'[PBR]) (HT)	ESty
	'Aviateur Blériot' (Ra)	CRHN EBls
	AVON ('Poulmulti'[PBR]) (GC)	EBls ETWh SApu SPer
	AWAKENING ('Probuzení') (ClHT)	CEnd CRos EBee EBls EDir EPfP ETWh LRHS MAsh MSwo SWCr
	AYA ('Poulren021'[PBR]) (Renaissance Series) (S) **new**	ETWh
	'Ayrshire Splendens'	see *R.* 'Splendens'
	BABE ('Raw1090') (F)	ESty
	'Baby Bio' (F/Patio)	NRog
	'Baby Faurax' (Poly)	EBls ETWh
	'Baby Katie' (Min)	NRog
	BABY LOVE ('Scrivluv'[PBR]) (Min/Patio)	WMal
	BABY MASQUERADE ('Tanba') (Min)	CGro MRav NRog SPer
	BABYFACE ('Rawril'[PBR]) (Min)	ESty
	BADMINTON GIRL ('Dicfiesta') (F)	IDic
	'Bajazzo' (HT)	SSea
	'Ballerina' (HM/Poly) ♀H6	Widely available
	BALMORAL ('Poulcas027'[PBR]) (Palace Series) (Patio)	EBls MAsh SWCr

	'Baltimore Belle' (Ra)	CRHN EBee EBls ETWh NLar
	banksiae (Ra)	SNig SRms SWeb
	- ***alba***	see *R. banksiae* var. *banksiae*
§	- var. ***banksiae*** (Ra/d)	CBcs CBod CRHN CSBt CTri CTsd EBls EHyd ELan EPfP ETWh LCro LOPS LPar LRHS SGsty SMad SSha WCot WLov XSen
	- 'Lutea' (Ra/d) 🏆H5	Widely available
	- 'Lutescens' (Ra)	EBee EBls WPGP
	- var. ***normalis*** (Ra)	CSBt EBls EPfP WCot WHer WPGP
I	- 'Rosea' (Ra)	ELan EPfP LPar NLar SGsty
	'Bantry Bay' (ClHT)	CArg CBod EBls ELan LSRN SOrN
	BARAKURA ('Beajap') (GC/S)	EBls
	BARBARA ('Raw1050')	LSRN
	BARBARA ANN	see *R.* SCENT FROM HEAVEN
	BARBRA STREISAND ('Wekquaneze') (HT)	LSRN MJon
	BARKAROLE ('Tanelorak') (HT)	SApu
	'Baron Girod de l'Ain' (HP)	EBee EBls ELon ETWh LSRN NLar NRog
	'Baroness Rothschild' ambig.	see *R.* 'Baronne Adolph de Rothschild', CLIMBING BARONNE EDMOND DE ROTHSCHILD
§	'Baronne Adolph de Rothschild' (HP)	EBls ETWh
	'Baronne Prévost' (HP)	EBls
	BARRY STEPHENS ('Horcabellero') (HT)	LSRN
	'Basye's Purple' (Ru)	ETWh
	BATHSHEBA ('Auschimbley'[PBR]) (Cl)	CGro CRos CSBt EPfP ESty LRHS MAsh MJon NLar SPer SWCr
	BEATRIX POTTER ('Beafolly') (S)	EBls
	BEAUTIFUL BRITAIN ('Dicfire') (F)	CBod
	BEAUTIFUL SUNRISE ('Bostimebide'[PBR]) (ClPatio)	SWCr
	BEAUTY STAR	see *R.* LIVERPOOL REMEMBERS
	BEHOLD ('Savahold') (Min)	NRog
	'Belinda' (HM)	EBls LSRN
§	BELLA ('Pouljill'[PBR]) (Renaissance Series) (S)	LSRN
	BELLA CHRISTINA ('Mandella') (F)	LSRN NRog
	BELLA DIANA ('Mandiana') (F)	LSRN NRog
	BELLA ROSA ('Chewnicebell') (F) **new**	EBls
	'Bellard' (G)	ETWh
	'Belle Amour' (A × D)	EBls ETWh NLar
	'Belle de Crécy' (G)	CTri EBls EPfP ETWh LRHS MAsh MNrw MPri NLar SPer
	BELLE DE JOUR ('Delijaupar') (F) **new**	ECnt ESty ETWh
	'Belle des Jardins' misapplied	see *R.* × *centifolia* 'Unique Panachée'
	BELLE EPOQUE ('Adasilthe'[PBR]) (HT)	SWCr
	BELLE EPOQUE ('Fryyaboo'[PBR]) (HT)	ESty LRHS MAsh MFry MJon
	BELLE HAPPINESS ('Meileodevin'[PBR]) (Cl)	NRog
	'Belle Isis' (G)	EBls ETWh NLar NRog SPer
	'Belle Lyonnaise' (ClT)	EBls
	'Belle Poitevine' (Ru)	NRog
	'Belle Vichyssoise' (N)	EBls
	BELMONTE ('Harpearl'[PBR]) (F)	LHkn
§	'Belvedere' (Ra) 🏆H6	ETWh NLar SPer
	BENITA ('Dicquarrel') (HT)	IDic
	BENJAMIN BRITTEN ('Ausencart'[PBR]) (S)	EHyd EPfP ESty LBuc LRHS NRHS SPer SWCr
§	'Bennett's Seedling' (Ra)	ETWh
	'Bérénice' Vibert (G)	NRog
	BERKSHIRE ('Korpinka') (GC) 🏆H6	EBls SApu SCob SSea
	BERRY DELIGHTFUL ('Chewdelight'[PBR]) (S)	EBls
	BERYL JOYCE ('Tan96145'[PBR]) (HT)	ESty LSRN
	BEST IMPRESSION ('Tan04247'[PBR]) (HT)	ECnt ESty
	BEST OF FRIENDS ('Pouldunk'[PBR]) (HT)	LSRN
	BEST WISHES ('Chessnut'[PBR]) (ClHT/v)	LSRN
	BETTY BOOP ('Wekplapic'[PBR]) (F)	MJon
	'Betty Curry' (HT)	NRog
	BETTY HARKNESS ('Harette'[PBR]) (F)	LHkn
	'Betty Prior' (F)	MJon
	'Betty Sherriff' (Ra)	ETWh GBin
	'Betty Uprichard' (HT)	EBls
	BETTY'S SMILE ('Websmile') (HT)	LSRN NRog
	'Bewitched' (HT)	LSRN
	BIDDULPH GRANGE ('Frydarkeye') (S)	MFry
	BIENVENUE ('Delrochipar') (Cl)	EBls ESty
	'Big Ben'	see *R.* 'Jack Hume'
§	'Big Chief' (HT)	NRog
	BIG PURPLE ('Stebigpu') (HT)	ECnt MJon NRog SApu
	BILLET DOUX ('Delrosar') (S)	ESty
	BIRTHDAY BOY ('Tan97607'[PBR]) (HT)	CBod CDoC ESty LSRN MRav NRog SApu SPoG
	BIRTHDAY GIRL ('Meilasso') (F)	CBod CDoC CGro CSBt EPfP ESty LRHS LSRN MAsh MFry MJon MRav NRog SApu SCob SCoo SPoG SSea SWCr
	BIRTHDAY SURPRISE ('Guesyoga') (F)	ESty
	BIRTHDAY WISHES (Patio)	see *R.* SHRIMP HIT (Patio)
	BIRTHDAY WISHES ('Guesdelay') (HT)	LSRN SOrN SSea
	'Bishop Darlington' (HM)	EBls
	BISHOP ELPHINSTONE ('Cocjolly') (F)	MJon
	BLACK BACCARA ('Meidebenne'[PBR]) (HT)	NRog SBmr
	BLACK GOLD ('Cleblack') (Min)	NRog
	'Black Jack' (Ce)	see *R.* 'Tour de Malakoff'
	BLACK JACK ('Minkco') (Min/Patio)	NRog
	'Black Prince' (HP)	EBls
	BLACKBERRY NIP ('Somnip'[PBR]) (HT)	ELon
	'Blairii Number Two' (ClBb)	CArg EBls ETWh NLar NRog
	'Blanche de Belgique' (A)	NRog
	'Blanche Double de Coubert' (Ru) 🏆H7	CArg CBcs CDoC CTri EBee EBls ECnt ELan EPfP ETWh LBuc LCro LOPS LRHS LSRN MFry MJon MSwo NLar SApu SCob SEND SPer WKif
	'Blanche Moreau' (CeMo)	EBls ETWh SPer
	'Blanchefleur' (Ce × G)	EBls ETWh NRog
	BLENHEIM ('Tanmurse') (GC)	SApu

	'Blessings' (HT)	CArg CBcs CSBt CTri EBls LBuc LSRN MAsh MGos MJon MRav NRog NTrD SApu SCob SPer SWCr
	'Bleu Magenta' (Ra) 🏆H6	CRHN EBls ETWh GBin IArd NLar NRog SSea
	BLISS ('Kormarzau'PBR) (F)	EBls
	BLOOM OF RUTH ('Harmedley'PBR) (HT)	ECnt ESty LHkn LSRN
	'Bloomfield Abundance' (Poly)	EBls ETWh MMuc
	'Bloomfield Courage' (Ra)	ETWh
	'Bloomfield Dainty' (HM)	EBls
	BLOOMING MARVELLOUS (Patio)	ESty
	'Blossomtime' (ClHT)	NRog SPer
	BLUE DIAMOND ('Athysumo'PBR) (HT)	ESty MFry
	BLUE FOR YOU ('Pejamblu'PBR) (F) 🏆H6	CDoC CEnd CGro CRos EBls ECnt ELan ELon EPfP ESty LBuc LCro LRHS MAsh MFry MGos MJon MPri NRHS SApu SCgs SCoo SMad SPoG SSea SWCr
	BLUE MOON ('Tannacht') (HT)	CDoC CTri EBls ELan MGos MRav NRog SApu SCob SPer SPoG SRGP SWCr
	BLUE PETER ('Ruiblun') (Min)	MJon
	BLUEBERRY HILL ('Wekcryplag') (F)	EBls
	'Blush Boursault' (Bs)	MMuc
	'Blush Damask' (D)	EBls
	'Blush Noisette'	see *R.* 'Noisette Carnée'
	'Blush Rambler' (Ra)	CRHN CSBt EBls EPfP ETWh MMuc SPer
	'Blushing Lucy' (Ra) 🏆H6	CRHN ETWh MNrw NLar
	'Bobbie James' (Ra) 🏆H6	CArg CRHN CTri EBee EBls EHyd EPfP ETWh LPar LRHS MNrw MRav MSwo NLar NRHS SApu SCob SPer SSea WFar
	'Bobby Charlton' (HT)	LSRN NRog
	BOBBY DAZZLER ('Smi133-02'PBR) (F)	CDoC ESty MRav
	'Bon Silène' (T)	EBls
	BONFIRE ('Bencincuenta') (Min)	NRog
	BONICA ('Meidomonac') (GC) 🏆H6	Widely available
§	BONITA ('Poulen009'PBR) (Renaissance Series) (S)	ECnt
	BONKERS ('Raw1249') (F) **new**	ESty
	'Bonn' (HM/S)	NRog
	BOOGIE-WOOGIE ('Poulyc006'PBR) (Courtyard Series) (ClHT)	ECnt
	BORDURE ABRICOT ('Delbora') (F)	EBls
	BORDURE CAMAIEU ('Delcapo') (S)	EBls
	BORN AGAIN	see *R.* RENAISSANCE
	BOSCOBEL ('Auscousin'PBR) (S)	CRos CSBt ECnt EPfP ESty LBuc LCro LRHS MJon NRHS SWCr
	'Botzaris' (D)	EBls ETWh
	'Bougainville' (N/T)	ETWh
	'Boule de Neige' (Bb)	CBcs CBod CTri EBls ECnt EPfP ETWh LCro LOPS LRHS LSRN MRav NLar NRHS SApu SCob SPer
	'Bouquet de Marie' (HP/N)	ETWh
	'Bouquet d'Or' (N)	EBls ETWh
	BOUQUET PARFAIT ('Lenbofa') (HM) **new**	EBls
	'Bouquet Tout Fait' misapplied	see *R.* 'Nastarana'
	'Bouquet Tout Fait' (N)	EBee ETWh
	BOWLED OVER ('Tandolgnil'PBR) (F) 🏆H6	ESty
§	***bracteata*** (S)	CHll CRHN EBls ECre ETWh EWes SSea
	BRAVE HEART ('Horbondsmile') (F)	CSBt MRav
	BREATH OF LIFE ('Harquanne'PBR) (ClHT)	CDoC EBls LHkn MFry MRav SApu SPer
	BREATHTAKING ('Hargalore'PBR) (HT)	ESty LHkn
	BRIAN STEAD ('Dictrophy') **new**	IDic
	BRIDE ('Fryyearn'PBR) (HT)	EBls LSRN MFry
	'Bride and Groom'PBR (HT)	CBod CDoC ESty LSRN MFry MRav SApu SCoo
	BRIDGE OF SIGHS ('Harglowing'PBR) (Cl)	CDoC ECnt ESty LBuc LHkn LRHS MAsh MFry SPoG SWCr
	BRIGHT AND BREEZY ('Dicjive') (F)	MJon
	BRIGHT AS A BUTTON ('Chewsumsigns'PBR) (S) 🏆H5	EBee EBls ETWh LRHS MAsh NLar SApu SPer SWCr
	BRIGHT FIRE ('Peaxi'PBR) (ClHT)	MSwo SPer
	BRIGHT FUTURE ('Kirora'PBR) (Cl)	CBod CDoC ELon ESty MJon SApu
	BRIGHT IDEAS ('Horcoffdrop') (ClHT)	CGro EBls LRHS MPri
	BRIGHT SMILE ('Dicdance') (F/Patio)	NRog
	BRILLIANT SWEET DREAM ('Frysassy') (Patio)	CSBt ECnt
	BROADLANDS ('Tanmirsch'PBR) (GC)	SApu
	BROTHER CADFAEL ('Ausglobe'PBR) (S)	CArg EHyd EPfP LRHS NRHS SCoo SWCr
	BROWN VELVET ('Maccultra') (F)	MJon SPer
	BROWNIE	see *R.* CHOCOLATE RIPPLES
§	***brunonii*** (Ra)	CExl EBls EWes WFar
	- HPA 1386	GGro
	- KR 10350	WPGP
	- PAB 3083	LEdu
§	- 'La Mortola' (Ra)	ETWh NLar
	BRUSH-STROKES ('Guescolour') (F)	ESty SApu
	BUCKLEBURY BOY ('Webspell') (Patio)	NRog
	'Buff Beauty' (HM) 🏆H6	CArg CBcs CDoC CEnd CGro CSBt CTri EBee EBls ECnt EPfP ETWh LCro LOPS MCot MFry MJon MRav MSwo NLar NRog SApu SCob SEND SPer WCFE WFar
	BUKAVU ('Lenbrirus') (HM)	NRog
	'Bullata'	see *R.* × *centifolia* 'Bullata'
§	'Burgundiaca' (G)	EBls ETWh
	Burgundian rose	see *R.* 'Burgundiaca'
§	BURGUNDY ICE ('Prose'PBR) (F)	CArg CBod EBee EBls EDir ELan EPfP LBuc LCro LOPS LRHS MAsh MFry MJon MRav MSwo NRHS SApu SCob SCoo SMad SPer SPoG SSea SWCr
	'Burgundy Iceberg'	see *R.* BURGUNDY ICE
	'Burgundy Rose'	see *R.* 'Burgundiaca'
	burnet, double pink	see *R. spinosissima* double, pink-flowered
	- - white	see *R. spinosissima* double, white-flowered

	BURNING DESIRE ('Frysizzle') (F)	MFry
	BUTTER CREAM ('Marbutter') (Patio)	NRog
	BUTTERCUP ('Ausband'[PBR]) (S)	LRHS
	BUXOM BEAUTY ('Korbilant'[PBR]) (HT) 🏆[H6]	CArg EBls ELon EPfP LRHS LSRN MGos MJon NRog SSea
	'C.F. Meyer'	see *R.* 'Conrad Ferdinand Meyer'
	CAFÉ AU LAIT ('Simgrey') (F)	ESty
	CAJUN MOON ('Wekonine') (HT)	NRog
	'Cajun Signature' (HT)	NRog
	'Cajun Sunrise' (HT)	NRog
	'Caledonian' (HT)	NRog
	CALENDAR GIRL ('Rawcalendar') (F)	NRog
	californica 'Plena'	see *R. nutkana* 'Plena'
	'Callisto' (HM)	ETWh NLar
§	CALYPSO ('Poulclimb'[PBR]) (ClHT)	SApu
	'Camayeux' (G)	EBls ETWh NLar NRog
	CAMBRIDGESHIRE ('Korhaugen'[PBR]) (GC)	CTri EBls ETWh SApu SCob SPer SSea
	CAMELOT ('Tan05372'[PBR]) (ClF)	ESty
	CAMILLE PISARRO ('Destricol') (F)	EBls ESty
	CAMPINA GOLD ('Viscopper') (F) **new**	MJon
	CANADIAN NORTHLIGHT ('Man-cl') (HT)	NRog
	'Canary Bird'	see *R. xanthina* 'Canary Bird'
	CANDY KISSES ('Simwatu') (HT)	ESty
	CANDY LAND ('Wekrosopela') (ClHT)	ECnt ESty MJon SSea
	CANDYFLOSS ('Raw1233') (F) **new**	ESty
	canina (S)	CArg CBTr CBod CCVT CGro CHab CLnd CPer CTri EHeP EPfP EPom GDam GMcL LBuc LCro LIns LOPS MRav NBwr NLar NWea SCob SEWo SPer WHlf WKor WMat WMou WTSh
	'Cantabrigiensis' (S) 🏆[H6]	EBls ETWh NRog SPer
	CANZONETTA ('Noa84497d') (F)	MAsh SWCr
	CAPEL MANOR HOUSE ('Beajammie') (ClS)	EBls
	'Capitaine John Ingram' (CeMo)	CArg EBls ETWh NLar
	'Captain Christy'	see *R.* 'Climbing Captain Christy'
	'Captain Hayward' (HP)	ETWh
	'Captain Scarlet' (ClMin)	ESty
	'Cardinal de Richelieu' (G)	CArg CBcs CTri EBls EPfP ETWh LCro LOPS LRHS MAsh MRav MSwo NLar NRog SCob SPer SPoG
	CARDINAL HUME ('Harregale') (S)	LHkn
	CAREFREE DAYS ('Meirivoui'[PBR]) (Patio) 🏆[H6]	CBod EBls LBuc LRHS MFry MPri NRHS SApu SPoG SSea
	CARIAD ('Auspanier'[PBR]) (HM)	MJon
	CARING FOR YOU ambig.	LSRN
	'Carmen' (Ru)	EBls
	'Carmenetta' (S)	EBls
	'Carol' (F)	see *R.* 'Carol Amling'
§	'Carol Amling' (F)	LSRN MJon
	CAROL ANN ('Peapost') (F)	LSRN
	'Caroline Testout'	see *R.* 'Madame Caroline Testout'
	CAROLINE VICTORIA ('Harprior'[PBR]) (HT)	LHkn LSRN SApu
	'Caroline's Heart' (S) **new**	EBls
	CAROLYN KNIGHT ('Austurner'[PBR]) (S)	CRos EHyd EPfP LCro LRHS LSRN NRHS SWCr
	CARON KEATING ROSE ('Harkoral'[PBR]) (F)	LHkn
	CARRIS ('Harmanna'[PBR]) (HT)	LHkn MAsh MFry MGos NRHS NTrD
§	CASINO ('Macca') (ClHT)	CTri EBls ETWh SPer
	'Castle Apricot'	see *R.* LAZY DAYS
	'Castle Cream'	see *R.* PERFECT DAY
	CASTLE OF MEY ('Coclucid') (F)	NRog
	'Castle Shrimp Pink'	see *R.* FASCINATION ('Poulmax')
	'Castle Yellow'	see *R.* SUMMER GOLD
	CATHERINE COOKSON ('Noscook') (HT)	NRog
§	'Cécile Brünner' (Poly) 🏆[H5]	CTri EBee EBls ELan ETWh LRHS LSRN MMuc NLar NRog NWea SPer
	CELEBRATING LIFE ('Harvixon') (F)	LHkn
§	CELEBRATION TIME ('Wekcobeju'[PBR]) (F) 🏆[H6]	MJon MRav NRog
§	'Céleste' (A) 🏆[H6]	CTri EBls EPfP ETWh GBin NLar SEND SPer
	'Célina' (CeMo)	GBin LSRN
	'Céline Forestier' (N)	CArg EBee EBls ETWh SPer
§	'Celsiana' (D) 🏆[H7]	EBls ETWh LRHS LSRN NLar NRog SPer
	CENTENAIRE DE LOURDES ('Delge') (F)	EBls
§	× ***centifolia*** (Ce)	EBls ETWh NRog SPer
§	- 'Bullata' (Ce)	EBls
§	- 'Cristata' (Ce) 🏆[H6]	CArg EBls ETWh LEdu NLar NRog SPer WBor
§	- 'De Meaux' (Ce)	EBls ETWh NLar SPer
§	- 'Muscosa' (CeMo)	EBls ETWh GBin LEdu NRog SCob
	- 'Parvifolia'	see *R.* 'Burgundiaca'
§	- 'Shailer's White Moss' (CeMo)	EBls ETWh NRog
	- 'Spong' (Ce)	EBls ETWh
§	- 'Unique' (Ce)	EBls ETWh
§	- 'Unique Panachée' (Ce)	EBls ETWh
	'Centifolia Variegata'	see *R.* × *centifolia* 'Unique Panachée'
	CENTRE OF ATTENTION ('Weksaqureref') (F) **new**	MJon
	CENTRE STAGE ('Chewcreepy'[PBR]) (S/GC) 🏆[H6]	LRHS MJon
	'Cerise Bouquet' (S) 🏆[H6]	EBls ETWh WSpi
	CHAMPAGNE CELEBRATION ('Frylimbo') (HT)	MFry
	CHAMPAGNE CELEBRATION ('Simluck') (F)	ESty
	CHAMPAGNE COCKTAIL ('Horflash') (F)	EDir NRog
§	CHAMPAGNE MOMENT ('Korvanaber'[PBR]) (F) 🏆[H6]	CArg CBcs CBod CDoC CEnd CGro CRos CSBt EBls ECnt ELan EPfP ESty LBuc LRHS LSRN MAsh MFry MGos MJon MPri MRav NRHS SApu SCob SMad SPer SPoG SSea SWCr
	'Champion of the World' (Bb)	EBls
	CHANDOS BEAUTY ('Harmisty'[PBR]) (HT) 🏆[H6]	CDoC CGro CRos ECnt ELon EPfP ESty ETWh EWTr LBuc LHkn LRHS LSRN MAsh MFry MGos MJon MRav NLar SApu SPer SPoG SSea SWCr
	'Chanelle' (F)	EBls NRog SDix SPer

CHANNABELLE ('Hartempter') (F)	LHkn
Chapeau de Napoléon	see *R.* × *centifolia* 'Cristata'
'Chaplin's Pink Climber' (Cl)	ETWh
CHARDONNAY ('Simtely') (F)	ESty
CHARISMA ('Jelroganor') (F)	MPri
CHARISMA ('Noa16071'[PBR]) (HT)	EBls EPfP LBuc LCro LRHS MFry SPoG
CHARISMATIC ('Decmatic') (Patio)	NRog
CHARLES AUSTIN ('Ausles') (S)	CDoC MGos MRav
CHARLES DARWIN ('Auspeet'[PBR]) (S)	EHyd EPfP LBuc LRHS MBNS NLar NRHS SCoo SPer SWCr
'Charles de Mills' (G) 𝒴H6	CBod CDoC CTri EBls ECnt EPfP ETWh LCro LOPS LRHS LSRN MCot MRav MSwo NLar NRog SPer WHer
CHARLES DICKENS ('Raw1064') (HT)	ESty
'Charles Mallerin' (HT)	EBls
CHARLIE'S ROSE ('Tanellepa') (HT) 𝒴H6	ESty LSRN SApu
CHARLOTTE ('Auspoly'[PBR]) (S) 𝒴H6	CRos EHyd ELan EPfP ESty LBuc LCro LOPS LRHS LSRN MBNS MJon MSwo NRHS SCoo SPer SWCr
CHARLOTTE VIELI ('Diclooker') (F)	IDic
CHARMING ('Kenslainte') (F) **new**	MJon
CHARTERED ('Diclingo') (F)	IDic
CHARTREUSE DE PARME ('Delviola') (S)	EBls ESty ETWh MRav NLar
CHATSWORTH ('Tanotax') (Patio/F) 𝒴H6	SPer
CHAWTON COTTAGE ('Harxcel')	LHkn
CH-CHING! ('Wekyesir') (HT) **new**	MJon
CHECKMATE ('Diclanky') (ClF)	CDoC IDic MRav SApu
§ CHEEK TO CHEEK ('Poulslas'[PBR]) (Courtyard Series) (ClMin)	EBls LRHS MAsh SApu
CHEERFUL CHARLIE ('Cocquimmer'[PBR]) (F)	LSRN MRav
CHELSEA BELLE ('Talchelsea') (Min)	NRog
CHERIE	see *R.* RED ABUNDANCE
CHERRY BONICA ('Meipeporia'[PBR]) (S)	CDoC CRos ECnt SWCr
CHERRY BRANDY '85 ('Tanryrandy'[PBR]) (HT)	CSBt
CHERRY HINTON ('Dicprolong') (S)	IDic
CHESHIRE ('Fryelise'[PBR]) (HT)	MFry
CHESTER CATHEDRAL ('Franshine') (HT)	MJon
'Chevy Chase' (Ra)	EBls LRHS MAsh SApu
'Chewton Rose' (S)	EBls
CHIANTI ('Auswine') (S)	EBls ETWh NLar
CHICAGO PEACE ('Johnago') (HT)	CArg EBls NRog SCob
CHIHULY ('Wekscemala') (F) **new**	MJon
CHILD OF ACHIEVEMENT	see *R.* BELLA
CHILD OF MY HEART ('Beapeace') (HT)	EBls
CHILD'S PLAY ('Savachild') (Min)	NRog
CHILTERNS ('Kortemma') (GC)	SCob
'Chinatown' (ClF) 𝒴H6	CArg CTri LRHS MAsh MPri NRog SApu SCob SCoo SPer SWCr
chinensis Jacq. (S)	EBls
– 'Minima' *sensu stricto* hort.	see *R.* 'Rouletii'
– 'Mutabilis'	see *R.* × *odorata* 'Mutabilis'
– 'Old Blush'	see *R.* × *odorata* 'Pallida'
– 'Semperflorens' (S)	EBls WCot
– var. ***spontanea*** (S)	WPGP
– 'White Beauty' (S)	WCot
CHLOE ('Poulen003'[PBR]) (Renaissance Series) (S)	ECnt ESty ETWh LSRN NLar
CHLOE'S STAR ('Pazstar') (Min)	NRog
'Chloris' (A)	EBee ETWh NLar NRog
CHOCOLATE DROP ('Simchocbab') (F) **new**	ESty
§ CHOCOLATE RIPPLES ('Simstripe') (Cl)	ESty
CHOIR OF ANGELS	see *R.* OUR JANE
CHRIS ('Kirsan'[PBR]) (ClHT)	CArg ESty LSRN MJon SApu
CHRIS BEARDSHAW ('Wekmeredoc'[PBR]) (HT)	MJon
CHRISTIAN DIOR ('Meilie') (HT)	EBls
CHRISTOPHER ('Cocopher') (HT)	LSRN
CHRISTOPHER COLUMBUS ('Poulbico'[PBR]) (F)	SApu
'Chrysler Imperial' (HT)	EBls
CHÂTEAU DE MUNSBACH ('Vel11mreal') (S) **new**	EBls
CHUCKLES ('Simmimi') (F)	ESty
CIDER CUP ('Dicladida') (Min/Patio)	NRog
CINCO DE MAYO	see *R.* CELEBRATION TIME
'Cinderella' ambig.	SWCr
'Cinderella' (Min)	CSBt
'Cinderella' (Ra)	EBee
CINDERELLA ('Korfobalt') (ClS)	ETWh MJon
CITY LIVERY ('Harhero 2000') (F)	LHkn
CITY OF CARLSBAD	see *R.* HANKY PANKY
'City of Leeds' (F)	MGos SPer
CITY OF LONDON ('Harukfore') (F)	CSBt EBls LRHS
CITY OF YORK	see *R.* 'Direktör Benschop'
CLAIR MATIN ('Meimont') (ClS)	EBls ETWh
CLAIRE AUSTIN ('Ausprior'[PBR]) (Cl)	CDoC CRos EHyd EPfP ESty LCro LRHS MAsh MJon MSwo NLar NRHS SCob SCoo SPoG
CLAIRE BEAR ('Webwelcome') (F)	NRog
'Claire Jacquier' (N)	EBls ETWh
CLAIRE MARSHALL ('Harunite'[PBR]) (F)	ECnt EPfP ESty LHkn LRHS SApu SRGP SSea
CLAIRE RAYNER ('Macpandem') (F/Patio)	MJon
CLAIRE ROSE ('Auslight'[PBR]) (S)	LSRN
'Clarence House' (Cl)	CGro EBls EPfP LRHS MAsh
CLARET ('Frykristal'[PBR]) (HT) 𝒴H6	EPfP MFry MJon MRav SApu
CLAUDE MONET ('Delstrirocrem'[PBR]) (Cl)	EBls ESty SSea
CLAUDE MONET ('Jacdesa') (HT)	EBls ESty

CLEAR COVER ('Poultc013') (Towne & Country Series) (GC/S)	ETWh
'Clementina Carbonieri' (T)	EBls ETWh
CLEO ('Beebop') (HT)	LSRN
'Cliff Richard' (F)	ESty LSRN NRog
'Climbing Alec's Red' (ClHT)	SPer
'Climbing Allgold' (ClF)	EDir
'Climbing Arthur Bell' (ClF)	CGro CSBt CTri ELon ESty ETWh MAsh MPri MSwo NRog SApu SCob SCoo SPer SPoG SRGP SSea SWCr
'Climbing Ballerina' (Ra)	CSBt
§ CLIMBING BARONNE EDMOND DE ROTHSCHILD ('Meigrisosar') (ClHT)	CSBt
CLIMBING BETTINA ('Mepalsar') (ClHT)	EBls
'Climbing Blue Moon' (ClHT)	ELan ELon ESty SApu SSea
§ 'Climbing Captain Christy' (ClHT)	EBls MAsh
'Climbing Cécile Brünner' (ClPoly) ♀H5	CArg CEnd CSBt CTri EBls ECnt EPfP ETWh LCro LOPS LSRN MCot MRav NRog SApu SCob SEND SNig SPer SSea SWCr
'Climbing Château de Clos-Vougeot' (ClHT)	EBls
§ 'Climbing Columbia' (ClHT)	EShb ETWh NRog
'Climbing Crimson Glory' (ClHT)	EBls EPfP ETWh NRog SSea
§ 'Climbing Devoniensis' (ClT)	EBls ETWh
'Climbing Ena Harkness' (ClHT)	CBod CRos EBls LHkn MRav NRog SPer SPoG SWCr
'Climbing Étoile de Hollande' (ClHT) ♀H5	CSBt CTri EBee EBls EDir ELon EPfP ETWh LBuc LCro LOPS MBNS MJon MPri MRav NRog SApu SMad SPer SPoG SSea SWCr WBor
'Climbing General MacArthur' (ClHT)	EBls
§ 'Climbing Golden Dawn' (ClHT)	EBls
'Climbing Home Sweet Home' (ClHT)	LSRN
'Climbing Iceberg' (ClF) ♀H5	Widely available
'Climbing Jazz'	see *R.* THAT'S JAZZ
'Climbing Josephine Bruce' (ClHT)	EBls ETWh
§ 'Climbing Lady Hillingdon' (ClT) ♀H4	CArg CGro EBls ELan EPfP ETWh LBuc LRHS LSRN MRav NLar SPer SSea SWCr
'Climbing Lady Sylvia' (ClHT)	CSBt EBls ESty ETWh LRHS LSRN NRHS NRog SPer
'Climbing Little White Pet'	see *R.* 'Félicité Perpétue'
'Climbing Madame Butterfly' (ClHT) ♀H6	EBls
'Climbing Madame Caroline Testout' (ClHT)	EBls ETWh NRog
'Climbing Masquerade' (ClF)	CBod CGro CTri EBls ELan ETWh MRav NRog SApu SCob SPer SSea
'Climbing Mrs Aaron Ward' (ClHT)	EBls
'Climbing Mrs Herbert Stevens' (ClHT)	EBls EPfP ETWh MRav NRog SPer
'Climbing Mrs Sam McGredy' (ClHT)	CArg CSBt EBls ETWh NRog
'Climbing Niphetos' (ClT)	EBls
'Climbing Ophelia' (ClHT)	EBls ETWh
CLIMBING ORANGE SUNBLAZE ('Meiji Katarsar') (ClMin)	SPer
§ 'Climbing Paul Lédé' (ClT)	CEnd EBls ETWh NLar
'Climbing Peace' (ClHT)	ETWh
§ 'Climbing Pompon de Paris' (ClMinCh)	EBls MNrw MRav SEND SMrm SPer
'Climbing Roundelay' (Cl)	EBls
'Climbing Ruby Wedding' (ClHT)	LSRN
'Climbing Shot Silk' (ClHT) ♀H6	EDir ETWh SPer
§ 'Climbing Souvenir de la Malmaison' (ClBb)	EBls ETWh SPer
'Climbing White Cloud'	see *R.* WHITE CLOUD ('Korstacha')
CLODAGH MCGREDY ('Macswanle'[PBR]) (F)	MJon
CLOUD NINE ('Fryextra'[PBR]) (HT)	MFry
'Clytemnestra' (HM)	EBls
COACHELLA ('Jackhill') (F)	NRog
COCO ('Korferse') (F)	LSRN
'Coconut Ice' (HT)	SCoo SWCr
COLCHESTER BEAUTY ('Cansend') (F)	ECnt
§ 'Colonel Fabvier' (Ch)	EBls ETWh NLar
colonial white	see *R.* 'Sombreuil'
COLORIFIC ('Wekplalajaro') (F) **new**	MJon
'Columbian'	see *R.* 'Climbing Columbia'
COMEBACK	see *R.* TIMELESS PINK
'Commandant Beaurepaire' (Bb)	EBls ETWh NRog
common moss	see *R.* × *centifolia* 'Muscosa'
COMMONWEALTH GLORY ('Harclue'[PBR]) (HT)	LHkn
'Compassion' (ClHT) ♀H6	Widely available
'Complicata' (G)	CBcs CTri EBls EPfP ETWh MRav NLar NRog SApu SEND SMad SPer
'Comte de Chambord' misapplied	see *R.* 'Madame Boll'
COMTESSE ANDRÉ D'OULTREMONT ('Vel15mkama') (HM) **new**	EBls
'Comtesse Cécile de Chabrillant' (HP)	EBls ETWh
'Comtesse de Lacépède' misapplied	see *R.* 'Du Maître d'Ecole'
§ 'Comtesse de Murinais' (DMo)	EBls
'Comtesse d'Oxford' (HP)	EBls
§ 'Comtesse du Caÿla' (Ch)	EBls
'Comtesse O'Gorman' (HP)	EBls
'Comtesse Vandal' (HT)	EBls
CONCERT	see *R.* CALYPSO
'Conchita' (Poly)	MBros
'Conditorum' (G)	EBls ETWh NLar NRog
CONGRATULATIONS ('Korlift') (HT)	CBcs CBod CSBt ECnt EDir IArd LCro LOPS LSRN MGos MJon MRav NRog SApu SCob SCoo SPer SWCr
§ 'Conrad Ferdinand Meyer' (Ru)	EBee EBls NRog SPer
CONSERVATION ('Cocdimple') (Min/Patio)	SCoo SWCr
CONSTANCE FINN ('Hareden'[PBR]) (F)	LHkn
'Constance Spry' (ClS) ♀H6	CArg EBee EBls EDir EHyd EPfP ETWh LCro LOPS LRHS MCot MGos MJon MMuc MRav MSwo

		NLar NRHS NRog SCob SCoo SEND SPer SWCr
§	'Cooperi' (Ra)	CRHN EBls EPfP ETWh SSea WKif WPGP
	Cooper's Burmese	see *R.* 'Cooperi'
	'Copenhagen' (ClHT)	EBls
	'Copper Delight' (F)	NRog
	COPPER LIGHTS ('Simhigh') (HT)	ESty
	'Coral Creeper' (ClHT)	CRHN
	'Coral Dawn' (ClHT)	EBls
	CORAL GEM ('Simplan') (HT)	ESty
	CORAL REEF ('Cocdarlee') (Min/Patio)	EDir
	CORAL SWEET DREAM ('Fryrader') (Patio)	MFry
	'Coralie' (D)	EBls
	'Cornelia' (HM) ♀H6	CArg CBcs CTri EBee EBls EPfP ETWh IArd LCro LOPS LRHS LSRN MCot MJon NLar NRog SCob SMad SPer
	CORONATION STREET ('Wekswetrup') (F)	LSRN
	'Coryana' (S)	EBls ETWh
	corymbifera (S)	EBls
	COSMOPOLITAN ('Simgrid') (HT)	ESty
	cottage maid	see *R.* × *centifolia* 'Unique Panachée'
	COTTAGE ROSE ('Ausglisten') (S)	LSRN
	COUNTESS OF WESSEX ('Beacream') (S)	EBls EPfP LRHS NRHS
	COUNTRY MUSIC ('Harcheer') (S)	LSRN NRog
§	COUNTY OF STAFFORDSHIRE ('Korsoalgu'[PBR]) (GC/S)	MJon
	COUNTY OF YORKSHIRE ('Korstarnow'[PBR]) (GC) ♀H6	EBls ESty
	COURAGE ('Poulduf'[PBR]) (HT)	ECnt
	'Cramoisi Supérieur' (Ch)	EBls ETWh
	CRAZY FOR YOU ('Wekroalt'[PBR]) (F) ♀H6	EBls ESty LSRN MJon SWCr
	CRAZY IN LOVE ('Raw1127') (S) **new**	ESty
	CREAM ABUNDANCE ('Harflax'[PBR]) (Abundance Series) (F)	LHkn SApu SSea
	CREAM DREAM ('Koromtar') (HT)	CTri NRog NTrD
	CREAMCRACKER ('Dicorigin') (F)	IDic
	CREAMSICLE (Min)	NRog
	CRÈME DE LA CRÈME ('Gancre'[PBR]) (ClHT)	CBod CDoC CRos CSBt EBee EBls ECnt ELan ESty ETWh LRHS MJon MRav NLar SApu SPer SPoG SSea SWCr
	'Crépuscule' (N)	EBee EBls ETWh NLar
	crested moss	see *R.* × *centifolia* 'Cristata'
	CRIMSON BLUSH ('Sieson') (A)	NRog
	CRIMSON CASCADE ('Fryclimbdown') (ClHT) ♀H6	CBod CDoC CGro EBls ELan ESty LBuc LRHS MAsh MFry MGos MRav MSwo SApu SPer SPoG
	crimson damask	see *R. gallica* var. *officinalis*
	'Crimson Descant' (ClHT)	ECnt
	'Crimson Glory' (HT)	CArg CTri EBls NLar
	'Crimson Shower' (Ra)	CArg CTri ELan ETWh LPar LRHS MBNS MMuc MSwo NRog SApu SPer WHer
	CRIMSON SWEET DREAM ('Frynogo') (Patio)	CSBt ECnt ESty MFry SCoo SWCr
	'Cristata'	see *R.* × *centifolia* 'Cristata'
	CROCUS ROSE ('Ausquest'[PBR]) (S) ♀H6	EHyd EPfP LCro LRHS NRHS SCob
	CROWN PRINCESS MARGARETA ('Auswinter'[PBR]) (Cl) ♀H6	CDoC CRos EHyd ELan EPfP ESty LBuc LCro LOPS LRHS LSRN MAsh NLar NRHS SCob SCoo SPer SPoG SWCr
	cuisse de nymphe	see *R.* 'Great Maiden's Blush'
	CUMBERLAND ('Harnext'[PBR]) (ClF)	ETWh LHkn NLar
	'Cupid' (ClHT)	EBls ETWh
I	'Cutie' (Patio)	ESty
	cymosa	EBls
	- 'Rebecca Rushforth' (Cl)	EBee WPGP
	'Cynthia Brooke' (HT)	EBls
	DACAPO ('Poulcy012'[PBR]) (Courtyard Series) (ClPatio)	ECnt
	'D'Aguesseau' (G)	ETWh
	DAILY SKETCH ('Macai') (F)	ESty
	'Dainty Bess' (HT)	EBls ETWh NLar
	'Dale Farm' (F/Patio)	NRog
	× ***damascena*** var. ***bifera***	see *R.* × *damascena* var. *semperflorens*
	- 'Kazanlik' (D)	EBls ETWh NRog
§	- 'Professeur Émile Perrot' (D)	NLar WFar
§	- var. ***semperflorens*** (D) ♀H6	EBls ETWh NLar NRog
	- 'Trigintipetala' misapplied	see *R.* × *damascena* 'Professeur Émile Perrot'
§	- 'Versicolor' (D)	EBls SPer SSea
§	'Dame de Coeur' (HT)	EPfP
	DAME JUDI DENCH ('Ausquaker'[PBR]) (HM)	CRos CSBt EPfP ESty LCro LRHS MBNS MJon MSwo NLar SCoo SWCr
	'Danaë' (HM)	EBls ETWh NRog
	DANCING FLAME ('Tucflame') (Min)	NRog
	DANCING PINK ('Hendan') (F)	NRog
	DANCING QUEEN ('Fryfestoon') (ClHT) ♀H6	CArg CDoC CGro EBls ECnt LBuc LRHS LSRN MAsh MFry MRav SApu SSea
	DANCING SUNSET ('Guesunusal') (ClHT)	ESty
	DANIEL ('Webwhite') (HT)	ESty
	DANNY BOY ('Dicxcon'[PBR]) (Patio)	IDic LSRN MJon
§	'Danse du Feu' (ClF)	CArg CBcs CSBt CTri EBls ELan ETWh LRHS MAsh MGos MJon MRav NRog SApu SCob SPer SWCr
	'Daphne' ambig.	EBls LSRN
	DARCEY BUSSELL ('Ausdecorum'[PBR]) (S) ♀H6	CGro CRos CSBt EBee ECnt EHyd ELan EPfP ESty LBuc LCro LOPS LRHS LSRN MAsh MGos MJon MSwo NLar NRHS SCoo SPer SPoG SWCr
	'Darius' (G)	NRog
	DARLING FLAME ('Meilucca') (Min)	EDir
	'Darling Jenny' (HT)	LSRN NRog
	DAVID WHITFIELD ('Gana') (F)	LSRN
	davidii (S)	EBls
	DAVID'S STAR ('Hordadstar') (HT)	LSRN NRog
	DAWN CHORUS ('Dicquasar') (HT) ♀H6	CDoC CSBt EPfP ESty LRHS MRav SApu SCob SPer SPoG SSea
	'Daybreak' (HM)	CTri EBls ETWh NLar NRog
	'De Meaux'	see *R.* × *centifolia* 'De Meaux'

'De Meaux, White'	see *R.* 'White de Meaux'
§ 'De Resht' (DPo) ♀H7	CArg CDoC CTri EBls ECnt EPfP ETWh LBuc LRHS MAsh MCot MJon MPri NLar SPer SSea
DEAR BARBARA ('Rawbar') (HT)	LSRN
DEAR DAD ('Smi87-02') (HT)	ESty
'Dear Daughter' (F)	ESty
DEAR JOAN ('Rawjo') (F)	LSRN
§ DEAR MARGARET ('Raw293') (HT)	LSRN
DEAR MICHAEL ('Raw1065') (F)	LSRN
'Dearest' (F)	CArg CTri NRog SCob SPer
'Debbie Thomas' (HT)	LSRN NRog
DEB'S DELIGHT ('Legsweet'[PBR]) (F)	LSRN MJon
'Debutante' (Ra) ♀H7	CRHN EBls ETWh
'Deep Secret' (HT)	CArg CBcs CSBt CTri EBls ECnt EDir ELan ELon EPfP ESty LBuc LRHS MAsh MCot MFry MJon MPri MRav NRog SApu SCoo SPer SSea SWCr
'Deidre Hall' (HT)	LSRN NRog
DELIGHTFUL ('Curspoglo') (ClMin)	ECnt ESty MJon
DELLA BALFOUR ('Harblend'[PBR]) (ClHT)	EBls LHkn SApu SSea
DESDEMONA ('Auskindling'[PBR]) (HM)	CRos ECnt EHyd EPfP LRHS MAsh MBNS MJon NLar NRHS
'Designer Sunset' (Patio)	EPfP MAsh
'Desperado' (HT)	NRog
§ 'Desprez à Fleur Jaune' (N)	EBls ETWh IArd
'Devoniensis' (ClT)	see *R.* 'Climbing Devoniensis'
DIAMOND ('Korgazell'[PBR]) (Patio) ♀H6	LSRN MJon SApu
'Diamond 60th Anniversary' (F) **new**	NTrD
DIAMOND ANNIVERSARY ('Morsixty') (Min)	LSRN
'Diamond Celebration' (HT)	LSRN
DIAMOND DAYS ('Hartribe'[PBR]) (HT)	CDoC ESty LHkn LSRN MRav SPoG
DIAMOND DAYS FOREVER ('Fryjess'[PBR]) (F)	ECnt LSRN MAsh MFry SApu
DIAMOND EYES ('Wekwibypur') (Min)	CBod CDoC ECnt ELon ESty MJon
'Diamond Jubilee' (HT)	CEnd CSBt EBls LRHS
DIAMOND JUBILEE ('Tan022260') (HT)	CArg ELan MFry NRog SPer
DIAMOND WEDDING ('Raw1150') (F)	ESty
'Diamond Wishes'	see *R.* MISTY HIT
DIANA ('Tananaid'[PBR]) (HT)	LSRN
DIANE BOYD ('Dicgalaxy') (S) **new**	IDic
DICK CLARK ('Wekfunk') (HT) **new**	MJon
DICK'S DELIGHT ('Dicwhistle') (GC)	LSRN
DIE WELT ('Diekor') (HT)	NRog
DIENIE STEWART ('Dicpraise') (F)	IDic
DINKY ('Velheav') (HM) **new**	EBls
DIORESSENCE ('Deldiore') (F)	ESty
§ 'Direktör Benschop' (ClF)	CGro EBls EPfP SWCr
DIXIELAND LINDA ('Beadix') (ClHT)	EBls LRHS MAsh
DIZZY HEIGHTS ('Fryblissful'[PBR]) (ClHT) ♀H6	ELon EPfP MFry MRav NLar SApu SGsty SPer SSea
'Docteur Grill' (T)	EBls
DOCTOR DICK ('Cocbaden') (HT)	NRog
'Doctor Huey' (Cl)	CRHN
DOCTOR JO ('Fryatlanta'[PBR]) (F)	MFry
DOCTOR JOHN DICKMAN ('Briman') (Min)	NRog
DOCTOR MICHAEL NOBLE ('Manmichael') (Min)	NRog
DOCTOR TOMMY CAIRNS ('Benwales') (Min)	NRog
DOCTOR TROY GARRET ('Weltroy') (Patio)	NRog
'Doctor W. Van Fleet' (Ra)	EBls
'Dogwood' (S)	NRog
DOLCE VITA ('Delcentoran') (F)	ESty MJon
DOLLY ('Poulvision') (F)	LSRN
DOMAINE DE CHANTILLY ('Delagak') (HT)	ESty
DONA MARTIN ('Mardona') (HT)	NRog
'Donald Prior' (F)	EBls
'Doncasteri'	EBls
DONNA ('Pekcoupamaple') (HT)	LSRN
'Doreen' (HT)	LSRN NRog
DORIS DAY ('Wekmajuchi') (F) **new**	MJon
DORIS MORGAN ('Brimorgan') (Min)	NRog
'Doris Tysterman' (HT)	CTri EBls NRog SCob SPer
DOROTHY ('Cocrocket'[PBR]) (F)	LSRN MRav
DOROTHY HOUSE ('Fryniffi') (F)	MFry
'Dorothy Perkins' (Ra)	CArg CBod CRHN CTri EBls EDir ETWh MFry MRav NPer NRog SApu SCob SPer
'Dortmund' (S) ♀H7	EBls ETWh SPer
DOUBLE DELIGHT ('Andeli') (HT)	EBls ELan ELon ESty LSRN MJon NRog SCob SPer SSea
DOUBLE GOLD ('Savadouble') (Patio)	NRog
DOUBLE TWIST ('Raw1222') (F) **new**	ESty
DOUGLAS ('Cocfresco') (F)	LSRN
DRAGA ('Bozdragfra') (Frayla Series) (S) **new**	ETWh
DREAM LOVER ('Peayetti'[PBR]) (Patio)	ESty MJon
'Dreaming Spires' (ClHT)	EDir MSwo SApu SPer
'Dresden Doll' (MinMo)	EBls
§ 'Du Maître d'Ecole' (G)	EBls WHer
DUBLIN BAY ('Macdub') (ClF) ♀H6	Widely available
'Duc de Guiche' (G) ♀H7	EBls EPfP ETWh MMuc WHer
'Ducher' (Ch/T)	ETWh
DUCHESS OF CORNWALL ('Tan97159'[PBR]) (HT) ♀H6	CDoC CSBt EBee EBls ECnt ELan ESty ETWh MFry MGos MRav NLar SApu SCoo SMad SPer SSea
DUCHESS OF DEVONSHIRE ('Stortebekerkal 2017') (HT)	MFry
'Duchess of Portland'	see *R.* 'Portlandica'
DUCHESS OF YORK	see *R.* SUNSEEKER
'Duchesse d'Angoulême' (Ce × G) ♀H7	EBls ETWh NRog
'Duchesse d'Auerstädt' (N)	EBls
'Duchesse de Berry' (G)	NRog
'Duchesse de Brabant' (HT)	EBls

	'Duchesse de Buccleugh' (G)	EBls ETWh
§	'Duchesse de Montebello' (G) ♀[H7]	EBls ETWh NLar
	'Duke of Edinburgh' (HP)	EBls
	DUKE OF EDINBURGH (Patio)	see *R.* THE GOLD AWARD ROSE
	'Duke of Wellington' (HP)	EBls ETWh
	'Duke of Windsor' (HT)	SPer
	DUNHAM MASSEY ('Beajelly') (S)	EBee EBls LRHS MAsh
	'Dunwich Rose' (SpH)	EBls EPfP ETWh MJon NLar NRog WCot
§	'Duplex' (S)	EBls ETWh NLar
	'Dupontii' (S) ♀[H6]	EBls ETWh
	'Dupuy Jamain' (HP)	EBls
	'Dusky Maiden' (F)	EBls ELon ETWh NLar
	'Dutch Gold' (HT)	CArg EDir MGos NRog SPer
	DYNAMIC DUO ('Fryvogue') (F)	ECnt
	DYNAMITE	see *R.* HIGH FLYER
	'E.H. Morse'	see *R.* 'Ernest H. Morse'
	'Earl of Eldon' (N)	ETWh
	'Easlea's Golden Rambler' (Ra) ♀[H5]	CArg EBls ETWh NLar
	EAST PARK ('Harjope'[PBR]) (HT)	LHkn
§	EASY DOES IT ('Harpageant'[PBR]) (F) ♀[H6]	CBod CDoC ECnt ELan ESty ETWh LHkn MJon MRav NLar
	EASY GOING ('Harflow'[PBR]) (F) ♀[H6]	IArd LHkn SWCr
§	EBB TIDE ('Weksmopur'[PBR]) (F)	CSBt EBls ECnt EPfP ESty LRHS MAsh MJon SApu SPoG SWCr
	ecae (S)	ETWh
	'Éclair' (HP)	EBls
	'Eddie Bailey' (Cl)	NRog
	'Eddie's Crimson' (*moyesii* hybrid)	LSRN
	'Eddie's Jewel' (*moyesii* hybrid)	EBls LSRN
	'Eden Rose' (HT)	NLar
	EDEN ROSE '88 ('Meiviolin') (ClHT)	EBls ETWh MJon SApu SGsty SPer SWCr
	'Edith Bellenden' (RH)	EBls
	EDITH HOLDEN ('Chewlegacy') (F)	EBls
	EDWARD'S ROSE ('Smi73/7/97') (F)	ELan ESty LSRN MRav
	eglanteria	see *R. rubiginosa*
	EGLANTYNE ('Ausmak'[PBR]) (S)	CRos EHyd ELan EPfP LCro LRHS NRHS SCob SPer SWCr
	'Eileen' (F)	NRog
	EIRENE ('Tan10696') (F)	CBod MFry
	'Eleanor' (Patio)	LSRN
	ELEANOR ('Poulberin'[PBR]) (S)	ECnt ETWh LSRN
§	***elegantula*** 'Persetosa' (S)	EBls ETWh
	'Elias' (S)	NRog
§	ELINA ('Dicjana') (HT) ♀[H6]	EBls ECnt LSRN MJon MRav NRog SPer
	ELIZABETH ASHBROOK ('Athybonper') (S)	MFry
	ELIZABETH CASSON ('Harkish'[PBR]) (F)	LHkn
	'Elizabeth Harkness' (HT)	LHkn SPer
	'Elizabeth Harwood' (Cl)	EBls
	ELIZABETH OF GLAMIS ('Macel') (F)	CTri EBls NRog SPer
	ELIZABETH STUART ('Maselstu') (Generosa Series) (S)	LSRN
	ELLE ('Meibderos'[PBR]) (HT)	LSRN
	ELLEN ('Auscup') (S)	LSRN
	'Ellen Willmott' (HT)	EBls ETWh
	'Elmshorn' (S)	EBls
	ELOISE ('Kirsandra'[PBR]) (HT)	LSRN MJon
	ELVIS ('Adablarop'[PBR]) (HT)	LSRN
	ELY CATHEDRAL ('Beajolly') (S)	EBls
	EMILIA MARIA	see *R.* LA ROSE DE MOLINARD
	EMILY ('Ausburton') (S)	LSRN
	EMILY BRONTË ('Ausearnshaw') (S)	CDoC CRos CSBt ESty LCro LRHS MJon SPer
	EMILY DAVIES ('Dicmars') (F)	IDic
	'Emily Gray' (Ra)	CRHN EBee EBls ETWh LRHS LSRN MPri NRog SCob SPer
	EMILY VICTORIA ('Boshipeacon') (F)	LSRN
	EMMA CLARE ('Sheriscarlet') (Patio)	NRog
	EMMA MAY ('Sherisilver') (HT)	NRog
	EMPEREUR CHARLES IV ('Vel15mscwi') (F) **new**	EBls
	'Empereur du Maroc' (HP)	EBls ETWh
	'Ena Harkness' (HT)	CDoC CTri EBls LHkn LRHS NRHS NRog SCob
	ENCHANTRESS ('Tan97281'[PBR]) (HT)	EBee EBls SSea
§	'Enfant de France' (HP)	EBls LSRN
	ENGLAND'S HEROES ('Webjack') (F)	NRog
	ENGLISH GARDEN ('Ausbuff') (S)	CArg ETWh LSRN SPer
	'English Miss' (F)	CArg CDoC CGro EBls ECnt LRHS MAsh MFry MGos MRav SApu SCob SPer SPoG SWCr
	ENGLISH SONNET	see *R.* SAMARITAN
	EQUITY ('Harplayer') (F)	LHkn
	'Erfurt' (HM)	EBee EBls ETWh
§	'Ernest H. Morse' (HT)	CSBt CTri EBls MJon NRog SPer
	ESCAPADE ('Harpade') (F) ♀[H6]	EBls NRog
	ESDAILE ROSE ('Cocglazer') (F) **new**	MJon
	'Esme' (HT)	ETWh
	ESPECIALLY FOR YOU ('Fryworthy'[PBR]) (HT) ♀[H6]	CSBt ESty LSRN MFry SApu SSea SWCr
	ESPERANZA ('Harquark'[PBR]) (S)	LHkn
	ESPRIT D'AMOUR ('Visamalbi') (S) **new**	MJon
	ESSEX ('Poulnoz') (GC)	SApu SCob SPer
	'Etain' (Ra)	ECnt
§	'Étendard' (ClHT)	EBls ETWh MRav NLar SPer SPoG SWCr
	ETERNAL PASSION ('Viskavepas') (F) **new**	MJon
	ETERNALLY YOURS ('Macspeego'[PBR]) (HT)	ESty MJon
	ETERNITY ('Noa150097') (F)	MAsh SWCr
	ETERNITY ('Ricity') (Min)	LRHS
	'Ethel' (Ra)	EBls ETWh LSRN NLar SApu
	'Étoile de Hollande' (HT)	CArg CDoC CTri EBee EBls EHyd LRHS LSRN MGos NLar SCob
	'Etoile de Lyon' (T)	EBls
	'Eugénie Guinoisseau' (Mo)	ETWh
	EUPHORIA ('Intereup'[PBR]) (GC/S)	SApu

	EUREKA ('Meizambaizt'PBR) (HT)	CEnd LRHS MJon
	'European Touch' (HT)	NRog
	EUSTACIA VYE ('Ausegdon') (S) **new**	CArg CGro MAsh NLar
	'Eva' (HM)	EBls
	'Evangeline' (Ra)	EBls NRog
	EVE RUGGIEN ('Adarylop') (HT)	LSRN
	EVELYN ('Aussaucer') (S)	CArg CSBt ESty ETWh LSRN MJon SApu
§	EVELYN FISON ('Macev') (F)	CSBt CTri EBls EDir LSRN NRog SCob SPer
	'Evelyn May' (HT)	EBls EPfP LRHS LSRN MAsh NRHS
	'Everest Double Fragrance' (F)	EBls
	EXCELLENT COVER ('Poultc017'PBR) (Towne & Country Series) **new**	CBod
	'Excelsa' (Ra)	CSBt CTri EBls EGrI EPfP ETWh IArd MAsh NRog SCob SGsty SPoG WHlf
	EYE OF THE STORM ('Wekeots') (F)	CDoC ETWh MJon NLar SApu
	EYE OF THE TIGER ('Chewbullseye'PBR) (*persica* hybrid) (S)	CDoC CEnd CGro CRos CWal EBls ECnt EHyd ELan EPfP ESty ETWh LRHS MAsh MFry MJon MPri NRHS SApu SMad SPoG SSea SWCr
	EYEOPENER ('Interop') (S/GC)	EBls
	EYES FOR YOU ('Pejbigeye') (F) 🏆H6	CEnd CGro CRos CSBt EBee EBls EPfP ESty ETWh LBuc LRHS MAsh MFry MJon MPri NLar NRHS SApu SMad SPoG SSea SWCr WCot WKif
	'F.E. Lester'	see *R.* 'Francis E. Lester'
§	'F.J. Grootendorst' (Ru)	EBls ETWh NRog WHer
	FAB AT 50 ('Woraunt') (F)	LSRN NTrD
	FABULOUS AT 40 ('Webcountry') (F)	LSRN
	FABULOUS AT 50 ('Rawfabsal') (F)	LSRN
	FABULOUS AT 65 ('Raw1041') (F)	LSRN
	FABULOUS AT 70	LSRN
	FABULOUS AT 80 ('Rawcox') (F)	LSRN
	FAB-U-LOUS! ('Forfab') (HT)	ESty
	'Fabvier'	see *R.* 'Colonel Fabvier'
	FAIR EVA ('Seaeva') (Ra/GC)	ESty
	FAIRHOPE ('Talfairhope') (Min)	NRog
	FAIRY QUEEN ('Sperien'PBR) (Poly/GC)	CBod
	'Fairy Rose'	see *R.* 'The Fairy'
	FAITH ('Horfaiwil') (HT)	NRog
	FAITHFUL ('Haressay'PBR) (F)	LHkn
	FAITHFUL FRIEND ('Beachallenge') (S)	EBls LSRN
	FALSTAFF ('Ausverse'PBR) (S)	CArg CRos CSBt EBee EHyd EPfP LCro LRHS LSRN MRav MSwo NLar NRHS SCob SCoo SPer SWCr
	FAMILY LIFE ('Hargladly') (F)	LHkn
	FANCY PANTS ('Kinfancy') (Min)	NRog
	'Fantin-Latour' (Ce) 🏆H6	CArg CBod CDoC CTri EBls ELan ETWh LEdu LRHS MCot MMuc NLar NRog SEND SPer
	fargesii hort.	see *R. moyesii* var. *fargesii*
	farreri f. ***persetosa***	see *R. elegantula* 'Persetosa'
§	FASCINATION ('Poulmax'PBR) (F) 🏆H6	CArg SApu SCob SPer
	FATHER'S FAVOURITE ('Gandoug'PBR) (F)	LSRN
	FAYE ('Mattgis') (HT) **new**	MJon
	fedtschenkoana Regel	EBls
	aff. ***fedtschenkoana***	ETWh
	FÉE DES NEIGES	see *R.* ICEBERG
	'Felicia' (HM) 🏆H6	CArg CSBt CTri EBee EBls ECnt ETWh EWTr LRHS MAsh MCot MJon MRav MSwo NLar NRog SApu SCob SEND SPer WKif
	FELICITAS ('Korberis'PBR) (S)	NRog
	'Félicité Parmentier' (A × D) 🏆H6	CArg EBls EPfP ETWh NLar NRog SPer
§	'Félicité Perpétue' (Ra) 🏆H6	CArg CBcs CBod CRHN CSBt CTri EBee EBls EHyd EPfP ETWh LRHS MRav MSwo NLar NRog SApu SCob SEND SPer SWCr WFar
	'Fellemberg' (ClCh)	ETWh
	FELLOWSHIP ('Harwelcome') (F) 🏆H6	CBod EBls EDir LCro LHkn LOPS SCob SSea SWCr
	'Ferdinand Pichard' (Bb) 🏆H6	CArg CBcs CRos CSBt CTri EBls ECnt EHyd ELon EPfP ESty ETWh LCro LOPS LRHS MAsh MCot MPri MRav NLar NRHS NRog SApu SMad SPer SSea SWCr WFar WKif
	FERDY ('Keitoli'PBR) (GC)	EBls SApu SPer
I	'Fern's Rose' (F)	LSRN
	ferruginea	see *R. glauca* Pourr.
	FESTIVAL ('Kordialo') (Patio)	MRav SPer
	FESTIVE JEWEL ('Beacost') (S)	EBls EPfP LRHS MAsh
	FETZER SYRAH ROSÉ ('Harextra'PBR) (S)	LHkn LRHS
§	'Feuermeer' (F)	NRog
	'Ffion' (Patio)	NRog
	FIGHTING TEMERAIRE ('Austrava'PBR) (S)	CRos EHyd EPfP LRHS NLar NRHS SWCr
	FIGURINE ('Benfig') (Min)	NRog
§	***filipes*** 'Kiftsgate' (Ra) 🏆H6	CArg CBcs CDoC CGro CSBt CTri EBee EBls ECnt ELan EPfP ETWh GKin LEdu LRHS MFry MJon NLar NRHS NRog NWea SApu SCob SPer SWCr WBor WKif
§	'Fimbriata' (Ru)	EBls ETWh LEdu SPer
	FIONA ('Meibeluxen') (S/GC)	EBls LSRN MSwo SEdd
	FIREBIRD ('Kortragoso'PBR) (F)	SApu
	'Firecracker' (F)	NRog
	FIRESTAR	see *R.* EASY DOES IT
	FIRST GREAT WESTERN ('Oracharpam'PBR) (HT)	CSBt ELon ESty MJon
	'Fisher and Holmes' (HP)	EBls
	FLAMING STAR ('Kortaltal') (HT)	EBls
	FLANDERS FIELD ('Horflan') (F)	NRog
	FLANDERS ROSE ('Beaknight') (F)	EBls
	FLIRT ('Korkopapp'PBR) (F)	MAsh
	'Flora' (Ra)	EBls ETWh
	'Flora McIvor' (RH)	EBls
	'Florence Mary Morse' (S)	SDix
	FLORENTINA ('Kortrameilo'PBR) (Cl)	EBls MJon
	FLOWER CARPET AMBER ('Noa97400a'PBR) (GC) 🏆H6	CDoC CGro CRos CSBt EBls EHyd EPfP LBuc LCro LOPS LRHS LSRN MAsh MPri NRHS NRog SPoG SSea

'Flower Carpet Coral'PBR (GC) 🏆H6	CGro CRos EBls EHyd EPfP LBuc LRHS LSRN MAsh MPri NRHS NRog SApu SPer SSea
FLOWER CARPET GOLD ('Noalesa'PBR) (GC)	CDoC CGro CRos EBls ECnt EHyd LBuc LRHS MAsh MPri NRHS NRog SApu SPoG SSea
FLOWER CARPET PINK	see *R.* PINK FLOWER CARPET
FLOWER CARPET PINK SUPREME ('Noa168098f') (GC)	EBls LRHS MAsh
FLOWER CARPET RED VELVET ('Noare'PBR) (GC/S) 🏆H6	CGro CRos EBls EHyd ELan EPfP LBuc LCro LOPS LRHS MAsh MPri NRHS NRog SCoo SPer
FLOWER CARPET RUBY (GC)	CDoC CRos EBls EHyd LBuc LRHS LSRN MAsh MPri NRHS NRog SApu SPoG
FLOWER CARPET SCARLET ('Noa83100b'PBR) (GC) 🏆H6	CRos EBls LBuc LCro LOPS LRHS MAsh NRHS NRog SSea
FLOWER CARPET SUNSET ('Deseo') (S)	CDoC CGro CRos LRHS MAsh MPri
§ FLOWER CARPET SUNSHINE ('Noason'PBR) (GC) 🏆H6	CRos EBls EHyd ELan LCro LOPS LRHS MAsh MPri NRHS NRog SCoo SPer
FLOWER CARPET WHITE ('Noaschnee') (GC) 🏆H6	CDoC CGro CRos EBee EBls ECnt EHyd ELan EPfP LCro LOPS LRHS LSRN MAsh MJon MPri NRHS NRog SApu SCoo SPer SPoG SSea SWCr
FLOWER POWER ('Frycassia'PBR) (Patio) 🏆H6	CDoC CSBt EBls ECnt ESty LCro LOPS LRHS MAsh MFry MGos MJon MPri MRav SApu SOrN SPoG SWCr
FLOWER POWER GOLD ('Fryneon') (Patio)	CBod CDoC CSBt EBls ECnt ESty LRHS MAsh MFry MPri NRHS SApu SOrN SPoG SWCr
§ ***foetida*** (S)	ETWh SPer
§ - 'Bicolor' (S)	EBls ETWh NLar NRog SPer
§ - 'Persiana' (S)	EBls
foliolosa	EBls
FOLKLORE ('Korlore') (HT)	NRog
'Follette' (Cl)	EBls
FOND MEMORIES ('Kirfelix'PBR) (Patio)	EBls ESty LSRN MJon SCoo SWCr
FOOLISH PLEASURE ('Decsure') (Patio)	NRog
FOR LOVE ('Webforlove') (F)	NRog
FOR YOU WITH LOVE ('Fryjangle') (Patio)	CDoC LSRN MAsh MFry SWCr
FOR YOUR EYES ONLY ('Cheweyesup'PBR) (S)	Widely available
FOREVER ROYAL ('Franmite') (F)	NRog
FORGET ME NOT ('Coccharm'PBR) (HT)	ESty
forrestiana (S)	EBls ETWh
× ***fortuneana*** (Ra)	EBls
Fortune's double yellow	see *R.* × *odorata* 'Pseudindica'
FOSTER'S RUBY GLOW ('Webdesire') (HT)	NRog
FOXY LADY ('Simmem') (HT)	ESty
FRAGONARD ('Delparviro'PBR) (HT)	EBls ESty
FRAGRANT CELEBRATION ('Beamerry') (Cl)	CGro EBls LBuc MAsh
FRAGRANT CLOUD ('Tanellis') (HT)	CArg CBcs CEnd CRos CTri EBls EDir ELan EPfP ETWh LBuc LRHS LSRN MAsh MGos MJon MRav NRog SCob SPer SPoG
'Fragrant Delight' (F) 🏆H6	CArg CDoC CSBt EBls EDir ELan MRav SCob
FRAGRANT DREAM ('Dicodour') (HT)	ESty SCob

FRAGRANT MEMORIES ('Korpastato'PBR) (HT)	CSBt
FRAGRANT PLUM ('Aroplumi') (HT)	ESty NRog
'Francesca' (HM)	EBls ETWh LSRN NLar NRog SPer
'Francis Copple' (S)	EBls
'Francis Dubreuil' (T)	EBls
§ 'Francis E. Lester' (HM/Ra) 🏆H6	CEnd CRos EBee EBls EHyd ELan EPfP ETWh LCro LRHS MCot NRHS SApu SPer SSea
× ***francofurtana*** misapplied	see *R.* 'Impératrice Joséphine'
'François Juranville' (Ra) 🏆H6	CArg CRHN EBee EBls EPfP ETWh LRHS MMuc MRav NLar NRog SApu SEND SPer WFar WHer
'Frau Astrid Späth' (F)	NRog
§ 'Frau Karl Druschki' (HP)	ETWh
'Fred Loads' (F) 🏆H7	EBls NRog
FREDDIE MERCURY ('Batmercury') (HT)	ESty LSRN NRog
FREE SPIRIT ('Fryjeru'PBR) (F) 🏆H6	ECnt MFry
FREEDOM ('Dicjem') (HT) 🏆H6	CArg CDoC CTri EBls ECnt EDir MFry MRav NRog SApu SCob SPer SWCr
'Frensham' (F)	EBls SSea
FRIEND FOR LIFE ('Cocnanne'PBR) (F) 🏆H6	ELan LSRN MRav
FRIENDS FOREVER ('Korapriber') (F) 🏆H6	CDoC CSBt EBls LRHS LSRN
FRIENDSHIP OF STRANGERS ('633D9') (Cl)	EBls
FRILLY CUFF ('Beajingle') (S)	EBee EBls EPfP LRHS MAsh
'Fritz Nobis' (S) 🏆H7	CArg ETWh NLar SPer
FROTHY ('Macfrothy') (Patio)	ECnt ESty MJon
'Frozen' (Min)	NRog
'Fru Dagmar Hastrup' (Ru) 🏆H7	CArg CBcs CBod CDoC CSBt CTri EBee EBls ECnt EPfP ETWh LBuc LRHS MAsh MFry MJon MSwo SApu SCob SEND SPer
'Frühlingsduft' (SpH)	ETWh NRog
'Frühlingsgold' (SpH) 🏆H7	CArg EBls ELan ETWh EWTr NLar NRog SCob SPer
'Frühlingsmorgen' (SpH) 🏆H7	EBls ETWh NRog SCob SPer
'Fyfield Princess' (F)	NRog
GAIANA (PatioHit Series)	MBros SPad
§ ***gallica*** (G)	EBls ETWh
§ - var. ***officinalis*** (G) 🏆H7	CRos CTri EBls EPfP ETWh GPoy LRHS MAsh MHer MNHC MRav NLar NRog SApu SRms WFar WHer
- 'Velutiniflora' (G)	EBls
§ - 'Versicolor' (G) 🏆H7	Widely available
GALWAY BAY ('Macba') (ClHT)	CArg CBod ETWh LRHS MAsh NLar SPer
GARDEN FUN	see *R.* GARTENSPASS
GARDEN OF ROSES	see *R.* JOIE DE VIVRE
'Gardeners' Glory'PBR (ClHT) 🏆H6	CArg CDoC CSBt ECnt ELan ESty LBuc LRHS MFry MGos MJon MPri MRav SApu SPoG SSea SWCr
GARDENERS' GOLD ('Harzoltan') (ClS)	LHkn
GARDENERS' JOY ('Beadrum') (S)	EBls
'Gardenia' (Ra)	EBls ETWh MMuc MSwo NLar SPer
'Gareth Davies' (HT)	NRog
'Garnette Carol'	see *R.* 'Carol Amling'
'Garnette Pink'	see *R.* 'Carol Amling'
§ GARTENSPASS ('Korgohowa'PBR) (F)	ETWh
'Gary Player' (HT)	NRog

'Gaujard'	see *R.* ROSE GAUJARD
'Gelbe Dagmar Hastrup'	see *R.* YELLOW DAGMAR HASTRUP
GEMINI ('Jacnepal') (HT)	ESty NRog
GEMMA ('Harlagoon'PBR) (F)	LHkn
'Général Kléber' (CeMo) 🏆H7	EBls
§ 'Général Schablikine' (T)	EBls ETWh NLar
GENESIS ('Fryjuicy'PBR) (Patio)	CGro MFry MRav
gentiliana misapplied	see *R.* 'Polyantha Grandiflora'
GENTLE HERMIONE ('Ausrumba'PBR) (S)	CDoC CRos EHyd ELan EPfP LBuc LCro LOPS LRHS MAsh MJon MSwo NRHS SCob SPoG SWCr
GENTLE TOUCH ('Diclulu') (Min/Patio)	CSBt MRav NRog SPer SWCr
GEOFF HAMILTON ('Ausham'PBR) (S)	LSRN MBNS SCob
'Geoffrey Smith' (Cl)	NDal NRog
GEORGE ('Simetna') (F)	ESty
GEORGE BEST ('Dichimanher'PBR) (Patio) 🏆H6	IDic LSRN MJon NRog
'George Dickson' (HT)	EBls
GEORGE'S PRIDE ('Manpride') (Min)	LSRN
'Georges Vibert' (G)	EBls ETWh NLar
'Geranium' (*moyesii* hybrid) 🏆H6	CArg CBcs CDoC CTri EBls ELan EPfP ETWh IArd MJon MRav NLar SApu SPer
GERBE D'OR	see *R.* CASINO
GERTRUDE JEKYLL ('Ausbord'PBR) (S) 🏆H6	Widely available
GETTYSBURG ('Poulen001'PBR) (F)	ETWh
'Ghislaine de Féligonde' (HM) 🏆H5	CBod EBee EBls EPfP ESty ETWh LRHS MAsh MCot NLar SApu SEND SPer SWCr WMal
GHITA	see *R.* MILLIE
§ GIARDINA ('Tan97289'PBR) (Cl)	ESty
gigantea	WPGP
gigantea × ***longicuspis***	WPGP
GIGGLES ('Frynoodle'PBR) (Patio)	MFry SCoo
GIGGLES ('Kingig') (Min)	NRog
GINGER SYLLABUB ('Harjolina'PBR) (ClHT)	ECnt ESty LHkn MGos SPer SPoG
GIPSY BOY	see *R.* 'Zigeunerknabe'
GIRLGUIDING UK CENTENARY ROSE ('Harnova') (F)	LHkn
GISELA'S DELIGHT ('Horpink') (S)	EBls
GLAD TIDINGS ('Tantide') (F)	CTri EBls NRog SPer
GLAMIS CASTLE ('Auslevel'PBR) (S)	CArg CTri SCob SCoo
glauca ambig.	EGrI GMcL MHer MSwo SCob WHlf
§ ***glauca*** Pourr. (S) 🏆H7	CBcs CKel CSBt CTri CWal EBee EBls ECha ECnt ELan ELon EPfP ETWh LEdu LRHS MJon MMuc MRav NBwr NLar NRog NWea SApu SEND SPer SPoG SSea WCot
'Glenfiddich' (F)	CArg CTri LSRN NRog SPer
'Glenn Dale' (Cl)	ETWh
GLOBAL BEAUTY ('Tan 94448') (HT)	CBod EBee ECnt ETWh MFry NLar SPer SSea
'Gloire de Bruxelles' (HP)	EBls
'Gloire de Dijon' (ClT)	CArg CEnd EBee EBls EDir ETWh LSRN NLar NRog NWea SCob SPer
'Gloire de Ducher' (HP)	EBls

'Gloire de France' (G) 🏆H7	CArg EBls ETWh WHer
'Gloire de Guilan' (D)	ETWh
'Gloire des Mousseuses' (CeMo)	EBls ETWh
'Gloire Lyonnaise' (HP)	EBls ETWh
glomerata (Cl)	WFar
- NJM 11.048	WPGP
'Gloria Mundi' (Poly)	EBls ETWh
GLORIANA ('Chewpope'PBR) (ClMin)	CArg CBod CDoC CGro ECnt ESty LBuc MAsh MJon NLar SMad SOrN SPer SPoG SSea SWCr
'Glory of Seale' (S)	SSea
GLOWING AMBER ('Manglow') (Min)	ESty NRog
GLYNDEBOURNE ('Harpulse'PBR) (S)	LHkn
GODSTOWE GIRL ('Harfurore') (HT)	LHkn
GOLD CHARM ('Chewalbygold') (Cl)	MAsh
'Goldbusch' (RH)	EBls
'Golden 50th Anniversary' (F) **new**	NTrD SWCr
'Golden Angel' (Min)	LRHS MAsh
GOLDEN ANGEL ('Poulpal056'PBR) (Patio) **new**	EBls
'Golden Anniversary' (Patio)	SSea
'Golden Autumn' (HT)	LSRN
GOLDEN BEAUTY ('Clebeau') (Min)	LRHS NLar
GOLDEN BEAUTY ('Korberbeni'PBR) (F) 🏆H6	CArg CEnd CGro EBee EBls ETWh MAsh MFry MJon SWCr
GOLDEN BERYL ('Manberyl') (Min)	LSRN NRog
GOLDEN CELEBRATION ('Ausgold'PBR) (S) 🏆H6	CArg CDoC CGro CRos CSBt ECnt EHyd EPfP ESty LCro LOPS LRHS LSRN MJon MSwo NLar NRHS SCoo SPer SPoG SWCr
'Golden Chersonese' (S)	NRog
'Golden Dawn' (ClHT)	see *R.* 'Climbing Golden Dawn'
GOLDEN DELICIOUS ('Wekgobafa') (HT)	ECnt ESty MJon
GOLDEN EUREKA ('Meikanaro'PBR) (F)	NRog
'Golden Gate' (Cl/T)	LPar
GOLDEN GATE ('Korgolgat'PBR) (ClHT) 🏆H6	EBls ECnt EPfP LBuc LRHS MJon NRHS SWCr
GOLDEN JEWEL ('Tanledolg'PBR) (F/Patio)	ESty
GOLDEN JUBILEE ('Cocagold') (HT)	CArg
GOLDEN MELODY ('Irene Churruca') (HT)	EBls
GOLDEN MEMORIES ('Korholesea'PBR) (F) 🏆H6	CArg CSBt EBls EHyd LBuc LRHS MAsh MGos MPri MRav SCoo SPer SWCr
'Golden Moment'PBR (HT)	ESty MRav
GOLDEN OLDIE ('Fryescape'PBR) (HT)	MFry
'Golden Rambler'	see *R.* 'Alister Stella Gray'
'Golden Showers' (Cl)	Widely available
§ GOLDEN SMILES ('Frykeyno'PBR) (F) 🏆H6	CArg CBod CDoC EBls ECnt ESty LRHS LSRN MAsh MFry MJon MPri SWCr
'Golden Unicorn' (S)	NRog
GOLDEN WEDDING ('Arokris') (F)	CBcs CDoC CGro CRos CSBt CTri EBls ECnt ELan EPfP IArd LCro LOPS LRHS LSRN MAsh MFry MGos

	MJon MRav NRHS NRog SApu SCob SOrN SPer SPoG SSea
GOLDEN WEDDING ANNIVERSARY (F)	LSRN NTrD SWCr
'Golden Wedding Celebration' (F)	CEnd LSRN
'Golden Wings' (S)	CArg CTri EBls ETWh GBin MCot MSwo NLar
'Goldfinch' (Ra)	CArg EBls EPfP ETWh LCro LOPS NLar NRog SApu SEND SPer SSha WFar
'Goldilocks' (F)	NRog
GOLDSTAR ('Candide') (HT)	ECnt
GOOD AS GOLD ('Chewsunbeam'[PBR]) (ClMin)	ECnt ESty MFry SPer SWCr
GORDON SNELL ('Dicwriter') (F)	IDic
GORDON'S COLLEGE ('Cocjabby'[PBR]) (F) ♀H6	MJon
GORGEOUS ('Poulpmt009'[PBR]) (HT)	CDoC CEnd CGro EPfP LBuc LRHS MAsh MPri
GORGEOUS GIRL ('Forshow') (HT)	ESty
GRACE ('Auskeppy'[PBR]) (S) ♀H6	CRos CSBt EHyd EPfP ESty LBuc LRHS LSRN MJon NRHS SCoo SPer SWCr
'Grace Abounding' (F)	LSRN NRog
'Grace Darling' (T)	EBls
GRACE DE MONACO ('Meimit') (HT)	EBls
GRACE DONNELLY ('Horlexstrip') (HT/F)	NRog
GRACE SHARINGTON ('Mangrace') (Patio)	NRog
'Graciously Pink' (Min)	EBls LRHS
GRAHAM THOMAS ('Ausmas') (S) ♀H6	CArg CRos CSBt EBee ECnt EHyd EPfP ESty LCro LRHS LSRN MCot MJon MSwo NLar NRHS SCob SEND SPer SPoG SSea SWCr
GRAND AWARD ('Poulcy014'[PBR]) (Courtyard Series) (ClF)	ETWh NLar
GRANDE AMORE ('Korcoluma') (HT)	see *R.* MY VALENTINE ('Korcoluma')
GRANDE AMORE ('Korliegra') (HT)	LRHS
'Grandma' (F)	LSRN
GRAND-MÈRE JENNY ('Grem') (HT)	EBls
'Grandpa Dickson' (HT)	CArg EBls MAsh MGos MJon SPer
GRANNY'S FAVOURITE (Patio/F)	LSRN
GREAT EXPECTATIONS ambig.	CBod CDoC SSea
GREAT EXPECTATIONS ('Jacdal') (F)	EDir
GREAT EXPECTATIONS ('Lanican') (HT)	CBcs
GREAT EXPECTATIONS ('Mackalves'[PBR]) (F)	EPfP IArd MGos MJon MRav SPer
§ 'Great Maiden's Blush' (A) ♀H7	EBls ETWh NLar NRog
GREAT NORTH EASTERN ROSE	see *R.* SIR GALAHAD
'Great Ormond Street' (F)	EBls
'Great Western' (Bb)	EBls
GREENALL'S GLORY ('Kirmac') (F/Patio)	MJon MRav
GREETINGS ('Jacdreco'[PBR]) (F)	CArg
'Grimpant Cramoisi Supérieur' (ClCh)	EBls
'Grootendorst'	see *R.* 'F.J. Grootendorst'
'Grootendorst Supreme' (Ru)	NRog
'Gros Chou de Hollande' (Bb)	EBls
GROSVENOR HOUSE (HT)	LRHS MAsh
GROUSE ('Korimro') (S/GC)	EBls ETWh NLar SEND SPer
GROUSE 2000 ('Korteilhab') (GC) ♀H6	SApu
'Gruss an Aachen' (Poly) ♀H6	EBls EPfP ETWh EWTr NLar NRog SPer
'Gruss an Teplitz' (China hybrid)	EBls ETWh NLar
GUIDING SPIRIT ('Harwolave') (Min/Patio)	LHkn
'Guinée' (ClHT)	CArg CRos EBls EHyd ELan EPfP ESty ETWh LCro MRav MSwo NLar SApu SPer WCot
GUIRLANDE D'AMOUR ('Lenalbi') (HM) **new**	EBls
GUIRLANDE ROSE ('Velwichba') (Ra)	EBls
'Gustav Grünerwald' (HT)	EBls
GUY SAVOY ('Delstrimen'[PBR]) (F)	EBls ESty ETWh LRHS MRav
GUY'S GOLD ('Harmatch'[PBR]) (HT)	LHkn LRHS MAsh SPoG
GWENT ('Poulurt') (GC)	CSBt SCob SEND SPer
gymnocarpa	EBls
GYPSY BOY	see *R.* 'Zigeunerknabe'
HAKA ('Poulcy023'[PBR]) (Cl)	MBros
HALLÉ ('Fryelectric'[PBR]) (HT)	MFry
'Hamburger Phönix' (Ra)	EBls
HAMILTON PRINCESS ('Harzinc') (HT)	CDoC LHkn SApu SSea
HAMPSHIRE ('Korhamp') (GC)	SCob
HÄNDEL ('Macha') (ClHT)	CBcs CBod CDoC CSBt CTri EBls EDir ELan EPfP ETWh LRHS MAsh MFry MGos MJon MPri MRav NLar NRog SApu SCob SCoo SPer SPlb SWCr
§ HANKY PANKY ('Wektorcent'[PBR]) (F)	CDoC CGro EBls ESty MJon MRav SApu
HANNAH GORDON ('Korweiso') (F)	EBls NRog SPer
'Hannah Hauxwell' (Patio/F)	NRog
HANNAH LUCY COCKROFT ('Rawgold') (HT)	NRog
'Hanne' (HT)	NRog
'Hansa' (Ru)	EBls ETWh LBuc NLar NRog SPer
HANSESTADT ROSTOCK ('Tan04603'[PBR]) (F)	MAsh SWCr
HAPPY 60TH BIRTHDAY	LSRN
HAPPY 70TH BIRTHDAY ('Rawday') (F)	LSRN
HAPPY 80TH BIRTHDAY	LSRN
HAPPY ANNIVERSARY ambig.	CSBt NLar
HAPPY ANNIVERSARY ('Bedfranc'[PBR]) (F)	LSRN MPri SCoo SWCr
HAPPY ANNIVERSARY ('Delpre') (F)	CRos CTri EHyd LRHS MAsh MRav NRHS SPoG
'Happy Birthday' (Min/Patio)	ESty LCro LOPS LSRN SSea SWCr
HAPPY COUPLE ('Simreg') (F)	ESty
HAPPY DAYS ('Harquad'[PBR]) (S)	CDoC MRav
HAPPY GARDENING ('Smi89-2-04') (HT)	ESty
HAPPY GOLDEN WEDDING	see *R.* GOLDEN SMILES

'Happy Memories' (F)	EBls LRHS
Happy Pearl Wedding (HT)	MFry SWCr
Happy Retirement ('Tantoras'[PBR]) (F) 🏆H6	CBcs EBls ELan EPfP ESty LBuc LCro LOPS LSRN MAsh MFry MJon MPri MRav SApu SCoo SPoG SSea SWCr
Happy Ruby Wedding ('Frynoble'[PBR]) (HT)	CBcs CDoC ELan MAsh MFry MJon MPri SSea SWCr
Happy Silver Wedding ('Frysilva') (F)	CDoC CRos LRHS LSRN MAsh MFry
Happy Times ('Bedone'[PBR]) (Patio/Min)	NRog NTrD
× ***harisonii*** (SpH)	EBls
§ - 'Williams' Double Yellow' (SpH)	EBls ETWh NLar
Harlow Carr ambig.	CDoC EHyd LRHS NRHS SCob
Harlow Carr ('Aushouse'[PBR]) (S)	CRos EPfP LBuc LSRN MAsh MJon MSwo SCob SCoo SPer
Harper Adams ('Fryflash'[PBR]) (F)	MFry
'Harpippin' (ClHT)	LRHS
Harrogate Rose ('Macmaryl') (HT)	MJon
'Harry Edland' (F)	CBod LCro LOPS LRHS
'Harry Wheatcroft' (HT)	CArg NRog SPer
Harvest Fayre ('Dicnorth') (F)	SPer
Havana Hit ('Poulpah032'[PBR]) (Patio)	EBls EPfP MPri
'Havering Rambler' (Ra)	ELon
'Hazel Le Rougetel' (Ru)	EBls WFar
Hazel McCallion ('Manhazel') (Patio)	NRog
'Headleyensis' (S)	EBls
Heart of Gold ('Coctarlotte'[PBR]) (HT) 🏆H6	CGro ECnt ESty MRav
Heart's Delight ('Webhawk') (F)	NRog
Heart's Desire ('Raw1063') (F)	ESty
Heathcliff ('Ausnipper'[PBR]) (S)	CSBt EPfP ESty MJon
Heather ('Poulcot007'[PBR])	LSRN
'Heather Muir' (*sericea* hybrid) (S)	EBls
Heather Sproul ('Sproheather') (Min)	NRog
'Heaven Scent' (F)	LRHS NRog
Heavenly Pink ('Lennedi') (HM) **new**	EBls
§ 'Hebe's Lip' (D × RH)	ETWh
'Helen Knight' (*ecae* hybrid) (S)	EBls ESty
Helena ('Poulna'[PBR]) (Renaissance Series) (S)	LSRN
helenae	EBee EBls ETWh GLog WPGP
- hybrid	ETWh
Helen's Trust ('Taytrust') (HT)	LSRN NRog
hemisphaerica (S)	EBls
Henri Delbard ('Delclaudibi') (HT) **new**	EBls ESty
§ 'Henri Martin' (CeMo) 🏆H7	CTri EBls ETWh LEdu NLar NRog SPer
Henri Matisse ('Delstrobla') (F)	ESty ETWh LRHS MRav NLar SPoG
'Henry Kelsey' (Cl/S)	EBls
§ 'Herbstfeuer' (RH)	EBls ETWh NLar

'Here's Sam' (HT)	LSRN NRog
Heritage ('Ausblush') (S)	EPfP ETWh SCob
'Hermosa' (Ch)	EBls ETWh NLar NRog
Hertfordshire ('Kortenay') (GC) 🏆H6	CBod MJon SCob SEND
Herzogin Christiana ('Korgeowim'[PBR]) (F)	EBls
'Hiawatha' (Ra)	EBls
× ***hibernica***	EBls
§ 'Hidcote Yellow' (Cl)	EBls ETWh SPer
Hidden Gem ('Gues11-50') (F)	ESty
High Flier ('Fryfandango'[PBR]) (ClHT)	EBls MFry
§ High Flyer ('Jacsat') (ClHT)	SSea
High Hopes ('Haryup'[PBR]) (ClHT)	EPfP NRog SApu SCob SPer SSea
'Highdownensis' (*moyesii* hybrid) (S)	EBls ELan
Highgrove ('Hornightshade') (Cl)	EBls EPfP ESty LBuc LRHS MPri NRog
'Highworth' (Ra) **new**	ESty
Hilde ('Benhile') (Min)	NRog
'Hillieri' (*moyesii* hybrid)	EBls
'Hippolyte' (G)	NLar NRog
hirtula (S)	EBls
Hollywood Star ('Reshollywood') (HT)	NRog
holodonta	see *R. moyesii* f. *rosea*
holy rose	see *R.* × *richardii*
Home Run ('Wekcisbako'[PBR]) (S) 🏆H6 **new**	MJon
Home Sweet Home ('Sim2008/10') (HT)	ESty
Home Sweet Redrow ('Dicprotector') (F)	IDic
Hommage à Barbara ('Delchifrou'[PBR]) (HT)	EBls EMul ESty ETWh MGos MRav NLar WKif
Honey Bunch ('Cocglen') (F)	MGos MRav SPer
Honey Dijon ('Weksproulses'[PBR]) (F)	ESty MJon
Honeybun ('Tan98264'[PBR]) (Patio)	ESty
Honeymoon	see *R.* 'Honigmond'
§ 'Honigmond' (F)	CBcs
'Honorine de Brabant' (Bb) 🏆H6	EBls ETWh LEdu NLar NRog
Hope for Justice ('P48b') (F)	MFry
Horatio Nelson ('Beahor') (S)	EBls
horrida	EBls
Hot Chocolate ('Wekpaltlez') (F) 🏆H6	CArg CDoC CEnd CGro CRos CSBt EBls ECnt ELan ELon EPfP ESty LBuc LRHS MAsh MFry MGos MJon MRav NRog SApu SCob SMad SPad SPer SPoG SSea SWCr
Hot Princess ('Tantocnirp') (HT)	NRog
Hot Tamale ('Jacpoy') (Min)	NRog
House Beautiful ('Harbingo') (Patio)	MRav
Huddersfield Choral Society ('Rawchor') (F)	NRog
'Hugh Dickson' (HP)	EBls ETWh LSRN NLar
hugonis	see *R. xanthina* f. *hugonis*
- 'Plenissima'	see *R. xanthina* f. *hugonis*
Hume's blush	see *R.* × *odorata* 'Odorata'

HUMMINGBIRD ('Tynpam') (F)	ESty
'Hunter' (Ru)	EBls
'Hurdalsrosa' (A)	NRog
HYDE HALL ('Ausbosky'[PBR]) (S)	EHyd LRHS
ICE CREAM ('Korzuri') (HT) 🏆H6	CArg CDoC ECnt ESty MJon MRav SApu SCob SCoo SPer SPoG SWCr
§ ICEBERG ('Korbin') (F) 🏆H6	Widely available
'Ilse Krohn Superior' (ClHT)	EBls
IMOGEN ('Austritch'[PBR]) (S)	CRos EHyd EPfP ESty LRHS MCot MJon NLar NRHS SWCr
IMPÉRATRICE FARAH ('Delivour') (HT)	ESty
§ 'Impératrice Joséphine' (Gn) 🏆H7	EBls ETWh NLar
'Impulse' (Patio)	NRog
IN MEMORY OF	LSRN
IN MEMORY OF MY CAT ('Webyum') (HT)	LSRN
IN MEMORY OF MY DOG ('Rawbark') (F)	LSRN
§ IN THE MOOD ('Wekfrancoly') (HT)	MJon
INCOGNITO ('Briincog') (Min)	NRog
INDIAN SUMMER ('Harwigwam') (ClMin)	ELon
INDIAN SUMMER ('Peaperfume') (HT) 🏆H6	CSBt MGos MRav SApu SWCr
INDIANNA MAE ('Beacrunch') (S)	EBls
'Indigo' (DPo)	EBls ETWh NLar
INFINITY ('Frytropic') (HT)	CArg EPfP LRHS
INGRID ('Maning')	LSRN NRog
INGRID BERGMAN ('Poulman'[PBR]) (HT) 🏆H6	CTri EBls ECnt ELon EPfP ETWh LRHS LSRN MFry MGos MJon MRav NRog SApu SSea SWCr
'Inspiration' (ClHT)	MAsh
INSPIRATION ('Nor19597') (HT)	SWCr
INSPIRE ('Frytempo') (HT)	CSBt ECnt MFry MJon
'Intermezzo' (HT)	EBls
INVINCIBLE ('Runatru') (F)	MFry
'Ipsilanté' (G)	EBls
'Irène Watts' (Ch)	CArg EBls LSRN NLar
'Irene's Delight' (HT)	ESty LSRN NRog
'Iridescent Pink' (S)	NRog
IRIS ('Coczero') (HT)	LSRN
IRIS ('Ferecha') (HT)	LSRN
IRISH EYES ('Dicwitness'[PBR]) (F) 🏆H6	CArg CGro ESty IArd MAsh MGos MRav SApu SCob SCoo SPer SWCr
IRISH HOPE ('Harexclaim'[PBR]) (F)	LRHS
IRISH WONDER	see *R.* EVELYN FISON
IRRESISTIBLE ('Tinresist') (Min/Patio)	NRog
'Isabel'	ETWh LSRN
ISABELLA ('Poulisab'[PBR]) (Renaissance Series) (S)	CBod ECnt NLar SPer
'Isabella Sprunt' (HT)	EBls
ISIS (HT)	see *R.* SILVER ANNIVERSARY ('Poulari')
ISN'T SHE LOVELY ('Diciluvit'[PBR]) (HT) 🏆H6	CArg EBls ELan ESty IDic LSRN NRog SApu
'Ispahan' (D) 🏆H6	CArg EBls EPfP ETWh LRHS MCot NLar NRog SApu WFar
IVOR'S ROSE ('Beadonald') (S)	EBls LRHS MAsh
IVORY CASTLE ('Guesoverlay') (HT)	CDoC SSea
IVORY ROMANTICA ('Meisabeyla'[PBR]) (HT)	LSRN
'Ivory Silk' (Min)	LSRN NRog
§ 'Jack Hume' (ClHT)	ESty
JACK WOOD ('Frydabble'[PBR]) (F)	MFry
JACK'S WISH ('Kirsil') (HT)	LSRN MJon
§ × *jacksonii* 'Max Graf' (GC/Ru)	ETWh NLar NRog SCob
– RED MAX GRAF	see *R.* ROTE MAX GRAF
'Jacky's Favorite' (F)	LSRN
Jacobite rose	see *R.* × *alba* 'Alba Maxima'
JACQUELINE DU PRÉ ('Harwanna') (S) 🏆H6	CArg EBls ECnt ESty ETWh LCro LHkn LRHS LSRN MCot MJon MRav NLar SApu SPer
JACQUELINE REDMILL ('Dicnuance') (F)	IDic
'Jacques Cartier' misapplied	see *R.* 'Marchesa Boccella'
JAM AND JERUSALEM ('Frymojo'[PBR]) (F)	CDoC CGro LRHS MAsh MFry MGos MJon MRav SWCr
JAMES GALWAY ('Auscrystal'[PBR]) (Cl)	CSBt EPfP ESty LBuc LRHS LSRN MAsh NLar NRHS SCoo SWCr
JAMES L. AUSTIN ('Auspike'[PBR]) (S)	CRos CSBt ECnt ESty LCro LRHS MAsh MJon SWCr
'James Mason' (G)	EBls NLar NRog
'James Mitchell' (CeMo)	EBls
'Jan Guest' (HT)	NRog
JANE AUSTEN ('Harzircon') (F)	LHkn
JANEEN ('Harultra') (F)	LHkn
JANE'S ROSE ('Webloxley') (F)	NRog
JANET ('Auspishus'[PBR]) (S)	LSRN
'Janet's Pride' (RH)	EBls
§ 'Japonica' (CeMo)	ETWh
§ JARDINS DE BAGATELLE ('Meimafris') (HT)	LSRN MJon SApu
JASMINA ('Korcentex'[PBR]) (ClHT)	CDoC EBls ESty ETWh LPar MJon NLar
'Jaune Desprez'	see *R.* 'Desprez à Fleur Jaune'
JAZZ (ClF)	see *R.* THAT'S JAZZ
'Jazz' (F)	LSRN
JEAN ('Cocupland'[PBR]) (Patio)	LSRN
JEAN KENNEALLY ('Tineally') (Min)	NRog
'Jean Mermoz' (Poly)	NRog
JEAN ROBIE ('Vismarok') (F) **new**	MJon
'Jean Rosenkrantz' (HP)	EBls NRog
JEAN STEPHENNE ('Velgrav') (HM) **new**	EBls
'Jeanne de Montfort' (CeMo)	ETWh
JEEPERS CREEPERS ('Scrivpinkedge') (GC) **new**	CDoC MJon
'Jenny Duval' misapplied	see *R.* 'Président de Sèze'
'Jenny Wren' (F)	EBls
JENNY'S ROSE ('Cansit') (F)	ECnt LSRN
'Jens Munk' (Ru)	EBls ETWh
JILL'S ROSE ('Ganjil'[PBR]) (F)	LSRN
JILLY JEWEL ('Benmfig') (Min)	LSRN NRog
JIVE ('Poulyc009'[PBR]) (Cl)	LSRN
'Jocelyn' (F)	LSRN
JOHANN WOLFGANG VON GOETHE ROSE	see *R.* PURE POETRY ('Tan04179') (HT)
JOHN BOY ('Chegem') (HT) **new**	MJon
'John Cabot' (S)	EBls
'John Gwilliam'	MAvo MHCG

	'John Hopper' (HP)	EBls ETWh NLar
	'John McCarthy' (Min)	NRog
	JOHN WILLAN ('Fryeager') (HT)	MFry
	JOHNNY PLUNKETT ('Dicgolf') (F)	IDic
§	JOIE DE VIVRE ('Korfloci 01'^{PBR}) (Patio/S) 🏆H6	CArg CBod CDoC CEnd CGro CSBt EBls ELan EPfP ESty ETWh LRHS MFry MJon MPri MRav NLar SApu SPer SPoG SSea SWCr
	JOLEEN ('Poulren032') (S)	ETWh
	'Josephine Bruce' (HT)	CBcs CTri EBls LSRN NRog SSea
§	JOSEPHINE ('Weksiamia') (HT)	LSRN MJon
	'Joseph's Coat' (ClS)	EBls ETWh IArd SCoo SWCr
	JOSIE WHITNEY ('Harfacey') (F)	LHkn
	'Journey's End' (HT)	NRog
I	'Joy' (F)	NRog
	JOY VIELI ('Dickaramel') (F)	IDic
	JUBILÉ PAPA MEILLAND ('Meiceazar'^{PBR}) (HT)	CSBt ESty MJon SSea
	'Jubilee Celebration' (F)	EHyd EPfP LRHS NRHS
	JUBILEE CELEBRATION ('Aushunter'^{PBR}) (S)	CRos CSBt EHyd LBuc LRHS NRHS SPer SPoG SWCr
	JUDE THE OBSCURE ('Ausjo'^{PBR}) (S)	EHyd EPfP ESty LBuc LRHS MGos MJon NRHS SCoo SPer SWCr
	JUDY GARLAND ('Harking') (F)	CSBt
	JUGENDLIEBE	see *R.* ARCHBISHOP DESMOND TUTU
	'Julia's Kiss' (HT)	NRog
	'Julia's Rose' (HT)	EBls LSRN MJon SPer
	JULIE Y ('Harbinger') (HT)	LHkn
	JULIET JACKSON-BONNER ('Rawjonber') (F)	NRog
	JULIO IGLESIAS ('Meistemon'^{PBR}) (F)	LSRN
	'Juno' (Ce)	EBls ETWh NLar
	JUST FOR YOU ('Gues 15-94') (F)	ESty
	JUST FOR YOU ('Moryou') (Min)	LSRN
	JUST JANE ('Raw1046') (F)	LSRN
	'Just Jenny' (Min)	LSRN NRog
	'Just Joey' (HT) 🏆H6	CArg CBcs CSBt CTri CWal EBls ECnt EDir ELan ELon ETWh IArd LCro LOPS LSRN MFry MGos MJon MRav NRog SApu SCob SPer SPoG SRGP SSea SWCr
	JUST ROBERT ('Raw1075') (F)	LSRN
	JUST STEVE ('Raw890') (F)	LSRN
	KAREN ('Franpur') (Min) **new**	MJon
	'Karlsruhe' (ClF)	EBls
	'Kasteel Hex' (S)	EBls
	'Katharina Zeimet' (Poly)	CTri EBls ETWh NRog
	'Kathleen' (HM)	EBls LSRN
	'Kathleen Ferrier' (F)	EBls
	'Kathleen Harrop' (Bb)	EBee EBls ETWh MMuc MSwo NLar NRog SEND SPer
	KATHLEEN JANE ('Horcoed') (S)	LSRN
	KATHLEEN'S ROSE ('Kirkitt') (F)	LSRN MJon
	KATHRYN ('Rawkat') (F)	LSRN NRog
	'Katie' (ClF)	LSRN
	KATIE'S ROSE ('Horrapture') (F)	LSRN
	KAY HAMILTON ('Cocbobo') (HT) **new**	MJon
	'Kazanlik' misapplied	see *R.* × *damascena* 'Professeur Émile Perrot'
	KEEP IN TOUCH ('Hardrama'^{PBR}) (F)	LHkn
	KEEP SMILING ('Fryflorida') (HT) 🏆H6	CDoC CGro EBls LRHS MFry MRav SPoG SSea
	KEEPSAKE ('Kormalda') (HT)	ESty
	'Keith Maughan' (Cl)	EBls LRHS MAsh
§	KENT ('Poulcov') (Towne & Country Series) (S/GC) 🏆H6	CDoC CSBt EBls ECnt ELan EPfP ESty ETWh LCro LOPS LSRN MFry MJon MMuc MRav MSwo NLar SApu SCob SEND SOrN SPer SPoG SSea SWCr
	KEROS ('Harpacific'^{PBR}) (S)	LHkn
	KEW GARDENS ('Ausfence'^{PBR}) (S) 🏆H6	EPfP LBuc LCro LRHS MJon NRHS SCoo
	'Kew Rambler' (Ra)	CRHN EBee EBls ETWh NLar SApu
	'Kiftsgate'	see *R. filipes* 'Kiftsgate'
	'Kiftsgate Superior' (S)	EBls
	'Kim' (Patio/F)	LSRN NRog
	KIND REGARDS ('Peatiger') (F)	LSRN
	'King's Ransom' (HT)	CSBt EBls MRav SCob SPer
	KISS ME KATE ('Kornagelio') (ClS)	EBls SApu SSea
	KISSES OF FIRE ('Chewmultiseek') (ClMin)	CDoC MAsh MRav NLar SSea
	KITTY ('Beaarty') (S)	EBls
	'Kitty Hawk' (Min)	NRog
	× ***kochiana***	EBls
	kokanica	WPGP
	KOKO LOCO ('Wekbijou') (F) **new**	EBls ESty MJon
	KOLO ('Poulcy033'^{PBR}) (Courtyard Series) (Cl)	ECnt
§	'Königin von Dänemark' (A) 🏆H7	CArg CBcs EBls EPfP ETWh GBin LCro LOPS LRHS LSRN MRav NLar SPer
§	'Kordes' Magenta' (S/F)	EBls WKif
	'Kordes' Robusta'	see *R.* ROBUSTA
	KORONA ('Kornita') (F)	NRog SPer
	'Korresia' (F) 🏆H7	CArg CDoC CSBt CTri EBee EBls ECnt ELon EPfP LRHS MAsh MJon MRav NRog SApu SCob SPer SPoG SWCr
	KRISTIN ('Benmagic') (Min)	NRog
	KRONENBOURG ('Macbo') (HT)	EBls
	KRONPRINSESSE MARY ('Poulcas018') (F)	CBod ETWh
	'Kronprinzessin Viktoria von Preussen' (Bb)	ETWh
	KYRA'S KISSES ('Horripple') (F)	NRog
	L.D. BRAITHWAITE ('Auscrim') (S)	CArg CTri EPfP LRHS MBNS MJon SCob
	'La Belle Distinguée' (RH)	ETWh
	'La Belle Sultane'	see *R.* 'Violacea'
	'La France' (HT)	EBls
	'La Mortola'	see *R. brunonii* 'La Mortola'
	'La Perle' (Ra)	CRHN
	'La Reine Victoria'	see *R.* 'Reine Victoria'
§	LA ROSE DE MOLINARD ('Delgrarose'^{PBR}) (S) 🏆H6	CArg ETWh MGos MRav NLar SApu
§	LA ROSE DE PETIT PRINCE ('Delgramau') (F)	EBls ESty ETWh
	'La Rubanée'	see *R.* × *centifolia* 'Unique Panachée'
	LA SÉVILLANA ('Meigekanu') (F/GC)	EBls MSwo SApu WCot WKif
	LA VILLA COTTA ('Korbamflu'^{PBR}) (L)	EBls
	'La Ville de Bruxelles' (D) 🏆H7	EBls ETWh NLar

LACE ('Frymoody') (HT) — LSRN
'Lady Alice Stanley' (HT) — EBls
'Lady Anne' (F) — LSRN NRog
'Lady Barnby' (HT) — EBls
'Lady Curzon' (Ru) — EBls
'Lady Elgin' — see *R.* THAÏS
LADY EMMA HAMILTON ('Ausbrother'^{PBR}) (S) ♀H6 — CRos EHyd EPfP ESty GBin LBuc LCro LRHS MAsh MCot MJon NRHS SCoo SPer
'Lady Gay' (Ra) — ETWh WBor
'Lady Hillingdon' (T) — EBls SRGP
'Lady Hillingdon' (ClT) — see *R.* 'Climbing Lady Hillingdon'
LADY MARMALADE ('Hartiger'^{PBR}) (F) — CArg CDoC CSBt ESty LBuc LHkn LRHS MAsh MFry MPri MRav SCoo SMad SPoG SSea SWCr
'Lady Mary Fitzwilliam' (HT) — EBls ETWh
LADY MITCHELL ('Haryearn') (HT) — ECnt LHkn
LADY OF MEGGINCH ('Ausvolume'^{PBR}) (S) — LRHS
LADY OF SHALOTT ('Ausnyson'^{PBR}) (S) ♀H6 — CRos ECnt EHyd ELan EPfP ESty LBuc LCro LOPS LRHS MCot MJon NRHS SCob SCoo SSea SWCr
LADY PENELOPE ('Chewdor'^{PBR}) (ClHT) — MFry MJon SWCr
§ 'Lady Penzance' (RH) — EBls
LADY ROSE ('Korlady') (HT) — MAsh
LADY RYDER OF WARSAW ('Harrelief') (S) — LHkn
LADY SALISBURY ('Auscezed'^{PBR}) (S) — EHyd EPfP LBuc LRHS NRHS SCoo SWCr
'Lady Sylvia' (HT) — EBls LSRN NRog
'Lady Waterlow' (ClHT) — EBee EBls ETWh SPer WSpi
laevigata (Ra) — EBls MMuc WPGP
- 'Anemonoides' — see *R.* 'Anemone'
L'AIMANT ('Harzola'^{PBR}) (F) ♀H5 — EBls LHkn LRHS MAsh MRav SApu
L'ALHAMBRA — see *R.* GIARDINA ('Tan97289') (Cl)
'Lamarque' (N) — EBls ETWh
LAMBADA ('Korapfhecki'^{PBR}) (S) — EBls
LANCASHIRE ('Korstesgli'^{PBR}) (GC) ♀H6 — ECnt ESty ETWh LSRN MJon MRav MSwo NLar SApu SCob SSea
LANCELOT ('Tan03542'^{PBR}) (Cl) — ESty
§ 'Lanei' (CeMo) — EBls ETWh NLar
LARA ('Wekplagneze') (HT) — MJon
LARISSA ('Korbaspro'^{PBR}) (F) **new** — WHlf
latibracteata — EBls
LAUDATIO — see *R.* TIMELESS PURPLE
LAURA FORD ('Chewarvel') (ClMin) ♀H5 — EBls ELan LRHS MAsh MFry MGos MJon MRav NRog SCoo SPer SPoG SWCr
'Laura Louisa' (Cl) — EBls ETWh LRHS NLar
'Laure Davoust' (Ra) — EBls ETWh MMuc NLar
LAVENDER DREAM ('Interlav') (S) — NRog
LAVENDER ICE ('Tan04249'^{PBR}) (F) — CBod EBee LCro LOPS SPoG SWCr
'Lavender Lassie' (HM) — EBls ETWh NLar SPer
'Lavender Pinocchio' (F) — EBls WKif
LAVENDER SYMPHONIE ('Meiptima') (Patio) — EBls NLar
LAVINIA — see *R.* LAWINIA
§ LAWINIA ('Tanklewi') (ClHT) ♀H6 — SApu
'Lawrence Johnston' — see *R.* 'Hidcote Yellow'
laxa — EBls
§ LAZY DAYS ('Poulkalm'^{PBR}) (F) — ECnt
LE ROUGE ET LE NOIR ('Delcart') (HT) — ELon ESty
'Le Vésuve' (Ch) — EBls ETWh
LEADING LADY ('Benuno') (Patio) — NRog
LEAH TUTU ('Hornavel') (S) — EBee EBls EPfP ESty LRHS MAsh
LEAPING SALMON ('Peamight'^{PBR}) (ClHT) ♀H6 — CArg CSBt EDir ELon ESty ETWh LSRN MGos MRav NLar SApu SCob SPer SWCr
'Leda' (D) — CArg EBls ETWh
LEGENDS — see *R.* JOSEPHINE
LEMON COUTURE ('Peacasino') (Patio) — CGro
'Lemon Pillar' — see *R.* 'Paul's Lemon Pillar'
LEMON TWIST ('Harquiz'^{PBR}) (Patio) — LHkn
LENKA ('Bozlenfra') (Frayla Series) (S) **new** — ETWh
LÉONARDO DE VINCI ('Meideauri'^{PBR}) (F) — CSBt
'Léonie Lamesch' (Poly) — EBls
'Léontine Gervais' (Ra) — CRHN EBls
'Leo's Eye' (Ra) — EPfP ETWh NLar WFar
LESLIE'S DREAM ('Dicjoon') (HT) — IDic
LEST WE FORGET ('Chewresolute') (S) **new** — MJon
LET FREEDOM RING ('Wekearman') (HT) — NRog
LET THERE BE LOVE ('Frysoda') (F) — CGro EBls LBuc LRHS MAsh MFry SWCr
LETCHWORTH CENTENARY ('Harjojo'^{PBR}) (Patio) — LHkn
LET'S CELEBRATE ('Fryraffles'^{PBR}) (F) ♀H5 — CDoC CGro EBls EPfP ESty LBuc LRHS MAsh MFry MPri MRav NRHS SPoG SWCr
LET'S DANCE ('Rawlik') (F) — NRog
'Leverkusen' (ClF) ♀H6 — CArg EBls ETWh NLar SCob SPer
'Ley's Perpetual' (ClT) — CArg EBls ETWh
× ***lheritieriana*** (Bs) — EBls
'Liberty Bell' (HT) — NRog
LICHFIELD ANGEL ('Ausrelate'^{PBR}) (S) ♀H6 — CRos EHyd EPfP LBuc LRHS MAsh NLar NRHS SCoo SWCr
LICHTKÖNIGIN LUCIA ('Korlillub') (S) — EBls
LIFE BEGINS AT 40! ('Horhohoho') (F) — LSRN NTrD
LIFELONG FRIEND ('Raw1168') (HT) — ESty
LIGHT FANTASTIC ('Dicgottago') (F) ♀H6 — CArg EPfP MFry NRog
LIGHTNING STRIKE ('Raw967') (F) — ESty
LILAC BOUQUET ('Chewlilacdays') (Cl) — CGro EBls ECnt ELon ESty LBuc LRHS MJon SSea
'Lilac Domino' (Ra) — ETWh
LILAC WINE ('Dicmulti') (F) ♀H5 — CBod CDoC IDic MJon MRav SApu
LILIANA ('Poulsyng'^{PBR}) (S) — EBee ECnt ETWh LSRN
LILLI MARLENE ('Korlima') (F) — CBod CTri EBee EBls NRog SCob SPer WKif
LINCOLN CATHEDRAL ('Glanlin'^{PBR}) (HT) — MJon SPer
LINCOLNSHIRE POACHER ('Glareabit') (HT) — ESty NRog
'Lincolnshire Yellow Belly' (F) — ESty
'Linville' (Min) — NRog
LINZI'S SMILE ('Wekscrivbeliac') (F) **new** — MJon

	LION'S FAIRY TALE	see *R.* CHAMPAGNE MOMENT
	LIONS INTERNATIONAL ('Frycharm'[PBR]) (HT)	MFry
	LISA ('Kirdisco') (F)	LSRN MJon
	LITTLE AMY ('Battamy') (Min)	LSRN NRog
	LITTLE ANGEL ('Poulpal038'[PBR]) (F)	CGro EBls EPfP LRHS
	'Little Buckaroo' (Min)	SPer
	LITTLE DIVA ('Simstep') (F) **new**	ESty
	'Little Dorrit' (Poly)	NRog
	LITTLE DUET ('Guesbliss') (F)	ESty
	'Little Emily' (Patio)	LSRN NRog
	'Little Fin' (Min)	LSRN NRog
	'Little Gem' (DPMo)	EBls ETWh
	LITTLE JACKIE ('Savor') (Min)	LSRN NRog
	LITTLE MUFF ('Horluisbond') (Min)	NRog
	LITTLE RAMBLER ('Chewramb'[PBR]) (MinRa) [H6]	CArg CBod CDoC CSBt EBls ECnt ELan ESty LCro LOPS LRHS MFry MGos MJon MRav NRHS SApu SCoo SPer SSea SWCr
	'Little White Pet'	see *R.* 'White Pet'
	LIVERPOOL HOPE ('Beapike')	EBls
§	LIVERPOOL REMEMBERS ('Frystar') (HT)	MFry
	LIVING DAYLIGHTS ('Fryradical') (F)	MFry
	'Living Fire' (F)	NRog
	LIZZY ('Tan10553'[PBR]) (ClMin) **new**	MJon
	LIZZY ('Tan99552')	SSea
	LOADS OF PINK ('Fialopi') (F)	NRog
	LOCHINVAR ('Ausbilda'[PBR]) (S)	LRHS
	'Lolabelle' (S)	ETWh
	'Long John Silver' (Cl)	EBls SApu
	longicuspis misapplied	see *R.* 'Mulliganii'
	longicuspis Bertol. (Ra)	NLar WPGP
§	- var. ***sinowilsonii*** (Ra)	ETWh
	LORD BYRON ('Meitosier') (ClHT)	ESty
	'Lord Penzance' (RH)	EBls ETWh NRog
	LORNA ('Cocringer') (F)	LSRN MJon
	LOTS OF LOVE ('Forchriso') (F)	ESty
	'L'Ouche' misapplied	see *R.* 'Louise Odier'
	'Louis XIV' (Ch)	EBls ETWh MCot
	LOUISA STONE ('Harbadge') (S)	LHkn
	LOUISE CLEMENTS ('Clelou') (S)	EBls MCot
	'Louise d'Arzens' (N)	EBls
	'Louise Estes' (HT)	NRog
§	'Louise Odier' (Bb)	CBod CTri EBls ECnt EPfP ETWh IArd LCro LOPS LRHS LSRN MCot MJon MRav NLar NRog SApu SPer SRGP
	LOVE & PEACE ('Baipeace'[PBR]) (HT) [H7]	ELan ESty NRog SApu
	LOVE EVERLASTING ('Horfrancis') (F)	NRog
	LOVE KNOT ('Chewglorious'[PBR]) (ClMin) [H6]	CArg CDoC CSBt ECnt EHyd ELan EPfP ESty LRHS MAsh MJon MRav NLar SWCr WHlf
	LOVE ME TENDER ('Forvend') (F) **new**	ESty
	'Love Never Dies' (Patio) **new**	NTrD
	LOVE SONG ('Wekstameda') (F) **new**	MJon
	LOVELY BOY ('Simjas') (HT)	ESty
§	LOVELY BRIDE ('Meiratcan'[PBR]) (Patio)	CRos EBls EHyd EPfP LRHS MAsh NRHS SApu SPoG
	LOVELY DAY ('Webpink') (Cl)	NRog
	LOVELY LADY ('Dicjubell'[PBR]) (HT) [H6]	CDoC CSBt EBls ECnt ELan ESty LSRN MJon MRav SApu SPer SSea
	LOVELY MEIDILAND	see *R.* LOVELY BRIDE
	LOVELY PARFUMA (F)	CDoC EBls
	LOVELY PINK ('Meinoplius'[PBR]) (F)	NRog
	'Lovers' Meeting' (HT)	SPer
	LOVESTRUCK ('Dicommatac') (F)	CArg CDoC CGro CSBt EBls ECnt ESty IDic LBuc LCro LRHS MAsh MFry MJon NLar SApu SCoo SSea SWCr
	LOVING MEMORY ('Korgund81') (HT)	CArg CSBt EBls ECnt EDir ESty IArd LCro LOPS LSRN MFry MGos MJon MPri MRav NRog NTrD SApu SCob SPer SPoG SSea SWCr
§	'Loving Mum'[PBR] (HT)	CSBt ESty
	'Lowri' (HT)	NRog
	LOWTHORPE DELIGHT ('Dicgoofy') (F)	IDic
§	***lucieae***	EGrI ETWh WPGP
	- 'Variegata' (Ra/v)	MJon
	LUCKY! ('Frylucy') (F) [H6]	CArg CDoC EBls EHyd EPfP ESty LRHS LSRN MAsh MFry MGos MJon MPri MRav NRog SApu SCoo SPer SPoG SSea SWCr
	LUCKY STAR ('Raw1142') (F)	ESty
	LUCKY STARS ('Kenhappy') (Patio) **new**	MJon
	LUCY ('Kirlis') (F)	LSRN MJon
	LUIS DESAMERO ('Tinluis') (Min)	NRog
	LULLABY ('Kenfrilpin'[PBR]) (ClF)	ESty MJon
	LUSATIA ('Korforst750'[PBR]) (F) **new**	MJon
	LUSCIOUS LUCY ('Tucklucy') (Patio)	LSRN
	LYDA ROSE ('Letlyda') (S)	EBls
	'Lykkefund' (Ra)	EBls ETWh
	LYNDA BELLINGHAM ('Harwise') (HT)	LHkn SSea
	LYNNE DE FONTVIVE ('Dicsystem') (F) **new**	IDic
	'Mabel Morrison' (HP)	EBls
	MaCartney rose	see *R. bracteata*, *R.* THE MCCARTNEY ROSE
	MACMILLAN NURSE ('Beamac') (S)	CBod CDoC CEnd EBls EPfP ESty ETWh LRHS MAsh MCot NRHS SCoo SWCr
	'Macrantha' (Gallica hybrid)	EBls
	macrophylla (S)	LEdu
	- B&SWJ 2603	WCru
	- GWJ 9306	WCru
	'Madame Abel Chatenay' (HT)	EBls
	'Madame Alfred Carrière' (N) [H5]	Widely available
	'Madame Alice Garnier' (Ra)	CRHN EBls ETWh NLar
	'Madame Antoine Mari' (T)	ETWh
§	'Madame Boll' (DPo)	CArg EBls ETWh LCro LSRN MSwo NRog SApu SWCr
	'Madame Butterfly' (HT)	EBls

§	'Madame Caroline Testout' (HT)	CTri EBls
	'Madame d'Arblay' (Ra)	ETWh
	'Madame de la Roche-Lambert' (DPMo)	EBls ETWh
	'Madame de Sancy de Parabère' (Bs)	EBls ETWh
	'Madame Driout' (ClT)	ETWh
	'Madame Ernest Calvat' (Bb)	EBls ETWh
	'Madame Eugène Résal' misapplied	see *R.* 'Comtesse du Caÿla'
§	'Madame Grégoire Staechelin' (ClHT) 🏆H6	CArg CTri EBls ECnt ELan EPfP ETWh LCro LOPS LRHS MJon MSwo NLar NRHS NRog SApu SCob SPer SPlb WKif
	'Madame Hardy' (D) 🏆H7	CBod CSBt EBls EHyd EPfP ETWh LCro LOPS LRHS LSRN MJon MRav MSwo NLar NRog SApu SPer WFar
	'Madame Isaac Péreire' (ClBb)	CArg CBcs CBod CDoC CGro CSBt CTri EBls ECnt EPfP ETWh GBin LCro LOPS MCot MRav MSwo NLar NRog SApu SCob SMad SPer WFar
	'Madame Jules Gravereaux' (ClT)	EBls
	'Madame Knorr' (DPo) 🏆H7	ECnt EPfP LRHS SPer
	'Madame Knorr' misapplied	see *R.* 'Madame Boll'
	'Madame Laurette Messimy' (Ch)	ETWh
	'Madame Lauriol de Barny' (Bb)	EBls ETWh NLar
	'Madame Legras de Saint Germain' (A × N)	EBls ETWh NLar NRog SPer
	'Madame Louis Laperrière' (HT)	EBls
	'Madame Louis Lévêque' (DPMo)	EBls ETWh NLar
	'Madame Pierre Oger' (Bb)	CArg CTri EBls ECnt ETWh NLar SPer
	'Madame Plantier' (A × N)	CArg NLar NRog SPer WFar
	'Madame Zöetmans' (D)	ETWh
	'Madeleine Seltzer' (Ra)	EBls ETWh
	'Madge' (HM)	SDix
	'Magenta' (S/F)	see *R.* 'Kordes' Magenta' (S/F)
	MAGIC CARPET ('Jaclover'PBR) (S/GC) 🏆H6	CDoC EBls MRav MSwo SApu SPer
	MAGIC MOMENT ('Forrusty') (HT)	ESty
	MAGIC SHOW ('Benjets') (Min)	NRog
	'Magna Charta' (HP)	EBls
	'Maid Marian' (HM)	SCoo
	'Maid Marion' (Ra)	LSRN
	MAID MARION ('Austobias'PBR) (HM)	LSRN
	'Maid of Kent'PBR (Cl)	LSRN NLar SCob SCoo SPer SWCr
	'Maiden's Blush' (A)	CArg CTri ELan LEdu LRHS MAsh NRog SCob SPer WHer
	'Maiden's Blush, Great'	see *R.* 'Great Maiden's Blush'
	'Maigold' (ClPiH) 🏆H6	CArg CBcs CGro CTri EBls EDir ELan EPfP ETWh LCro LOPS LRHS MAsh MGos MJon MRav MSwo NLar NRog SCob SMad SPer SRGP
	Maltese rose	see *R.* 'Cécile Brünner'
	MALVERN HILLS ('Auscanary'PBR) (Ra) 🏆H5	CRos CSBt EBee EPfP ESty LRHS MCot MJon NLar SCoo SPer
	'Maman Cochet' (T)	EBls
	MAMMA MIA! ('Fryjolly'PBR) (HT) 🏆H6	CDoC CGro EBls ECnt EPfP ESty LRHS MAsh MFry MRav SApu SPoG
	'Mandarin' (F)	SCob
	MANDARIN ('Korcelin') (Min)	EBls ESty MRav
	MANDARIN ('Korlisuha'PBR) (Min) **new**	CDoC
	'Manning's Blush' (RH)	EBls
	'Mannington Cascade' (Ra)	EBls
	'Mannington Mauve Rambler' (Ra)	EBls ESty
	MANY CONGRATULATIONS ('Forshelly') (F)	ESty
	MANY HAPPY RETURNS ('Harwanted') (F) 🏆H6	CBcs CBod CDoC CGro CRos CSBt EBls ECnt EPfP LHkn LRHS LSRN MAsh MFry MGos MJon MPri MRav NRHS NRog SApu SCob SWCr
	MANY THANKS ('Darmilbou') (F) **new**	MJon
§	'Marchesa Boccella' (DPo) 🏆H7	CArg CBcs CTri EPfP ETWh LRHS MPri NLar NRog SApu SPer SWCr WHer
	'Marchioness of Salisbury' (HT)	EBls
	'Maréchal Davoust' (CeMo)	NRog
	'Maréchal Niel' (N)	EBls EShb ETWh NLar NRog SPer SSea
	MARGARET ('Raw293') (HT)	see *R.* DEAR MARGARET
	'Margaret' (HT)	LSRN
	MARGARET GREVILLE ('Beajoker') (S)	EBls
	MARGARET MERRIL ('Harkuly') (F)	Widely available
	MARGARET'S SMILE ('Dewlp1') (HT)	NRog
	'Margo Koster' (Poly)	NRog
	'Marguerite Hilling' (S)	CTri EBls ETWh MSwo NRog
	MARIA ('Poulen010'PBR) (Renaissance Series) (S) **new**	ETWh
	MARIANA LILY ('Rawaninly')	NRog
	'Marie Bugnet' (Ru)	EBls
	'Marie Louise' (D)	EBls ETWh
	'Marie Pavič' (Poly)	ETWh NLar
	'Marie-Jeanne' (Poly)	EBls
	'Marigold' (HT) **new**	CDoC
	MARIGOLD SWEET DREAM ('Fryprospa') (Patio)	ECnt MFry
	MARILYN MONROE ('Weksunspat') (HT)	MJon
	MARJORIE FAIR ('Harhero') (Poly/S) 🏆H6	EBls ELan EPfP NRog SCob SRGP
	MARLON'S DAY ('Wrimarlon') (HT)	NRog
	'Martha' (Bb)	EBls LSRN
	'Martha's Choice' (HT)	NRog
	'Martin Frobisher' (Ru)	EBls
I	'Mary' (Poly)	LSRN
	'Mary B' (F)	NRog
	MARY BERRY ('Harupon') (HT)	ESty LHkn LRHS SApu SSea
	MARY JEAN ('Haryen') (HT)	LHkn
	'Mary Manners' (Ru)	EBls
	MARY ROSE ('Ausmary') (S)	CRos CSBt EHyd ELan EPfP LRHS LSRN MJon NRHS SCob SPoG
	'Masquerade' (F)	CDoC CGro CTri EBls ELan NLar NRog SPer
	MATADOR ('Tanrodat'PBR) (HT) **new**	CDoC
	MATANGI ('Macman') (F) 🏆H6	NRog
	MATAWHERO MAGIC	see *R.* SIMPLY THE BEST
	MATCHMAKER ('Dicnarrow') (F)	CSBt SApu
	MATHILDE ('Poulren026') (Renaissance Series) (S) **new**	ETWh
	'Maurice Bernardin' (HP)	EBls

	Name	Suppliers
	MAURICE UTRILLO ('Delstavo') (HT)	ESty
	MAVERICK ('Mavrik') (HT)	NRog
	'Max Graf'	see *R.* × *jacksonii* 'Max Graf'
	'Maxima'	see *R.* × *alba* 'Alba Maxima'
	MAXIMA ROMANTICA ('Meikerira'[PBR]) (HT)	EBls ELon
	'Maxime Corbon' (Ra)	ETWh
	'May Queen' (Ra)	CRHN EBls ETWh NLar SEND
	'McCartney Rose'	see *R.* THE MCCARTNEY ROSE
	'McGredy's Sunset' (HT)	EBls NRog
	'McGredy's Yellow' (HT)	NRog
	'McMillan's Pink' (HT)	NRog
§	MEDLEY RUBY ('Noa140715'[PBR]) (Min)	SPoG
	'Meg' (ClHT)	CArg EBls ETWh LSRN MCot NLar
	'Meg Merrilies' (RH)	EBls
	MELODY MAKER ('Dicqueen') (F)	NRog
	MEMORY LANE ('Peavoodoo'[PBR]) (F)	LSRN
	MERCY ROSE ('Harport') (F)	LHkn
	'Merlot' (Min)	LSRN
	'Mermaid' (Cl) ♀H5	CArg CBcs CRos CSBt CTri EBls EHyd EPfP ETWh LRHS MJon NLar NRHS NRog SApu SCob SEND SNig SSea
§	'Mevrouw Nathalie Nypels' (Poly)	CArg CBod EBls ETWh
	MICHAELA'S ROSE ('Rawpurpink') (HT)	NRog
	'Michelle Cholet' (Min)	NRog
	× ***micrugosa***	EBls
	- 'Alba'	EBls
	MIDDLESBOROUGH FOOTBALL CLUB ('Horflame') (HT)	LSRN NRog
	MIDNIGHT BLUE ('Wekfabpur') (S)	CDoC EBls ECnt ESty MGos MJon
	MIDSUMMER NIGHT'S DREAM ('Rawroyal') (F)	ESty
	MIDSUMMERSNOW ('Vissnowit') (F) **new**	MJon
	MIKE THOMPSON ('Sherired') (HT)	NRog
	MILEVA ('Bozmilefra') (Frayla Series) (S) **new**	ETWh
§	MILLIE ('Poulren013'[PBR]) (Renaissance Series) (S) ♀H6	CArg CBcs CBod CEnd EBls ECnt ELan ESty ETWh LBuc LCro LRHS LSRN MGos MJon MPri NLar NRHS SApu SCoo SOrN SPoG SRGP SWCr
	MILLIE ROSE ('Wekblunez'[PBR]) (HT)	MJon SApu SWCr
	MILLIONAIRE ('Peazara') (F)	LSRN
	MIND GAMES ('Dickylie') (F)	MJon
	MINERVA ('Visancar') (F)	CSBt ESty MJon SSea
	'Minnehaha' (Ra)	EBls NRog SSea
	MINNIE PEARL ('Savahowdy') (Min)	NRog
	MINNIE THE MOOCHER ('Webriva') (Min)	NRog
	'Minniehaha' (Ra) **new**	CBod
	MIRANDA ('Ausimmon'[PBR]) (S)	ETWh
	mirifica stellata	see *R. stellata* var. *mirifica*
	MISCHIEF ('Macmi') (HT)	LSRN NRog SPer
	MISS ALICE ('Ausjake'[PBR]) (S)	LSRN
	MISS CONGENIALITY	see *R.* STUART
	MISS DIOR ('Harencens'[PBR]) (S)	LHkn
	'Miss Edith Cavell' (Poly)	EBls ETWh
	MISS FLIPPINS ('Tuckflip') (Min)	NRog
	MISS HARP ('Tanolg') (HT)	NRog
	MISS KATE ('Dicpredict') (F)	IDic
	'Miss Lakeland' (Min)	NRog
	MISS SCARLET ('Forbright') (Cl)	ESty
	MISSING YOU ('Raw1107') (S) **new**	ESty
§	'Mister Lincoln' (HT)	EBls EDir SPer
§	MISTY HIT ('Poulhi011'[PBR]) (PatioHit Series) (Patio)	CGro EBls ECnt LRHS LSRN NRHS
	MITSOUKO ('Delnat') (HT)	ESty
	MODERN SLAVERY ('Dicpowwow') (F)	IDic
	MOKAROSA ('Frywitty'[PBR]) (F) **new**	ECnt ESty MJon
	MOLINEUX ('Ausmol'[PBR]) (S) ♀H6	CRos EHyd LRHS LSRN MAsh MJon NLar NRHS SPer
	'Molly Sharman-Crawford' (HT)	EBls
	MOM ('Rawtoks') (F)	LSRN NRog
	MOMENT IN TIME ('Korcastrav'[PBR]) (F) ♀H6	CArg CBod CDoC CSBt EBee ECnt MAsh MJon MPri MRav SPer SPoG SWCr
§	MONICA BELLUCCI ('Meimonkeur'[PBR]) (HT)	ESty NRog
	'Monique' (HT)	EBls
	MONSIEUR PÉLISSON	see *R.* 'Pélisson'
	MOODY BLUE ('Fryniche') (HT)	CDoC ECnt EPfP LBuc LRHS MAsh MFry MRav
	MOON DANCER ('Fordan') (Cl) **new**	ESty
	'Moonlight' (HM)	CArg CTri EBls ETWh LPar MCot MRav MSwo NRog SCob SPer SWCr
	MOONSTONE ('Wekcryland') (HT)	NRog
	MOORCROFT ('Guesyearn') (F)	ESty
	'Morletii' (Bs)	ETWh MMuc SEND
	MORNING BLUSH ('Siemorn') (A)	NRog
	'Morning Jewel' (ClF) ♀H7	LHkn MJon NRog SPer
	MORNING MIST ('Ausfire') (S)	EPfP LRHS
§	'Morsdag' (Poly/F)	LSRN
	MORTIMER SACKLER ('Ausorts'[PBR]) (S) ♀H6	EHyd EPfP LBuc LRHS MAsh MCot MJon NRHS SCoo SPer
	moschata (Ra)	EBls ETWh SSea
	- 'Autumnalis'	see *R.* 'Princesse de Nassau'
	- var. ***nepalensis***	see *R.* ***brunonii***
	MOTHER'S DAY	see *R.* 'Morsdag'
I	'Mother's Day'	SPer
	MOTHER'S JOY ('Horsiltrop') (F)	LSRN
	MOTHER'S LOVE ('Tinlove') (Min)	NRog
	MOULIN ROUGE ('Simmarg') (HT)	ESty
	MOUNT AORANGI ('Sanaran') (HT)	ESty
	MOUNTAIN SNOW ('Aussnow') (Ra)	LRHS
	MOUNTBATTEN ('Harmantelle') (F) ♀H6	EBls ELan LHkn MRav SCob SPer SPoG
§	'Mousseline' (DPoMo)	CArg EBls ETWh NLar NRog
	'Mousseuse du Japon'	see *R.* 'Japonica'
	moyesii (S)	CTri EBls ELan ETWh GGro NRog NWea
§	- var. ***fargesii*** (S)	EBls ETWh
	- ***holodonta***	see *R. moyesii* f. *rosea*

	Name	Suppliers
§	- f. ***rosea*** (S)	EBls
	'Mr Lincoln'	see *R.* 'Mister Lincoln'
	'Mrs Anthony Waterer' (Ru)	ETWh
	'Mrs Foley Hobbs' (T)	ETWh
	'Mrs Honey Dyson' (Ra)	ETWh
	'Mrs John Laing' (HP)	EBls ETWh NLar
	'Mrs Miniver' (HT) **new**	CSBt
	'Mrs Oakley Fisher' (HT)	EBls ETWh MCot NLar
	'Mrs Paul' (Bb)	ETWh
	'Mrs Reynolds Hole' (T)	ETWh
	'Mrs Sam McGredy' (HT)	EBls
	'Mrs Yamada' (Bb)	EBls
	'Muff's Pet' (Min)	NRog
	'Mulliganii' (Ra)	EBls EPfP ETWh GKin SPer
	multibracteata (S)	EBls ETWh GLog
	multiflora (Ra)	EBls ETWh LBuc NBwr
	- 'Carnea' (Ra)	EBls
§	- 'Grevillei' (Ra)	ETWh MCot MMuc WFar
	- 'Platyphylla'	see *R. multiflora* 'Grevillei'
	- var. ***watsoniana***	see *R. watsoniana*
	MUM IN A MILLION	see *R.* MILLIE
	MUMMY	see *R.* NEWLY WED
	mundi	see *R. gallica* 'Versicolor'
	MUNSTEAD WOOD ('Ausbernard'PBR) (S) 🏆H6	CRos EBee ECnt EHyd EPfP ESty LBuc LCro LRHS LSRN MCot MJon MSwo NRHS SCob SCoo SPoG SWCr WSpi
	murielae	EBls
	'Murjami'	EBls
	'Muscosa Alba'	see *R.* × *centifolia* 'Shailer's White Moss'
	'Mutabilis'	see *R.* × *odorata* 'Mutabilis'
	MY BROTHER ('Raw1056') (F)	ESty
	MY DAD ('Boselftay'PBR) (F)	CBcs CBod CDoC CSBt EBls LSRN SApu SWCr
	'My Darling Husband' (F)	LSRN
	'My Darling Wife' (F)	LSRN
	MY GIRL ('Tan00798'PBR) (HT)	CDoC EBee SSea
	'My Joy' (HT)	LSRN NRog
	MY LOVELY FRIEND ('Fryvanity') (HT)	ECnt
	'My Lovely Mum' (F)	MFry SWCr
	MY MUM ('Webmorrow'PBR) (F)	CBcs CBod CSBt ESty LSRN SApu SCoo SWCr
	MY NAN ('Fornan') (HT)	ESty
	MY SISTER ('Raw1052') (F)	ESty
§	MY VALENTINE ('Korcoluma'PBR) (HT) 🏆H6	CArg CSBt LSRN
	MY VALENTINE ('Mormyval') (Min)	EBls LSRN
	MYRIAM ('Cocgrand') (HT)	LSRN
	MYSTERY GIRL ('Dicdothis'PBR) (HT)	NRog
	MYSTIC ('Bozedib022') (Taste of Love Series) (S) **new**	ETWh
	MYSTIQUE ('Kirmyst') (F)	MJon
§	NADIA ('Poulen007'PBR) (Renaissance Series) (S) **new**	ETWh
	NADIA ZEROUALI ('Bozedib021') (Taste of Love Series) (S) **new**	ETWh
	NAHÉMA ('Deléri') (ClHT)	EBls
	NANCY ('Poulninga') (Renaissance Series) (S)	ETWh LSRN
	NANCY JEAN ('Ricnancy') (Patio)	LSRN NRog
	nanothamnus	SPtp
	'Naomi' (HT)	LRHS LSRN MAsh SWCr
	NAOMI ('Poulren022'PBR) (Renaissance Series) (S) **new**	ETWh LBuc MAsh
	'Narrow Water' (Ra) 🏆H6	CArg EBls ETWh NLar
§	'Nastarana' (N)	EBls ETWh NLar
	NATALIE ('Poulren014'PBR) (Renaissance Series) (S)	ETWh LSRN NLar
	NATALIJA ('Boznatafra') (Frayla Series) (S) **new**	ETWh
	NATANIA ('Dicseduce') (F)	IDic
	NATASHA RICHARDSON ('Harpacket'PBR) (F)	LHkn LRHS MRav
	'Nathalie Nypels'	see *R.* 'Mevrouw Nathalie Nypels'
	'National Trust' (HT)	CArg CTri EDir IArd MFry NRog SCob SCoo SPer SWCr
	NELSON'S JOURNEY ('Beaflirt') (S)	EBls
	'Nelson's Pride' (F)	EBls
	NEON STAR ('Weknecofloc') (Patio) **new**	MJon
	NEPTUNE ('Wekhilpurnil') (HT) **new**	MJon
	'Ness' (S) **new**	ETWh
	'Nestor' (G)	ETWh
	'Nevada' (S)	CArg CTri EBls EPfP ETWh IArd LEdu MRav NLar NRog SCob SPer
	NEVER FORGOTTEN ('Gregart') (HT)	LSRN
	NEW AGE ('Wekbipuhit'PBR) (F)	MJon
	NEW ARRIVAL	see *R.* 'Red Patio'
	NEW BEGINNINGS ('Korprofko'PBR) (F) 🏆H5	EBls LSRN SWCr
§	'New Dawn' (Cl) 🏆H7	Widely available
	'New Home'	LSRN
	NEW ZEALAND ('Macgenev') (HT)	MJon
§	NEWLY WED ('Dicwhynot'PBR) (Patio) 🏆H6	LSRN SSea
	NEWSFLASH ('Kendutch'PBR) (F) 🏆H5	CBod ESty ETWh MJon
	NICE DAY ('Chewsea'PBR) (ClMin)	CTri EPfP ESty LRHS MFry MRav SApu SCoo SPer SPoG SWCr
	'Nicola' (F)	LSRN
	NIGHT LIGHT ('Poullight'PBR) (Courtyard Series) (ClHT)	ECnt SApu
	NIGHT OWL ('Wekpurosot') (Cl)	CBod CDoC CEnd ELon ESty ETWh GBin LRHS LSRN MJon MRav NLar NPoe NRog SHor SPer SPoG SSea
	NINA ('Mehnina'PBR) (S)	LSRN
	NINA ('Poulren018'PBR) (Renaissance Series) (S)	ECnt ETWh
	NINA NADINE ('Kirhand') (F)	MJon
	NIPPER ('Hareco'PBR) (GC)	LHkn
	nitida	EBls GMcL NBwr NWea SCob SPer
	NOBLE ANTONY ('Ausway'PBR) (S)	EPfP
§	'Noisette Carnée' (N) 🏆H7	CArg CTri EBee EBls EPfP ETWh GBin LRHS LSRN MBNS MCot MRav NLar NRHS NRog SApu SCob SPer SSea SWCr WBor
	NORFOLK ('Poulfolk') (GC)	CTri EBls ETWh MSwo SApu SCob SWCr
	'Norma Major' (HT)	NRog
	NORTHAMPTONSHIRE ('Mattdor') (GC)	SCob
	'Northwest' (HT)	NRog
	'Norwell' (Ra)	MNrw WFar
	'Norwich Castle' (F)	EBls
	NORWICH CATHEDRAL ('Beacath') (HT)	EBls

	'Norwich Union' (F)	EBls
	NOSTALGIA ('Savarita') (Min)	CGro EPfP LBuc LRHS MAsh
§	NOSTALGIA ('Taneiglat'[PBR]) (HT) ♀H6	CEnd CSBt CWal EBls ECnt EDir ELon ESty MFry MGos MJon MRav SApu SCoo SMad SPer SPoG SSea SWCr
	NOSTALGIE	see *R.* NOSTALGIA
	'Notre-Dame de Calais' (Cl)	EBee EBls EPfP LRHS
	NOVALIS ('Korfriedhar'[PBR]) (F)	EBls
	'Nozomi' (ClMin/GC)	CTri EBls ELan ESty ETWh MJon NLar NRog SApu SPer SWCr
	'Nuits de Young' (CeMo) ♀H7	CArg EBls EPfP ETWh NLar SApu
	'Nur Mahal' (HM)	CArg EBls ETWh
	NURSE TRACEY DAVIES ('Frykookie'[PBR]) (F) ♀H6	MAsh MFry SWCr
	nutkana (S)	EBls
§	- var. ***hispida*** (S)	EBls
§	- 'Plena' (S/D) ♀H7	EBls ETWh GKin WHer
	'Nymphenburg' (HM)	ETWh SPer
	'Nyveldt's White' (Ru)	EBls
	OCTAVIA HILL ('Harzeal'[PBR]) (F)	ETWh LHkn MRav SPer
	× ***odorata*** 'Fortune's Double Yellow'	see *R.* × *odorata* 'Pseudindica'
	- 'Hume's Blush Tea-scented China' (ClCh)	ETWh
§	- 'Mutabilis' (Ch) ♀H5	Widely available
§	- 'Ochroleuca' (Ch)	ETWh
I	- 'Odorata' (Ch)	EBls
	- old crimson China (Ch)	EBls
§	- 'Pallida' (Ch)	EBls EPfP ETWh LRHS MCot NLar SCob WCot
§	- 'Pseudindica' (ClCh)	EBls IArd
§	- Sanguinea Group (Ch)	EBls ILea LRHS XSen
	- - 'Bengal Crimson' (Ch) ♀H5	CRHN CRos ECre EHyd ELan EPfP ETWh LRHS NRHS SDix SPoG WAvo WCFE WCot WKif
	- - 'Bob's Beauty' (Ch)	WCot
§	- 'Viridiflora' (Ch)	EBee EBls ETWh LEdu NRog SCob SPer SSea WCot WHer
	ODYSSEY ('Franski'[PBR]) (F)	ESty MJon NRog
	officinalis	see *R. gallica* var. *officinalis*
	OH WOW! ('Wekspitrib'[PBR]) (ClHT)	CDoC ECnt ESty MJon SSea
	OL' BLUE EYES ('Wekyolovefoy') (F) **new**	MJon
	old blush China	see *R.* × *odorata* 'Pallida'
	old cabbage	see *R.* × *centifolia*
	OLD GLORY ('Benday') (Min/Patio)	NRog
	OLD JOHN ('Dicwillynilly') (F)	LSRN
	old pink moss rose	see *R.* × *centifolia* 'Muscosa'
	OLD PORT ('Mackati') (F)	ELon ESty IArd MJon SApu
	old red moss	see *R.* 'Henri Martin', *R.* 'Lanei'
	old velvet moss	see *R.* 'William Lobb'
	'Old Velvet Rose'	see *R.* 'Tuscany'
	old yellow Scotch (SpH)	see *R.* × *harisonii* 'Williams' Double Yellow'
	OLIVERA ('Bozolivfra') (Frayla Series) (S) **new**	ETWh
	OLIVIA ROSE AUSTIN ('Ausmixture'[PBR]) (S)	CGro CRos CSBt EHyd ELan EPfP ESty GBin LCro LOPS LRHS MCot MJon NRHS SCoo SPer SPoG SWCr
	OLIVIA ROSE ('Wisnut') (Min)	NRog
	OLIVIA ('Wekquahofa') (HT)	LSRN MJon
	'Olympic Flame' (F)	MAsh
	'Omar Khayyám' (D)	EBls ETWh NLar NRog
§	'Ombrée Parfaite' (G)	NRog
	omeiensis	see *R. sericea* subsp. *omeiensis*
	ONE IN A MILLION ('Poulren024'[PBR]) (S)	ETWh MAsh NLar SWCr
	OOH LA LA ('Gues05-64') (F)	ESty
	OOPS A DAISY ('Gues11-13') (F) **new**	ESty
	OPEN ARMS ('Chewpixcel'[PBR]) (ClMin) ♀H6	CRos EBls EPfP LCro MFry MJon SApu SMad SPer SSea SWCr
	'Ophelia' (HT)	EBls
	ORANGE BLOSSOM SPECIAL ('Smi 5202'[PBR]) (ClMin)	ESty SSea
	'Orange Sensation' (F)	CTri NRog
§	ORANGE SUNBLAZE ('Meijikatar'[PBR]) (Min)	SCob SCoo SPer SWCr
	'Orange Triumph' (Poly)	EBls
	ORANGES AND LEMONS ('Macoranlem') (F)	CArg CDoC EBls ESty MJon SApu SCob SSea SWCr
	'Orpheline de Juillet'	see *R.* 'Ombrée Parfaite'
	OTHELLO ('Auslo'[PBR]) (S)	SPer
	OUR BETH ('Beacarol') (S)	CEnd EBls EPfP LRHS LSRN MAsh
	OUR BRIAN ('Wekx965-1') (HT) **new**	MJon
	'Our Dream' (Patio)	EBls MAsh
	OUR ENDEAVOUR ('Bra063') (F)	NRog
	OUR GEORGE ('Kirrush') (Patio)	LSRN MJon
	OUR HILDA ('Lancoro') (F)	LSRN
§	OUR JANE ('Horengland') (F)	LSRN NRog
	OUR JUBILEE ('Coccages') (HT)	ESty
	'Our Millie' (HT)	LSRN NRog
	OUR MOLLY ('Dicreason') (GC/S)	IDic LSRN MJon SPer
	OUT OF THE BLUE ('Simblue') (F)	ESty
	OVER THE MOON ('Oraclelon') (HT)	ESty NRog
	OXANA ('Dicovadatop') (F)	IDic SApu
	OXFORDSHIRE ('Korfullwind'[PBR]) (GC) ♀H6	SCob SWCr
	'Ozena'	SSea
	PADDY MCGREDY ('Macpa') (F)	NRog
	PADDY STEPHENS ('Macclack'[PBR]) (HT) ♀H6	MJon
	PAISLEY ABBEY ('Harrestore'[PBR]) (S)	LHkn
	PANACHE ('Poultop'[PBR]) (Patio/Min)	EBls ECnt LRHS MPri
	PAPA MEILLAND ('Meisar') (HT)	CSBt CTri EBls NRog SPer SSea
	PAPER ANNIVERSARY (Patio)	LSRN
	PAPI DELBARD ('Delaby') (ClHT)	CArg EBee EBls ETWh LSRN MGos NLar
	'Papillon' (Ch)	EBls
	PAPWORTH'S PRIDE ('Beamelon') (S) **new**	MAsh
§	'Para Ti' (Min)	SPer
I	'Parade' (Cl) ♀H6	CArg EBls ETWh LSRN MFry NLar SWCr
	'Parkdirektor Riggers' (Cl)	EBls ETWh LCro LOPS NLar SCob SPer
	Parks's yellow China	see *R.* × *odorata* 'Ochroleuca'
	PARKY ('Harpresto'[PBR]) (S)	LHkn
	Parson's pink China	see *R.* × *odorata* 'Pallida'

PARTRIDGE ('Korweirim') (GC)	EBls SPer
'Party Girl' (Min)	NRog
parvifolia	see *R.* 'Burgundiaca'
PASCALI ('Lenip') (HT)	CArg CBcs CTri EBls EDir NRog SCob SWCr
PAT AUSTIN ('Ausmum'^{PBR}) (S)	CArg CTri EPfP ETWh LSRN SCob
PATRICIA KENT ('Harmerry'^{PBR}) (S)	CBod LHkn
PATRICIA MAY ('Dicscenic') (F)	IDic
'Paul Crampel' (Poly)	NRog
'Paul Dauvesse' (Ra)	ETWh
'Paul Lédé' (ClT)	see *R.* 'Climbing Paul Lédé'
PAUL MCCARTNEY (HT)	see *R.* THE MCCARTNEY ROSE
'Paul Neyron' (HP)	EBls ETWh
'Paul Noël' (Ra)	CRos ETWh LSRN
'Paul Ricault' (Ce × HP)	EBls ETWh NLar
PAUL SHIRVILLE ('Harqueterwife'^{PBR}) (HT)	EBls SPer
'Paul Transon' (Ra) ♀^{H6}	CRHN CRos EBls EPfP ETWh LRHS MMuc NLar SEND WHer
'Paul Verdier' (Bb)	EBls
'Paula's Rose' (Patio)	LSRN NRog
§ 'Paulii' (Ru/GC)	EBls WSpi
'Paulii Alba'	see *R.* 'Paulii'
'Paul's Early Blush' (HP)	EBls
'Paul's Himalayan Musk' (Ra) ♀^{H6}	Widely available
§ 'Paul's Lemon Pillar' (ClHT)	CArg EPfP ETWh NLar NRog SPer
'Paul's Scarlet Climber' (Cl/Ra)	CArg CBod CDoC EBls ETWh LBuc LCro LOPS LRHS MPri MRav MSwo SCob SCoo SPer SWCr
'Paul's Single White Perpetual' (Ra)	CTri EBls ETWh
PAWS ('Beapaw') (S)	EBls
'Pax' (HM)	EBls ETWh NRog WKif
PEACE ('Madame A. Meilland') (HT) ♀^{H6}	CArg CBcs CEnd CSBt CTri EBls ECnt ELan EPfP LCro LOPS LRHS LSRN MAsh MFry MPri MRav NRHS NRog SApu SCob SPer SPoG SSea SWCr
PEACEKEEPER ('Harbella'^{PBR}) (F)	LHkn
PEACH ('Bozvaz019') (Vaza Series) (S) **new**	ETWh
'Peach Grootendorst' (Ru)	ETWh
PEACHY ('Macrelea') (HT)	EBls EPfP MAsh SPoG
PEAR ('Bozedib023') (Taste of Love Series) (S) **new**	ETWh
PEARL ('Korterschi'^{PBR}) (F) ♀^{H6}	EBls LRHS MRav
PEARL ('Wekpearl') (HT)	CSBt
§ PEARL ABUNDANCE ('Harfrisky'^{PBR}) (F)	LHkn NTrD SApu
PEARL ANNIVERSARY ('Whitston'^{PBR}) (Min/Patio)	CDoC ESty LCro LOPS LSRN MRav SApu SSea
PEARL DRIFT ('Leggab') (S)	CEnd EBls ETWh MCot MSwo NRog SPer SWCr
PEAUDOUCE	see *R.* ELINA
PEEL BROW GOLD ('Braapple') (HT)	NRog
§ 'Pélisson' (CeMo)	EBls
§ ***pendulina***	EBls ETWh WOut
- 'Nana'	NWad
pendulina* × *pimpinellifolia	see *R.* × *reversa*
'Penelope' (HM) ♀^{H5}	CArg CDoC CSBt CTri EBee EBls ECnt ELan EPfP ETWh LCro LOPS LRHS LSRN MAsh MCot MFry MJon MNrw MRav NLar NRog SCob SPer SSea SWCr

'Penelope Hobhouse' (HM)	EBls
PENNI OUR SPECIAL GIRL ('Raw1130') (F)	ESty
PENNY LANE ('Hardwell'^{PBR}) (ClHT) ♀^{H6}	CArg CSBt EBee EBls ECnt EDir ELan EPfP ETWh LBuc LCro LHkn LOPS LRHS MAsh MFry MGos MJon MRav NLar SApu SCob SCoo SOrN SPer SPoG SSea SWCr
PENNY LANE ('Talpen') (Min)	MSwo
× ***penzanceana***	see *R.* 'Lady Penzance'
PEPPERMINT SPLASH	see *R.* RACHEL LOUISE MORAN
PERCEPTION ('Harzippee'^{PBR}) (HT)	LHkn NRog
PERENNIAL BLUE ('Mehv9601') (Ra) ♀^{H6}	CDoC EBls ESty MRav SApu SCoo SSea SWCr
PERENNIAL BLUSH ('Mehbarbie'^{PBR}) (Ra) ♀^{H6}	CArg CDoC ELan ESty MRav SApu
§ PERFECT DAY ('Poulcrem') (F)	ECnt
PERFECT GENTLEMAN ('Raw1059') (F)	ESty
PERFECT HARMONY ('Tangustedv') (HT)	EBls ESty SSea
PERFECT MATCH ('Hartie') (F)	LHkn NTrD
PERFECT PET ('Smi 122204'^{PBR}) (F)	ESty
'Pergolèse' (DPo)	EBls ETWh
§ 'Perle d'Or' (Poly) ♀^{H6}	EBls ETWh NLar NRog SDix SPer
PERPETUALLY YOURS ('Harfable'^{PBR}) (Cl)	CGro LHkn MRav NLar NRog
PERSIAN MYSTERY ('Hartroy') (*persica* hybrid)	LHkn
Persian yellow	see *R. foetida* 'Persiana'
persica	SBrt
PETER BEALES ('Cleexpert') (S)	EBls
PETER COTTONTAIL ('Marpeter') (Patio)	NRog
§ PETER COTTRELL ('Harentente'^{PBR}) (F)	LHkn
PETER JAMES RICHARDSON ('Dicpaspa') (F) **new**	IDic
PETER PAN ('Chewpan'^{PBR}) (Min) ♀^{H6}	MJon
PETER PAN ('Sunpete') (Patio)	MAsh
'Petite de Hollande' (Ce)	EBls ETWh NLar SPer
'Petite Lisette' (Ce × D)	NLar
'Petite Orléannaise' (Ce)	EBls
PHAB GOLD ('Frybountiful'^{PBR}) (F)	MFry
PHEASANT ('Kordapt') (GC)	EBls MJon SApu
PHILLIPA ('Poulheart'^{PBR}) (S)	ETWh LSRN SApu
PHOEBE (Ru)	see *R.* 'Fimbriata'
phoenicea	EBls
'Phyllis Bide' (Ra) ♀^{H6}	CArg EBee EBls EHyd ELan EPfP ETWh IArd LCro LOPS LRHS MBNS MCot MJon MSwo NLar NRog SApu SPer SSea SWCr WKif
PICCADILLY ('Macar') (HT)	CSBt CTri NRog SCob
PICCOLO ('Tanolokip') (F/Patio)	MJon SApu
'Piccolo Pete' (S)	NRog
'Picture' (HT)	NRog SPer
PIERRE CARDIN ('Meilolipo'^{PBR}) (HT)	ESty

	PIERRINE ('Micpie') (Min)	NRog
	PIGALLE '84 ('Meicloux') (F)	SCoo
	'Pilgrim'	see *R.* THE PILGRIM
	pimpinellifolia	see *R. spinosissima*
	- 'Altaica'	see *R. spinosissima* 'Grandiflora'
	- double yellow-flowered	see *R.* × *harisonii* 'Williams' Double Yellow'
	PINK ABUNDANCE ('Harfrothy'PBR) (Abundance Series) (F)	CArg LHkn SApu
	PINK BELLS ('Poulbells') (GC)	CBod CGro EBls SApu SPer
	'Pink Bouquet' (Ra)	CRHN
	PINK CHAMPAGNE ('Forchamp') (Cl)	ESty
	'Pink Favorite' (HT)	NRog SCob SPer
	PINK FIZZ ('Poulycool') (ClPatio)	ECnt
§	PINK FLOWER CARPET ('Noatraum') (GC) 𝕐H6	CDoC CGro CRos CSBt CTri EBee EBls ECnt EHyd LCro LOPS LRHS LSRN MAsh MJon MPri NRHS NRog SApu SCoo SEND SPer SPoG SSea SWCr
	'Pink Garnette'	see *R.* 'Carol Amling'
	'Pink Grootendorst' (Ru)	EBls EPfP ETWh LEdu NLar NRog SCob SPer
	'Pink Gruss an Aachen' (F)	EBls ETWh
§	PINK HIT ('Poultipe'PBR) (Min/Patio)	EBls ECnt LRHS LSRN NRHS
	'Pink Leda' (D)	ETWh
	PINK MARTINI ('Tan04608'PBR) (HT)	CBod CDoC EBee EBls MFry MRav SSea
	pink moss	see *R.* × *centifolia* 'Muscosa'
	PINK PARADISE ('Delfluoros'PBR) (HT)	EBls ETWh
	'Pink Parfait' (F)	NRog SPer
	PINK PERFECTION ('Korpauvio'PBR) (HT) 𝕐H5	CEnd CSBt ECnt EPfP LRHS MAsh SSea
	'Pink Perpétué' (Cl)	CArg CBod CSBt CTri EBls ECnt EPfP ETWh MRav NLar SCob SCoo SPer SPoG SRGP SWCr
	PINK PIROUETTE ('Harboul'PBR) (Patio)	LHkn
	'Pink Prosperity' (HM)	EBls NRog
	'Pink Showers' (ClHT)	MSwo
	PINK SKYLINER ('Franwekpink'PBR) (ClS)	MJon
	PINK TOPAZ ('Manpaz') (Min)	NRog
	PINNACLE ('Beniowa') (F)	NRog
	PIPPIN ('Beajaffa') (S)	EBls MAsh SSea SWCr
	PIROUETTE ('Poulyc003'PBR) (ClS)	EBls ECnt MAsh SWCr
	PLAYGROUP ROSE ('Horsun') (F)	NRog
	PLEINE DE GRÂCE ('Lengra') (S)	LEdu NRog
	'Plentiful' (F)	EBls
	POETRY IN MOTION ('Harelan'PBR) (HT)	CArg EBls LHkn NRog
	POLAR STAR ('Tanlarpost') (HT)	CArg CSBt EBls ECnt EDir MFry NRog SCob SPer
	'Polly' (HT)	LSRN NRog
	'Polonaise' (S)	NRog
§	'Polyantha Grandiflora' (Ra)	EBls ETWh SVic
	pomifera	see *R. villosa* L.
	'Pompon Blanc Parfait' (A)	EBls ETWh NRog
	'Pompon de Bourgogne'	see *R.* 'Burgundiaca'
	'Pompon de Paris' (ClMinCh)	see *R.* 'Climbing Pompon de Paris'
	'Pompon de Paris' (MinCh)	WAbe WKif
	POPPY ROSE (HM) **new**	EBls
	PORT SUNLIGHT ('Auslofty'PBR) (HM) 𝕐H6	CGro CRos EHyd EPfP LRHS MAsh NRHS SWCr
	Portland rose	see *R.* 'Portlandica'
	'Portland Trailblazer'	see *R.* 'Big Chief'
§	'Portlandica' (Po)	EBls ETWh LRHS SPer
	POUR TOI	see *R.* 'Para Ti'
	POWER POINT ('Bennovecientos') (Patio)	NRog
	'Prairie Clogger' (S)	NRog
	prairie rose	see *R. setigera*
	'Prairie Star' (S)	NRog
	prattii	EBls
	'Precious Amber' (F)	EBls LBuc LRHS MAsh
	PRECIOUS GOLD ('Noa55504') (F)	EBls LRHS MAsh MFry WHlf
	PRECIOUS GRANDDAUGHTER ('Raw1193') (F)	ESty
	PRECIOUS GRANDSON ('Raw1088') (F)	ESty
	PRECIOUS LOVE ('Kirlowo'PBR) (F)	EBls LBuc LRHS MAsh MJon SWCr
	'Precious Memories' (Min)	LSRN
	PRECIOUS MEMORIES ('Dichello'PBR) (F)	ESty
	'Precious Platinum' (HT)	MJon SPer
	PRECIOUS TIME ('Oramarpa'PBR) (HT)	ESty MJon
	PRESIDENT ARMAND ZINSCH ('Delzinsch') (HT)	EBls
§	'Président de Sèze' (G) 𝕐H6	CArg EBls ETWh
	'President Herbert Hoover' (HT)	EBls
	'Prestige' (S)	NRog
	PRETTY IN PINK ('Dicumpteen'PBR) (GC) 𝕐H6	ECnt ELan
	PRETTY JESSICA ('Ausjess') (S)	CGro LSRN MGos MRav NLar SPer
	PRETTY LADY ('Scrivo'PBR) (F) 𝕐H6	MJon
	PRETTY POLLY ('Meitonje') (Min) 𝕐H6	CBod EDir EHyd EPfP ESty LCro LRHS MAsh MFry MRav SCob SCoo SPoG SWCr
	PRIDE & PREJUDICE ('Harwindow'PBR) (F)	LHkn
	PRIDE OF CHESHIRE ('Wekosupalz'PBR) (HT)	MJon
	PRIDE OF ENGLAND ('Harencore'PBR) (HT)	LHkn NTrD
	'Pride of Lakeland' (HT)	NRog
	PRIDE OF SCOTLAND ('Macwhitba') (HT)	MJon
	'Pride of Seale' (Cl) **new**	SSea
	'Prima Ballerina' (HT)	CArg CTri EBls EDir EPfP LRHS NRog SPer
	primula	ETWh MJon NRog
	PRINCE CASPIAN	see *R.* IN THE MOOD
	'Prince Charles' (Bb)	EBls ETWh NLar WKif
	PRINCE JARDINIER ('Meitroni'PBR) (HT) 𝕐H6	CArg ESty
	PRINCESS ('Korspobux'PBR) (HT)	ECnt NRog
	PRINCESS ALEXANDRA ('Pouldra'PBR) (Renaissance Series) (S) 𝕐H6	CBod ECnt ETWh NLar
	PRINCESS ALEXANDRA OF KENT ('Ausmerchant'PBR) (S)	CDoC CRos CSBt EHyd ELan EPfP ESty LRHS MAsh NRHS SPer SWCr

PRINCESS ALICE ('Hartanna') (F)	LSRN NRog
PRINCESS ANNE ('Auskitchen'^{PBR}) (S) 𝕐H6	CSBt ECnt EHyd EPfP LBuc LRHS MJon MSwo NRHS SWCr
PRINCESS CLAIRE OF BELGIUM ('Visbonpa') (HT) **new**	MJon
'Princess Louise' (Ra)	EBls ETWh
PRINCESS NOBUKO ('Coclistine'^{PBR}) (HT)	NRog
PRINCESS OF WALES ('Hardinkum'^{PBR}) (F) 𝕐H6	EBls LHkn MRav SApu SPer SWCr
§ 'Princesse de Nassau' (Ra)	EBls ETWh
'Princesse Louise' (Ra)	EBls
'Princesse Marie' misapplied	see *R.* 'Belvedere'
'Princesse Marie' Jacques (Ra)	EBls
'Prolifera de Redouté' misapplied	see *R.* 'Duchesse de Montebello'
PROPER JOB ('Tan02733'^{PBR}) (HT)	CBod CDoC EBee EBls ECnt ETWh MFry NLar SPer SSea
'Prosperity' (HM) 𝕐H6	CArg CBod CTri EBls ELan ETWh MCot MJon NLar NRog SPer
PROSPERO ('Auspero') (S)	ETWh
PUMPKIN PATCH ('Wekmongros') (F) **new**	MJon
PURE DELIGHT ('Guesrave') (HT) **new**	MJon
PURE GOLD ('Harhappen'^{PBR}) (S)	LHkn
§ PURE POETRY ('Jacment') (F)	LRHS
§ PURE POETRY ('Tan04179') (HT)	EBee EBls EDir ELon ETWh MFry NLar SApu SPer SSea
'Purezza' (Ra)	EBls NLar
'Purity' (ClHT)	ETWh
PURPLE EDEN	see *R.* EBB TIDE
PURPLE MOON ('Dicmover') (F)	SApu
PURPLE SKYLINER ('Franwekpurp'^{PBR}) (ClS)	CBod EBls LRHS MJon MPri SApu SPoG
PURPLE TIGER ('Jacpurr'^{PBR}) (F)	EDir ESty SApu SCob
'Purpurtraum' (Ru)	SApu
quatre saisons	see *R.* × *damascena* var. *semperflorens*
'Quatre Saisons Blanche Mousseuse' (DMo)	EBls ETWh NLar
QUEEN ANNE ('Austruck'^{PBR}) (S)	ESty LSRN
QUEEN ELIZABETH	see *R.* 'The Queen Elizabeth'
QUEEN MOTHER ('Korquemu') (Patio) 𝕐H6	CSBt ELan EPfP MRav SPer SWCr
QUEEN OF BHUTAN ('Harworld') (F)	LHkn
'Queen of Bourbons' (Bb)	EBls ETWh LEdu NLar NRog
QUEEN OF DENMARK	see *R.* 'Königin von Dänemark'
QUEEN OF HEARTS (HT)	see *R.* 'Dame de Coeur'
QUEEN OF SWEDEN ('Austiger'^{PBR}) (S)	CGro CRos ECnt EHyd EPfP LBuc LRHS MJon MSwo NLar NRHS SCoo SPer SWCr
QUEEN'S LONDON CHILD ('Harlisted') (Patio)	LHkn
'Quietness' (S)	NRog
'Rachel' (HT)	CArg CDoC LBuc LRHS LSRN MAsh MPri SWCr
RACHEL ('Booyol') (S)	EBee
RACHEL ('Tangust'^{PBR}) (HT) 𝕐H6	CEnd CSBt EBls EPfP ESty ETWh MFry MJon MRav SApu SPoG SSea
'Rachel Kathleen' (F)	NRog
§ RACHEL LOUISE MORAN ('Jacdrama'^{PBR}) (HT)	ESty
RACQUEL ('Poulren023'^{PBR}) (S)	ETWh
RACY LADY ('Dicwaffle'^{PBR}) (HT)	NRog
RADIANT ('Benrad') (Min)	NRog
'Rambling Rector' (Ra) 𝕐H6	Widely available
RAMBLING ROSIE ('Horjasper'^{PBR}) (Ra) 𝕐H6	CArg CBod CDoC CRos CSBt EBee EBls ECnt EPfP ESty ETWh LSRN MJon MSwo NLar NRog SApu SSea WCot
'Ramona' (Ra)	EBls ETWh
RANDY SCOTT ('Siljonscott') (HT)	NRog
RASPBERRY CREAM TWIRL ('Meiteratol'^{PBR}) (ClHT)	EBls EPfP LRHS MAsh
RASPBERRY QUEEN ('Tanneidol') (F)	MFry
'Raspberry Royale' (F/Patio) 𝕐H6	CDoC EBls EPfP MAsh SPoG
'Raubritter' ('Macrantha' hybrid)	CBod EBls ETWh NLar SPer
RAYMOND BLANC ('Delnado') (HT)	ETWh LSRN MRav NLar
'Raymond Carver' (S)	EBee EBls LRHS MAsh
REBECCA (Patio)	ESty LSRN
'Rebecca Claire' (HT)	LSRN
REBECCA MARY ('Dicjury'^{PBR}) (F)	CBod IDic MJon
REBEKAH HIT ('Poulpah046') (Patio) **new**	LCro
RECONCILIATION ('Hartillery'^{PBR}) (HT)	LHkn
RED 4 ('Rawarrow') (HT)	NRog
§ RED ABUNDANCE ('Harkimono'^{PBR}) (Abundance Series)	CBod EBls LHkn SApu
RED BELLS ('Poulred') (Min/GC)	SApu XSen
RED BLANKET ('Intercell') (S/GC)	SPer
RED COAT ('Auscoat') (F)	NRog
RED DEVIL ('Dicam') (HT)	CArg MJon NRog
I 'Red Dragon' Cants (F) **new**	MJon
RED EDEN ROSE ('Meidrason'^{PBR}) (Cl)	ESty SSea
RED FINESSE ('Korvillade'^{PBR}) (F) 𝕐H6	CArg ETWh NRog
RED FLAME ('Adabaring'^{PBR}) (ClHT)	CGro EBls EPfP LBuc MAsh
'Red Grootendorst'	see *R.* 'F.J. Grootendorst'
RED HAT LADY ('Harpeep'^{PBR}) (F)	LHkn
RED LETTER DAY ('Beajackdaw') (S)	EBls LRHS MAsh NRHS
'Red Max Graf'	see *R.* ROTE MAX GRAF
red moss	see *R.* 'Henri Martin'
RED NEW DAWN	see *R.* 'Étendard'
§ 'Red Patio' (F/Patio)	LSRN NTrD
RED PERFUMELLA ('Meikeneza'^{PBR}) (HT)	ELan NRog
'Red Phenomenon' (Ru) **new**	MJon
RED RASCAL ('Jacbed') (S/Patio)	CSBt MFry SApu
red rose of Lancaster	see *R. gallica* var. *officinalis*

	RED SPLENDOUR ('Davona') (F)	NRog
	'Red Wing' (S)	EBls
	REDOVA ('Poulcy030'^{PBR}) (Courtyard Series) (Cl)	ECnt MAsh MBros
	REGENSBERG ('Macyoumis'^{PBR}) (F/Patio)	CBod LEdu SPer
	'Reine des Violettes' (HP) ♀^{H6}	CBod EBls ELon EPfP ETWh IArd LCro LOPS LSRN MCot MPri NLar SPer
§	'Reine Victoria' (Bb)	CDoC EBls ETWh LCro LOPS NLar NRog SPer
§	REMEMBER ('Poulht001'^{PBR}) (HT) ♀^{H6}	EBls ECnt EPfP LBuc LRHS NRHS NRog SPoG
	REMEMBER ME ('Cocdestin') (HT) ♀^{H6}	CArg CDoC CGro CSBt EBls ECnt ELan EPfP ESty IArd LCro LOPS LRHS LSRN MAsh MFry MGos MJon MRav NRog SApu SCob SCoo SPer SPoG SWCr
	REMEMBRANCE ('Harxampton') (F)	CArg CBod CGro CRos CSBt EBls EPfP ESty LBuc LHkn LRHS LSRN MAsh MFry MJon MPri MRav NTrD SApu SCob SCoo SPer SPoG SWCr
§	RENAISSANCE ('Harzart'^{PBR}) (HT)	CArg EDir LHkn WHlf
	'René André' (Ra)	CRHN EBee ETWh NLar
	'Rescht'	see *R.* 'De Resht'
	'Rêve d'Or' (N)	EBls ETWh
	'Réveil Dijonnais' (ClHT)	EBls
§	× ***reversa*** **new**	NBwr
	RHAPSODY IN BLUE ('Frantasia'^{PBR}) (S) ♀^{H6}	Widely available
	RHUBARB AND CUSTARD ('Raw1138') (F)	ESty
	RICHARD PORSON ('Beajuniper') (S)	EBls
§	× ***richardii***	EBls ETWh
	RICK STEIN ('Tan96205'^{PBR}) (HT)	LSRN
	'Rita' ambig.	WKif
	'River Gardens'	NPer
	'Rivers's George IV' (Ch)	ETWh NLar
	ROALD DAHL ('Ausowlish'^{PBR}) (S)	CDoC CRos CSBt EHyd ELan EPfP ESty LCro LRHS MAsh MJon MSwo NLar NRHS SCoo
	'Robert le Diable' (Ce × G)	EBls ETWh SPer
	ROBERT WINSTON ('Harsunup') (F)	LHkn
	ROBIN ALONSO ('Alorobin') (Patio)	NRog
	'Robin Hood' (HM)	EBls ETWh NLar
	ROBIN REDBREAST ('Interrob') (Min/GC)	EBls
§	ROBUSTA ('Korgosa') (Ru)	EBls
	ROCK & ROLL ('Wekgobnez') (HT)	CSBt ELon ESty LSRN MJon
	'Roger Lambelin' (HP)	EBls
	ROMANCE ('Tanezamor'^{PBR}) (S)	LSRN
	ROMANZE ('Tan03434'^{PBR}) (HT)	CArg
	'Rosa Mundi'	see *R. gallica* 'Versicolor'
	ROSALITA ('Lentrihel') (HM) **new**	EBls
	ROSARIUM UETERSEN ('Kortersen') (ClHT)	EBls
	'Rose à Parfum de l'Haÿ' (Ru)	CTri
	'Rose Ball' (S)	EBls LRHS
§	'Rose d'Amour' (S) ♀^{H6}	EBls
I	'Rose de Alhambra' (DPo) **new**	MJon
	'Rose de Meaux'	see *R.* × *centifolia* 'De Meaux'
	'Rose de Meaux White'	see *R.* 'White de Meaux'
	'Rose de Rescht'	see *R.* 'De Resht'
	ROSE DES CISTERCIENS ('Delarle') (HT)	ESty ETWh LRHS NLar
	'Rose des Maures' misapplied	see *R.* 'Sissinghurst Castle'
	'Rose du Maître d'Ecole'	see *R.* 'Du Maître d'Ecole'
	'Rose du Roi' (HP/DPo)	EBls ETWh NRog
	ROSE FOR ELAINE ('Rawdenqueen') (HT)	LSRN NRog
§	ROSE GAUJARD ('Gaumo') (HT)	CArg EBls LRHS MAsh
	ROSE SYNACTIF BY SHISEIDO	see *R.* LA ROSE DE PETIT PRINCE
	ROSÉE DE MATIN ('Evematch'^{PBR}) (S)	EBls
	'Rose-Marie Viaud' (Ra)	EBls ETWh MMuc
	ROSEMARY HARKNESS ('Harrowbond') (HT)	ESty LHkn SPer SRGP
	'Rosemary Rose' (F)	NRog SPer
	ROSEMOOR ('Austough'^{PBR}) (S) ♀^{H6}	CRos EHyd LBuc LRHS NRHS SPer SWCr
	'Roseraie de l'Haÿ' (Ru) ♀^{H7}	Widely available
	ROSEROMANTIC ('Korumneza'^{PBR}) (F)	SApu
	ROSIE ('Benros') (Min)	LSRN
	ROSSETTI ROSE ('Harjug'^{PBR}) (F)	LHkn
	'Rosy Cheeks' (HT)	MAsh SWCr
	ROSY CUSHION ('Interall') (S/GC)	EBls ETWh NLar NRog SApu SPer WKif
	ROSY FUTURE ('Harwaderox') (F/Patio)	LHkn
	'Rosy Mantle' (ClHT)	CSBt EBls SPer
§	ROTARY SUNRISE ('Fryglitzy') (HT)	LRHS MFry
§	ROTE MAX GRAF ('Kormax') (GC/Ru)	EBls
§	'Rouletii' (Min)	ITim WFar
	'Roundelay' (HT)	EBls ETWh
	ROXANNE PALLETT ('Oradal') (HT)	MJon
	roxburghii	ETWh LEdu
	- PAB 7331	LEdu
	- f. ***normalis***	EBls
§	ROYAL BROMPTON ROSE ('Meivildo') (HT)	ELon ESty
	ROYAL CELEBRATION ('Wekbiphitsou') (F)	MJon
	ROYAL COPENHAGEN	see *R.* REMEMBER ('Poulht001')
	'Royal Gold' (ClHT)	EBls EDir NRog
	'Royal Highness' (HT)	NRog
	ROYAL JUBILEE ('Auspaddle'^{PBR}) (S)	CSBt EPfP LCro LOPS MAsh SCoo SPer SWCr
	'Royal Occasion' (F)	SPer
	ROYAL PARFUMA ('Kordiagraf'^{PBR}) (HT)	EBls ECnt
	ROYAL PARKS ('Harlyric'^{PBR}) (HT)	LHkn
	ROYAL PHILHARMONIC ('Hardeed'^{PBR}) (HT)	LHkn
	ROYAL SALUTE ('Macros') (Min)	NRog
	ROYAL WILLIAM ('Korzaun') (HT) ♀^{H6}	CArg CDoC CSBt CTri EBls ELan LBuc LCro LRHS LSRN MAsh MFry MGos MPri MRav NRog SApu SCob SPer
§	***rubiginosa***	CCVT CPer EBls ETWh GPoy LBuc NBwr NWea SCob SPer WHlf WKor WMou WTSh
	rubra	see *R. gallica*
	rubrifolia	see *R. glauca* Pourr.
	'Rubrotincta'	see *R.* 'Hebe's Lip'

RUBY ANNIVERSARY ('Harbonny'[PBR]) (Patio)	CDoC CGro CRos CSBt EBls EHyd ELan ELon EPfP ESty LBuc LCro LHkn LOPS LRHS LSRN MAsh MFry MRav MSwo SApu SCob SCoo SPer SPoG SSea SWCr
'Ruby Baby' (Min)	NRog
RUBY CELEBRATION ('Peawinner'[PBR]) (F) ♀H6	CBod EBls ELan ELon ESty MRav SApu
'Ruby Pendant' (Min)	NRog
RUBY RIBBON ('Harruby') (Patio)	LHkn
RUBY ROMANCE	see *R.* MEDLEY RUBY
RUBY RUBY	see *R.* RUBY SLIPPERS
§ RUBY SLIPPERS ('Weksactrumi') (Min)	LRHS NRHS SPoG
'Ruby Wedding' (HT)	CArg CBcs CDoC CEnd CRos CSBt CTri EBee ECnt ELan EPfP IArd LRHS LSRN MAsh MFry MGos MJon MRav NRHS NRog SApu SCob SPer SWCr
'Ruby Wedding Anniversary' (F)	LSRN NTrD
rugosa (Ru)	CArg CBod CGro CLnd CPer CTri EPfP EPom GAbr GArf LBuc MRav NBwr NWea SCob SPlb WFar WMat WMou WTSh
- 'Alba' (Ru)	Widely available
- 'Rubra' (Ru)	CBTr CBcs CBod CCVT CSBt CTri EBee ELan EPfP EPom GArf GMcL LBuc LCro LOPS LPar MJon NLar NWea SEWo SEdi SPer SPoG SSea SVic
- var. ***ventenatiana*** (Ru)	EBls
'Rugosa Atropurpurea' (Ru)	EPom NRog
'Rural England' (Ra)	EBee EBls LRHS MAsh
'Russelliana' (Ra)	ETWh
SABRINA ('Meiptorius'[PBR]) (Cl) **new**	SSea
'Sadler's Wells' (S)	EBls
'Safrano' (T)	EBls
SAINT BONIFACE ('Kormatt') (F/Patio)	CSBt
SAINT CHRISTOPHER ('Harcogent'[PBR]) (HT)	LHkn
SAINT DUNSTAN'S ROSE ('Kirshru') (S)	MJon
SAINT EDMUNDS ROSE	see *R.* BONITA
SAINT ETHELBURGA ('Beabimbo') (S)	EBls EPfP LRHS MAsh MCot
SAINT JOHN ('Harbilbo') (F)	LHkn
Saint John's rose	see *R.* × *richardii*
Saint Mark's rose	see *R.* 'Rose d'Amour'
'Saint Nicholas' (D)	EBls
SAINT RICHARD OF CHICHESTER ('Harklement'[PBR]) (S)	LHkn
SAINT SWITHUN ('Auswith'[PBR]) (S)	EHyd EPfP ESty LRHS MAsh NRHS SCoo SWCr
'Salet' (DPMo)	EBls ETWh NLar
'Sally Holmes' (S) ♀H6	EBls ECnt ETWh LSRN MCot MRav NLar SApu SEND SPer
SALLY'S ROSE ('Canrem') (HT)	EBls ECnt LSRN
SALSA	see *R.* CHEEK TO CHEEK
SALVATION ('Harlark'[PBR]) (F)	ESty LHkn
§ SAMARITAN ('Harverag') (HT)	CSBt LHkn SApu SWCr
sancta	see *R.* × *richardii*
'Sander's White Rambler' (Ra) ♀H6	CEnd CRHN CTri EBee EBls EPfP ETWh MCot MSwo NLar NRHS NRog SPer WFar
SANDRA ('Koreinek') (HT)	LSRN
SANDRA ('Poulen055'[PBR]) (Renaissance Series) (S)	ETWh LSRN NLar
SANDRA ('Sandkor') (HT)	NRog
SANDRA LORRAINE ('Rawsand') (F)	NRog
SANDRINGHAM ('Beamolly') (S)	EBee EBls EPfP ESty LRHS MAsh
'Sandringham Centenary' (HT)	EBls
'Sanguinea'	see *R.* × *odorata* Sanguinea Group
SANTANA ('Tan06300'[PBR]) (HT) **new**	LPar
SARAH (HT)	see *R.* JARDINS DE BAGATELLE
SARAH ELIZABETH ('Athygrafos') (F)	MFry
'Sarah van Fleet' (Ru)	CBod CDoC CTri EBls ETWh IArd MSwo NLar NRog SApu SCob SPer
SARAH, DUCHESS OF YORK	see *R.* SUNSEEKER
'Satchmo' (F)	NRog
SAVOY HOTEL ('Harvintage') (HT)	CArg EBls LHkn MFry SApu SCob SPer
'Saxilby Belle' (Min)	NRog
'Scabrosa' (Ru) ♀H7	EBls ECnt EPfP ETWh LBuc LRHS MAsh MJon NLar NRog NWea SPer
SCARLET FIRE	see *R.* 'Scharlachglut'
SCARLET GLOW	see *R.* 'Scharlachglut'
SCARLET HIT ('Poulmo'[PBR]) (PatioHit Series) (Min/Patio)	EBls ECnt LRHS LSRN NRHS
SCARLET PATIO ('Kortingle') (Patio)	CRos MAsh SPoG
SCARLET TOWER ('Wekpaltsindra') (Cl) **new**	MJon
§ SCENT FROM HEAVEN ('Chewbabaluv') (ClHT)	CDoC CEnd CGro CRos CSBt EBls ECnt ELan ELon EPfP ESty ETWh LBuc LCro LOPS LSRN MAsh MFry MGos MJon NLar SApu SCoo SMad SPer SPoG SSea SWCr
SCENTED CARPET ('Chewground'[PBR]) (GC) ♀H6	CDoC ECnt ETWh MJon NLar SApu
SCENTED GARDEN ('Chewscentity') (S)	CDoC CSBt ESty MJon
SCENTED MEMORY ('Poulht002'[PBR]) (HT)	ECnt
SCENTIMENTAL ('Wekplapep'[PBR]) (F)	CGro EBls ELan EPfP ESty LRHS MGos MRav SApu SMad SWCr
SCENT-SATION ('Fryromeo'[PBR]) (HT)	CDoC MRav SPoG
SCENTSATIONAL ('Savamor') (Min)	NRog
SCEPTER'D ISLE ('Ausland'[PBR]) (S)	CRos CSBt EHyd EPfP LRHS LSRN MAsh MCot NLar NRHS SCoo SPer
§ 'Scharlachglut' (ClS)	EBls ETWh MJon SPer
SCHLOSS BAD HOMBURG	see *R.* 'Alibaba'
'Schneelicht' (Ru)	NRog
SCHNEEWITTCHEN	see *R.* ICEBERG
§ 'Schneezwerg' (Ru) ♀H7	EBls ETWh NLar NRog
'Schoolgirl' (ClHT)	CArg CBcs CDoC CTri EBls ELan EPfP ETWh LBuc LCro LOPS LRHS MAsh MFry MPri MRav MSwo NRog SApu SCob SPer SRGP SWCr
Scotch rose	see *R. spinosissima*
Scotch yellow (SpH)	see *R.* × *harisonii* 'Williams' Double Yellow'
'Sea Foam' (S)	WHlf
SEA OF FIRE	see *R.* 'Feuermeer'
'Seagull' (Ra) ♀H6	CArg CTri EBls ECnt EDir EPPr EPfP ETWh LCro LEdu LRHS

	LSRN MAsh MJon NLar NRog SApu SCob WHer
'Seale Pink Diamond' (S)	SSea
'Seale White Rambler' (Ra)	SSea
SEALED WITH A KISS ('Simwhat') (HT)	ESty
'Sealing Wax' (*moyesii* hybrid)	ETWh
SECRET SMILE ('Dicswifty') (F)	IDic
SELFRIDGES ('Korpriwa') (HT)	ESty NRog
'Semiplena'	see *R.* × *alba* 'Alba Semiplena'
sempervirens (Ra)	EBls
SERENITY ('Poulht009'[PBR]) (HT)	EPfP ESty
sericea var. ***morrisonensis*** B&SWJ 7139	WCru
§ - subsp. ***omeiensis***	LEdu WPGP
- - BWJ 7550	WCru
- - PAB 2883	LEdu
- - f. ***pteracantha*** (S)	CTri EBee EBls ELan EPfP ETWh GKev IDee NLar NRog NWea SApu SPer SSea
- subsp. ***sericea*** **new**	LEdu
§ ***setigera***	EBls
setipoda	EBls
seven sisters rose	see *R. multiflora* 'Grevillei'
SEXY REXY ('Macrexy') (F)	CArg CBcs CBod EBls EDir LSRN MAsh MGos MJon NRog SCob SPer SPoG SWCr
'Shailer's White Moss'	see *R.* × *centifolia* 'Shailer's White Moss'
SHANTY ('Tan96191') (F)	ESty
SHEER SILK ('Harpatter'[PBR]) (Patio)	LHkn
SHEILA'S PERFUME ('Harsherry') (F) ♀H6	CArg CDoC CEnd EBls ECnt ELan EPfP ESty LRHS LSRN MAsh MFry MGos MJon MRav SApu SPoG SWCr
SHINE ON ('Dictalent'[PBR]) (Patio) ♀H6	MFry
SHIRYNNE COWAN ('Manian') (Patio)	NRog
'Shot Silk' (HT)	SCob
SHOW STOPPER ('Benseah') (Patio)	NRog
SHOWMEE MUSIC ('Chewdaybell') (GC)	CDoC
SHOWMEE SUNSHINE ('Kenveron') (GC)	CDoC
SHOWSTAR	see *R.* 'Loving Mum'
'Showtime' Lindquist (HT)	EBls MAsh
SHOWTIME ('Baitime') (ClS)	SPoG
§ SHRIMP HIT ('Poulshrimp'[PBR]) (Patio)	EBls ECnt SPoG
SHROPSHIRE STAR ('Chewsummit') (ClS)	ELon ESty SSea
SIGHTSAVER ('Fryaffair'[PBR]) (HT)	MFry
SIGNATURE ('Jacnor') (HT)	NRog
'Silver 25th Anniversary' (F)	LPar
SILVER ANNIVERSARY ambig.	CArg CGro LSRN NLar
SILVER ANNIVERSARY ('Meiborfil') (HT)	ELon
§ SILVER ANNIVERSARY ('Poulari') (HT) ♀H6	CBod CDoC CEnd CRos CSBt EBls ECnt EHyd ELan LRHS LSRN MAsh MFry MGos MJon MPri MRav NRHS NRog SApu SCoo SPer SPoG SSea SWCr
SILVER CELEBRATION ('Guescloud') (F)	ESty
'Silver Jubilee' (HT)	CArg CBcs CTri EBls IArd LRHS MAsh MJon MRav NRHS NRog SCob SPer SWCr
SILVER SHADOW ('Frystereo'[PBR]) (HT)	ECnt ESty SApu
'Silver Wedding' (HT)	CBcs CDoC CTri EBls ELan IArd MRav MSwo NRog NTrD SCob SPer SWCr
'Silver Wedding Celebration' (F)	ESty LSRN
SILVER WISHES	see *R.* PINK HIT
SIMBA ('Korbelma') (HT)	LSRN
'Simone' (HT)	EBee ETWh
SIMPLE GOLD ('Harsymbol') (S)	LHkn
SIMPLE PEACH ('Harwarmth') (S)	LHkn
SIMPLE YELLOW ('Harsonnet') (S)	LHkn
SIMPLY GORGEOUS ('Formaui') (HT)	ESty
SIMPLY SALLY ('Harpaint'[PBR]) (Patio)	LHkn LSRN
§ SIMPLY THE BEST ('Macamster'[PBR]) (HT) ♀H6	CArg CDoC CEnd CGro CSBt EBls EDir ELan EPfP ESty LRHS LSRN MAsh MFry MGos MJon MPri MRav NRHS SApu SCob SCoo SPer SPoG SWCr
sinowilsonii	see *R. longicuspis* var. *sinowilsonii*
'Sir Cedric Morris' (Ra)	EBls ETWh SSea
SIR DAVID MICHELS ('Dewraw4') (S)	NRog
'Sir Frederick Ashton' (HT)	EBls
§ SIR GALAHAD ('Hareasy') (F)	LHkn
'Sir Galahad' white-flowered	see *R.* SIR GALAHAD
SIR HENRY CECIL ('Webpegasus') (F)	LSRN
SIR JOHN BETJEMAN ('Ausvivid'[PBR]) (S)	EHyd EPfP LBuc LRHS MAsh MSwo NRHS
SIR JOHN MILLS ('Beadaffy') (Cl)	EBls
'Sir Joseph Paxton' (Bb)	ETWh
SIR PAUL SMITH ('Beapaul') (ClHT)	EBls EPfP LRHS MAsh
SIR WALTER RALEIGH ('Ausspry') (S)	MGos MRav
§ 'Sissinghurst Castle' (G)	EBls
SISTER ELIZABETH ('Auspalette'[PBR]) (S)	LSRN
'Skyrocket'	see *R.* 'Wilhelm'
SMALL TALK ('Kirsmata') (Patio) **new**	MJon
SMARTY ('Intersmart') (S/GC)	EBls SPer
SMILING EYES ('Chewrocko'[PBR]) (S/GC)	EBls EPfP ETWh LRHS
SNAZZEE ('Wekzazette'[PBR]) (F)	ECnt ESty MJon
SNOW BUNNY ('Korsnokinu'[PBR]) (Min)	EBls SApu
SNOW CARPET ('Maccarpe') (Min/GC)	MJon
'Snow Dwarf'	see *R.* 'Schneezwerg'
SNOW GOOSE ('Auspom'[PBR]) (ClS)	EBee EPfP LRHS MAsh MJon NLar SPer SWCr
SNOW HIT ('Poulsnows'[PBR]) (Min/Patio)	ECnt
'Snow Queen'	see *R.* 'Frau Karl Druschki'
SNOW QUEEN ('Simseen') (HT)	ESty

Snowball ('Macangeli') (Min/GC)	LSRN
Snowcap ('Harfleet'PBR) (Patio)	ESty LHkn
'Snowdon' (Ru)	EBls
Soeur Emmanuelle ('Delamo'PBR) (S)	ESty ETWh LSRN MRav
Solar Flair ('Benbaas') (Patio)	NRog
'Soldier Boy' (Cl)	EBls ETWh NLar
'Soleil d'Or' (S)	EBls
Soleil Vertical ('Delsov') (Cl)	EBls ELan ESty MJon
Solitaire ('Macyefre') (HT)	MJon
Solo Mio ('Poulen002') (S)	see *R.* Sophia
§ 'Sombreuil' (ClT)	CArg EBls EPfP ETWh IArd MAsh NLar SApu SPer
Someday Soon ('Seasoon') (Min)	NRog
Something Special ('Macwyo'PBR) (HT)	ESty MJon
Sommergold ('Noa51071'PBR) (Cl)	LBuc LRHS
§ Sophia ('Poulen002'PBR) (Renaissance Series) (S)	ECnt ETWh NLar
'Sophie's Perpetual' (ClCh)	CTri EBls ETWh
Sophy's Rose ('Auslot'PBR) (S)	LSRN
Sorbet Fruité ('Meihestries'PBR) (ClF)	SSea
soulieana (Ra/S)	ETWh
'Soupert et Notting' (DPoMo)	ETWh SPer
'Southampton' (F) ♀H6	CArg EBls LSRN NRog SPer SSea
Southern Belle ('Wekspopoc') (HT)	ESty MJon
'Souvenir d'Alphonse Lavallée' (ClHP)	EBls
Souvenir de Baden-Baden ('Korsouba'PBR) (HT)	EBls
'Souvenir de Claudius Denoyel' (ClHT)	CArg EBls ETWh NRog SPer
'Souvenir de Jeanne Balandreau' (HP)	EBls ETWh
'Souvenir de la Malmaison' (ClBb)	see *R.* 'Climbing Souvenir de la Malmaison'
'Souvenir de la Malmaison' (Bb)	CArg EBls ETWh MRav NRog
Souvenir de Louis Amade ('Delilac') (S)	EBls
'Souvenir de Madame Auguste Charles' (Bb)	ETWh
'Souvenir de Madame Léonie Viennot' (ClT)	EBls ETWh
'Souvenir de Pierre Vibert' (DPMo)	ETWh
'Souvenir de Saint Anne's' (Bb)	EBls ETWh
'Souvenir d'Elise Vardon' (T)	EBls
'Souvenir du Docteur Jamain' (ClHP)	CSBt EBee EBls ECnt ELan ELon EPfP ESty ETWh LCro LOPS LSRN MGos MRav NLar SApu SCob SPer SPoG WFar WKif
'Souvenir d'un Ami' (T)	EBls
spaldingii	see *R. nutkana* var. *hispida*
'Spanish Beauty'	see *R.* 'Madame Grégoire Staechelin'
Sparkle ('Frymerlin'PBR) (HT)	ECnt ESty LBuc MAsh MFry SWCr
Sparkler	see *R.* Kent
Sparkling Burgundy ('Raw1007') (F)	ESty
Sparkling Scarlet ('Meihati') (ClF)	MAsh
Special Anniversary ('Whastiluc'PBR) (HT) ♀H6	CBcs CBod CDoC CGro CRos CSBt EBls ECnt ELan ELon EPfP ESty ETWh LCro LOPS LRHS LSRN MAsh MFry MJon MPri MRav NLar NRHS SCoo SPoG SSea SWCr
Special Child ('Taniripsa'PBR) (F/Patio) ♀H6	CDoC ELan MJon MRav SApu SSea SWCr
'Special Dad' (HT)	CGro LCro NTrD
'Special Daughter' (F)	LSRN NTrD
Special Event ('Meibrelon') (HT)	ESty
Special Friend ('Kirspec'PBR) (Patio)	EBls ESty LSRN MJon SApu SCoo SWCr
'Special Grandad' (Patio)	LSRN NTrD
Special Grandchild ('Flimika') (F)	ESty
Special Grandma (F)	ESty LSRN NTrD
Special Grandpa (F)	ESty
Special Memories ('Fortop') (F)	ESty
'Special Mum' (F)	LCro LSRN NTrD
Special Occasion ('Fryyoung'PBR) (HT)	MFry MGos MRav SCoo SWCr
Special Son (F)	ESty
'Spectabilis' (Ra)	EBls ETWh
Spectacular	see *R.* 'Danse du Feu'
'Spencer' misapplied	see *R.* 'Enfant de France'
Spice of Life ('Diccheeky'PBR) (F/Patio)	EBls
§ ***spinosissima***	CArg CCCN CSde EBls ELan ETWh NBwr NRog NWea SCob SPer WKor WTSh
- 'Andrewsii' ♀H7	MRav
- 'Cedric Morris'	WCot WMal
§ - double, pink-flowered	WBor
§ - - white-flowered ♀H7	EBls ECha ETWh LEdu
- 'Falkland'	ECha
§ - 'Grandiflora'	EBls ETWh
- 'Marbled Pink'	ETWh
- 'Mary, Queen of Scots'	EBls ETWh GBin NLar SRms
- 'Merthyr Mawr'	WCot
- 'Mrs Colville'	EBls
- 'Single Cherry'	EBls
- 'William III'	EBls EWes WCot WMal
Spirit of Freedom ('Ausbite'PBR) (S)	EPfP LRHS MAsh NRHS SCoo SWCr
§ 'Splendens' (Ra)	EBls ETWh
St Clare ('Horbamber') (F)	EBls
St Helena ('Canlish') (F)	ECnt
Stamford's Sanctuary ('Beajealous') (Cl)	EBls
'Stanwell Perpetual' (SpH) ♀H7	CArg EBls ETWh MCot NLar
'Star Appeal' (GC) **new**	CDoC
Star Dust ('Morstar') (Min)	ELon
'Star of Waltham' (HP)	ETWh
'Star Performer'PBR (ClPatio)	CDoC CSBt ECnt EPfP ESty LRHS MAsh MJon SApu SPoG SWCr WHlf
Starlight Express ('Trobstar'PBR) (Cl)	CDoC CGro ELon LBuc LRHS MAsh MFry MGos MPri SPer
Starlight Symphony ('Harwisdom') (ClS)	CArg CDoC CEnd CGro EBls ECnt ELan ELon EPfP ESty LBuc LCro LHkn LRHS MAsh MFry MGos MJon SPer SSea
Starry Eyed ('Horcoexist') (Patio)	CDoC NRog
Starship ('Bristar') (Patio)	NRog

	STELLA (HT)	LSRN
§	***stellata*** var. ***mirifica***	ETWh
	STÉPHANIE D'URSEL ('Vel15fchpo') (HM) **new**	EBls
	'Stephen'	LSRN
	STEPHEN RULO ('Wecrulo') (F)	NRog
	STOP STREET ('Kordorsten')	NRog
	'Storm Cloud' (Cl) **new**	SSea
	STORYTELLER ('Diccayman') (F)	IDic MJon
	STRANGE BREW ('Mattbre') (F) **new**	MJon
	STRAWBERRIES AND CREAM ('Geestraw') (Min/Patio)	ESty
	STRAWBERRY FAYRE ('Arowillip') (Min/Patio)	ESty MRav SPoG
	STRAWBERRY HILL ('Ausrimini'PBR) (Cl) ♀H6	CSBt EHyd EPfP ESty LCro LOPS LRHS MAsh MJon NLar NRHS SCoo SWCr
	STRIKE IT RICH ('Wekbepmey'PBR) (HT) ♀H6	CDoC ESty MGos MJon MRav SApu
	'Stromboli' (F)	EDir
§	STUART ('Wekpurmebep') (F) **new**	MJon
§	SUE HIPKIN ('Harzazz'PBR) (HT)	ESty MRav
	'Suffolk' (HT)	SCob
	SUFFOLK ('Kormixal') (S/GC) ♀H6	CSBt EBls SCob
	suffulta	see *R. arkansana* var. *suffulta*
	SUGAR AND SPICE ('Peaallure'PBR) (Patio)	SPoG
	SUGAR MOON ('Wekmemolo') (HT) **new**	ESty MJon
	SUGAR 'N' SPICE ('Tinspice') (Min)	CDoC MRav
	SUMA ('Harsuma') (GC)	ESty
	SUMMER BEAUTY ('Kororbe'PBR) (F) ♀H6	CArg EBls SWCr
	SUMMER FRAGRANCE ('Tanfudermos') (Castle Series) (HT)	EBls
§	SUMMER GOLD ('Poulreb'PBR) (F)	MAsh SWCr
	'Summer Holiday' (HT)	SPer
	SUMMER LOVE ('Franluv') (F)	CBcs
	SUMMER LOVING ('Raw1152') (Cl)	ESty
	SUMMER MAGIC ('Websplash') (F)	NRog
	SUMMER MEMORIES ('Koruteli'PBR) (Palace Series) (F)	EBls ETWh NLar
	SUMMER SNOW ('Weopop') (Patio)	MJon
	SUMMER SONG ('Austango'PBR) (S)	EHyd EPfP ESty LRHS LSRN MJon
	'Summer Sunrise' (GC)	EBls
	'Summer Sunset' (GC)	EBls
	SUMMER SWEETHEART ('Harquasar'PBR) (ClMin)	LHkn
	SUMMER WINE ('Korizont'PBR) (ClHT) ♀H6	CDoC CGro CSBt EBls ECnt EPfP ESty ETWh LRHS MAsh MJon SApu SPer SPoG SWCr
	SUMMERTIME ('Chewlarmoll'PBR) (ClPatio) ♀H6	CArg CDoC CSBt EBls ECnt ELan EPfP MFry MGos MJon MPri MRav SApu SPer SPoG
	SUN HIT ('Poulsun'PBR) (PatioHit Series) (Min/Patio)	EBls ECnt MRav SPoG
	'Sunblaze'	see *R.* ORANGE SUNBLAZE
	SUNBLEST ('Landora') (HT)	MRav NRog SCob
	SUNCHARM ('Harfab'PBR) (Patio)	LHkn
	SUNDERLAND SUPREME ('Nossun') (HT)	NRog
	'Sunfire' Barni (F)	ECnt
	SUNNY ABUNDANCE (Abundance Series)	see *R.* PETER COTTRELL
	SUNNY DAY ('Savasun') (S)	ETWh
	SUNNY SKY ('Koraruli'PBR) (HT)	CRos CSBt ECnt EHyd EPfP LBuc LRHS MAsh MFry MGos MJon MPri NRHS SCoo SPer SPoG SWCr
	SUNNY SKY ('Korvestavi') (HT)	CDoC
	SUNRISE ('Kormarter') (S)	EPfP ESty NRog SApu SPoG
§	SUNSEEKER ('Dicracer') (F/Patio) ♀H6	CGro MAsh MFry MRav SPoG
	SUNSET BOULEVARD ('Harbabble'PBR) (F)	SPer SWCr
	SUNSET CELEBRATION	see *R.* WARM WISHES
	SUNSET GLOW	see *R.* 'Alibaba'
	SUNSET STRIP ('Arocore') (Min)	NRog
	SUNSHINE BABYLON EYES ('Intereybabnus') (Babylon Eyes Series) (*persica* hybrid)	SGsty
	SUNSWEPT ('Benbrett') (Min)	NRog
	SUPER DOROTHY ('Heldoro') (Ra) ♀H6	LSRN MJon SSea
	SUPER ELFIN ('Helkleger'PBR) (Ra)	CBod CDoC CRos LRHS MFry MJon MRav NLar SApu
	SUPER EXCELSA ('Helexa') (Ra) ♀H6	CBod EBls ELan MJon SApu
	SUPER FAIRY ('Helsufair'PBR) (Ra) ♀H6	CBod CDoC EBee EBls ECnt ETWh LSRN MFry MGos MJon MRav NLar SApu SSea
§	SUPER STAR ('Tanorstar') (HT)	CArg EBls MJon
	SUPER TROUPER ('Fryleyeca'PBR) (F) ♀H6	CArg CBod CDoC CGro CSBt EBls ECnt ELan ESty LRHS LSRN MAsh MFry MRav SApu SCoo SPad SPer SSea SWCr WBor WCot
	'Surpasse Tout' (G)	EBls ETWh
§	'Surpassing Beauty of Woolverstone' (ClHP)	EBls
	SURREY ('Korlanum') (GC) ♀H6	CDoC CSBt CTri EBls ESty ETWh LCro LOPS LSRN MRav MSwo NLar SApu SCob SOrN SPer SSea SWCr
	SUSAN ('Poulsue') (S)	ECnt LSRN NLar
	SUSAN DANIEL ('Harlady') (F)	LHkn
	SUSAN HAMPSHIRE ('Meinatac') (HT)	EBls
	SUSAN WILLIAMS-ELLIS ('Ausquirk'PBR) (S)	CRos EHyd EPfP LRHS MJon NLar NRHS SPoG
	SUSIE ('Harwhistle') (ClPatio)	ECnt ESty LHkn LSRN MJon
	SUSSEX ('Poulave') (GC)	CBod CSBt EBls MSwo SCob SMad SOrN SPer SWCr
	'Sutter's Gold' (HT)	EBls
	SWAN LAKE ('Macmed') (Cl)	CArg CEnd EBls ECnt ELan EPfP ETWh MFry NLar SCob SPer
	SWANY ('Meiburenac') (Min/GC)	CBod EBls ESty MSwo SApu SPer
	SWEET CAROLINE ('Micaroline') (Min)	LSRN NRog
	SWEET CHILD OF MINE (HT)	ESty SSea

SWEET DREAM ('Fryminicot') (Patio) ♀H6	CArg CBod CDoC CGro CSBt CTri EBls EDir EPfP LCro LOPS LRHS LSRN MAsh MFry MGos MJon MRav NRog SApu SCob SPer SPoG SSea SWCr
'Sweet Fairy' (Min)	CSBt
SWEET HAZE ('Tan97274'PBR) (F) ♀H6	MRav SPer
SWEET HONEY ('Korkularis') (HT)	EBls NLar
SWEET HONEY ('Kormecaso'PBR) (F)	CArg CDoC CGro ECnt ESty ETWh LBuc LCro MAsh MJon
SWEET JESSICA ('Wekneflocjuc') (F)	ESty MJon
SWEET JULIET ('Ausleap') (S)	MJon MSwo
SWEET LIZZIE ('Webevening') (HT)	NRog
SWEET MAGIC ('Dicmagic'PBR) (Min/Patio) ♀H6	EDir MRav SCob SCoo SPoG SWCr
SWEET MEMORIES ('Whamemo') (Patio)	CDoC EBls ECnt ELan EPfP ESty LRHS MJon MPri MRav NRHS SCob SCoo SOrN SPer SPoG SSea SWCr
§ SWEET PARFUM DE PROVENCE ('Meiclusif'PBR) (HT) ♀H6	CArg EBls ECnt ELan ELon EPfP LRHS LSRN NRHS
SWEET REMEMBRANCE ('Kirrans') (HT)	MJon SCoo SWCr
'Sweet Revelation'	see *R.* SUE HIPKIN
SWEET SYRIE ('Harwilling') (Cl)	CDoC ESty LHkn LRHS
'Sweet Wonder' (Patio)	EPfP
sweginzowii	EPPr EWld GLog
'Sydonie' (HP)	ETWh
'Sylvia Dot' (F)	LSRN
'Sympathie' (ClHT)	EBls SPer
TAKE IT EASY ('Wekyoopedko') (F) **new**	MJon
TALL STORY ('Dickooky') (F) ♀H6	CBod EBee EBls ETWh SApu
TAM O'SHANTER ('Auscerise'PBR) (S)	EPfP
TAMMY CLEMONS ('Declemons') (Patio)	NRog
TANGERINE TANGO ('Cheworangemane') (Cl)	MJon SSea
TANGO SHOWGROUND ('Chewpattens'PBR) (GC)	ESty
TATTON ('Fryentice'PBR) (F)	EBls MJon MRav
§ 'Tausendschön' (Ra)	EBls
TAXANDRIA ('Viscampina') (S) **new**	MJon
TEAR DROP ('Dicomo') (Min/Patio)	MFry SApu SCob
TEASING GEORGIA ('Ausbaker'PBR) (Cl) ♀H6	CRos ECnt EHyd EPfP ESty LBuc LRHS LSRN MJon MSwo NRHS SCob SCoo SPer SWCr
'Temple Bells' (ClMin/GC)	NRog
TEMPTRESS ('Korramal') (ClS) ♀H6	EPfP LRHS
TENACIOUS ('Macblackpo'PBR) (F)	ESty MJon
TEQUILA SUNRISE ('Dicobey') (HT) ♀H6	CArg CGro CTri EBls ELan EPfP ESty LBuc MFry MGos MJon MRav NRog SApu SPer SSea SWCr
TESS OF THE D'URBERVILLES ('Ausmove'PBR) (S)	CRos EHyd EPfP ESty LRHS MSwo NLar NRHS SCoo
'Tessa' (F)	LSRN
§ THAÏS ('Memaj') (HT)	EBls
'Thalia' (Ra)	EBls
THANK YOU ('Chesdeep'PBR) (Patio)	ESty LCro LOPS LSRN SWCr
§ THAT'S JAZZ ('Poulnorm'PBR) (Courtyard Series) (ClF)	CArg ECnt LSRN MFry MJon
THE ALBRIGHTON RAMBLER ('Ausmobile'PBR) (Ra)	CRos EBee EHyd EPfP LRHS MAsh MSwo NLar NRHS SCoo
THE ALEXANDRA ROSE ('Ausday') (S)	EPfP
§ THE ALNWICK ROSE ('Ausgrab'PBR) (S)	CRos EHyd EPfP LBuc LRHS MAsh MGos MJon MSwo NLar NRHS SCob SCoo SPer SWCr
THE ANCIENT MARINER ('Ausoutcry') (S)	EHyd LCro LOPS LRHS MAsh NLar NRHS SCoo
THE ANNIVERSARY ROSE (HT)	see *R.* SWEET PARFUM DE PROVENCE
THE BEE'S KNEES ('Guesbehold') (F)	ESty
THE BOSWORTH ROSE ('Raw1014') (F)	ESty
'The Boy's' (F)	NRog
'The Bride' (T)	ETWh MAsh
THE BROWNIE ROSE ('Harlassie'PBR) (F)	LHkn
THE CHESHIRE REGIMENT ('Fryzebedee') (HT)	MFry
THE CHURCHILL ROSE ('Horoften') (S)	EBee EBls LRHS MAsh
THE CORPS ROSE ('Mattstrip') (F) **new**	MJon
THE COVENTRY CATHEDRAL ROSE ('Smi72-02') (F)	ESty
THE DEBBIE PHILLIPS ROSE ('Harverve') (HT)	LHkn
THE DIAMOND WEDDING ROSE ('Meidiaphaz') (HT)	EBls ELan ESty LSRN MAsh SWCr
'The Doctor' (HT)	EBls
THE EVE ROSE ('Harwinsome') (F)	LHkn
§ 'The Fairy' (Poly) ♀H6	Widely available
THE FEMININE TOUCH ('Wekmootono'PBR) (F)	MJon SApu
'The Garland' (Ra) ♀H6	CArg EBee EBls EPfP ETWh GBin MMuc NLar SApu SPer
THE GENEROUS GARDENER ('Ausdrawn'PBR) (Cl) ♀H6	CDoC CRos CSBt EBee EHyd ELan EPfP ESty LBuc LCro LRHS LSRN MAsh MCot MGos MJon MSwo NRHS SCob SCoo SPer SSea SWCr
§ THE GOLD AWARD ROSE ('Poulac008'PBR) (Palace Series) (Patio)	ECnt
THE INGENIOUS MR FAIRCHILD ('Austijus'PBR) (S)	EPfP SCoo
THE JUBILEE ROSE ('Poulbrido'PBR) (F)	ECnt
THE LADY ('Fryjingo'PBR) (S)	ESty
THE LADY GARDENER ('Ausbrass'PBR) (S)	CRos EHyd ELan EPfP ESty LRHS MAsh MBNS NLar NRHS SCoo SWCr
THE LADY OF THE LAKE ('Ausherbert'PBR) (Ra)	CRos EHyd EPfP LRHS MAsh NLar NRHS SCob SCoo
THE LADY'S BLUSH ('Ausoscar'PBR) (S)	EHyd EPfP LRHS
THE LAKELAND ROSE ('Harspiral') (Cl)	LHkn MJon SApu
THE LARK ASCENDING ('Ausursula'PBR) (S)	EHyd LBuc LCro LRHS MCot NRHS SCoo
THE LEONARD CHESHIRE HOME	see *R.* NADIA

	THE MARC BOLAN ROSE ('Diclorilia') (ClF) **new**	MJon
	'The Margaret Coppola Rose'	see *R.* WHITE GOLD
	THE MAYFLOWER ('Austilly'[PBR]) (S) ℘H6	CRos CSBt EPfP LBuc LRHS MJon MSwo NRHS SPer SWCr
	THE MAYOR ('P48a') (F)	MFry
§	THE MCCARTNEY ROSE ('Meizeli') (HT)	LSRN MJon SApu
	THE MILL ON THE FLOSS ('Austulliver') (S)	CRos EPfP ESty LCro LRHS MJon NLar SWCr
	'The New Dawn'	see *R.* 'New Dawn'
	'The One and Only' (HT)	LRHS
	THE PAINTER ('Mactemaik'[PBR]) (F)	LSRN MJon
	THE PERSE ROSE ('Beajargon') (S)	EBls
§	THE PILGRIM ('Auswalker') (S) ℘H6	CRos CSBt EHyd EPfP ESty LBuc LCro LRHS LSRN MAsh MJon NLar NRHS SCoo SPer SPoG SWCr
	THE POET'S WIFE ('Auswhirl'[PBR]) (S)	CDoC CRos CSBt ECnt EHyd EPfP ESty LRHS MAsh NRHS SCoo SPoG
	THE PRINCE'S TRUST ('Harholding'[PBR]) (Cl)	LHkn LRHS
§	'The Queen Elizabeth' (F)	CArg CBod CSBt CTri EBls EDir ELan LCro LHkn LOPS LRHS LSRN MFry MGos MRav NRog NTrD SApu SCob SPer SSea SWCr
	THE QUEEN'S JUBILEE ROSE ('Beajubilee') (S)	CEnd EBls LRHS MAsh
	THE ROTARIAN	see *R.* ROTARY SUNRISE
	'The Royal Brompton Rose'	see *R.* ROYAL BROMPTON ROSE
I	'The Rugby Rose' (HT)	LSRN
	THE SHEIKH KHALIFA ROSE ('Dickoolkid') (Patio)	IDic
	THE SHIRE	see *R.* CELEBRATION TIME
	THE SIMPLE LIFE ('Hartrifle'[PBR]) (Cl)	LHkn MJon MRav SApu SSea
	THE SOHAM ROSE	see *R.* PEARL ABUNDANCE
	THE SOROPTIMIST ROSE ('Benstar') (Patio)	MJon NRog
	THE SUN AND THE HEART ('Hartyre') (S)	LHkn
	THE TIMES ROSE ('Korpeahn') (F) ℘H6	ECnt SCob
	THE WAINWRIGHT ROSE ('Frylovely') (HT)	NRog
	THE WEDGWOOD ROSE ('Ausjosiah'[PBR]) (ClS)	EHyd EPfP LRHS NRHS
	THE WREN ('Kormamtiza'[PBR]) (F/Patio)	EBls EPfP
	THE YORKSHIRE REGIMENT ('Webterrific') (F)	NRog
	'Thelma' (Ra)	EBls
	THEO CLEVERS ('Bozkatafra') (Taste of Love Series) (S) **new**	ETWh
	'Thérèse Bugnet' (Ru) ℘H7	EBls NRog
	THINKING OF YOU ('Frydandy'[PBR]) (HT) ℘H6	CDoC EBls EDir ELon EPfP ESty LRHS LSRN MAsh MFry MJon SApu SCoo SPer SSea SWCr
	THIS IS THE DAY ('Sproday') (Min)	NRog
	THIS MORNING ('Harzephyr') (S)	LHkn
	'Thisbe' (HM)	EBls ETWh
	THOMAS À BECKET ('Auswinston'[PBR]) (S)	CGro CRos ECnt EHyd EPfP ESty LCro LOPS LRHS MAsh MSwo NLar NRHS SPer SWCr
	'Thoresbyana'	see *R.* 'Bennett's Seedling'
	THOUSAND BEAUTIES	see *R.* 'Tausendschön'
	threepenny bit rose	see *R. elegantula* 'Persetosa'
	THUMBS UP ('Hornothing') (S)	EBls
	TICKLED PINK ('Fryhunky'[PBR]) (F) ℘H6	CArg CTri EBls LCro LRHS LSRN MAsh MFry MJon MRav NRog SApu SPer SPoG SSea SWCr
§	TIMELESS CREAM ('Noa1112130'[PBR]) (HT)	CRos EBls LBuc MAsh SWCr WHlf
§	TIMELESS PINK ('Noa1811108'[PBR]) (HT)	CRos EBls LBuc LCro MAsh WHlf
§	TIMELESS PURPLE ('Noa38121'[PBR]) (HT)	CRos EBls LBuc LCro MAsh WHlf
	TIMES PAST ('Harhilt'[PBR]) (ClHT)	ELon ETWh LHkn MRav SApu SPoG
	'Tina Turner' (HT)	LSRN NRog
	TIP TOP ('Tanope') (F/Patio)	NRog
	'Tipo Ideale'	see *R.* × *odorata* 'Mutabilis'
	TITANIC ('Macdako'[PBR]) (F)	ESty MJon
	'Toby Tristam' (Ra)	CRHN
	TOGETHER FOREVER ('Dicecho'[PBR]) (F)	EBls LSRN MAsh MFry SWCr
	TOGMEISTER ('Beahappy') (F)	CEnd EBee EBls LRHS MAsh NRHS
	'Tom Marshall' (Ra)	ETWh LSRN
	'Tom Wood' (HP)	ETWh
	'Tony Bracegirdle' (HT)	NRog
	'Tony Jacklin' (F)	LSRN NRog
	TOO HOT TO HANDLE ('Macloupri') (ClS)	MJon
	TOOTS ('Braable') (Patio)	NRog
	TOP MARKS ('Fryministar') (Min/Patio)	MFry MRav SApu SCob SCoo SPer SWCr
	TOPAZ JEWEL	see *R.* YELLOW DAGMAR HASTRUP
	'Topsi' (F/Patio)	NRog SPer
	TOTTERING-BY-GENTLY ('Auscartoon') (S)	CRos ELan EPfP ESty LRHS MAsh MCot NLar SPer
§	'Tour de Malakoff' (Ce)	EBls NLar SPer
	TOWER BRIDGE ('Haravis') (HT)	LHkn
	TOYNBEE HALL ('Korwonder') (F)	EBls LRHS
	TRADITION (ClHT)	see *R.* TRADITION '95
§	TRADITION '95 ('Korkeltin'[PBR]) (ClHT)	ETWh NLar
	TRANQUILITY ('Barout') (HT)	CGro EHyd EPfP LRHS MSwo NRHS SCoo SWCr
	TRANQUILLITY ('Ausnoble'[PBR]) (S)	CRos CSBt ECnt ESty LBuc MJon SCoo SPer
	'Treasure Trove' (Ra)	CRHN EBls
§	TRENCIN ('Poulcas066') (Castle Series) (F) **new**	ETWh
	'Tricolore de Flandre' (G)	EBls ETWh
	'Trier' (Ra)	EBls ETWh WMal
	'Trigintipetala' misapplied	see *R.* × *damascena* 'Professeur Émile Perrot'
	'Triomphe des Noisettes' ambig. (N)	ETWh
	'Triple Delight' (S)	LSRN NRog
I	'Trish's Rose' (Ru)	LSRN
	TROIKA ('Poumidor') (HT)	ELon LRHS MAsh SPer
	TROPICAL TWIST ('Jacorca') (Min)	NRog
	'Tropicana'	see *R.* SUPER STAR
	TRUE FRIEND ('Smi35-2-02') (F)	ESty
	'Truly Loved' (F)	LSRN MAsh
	'Truly Scrumptious'[PBR] (HT)	MRav
	TRUMPETER ('Mactru') (F) ℘H6	CArg CGro CTri EBee ECnt EDir IArd LBuc MAsh MFry MJon MRav NRog SPer SPoG WKif
§	'Tuscany' (G)	EBls

'Tuscany Superb' (G) 🏆H7	CArg CBcs CDoC CRos CSBt CTri EBee EBls ELan EPfP ETWh LCro LEdu LOPS LRHS LSRN MCot MGos MRav NLar NRog SCob SPer SSea WBor WFar WHer WKif
Twenty-one Again! ('Meinimo') (HT)	LSRN
Twice in a Blue Moon ('Tan96138'[PBR]) (HT) 🏆H6	CArg CDoC CGro CSBt EBls ECnt ELon ESty LRHS MFry MJon MRav SApu SCob SCoo SPer SPoG SSea SWCr WKif
Twiggy's Rose ('Harteam'[PBR]) (F)	LHkn
Twilight Zone ('Wekebtidere') (HT)	ECnt ESty MJon
Twist ('Poulstri'[PBR]) (Courtyard Series) (ClPatio)	CArg ECnt LSRN SApu
Tynwald ('Mattwyt') (HT)	SPer
'Ulrich Brünner'	see *R.* 'Ulrich Brünner Fils'
§ 'Ulrich Brünner Fils' (HP)	EBls
Unbridled ('Decbridled') (Patio)	NRog
'Uncle Bill' (HT)	EBls
Uncle Walter ('Macon') (HT)	EBls
'Unique Blanche'	see *R.* × *centifolia* 'Unique'
Utopia ('Delsimros') (F) **new**	MJon
Valentine Heart ('Dicogle') (F) 🏆H6	CArg CSBt ESty IArd LSRN MRav SApu SPoG
Vanessa Bell ('Auseasel'[PBR]) (S)	CGro CRos CSBt ESty LRHS MJon MSwo NLar SCoo SWCr
'Vanity' (HM)	EBls
Varenna Allen ('Harmode'[PBR]) (F)	LHkn
'Variegata di Bologna' (Bb)	EBls EPfP ETWh NLar NRog
'Vatertag' (Min)	LSRN
Vavoom ('Wekjutono') (F) **new**	MJon
'Veilchenblau' (Ra) 🏆H7	Widely available
'Velindre' (HT)	MJon
Velvet Fragrance ('Fryperdee') (HT)	CArg CSBt ECnt ESty MFry MGos MRav SApu SCob SPoG
'Vera Parker' (Min)	NRog
Veronica Arnott ('Harjob') (S)	LHkn
Veronica Margaret ('Dicpursue') (F)	IDic
'Verschuren' (HT/v)	ESty
'Versharben'	SSea
versicolor	see *R. gallica* 'Versicolor'
Veterans' Honor ('Jacopper') (HT)	NRog
'Vick's Caprice' (HP)	EBls ETWh NLar
'Vicomtesse Pierre du Fou' (ClHT)	EBls
Victoria ('Simlast') (HT)	ESty
Victoria Joy ('Diciwill') (F)	IDic
Victoria Pendleton ('Harpace'[PBR]) (F)	LHkn
Vidal Sassoon ('Macjuliat'[PBR]) (HT)	MJon
'Village Maid'	see *R.* × *centifolia* 'Unique Panachée'
§ ***villosa*** L.	EBls ETWh WKor
Vintage Classic (F) **new**	MJon
§ 'Violacea' (G)	EBls ETWh
Violet Cloud ('Harquick'[PBR]) (Min)	CDoC CGro LHkn MGos MRav
'Violette' (Ra)	EBls ESty ETWh SPer WFar WHer
'Violinista Costa' (HT)	EBls
Virginia McKenna OBE ('Harsong') (S)	LHkn LSRN
virginiana 🏆H7	EBls NWea SCob SDix
- 'Plena'	see *R.* 'Rose d'Amour'
'Viridiflora'	see *R.* × *odorata* 'Viridiflora'
Vision of Hope ('Webjuly') (F)	NRog
'Vivid' (Bourbon hybrid)	EBls
Voice of Thousands ('Horsunsmile') (F)	NRog
Walferdange ('Lenwal') (HM) **new**	EBls
Wallace Hartley ('Horlazarus') (F)	NRog
Waltz ('Poulkrid'[PBR]) (Courtyard Series) (ClPatio)	ECnt LSRN
'Waltz Time' (HT)	EDir
Warm Welcome ('Chewizz') (ClMin) 🏆H6	CBcs CBod CDoC CEnd CGro CRos EBls ECnt ELan EPfP ESty LCro LOPS LSRN MAsh MFry MJon MRav NPoe NRog SApu SCoo SMad SPer SPoG SSea SWCr
§ Warm Wishes ('Fryxotic'[PBR]) (HT) 🏆H6	CEnd CSBt EBls ECnt EDir EPfP LBuc LRHS LSRN MAsh MFry MGos MJon MRav NRHS SCob SPer SSea SWCr
Warwickshire ('Korkandel') (GC)	EBls SCob
§ ***watsoniana*** (Ra)	EBls EBtc
WB Yeats ('Dicoodles') (F)	IDic MJon SApu
webbiana	ETWh
Wedding Bells ('Korsteflali'[PBR]) (HT)	EPfP LSRN MJon NRog
Wedding Celebration ('Poulht006'[PBR]) (HT)	CBod EBls ECnt
'Wedding Day' (Ra)	Widely available
'Weetwood' (Ra)	CRHN
Weisse Wolcke	see *R.* White Cloud ('Korstacha')
Well-Being ('Harjangle'[PBR]) (S)	CArg CGro ELon LHkn
'Welsh Gold' (Patio)	NRog
Welwyn Garden Glory ('Harzumber'[PBR]) (HT)	LHkn
'Wendy Cussons' (HT)	CTri EBls NRog SApu SCob SPer SSea
Westerland ('Korwest') (S) 🏆H6	CDoC EBls ETWh LPar LRHS MJon MRav NLar NRog SHor
Where the Heart Is ('Cocoplan'[PBR]) (HT)	ESty
Whirlaway ('Decwhirl') (Patio)	NRog
Whisky Mac ('Tanky') (HT)	CBcs CDoC CGro CSBt CTri EBee EBls EDir ELan ELon LSRN MGos MJon MRav NRog SApu SCob SPer
'White Bath'	see *R.* × *centifolia* 'Shailer's White Moss'
'White Cécile Brünner' (Poly)	EBls
§ White Cloud ('Korstacha'[PBR]) (ClHT)	CDoC EDir ESty LRHS MJon SApu SSea
'White Cockade' (ClHT)	EBls EDir ETWh MSwo SPer
White Cover	see *R.* Kent
§ 'White de Meaux' (Ce)	EBls
White Diamond ('Interamon'[PBR]) (F)	ECnt EDir
White Fox Rose ('Harzebek') (F)	LHkn LRHS
§ White Gold ('Cocquiriam'[PBR]) (F) 🏆H6	CSBt

'White Grootendorst' (Ru) — EBls ETWh
WHITE LIQUORICE ('Wekdidusinra') (F) **new** — MJon
'White Maman Couchet' (HT) — EBls
WHITE MEIDILAND ('Meicoublan') (S/GC) — LRHS LSRN MAsh SWCr
white moss — see *R.* × *centifolia* 'Shailer's White Moss', *R.* 'Comtesse de Murinais'
'White New Dawn' (Cl) — EBls
'White Patio' (Min/Patio) — CRos EBls LRHS MAsh SPoG
WHITE PERFUMELLA ('Meicalanq'PBR) (HT) — ELan ESty LSRN NRog
§ 'White Pet' (Poly) ♀H6 — CArg CBod CTri EBee EBls ECnt ELan EPfP ETWh LCro LOPS LRHS LSRN MCot MJon MRav NLar NPoe NRog SApu SCob SEND SPer SWCr WKif
white Provence — see *R.* × *centifolia* 'Unique'
white rose of York — see *R.* × *alba* 'Alba Semiplena'
WHITE SKYLINER ('Franwekwhit'PBR) (ClS) — MJon SSea
WHITE STAR ('Harquill') (ClHT) ♀H5 — ECnt LHkn MAsh MJon MRav SSea
WHITE WEDDING ('Tan02360') — NTrD
'White Wings' (HT) — CArg EBls ETWh WKif
wichurana — see *R. lucieae*
'Wickwar' (Ra) ♀H6 — EBls ETWh NLar
WILD BLUE YONDER ('Wekisosblip') (HT) **new** — MJon
'Wild Eagle' (Ru) **new** — MJon
WILD EDRIC ('Aushedge'PBR) (Ru) ♀H6 — ECnt MJon MMuc SCoo
'Wild Horse' (Ru) **new** — MJon
WILD ROVER ('Dichirap') (F) ♀H6 — CBod CDoC EBls ELon ESty MFry MJon SApu
WILDEVE ('Ausbonny'PBR) (S) ♀H6 — EHyd LRHS MJon NRHS SWCr
WILDFIRE ('Fryessex'PBR) (Patio) — CArg CGro EBls ECnt ESty LRHS MAsh MFry MGos MRav SApu SPoG SWCr
§ 'Wilhelm' (HM) — EBls ETWh SPer
WILLIAM AND CATHERINE ('Ausrapper'PBR) (S) — EPfP LCro
'William Cobbett' (F) — SSea
§ 'William Lobb' (CeMo) ♀H7 — CArg CBcs CDoC EBls EHyd EPfP ETWh LRHS MCot MNrw MRav NLar NRHS NRog SCob WHer WKif
WILLIAM MORRIS ('Auswill'PBR) (S) — CSBt
WILLIAM SHAKESPEARE ('Ausroyal') (S) — SCob
WILLIAM SHAKESPEARE 2000 ('Ausromeo'PBR) (S) — CArg CSBt ESty MJon NLar SCob
'William Tyndale' (Ra) — ETWh
'Williams' Double Yellow' — see *R.* × *harisonii* 'Williams' Double Yellow'
willmottiae — ETWh
WILTSHIRE ('Kormuse') (S/GC) ♀H6 — CSBt CTri EBls ETWh MRav NLar SApu SCob SEND SSea
WIMI ('Tanrowisa') (HT) — NRog
WINCHESTER CATHEDRAL ('Auscat') (S) — CArg CRos CTri EHyd EPfP LCro LOPS LRHS LSRN MAsh MJon MSwo NLar NRHS SCob SCoo SPer SPoG
WINDRUSH ('Ausrush') (S) — ETWh
WINE AND DINE ('Dicuncle') (GC) — EBls
WING-DING ('Wekairyven'PBR) (Poly) **new** — MJon
WINTER SUN ('Korbatam'PBR) (HT) — EBls
WISLEY 2008 ('Ausbreeze'PBR) (S) — CSBt EHyd EPfP LBuc LRHS MAsh NRHS SCoo SWCr
WIZARD (HT) — NRog
'Woburn Abbey' (F) — EBls
WOLLERTON OLD HALL ('Ausblanket'PBR) (Cl) — CRos CSBt EBee EHyd EPfP ESty LBuc LCro LRHS MAsh MJon MSwo NLar NRHS SCoo SPer SWCr
'Wolley-Dod' — see *R.* 'Duplex'
WONDERFUL HUSBAND ('Raw982') (F) — ESty
WONDERFUL NEWS ('Jonone'PBR) (Patio) — ESty MJon
WONDERFUL WIFE ('Raw1025') (HT) — ESty
WONDERFUL YOU ('Smi 170-2-4') (HT) — ESty
woodsii (S) — EBls
- var. ***fendleri*** — EBls ETWh
- var. ***ultramontana*** — EBls
'Woolverstone Church Rose' — see *R.* 'Surpassing Beauty of Woolverstone'
WORCESTERSHIRE ('Korlalon'PBR) (GC) ♀H6 — MJon MRav SApu SPer
WYMONDHAM ABBEY ('Beadevil') (ClHT) — EBls LRHS MAsh
xanthina Lindl. — LShi
§ - 'Canary Bird' (S) ♀H6 — CArg CBcs CDoC CSBt EBee EBls ECnt ELan EPfP ESty ETWh LRHS LSRN MAsh MFry MGos MJon MRav NLar SApu SCob SPer SPoG SSea SWCr SWvt
§ - f. ***hugonis*** — EBls ELan ETWh NLar NRog SPer
X-RATED ('Tinx') (Min) — NRog
YABBA DABBA DOO ('Wekruneflo') (S) **new** — MJon
YARDLEY BAROQUE ('Beayar') (HT) — EBls
'Yellow Cécile Brünner' — see *R.* 'Perle d'Or'
§ YELLOW DAGMAR HASTRUP ('Moryelrug') (Ru) — ETWh NRog SApu
YELLOW FLOWER CARPET — see *R.* FLOWER CARPET SUNSHINE
'Yellow Mutabilis' (Ch) — EBls
'Yellow Patio' (Min/Patio) — CRos MAsh SCob SPoG
yellow Scotch — see *R.* × *harisonii* 'Williams' Double Yellow'
YELLOW SUNBLAZE ('Meitrisical') (Min) — CSBt
'Yesterday' (Poly/FCl) ♀H6 — EBls ETWh NLar SCob
'Yolande d'Aragon' (HP) — EBls ETWh
York and Lancaster — see *R.* × *damascena* 'Versicolor'
YORK MINSTER ('Harquest') (F) — LHkn MRav
YORKSHIRE ('Korbarkeit'PBR) (GC) — EBls
YORKSHIRE BANK ('Rutrulo') (HT) — MFry
'Yorkshire Lady' (HT) — LSRN NRog
YORKSHIRE PRINCESS ('Dicmouse') (Patio) — IDic MJon MRav
YOU ARE MY SUNSHINE ('Frykwango'PBR) (HT) ♀H6 — NTrD
'You Only Live Once' (F) — LSRN
YOUNG AT HEART ('Raw922') (F) — ESty
YOUNG LOVE — see *R.* ARCHBISHOP DESMOND TUTU
YOUNG LYCIDAS ('Ausvibrant'PBR) (S) — CSBt EPfP LBuc LRHS LSRN MAsh MBNS NRHS SWCr

'Your Wedding Day' (F)	NTrD
YOU'RE BEAUTIFUL ('Fryracy'PBR) (F) ♀H6	CDoC CSBt EBee EBls ECnt EDir ELan LBuc LCro LOPS LRHS MAsh MFry MJon MRav NRHS SApu SPer SPoG SWCr
YOURS IN CONTINUED FRIENDSHIP ('Harpal') (F)	LHkn
YVES PIAGET	see *R.* ROYAL BROMPTON ROSE
'Yvonne Rabier' (Poly) ♀H6	EBls ETWh SPer
'Zéphirine Drouhin' (Bb)	Widely available
§ 'Zigeunerknabe' (S)	CBod EBls ETWh NLar SPer WFar
'Zoe'	LSRN

Roscoea ✿ (*Zingiberaceae*)

alpina	CBro CExl CMiW EAri EPot GEdr GKev NBPC NHar WCru WFar XLum
- f. ***pallida*** **new**	GEdr
- short	WCru
§ ***auriculata*** ♀H5	CAvo CBro CLAP CTsd EAri EBee EMor EPfP EPot GEdr GKev ITim LAma LBar LEdu MAsh NChi NWad SChF SDeJ SDir SPer WCru WHil
- B&SWJ 2594	WCru
- B&SWJ 2687	WCru
- GWJ 9230	WCru
- brown-stemmed × ***purpurea***	CJun
- early-flowering	WCru WFar
- 'Floriade'	CAvo CJun EBee LAma SDir SPVi WFar WPGP WSHC
- green-stemmed × ***purpurea***	CJun
- late-flowering	WCru
- 'White Cap'	CJun EBee
auriculata* × *cangshanensis	WCru
auriculata* × *purpurea	WCru
australis	EBee ELon GEdr GGro MNrw WCru WFar WThu
'Ballyrogan White'	NHar
× ***beesiana*** ♀H5	CAvo CBcs CBod CDTJ EBee EPfP NCth NHar SMHy WFar
- 'Ballyrogan Purple'	CJun
- Cream Group	CJun EBee ELon LAma NBir SDeJ SDir WCru
- Gestreept Group	CBro CLAP ECha EHyd EPot EWoo GEdr GKev LAma LBar LRHS MHol NBPC NRHS SDir WCru
- - white-flowered	GKev
- 'Lemon and Lavender'	CJun NHar
- 'Monique'	CDTJ CJun EAri EBee EPfP NHar WFar
- 'Moonlight'	CJun NHar
bhutanica PAB 3826	LEdu WFar
Blackthorn strain	WCru WHil
cangshanensis	CMiW GKev WFar
- BWJ 7848	SPVi WCru
cautleyoides	CAby CAvo CBro CMiW CRos CWCL ECha EGrl EHyd EMor EPot GKev LAma LRHS MHid MNrw NChi NGdn NHar NLar NRHS WCot WCru WFar WSHC
- blue-leaved	NHar
- var. ***cautleyoides*** white-flowered	CAby
- 'Crûg's Late Lemon'	WCru WFar
- 'Early Purple'	CJun
- 'Ice Age'	CDor CMiW ELon
- 'Jeffrey Thomas' ♀H5	CBro CJun EHyd LAma LRHS NRHS WHil
- 'Last Emperor'	CLAP
- 'Lemon Giraffe'	CJun
- mauve-flowered	WHil
- 'Nguluko Village'	WFar
- 'Pennine Purple'	NHar
- var. ***pubescens***	CJun
- 'Purple Giant'	CJun WHil
- 'Purple Queen' ♀H5	WFar
- purple-flowered	CBod CMiW
- 'Reinier'	CJun
- f. ***sinopurpurea***	GKev
- 'Vanilla'	CJun LEdu
- 'Vien Beauty'	NHar
- 'Wine Red'	WHil
- 'Yeti'	CJun
aff. ***cautleyoides***	SPlb
cautleyoides* × *humeana	NHar
forrestii f. ***forrestii***	NHar
'Harvington Evening Star'	CJun CKel CLAP ECha EHyd LRHS NHar NRHS WFar
Harvington hybrids	NHar
'Harvington Imperial'	NHar
'Harvington Raw Silk' ♀H5	CBro CJun CLAP ECha EHyd LEdu LRHS NHar NRHS WFar
'Harvington Royale'	CJun EHyd LRHS NHar NRHS WFar
'Harvington Summer Deep Purple' **new**	WFar
humeana	CBro CMiW CRos EAri EHyd EPot GEdr GKev LRHS NHar NRHS WFar WThu
- from Cruickshank Botanic Garden	NHar
- f. ***alba***	CJun NHar
- 'Long Acre Sunrise'	CJun
- f. ***lutea*** ♀H5	CJun GEdr NHar WFar
- purple-flowered	ECha EHed
- 'Purple Streaker'	CJun
- 'Rosemoor Plum'	CAby CJun CMiW WHil
- 'Snowy Owl'	CJun GEdr MHid WFar
- 'Stephanie Bloom' ♀H5	EBee EBlo NHar
- 'Two Tone'	CJun
- f. ***tyria*** ♀H5	CJun
- - Inkling Group	NHar
'Ice Maiden'	CJun
'Kew Beauty' ♀H5	CAby CBcs CBro CExl CJun CLAP CMiW EBee ECha EHed EHyd EMor EPfP LBar LRHS NFav NHar NRHS SPoG WFar WGwG
'McBeath's Pink'	EHyd NHar NRHS SPVi WFar
nepalensis	CJun
praecox	GEdr
procera misapplied	see *R. auriculata*
procera Wall.	see *R. purpurea*
'Purple King'	CJun
§ ***purpurea***	CAvo CBcs CBro CDTJ ECha EGrl EHyd ELan ELon EPfP EWoo GKev LAma LRHS MAsh NBPC NBir NChi NGdn NLar NRHS SPer SPlb SPoG WBor WCAu WCru WFar WGwG WHer
- CC 3628	CExl
- HWJK 2020	SPVi WCru
- HWJK 2169	WCru
- HWJK 2175	WCru
- HWJK 2400	WCru WFar
- HWJK 2407	WCru
- MECC 2	CJun
- MECC 10	CJun
- 'Ant Marian'	GKev IPot
- 'Arapahoe' **new**	CBor
- Blackthorn hybrids	CLAP NHar
- bronze-leaved	CMiW
- 'Brown Peach'	EMor

- 'Brown Peacock'	CAvo CJun EMor GKev IPot LAma NHar SDir SPVi WCot WCru WFar
- 'Butterfly'	WFar
- 'Cinnamon Stick'	CJun CLAP CWGN ECtt EHed EMor GBin GKev NHar SPVi WCot
- 'Coushatta' **new**	CBor
- Emperor Group	NHar
- 'Harvington Imperial'	SPVi
- 'Julie's Glory'	WFar
- 'Navajo' **new**	CBor
- 'Nico'	CJun EAri ELan
- 'Omaha' **new**	CBor
- pale-flowered	WFar
- 'Peacock'	CJun EMor GKev WHil
- 'Peacock Eye'	CJun GEdr LAma WFar
- var. ***procera***	see *R. purpurea*
- 'Red Foot'	WFar
- 'Red Gurkha'	see *R. purpurea* f. *rubra*
- 'Red Riding Hood'	WFar
- red-stemmed	NHar
- Royal Purple hybrids	CJun MAsh NHar SPVi WPGP
§ - f. ***rubra*** 🏆H5	Widely available
- - 'Gurkha Redstem'	CJun CLAP SPVi SPoG WCru WFar
- 'Salt 'n' Pepper'	EMor GKev
- 'Snow Goose'	WCru
- 'Spice Island'	CJun CLAP CSpe CWGN ECtt GEdr IPot MMrt MPkF SEdd SMad SPVi SPoG WCot WFar XSte
- Sultan Group	NHar SPVi WHoo
- 'Summer Snow'	WFar
- tall	WCru
- 'Twin Towers'	EMor GKev
- 'Vannin'	CJun LEdu SPVi WCru WFar
- 'Vincent'	CJun EBee EMor EPot GKev LAma WFar
- 'Wisley Amethyst'	CBro CJun EBee EHyd MNrw NHar NRHS WFar
schneideriana	CJun GKev WFar WThu
scillifolia	CBro CRos EAri EHyd GEdr LRHS NBir NRHS SDeJ SPlb
- f. ***atropurpurea***	CMiW EPot EWld GKev WCru WThu
- black-flowered	NHpl
- pink-flowered miniature **new**	CBor
- f. ***scillifolia***	EWld GGro MPie NHpl WCru WFar WThu
aff. ***scillifolia*** purple-flowered	GEdr
'Snow Queen'	NHar
'Summer Deep Purple' 🏆H5	CJun EHyd LRHS NHar NRHS WFar
tibetica	CWCL EAri GArf GEdr GKev SPlb WCru WFar WSHC WThu
- ACE 2538	WCru
- BWJ 7878	WCru
- f. ***atropurpurea*** BWJ 7640	WCru
- narrow-leaved	GGro
- f. ***rosea***	WCru
I - white-flowered	GRum
'Two Tone'	CJun NHar
wardii 🏆H5	CExl

rosemary see *Salvia rosmarinus*

Rosmarinus see *Salvia* (Ro)

corsicus 'Prostratus'	see *Salvia rosmarinus* Prostrata Group
× ***noeanus***	see *Salvia* × *lavandulacea* (de Noé) Roma-Marzio & Galasso
officinalis	see *Salvia rosmarinus*
- f. ***albiflorus***	see *Salvia rosmarinus* Albiflora Group
- var. ***angustissimus***	see *Salvia rosmarinus* Angustifolia Group
repens	see *Salvia rosmarinus* Prostrata Group

Rostrinucula (*Lamiaceae*)

dependens	CBcs CMCN CTsd EBee EHed EPfP ESwi EWes IDee LCro LPar LRHS NLar SBrt SMrm SPad WCFE
- 'Happy Cascade' **new**	LPar
sinensis	CExl

Rosularia (*Crassulaceae*)

§ ***aizoon***	CRos EHyd LRHS NRHS SRms WFar
alba	see *Sedum sedoides* var. *album*
§ ***chrysantha***	CRos EDAr EHyd EPot LRHS NHpl NRHS SPlb SRms WAbe WFar
crassipes	see *Rhodiola wallichiana*
hirsuta	NHpl
libanotica RCB RL 20	WCot
§ ***muratdaghensis***	SPlb
pallida A. Berger	see *R. chrysantha*
pallida Stapf	see *R. aizoon*
pallida ambig.	EPot
platyphylla misapplied	see *R. muratdaghensis*
rechingeri	GArf SRms
sedoides	see *Sedum sedoides*
sempervivum	EWes WThu
§ - subsp. ***glaucophylla***	CRos EHyd LRHS NRHS SPlb SRms WFar WThu
serpentinica	EWes WAbe
spatulata hort.	see *R. sempervivum* subsp. *glaucophylla*

Rotheca (*Lamiaceae*)

§ ***myricoides*** 'Ugandense' 🏆H1b	CCCN CHII ELan EShb SMrm WSFF

Roystonea (*Arecaceae*)

regia **new**	EAri NPlm

Rubia (*Rubiaceae*)

peregrina	GPoy
tinctorum	CHab CHby GJos GPoy MNHC SRms WSFF

Rubus ✿ (*Rosaceae*)

RCB/Eq C-1	WCot
acuminatus	ESwi LEdu SBrt
alceifolius Poir.	SDys
- B&SWJ 1833	WCru
arcticus	LEdu NHar SHar WKor WPGP XLum
- subsp. ***stellarcticus*** 'Beata' (F)	LEdu
- - 'Linda' (F)	LEdu
- - 'Tarja' (F) **new**	LEdu
bambusarum	EBee EShb GGro MRav NLar WCFE WCru
'Benenden' 🏆H5	CBcs CExl CKel CTri EBee EHyd ELan EPfP GKin LRHS LSRN MBNS MMrt MMuc MRav NBid NLar SPer SPhx WCFE WLov WSpi
'Betty Ashburner'	CAgr CBcs CDoC EHeP EPPr GLog GMcL MCoo MGos MRav NLar SCob SPer SPoG XLum
biflorus 🏆H6	LEdu LRHS MBlu MMuc SEND WKor
'Boysenberry' (F)	CArg CMac EDir EHyd LEdu LRHS MAsh

boysenberry, thornless (F)	CDoC CMac LBuc LSRN NRog SPer WLea
buergeri B&SWJ 5555	WCru
caesius	NRog WCot WKor
calophyllus	CBcs CKel EBee EPfP ESwi LRHS WPGP
- PAB 13.171	LEdu WPGP
calycinoides Hayata ex Koidz.	see *R. rolfei*
calycinoides ambig.	EHeP
calycinoides Kuntze	GKev MGil SGol
chamaemorus	GPoy
- 'Nyby'	WKor
cockburnianus (F)	CBcs EHeP ELan EPfP GMcL LBuc LCro LOPS LPar LShi LSto MAsh MMuc MRav MSwo NLar NSti NWea SCob SPer SPlb SRms WSpi
- 'Goldenvale' ♀H6	CBcs CDoC CKel EHyd ELon EPfP GMcL LRHS LSto MAsh MBlu MGos MMuc MRav MSwo NBir NLar NSti SEND SPer SPoG SRms WBor WFar
crataegifolius	MRav
discolor	NWea
flagelliflorus	NLar
fockeanus misapplied	see *R. rolfei*
formosensis	SBrt
- B&SWJ 1798	CBod EBee ESwi WCru
formosensis* × *reflexus var. ***lanceolobus*** **new**	WPGP
fruticosus agg.	CArg NWea SCob WSFF
- 'Adrienne' (B)	CAgr CDoC CHab CSBt LEdu MAsh MTrO NRog SBdl SCoo SRms SSFr
- 'Apache' (B)	CHab CRos LCro LOPS LRHS MNHC MTrO SKee SPoG
- 'Ashton Cross' (B)	SBmr SSFr
- 'Asterina' (B)	CMac
- 'Bedford Giant' (B)	CHab CSBt LSRN MAsh MGos NRog NWea SBmr SCoo SSFr
- 'Black Butte' (B)	CHab EPom NBwr NRog SVic
- 'Black Cascade'	see *R. fruticosus* agg. 'Dart's Black Cascade'
- 'Black Satin' (B)	CAgr EDir NLar NRog SEdi SVic
- 'Čačanska Bestrna' (B)	NRog
- 'Chester' (B)	CMac CRos EBee EDir EHyd EPom LEdu LRHS NRHS NRog SKee
§ - 'Dart's Black Cascade' (B)	EPom LCro LOPS SCoo
- 'Fantasia' (F)	NRog
- 'Helen' (B)	CAgr NRog SBmr SSFr
- 'Himalayan Giant' (B)	CHab NBwr NLar NRog
- 'Karaka Black'PBR (B)	CHab EPom LBuc MAsh NRog SBmr SPoG SSFr SVic
- 'Loch Maree'PBR (B/d)	CHab EPom LEdu NRog
- 'Loch Ness' (B) ♀H6	CAgr CArg CHab CMac CRos EHyd EPom IArd LCro LOPS LRHS LSRN NRHS NRog NWea SBmr SCoo SKee SSFr SVic
- 'Loch Tay'PBR (B) ♀H6	CArg CHab CMac CRos EHyd EPom LRHS NRHS NRog SPoG
- LOWBERRY LITTLE BLACK PRINCE (B)	SBmr SCoo
- 'Merton Thornless' (B)	CDoC CPer CSBt CTri EDir LBuc LEdu LSRN MAsh MGos NBwr NRog NWea SBdl SCoo SRms
- 'Navaho' (B)	CHab CRos EBee EPfP MNHC NRHS NRog SPoG
- 'Navaho Big and Early' (B)	LRHS SBmr
- 'Obsidian' (B)	LEdu
- 'Oregon Thornless' (B)	CAgr CSBt EDir EPfP LCro LOPS LRHS LSRN MAsh MRav MTrO NLar NRog NWea SBmr SCoo SEdi SGbt SPer SPoG SRms SSFr SVic WMat
- 'Ouachita'PBR (B)	CMac CRos EPfP LCro LOPS LRHS MTrO NRHS NRog SKee SPoG
- 'Purple Opal' (B)	LCro LOPS
- 'Reuben'PBR (B)	CHab CRos EHyd EPfP EPom LBuc LCro LOPS LRHS MTrO NRHS NRog SKee SPoG SRms WMat
- 'Thornfree' (B)	CAgr CTri EPfP MTrO NLar NRog SBmr SGbt WMat
- 'Triple Crown' (B)	CHab CMac MCoo
- 'Variegatus' (v)	CMac MBlu WCot
- 'Waldo' (B)	CAgr CDoC CPer LBuc LEdu LSRN MAsh MGos NRog SBdl SBmr SCoo SRms SSFr
'Glencoe' (B)	CMac EPom SVic
henryi	CBcs EBee GBin NLar SPoG WBor
- var. ***henryi***	WCru
ichangensis	CBcs ESwi NLar WJur
idaeus	GPoy LRHS
- 'All Gold' (F) ♀H6	CDoC CMac CPer EPfP EPom NBwr NLar NRog SCoo SPer SRms SVic WMat
- 'Alpengold'PBR (F)	CAgr CRos EBee LOPS LRHS MCoo SPoG
- 'Aureus' (F)	ECha MRav NBid WCot
- 'Autumn Amber' (F)	CMac LRHS NRog
- 'Autumn Bliss' (F) ♀H6	Widely available
- 'Autumn Treasure'PBR (F)	EPom SVic
- 'Black Jewel' (F)	LOPS NRog SBmr
- BONBONBERRY YUMMY ('Jdeboer19') (F) **new**	SBmr
- 'Cascade Delight' (F)	CArg CRos CSBt EHyd EPom LOPS LRHS MAsh NRHS NRog SBmr
- 'Chemainus' (F)	EDir EPom
- 'Erika'PBR (F)	CDow CRos EBee EHyd EPom LCro LRHS MCoo NLar NRHS NRog SRms WMat
- 'Fallgold' (F)	SKee
- 'Glen Ample'PBR (F) ♀H6	Widely available
- 'Glen Clova' (F)	CAgr CDoC CRos CSBt CTri EBee EHyd LRHS LSRN MAsh MGos NBwr NLar NRHS NWea SEdi SGbt SKee SPoG SRms WMat
- 'Glen Dee' (F)	CMac SBmr SRms
- 'Glen Doll'PBR (F)	CAgr MAsh NLar NRHS SCoo SRms WMat
- 'Glen Fyne'PBR (F)	CAgr NRog
- 'Glen Lyon' (F)	CArg CSBt EPfP LBuc MAsh NRog SBdl SCoo SEdi
- 'Glen Magna'PBR (F) ♀H6	CAgr CArg CSBt MAsh SCoo SEdi SKee SRms
- 'Glen Moy'PBR (F)	CAgr CArg EPfP MAsh MGos NWea SCoo SPer
- 'Glen Prosen'PBR (F)	CAgr CDoC CPer CSBt MAsh MGos MPri NRog NWea SCoo SEdi SPlb SPoG SRms SSFr WMat
- 'Heritage' (F)	LSRN MAsh SCoo SRms
- HIMBO TOP ('Rafzaqu'PBR) (F)	NRog
- 'Joan J'PBR (F) ♀H6	CArg CMac EPom LBuc LSRN NRog SBdl SBmr SPer SRms SSFr
- 'Korpiko' (F)	NRog
- 'Leo'PBR (F)	CSBt LCro MAsh NRog SCoo SKee SRms SSFr
- LOWBERRY LITTLE RED PRINCESS (F)	SCoo
- 'Malling Admiral' (F) ♀H6	CSBt CTri EPfP EPom LSRN MAsh NRog NWea SCoo SKee SPer
- 'Malling Delight' (F)	NBwr SCoo SEdi SPlb
- 'Malling Jewel' (F) ♀H6	CAgr CArg CDoC CSBt CTri EPfP EPom LBuc LSRN MAsh MPri NBwr NRog NWea SEdi SKee SPer SRms
- 'Malling Juno'PBR (F)	CMac SVic

- 'Malling Minerva' (F)	CAgr EPom NRog SRms SVic
- 'Octavia'PBR (F)	CAgr CArg CDoC EPom LBuc MAsh MCoo NLar NRHS NRog NWea SBdl SEdi WMat
- 'Paris'PBR (F)	EPom
- 'Polka'PBR (F) 🏆H6	CArg CDoC CRos EHyd EPfP EPom LBuc LCro LOPS LRHS LSRN MAsh MCoo MRav NRHS NRog SBdl SBmr SCoo SKee SPer SRms SSFr WMat
- PRIMEBERRY AUTUMN FIRST (F)	LRHS
- RUBY BEAUTY ('Nr7'PBR) (F)	CDoC CSBt EHyd EPom LBuc LCro LOPS LSRN MGos MNHC MPri NRHS SCoo SPoG SRms
- 'Sanibelle' (F)	LRHS
- 'Sugana'PBR (F)	LCro LRHS NRog
- 'Tadmor'PBR (F)	CArg CRos EHyd EPom LCro LRHS NRHS SRms WMat
- 'Tulameen' (F) 🏆H6	Widely available
- TWOTIMER SUGANA YELLOW (F)	LRHS SRms
- 'Zeva' (F)	SRms
illecebrosus (F)	LEdu WKor XLum
irenaeus	LEdu SEND
Japanese wineberry	see *R. phoenicolasius*
'Jungle Karlostachys'	WPGP
'Kenneth Ashburner'	NLar
laciniatus 'Thornless Evergreen'	NRog
lambertianus PAB 8931	LEdu
- var. ***glandulosus*** B&SWJ 14507	WCru
leucodermis	WKor
lineatus	CBcs CDTJ CKel CMCN EHyd EPfP EWes GBin LEdu LRHS MCot WCru WJur WPGP
- B&SWJ 11261 from Sumatra	WCru
- HWJ 892 from Vietnam	WCru
- HWJK 2045 from Nepal	WCru
- PAB 13.163	LEdu
- from Vietnam	SBrt WPGP
× ***loganobaccus*** (F)	CMac
- 'Ly 59' (F)	EPfP MMuc SKee SRms
- 'Ly 654' (F) 🏆H5	CMac CRos CSBt EHyd EPom LBuc LRHS NRHS NRog SBmr SPer SSFr SVic
- thornless (F)	CAgr CDoC CTri EPfP EPom LEdu MAsh SCoo SEdi SPoG WMat
malvaceus FMWJ 13324	WCru
'Margaret Gordon'	MRav
microphyllus 'Variegatus' (v)	MRav
§ ***nepalensis***	CAgr GKev LEdu WKor WPGP
- CC 7626	GGro
niveus	WKor
nutans	see *R. nepalensis*
occidentalis	WKor
odoratus	CAgr CBcs ELan EPPr EPfP LEdu MBlu NBid NLar SPer WBor WKor
palmatus var. ***coptophyllus***	MMuc
paniculatus CC 7635	GGro
parkeri PAB 6891	LEdu
parviflorus	WKor
- 'Bill Baker'	LEdu
- double-flowered (d)	EPPr
parvus	LEdu
pectinellus var. ***trilobus*** B&SWJ 1669B	WCru
peltatus	NLar
pentalobus	see *R. rolfei*
§ ***phoenicolasius***	CAgr CBcs CBod CCCN CKel CMac ELan EPPr EPfP LCro LEdu LOPS LRHS MBlu MCoo MRav NRog SBmr SPer SPoG SPre SVic WBor WFar WKor WPGP
reflexus var. ***hui***	EShb
§ ***rolfei***	GGro MCoo NWad
- B&SWJ 3546 from Taiwan	WCru
- B&SWJ 3878 from the Philippines	WCru
- 'Emerald Carpet' 🏆H5	CAgr NLar
rosifolius 'Coronarius' (d)	CBcs EBee GBin MHol MNrw NLar WCot WTyc
rubrisetulosus PAB 9532	LEdu
'Rushbrook Redleaf'	SBrt
saxatilis	WKor
setchuenensis	CMCN EPPr NLar
'Silvan' (F)	SEND
spectabilis	EPPr LEdu MGil MRav WKor
- 'Flore Pleno'	see *R. spectabilis* 'Olympic Double'
§ - 'Olympic Double' (d)	Widely available
splendidissimus B&SWJ 2361	WCru
squarrosus	ELon EShb SMad WFar
'Sunberry' (F)	CCCN LEdu NRog SBmr
swinhoei B&SWJ 1735	WCru
taiwanicola	GGro NWad
- B&SWJ 317	ESwi
Tayberry Group (F)	CRos CSBt CTri EHyd GDam LRHS LSRN MGos NLar NRHS SBmr SPer SRms SVic
- 'Buckingham' (F)	CArg CMac EDir EHyd EPom LBuc LCro LRHS NLar NPer NRog SBmr SEdi SVic WMat
- 'Medana Tayberry' (F)	CAgr CTri EPfP LCro LEdu LRHS MAsh MNHC NLar NRog NWea SEdi SKee SPoG WMat
- 'Tayberry' (F) 🏆H5	CDoC EDir SCoo
- thornless	WLea
§ ***thibetanus*** 🏆H6	CBcs CBod CDoC CEme CKel CMac EBee EHeP EHyd ELan EPfP GBin LRHS MBriF MGos MMuc MRav MSwo NLar SCob SDix SEND SPer SPoG SWvt WSpi
- 'Silver Fern'	see *R. thibetanus*
treutleri B&SWJ 2139	WCru
tricolor	CAgr CBcs CBod CDoC CSBt CTri EHeP ELan GGro GKev GMcL MBlu MCoo MMuc MRav MSwo NLar SCob SDix SGol SPer
trilobus B&SWJ 9096	WCru
'Tummelberry' (F)	EHyd NRog SVic
ulmifolius 'Bellidiflorus' (d)	EHeP EPPr MRav NLar
ursinus	SVic WKor
xanthocarpus	LEdu NLar XLum

Rudbeckia (*Asteraceae*)

AUTUMN SUN	see *R. laciniata* 'Herbstsonne'
'Berlin'	EBee LRHS NRHS
californica B&SWJ 14105	WCru
deamii	see *R. fulgida* var. *deamii*
fulgida	SWvt WFar
- 'American Gold Rush'PBR **new**	LBar
- 'City Garden'	GBin LRHS NLar SRms WFar
§ - var. ***deamii*** 🏆H6	Widely available
- 'Early Bird Gold'	CWGN ECtt EHyd EPfP GBin GMaP LBar LCro LRHS MHol NGrs NLar NRHS SAko SCob WCAu WFar

- 'Forever Gold'	NCth SEdd SMad
- var. ***fulgida***	EBee EPfP LEdu SPoG
- 'Little Goldstar'[PBR]	CBod CKno CRos ECtt EHyd ELan EPfP LBar LCro LOPS LRHS MACG MAsh MPri MTin NGrs NLar NRHS SCob SCoo SPoG SRms WFar WHil
§ - var. ***speciosa*** 🏆H6	CBod EBee ECha ECtt EHyd ELan ELon EPfP GAbr GBin LRHS MMuc NRHS SEND SHar SPlb SPtp SRms SWvt WFar WOld XLum
- var. ***sullivantii***	CDoC EMor
- - 'Goldsturm' 🏆H6	Widely available
- - 'Pot of Gold'	NBPC NLar SCob
- VIETTE'S LITTLE SUZY ('Blovi')	CBod EBlo EHyd EPfP LBar LRHS LSou WFar
gloriosa	see *R. hirta*
§ ***hirta***	NRHS SRms SIvy
- AUTUMN COLORS (mixed)	CWnw EBee EHyd ELan EPfP LCro LRHS NRHS
- (Big Smileyz Series) 'Big Kiss Smileyz' **new**	LBar
- - 'Big Love Smileyz' **new**	LBar
- - 'Big Smile Smileyz' **new**	LBar
- 'Cappuccino'	EBee EHyd ELan EPfP LRHS NRHS
- CHEROKEE SUNSET (mixed) (d)	CSpe
- 'Cherry Brandy'	CSpe LRHS MNHC NLar SPhx
- CHIM CHIMINEE (mixed)	SCoo
- 'Goldilocks'	SVic
- 'Indian Summer' 🏆H3	CRos EBee EHyd EPfP LRHS MNHC NRHS SPhx
- 'Irish Eyes'	SPhx SVic
- 'Marmalade'	EPfP SPhx SVic
- 'Prairie Sun'	CRos EBee EHyd EPfP LRHS MBros MDon NGrs NRHS SPhx WHil WHlf
- SAHARA (mixed) **new**	CWnw
- (Smileyz Series) 'Garden Smileyz'	see *R. hirta* (Smileyz Series) 'Glowing Smileyz'
- - 'Giggling Smileyz'[PBR] **new**	LBar
§ - - 'Glowing Smileyz'[PBR] **new**	LBar
- - 'Laughing Smileyz'[PBR] **new**	LBar
- - 'Loving Smileyz' **new**	LBar
- (Sunbeckia Series) SUNBECKIA ALICIA	LBar LRHS
- - SUNBECKIA EMELIA ('Bullrudi 05'[PBR])	LBar
- - SUNBECKIA OLIVIA	LRHS
- - SUNBECKIA PAULINA **new**	LBar
- - SUNBECKIA SOPHIA	LBar
- (Toto Series) 'Toto' 🏆H3	GKev LCro LOPS LRHS SWvt
- - 'Toto Lemon'	LRHS
- - 'Toto Rustic'	LRHS
JULY GOLD	see *R. laciniata* 'Juligold'
laciniata	CKno CMac CSpe EBee ELan EPPr GElm GQue LEdu MNrw NDov NGBl NLar SMHy SPeP SPhx SRms WChS WCot XLum
- 'Golden Glow'	see *R. laciniata* 'Hortensia'
- 'Goldquelle' (d)	Widely available
§ - 'Herbstsonne' 🏆H6	Widely available
§ - 'Hortensia' (d)	EBee EPPr MAvo MRav NGBl WBrk WCot WFar WHoo WOld
§ - 'Juligold'	CBod CRos EBee EBlo ECtt EHyd ELon EPfP EShb LBar LRHS MBNS MPie NGdn NLar NRHS SMrm SPoG WSpi

- 'Starcadia Razzle Dazzle' 🏆H6	ECha EWld MACG SAko WCot WFar
maxima	Widely available
- 'Golda Emanis' **new**	ECha
missouriensis	CRos CSpe EAJP EHyd EPfP LPla LRHS MNrw NRHS
- 'Fairly Free'	MNrw
mollis	CRos EHyd LRHS NRHS
newmannii	see *R. fulgida* var. *speciosa*
nitida	WSpi
occidentalis	EHyd LRHS NChi NRHS
- 'Black Beauty'[PBR]	WSpi
- 'Green Wizard'	CBod CMac CRos EBee EHyd ELan ELon EPfP GBin LRHS LShi MCot NGBl NLar NRHS NSti SBls SCob SMrm SPeP SRms WGwG WPnP WSpi
* ***paniculata***	CDor ECha NGBl WCot
'Peking'[PBR]	EPfP MHol
purpurea	see *Echinacea purpurea*
speciosa	see *R. fulgida* var. *speciosa*
subtomentosa	CRos EHyd EPfP EWes LEdu LRHS MACG MMuc NDov NRHS NSti SDix SMHy WCot WOld WSpi XLum
- 'Henry Eilers'	Widely available
- 'Little Henry'[PBR]	CBcs CBod CKno CNor CTtf EAJP EBee ECtt EHyd ELon EPfP EShb LRHS MAsh MAvo MBNS MBel MHer MHol MSpe MTin NCth NFav NGrs NRHS SCob SPoG WFar WHlf
- 'Loofahsa Wheaten Gold' 🏆H6	ECha GBin LEdu MAvo NDov SHar WCot WGoo
- 'Poligny'	MNrw
Summerina Series	CDoC LRHS SCob
- SUMMERINA BROWN ('Et Rdb 03'[PBR])	CKno CRos EHyd EPfP LRHS NGBl NRHS SCob SMad SPoG WCot
- SUMMERINA BUTTERSCOTCH BISCUIT ('Et Rdb 410'[PBR])	CRos EPfP LBar LRHS
- SUMMERINA ELECTRA SHOCK ('Et Rdb 404'[PBR])	EPfP LRHS
- SUMMERINA FRINGLE FUDGE **new**	LBar
- SUMMERINA ORANGE ('Et Rdb 01'[PBR])	CRos EHyd EPfP LPla LRHS NRHS SCob SGBe SMad SPad SPoG SRkn XSte
- SUMMERINA PECAN PIE ('Et Rdb 401'[PBR])	EBee EPfP LRHS SPad
- SUMMERINA PUMPERNICKEL ('Et Rdb 402'[PBR])	EBee EPfP LBar LRHS
- SUMMERINA YELLOW ('Et Rdb 02'[PBR])	CRos EHyd EPfP LRHS MBNS NGBl NGrs NRHS SCob SGBe SPoG SRkn WCot
TIGER EYE GOLD ('Syntigeygol')	SPoG
triloba 🏆H6	CRos CSpe ECha EHyd EMor EPfP LRHS MNrw NCth NGBl NGdn NRHS SCob SDix SHar SPhx WCAu WSpi
- 'Blackjack Gold'	EAJP EBlo EDAr
- 'Prairie Glow'	CAby CBcs CDor CSpe EAJP EBee ECha EDAr EHyd EPfP LEdu LRHS MACG MHol MNrw NCth NGBl SCob SCoo SMad SMrm SPer SPhx SRkn WGwG WHil WPnP

rue see *Ruta graveolens*

Ruellia (*Acanthaceae*)

amoena	see *R. brevifolia*
§ ***brevifolia***	ECre WFib
humilis	EBee ECha GEdr MNrw SBrt
macrantha	CCCN EShb
strepens	EBee SBrt
tweediana	EShb WFib
- 'Katie'	EAri
- pink-flowered	EShb

Rulingia (*Sterculiaceae*)

hermanniifolia	WAbe

Rumex (*Polygonaceae*)

acetosa	CAgr CBod CCBP CHab CHby CLau CTsd ENfk GPoy MCoo MHer MHoo MNHC NBir SPhx SRms WCot WHer WJek WSFF WWild
- 'Abundance'	CLau LEdu
- subsp. ***acetosa*** 'Saucy' (v)	LEdu MHol WCot
- broad-leaved	SVic
- 'De Belleville'	CLau
- 'Profusion'	GPoy
- red-veined	LCro LOPS
acetosella	CAgr CHab SRms WSFF
alpinus	LEdu SBrt WCot WPGP
flexuosus	CSpe GGro SPtp
hydrolapathum	CHab LPfP MMuc SEND SPlb WCot WSFF
patientia	CBod CHab CLau
sanguineus	CWat EGrI ENfk EShb LEdu LPfP LShi MHoo NLar NQui SRms XLum
- var. ***sanguineus***	CBod CHby ELan GQue MHer MNHC NBro NGrd SMrm WFar WHer
scutatus	CBod CCBP CHby ENfk GPoy MHoo MNHC NGrd SPlb SRms WJek
- 'Armenian Steel'	LEdu
- subsp. ***induratus***	SEND
- 'Silver Shield'	EPPr LEdu MHer NGrd SRms WFar

Rumohra (*Dryopteridaceae*)

adiantiformis 🏆^{H3}	CBdn CCCN CRos EHyd LEdu LRHS MAsh NRHS SEND WFib

Rungia (*Acanthaceae*)

klossii	ENfk WJek

Ruschia (*Aizoaceae*)

putterillii	EAri SPlb
spinosa	EAri SPlb
tumidula	SPlb
uncinata	EAri

Ruschiella (*Aizoaceae*)

argentea	SSim

Ruscus ✿ (*Asparagaceae*)

aculeatus	CBcs CMac ELan EPfP GPoy LEdu LPal LPar LRHS MGil NFav NLar NWea SPlb SRms SWvt WMou
- hermaphrodite	ELan EPfP MNrw SEND WAvo
- (f)	NFav SCob WSpi
- var. ***angustifolius*** (f)	WCru
- - PAB 254	LEdu
- 'John Redmond'^{PBR} (f/m) 🏆^{H5}	CBcs ELan EPfP NHol NWad SPer SWvt WFar WSpi
- var. ***platyphyllus*** B&SWJ 15015 **new**	WCru
* - 'Wheeler's Variety' (f/m)	CJun MRav
colchicus	WPGP
- PAB 1753	LEdu
hypoglossum	CBcs CMac IArd SEND WCot WSpi
hypophyllum B&SWJ 15009	WCru
× ***microglossus*** (f) B&SWJ 14041	WCru
racemosus	see *Danae racemosa*

Ruspolia (*Acanthaceae*)

hypocrateriformis	CCCN

Ruspolia × *Ruttya* see × *Ruttyruspolia*

Russelia (*Plantaginaceae*)

§ ***equisetiformis*** 🏆^{H1c}	WFib
- 'Lemon Falls' 🏆^{H1c}	WFib
- 'Tangerine Falls'	WFib
juncea	see *R. equisetiformis*

Ruta (*Rutaceae*)

chalepensis	XLum
corsica	MHoo XLum
graveolens	CBod CCBP CHab ENfk GPoy GQue MHoo MNHC SVic WJek XLum XSen
- 'Alderley Blue'	WJek
- 'Jackman's Blue'	CBcs EGrI ELan EPfP GPoy MHer MNHC MRav MSwo SRms SWvt WFar WSpi XLum
- 'Variegata' (v)	LShi MHoo MNHC NPer SRms

Ruttya (*Acanthaceae*)

fruticosa	CCCN

× *Ruttyruspolia* (*Acanthaceae*)

lutea	CCCN
'Phyllis van Heerden'	CCCN

S

Sabal (*Arecaceae*)

§ ***bermudana***	NPlm
causiarum	NPlm
etonia	NPlm
maritima **new**	NPlm
§ ***mexicana***	NPlm
minor	CPHo LPal NPlm SPlb
palmetto	EOli LPal NPlm
princeps	see *S. bermudana*
texana	see *S. mexicana*
uresana	LPal LRHS NPlm
yapa	NPlm

Sabatia (*Gentianaceae*)

angularis **new**	CSpe

Saccharum (*Poaceae*)

arundinaceum	CKno
officinarum	SPlb
- purple-stemmed	SPlb WCot
- var. ***violaceum***	SDix
ravennae	EBee SBls SMad SPlb

sage see *Salvia officinalis*

sage, annual clary see *Salvia viridis*

sage, biennial clary see *Salvia sclarea*

sage, pineapple see *Salvia elegans*

Sagaretia (*Rhamnaceae*)

§	***thea***	CMen
	theezans	see *S. thea*

Sagina (*Caryophyllaceae*)

	subulata	LRHS NBwr SVic WSFF XLum
	- var. ***glabrata***	MAsh SRot
§	- - 'Aurea'	EBou ECha ECtt EDAr ELan EPfP GMaP MAsh MHer NHpl SJap SPoG SRms SRot
	- 'Lime Moss' new	WWke
	- 'Supreme'	EPfP LRHS

Sagittaria (*Alismataceae*)

	graminea	LLWG SBrt
	- 'Crushed Ice' (v)	LLWG
	japonica	see *S. sagittifolia*
	lancifolia	LLWG
	latifolia	CAgr CToG LPfP NPer
§	***sagittifolia***	CPud CToG CWat EWat LLWG LPfP MWts WHlf WMAq XLum
	- var. ***leucopetala***	WMAq
	- - 'Flore Pleno' (d)	CWat EWat LPfP NPer XLum

Saintpaulia see *Streptocarpus* (AV)

Salicornia (*Amaranthaceae*)

	europaea	SVic

Salix ✿ (*Salicaceae*)

	acutifolia	WeWi
	- 'Blue Streak' (m) ♀H6	CEnd EPfP EWes MBlu NBir NLar WMou
	'Aegma Brno' (f)	WMou
	aegyptiaca	EBtc MBlu WMou
	alba	CBTr CCVT CHab CLnd CPer LBuc LIns LMaj LPar LSto MAsh NBwr NRog NWea SCob SEWo WMou WTSh WeWi
	- f. ***argentea***	see *S. alba* var. *sericea*
	- 'Aurea'	WCot WMou
	- var. ***caerulea***	CAco EHeP NRog NWea WMou
	- 'Cardinalis' (f)	WeWi
	- 'Chermesina' hort.	see *S. alba* var. *vitellina* 'Britzensis'
	- 'Flame'	EHeP
	- 'Golden Ness' ♀H6	CRos EBee EHyd EPfP GQue LRHS MAsh MBlu MTrO NLar NOra NRHS WFar WMat WeWi
	- 'Hutchinson's Yellow Bark'	MTrO NLar NWea WeWi
	- 'Liempde' (m)	EHeP SCob
	- 'Raesfeld' (m)	WeWi
§	- var. ***sericea*** ♀H6	CLnd EPfP LShi MBlu MRav NLar NRog NWea SPer WCot WMou
	- 'Splendens'	see *S. alba* var. *sericea*
	- 'Tristis' misapplied	see *S.* × *sepulcralis* var. *chrysocoma*
§	- 'Tristis' ambig.	CBTr CBrac CLnd CTri ELan IPap LMaj LRHS MGos MRav MSwo MTrO NBwr NOra SCob SEWo
	- var. ***vitellina***	EHeP LBuc LSto MBNS MMuc NLar NRog NWea SRms WWbk
§	- - 'Britzensis' (m)	Widely available
	- - 'Nova'	ELan
§	- - 'Yelverton' ♀H6	CRos EBee EHyd EPfP LRHS LSto MAsh MTrO NLar NOra NOrn NRHS SPoG WFar WMat WeWi
	- 'Vitellina Tristis'	see *S. alba* 'Tristis' ambig.
§	***alpina***	NHar
	'Americana' (m)	SWeb WeWi
	amplexicaulis 'Pescara' (m)	WeWi
	apennina new	WeWi
	apoda	WeWi
	appendiculata	WeWi
§	***arbuscula***	ELan
	arenaria	see *S. repens* var. *argentea*
	aurita	MMuc NWea
	babylonica	CAco CEnd LPal LPar SArc WMou
	- 'Annularis'	see *S. babylonica* 'Crispa'
	- 'Bijdorp'	NLar
§	- 'Crispa'	ELan GBin MMrt NLar NQui NSti SMad SPoG WFar
	- 'Pan Chih-kang'	NLar
	- var. ***pekinensis***	CWal
	- - 'Pendula'	IArd
§	- - 'Tortuosa' (f)	CAco CBcs CSBt EDir ELan EPfP GMcL IPap LPar LRHS LSto MGos MMuc NGrd NLar NOrn NPer SEND SGol SGsty SPer SPlb SRHi SRms WFar WHtc WeWi
*	- 'Tortuosa Aurea'	MDon SWvt
	bebbiana	CBTr WeWi
	bockii	CKel EHyd EPfP ESwi LRHS SBrt SDys SPlb
§	'Bowles's Hybrid'	EHeP WMou
	'Boydii' (f) ♀H7	ELan EPfP EPot GAbr GEdr GJos GKev GMaP ITim LRHS MGos NBir NBwr NFav NPoe NSla SAko WAbe WFar WLov
	burjatica 'Korso'	WeWi
	caesia	WeWi
	× ***calliantha*** 'William Rogers' new	WeWi
	candida	LSto WFar WeWi
	× ***canescens***	GKev WeWi
	cantabrica	WeWi
	caprea	CArg CBTr CBcs CCVT CHab CLnd CPer CTri EHeP EPfP LBuc NBwr NRog NWea SCob SEWo SPer WMou WSFF WTSh
§	- 'Kilmarnock' (m)	Widely available
	- var. ***pendula*** (f)	see *S. caprea* 'Weeping Sally'
	- - (m)	see *S. caprea* 'Kilmarnock'
	- 'Silberglanz'	WeWi
§	- 'Weeping Sally' (f)	WMat
	caprea × ***lanata***	NBwr
	capusii	LEdu WPGP
	cashmiriana	GEdr
	caspica	WeWi
	'Chrysocoma'	see *S.* × *sepulcralis* var. *chrysocoma*
	cinerea	CBTr CBcs CTri LSto NTrD NWea SCob SEWo WMou WTSh WeWi
	'Coire Kander'	EBee GKev
	daphnoides	CBTr CBcs CCVT CLnd CMac CPer EPfP LMaj MGos MMuc MSwo NLar NRog NWea SCob SEND SPer SRms WMou WSFF
	- 'Aglaia' (m) ♀H6	CTri
	- 'Continental Purple'	LSto WeWi
	- 'Netta Statham' (m)	WeWi
	- 'Oxford Violet' (m)	WeWi
	- 'Sinker'	WeWi
	× ***dasyclados***	WWbk
	- 'Grandis'	NWea
§	× ***doniana*** 'Kumeti'	WeWi
	'E.A. Bowles'	see *S.* 'Bowles's Hybrid'
§	***elaeagnos***	CCVT CPer EHeP EPfP GMcL LShi MMuc NWea SCob SMHy SPer WMou WSpi
§	- subsp. ***angustifolia*** ♀H6	ELan EPfP LShi MMuc MRav MSwo NLar SEND SRms WeWi
	'Elegantissima'	see *S.* × *pendulina* var. *elegantissima*

	exigua $\mathbb{Y}^{H5}$	CBcs CEme CLnd ELan EPfP EWes IDee LEdu LPar MBlu MBrN MGos MSwo NLar NWea SChF SCob SEdd SMad SMrm SPer WMou WPGP WSpi WeWi
	fargesii $\mathbb{Y}^{H6}$	CBcs CBod CBrac CDoC CEnd CExl CKel CMac EBee EHyd ELan EPfP GBin GGro LRHS MBlu MGos MMuc MRav NBid NFav NOra SBrt SCob WCru WFar WLov
	fargesii* × *magnifica	EHed
	formosa	see *S. arbuscula*
§	× ***fragilis***	CCVT CHab CLnd CPer EHeP LSto NWea WMou WTSh
	- 'Basfordiana' (m)	CLnd MBNS WMou
	- 'Bouton Aigu'	WCot WeWi
	- var. ***decipiens***	LSto
	- 'Flanders Red' (f)	WWbk WeWi
§	- var. ***furcata***	EDAr GEdr GKev LShi
	- 'Golden Willow'	WeWi
	- 'Jaune de Falaise'	WeWi
	- 'Jaune Hâtive'	WeWi
	- 'Laurina'	WeWi
	- 'Parsons'	WeWi
	- var. ***russelliana*** **new**	WeWi
	- 'Sanguinea' **new**	WeWi
	fruticulosa	see *S.* × *fragilis* var. *furcata*
	'Fuiri-koriyanagi'	see *S. integra* 'Hakuro-nishiki'
	furcata	see *S.* × *fragilis* var. *furcata*
	glabra	WeWi
	'Golden Curls'	see *S.* × *sepulcralis* 'Erythroflexuosa'
	gracilistyla	NWea WMou
§	- 'Melanostachys' (m) $\mathbb{Y}^{H5}$	CBod EHed ELan EPfP GBin GQue LRHS MAsh MBNS MBlu MGos MMuc MRav NBir NLar NWea SBrt SRms WBor WFar WHlf WLov WeWi XSte
	- 'Mount Aso'	CGBo CMCN EBee EHed ELon EPfP EWes IDee LCro LEdu LOPS LPar LRHS MGos MMrt NLar SBrt SEdd SMad SPtp SRms WCot WFar WHlf WLov WPGP WeWi XSte
	hastata 'Wehrhahnii' (m) $\mathbb{Y}^{H6}$	CBcs EBee EHeP ELan EPfP GMcL LRHS MAsh MBlu MMrt MMuc MRav MSwo NBir NBwr NLar SCob
	helvetica $\mathbb{Y}^{H7}$	CBcs CEme CKel CMac EBee EHeP ELan EPfP GMcL LPar LRHS MAsh MBlu MRav NBir NLar NWea WFar WeWi
	herbacea	EPot GEdr WAbe
	hibernica	see *S. phylicifolia*
I	***himalayas***	WeWi
	hookeriana	CExl MBlu MBrN MCoo WMou WeWi
	humilis **new**	WeWi
	incana	see *S. elaeagnos*
	integra	WeWi
	- 'Albomaculata'	see *S. integra* 'Hakuro-nishiki'
	- 'Flamingo'PBR	ELan MDon NLar SPoG WTSh
§	- 'Hakuro-nishiki' (v) $\mathbb{Y}^{H5}$	Widely available
	- 'Pendula' (f)	CEnd MAsh NOrn WHtc
	irrorata $\mathbb{Y}^{H5}$	CLnd EPfP EWTr LPar MBlu MSwo MTrO NOra WMat WeWi
	'Jacquinii'	see *S. alpina*
§	***koriyanagi***	NLar WeWi
	'Kumeti'	see *S.* × *doniana* 'Kumeti'
	'Kuro-me'	see *S. gracilistyla* 'Melanostachys'
	lanata $\mathbb{Y}^{H7}$	CBcs CBor CMac EHeP ELan ELon EPfP GAbr GKev GMcL GQue LRHS MAsh MGos NBir NLar NWea SPer WCFE

	lapponum	LEdu MMuc NLar SRms
	- from Glen Doll, Scotland **new**	GKev
	- from Glen Lochay, Scotland **new**	GKev
	- compact	GKev
	- 'Corrieshalloch'	GKev
	lasiolepis	WeWi
	magnifica	CExl CKel EPfP GBin LEdu LRHS MMrt MMuc WCot WFar WHer WMou WPGP WSpi WeWi XSte
	'Mark Postill' (f)	EHyd GBin MMuc SAko
	matsudana 'Tortuosa'	see *S. babylonica* var. *pekinensis* 'Tortuosa'
	- 'Tortuosa Aureopendula'	see *S.* × *sepulcralis* 'Erythroflexuosa'
	'Melanostachys'	see *S. gracilistyla* 'Melanostachys'
	mielichhoferi	WeWi
	miyabeana	WWbk WeWi
	× ***mollissima*** var. ***hippophaifolia***	WeWi
	- 'Pheasant Brown'	WeWi
	moupinensis	CBcs EPfP
§	***myrsinifolia***	ELan LSto MBlu MMuc NLar NWea WBor WLov WeWi
	myrsinites var. ***jacquiniana***	see *S. alpina*
	myrtilloides 'Pink Tassels' (m)	NHar SBrt
	nakamurana var. ***yezoalpina***	CDoC CKel CRos EBee EHyd ELan GAbr GEdr LRHS MBlu MMrt MMuc MRav NFav NHar NLar NRya SMad WFar WLov WeWi
	nigricans	see *S. myrsinifolia*
	nivalis	see *S. reticulata* subsp. *nivalis*
§	× ***pendulina*** var. ***elegantissima***	WeWi
	pentandra	CLnd LSto NLar NWea WMou WeWi
§	***phylicifolia***	NWea WMou WeWi
	pseudopentandra	WeWi
§	***purpurea***	CBTr CCVT CPer GMcL NWea SWeb WMou WWbk WeWi
	- 'Brittany Blue'	WeWi
	- 'Brittany Green' (f)	WeWi
	- 'Carl Jensen'	WeWi
	- 'Dark Dicks' (f)	NLar WSFF WWbk WeWi
	- 'Dicky Meadows' (m)	LSto WeWi
*	- 'Elegantissima'	WeWi
	- 'Goldstones'	NLar WeWi
	- f. ***gracilis***	see *S. purpurea* 'Gracilis'
§	- 'Gracilis'	LPar MMuc NBwr NLar NWea SCob WCot WeWi
	- 'Green Dicks'	LSto WeWi
	- 'Helix'	see *S. purpurea*
	- 'Howki' (m)	WMou
	- 'Irette' (m)	WeWi
	- 'Jagiellonka' (f)	WeWi
	- var. ***japonica***	see *S. koriyanagi*
	- 'Lancashire Dicks' (m)	WeWi
	- 'Leicestershire Dicks' (m)	WeWi
	- 'Light Dicks'	WeWi
	- 'Nancy Saunders' (f) $\mathbb{Y}^{H6}$	EShb EWld GLog LEdu LSto MBNS MBlu MBow MBrN NBir NLar NOrn NSti SDix SMHy WCot
I	- 'Nicholsonii Purpurascens'	WeWi
	- 'Norbury'	WeWi
	- 'Pendula' $\mathbb{Y}^{H6}$	CBod CCVT CEnd CMac LRHS MAsh MSwo NOrn NRog NWea
	- 'Procumbens'	WeWi
	- 'Richartii' (m) **new**	WeWi
	- 'Whipcord'	WeWi
	pyrenaica	EWes

pyrifolia	LSto WeWi
radinostachya KR 7622	WPGP
repens	NWea SRms
§ - var. ***argentea***	EHyd MMuc MRav SCob SPer WFar
- 'Armando'PBR	WFar
reticulata 🏆H7	EPot GKev NBir NSla WAbe WFar
§ - subsp. ***nivalis***	EPot LShi
retusa	NBir
rosmarinifolia misapplied	see *S. elaeagnos* subsp. *angustifolia*
rosmarinifolia L.	EPfP NLar SCob WeWi
'Roth Cheviot'PBR **new**	WeWi
'Roth Hambleton'PBR **new**	WeWi
'Roth Mourne'PBR **new**	WeWi
× ***rubens***	see *S.* × *fragilis*
× ***rubra*** 'Eugenei' (m)	MBlu WWbk
- 'Harrison's' (f)	LSto
- 'Harrison's Seedling B' **new**	WWbk
sachalinensis 'Kioryo'	WeWi
schraderiana	WeWi
schwerinii	CBTr WeWi
× ***sepulcralis*** 'Caradoc'	LPar WeWi
§ - var. ***chrysocoma*** 🏆H5	Widely available
- 'Dart's Snake' (m)	ELan EShb LPar LShi MAsh MRav NLar WCot WFar
§ - 'Erythroflexuosa' (m) 🏆H5	CBcs CEnd EBee ELan EPfP LPar LRHS MAsh MGos MMrt MMuc MTrO NOra NOrn NTrD NWea SCob SEND SGsty SLim SPer SPoG SRHi WCFE WHlf WMat WeWi
× ***sericans***	WeWi
serpyllifolia	GKev
- 'Chamonix'	NSla
serpyllum	see *S.* × *fragilis* var. *furcata*
sessilifolia	WeWi
'Setsuka'	see *S. udensis* 'Sekka'
silesiaca	WeWi
sitchensis	WeWi
subopposita	MGil MMuc SBrt
I 'Super Willow' **new**	WWbk
triandra	NWea WMou WeWi
- 'Belge'	WeWi
- 'Black Hollander' (m)	NLar
- 'Black Maul'	LSto WeWi
- 'Faux Plant de Tourraine'	WeWi
- 'Grisette Noire'	WeWi
- 'Long Bud'	WeWi
- 'Noir de Challans'	WeWi
- 'Noir de Villaines' (m)	WeWi
- 'Rouge d'Orléans'	EBtc
- 'Sarda' **new**	WWbk
- 'Whissander'	WeWi
udensis 'Golden Sunshine'PBR	CBcs CKel CMac CRos EBee EHyd EPfP LRHS MAsh MMrt NEoE NLar NRHS SEdd SPer SSta XSte
§ - 'Sekka' (m)	CBcs LSto MBlu NBir NWea WMou
'Ulbrichtweide'	WeWi
viminalis	CBTr CCVT CDoC CPer EHeP EPfP GMcL LBuc LSto MMuc NWea SCob SEWo SVic WMou WSFF WWbk
- 'Black Satin'	WeWi
- cane osier **new**	WeWi
- 'Mulattin'	WeWi
- 'Reader's Red' (m)	WeWi
- 'Riefenweide'	WeWi
- 'Stone Osier'	WeWi
- 'Suffolk Osier'	WeWi
vitellina 'Pendula'	see *S. alba* 'Tristis' ambig.
'Yelverton'	see *S. alba* var. *vitellina* 'Yelverton'

Salpiglossis (*Solanaceae*)

sinuata Royale Series 🏆H2	LCro LOPS

Salvia ✿ (*Lamiaceae*)

from Catamarca, Argentina	CFoP SDys
from Guatemala **new**	CFoP
abrotanoides (Pe)	XLum
absconditiflora	XSen
acerifolia	CFoP SDys
acetabulosa	see *S. multicaulis*
African hybrid **new**	CFoP
'African Sky'	CCBP CFoP ECre ECtt EHyd EPPr EPfP EPri EWld EWoo IPot MAvo MCot MHer MPie MIdl NGrs NRHS SBut SDys SEdd SIvy SMHy SPhx WAvo WWke
§ ***africana***	CFoP EBee
africana-caerulea	see *S. africana*
africana-lutea	see *S. aurea*
agnes	SAng SDys
'Alegría'	CFoP SDys
algeriensis	LRHS
'Allen Chickering'	SDys
'Amante'	CBcs CFoP CKel CWGN EBee ECtt EGrI ENfk EWld MPri SDys SIvy WFar WHlf WNPC
amarissima	CFoP
'Amber'	LPla
ambigens	see *S. guaranitica*, *S. guaranitica* 'Blue Enigma'
'Amena'	SDys
AMETHYST LIPS ('Dyspurp')	Widely available
'Amigo' **new**	SIvy
'Aminia'	CFoP
'Amistad'PBR 🏆H3	Widely available
'Amparito'	XSen
ampelophylla	SDys
§ ***amplexicaulis***	CFoP MACG NLar SRms XSen
'Angel Wings' **new**	SDys
angustifolia Cav.	see *S. reptans*
angustifolia Mich.	see *S. azurea*
'Anna'	SDys
'Annabel' **new**	MHoo
'Anthony Parker'	CFoP
apiana	EWld SAng SPlb SRms SVen XSen
(Arctic Blaze Series) ARCTIC BLAZE PURPLE ('Novasalpur')	XSen XSte
- ARCTIC BLAZE RED ('Novasalred')	XSen
argentea 🏆H4	CBcs CBod CDor CFoP CKel CRos CSpe CTsd EBlo ECha EHyd ELan EPfP EWoo LRHS MHoo NRHS SMad SPer WCAu WKif XSen
- 'Artemis'	LSun
arizonica	CFoP EWld MAsh SDys SIvy WSHC
atrocyanea	CFoP CSpe ECre EWes EWld MAsh MAvo MGil SDys SIvy SMHy WAvo WSHC
atropatana	WCot
aucheri	CFoP
§ ***aurea***	CBcs CFoP EPri SEle SPlb SSha XLum
- 'Kirstenbosch'	CFoP CTtf ECtt EPri EWld SEdd WCot WKif
aurita	CFoP
'Azure Snow' (Color Spires Series)	LBar SHar WTor
§ ***azurea***	NBPC SPhx SPlb XSen
- var. ***grandiflora***	WCot
bacheriana	see *S. buchananii*
'Ballerina'	XSen
§ ***barrelieri***	CFoP EPri ESwi
'Barwinnock Dwarf Blue' (Ro)	WHer

'Bee's Bliss'	XSen
'Belhaven'	EBee EPPr SRms
benthamiana	SDys
bicolor	see *S. barrelieri*
biserrata	CFoP
BLACK & BLOOM ('Balsaloom')	CDoC CFoP CRos CSpe CWGN EBee ECtt LRHS LWaG MAsh
'Black Knight'	CFoP MAsh
blancoana	see *S. lavandulifolia* subsp. *blancoana*
blepharophylla	CFoP EPPr MHoo WAvo XSen
- 'Diablo'	ECtt EWld
- 'Painted Lady'	MAsh SDys
'Bleu Armor'^{PBR}	NCth SPhx XSen
'Blue Cascade' (Ro)	SGBe
'Blue Chiquita' pale form	CFoP
'Blue Haze' (Pe)	SRHi
'Blue Merced'	MAsh SDys SIvy
§ 'Blue Note'^{PBR}	Widely available
'Blue Sky'	EWld MPri MidI WFar
'Blue Spire' (Pe) ♀H5	Widely available
bogotensis	CFoP
bowleyana	CFoP EWld
brandegeei	SAng
'Bright Eyes' (Suncrest Series)	CWGN IPot
broussonetii	CFoP
§ ***buchananii*** ♀H2	CFoP EWld MAsh MHoo MRav SDys SRkn WKif
bulleyana misapplied	see *S. flava* var. *megalantha*
bulleyana Diels	CBcs CExl EWes GPSL LBar MHoo NQui
- 'Blue Lips'	CBod EBee IPot MidI
bullulata	CFoP EPri
- pale blue-flowered	CFoP EWld SDys SIvy
'Buttermilk' **new**	WNPC
cacaliifolia ♀H2	CExl CFoP CSde CWCL EBee ECtt EWld MAsh MHer MidI SDys SRkn WAvo
caerulea misapplied	see *S. guaranitica*, *S. guaranitica* 'Black and Blue'
caerulea L.	see *S. africana*
caespitosa	XSen
campanulata	CFoP
- B&SWJ 9232	WCru
- CC **new**	GGro
- GWJ 9232 **new**	GGro
- GWJ 9294	WCru
- var. ***hirtella*** GWJ 9397	WCru
canariensis	CFoP CWal WCot WFar
- f. ***albiflora***	CFoP
- f. ***candidissima***	CFoP
candelabrum ♀H3	CFoP CKel ECre MHer WKif XSen
canescens	XSen
cardinalis	see *S. fulgens*
carnea	CFoP MAsh
- from Valle de Bravo, Mexico	SDys
'Cavalieri d'Alto'	MAvo MidI SPhx
'Cavaliero Celeste'	SPhx
caymanensis	CFoP
§ ***chamaedryoides***	CFoP ELan MAsh MHoo SBrt SIvy SPhx XSen
- var. ***isochroma***	EPfP EWld MAsh SDys WPGP XSen
- 'Marine Blue'	MAsh MCot
- silver-leaved	CSpe SPhx WPGP XLum
chamelaeagnea	CFoP EPPr EWoo SDys XSen
'Cherbourg'	XSen
CHERRY LIPS ('Dysceri')	CAby CBod ECtt EShb EWes LBar LSou MACG MAsh MBNS MBros MNHC MPnt MPri NDov WHlf WNPC WWke
'Cherry Pie'	CWGN ENfk MidI SIvy WHlf WNPC
'Cherry Queen'	CWGN MAsh WOut
chiapensis	CFoP MAsh SDys
chionophylla	CFoP
'Christine Yeo'	CFoP EBee ECtt EGrI ELon EPPr EPri EWld MAsh MidI SDys SEND SIvy WAvo WHlf WKif XSen
chrysophylla	CFoP SDys
'Château Cathare'	XSen
cleistogama misapplied	see *S. glutinosa*
clevelandii	CFoP MHer SAng
- 'Winnifred Gilman'	SDys
clinopodioides	CFoP EBee SDys
'Clotted Cream'	CBcs CDoC CWGN EBee ENfk EPfP LRHS LWaG MHoo MNHC MidI SIvy WFar WHlf WHoo WMal
coahuilensis misapplied	see *S. greggii* × *serpyllifolia*
coahuilensis ambig.	MAsh SIvy SMrm SRkn WSHC XLum
coccinea 'Brenthurst'	WHlf
- 'Forest Fire'	CFoP
- (Nymph Series) 'Coral Nymph'	CFoP LDai
- - 'Lady in Red' ♀H3	EWld
cocuyana B&SWJ 14861	WCru
concolor misapplied	see *S. guaranitica*
concolor Lamb. ex Benth.	EPPr EWld SDys SIvy
confertiflora	Widely available
congestiflora	CFoP
'Cool Cream' **new**	CWGN
corrugata	CBod CElw CFoP CKel CTsd EAri EBee ECtt EWld IPot MAsh MCot MHer SDys SEdd SIvy SPhx WFar
'Courson Pink' **new**	WHoo
'Crazy Dolls'	CFoP ECtt SDys SIvy
'Crème Caramel'	EBee ECtt MAsh MAvo MidI SDys
cuatrecasana	CFoP
curviflora	CElw CFoP EAri EWld IPot MAsh SDys SEle SIvy SRkn WAvo WBor
- 'Tubular Bells'	MHoo WFar
cuspidata subsp. ***gilliesii***	CFoP EWld
cyanescens	CFoP CSpe EPot XSen
cyanicalyx	CFoP SDys
cyclostegia	CExl
'Dad's Brown Trousers' **new**	SIvy
daghestanica	CSpe
'Dancing Dolls'	CMiW CWGN EWoo IPot LRHS MidI XSen
I ***dangitalis*** SDR 4332	CExl
darcyi misapplied	see *S. roemeriana*
darcyi J. Compton	CExl CFoP EWes EWld SDys WSHC XLum
- peach-flowered	CSpe
'Dark Red Dream' **new**	SDys
'Day Glow'	CChe ECtt MidI SAdn
deserta	GGro GQue LRHS SBrt SPhx WCot
- from Kazakhstan	GGro
desoleana	CFoP
'Didi'	NDov
discolor	CFoP CHll CSpe ECtt EPPr EWTr EWld LDai MAsh MHer MidI SAng SDys SIvy WAvo WHlf WTyc
disermas	SPlb
disjuncta	SBrt
dolichantha	NLar
dolomitica	CFoP
dombeyi	CAby CFoP ECre EWld SDys SIvy WAvo WPGP
dominica	CFoP
dorisiana	MAsh MHer SDys SVen
'Dorset Wonder'	NDov
durifolia	CFoP
'Dyson's Crimson'	CFoP CSde ECtt ELan ELon MCot SDys SPhx WTre
'Dyson's Gem'	ECtt MAvo SDys
'Dyson's Joy' ♀H3	CAby CBcs CBod CDoC CSpe ECtt EPPr EWld LRHS MAsh MAvo MCot

	MHer MidI SDys SIvy SRkn WHlf XSen
eigii	CFoP
eizi-matudae	CFoP SDys
§ ***elegans***	CBor CHll CKel CLau CPla CWal EBee EWes EWhm IDee LWaG NPol SEdi WFar WHer XLum XSen
- 'Golden Delicious'	CAby CBod CFoP EBee ENfk EPPr EWes EWld MBriF NBwr SMrm SRms WFar
- 'Honey Melon'	CBod CFoP ENfk EWhm MAsh SDys SRms
- 'Lemon' **new**	CBod
- 'Scarlet Pineapple'	CBod CExl ELan ENfk EWld GPoy MBow MHer MHoo MNHC SCoo SDys SIvy SMrm SPoG SRms SVen WJek
- 'Sonoran Red'	SDys
- 'Tangerine'	CBod CLau CTsd ENfk EWhm LCro LOPS MBow MHer MHoo MNHC NQui SMrm SRms WJek
EMBER'S WISH ('Sal 0101'PBR)	CBcs CRos CWnw EBee ECtt EGrl EHyd ELan EPfP EWoo LBar LCro LRHS MAsh MHoo MNrw MSpe MidI NRHS SCob SCoo SDys SEle SGBe SIvy SPoG SRkn WCav WFar WHlf
'Endless Love'	EBee MidI NDov SRms
eremostachya	CFoP
'Eveline'	CFoP CKno CMac CWGN EBee ECtt LBar MidI NLar SHar SRms STPC
'Fancy Dancer' **new**	CWGN
farinacea 'Fairy Queen'	SDys
- 'Midnight Candle'	CCht LRHS NCou NRHS
- 'Rhea'	SPoG
- SALLYFUN DEEP OCEAN ('Dsaldpocn'PBR) **new**	MPri
- 'Strata'	MBros SPoG
- 'Victoria'	MDon
'Filigran' (Pe)	CBod EHyd EPfP GBin LRHS LSou LSto MBel NLar NRHS SBrt SMad SPoG WSpi XSen
'Fire Dancer' (Suncrest Series)	LRHS MidI XSen
'Flamenco Rose' (Suncrest Series)	ELan LRHS MidI XSen
§ ***flava*** var. ***megalantha***	CAby CBod CFoP EHyd ESwi GGro LRHS LSRN LShi NRHS SIvy XSen
'Flower Child'	CSpe ECtt IPot SDys WFar
forreri	EBee MAsh SDys SIvy
- 'Karen Dyson'	SDys
§ ***forsskaolii***	CBod CCBP CElw CExl CFoP EPfP EWoo GAbr GGro GKev MMuc MNrw MRav MSpe NChi NLar NQui NSti SAko SEND SPtp WCAu WCot WFar WTre XLum XSen
- white-flowered	CFoP EBee
§ ***fruticosa***	EHyd LRHS SPhx SRms XSen
§ ***fulgens*** ♀H3	CFoP EWld MAsh SDys SIvy SRkn WFar WHer
- from Mount Popocatépetl, Mexico	CFoP
- green calyx	CFoP
gachantivana	CFoP
'Gea Viola' **new**	SDys
gesneriiflora	ECtt
- mountain form	ECre SDys
'Gigi'	WFar
glabrescens B&SWJ 11152	WCru
* - var. ***robusta*** B&SWJ 11147	WCru
§ ***glutinosa***	CBod CFoP CMac CSpe EBee EWld GGro LDai MMuc NBro NLar NSti SEdd SIvy WCAu WFar XLum XSen
grahamii	see *S. microphylla* var. *microphylla*
'Great Comp'	NDov SDys
greggii	EPfP EWes NRHS SPlb SRms WKif XLum
- CD&R 1148	SDys
- 'Alba'	CBod MidI XLum XSen
- 'Blue Note'	see *S.* 'Blue Note'
- 'Blush Pink'	see *S. microphylla* 'Blush Pink'
- 'Caramba' (v)	CDow
§ - 'Desert Blaze' (v)	CWGN EAJP ELan EPfP LRHS MRav MidI NRHS SDys SPoG WAvo XLum
- 'Devon Cream'	see *S. greggii* 'Sungold'
- 'Diane'	MAsh
- 'Emperor'	CFoP CWGN EBee EPri EWTr EWes MAvo MBel MBrN MidI SEle SIvy WFar WHlf
- 'Flame'	CWGN EBee ELan EPfP LRHS MidI
- 'Icing Sugar'PBR	Widely available
- 'Lara'	ECtt LEdu MAvo WHlf
- 'Lipstick'	CExl EBee ECtt EHyd ENfk EPfP LCro LOPS LRHS LSto MAsh MidI NBwr NRHS SSut XSen
- 'Magenta'	CFoP
- 'Peach' misapplied	see *S.* × *jamensis* 'Pat Vlasto'
- 'Peach'	CFoP CWGN EPfP MAsh MidI SDys XLum
- 'Pink Preference'	CFoP MAsh SDys
- 'Purple Pastel'	LRHS MidI
- 'Raspberry Red'	EPri XLum
- 'Rose Pink'	LRHS MHoo
- salmon-flowered	MidI
- 'Sierra San Antonio'	see *S.* × *jamensis* 'Sierra San Antonio'
- 'Sparkler'	see *S. greggii* 'Desert Blaze'
- 'Stormy Pink'	CSpe ECtt EWTr IPot MAsh MBriF MCot MNrw MPie MidI WFar WKif WTre
- 'Strawberries and Cream'	MidI SIvy
- 'Strawberry Delight' **new**	SDys
§ - 'Sungold'	CWGN ECtt EPfP MAsh MHoo SDys SPhx WFar XSen
- variegated (v)	XSen
- yellow-flowered	XLum
greggii* × *serpyllifolia	CSpe MAsh MHoo MidI SDys SMHy
§ ***guaranitica***	CHll ECtt MHer MidI WKif WPGP WTre XLum
- 'Argentina Skies'	CDow CFoP ECtt EGrl EPPr SDys SIvy SMrm
- 'Black and Blue'	Widely available
§ - 'Blue Enigma' ♀H3	Widely available
- 'Costa Rica Blue'	EAri LPla SDys SIvy WKif
- 'Indigo Blue'	MAsh
- large-flowered **new**	CFoP
- 'Midnight'	CFoP CSpe
- purple-flowered	EPPr SDys
- 'Rhythm and Blues' (Bodacious Series)	LRHS
- 'Super Trouper'	ECtt EWld IPot MidI SDys WWke
- violet-flowered	SDys
'Guarini'	SDys
haematodes	see *S. pratensis* Haematodes Group
haenkei	CElw
- 'Prawn Chorus'	CFoP EWld MAsh
'Hannah'	MAvo
heldreichiana	XSen
hians	CBod CTsd EBee EHed ESwi LShi SRms
- CC 1787	CExl
hierosolymitana	EBee EHyd LRHS NRHS SPhx XSen
hispanica misapplied	see *S. lavandulifolia*
holwayi	SDys
'Hooksgreen' **new**	MHoo
horminum	see *S. viridis* var. *comata*

	Name	Suppliers
§	'Hot Lips' ♀H5	Widely available
	huberi	SAng
	'Hybrida' (Pe)	WMal
	'I Cavalieri del Tau'	Midl SDys WFar WHlf
	'Indiansummer'	SDys
	indica	CFoP LRHS SPhx
	'Indigo Spires'	CDow CExl CFoP CSpe CWGN ECre ECtt MAsh MBrN Midl NDov SDix SDys SEle SMrm SPhx WAvo WFar WKif WOld XLum
	interrupta	CFoP EWld MCot XSen
	involucrata ♀H3	CAby CHll CWal MCot NBro SDys SMrm SVen WSHC
	- 16339	EGrl
	- 'Bethellii' ♀H3	CBod CKel CSde CTsd CWCL EBee ECtt ELan EPfP EWes EWld EWoo LRHS MAsh MHer MNrw MPie SDys SEdd SMrm SRkn WFar WKif WSHC WSpi XLum
	- 'Boutin' ♀H3	CFoP EBee EPPr MAsh MHol SDys SEle
§	- 'Hadspen'	CFoP CRHN CSpe EBee EPPr EPri EWes SIvy WAvo WHer
	- 'Mrs Pope'	see *S. involucrata* 'Hadspen'
	involucrata* × *wagneriana	SDys
	iodantha	CFoP
	'Jackson's Cassis'	MHoo
	'Jackson's Kir Royale'	MHoo
	'Jackson's Purple'	MHoo
	× *jamensis*	MAsh
	- 'Amarillo'	SDys
	- 'Blue Amor'	CGBo CWnw NCth
	- 'California Sunset'	ECtt MAsh Midl XSen
	- 'Dark Dancer'	MAsh SDys
	- 'Devantville'	XLum
	- 'Dysons' Orangy Pink'	NDov SDys
	- 'El Durazno'	XSen
	- 'Flammenn'[PBR]	CRos EHyd EPfP LRHS NRHS XSen
	- 'Golden Girl'	CFoP CSpe CWGN EBee EWoo Midl WSHC
	- (Heatwave Series) 'Heatwave Blast'[PBR]	Midl XSen
	- - HEATWAVE BLAZE ('Eggben005')	Midl XSen
	- - 'Heatwave Glimmer'[PBR]	CFoP CSpe EPfP LRHS MCot Midl WSHC XSen
	- - 'Heatwave Glitter'[PBR]	Midl XSen
	- - HEATWAVE SCORCHER	CFoP
	- - HEATWAVE SPARKLE ('Eggber004')	Midl XSen
	- 'James Compton'	LPla SMrm XSen
	- 'Javier' ♀H4	CFoP CSpe ECtt EPPr EPri EWld EWoo LSto MAsh Midl SDys SIvy
	- 'Kentish Pink'	SDys SIvy
	- 'La Luna'	ECtt ELan EPPr EShb MAsh MPie MRav Midl NDov WSHC XLum XSen
	- 'La Siesta'	EBee IPot MAsh MPie XSen
	- 'La Tarde'	MAsh
	- 'Lemon Light'	ELan EPfP IPot MAvo Midl SPer XSen XSte
	- 'Lemon Sorbet'	WNPC
	- 'Los Lirios'	CSpe MCot WAvo
	- 'Maraschino'	ECtt MAsh Midl SDys SIvy SRms XLum
	- 'Melen'[PBR]	CRos CWnw EBee ECul EPfP LRHS SPhx SRms XSen
	- 'Moonlight Over Ashwood' (v)	MAsh WSHC
	- 'Moonlight Serenade'	MAsh SDys WHlf
§	- 'Pat Vlasto'	CFoP
	- 'Peter Vidgeon' ♀H4	Widely available
	- pink-flowered	SBls
	- 'Pleasant Pink'	MAsh
	- 'Pluenn'[PBR]	CKel CRos CWnw EHyd EPfP LRHS LSRN NCth NRHS XSen
	- 'Raspberry Royale'	ECtt EHyd EPri EWhm IPot MAsh MHoo MPie NRHS SDys SMrm XLum XSen
	- 'Red Velvet'	ECtt MAsh MCot SDys SPhx WAvo WBrk WHrl WSHC
	- RÊVE ROUGE ('Fauresal02'[PBR])	EPfP EWoo LRHS XSen XSte
	- 'Señorita Leah'	CFoP CWGN ENfk MAsh MCot NDov SDys WFar
	- 'Shell Dancer'[PBR]	CWGN LRHS Midl XSen XSte
§	- 'Sierra San Antonio'	EPfP IPot LRHS MAsh Midl NRHS SDys SMrm XLum XSen
	- 'Stormy Sunrise'	SDys
§	- 'Trebah'	CBod CDow CFoP CGBo ECre ENfk MAsh MHoo MSpe Midl SDys WKif
	- 'Trenance'	ECre MHer WMal
	- VIOLETTE DE LOIRE ('Barsal'[PBR])	CWnw ECul LRHS LSRN NCth SPhx SRms
	'James Curry'	CFoP SMHy
	japonica* var. *formosana NMWJ 14469	WCru
	'Jean's Jewel'	CFoP Midl SDys
	'Jean's Purple Passion'	MAsh SDys
	JEMIMA'S GEM ('Jemco') **new**	WNPC
§	'Jeremy'	ECtt LRHS MNrw Midl SDys SRms WOut
	'Jezebel' ♀H3	CFoP ECtt EPfP GBin Midl NRHS SDys WHlf
	'Joan'	CFoP CWGN EPPr MAsh MAvo MBriF MCot MHol SDys
	judaica	MSpe XSen
	jurisicii	CFoP SAng XLum XSen
	karwinskyi	ECre SDys SIvy
	karwinskyi* × *univerticillata	SDys
	keerlii	CFoP
	'Kisses and Wishes'	CFoP CNor EBee ECtt ENfk LBar LCro LSvl MHoo MPri MSpe Midl NLar SHar SRkn WNPC WTor
	koyamae	CFoP EBee EWld
	- B&SWJ 10919	GGro WCru
	'Krystle Pink'	Midl WHlf
	'La Grande Boom' **new**	SDys
	'La Mancha'	ECtt ENfk MAsh MHoo SDys WCot WFar WHlf
	LACEY BLUE ('Lisslitt'[PBR]) (Pe)	CBod CKel CRos CWGN EBee EHyd EPfP LCro LRHS MAsh NLar NRHS SCob SWvt XSen
	'Lady Camilla' **new**	MHoo
	'Lady Jane' **new**	MHoo
	'Lalarsha'	CFoP ECtt ELan MAsh MCot NDov SDys
	lanceolata	CFoP CSpe EWld LRHS
	× *lavandulacea* misapplied (Ro)	see *S. rosmarinus* Prostrata Group
§	**× *lavandulacea*** (de Noé) Roma-Marzio & Galasso (Ro)	XSen
§	***lavandulifolia***	CFoP CRos EBee EHyd ELan EPfP EWes GPoy LRHS LWaG MAsh MHer MHoo MNHC MRav SAng SBut SRms WHoo WJek WKif XLum XSen
§	- subsp. ***blancoana***	ECha SPhx XSen
	- 'Roquefure'	XSen
	- subsp. ***vellerea***	XSen
	lavanduloides	CFoP
	'Lavender Dilly Dilly'	ENfk MAvo SIvy
	lemmonii	see *S. microphylla* var. *wislizeni*
	'Lemon Pie'	CFoP CSpe Midl SDys WHlf WNPC

* ***lepechinia*** **new**	CFoP
leptophylla	see *S. reptans*
leucantha 𝒀^{H2}	CCBP CMCN EAri ECre ELan EPPr EWld MAsh MGil MNrw MPie MRav SPlb SRkn SVen WFar WHer WKif
- Danielle's Dream ('Ferpink')	CFoP
- 'Eder' (v)	MAsh SDys
- 'Northcourt' **new**	SVen
- 'Purple Velvet'	CFoP CSpe EBee ECtt MAsh MHer SDys SIvy WAvo WFar WTyc
- 'Santa Barbara'	CFoP LRHS MAsh SDys WFar
- 'White Mischief'	SDys SIvy
leucocephala	CFoP SDys
leucophylla	SAng
libanensis	SDys
'Lilac Lipstick' (Fashionista Series) **new**	LBar
littae	SDys
'Little Azur'	ECtt ENfk EPPr SDys
Little Lace ('Novaperlac') (Pe)	LRHS
'Little Spire'^{PBR} (Pe)	Widely available
'Longin' (Pe)	CKel XLum
longispicata	CFoP
longistyla	SDys SVen
Love and Wishes ('Serendip6'^{PBR})	Widely available
lycioides misapplied	see *S. greggii* × *serpyllifolia*
lycioides A. Gray	CFoP SDys WAvo
lyrata 'Burgundy Bliss'	see *S. lyrata* 'Purple Knockout'
§ - 'Purple Knockout'	CKel EHyd EPfP LRHS NRHS SAng XSen
- 'Purple Vulcano'	see *S. lyrata* 'Purple Knockout'
macellaria misapplied	see *S. microphylla*
macrophylla	CFoP SDys WPGP
- purple-leaved	CFoP SDys WHil WPGP
- upright	WHil
'Madeline'^{PBR}	CBod CFoP CWGN EHyd EPfP GMaP LBar LCro LRHS LSou MHol MNrw Midl NCth SPer
madrensis	CFoP SDys
'Magenta Magic'	CFoP EWld IPot SDys
'Magic Potion'	CWGN
'Mas de Lunès'	XSen
'Mauve Lips' **new**	WNPC
'Mauve Midget' **new**	SDys
melaleuca B&SWJ 14863	WCru
mellifera	CFoP SAng
'Merlin's Magenta'	ENfk
Mesa Azure ('Mes Azur')	CFoP
mexicana 'Limelight'	CFoP ESgI
- var. ***minor***	EWld SDys SIvy
§ ***microphylla***	CBod CMac CTri EGrI EWes EWhm GMcL MBow MHoo SVen XLum
- 'Albert'	LCro
- 'Aphrodite' **new**	Midl
- 'Baby Doll'	Midl
- 'Belize'	CFoP MAsh
- 'Blind Faith'	CSpe MAvo
- 'Blue Monrovia'	IPot LRHS MRav SEdd
§ - 'Blush Pink'	CTtf MAvo SDys
- 'Bordeaux'	CFoP CSpe ILea LRHS Midl SIvy SPhx XSte
- 'Cerro Potosí' 𝒀^{H4}	Widely available
- 'Chalk White'	GBin SDys SMHy SPhx
- Glacier	see *S. microphylla* 'Gletsjer'
§ - 'Gletsjer' **new**	EWld XSen
- 'Hot Lips'	see *S.* 'Hot Lips'
- 'Kew Red'	MHoo MNrw WAvo WBrk
- 'Little Kiss' **new**	XSen
I - 'Lutea'	CDow ENfk MAsh SDys
- 'Maroon'	CFoP EPfP EPri MAvo MCot Midl SDys SEdd WCot
§ - var. ***microphylla***	CDow CFoP CRHN CTri ECtt ENfk EPPr LCro LSRN MCot MHer MHoo MNHC MRav SAng SEND SRkn SRms SVic XLum
I - - 'Blackcurrant' **new**	CBod
- - 'La Foux'	SMrm SPhx WAvo
- - 'Newby Hall'	CSde ECtt EPfP EWes LRHS MAvo SPhx WSHC
- var. ***neurepia***	see *S. microphylla* var. *microphylla*
- 'Norwell'	MNrw
- 'Orange Door'	SDys
- orange-red-flowered	MRav
- 'Oregon Peach'	EPfP NRHS
- 'Oxford'	EGrI Midl
- 'Pink Blush'	CWGN ECtt ELan ELon EPfP MAsh MCot MHer MHoo MNHC SEND SMrm SRkn WAvo WHoo WKif XSen
- 'Robin's Pride'	ECtt SDys
- 'Rodbaston Rosy Cheeks'	MSCN
- 'Ruby Star'	ECtt IPot NCth
- 'San Carlos Festival'	ECtt MAsh Midl SDys
- 'Trelawny Rose Pink'	see *S.* 'Trelawney'
- 'Trelissick Creamy Yellow'	see *S.* 'Trelissick'
- 'Trewithen Cerise'	see *S.* 'Trewithen'
- 'Wendy's Surprise'	CWGN ECtt EWld MCot SDys SRkn
- 'Wild Watermelon'	CWGN EBee ECtt EWTr EWes EWld GPSL IPot MAsh MAvo MHer Midl NQui SDys SIvy
- 'Wine and Roses' **new**	ECtt ENfk SDys SIvy WHlf
§ - var. ***wislizeni***	CElw
- 'Wollerton White'	MCot MRav
'Midnight Model' (Fashionista Series) **new**	LBar
miltiorrhiza	CFoP CSpe GGro MHoo XLum XSen
miniata	SIvy
(Mirage Series) Mirage Burgundy ('Balmirbur'^{PBR}) **new**	CFoP
- Mirage Cherry Red ('Balmircher'^{PBR})	CBod LCro LRHS MACG WFar
- Mirage Cream ('Balmircemi') Darwin Perennials, 2019	CBod WFar WHil
- Mirage Deep Purple ('Balmirdepur'^{PBR})	CBod EPfP LCro LRHS MACG WFar
- Mirage Hot Pink ('Balmirhopi') **new**	LCro MACG
- Mirage Neon Rose ('Balmirnose')	LRHS
- Mirage Soft Pink ('Balmirsopin')	CBod EBee EPfP WFar
- Mirage Violet ('Balmirvio'^{PBR}) **new**	EPfP
moorcroftiana	SBls
muelleri misapplied	see *S. greggii* × *serpyllifolia*
muelleri ambig.	CPla CSpe
'Mulberry Jam'	CCBP CDow CFoP EBee ECtt ELan EWoo MAsh MCot Midl SDix SDys SEle SIvy SRkn WFar WKif
§ ***multicaulis*** 𝒀^{H3}	CFoP MAsh XSen
munzii	CFoP SDys
Mystic Spires Blue ('Balsalmisp'^{PBR})	CFoP CRos CSpe CWGN ECtt EPfP MBros MHer NGrs NRHS SPoG WHlf
'Nachtvlinder' 𝒀^{H5}	Widely available
namaensis	CFoP EWld WKif
nana 'Curling Waves'^{PBR}	CWGN EPfP MHoo MSCN WSHC
'Naomy Tree' **new**	SDys
napifolia	EWes MNrw NLar
- 'Baby Blue'	MHoo
'Nel'	EBee WMal

	nemorosa	CBod LSRN SPhx SRms XLum XSen
	- 'Amethyst' 𝕐H7	Widely available
	- 'Blaureiter'	EBee
	- BLUE BOUQUETTA ('Alkif')	CWGN LBar LSou MHol MidI NBPC NLar SDys SPad WNPC
	- BLUE MOUND	see *S.* × *sylvestris* 'Blauhügel'
	- 'Bordeau Steel Blue'	EHyd ELon LRHS NRHS SRms
	- 'Caradonna' 𝕐H7	Widely available
	- 'Caradonna Compact' **new**	CBod
	- 'Crystal Blue' (Color Spires Series)	CWGN IPot LBar LCro LRHS MidI NCth SEdd SHar SHor
	- EAST FRIESLAND	see *S. nemorosa* 'Ostfriesland'
	- 'Giovanni'	MidI
	- 'Jan Spruyt'	NDov
	- 'Little Friesland'	EHyd LRHS NRHS
	- 'Lubecca' 𝕐H7	CRos ECtt EHyd EPfP LBar LRHS MidI NDov NGdn NLar SPer SPhx WCAu WFar XSen
	- LYRICAL SILVERTONE ('Balyricsil'PBR)	LBar WFar
	- LYRICAL WHITE	see *S. nemorosa* (Sensation Series) SENSATION WHITE
	- MARCUS ('Haeumanarc'PBR)	CBod CRos EBee ECtt EHyd ELan ELon EPfP LBar LRHS LSRN MBNS MRav MTin NRHS SDys SPoG WFar
	- 'New Dimension Blue'	CGBo EAJP LBar MACG MidI WCav WFar WHil WPnP
	- 'New Dimension Rose'	LBar MACG MidI NLar
§	- 'Ostfriesland' 𝕐H7	Widely available
	- 'Pink Beauty'	CBcs CRos EHyd EPfP LRHS LSto NRHS
	- 'Pink Friesland'PBR	CAby CBod CCht CDor ECtt EPfP GMaP LSou NGdn NRHS SCob WSpi
	- 'Plumosa'	see *S. nemorosa* 'Pusztaflamme'
§	- 'Pusztaflamme' 𝕐H7	EBee ECha EPfP MRav
	- 'Rose Queen'	CBod CKel EShb EWTr EWld EWoo GMaP NBPC NBir NLar SCob SPer SPhx WCot WFar WPnP XLum XSen
	- 'Rosenwein'	CDor CRos EHyd LBar LDai LRHS NRHS SGbt SPhx XSen
	- SALLYROSA JUMBO PINK (Sallyrosa Series)	CFoP
	- (Salute Series) 'Salute Ice Blue' **new**	LBar
	- - 'Salute Light Pink' **new**	LBar
	- - 'Salute White' **new**	LBar
	- 'Salvatore Blue' **new**	LBar
	- 'Schwellenburg'	CKno CRos EAJP ECtt EShb EWes LBar LCro LRHS MNrw NLar NRHS
	- (Sensation Series) SENSATION BLUE ('Florsalvioblu'PBR)	CRos EHyd LRHS NRHS
	- - SENSATION BLUE IMPROVED	MidI
	- - SENSATION DEEP BLUE ('Florsaldblue')	CRos EBee EHyd ELon LRHS LSou MidI NRHS WHlf
	- - SENSATION DEEP ROSE ('Flor Sal Roz')	CBod NRHS WCav
	- - SENSATION DEEP ROSE IMPROVED	MidI SPoG WHlf
	- - SENSATION MEDIUM PINK ('Florsalpi')	CRos
	- - SENSATION MEDIUM WHITE ('Florsalmwh') **new**	WHlf
	- - SENSATION PINK	LRHS MidI NRHS
	- - SENSATION ROSE	CRos EGrI EHyd LBar LCro LOPS LRHS LSRN LSou MAvo MHol MMrt MidI NRHS SCob SHar SRms
§	- - SENSATION WHITE ('Florsalwhite')	CBod CRos CWGN EHyd GKev LRHS MBel MidI NRHS SCob
§	- subsp. ***tesquicola***	NLar SPhx WFar
§	- 'Violet Queen'	CBod CGBo LSun SBls
	- 'West Friesland'	see *S. nemorosa* 'Violet Queen'
	- 'Wesuwe'	ECha ELon MidI NDov
	'Neon'	CFoP EBee ECtt MidI WAvo WHlf WNPC WWke
	neurepia	see *S. microphylla* var. *microphylla*
	nipponica	CFoP EBee SBrt
	- B&SWJ 5829	GGro WCru
	nubicola	CExl ESwi GPoy
	- CC 6306	GGro
	aff. ***nubicola*** HPA 1355	GGro
	'Nuchi'	EHyd LRHS MidI NRHS SPoG SRms WHlf
	nutans	EPri GElm GGro LBar MHoo SAng SPhx XSen
	officinalis misapplied (Ro)	see *S. rosmarinus*
	officinalis L.	Widely available
	- 'Albiflora'	CBcs CBod ECha MBriF MHoo WJek XSen
	- 'All Gold' **new**	NBwr
	- 'Aurea' ambig.	GPoy MHoo SCob
	- 'Berggarten' 𝕐H5	CCBP CLau ECha EWhm GBin LRHS MHer MRav SPhx WHer XLum XSen
	- 'Berggarten Variegated' (v) **new**	EWhm
	- 'Blackcurrant'	CLau WFar
§	- broad-leaved	CLau MHer SEdi WJek
	- 'Crispa'	XSen
	- 'Grete Stölzle'	LPla XSen
	- 'Grower's Friend'	CTsd
§	- 'Icterina' (v) 𝕐H5	Widely available
	- ***latifolia***	see *S. officinalis* broad-leaved
	- narrow-leaved	see *S. lavandulifolia*
	- 'Nazareth'	XSen
	- ***prostrata***	see *S. lavandulifolia*
	- 'Purpurascens' 𝕐H5	Widely available
	- 'Robin Hill'	EHyd LRHS NRHS
	- 'Tricolor' (v)	CBcs CBod EBee EHyd ELan ENfk EPfP EWhm GMcL GPoy LRHS LShi MAsh MHer MHoo MNHC NBwr SCob SEdi SPer SPoG SRms WFar WJek
	- 'Variegata'	see *S. officinalis* 'Icterina'
	- variegated (v)	MHer
	- 'Würzburg'	XSen
	omeiana	CFoP
	- BWJ 8062	WCru
	- 'Crûg Thundercloud'	ESwi SBrt WCru
	oppositiflora misapplied	see *S. tubiflora*
	oppositiflora ambig.	CFoP SDys
	'Orchid Glow' (Suncrest Series)	CWGN ELan LRHS MidI NCth XSen
	oxyphora	CFoP EWld MHer MPie MidI SDys SEdd SIvy WFar WOld
	pachyphylla	XSen
	'Pakhuis Pass'	CFoP
	pallida	CFoP
	'Pam's Purple'	MAsh
	'Pasadena'	EWld SDys
§	***patens*** 𝕐H3	CAby CFoP CSde CSpe EBee ECha ECtt EPfP LCro LOPS LRHS MAsh MHer MHoo MRav NGdn SDix SDys SRms WFar WKif WSHC WSpi WWFP
	- 'Alba' misapplied	see *S. patens* 'White Trophy'
	- 'Blue Angel'	CCht CWGN CWal EHyd EPfP EWes LEdu LRHS SBls
*	- 'Blue Trophy'	MidI
	- 'Cambridge Blue' 𝕐H3	CAby CExl CFoP CSpe CWGN EBee ECtt EHyd ELan EPfP EWoo LRHS MAsh MHer MHoo MRav MidI NLar NPer NRHS SAng SDys SMrm WFar WSHC

	- 'Chilcombe'	CAby SDys
	- 'Dot's Delight'	CExl CFoP CSpe ECtt EWld IPot LRHS SDys WSHC
	- 'Guanajuato'	CExl CSBt ECtt EWld EWoo MHoo MIdl NLar SAng SDys SHar SMrm WKif WSHC
	- large	CFoP CSpe
	- light blue-flowered	EHyd LRHS NRHS
	- OCEANA BLUE ('Salsyll')	EBee MIdl
	- 'Oxford Blue'	see *S. patens*
	- (Patio Series) 'Patio Deep Blue'	CBod CWGN EPfP MBros MHoo SPoG WHil WTor
	- - 'Patio Sky Blue'	CBod MHoo SCoo WHil WSpi
	- 'Pink Ice'	CFoP ECtt EWld MIdl SDys
	- pink-flowered	WSHC
	- 'Royal Blue'	see *S. patens*
§	- 'White Trophy'	CExl CFoP CSde ECtt EWes LRHS MHoo MIdl SDys SMrm
	'Peach Cobbler'	CWGN ENfk EPPr MAvo MIdl WHlf WNPC
	'Peach Parfait'	CWGN MAvo MIdl NCth SDys WAvo WHlf WNPC WWke
	'Peaches and Cream'	MIdl
	'Penny's Laugh' **new**	CFoP
	'Penny's Smile'	CElw CFoP CMac ELon IPot MAsh MCot MSCN MIdl SDys SIvy SPhx WFar WSHC WWke
	'Peru Blue'	CFoP SDys
	'Phyllis' Fancy'	CFoP CSde CSpe CWGN EBee ECre ENfk EWes EWld LPla MAsh MBrN MCot MHer MPie MIdl NDov SAng SDys SIvy SPlb SRms WAvo WBor WFar WHlf WKif WWke
	'Pink Lace'	ECtt SBut SDys
	PINK LIPS	see *S.* 'Jeremy'
	'Pink Pong' **new**	CWGN SDys SIvy
	pisidica	XSen
	polystachya	SEdd
	'Porthos' **new**	XSen
	pratensis	CBee CBod CCBP EPfP GJos LCro LOPS MRav SPhx SRms WCot WWild XSen
	- W&B BGH-3	WCot
	- (Ballet Series) 'Rose Rhapsody'	CDor EAJP EPPr EPfP LBar LDai MMrt NLar SBls SPhx XSen
	- - 'Sky Dance'	CDor EAJP LSun MIdl NLar
	- - 'Swan Lake'	CDor EBee MACG NLar SBls SPhx SPlb XSen
	- - 'Sweet Esmeralda'	CDor EBee EGrl EPfP MACG NGdn NLar SPhx XSen
	- - 'Twilight Serenade'	CDor EBee EBou ECtt ELan EPPr EPfP LRHS NLar SBls SPhx XSen
	- 'Dear Anja'	see *S.* × *sylvestris* 'Dear Anja'
§	- Haematodes Group ♀H7	LDai MNrw SRms
	- 'Indigo' ♀H7	CAby CBWd CRos ECtt EHyd ELon GMaP LCro LRHS MAsh MRav NLar NRHS SMrm SPhx SPoG WCot WPGP
	- 'Lapis Lazuli'	EBee EWes LPla LRHS MPri
	- 'Pink Delight' PBR	EBee ECtt EHyd EPfP LRHS NBPC NLar NRHS SRms
	- 'Rosea'	ECha
	- 'White Swan'	LRHS
	'Pretty in Pink' (Fashionista Series) **new**	LBar SDys
	procurrens	CFoP EBee EWld XSen
	przewalskii	CExl CFoP EHyd GGro LRHS NRHS XSen
	- ACE 1157	WCru
	- BWJ 7920	GGro WCru XLum
	- var. ***przewalskii*** **new**	MHoo
	'Purple Majesty'	ECtt SDys SMrm WKif WSpi XLum
	'Purple Queen'	CElw CFoP EBee ENfk EPfP EShb MCot NRHS SDys SEle SPhx WFar
	'Purple Rhythm' (Bodacious Series)	LRHS
	purpurea	LSRN
	'Radio Red'	CBod CWGN LBar MIdl WFar WHil
	radula	CFoP EWld
	'Raspberry Truffle'	SDys
	raymondii subsp. ***raymondii***	CFoP
	recognita	CSpe MHoo XSen
	'Red Swing' PBR	EBee EHyd EWoo LRHS LShi MIdl NRHS
	regeliana misapplied	see *S. virgata* Jacq.
	regla	CFoP CHll MAsh SDys WBor WPGP
	repens	WSHC
§	***reptans***	ECha EPri SBrt
	- from western Texas	SAng SDys WCot WFar
	- 'Summer Skies'	MIdl
	'Ribambelle' ♀H3	EAJP MAsh MCot WMal XLum
	ringens	XSen
	'Rocketman' (Pe)	LRHS
	ROCKIN' DEEP PURPLE ('Bbsal09001')	CPla CRos ENfk LRHS MIdl
	ROCKIN' FUCHSIA ('Bbsal00301')	CAby CRos
§	***roemeriana***	CFoP CSpe
	- 'Arriba'	EDAr
	- 'Hot Trumpets'	EHyd EPfP LBar LBuc LRHS MHoo NRHS
	'Rolando'	CFoP SDys
	'Rose Queen' ambig.	MHoo
§	***rosmarinus*** (Ro)	Widely available
§	- Albiflora Group (Ro)	CBcs CCBP CLau EHyd ENfk EPfP EWhm LRHS MHoo MMrt MNHC NPol SCob SDow SPlb SPoG SRms WGwG WJek XSen
	- - 'Lady in White' (Ro)	CRos CSBt EHyd ELan EPfP LRHS NRHS SPer SPoG SRms WGwG WJek
	- 'Abraxas' (Ro)	CBod MHer WFar
	- 'Alderney' (Ro)	WGwG WJek
	- 'Amethyst Beauty' (Ro)	SDow
§	- (Angustifolia Group) 'Benenden Blue' (Ro) ♀H4	CSBt ECha ELan GPoy LRHS MHoo SPer SPlb SPoG SRms WGwG WJek WSpi XSen
	- - 'Corsican Blue' (Ro)	CWnw GPoy MHer SDow SPer SRms WGwG
	- 'Arp' (Ro)	CBod ENfk MHoo SEdi SRms WGwG XSen
§	- 'Aurea' (Ro/v)	MHoo SRms WHer WJek
	- 'Aureovariegata' (Ro)	see *S. rosmarinus* 'Aurea'
	- 'Barbecue' PBR (Ro)	CLau ECul ENfk EWhm SRms XSen
	- 'Blue Lagoon' (Ro)	CBod CBrac CCBP CDoC CLau ECul ENfk EWhm MHer MHoo MNHC SGBe SRms SSha WGwG WHer WJek
	- 'Blue Rain' (Ro)	CBod EWhm MHer MSwo NQui WFar WGwG WHer
	- 'Blue Winter' (Ro)	CBod
	- 'Bolham Blue' (Ro)	CRos
	- 'Capercaillie' (Ro)	SDow WGwG
	- 'Cascade' (Ro)	LRHS
	- 'Collingwood Ingram' (Ro)	see *S. rosmarinus* (Angustifolia Group) 'Benenden Blue'
	- 'Farinole' (Ro)	MNHC SRms WGwG
	- 'Fota Blue' (Ro)	CLau CTsd EHyd EWhm IArd LRHS MHer MHoo NPol NRHS SDow SRms SVen SWvt WGwG WJek WMal
	- 'Foxtail' (Ro)	CDoC CGBo CLau ENfk EPfP EWhm MHoo SGBe SRms WJek XSen
	- 'Golden Rain' (Ro)	see *S. rosmarinus* 'Joyce DeBaggio'
	- 'Gorizia' (Ro)	LRHS SDow SRms

- 'Green Ginger' (Ro) ♀H4	CBod CLau EBee ECha ELan EPfP EWhm GBin LRHS MGos MHer MHoo MNHC MRav NPer SCob SDow SPoG SRms SSha SVen WGwG WJek
- 'Guilded' (Ro)	see *S. rosmarinus* 'Aurea'
- 'Haifa' (Ro)	CCBP CLau CSde ENfk EWhm MHoo SEdi SRms WGwG XSen
- 'Heavenly Blue' (Ro)	WGwG WHer
- 'Iden Blue Boy' (Ro)	SRms
- 'Ingauno' (Ro) **new**	EWhm
- 'Jekka Blue' (Ro)	WJek
§ - 'Joyce DeBaggio' (Ro/v)	MHer SDow WGwG WHer
- 'King Hussein' (Ro) **new**	MHoo
- 'Knightshayes Blue' (Ro)	CRos EHyd LRHS NRHS
- 'Lilies Blue' (Ro)	GPoy WGwG
- 'Lockwood Variety' (Ro)	see *S. rosmarinus* (Prostrata Group) 'Lockwood de Forest'
- 'Majorca Pink' (Ro)	CBcs CBod CBrac CLau CSBt CSpe EFPl ENfk EPfP EWhm LRHS MHer MNHC SDow SGBe SPer SRms WGwG WHer WJek WMal XLum XSen
- 'Marenca' (Ro)	MNHC SRms WGwG
- 'McConnell's Blue' (Ro) ♀H4	CBod EHeP EHyd EPfP EWhm LRHS MGos NRHS SDow SRms WGwG WHer WJek
* - 'Miss Jessopp's Prostrate' (Ro)	NBwr SEdi
- 'Miss Jessopp's Upright' (Ro) ♀H4	Widely available
- 'Pointe du Raz' (Ro)	CDoC CKel CWnw EPfP EWhm SRms WGwG WSpi XSen
- 'Primley Blue' (Ro)	CLau EBou ECtt EWhm MHoo MRav SRms SVic WGwG WJek
§ - Prostrata Group (Ro)	Widely available
- - 'Capri' (Ro)	EPfP LSto SCgs SCob SRms WFar WJek
- - 'Jackman's Prostrate' (Ro)	GBin SDix
§ - - 'Lockwood de Forest' (Ro)	WGwG WHer
- - 'Rampant Boule' (Ro)	CBod CLau EWhm GQue MHoo SDow SRms WGwG WHtc WJek XLum XSen
- - 'Sea Level' (Ro)	MHer WGwG
- - 'Sheila Dore' (Ro)	SPlb SVen
- - white-flowered (Ro)	GPoy
- - 'Whitewater Silver' (Ro)	CCoa ELan EWhm LRHS MBros SMad SPad WJek
- 'Punta di Canelle' (Ro)	XSen
- 'Pyramidalis' (Ro)	CBod SSha XSen
- 'Rex' (Ro)	SRms WGwG XSen
- 'Roman Beauty'PBR (Ro)	CBcs CBod CKel CRos CSBt EBee EHyd EPfP EWhm LCro LRHS LSRN NRHS SGBe SRms SSha SWvt WFar WHer WHlf WSpi WTyc
- 'Rosea' (Ro)	CCBP CRos ELan ENfk EPfP EWTr EWhm GPoy LRHS MHer MHoo MNHC NRHS SCob SDow SEND SPoG SRms SVen WAvo WGwG WJek
- 'Salem' (Ro)	MHer
- 'Severn Sea' (Ro) ♀H4	CBcs CBod CLau CRos CSBt CSde CTri ECtt ELan EPfP EWhm GPoy LRHS MGos MHoo MNHC MRav MSwo NRHS SEdi SPer SRms SSut SVen SVic WAvo WGwG WHtc WJek WSpi
- 'Shimmering Stars' (Ro)	WGwG
- 'Silver Sparkler' (Ro)	WFar WHer
- 'Sissinghurst Blue' (Ro) ♀H4	CBod CCBP CDoC CKel CRos CSde EBee ELan EPfP EWTr LRHS MHer MNHC MRav NBwr NRHS SDow SPer SPlb SRms SWvt WGwG

- 'Sorcerer's Apprentice' (Ro)	SDow
- 'Spice Island' (Ro)	SPer XSen
- 'Sudbury Blue' (Ro)	CBod CLau CTsd EWhm MHoo SAko SDow SRms SSha SVic WGwG
- 'Sunkissed'PBR (Ro)	LCro SGBe SRms
- 'Tuscan Blue' (Ro)	CBcs CKel CLau CWal ECha ECtt EHyd EPfP EWhm LRHS MBow MHer MHoo MSwo NBwr NRHS SPer SRms WGwG XSen
- 'Variegata' (Ro)	see *S. rosmarinus* 'Aurea'
- 'Vatican Blue' (Ro)	WJek
- WILMA'S GOLD ('Wimtim01'PBR) (Ro)	CLau
'Royal Bumble' ♀H4	Widely available
'Royal Crimson Distinction'PBR	LBar SHar
rubescens B&SWJ 14368	WCru
- subsp. ***dolichothrix***	CFoP
rutilans	see *S. elegans*
sagittata	CFoP EBee EWld MHer SDix SPlb
- purple-leaved **new**	CFoP
'Saint Jean de Beauregard'	WFar
'Sally Light Blue'	MIdl
SALLYFUN BLUE ('Dansalfun1')	MPri
SALMIA DARK PURPLE	LSou WFar
SALMIA ORANGE **new**	LCro
SALMIA PINK	LCro LSou WFar
'Salmon Dance'	CBod CWGN ECtt EHyd EMor EPPr EWld IPot LCro LRHS MAvo NRHS WNPC
scabra	CFoP EBee XSen
- 'Good Hope' **new**	LBar
schlechteri	CFoP
sclarea	CBod CHby EBou ENfk GPoy LWaG MHoo MNHC MIdl NLar SEdi SRms SVic XLum XSen
- var. ***sclarea***	EPfP EWoo
- var. ***turkestanica*** hort.	see *S. sclarea* var. *turkestaniana* 'Vatican Pink'
- var. ***turkestaniana*** (Bruant) Mottet	CAby CDor
§ - - 'Vatican Pink'	CDor CHll CSpe CTtf EAJP ECha EHyd EPfP LRHS LSRN LSun MRav NRHS SAng SPer SPhx SRkn WKif
§ - - 'Vatican White'	CFoP CSpe EAJP EBee ECha EHyd LBar LDai LRHS NLar NRHS SPhx SWvt WFar XSen
- white-bracted	see *S. sclarea* var. *turkestaniana* 'Vatican White'
'Sebastian'	CFoP MIdl SEle
semiatrata misapplied	see *S. chamaedryoides*
semiatrata ambig.	CFoP EWld SPhx
semiatrata Zucc.	CSpe EPPr
serboana	EBee EPfP EWld SAko WKif WPGP
- B&SWJ 10236	WCru
'Serenade'	CBod ELon MIdl NDov SDys WCot WHoo
serpyllifolia	XSen
'Shame'	MAvo NDov
'Shirley Dyson' **new**	SDys
'Silas Dyson'	CDow CFoP CTtf EBee ECre ECtt ELon EPfP EWTr EWld MAsh MAvo MCot NDov NGrs NRHS SDys SIvy SPoG WAvo WBrk WFar WKif WSHC
'Silke's Dream'	CFoP EBee ECtt EPfP MAsh MCot SDys WAvo WMal XSen
'Silke's Red'	SDys WFar
'SoCool Pale Blue'	ECtt SDys

	'SoCool Purple'	SDys
	somalensis	CFoP EBee EWld
	'Southern Belle'	SDys
	spathacea ♀H4	CFoP WOut XSen
	splendens	CFoP
	- 'Jimi's Good Red'	SDys
	- 'Lighthouse Purple'	CSpe
	- 'Red Indian'	SDys
	- 'São Borja'	SDys
	- 'Vanguard' ♀H3	MPri
§	- 'Van-Houttei' ♀H3	CFoP SDys
	'Spring King'	SDys
	stachydifolia	CFoP WPGP
	- CDPR 3071	EBee WPGP
	'Stephanie'	SDys
	stepposa	GBin
	stolonifera	CFoP CSde CSpe ECre EPPr EWes EWld EWoo MAsh MAvo MHer SDys SIvy SMHy WAvo WPGP
	- 723	SEdd
	striata	SDys
	- from Peru **new**	CFoP
	- pink-flowered	CFoP
	- red-flowered	CFoP
	styphelus	CFoP MidI SDys
	subrotunda	CFoP SDys
	- 'Caitymary'	CFoP
	'Sue Templeton'	CFoP
	'Sunset Strip'	CDow
	× ***superba***	CBod EBee ECha ECtt EHyd ELan EPfP LRHS LSRN LShi NRHS SDix SGbt SPer SRms WCAu WHoo
	- 'Adrian'	ECtt ELon EPfP LSRN SAng SPoG WCot
	- 'Lyon Rose'	EBee
§	- 'Merleau'	EHyd LBar LRHS
	- 'Merleau Blue'	see *S.* × *superba* 'Merleau'
	- 'Merleau Pink'	EHyd
	- 'Merleau Rose'	EBee LBar MRav SRms
	- 'Merleau White' **new**	LBar
*	- 'Rosea'	EBee
	- 'Rubin' ♀H7	ECtt
I	- 'Superba'	CAby ECtt MRav SPhx SRkn
	× ***sylvestris*** APRIL NIGHT ('Dsalrs203')	LBar NCth
§	- 'Blauhügel' ♀H7	CBWd CBod CDoC CRos ECha ECtt EHyd ELan EPfP EShb GBin LCro LRHS LSto MArl MAvo MPri MRav NDov NRHS SCob SCoo SPer SPhx SRms WCAu WHoo XSen
§	- 'Blaukönigin'	CDor CKel CNor CRos CSBt EHyd ELon EPfP GMaP LRHS MidI NLar NRHS SBls SPlb SPoG SRms SWvt WCot WFar WOld XLum
	- BLUE MARVEL ('Balsalarv'PBR)	CBod LBar LCro LOPS LRHS LSou MDon MHol MidI SCob SPoG SRms WHil
	- BLUE QUEEN	see *S.* × *sylvestris* 'Blaukönigin'
§	- 'Dear Anja'	CBod EBee ECtt GElm LCro LOPS LRHS MBel MidI NCth NDov SHor WCot
	- 'Lye End'	MRav WCot
	- (Lyrical Series) LYRICAL BLUES ('Balyriclu'PBR)	EPfP LBar WHil
	- - LYRICAL ROSE ('Balyricose'PBR)	LBar SPoG WHil
§	- 'Mainacht' ♀H7	Widely available
	- MAY NIGHT	see *S.* × *sylvestris* 'Mainacht'
	- 'Negrito'	EBee ECtt LBar NLar
	- 'Pink Field'PBR **new**	NCth
	- 'Rhapsody in Blue'PBR	EPfP LBar MHol MidI NLar WCot
	- 'Rose Marvel'PBR	CBod LBar LRHS MPri MidI WHil
	- 'Rose Queen'	CBWd CBod CMac CRos CSBt ECha EHyd ELan EPfP EShb LCro LOPS LRHS LSto MRav NRHS NSti SCoo SGbt SPer SPhx SPoG SRms SWvt XLum XSen
	- 'Rügen'	CRos EHyd ELon GQue LRHS NRHS WCAu
	- 'Schneehügel'	Widely available
	- SKY BLUE MARVEL ('Balsalskarv') **new**	MDon
	- 'Tänzerin' ♀H7	EBee ECtt GBin LRHS MidI NDov NLar
	- 'Viola Klose' ♀H7	CBWd CBod CRos EBee EBlo ECha ECtt EHyd ELan EPfP EShb GElm LBar LCro LOPS LRHS LSRN LSou MAvo MCot MNrw MidI NBPC NCth NDov NGdn NLar NRHS SRms
	tachiei hort.	see *S. forsskaolii*
	taraxacifolia	LBar XSen
	tesquicola	see *S. nemorosa* subsp. *tesquicola*
	texana	CFoP
	'Theresia'	EBee
	thymoides	WOut
	tiliifolia	SRms
	tomentosa	XSen
	transsylvanica	LDai MHoo SRms XSen
	- 'Blue Spire'	NGrs SPhx SRkn
	'Trebah Lilac White'	see *S.* × *jamensis* 'Trebah'
§	'Trelawney'	ECtt EHyd EPPr EWld LRHS MCot MHer MHol MHoo MPie MidI NRHS SGbt
§	'Trelissick'	CGBo EBee EHyd ENfk LRHS MAsh MCot MHer MHoo MSpe MidI NLar NRHS SDys SEND SEle SRkn
§	'Trewithen'	CBod CExl ECre EWoo MHoo MidI XLum
	trijuga	CFoP
	triloba	see *S. fruticosa*
§	***tubiflora*** ♀H2	CFoP ECre MAsh
	'Tutti Frutti'	MAvo MidI WHoo
	uliginosa ♀H4	Widely available
	- 'Ballon Azul'	CBod CCBP CSde CSpe EBee EBtc ECha ECtt ELan EPPr EShb EWes LRHS MAsh MidI SDys SEdd SEle SIvy SPoG SPtp WSHC
	- 'Reach for the Skies'	SPtp
	'Ultra Violet'	CWGN EPfP LRHS
	urica	CFoP
	- short	SDys
	'Valerie'	MPie SDys
	'Van-Houttei'	see *S. splendens* 'Van-Houttei'
	'Vanity Fair' (Fashionista Series) **new**	LBar
	'Vatican City'	see *S. sclarea* var. *turkestaniana* 'Vatican White'
	verbenaca	MHer NMir WWild XSen
	verticillata	CCBP CWCL EPfP GQue LEdu NLar SPhx SRms WFar
§	- 'Alba'	CDor EBee EMor EPPr EPfP GQue LRHS MRav MidI NGdn NLar NRHS SCob SPer WCAu XSen
	- 'Hannay's Blue'	CDor ECha EPPr GMaP LPla MAvo MidI SMHy SMrm SPhx WCAu WFar WHrl XSen
	- 'Hannay's Purple'	ECtt EPPr EWld MidI
	- 'Purple Fairy Tale' **new**	WWke
	- 'Purple Rain'	Widely available
	- 'Smouldering Torches'	EBee MAvo NDov SCob SPhx
	- 'White Rain'	see *S. verticillata* 'Alba'
	villicaulis	see *S. amplexicaulis*
	'Violin Music'PBR	EBee ECtt EHyd LRHS MHer MidI NRHS SPhx SRkn
§	***virgata*** Jacq.	CFoP EBee XSen

- 'Alba'	WOut
viridis	CBod CHby MHoo MNHC NLar SDys
- 'Blue Denim'	LOPS
- 'Blue Monday' **new**	CBod
- blue-flowered	LCro LOPS
- Claryssa Series	SRms
§ - var. ***comata***	CBod CFoP
- (Marble Arch Series) 'Marble Arch Blue'	CSpe
- - 'Marble Arch White'	WFar
viscosa ambig.	CFoP SBut
vitifolia	CFoP SAng SDys WAvo WKif
'Walsingham White' **new**	ENfk
'Waverly'	CFoP EBee EPPr EWTr EWld LAlb MAsh MBriF MHer MHtn SDys SEle
'Wendy's Wish'[PBR]	Widely available
× ***westerae***	CFoP
§ ***yangii*** (Pe)	CKel CWal MGil MHer MNHC WChS WKif
- 'Blue Jean Baby' (Pe) **new**	LBar LCro WHil
- 'Blue Shadow' (Pe)	EHyd NLar
- BLUE SPRITZER ('Balperobritz') (Pe)	EBlo LBar LRHS
- 'Blue Steel' (Pe)	CBod SBls
- 'CrazyBlue' (Pe) **new**	LBar
- SILVERY BLUE ('Lissvery'[PBR]) (Pe)	CBcs CBod CMac EHyd LRHS MMrt NLar NRHS WNPC XSen
- 'Taiga' (Pe) **new**	CWal
yunnanensis	CFoP
aff. ***yunnanensis*** BWJ 7874	ESwi

Salvinia (*Salviniaceae*)

natans	CBen LLWG LPfP

Sambucus ✿ (*Adoxaceae*)

'14th December'	WCot
'Black Cherry'	WCot
caerulea	see *S. nigra* subsp. *caerulea*
'Cappuccino' **new**	WCot
'Chocolate Marzipan'	EBee WCot
coraensis	see *S. williamsii* subsp. *coreana*
ebulus	EBee EPPr LEdu LShi NSti SMad WCot
- B&SWJ 15307	WCru
- var. ***deborensis*** **new**	LEdu
'Ed's Brown' **new**	WCot
'Florence'	WCot
formosana	WCot
'Gate into Field'	WCot
* ***himalayensis***	WCot
§ ***javanica***	WCot
mexicana B&SWJ 10349	WCot WCru
'Milk Chocolate'	CTsd EHed GBin MPie SEdd SPad WCot
'Milk Chocolate Orange'	WCot
miquelii	LShi WCot
nigra	CArg CBTr CBcs CBod CCVT CPer EHeP EPom GDam GMcL GPoy LBuc LIns NBwr NTrD NWea SCob SEWo SVic WJur WKor WMat WMou WSFF WTSh
- 'Albomarginata'	see *S. nigra* 'Marginata'
- 'Ardwall'	CAgr EPPr GBin WCot
- 'Aurea'	CBcs CMac EHeP EPom GMcL NBwr SCob SPer WCot
- 'Aureomarginata' (v)	ELan EPPr MMuc MRav SEND WCot WFar
- 'Beaujolais'	NLar
- BLACK BEAUTY	see *S. nigra* f. *porphyrophylla* 'Gerda'
- BLACK LACE	see *S. nigra* f. *porphyrophylla* 'Eva'
- 'Bont Oosterwoldë'	WCot
- 'Bradet'	CAgr WCot WFar
- 'Broadway' (v)	WCot
- 'Cae Rhos Lligwy'	CAgr WCot WHer
§ - subsp. ***caerulea***	SMad WCot WKor WPGP
- subsp. ***canadensis***	WKor
- - 'Adams' (F)	WCot
- - 'Aurea'	NWea WCot
- - 'Johns'	CAgr WCot
- - 'Maxima'	SDix SMad WCot
- - 'Rubra'	WCot
- - 'York' (F)	CAgr WCot
- 'Castledean'	WCot
- 'Dart's Greenlace'	WCot
- 'Dolomite' (v)	WCot
- 'Donau'	CAgr WCot
- 'Frances' (v)	EPPr WCot
- 'Franzi'	CAgr WCot
- 'Fructuluteo'	WCot
- 'Godshill' (F)	CAgr WCot
- GOLD SPARK ('Alcsam') (v)	CBod NEoE
- GOLDEN TOWER ('Jdeboer001'[PBR])	CDoC CWnw LCro LPar LRHS SPoG
- 'Haidegg 17' (F)	CAgr
- 'Haschberg'	CAgr SVic WCot
- 'Heterophylla'	see *S. nigra* 'Linearis'
- 'Hillier's Dwarf'	WCot
- 'Ina'	CAgr WCot
- 'Körsör' (F)	NLar WCot
- f. ***laciniata*** ♀H6	CBcs EBee EHeP EHyd ELan EPfP LRHS MBlu MMuc MRav NLar SCob SDix SPoG WCot WFar
§ - 'Linearis'	EHed MMrt MRav NLar WCot
- 'Long Tooth'	WCot
- 'Lutea Punctata'	WCot WFar
- 'Madonna' (v)	EPfP LEdu MBlu MRav NLar NPol NQui SMad SMrm SPoG WAvo WCot WHtc
§ - 'Marginata' (v)	CMac EHeP GBin MHer MRav NBwr WCot WFar
- 'Marion Bull' (v)	WCot
I - 'Marmorata'	NLar WCot
- 'Mint Julep'	WCot
I - 'Monstrosa'	WCot
- 'Nana'	WCot
- 'Naomi'	WCot
- 'Norfolk Speckled' (v)	WCot
- 'Pingo Trail'	WCot
- 'Plena' (d)	WCot
- f. ***porphyrophylla*** BLACK TOWER ('Eiffel 1'[PBR])	Widely available
- - BLUE SHEEN ('Hyfsheen')	CBod CRos EHyd EPfP LRHS MGos SCoo WCot WHlf
§ - - 'Eva'[PBR] ♀H6	Widely available
§ - - 'Gerda'[PBR] ♀H6	Widely available
§ - - 'Guincho Purple'	CBcs CTri EGrl EHeP EPPr EPfP GMcL LRHS MRav NLar NWea SPlb WCot WFar
§ - - LACED UP ('Snr1292') **new**	NLar
- - 'Purple Pete'	WCot
- - 'Thundercloud' ♀H6	ELon MAsh MNrw NEoE NLar WCot WFar
- 'Pulverulenta' (v)	MRav NQui SMad SRms WCot WFar
- 'Purpurea'	see *S. nigra* f. *porphyrophylla* 'Guincho Purple'
- 'Pyramidalis'	MRav WCot
- 'Riese aus Vossloch'	WCot
- 'Robert Piggin' (v)	WCot
- var. ***rotundifolia***	WCot
- 'Sambu' (F)	CAgr WCot
- 'Samdal' (F)	CAgr WCot WFar
- 'Samidan' (F)	CAgr WCot
- 'Samnor' (F)	CAgr WCot

– 'Sampo' (F)	CAgr WCot
– 'Samyl' (F)	CAgr WCot
– 'Serenade'	CBcs CBod CPla CRos EBee EHyd GBin LRHS MMrt NEoE NLar NRHS SCob WCot WFar
– STRAIT LACED	see *S. nigra* f. *porphyrophylla* LACED UP
– 'Urban Lace'	CAgr WCot
– 'Variegata'	see *S. nigra* 'Marginata'
– f. ***viridis***	CAgr WCot
'Ocean Depths'	GBin NEoE
palmensis	WCot
racemosa	NWea WCot WKor
– 'Altamont'	WCot
– 'Aurea'	NBwr WFar
– var. ***callicarpa***	WCot WFar
– subsp. ***kamtschatica***	WCot
– LEMONY LACE ('Smnsrd4')	EHed LPar LRHS NLar
– var. ***melanocarpa***	WCot
– 'Plumosa Aurea'	EHeP EPfP GMcL LPar MGos MRav MSwo NBwr NLar NWea SCob SRms WAvo WCot
– var. ***pubens***	WCot
§ – var. ***sieboldiana***	WCot
– 'Sutherland Gold' ♀H7	Widely available
– 'Tenuifolia'	WCot
sieboldiana	see *S. racemosa* var. *sieboldiana*
× ***strumpfii*** SERENADE ('Jonade')	LCro SGBe
SUNNY DAYS ('Jonsun')	LRHS NLar WNPC
I 'The Sweet One'	WCot
tigranii	WCot WFar
'Vermilion Summers'	WCot
WELSH GOLD ('Walfinb'PBR)	CRos EHyd LRHS MAsh SPoG
wightiana	see *S. javanica*
§ ***williamsii*** subsp. ***coreana***	WCot

Sandersonia (*Colchicaceae*)

aurantiaca	CAvo EPot GKev LAma SBrt SDeJ SDir

Sanguinaria (*Papaveraceae*)

canadensis	CAvo CBor EAri EGrI EHyd EPPr EPot GAbr GEdr GKev GPoy ILea LAma LEdu LRHS MHoo MMuc NHol NHpl NRHS SMHy WFar WPnP
– f. ***multiplex*** (d)	CBor EHyd NBir NRHS WSHC
– – 'Plena' (d) ♀H5	EAri EBee ECha EHyd EMor EPfP GEdr GKev GPoy ILea LAma LRHS MAvo MCor NBPC NFav NHar NHol NHpl NPoe NRHS NRya NSla SDeJ WFar WPnP
– pink-flowered	GEdr

Sanguisorba ✿ (*Rosaceae*)

DJHC 143 **new**	NDov
from Japan	GGro LPla MAvo
§ ***albiflora***	CDoC CKno ECha EPfP EShb EWhm GBee GGro ILea LEdu LRHS LShi MMuc MNrw MRav MidI NDov NGdn NLar SEND SPhx SRkn WCAu
– 'Cindy's Tall White'	SPVi
'All Time High'	GBin LEdu NDov WCAu
alpina	GLog MMuc SEND
'Ankum's Thums'	MAvo MHol
applanata	EBlo GGro SBrt SSut WCot WFar WPGP
§ ***armena***	LEdu MNrw SPVi WFar
'Autumn Bliss'	GMaP
'Autumn Red'	MAvo
'Beetlewings'	NDov
'Blackthorn'	CBWd CKno ECtt GMaP LPla LRHS MBel NDov NLar SMHy SMad SPhx WCAu WCot WHoo WTor
'Burr Blanc'	CKno GMaP MSpe SMHy SPhx
'Bury Court' **new**	NDov
canadensis	Widely available
– 'Twisty'	LPla
'Candy Floss'	MAvo SPVi WHoo
'Cangshan Cranberry'	CBWd EBee ECha ECtt GMaP ILea LPla LRHS MAvo MBel NDov NLar SHor SMHy SMad WCAu WCot
'Ccc'	MAvo
'Chocolate Tip'	CDor EBee ECtt EPPr ILea NGrd SEdd SPVi WFar
'Coen's Cranberry'	NDov
dodecandra	EBee
'Foxtail'	MAvo SPVi
'Frilly Green'	see *S. armena*
hakusanensis	CBod CKno EBee ECha EMor EWhm GMaP LEdu LShi MBriF MNrw NBir NBro NChi NFav NGBl NLar SBut SPVi SPeP SPhx WCAu WCot WFar
– B&SWJ 8709	WCru
– 'Alster Luft'	SPVi
– 'Lilac Squirrel'	Widely available
'Hendrickx'	LEdu
'Ivory Towers'	MAvo SPhx WFar
'John Coke'	NLar
'Joni'	CKno MACG
'Little Angel'	Widely available
'Maartjes Merlot'	SPVi
magnifica	EWes LEdu
– ***alba***	see *S. albiflora*
menziesii ♀H7	Widely available
– 'Dali Marble' (v)	ECtt GQue NLar
– 'Misbourne'	LPla
– 'Wake Up'	NDov
§ ***minor***	CAgr CBod CCBP CHby CLau GJos GPoy GQue LEdu MBow MHer MHoo MNHC NPol SPhx SPlb SRms WHer WHlf WWild XLum
– subsp. ***minor***	CHab
'Misbourne Pink'	LPla
'Miss Elly'	NDov SPVi
'Nettlesworth Wand'	SMHy SPhx
obtusa	Widely available
– 'Chatto'	CTtf GBee MAvo NLar SPVi WMal WPGP
– silver-leaved	MNrw WFar
– white-flowered	EBee MBel WPGP
officinalis	CHab CSpe EGrI GJos GKev GQue LShi LSto MACG MBow MHer MHoo NMir NPol SCob SPer SPhx SRms WCAu WFar
– CDC 262	EPPr LEdu SMHy SPhx
– CDC 282	CSpe SPhx
– CDC 292	WCot
– DJHC 535	LEdu NLar
– 'Arnhem'	CDor CKno EBee ECtt EPPr GPSL ILea LEdu LRHS NDov NLar SEdd SMHy SMrm SPhx WCAu WCot WTor
– 'Burgundy Buttons'	CRos LRHS NDov
– 'Crimson Queen'	EBee ECtt GMaP GQue MBel MidI NLar
– dark-flowered	MAvo WMal
– early-flowering	GMaP
– 'False Tanna'	WFar
– 'Lemon Splash' (v)	EBee ECtt LEdu LShi WCot WFar WPGP
– 'Lum'	MAvo NDov

- 'Martin's Mulberry'	EBee EWes LEdu MAvo MNrw NDov WTor
- 'Morning Select'	EBee EPPr GMaP NLar
- 'Red Buttons'	MAvo NDov WMal
- 'Red Thunder'	CBWd CSpe EBee ECtt EPPr EWhm EWoo GMaP GPSL ILea LCro LEdu LOPS LRHS MAvo MBel MHol NLar SPVi WCAu WCot WGwG WPGP WTor
- 'Shiro-fukurin' (v)	EBee ECtt EShb EWes EWhm GMaP LEdu MBel MHol MNrw MSpe NLar WCot WFar WHer WSHC
- 'Tsetseguun'	LEdu LRHS MAvo SPhx WPGP
- 'White Tanna'	SCob
parviflora	see *S. tenuifolia* var. *parviflora*
pimpinella	see *S. minor*
'Pink Brushes'	CKno CTtf ECtt EMor GMaP GQue ILea IPot LBar LRHS MACG MAvo MBriF MNrw NCth NDov NGrd NLar SPVi WCAu
'Pink September'	MAvo MHol
'Pink Tanna'	Widely available
'Prim and Proper'	MAvo MHol
'Proud Mary'	NDov
'Purple Tails'	MAvo
'Raspberry Coulis'	MAvo NDov WMal
'Raspberry Mivvi'	SPhx WMal
'Red Busby'	MAvo SMHy
'Rock and Roll'	CKno EBee ECtt EMor EPPr GBee MBNS MSpe NLar
'Ruby Velvet'	IPot MNrw
'Sangria'	MAvo MHol
'Sanguine Dwarf'	MAvo
'Scapino'	ESwi MAvo SMHy
sitchensis	see *S. stipulata*
'Skinny Fingers' **new**	MAvo
§ ***stipulata***	CMac EBee EBlo EHyd LEdu LPla LRHS MHer MNrw NRHS
- var. ***riishirensis***	EMor EPPr MNrw WCAu WFar
'Sussex Prairies Cheyenne'	SPVi
'Sussex Prairies Iroquois'	SPVi
'Sussex Prairies Iroquois Alba'	SPVi
'Sussex Prairies Navaho'	SPVi
'Swarm'	MAvo
'Tanna' ♀H7	Widely available
tenuifolia	ECha LShi NChi NGBl NGrd NLar SPhx WCot
- from Ernst Pagels	MAvo
- var. ***alba***	Widely available
- - CDC	MRav
- - 'Korean Snow'	EPPr GElm GMaP ILea LEdu LPla LRHS NDov SPhx SSut
- 'Atropurpurea' **new**	NLar
- 'Big Pink'	MAvo MNrw MidI WFar
- 'Bordeaux'	CDor EBee ECtt GElm
- 'Henk Gerritsen'	MAvo NLar SEdd SPVi WCAu WFar
§ - var. ***parviflora***	EMor LEdu LShi MAvo NLar SBut WHoo WPGP
- 'Pieters'	MAvo
- 'Pink Elephant'	CBWd CKno EBee ECha ECtt EMor EPPr EWhm GJos GKev GMaP GQue ILea LDai LRHS MAvo NLar SCob SEdd SMad SPVi WCAu WFar
- pink-flowered	SMHy
- var. ***purpurea***	EBee GBin MBNS
- 'Purpurea'	CKno EBee EPPr GPSL GQue ILea LPla MAvo NFav SPhx WCAu WCot WPGP
- 'Stand Up Comedian'	GQue LEdu MNrw NDov NLar SHar WPGP
- 'Strawberry Frost'	MAvo MHol SMHy
- 'Strawberry Fruli'	LEdu WPGP
- 'Sturdy Guard'	EPPr LEdu NLar
- 'The Invisible'	SPVi WCAu
- 'White Tanna'	EPPr GQue LEdu SPVi
'White Tails' **new**	MAvo
'Woottens'	LPla

Sanicula (*Apiaceae*)

§ ***epipactis*** ♀H7	CBor CCBP CDor CElw CRos ECha EGrI EHyd EMor EPfP EPot GBin GEdr GKev GMaP GQue LCro LRHS NBir NBro NChi NFav NRHS NRya WCot WHoo WKif WMal WSHC
- 'Harry Foley' (v)	GEdr NWad
- 'Thor' (v)	ECha EWes GBin GEdr GQue MNrw NBir NGrd SPVi WAbe
europaea	CEls CTtf GPoy NGrd NMir

Sansevieria (*Asparagaceae*)

bacularis **new**	NHrt
- 'Mikado'	LCro LOPS NHrt
'Black Coral' **new**	NHrt
'Black Dragon' **new**	NHrt
cylindrica	CDoC EShb NHrt SPlb
- 'Motum Kenya' **new**	LCro
- 'Straight'	NHrt SPad
'Fernwood Mikado' **new**	NHrt
kirkii **new**	NHrt
§ - 'Farah'^{PBR} **new**	LCro
- 'Friends'	see *S. kirkii* 'Farah'
- 'Silver Blue' (v) **new**	LCro
masoniana 'Victoria' **new**	LCro
trifasciata	CWal LWaG NGKo NHrt
- 'Diamond Flame'^{PBR} **new**	NHrt
- 'Golden Hahnii' (v) ♀H1b	EShb NHrt
- 'Hahnii' ♀H1b	EShb LCro NGKo NHrt
- var. ***laurentii*** (v) ♀H1b	CDoC LCro LOPS NHrt
- 'Moonshine' ♀H1b	CDoC EShb LCro NHrt
- 'Silver Flame' (v) **new**	LCro
zeylanica	LCro LOPS NHrt
- 'Silver Flame'^{PBR} **new**	NHrt

Santolina ✿ (*Asteraceae*)

'Apple Court'	EHyd
benthamiana	EBtc XSen
§ ***chamaecyparissus***	Widely available
- var. ***corsica*** misapplied	see *S. chamaecyparissus* 'Nana'
- subsp. ***insularis***	XSen
- 'Lambrook Silver'	CBod CFis CKel CRos EBee EHyd ENfk EPfP LRHS MHoo NLar NRHS SCoo XSen
- 'Lemon Queen'	CBod CCBP CRos EGrI ELon ENfk EPfP EWhm LRHS MSwo NBir NLar NRHS SCob SRms XSen
- subsp. ***magonica***	EBtc XSen
§ - 'Nana' ♀H5	CRos EHyd EPfP LRHS MAsh MHer MRav MSwo SCob SGBe SRGP SRms XSen
- 'Pretty Carroll' ♀H5	CBod CDoC CKel CRos EBee EBtc ELan EPfP LRHS LSRN NLar SPoG WFar
- 'Small-Ness'	EBtc EPfP LRHS MHer NLar SRms SWvt WAbe WHer XSen
etrusca	CBod EBtc ECha LRHS LShi MHoo XSen
impressa	XSen
incana	see *S. chamaecyparissus*
* ***lindavica***	CKel EBtc XSen
pectinata	see *S. rosmarinifolia* subsp. *canescens*
pinnata	CTri EBtc
§ - subsp. ***neapolitana*** ♀H5	ECha ELan ENfk EPfP MRav SCob SDix SEND

- - cream-flowered	see *S. pinnata* subsp. *neapolitana* 'Edward Bowles'
§ - - 'Edward Bowles'	Widely available
- - 'Sulphurea'	CDoC CKel CRos EGrI EHyd EPfP LRHS SPer SPhx WKif
rosmarinifolia	CBod CCBP CRos EHeP EHyd GPoy GQue LRHS MHoo MRav NRHS SCob SPlb SRms XSen
I - 'Caerulea'	XSen
§ - subsp. ***canescens***	EBtc EGrI
- 'Green Fizz'	WFar
- 'Lemon Fizz' ♀H5	Widely available
§ - subsp. ***rosmarinifolia***	CEme ECha ELan ENfk EPfP LShi MHer MHoo MNHC MRav NBwr SAng SCob SDix SPer SRms SWvt WFar WSHC XLum XSen
- - 'Primrose Gem' ♀H5	CBcs CBod CCBP CDoC CKel CRos CSBt CTri EAJP ECha EGrI ELon EPfP LRHS MAsh MAvo MSwo NRHS SCob SEND SGbt SPer SRms SWvt XSen
- - white-flowered	WHer
SHADES OF JADE ('Sant101')	EBtc SCob SRms
tomentosa misapplied	see *S. pinnata* subsp. *neapolitana*
villosa	EBtc XSen
virens	see *S. rosmarinifolia* subsp. *rosmarinifolia*
viridis	see *S. rosmarinifolia* subsp. *rosmarinifolia*
'Yellow Buttons'	LRHS

Sanvitalia (*Asteraceae*)

AZTEKENGOLD	see *Melampodium montanum* AZTEC GOLD
procumbens misapplied	see *Melampodium montanum*

Sapindus (*Sapindaceae*)

mukorossi	WJur
- B&SWJ 14689	WCru

Saponaria (*Caryophyllaceae*)

'Bressingham' ♀H5	CBod ECha EDAr EPot WAbe WFar WIce WTor
Bressingham hybrid	MAsh
caespitosa	EWes
intermedia	NDov WCot
× ***lempergii*** 'Fritz Lemperg'	NDov WCot WMal
- 'Max Frei'	EBee ECtt ELon EPPr LCro LOPS LPla MCot MRav NDov SGro SPhx WCot WMal XLum
ocymoides ♀H5	EBee ECha ELan EPfP GMcL LBar LShi MAsh MHol MNHC NHpl SBls SPlb SPoG SRms XLum
- 'Alba'	NSla WFar
- 'Snow Tip'	GRum LBar NGdn
officinalis	CBod CBor CCBP ENfk EWhm GBin GPoy GQue LShi MBow MHer MHoo MNHC SMrm SPlb SRms WCAu WHer WSFF
- 'Alba Plena' (d)	EBee NLar SEND WCAu WFar XLum
- 'Betty Arnold' (d)	ECtt EMor EPPr EWes LPla LShi WCot WGob WJam
- 'Flore Pleno' (d)	CBod GAbr LShi WFar
- 'Red Splash'	WFar
- 'Rosea Plena' (d)	CMac EBee ELan EPfP LEdu LRHS MCot MHer MHol MMuc NBPC NBid NBir NGdn SEND SMrm SPer WFar WGwG
- 'Rubra Plena' (d)	CCBP EPPr EWes MMuc WGob
× ***olivana*** ♀H5	ECtt EPot GArf GMaP GRum MAsh NLar XLum
pumila	EDAr
zawadskii	see *Silene zawadskii*

Saracha (*Solanaceae*)

punctata B&SWJ 14882	WCru
quitensis B&SWJ 14748	WCru

Sarcandra (*Chloranthaceae*)

§ ***glabra***	GPoy
- B&SWJ 11102	WCru

Sarcococca ✿ (*Buxaceae*)

confusa ♀H5	Widely available
hookeriana	ELon EPfP EWoo GDam GKin LSRN MBlu MSwo NFav NLar NWad SGbt SWvt SavN WFar WHlf WPGP WSpi
- B&SWJ 2585	WCru
- HWJK 2393	WCru
- HWJK 2428	WCru
- var. ***digyna***	Widely available
- - SDR 7816	GKev
- - 'Purple Stem' ♀H5	CBcs CBod CDoC CEnd CExl CJun CKel CTri CWnw EBee ELan EPfP GKin LAlb LCro LEdu LOPS LRHS LSto MAsh MGos MNrw NLar SCob SCoo SPer SPoG SWvt WCru WSpi
§ - - 'Tony Schilling'	CExl CJun WCru
- var. ***hookeriana***	CJun GDam LSRN WJur
- - GWJ 9222	WCru
- - GWJ 9344	WCru
- - GWJ 9369	WCru
- - HWJK 2102	WCru
- - HWJK 2366	WCru
- - HWJK 2393	WCru
- - 'Daman'	CExl
- - 'Ghorepani' ♀H5	CRos EHyd LCro LOPS LRHS NRHS
- var. ***humilis***	Widely available
- - FRAGRANT MOUNTAIN ('Sarsid2') **new**	LCro
- - FRAGRANT VALLEY ('Sarsid1') **new**	LCro
- WINTER GEM ('Pmoore03'PBR)	CBod CDoC CMac CRos CSBt EBee ECha EHyd ELon EPfP LCro LOPS LRHS LSRN MAsh MGos MSwo NFav NGrs NHol NLar NRHS SCob SGBe SPoG SRHi SRkn WFar WHlf
orientalis	CBct CExl CJun CKel CMCN CRos EBee EHyd ELon EPfP ESwi GKev IDee LRHS MAsh NLar NRHS NWad SPoG SPtp WJur WLov WPGP WSpi
'Roy Lancaster'	see *S. ruscifolia* var. *chinensis* 'Dragon Gate'
'Rudolph'	CDoC CJun CKel
ruscifolia	Widely available
- var. ***chinensis***	CJun WCru WPGP
§ - - 'Dragon Gate' ♀H5	CDoC CExl CJun CKel CRos EBee EGrI EHyd ELan ELon EPfP GKev LRHS LSRN LSto MAsh MGos NCth NRHS SPoG SWvt WCru WPGP WSpi XSte
saligna	CBcs CJun EBee EPfP MRav WCru
- HWJK 2428	WCru
- MF P2056	WCru
- NJM 12.043	WPGP
I ***taiwaniana*** RWJ 9999	WCru
trinervia B&SWJ 9500	WCru
vagans B&SWJ 7285	WCru
- B&SWJ 9760 from Vietnam	WCru
- B&SWJ 9766 from Vietnam	WCru
aff. ***vagans*** B&SWJ 7265 from north Thailand	WCru

wallichii	CBcs CBod CExl ELon EPfP LEdu LRHS MBlu MGil SPoG WCot WLov WPGP
- B&SWJ 2291	CJun WCru
- GWJ 9427	WCru
- HWJK 2425	WCru
- HWJK 2428	WCru
- PAB 13.077	IKel LEdu
aff. ***wallichii***	EBee
- NJM 12.043	WPGP
zeylanica B&SWJ 10199	WCru
- var. ***brevifolia*** GWJ 9480	WCru
- - GWJ 9483	WCru

Sarcopoterium (*Rosaceae*)

spinosum	CKel SVen

Sarcostemma see *Cynanchum*

stipitatum	see *Philibertia stipitata*

Sarmienta (*Gesneriaceae*)

repens	see *S. scandens*
§ ***scandens*** 🏆H1c	CExl WAbe WPGP

Sarothamnus see *Cytisus*

Sarracenia ✿ (*Sarraceniaceae*)

× ***ahlesii***	CHew WFar
- (*S. alata* 'Red Throat' × (× *areolata*))	WFar
alata	NWac SHmp WFar WSSs
- from Desoto National Forest, Mississippi	NWac
- from George County, Mississippi	WFar
- from Nicholson County, Mississippi	WFar
- from Robertson County, Texas	NWac WFar
- var. ***alata***	CHew
- all green	SHmp
- var. ***atrorubra***	CHew
- 'Black Tube' 🏆H3	NWac WFar WSSs
- 'Black Tube' × ***oreophila***	WFar
- 'Citronelle'	WFar
- heavily veined	NWac SHmp WSSs
- - from East Texas	WFar
- large lid, robust, from Texas	WFar
- var. ***nigropurpurea***	CHew WSSs
- var. ***ornata***	CHew WSSs
- pubescent	SPlb WSSs
- - from Deer Park, Alabama	NWac WFar
- 'Red Lid'	NWac WSSs
- 'Red Lid' × ***purpurea*** subsp. ***venosa***	WFar
- var. ***rubrioperculata***	CHew WSSs
- veined, from Angelina County, Texas	WFar
- wavy lid	NWac SHmp WSSs
- white-flowered	NWac WSSs
alata × ***flava***	see *S.* × *soperi*
alata × ***leucophylla***	NWac
alata × ***oreophila***	WFar
alata × (× ***willisii***)	WFar
'Anne Carlisle' 🏆H3 **new**	NWac
× ***areolata***	CHew NWac SHmp WFar WSSs
'Asbo' **new**	NWac
'Barbapapa'	NWac WFar
'Bloodwulf' **new**	WFar
'Camisole' **new**	NWac WFar
'Camisole' × 'Jenny Helen'	WFar
× ***catesbaei***	CHew NWac SHmp WFar WSSs
- (*S. flava* × *purpurea* subsp. *purpurea* f. *heterophylla*)	WFar
- 'Heterophylla'	WFar
- Melanorhoda Group	WFar
- Melanorhoda Group × (× ***moorei*** 'Marston Clone')	WFar
- snakeskin-veined	WFar
× ***catesbaei*** × (× ***excellens***)	WFar
× ***catesbaei*** × ***flava***	WFar
× ***catesbaei*** × ***leucophylla***	WFar
× ***catesbaei*** × (× ***popei***)	WFar
× ***catesbaei*** × ***purpurea*** subsp. ***purpurea*** **new**	WFar
× ***catesbaei*** × ***rubra***	WFar
× ***chelsonii***	NWac WFar
× ***chelsonii*** × ***flava*** var. ***ornata***	WFar
× ***courtii***	SHmp WFar
× ***courtii*** × ***purpurea*** subsp. ***venosa*** ruffled lid	WFar
'Dainty Maid'	WFar
'Dana's Delight' **new**	WFar
'Daniel Rudd'	WFar
'Dawn Prince' **new**	WFar
'Decora'	WFar
'Devil's Stick' **new**	WFar
'Diane Whittaker'	NWac WFar WSSs
'Dixie Lace' 🏆H3	NWac
'Dutch Stevens' 🏆H3	SHmp WFar
'Eva' 🏆H3	NWac SHmp WFar WSSs
'Evendine'	NWac WFar
× ***excellens***	CHew NWac WFar WSSs
- 'Judy'	WFar
- 'Loch Ness'	NWac WFar
× ***excellens*** × ***leucophylla***	WFar
× ***excellens*** × ***leucophylla*** × ***rubra*** subsp. ***gulfensis***	WFar
× ***excellens*** × (× ***readei***)	WFar
× ***excellens*** × ***rubra***	WFar
× ***exornata***	NWac SPlb SRms WFar
- 'Peaches'	NWac WFar WSSs
'Fiona'	NWac SHmp
flava	LCro LOPS NWac WSSs WTyc
- from Bay County, Florida	NWac
- from Marston Exotics	NWac
- from McClellanville, South Carolina	NWac
- all green giant	see *S. flava* var. *maxima*
- var. ***atropurpurea***	NWac SHmp WFar WSSs
- - from Blackwater, Florida	NWac WFar
- - from North Carolina	WFar
- - from Wewahitchka, Florida	WFar
- var. ***cuprea***	CHew NWac SHmp WFar WSSs
- - from North Carolina	NWac WFar
- var. ***flava***	CHew NWac WSSs
- - from Prince George County, Virginia	WFar
- - 'Bronze Blush'	WFar
- - 'Marston Dwarf'	WFar
- 'Goldie'	WFar
§ - var. ***maxima***	CHew NWac SHmp WFar WSSs
- var. ***maxima*** × (× ***moorei*** 'Brooks's hybrid')	SPlb

- var. ***maxima*** × ***oreophila*** heavily veined	WFar
- var. ***maxima*** × (× ***popei***)	
- 'Slack's Max' ℽH4 **new**	NWac
- var. ***ornata***	CHew NWac SHmp WFar WSSs
- - from Apalachicola, Florida	NWac WFar
- - from Bay County, Florida	NWac WFar
- var. ***rubricorpora***	CHew NWac SHmp SPlb WSSs
- - from Apalachicola, Florida	WFar
- - 'Burgundy'	WFar WSSs
- - 'Claret'	WFar WSSs
- - 'Claret' × ***oreophila*** × ***purpurea***	WFar
- var. ***rugelii***	CHew NWac SHmp SPlb WSSs
- - from Milton County, Florida	WFar
- - from N. Florida	WFar
- - from Prince George County, Virginia	WFar
- - from Telogia, Florida	WFar
- - giant and robust	WFar
- - wavy lid	WFar
- 'Strained' **new**	NWac
- f. ***viridescens***	CHew
flava × (× ***willisii***)	WFar
× ***formosa***	NWac WFar
'Frogita'	WFar
'Gelber Schnee' **new**	WFar
'Ghost'	WFar
× ***gilpinii*** **new**	NWac
'Giraffe' **new**	WFar
'God's Gift'	NWac WFar
'Green Goddess' **new**	WFar
× ***harperi***	NWac WFar
'Hugh Jampton'	WFar
'Hummer's Hammerhead'	WFar
'Imhotep' **new**	WFar
'Jagger' **new**	WFar
'Jedi'	WTyc
'Johnny Marr' ℽH4	SHmp
'Joyce Cooper'	CHew
'Judith' **new**	NWac
'Judith Hindle' ℽH3	NWac SHmp WFar WSSs
'Judith Hindle' × (× ***moorei*** 'Elizabeth')	WFar
'Juthatip Soper' ℽH3	NWac SHmp WFar WSSs
'Kaspar Hauser' **new**	WFar
'Ladies in Waiting' ℽH3	NWac WFar
'Laughing Wizard' **new**	WFar
leucophylla	CDoC NWac SHmp SPlb SRms WFar WSSs WTyc
- from Ben's Bog, Baldwin County, Alabama	NWac
- from Okaloosa Co., Florida	NWac SHmp
- from Perdido, Alabama	NWac WFar
- from Southern Eglin Reserve, Oskaloosa County, Florida	NWac
- var. ***alba***	CHew WSSs
- anthocyanin-free **new**	WFar
- 'Cronus' **new**	WFar
- 'Deer Park Alabama'	SHmp WSSs
- green	WSSs
- - from Milton, Florida	WFar
- green and white	NWac WSSs
- var. ***leucophylla***	CHew
- pubescent	WFar WSSs
- - from Deer Park, Alabama	SHmp
- red and white	WFar
- 'Schnell's Ghost' ℽH3	NWac SHmp WFar WSSs
- 'Tarnok'	NWac WFar WSSs
- f. ***viridescens***	CHew NWac WSSs
- white-topped	WFar
leucophylla × (× ***moorei***)	WFar
leucophylla × ***oreophila***	NWac WFar
leucophylla × (× ***popei***)	NWac WFar
leucophylla × (× ***readei***)	WFar
'Lovebug' **new**	WFar
'Lynda Butt' ℽH3	NWac SHmp WFar WSSs
'Mardi Gras'	WFar
'Maria Marten' **new**	WFar
'Maroon'	NWac
'Mieke' **new**	NWac
× ***miniata***	SHmp WFar WSSs
minor	NWac SHmp WFar WSSs
- from Pine Mountain, Georgia	WFar
- from Waycross, Georgia	WFar
- var. ***minor***	CHew
§ - 'Okee Giant'	NWac WSSs
- 'Okefenokee Giant'	see *S. minor* 'Okee Giant'
- var. ***okefenokeensis***	CHew NWac WFar WSSs
- - from Deeland County, Florida	WFar
- - from Waycross, Georgia	NWac WFar
- var. ***okefenokeensis*** × (× ***willisii***)	WFar
minor × ***oreophila***	WFar
minor × ***rubra***	WFar
× ***mitchelliana***	CHew NWac SHmp WFar WSSs
- 'Bella' ℽH3	NWac SHmp WFar WSSs
- 'Mr Purplehaze' ℽH3	SHmp WFar WSSs
- pale	WFar
- 'Rita Soper' ℽH3	NWac SHmp
- 'Victoria Morley' ℽH3 **new**	NWac
× ***mooreana*** **new**	NWac
× ***moorei***	CHew NWac SHmp WFar WSSs
- (*S.* × *mitchelliana* 'Rita Soper') × (× *moorei* 'Leah Wilkerson')	SHmp WFar
- 'Adrian Slack'	CHew WFar WSSs
- 'Brooks's Hybrid' ℽH4	CHew NWac SHmp SPlb WFar WSSs
- Gulf Coast form	SHmp
- 'Leah Wilkerson'	CHew NWac WFar WSSs
- 'Marston Clone'	NWac WFar
- 'Marston Mill'	WFar
- 'Peaches'	WFar
- 'Welsh Dragon'	WFar
× ***moorei*** × (× ***readei***)	WFar
'Nicely Inconspicuous' **new**	WFar
oreophila	NWac SHmp SPlb WSSs
- from Boaz, Alabama	NWac WFar
- from Boaz, Alabama × ***purpurea*** subsp. ***venosa***	WFar
- from Cherokee, Alabama	WFar
- from DeKalb, Illinois **new**	WFar
- from Sand Mountain, Georgia	NWac WFar
- heavily veined	WFar
- var. ***oreophila***	CHew
- var. ***ornata***	CHew
- purple throat	NWac
oreophila × ***purpurea***	NWac
oreophila × ***purpurea*** subsp. ***venosa***	WFar
× ***popei***	WFar WSSs
× ***popei*** × ***purpurea*** subsp. ***venosa***	WFar
× ***popei*** × (× ***swaniana***)	WFar
'Pout' **new**	WFar
'Pretty 'n' Pink'	WFar
'Pseudo-Judy'	NWac

psittacina	NWac SHmp SRms WSSs
* - f. ***heterophylla***	NWac
- var. ***okefenokeensis***	CHew
- var. ***psittacina*** 🏆H3	CHew
purpurea	NWac SPlb WCot WTyc
- subsp. ***purpurea*** 🏆H6	CHew SHmp WSSs WFar
- - f. ***heterophylla*** 🏆H6	NWac WSSs
- - 'Lake Hiron'	WFar
- subsp. ***venosa***	CHew NWac SHmp SPlb WSSs
- - var. ***burkii*** 🏆H3	NWac SHmp WFar WSSs
- - var. ***montana*** new	NWac
× ***readei***	NWac SHmp WFar WSSs
'Red Sentinel' new	WFar
'Redneck' new	NWac
× ***rehderi***	SHmp WFar WSSs
rubra	NWac WSSs
- subsp. ***alabamensis*** 🏆H3	CHew SHmp WSSs
- subsp. ***gulfensis***	CHew NWac SHmp WSSs
* - - f. ***heterophylla*** from Yellow River, North Florida	NWac
- - f. ***luteoviridis***	WSSs
- subsp. ***jonesii***	CHew NWac SHmp WFar WSSs
- - from McClures Bog, North Carolina	NWac WFar
* - - f. ***heterophylla***	WFar
- - f. ***viridescens***	WSSs
- subsp. ***rubra***	CHew SHmp WSSs
- - long lid	NWac WFar
- subsp. ***wherryi***	CHew NWac WSSs
- - 'Chatom Giant'	NWac WFar
- - giant	WSSs
- - yellow-flowered	WSSs
'Scarlet Belle'	NWac SHmp WFar
'Scarlet Empress' new	WFar
'Skywatcher' new	WFar
× ***slackii***	NWac
§ × ***soperi***	CHew SHmp
- (*S. alata* × *S. flava* var. *maxima*)	NWac WFar WSSs
- (*S. alata* 'Red Lid' × *flava* var. *rubricorpora*)	WFar
- (*S. alata* 'Red Lid' × *flava* var. *rubricorpora* 'Burgundy')	WFar
- all red	SHmp
× ***swaniana***	NWac SHmp SRms WFar
'Tara'	WTyc
'True Blood'	WFar
'Tygo'PBR	NWac SHmp
'Velvet'	NWac
'Vogel' 🏆H3	NWac SHmp WFar WSSs
× ***willisii***	NWac WFar
× ***wrigleyana***	NWac SRms WFar WTyc

Saruma (*Aristolochiaceae*)

henryi	CAby EMor EPfP EPot ESwi EWld GEdr GGro GKev GLog LBar LEdu MPie NLar SBls SBrt SMad WCot WCru WFar WSHC

Sasa (*Poaceae*)

disticha 'Mirrezuzume'	see *Pleioblastus pygmaeus* 'Mirrezuzume'
glabra f. ***albostriata***	see *Sasaella masamuneana* 'Albostriata'
kurilensis	MWht
§ - 'Shima-shimofuri' (v)	EShb
- 'Shimofuri'	see *S. kurilensis* 'Shima-shimofuri'
§ ***palmata***	LCro LOPS MMuc SArc
- f. ***nebulosa***	CBcs LPal LPar MWht NLar SArc
- var. ***niijimae***	MWht
tessellata	see *Indocalamus tessellatus*
tsuboiana	CBcs LPal MWht NLar SGol
§ ***veitchii***	CBcs ECha GArf LPal MMuc MRav MWht NLar SCob SGol WFar

Sasaella (*Poaceae*)

§ ***masamuneana*** 'Albostriata' (v)	MWht
§ ***ramosa***	CBcs GBin MWht

Sassafras (*Lauraceae*)

albidum	CBcs CKel CMCN EHyd ELan EPfP LRHS MAsh MMrt MPkF NLar SPoG WPGP

satsuma see *Citrus reticulata*

Satureja ✿ (*Lamiaceae*)

biflora	WJek
coerulea 🏆H5	EWes XSen
douglasii	CBod WJek
- 'Indian Mint'PBR	ENfk MHer SRms
hortensis	CBod ENfk LCro LOPS MHer MHoo MNHC SRms SVic WJek
intricata	XSen
montana	CBod CCBP CHby CLau EBou ELan ENfk EWhm GJos GPoy GQue LCro LOPS MBros MHer MHoo MNHC NGrd SEND SPhx SRms SVic WJek XSen
* - ***citriodora***	GPoy MHer MHoo XSen
§ - subsp. ***illyrica***	CCBP MHoo SPhx WJek XLum XSen
- 'Purple Mountain'	GPoy MHer
- ***subspicata***	see *S. montana* subsp. *illyrica*
repanda	see *S. spicigera*
§ ***spicigera***	CBod EBou ENfk EPot EWhm LEdu MHer MHoo SPhx SRms WJek XLum XSen
* - 'Prostrata'	CLau
thymbra	SPhx SRms

Sauromatum (*Araceae*)

gaoligongense	WCot
giganteum	GKev
guttatum	see *S. venosum*
§ ***venosum***	CBor CExl CPla CRos EBee EGrl EHyd EPfP EWld GKev LAma LEdu LRHS NGKo NRHS SPlb WCot WTyc XLum

Saururus (*Saururaceae*)

cernuus	CBen CPud CToG CWat ELan LLWG LPfP WHlf WMAq XLum
- 'Hertford Streaker' (v)	WCot
chinensis	LLWG LPfP SBrt
- PB 95-85	GGro WFar

Saussurea (*Asteraceae*)

centiloba subsp. ***pachyneura*** W&O 7247	GGro
costus	GGro GPoy
nepalensis	GKev
pseudoalpina	WCot
stella	GKev

savory, summer see *Satureja hortensis*

savory, winter see *Satureja montana*

Saxegothaea (*Podocarpaceae*)

conspicua	CBcs IArd IDee NLar
- 'Ray Wood'	WPGP

Saxifraga ✿ (Saxifragaceae)

acerifolia (5) GEdr
'Ada' (× *petraschii*) (7) WHoo
§ 'Afrodite' (*sempervivum*) (7) WAbe
aizoides (9) GKev
'Akibare' (*fortunei*) (5) GEdr
'Alan Hayhurst' (8) EPot NSla NWad WAbe
'Alan Martin' (× *boydilacina*) (7) EPot EWes NBwr
'Alba' ambig. CRos EHyd LRHS NRHS
'Alba' (× *apiculata*) (7) ♀H5 EPot MAsh NBwr SPlb SRms
'Alba' (*oppositifolia*) (7) ELan EWes NWad WAbe
'Alba' (*dinnikii*) (7) EPot
'Albertii' (*callosa*) see *S.* 'Albida'
§ 'Albida' (*callosa*) (8) NWad WAbe
'Aldo Bacci' (Milford Group) (7) NSla
'Alfons Mucha' (7) EPot
'Allendale Bamby' (× *lismorensis*) (7) EPot NBwr
'Allendale Beauty' (7) WAbe
'Allendale Billows' (7) NSla
'Allendale Bonny' (7) EPot NSla WAbe
'Allendale Bravo' (× *lismorensis*) (7) WHoo
'Allendale Charm' (Swing Group) (7) EPot GKev WAbe WHoo
'Allendale Chick' (7) NBwr
'Allendale Desire' (7) WAbe
'Allendale Elf' (7) WHoo
'Allendale Elite' (7) WAbe
'Allendale Fairy' (7) WHoo
'Allendale Goblin' (7) WOld
'Allendale Grace' (7) WAbe
'Allendale Harvest' (7) WAbe
'Allendale Jinn' (7) NSla
'Allendale Jo' (7) WAbe
'Allendale Snow' (× *rayei*) (7) EWes
alpigena (7) NSla WAbe
ALPINO EARLY LIME ('Sax20007') (15) LCro LRHS WFar
ALPINO EARLY PICOTEE ('Saxz0010'PBR) (× *arendsii*) (15) LCro LRHS
ALPINO EARLY PINK HEART ('Saxz0008'PBR) (× *arendsii*) (15) LRHS
ALPINO EARLY PINK ('Saxz0009'PBR) (× *arendsii*) (15) LCro LRHS
ALPINO EARLY WHITE ('Saxz0001') (× *arendsii*) (15) LRHS
ALPINO RED ('Saxz0014') (× *arendsii*) (15) **new** LCro
'Amberglow' (× *anglica*) (7) EPot NSla
'Amberine' (× *anglica*) (7) WHoo
× ***andrewsii*** (8 × 11) XLum
angustifolia Haw. see *S. hypnoides*
'Anna' (× *fontanae*) (7) EPot
'Anneka Hope' (8) GKev
'Antonio Vivaldi' (7) NBwr
'Aphrodite' (*sempervivum*) see *S.* 'Afrodite'
× ***apiculata*** *sensu stricto* hort. see *S.* 'Gregor Mendel'
× ***apiculata*** (7) GMaP MAsh
'Apple Blossom' (Mossy Group) (15) ECtt EPfP NEoE NRya
§ 'Arco' (× *arco-valleyi*) (7) EPot
× ***arco-valleyi*** *sensu stricto* hort. see *S.* 'Arco'
× ***arendsii*** purple-flowered (15) CPla MMuc NBwr SCob SPlb
– white-flowered SCob
'Arleta' (Southside Seedling Group) (8) WIce
'Assimilis' (× *petraschii*) (7) EPot
'Atropurpurea' (*paniculata* subsp. *cartilaginea*) (8) GMaP NFav NHol NSla WFar WHoo WIce XLum
'Audrey Lowe' (*oppositifolia*) (7) WAbe
'Auguste Renoir' (Decora Group) (7) NSla
'Aurea' (*umbrosa*) see *S.* 'Aureopunctata'
'Aurea Maculata' (*cuneifolia*) see *S.* 'Aureopunctata'
§ 'Aureopunctata' (× *urbium*) (11/v) CMac CTri CTtf EBou ECha EHyd ELan EPfP GAbr GKev GMaP LEdu LRHS MHer MPie MPnt MRav NRHS SCoo SMad SPer SPlb SPoG SRms SRot WFar XLum
'Autumn Tribute' (*fortunei*) (5) GEdr WAbe WFar
'Ayako' (*fortunei*) (5) GEdr WFar
'Balcana' (*paniculata*) (8) WAbe
'Baldensis' see *S. paniculata* var. *minutifolia*
'Ballawley Guardsman' (Mossy Group) (15) NFav
'Beatles' (Beat Group) (7) NSla
§ 'Beatrix Stanley' (× *anglica*) (7) CRos EHyd LRHS MHer NRHS
'Beautiful Girl' (*fortunei*) (5) WFar
'Becky Foster' (× *borisii*) (7) EPot
'Ben Loyal' (× *concinna*) (7) WAbe
'Beni-karen' (*fortunei*) (5) GEdr WFar
'Beni-kirin' (*fortunei*) (5) GEdr WFar
'Benimine' (*fortunei*) (5) GEdr WFar
'Beni-tsukaji' (*fortunei*) (5) NBro SHeu
'Beni-tsukasa' (*fortunei*) (5) ECtt GEdr GMaP NHar NHpl NLar WFar
'Beni-zakura' (*fortunei*) (5) GEdr WFar
'Benny' (8) **new** NSla
'Berenika' (× *bertolonii*) (7) EPot
'Bertramka' (Holenka's Miracle Group) (× *megaseiflora*) (7) NSla
× ***biasolettoi*** *sensu stricto* hort. see *S.* 'Phoenix'
× ***biasolettoi*** Sünd. (7) CRos EHyd LRHS NRHS
'Bizourtouse' (× *luteopurpurea*) (7) NSla
'Black Beauty' (15) ECtt NWad
BLACK RUBY (*fortunei*) (5) Widely available
'Blackberry and Apple Pie' (*fortunei*) (5) ♀H4 CExl CRos ECtt EHyd EPfP LRHS NRHS SGro SMad SWvt WFar
'Bob Hawkins' (Mossy Group) (15/v) NHol NWad
'Bohemia' (7) NSla WAbe
'Bohemian Karst' (Prominent Group) (7) WAbe
'Boston Spa' (× *elisabethae*) (7) CRos EHyd LRHS MAsh MHer NBPC NLar NRHS SPlb
'Bridget' (× *edithae*) (7) EHyd NRHS
'Brookside' (*burseriana*) (7) EPot NBwr
'Bryn Llwyd' (Vanessa Group) (7) WAbe
× ***burnatii*** (8) CRos EHyd LRHS NRHS NSla WFar
burseriana (7) WAbe
'Bychan' (*fortunei*) (5) WAbe
caesia L. (8) SRms
§ ***callosa*** (8) ♀H5 CRos EDAr EHyd GKev LRHS MHer MMuc NRHS SEND WAbe

§	- subsp. ***catalaunica*** (8)	WAbe
	- ***lingulata***	see *S. callosa*
	callosa* × *cochlearis	see *S.* Silver Farreri Group
	× ***canis-dalmatica***	see *S.* 'Canis-dalmatica'
§	'Canis-dalmatica' (× *gaudinii*) (8)	CRos CTtf EBou ECtt EHyd GAbr GArf GKev GQue LRHS NBwr NRHS NWad SIvy WFar WTor
	'Carniolica' (× *engleri*) (8)	WAbe
§	'Carniolica' (*paniculata*) (8)	NBro NHol NWad
	carolinica	see *S.* 'Carniolica' (*paniculata*)
	cartilaginea	see *S. paniculata* subsp. *cartilaginea*
	catalaunica	see *S. callosa* subsp. *catalaunica*
	cebennensis (15)	NBwr
	- dwarf (15)	WAbe
	'Celebration'	WAbe
	cespitosa (15)	WAbe
	'Chambers' Pink Pride'	see *S.* 'Miss Chambers'
	'Charles Chaplin' (7)	NBwr
	CHEAP CONFECTIONS (*fortunei*) (5)	ECtt EHed GEdr MHtn SGro SPoG WFar
	CHERRY PIE (*fortunei*) (5)	GEdr NBPC NBir NHpl WFar
	'Chodov' (Holenka's Miracle Group) (× *megaseiflora*) (7)	EPot
	cinerea (7)	WAbe
	'Cio-Cio-San' (Vanessa Group) (7)	EPot
	'Claire Felstead' (7)	WAbe
	'Clare' (× *anglica*) (7)	NHol
	'Clare Island' (*rosacea*) (15)	SLee
§	'Clarence Elliott' (London Pride Group) (*umbrosa*) (11) ♀H5	EBou ECtt EPPr EWes GJos GKev GMaP NDov NFav NRya NWad WFar WIce WTor
	'Claude Monet' (Impression Group) (7)	EPot NSla
	'Claudia' (× *borisii*) (7)	NSla
	'Cloth of Gold' (*exarata* subsp. *moschata*) (15)	CRos ECha ECtt EHyd ELan EPfP LRHS MAsh MAvo NEoE NFav NHol NHpl NRHS NWad SPlb SPoG SRms SRot WIce
	cochlearis (8)	CRos CTri EDAr EHyd NBro NRHS NSla WAbe
	- hybrid (8)	MAsh
	'Cockscomb' (*paniculata*) (8)	ECtt ITim NWad
	× ***concinna*** 'Helvellyn' (7)	WAbe
	'Conwy Snow' (*fortunei*) (5) ♀H4	WAbe WFar
	'Conwy Star' (*fortunei*) (5)	GEdr WAbe WFar
	'Coolock Gem' (7)	WAbe WHoo
	'Coolock Kate' (7) ♀H5	EPot NSla WAbe WFar WHoo
	'Corennie Claret'	see *S.* 'Glowing Ember'
*	× ***correvensis***	EBou
	'Correvoniana' misapplied	see *S.* 'Lagraveana'
	'Correvoniana' Farrer (*paniculata*) (8)	MHer MMuc SEND WHoo XLum
	cortusifolia (5)	NBPC WHlf
	- var. ***stolonifera*** (5)	CBct XLum
	COTTON CROCHET (*fortunei*) (5/d)	ECtt GEdr NBro SHeu WFar
	cotyledon (8)	CRos EHyd LEdu LRHS NRHS SGro WAbe WCFE
	COVENTRY TEARS	see *S.* 'Slzy Coventry' (× *proximae*)
§	'Cranbourne' (× *anglica*) (7) ♀H5	CRos EHyd EPot LRHS NRHS NSla
	'Crenata' (*burseriana*) (7) ♀H5	CRos EHyd NRHS
	'Crimson Rose' (*paniculata*)	see *S.* 'Rosea' (*paniculata*)
	'Crinoline' (7)	NSla WAbe
§	***crustata*** (8)	EPot GKev WAbe WThu XLum
	- var. ***vochinensis***	see *S. crustata*
	CRYSTAL PINK (*fortunei*) (5/v)	CExl EBee ECtt NBPC NHpl WCot WFar
	'Crystalie' (× *biasolettoi*) (7)	EHyd NRHS
	'Cultrata' (*paniculata*) (8)	NBro
	'Cumulus' (7) ♀H5	EPot GKev SPlb
§	***cuneifolia*** (11)	MHer NWad XLum
	'Cuscutiformis' (*stolonifera*) (5)	CAby CElw CExl EWld GEdr MAvo MSCN SGro SMrm SRms WBor WFar XLum
	dahurica	see *S. cuneifolia*
	'Dai Uchu' (*fortunei*) (5)	GEdr
	'Dainty Dame' (× *arco-valleyi*) (7)	EHyd NRHS
	'Dana' (Prichard's Monument Group) (× *megaseiflora*) (7)	EPot
	'Darcies Cross'	EDAr
	'Dawn Frost' (7)	EPot
	'Delia' (× *hornibrookii*) (7)	EPot
	'Dentata' (× *urbium*)	see *S.* (London Pride Group) 'Dentata' (× *polita*)
§	'Dentata' (London Pride Group) (× *polita*) (11)	CElw CMiW ECha LEdu LPla MMuc MPnt SMHy
I	'Diana' (× *lincolni-fosteri*) (7)	WIce
	diapensioides (7)	NSla WAbe
	dinnikii (7)	WAbe
	× ***dinninaris*** (7)	EPot NSla WAbe
	'Doctor Clay' (*paniculata*) (8)	CRos ECtt EHyd EPot GKev LRHS NHol NRHS NRya NSla NWad SPlb
	'Doctor Ramsey' (8)	CRos EHyd EWes GArf LRHS NRHS NWad
	'Doctor Watson' (7)	EPot
	'Donald Mann' (15)	EWes
	'Donnington Veil' (7)	NSla
	'Dotty Darcy' (8) **new**	EDAr
	'Drakula' (*ferdinandi-coburgi*) (7)	CRos EHyd LRHS NRHS NSla
	'Earl Grey' (8)	GKev NSla WAbe
	'Eiga' (*fortunei*) (5)	GEdr WFar
	'Elegance'	WFar
	'Elf' (7)	see *S.* 'Beatrix Stanley'
	'Elf' (*exarata* subsp. *moschata*) (15)	MAsh SRms
	'Elf Rose' (15)	CRos EHyd EPfP LRHS NEoE NRHS SCoo SPoG
	'Elizabeth Sinclair' (× *elisabethae*) (7)	GKev
	'Elliott's Variety'	see *S.* 'Clarence Elliott' (*umbrosa*)
	'Emil Holub' (Ethography Group) (7)	NBwr
	epiphylla (5) BWJ 8177	WCru
	erioblasta (15)	WAbe
	'Esther' (× *burnatii*) (8)	CRos EBou EHyd GKev GMaP LRHS NRHS NSla NWad SLee WHoo
§	'Eulenspiegel' (× *geuderi*) (7)	EPot NBwr
	'Eva Hanzliková' (× *izari*) (7)	EPot NSla
	'Excellent' (Exclusive Group) (7)	NSla
	'Exee' (7)	NSla
	fair maids of France	see *S.* 'Flore Pleno'
	'Fairy' (*exarata* subsp. *moschata*) (15)	NBir NEoE
	× ***farreri*** hort.	see *S.* 'Reginald Farrer' (Silver Farreri Group)
	× ***farreri*** (15)	WFar WIce
§	***federici-augusti*** (7)	WFar
§	- subsp. ***grisebachii*** (7) ♀H5	CRos EHyd GKev LRHS NRHS NSla WAbe WFar
	- subsp. ***grisebachii* × *sempervivum*** (7) **new**	NSla

ferdinandi-coburgi (7)	NSla WAbe
§ - subsp. ***chrysosplenifolia*** var. ***rhodopea*** (7)	CRos EHyd LRHS NRHS
- var. ***pravislavii***	see *S. ferdinandi-coburgi* subsp. *chrysosplenifolia* var. *rhodopea*
- var. ***radoslavoffii***	see *S. ferdinandi-coburgi* subsp. *chrysosplenifolia* var. *rhodopea*
'Findling' (Mossy Group) (15)	ECtt EPfP NWad SPoG WAbe WIce
'Firebrand' (× *kochii*) (7)	WAbe
'Flavescens' misapplied	see *S.* 'Lutea' (*paniculata*)
'Fleece' (15)	LLWG NHpl
§ 'Flore Pleno' (*granulata*) (15/d)	CElw CMiW EWes LEdu NBir
'Flowers of Sulphur'	see *S.* 'Schwefelblüte'
fortunei (5) ♀H4	CMac NBir SCob SRms WAbe WFar
- f. ***alpina*** (5)	NBro
- var. ***obtusocuneata*** (5)	GEdr WAbe
- pink-flowered (5)	WAbe
'Four Winds' (Mossy Group) (15)	EWes SPoG
'Francis Cade' (8)	EPot GAbr NSla WAbe
'Freckles'	GKev NHpl SGro
frederici-augusti	see *S. federici-augusti*
'Frederik Chopin' (7)	EPot NBwr
'Fumiko' (*fortunei*) (5)	SPlb WAbe
'G.W. Gould No. 2'	EPot
'Gaia' (fortunei) (5)	LEdu
'Gaiety' (15)	CRos EHyd LRHS NEoE NRHS SPoG
× ***gaudinii*** (8)	XLum
'Gelber Findling' (7)	EPot
'Gelbes Monster' (*fortunei*) (5)	EBee ECtt ELan GEdr LBar NHar NHpl NLar SMrm WCot WFar WSpi
'Gem' (× *irvingii*) (7)	CRos EHyd LRHS NRHS
'Gemma' (× *megaseiflora*) (7)	EHyd NRHS
× ***geuderi*** *sensu stricto* hort.	see *S.* 'Eulenspiegel'
§ × ***geum*** (11)	CTtf ECha EPPr GBin MRav SDix WFar
- Dixter form (11)	ECha EWes LEdu NDov NFav SMHy
'Gina Lollobrigida' (Blues Group) (7)	EPot
'Ginkgo 98' (*stolonifera*) (5)	GGro WFar
'Glauca' (*paniculata* var. *brevifolia*)	see *S.* 'Labradorica'
'Gleborg' (Mossy Group) (15)	SPoG
'Gloria' (*burseriana*) (7)	CRos EHyd EPot LRHS MAsh NBwr NRHS NSla WIce
§ 'Glowing Ember' (Mossy Group) (15)	EWes
'Gokka' (*fortunei*) (5)	NHar NHpl SHeu XSte
'Golden Falls' (Mossy Group) (15/v)	SPlb SPoG
GOLDEN PRAGUE (× *pragensis*)	see *S.* 'Zlatá Praha'
'Gosho-guruma' (*stolonifera*) (5) **new**	GGro
'Grace Farwell' (× *anglica*) (7)	NLar
granulata (15)	EWes GJos NAts
'Gratoides' (× *grata*) (7)	EPot
§ 'Gregor Mendel' (× *apiculata*) (7) ♀H5	CRos EHyd LRHS NBwr NLar NRHS NSla SRms WAbe WHoo
grisebachii	see *S. federici-augusti* subsp. *grisebachii*
- subsp. ***montenegrina***	see *S. federici-augusti*
'Haagii' (× *eudoxiana*) (7)	CTri GKev
'Hakubai' (*fortunei*) (5)	GEdr WFar
'Hare Knoll Beauty' (8)	CBor CRos EDAr EHyd EPot GKev LRHS NBwr NFav NHol NHpl NRHS NSla NWad WAbe WFar WIce
'Harlow Car' (× *anglica*) (7)	EPot NSla
'Harold Bevington' (*paniculata*) (8)	NSla
'Harvest Moon' (*stolonifera*) (5)	WFar WHer
'Helga Hufflepuff' (*cortusifolia*) (5)	SGro
'Herbert Cuerden' (× *elisabethae*) (7)	EPot
'Hi-Ace' (Mossy Group) (15/v)	NHpl SPlb
'Highlander Red' (Mossy Group) (15)	LCro NBwr
'Highlander Rose Shades' (Mossy Group) (15)	LRHS
'Highlander White' (Mossy Group) (15)	LBar LRHS NBwr WWke
'Hime' (*stolonifera*) (5)	GGro SRms
'Hindhead Seedling' (× *boydii*) (7)	CRos EDAr EHyd LRHS NRHS WAbe
'Hi-no-mai' (*fortunei*) (5)	GEdr WFar
'Hiogi' (*fortunei*) (5)	GEdr WFar
hirsuta (11)	CMac ESwi EWld LEdu MMuc MNrw SBrt WCot WCru
'Hirsuta' (× *geum*)	see *S.* × *geum*
§ 'Hirsuta' (*paniculata*) (8)	WFar
'Hirtella' misapplied	see *S.* 'Hirsuta' (*paniculata*)
'Hirtella' Ingwersen (*paniculata*) (8)	EPot
'His Majesty' (× *irvingii*) (7)	EPot
'Hiten' (*fortunei*) (5)	EBee
'Hitomebore' (*fortunei*) (5)	WFar
hostii (8)	GArf GKev NWad XLum
- subsp. ***hostii*** (8)	XLum
- - var. ***altissima*** (8)	XLum
- subsp. ***rhaetica*** (8)	NBro WThu XLum
'Hsitou Silver' (*stolonifera*) (5)	WCot
'Hyoseki' (*fortunei*) (5)	GEdr WFar
§ ***hypnoides*** (15)	WAbe
'Iceland' (*oppositifolia*) (7)	EWes WAbe
imparilis (5)	WCru
'Ingeborg' (Mossy Group) (15)	CElw SLee
'Irene Bacci' (× *baccii*) (7)	EPot
× ***irvingii*** *sensu stricto* hort.	see *S.* 'Walter Irving'
'Iyo Haksui' (*fortunei*) (5)	GEdr WFar
× ***jacggiana***	NSla
'James' (7)	NSla
'Jan Neruda' (× *megaseiflora*) (7)	EPot
'Jan Palach' (× *krausii*) (7)	NBwr
'Jan Preisler' (Conspecta Group) (7)	EPot NBwr
'Jaromir' (8)	NSla WAbe
'Jenkinsiae' (× *irvingii*) (7)	EDAr EHyd EPot MMuc NBwr NLar NRHS NSla WAbe WIce
'Joachim Barrande' (× *siluris*) (7)	EPot
§ 'Johann Kellerer' (× *kellereri*) (7)	EPot
'John Byam-Grounds' (Honor Group) (7)	WAbe
'John Tomlinson' (*burseriana*) (7)	NSla
'Jorg' (× *biasolettoi*) (7)	EPot
'Josef Čapek' (Holenka's Miracle Group) (× *megaseiflora*) (7)	EPot

'Joy' — see *S.* 'Kaspar Maria Sternberg'
§ ***juniperifolia*** (7) — EDAr NBwr SRms XLum
'Jupiter' (Holenka's Miracle Group) (× *megaseiflora*) (7) — EPot
× ***karacardica*** (7) — NSla
karadzicensis* × *scardica (7) — EPot
'Karel Čapek' (Prichard's Monument Group) (× *megaseiflora*) (7) — CRos EHyd EPot LRHS NRHS
'Karlštejn' (× *borisii*) (7) — EPot NBwr
§ 'Kaspar Maria Sternberg' (× *petraschii*) (7) 🏆H5 — CRos EHyd LRHS NRHS
'Kathleen' (× *polulacina*) (7) — EPot
'Kathleen Pinsent' (8) — WAbe
'Kath's Delight' (8) — GKev
'Katrin' (× *borisii*) (7) — NSla
'Kawazu-beni' (*fortunei*) (5) — GEdr WFar
× ***kellereri*** *sensu stricto* hort. — see *S.* 'Johann Kellerer'
'King Lear' (× *bursiculata*) (7) — CRos EHyd EPot NRHS
'Kinki Purple' (*stolonifera*) (5) — CDTJ CDoC CSpe CTsd EMor EPPr EPri EShb EWld WCru WFar WPnP WTyc
'Kirke' (7) — EPot
'Klondike' (× *boydii*) (7) — EPot NSla WAbe
'Knapton Pink' (Mossy Group) (15) — GBin NEoE SPoG WIce
'Kokoryu-nishiki' (*fortunei*) (5) — GEdr WFar
'Komochi-daimonji' (*fortunei*) (5) — GEdr WFar
'Korin' (*fortunei*) (5) — WFar
'Labe' (× *arco-valleyi*) (7) — EHyd LRHS NRHS
§ 'Labradorica' (*paniculata*) (8) — NRya
'Lady Beatrix Stanley' — see *S.* 'Beatrix Stanley'
§ 'Lagraveana' (*paniculata*) (8) 🏆H5 — CRos EHyd GKev LRHS NBwr NRHS SLee WFar
'Laka' (7) — NSla
× ***landaueri*** *sensu stricto* hort. — see *S.* 'Leonore'
'Lantoscana' (*callosa* subsp. *callosa* var. *australis*) (8) — GKev
'Lantoscana Superba' (*callosa* subsp. *callosa* var. *australis*) (8) — NWad
'Lemon Puff' — EDAr NBwr NWad WFar
'Lenka' (× *byam-groundsii*) (7) — EPot NSla
'Leo Gordon Godseff' (× *elisabethae*) (7) — EHyd LRHS NRHS NSla
'Leonardo da Vinci' (7) — EPot WAbe
§ 'Leonore' (× *landaueri*) (7) — EHyd LRHS NRHS
'Letchworth Gem' (London Pride Group) (× *urbium*) (11) — CRos EHyd EPPr GAbr LRHS NRHS WFar
'Lidice' (7) — WHoo
lilacina (7) — NSla WAbe
'Lilliput' (*stolonifera*) (5) **new** — GGro WFar
'Limelight' (*callosa* subsp. *callosa* var. *australis*) (8) — NWad
'Lincoln Foster' (8) — EDAr NWad
lingulata — see *S. callosa*
'Lismore Carmine' (× *lismorensis*) (7) — EPot NBwr
'Lismore Mist' (× *lismorensis*) (7) — EPot NBwr
'Lissadell' (*callosa*) (8) — GKev
* 'Little Piggy' (*epiphylla*) (5) — SHar WCru
llonakhensis (1) — WAbe
'Lohmuelleri' (× *biasolettoi*) (7) — GKev
London Pride Group — WBrk
longifolia (8) — EHyd GEdr NHpl NRHS NSla
- hybrids — GKev
'Louis Armstrong' (Blues Group) (7) — NBwr WAbe
LOVE ME — see *S.* 'Miluj Mne'
lowndesii (7) — WAbe
'Lutea' (*aizoon*) — see *S.* 'Lutea' (*paniculata*)
§ 'Lutea' (*paniculata*) (8) — EBou GMaP NBro NHol NRya NSla NWad SHar
'Lydia' (× *hornibrookii*) (7) — NSla WAbe
macedonica — see *S. juniperifolia*
'Maigrün' (*fortunei*) (5) — EBee
'Mai-hime' (*fortunei*) (5) — GEdr WFar
'Major' (*cochlearis*) (8) — GKev
marginata (7) 🏆H5 — GKev NSla WAbe
- var. ***balcanica*** — see *S. marginata* subsp. *marginata* var. *rocheliana*
- var. ***bubakii*** (7) — NSla
- subsp. ***marginata*** var. ***boryi*** (7) — EHyd LRHS NRHS
- - var. ***coriophylla*** (7) — WAbe
§ - - var. ***rocheliana*** (7) — EHyd LRHS NRHS
'Maria Luisa' (× *salmonica*) (7) — WAbe
'Marianna' (× *borisii*) (7) — EPot
'Maroon Beauty' (*stolonifera*) (5) — EBee ECtt EPPr MCot NBid WCot WFar
'Marsyandi' (*andersonii*) (7) — WAbe
'Marto Hot Rose' (× arendsii) (Marto Series) (15) — CBod
'Mary Golds' (Swing Group) (7) — GKev NLar NSla
'Masami' (*fortunei*) (5) — GEdr
'Matthew Ruane' (8) **new** — GKev
× ***megaseiflora*** *sensu stricto* hort. — see *S.* 'Robin Hood'
mertensiana (6) — NBir WSHC
'Meteor' (7) — NHol NSla
'Mikawa-beni' (*fortunei*) (5) — GEdr WFar
§ 'Miluj Mne' (× *poluanglica*) (7) — NSla WHoo WIce
'Minor' (*cochlearis*) (8) 🏆H5 — CRos EHyd GKev LRHS NRHS
'Minor Glauca' (*paniculata*) — see *S.* 'Labradorica'
§ 'Miss Chambers' (London Pride Group) (11) — CBod CKel CMac EWes LPla SMHy WBrk WCot WFar WSHC
'Moe' (*fortunei*) (5) 🏆H4 — GEdr WFar
'Mollie Broom' (7) — WAbe
'Momo Tarou' (*fortunei*) (5) — GEdr
'Mona Lisa' (× *borisii*) (7) — GKev WAbe
'Monarch' (8) 🏆H5 — CRos EDAr EHyd EWes GAbr GKev ITim LRHS NFav NHpl NRHS NWad WAbe WFar WIce
'Moonlight' (× *boydii*) — see *S.* 'Sulphurea'
Mossy Group (15) — LRHS MBros MHol
- pink-flowered (15) — GAbr MMuc SPoG
- red-flowered (15) — SPoG
- white-flowered (15) — MMuc
'Mossy Triumph' — see *S.* 'Triumph'
'Mount Nachi' (*fortunei*) (5) 🏆H4 — EHyd EPfP EWes GAbr GEdr GMaP LRHS NBro NHar NHpl NRHS SPlb WAbe WFar WSpi
'Mrs Helen Terry' (× *salmonica*) (7) 🏆H5 — CRos EHyd GArf LRHS NRHS
'Mugen' (*fortunei*) (5) **new** — WFar
'Myra' (× *anglica*) (7) — WHoo

'Myriad' (7)	WAbe
'Myriad Seedling' (7)	EPot
'Namiyama' (*fortunei*) (5)	GEdr WFar
'Nancye' (× *goringiana*) (7)	NSla
'Nezu-jinja' (*stolonifera*) (5) **new**	GGro
'Nicholas' (8)	GKev NHpl
'Nottingham Gold' (× *boydii*) (7)	EPot
'Nouhime' (*fortunei*) (5)	GEdr WFar
§ ***obtusa*** (7)	MHer
'Ogon-no-mai' (*fortunei*) (5)	GEdr WFar
'Oh Yes' (*cochlearis*) (8)	WAbe
oppositifolia (7)	NHol NSla SPlb SRms WAbe
- subsp. ***oppositifolia*** var. ***latina*** (7)	ELan GArf GKev
'Ottone Rosai' (Toscana Group) (7)	NSla
'Pablo Picasso' (Conspecta Group) (7)	NSla
paniculata (8)	EDAr GKev GMaP NSla SPlb SRms WAbe
- from Gorges du Verdon, France	GKev
§ - subsp. ***cartilaginea*** (8)	GKev
- subsp. ***kolenatiana***	see *S. paniculata* subsp. *cartilaginea*
§ - var. ***minutifolia*** (8)	CRos EDAr EHyd GQue LRHS NBro NBwr NHpl NRHS NRya NSla SLee SPlb WAbe WHoo WIce
'Paradisiac' (7) **new**	NSla
paradoxa (15)	CRos EHyd EPot LRHS NHol NRHS NWad
'Parcevalis' (× *finnisiae*) (7 × 9)	WAbe
'Paul Cézanne' (Decor Group) (7)	NSla
'Paul Gauguin' (Conspecta Group) (7)	EPot
'Paul Rubens' (7)	WAbe
'Peach Melba' (7) ♀H5	CRos EHyd EPot LRHS NBwr NHpl NLar NRHS NSla WHoo WIce
'Pearl Rose' (× *anglica*) (7)	EPot
'Pearly King' (Mossy Group) (15)	ECtt GMaP WAbe WCav
'Penelope' (× *boydilacina*) (7)	CRos EHyd EPot LRHS NLar NRHS NSla WHoo
'Peter Burrow' (× *poluanglica*) (7)	EPot
'Peter Pan' (Mossy Group) (15)	CRos ECtt EHyd EPfP GMaP LRHS MHer NHol NLar NRHS NWad SPoG WCav WFar
'Petra' (7)	EPot
§ 'Phoenix' (× *biasolettoi*) (7)	EHyd NRHS
'Pink Candy' (*fortunei*) (5)	WFar
'Pink Cloud' (*fortunei*) (5)	EPri GEdr NBPC NBro NHar WAbe WFar
'Pink Haze' (*fortunei*) (5) ♀H4	GEdr WAbe WFar
'Pink Melba' (7)	CRos
'Pink Mist' (*fortunei*) (5)	GEdr WAbe WFar
'Pink Pagoda' (*nipponica*) (5)	EBee WCot WCru WFar
'Pink Star' (× *boydilacina*) (7)	EPot GMaP NLar
'Pixie' (15)	ECtt MAsh NBwr NHol NRya NWad SLee SPoG SRms SRot WFar WIce
'Pixie Alba'	see *S.* 'White Pixie'
'Pixie Pearls' (Mossy Group) (15) **new**	EDAr
'Plena' (*granulata*)	see *S.* 'Flore Pleno'
'Poils Hirsutes' (*stolonifera*) (5)	GGro
'Polar Drift'	CRos EHyd EPot LRHS NRHS NSla NWad WAbe WFar WIce
poluniniana (7)	WAbe
poluniniana × 'Winifred' (× *poluanglica*) (7)	EPot NBwr
'Pomona Sprout' (*cortusifolia*) (5)	SGro
'Pompadour' (15)	NEoE
'Popelka' (*marginata* subsp. *marginata* var. *rocheliana*) (7)	EHyd NRHS
'Portae' (× *fritschiana*) (8)	XLum
'Precious Piggy' (*epiphylla*) (5)	WCru
'Primrose Dame' (× *elisabethae*) (7)	EPot
'Primulaize Salmon' (9 × 11)	NHar
'Primuloides' (*umbrosa*) (11)	MMuc SRms SRot SWvt
'Primuloides' variegated (*umbrosa*) (11/v)	SRms
'Prince Hal' (*burseriana*) (7)	CRos EHyd EPot LRHS NRHS
'Princess' (*burseriana*) (7)	CRos EHyd EPot LRHS NRHS NSla
'Probynii' (*cochlearis*) (8)	EPot NBwr NSla WAbe WFar
× ***prossenii*** *sensu stricto* hort.	see *S.* 'Regina'
'Pseudo-valdensis' (*cochlearis*) (8)	WAbe
pubescens (15)	WAbe
- subsp. ***iratiana*** (15)	WAbe
'Punctatissima' (*paniculata*) (8)	NWad
'Purple Piggy' (*epiphylla*) (5)	WCru
'Purple Robe' (× *arendsii*) (15) **new**	LBar
'Purpurea' (*fortunei*)	see *S.* 'Rubrifolia'
'Pyramidalis' (*cotyledon*) (8)	GKev XLum
'Rachel' (8)	GKev
'Rainsley Seedling' (8)	EPot GKev NBro NBwr
'Ray Woodliffe' (× *dinninaris*) (7)	WAbe
'Red Poll' (× *poluanglica*) (7)	NHpl WAbe
* 'Regent'	WAbe
§ 'Regina' (× *prossenii*) (7)	EDAr
§ 'Reginald Farrer' (Silver Farreri Group) (8) ♀H5	WAbe
'Rembrandt van Rijn' (7)	EPot
retusa (7)	WAbe
'Rex' (*paniculata*) (8)	CMac NWad
§ 'Robin Hood' (× *megaseiflora*) (7)	WHoo
'Rocco Red' (× *arendsii*) (15)	CBod EPfP LBar LRHS MACG WWke
'Rockies White' (× arendsii) (Rockies Series) (15)	LRHS
'Rockrose' PBR (× *arendsii*) (15)	SPoG
§ 'Rockwhite' (× *arendsii*) (15)	WIce
'Rokujō' (*fortunei*) (5) ♀H4	NBro NFav NLar SHeu
'Rosa Tubbs' (8)	EWes
'Rosea' (× *arendsii*) (15)	SCob
§ 'Rosea' (*paniculata*) (8) ♀H5	GMaP LLWG MMuc NBro NRya NSla SEND SRms WFar
'Rosina Sündermann' (× *rosinae*) (7)	CRos EHyd LRHS NRHS
rotundifolia (12)	CElw ECha MPnt WBor
- subsp. ***chrysospleniifolia*** var. ***rhodopea*** (12)	NBwr
'Rubin' (× *hornbrookii*) (7)	MHer
'Rubra' (*aizoon*)	see *S.* 'Rosea' (*paniculata*)

§ 'Rubrifolia' (*fortunei*) (5) ♀H4 — CMac ECha ECtt GAbr GEdr GMcL LEdu LRHS NBPC NBro NHpl SMad SWvt WCot WCru WFar WPnP
* 'Ruby Red' — EDAr
* 'Ruby Wedding' (*cortusifolia*) (5) — WFar
'Ruth Draper' (*oppositifolia*) (7) ♀H5 — WAbe
'Saint John's' (8) — GKev WAbe
× ***salmonica*** *sensu stricto* hort. — see *S.* 'Salomonii'
§ 'Salomonii' (× *salmonica*) (7) — SRms
sancta (7) — CRos EHyd LRHS NRHS NSla SRms
- subsp. ***pseudosancta*** — see *S. juniperifolia*
- - var. ***macedonica*** — see *S. juniperifolia*
'Saotome' (*fortunei*) (5) — GEdr
sarmentosa — see *S. stolonifera*
'Satchmo' (Blues Group) (7) — NBwr NSla
'Saturn' (× *megaseiflora*) (7) — EPot
(Saxony Series) 'Saxony Red' (× arendsii) (15) — CBod EPfP NBwr
- 'Saxony White' (× arendsii) (15) — CBod
'Sázava' (× *poluluteopurpurea*) (7) — NSla
§ ***scardica*** (7) — GArf NBro
- var. ***dalmatica*** — see *S. obtusa*
- subsp. ***korabensis*** (7) — EPot
§ 'Schelleri' (× *petraschii*) (7) — EPfP SCoo SPoG
'Schneeteppich' (15) — LBar
§ 'Schwefelblüte' (15) — EHyd GMaP NRHS
sempervivum (7) — NGdn WFar
'Seren y Gwanwyn' (*oppositifolia*) (7) — WAbe
'Setsu-gekka' (*stolonifera*) (5/v) **new** — GGro
'Shaggy Hair' (*stolonifera*) (5) — WFar
'Shanghai' (*stolonifera*) (5) — GGro
'Sherlock Holmes' (7) — ECha WAbe
'Shimanami' (*fortunei*) (5) — EMor MNrw NHar
'Shimmy' — WAbe
'Shiomoe' (*fortunei*) (5) — GEdr WFar
'Shiranami' (*fortunei*) (5) ♀H4 — CBcs ECtt EHed ELan EWes GEdr GGro LSun MMrt NHpl SMad SPlb WCot WFar WSpi
'Sibyll Trelawney JP' (*fortunei*) (5) — EBee EPfP GPSL LBar MPie NHar WFar
§ 'Silver Cushion' (15/v) — CRos CTri EHyd ELan LRHS NFav NHpl NRHS SPlb SPoG SRms SRot WAbe WIce
'Silver Hill' (*paniculata*) (8) — NSla
'Silver Maid' (× *engleri*) (8) — ITim NBwr NSla
'Silver Mound' — see *S.* 'Silver Cushion'
'Silver Velvet' (*fortunei*) (5/v) — ECtt GMcL NBPC NHpl SHeu WCot
'Sissi' (7) — ECha EPot
'Slack's Ruby Southside' (Southside Seedling Group) (8) ♀H5 — NBwr NSla NWad WCav WFar WIce
'Slack's Supreme' (8) — NSla NWad WFar
'Slack's Vesuvius' (8) — WFar
§ 'Slzy Coventry' (× *proximae*) (7) — EPot
'Snowcap' (*pubescens*) (15) — WAbe
'Snowflake' (Silver Farreri Group) (8) ♀H5 — CRos EHyd LRHS NRHS WAbe
Southside Seedling Group (8) — Widely available
- 'Southside Star' (8) ♀H5 — LEdu NHpl WAbe
'Spartakus' (× *apiculata*) (7) — NBwr
spathularis (11) — MACG WCot
'Splendens' (*oppositifolia*) (7) ♀H5 — GAbr GKev SRms WAbe
'Spotted Dog' — see *S.* 'Canis-dalmatica'
'Sprite' (15) — SPoG
spruneri (7) — EHyd LRHS NRHS
'Stansfieldii' (*rosacea*) (15) — EBou SPlb SPoG
'Starfire' (8) — NHar WThu
'Starlight' (8) — GKev
startorii — see *S. scardica*
stolitzkae (7) — EPot
§ ***stolonifera*** (5) ♀H2 — CSpe ECha EShb GGro LCro LDai LWaG NBro SDix SWvt WCot WFar
- large-flowered (5) — WCot
stribrnyi (7) — GKev WHoo
* - var. ***degenii*** (7) — NSla
'Sturmiana' (*paniculata*) (8) — SRms
'Sue Tubbs' (8) — GKev
'Suendermannii' (× *kellereri*) (7) — CRos EHyd GKev LRHS NRHS
'Suendermannii Major' (× *kellereri*) (7) — EHyd LRHS NRHS
SUGAR PLUM FAIRY ('Toujya') (*fortunei*) (5) ♀H4 — ECtt EHed SHeu WFar XSte
§ 'Sulphurea' (× *boydii*) (7) — CRos EHyd LRHS NRHS NSla WHoo
'Superba' (*callosa* subsp. *callosa* var. *australis*) (8) — NSla
'Symons-Jeunei' (8) — NWad
'Tamayura' (*fortunei*) (5) — GEdr
'Tenerife' (Swirly Group) (7) — EWes WAbe
'Theoden' (*oppositifolia*) (7) — EWes GArf WAbe
'Theresa Cooper' (7) — EPot
'Thór Heyerdahl' (Ocean Group) (7) — EPot
tombeanensis (7) — EPot WAbe
TOURAN DEEP RED ('Rockred') (Mossy Group) (15) — EHyd EPfP LBuc LRHS NRHS
TOURAN LARGE WHITE ('Rocklarwhi'PBR) (Mossy Group) (15) — EHyd EPfP LRHS NRHS
TOURAN PINK (× *arendsii*) (15) — EPfP LRHS
TOURAN RED ('Saxz0006') (× *arendsii*) (15) — SPoG WIce
TOURAN WHITE — see *S.* 'Rockwhite' (× *arendsii*)
TOURAN WHITE IMPROVED ('Saxz0004'PBR) (× *arendsii*) (15) — LCro SPoG WIce
'Tricolor' (*stolonifera*) (5) ♀H2 — CDoC WCot WFar
§ 'Triumph' (× *arendsii*) (15) — CPla GMaP LLWG MAsh MAvo SCoo SPoG
'Tumbling Waters' (8) ♀H5 — CBor CRos EHyd EPot LEdu LRHS NBwr NFav NHol NHpl NRHS NSla NWad WAbe
§ 'Tvoje Píseň' (× *poluanglica*) (7) — WHoo
§ 'Tvůj Prítel' (× *poluanglica*) (7) — GArf
§ 'Tvůj Úsměv' (× *poluanglica*) (7) ♀H5 — GKev NBPC NHpl NLar
§ 'Tvůj Úspěch' (× *poluanglica*) (7) — EPot
'Two Kings' (*fortunei*) (5) — WFar
'Tycho Brahe' (× *doerfleri*) (7) — WAbe
'Tysoe' (7) — EPot
'Tysoe Blush' (Blues Group) (7) — NBwr NSla WFar

'Tysoe Burgundy' (Blues Group) (7) — NSla WFar
'Tysoe Everest' (7) — EPot WAbe
'Tysoe Makalu' (7) — NSla WAbe
'Tysoe Pink-Perfection' (Blues Group) (7) — NSla
'Tysoe Splendour' (Blues Group) (7) — NSla
'Uchiwa' (*stolonifera*) (5) **new** — GGro
umbrosa (11) — CMac CRos EDAr EHeP EHyd EPfP GAbr LEdu LRHS MMuc MRav NRHS SCgs SEND SHar SPlb SPoG SRms SRot SWvt WFar XLum
* - ***subinteger*** — MMuc
× ***urbium*** (11) ♀H5 — CCBP CKel CTri CTtf EGrI EHyd ELan EPfP EWoo GMaP GQue LBar LCro LEdu LRHS LSto LWaG MBel NSti SBut SCob SEdd SPer SRms WCAu WHlf WHoo WPnP WSpi WTor
'Vaccariana' (*oppositifolia*) (7) — EPot SHar
'Valborg' — see *S.* 'Cranbourne'
'Valentine' — see *S.* 'Cranbourne'
I 'Variegata' (*cuneifolia*) (11/v) — CRos EBou ECtt EHyd EPfP LRHS NFav NHol NHpl NRHS NRya NWad SLee SPlb SPoG WBrk WHoo WIce
I 'Variegata' (*exarata* subsp. *moschata*) (15/v) — GMaP
'Variegata' (*umbrosa*) — see *S.* 'Aureopunctata'
I 'Variegata' (× *urbium*) (11/v) — EBee EPfP GPSL LBar NLar SCob SPtp SRms WFar WHoo WTor
vayredana (15) — WAbe
'Večerní Hvězda' (7) — WAbe
veitchiana (5) — GGro NBro WFar XLum
'Verona' (× *caroli-langii*) (7) — WAbe
'Vikos Gold' (7) — EPot WAbe
'Vincent van Gogh' (× *borisii*) (7) — EPot
'Vladana' (× *megaseiflora*) (7) — EHyd GArf NRHS NSla
'Vreny' (8) — GKev
'Wada' (*fortunei*) (5) — CMac CSpe ECtt EPri GArf GKev GMaP LRHS MNrw NBir NBro NHar NRHS SHar SRms WCot WFar WOld WSHC
'Walpole's Variety' (8) — NWad
'Walter Ingwersen' (*umbrosa*) (11) — SRms
§ 'Walter Irving' (× *irvingii*) (7) ♀H5 — NSla WAbe
'Welsh Dragon' (15) — WAbe WFar
'Welsh Red' (15) — WAbe
'Welsh Rose' (15) — WAbe
'Wheatley Rose' (7) — CRos EHyd LRHS NRHS
'White Delight' (× *megaseiflora*) (7) — CRos EHyd LRHS NRHS NSla
§ 'White Pixie' (15) — CPla ECtt EDAr EPfP MHer NEoE NFav NHol NRya NWad SLee SPlb SPoG SRms SRot WCAu WFar WIce
'White Star' (*fortunei*) (5) — EHyd LRHS NRHS
'White Star' (× *petraschii*) — see *S.* 'Schelleri'
'Whitehill' (8) ♀H5 — CRos EBou EDAr EHyd ELan EPot GEdr GMaP LRHS NBwr NFav NRHS NRya NSla NWad SGro SLee WHoo
'William Shakespeare' (Blues Group) (7) — NBwr WAbe
'Winifred' (× *anglica*) (7) — EPot WAbe
'Winifred Bevington' (8 × 11) — CRos CTtf EAJP EBou EDAr EHyd GBin GEdr GMaP LRHS MBel NBro NBwr NFav NHpl NLar NRHS NRya NWad SGro SIvy SLee SRms WAbe WCav WFar WHoo WIce WTor
'Winston Churchill' (15) — CRos EHyd EPfP LRHS NBwr NEoE NHol NRHS NWad
I 'Winston Churchill Variegata' (15/v) — NHol WIce
'Winton' (× *paulinae*) (7) — EPot
'Wisley' (*federici-augusti* subsp. *grisebachii*) (7) ♀H5 — GKev
YOUR FRIEND — see *S.* 'Tvůj Prítel'
YOUR GOOD FORTUNE — see *S.* 'Tvůj Úspěch'
YOUR SMILE — see *S.* 'Tvůj Úsměv'
YOUR SONG — see *S.* 'Tvoje Píseň'
YOUR SUCCESS — see *S.* 'Tvůj Úspěch'
× ***zimmeteri*** (8 × 11) — NSla
§ 'Zlatá Praha' (× *pragensis*) (7) — EPot WAbe
'Zlatý Kůň' (× *laeviformis*) (7) — EPot

Scabiosa (*Caprifoliaceae*)

africana — CElw
- 'Jocelyn' — SHar
alpina L. — see *Cephalaria alpina*
argentea — EWes WPGP
- PAB 1229 — LEdu
atropurpurea — LCro
- 'Ace of Spades' — EPfP LRHS
- 'Beaujolais Bonnets' — CRos EHyd EPfP LRHS SBls WHlf
- 'Black Knight' — CSpe LCro LOPS SPhx
- BLACKBERRY SCOOP ('Dblckbry'PBR) (Scoop Series) — IPot LBar WHil
§ - 'Chile Black' — CBcs EAJP EHyd ELan EPfP ETod LShi NLar NRHS SCob SPer SPoG SRkn SWvt
§ - 'Chilli Pepper' — LRHS
- 'Derry's Black' — CSpe
- 'Fata Morgana' — CKel
banatica — see *S. columbaria*
'Barocca' — CWGN EBee ELan EPfP ETod LRHS NLar SCob SRms WHlf
'Blackberry Fool' (Dessert Series) — SCob
BLUE DIAMONDS ('Kiescalibu') — GJos WFar
'Blue Mound' — SPhx
'Blueberry Muffin' (Dessert Series) — SCob
§ 'Butterfly Blue' — Widely available
caucasica — CMac CWal EHyd EPfP GKev LRHS NRHS XSen
- var. ***alba*** — CBcs EPfP MBel NGBl
- 'Blauer Atlas' — NCth
- 'Blausiegel' — EShb LBar LRHS MRav SGbt WHoo
- 'Clive Greaves' ♀H4 — EBee ECha GMaP LBar MBNS MBel NCth NLar SGbt SMrm SPad SPer SRms SWvt WCAu WFar
- 'Deep Waters' — LRHS SPtp
- 'Fama' — CSpe NBir NGBl NLar SPlb SRms WFar WHoo
- 'Fama Deep Blue' — CDor LRHS MACG MCot MHol NCou NCth NRHS SHar WFar WHlf
- 'Fama White' — EHyd LRHS MACG MCot NCth NRHS SHar WHlf
- 'Goldingensis' — MACG WHil
- House's hybrids — CSBt NGdn SRms
- 'Isaac House' — WFar XLum
- 'Kompliment' — WFar

- 'Miss Willmott' ♀^{H4}	EBee ECha ECtt EHyd EShb GBin LRHS LSto MArl MBel MHer MRav NCth NLar NRHS SGbt SPad SPer SWvt WCAu WGwG XSen
- Perfecta Series	EHyd GMcL LRHS MACG NGdn NLar NRHS SCob SEdd SPoG
- - 'Perfecta Alba'	CDor CRos EHyd EPfP EShb ETod EWoo GMaP LBar LCro LRHS NLar NRHS SBut SCob SPer SPoG SPtp WCAu WHoo WPnP WWke XLum
- - 'Perfecta Blue'	CDor EPfP ETod EWoo GMaP LBar LSto NLar XLum
- - 'Perfecta Lilac Blue'	SPer
- 'Stäfa'	CBod EBee ECha EHyd LBar LRHS MBel MHer NLar SCob SGbt WHoo
'Cherry Pie' (Dessert Series)	SCob
CHERRY VANILLA SCOOP ('Dchrunscop') (Scoop Series)	LBar WHil
'Chile Black'	see *S. atropurpurea* 'Chile Black'
'Chile Pepper'	see *S. atropurpurea* 'Chilli Pepper'
§ ***columbaria***	CAby CCBP CHab CRos EBee EHyd GBee GQue LCro LRHS MBow NGrd NMir NRHS SBut SPhx WHer WOut WSFF WWild XSen
* - ***alpina***	GKev
- 'Big Blue'	EPfP LRHS
- 'Blue Note'^{PBR}	LBar LRHS MACG MPri
- blue-flowered	NHpl
- (Flutter Series) FLUTTER DEEP BLUE ('Balfluttdelu'^{PBR})	CBod LBar LRHS LSou MDon MHol WHil
- - FLUTTER PURE WHITE ('Bafflutturite'^{PBR})	LBar MACG MDon MPri
- - FLUTTER ROSE PINK ('Balfluttropi'^{PBR})	CBod EPfP LBar LRHS LSou MDon MHol SCoo WHil WWke
- 'Mariposa Blue'^{PBR}	CBod LBar LRHS MACG MDon MHol MPri NBir NRHS WHil WWke
- 'Mariposa Blush'	LRHS WHil
- 'Misty Butterflies'	CAby ECtt GJos LRHS NGdn NLar SBls SEdd SGBe SRms WFar
- 'Nana'	EHyd EPfP GArf GQue LRHS LSun NBir NGdn NRHS WAbe WCFE XLum
§ - subsp. ***ochroleuca***	CAby CCBP CDor CElw CKno CSpe CTtf ECha EHyd EPfP EWoo GElm LRHS NBir NGBl SBut SHar SPeP SPhx SPoG SRms SSut WCAu WWke XSen
- - 'Moon Dance'	CDor CRos CWGN EAJP EHyd EMor EShb LRHS LSun MACG NRHS SAko SCob SEdd SGBe SGbt SPoG WCot WHil WHoo
- 'Pincushion Blue'	EHyd LRHS MACG NRHS
- 'Pincushion Pink'	EBou EHyd GJos LRHS LSun MACG NGdn NRHS
cretica	XLum XSen
drakensbergensis	GBin GKev LRHS SPtp
GELATO BLUEBERRY (Gelato Series) **new**	LBar
gigantea	see *Cephalaria gigantea*
graminifolia	EBee EHyd LRHS NBir NRHS SGro SRms XLum XSen
'Helen Dillon'	EWes
'Irish Perpetual Flowering'	see *S.* 'Butterfly Blue'
japonica var. ***alpina***	EBee EPfP GGro GKev NGdn SPhx SPtp WFar WHoo XLum XSen
- - 'Blue Star'	EBee SGbt
- - pink-flowered	NBir
- - 'Ritz Blue'	GRum LBar LRHS MACG MHer WCav WHil
- - 'Ritz Rose'	LBar MACG
Kudo Series	CBod CNor CRos CWGN ECtt EHyd ELan EPfP LRHS LSou MHol NLar NRHS NSti SCoo SHar SMrm SPad SPoG SWvt WHil WHlf WNPC XSte
- KUDO PINK ('Ichpin'^{PBR}) **new**	LBar LCro MPri SOrN
- KUDO WHITE ('Ichwit')	CBod CRos CWGN ECtt ELan LBar LCro LRHS LSou MBros MHol MPnt NSti SGBe SHar SOrN WHil WNPC XSte
lachnophylla	SPhx WCot
LAVENDER SCOOP ('Dlvndrscop') (Scoop Series)	LBar WHil WHlf
'Little Cracker'	GBin LRHS
'Little Emily'	ELon
lucida	CBod EHyd EPfP GKev LRHS MMuc MRav NLar NRHS SEND SGbt WCAu XLum
MARSHMALLOW SCOOP ('Dmarshscop') (Scoop Series)	LBar WHil WHlf
'Midnight Moon'	LBar
minoana	XSen
'Miss Havisham'	CElw EWes MNrw WHoo
'Misty Pink'	EPfP
montana Mill.	see *Knautia arvensis*
ochroleuca	see *S. columbaria* subsp. *ochroleuca*
parnassi	see *Pterocephalus perennis*
'Perpetual Flowering'	see *S.* 'Butterfly Blue'
PINK BUTTONS ('Walminipink')	LRHS
'Pink Diamonds'	CBod ELan EPfP LRHS WFar
'Pink Mist'	CRos EBee ECtt EHyd ELan EPfP GBin LBar LCro LRHS MAsh MPie NBir NHpl NLar NRHS SCob SCoo SPer SPoG SRms WHlf WTor
pterocephala	see *Pterocephalus perennis*
RASPBERRY SCOOP ('Draspscop') (Scoop Series)	LBar WHil WHlf
'Raspberry Sorbet' (Dessert Series)	SCob
RED VELVET SCOOP ('Drevelscop') (Scoop Series)	WHil
rhodopensis	EBee
'Rosie's Pink'	ECtt
rumelica	see *Knautia macedonica*
'Satchmo'	see *S. atropurpurea* 'Chile Black'
speciosa 'Maharajah'	SPtp
stellata	SPhx
STRAWBERRY SCOOP ('Dstrawscop') (Scoop Series)	WHil
succisa	see *Succisa pratensis*
tatarica	see *Cephalaria gigantea*
triandra	ECha EShb
TUTTI FRUTTI SCOOP ('Dtutfrscop') (Scoop Series) **new**	WHil
VANILLA SCOOP ('Dvanilscop') (Scoop Series)	WHlf
'Vivid Vi'^{PBR}	CAby CBod CDor CRos EBee ECtt EHyd ELan EPfP LBar LRHS LSRN MMuc MNrw NHpl NLar NRHS

Scadoxus ✿ (*Amaryllidaceae*)

membranaceus	WCot WMal
multiflorus	CCCN GKev LAma SDeJ SDir
§ - subsp. ***katherinae*** ♀^{H1b}	WCot
§ - subsp. ***multiflorus***	WCot

natalensis see *S. puniceus*
§ ***puniceus*** GKev WCot

Scaevola (*Goodeniaceae*)

aemula 'Abanico Blue' LSou
- 'Abanico Rose' LSou
- 'Abanico White' LSou
- 'Blue Fan' see *S. aemula* 'Blue Wonder'
- BLUE PRINT ('Kingscablin') LSou
§ - 'Blue Wonder' NPer SWvt
- 'Fancy' LSou
- 'Zig Zag'PBR CCCN
BLAUER FACHER ('Saphira'PBR) CCCN
'Mini Blue' CCCN
'Topaz Pink' LSou

Sceletium (*Aizoaceae*)

tortuosum SPlb

Schefflera (*Araliaceae*)

NJM 13.128 WPGP
alpina CBct CExl MPkF XVPe
- B&SWJ 8247 WCru
- B&SWJ 11827 WCru
- HWJ 936 WCru
- NJM 09.140 EBee WPGP
- NJM 09.157 WPGP
- large-leaved WWJ 11999 WCru
arboricola ♀H1c CDoC SEND
- 'Gold Capella' ♀H1c LCro NHrt NPlm SEND
- 'Nora' new LCro
- variegated (v) SEND
bodinieri new WPGP
brevipedicellata CDTJ
- HWJ 870 WCru
- KWJ 12224 WCru
aff. ***brevipedicellata*** IKel
- NJM 10.102 WPGP
§ ***chapana*** B&SWJ 11833 WCru
- B&SWJ 11848 WCru
- HWJ 983 WCru
delavayi CBct CDTJ CExl IKel WCru WPGP
digitata CTrC IKel
enneaphylla HWJ 1018 WCru
fantsipanensis B&SWJ 11666 WCru
- B&SWJ 11671 WCru
gracilis CBct EBee
- HWJ 622 WCru
- HWJ 878 WCru
gracilis* × *taiwaniana WCru
hoi B&SWJ 11747 WCru
kornasii B&SWJ 11830 WCru
- HWJ 918 WCru
macrophylla B&SWJ 8210 WCru
- B&SWJ 9788 WCru
- B&SWJ 11842 WCru
- WWJ 11681 WCru
microphylla B&SWJ 3872 WCru
multinervia B&SWJ 11727 WCru
aff. ***myriocarpa*** B&SWJ 11828 WCru
pauciflora WWJ 11986 WCru
rhododendrifolia CBcs CBct CDTJ CDoC CExl EBee IKel WPGP
- GWJ 9375 WCru
shweliensis NJM 13.130 WPGP
taiwaniana ♀H4 CAbb CBct CCht CDTJ CExl CTsd EBee IKel MPkF WCot WPGP XVPe
- B&SWJ 3575 WCru
- B&SWJ 3788 WCru
- B&SWJ 7096 WCru
- RWJ 10000 WCru
- RWJ 10016 WCru
trevesioides BWJ 15158 WCru
trianae B&SWJ 14313 WCru
vietnamensis see *S. chapana*
aff. ***alpina*** new CDTJ XSte

Schima (*Theaceae*)

argentea CBcs CCCN CExl CTsd EBee WPGP
aff. ***argentea*** NJM 13.042 WPGP
khasiana CBcs WPGP
- PAB 3447 EBee LEdu
wallichii CExl

Schinus (*Anacardiaceae*)

latifolius ESwi LAlb
lentiscifolius SPlb SVen
molle CKel SPlb
montanus SPlb
patagonicus MGil
polygama MGil SPlb

Schisandra (*Schisandraceae*)

arisanensis CRHN MBlu NLar WPGP
- B&SWJ 3050 WCru
arisanensis* × *sphaerandra CRHN
chinensis CAgr CBcs CKel CRHN GKev GPoy LEdu MGil MSwo NLar SBrt WPGP
- B&SWJ 4204 WCru
- B&SWJ 4611A WCru
- B&SWJ 4611B WCru
- 'Bere' LEdu WPGP
- 'Sadova No.1' CAgr
grandiflora ♀H4 CBcs CBod CRos ELan EPfP ESwi GBin LRHS MBlu WHlf WPGP
- B&SWJ 2245 WCru WSHC
- PAB 3673 LEdu
- WJC 13666 WCru
- var. ***cathayensis*** see *S. sphaerandra*
- 'Jamu' (m) CRHN WCru
- 'Lahlu' (f/F) CRHN WCru
aff. ***grandiflora*** CRHN
- WJC 13817 WCru
grandiflora* × *rubriflora MMuc WCru
henryi subsp. ***yunnanensis*** B&SWJ 6546 WCru
incarnata BWJ 7898 WCru
incarnata* × *rubriflora WCru
lancifolia MBlu
nigra see *S. repanda*
perulata FMWJ 13100 WCru
aff. ***plena*** HWJ 664 WCru
propinqua subsp. ***sinensis*** CMac CRHN LEdu NLar WPGP
- - BWJ 8148 WCru
§ ***repanda*** B&SWJ 5897 WCru
- B&SWJ 11455 WCru
rubriflora ♀H5 CTri EPfP LRHS MBlu MGos SDix WCFE WPGP
- BWJ 7557 CRos WCru
- (f) WSHC WSpi
- 'Bodnant Redberry' (f) WCru
§ ***sphaerandra*** CBcs CRHN MBlu
- BWJ 7739 WCru
- BWJ 8082 WCru
sphenanthera CKel EBee MBlu NLar WSHC
- BWJ 8151 WCru

Schizachyrium (*Poaceae*)

§ ***scoparium*** CKno CWal EPfP LRHS NRHS SBls SCob SPeP XLum
- 'Blaze' CBWd EMor NDov SBls

- 'Blue Heaven'	ELon IPot LEdu MAvo NDov SCoo SEdd SMHy WPGP WSpi
- 'Cairo'	EBee IPot
- 'Camper' **new**	SBls
- 'JS Red Frost' **new**	IPot
- 'Prairie Blues'	CBod CSpe EBou EPfP LSun MACG NDov SBls SCoo SEdd SPoG WCot
- 'Standing Ovation'	CSpe EMor LCro LOPS NCth NDov SCoo
- 'The Blues'	IPot

Schizocarphus (*Asparagaceae*)

nervosus	WCot

Schizocodon see *Shortia*

Schizophragma (*Hydrangeaceae*)

fauriei	NLar
- B&SWJ 1701	WCru
- B&SWJ 6831	WCru
- B&SWJ 7052	WCru
- CWJ 12405	WCru
- CWJ 12433	WCru
- 'Angel Wings' **new**	LCro MBlu
- WINDMILLS ('Plooster')	CKel CMil LRHS WHlf WLov
hydrangeoides	CBcs CCCN CKel EBee EHyd ELan EPfP EWTr IDee LCro LOPS LRHS MBlu MGos NRHS SCob SGol SPer SPoG SWvt WSpi
- 'Brookside Littleleaf'	see *Hydrangea anomala* subsp. *petiolaris* var. *cordifolia* 'Brookside Littleleaf'
- var. ***concolor*** B&SWJ 5954	WCru
- - 'Moonlight' 🏆^{H5}	CBcs CDoC CKel CMac CRos CWGN EHyd ELan EPfP LPal LRHS MBlu MGil MGos MMuc NLar NRHS SGol SPoG SRHi SSha SWvt WCot WCru WPGP
- var. ***hydrangeoides*** B&SWJ 5489	WCru
- - B&SWJ 5732	WCru
- - 'Iwa Garami'	NLar
- - 'Roseum' 🏆^{H5}	CArg CBcs CCCN CDoC CMac CMil ELan EPfP EWes IArd MBlu MGil MGos SCob SGol SPer SSha SWvt WCot WCru WLov
- 'Rose Sensation'	CBod CCCN CKel CRos EBee EHyd EPfP LRHS MDon MHtn NLar NRHS SGol SPoG SRHi WLov
- 'Shiro-dai-fukurin' (v) **new**	WCot
- SNOW SENSATION ('Minsnow3')	NLar
- var. ***taquetii*** B&SWJ 8771	WCru
- - 'Cheju's Early'	WCru
- var. ***ullungdoense*** B&SWJ 8505	WCru
- - B&SWJ 8522	WCru
- var. ***yakushimense*** B&SWJ 6119	WCru
integrifolium 🏆^{H5}	CBcs CCCN CKel CRHN EBee EHyd ELan EPfP GKev LRHS MBlu NLar SPer WKif WPGP
- BWJ 8150	WCru
molle HWJ 1011	WCru
- WWJ 11905	WCru

Schizostylis see *Hesperantha*

Schlumbergera (*Cactaceae*)

× ***buckleyi*** 🏆^{H1b} **new**	CWal
'Thor Wild Cactus Orange' **new**	LCro
truncata **new**	CWal

Schoenoplectus (*Cyperaceae*)

§ ***lacustris***	CPud CWat LLWG LPfP
§ - subsp. ***tabernaemontani***	CSpe LLWG LPfP
- - 'Albescens' (v)	CBen CWat MMuc MNrw XLum
- - 'Zebrinus' (v)	CBen CPud CWat ELan MNrw SPlb WMAq XLum

Schoenus (*Cyperaceae*)

pauciflorus	LLWG

Sciadopitys (*Sciadopityaceae*)

verticillata 🏆^{H6}	CAco CBcs CMCN CMac CSBt EHed EPfP GKin LAlb LMaj LPar LRHS MAsh MBlu MGil MGos MMuc MPkF NHol NWea SCoo SEND SLim SPoG SSha SWvt XSte XVPe
- 'Eiffel Tower' **new**	CAco
- 'Firework'	CKen
- 'Globe'	CKen
- 'Gold Star'	CKen NLar
- 'Goldammer'	CAco
- 'Golden Rush'	CKen
- 'Goldmahne'	CKen
- 'Grüne Kugel'	CKen MAsh
- 'Jeddeloh Compact'	CKen
- 'Koja Maki'	NLar
- 'Kupferschirm'	CKen
- 'Marylin Monroe'	NLar
- 'Mecki'	CKen
- 'Megaschirm'	CAco CKen
- 'Mireille' **new**	CAco
- 'Ossorio Gold'	CAco CKen
- 'Perlenglanz'	CAco CKen
- 'Picola'	CKen MAsh
- 'Pygmy'	CKen
- 'Richie's Cream'	CKen
- 'Richie's Cushion'	CKen
- 'Shorty'	CKen
- 'Speerspitze'	CKen
- 'Star Wars'	CKen
- 'Starburst'	CKen
- 'Sternschnuppe'	CAco CKen NLar
- 'Tsai Cheng'	NLar
- variegated	CAco
- 'Wintergreen'	CKen

Scilla (*Asparagaceae*)

adlamii	see *Ledebouria cooperi*
× ***allenii***	NRog
amethystina	see *S. litardierei*
amoena	GKev NRog WCot
autumnalis	CAvo EHyd EPot GKev LAma NRHS NRog SChr WShi WThu
- subsp. ***fallax***	NRog
- white-flowered	NRog
bifolia 🏆^{H6}	CAvo EPot GKev LAma LRHS NRog SDeJ WCot WShi
- 'Alba'	CAvo GKev LAma NRog SDeJ
- 'Norman Stevens'	NRog
- 'Rosea'	CAvo CRos EHyd ERCP GKev LAma LRHS NRHS NRog SDeJ WHlf
bithynica 🏆^{H6}	CFis GKev NRog WCot WShi
'Blue Giant'	CAvo ELan EPfP EPot ERCP GKev LAma LRHS NRog WCot WHlf
campanulata	see *Hyacinthoides hispanica*
chinensis	see *S. scilloides*
cilicica	GKev NRog WCot
dracomontana	see *Merwilla dracomontana*
§ ***forbesii***	EHyd EPot ETay GKev LAma LCro LRHS NBir NHpl NRHS NRog SDeJ SRms WShi

- 'Violet Beauty'	GKev LAma SDeJ
- 'Zwanenburg'	NRog
greilhuberi	CBor EPPr EPri NDry NRog SGro WCot
hohenackeri	GKev NRog WCot WThu
- BSBE 811	WCot
§ ***hughii***	CBro NRog
hyacinthoides	CMiW ERCP GKev NRog SDir WCot
- 'Blue Arrow'	EPfP GKev LAma LHWs SDir WFar
ingridiae	NRog WCot
italica	see *Hyacinthoides italica*
japonica	see *S. scilloides*
liliohyacinthus	CAvo CBro CToG GKev NRog NWad WCot WShi
- 'Alba'	CAvo
§ ***litardierei*** 🏆H6	EPPr EPot EPri ERCP EWTr GKev LAma NRog SDeJ SPhx WShi
lochiae	NBwr
luciliae misapplied	see *S. forbesii*
luciliae ambig.	EHyd LCro LRHS NRHS NRog SEND
luciliae (Boiss.) Speta 🏆H6	CAvo LCro SDeJ SPer
- 'Alba'	ECha EHyd ETay LHWs LRHS MBros NHpl NRHS NRog SDeJ SPer WHlf
§ - Gigantea Group	GKev LAma NRog
- - 'Alba'	EPot GKev NRog
- 'Rosy Queen'	GKev
lutea hort.	see *Ledebouria socialis*
madeirensis	CHll WCot
melaina	GKev NRog WCot
- 'Vaclav'	NRog
mesopotamica	GKev NRog
messeniaca	GKev NRog
- MS 38 from Greece	WCot
mischtschenkoana 🏆H6	CAby CAvo CRos EHyd EPot EWld LCro LOPS LRHS NRHS SDeJ WShi
§ - 'Tubergeniana' 🏆H6	GKev LAma NRog WCot
monanthos	GKev
monophyllos	GKev NRog WCot
morrisii	GKev NRog
natalensis	see *Merwilla plumbea*
non-scripta	see *Hyacinthoides non-scripta*
nutans	see *Hyacinthoides non-scripta*
obtusifolia subsp. ***intermedia***	WCot
persica 🏆H4	GKev NRog WCot
peruviana	Widely available
- SB&L 20/1	WCot
- 'Alba'	CBro CWCL ECha EPri EWes MPtr NHpl WCot WHlf XLum
- 'Blue Moon'	CDoC CRos EPfP LRHS
- Carribean Jewels Series	MHol
- - 'Sapphire Blue'	MHtn WFar
- 'Hughii'	see *S. hughii*
- var. ***ifniensis***	WCot
- var. ***venusta*** S&L 311/2	WCot
- 'White Moon'	EBee EHed ERCP GKev LAma
'Pink Giant'	CAvo ECha EHyd ELan EPfP EPot ERCP ETay LCro LOPS LRHS MPie NBir NRHS NRog SDeJ WHlf XLum
pratensis	see *S. litardierei*
puschkinioides	GKev NRog
ramburei	GKev
rosenii	CBor GKev NRog
- 'Alba'	NRog
- 'Bakuriani'	NRog
- 'Caucasian Giant'	NRog
- 'Cloudy Sky'	WCot
'Rosiba'	NRog
sardensis 🏆H6	ECha EHyd EPot ERCP GKev LAma LRHS NRHS NRog SDeJ SRms WCot WShi
§ ***scilloides***	EPot GKev
* - 'Alba'	SDeJ
siberica 🏆H6	CAby CRos EHyd ELan EPfP EShb ETay GKev LAma LCro LOPS LRHS NRHS NRog SPer WShi
- 'Alba'	EPot EShb GKev LAma NRog SDeJ WShi
- subsp. ***armena***	GKev NRog
- 'Boreas'	GKev
- 'Enem'	GKev
- 'Spring Beauty'	CAvo CRos EHyd EPot ERCP GKev LAma LRHS NRHS NRog SDeJ SRms
siehei 'Rosea'	GKev NHpl NRog
'Tubergeniana'	see *S. mischtschenkoana* 'Tubergeniana'
'Valentine Day'	EPot
verna	GKev WAbe WShi WThu
vicentina	see *Hyacinthoides vincentina*
violacea	see *Ledebouria socialis*
vvedenskyi	NRog

Scindapsus (*Araceae*)

aureus	see *Epipremnum aureum*
pictus (v)	NHrt
- 'Argyraeus' 🏆H1a	EShb NHrt
- 'Trebie' **new**	NHrt

Scirpus (*Cyperaceae*)

cernuus	see *Isolepis cernua*
'Green Mist'	WCot
lacustris	see *Schoenoplectus lacustris*
- 'Spiralis'	see *Juncus effusus* f. *spiralis*
maritimus	see *Bolboschoenus maritimus*
tabernaemontani	see *Schoenoplectus lacustris* subsp. *tabernaemontani*

Scleranthus (*Caryophyllaceae*)

biflorus	CBor CPla CTrC EDAr EPot EWes GBin GQue LEdu MAsh SPlb WFar XLum
uniflorus	CPla CTrC EPot GArf LEdu NHpl SMad SPlb SRot XLum XSte
- compact	WSFF
- 'Selected Bronze'	ELon

Sclerochiton (*Acanthaceae*)

harveyanus	EShb

Scoliopus (*Liliaceae*)

hallii	GBin GKev MNrw NHar

Scolopendrium see *Asplenium*

Scopolia (*Solanaceae*)

anomala HWJK 2252	WCru
- PAB 4925	LEdu
carniolica	CTtf EAri ECha EPPr EWld GBin GPoy ILea LEdu NChi NLar NSti SBls SPlb WCru WFar WPav WSHC XLum
- from Poland	LEdu
§ - var. ***brevifolia***	CTtf EBee EBlo EHed EHyd EPPr EPfP EWld LEdu LRHS MPie NRHS WCot WPGP WPav
- 'Zwanenburg'	CBor EPPr EWes LEdu NLar WFar XLum
hladnikiana	see *S. carniolica* var. *brevifolia*
stramoniifolia	WPav

Scorzonera (*Asteraceae*)

hispanica 'Long Black Maxima'	SVic

Scorzoneroides (*Asteraceae*)

	autumnalis	CHab NMir

Scrophularia (*Scrophulariaceae*)

	aquatica misapplied	see *S. auriculata*
§	***auriculata***	CHab CPud LPfP NPer WHer
§	- 'Variegata' (v)	CBct ECha EHyd EPfP GLog LBar LPfP LRHS MHer NRHS NSti SGbt SHar SPer
	buergeriana 'Lemon and Lime' misapplied	see *Teucrium viscidum* 'Lemon and Lime'
	calliantha	SBrt SPtp WMal
	macrantha	WHil
	- 'Cardinal Red'	LBar SPad
	nodosa	GPoy NMir WHer
	- variegata	see *S. auriculata* 'Variegata'
	vernalis	CBgR

Scutellaria (*Lamiaceae*)

§	***alpina***	GKev SPlb SRms
	- 'Arcobaleno'	GEdr
	- 'Sapphire'	LRHS
	altissima	ECha EMor GJos GPSL NBro NGrd SBut SPlb WFar XSen
	- pink-flowered **new**	WFar
	baicalensis	CSpe GJos GPoy MGil MHoo
	canescens	see *S. incana*
	costaricana	CCCN
	galericulata	CBod CHab CPud ENfk GPoy LEdu LLWG MBow MHer MHoo NAts SPhx
	hastata	see *S. hastifolia*
§	***hastifolia***	CTri EBou GJos
§	***incana***	CAby CBWd CFis CSpe ECha MAvo SMrm SPhx WCot WSHC WTor
	- white-flowered **new**	SPhx
	indica	GEdr
	- var. ***japonica***	see *S. indica* var. *parvifolia*
§	- var. ***parvifolia***	EBou EWes GEdr GMaP ITim NBir SLee WFar
	- - 'Alba'	SLee WAbe
	integrifolia	CAby SPhx
	laeteviolacea	WAbe
	lateriflora	GJos GPoy MGil SRms
	- PAB 3921	LEdu
	maekawae	EBee
	orientalis	EDAr WAbe
	ovata subsp. ***ovata*** **new**	LBar
	pontica	SPhx XSen
	red-flowered	CCCN
	resinosa 'Smokey Hills' **new**	LBar
	salviifolia **new**	XSen
	scordiifolia	CFis CSpe ECha MACG NRya SBut SHar SRms WCav WFar WJam
	- 'Seoul Sapphire'	GBin LEdu SPtp
	serrata	LPla
	SHERBERT LEMON ('Yascut')	LBar
	suffrutescens	ESgI MHoo XSen
	- 'Texas Rose'	CSpe EDAr EPfP GEdr LBar NHpl SLee SRot WAbe WFar WHoo WIce WTor
	supina	see *S. alpina*
	tournefortii	ECtt EHyd GJos LPla LRHS NRHS
*	***zhongdianensis***	EPPr MAvo MSpe

seakale see *Crambe maritima*

Searsia (*Anacardiaceae*)

§	***incisa***	SPlb

Sebaea (*Gentianaceae*)

	rehmanii	SPlb
	thomasii	GEdr WAbe
	- 'Bychan'	WAbe

Securigera (*Fabaceae*)

§	***varia***	CDor EWld GJos LEdu LRHS MMuc SEND SRms XLum

Sedastrum see *Sedum*

× *Sedeveria* (*Crassulaceae*)

	'Darley Dale'	SEdd
	'Harry Butterfield'	SEdd WCot
	hummellii **new**	EAri SEdd
	- 'Green Rose' **new**	SEdd
	'Letizia'	SEdd

Sedum ✿ (*Crassulaceae*)

	'Abbey Dore'	see *Hylotelephium* 'Abbey Dore'
	acre	CRos CTri EHyd EPfP GPoy GQue LRHS MAsh MNHC NMir NRHS SPlb XLum
	- 'Aureum'	CSBt EDAr ELan MAsh NHpl NLar NRya SLee SPoG SRms SSim WCot WIce WWke XLum
	- 'Elegans'	ECtt
	- 'Golden Queen'	CRos EBou EHyd LRHS NHpl NRHS SPlb SPoG SRms
	- 'Minus'	CRos EHyd LRHS NFav NRHS SRms
§	- subsp. ***neglectum*** var. ***majus***	NLar
	- 'Oktoberfest'	LBar
	adolphi	SEdd
	aizoon	SPlb WFar XLum
	- 'Aurantiacum'	see *S. aizoon* 'Euphorbioides'
§	- 'Euphorbioides'	ECha ECtt LDai LShi MHer MMuc MRav NLar SEND SPlb XSen
§	- subsp. ***maximowiczii***	NWad
	alatum	WFar
	albescens	see *S. forsterianum* f. *purpureum*
	alboroseum	see *Hylotelephium erythrostictum*
§	***album***	CRos EHyd GJos LRHS MMuc NBro NRHS SEND SRms XLum
	- chocolate-leaved	GRum
	- 'Coral Carpet'	CKel EBou ECtt ELan EPPr EPfP GKev MAsh MRav NBwr NHpl NLar NRya SCoo SLee SPoG WFar XLum
	- subsp. ***teretifolium*** var. ***micranthum*** 'Chloroticum'	NFav XLum
§	- - var. ***murale***	CTri EHyd LRHS NHpl NRHS WFar XLum
	alpestre	XLum
	altissimum	see *S. sediforme*
	anacampseros	see *Hylotelephium anacampseros*
	anglicum	SSut
	athoum	see *S. album*
	AUTUMN JOY	see *Hylotelephium* (Herbstfreude Group) 'Herbstfreude'
	batallae ISI 1496	NWad
	beauverdii subsp. ***vietnamense*** HWJ 824	WCru
	'Bertram Anderson'	see *Hylotelephium* 'Bertram Anderson'
	beyrichianum misapplied	see *S. glaucophyllum*
	brevifolium	EWes NHpl
§	- var. ***quinquefarium***	WIce
	burrito	CDoC CPla EShb SIvy
	'Carl'	see *Hylotelephium* 'Carl'

cauticola	see *Hylotelephium cauticola*
clavatum ISI 1161	NWad
compressum	see *S. palmeri* subsp. *palmeri* tetraploid
confusum Hemsl.	SEND SEdd SIvy WMal
crassipes	see *Rhodiola wallichiana*
crassularia	see *Crassula setulosa* 'Milfordiae'
cryptomerioides B&SWJ 054	WCru
dasyphyllum	NBir NHpl NRya SLee SPlb SRms WCot
- subsp. ***dasyphyllum*** 'Lilac Mound'	NFav
dendroideum subsp. ***praealtum***	NWad SChr SEND
divergens	GKev XLum
douglasii	see *S. stenopetalum* 'Douglasii'
'Dudley Field'	EPot
'Eleanor Fisher'	see *Hylotelephium telephium* subsp. *ruprechtii*
ellacombeanum	see *S. kamtschaticum* var. *ellacombeanum*
'Elworthy Rose'	CElw
erythrostictum	see *Hylotelephium erythrostictum*
ewersii	see *Hylotelephium ewersii*
fabaria	see *Hylotelephium telephium* subsp. *fabaria*
fastigiatum	see *Rhodiola fastigiata*
floriferum	see *S. kamtschaticum* var. *floriferum*
forsterianum new	NWad
- subsp. ***elegans***	SEND SPlb XLum
- - 'Silver Stone'	MMuc
§ - f. ***purpureum***	NRya
furfuraceum	NHpl NWad SPlb WAbe
§ ***glaucophyllum***	EDAr XLum
'Gold Mound'	LLWG NHpl SCoo SEdd SPoG
Herbstfreude Group	see *Hylotelephium* Herbstfreude Group
hernandezii	SSim
- FO 199	NWad
heterodontum	see *Rhodiola heterodonta*
hidakanum	see *Hylotelephium pluricaule*
himalense misapplied	see *Rhodiola* 'Keston'
hispanicum	SPlb
- 'Blue Carpet'	EPPr LRHS NHpl SSim WFar
- ***glaucum***	see *S. hispanicum* var. *minus*
§ - var. ***minus***	ECtt MMuc NHpl SEND SPlb WCot
'Honey Gold'	NLar WMal
humifusum	EPot NHpl SPlb WAbe WFar
§ ***hybridum***	XLum
- 'Czar's Gold'	GJos NGdn
'Indian Chief'	see *Hylotelephium* (Herbstfreude Group) 'Herbstfreude'
indicum var. ***yunnanense***	see *Sinocrassula yunnanensis*
integrifolium	see *Rhodiola integrifolia*
'Joyce Henderson'	see *Hylotelephium* 'Joyce Henderson'
kamtschaticum ♀H5	GJos
- B&SWJ 10870	WCru
§ - var. ***ellacombeanum*** ♀H5	CRos EHyd LRHS MAsh MMuc NRHS SEND SRms WCot XLum
- - B&SWJ 8853	WCru
§ - var. ***floriferum***	XSen
§ - - 'Weihenstephaner Gold'	CTri EBou ECtt ELan EPfP GJos GKev GMaP MHer MMuc MRav NBir NSla SLee SPlb SPoG SRms SRot WCav WFar WIce XLum XSen
- var. ***kamtschaticum*** 'Variegatum' (v) ♀H5	CRos EBou EHyd ELan EPfP GAbr LBar LLWG LRHS MHer MMuc NHpl NRHS NSla SLee SPoG SRms SRot SSim SWvt WIce XLum
'Katharine's Gold'	MNrw
lineare	CDoC
- 'Variegatum' (v)	LRHS XLum
'Little Dove'	SGro
'Little Gem'	see × *Cremnosedum* 'Little Gem'
'Little Missy'	see *Crassula pellucida* subsp. *marginalis* 'Variegata'
lucidum new	SEdd
× ***luteoviride***	NWad
§ ***lydium***	CTri EGrI NHpl SLee SPlb
- 'Bronze Queen'	see *S. lydium*
makinoi	SSim
'Manoir de Gaudon'	WCot
'Matrona'	see *Hylotelephium* 'Matrona'
maweanum	see *S. acre* subsp. *neglectum* var. *majus*
maximowiczii	see *S. aizoon* subsp. *maximowiczii*
mendozae	EAri SEdd SSim
middendorffianum	MBrN MHer MMuc SRms SRot XLum
§ ***montanum***	MMuc
moranense	MMuc XLum
morganianum ♀H2	CSBt EShb LCro NCft NMen NWad SIvy
morrisonense B&SWJ 7078	WCru
'Mr Goodbud'	see *Hylotelephium* 'Mr Goodbud'
'Munstead Red'	see *Hylotelephium* 'Munstead Red'
murale	see *S. album* subsp. *teretifolium* var. *murale*
nevii misapplied	see *S. glaucophyllum*
nevii ambig.	SPlb
nicaeense	see *S. sediforme*
niveum	EPot
nussbaumerianum ♀H2	LLWG NWad SEdd SIvy
obtusatum misapplied	see *S. oreganum*
§ ***obtusatum*** A. Gray	NBro NSla
obtusifolium	SGro
- var. ***listoniae***	EDAr MHer
ochroleucum	NWad WCot WFar
- subsp. ***montanum***	see *S. montanum*
oppositifolium	see *S. spurium* 'Album'
§ ***oreganum***	ECha GAbr GKev GMaP LBar MHer NBir NBwr NFav SLee SMad SPlb SRms SRot XLum
- 'Procumbens'	see *S. oreganum* subsp. *tenue*
§ - subsp. ***tenue***	NHol NRya NWad
§ ***oregonense***	CRos EHyd LRHS MHer NRHS WFar
'Oriental Dancer'	see *Hylotelephium* 'Oriental Dancer'
pachyclados	see *Rhodiola pachyclados*
palmeri	EAri EDAr MRav NBir SChr XLum
§ - subsp. ***palmeri*** tetraploid	SEND SIvy
pilosum	GKev WAbe
'Pink Dove'	SGro
pluricaule	see *Hylotelephium pluricaule*
polytrichoides 'Chocolate Ball'	CPla NHpl SLee SSim
populifolium	see *Hylotelephium populifolium*
pulchellum	LBar WFar
quinquefarium	see *S. brevifolium* var. *quinquefarium*
'Red Cauli'	see *Hylotelephium* 'Red Cauli'
'Red Star'	MAvo
reflexum L.	see *S. rupestre* L.
- 'Cristatum'	NHpl NRya SCgs
- red-leaved	GRum NHpl
rhodiola	see *Rhodiola rosea*
rosea	see *Rhodiola rosea*
'Roy Lancaster'	LShi
rubroglaucum misapplied	see *S. oregonense*
rubroglaucum Praeger	see *S. obtusatum* A. Gray
× ***rubrotinctum*** ♀H3	CBod SEND SEdd SIvy SSim

	- 'Aurora' ♀H2	CDoC SIvy
	'Ruby Glow'	see *Hylotelephium* 'Ruby Glow'
§	***rupestre*** L.	CPla EGrl ELan GJos GQue LBar MMuc MNHC NBwr SEND SPlb SRms SRot WFar XLum
	- 'Angelina'	CBod CKno EBou EPPr EWes LRHS MHer NBir NBwr NDov NHol NWad SCoo SLee SPoG SSim WCot WFar WIce WWke XLum
	- 'Aureum'	LShi WFar
	- 'Blue Cushion'	LShi
	- 'Monstrosum Cristatum'	NBir SSut WCot WFar XLum
	- 'Yellow Cushion'	MAvo XSte
	ruprechtii	see *Hylotelephium telephium* subsp. *ruprechtii*
	'Sandra Mottram'	NWad
	sarcocaule hort.	see *Crassula sarcocaulis*
	sarmentosum	XLum
§	***sediforme***	CKel MMuc SEND SRms SSim
	- nicaeense	see *S. sediforme*
§	***sedoides*** var. ***album***	EBou NHpl SCoo SPoG SRms XLum
	selskianum	GJos NLar XLum
	sexangulare	CKel EBou ELon EPfP GJos MHer MMuc NFav NRya SPlb SRms XLum
	- f. ***elatum***	WFar
	- 'Weisse Tatra'	WFar
	sibiricum	see *S. hybridum*
	sieboldii	see *Hylotelephium sieboldii*
	'Silvermoon'	NWad
	spathulifolium	CTri ECha EPot
	- Atropurpureum Group	GQue SRot
	- 'Cape Blanco' ♀H5	Widely available
	- 'Purpureum' ♀H5	CRos CTri CWCL EBou ECtt EDAr EHyd ELan EPfP EPot GAbr GArf GJos GKev GMaP LRHS MHer NHol NHpl NRHS NRya NWad SCoo SLee SPlb SPoG SSim WAbe XLum
	- 'William Pascoe'	EPot
	spectabile	see *Hylotelephium spectabile*
	spinosum	see *Orostachys spinosa*
	spurium	GJos GKev MAsh MMuc SEND SRms WFar XSen
§	- 'Album'	NRya XLum
	- 'Atropurpureum'	ECha XLum
	- 'Coccineum'	GJos GQue MMuc SEND
	- DRAGON'S BLOOD	see *S. spurium* 'Schorbuser Blut'
	- 'Erdblut'	CTri
	- 'Fuldaglut'	CRos CTri EBou ECtt EGrl EHyd EPPr LRHS MNrw NRHS NRya SMrm SRms
	- 'Green Mantle'	ECha
	- 'John Creech'	ECtt
	- PURPLE CARPET	see *S. spurium* 'Purpurteppich'
	- 'Purpureum'	NBwr SLee SRms
§	- 'Purpurteppich'	ECtt MRav NBro NLar NWad SRms SVen
	- 'Roseum'	SRms
	- 'Ruby Mantle'	GKev GMcL NBro NEoE SPoG SRms SWvt XLum
§	- 'Schorbuser Blut' ♀H5	CGBo CRos CSBt ECha ECtt EHyd ELan EPPr EPfP GKev LLWG LRHS LSto MBow MCot NBir NBwr NRHS NRya NSla SEdd SLee SPlb SRms SRot SSim WFar WHoo WIce XLum
I	- 'Splendens Roseum'	XLum
	- 'Summer Glory'	NLar
§	- 'Tricolor' (v)	CTri EBou ECha EDAr EPfP GEdr GKev LBar LShi MHer MRav NHol NRya NWad SIvy SLee SPlb SPoG SRot SSim XLum
	- 'Variegatum'	see *S. spurium* 'Tricolor'
	- 'Voodoo'	CPla CWCL EBou EPfP EWes LBar LShi MHer NBro NDov NGdn XLum
	stahlii	SIvy WOld
	stefco	XLum
	stenopetalum	SPlb
§	- 'Douglasii'	MHer SRms
	'Stewed Rhubarb Mountain'	see *Hylotelephium* 'Stewed Rhubarb Mountain'
	stribrnyi	see *S. urvillei* Stribrnyi Group
	suaveolens **new**	SEdd
	subtile PB 08-639	GGro
	takesimense	NBir XLum
	- B&SWJ 8493	WCru
	- B&SWJ 8518	WCru
	- ATLANTIS ('Nonsitnal') (v) **new**	LBar LCro MBel WCot WHlf
	tatarinowii	see *Hylotelephium tatarinowii*
	telephium	see *Hylotelephium telephium*
	ternatum	EDAr MHer
	tetractinum 'Coral Reef'	NBir SRms XLum
	trollii	see *Rhodiola saxifragoides*
	urvillei Sartorianum Group	XLum
§	- Stribrnyi Group	XLum
	ussuriense	see *Hylotelephium ussuriense*
	valens	SPlb
	'Vera Jameson'	see *Hylotelephium* 'Vera Jameson'
	verticillatum	see *Hylotelephium verticillatum*
	viviparum	see *Hylotelephium viviparum*
	'Washfield Purple'	see *Hylotelephium telephium* (Atropurpureum Group) 'Purple Emperor'
	'Weihenstephaner Gold'	see *S. kamtschaticum* var. *floriferum* 'Weihenstephaner Gold'
	weinbergii	see *Graptopetalum paraguayense*
	yezoense	see *Hylotelephium pluricaule*
	yunnanense	see *Rhodiola yunnanensis*

Seemannia (*Gesneriaceae*)

§	***gymnostoma*** **new**	WFar
§	***nematanthodes***	SBrt
	- 'Evita'	EShb WCot WFar
§	***sylvatica***	EShb WFar
	- PB 12-738 **new**	WFar
	- 'Bolivian Sunset'	WDib

Selaginella (*Selaginellaceae*)

braunii	WCot
helvetica	EBee WSHC XLum
kraussiana ♀H2	CBrP CKel CTsd ESwi GArf ISha
- 'Aurea'	CCCN EHyd ELan ISha LRHS MAsh NRHS
- 'Brownii' ♀H2	CCCN
- 'Gold Tips'	CBod CCCN EHed EHyd ELan ESwi GGro LRHS MAsh NRHS
lepidophylla	GKev ISha LAma SVic
martensii 'Jori' (v)	WCot
moellendorfii	EHyd LPal LRHS NRHS
uncinata ♀H1b	EHyd NRHS

Selenicereus (*Cactaceae*)

grandiflorus **new**	EAri
validus **new**	NPlm

Selinum (*Apiaceae*)

CC 6869	GGro MSpe
KWJ 12281 from northern Vietnam	WCru
alatum	WCru
candollei HWJK 2329	WCru
carvifolium	CCBP CExl CMac ELan EMor GElm LDai LEdu LLWG MHol MNrw NLar SEdd SPtp WCot

- HWJK 2347	ESwi WCru
- PAB 2676	LEdu
cryptotaenium	ELan
- FMWJ 13250	SPtp WCru
- PAB 8948	LEdu
filicifolium	EBee LLWG MHol MNrw SMad WCot
tenuifolium	see *S. wallichianum*
§ ***wallichianum*** ♀H6	Widely available
- CC 6869	GKev
- EMAK 886	EBee
- HPA 1389	GGro
- HWJK 2347	WCru
- PAB 3579	LEdu WPGP
- PAB 8969	LEdu WPGP
- WJC 13656 from Sikkim	WCru
- from Bhutan	WPGP
- from Manipur	WPGP
- from Nagaland, India	WPGP

Selliera (*Goodeniaceae*)

radicans	GAbr LShi

Semele (*Asparagaceae*)

androgyna	CRHN EShb WCot

Semiaquilegia (*Ranunculaceae*)

§ ***adoxoides***	GGro GKev
- double-flowered (d)	GKev
- white/cream-flowered (mixed) **new**	CBor
§ ***ecalcarata*** ♀H5	CDor CSpe EBee EMor EWld GArf GKev LDai MNrw NGdn NHpl SBut SRms
'Moody Blues'	CBor WFar
simulatrix	see *S. ecalcarata*
'Sugar Plum Fairy'	CBor CRos EHyd EPfP LRHS LSto NRHS SPoG WFar
'Tinkerbell'	CBor WFar

Semiarundinaria (*Poaceae*)

§ ***fastuosa*** ♀H6	CBcs CJun EPfP LPal LPar MAsh MMuc MWht SArc SBGi SEND SPlb
- var. ***viridis***	MWht WCru
kagamiana	EPfP MMuc MWht
§ ***lubrica***	MWht
makinoi	MWht
nitida	see *Fargesia nitida*
§ ***okuboi***	CBdn MWht
villosa	see *S. okuboi*
yamadorii	MWht
yashadake	MWht
- f. ***kimmei***	CBod CRos EHyd EPfP GMcL LPal LRHS MAsh MMuc MWht NLar NRHS SEND SPoG WHlf

Semnanthe see *Erepsia*

Sempervivella see *Rosularia*

Sempervivum ✿ (*Crassulaceae*)

'Aaroundina'	NMen
'Abba'	NMen
'Abbe'	NMen
'Achalm'	NMen
acuminatum	see *S. tectorum* var. *glaucum*
'Adamina'	NMen SSem
'Adelaar'	NMen
'Adelmoed'	NMen
'Ageet'	NMen
§ 'Aglow'	CBod LBar LCro WHil
'Aida'	NMen
'Aladdin'	NMen SRms
'Albertine' **new**	NMen
'Alchimist'	NMen SSim XLum
'Aldo Moro'	NMen WIce XLum
'Alenco'	NMen
'Alesia'	NMen
'Alfons-Roelands'	NMen
'Aline'	NMen
allionii	see *Jovibarba allionii*
'Alluring'	NMen
'Almaros' **new**	NMen
'Alpha'	NMen SRms XLum
altum	CRos EHyd LRHS NRHS SPlb SRms XLum
'Amanda'	MBrN NMen SRms WHoo
'Ambergreen'	NMen
'Americanos'	NMen
'Andinn Tunrida'	NMen
andreanum	see *S. tectorum* var. *alpinum*
'Andrenor'	NMen
'Andrenor' sport	NMen
'Antiquity'	WFar
'Apache' Haberer	NMen
'Apanatschi'	NMen
'Apollo'	XLum
'Apollo's Frog'	NMen
'Apple Blossom'	NMen
APPLETINI (Chick Charms Series)	see *S.* 'Reinhard'
'Apricot'	NMen
'Aqua'	NMen
arachnoideum ♀H7	Widely available
- from the Abruzzi, Italy	NMen SLee
- from Zermatt, Switzerland	XLum
- 'Ararat'	SDys
- var. ***bryoides***	CRos EHyd LRHS NRHS SRms SSem WFar
- 'Clärchen'	EDAr MSCN NMen WAbe XLum
- CORAL RED ('Belsemred1'PBR) **new**	LCro
- cristate	XLum
* - ***densum***	EDAr EPPr SSem WAbe
- subsp. ***doellianum***	see *S. arachnoideum* subsp. *tomentosum* var. *glabrescens*
§ - 'Emily' **new**	LCro
- giant	WFar
- 'Laggeri'	see *S. arachnoideum* subsp. *tomentosum* (C.B. Lehm. & Schnittsp.) Schinz & Thell.
- 'Opitz'	SRms
- 'Peña Prieta'	XLum
- 'Piletina'	WFar
- 'Red Papaver'	EPot EShb LRHS
- 'Red Wings'	NMen XLum
- 'Rheinkiesel'	XLum
- 'Rubin'	CGBo MCot NHpl SSim WFar
- 'Rubrum'	CDoC CRos EBou EWoo GKev GMaP LRHS NRHS SPlb SSem WFar XLum
- 'Spider's Nest'	WFar
- 'Spider's Web'	WFar
- subsp. ***tomentosum*** misapplied	see *S. × barbulatum* 'Hookeri'
- subsp. ***tomentosum*** ambig.	EBou EPot EWoo XLum
§ - subsp. ***tomentosum*** (C.B. Lehm. & Schnittsp.) Schinz & Thell. ♀H7	CRos EDAr EHyd EPot NFav NPer NRHS NSla NWad SPlb SRms SSem WAbe
§ - - var. ***glabrescens***	SDys XLum
- - 'Minor'	EDAr SSim WFar
- - 'Minus'	EPfP LRHS
§ - - 'Stansfieldii'	CRos EHyd EPPr LRHS NRHS SLee SRms WFar
- 'Web Cluster'	WFar
- 'Whisper' **new**	EDAr

§	- 'White Christmas'	MHer NMen
	arachnoideum* × *montanum	see *S.* × *barbulatum*
	arachnoideum* × *nevadense	SDys
	arachnoideum* × *pittonii	NMen SRms WAbe
	arenarium	see *Jovibarba arenaria*
	'Argus Eye'	NMen
	'Arondina'	NMen
	'Arrowheads Red'	NMen
	'Artist'	NMen
	'Ashes of Roses'	EGrI MSCN NHol NMen XLum
	'Astrid'	NMen
	'Athen'	NMen
	'Atlantic'	SRms
	atlanticum	MMuc NMen SLee SSem
	- from Oukaïmeden, Morocco	NMen SRms
	- 'Edward Balls'	NMen SDys SRms WFar
	'Atlantis' ambig.	NFav NMen SRms
	'Atropurpureum' ambig.	EGrI EPot MBrN NMen WFar
	'Attraction'	NMen
	'Aureum'	see *Greenovia aurea*
	'Averil'	NMen
	'Babette'	NMen
	'Baby Skrocki'	NMen
	balcanicum	NMen SRms XLum
	ballsii	CRos EHyd LRHS NMen NRHS SRms
	- from Smólikas, Greece	NMen
	- from Tschumba Petzi, Greece	SDys XLum
	'Banderi'	NMen
	'Bandi'	NMen
	'Banjo'	NMen
	'Banyan'	CRos EHyd LRHS NRHS SRms SSem
§	× ***barbulatum***	SDys
§	- 'Hookeri'	CTri EDAr GKev NMen NSla SSim WAbe WHoo XLum
	'Baronesse'	NMen
	'Bascour Zilver'	SRms
	'Be Mine'	MSCN
I	'Beate' G. Dillmann	NMen
	'Beatles Memory'	NMen
	'Beaute'	NMen
	'Beautiful'	NMen
	'Bedazzled'	NMen
	'Bedivere'	NMen SRms
	'Bedivere Crested'	NMen
*	'Bedley Hi'	NMen
	'Begbroke' **new**	EDAr
	'Bella Donna'	NMen
	'Bella Meade'	NMen SRms
	'Bellotts Pourpre'	NMen
	'Benala'	NMen
	'Bennerbroek'	NMen
	'Berello' **new**	EDAr
	'Bernstein'	EDAr EPPr GKev MHer NMen NWad SLee WIce XLum
	Berry Blues (Chick Charms Series)	see *S.* 'Pacific Blue Ice'
	'Beta'	NMen WAbe XLum
	'Bethany'	NWad
	'Bianca'	NMen
	'Big Blue'	SSem
	'Bijou'	NMen
	Bing Cherry (Chick Charms Series)	see *S.* 'Aglow'
	'Birchmaier'	NMen
	'Bitter Chocolate'	NMen
	'Björn'	NMen
	'Black Beauty'	EBou EPot NMen
	'Black Cap'	NMen
	'Black Knight'	CRos EHyd LRHS MHer NRHS SPlb SRms SSem WHoo
	'Black Mini'	GKev NBir NMen SLee SRms
	'Black Mountain'	EMul GKev NMen
	'Black Rose'	NMen
	'Black Velvet'	NMen
	'Black Widow'	NMen
	'Blade of Steel'	NMen
	'Blauer Ritter'	NMen
	'Blood Tip'	CRos EHyd EWoo GKev LRHS LSun MHer NHol NMen NRHS NRya NWad SEND SPlb SPoG SRms WFar
	'Bloody Goose'	NMen
	'Bloody Mary'	NMen
	'Blue Angel'	NMen
	'Blue Bird'	NMen
	'Blue Boy'	CRos EBou EHyd EPPr EWoo LRHS MSCN NMen NRHS SCoo SPlb SPoG SRms SSem WFar
	'Blue Knight'	NMen
	'Blue Lady'	NMen
	'Blue Moon'	NMen SSem
	'Blue Time'	WFar WHoo XLum
	'Blush'	NMen
	'Blushes'	SSem
	'Boissieri'	see *S. tectorum* subsp. *tectorum* 'Boissieri'
	'Bokkenrijders'	NMen
	'Bold Chick'	NMen
	'Booth's Red'	NMen
	borisii	see *S. ciliosum* var. *borisii*
	borissovae	EPot NMen SDys
	'Boromir'	NMen XLum
	'Boule de Neige'	EPot NMen NRya WFar
	'Bowles's Variety'	NMen
I	'Braunella'	NMen
	'Brilland Red Brun'	NMen
	'Britta'	NMen SDys
	'Brock'	CRos EHyd LRHS NRHS SRms SSem
	'Bronco' ♀H5	CRos EBou EGrI EHyd EPfP GBin LRHS MMuc NHol NMen NRHS NRya NWad SEND SLee SRms SRot SSem SSim WBrk WCot WFar WPGP XLum
	'Bronze Pastel'	NHpl NMen NSla SRms SSem
	'Brown Owl'	EBou EDAr NMen SRms SSem
	'Brownii'	NMen
	'Brunhilde'	NMen
	bungeanum hort.	NMen
	'Burgundy'	NMen
	'Burning Bush'	WFar
	'Burning Desire'	NMen
	'Burnished Bronze'	NMen
	'Burnt Embers'	NMen
	'Butterbur'	NMen
	'Butterfly'	NMen
	'Butterpat' **new**	NMen
	'Café'	MSCN NHol NMen NSla SRms
*	***calabricum***	NHol
	calcareum	CRos EBou EHyd EPot GKev GQue LRHS MCot MMuc MPnt NBro NHol NHpl NMen NRHS SArc SCoo SEND SEdd SGro SPlb SPoG SRms SSem SSim WFar XLum
	- GDJ 92.16 from Petite Ceüse, France	SRms
	- from Cleizé, France	see *S. calcareum* 'Limelight'
	- from Col Bayard, France	NMen
	- from Colle St Michel, France	SRms
	- from Queyras, France	NMen
	- from Triora, Italy	EMul NMen

- 'Atropurpureum'	CCal
- 'Benz'	SDys
- 'Button'	WFar
- 'Extra' ♀H5	CCal EDAr EWes MSCN NMen SRms SSem WFar
- 'Greenii'	CRos EHyd LRHS MSCN NMen NRHS SPlb SRms
§ - 'Grigg's Surprise'	NMen SPlb
- 'Guillaumes' ♀H5	CRos EHyd LRHS NMen NRHS SRms SSem SSim WHoo
§ - 'Limelight'	CRos EHyd LRHS NMen NRHS SLee SSem WHoo
- 'Monstrosum'	see *S. calcareum* 'Grigg's Surprise'
§ - 'Mrs Giuseppi'	EGrI EWoo GAbr LBar LCro LSun NHpl NMen SEdd SGro SRms SSem WAbe WFar WIce XLum
- 'Nigricans'	EDAr NMen
- 'Pink Pearl'	MSCN NMen SDys SPlb XLum
- 'Sir William Lawrence' ♀H5	CCal CRos EBou EDAr EGrI EHyd LRHS NMen NRHS SGro SLee SRms SRot SSem WAbe XLum
'Cameo'	see *Jovibarba heuffelii* var. *glabra* 'Cameo'
'Campagha'	NMen
'Canada Kate'	NMen
'Cancer'	XLum
'Candy Floss'	NMen
cantabricum	MMuc NMen WFar XLum
- from Navafria, Spain	NMen
- from Ticeros	XLum
- from Valvanera, Spain	NMen
- subsp. ***guadarramense***	see *S. vicentei* subsp. *paui*
- - from Pico del Lobo, Spain, No 1	SRms
- subsp. ***urbionense***	SRms
'Cantal' **new**	NMen
'Caramel'	NMen
'Carlo's II'	NMen
'Carmen'	NMen
'Carneum'	NMen
'Carnival'	NMen
'Casablanca'	NMen
'Caspara'	NMen
caucasicum	CRos EHyd LRHS NMen NRHS SRms XLum
'Cavo Doro'	NMen
'Celon'	NMen
'Centaurus'	WHlf
'Centennial'	NMen SSem
charadzeae	XLum
CHERRY BERRY (Chick Charms Series)	see *S.* 'Rocknoll Rosette'
'Cherry Dream'	EDAr NMen SSem
'Cherry Frost'	NHol NMen XLum
'Cherry Glow'	see *Jovibarba heuffelii* 'Cherry Glow'
'Cherry Tart'	NMen SPlb SSem
'Chilli Pepper'	MSCN
'Chivalry'	NMen
'Cho'	NMen
'Chocolate'	NHpl WAbe
CHOCOLATE KISS (Chick Charms Series)	see *S.* 'Pacific Devils Food'
'Choctaw'	NMen
'Cholie'	GKev NMen
'Christmas Time'	NMen
chrysanthum	EDAr SSim
ciliosum ♀H7	EDAr NRya SPlb SRms
- from Alí Butús, Bulgaria	SDys
§ - var. ***borisii***	EPPr GKev NRya SSem WAbe WFar
- var. ***borisii*** × ***ciliosum*** var. ***ciliosum***	CTri
- subsp. ***octopodes***	NMen
'Cindy'	SRms

CINNAMON STARBURST (Chick Charms Series)	see *S.* 'Jeanne d'Arc'
'Claey's Fluweel'	NMen
'Clara Noyes'	NMen
'Clare'	MHer NMen
'Classic Rock'	NMen
'Clemanum'	NMen
'Cleveland Morgan'	XLum
'Climax' ambig.	EPfP WFar
'Climax' Ford	NMen
'Cobweb Capers'	NMen
'Cobweb Centres'	EWes NMen
'Colchicum'	SRms
'Collecteur Anchisi'	SDys
'Commander Hay'	CTri EWes GKev GMaP MSCN NHpl NMen NPer NRya SRms XLum
'Comte de Congae'	NMen
'Congo'	NMen XLum
'Cono' **new**	NMen
'Corio'	NMen
'Corona'	NMen
'Coronet'	NMen
'Corsair'	EPPr GKev MBrN MMuc NMen SRms SSem WBrk WFar
COSMIC CANDY (Chick Charms Series)	see *S.* 'Urmina'
COTTON CANDY (Chick Charms Series)	see *S. arachnoideum* 'Emily'
CRANBERRY COCKTAIL (Chick Charms Series)	see *S.* 'Killer'
'Cream Tea'	NMen
'Crimson Velvet'	NMen XLum
'Crimson Webb'	WFar
'Cripello'	NMen
§ 'Crispyn' ♀H5	CCal CRos EHyd EPot LRHS MMuc MSCN NMen NRHS SEND SRms SSem WFar
'Crows'	NMen
'Crucify'	NMen
'Cupream'	NMen SRms
'Cyclops'	NMen
'Dakota'	NMen
'Dallas'	NMen SRms
'Damask'	EMul MSCN NMen
'Dancer's Veil'	NMen
'Danji'	NMen
'Darjeeling'	NMen
'Dark Beauty'	CRos EHyd LRHS NHol NRHS NSla SRms SSem WAbe WCAu WCot
'Dark Cloud'	NMen WHoo XLum
'Dark Point'	NMen
'De Kardijk'	NMen
'Deep Fire'	NMen SRms SSem
× ***degenianum***	NMen XLum
'Delta' ♀H5	NMen WHoo
densum	see *S. tectorum*
'Desert Dream'	WFar
'Devil's Teeth'	MSCN
'Devil's Touch'	SSem
'Devon Glow'	MSCN
'Dippy Dame'	NMen
'Dipsy' **new**	NMen
'Director Jacobs'	NHpl NMen
'Direktor General'	NMen
'Disney Festival' **new**	WFar
'Doeskin'	SSem
'Dolfien'	NMen
'Dolle Dina's'	NMen
dolomiticum	NMen XLum
dolomiticum × ***montanum***	NBro NMen
'Donarrose'	NMen
'Donnerlüttchen'	NMen SSem

'Dornröschen'	NMen
'Downland Queen'	NMen
'Dr Fritz Köhlein'	NMen SSem
'Dragoness'	NMen SSem
'Dream Catcher'	NMen
'Dune'	NMen
'Dusty' **new**	EDAr
'Dyke'	CTri NMen
dzhavachischvilii	NMen XLum
'Edge of Night'	SRms
'Edwardine'	NMen
'Edwina'	SSem
'Eefje'	NMen
'Eisbär'	SSem
'El Greco'	NMen
'El Misti' **new**	NMen
'El Toro'	NHpl NMen SSem
'Electra'	SSem
'Elene'	MPnt
'Elgar'	NMen
'Elva'	NMen
'Elvis'	EMul NMen SLee
'Emerald Empress'	NMen
'Emerald Giant'	SRms
'Emerald Haze'	WFar
'Emerald Lustre'	WFar
'Emerson's Giant'	NMen SRms
'Emmchen'	NMen
'Engle's'	CRos CTri EHyd GKev LRHS MMuc NMen NRHS SEND SPlb SRms SSem WFar
'Engle's 13-2'	NMen
'Engle's Rubrum'	NMen NRya
'Eos'	NMen
'Erdbeermond'	NMen
erythraeum	CRos EHyd LRHS NHpl NMen NRHS SPlb SRms SSem
- from Mesta Valley, Bulgaria	NMen
'Essence of Lime'	NMen
'Euphemia'	NMen
'Evening Glow'	NMen
'Excalibur'	NMen
'Exhibita'	SDys SRms
'Exorna'	NMen SSem
'Eyjafjalla'	SSem
'Fair Lady'	NMen
'Fairy'	NMen
'Fame'	NMen SPlb
'Famke'	SSem
'Faramir'	NMen
'Farida'	NMen
§ 'Fashion Diva' **new**	LCro
'Fat Jack'	NMen
× ***fauconnetii***	LRHS NMen
- 'Rubellum'	EDAr NMen
- 'Thompsonii'	SRms
'Feldmaier'	NMen WFar
'Fernanda'	NMen
'Fernwood'	NMen
'Fernzünder'	SSem
'Festival'	NMen
'Fiery Furness'	NMen
'Fiesta' ambig.	NMen
'Fifty One Shades'	WFar
× ***fimbriatum*** 'Joy of Life'	SSem SSim
'Finerpointe'	NMen
'Fire Flies'	NMen
'Fire Glint'	EMul NMen SRms WFar
'Firebird'	NMen
'Firgrove Early Riser'	NMen
'Firlefanz'	SSem
'First Try'	NMen
flagelliforme	XLum

'Flaming Heart'	MBrN NMen
'Flaming Sword'	NMen
'Flaming Web'	WFar
'Flamingo'	NMen
'Flanders Passion'	EWes NMen SRms SSem
'Flasher'	NMen SSem SSim
'Fluweel'	NMen
'Forden'	NMen
'Ford's Amiability'	SDys
'Ford's Giant'	XLum
'Ford's Shadows'	SDys
'Ford's Spring'	EDAr NMen SRms SSem
'Foxy Lady' **new**	NMen
'Freckles'	NMen
'Fronika'	NMen
'Frosty'	NMen SRms
'Fuego' ♀H5	CCal CRos EHyd LRHS NMen NRHS SRms SSem
'Fuji'	NMen
× ***funckii***	EGrI MBrN NMen XLum
'Fuzzy Wuzzy'	NMen
'Gabrielle'	SSem
'Galadriel'	SSem
'Galahad'	NMen
'Galaxis'	NMen
'Galifa'	SSem
'Gallivarda' ♀H5	CRos EHyd LRHS NMen NRHS
'Gambol'	NWad
'Gamma'	NMen SRms
'Gangster' **new**	NMen
'Gargamel'	SSem
'Garnet'	NMen
'Gay Jester'	CTri NMen SLee WHoo
'Gazelle'	XLum
'Georgette'	NMen XLum
'Georgia Rowan'	NMen
'Ginger Nut'	NMen
'Ginnie's Delight'	NMen
'Gipsy'	NMen
giuseppii ♀H7	CRos EHyd GKev LRHS NRHS SRms
- from Peña Espigüete, Spain	SDys SRms
'Gizmo'	NMen
'Glaucum'	see *S. tectorum* var. *glaucum*
'Glaucum Minor'	NMen
globiferum subsp. ***globiferum*** 'Minor'	XLum
'Gloriosum' ambig.	NMen
'Glowing Embers'	NMen XLum
'Glückskinder'	NMen
'Godaert'	MMuc SEND XLum
'Gog'	NMen
'Gold Nugget' (Chick Charms Series) **new**	CBod LBar LCro WHil
'Golden Valley' **new**	NMen
'Goldie'	NMen
'Goldmarie'	NMen SSem
'Goldschatz'	NMen
'Goovy'	NMen
'Granada'	NMen
'Granat'	MHer NMen SRms XLum
'Granby'	SDys
'Grand Mère'	NMen
grandiflorum	NMen WThu XLum
- 'Fasciatum'	NMen
'Grannie's Favourite'	NMen
'Grapetone'	NMen SDys
'Gratiana'	NMen
'Graupurpur'	XLum
'Green Apple'	NMen SDys
'Green Caro'	NMen
'Green Disk'	SRms

	'Green Dragon'	CRos EGrI EHyd EWoo LRHS MSCN NMen NRHS SRms
	'Green Ice'	NMen SLee SSem
	'Green Wheel'	NMen
	'Greenwich Time'	EDAr NMen
*	***greigii***	MSCN
	'Grey Dawn'	CRos EHyd LRHS NMen NRHS SRms XLum
	'Grey Ghost'	NMen SSem SSim
	'Grey Lady'	NMen
	'Grey Owl'	CRos EHyd EWoo LRHS NMen NRHS SRms WFar
	'Grey Velvet'	NMen
	'Greyfriars'	CRos EHyd EWoo LRHS NMen NRHS SRms SSem
	'Greyolla'	NMen
	'Grünschnabel'	XLum
	'Grunspur'	NMen
	'Gulle Dame'	NMen SRms
	'Gummibärchen'	NMen
	'Gwendolyn' **new**	NMen
	'Gwiazda'	GBin WFar
	'Halley'	NMen
I	'Hall's Hybrid'	MSCN NBro NMen SRms
	'Happy'	EMul NMen SLee SRms SSem
	'Harriet'	NMen
	'Hart'	NMen SSem
	'Havana'	NMen
	'Havendijker Splitt'	NMen
	'Havendijker Teufel'	SSem
	'Havendijks Black' **new**	NMen
	'Havendijks Millenium'	NMen
	'Havendijks Perfection' **new**	NMen
	'Havendijks Pride'	NMen
	'Hayling'	EDAr EHyd EWes NMen NRHS NWad SRms SSem SSim WFar XLum
	'Haynaldii'	NMen
	'Heigham Red'	CRos EBou EHyd EMul GKev LRHS NMen NRHS SRms SSem WFar WIce
	'Heike'	NMen
	'Heiko'	NMen
	'Helen'	NMen WFar
	'Heliotroop'	NMen SDys
	helveticum	see *S. montanum*
	'Hermann Näpfel'	NMen
	'Hermine'	NMen
	'Hester'	MBrN NBro NMen
	'Hey-hey'	CRos EGrI EHyd LRHS MBrN NMen NRHS SEdd SPlb SSem WCot XLum
	'Hidde'	EGrI NMen SPlb
	'Highland Mist'	NMen
	'Hirsutum'	see *Jovibarba allionii*
	hirtum	see *Jovibarba hirta*
	'Honigmond'	NMen SSem SSim
	'Honymoon'	NMen
	'Hookeri'	see *S. × barbulatum* 'Hookeri'
	'Hopi'	NMen
	'Hortulanus Smit'	XLum
	'Hot Boyz'	NMen
	'Hot Peppermint'	NMen
	'Hualalāi'	NMen
	'Hula Girl' **new**	NMen
	'Hullabaloo'	NMen
	'Hurricane'	EMul NMen
	'Icicle'	CRos EHyd LRHS MSCN NBro NHol NMen NRHS SRms
	imbricatum	see *S. × barbulatum*
	'Impact'	NMen
	'Imperial'	NMen SPlb
	'Ingemarie'	NMen
	ingwersenii	NMen XLum
	ingwersenii × pumilum	NMen SRms
	'Intensity' **new**	NMen
	'Irazu'	CRos EDAr EHyd EPot LRHS MSCN NMen NRHS SDys SRms SSem WHoo
	'Isaac Dyson'	SDys SLee SRot SSem
	'Isabelle'	NMen
	italicum	XLum
	'Itchen'	NMen
	'Ivonne'	NMen
	'Iwo'	NMen
	'Jack Frost'	NBro NMen XLum
	'Jacquette'	NMen
	'Jade' ambig.	NMen
	'Jadestern'	NMen
I	'Janus'	NMen
§	'Jeanne d'Arc' **new**	LCro
	'Jelly Bean'	NMen
	'Jet Stream' 🏆H5	CRos EHyd LRHS NMen NRHS SDys SPlb SRms SSem WFar
	'Jewel Case'	CRos EHyd LRHS NRHS SRms
	'Jim Knopf'	NMen
I	'John Hobbs seedling No. 2'	NMen
	'John T' × 'Saffron'	NMen
	'Joke'	NMen
	'Jolly Green Giant'	NMen
	'Jo's Spark'	NMen
	'Jubilee'	ELan MAsh MHer NMen SRms XLum
	'Jubilee Tricolor'	NBwr NHol NMen SPlb SSim WAbe WFar
	'Jungle Fires'	CCal SDys SRms WHoo
	'Jungle Shadows'	NMen NWad XLum
	'Jupiter'	GKev XLum
	'Jurrina'	NMen
	'Justine's Choice'	NMen SRms
	'Kai'	NMen
	'Kappa'	EDAr NBro NMen SDys
	'Karin'	NMen SSem
	'Katmai'	NMen NSla
	'Kautangel' **new**	NMen
	'Keder'	NMen
	'Keiko'	NMen
	'Kelly Jo'	EWoo WBrk
	'Kermit'	NMen
	KEY LIME KISS (Chick Charm Series)	see *Jovibarba allionii*
	'Khaleesi'	WFar
	'Kiara'	NMen
	'Kibo'	NMen
	'Kidlington'	NMen
	'Kildare'	NMen
§	'Killer' **new**	LCro NMen
	'Kim'	NMen
	'Kimba'	NMen
	'Kimble'	NMen
	'Kimono'	NMen NWad
	kindingeri	NMen SRms XLum
	'King Alfred' **new**	NMen
	'King George'	CTri EBou EDAr GKev MMuc NMen SEND SRms WHoo XLum
	'King Lear'	NMen
	'Kip'	NMen
	'Kismet'	NMen
	'Kohala'	SSem
	'Koko Flanel'	CCal NMen SRms SSem
	'Korspel Beauty'	NMen
	'Korspel Cherry'	NMen
	'Korspel Prince'	NMen
	'Korspel Sport'	NMen
	'Korspelsegietje'	NMen SRms
	kosaninii	NMen
	– from Koprivnik, Slovenia	MSCN WAbe XLum

	- 'Hepworth'	EDAr SPlb
	'Kramer's Spinrad'	EPPr GKev NMen SPlb SRms WFar WHoo WThu
	'Krankii'	XLum
	'Krater'	NMen
	'Lady Di'	NMen
	'Lamia'	NMen
	'Lancer'	NMen
	'Landemine'	NMen SSem
	'Latex'	SSem
	'Laura Lee'	MMuc NMen SEND
	'Lavender and Old Lace'	CRos EHyd LRHS MSCN NMen NRHS SPlb SRms SSem WFar WIce XLum
	'Lavenderspross'	NMen
	'Le Congai'	NMen
	'Legolas'	NMen
	'Lemon Babies' **new**	NMen
	'Leneca'	NMen
	'Lennik's Glory'	see *S.* 'Crispyn'
	'Lennik's Sport'	XLum
	'Lentezon'	NMen
	'Leocadia's Nephew'	NMen
	'Leopold'	SSem
	leucanthum	EDAr XLum
	'Lilac Queen'	NMen
	'Lilac Time' ♀H5	CCal CRos EHyd EPPr LRHS MBrN MHer MSCN NMen NRHS SPlb SRms SSem WFar XLum
	'Lilehammer'	NMen
	'Limbo'	NMen
	'Limburg'	NMen
	'Lion King'	CCal MSCN NMen
	'Lioness'	NMen
	'Lipari'	LRHS SRms WCot XLum
	'Lipstick'	GQue NMen
	'Little Fiirt'	MSCN
	'Little Rock'	NMen
	'Lively Bug'	CRos EHyd EPPr EPot LRHS MSCN NMen NRHS SDys SLee SRms SSem XLum
	'Lloyd Praeger'	see *S. montanum* subsp. *stiriacum* 'Lloyd Praeger'
	'Long Shanks'	MSCN
	'Lonzo'	NMen SRms
	'Lord Alan'	GKev NMen
	'Lord Morton'	NMen
	'Lovely Roset'	NMen
	'Lucy Liu'	NMen SSem
	'Ludmila'	NMen
	'Luftsprung'	NMen
	'Lumeseen'	NMen
	'Luminosity' **new**	NMen
	'Lynn's Choice'	NMen NWad
	'Lyra'	NMen
	macedonicum	NMen SPlb SRms XLum
	'Magic Morning'	SSem
	'Magic Spell'	NMen
	'Magical'	NMen
	'Magnificum'	NMen XLum
	'Mahogany'	CTri EGrI GKev MHer MSCN NHol NMen NRya SRms XLum
	'Mai Appel'	NMen
	'Maia'	SSim
	'Maigret'	NMen SSem
	'Majanka'	NMen
	'Majestic'	NMen
	'Malby's Hybrid'	see *S.* 'Reginald Malby'
	'Manhattan' **new**	NMen
	'Maria Laach'	NMen
	'Marijntje'	NMen
	'Mariska'	NMen
	'Marjory'	NMen
	'Marland Ruby'	NMen WCot
	'Marmalade'	NMen
§	***marmoreum***	EHyd NMen NRHS SRms
	- from Börzöny, Hungary	XLum
	- from Kanzan Gorge, Bulgaria	XLum
	- from Okol, Albania	NMen
	- 'Brunneifolium'	XLum
	- subsp. ***marmoreum*** var. ***dinaricum***	MHer NMen
§	- - 'Rubrifolium'	XLum
	'Marshall'	NMen
	'Marsupilami'	NMen
	'Mary-Beth'	NMen
	'Matthew's Day Dream'	GKev NMen SSim
	'Mauvine'	NWad XLum
	'Mavina' **new**	NMen
	'May Red'	NMen
	'Mayfair'	NMen
	'Maytime'	NMen SSem
	'Meadow Blaze'	WFar
	'Melanie'	MBrN NMen SSem
	'Mercury'	CRos EHyd LRHS NBro NMen NRHS SRms
	'Merlin'	MSCN
	mettenianum	NMen
	'Michael'	SSem
	'Mickey Mouse'	NMen
	'Midas'	CRos EHyd EMul LRHS NRHS SRms
	'Mike' **new**	NMen
	'Mini Frost'	NMen
	MINT MARVEL (Chick Charms Series)	see *S. calcareum* 'Mrs Giuseppi'
	'Minuet'	NMen
	'Mira'	MHol
	'Moerkerk's Merit'	NMen XLum
	'Mona Lisa'	NMen
	'Mondstein'	MSCN NMen SRms
	'Monseigneur Desmet'	GQue
§	***montanum***	XLum
	- from Haute-Loire, France	XLum
	- from Mont Aigoual, France	XLum
	- from the Pyrenees	XLum
	- from Vallée d'Estaing, France	XLum
	- 'Caesar'	MSCN
	- subsp. ***carpaticum*** 'Cmiral's Yellow'	EDAr GKev WAbe WFar
	- subsp. ***montanum*** var. ***braunii***	LRHS
	- 'Rubrum'	see *S.* 'Red Mountain'
	- subsp. ***stiriacum***	SRms XLum
§	- - 'Lloyd Praeger'	NMen SDys
	'More Honey'	NMen
	'Morning Glow'	NMen
	'Moss Rose'	NMen
	'Mount Hood'	CRos EHyd LRHS NMen NRHS SRms
	'Mount Skippet'	NMen
	'Mount Usher'	NMen
	'Mulberry Wine'	EDAr SRms SSem WHoo
	'Mystic'	MBrN NMen SSem
	'Naemi'	NMen
	'Neon'	NMen
§	'Neptune'	LBar LCro WFar
*	***netaginatum***	XLum
	nevadense	GArf NMen NRya NSla SRms
	- 'Hirtellum'	SRms
	'New Rose'	WFar XLum
	'Nico'	NMen NWad SRms
	'Night Detector'	NMen
	'Nigrum'	see *S. tectorum* 'Nigrum'
	'Niobe'	NMen

	'Nocturno'	NMen XLum
	'Noellie'	NMen
	'Noir'	EHyd EPfP GKev LRHS NBro NMen NRHS SSem WFar XLum
	'Norbert'	NMen SRms XLum
	'Nörtofts Beauty'	NMen
	'Nouveau Pastel'	NMen XLum
	'Nova'	NMen
	'Novalis'	NMen
	'Obaldina'	NMen
	'Oberon'	NMen
	'Obsession'	WFar
	'Ockerwurz'	WFar
	'Octet'	NMen
	octopodes	NBir NRya XLum
	– var. ***apetalum***	EPPr MSCN NMen WHoo
	'Oddity'	LRHS MBrN MHer NMen NWad WFar
	'Oh My'	NMen
	'Ohio Burgundy'	CRos EHyd LRHS MSCN NMen NRHS SRms WAbe WFar
	'Ohu ôm Ohu' **new**	NMen
	'Olcina'	NMen
	'Old Man Sage'	SPlb
	'Olivia'	NMen
	'Omega'	NMen
	'One Hundred' **new**	NMen
	'Orange Glow'	SSem
	'Orestes'	NMen
	'Orion' **new**	EMul
	'Ornatum'	MHer WAbe
	ossetiense	NMen XLum
	'Othello' ♀H5	CTri NBir NMen SRms SSem WCot WPGP XLum
	'Ottelein'	NMen
	'Pachamama'	NMen
	'Pacific Blazing Star'	NMen SSem
§	'Pacific Blue Ice'	LCro SSem
	'Pacific Charm'	NMen
	'Pacific Dawn' **new**	NMen
§	'Pacific Devils Food'	LBar LCro NMen
	'Pacific Evening Star' **new**	NMen
	'Pacific Hazy Embers'	NMen
	'Pacific Knight' **new**	NMen
	'Pacific Opal'	NMen
	'Pacific Purple Shadows'	EMul NMen WFar
	'Pacific Second Try'	NMen
	'Pacific Sexy'	NMen SSem
	'Pacific Sunset'	NMen
	'Pacific Tart' **new**	NMen
	'Packardian'	NMen NWad
	'Painted Lady'	NMen
	'Palissander'	EMul NMen WHlf XLum
	'Pallas'	XLum
	'Pandaros'	SSem
	'Papucchini'	NMen
	'Passionata'	EMul NMen SSem
	'Pastel'	CTri MHer SLee
	patens	see *Jovibarba heuffelii*
	'Patrician'	NMen SRms
	'Pavilion'	NMen
	'Peggy'	CCal NMen
	'Pekinese'	CRos EBou EHyd LRHS MBrN NBro NMen NRHS SRms SSim WBrk XLum
	'Persephone'	NMen
	'Peterson's Ornatum'	SDys
	'Petsy'	EDAr NMen SRms
	'Phoebe'	NMen
	'Picasso'	NMen SSem
	'Pilatus'	EPfP SRms WFar XLum
	'Pine Cone'	NMen
	'Pink Astrid'	NMen
	'Pink Cloud'	NMen SSem

	'Pink Delight'	MSCN
	'Pink Flamingoes'	NMen SSem
	'Pink Globe' **new**	EDAr
	'Pink Grapefruit'	NMen
	'Pink Lemonade'	NMen SSem
	'Pink Mist'	SRms
	'Pink Puff'	NMen
	'Pinkerton'	SSem
	'Pinochio'	NMen
	'Pip' **new**	NMen
	'Pippin'	NMen SRms SSem
	pittonii ♀H5	NMen WAbe XLum
	'Pixie'	NMen
	'Plum Frosting'	MSCN NMen WFar
	PLUM PARFAIT (Chick Charms Series)	see *S.* 'Prairie Sunset'
	'Plumb Rose'	NMen
	'Plush'	NMen
	'Pluto'	NMen XLum
	'Poke Eat'	EMul
	'Polaris'	NMen SSem
	'Poldark'	NMen
	'Pompeja'	NMen
	'Poollicht'	SSem
	'Popocatepetl'	SSem
I	'Powellii'	NMen SLee
§	'Prairie Sunset'	LCro NMen WHil
	'President Arsac'	XLum
	'Princess Little'	NMen
	'Probus'	NMen
	'Procton'	NMen
	'Proud Zelda'	MSCN NMen SSem
	'Pseudo-ornatum'	SRms
	pulchellum	XLum
	'Pumaros'	SDys
	pumilum	CRos EHyd LRHS NMen NRHS SRms
	– from Techensis, Caucasus Mountains	SRms
	– 'Sopa'	MSCN
	'Purdy'	EDAr NHpl NMen WAbe
	'Purdy's 50-6'	EMul NMen
	'Purdy's 70-40'	NMen
	'Purdy's 90-1'	NMen
	'Purdy's Big Red'	NMen
	'Purple Beauty'	NMen
	'Purple Dazzler'	EMul NMen
	'Purple Haze'	NMen WFar
	'Purple King'	NMen SDys
	'Purple Queen'	CRos EHyd EPPr LRHS NMen NRHS NRya SRms SSem WFar
	'Purple Shadows'	NMen
	'Purple Violet'	NMen
	'Purpurkranz'	NMen
	'Pygmalion'	NMen
	'Queen Amalia'	see *S. reginae-amaliae*
	'Queen Elizabeth'	SSem
	'Quintessence'	MSCN NMen SRms
	'Ramses'	SDys
	'Raspberry Ice'	GKev MSCN NBro NHpl NMen
	'Rauer Kulm'	NMen
	'Rauhreif'	XLum
	'Ravenheart'	MSCN
	'Rebecca'	GKev
	'Red Ace'	EMul NBro NEoE WFar
	'Red Beam'	EDAr EHyd NMen NRHS
	'Red Chief'	EPfP GKev LRHS XLum
	'Red Cross'	NMen
	'Red Delta'	NBir NMen WCot WPGP
	'Red Devil'	CRos EGrI EHyd EWoo LRHS NMen NRHS SPlb SRms SSem WHoo
	'Red Heart'	CCal
	'Red King'	NMen

	'Red Lion'	NMen
§	'Red Mountain'	EWoo LSun NMen NRya SLee SRms
	'Red Pink'	NMen
	'Red Pluche'	NMen
	'Red Robin'	NMen
	'Red Shine'	NMen
	'Red Spider'	EDAr NBro NMen
	'Red West'	NMen
	'Regal'	NMen
	'Regenbogen'	SSem
	'Regensburger Knirps'	NMen
	'Regensburger Kokon'	NMen
	reginae	see *S. reginae-amaliae*
§	***reginae-amaliae***	CRos EHyd GKev LRHS NMen NRHS SRms XLum
	- from Kambeecho, Greece, No 2	SDys
	- from Sarpun, Turkey	SDys
§	'Reginald Malby'	CRos EHyd LRHS NMen NRHS SRms
§	'Reinhard' 🏆H5	CCal CRos EDAr EHyd EPot GKev GMaP LCro LRHS MAsh MBrN MHer MSCN NHpl NMen NRHS NRya SLee SPlb SRms SRot SSem SSim WBrk WFar WHoo WIce
	'Remus'	ELan NMen SRms
	'Rex'	NMen
	'Rhöne'	NMen
	'Rhubarb Crumble'	NMen
	'Rio de Janeiro'	NMen
	'Rita Jane'	NMen SSem
	'Robin'	NBro NHol NMen NSla SRms XLum
	'Robson' **new**	NMen
§	'Rocknoll Rosette'	LCro
	'Rococo'	NMen
	'Romantic Knights'	NMen
	'Romantik Ritter'	NMen
I	'Ronsdorfer Hybride'	NMen
	'Roosemaryn'	EDAr
	'Rosa Mädchen'	NMen SSem
	'Rosenherz'	SSem
	'Rosenhügel'	NMen SSem
	× ***roseum***	NMen
	'Rosie'	CCal CRos EHyd EPot GMaP LRHS MAsh MMuc MSCN NHol NMen NRHS NSla SLee SRms SSim WBrk WFar WIce
	'Rosy Glow' **new**	EDAr
	'Rotes Meer' **new**	NMen
	'Rotkopf' 🏆H5	CCal CRos EHyd LRHS MSCN NMen NRHS NWad SEdd SSem XLum
	'Rotmantel'	NMen
	'Rotund'	MSCN
	'Royal Opera'	EPot NMen
	'Royal Ruby'	NMen SLee
	'Royal Twist' **new**	EDAr
	'Rubikon Improved'	NMen
	'Rubin'	CGBo CKel CTri EBou EPfP LLWG LRHS MAsh MHol NBir NHpl NMen SPoG SRms SSem SSim WAbe WIce XLum
I	'Rubra Ash'	NMen
I	'Rubra Ray'	CCal NMen
	'Rubrifolium'	see *S. marmoreum* subsp. *marmoreum* 'Rubrifolium'
	'Ruby Heart'	CBod MBros SSim
	'Ruby Meadows'	WFar
	'Russian River'	WHoo
	'Rusty'	NMen
	ruthenicum	CRos EHyd EPPr LRHS NMen NRHS NRya SRms XLum
	- 'Regis-Fernandii'	XLum
	'Ruth's Choice'	WFar
	'Saffron'	NMen
	'Saga'	NMen
	'Samwise'	NMen
	'Sanford's Hybrid'	NMen
	'Sanne'	NMen
	'Santis'	GKev NMen
	'Sarah'	NMen
	'Sardonyx' **new**	NMen
	'Sarotte'	NMen
	'Sassy Frass'	NMen
	'Saturn'	NMen SRms WFar
	schlehanii	see *S. marmoreum*
	schnittspahnii	XLum
	'Schwarze Rose'	NMen SSem
	'Scooby'	WFar
	'Sea Coral' **new**	NMen
	'Seerose'	SSem
	seguieri	XLum
	'Seminole'	NMen
	'Seneca'	NMen
	'Sephora'	NMen
	'Seren'	GBin
	'Sharon's Pencil'	NMen
	'Sha'uri'	NMen
	'Sheila'	GAbr
	'Shepherd's Warning'	WFar
	'Shirley Moore'	NMen
	'Shirley's Joy'	NMen XLum
	'Show Baby'	NMen
	'Sideshow'	NMen
	'Sigma'	NMen
	'Silberand'	LRHS
	'Silberkarneol' misapplied	see *S.* 'Silver Jubilee'
	'Silberkarneol' ambig.	EGrI SEdd
	'Silberspitz'	CRos EHyd LRHS MHer NBro NMen NRHS SPlb SRms
	'Silver Andre'	NMen
§	'Silver Jubilee'	CRos EHyd GQue LRHS NBro NMen NRHS NRya SPlb SRms WFar WHoo XLum
	SILVER SUEDE (Chick Charms Series)	see *S.* 'Neptune'
	'Silver Thaw'	EHyd NRHS
	'Silverine'	NMen
	'Silvertone'	EDAr NMen
	'Simonkaianum'	see *Jovibarba hirta*
	'Simply Nightfall'	SSim
	'Sioux'	MBrN NMen SSem
	'Sirius'	GBin LLWG MHol NMen
	'Skrocki's Beauty'	NMen SRms WFar
	'Skrocki's Bronze'	CRos EHyd LRHS NRHS
	'Smaragd'	NMen XLum
	'Smit's Seedling'	NMen
	'Smokey Jet'	NMen
	'Snow Baby' **new**	NMen
	'Snowberger'	EBou EMul NMen SRms
	soboliferum	see *Jovibarba sobolifera*
	'Solamith'	NMen
	'Solar Meadows'	WFar
	'Sombrero'	NMen
	'Sonnenkuss'	SSem
	'Soothsayer'	NMen
	sosnowskyi	NMen XLum
	'Soul'	CCal NMen
	'Space Dog'	NMen
	'Spangle'	NMen
	'Spangle' sport	NMen
	'Spanish Dancer'	NMen
	'Spartan's Sunrise'	WFar
	'Spherette'	MBrN NMen WAbe
	'Spicatogne Valias' **new**	EDAr
	'Spice'	NMen
	'Spider's Lair' 🏆H5	EPot SLee SRms

	'Spiver's Velvet'	NMen
	'Sponnier'	XLum
	'Spring Beauty'	NMen
	'Springmist'	CRos EHyd LRHS NRHS SRms SSem
	'Sprite'	CRos EHyd LRHS NMen NRHS SDys SRms SSem SSim
	'Squib'	CCal EDAr MSCN NMen
	'Standard Green'	CBod CCal LLWG
	stansfieldii	see *S. arachnoideum* subsp. *tomentosum* 'Stansfieldii'
	'Starburst'	CRos EHyd LRHS NMen NRHS
	'Starion'	NMen
	'State Fair'	NMen NSla SSem
	'Steerosentern'	NMen
	STRAWBERRY KIWI (Chick Charms Series)	see *S.* 'Fashion Diva'
	'Strawberry Sundae'	NFav
	'Strawberry Vale' **new**	EDAr
	'Strider'	NMen
	'Stuffed Olive'	NMen SDys SLee SRms
	'Sugary'	NMen
	'Suite Minuet'	SSem
	'Sun Kiss'	NMen
	'Sun Waves'	SDys
	'Sunburst'	SSim
	'Sunray Desire'	NMen
	'Sunrise'	NMen
	'Super Dome'	NMen
	'Superama'	NMen
	'Supernova'	NMen
	'Svava'	NMen
	'Sweet Brown Sugar'	NMen
	'Sweetheart'	NMen
	'Syston Flame'	NMen
	'Tamberlane'	EDAr
	'Tarita'	NMen
	'T'Boz'	NMen
§	***tectorum*** 🏆^{H7}	CTri ELan GPoy MHoo MNHC SPlb SSem XLum
§	- var. ***alpinum***	CRos EHyd LRHS NBro NRHS SRms
	- var. ***andreanum***	XLum
	- 'Atropurpureum'	ELan SRms
	- 'Atroviolaceum'	NMen SPlb XLum
*	- 'Aureum'	NMen
	- var. ***boutignyanum***	SRms
	GDJ 94.04 from Route de Tuixén, Spain	
§	- var. ***glaucum***	NMen XLum
	- 'Mettenianum'	XLum
	- monstrose	SPlb SRms
	- 'Murale'	XLum
§	- 'Nigrum'	EGrl MHer NBro SDys XLum
	- 'Red Flush'	MBrN NMen
	- 'Royanum' 🏆^{H7}	MSCN NMen SRms
*	- subsp. ***sanguineum***	SSim
	- 'Sunset'	EWes NMen SDys SSim
§	- subsp. ***tectorum*** 'Boissieri'	NMen
	- - 'Triste'	NHpl NMen SSim XLum
	- 'Violaceum'	EBou NMen SPlb SRms
	'Teddy Bear'	MSCN NMen
	'Tederheid'	NMen
	'Teide'	SSem
	'Telfan'	NMen
	'Terlamen'	NMen
	'Terracotta Baby'	CCal NMen SLee SSim WFar
	'Tesoro'	NMen SSem
	'Thayne'	NMen
	'The Flintstones'	NMen SSim
	'The Platters'	NMen
	'The Red Carpet' **new**	NMen
	'Thistle Hill'	NMen
	'Thunder'	NMen
	'Tiger Bay'	NMen
	'Timmy'	NMen
	'Tinner Bell'	NMen
	'Tintenblut'	NMen SSem
	'Tintinabulum'	NMen
	'Tip Top'	EPot NMen WFar
	'Tipsy'	NMen
	tissieri	XLum
	'Titania'	NMen
	'Tjabine'	NMen
	'Tohuwabohu' **new**	NMen
	'Tommella'	XLum
	'Topaz'	NMen SRms XLum
	'Tordeur's Memory'	NMen SEND SRms
	'Tormulin'	LRHS
I	'Tourmalyi'	NMen
	'T'Pol'	NMen
	'Tracy Sue'	XLum
	'Traffic Lights'	SSem
	'Trail Walker'	NMen SRms
	transcaucasicum	EDAr XLum
	'Tree Beard'	NMen
	'Trine'	NMen
	'Tristesse' 🏆^{H5}	NMen SSem
	'Troika'	NMen
	'Trude'	NMen
	'Truva'	NMen
	'Twilight Blues'	CCal CRos EHyd LRHS NRHS SRms
	'Twist'	NMen
	'U4'	NMen
	'Udine'	NMen
	'Uralturmalin'	NMen
	'Uranus'	XLum
	'Urmel'	NMen
§	'Urmina'	LCro NMen
	'Utopian'	EGrl LRHS
	× ***vaccarii***	XLum
	'Van der Steen'	NMen
	'Vanbaelen'	NMen SDys
	'Vasi Petru'	NMen
	'Vega'	MHol
	'Venus'	NMen XLum
	'Veronique' **new**	NMen
	'Veuchelen'	EDAr
	'Veughelen'	NMen SSem
	vicentei	NMen WFar
	- from Gaton, Spain	NMen
§	- subsp. ***paui***	NSla
	'Video'	NMen
	'Viking'	NMen
	'Violet Queen'	NMen
	'Virbinis' **new**	EDAr
	'Virgil'	MBrN MSCN NMen NWad SDys SPlb SSem WAbe WCot WFar WIce
I	'Virginius'	NMen
	'Vossa Nova' **new**	NMen
	'Vulcano'	NMen
	'Walnut Tree' **new**	NMen
	'Wasti'	NMen
	'Waterlily'	NWad
	'Watermelon Rind'	NMen
	'Web of Intrege' **new**	NMen
	webbianum	see *S. arachnoideum* subsp. *tomentosum* (C.B. Lehm. & Schnittsp.) Schinz & Thell.
	'Webbyola'	NMen
	'Webster' **new**	NMen
	'Weitblick'	SSem
	'Wendy'	NMen
	'Westerlin'	NMen
	'Wheel of Fire'	NMen
	'White Christmas'	see *S. arachnoideum* 'White Christmas'

	'White Ladies'	NMen
	'Whitening'	WFar
	× ***widderi***	NMen
	'Wilhelm Tell'	NMen
	'Wine Queen'	NMen
	'Winsome'	NFav NWad
	'Wok'	NMen
I	'Woolcott's Variety'	NBir NMen SRms
	wulfenii	XLum
	- subsp. ***juvanii***	XLum
	'Yanisha'	NMen
	'Yolanda'	NMen
	'Yvette'	NMen
	'Zaccour'	NMen
	'Zackenkrone'	NMen
	'Zannalee'	NMen
	'Zeeuwse Winner'	NMen
	'Zelca'	NMen
	zeleborii	NMen
	'Zenith'	NMen SRms
	'Zenocrate'	NHol
	'Zepherin'	NMen
	'Zilver Moon'	NMen
	'Zilver Snowflake'	NMen
	'Zilver Suzanna'	NMen
	'Zilverprinsesje'	NMen
	'Zircon'	NMen
	'Zone'	EMul NMen
	'Zorba'	NMen
	'Zulu'	NMen
	'Zwergengnom' **new**	NMen

Senecio (*Asteraceae*)

	antandroi **new**	EAri
	anteuphorbium	see *Kleinia anteuphorbium*
	articulatus	see *Curio articulata*
§	***barbertonicus***	EShb NHrt
	bidwillii	see *Brachyglottis bidwillii*
	candicans misapplied	see *Jacobaea maritima*
	candidans ANGEL WINGS ('Senaw'PBR)	CBcs CBod CKel CSBt CWGN CWnw ECtt ELan EPfP LCro LOPS LRHS MBros NHpl NSti SIvy SMad SPeP SRkn WCot WHlf XSte
	chrysanthemoides misapplied	see *Euryops chrysanthemoides*
	cineraria	see *Jacobaea maritima*
	cinerascens	SVen
	citriformis	see *Curio citriformis*
	coccinilifera hort.	see *Kleinia grantii*
	compactus	see *Brachyglottis compacta*
	confusus	see *Pseudogynoxys chenopodioides*
	crassissimus	EShb LWaG
	cristobalensis	see *Roldana cristobalensis*
	'Donkey's Ears' **new**	CBod LBar
	doria	EPfP EShb MMuc SAko SDix WHrl
	elegans	SVen
	ficoides	see *Curio ficoides*
	gerberifolius B&SWJ 10357	WCru
	- B&SWJ 10361	MHol WCru
	'Gregynog Gold'	see *Ligularia* 'Gregynog Gold'
	greyi misapplied	see *Brachyglottis* (Dunedin Group) 'Sunshine'
	greyi Hook. f.	see *Brachyglottis greyi* (Hook. f.) B. Nord.
	haworthii	see *Caputia tomentosa*
	herreianus	LCro NHrt SIvy
	hoffmannii	EShb
	kleinia	see *Kleinia neriifolia*
	kleiniiformis	EShb
	laxifolius hort.	see *Brachyglottis* (Dunedin Group) 'Sunshine'
	leucostachys misapplied	see *S. viravira*
	macroglossus	CHll EShb
	- 'Variegatus' (v) ♀H1c	EAri EShb
	madagascariensis	see *Kleinia madagascariensis*
	mandraliscae	see *Curio talinoides* subsp. *mandraliscae*
	maritimus	see *Jacobaea maritima*
	mikanioides	see *Delairea odorata*
	monroi	see *Brachyglottis monroi*
	oxyriifolius **new**	EAri
	peregrinus **new**	LCro
	petasitis	see *Roldana petasitis*
	picticaulis	see *Kleinia picticaulis*
	polyodon var. ***polyodon***	CKel EPfP GBee GBin LRHS MMuc NFav SBut SWvt WCAu WWFP
	- var. ***subglaber***	CCCN CSpe EAJP EWes EWld GElm GLog GQue MHol MNrw MPie NCth SRms SSut WBor WTyc
	- - 'Joe's Old Rose'	EPPr
	- - 'Joe's White'	EPPr
	przewalskii	see *Ligularia przewalskii*
	pulcher	CDTJ MHol SHar SMrm
	reinoldii	see *Brachyglottis rotundifolia*
	rowleyanus	see *Curio rowleyanus*
	scandens	see *Delairea odorata*
	seminiveus	EBee
	serpens	see *Curio repens*
§	***smithii***	ELan NBid WWtn
	squalidus subsp. ***aethnensis***	WCot
	'Sunshine'	see *Brachyglottis* (Dunedin Group) 'Sunshine'
	talinoides 'Himalaya' misapplied (green-leaved)	see *S. barbertonicus*
	tamoides	SPlb
	tanguticus	see *Sinacalia tangutica*
§	***viravira***	EPri EShb MCot SMrm SPhx WSHC
	vitalis	see *Curio talinoides* subsp. *cylindricus*

Senna (*Fabaceae*)

	alexandrina	CCCN EShb
	artemisioides ♀H1b	WCot
§	***candolleana***	CCCN
§	***corymbosa***	CBcs CCCN CHll CRHN CTri ECre IDee SMrm
	× ***floribunda***	SBrt
	hebecarpa	SBls SBrt
§	***marilandica***	CSpe EBee LRHS MGil
	obtusa Clos	see *S. candolleana*
	septemtrionalis	CCCN EHyd LRHS

Sequoia (*Cupressaceae*)

	sempervirens ♀H6	CAco CBcs CCVT CLnd CMCN CMen CPer CTsd EPfP IPap LMaj MBlu MGil MMuc NOra NWea SArc SCob SEND SGol SSha WMat WMou WTSh
	- 'Adpressa'	CAco LRHS MGos SCoo
	- 'Cantab'	WMou
	- 'Filoli'	CAco
	- 'Henderson Blue'	SLim
	- 'Korbel KT'	SMad
	- 'Prostrata'	EWhm

Sequoiadendron (*Cupressaceae*)

	giganteum ♀H6	Widely available
	- 'Barabits Requiem'	CAco MBlu
	- 'Bultinck Yellow'	MBlu
	- 'Chief'	NLar
	- 'French Beauty'	NLar
	- 'Glaucum'	CAco LPar LRHS MBlu SGsty SLim

* - 'Glaucum Compactum' MBlu
- 'Greenpeace' MBlu
- 'Kaatje' SLim
- 'Kyoxonera' NLar
- 'Lighting Green' NLar
- 'Little Stan' NLar SLim
- 'Pendulum' CAco CCVT ELan ESwi LPar MBlu SLim WLea
- 'Pierie' NLar
- 'Powdered Blue' NLar

Serapias (*Orchidaceae*)

lingua peach-flowered WMal

Serenoa (*Arecaceae*)

repens NPlm
- silver-leaved **new** NPlm

Sericocarpus (*Asteraceae*)

asteroides GArf GKev

Seriphidium see *Artemisia*

Serratula (*Asteraceae*)

bulgarica see *Klasea bulgarica*
coronata see *Klasea coronata*
- subsp. ***insularis*** see *Klasea coronata* subsp. *insularis*
gmelinii see *Klasea radiata* subsp. *gmelinii*
lycopifolia see *Klasea lycopifolia*
shawii see *S. tinctoria* var. *seoanei*
tinctoria NLar SBut SPhx
§ - var. ***seoanei*** Widely available

Serruria (*Proteaceae*)

florida SPlb
phylicoides SPlb

Sesbania (*Fabaceae*)

punicea CCCN WJur

Seseli (*Apiaceae*)

elatum PAB 9228 SPhx
- subsp. ***osseum*** ELan LRHS SPhx SPtp WHil
globiferum SPhx
gracile CSpe ECha SPhx
gummiferum CAby CSpe EAJP ELan LDai SPhx SPtp WHil WSHC
hippomarathrum CElw CSpe ECha ELan EPPr MAvo MNrw NGrd SBrt SPhx WCot WFar WHrl
lehmannii WCot
§ ***libanotis*** EBee ECha EPPr GBin LEdu LRHS NLar SPhx WFar
montanum CMiW CSpe EBee LPla MAvo NDov SBut SHar WCot
petraeum WHil
transcaucasicum LEdu
- B&SWJ 15352 WCru

Sesleria (*Poaceae*)

§ ***albicans*** CBod EPPr
§ ***argentea*** CKno SCoo SPoG
autumnalis ♀H7 CBWd CBar CKel CKno CWnw EBee ELon EPPr EWes EWoo GBin GMaP LCro LOPS SCob SHar SPhx WChS WSpi XLum
caerulea CKno CSde EGrl ELan EPfP GMaP GQue LCro LEdu LPal LRHS SCob SPhx SPoG XLum
- subsp. ***calcarea*** see *S. albicans*
- 'Malvern Mop' EBee WCot WHrl
* ***candida*** EPPr
cylindrica see *S. argentea*
'Greenlee' CKno LPla
heufleriana CBWd CBod EPPr GBin LCro LPla NRya SPhx SPlb SPtp WCot WSpi
insularis EPPr EShb
nitida CBWd CKno GMaP LEdu SPhx WChS XLum
sadleriana EBee EPPr

Setaria (*Poaceae*)

italica 'Red Jewel' CSpe
macrostachya SPhx
palmifolia ♀H2 CBod EPPr EShb MPie SBls SBrt SDix SIvy SPlb
viridis WCot

Setcreasea see *Tradescantia*

shaddock see *Citrus maxima*

Sharon fruit see *Diospyros kaki*

Shepherdia (*Elaeagnaceae*)

argentea NLar WKor

Shibataea (*Poaceae*)

kumasaca ♀H6 CAbb CBcs LEdu MWht SCob SGol

Shortia (*Diapensiaceae*)

galacifolia EPot
soldanelloides GEdr
- var. ***magna*** EPot
uniflora EPot

Sibbaldia (*Rosaceae*)

cuneata HPA 1390 GGro
procumbens GKev

Sibbaldiopsis (*Rosaceae*)

§ ***tridentata*** GArf GKev SBrt

Sibthorpia (*Plantaginaceae*)

europaea CExl

Sida (*Malvaceae*)

hermaphrodita EBee SBls SBrt WHil

Sidalcea ✿ (*Malvaceae*)

'Brilliant' CBcs CBod CNor GBin ILea MNrw NBir NHsp SPer WCAu WFar
campestris from Oregon, USA NFav
candida CBod CRos ECtt EHyd ELan EWoo GMaP MBNS MMuc MRav NChi NGBl NGdn NLar NRHS NSti SGbt SPer WCAu WCot
- 'Bianca' ELan EMor EPfP LSun NFav NLar SBut WFar
'Candy Girl' CBod NHsp NLar SGBe WCot WFar
'Crimson King' WFar
'Croftway Red' CBod CBor CRos EBee ELan LRHS MAvo NBPC NBro NGdn NHol NHsp NRHS NWad SPer SWvt WFar
'Elsie Heugh' ♀H7 Widely available
LILAC CANDICE ('Midawioha') NHsp WFar
'Little Princess'PBR CBor EBee EHyd EPfP EWes GKev LRHS MNrw NBPC NGdn NHsp NLar NRHS SPoG WCot WFar
'Loveliness' EBee ECtt EHyd ELan LRHS LSou MAvo MBel MRav NBro NDov NHsp NRHS NWad SPoG WFar WWke

malviflora	SRms
- subsp. ***purpurea***	EHyd LRHS
'Monarch'	WFar
'Moorland Rose Coronet'	WFar
'Mr Lindbergh'	LBar MACG NHsp NLar SPer WCFE
'Mrs Borrodaile'	MRav NBro NEoE NGdn NLar WFar
'Mrs Galloway'	NHsp
'My Love'	ECha NDov NHsp
'Nimmerdor'	EBlo NHsp
'Oberon' ♀H7	CRos EBee EBlo EHyd LBar LRHS MRav NRHS
oregana	NGdn
- subsp. ***spicata***	WFar
'Party Girl'	CGBo CRos CSBt EAJP EBee EHyd ELan EMor EPfP GKev LRHS LSun MNHC MRav NBPC NBro NFav NGdn NLar NRHS SBut SCob SCoo SGBe SPlb SPoG WFar WPnP XLum
'Purpetta'	EPfP NEoE NGBl NHsp NLar
'Reverend Page Roberts'	MRav WCot
'Rosaly'	CSpe ELan MACG NFav NHsp NLar WFar
'Rosanna'	CRos EBou EHyd EPfP GMaP LRHS NHsp NLar NRHS
'Rose Bouquet'	NHsp
'Rose Bud'	NHsp WFar
'Rose Queen'	CRos EBee ECha EHyd GKev LRHS MAvo MRav NBro NHol NHsp NRHS SGbt SHar SPer SRms WFar
'Rosy Gem'	SCob
Stark's hybrids	CBod EHyd LRHS NFav NRHS SRms
'Sussex Beauty'	CBor LSou MAvo MBel MHol MRav NCth NDov NGdn NHsp SCoo SMrm SPoG WCot WFar
'Wensleydale'	CRos EBlo EHyd LRHS NHsp NRHS WFar
'William Smith' ♀H7	CRos EBee ECha ECtt EHyd EPfP EWTr EWes GBin LRHS MArl MAvo MBel MMuc MRav NBir NGdn NHsp NLar NRHS SEND SGbt WFar
'Wine Red'	CBod EBee EHyd EPfP GPSL LRHS LSou MNrw NFav NGdn NHsp NRHS SPoG SWvt

Sideritis (*Lamiaceae*)

syriaca	MHer SBls XSen
- RCB UA 2	WCot

Sieversia (*Rosaceae*)

§ ***pentapetala***	GEdr GKev WAbe
- 'Flore Pleno' (d)	WAbe

Silaum (*Apiaceae*)

silaus	SPhx

Silene (*Caryophyllaceae*)

RBS	EPPr
acaulis	EDAr EPot GJos GKev SLee SRms WAbe WIce
§ - subsp. ***acaulis***	SPlb SRms WIce
- 'Alba'	EPot WAbe
- 'Blush'	EDAr NSla WAbe
- 'Correvoniana'	NLar
- subsp. ***elongata***	see *S. acaulis* subsp. *acaulis*
- 'Frances'	EDAr ITim NBwr NLar NRya NSla SLee SRot WAbe
- 'Helen's Double' (d)	GArf
- 'Mount Snowdon'	ELan EWes GArf NBwr NHpl NLar SLee SPlb SPoG SRms WFar WHoo
- 'Pedunculata'	see *S. acaulis* subsp. *acaulis*
alba	see *S. latifolia* subsp. *alba*
§ ***alpestris***	SBut SHar SRms
- 'Flore Pleno' (d) ♀H7	EBou EDAr EWes NSla WIce
- 'Starry Dreams'	CRos CSpe EHyd LRHS NRHS
aomorensis	GGro
× ***arkwrightii***	see *Lychnis* × *arkwrightii*
armeria	SDys
- 'Electra'	CSpe CTtf MNHC
asterias	CBor CPla ECha EPPr EWld GElm GGro GJos MNrw SBrt
atropurpurea	see *Lychnis viscaria* subsp. *atropurpurea*
caroliniana subsp. ***wherryi*** 'Short and Sweet'	CBor
coeli-rosa 'Blue Angel'	SPhx
'Confetti'	CPla CSpe EAJP ECha EShb GJos SPtp
'Country Comet'	NChi
§ ***davidii***	GKev
delavayi	GJos
§ ***dioica***	CCBP CHab CTtf EBee EBou EMor GJos GQue LCro LOPS MBow MHer MNHC NAts NGrd NLar NMir SBut SCgs SPhx SPoG SRms WSFF WShi WWild
- 'Clifford Moor' (v)	ECtt MHer NSti SCoo
- 'Compacta'	see *S. dioica* 'Minikin'
- 'Firefly'PBR (d)	CDor CMac ECtt NSti SWvt WSHC
§ - 'Flore Pleno' (d)	CBor EGrI GElm MHol MRav NBid NBro NGdn WHoo
- golden-leaved	CBor LShi
§ - 'Graham's Delight' (v)	NFav
- 'Inane'	WMal WSHC
- 'Innocence'	NGrd
§ - 'Minikin'	NGdn
- 'Purple Prince'	LBar MMuc SEND
- 'Purple Rim' **new**	LBar
I - 'Ray's Golden Campion'	EMor EPPr LBar NWad
- 'Rollie's Favorite'PBR	CBor CRos EBee ECtt EHyd EMor EPfP LBar LRHS LSou MHol MNrw MPri NDov NRHS NSti SPoG WCAu
- 'Rosea Plena' (d)	MHer WSHC
- 'Rubra Plena'	see *S. dioica* 'Flore Pleno'
- 'Stella'	NGrd
- 'Thelma Kay' (d/v)	NGdn
- 'Valley High' (v)	EBee ECtt WCot
- 'Variegata'	see *S. dioica* 'Graham's Delight'
fabaria	CSpe
subsp. ***domokina*** **new**	
§ ***fimbriata***	CAby CSpe CTtf EBee ECha ELan EMor EPPr EShb GElm ILea LPla MCot MMrt MNrw MRav MSCN NLar NSti SBut SDix SMrm WCAu WCot WFar WKif
frivaldskyana	SPhx
'Frivola Rose'	EWes LBar LPla MHol
fruticosa **new**	GElm
hookeri	GBin SPlb
- Ingramii Group	WAbe
inflata	see *S. vulgaris* subsp. *vulgaris*
'Jiggy Pink'	LBar LRHS
'Jiggy White'	LBar LRHS
kantzeensis	see *S. davidii*
keiskei	GJos
- var. ***akaisialpina***	NSla
- - f. ***leucantha***	NSla
- var. ***minor***	EHyd EWes LRHS NRHS WAbe
laciniata 'Starburst'	CSpe
latifolia	CHab GJos MHer MNHC NGrd NMir WSFF
§ - subsp. ***alba***	GJos GQue LRHS SPhx
maritima	see *S. uniflora*
multifida	see *S. fimbriata*
multiflora	EPPr
nigrescens	EDAr

noctiflora	CHab WSFF
nutans	LEdu NAts SBut SPhx SRms WSFF
pusilla	EDAr GJos NHpl NLar
quadridentata	see *S. alpestris*
regia	CSpe SPhx WHil WKif
rubra	see *S. dioica*
sachalinense	GGro
schafta ♀^{H5}	CTri ECha EGrI EPfP GJos GKev LRHS MAsh MMuc MPie MRav NBid SBls SEND SLee SRms WHoo XLum
- 'Persian Carpet'	EBou
- 'Shell Pink'	CRos ECha EHyd EPfP EWes GJos LRHS LSun MMuc NBid NRHS NSla SEND WHoo
sieboldii	see *Lychnis coronata* var. *sieboldii*
SPARKLING ROSE ('Insilsparo'^{PBR})	CRos LRHS MHol
stellata	SPhx
tatarica	GGro
§ ***uniflora***	CHab EPfP GJos LRHS MMuc NAts NBro NBwr SBut SPlb SRms SSut WCav
- 'Alba Plena'	see *S. uniflora* 'Robin Whitebreast'
I - 'Compacta'	SPhx
§ - 'Druett's Variegated' (v)	CBod CRos CTri EBou ECha ECtt EHyd ELan ELon EPot EWes LLWG LRHS MAsh NBwr NFav NHpl NRHS SPlb SPoG SRms SRot WCav WIce XLum
- 'Flore Pleno'	see *S. uniflora* 'Robin Whitebreast'
- pink-flowered	SBut
§ - 'Robin Whitebreast' (d)	ECha EPfP GBin LRHS NBid NBro SPhx SRms WSHC XLum
- 'Rosea'	ECtt EMor GJos MHol MMuc NHpl SLee SPlb SRot
- 'Variegata'	see *S. uniflora* 'Druett's Variegated'
- WEISSKEHLCHEN	see *S. uniflora* 'Robin Whitebreast'
- 'White Bells'	CTri WKif
viridiflora	SPhx
§ ***vulgaris***	CAgr CHab GJos MMuc MNHC NMir SBut SPhx SRms WHer WOut
- subsp. ***maritima***	see *S. uniflora*
§ - subsp. ***vulgaris*** new	CBod
wallichiana	see *S. vulgaris*
'Wisley Pink'	ECtt
yunnanensis	SPhx WSHC
§ ***zawadskii***	GGro GJos GKev MMuc SBrt SEND SPhx

Siler (*Umbelliferae*)

montanum	see *Laserpitium siler*

Silphium (*Asteraceae*)

albiflorum	SBrt
integrifolium	LPla SPhx WCot XLum
laciniatum	CMac CSpe EBee LEdu LShi SBrt SPhx XLum
mohrii	ECha GElm LPla SBut SPhx
perfoliatum ♀^{H7}	CSpe EBee EHyd GPoy GQue LEdu LRHS MMuc NDov NLar NRHS SBls SDix SEND SMrm SPhx WCAu WCot XLum
- var. ***connatum***	SPhx
- 'Maya' new	LBar WCot
simpsonii	SBrt
terebinthinaceum	CSpe SBrt SPhx WCot XLum
trifoliatum	EPPr SPhx WCot

Silybum (*Asteraceae*)

marianum	CCBP EHyd ELan GPoy LRHS MHoo MNHC NBir SPhx SRms
- white	SPhx

Sinacalia (*Asteraceae*)

§ ***tangutica***	ECha GGro GQue NBid NLar NSti SDix WCot

Sinapis (*Brassicaceae*)

alba	SVic

Sinarundinaria (*Poaceae*)

anceps	see *Yushania anceps*
jaunsarensis	see *Yushania anceps*
murielae	see *Fargesia murielae*
nitida	see *Fargesia nitida*

Sinningia (*Gesneriaceae*)

calcaria	WDib
canescens ♀^{H1a}	WDib
§ ***cardinalis***	WDib
conspicua	WDib
iarae	WDib
nivalis	WDib
speciosa 'Blanche de Méru'	SDeJ
- 'Corina' new	LCro
- 'Defiance'	SDeJ
- 'Hollywood'	LCro SDeJ
- 'Kaiser Friedrich'	SDeJ
- 'Kaiser Wilhelm'	SDeJ
- 'Mont Blanc'	SDeJ
- 'Violacea'	LCro
tuberosa	MCot
tubiflora	EAJP EShb EWld LEdu SBrt WCot WFar WKif XLum

× *Sinocalycalycanthus* see *Calycanthus*

Sinocalycanthus see *Calycanthus*

Sinocrassula (*Crassulaceae*)

§ ***yunnanensis***	CDoC EShb GKev NHpl SEdd SMrm SPlb SSim

Sinofranchetia (*Lardizabalaceae*)

chinensis	CRHN WJur WPGP
- DJHS 4117	WCru

Sinojackia ✿ (*Styracaceae*)

xylocarpa	CBcs CMCN EHed

Sinopodophyllum (*Berberidaceae*)

§ ***hexandrum***	EBee ELan EMor EWTr GBin GGro GKev GMaP GPoy GQue ILea LPla MBel MNrw MRav NBid NBir NChi NLar SMad SPlb WAvo WCot WKor WPnP WSHC WTyc
- from Kangding, Mugecuo Lake, Sichuan, China	SBrt
§ - var. ***chinense***	GEdr GKev LEdu
- - BWJ 7908	WCru
- - SDR 4409	CExl
- 'Chinese White'	CExl
§ - var. ***emodi***	ECha ITim
- - 'Majus'	CMiW GBin IPot MCot

Sinowilsonia (*Hamamelidaceae*)

henryi	WJur

Siphocranion (*Lamiaceae*)

§ ***macranthum***	EBee EWes WPGP

Sisyrinchium (*Iridaceae*)

× ***anceps***	see *S. angustifolium*
§ ***angustifolium***	CWCL EGrI LSun NBir NChi SPlb SRms WBrk WCav

- f. ***album***	LBar MCot NChi NLar
§ ***arenarium***	CWCL GArf
bellum hort.	see *S. idahoense* var. *bellum*
bermudiana	see *S. angustifolium*
'Biscutella'	CBod CKno EPfP ESgI EWoo GElm GMaP LBar LEdu MACG NFav SLee SMHy SPlb SRot WCav WFar WHoo WKif WWke
'Blue France'	EPot
'Blue Ice'	GPSL LRHS NLar WAbe
'Blue Skies'	WCav
boreale	see *S. californicum*
brachypus	see *S. californicum* Brachypus Group
'Californian Skies'	CAby CBor CElw CExl CKno CRos EAJP EBee ECha ECtt EHyd EPot EWoo GMaP LRHS NBir NDov NRHS NSla SMrm SRms SWvt WAvo WIce WKif
§ ***californicum***	CBen CDoC EWoo GKev GQue LLWG LPfP WMAq XLum
§ - Brachypus Group	CTri EBou EMor EPfP GAbr NBir NFav SPlb SWvt WKif
- 'Yellowstone'	CSBt GMcL LBar SRms WWke
* ***capsicum***	CExl
convolutum	NDov
- B&SWJ 9117	WCru
cuspidatum	see *S. arenarium*
'Deep Seas'	EDAr
depauperatum	CBor EDAr NFav
'Devon Skies'	CElw CRos CWCL ECtt EHyd ESgI GArf LBar LLWG LRHS MACG MEch MNrw NBwr NLar NRHS SGro SRms SWvt WAbe
douglasii	see *Olsynium douglasii*
'Dragon's Eye'	CElw CKno CPla EDAr ESgI EWes LBar MBrN MHer SRot WAbe WFar WHoo WIce
'E.K. Balls'	Widely available
graminoides	NWad
grandiflorum	see *Olsynium douglasii*
'Hemswell Sky'	ECtt GAbr NLar
'Iceberg'	CBor CElw EAJP ECha EWes
idahoense	ECha GAbr NDov NHpl SPlb SRms
§ - var. ***bellum***	CGBo EBou EPfP NFav SRms XLum
- - pale-flowered	CKno SMHy
- - 'Rocky Point'	CRos EHyd EPfP EWes LRHS NRHS SCoo SPoG WFar
- var. ***macounii***	ELan GPSL SPlb
§ - - 'Album' ♀H4	CElw EWes MMrt NBwr NFav WAbe WFar WIce
'Janet Denman' (v)	CBor ECha EDAr ESgI EWes SEdd SRot WFar
junceum	see *Olsynium junceum*
littorale	CExl
macrocarpon misapplied	see *S. macrocarpum*
§ ***macrocarpum***	CBor EWld
'Marchants Seedling'	SMHy
'Marion'	ECtt MBrN WHoo
'May Snow'	see *S. idahoense* var. *macounii* 'Album'
'Miami'	EWoo
montanum	NHpl
montanum × ***nudicaule***	GAbr
narcissiflorum	GArf
'North Star'	see *S.* 'Pole Star'
nudicaule	CBor NWad
palmifolium	CSpe EAri LEdu LPla MHer MNrw SMad WFar XLum
patagonicum	CExl GKev
§ 'Pole Star'	NLar
'Quaint and Queer'	CCCN CExl EAJP ECha EShb EWoo MBrN MNrw NBir NSla SAng SMHy WAvo WJam WSHC
'Raspberry'	CKno ECha ESgI EWoo WFar
'Sapphire'	CAby CBor CCCN CKno ECtt EDAr ELan EWoo LBar MAvo MBow MHol NHpl NLar NWad SPoG WWke
§ ***striatum***	Widely available
§ - 'Aunt May' (v)	CCCN CKel CMac ECha EPfP EWoo GMaP LBar LRHS LSRN MBel MGos MRav MSpe NHpl NRHS NSti SCob SIvy SPoG SRms SWvt WCot
- 'Variegatum'	see *S. striatum* 'Aunt May'
aff. ***unispathaceum*** B&SWJ 10683	WCru
'Wisley Blue' **new**	NGrs

Sium (*Apiaceae*)

sisarum	CLau ECha LEdu MBriF NDov SDix SPhx WKor WSFF

Skimmia ✿ (*Rutaceae*)

anquetilia	CMac
- (m)	WCru
- (f)	WCru
arborescens B&SWJ 11799	WCru
- B&SWJ 13902	WCru
- PAB 8774	LEdu
- subsp. ***nitida*** B&SWJ 8239	WCru
arisanensis B&SWJ 7114	WCru
- CWJ 12417	WCru
black-fruited B&SWJ 8259 from northern Vietnam (f/m)	WCru
× ***confusa*** 'Kew Green' (m) ♀H5	Widely available
japonica	CDoC CMac EGrI EHeP MGos NWea SCob SGsty SSta SavN WFar WJur
- (f)	CMac CTri EPfP GMcL SRms
- B&SWJ 5053(f)	WCru
- B&SWJ 5053 (m)	WCru
- 'Alba'	see *S. japonica* 'Wakehurst White'
- 'Attraction'	EBee MGos
- 'Bowles's Dwarf Female' (f)	CEnd MRav MWht
- 'Bowles's Dwarf Male' (m)	NWad
- 'Bronze Knight' (m)	CBod CMac MRav NLar NWad SRms
- 'Carberry' (f)	CMac
- 'Chameleon' (f)	EHeP GMcL
- 'Dad's Red Dragon' (f)	CDoC CMac SRms
- DELIGHT ('Delibolwi'PBR)	CDoC
- 'Emanuella'	SGsty
- 'Finchy'PBR (m)	CRos EHyd EPfP LRHS MAsh NLar NRHS
- 'Foremanii'	see *S. japonica* 'Veitchii'
§ - 'Fragrans' (m) ♀H5	CDoC CMac CRos CSBt CTri EBee EHyd EPfP LCro LOPS LPal LRHS LSRN MAsh MGos MRav NBwr NLar NRHS SCob SPer SPoG SRms SWvt WFar
- 'Fragrant Cloud'	see *S. japonica* 'Fragrans'
- 'Godrie's Dwarf' (m)	CRos EHyd LPar LRHS MAsh NLar NRHS WFar
- 'Humpty Dumpty' (f)	WFar
- var. ***intermedia*** f. ***repens***	see *S. japonica* subsp. *japonica* var. *intermedia*
§ - subsp. ***japonica*** var. ***intermedia*** B&SWJ 5560	WCru
- - B&SWJ 11165	WCru

- 'Kew White' (f) CBcs CBrac CDoC CRos EHyd ELan ELon EPfP GMcL IArd LCro LOPS LPar LRHS MAsh MGos MRav NHol NRHS NWad SPer SSta SWvt
- LUWIAN ('Wanto') (m) EHyd LRHS
- 'Macpenny Dwarf' (m) CMac SRms
- 'Magic Marlot'[PBR] (m/v) CRos EHyd EPfP GMcL LCro LRHS MAsh MGos MRav NHpl SPoG SWvt
- 'Marlot' (m) CDoC CRos EHyd EPfP LRHS MAsh NLar NRHS SPoG WLea
- 'Mystic Marlot'[PBR] LRHS MAsh
- 'Nymans' (f) ♀H5 CDoC CEnd CRos CTsd EHyd ELan EPfP GBin GMcL LCro LOPS LRHS MAsh MGos MRav NBwr NGrs NRHS SCob SPoG SRms SWvt
- OBSESSION ('Obsbolwi'[PBR]) (m/f) GMcL LCro LOPS LPar LSRN MAsh MGos WLea
- 'Olympic Flame' (f) CBod CDoC CRos EHyd EPfP IArd LRHS MAsh MBlu NRHS SPoG
- 'Pabella'[PBR] (f) CDoC ELan LPar LRHS MAsh SPoG
- 'Perosa'[PBR] (m) **new** LCro
- 'Pigmy' (f) CExl
- PINK DWARF ('Moerings 47'[PBR]) CDoC
- 'Red Diamonds' NRHS
- 'Red Princess' (f) CDoC MAsh
- 'Red Riding Hood' (f) CBod CRos EHyd ELon LCro LRHS MAsh MMrt NLar NRHS NWad SPer WCot
- 'Redruth' (f) CBcs CMac CSBt LSto MAsh SEND WAvo

§ - subsp. ***reevesiana*** CBcs CBod CBrac CMac CSBt CTri EGrI EHyd ELan EPfP GBin GMcL LCro LOPS LRHS MGos MRav MSwo NBwr SCob SPoG SRms SWvt
- - B&SWJ 3763 MAsh WCru
- - 'Chilan Choice' (f/m) WPGP
- - var. ***reevesiana*** B&SWJ 3544 WCru

§ - Rogersii Group CMac CTri
- - 'Nana Mascula' (m) CTri
- - 'Rockyfield Green' MAsh
- - 'Rogersii' (f) CMac
- 'Rubella' (m) ♀H5 Widely available
- RUBESTA ('Moerings3'[PBR]) CDoC NLar
- RUBESTA OPTIMA ('Moeropti'[PBR]) LRHS NLar
- 'Rubinetta' (m) CBar IArd MAsh
- 'Ruby Dome' (m) CDoC LRHS NWad
- 'Ruby King' (m) IArd LSRN NLar
- 'Scarlet Dwarf' (f) NHol WAvo
- SEDUCTION ('Redbolwi'[PBR]) MGos
- 'Snow White'[PBR] (m) EBee LRHS WAvo
- 'Tansley Gem' (f) EHyd LRHS MAsh MWht SPoG
- 'Temptation'[PBR] (f) CDoC CRos EHyd ELan EPfP LCro LOPS LRHS NRHS
- 'Thereza'[PBR] (m) EBee MAsh

§ - 'Veitchii' (f) CBar CBcs CBrac CDoC CKel CMac CSBt CTri EHeP EHyd EPfP LRHS LSRN MGos MRav NBwr NRHS SEND SLim SPer SPoG SRms SWvt

§ - 'Wakehurst White' (f) CBcs CMac CSBt CTri EBee EPfP LRHS MAsh MRav NWad SPoG SRms
- 'White Bella' (m) EHyd LRHS NRHS
- WHITE DWARF ('Moerings 1'[PBR]) LRHS
- WHITE GLOBE ('Fm1'[PBR]) (m) **new** NGrs
- 'Winifred Crook' (f) EHyd
- 'Winnie's Dwarf' MAsh
- 'Wisley Female' (f) CTri

laureola SRms WJur
- GWJ 9364 WCru
- 'Kew Green' EGrI
- subsp. ***laureola*** HWJK 2095 WCru
- subsp. ***multinervia*** GWJ 9374 WCru

reevesiana see *S. japonica* subsp. *reevesiana*
rogersii see *S. japonica* Rogersii Group
'Snowman' WCFE

Smallanthus (*Asteraceae*)

sonchifolius LEdu LWaG
- 'Morado' WPGP

Smilacina see *Maianthemum*

Smilax (*Smilacaceae*)

B&SWJ 6628 from Thailand WCru
aspera CMac EShb ESwi LEdu WCru WPGP
china B&SWJ 4427 WCru
discotis SEND
glaucophylla B&SWJ 2971 WCru
nipponica B&SWJ 4331 WCru
rotundifolia LEdu
sieboldii LEdu MRav
- B&SWJ 744 WCru

Smyrnium (*Apiaceae*)

olusatrum CCBP CHab CSpe GJos LEdu LRHS SPhx SPtp SRms WHer WSFF
- Cretan giant LEdu WPGP
perfoliatum CSpe EBee ELan EPfP EWes GBin LCro LEdu LOPS NAts NBir SAng SDix SPhx WCot WMal WSHC
rotundifolium WCot
- PAB 6714 LEdu WPGP

Solandra (*Solanaceae*)

grandiflora misapplied see *S. maxima*
hartwegii see *S. maxima*
§ ***maxima*** CCCN

Solanum (*Solanaceae*)

aerial-rooting climbing species B&SWJ 14398 WCru
atropurpureum CDTJ EWld SPlb WCot
betaceum (F) CCCN CDTJ EAri EShb SVic XVPe
- yellow-fruited (F) SPlb
burchellii SPlb
capsicastrum see *S. pseudocapsicum*
conchifolium hort. see *S. linearifolium*
crispum 'Autumnale' see *S. crispum* 'Glasnevin'

§ - 'Glasnevin' ♀H4 Widely available
dulcamara GPoy
- 'Variegatum' (v) CMac MAsh
jasminoides see *S. laxum*
laciniatum CCCN CDTJ CExl EAri EWld SArc SEND SMrm SPlb SVen

§ ***laxum*** CKel CMac EBee EHyd LRHS MRav NRHS SGsty SPer SRms SWvt
- 'Album' ♀H4 Widely available
- 'Album Variegatum' (v) SCob

* - 'Aureovariegatum' (v) CMac EBee SPlb
- 'Coldham' EPPr MNrw SDix
- 'Crèche du Pape' ECha LRHS SRms

§ ***linearifolium*** CSpe

lycopersicum MBros SVic
mammosum CDTJ WJur
marginatum SPlb
muricatum (F) CCCN SPlb
- 'Pepino Gold' (F) EShb
§ ***pseudocapsicum*** 🏆H1c SPlb
- variegated (v) WCot
pyracanthum CDTJ CTtf ECre SArc SPlb WCot
quitoense (F) CDTJ EAri SPlb
rantonnetii see *Lycianthes rantonnetii*
sisymbriifolium SPlb
aff. ***stenophyllum*** B&SWJ 10744 WCru
umbelliferum var. ***incanum*** SBrt
villosum SVen
wendlandii CCCN CHll

Soldanella (*Primulaceae*)

alpina CTsd EBee EMor GKev NSla SRms SRot WAbe
I - 'Alba' CTtf GEdr NSla
carpatica CBor CTtf EPot GEdr GKev LEdu SPlb WAbe WPGP
- 'Alba' CTtf LEdu
carpatica* × *pusilla CTtf MNrw NRya SBut WAbe WSHC
carpatica* × *villosa LEdu
cyanaster CTtf GAbr GBin GJos GLog LEdu NHpl NQui
dimoniei CTtf EPot GArf GKev LEdu WFar
hungarica GEdr
minima EPot GEdr GJos GKev LEdu WAbe
montana CPla CTtf EMor EWld GBin GJos GKev LEdu MBel NLar WBor WTyc XBar
- hybrid NSla
pindicola GEdr LEdu
pusilla GKev
'Spring Symphony' CElw CWCL ELan EPot GArf GBin GEdr GKev GMaP GPSL LEdu MNrw NBro NBwr NHar NWad SAko SPoG WFar WPnP
'Sudden Spring' CElw GBin LEdu NWad WAbe
villosa 🏆H6 CElw CTtf GAbr GBin GEdr GKev GLog GPSL LEdu NHar NWad WSHC

Soleirolia (*Urticaceae*)

soleirolii CDoC CKel CTri CWal ELan EPot LCro LLWG LOPS LWaG SEND SMad SPer SPtp SVic SWvt WHer XLum
- 'Argentea' see *S. soleirolii* 'Variegata'
§ - 'Aurea' CWal ELan EPot LWaG NBid NHpl SIvy SPtp SVic SWvt
- 'Golden Queen' see *S. soleirolii* 'Aurea'
- 'Minty' **new** LWaG
- 'Silver Queen' see *S. soleirolii* 'Variegata'
§ - 'Variegata' (v) ELan LLWG SPtp SVic

Solenopsis (*Campanulaceae*)

axillaris see *Isotoma axillaris*

Solenostemon ✿ (*Lamiaceae*)

scutellarioides 'Angel of the North' WDib
- 'Autumn Rainbow' WDib
- 'Beauty of Lyons' WDib
- 'Brilliant' (v) WDib
- 'Bronze Pagoda' WDib
- BURGUNDY WEDDING TRAIN ('Kakegawa Ce10') WDib
- CAMPFIRE ('Uf12823') MBros WHil
- 'Chamaeleon' (v) WDib
- 'Chocolate Covered Cherry' (v) **new** LCro WHlf
- 'Chocolate Mint' (v) **new** LCro
- 'City of Sunderland' WDib
- 'Combat' (v) 🏆H1c WDib
- 'Crimson Ruffles' (v) 🏆H1c WDib
- 'Dazzler' (v) WDib
- 'Durham Gala' 🏆H1c WDib
- 'Firelight' (v) WDib
- (FlameThrower Series) FLAMETHROWER SALSA ROJA ('Uf15-97-9') (v) **new** MPri
- - FLAMETHROWER SALSA VERDE ('Uf14-24-1') (v) **new** MPri
- 'Gay's Delight' 🏆H1c MPri
- HENNA ('Balcenna'PBR) (v) 🏆H1c ECtt MPri
- 'Illumination' WDib
- 'Inky Fingers' (v) WDib
- 'Juliet Quartermain' 🏆H1c WDib
- 'Jupiter' WDib
- 'Kentish Fire' (v) WDib
- 'Kiwi Fern' (Stained Glassworks Series) (v) WDib
- 'Lemon Chiffon' WDib
- 'Lime Delight' **new** LCro
- 'Lord Falmouth' (v) 🏆H1c WDib
- 'Mrs Pilkington' (v) WDib
- 'Muriel Pedley' (v) WDib
- 'Paisley Shawl' (v) WDib
- 'Peter Wonder' (v) WDib
- 'Pineapple Beauty' (v) 🏆H1c WDib
- 'Pineapplette' (v) 🏆H1c WDib
- 'Pink Chaos' (v) 🏆H1c WDib
- 'Red Angel' (v) WDib
- 'Red Velvet' (v) WDib
- 'Rose Blush' (v) WDib
- 'Roy Pedley' (v) 🏆H1c WDib
- 'Royal Scot' (v) 🏆H1c WDib
- 'Saturn' (v) MBros MDon WDib
- 'The Flume' WDib
- 'Timotei' WDib
- TRUSTY RUSTY ('Uf06419'PBR) (v) 🏆H1c MPri
- 'Walter Turner' (v) 🏆H1c WDib
- 'Winsome' (v) 🏆H1c WDib
- 'Winter Sun' (v) WDib
- 'Wisley Tapestry' (v) 🏆H1c WDib

Solidago (*Asteraceae*)

'Autumn Blaze' WFar
BABYGOLD see *S.* 'Goldkind'
'Ballardii' SRms
brachystachys see *S. cutleri*
caesia CTtf EBee EWes NBir SAko WFar WOld
- 'Maryland' **new** SHar
canadensis CTri SEND SPlb WBrk WFar WHer WOld XLum
- var. ***scabra*** NFav
'Citronella' GQue
'Cloth of Gold' CBod CMac EHeP EPfP LRHS NHol SGbt SPoG SWvt WOld
§ 'Crown of Rays' CRos ELan EPfP GBin LRHS MRav NLar NRHS SAko SCob WFar
§ ***cutleri*** EBou EDAr NLar SPlb SRms WFar

I	- ***nana***	SLee
	'Dennis Strange'	MAvo MHol WCot
	'Ducky'	SCob
	'Early Bird'	WFar
	flabelliformis	WCot
§	***flexicaulis***	GMaP SAko SPhx WCot XLum
	- 'Variegata' (v)	EBee EHyd EShb GMaP LRHS NLar NRHS WFar XLum
	'Foxbrook Fountain'	MAvo
	'Foxbrook Gold'	ECha MAvo MHol WFar
	'Gardone' ♀H7	WFar
	gigantea	WFar
	glomerata	MMuc NLar SEND SMrm
	GOLDEN BABY	see *S.* 'Goldkind'
§	'Golden Dwarf'	CWCL SPoG SRms XLum
	'Golden Fleece'	see *S. sphacelata* 'Golden Fleece'
	'Golden Thumb'	see *S.* 'Queenie'
	'Goldenmosa' ♀H7	CMac CSBt EWes GMaP SPer WCAu WFar
	'Goldilocks'	SRms
§	'Goldkind'	CSBt CTri EBee EBou EHyd ELan EPfP GMcL LRHS NRHS SCob SRms SWvt WBrk WCav WFar
	GOLDZWERG	see *S.* 'Golden Dwarf'
	'Hiddigeigei' (v)	SPtp WCot WFar
	hybrida	see *S.* × *luteus*
	latifolia	see *S. flexicaulis*
	'Laurin'	NLar XLum
	'Ledsham'	CAby CBod CRos ECtt EHyd GBin LRHS NRHS SPoG
	'Lena'	SRms
	'Linner Gold'	SAko
	'Little Gem'	LRHS
	'Little Lemon' PBR	EBee LRHS MTin NEoE NLar
§	× ***luteus***	EBee SRms WFar XLum
	- 'Lemore' ♀H7	CBod CDor CKno CMiW CTtf EBee ECha EPPr EPfP EShb GMaP LDai LRHS LSou MSpe NSti NWsh SAko SBut SMrm SPer SPhx SPoG SRms WCot WFar WOld XLum
	ohioensis	NLar XLum
	- 'Four Seasons'	GBin
§	***ptarmicoides***	XLum
§	'Queenie'	MHer
	riddellii	XLum
	rigida	SMrm
	- subsp. ***humilis*** 'Golden Rockets'	SPhx
	rugosa	ECha MBriF MMuc SEND SPhx WCot
	- 'Fireworks' ♀H7	CAby CBod CCBP CKno CMac CTtf ECha ECtt ELon EPPr EShb GBin GQue LShi MAvo MBriF MSpe NLar SAko SDys SPhx SRms WBrk WCAu WCot WFar WHoo WOld XLum
	- 'Loydser Crown'	ELon MAvo NDov SAko WCot
	sempervirens	WFar WOld
	- 'Goldene Wellen'	SAko
	shortii 'Solar Cascade'	SAko
	speciosa	SPhx WCot
§	***sphacelata*** 'Golden Fleece'	CBcs EHyd ELan EPfP SRms
	STRAHLENKRONE	see *S.* 'Crown of Rays'
	'Super'	WCot
	SWEETY ('Barseven' PBR)	EHyd LBar LRHS NRHS WHil
	'Tom Thumb'	MRav NBir SRms
	uliginosa	EShb NLar
	virgaurea	CBee GPoy MHer MMuc MNHC NAts NLar SMrm SRms WHer
	- var. ***cambrica***	see *S. virgaurea* subsp. *minuta*
	- subsp. ***leiocarpa***	WFar
§	- subsp. ***minuta***	GArf GBin GRum NBwr
	'Yellow Springs'	GJos
	'Yellow Stone'	EBee EHyd ELan LRHS

× *Solidaster* see *Solidago*

	hybridus	see *Solidago* × *luteus*

Sollya (*Pittosporaceae*)

	fusiformis	see *S. heterophylla*
§	***heterophylla***	Widely available
	- 'Alba'	CBcs CCCN CRos EHyd ELan EPfP ETho LRHS NRHS SCoo SEle SPer SPoG SWvt
	- 'Pink Charmer'	CBcs CKel EHyd ELan EPfP ETho LRHS SEle SPer SPoG WHlf
	- pink-flowered	CCCN CSBt CTsd SCoo SWvt

Solms-laubachia (*Brassicaceae*)

	eurycarpa	GKev

Sonchus (*Asteraceae*)

	arboreus	SIvy
	canariensis new	EAri
	congestus Willd. new	EAri
	fruticosus	EAri SIvy SPlb
	tenerrimus	SPlb
	subsp. ***tenerrimus***	

Sophora (*Fabaceae*)

	cassioides	MGil
	- NJM 08.008	WPGP
§	***davidii***	CBcs CExl CKel EAri EBee ELon EPfP ESwi LEdu LRHS MBlu SNig SPoG WCot WJur WLov
	flavescens	SBrt
	howinsula	WCot
	japonica	see *Styphnolobium japonicum*
§	'Little Baby'	CDoC CKel ELan EPfP MGil MGos SEle SIvy SPoG SWvt WLov
	longicarinata	WPGP
	macrocarpa	SWvt
	microphylla	CTri
	molloyi 'Dragon's Gold'	CBcs CKel EAri EBee ELan ELon EPfP LRHS MAsh SCoo SEND SEle SPoG SWvt XSte
	prostrata misapplied	see *S.* 'Little Baby'
	prostrata ambig.	SavN
	prostrata Buchanan	CMac WJur
	SUN KING ('Hilsop' PBR) ♀H4	CBcs CDoC CKel CRos CWGN EDir EHyd ELan EPfP EWes LMaj LRHS LSRN MGos MPkF NRHS SCoo SMad SPoG SWvt WCot XVPe
	tetraptera	CBcs CTsd EAri EHyd EPfP LRHS SEND SWvt WJur WPGP
	viciifolia	see *S. davidii*

Sorbaria (*Rosaceae*)

	aitchisonii	see *S. tomentosa* var. *angustifolia*
	arborea	see *S. kirilowii*
§	***kirilowii***	CExl CMac MRav NLar SMad
	lindleyana	see *S. tomentosa*
	sorbifolia	CBcs CMCN EHeP ELan GMcL IDee MGil MMuc SCob SEND SPer SPlb WFar
	- PINK HOPI ('Cousorb05')	NCth SGol
	- 'Sem' PBR ♀H5	Widely available
§	***tomentosa***	GBin
§	- var. ***angustifolia*** ♀H5	CEme CTri EHyd ELan EPfP LRHS MMuc MRav NBid SEND

× *Sorbaronia* (*Rosaceae*)

	fallax	NLar
	- 'Likjornaja' (F)	LRHS NLar WHtc

× *Sorbopyrus* (*Rosaceae*)

§ ***auricularis*** 'Shipova' (F)	CAgr MAsh WMat

Sorbus ✿ (*Rosaceae*)

KR 100	MVil
NJM 09.203	WPGP
adamii	CMCN
alnifolia	CLnd CMCN CPer EPfP MBlu
- B&SWJ 8461	WCru
- B&SWJ 10948	WCru
- 'Red Bird'	EBee EPfP LRHS MBlu MTrO NOra
'Amber Light'	EBee MTrO NLar NOra SGbt SOrN WMat
americana	NRog NWea
amoena	EGrI SPtp
'Apricot'	CEnd
'Apricot Queen'	CLnd EDir MDon NRog SGol WFar
aria	CBTr CCVT CHab CLnd CPer CTri EHeP IPap LBuc LPar MGos MMuc NBwr NRog NWea SCob SEND SGol WKor WMou WTSh
- 'Aurea'	CLnd EHeP
- 'Chrysophylla'	CSBt NRog
- 'Decaisneana'	see *S. aria* 'Majestica'
- 'Lutescens' ♀^{H6}	Widely available
- 'Magnifica'	CLnd EBar ELan LPar NBwr NWea SEWo
§ - 'Majestica' ♀^{H6}	CCVT CLnd CMac EBee EDir EHeP MRav NBwr NRog NWea SCob WFar WHtc
- 'Mitchellii'	see *S.* 'John Mitchell'
aria × ***pseudovilmorinii***	EBee MTrO WPGP
arnoldiana 'Golden Wonder'	see *S.* 'Lombarts Golden Wonder'
aronioides misapplied	see *S. caloneura*
aronioides Rehder	GKev
§ ***aucuparia***	Widely available
- 'Aspleniifolia'	CCVT CMCN CMac CPer CSBt EBar EBee EDir EHeP EPom EWTr IPap LRHS MGos MNic MRav MTrO NBwr NLar NOra NOrn NRHS NRog NWea SCob SLim WFar WHtc WMat WMou
- subsp. ***aucuparia***	CDoC
§ - 'Beissneri'	CAgr EHeP MRav NRog NWea WHtc
- CARDINAL ROYAL ('Michred')	CCVT CDoC CLnd EDir EHeP IPap LRHS MMuc NBwr SCob SCoo SEWo WHtc
- 'Dirkenii'	WHtc WMat
§ - var. ***edulis*** (F)	CArg EHeP LBuc
- - 'Rossica' misapplied	see *S. aucuparia* var. *edulis* 'Rossica Major'
§ - - 'Rossica Major'	EDir EHeP MMuc SEWo WHtc
§ - 'Fastigiata'	CEnd CTri EPfP GKin LPar
- 'Fingerprint'^{PBR}	EBee MTrO NLar NOra
- 'Hilling's Spire'	CPer
- subsp. ***maderensis***	MBlu WLov
- ***pluripinnata***	see *S. scalaris* Koehne
- var. ***rossica*** Koehne	see *S. aucuparia* var. *edulis*
- 'Sheerwater Seedling' ♀^{H6}	Widely available
- 'Wettra'	SGsty
- var. ***xanthocarpa***	NRog
§ ***aucuparia*** × ***scalaris***	CPer NOrn
AUTUMN SPIRE ('Flanrock') ♀^{H6}	CBcs CBod CDoC CEnd CKel CLnd CWnw EBee ELan EPfP LRHS LSRN MAsh MDon MGos MTrO NOra NWea SCoo SGol SGsty SLim SOrN SPer SPoG SRHi SWvt WHtc WMat
§ ***bissetii***	LRHS MTrO NOra WLov
- Yu 14299	WCru
- PEARLS	see *S. bissetii*
brevipetiolata B&SWJ 11771	WCru
bulleyana	MVil
- KR 2809	WCru
- MF 96170	GKev
§ ***caloneura***	EBee EPfP LEdu MBlu SPtp WLov WPGP
- Guiz 80	WCru
§ ***carmesina***	CPer EPfP MTrO NLar NOra SPtp WMat
- B&L 12545	EBee EPfP GKev WCru
- 'Emberglow'	see *S. carmesina*
cashmiriana misapplied pink-fruited	see *S. rosea*
cashmiriana Hedl. ♀^{H6}	CBcs CCVT CLnd CMCN CMac CTri CWal EHyd ELan EPfP EPom GKev IPap LRHS MBlu MGos MMuc MRav MSwo MTrO NLar NOrn SCob SGol SPer SPoG WMat WMou
aff. ***cashmiriana*** ambig.	EDir EHeP LCro MAsh NBwr NHol NOra SRHi WFar WTSh
- B 751	WCru
chamaemespilus	WThu
'Chinese Lace'	Widely available
§ ***commixta***	CBod CEnd CKel CLnd CMCN CPer CWnw EDir EHeP EWTr LCro LMaj MBlu MDon MGos MSwo MTrO NOrn NRog SGol SLim SPer
- B&SWJ 10839	WCru
- B&SWJ 11043	WCru
- B&SWJ 12640 from Ulleungdo, South Korea	WCru
- 'Carmencita'	EWTr MBlu
- 'Embley' ♀^{H6}	CBcs CCVT CLnd CMCN CSBt CTri EHeP EPfP LCro LOPS MBlu MGos MMuc MRav NOrn NWea SCob SEND SGol SPer WHtc
- OLYMPIC FLAME	see *S. ulleungensis* 'Olympic Flame'
- 'Ravensbill'	EBee EPfP MTrO NLar NOra NWea SCoo SGbt SGol WHCr WMat
- var. ***rufoferruginea*** B&SWJ 11486	WCru
aff. ***commixta***	CBod WTSh
conradinae Koehne	see *S. esserteauana*
'Copper Kettle' ♀^{H6}	CBcs EBee EPfP MAsh MBlu MTrO NLar NOra NOrn SCoo SGol WHCr WMat WMou
'Coral Beauty'	CLnd
corymbifera	GKev
- WWJ 11860	WCru
'Covert Gold'	CEnd
'Croft Coral'	MAsh MTrO NLar NOra WHtc
cuspidata	see *S. vestita*
decora var. ***nana***	see *S. aucuparia* 'Fastigiata'
devoniensis	CPer
- 'Devon Beauty'	CAgr
discolor misapplied	see *S. commixta*
discolor (Maxim.) Maxim.	EDir IPap MBlu MTrO NWea
- MF 96172	MAsh
- MF 97103	WCru
domestica	CLnd CPer MMuc NRog NWea SEND WJur
- 'Maliformis'	see *S. domestica* f. *pomifera*
§ - f. ***pomifera***	LEdu
§ - f. ***pyrifera***	LEdu
- 'Pyriformis'	see *S. domestica* f. *pyrifera*
- 'Rosie'	CAgr
dunnii	WPGP
'Eastern Promise' ♀^{H6}	CPer EPfP EPom LCro MAsh MBlu MSwo MTrO NLar NOra NOrn NRog NWea SCob SCoo SGbt SLim WHCr WHtc WMat WMou
§ ***eburnea***	GKev

	- Harry Smith 12799	NHar WPGP
	eleonorae	SPtp WPGP
§	***esserteauana***	CLnd
	'Ethel's Gold'	MBlu
	eugenii-kelleri	GKev
	fansipanensis NJM 09.176	WPGP
	'Fastigiata'	see *S. aucuparia* 'Fastigiata', *S.* × *thuringiaca* 'Fastigiata'
	filipes	GKev
	folgneri 'Emiel' ♀H6	CBcs EPfP IArd MBlu NOra WMat
	- 'Lemon Drop'	CEnd CLnd EBee MBlu NOra SCoo WMat
	foliolosa	CLnd
	forrestii ♀H6	EBee GKev MMuc MVil SPtp WHtc
§	***frutescens*** ♀H6	ELan MVil NWad
	fruticosa 'Koehneana'	see *S. koehneana* C.K. Schneid.
	'Ghose'	EBee WMat
	glabrescens	LEdu
§	***glabriuscula***	WJur
	'Glendoick Spire'	EBee LRHS MTrO NOra WMat
	'Glendoick White Baby'	MTrO NOra WMat
	globosa HWJ 537	WCru
	'Golden Wonder'	see *S.* 'Lombarts Golden Wonder'
	gonggashanica	EPfP GEdr LRHS SPtp WPGP
§	***graeca***	GKev WCot
	'Granatnaja'	see × *Crataegosorbus* 'Granatnaja'
	granulosa HWJ 1041	WCru
	harrowiana	LEdu LRHS MTrO WLov WMat WPGP
	- KW 21009	WPGP
	- from Burma	WPGP
	- from Yunnan	WPGP
	- pink-fruited **new**	WPGP
	hedlundii	CExl EPfP LRHS MTrO NLar NOra WMat WPGP
	- GWJ 9363	WCru WPGP
	- KR 1687	WPGP
	- KR 1810	WPGP
	- WJC 13806	WCru
	helenae	MTrO NOra WPGP
	- EN 3088	GKev WPGP
	hemsleyi	CExl CLnd SPtp WPGP
	- 'John Bond' ♀H6	LRHS MTrO NLar NOra WHtc WMat
	henryi	MTrO
	× ***hostii***	CLnd
	hugh-mcallisteri	MVil
	- CLD 310	GKev MVil
	hupehensis misapplied	see *S. pseudohupehensis*
	- 'November Pink'	see *S. pseudohupehensis*
	- 'Rosea'	see *S. pseudohupehensis*
	- white-berried	see *S. glabriuscula*
	aff. ***hupehensis***	CSBt EHeP NBwr NOra NOrn NRog SGol WFar WTSh
	hybrida L. 'Gibbsii' ♀H6	EPfP MAsh MDon MTrO NOra NOrn WMat
	incana	LMaj
	insignis	WLov WPGP
	- from Arunachal Pradesh, India	WPGP
	- from Nepal	WPGP
	intermedia	CAco CBTr CCVT CLnd CSBt CTri EHeP IPap LMaj LPar NBwr NRog NWea SCob SEND SGol
	- 'Brouwers'	CLnd EHeP WMou
	japonica	EBee NOra WMat
	- B&SWJ 10813	WCru
	- B&SWJ 11048	WCru
§	'John Mitchell' ♀H6	CAgr CBcs CEnd CLnd CMCN CRos EBee EHeP EPfP MBlu MGos MTrO NLar NOra SLim SPoG WMat
	'Joseph Rock'	Widely available
	aff. ***karchungii***	EBee
	- AGS/ES 347	WPGP
I	***keenanii*** NJM 13.050	WPGP
	keissleri	EBee
	- NJM 11.004	WPGP
	- PAB 7916	LEdu
	'Keith Rushforth'	WCru
§	× ***kewensis***	CLnd SPlb
	khumbuensis	GKev SPtp
	'Kirsten Pink'	CCVT EHeP SPer
	koehneana misapplied	see *S. frutescens*
§	***koehneana*** C.K. Schneid.	CLnd CMCN GKev MMrt WCru
	aff. ***koehneana*** C.K. Schneid.	see *S. eburnea*, *S. tenuis*
	lanata misapplied	see *S. vestita*
	latifolia	NWea
	'Leonard Messel' ♀H6	EPfP MAsh MTrO NOra SGbt WMat
§	'Lombarts Golden Wonder'	CLnd EDir EHeP MMuc NBwr NLar NWea
*	***maculata*** KR 5334	GKev MVil
	matsumurana misapplied	see *S. commixta*
	matsumurana (Makino) Koehne	EBee IArd WPGP
	'Matthew Ridley'	EBee ELan
	megalocarpa	CMCN WJur WPGP
	- var. ***cuneata***	WPGP
	meliosmifolia	SPtp
	- B&SWJ 11709	WCru
	microphylla agg.	CMCN EPfP GKev
	- GWJ 9252	WCru
	monbeigii (Cardot.) N.P. Balakr.	MGil
	moravica 'Laciniata'	see *S. aucuparia* 'Beissneri'
	muliensis F 22177	GKev
§	***munda***	MMuc WCFE
	needhamii NJM 11.005	EBee WPGP
	'Nevezhinskaja'	MBlu
	olivacea	GKev SPtp
	aff. ***ovalis*** H 1948	EBee
	pallescens 'White House Farm'	WPGP
	paniculata NJM 13.067	WPGP
	- NJM 13.092	WPGP
	- PAB 9831	LEdu
	parvifructa	GKev WPGP
	'Peaches and Cream'	LCro LOPS
	'Pearly King'	CPer MAsh
§	'Pink Pearl'	EPfP NOra
	'Pink-Ness'	EPfP MBlu MTrO NLar NOra SCoo WLov WMat
	pohuashanensis misapplied	see *S.* × ***kewensis***
	pohuashanensis ambig.	CMCN
	poteriifolia ♀H5	GEdr GKev NHar
	prattii misapplied	see *S. munda*
	- var. ***subarachnoidea***	see *S. munda*
	aff. ***prattii*** **new**	CPer
§	***pseudohupehensis*** ♀H6	Widely available
§	- 'Pink Pagoda'	see *S. pseudohupehensis*
	pseudovilmorinii	CBcs EBee GKev LRHS MGil MNic MTrO NOra NWea WCru WMat
	- SBEC 974	WPGP
	randaiensis	EBee SPlb WPGP
	- B&SWJ 156	WPGP
	- B&SWJ 3202	NWad WCru
	reducta ♀H5	GBin GEdr GKev MMuc MVil NFav NHar NHol NLar NSla WLov
	aff. ***reducta***	SRms
	reflexipetala misapplied	see *S. commixta*
	rehderiana misapplied	see *S. aucuparia*
	rehderiana Koehne	GKev MVil
	'Rose Queen'	MBlu MTrO NOra
§	***rosea***	EBee ELan EPfP GKev LRHS MTrO NOra NWea WMat

	- SEP 492	WCru WPGP
	- 'Rosiness'	see *S. rosea*
	'Rowancroft Coral Pink'	EBee
	rubescens	GKev
	rufopilosa	MVil
	rupicola	NWea
	rushforthii KR 5789	EBee GKev
	'Salmon Queen'	CLnd EHeP
	sargentiana ♀H6	CBTr CBcs CCVT CEnd CLnd CMCN CMac CTri EBee EHeP ELan EPfP MBlu MGos MRav MSwo MTrO NLar NOra NOrn NRog NWea SLim SPoG WHtc WJur WMat
	scalaris misapplied	see *S. aucuparia* × *S. scalaris*
	scalaris ambig.	CBcs CBod CMCN CPer ELan GKev MAsh MSwo MTrO NOra NRog NWea SPoG
§	***scalaris*** Koehne	CEnd CTri MBlu WJur WMat
	'Schouten'	EHeP
	scopulina misapplied	see *S. aucuparia* 'Fastigiata'
	section *Discolores*	MTrO
	- KR 5585	MVil WCru WPGP
	- KR 6308	WCru
	setschwanensis	CMCN
	'Showa'	GKev
	- KR 5585	WPGP
§	***splendens***	CLnd LRHS NLar WJur
	- CH 7122 **new**	WPGP
	subulata HWJ 925	WCru
	- KWJ 12272	WCru
	'Sunshine'	CCVT CLnd EHeP LRHS MAsh MGos MMuc MTrO NOra SEND SGol WHtc
§	***tenuis***	GKev
	thibetica	WJur
	aff. ***thibetica*** BWJ 7757a	WCru
	thomsonii GWJ 9363	WCru
	- WWJ 12004	WCru
§	× ***thuringiaca*** 'Fastigiata'	EBar EHeP NBwr NWea SCoo WMat
	tianschanica	WCru
	'Titan'	EPfP MBlu
	torminalis	Widely available
	ulleungensis	WPGP
	- B&SWJ 12640	WCru
	- 'Dodong'	LRHS MNic SGsty
§	- 'Olympic Flame' ♀H6	Widely available
	umbellata var. ***cretica***	see *S. graeca*
	ursina (Wall. ex G. Don) S. Schauer	see *S. foliolosa*
§	***vestita***	WCru
	vexans	GBin
	vilmorinii ♀H6	Widely available
	- 'Pink Charm'	EPfP LRHS MNic MTrO NOra SGol WMat
	- 'Robusta'	see *S.* 'Pink Pearl'
	aff. ***vilmorinii***	CWnw EHeP GKin MTrO SRHi WHtc
	- KR 5100 **new**	MVil
	- KR 6453	WCru WPGP
	wallichii NJM 13.127	WPGP
	wardii	EPfP LRHS MBlu NOra
	- KR 21127	EBee WPGP
	'White Wax'	CBod CCVT EHeP MGos NWea SPer
	'Wilfrid Fox'	CCVT EHeP MGos
	wilsoniana misapplied	see *S. splendens*
	wilsoniana C.K. Schneid. PW 47 **new**	WPGP
	'Wisley Gold' ♀H6	CBod LRHS MTrO NOra NWea SCoo SGbt SLim WMat WMou
	yuana	WPGP
	zahlbruckneri C.K. Schneid.	WPGP

Sorghastrum (*Poaceae*)

	avenaceum	see *S. nutans*
§	***nutans***	EBou EPPr SBls
	- 'Indian Steel'	ECha NDov XLum
	- 'Sioux Blue'	NDov

sorrel, common see *Rumex acetosa*

sorrel, French see *Rumex scutatus*

Souliea see *Actaea*

Sparaxis (*Iridaceae*)

'Bright Star'	GKev
bulbifera	WHil
elegans	CBor SPlb WHil
- white-flowered	CBor WHil
grandiflora subsp. ***acutiloba***	CBor CPbh NRog
- subsp. ***fimbriata***	NRog
- subsp. ***grandiflora***	CPbh
'Moonlight'	GKev
pillansii **new**	CBor
'Red Reflex'	GKev
roxburghii **new**	CBor
'Skyline'	GKev
'Sunshine'	GKev NRog
tricolor	CPla GKev LAma SDeJ
villosa	NRog

Sparganium (*Sparganiaceae*)

§	***erectum***	CPud CWat LPfP NMir NPer WMAq WSFF XLum
	ramosum	see *S. erectum*

Sparrmannia (*Malvaceae*)

africana ♀H1c	CCCN CHll EAri ELan EShb SEND SPlb SVen WCot
- 'Flore Pleno' (d)	CBcs

Spartina (*Poaceae*)

pectinata	XLum
- 'Aureomarginata' (v)	CBod CWCL ELan EPfP GMaP GMcL MACG MMuc NFav NWsh SEND SPer XLum

Spartium (*Fabaceae*)

junceum ♀H5	CBcs CBod CCCN CDoC CMac EHeP ELan ELon EPfP LRHS NFav NSti SArc SEND SPer SRms WAvo WJur XSen
- 'Brockhill Compact'	CDoC CKel EHyd EPfP

Spartocytisus see *Cytisus*

Spathantheum (*Araceae*)

orbignyanum	GKev SBrt WCot

Spathipappus see *Tanacetum*

Spathiphyllum (*Araceae*)

BINGO CUPIDO ('Spapril'PBR) **new**	LCro
'Lima'PBR **new**	NHrt
'Sweet Lauretta'PBR **new**	LCro NHrt NTrD
wallisii	NHrt SPre
- 'Bellini'	LCro LOPS NHrt

Spathodea (*Bignoniaceae*)

campanulata	SPlb

spearmint see *Mentha spicata*

Speirantha (*Asparagaceae*)

	convallarioides	see *S. gardenii*
§	***gardenii***	CBct CDTJ EHed EPPr ESwi LEdu MHol MNrw WCru WPGP WSHC

Sphacele see *Lepechinia*

Sphaeralcea (*Malvaceae*)

	ambigua	SPlb
	'Childerley'	CDor CSpe EAri ECtt MHol SMad SPad SPoG WCot WMal
	coccinea	CSpe SPlb
	fendleri	CCCN CSde
	'Hopleys Lavender'	CCCN SWvt
	incana	CCCN CSde LPla MGil SIvy WMal
	- 'Sourup'	ECtt SMHy WCot
	malviflora	CDTJ
	miniata	CCCN
	munroana	CCCN ECtt ELan SMad SRkn
	'Newleaze Coral'	CCCN EAri EWld MAsh MGil MNrw SIvy SMad SPad SPoG SRkn SWvt WBor WCot WFar WLov WMal
	'Newleaze Pink'	SRkn
	remota	CExl SPlb
	umbellata	see *Phymosia umbellata*

Sphagneticola (*Asteraceae*)

§	***trilobata***	LLWG

Sphenomeris (*Dennstaedtiaceae*)

	chinensis B&SWJ 6108	WCru

Spigelia (*Loganiaceae*)

	marilandica	CBor EBee GKev LBar SMad WCot WHil WSHC

Spilanthes (*Asteraceae*)

	acmella misapplied	see *Acmella oleracea*
	oleracea	see *Acmella oleracea*

Spiloxene see *Pauridia*

spinach see AGM Vegetables Section

Spiraea (*Rosaceae*)

	alba var. ***latifolia***	MMuc
	albiflora	see *S. japonica* 'Albiflora'
	arborea	see *Sorbaria kirilowii*
	arcuata	NBwr
§	'Arguta' ♀H6	Widely available
	× ***arguta*** 'Bridal Wreath'	see *S.* 'Arguta'
	aff. 'Arguta'	EPau GMcL NBwr SRHi WHtc
	betulifolia	MRav WFar
	- var. ***aemiliana***	MMuc
	- PINK SPARKLER ('Courispi01'PBR) **new**	WHlf
	- 'Tor'	EPPr GKev LPar NLar
	- 'Tor Gold'PBR	CBcs EHed ELan LRHS MMrt MRav SPoG
	× ***billardii*** misapplied	see *S.* × *pseudosalicifolia*
	blumei CWJ 12829	WCru
	× ***bumalda*** 'Wulfenii'	see *S. japonica* 'Walluf'
	callosa 'Alba'	see *S. japonica* 'Albiflora'
	canescens	CExl GKin
	× ***cinerea*** 'Grefsheim' ♀H6	CBcs CBod CSBt EHeP ELan LBuc LPar NLar SCob SPer SPlb
	crispifolia misapplied	see *S. japonica* 'Bullata'
	densiflora	GKev
	- var. ***splendens***	SBrt
	DOUBLE PLAY BIG BANG	see *S.* 'Tracy'
	douglasii	CMac
	formosana B&SWJ 1597	CExl WCru
	fritschiana	CMac
	hayatana	GKev SBrt
	- RWJ 10014	WCru
	hendersonii	see *Petrophytum hendersonii*
	japonica var. ***acuminata***	MVil
§	- 'Albiflora'	CBod CBrac CEme CKel CMac CSBt CTri EFPl EHeP EHyd ELan EPfP GMcL LRHS MRav MSwo NBwr NLar NRHS NWad NWea SGbt SRms SWvt WFar
	- 'Alpina'	see *S. japonica* 'Nana'
	- 'Alpine Gold'	NEoE
	- 'Anthony Waterer' (v)	Widely available
	- 'Barkby Gold'	EHeP
§	- 'Bullata'	CMac NBwr NLar WAbe
	- 'Candlelight' ♀H6	CBod CSBt ELan EPfP GBin GKin GMcL LRHS MAsh SCob SCoo SGol SPoG SWvt
	- 'Country Red'	NBwr
	- 'Crispa'	EPfP NBwr NEoE NWad WFar
	- 'Dart's Red' ♀H6	EDir EHeP GKin
	- (Double Play Series) DOUBLE PLAY ARTISAN ('Galen')	SPoG
	- - DOUBLE PLAY GOLD ('Yan')	SPoG
	- 'Firelight'	CBod CDoC CGBo CRos CSBt CTsd EBee EDir ELan ELon EPau EPfP GKin GMcL LRHS MAsh MGos MSwo NBwr NHol NLar NWad SCob SCoo SGol SPer SRms SWvt WBor
§	- var. ***fortunei*** 'Macrophylla'	WLov
	- 'Froebelii'	EBee GMcL
§	- 'Genpei'	CChe CMac MAsh NBwr SGol SPer SPoG SRms
	- 'Gold Mound'	CBar CBod CBrac CMac EBee EHeP ELan EPfP GMcL MAsh MGos MRav MSwo NBwr NLar SCob SCoo SGol SPer SPlb SRms WFar WHtc
	- GOLDEN PRINCESS ('Lisp') ♀H6	CDoC CMac CRos CTri EHyd ELan EPfP GMcL LBuc LRHS MAsh MGos NBwr SCoo SGol SPer SRms WFar
	- 'Goldflame'	Widely available
	- 'Little Princess'	CBcs CBod CDoC CGBo CMac CRos EBee EDir EHeP EHyd ELan GMcL LRHS MAsh MRav MSwo NBwr NRHS NWea SCob SCoo SGol SGsty SPer SRHi SRms SWvt WFar WHtc
	- MAGIC CARPET ('Walbuma'PBR) (v) ♀H6	CBcs EHyd EPfP GMcL LBuc LRHS MAsh MMuc NLar NRHS SCoo SPoG SRms
	- 'Magnifica'	see *S. japonica* var. *fortunei* 'Macrophylla'
§	- 'Nana' ♀H6	CSBt MAsh SRms
	- 'Neon Flash' **new**	WHlf
	- 'Nyewoods'	see *S. japonica* 'Nana'
	- 'Nyewoods Gold'	CMac
	- 'Odessa'PBR	GKev
	- 'Shiburi'	see *S. japonica* 'Albiflora'
	- 'Shirobana' misapplied	see *S. japonica* 'Genpei'
	- 'Shirobana'	see *S. japonica* 'Albiflora'
	- 'Stanton Gold'	WCFE
	- WALBERTON'S PLUMTASTIC ('Walplum') **new**	LBuc WNPC
§	- 'Walluf'	CMac CTri GBin
	- 'White Cloud'	CDoC

- 'White Gold'[PBR]	CKel CMac CRos CSBt EHyd ELan EPfP GMcL LRHS LSou MAsh NEoE NHol NRHS NWad SCoo SPer SPoG SRms SWvt WFar
× ***margaritae***	SWvt
media DOUBLE PLAY BLUE KAZOO ('Smsmbk') (Double Play Series) **new**	EHed
micrantha	CExl
nipponica 'Halward's Silver'	MRav NEoE
- 'June Bride'	CBod MACG
§ - 'Snowmound' 🏆H6	Widely available
- var. ***tosaensis*** misapplied	see *S. nipponica* 'Snowmound'
palmata 'Elegans'	see *Filipendula purpurea* 'Elegans'
prunifolia (d)	CBod CMac EPfP LRHS MRav NLar SPer WAvo WCFE WFar
× ***pseudosalicifolia*** 'Triumphans'	EHeP MMuc SPer
rosthornii	GKev
salicifolia	WFar
SPARKLING CHAMPAGNE ('Lonspi'[PBR])	CBod CSBt LCro LRHS LSRN NEoE NWad SCob SGBe
SUNDROP ('Bailcarol')	LSou
tarokoensis	CMCN
thunbergii 🏆H6	CBcs CBrac CMac CTri EHeP EPfP MMuc MRav NWea SBrt SCob SPer SRms
- 'Fujino Pink'	CRos LRHS
- 'Golden Times'	SPoG
- 'Mellow Yellow'	see *S. thunbergii* 'Ōgon'
- 'Mount Fuji'	CMac MRav WFar
§ - 'Ōgon'	EPfP NLar WFar
* - 'Variegata' (v)	SRms
§ 'Tracy'[PBR]	LRHS MMrt NEoE SCob SMad WCot
ulmaria	see *Filipendula ulmaria*
× ***vanhouttei***	CMac CTri ELan LPar MMuc MRav MSwo NBwr SEND SGsty SRms SavN WFar
- 'Gold Fountain'	CBod CMac ELan EPfP GKev LPar LSRN MAsh MMuc NHol NLar SCoo SEND SPer WFar WHtc
- 'Pink Ice' (v)	CBod CMac CRos EHyd EPfP LRHS MAsh MRav NBwr NLar SPer SPlb SPoG SWvt WFar
veitchii	GLog MRav
venusta 'Magnifica'	see *Filipendula rubra* 'Venusta'

Spiranthes (*Orchidaceae*)

aestivalis	NLAp
cernua	NLAp
ochroleuca	NLAp
odorata 'Chadd's Ford' 🏆H4	CBod CExl EGrI EHed LBar MHer MHtn SBls SCoo SPoG WTor XSte
sinensis	NLAp
spiralis	GKev NLAp

Spodiopogon (*Poaceae*)

sibiricus	CKno EPPr GBin LDai SPeP SPtp XLum
- 'West Lake'	MAvo NDov

Sporobolus (*Poaceae*)

airoides	CKno EPPr
heterolepis	CBWd CKno CSpe EBee ECha EPfP EWes GBin GMaP LEdu LRHS MBel NDov SMHy SPtp WCot WPGP
- 'Cloud'	NDov
I - 'Wisconsin Strain'	CSpe EBee SBls
'JS Delicatesse'	CAby EPfP LRHS WTor
wrightii	CKno EPPr SBls WAvo

Sprekelia (*Amaryllidaceae*)

formosissima	EShb GKev LAma LEdu SDeJ SDir

squashes see AGM Vegetables Section

Stachys (*Lamiaceae*)

aethiopica 'Danielle'	see *S. thunbergii* 'Danielle'
§ ***affinis***	GPoy LEdu SPlb SVic
'Bello Grigio'	MHol
betonica	see *Betonica officinalis*
§ ***byzantina***	Widely available
§ - 'Big Ears'	Widely available
§ - 'Cotton Boll'	CBod CRos ECha EGrI LRHS SRms WFar XSen
- 'Countess Helen von Stein'	see *S. byzantina* 'Big Ears'
- 'Fuzzy Wuzzy'	WFar
- gold-leaved	see *S. byzantina* 'Primrose Heron'
- large-leaved	see *S. byzantina* 'Big Ears'
- 'Limelight'	SAng WCot XLum
§ - 'Primrose Heron'	ECha EGrI GBin GKev GMaP LBar MAsh MRav NLar NRHS SMrm SPer SWvt WCAu WFar WMal XLum
- 'Pure Cotton'	SBls
- 'Sheila McQueen'	see *S. byzantina* 'Cotton Boll'
- 'Silky Fleece'	EBou ECha ELan EPfP LRHS NLar SRms XSen
- 'Silver Carpet'	Widely available
chamissonis var. ***cooleyae***	GBin
citrina	LPla SLee WAbe XSen
coccinea	GEdr
cretica	XSen
densiflora	see *S. monieri* (Gouan) P.W. Ball
discolor	see *Betonica nivea*
germanica	NAts
grandiflora	see *Betonica macrantha*
'Hidalgo'	SRms
lanata Jacq.	see *S. byzantina*
lavandulifolia	WAbe
macrantha	see *Betonica macrantha*
- 'Hummelo'	see *Betonica officinalis* 'Hummelo'
mexicana misapplied	see *S. thunbergii*
monieri misapplied	see *Betonica officinalis*
monieri ambig.	CBor EPfP NLar NSti
- white-flowered	EBee
§ ***monieri*** (Gouan) P.W. Ball	LEdu
* - 'Rosea'	CBWd EBee EMor LEdu NDov NLar SRms
nivea	see *Betonica nivea*
officinalis	see *Betonica officinalis*
olympica	see *S. byzantina*
ossetica	see *Betonica nivea* subsp. *ossetica*
palustris	CHab CPud CWat EWat LLWG LPfP MCoo MMuc NLar SEND SPhx SRms
- from Islay, Hebrides	MMuc SEND
recta	CBee SBut WCAu
setifera	MHol XLum
spicata	see *Betonica macrantha*
sylvatica	CHab WHer WSFF WWild
'The Bride'	NDov
thirkei	SAng WCot
§ ***thunbergii***	MBrN MBriF MNHC WKif
§ - 'Danielle'	CBod CBor ECtt EGrI EPfP NLar SDys SRkn SRms WMal
tuberifera	see *S. affinis*

Stachyurus (*Stachyuraceae*)

chinensis	CBcs CBod CJun CMCN CTri EBee EWes MVil NLar

- 'Celina' ♀H5	CJun CRos EHed EHyd ELon EPfP ESwi GKin LRHS MBNS MGos NLar NRHS SPoG WPGP XSte
- 'Goldbeater'	NLar
- 'Joy Forever' (v) ♀H5	CBcs CDoC CEnd CKel CMac EHyd EPfP ESwi LRHS MGos MMrt NLar SPer SPoG SSta SWvt WKif
- 'Senna'	NLar
- 'Wonderful Image'	ESwi
himalaicus	NLar
- HWJK 2035	WCru
- pink-flowered	see *S. himalaicus* subsp. *purpureus*
§ - subsp. ***purpureus*** HWJK 2052	WCru
aff. ***macrocarpus*** B&SWJ 14678	WCru
'Magpie' (v)	SSha
praecox ♀H5	Widely available
- B&SWJ 8898	WCru
- B&SWJ 10899	IDee LCro WCru
- var. ***leucotrichus***	CJun NLar
- var. ***matsuzakii***	CJun NLar
- - B&SWJ 11229	WCru
- 'Petra'	CJun
retusus	CExl
'Rubriflorus'	EBee ELon EPfP MAsh WPGP
salicifolius	CBcs CExl CJun EBee EPfP IArd IDee LRHS SPoG SSta WPGP XSte
sigeyosii	CBcs CExl EBee SSta WPGP
- B&SWJ 6915	WCru
- CWJ 12420	WCru
aff. ***szechuanensis***	CExl
- BWJ 8153	WCru
yunnanensis	CJun NLar WPGP

Stangeria (*Stangeriaceae*)

eriopus	LPal

Stapelia (*Apocynaceae*)

sp.	SCoo SPoG
grandiflora	SSim
marmoratum	see *Orbea variegata*
variegata	see *Orbea variegata*

Staphylea ✿ (*Staphyleaceae*)

bumalda	CBcs CJun LEdu NLar
- B&SWJ 11053	WCru
- B&SWJ 12744 from Korea	WCru
colchica	CBcs CMCN CRos EHyd ELan EPfP EWTr EWes LEdu LMaj LPar LRHS MGos MMrt MRav SPer WHlf WJur WKif
- B&SWJ 16009 **new**	WCru
holocarpa	CJun
- 'Innocence'	CBcs WPGP
- var. ***rosea***	CBcs CJun CMCN MBlu SWvt WKif WPGP
pinnata	CAgr CBcs CJun EPfP MCoo NLar SEND WHtc WJur XSte
- B&SWJ 15319 **new**	WCru
- PAB 8427	LEdu
trifolia	CAgr EBee EHed EPfP WHtc WJur

Statice see *Limonium*

Stauntonia (*Lardizabalaceae*)

from northern Vietnam	WCru
aff. ***chinensis*** DJHV 06175	WCru
hexaphylla	CBcs CBrac CCCN CRHN CTri CWGN EBee EGrI EHyd EPfP ESwi LPal LRHS MAsh MGil NLar SAdn SNig SPer SPoG SSta
- B&SWJ 4858	WCru
- B&SWJ 14655	CKel ESwi WCru
libera KWJ 12218	WCru
obovata CWJ 12353	WCru
obovatifoliola B&SWJ 3685	WCru
purpurea	WPGP
- B&SWJ 3690	WCru
yaoshanensis B&SWJ 8223	WCru
- FMWJ 13171	WCru
- HWJ 1024	WCru

Steganotaenia (*Apiaceae*)

araliacea **new**	WCot

Stegnogramma (*Thelypteridaceae*)

pozoi	EFer

Stellaria (*Caryophyllaceae*)

graminea	CHab
holostea	CHab MBow NBir WShi

Stemmacantha see *Rhaponticum*

Stenanthium (*Melanthiaceae*)

gramineum	EBee EWes

Stenocactus (*Cactaceae*)

LAU 1377 **new**	NMen
multicostatus ♀H1c **new**	NMen
- SB 1565 **new**	NMen
vaupelianus **new**	NMen

Stenocereus (*Cactaceae*)

dumortieri **new**	NPlm
marginatus	see *Pachycereus marginatus*
thurberi **new**	NPlm

Stenomesson (*Amaryllidaceae*)

pearcei	CBor GKev

Stenotaenia (*Apiaceae*)

macrocarpa **new**	WCot

Stenotaphrum (*Poaceae*)

secundatum	EShb
- 'Variegatum' (v)	EShb XLum

Stephanandra (*Rosaceae*)

incisa	CExl
§ - 'Crispa'	CBcs CDoC CMac CTri EBee EGrI EHeP ELan EPfP GArf GKin GMcL LPar LRHS MBlu MRav NHol SCob SGbt SPer SRms WFar WHtc
- 'Prostrata'	see *S. incisa* 'Crispa'
tanakae	CBcs CExl CMac EBee ELan EPfP MBlu MGil MRav SPer SRms

Stephania (*Menispermaceae*)

aff. ***hernandiifolia*** B&SWJ 14950	WCru
japonica CWJ 12823	WCru
aff. ***tetrandra*** WWJ 11896	WCru

Stephanotis (*Apocynaceae*)

floribunda ♀H1a	CBcs CCCN CDoC LCro LOPS SPre WFib

Sterculia (*Malvaceae*)

rupestris	see *Brachychiton rupestris*

Sternbergia (*Amaryllidaceae*)

	candida	CBro NRog
§	***clusiana***	NRog
	colchiciflora	NRog
	fischeriana	CBro
	greuteriana	EPot GKev NRog
	lutea 🏆H4	CBro CTri ECha EHyd ELan EPot ERCP EWes GKev LAma LCro LOPS LRHS NRHS NRog SDeJ SGro WHoo WIce XLum
	- from Bisceglie, Italy	NRog
	- from Iran	NRog
	- Angustifolia Group	CAvo CBro WCot
	- var. ***graeca***	NRog
	macrantha	see *S. clusiana*
	sicula	CBro EPot GKev NRog
	- 'Arcadian Sun'	GKev NRog
	- 'Dodona Gold'	CBor GKev NRog
	- 'John Marr'	WCot WThu
	vernalis	NRog

Stetsonia (*Cactaceae*)

	coryne **new**	LCro NCft NPlm

Stevia (*Asteraceae*)

	rebaudiana	CBod CCBP CGro ENfk GPoy LCro LShi MHoo MNHC SPre SRms SVic WCot WJek

Stewartia ✿ (*Theaceae*)

	gemmata	see *S. sinensis*
	'Korean Splendor'	see *S. pseudocamellia* Koreana Group
	koreana	see *S. pseudocamellia* Koreana Group
	monadelpha	CBcs CJun EHed IDee LMaj LRHS MBlu MPkF NLar
	ovata	CJun
	pseudocamellia 🏆H5	Widely available
	- B&SWJ 11044 from North Japan	WCru
§	- Koreana Group 🏆H5	CBct CEnd CJun CMCN EPfP GKin LRHS MPkF NLar SChF SLim
	- 'Ogisu'	IArd IDee NLar
	pteropetiolata B&SWJ 11726	WCru
	- NJM 10.107	WPGP
	- WWJ 11939	WCru
	rostrata	CBcs CJun CLnd CMCN EBee EGrI LMaj LRHS MBlu MPkF NLar SPtp WPGP XSte
	- 'Hulsdonk Pink'	CJun
	serrata	CJun CMCN MPkF WCru
§	***sinensis*** 🏆H5	CBcs CCCN CDoC CJun EPfP IArd IDee LMaj MBlu MPkF NLar SAko SPtp WPGP

Stigmaphyllon (*Malpighiaceae*)

	ciliatum	CCCN
	littorale	CCCN

Stipa (*Poaceae*)

	arundinacea	see *Anemanthele lessoniana*
	barbata	CSpe ECha EPPr ESwi ETod XSen
	brachytricha	see *Calamagrostis brachytricha*
§	***calamagrostis*** 🏆H4	CBWd CElw CWCL CWal EBee ECha EHyd ELan EMor EPPr EShb GDam GElm GMaP LCro LOPS LRHS MRav NBro NDov NRHS SBls SCob SDix SEND SRms WCAu XSen
	- 'Allgäu' 🏆H4	ECha SMHy WCot
	- 'Lemperg' 🏆H4	NDov
	capillata	CSpe EPPr EWhm GBin LRHS SHor XSen
	- 'Brautschleier'	MDon
*	- 'Lace Veil'	WAvo
	elegantissima	CDoC
	extremiorientalis	EPPr
	gigantea 🏆H4	Widely available
	- 'Alberich'	ECha
	- 'Gold Fontaene' 🏆H4	CKno EPPr EPfP EWes GBee LEdu LRHS MAvo MNrw NDov SMHy SMad WChS WCot
	- 'Goldilocks'	CKno CRos ECha EHyd LEdu LRHS NRHS SMHy
	- 'Pixie'	CRos EBee EHyd EPPr EPfP LRHS NRHS
	ichu 🏆H4	CElw CKno CRos CSpe EAJP ECha EHyd GElm LRHS LSun MAvo NDov NRHS SDix SMHy SPhx
	lasiagrostis	see *S. calamagrostis*
	lessingiana 🏆H5	CExl EPPr LRHS SBls SEND SPhx
	parviflora **new**	XSen
	pennata	CKel CPla LRHS MACG XSen
	pseudoichu 🏆H5	CBod CCht ECha ELan EPPr GElm LPla LRHS MAvo NCth NWsh SMHy SPeP SPtp WCot WHoo WPGP
	- RCB/Arg Y-1	EBee ELon
	pulcherrima	EPPr
	robusta	EPPr
	splendens misapplied	see *S. calamagrostis*
	splendens Trin.	ECha EPPr SAko
	tenacissima	CBWd GMcL
	tenuifolia misapplied	see *S. tenuissima*
	tenuifolia Steud.	LRHS MRav NBir NBro XLum XSen
§	***tenuissima*** 🏆H4	Widely available
	- 'Wind Whispers'	CBod CExl LEdu LRHS MBel SIvy SMHy SPtp

Stoebe (*Asteraceae*)

	alopecuroides	SPlb

Stokesia ✿ (*Asteraceae*)

	cyanea	see *S. laevis*
§	***laevis***	ECha EGrI EHyd EPfP LRHS NLar NRHS SGBe SPlb SRms WCAu
	- 'Alba'	ECha EGrI EHyd ELan EPfP EPri GPSL LEdu LRHS MBel MRav NLar SGBe WCAu
	- 'Blue Frills'	ECtt EPfP
	- 'Blue Star'	CAby CBcs CBod CDor CRos CWGN EBee ELan ELon EMor EPfP EWoo GElm LRHS LSou MACG MBel MHer MRav NBPC NRHS SGbt SMrm SPer SPoG SRkn SWvt WSHC
	- 'Color Wheel'	ECtt LBar
	- 'Divinity'	CRos ECtt LBar LRHS SCob
	- 'Klaus Jelitto'	CDor CNor ECtt EHyd EMor GElm LBar LEdu LRHS MPie SCob SGbt SHar SPoG
	- 'Mary Gregory'	CBod CMac CNor CRos EBee EBlo ECtt ELan EMor EPfP EWTr LBar LRHS MACG MBel MRav NBPC NLar NRHS SCob SGbt SMrm SWvt WSHC
	- 'Mega Mels' **new**	LCro
§	- 'Mel's' PBR	CRos ECtt EHyd LBar LRHS NRHS SHar
	- MEL'S BLUE	see *S. laevis* 'Mel's'
	- 'Mini Mels' **new**	LBar
	- 'Omega Skyrocket'	SRms
	- 'Peachie's Pick'	ECtt EMor SPad
	- 'Purple Parasols'	CDor CMac CRos CWGN EBee ECtt EPfP LBar LEdu LRHS LSou MBel NLar NRHS SGbt SPoG SWvt

- 'Silver Moon'	CDor CNor ECtt EMor EPfP GBin LRHS NBPC NLar NRHS SGbt SMrm SPer
§ - 'Träumerei'	CBod CWGN EBee ECtt EPfP LBar LRHS MPie NRHS SGbt SMrm XLum
- 'White Star'	see *S. laevis* 'Träumerei'

Stranvaesia see *Photinia*

× *Stranvinia* see *Photinia*

Stratiotes (*Hydrocharitaceae*)

aloides	CBen CPud CWat EWat LCro LLWG LOPS LPfP MWts NPer SVic WMAq WPnP

strawberry see *Fragaria*; see also AGM Fruit Section

Strelitzia (*Strelitziaceae*)

alba	CCCN NPlm
juncea	LPal
nicolai	CCCN CDoC LCro LPal NHrt NPer NPlm SPlb
reginae 🏆H1b	CAbb CCCN CDoC CPla CTsd ELan ETod LCro LOPS LPal NHrt NPer NPlm SArc SPlb WHlf
- 'Kirstenbosch Gold'	CCCN LPal

Streptanthus (*Brassicaceae*)

farnsworthianus	CSpe

Streptocarpella see *Streptocarpus*

Streptocarpus ✿ (*Gesneriaceae*)

'8e-Ajisai' (AV)	WDib
'Abigail' **new**	WDib
'Adele'	WDib
'Ae-Amur Elit' (AV)	WDib
'Ajohn's Fruit Cocktail' (AV)	WDib
'Ajohn's Yellow Submarine' (AV)	WDib
'Alamo Quest' (AV)	WDib
'Alana'	WDib
'Alan's Fallen Angel' (AV/d/v)	WDib
'Alan's White Feather' (AV)	WDib
'Albatross'	WDib
'Alchemy Yellow Star' (AV)	WDib
'Alissa'	WDib
'Allegro Appalachian Trail' (AV)	WDib
'Always Pink' (AV)	WDib
'Amanda' Dibley	WDib
'Amazing Grace' (AV)	WDib
'Ambiente' 🏆H1c	WDib
'Amethyst' (AV)	WDib
'Amy'	WDib
'Anne' (d)	WDib
'Anouk' (AV)	WDib
'An-Rio Rita' (AV)	WDib
'Anthoflores Edith' (AV)	WDib
'Anwen'	WDib
'Apache Magic' (AV)	WDib
'Apache Maiden' (AV/v)	WDib
'Apache Thunderbolt' (AV)	WDib
'Aussie Magic' (AV)	WDib
'Austin's Smile' (AV)	WDib
'Awena'	WDib
'Baby Brian' (AV)	WDib
baudertii	WDib
'Beacon Trail' (AV)	WDib
'Beatrice Trail' (AV)	WDib
'Bella'	WDib
'Berry Splash' (AV/v)	WDib
'Bethan' 🏆H1c	LCro WDib
'Betty Stoehr' (AV)	WDib
'Bianca'	WDib
'Black Panther'	WDib
'Bliznecy' (AV)	WDib
'Bloomlover's Cat' (AV/d)	WDib
'Blue Dragon' (AV/d)	WDib
'Blue Frills' 🏆H1c	WDib
'Blue Gem'	WDib
'Blue Leyla'	see *S.* 'Leyla'
'Blue Moon'	WDib
'Blue Nymph'	WDib
'Blue Tail Fly' (AV)	WDib
'Blushing Ivory' (AV)	WDib
'Bob Serbin' (AV/d)	WDib
'Bob's Omega' (AV)	WDib
'Bourane' (AV/v)	WDib
'Boysenberry Delight'	WDib
'Branwen'	WDib
brevipilosus (AV)	WDib
'Bristol's Black Bird'	WDib
'Bristol's Very Best'	WDib
'Buffalo Hunt' (AV/d)	WDib
caeruleus	WDib
'Caitlin'	WDib
'Calico Beauty' (AV)	WDib
candidus	WDib
'Candy Fountain' (AV)	WDib
'Candy Swirls' (AV)	WDib
'Cappuccino'	WDib
'Cariad'	WDib
'Carnival' **new**	WDib
'Carol'	WDib
'Carys' 🏆H1c	WDib
'Cathedral' (AV)	WDib
caulescens	WDib
- var. ***pallescens***	see *S. pallidiflorus*
'Cedar Creek Trail of Hope' (AV)	WDib
'Celebration'	WDib
'Chantaspring' (AV)	WDib
'Chanticleer' (AV/d)	WDib
'Charlotte' 🏆H1c	WDib
'Cherokee Trail' (AV/v)	WDib
'Cherries 'n' Cream' (AV)	WDib
'Chiffon Fiesta' (AV)	WDib
'Chiffon Pageant' (AV)	WDib
'Chiffon Vesper' (AV)	WDib
'Chloe'	WDib
'Cirelda' (AV)	WDib
'Constant Nymph'	WDib
'Country Romance' (AV/d)	WDib
'Crimson Ice' (AV)	WDib
'Crowning Glory' (AV)	WDib
'Crystal Beauty'	WDib
'Crystal Blush'	WDib
'Crystal Charm'	WDib
'Crystal Dawn'	WDib
'Crystal Ice' PBR 🏆H1c	LCro LOPS WDib
'Crystal Snow'	WDib
'Crystal Wonder'	WDib
'Cupid's Jewel' (AV)	WDib
'Cupie Doll' (AV)	WDib
cyaneus	WDib
- subsp. ***polackii***	WDib
'Cynthia'	WDib
'Daphne'	WDib
'Dawn Michelle' (AV)	WDib
'Dee'	WDib
'Deep Sky' (AV)	WDib

'Delft' (AV/d)	WDib
'Delia'	CSpe WDib
'Denim'	WDib
denticulatus	WDib
'Diana'	WDib
'Dibley's Beate' (AV)	WDib
'Dibleys Kaarina' (AV)	WDib
'Dibley's Leopold' (AV)	WDib
'Dibleys Marion' (AV)	WDib
'Dibleys Mercedes' (AV)	WDib
'Dibley's Pat' (AV)	WDib
'Dinas'	WDib
'Ds-Horus'	WDib
dunnii	WDib
'Dwynwen'	WDib
'Edee's Rosebud Trail' (AV/d)	WDib
'Ek-Afrodita' (AV/v)	WDib
'Ek-Gost'ya iz Budushchego' (AV)	WDib
'Ek-Sady Semiramidi' (AV)	WDib
'Ek-Shedevr Khudozhnika' (AV)	WDib
'Ek-Snezhnyi Bars' (AV)	WDib
'Ek-Vrata Raia' (AV)	WDib
'Elin'	WDib
'Elsi'	WDib
'Emerald Love' (AV)	WDib
'Emily'	WDib
'Ethel's Wild Side' (AV)	WDib
'Eve'	NWad WDib
'Faith' **new**	WDib
'Falling Stars' ♀H1c	CSpe WDib
'Favorite Child' (AV)	WDib
'Festival Wales'	WDib
'Fiesta'	WDib
'Fiona'	WDib
'Fire Mountain' (AV)	WDib
'Flashy Angel' (AV/v)	WDib
'Flashy Trail' (AV)	WDib
floribundus	WDib
'Flower Drum' (AV)	WDib
formosus	WDib
'Franken Skye'	WDib
'Freya'	WDib
'Frosty Diamond' ♀H1c	WDib
gardenii	WDib
'Gecko's Vespa Vino' (AV)	WDib
'Gillian' (AV/d)	WDib
glandulosissimus ♀H1c	WDib
'Gloria' ♀H1c	WDib
'Gold Dust'	WDib
'Gold Rose'	WDib
'Goluboi Tuman' (AV)	WDib
'Grandmother's Halo' (AV)	WDib
'Green Dragon' (AV)	WDib
'Green Lace' (AV/d)	WDib
'Gwen'	WDib
'Halo's Aglitter' (AV)	WDib
'Hand-picked' (AV/v)	WDib
'Hannah' ♀H1c	CSpe WDib
'Happy Cricket' (AV)	WDib
'Harlequin Blue' PBR ♀H1c	LCro LOPS WDib
'Harlequin Damsel'	WDib
'Harlequin Dawn'	WDib
'Harlequin Delft'	WDib
'Harlequin Lace' PBR ♀H1c	WDib
'Harlequin Purple'	WDib
'Harlequin Rose'	WDib
'Harriet'	WDib
'Hayley'	WDib
'Heaven's A-calling' (AV)	WDib
'Heidi'	WDib
'Helen'	WDib
'Hope'	WDib
'Hot Summer Day' (AV)	WDib
'Ian-Minuet' (AV/d)	WDib
'In the Pink' (AV)	WDib
'Indian Trail' (AV)	WDib
'Indigo Ruffles' (AV)	WDib
'Iona'	WDib
ionanthus subsp. ***grotei*** (AV)	WDib
- subsp. ***ionanthus*** (AV)	WDib
- subsp. ***rupicola*** (AV)	WDib
- subsp. ***velutinus*** (AV)	WDib
'Isabella'	WDib
'Island Breezes' (AV)	WDib
'Jacquie'	WDib
'Jennifer' ♀H1c	WDib
'Jenny Lilac' (AV/d)	WDib
'Jessica' ♀H1c	WDib
'Joanna'	WDib
johannis	WDib
'Joli Concerto' (AV)	WDib
'Jolly Champ' (AV)	WDib
'Jolly Gala' (AV)	WDib
'Jolly Gold' (AV)	WDib
'Jolly Orchid' (AV/d)	WDib
'Jolly Prize' (AV/d)	WDib
'Jolly Sun Chaser' (AV/d)	WDib
'Jolly Texan' (AV/d)	WDib
'Joy'	WDib
'Karen'	WDib
'Katie' PBR ♀H1c	WDib
kentaniensis	WDib
'Kim' ♀H1c	CSpe WDib
kirkii	WDib
'Kosmicheskaia Legenda 2' (AV)	WDib
'Kostina Fantaziia' (AV)	WDib
'Laura' ♀H1c	WDib
'Leah'	WDib
'LE-Karusel' (AV/v)	WDib
'LE-Macho' (AV)	WDib
'Lemon Sorbet'	WDib
'Letnaya Noch' (AV)	WDib
'Letnie Sumerki' (AV)	WDib
§ 'Leyla' PBR	WDib
'Lil Bit O'Irish' (AV)	WDib
'Lilla Blaklockan' (AV)	WDib
'Little Axel' (AV)	WDib
'Little Bo Peep' (AV)	WDib
'Little Chatterbox' (AV)	WDib
'Little Seagull' (AV)	WDib
'Lollipop' (AV)	WDib
'Looking Glass' (AV)	WDib
'Louise'	CSpe WDib
'Louisiana Lullaby' (AV/d)	WDib
'Love Spots' (AV)	WDib
'Lucky Ladybug' (AV)	WDib
'Lucy'	WDib
'Luminescence' (AV)	WDib
'Lyndee'	WDib
'Lynne'	WDib
'Lyon's Minnie-HaHa' (AV)	WDib
'Lyon's Plum Pudding' (AV)	WDib
'Maassen's White'	WDib
'Mac's Black Jack' (AV)	WDib
'Mac's Blowing Bubbles' (AV)	WDib
'Mac's Carnival Clown' (AV)	WDib
'Mac's Glacial Grape' (AV)	WDib
'Mac's Just Jeff' (AV)	WDib
'Mac's Nocturne' (AV/d)	WDib
'Mac's Rouge Rogue' (AV)	WDib

'Mac's Southern Springtime' (AV/d)	WDib
'Madison Red' (AV) new	LCro
'Manon'	WDib
'Margaret' Gavin Brown	WDib
'Marie'	WDib
'Marion'	CSpe WDib
'Ma's Ching Dynasty' (AV/d)	WDib
'Ma's Easter Parade' (AV)	WDib
'Matilda'	WDib
'Megan'	WDib
'Melanie' Dibley	WDib
'Menai'	WDib
meyeri	WDib
'Midget Silver Fox' (AV/v)	WDib
'Midnight Flame' (AV/d)	WDib
'Mikinda Girl' (AV/v)	WDib
'Minnie'	WDib
modestus	WDib
'Myfanwy'	WDib
'MyJoy' (MyViolet Series) (AV)	WDib
'Nadine'	WDib
'Natalie'	WDib
'Nerys'	WDib
'Ness' Antique Red' (AV)	WDib
'Ness' Cherry Smoke' (AV)	WDib
'Ness' Crinkle Blue' (AV/d)	WDib
'Ness' Midnight Fantasy' (AV)	WDib
'Ness' Orange Pekoe' (AV)	WDib
'Ness' Satin Rose' (AV)	WDib
'Ness' Sheer Peach' (AV)	WDib
'Neverfloris' (AV)	WDib
'Newtown Ohio' (AV)	WDib
'Nia'	WDib
'Nicola'	WDib
nitidus (AV)	WDib
'Norseman' (AV)	WDib
'Number 32' (AV)	WDib
'Ode to Beauty' (AV)	WDib
'Ode to Grace' (AV)	WDib
'Okie Easter Bunny' (AV)	WDib
'Oksana' (AV)	WDib
'Olivia'	WDib
'Optimara Little Moonstone' (AV)	WDib
'Otoe' (AV/d)	WDib
'Padarn'	WDib
§ ***pallidiflorus***	WDib
'Parnikovyi Effekt' (AV)	WDib
'Pat Champagne' (AV/v)	WDib
'Pat Tracey' (AV)	WDib
'Paula'	WDib
'Pearl' ♀H1c	CSpe WDib
pentherianus	WDib
'Pink Leyla' ♀H1c	WDib
'Pink Mint' (AV/d)	WDib
'Pink Souffle'	WDib
'Pixie Blue' (AV)	WDib
'Pixie Pink' (AV)	WDib
'Podvenechnaia' (AV/d)	WDib
'Polka-Dot Purple' ♀H1c	WDib
'Polka-Dot Red'	WDib
polyanthus subsp. ***dracomontanus***	WDib
'Powder Keg' (AV/d)	WDib
'Powwow' (AV/d/v)	WDib
'Prancing Pony' (AV)	WDib
primulifolius	WDib
prolixus	WDib
'Purple Passion' (AV)	WDib
'Purple Velvet'	CSpe WDib
'Rainbow's Limelight' (AV/d)	WDib
'Rainbow's Quiet Riot' (AV)	WDib
'Ramblin' Amethyst' (AV)	WDib
'Ramblin' Lassie' (AV)	WDib
'Ramblin' Spots' (AV/v) new	WDib
'Ramblin' Sunshine' (AV)	WDib
'Raspberry Crisp' (AV)	WDib
'Rebel's Amy' (AV)	WDib
'Rebel's Splatter Kake' (AV)	WDib
'Rebel's Strawberry Bites' (AV)	WDib
'Red Lantern' (AV/d)	WDib
'Reflections of Spring' (AV/d)	WDib
rexii	WDib
'Rhapsodie Clementine' (AV)	WDib
'Rhiannon'	WDib
'Rob's Argyle Socks' (AV/d)	WDib
'Rob's Bed Bug' (AV/v)	WDib
'Rob's Chilly Willy' (AV/d/v)	WDib
'Rob's Dust Storm' (AV/d)	WDib
'Rob's Flim Flam' (AV)	WDib
'Rob's Hot Tamale' (AV)	WDib
'Rob's Ice Ripples' (AV/d)	WDib
'Rob's Jitterbug' (AV)	WDib
'Rob's Love Bite' (AV/d)	WDib
'Rob's Mad Cat' (AV/d)	WDib
'Rob's Melon Wedges' (AV)	WDib
'Rob's Peedletuck' (AV)	WDib
'Rob's Pewter Bells' (AV)	WDib
'Rob's Sarsparilla' (AV/d)	WDib
'Rob's Scrumptious' (AV)	WDib
'Rob's Shadow Magic' (AV/d/v)	WDib
'Rob's Slap Happy' (AV/v) new	WDib
'Rob's Smarty Pants' (AV/d)	WDib
'Rob's Vanilla Trail' (AV/d)	WDib
'Rob's Wooloomooloo' (AV/d)	WDib
'Rose Halo'	WDib
'Rosebud'	WDib
(Roulette Series) 'Roulette Azur' PBR ♀H1c	WDib
– 'Roulette Cherry'	WDib
'Rs-Barbie' (AV)	WDib
'Rs-Bog Solntsa' (AV/d)	WDib
'Rs-Boyarinya' (AV)	WDib
'Rs-Gertsogninea' (AV)	WDib
'Rs-Iolanta' (AV/v)	WDib
'Rs-Kabaret' (AV)	WDib
'Rs-Korrida' (AV)	WDib
'Rs-Romantika' (AV)	WDib
'Rs-Strast' (AV)	WDib
'Rs-Utonchennyy-vkus' (AV)	WDib
'Rs-Vodevil' (AV/v)	WDib
'Rubina' PBR	WDib
'Rubina Pink' ♀H1c	WDib
'Ruby'	WDib
'Ruffled Skies' (AV)	WDib
'Ruth'	WDib
'Sadie'	WDib
'Sally'	WDib
'Sandra'	WDib
'Santa Anita' (AV)	WDib
'Sapphire Halo' (AV)	WDib
'Sarah'	WDib
saxorum	CCCN EAri LSou WDib
– compact ♀H1c	CCCN WDib
'Scarlett'	WDib
'Senk's Arctic Fox' (AV)	WDib

'Senk's Vespa Verde' (AV) **new**	WDib
'Seren'	WDib
'Sharon's Way' (AV) **new**	WDib
shumensis (AV)	WDib
'Shy Blue' (AV)	WDib
'Sian'	WDib
silvaticus	WDib
'Silverglade Beads' (AV)	WDib
'Sioned' ♀H1c	WDib
'Sky Bells' (AV/v)	WDib
'Sky Trail' (AV)	WDib
'Snow Leopard' (AV)	WDib
'Snow White' ♀H1c	CSpe WDib
'Sparkleberry' (AV)	WDib
'Special Treat' (AV)	WDib
§ 'Stella' Fleischle (Marleen Series) ♀H1c	WDib
'Stephanie'	WDib
stomandrus	WDib
'Sun Sizzle' (AV)	WDib
'Sunkissed Rose' (AV)	WDib
'Susan' ♀H1c	WDib
'Sweet Melys'	WDib
'Sweet Rosy'	WDib
'Taffeta Blue' (AV/d)	WDib
'Tanga'	see *S.* 'Stella' Fleischle
'Tanya'	WDib
'Teleri'	WDib
'Texas Hot Chili'	CSpe WDib
'The King' (AV)	WDib
'The Madam' (AV)	WDib
thompsonii	WDib
THREE SISTERS (mixed)	WDib
'Tiger' (AV/v)	WDib
'Tina' ♀H1c	WDib
'Tina's April Fantasy' (AV)	WDib
'Titania'	WDib
'Top Dark Blue' (AV)	LCro
'Toy Castle' (AV)	WDib
'Tracey'	WDib
'Tula' (AV)	WDib
'Two-w Miss Sophie' (AV/d)	WDib
'Vallartas Campanas Moradas' (AV)	WDib
'Valor'	WDib
vandeleurii	WDib
variabilis	WDib
'Warm Sunshine' (AV)	WDib
wendlandii	WDib
'Wendy'	WDib
'Whirligig Star' (AV)	WDib
'White Butterfly' ♀H1c	WDib
'Wiesmoor Red'	WDib
'Wild Irish Rose' (AV)	WDib
'Winifred'	WDib
'Wisteria' (AV/d)	WDib
'Wrangler's Jealous Heart' (AV)	WDib
'Wrangler's Snowfield's' (AV/v)	WDib
'Yesterday's Child' (AV)	WDib
'Zivai' (AV/d)	WDib
'Zoe'	WDib

Streptopus (*Liliaceae*)

amplexifolius	EBee ESwi EWld GBin GKev MNrw WCru WSHC
- var. ***papillatus***	GEdr
roseus	WCru
streptopoides	EBee EHed EHyd EPPr LEdu LRHS NBro

Streptosolen (*Solanaceae*)

jamesonii ♀H1c	CCCN CHll EShb SWvt WFib

Strobilanthes (*Acanthaceae*)

CC 4071	CExl
CC 4573	CExl
angustifrons	SBrt
anisophylla	EShb WSpi
- BRUNETTHY ('Lankveld15'PBR)	WHlf
atropurpurea misapplied	see *S. attenuata*
atropurpurea Nees	see *S. wallichii*
§ ***attenuata***	CRos EBee ECtt EGrI EHyd GGro ILea LEdu LRHS MHer MPie MRav NChi NRHS NSti SBut SDix SPoG WCot WCru WSpi
- 'Blue and White'	EBee
- 'Blue Carpet'	ESwi NDov
- 'Latham's Form'	ESwi
- subsp. ***nepalensis***	GGro XLum
dyeriana ♀H1b	EShb SPlb WCot
flexicaulis B&SWJ 354	EPPr ESwi WCru
aff. ***flexicaulis*** CMBTW 1531 **new**	GGro
heyneana **new**	GGro
aff. ***inflata*** B&SWJ 7754	WCru
* ***lactea***	EShb
nutans	EBee ESwi EWld GGro NSti SBrt WBor WHil XLum
'Orizaba' **new**	EShb
pentastemonoides	EPPr
rankanensis	EPPr GPSL ILea SDys SMHy WHil XLum
- B&SWJ 1771	WCru
- marbled-flowered CMBTW 1484 **new**	GGro
violacea misapplied	EShb
§ ***wallichii***	CMac EBee EPfP ESwi EWes EWld MMuc NSti SEND WCAu WCru WMal
- from Picton	WFar

Stromanthe (*Marantaceae*)

amabilis	see *Ctenanthe amabilis*
sanguinea ♀H1b	NHrt
- 'Triostar'PBR (v)	LCro NHrt

Strongylodon (*Fabaceae*)

macrobotrys	CCCN WFib

Strophanthus (*Apocynaceae*)

speciosus	CCCN CHll EShb

Strumaria (*Amaryllidaceae*)

aestivalis	NRog
discifera subsp. ***bulbifera***	WCot
gemmata	NRog
salteri	NRog
tenella subsp. ***tenella***	NRog
truncata	NRog
watermeyeri subsp. ***watermeyeri***	NRog

Struthiopteris (*Blechnaceae*)

niponica	see *Blechnum niponicum*

Stuartia see *Stewartia*

Stylidium (*Stylidiaceae*)

graminifolium	CTsd SPlb

Stylophorum (*Papaveraceae*)

diphyllum	EMor EWld LEdu MAvo WCru WPGP WPnP
lasiocarpum	CExl CSpe EMor EPPr EWld GEdr GGro NBid NSti WCru WPnP
sutchuenense	GGro

Styphelia (*Ericaceae*)

colensoi	see *Leucopogon colensoi*

Styphnolobium (*Fabaceae*)

§ ***japonicum***	CAco CBcs CHab CMCN CMac EPfP IPap LPar SPer SPlb WTSh
- 'China Gold'	EBee SPoG
- 'Flavirameum'	SMad
- 'Gold Standard'	MTrO NLar
- 'Pendulum'	LPar MPri
- 'Regent'	LPar

Styrax ✿ (*Styracaceae*)

NJM 11.013 from Guizhou, China	WPGP
NJM 11.085 from Guizhou, China	WPGP
americanus	EPfP
- Kankakee form	WPGP
confusus	CExl
dasyanthus	CExl
faberi	CExl
formosanus	CBcs CExl CJun EPfP MBlu SChF
var. ***formosanus***	WPGP
- - B&SWJ 3803	WCru
- - B&SWJ 6786	WCru
- var. ***hayatiana*** B&SWJ 6823	WCru
grandiflorus	CExl
hemsleyanus ♀H5	CExl EGrI EPfP IDee LEdu MBlu NLar SPtp
hookeri	CExl LEdu WPGP
japonicus	CBcs CDoC CExl CLnd CMCN CRos CTri EHyd ELon EPfP GKin IPap LEdu LMaj LRHS LSRN MAsh MBlu MGos MRav MVil NLar SGol SPer SPoG WPGP
- B&SWJ 4405	WCru
- B&SWJ 8770	WCru
- B&SWJ 11078	WCru
- Guiz 216	CExl WPGP
§ - Benibana Group	WPGP
- - 'Pink Chimes'	CBcs CExl CJun CMCN EHed GKin LMaj LRHS MBlu MPkF MTrO NLar NOra SRHi WMat XSte
- 'Carillon'	LMaj
- 'Evening Light'PBR	CBcs SRHi
- 'Fargesii' ♀H5	CBcs CDoC CExl CJun LRHS XSte
- 'Fragrant Fountain'	CBcs LPar LRHS MBlu MPkF NLar SGsty XSte
- 'June Snow'PBR	LPar NLar XSte
§ - MARLEY'S PINK PARASOL ('JLWeeping')	NLar
- 'Momo-shidare'	see *S. japonicus* MARLEY'S PINK PARASOL
- 'Pendulus'	CBcs EPfP NLar WPGP
- 'Pink Bells Compacta' **new**	NLar
I - 'Pink Snowbell'	LRHS
- 'Purple Dress' ♀H5	CBcs CJun EPfP MBlu MPkF NLar
- 'Roseus'	see *S. japonicus* Benibana Group
- SNOWCONE ('Jfs-D')	CBcs LMaj SGsty
- 'Snowfall'	CJun EHed NLar
- 'Sohuksan' ♀H5	CBcs CExl CJun MBlu WPGP
aff. ***japonicus*** B&SWJ 14182 from Heuksando, South Korea	WCru
limprichtii	CExl
obassia	CBcs CLnd CMCN EPfP IDee LMaj LRHS MBlu NLar SChF SPtp WGob WJur WPGP
- B&SWJ 6023	WCru
- B&SWJ 10890	WCru
odoratissimus	CExl WPGP
officinalis	CJun
- NJM 12.007 **new**	WPGP
redivivus	CJun
serrulatus	CExl
shiraianus	CExl MBlu NLar WPGP
tonkinensis FMWJ 13134	WCru
'Wespelaar'	EPfP WPGP
wilsonii	CExl EBee
wuyuanensis	CBcs WPGP

Succisa (*Caprifoliaceae*)

§ ***pratensis***	Widely available
- 'Alba'	EWes
- 'Buttermilk'	CDor EWes LEdu WHoo
- 'Cassop'	GEdr
- 'Derby Purple'	CSpe SPhx WHoo
- early-flowering	LEdu
- 'Peddar's Pink'	EWes LLWG LRHS SPhx

Succisella (*Caprifoliaceae*)

inflexa	CAby ECha MSpe NFav SPhx WCAu
I - 'Alba'	MSpe
- 'Frosted Pearls'	CBWd CDor CElw CFis EBee ECha GBin MACG MAvo MHer NLar SBls SBut SHar

Sulcorebutia see *Rebutia*

rauschii	see *Rebutia pulchra*

sunberry see *Rubus* 'Sunberry'

Sutera (*Scrophulariaceae*)

cordata	see *Chaenostoma cordatum*
Scopia Series	see *Chaenostoma cordatum* Scopia Series

Sutherlandia ✿ (*Fabaceae*)

frutescens	SPlb
montana	CSpe SBrt

Swainsona (*Fabaceae*)

galegifolia 'Albiflora'	CHll

sweet cicely see *Myrrhis odorata*

sweet corn see AGM Vegetables Section

sweet pepper see *Capsicum*; also AGM Vegetables Section

Swertia (*Gentianaceae*)

bimaculata	ECha
- PAB 8845	LEdu
perennis	GEdr

Syagrus (*Arecaceae*)

§ ***romanzoffiana***	EAri LRHS NPlm
weddelliana	see *Lytocaryum weddellianum*

× *Sycoparrotia* (*Hamamelidaceae*)

semidecidua	CBcs CBct CCCN CJun EBee EPfP LMaj MBlu NLar NOrn SSta
- 'Purple Haze'	CBcs CJun IArd IDee NLar

Sycopsis (*Hamamelidaceae*)

sinensis	CBcs CBod CCCN CExl CJun CKel EBee EHyd EPfP GBin IDee LEdu LMaj MGil MMuc NLar SSta SWvt WPGP

Symphoricarpos (*Caprifoliaceae*)

albus	CAco CBee CMac CPer EHeP ELan MSwo NWea SCob WTSh
- 'Constance Spry'	SRms
§ - var. ***laevigatus***	LBuc
× ***chenaultii***	EHeP SRms
- 'Hancock'	CBod CMac EBee EHeP ELan EPfP GMcL MRav MSwo NBwr SCob SPer
× ***doorenbosii*** 'Magic Berry'	CBrac EBee EHeP MRav NWea SCob SGbt
- 'Mother of Pearl'	EDir EHeP EPfP LCro LPar MRav NWea SCob SPer SRms WHtc
- 'White Hedge'	EHeP GMcL LBuc LPar NBwr NWea SGbt SPer SPlb
guatemalensis B&SWJ 1016	WCru
MAGICAL CANDY ('Kolmcan'PBR)	CBod CRos EHyd LCro LRHS LSRN MPri NEoE NRHS SPoG
MAGICAL GALAXY ('Kolmgala'PBR)	CBod CRos EHyd EPfP LCro LRHS MPri NRHS SPoG
MAGICAL SWEET ('Kolmaswet'PBR)	CRos EHyd LCro LRHS NRHS SPoG
orbiculatus 'Bowles's Golden Variegated'	see *S. orbiculatus* 'Foliis Variegatis'
§ - 'Foliis Variegatis' (v)	CMac CTri MRav
- 'George Gardiner'	CMac
- 'Variegatus'	see *S. orbiculatus* 'Foliis Variegatis'
rivularis	see *S. albus* var. *laevigatus*

Symphyandra see *Campanula*

asiatica	see *Hanabusaya asiatica*

Symphyotrichum (*Asteraceae*)

§ × ***amethystinum***	MNrw WCot
- 'Freiburg'	ELon EPPr LShi MNrw NDov WOld
'Anja's Choice'	EBee EPPr
'Ann Leys'PBR	EBee LBar MNrw WCot
'Aqua Compact' (Autumn Jewels Series)	CBod EHyd LRHS NRHS SGBe
'Beauté du Nord'	WCot
'Bee Lee Elliott'	SPhx
'Blue Butterfly'	SPhx WOld XLum
'Blütenregen'	MNrw WCot WFar
chilense 'Purple Haze'	EPPr
§ ***ciliolatum***	LRHS
'Claudia'	WOld
'Climax' Vicary Gibbs	MNrw WFar WOld
'Coombe Fishacre' 🏆H7	CDor EBee ECtt ELan ELon GQue ILea LEdu LRHS MNrw NDov NLar SPeP SPhx SRms SWvt WCAu WCot WHoo WOld WSpi
§ ***cordifolium***	SPhx
- from Piney Fork	EPPr
- 'Aldebaran'	LEdu WOld
- 'Blue Heaven'	MNrw SAko WCAu
- 'Chieftain' 🏆H7	MHCG SPhx WOld
- 'Elegans'	EBee SDix WOld
- 'Ideal'	NLar SPhx XLum
- 'Silver Spray'	CKno ECtt ELon GMaP ILea WOld XLum
- 'Sweet Lavender' 🏆H7	WOld
- 'White Chief'	WOld
'Diamond Jubilee'	MAvo WOld
dumosum 'Beryll'	WFar
- 'Biteliness'	NLar
- 'Blue Lapis'	WFar
- SAPPHIRE ('Kiesapphire'PBR) (Autumn Jewels Series)	CChe ELon LRHS LSRN NCou SRkn SWvt XLum
§ ***ericoides***	WOld
- 'Blue Star' 🏆H7	CDor CTtf EHyd ELon LRHS NFav NLar SMHy SPer WOld
- 'Blue Wonder'	CBod ELon MNHC XLum
- 'Brimstone' 🏆H7	WOld
- 'Cinderella'	EBee ELon NSti WOld
- 'Cirylle'	LEdu SMHy
- 'Constance'	MCot WOld
- 'Deep Danziger'	SAko SPhx XLum
- 'Erlkönig'	EBee ELon EPri EShb GQue LEdu NGdn NLar SDix SWvt WCAu WCot WOld
- 'Esther'	ECha ECtt MMrt MNrw WOld XLum
- 'First Snow'	WCot WFar
- 'Golden Spray' 🏆H7	EBee ECtt ELan ELon EPfP EWes GMaP GQue NLar SPer WOld
- 'Herbstmyrte'	EHyd LRHS NRHS
- 'Monte Cassino'	see *S. pilosum* var. *pringlei* 'Monte Cassino'
- 'Pink Cloud' 🏆H7	CBWd CBod ECtt EHyd ELan ELon EPfP EPri EShb GQue LEdu LRHS LSto MBel NCth NLar NWad SAko SDix SHar SPer SPhx WCAu WMal WOld WTre XLum
- var. ***prostratum***	EPot MRav SAko XSen
§ - - 'Snow Flurry' 🏆H7	CSpe ECha ECtt ELon EShb GBin GQue LEdu LPla MAvo MNrw NLar SAko SMHy SMrm SWvt WCAu WCot WHoo WOld WPGP XLum
- 'Rosy Veil'	NBir NGdn WOld
- 'Schneegitter'	SAko XLum XSen
- 'Schneetanne'	SAko
- 'Vimmer's Delight'	ECtt LPla WCot WFar WMal
- 'White Heather'	ECtt NLar WOld
- 'Yvette Richardson'	ECtt SMHy WOld
'Ethereal'	WHoo
§ ***falcatum***	WCot
- var. ***commutatum***	WCot XLum
§ ***foliaceum***	EWTr
- from Montana	EPPr
- var. ***parryi***	ECha
'Foxbrook Fairy' (*ericoides*)	MAvo
GRANAT ('Kiastgranat') (Autumn Jewels Series)	SGBe
§ ***greatae***	EBee
'Herfstweelde'	LEdu MNrw
'Hill Close Blue'	MAvo MHCG
'Hon. Vicary Gibbs' (*ericoides* hybrid)	WOld
'Jessica Jones'	WOld
'Johan' **new**	LEdu
§ ***laeve***	CDor LEdu NLar SPhx
- 'Anneke Van der Jeugd'	MNrw WFar
§ - 'Arcturus'	CDor CElw LEdu MAvo MBel MNrw NBir SDix WCot WFar WOld XLum
- 'Black Ice'	MAvo
- 'Blauschleier'	NLar
- 'Blue Bird'	WOld
§ - 'Calliope'	CElw CKno EBee ECtt EShb GBin GMaP ILea LEdu MCot MHol MMuc MNrw MSpe NBid NLar NWsh SBut SEND SMrm SPhx SWvt WBor WFar WKif WOld WPGP WSpi

	- 'Cally Compact'	GQue MHol NLar WFar
	- 'Climax'	CElw EBee ELan MMuc MRav NBid NSti SDix SEND SMrm WBrk XLum
	- 'Glow in the Dark'	ECha EPPr LEdu MAvo MSpe NCth SPeP WBrk WCAu WCot WHoo WMal WOld WPGP
	- 'Jane Ward'	MNrw
	- 'Les Moutiers'	CDor CTtf EPPr LEdu LSto MAvo MNrw SDix WBrk WFar WMal WOld
	- 'Nightshade'	EPPr MAvo MNrw WFar WOld
	- 'Orpheus'	ECha GBin LEdu MAvo MNrw WBrk WFar WMal WOld
	- 'Sharon'	MNrw
	- 'Vesta'	ECtt WOld
§	- 'White Climax'	CDor MNrw WCot
	- white-flowered	WBrk WOld
	lanceolatum 'Edwin Beckett'	MNrw SWvt WFar WOld
	- subsp. ***lanceolatum*** **new**	SMHy
§	***lateriflorum***	SWvt WOld
	- 'Bleke Bet'	WCot WFar
	- 'Buck's Fizz'	WOld
	- 'Chloe'	CDor MNrw NCth NLar SHar SMHy SPhx WCot WFar WOld
	- var. ***horizontale*** $\mathbb{Y}^{H7}$	CAby CBod CRos EBee ECha ECtt ELan ELon EPPr EPfP GKev GQue LRHS LShi LSto MRav NBro NGdn NWad SCob SDix SGbt SMHy SPer SPlb SRms SWvt WCAu WOld WSpi
	- 'Lady in Black'	CBcs CMac CSpe EAJP ECtt EHyd ELan ELon EPfP EWoo GMaP ILea LEdu LRHS LSto MNrw MRav NBir NLar NRHS NSti SCob SMrm SPhx SRms SSut SWvt WFar WOld XLum
	- 'Lovely'	WCot
	- 'Prince'	CDor CMac CSBt ECha ECtt ELan ELon EPfP EWes EWoo GMaP LRHS MHer MNrw MRav NBir NGdn NRHS NSti SPeP SPoG SRms WCAu WFar WOld WSpi
	'Little Carlow' (*cordifolium* hybrid) $\mathbb{Y}^{H7}$	Widely available
	'Little Dorrit' (*cordifolium* hybrid)	ECtt NWsh
	(Newstars Series) 'Newstars Fantasy'	MAvo
	- 'Newstars Glory'	WFar
	'Nicholas'	ECtt MACG WCot WFar WOld
	'Nineteen'	MAvo WOld
	'Noreen'	ECha MAvo MHCG WOld
§	***novae-angliae***	WOld
	- 'Abendsonne'	SAko
	- 'Alex Deamon'	ELon SMHy WBrk WOld
	- 'Anabelle de Chazal'	ECtt ELon WFar WOld XLum
	- 'Andenken an Alma Pötschke'	Widely available
	- 'Andenken an Paul Gerber' $\mathbb{Y}^{H7}$	ECtt EHyd ELon EPfP IPot LRHS MAvo MNrw NLar NRHS SAko SRGP WCAu WOld XLum
	- 'Augusta'	ELon MACG NLar SAko SPhx WBrk WOld
	- AUTUMN SNOW	see *S. novae-angliae* 'Herbstschnee'
	- 'Badsey Pink' $\mathbb{Y}^{H7}$	GQue WCot WOld
	- 'Barr's Blue'	CMac EBee ECtt EHyd ELan ELon EPfP IPot LRHS MAvo MMuc NLar NWsh SCob SEND SPer SRms WBrk WCAu WOld WSFF XLum
	- 'Barr's Pink'	CMac EBee ECtt EHyd ELan ELon EPfP LRHS MAvo MPie NRHS SRms WBrk WFar WOld WSFF
	- 'Barr's Purple' $\mathbb{Y}^{H7}$	ECtt LSto MAvo WBrk WCFE WOld
	- 'Barr's Violet'	CDow ECtt MACG MAvo NSti SRms WBrk WCot WFar WOld
	- 'Betel Nut'	EPPr WOld
	- 'Beth Picton' **new**	WOld
	- 'Bishop Colenso'	EPPr LPla LShi SPhx WBrk
	- 'Blackheart'	ELon
I	- 'Brightness'	WCot
	- 'Brockamin'	EPPr MNrw WBrk
	- 'Brunswick' $\mathbb{Y}^{H7}$	MAvo WFar WOld
	- 'Christopher Harbutt'	LEdu
	- 'Colwall Century' $\mathbb{Y}^{H7}$	MAvo WBrk WOld
	- 'Colwall Constellation'	ELon WBrk WOld
	- 'Colwall Galaxy'	WBrk WOld
	- 'Colwall Orbit'	ECtt ELon WBrk WOld
	- 'Connie'	MNrw
	- 'Constanze'	EBee ECtt ELon MAvo WOld
	- 'Crimson Beauty'	ECtt ELon MHCG MHer MNrw SAko WBrk WFar WOld
	- 'Dapper Tapper'	ECtt ELon MAvo WCot WOld
	- 'Dark Desire'	MNrw
	- 'Early Bird'	ELon SEdd
	- 'Evensong'	ECtt MPie WBrk WOld
	- 'Festival'	WBrk
	- 'Foxy Emily'	ECtt MHCG WBrk WOld
	- 'Guido en Gezelle'	ELon MAvo MNrw WOld
	- 'Harrington's Pink'	Widely available
	- 'Harrington's Red' **new**	WOld
	- 'Helen Picton' $\mathbb{Y}^{H7}$	CDor CDow ECtt ELon EPPr IPot LEdu LRHS LSto MAvo MBrN MHer MPie MSpe NLar NWsh SBea SMHy SRms WBrk WCAu WFar WHoo WOld
	- 'Herbstflieder'	EBee
§	- 'Herbstschnee'	Widely available
	- 'Hoo House'	WHoo
	- 'Ivy Patterson'	MAvo
	- 'James' $\mathbb{Y}^{H7}$	EPPr MAvo WOld
	- 'James Ritchie' $\mathbb{Y}^{H7}$	CDow CTtf ECtt IPot MCot WCAu WHoo WMal WOld
	- 'John Davis' $\mathbb{Y}^{H7}$	MAvo MNrw WOld
	- 'John Dickinson'	WBrk WOld
	- 'Jon Baker'	WBrk
	- 'Kate Deamon'	ECtt WOld
	- 'Kylie'	ECtt EPPr LRHS LSRN MNrw MPie SMHy SPhx WCot WFar WMal WOld
	- 'Lachsglut' $\mathbb{Y}^{H7}$	ELon EPPr LEdu MAvo NLar SAko SMrm WCot WOld
	- 'Ladies Day'	WOld
	- 'Little Bella'	ECtt WOld
	- 'Lou Williams'	CDow ECtt ELon MNrw NLar WFar WOld
I	- 'Lucida'	SRms WOld
	- 'Lye End Beauty'	CDor CDow ECtt ELon MAvo MHer MNrw MPie WBrk WCot WFar WMal WOld
	- 'Mabelle'	WOld
	- 'Mandie's Choice'	WCot
	- 'Marina Wolkonsky'	CBWd CDow CMiW ECtt ELon EWes IPot LEdu LPla MACG MNrw MSpe NLar SAko SMHy SPhx SRms WBrk WCot WFar WKif WMal WOld
	- 'Millennium Star'	ECtt ELon SAko WBrk WOld
	- 'Miss K.E. Mash'	ECtt NLar SRGP WBrk WCAu WFar WOld
	- 'Mrs S.T. Wright'	CTri ECtt EWes LEdu MBrN MNrw NWsh WBrk WFar WOld XLum
	- 'Mrs S.W. Stern'	WBrk WOld
	- 'Nachtauge'	SAko
	- 'Naomi'	WBrk WOld
	- 'Patricia'	MAvo
	- 'Percy Picton'	LEdu

- 'Pink Parfait'	ECtt GBee LShi MACG MAvo NGdn SRms WCot WFar WOld
- 'Pink Victor'	CTtf EPPr SRms WFar
- 'Pride of Rougham'	ECtt EWes MAvo SAko WBrk
- 'Primrose Upward'	ECtt MNrw NDov NWsh SAko SMHy SPhx WChS WCot WOld
- 'Purple Cloud'	ECtt ELon MHer NGdn WBrk WOld
I - 'Purple Dome'	Widely available
- 'Purple Paradise'	WOld
- 'Quinton Menzies' 🏆H7	ELon MAvo NLar SMHy WOld
- 'Red Cloud'	ECtt ELon LEdu MAvo MHer WOld
- 'Rosa Sieger' 🏆H7	ECtt ELon EPPr GMaP MAvo MNrw MSpe NGdn SBut SMHy WBrk WChS WFar WHoo WMal WOld XLum
- 'Rose Williams'	MAvo MPie
- 'Röter Stern'	ECtt MPie WOld
- 'Röter Turm'	SAko
- 'Rougham Purple'	EWes XLum
- 'Rougham Violet'	WBrk
- 'Rubinschatz'	EBee ECtt ELon IPot MAvo NLar NWsh SAko SRms WOld XLum
- 'Rudelsburg'	CDow ECtt ELon IPot MAvo NLar SHar WOld
- 'Rudolph'	ECtt EWes
- 'Saint Michael's'	WBrk WFar WOld
- 'Sayer's Croft'	CDow ECtt ELon SRms WCot WFar WHoo WOld
- 'Schneehügel'	CDow
- SEPTEMBER RUBY	see *S. novae-angliae* 'Septemberrubin'
§ - 'Septemberrubin'	ECtt ELan ELon EPPr EPfP GJos GQue IPot LEdu LPla MAvo MMuc MRav NSti NWsh SBut SEND SRms WCAu WFar WOld WSpi WTyc XLum
- 'Treasure'	ECtt ELon EPPr EWes SMrm SPhx SRGP WBrk WOld
- 'Vibrant Dome'	EHyd ELon LRHS MNrw NLar NRHS
- 'Violet Dusk'	ELon WBrk
- 'Violet Haze'	ELon WBrk
- 'Violetta'	EBlo ECha ECtt EHyd GMaP ILea IPot LRHS MAvo MNrw MPie NRHS SPhx WBor WBrk WCAu WFar WKif WOld
- 'W. Bowman'	ECtt MNrw NLar WBrk WOld
- 'Warm Throng'	WCot
- 'Wineflower'	MAvo MCot
- 'Wow'	CDor ELon SMrm
§ ***novi-belgii***	GElm WHer
- 'Ada Ballard'	CFis CMac EBee LDai LRHS LSRN NGrd NRHS WFar WOld
- 'Albanian'	SRms WOld
- 'Alderman Vokes'	WOld
- 'Algar's Pride'	WFar WOld
- 'Alice Haslam'	CMac EHyd ELan EPfP LRHS NBir NLar NRHS SRGP SRms WCAu WFar WOld XLum
- 'Anita Ballard'	WOld
- 'Anita Webb'	CDor CTtf NBir WOld
- 'Anneke'	EGrI NLar WOld
- 'Apollo'	EHyd LBar LRHS NLar NRHS SCob SEdd WFar WOld
- 'Apple Blossom'	WFar WOld
- 'Audrey'	CDor CMac EHeP EPfP GMaP LSRN MBNS NGdn SRms WFar WOld
- 'Autumn Beauty'	WOld
- 'Autumn Days'	WOld
- 'Autumn Glory'	WOld
- 'Autumn Rose'	WOld
- 'Baby Climax'	WOld
- BAHAMAS ('Dasone') (Island Series)	CBod EHyd EPfP LBar LRHS NRHS NWsh SCob SPoG SRms SWvt WCot
- BARBADOS ('Dastwo') (Island Series)	CBod EHyd EPfP LRHS NBir NLar NRHS SCob SPoG SWvt WCot WFar
- 'Beauty of Colwall'	WOld
- 'Beechwood Beacon'	WFar
- 'Beechwood Challenger'	MHCG MNrw MPie NWad WOld
- 'Beechwood Charm'	CTtf WFar WOld XLum
- 'Beechwood Rival'	CDor CTri
- 'Blandie'	WOld
- 'Blauglut'	LShi WFar WOld
- 'Blue Baby'	CMac MPie
- 'Blue Bouquet'	CTri SRms WFar WOld
- 'Blue Boy'	WOld
- 'Blue Danube'	WOld
- 'Blue Eyes'	WOld
- 'Blue Gown'	GQue WOld
- 'Blue Lagoon'	CDor GMcL LSRN MACG WBrk WCAu WOld XLum
I - 'Blue Moon'	CDor WFar WOld
- 'Blue Radiance'	WOld
- 'Blue Spire'	SPhx WOld
- 'Blue Whirl'	WOld
- 'Boningale Blue'	WOld
- 'Boningale White'	MHCG NHol SAko WFar WOld
- 'Bonnie'	WOld
- 'Bridgette'	CBod
- 'Bright Eyes'	WOld
- 'Brightest and Best'	WOld
- 'Brigitte'	CDor EWTr NLar
- 'Cameo'	WOld
- 'Cantab'	WOld
- 'Carlingcott'	WOld
- 'Carnival'	CMac LDai WOld
- 'Cecily'	WOld
- 'Charles Wilson'	WOld
- 'Chatterbox'	CDor EHyd ELan EPfP LRHS MRav NRHS SRms WFar WOld
- 'Chelwood'	WFar WOld
- 'Chequers'	MBNS MHer SGbt SRms WFar WOld
- 'Christina'	see *S. novi-belgii* 'Kristina'
- 'Christine Soanes'	WOld
- 'Cliff Lewis'	WFar WOld
- 'Climax Albus'	see *S. laeve* 'White Climax'
- 'Cloudy Blue'	WOld
- 'Colonel F.R. Durham'	WOld
- 'Coombe Gladys'	WOld
- 'Coombe Margaret'	WOld
- 'Coombe Radiance'	WOld
- 'Coombe Rosemary'	NLar WBor WOld
- 'Coombe Violet'	WOld
- 'Countess of Dudley'	CFis WFar WOld
- 'Crimson Brocade'	CDor EHyd ELan EPfP EWTr LRHS NLar NRHS SAko SCob SPoG SRms SWvt WFar
- 'Dandy'	CMac EHyd ELan EPfP LRHS NBir NGdn NRHS SGbt SRms WFar WGwG WOld
- 'Daniela'	SRms WBrk WFar WOld
- 'Dauerblau'	WOld
- 'Davey's True Blue'	CTri WFar WOld XLum
- 'David Murray'	WOld
- 'Dazzler'	CDor WFar WOld
- DEBBIE ('Dasdebi'[PBR]) (Mystery Lady Series) (d)	NBir
- 'Destiny'	WOld
- 'Diana'	ECtt
- 'Diana Watts'	WOld
- 'Dietgard'	WFar WOld
- 'Dolly'	NBir SRms WOld
- 'Dora Chiswell'	WOld
- 'Dusky Maid'	ELon WFar WOld
- 'Elizabeth Hutton'	SRGP WFar WOld
- 'Elsie Dale'	WOld

- 'Elta' WOld
- 'Erica' CElw WOld
- 'Ernest Ballard' WOld
- 'Eva' ELon SRms WOld
- 'Eventide' CTri LSRN WOld XLum
- 'Fair Lady' WOld
- 'Faith' WFar WOld
- 'Farncombe Lilac' MAvo SRms
- 'Feckenham Rival' WMal WOld
- 'Fellowship' ♀H6 CDor CTtf EBee ECha ECtt EHyd ELon EPfP LEdu LRHS MMuc MNrw NCth NLar NRHS SAko SEND SEdd SHar SRms SWvt WCAu WCot WFar WHlf WOld XLum
- 'Flamingo' SRms WCAu WOld
- 'Fran' WOld
- 'Freda Ballard' ECtt EHyd GMaP LRHS LSto NRHS WFar WOld
- 'Freya' CElw LSRN SRms WOld WSHC
- 'Fuldatal' WFar WOld
- 'Gayborder Blue' WFar WOld
- 'Gayborder Royal' WFar WOld
- 'Goliath' WOld
- 'Grey Lady' WFar WOld
- 'Guardsman' WOld
- 'Gulliver' SRms WBrk WFar WOld
- 'Gurney Slade' CDor WFar WOld
- 'Guy Ballard' WOld
- 'Harrison's Blue' CDor WOld
- 'Heinz Richard' CFis ECha MHer NBir NGdn SRms WOld
- 'Helen' ELon WOld
- 'Helen Ballard' NBid SRms WFar WOld
- 'Herbstgruss vom Bresserhof' EHyd EWTr LRHS NLar NRHS SAko WFar WOld XSen
- 'Hilda Ballard' WOld
- 'Ilse Brensell' WOld
- 'Irene' WOld
- 'Janet McMullen' WOld
- 'Janet Watts' WOld
- 'Jean' ELon SRms WFar WOld
- 'Jean Gyte' WOld
- 'Jeanette' SRms WFar WOld
- 'Jenny' CBod CSBt ECtt EHyd ELan EPPr EPfP EWoo GMaP LRHS LSRN LShi MHer MRav NBid NBir NGdn NHol NRHS SCob SGbt SPeP SPer SRGP SRms SWvt WCAu WFar WOld XLum
- 'Jollity' WOld
- 'Jugendstil' XLum
- 'Julia' WOld
- 'Kassel' SRms WFar WOld
- 'King of the Belgians' WFar WOld
- 'King's College' WOld

§ - 'Kristina' CRos ECha EHyd GMcL LRHS MNrw MRav NBir NRHS SDix SRGP WFar WOld

- 'Lady Frances' SRms WOld
- 'Lady in Blue' CBod CRos CSBt ECtt EHyd ELan EPfP EWoo LEdu LRHS LShi MBNS MGos NGdn NGrd NRHS NWad SGbt SPer SPoG SRms SSut SWvt WCAu WFar WGwG WOld XSen
- 'Lassie' NWsh SRms WFar WOld
- 'Lavender Dream' WOld
- 'Lawrence Chiswell' WFar WOld
- 'Leuchtfeuer' **new** SAko
- 'Lisa Dawn' WFar WOld
- 'Lisette' LEdu WOld
- 'Little Boy Blue' CDor SRms WOld XLum
- 'Little Man in Blue' CDor WOld
- 'Little Ness' GKev MNrw NWsh WFar WMal
- 'Little Pink Beauty' CCBP CRos ECtt EGrl EHeP EHyd ELan EPfP GMcL LRHS MBNS NGdn NGrd NHol NRHS NWad SPer SRGP SRms WCAu WFar WOld
- 'Little Pink Lady' SRms WFar WOld
- 'Little Pink Pyramid' SRms WOld
- 'Little Red Boy' WOld
- 'Madge Cato' SRms WOld
- 'Mammoth' WOld
- 'Margery Bennett' WOld
- 'Marie Ann Neil' SRms WOld
- 'Marie Ballard' CAby CBod CDor CMac CRos CSBt CTtf EHyd GMaP GQue LEdu LRHS MHer MPie MRav NGdn NHol NLar NPer NRHS SBea SCob SGbt SPer SRms SWvt WCAu WFar WOld XLum
- 'Marie's Pretty Please' WOld
- 'Marie-Theres' SAko
- 'Marjorie' LSRN WOld XLum
- 'Mauve Magic' SRms WFar WOld
- 'Melbourne Magnet' WOld
- 'Midget' WOld
- 'Mistress Quickly' ECtt WFar WOld
- 'Mittelmeer' WOld XLum
- 'Mount Everest' CDor NCth WOld
- 'Mrs Leo Hunter' WOld
- 'Nachtlicht' SAko
- 'Neron' MNrw MPie NDov SHar WCAu WFar WMal WOld
- 'Nesthäkchen' WOld
- 'Niobe' WOld
- 'Norman's Jubilee' EHyd EPfP NBir NRHS WFar WOld
- 'Nursteed Charm' WOld
- 'Pamela' CTtf WOld
- 'Patricia Ballard' (d) CBcs CBod CDor CMac CRos CSBt EBee EBou EHyd ELan EPfP GMaP LCro LOPS LRHS MHer NBir NGrd NLar NPer NRHS NWad SPer WCAu WFar WOld
- 'Peace' WOld
- 'Percy Thrower' CDor WOld
- 'Peter Chiswell' SRms WOld
- 'Peter Harrison' EHyd GMaP LRHS NBir NRHS WOld XLum
- 'Peter Pan' SCob
- 'Pink Buttons' MAvo NDov
- 'Pink Lace' MBNS WOld
- 'Plenty' WOld
- 'Porzellan' CElw ECtt LEdu MAvo MBNS MNrw NGdn NGrd NLar WCot WFar WMal WOld WPGP
- 'Pride of Colwall' SRms WOld
- 'Priory Blush' CDor SRms WOld
- 'Professor Anton Kippenberg' EHyd ELan EPfP GMaP LRHS MNrw MRav NGrd NLar NRHS SAko SPer SRms SWvt WFar WOld XLum
- 'Prosperity' WOld
- 'Purple Dome' CSBt CTtf ECha EGrl ELan LEdu LOPS LSRN MHer NBir NCth SBut SDix SHar SOrN SRkn WChS WFar WOld
- 'Purple Dream' WFar
- 'Ralph Picton' WFar WOld
- 'Red Robin' LShi
- 'Red Sunset' SRms
- 'Rembrandt' LDai MArl NGdn
- 'Remembrance' CDor SRms WFar WOld
- 'Reverend Vincent Dale' WOld
- 'Richness' CTtf WOld
- 'Rose Bonnet' CSBt SPlb WFar WOld
- 'Roseanne' WOld
- 'Rosebud' Ballard (d) CDor WOld

- 'Rosenquartz'	NLar WFar
- 'Rosenwichtel'	CDor NLar SRms WOld
- 'Royal Blue'	WOld
- 'Royal Ruby'	CFis EBee ECtt NLar SRms WOld XLum
- 'Royal Velvet'	WOld
- 'Rozika'	MNrw
- 'Rufus'	NWsh WFar WOld
- 'Saint Egwyn'	WOld
- 'Sam Banham'	MNrw WFar WOld
- SAMOA ('Dasthree') (Island Series)	EHyd EPfP LBar LRHS LSou NLar NRHS SPoG SRms WCot
- 'Sandford White Swan'	MHer WFar WOld
- 'Sarah Ballard'	NLar WFar WOld
§ - 'Schneekissen'	ECtt EHyd ELan EPfP GKev GMaP LRHS LShi MBNS MHer NRHS SRms SWvt WFar WOld XLum
- 'Schneezicklein'	GBin
- 'Schöne von Dietlikon'	CKno SAko WFar WOld XLum
- 'Schoolgirl'	CTtf WOld
- 'Sheena'	WFar WOld
- 'Silberblaukissen'	WOld
- SNOW CUSHION	see *S. novi-belgii* 'Schneekissen'
- 'Snowdrift'	WGwG
- 'Snowsprite'	CBod CSBt EHyd ELan EShb LRHS NLar NRHS SGbt SRms WOld XLum
- 'Sonata'	GMaP WOld
- 'Sophia'	WOld
- STARLETTA BLUE ('Asflo Blue')	NBir
- 'Starlight'	CDor GMcL NLar WCAu WFar
- 'Steinebrück'	WOld
- 'Sterling Silver'	WOld
- 'Sunset'	WOld
- 'Sweet Briar'	WOld
- 'Terry's Pride'	SRms WFar WOld
- 'The Archbishop'	ECtt WOld
- 'The Bishop'	WOld
- 'The Cardinal'	WOld
- 'The Dean'	WOld
- 'The Sexton'	WOld
- 'Thundercloud'	CDor WOld
- 'Timsbury'	CDor CTtf SRms WOld
- TONGA ('Dasfour') (Island Series)	EHyd EPfP LRHS MACG NLar NRHS NWsh SCob SPoG SRms SWvt
- 'Tovarich'	WOld
- 'Trudi Ann'	NBir WOld
- 'Twinkle'	WOld
- 'Victor'	WOld
- 'Vignem'	NSti
- 'Violet Lady'	WOld
- 'Waterperry'	WBrk WOld
- 'White Ladies'	CBcs CRos EHyd GMaP LCro LOPS LRHS MMuc MNrw NLar NRHS SCob WCAu XLum
- 'White Swan'	ECtt
- 'White Wings'	LSto WOld
- 'Winston S. Churchill'	CAby CDor EHyd ELan EPfP GMaP LEdu LRHS MBel MHer MPie NRHS SPer SPlb SPoG SRGP WCAu WOld WTor
- 'Zwergenhimmel'	SAko
§ ***oblongifolium***	LRHS NWsh XSen
§ - 'Fanny's'	ECtt NWad
- 'October Skies'	EBee EWes MNrw SHar XSen
- 'Raydon's Favorite' **new**	SMHy
'Ochtendgloren' (*pilosum* var. *pringlei* hybrid) ♀^{H4}	CDor CTtf EBee ECtt ELon EPPr EWes MACG MAsh MHol MMuc MNrw NCth NLar SMHy WHoo WMal WOld
§ 'Oktoberlicht'	EPPr MNrw NCth SHar WHoo WOld
§ ***oolentangiense***	SPhx
'Orchidee'	ECtt EShb EWes MAvo WMal WOld
'Photograph' ♀^{H7}	CTtf ECtt EHyd EWes LEdu LRHS MPie MRav NCth NLar NRHS SMrm WOld WPGP
§ ***pilosum***	WCot WFar WOld
§ - var. ***pringlei*** ♀^{H7}	ECha EWes MMuc NWad
- - double-flowered (d)	WOld
§ - - 'Monte Cassino'	CSBt GQue LEdu LRHS MBNS NBro SEdd SMHy SPer SPhx SRms WCAu WMal WSpi XLum
- - 'October Glory'	ECtt WFar
- - 'Phoebe'	WOld
'Pink Star'	CRos ECtt EHyd ELon GMaP LEdu LRHS MNrw MRav NRHS NSti SPhx WCAu WFar XLum
'Pinwheel'	LEdu WCot
'Pixie Dark Eye' (*ericoides* hybrid)	EBee ECtt SDix SRms WCot WOld
'Pixie Red Eye' (*ericoides* hybrid)	EBee ELon LEdu WCot WFar
'Prairie Perse' **new**	WCot
'Prairie Pink'	WOld
'Prairie Purple'	CDor ECha ECtt ELon NDov SMHy SPhx WCot WFar WHoo WMal WOld
'Prairie Sky'	ECha
'Primrose Path'	CDor ECha ECtt EPPr LEdu MNrw SPhx WBrk WCot WFar WOld
§ ***puniceum***	MMuc SEND WOld XLum
'Purple Diamond' (Autumn Jewels Series)	SGBe WFar
'Ringdove' (*ericoides* hybrid) ♀^{H7}	MAvo NCth NSti SMHy SWvt WCot WOld
'Rose Crystal' (Autumn Jewels Series)	SGBe
'Rose Glow'	EPPr
'Rose Quartz' (Autumn Jewels Series)	NLar SGBe
'Rose Queen'	MACG MMrt MNrw MPie NWsh SRms WOld
× ***salignum*** Scottish form	WOld
'Sea Spray'	WCot
§ ***sericeum***	SPhx
'Soft Lass'	WCot
'Star of Chesters'	MAvo
'Sunhelene'	EBee ECtt ELon WCot
SUNPLUM ('Danasplum'[PBR])	CTtf
'Superstar'	MNrw NDov SPhx WHoo WMal WOld
§ ***tradescantii***	MBNS NSti SMad WBrk WCot
'Treffpunkt'	GBin MAvo MNrw NLar SAko SMHy
§ ***turbinellum*** ambig.	EWTr LSun WCAu WPGP
turbinellum misapplied ♀^{H6}	CFis ELon EPfP EWes LRHS LSto NGdn SMHy SPhx SRkn SWvt
turbinellum Lindl.	EBee EPfP EWTr LEdu NQui SSut WCot WOld WPGP
- 'El Fin'	MNrw
- hybrid	CTtf SDix WOld WSpi
- 'Leaflet' **new**	SMHy WOld
'Vasterival'	EPPr EWoo IPot LEdu MHer MPie NCth NDov SHar WCAu WPGP XLum
'Wood's Blue'	EHyd LRHS NRHS
'Wood's Pink'	CBod EHyd LRHS NRHS WCAu

Symphytum (*Boraginaceae*)

'Angela Whinfield'	LPla LShi WMal
asperum	CCBP ECha EPPr MRav NLar
* ***azureum***	EBee LPla MBel MNrw NChi WCAu
'Belsay Gold'	NBid NBir SDix
'Bocking'	see *S.* × *uplandicum* 'Bocking 4', 'Bocking 14'

	bulbosum PAB 4886	LEdu
	caucasicum	ECha LEdu MHoo NLar SRms WWtn XLum
	cordatum	EPPr LEdu MNrw WPGP
§	'Goldsmith' (v)	EBee ECha ELan EPfP GKev LRHS MBriF MCot MHol MSCN NBPC NBid NBir NLar NPer SCob SGbt SPoG WCAu WFar
	grandiflorum	CMac CTri GKev GPoy LEdu LWaG
	'Hidcote Blue'	CBod CRos CTri ECha ECtt EHyd EMor EPPr EPfP LRHS LShi MHoo MMuc NBro NRHS SEND SMrm SPoG SRms WGwG WPnP WWtn
	'Hidcote Blue' × ***tuberosum***	EMor
§	'Hidcote Pink'	CBod CRos ECha ECtt EHyd EMor EPPr EPfP LRHS LShi MHoo MMuc MNrw NBir NLar NRHS NSti SEND SMrm SPer SRms WCAu WFar WGwG WPnP WWtn XLum
	'Hidcote Variegated' (v)	CMac SRms
	ibericum	CAgr CBod CCBP ECha EGrI EHyd EMor GKev GMaP GPoy LRHS LShi MHoo MMuc NRHS NSti SEND SMrm SRms WGwG WWtn
	- 'All Gold'	EBee ECha EHyd LRHS LShi MNrw NRHS WFar
	- 'Blaueglocken'	ECha
	- 'Gold in Spring'	WFar
	- 'Jubilee'	see *S.* 'Goldsmith'
	- 'Lilacinum'	WHer
	- variegated (v)	MHoo
	- 'Variegatum'	see *S.* 'Goldsmith'
	- 'Wisley Blue'	CAgr CBcs CBod LRHS NLar SCob WCAu WFar
	'Lambrook Sunrise'	CFis CMac NBro SRms WCot
	'Langthorns Pink'	EBee NLar
	officinale	CAgr CBod CHab EBee ENfk GJos GPoy GQue MHer MHoo MNHC NPer SPer SPoG SRms WCAu WHer WWild XLum
	- blue-flowered	MHoo
	- var. ***ochroleucum***	WHer
	orientale	CCBP EBee EPPr GJos MBel MNrw
	peregrinum	see *S.* × *uplandicum*
	'Romanian Red'	SDix
	'Roseum'	see *S.* 'Hidcote Pink'
	'Rubrum'	CBod CTtf EHyd ELan EPfP EWes LRHS MHoo NBPC NBro NLar NRHS SPer WCAu XLum
	tuberosum	CFis EPPr GPoy LEdu LPla MHer MMuc NGrd NWad WBor WCot WFar WHer XSen
§	× ***uplandicum***	CLau CTri GPoy MMuc SVic
	- 'Axminster Gold' (v)	WCot
§	- 'Bocking 14'	CAgr CHby GAbr LCro LEdu LOPS MHoo NGrd SRms WSFF XLum
§	- 'Bocking 4'	CAgr
	- 'Droitwich' (v)	WCot
	- 'Moorland Heather'	CDor CSpe CTtf EAJP ECha EMor LEdu LPla LRHS MBriF MHer MHoo MMrt MNrw MPie SPhx WCot WMal WWFP
	- 'Padworth Purple'	LEdu
	- purple-flowered	MMuc
	- 'Variegatum' (v)	CTtf ECtt EHyd EWes LRHS NBir NGdn WAvo WSpi

Symplocos (*Symplocaceae*)

paniculata new	WJur

Synadenium (*Euphorbiaceae*)

grantii 'Rubrum'	EShb

Syncarpha (*Asteraceae*)

vestita	SPlb

Syncolostemon (*Lamiaceae*)

'Candy Kisses'	WCot

Syneilesis (*Asteraceae*)

aconitifolia	ESwi EWld GEdr WCot
- B&SWJ 879	LEdu WCru
subglabrata B&SWJ 298	ESwi
- NMWJ 14528	WCru
aff. ***tagawae*** B&SWJ 11191	WCot

Syngonium (*Araceae*)

'Arrow' (v) new	LCro
podophyllum 🏆^{H1a}	CDoC
- 'Pixie'	CDoC

Synnotia see *Sparaxis*

Synthyris (*Plantaginaceae*)

laciniata	EDir
missurica subsp. ***missurica***	EBee GKev WFar
- subsp. ***stellata***	CAby CBWd CBod CMiW EBee ECha ECtt EHed EHyd EPfP EPri EWes GAbr GBin GElm GMaP LBar LEdu LRHS LSto MMrt MPie NBir NHpl NRHS NSti WSHC

Synurus (*Asteraceae*)

excelsus	GGro

Syringa ✿ (*Oleaceae*)

	afghanica misapplied	see *S. protolaciniata*
	BLOOMERANG DARK PURPLE ('Smsjbp7'^{PBR})	CRos CWGN EPfP LCro LOPS LPar LSRN MAsh NLar SGol SPoG WSpi
	BLOOMERANG PINK PERFUME	see *S.* 'Pink Perfume'
	BLOOMERANG PURPLE ('Penda')	CRos LRHS NRHS
	× ***chinensis***	EPfP
	- 'Bicolor'	WGob
	- 'Saugeana'	MBlu MMuc SPer
	× ***diversifolia***	MBlu NLar
	emodi 'Aurea'	EPfP
	- 'Aureovariegata'	see *S. emodi* 'Variegata'
	- 'Elegantissima' (v)	CBcs CEnd CMac ELan SPoG
§	- 'Variegata' (v)	EHyd EPfP LRHS NLar
	× ***hyacinthiflora*** 'Clarke's Giant'	SGol
	- 'Dark Night'	WGob
	- 'Esther Staley' 🏆^{H6}	EPfP LPar MACG MRav WGob
	- 'Maiden's Blush' 🏆^{H6}	EPfP SGol
	- 'Pocahontas' 🏆^{H6}	WGob
	- 'Sweetheart' (d)	NOra WMat
	JOSÉE ('Morjos 060f')	ELan ELon EPfP MAsh NLar SGol SWvt WFar WGob WHtc WLov
	× ***josiflexa***	CExl
	- 'Agnes Smith'	CMac LPar NLar SCob WSpi
	- 'Bellicent' 🏆^{H6}	CBod CEnd CKel CMac CRos EHyd ELan EPfP GMcL LRHS MAsh MMuc MRav NLar NRHS SMad SNig SPer SPoG SRms SWvt WAvo WCFE WFar WHtc WLov WSpi
	- 'James MacFarlane'	NLar
	- 'Redwine'	LRHS
§	- 'Royalty'	SCob
	josikaea	CAco CMCN CSBt NLar SPer WMat
	- 'Oden'	WMat
	komarowii	ESwi GGGa MGil
§	- subsp. ***reflexa***	EPfP MBlu NLar WHlf WPGP

§ × ***laciniata*** Mill. — CKel CTsd EBee EHed EHyd ELan EPfP LRHS MRav SPer WAvo WCFE WHtc WLov WPGP
'Lark Song' — NLar
meyeri — SVen
- (Flowerfesta Series) FLOWERFESTA PINK ('Anny200817'PBR) — LCro LOPS WHlf
- - FLOWERFESTA PURPLE ('Anny200809'PBR) — LCro LOPS WHlf
- - FLOWERFESTA WHITE ('Anny200810'PBR) — LCro LOPS WHlf
§ - 'Palibin' 🏆H5 — Widely available
microphylla — see *S. pubescens* subsp. *microphylla*
'Minuet' — CBcs LBuc SGol
'Miss Canada' — NLar SCob
oblata — CMCN
palibiniana misapplied — see *S. meyeri* 'Palibin'
patula misapplied — see *S. meyeri* 'Palibin'
patula (Palib.) Nakai — see *S. pubescens* subsp. *patula*
pekinensis — see *S. reticulata* subsp. *pekinensis*
× ***persica*** 🏆H6 — CExl EPfP MGos MRav NLar NWea SPer WFar WGob
- 'Alba' 🏆H6 — MRav WAvo WFar WGob
- var. ***laciniata*** — see *S.* × *laciniata* Mill.
§ 'Pink Perfume'PBR — CMac CRos EHyd ELon EPfP EWTr LCro LPar LRHS LSRN MAsh MTrO NOra NOrn NRHS SGol SPoG WSpi
pinnatifolia — CBcs CKel ELan GBin LRHS NLar WCFE WPGP
× ***prestoniae*** 'Desdemona' — EHyd MMuc
- 'Elinor' 🏆H6 — CKel ELan EPfP LRHS MRav
- 'Nocturne' — WFar
- 'Royalty' — see *S.* × *josiflexa* 'Royalty'
§ ***protolaciniata*** — EShb SGsty
pubescens subsp. ***julianae*** 'George Eastman' — MGos MRav
§ - subsp. ***microphylla*** — LSto
- - 'Superba' 🏆H6 — Widely available
§ - subsp. ***patula*** — CMac EHyd EPfP LRHS MMuc MRav NRHS SVen
- - 'Miss Kim' 🏆H6 — Widely available
'Red Pixie' — CDoC CKel CRos EBee EHyd EMil EPfP LCro LOPS LRHS MAsh MDon MGos MMrt NOrn NRHS SCoo SGsty SRkn WGob
reflexa — see *S. komarowii* subsp. *reflexa*
reticulata — CMCN MBlu WJur
- 'Ivory Silk' — EBtc WMat
§ - subsp. ***pekinensis*** — CMCN
- - CHINA SNOW ('Morton') 🏆H6 — NOrn
- - 'Yellow Fragrance' — MBlu NLar
SUGAR PLUM FAIRY ('Bailsugar') (Fairytale Series) — NLar
× ***swegiflexa*** — CExl
tomentella — EBee SRms WCFE WPGP
- subsp. ***sweginzowii*** — CBcs CWCL EPPr EShb GKin MHtn NLar SNig SPer WBor WSpi
- subsp. ***yunnanensis*** — CExl GKev SBrt
velutina Kom. — see *S. pubescens* subsp. *patula*
villosa — SPlb
I - 'Aurea' — LRHS
vulgaris — CAco EDir EHeP LPar LSto NWea
- var. ***alba*** — LPar
- 'Amethyst' — CBod EPfP
§ - 'Andenken an Ludwig Späth' 🏆H6 — Widely available
- 'Aurea' — MRav WAvo WFar WHtc
- BEAUTY OF MOSCOW — see *S. vulgaris* 'Krasavitsa Moskvy'
- 'Belle de Nancy' (d) — CBod CCCN CDoC CKel EDir ELan ELon GMcL IPap LPar MAsh MDon MMuc MRav NOrn SEND SGol SGsty SWvt
- CARPE DIEM — see *S. vulgaris* 'Evert de Gier'
- 'Charles Joly' (d) 🏆H6 — Widely available
- 'Comtesse d'Harcourt' — EPfP SPer
- 'Congo' — WGob
- 'Dappled Dawn' (v) — MMrt
- 'Dark Koster' — WGob
- DENTELLE D'ANJOU ('Mindent') — CDoC CKel
- 'Dwight D. Eisenhower' 🏆H6 — WGob
- 'Edward J. Gardner' (d) 🏆H6 — SEND
§ - 'Evert de Gier'PBR — CBcs CBod GAbr NLar WHlf WSpi WTyc
- 'Firmament' 🏆H6 — MRav SEND SPer WGob WSpi
- FRAU HOLLE — LRHS
- 'Général Pershing' Lemoine, 1924 (d) — LRHS WSpi
- 'Hope' — see *S. vulgaris* 'Nadezhda'
- 'Katherine Havemeyer' (d) 🏆H6 — Widely available
§ - 'Krasavitsa Moskvy' (d) 🏆H6 — CBod CCVT CDoC CTri CWCL EDir ELon EPfP EWes GMcL LRHS MAsh MRav MTrO NLar NOra WHtc WMat WSpi
- 'Lila Wonder'PBR — CBod EPfP SPoG WGob
- 'Madame Antoine Buchner' (d) 🏆H6 — LPar WSpi
- 'Madame Florent Stepman' — CBod CMac CWCL EPau EPfP GMcL LRHS SRHi WFar WSpi
- 'Madame Lemoine' (d) 🏆H6 — Widely available
- 'Marlyensis Pallida' **new** — NBwr
- 'Michel Buchner' (d) — CBcs CDoC CKel GMcL LMaj LRHS MBlu MDon MGos NLar NOra SCob SCoo SPer WHtc WMat
- 'Mrs Edward Harding' (d) 🏆H6 — EPfP GMcL LRHS MRav NLar NWea
§ - 'Nadezhda' (d) — CBod CKel EBee EDir GAbr LPar LRHS WGob
- 'Paul Thirion' (d) — CBod LRHS
- 'Perle von Stuttgart' — LRHS
- 'Président Grévy' (d) — CKel CWCL EDir EPfP MAsh SGol SPer SPoG
- 'President Lincoln' — WGob
- 'Président Poincaré' (d) — WGob
- 'Primrose' 🏆H6 — CBcs CBod CCCN CMac EBee ELan EPfP IPap LRHS MACG MAsh MGos MTrO NOra NOrn SCob SCoo SEND SGol SPer SPoG WGob WMat WSpi
- 'Prince Wolkonsky' (d) — CKel EDir ELan EPfP LRHS LSRN MAsh MGos MTrO NOra SGsty SPer WFar WGob
- 'Princesse Sturdza' — EPfP NOra WHtc
- 'Professor Hoser' — WGob
- ROSE DE MOSCOU ('Minkarl'PBR) — SCob
- 'Ruhm von Horstenstein' — LPar
- 'Sarah Sands' — LRHS WGob
- 'Sensation' 🏆H6 — Widely available
- 'Souvenir d'Alice Harding' (d) 🏆H6 — LMaj
- 'Souvenir de Louis Spaeth' — see *S. vulgaris* 'Andenken an Ludwig Späth'
- variegated (v) — EWes
- variegated double (d/v) — WCot
- 'Viviand-Morel' (d) — CMac
- 'Wedgewood Blue' — WGob
- 'Znamya Lenina' — WSpi
wolfii — EBtc GKev NLar

Syzygium (*Myrtaceae*)

	paniculatum	CExl WJur
	zeylanicum	EShb

T

Tabernaemontana (*Apocynaceae*)

	coronaria	see *T. divaricata*
§	***divaricata***	CCCN WFib

Tacca (*Taccaceae*)

	integrifolia	LPal

Taccarum (*Araceae*)

	weddellianum	WCot

Tacitus see *Graptopetalum*

Taenidia (*Apiaceae*)

	integerrima	SPhx

Tagetes (*Asteraceae*)

	'Cinnabar'	CSpe GBin
	erecta	SCob SVic
	- INCA I ORANGE (Inca I Series) ♀H2	LCro
	- 'Taishan'	MBros
	- 'Vanilla'	MBros
	lemmonii	SDix
	- 'Martin's Mutant'	SDix
	'Lemon Gem'	MBros
	lucida	CSpe ENfk LEdu MHer SRms SVic WFar WJek
	patula	SCob SVic
	- 'Alumia Vanilla Cream' (Alumia Series)	CSpe
	- Bonanza Series (d) ♀H2	LCro LOPS MBros
	- - BONANZA BEE ('Pas2258') (d)	MBros
	- - 'Bonanza Bolero' (d)	MBros
	- - BONANZA ORANGE ('Pas91617') (d)	MBros
	- - BONANZA YELLOW ('Pas2276') (d)	MBros
	- 'Dainty Marietta' ♀H2	LCro LOPS
	- DWARF DOUBLE MIXED (d)	LCro
	- 'Fireball' (d) ♀H2	CSpe
	- FRENCH FANCY (mixed) (d)	LCro
	- Hero Series **new**	MBros
	- 'Strawberry Blonde' (d)	MBros
	tenuifolia 'Golden Gem'	LCro LOPS MBros
	zypaquirensis B&SWJ 14840	WCru

Taiwania (*Cupressaceae*)

	cryptomerioides	CAco IArd IDee SLim

Talbotia (*Velloziaceae*)

§	***elegans***	SBrt

tamarillo see *Solanum betaceum*

tamarind see *Tamarindus indica*

Tamarindus (*Fabaceae*)

	indica (F)	SPlb

Tamarix (*Tamaricaceae*)

	gallica	NWea SArc SWeb
	hampeana	SEND
	'Hulsdonk White'PBR	CBcs CCCN EDir SPer
§	***parviflora*** ♀H5	CMac EHyd EPfP LPar LRHS NRHS
	pentandra	see *T. ramosissima*, *T. ramosissima* 'Rosea'
	ramosissima	CBod CCCN CTri EBee EPfP LPar MAsh SGsty SRms
	- 'Pink Cascade' ♀H5	CBcs CBod CCCN CMac EBee EDir ELan EPfP LCro LOPS MBlu MGos MRav SCob SEdd SGbt SPer SPoG SSha SWvt
§	- 'Rosea'	CBcs
§	- 'Rubra'	CBod EPfP GMcL LPar SCob SEND SEdd SPer
	- 'Summer Glow'	see *T. ramosissima* 'Rubra'
	tetrandra ♀H5	Widely available
	- var. ***purpurea***	see *T. parviflora*

Tanacetum ✿ (*Asteraceae*)

§	***argenteum***	MRav
	- subsp. ***canum***	EDAr
	aureum	CKel
§	***balsamita***	CBod CCBP CHby EBee ENfk EPPr GJos GPoy MHer MHoo MMuc MNHC NGrd SEND SRms WHer WJek WSFF XLum
§	- subsp. ***balsamita***	GPoy GQue SRms WJek
§	- subsp. ***balsamitoides***	CBod MHer SRms
	- var. ***tanacetoides***	see *T. balsamita* subsp. *balsamita*
	- ***tomentosum***	see *T. balsamita* subsp. *balsamitoides*
	camphoratum	SRms
§	***cinerariifolium***	CBod GPoy MNHC
§	***coccineum***	SVic WFar
	- 'Alfred'	MNrw
	- 'Bees' Pink Delight'	LRHS
	- 'Duro'	EHyd LRHS NRHS
	- 'Eileen May Robinson'	LBar LRHS SGbt
	- 'Garden Treasure'	NCth
	- 'H.M. Pike'	EBee
	- 'James Kelway'	EPfP
	- 'Laureen'	LBar WNPC
	- 'Laurin'	EBlo ECtt EHyd LRHS MHol NBPC NRHS
	- Robinson's crimson-flowered	EHyd LRHS NRHS
	- - giant-flowered	EHyd LRHS NRHS SRms
	- - pink-flowered	EAJP EBee EBou EHyd ELan EPfP GMaP LBar LRHS MHol SCob XLum
	- - red-flowered	CBod CSBt CWnw EAJP EBou EHyd ELan EPfP GMaP GMcL LBar LRHS MBNS MHol SCob SPlb SVic SWvt WHlf XLum
	- - rose-flowered	CSBt LPal MBNS
	- 'Scarlet Glow'	LBar NCth
	- 'Snow Cloud'	ECtt LBar LRHS NCth
	- 'Vanessa'	MNrw
§	***corymbosum***	NLar WCot
	- 'Bukke'	LEdu
	- 'Festtafel'	LEdu LPla
	densum	WCFE
	- subsp. ***amani***	CKel ECha GKev GMaP SEND XSen
	- - 'Beth Chatto'	XSen
§	***haradjanii***	EBou SGro WKif
	macrophyllum misapplied	see *Achillea grandifolia* Friv.
§	***macrophyllum*** (Waldst. & Kit.) Sch.Bip.	EBee ECtt EPPr SPhx WBor
	- 'Cream Klenza'	WCot
	niveum	ECha SDix WCot XSen

	- 'Jackpot'	ECha ELan EWes SBls SHar SWvt WHil
§	***parthenium***	CBod CCBP CHab CHby EMor ENfk GPoy GQue LCro LOPS MHer MHoo MNHC NPer SRms SVic WFar WHer XLum
	- 'Aureum'	CBod CTtf EBou ECha ELan EMor ENfk EWes EWhm GPoy MHer MHoo MNHC SPlb SRms SWvt WCot WFar WHer WHil WHoo XLum
	- double white-flowered (d)	CTtf MHoo NPer SRms
	- 'Golden Ball'	WFar
	- 'Golden Moss'	EMor XLum
	- 'Magic Lime Green'	MNrw WFar
	- 'Malmesbury'	MHoo WHer
	- 'Plenum' (d)	MNrw
§	- 'Rowallane' (d)	MMuc SEND WCot
	- 'Selma Star' (d)	MNrw WFar WHer
	- 'Sissinghurst White'	see *T. parthenium* 'Rowallane'
	- 'White Bonnet' (d)	WHer WMal
	poteriifolium	EBlo EHyd LRHS MAvo NRHS
	ptarmiciflorum 'Silver Feather'	SRms SVen
	RADIANT DEEP PINK ('Tntadp')	LBar MHol WNPC
	RADIANT LIGHT PINK ('Tntalp')	LBar WNPC
	vulgare	CCBP CHab CHby CWal ECha ECtt ENfk GBin GJos GPoy GQue IRos LCro LOPS MACG MHer MHoo NGrd NMir SRms SVic WFar WSFF XSen
	- 'All Gold'	MBriF SMad SRms
	- var. ***crispum***	EBee ENfk MRav SMad SRms WFar
	- 'Golden Fleece'	CSpe ECtt EWes GMcL WCot
	- 'Isla Gold' (v)	CDor ECtt EWes LDai LEdu MBriF MHer MMuc NBid SEND SMrm WCAu WCot WFar
	- 'Silver Lace' (v)	EBee WFar

Tanakaea (*Saxifragaceae*)

	radicans	WSHC

tangelo see *Citrus* × *aurantium* Tangelo Group

tangerine see *Citrus reticulata* Tangerine Group

tangor see *Citrus* × *aurantium* Tangor Group

Tara (*Fabaceae*)

§	***spinosa***	EAri SPlb WJur

Taraxacum (*Asteraceae*)

	faeroense	NPoe WCot
	leucanthum	GGro
	officinale agg.	CHab SVic
	pseudoroseum	GGro NPoe WFar
	rubrifolium	WFar

tarragon see *Artemisia dracunculus*

Tasmannia (*Winteraceae*)

§	***lanceolata***	Widely available
	- (f)	EHed SPer
	- (m)	SPer
	- 'Red Spice'	EPfP LRHS LSRN SEle
	- 'Suzette' (v)	MBlu SRms

Taxodium ✿ (*Cupressaceae*)

	ascendens 'Nutans'	see *T. distichum* var. *imbricarium* 'Nutans'
	distichum	Widely available
	- 'Cascade Falls'	CAco LRHS MBlu MTrO NOra SLim
	- var. ***imbricarium***	CAco CMCN LRHS
§	- - 'Nutans'	CAco CBcs EPfP IArd MBlu MTrO SLim WMat
	- 'Little Leaf'	SLim
	- 'Little Twister'	SLim
	- 'Minaret'	MBlu
*	- 'Pendulum'	IDee
	- 'Pévé Minaret'	CMen LRHS MGil NOra SArc SLim
	- 'Pévé Yellow'	MBlu SLim
	- 'Schloss Herten'	SLim
	- 'Secrest'	MBlu
	- SHAWNEE BRAVE ('Mickelson')	MBlu SLim
	mucronatum	CAco CExl
	- NJM 09.037	WPGP

Taxus ✿ (*Taxaceae*)

	baccata ♀H7	Widely available
	- 'Aldenham Gold'	CKen
	- 'Amersfoort'	CAco NLar
	- 'Argentea Minor'	see *T. baccata* 'Dwarf White'
	- Aurea Group	ELan MDon NWea SRms SSha
I	- 'Aureomarginata' (v)	CBcs MAsh SWvt
	- 'Autumn Shades'	LRHS NLar
	- 'Barabits' Express'	CAco
	- 'Bence'	CAco
	- 'Black Rod'	CKen
	- 'Corleys Coppertip'	CKen ELan NLar
	- 'Cristata'	CKen MBlu NLar
	- 'David'	CAco EPfP IArd LCro LRHS MDon MGos NLar SCoo SLim SPoG SSha SWvt
	- 'Dorothea'	NLar
	- 'Dovastoniana' (m or f)	CAco NLar NWea
	- 'Dovastonii Aurea' (m or f/v)	CAco CBcs GKin LSto MBlu NLar SGol SRms
§	- 'Dwarf White' (v)	NLar
	- 'Elegantissima' (f/v)	EPfP LMaj NWea SCoo SLim SPoG SSha
§	- 'Fastigiata' (f) ♀H7	Widely available
	- Fastigiata Aurea Group	CAco CWnw EHeP EPfP GMcL GQue IArd LCro LMaj LPar LRHS MAsh MGil MGos NBwr NLar NOrn NWea SArc SCob SGol SGsty SRms SWeb
	- 'Fastigiata Aureomarginata' (m/v) ♀H7	CMac CSBt EPfP LBee LRHS LSto MGos MSwo NBwr SCoo SLim SPer SPoG SSha SWvt WTSh
	- 'Fastigiata Robusta' (f)	CAco CSBt CWnw EDir ELan EPfP GMcL LCro LMaj LRHS LWaG MAsh MGos MSwo MTrO NLar SCoo SGsty SLim SPoG SSha WMat
	- 'Globus'	CAco
	- 'Goldener Zwerg'	MBlu
	- 'Gracilis Pendula'	SMad
	- 'Graciosa'	NLar
	- 'Grayswood Hill'	WFar
	- 'Great Column'	MBlu
	- 'Green Column'	NLar
	- 'Green Diamond'	MBlu NLar
	- 'Hibernica'	see *T. baccata* 'Fastigiata'
	- 'Icicle' ♀H7	CAco LRHS MAsh NHol NLar SLim
	- 'Itsy Bitsy'	CKen
	- 'Ivory Tower'	CAco CKen LRHS NHol NLar SLim
	- 'Jack's Gold'	NLar
	- 'Klitzeklein'	CKen NLar
	- 'Lakatos'	CAco
	- 'Luca' PBR	CAco NLar
	- 'Lutea' (f)	CAco SLim
	- 'Micro'	CKen MAsh NLar
	- 'Nutans'	CKen

	- 'Overeynderi'	CAco
	- 'Pendula'	CAco
	- 'Pygmaea'	CKen
	- 'Renke's Kleiner Grüner'	LRHS
	- 'Repandens' (f) 🏆H7	CAco GMcL IArd LIns LRHS SavN WFar WSpi
I	- 'Repens Aurea' (v) 🏆H7	CBcs CMac EPfP SCoo SLim SRms SSha WFar WSpi
	- 'Rushmore'	NLar
	- 'Semperaurea' (m) 🏆H7	CBcs CMac LBuc LPar LRHS MAsh NBwr NLar NWea SCoo SGol SLim SPoG SSha WSpi
	- 'Standishii' (f) 🏆H7	Widely available
	- 'Stove Pipe'	CKen
	- 'Summergold' (v)	CBrac ELan GMcL LCro LIns LRHS LSto NBir NBwr NLar SCoo SGsty WHtc WSpi
	- 'Sussex Yellow' **new**	CBod
	- 'Washingtonii' (v)	LPar
	- 'Zöld'	CAco
	cuspidata	CAco CMen
	- 'Aurescens' (v)	CKen
	- 'Minuet'	CKen
	- var. ***nana*** hort. ex Rehder	CAco
	- 'Silver Queen'	CAco SLim
	× ***media*** 'Brownii'	CAco
	- 'Densiformis' **new**	CAco
	- 'Green Mountain' **new**	CAco
	- 'Hicksii' (f)	CAco GMcL LBuc LIns LMaj NBwr NWea SGol SGsty
	- 'Hillii'	CAco LBuc LIns LPar SGsty
	- 'Nixe'	SLim
§	- 'Oene'PBR **new**	CAco
	- RISING STAR	see *T.* × *media* 'Oene'
	- 'Stefania'PBR **new**	CAco
	- 'Tymon'PBR	MGos NLar
	- 'Viridis'	CAco
	wallichiana	CAco IDee

tayberry see *Rubus* Tayberry Group; see also AGM Fruit Section

Tecoma (*Bignoniaceae*)

	capensis 🏆H1c	CHII CRHN CSBt SVen
	- 'Lutea'	EShb
	- yellow-flowered	CHII WLov
	ricasoliana	see *Podranea ricasoliana*
	stans 🏆H1c	WJur

Tecomanthe (*Bignoniaceae*)

	speciosa	CRHN

Tecomaria see *Tecoma*

Tecophilaea (*Tecophilaeaceae*)

	cyanocrocus 🏆H3	CBor EHyd EPot GKev LAma LRHS NDry NRHS NRog
	- 'Leichtlinii' 🏆H3	CAvo CBor EHyd EPot GKev LAma LRHS NDry NRHS NRog SDeJ
	- 'Purpurea'	see *T. cyanocrocus* 'Violacea'
	- Storm Cloud Group	EPot GKev LAma
§	- 'Violacea'	CAvo CBor EHyd EPot GKev LAma LRHS NDry NRHS NRog
	violiflora	NRog

Tectona (*Verbenaceae*)

	grandis	EBee

Telekia (*Asteraceae*)

§	***speciosa***	CAby CMac CSpe CWal EBee EHyd EPfP GAbr GJos GLog LBar LEdu LRHS NBro NChi NGBl NLar NRHS NSti SBls SDix SEND SPlb SRms WBor WBrk WCAu WHoo

Telesonix see *Boykinia*

Teline see *Genista*

Tellima (*Saxifragaceae*)

	grandiflora	Widely available
	- 'Bob's Choice'	WCot
	- 'Delphine' (v)	EPPr MBriF WCot XLum
	- 'Forest Frost'	CBod CMac EBee EHyd ELan EMor EPPr EPfP EShb GElm LRHS LSto MBNS MBel MBriF MPnt NLar NRHS SWvt WCAu WCot
	- Odorata Group	ECha WCot
	- 'Purpurea'	see *T. grandiflora* Rubra Group
	- 'Purpurteppich'	EBlo EHyd EMor EPPr EPfP GPSL LRHS MPnt MRav NRHS SWvt WCot
§	- Rubra Group	CBod CBro CMac CTri CTtf ECha EHeP ELan EMor EPfP EWoo GMaP GQue LRHS MBriF NChi NLar NPer NSti SCob SPer SPlb SRms SWvt WCAu WCot WFar WHoo WPnP
	- 'Silver Select'	EPPr

Telopea (*Proteaceae*)

	'Braidwood Brilliant'	XSte
§	'Bridal Gown'PBR	CCCN
	'Emperor's Torch'	LRHS XSte
	oreades	LRHS SPlb
	SHADY LADY CRIMSON ('T90101'PBR)	CCCN XSte
	SHADY LADY RED **new**	CCCN
	SHADY LADY WHITE	see *T.* 'Bridal Gown'
	SHADY LADY YELLOW	CCCN XSte
	speciosissima	CCCN LRHS SPlb
	- 'Red Embers'	XSte
	truncata	CCCN SPlb
	white-flowered	XSte

Temu see *Blepharocalyx*

Tephrocactus (*Cactaceae*)

§	***articulatus***	EAri SPlb
§	***molinensis*** **new**	SPlb

Tephroseris (*Asteraceae*)

	integrifolia subsp. ***capitata***	GEdr SPlb

Ternstroemia (*Pentaphylacaceae*)

	chapaensis WWJ 11918	WCru
	gymnanthera	WCru
	kwangtungensis FMWJ 13402	WCru
	luteoflora FMWJ 13360	WCru

Tetracentron (*Trochodendraceae*)

§	***sinense***	CBcs CMCN EPfP ESwi MBlu WPGP
	- WJC 13818 from the Himalaya	WCru
	- var. ***himalense***	see *T. sinense*

Tetradium (*Rutaceae*)

§	***daniellii***	CBcs CMCN EBee ELan EPfP ESwi IArd LAlb LEdu LMaj LPar SAko SEND SPtp WJur WMat WPGP
	- from Korea	WPGP
§	- Hupehense Group	CMCN MCoo NLar
	fraxinifolium PAB 9101	LEdu
	- WJC 13750	WCru

aff. ***fraxinifolium*** WWJ 11615	WCru
glabrifolium B&SWJ 6882	WCru
- CWJ 12364	WCru
ruticarpum	MBlu WPGP
- B&SWJ 3541	WCru

Tetragonolobus see *Lotus*

Tetraneuris (*Asteraceae*)

§ ***grandiflora***	SPlb
scaposa	EPot
torreyana	GEdr

Tetrapanax ✿ (*Araliaceae*)

§ ***papyrifer*** 🏆H3	CDTJ CDoC EAri ELan ESwi LPal MPie SDix SEND SVen WLov
- B&SWJ 7135	WCru
- NMWJ 14580	WCru
- 'Empress'	WCru
- 'Meifeng'	WCru
- 'Rex'	Widely available

Tetrapathaea see *Passiflora*

Tetrastigma (*Vitaceae*)

obtectum	CCCN CRHN CTsd EShb EWld SEND

Teucrium (*Lamiaceae*)

* ***ackermannii*** 🏆H5	CBcs CWnw LRHS MHer MHol NBwr NCou SGro WAbe WHoo WIce WMal WPGP WTor XSen XSte
* ***armenum***	EBou
aroanium	EPot GEdr WMal XSen
asiaticum	XSen
botrys	MHer
chamaedrys misapplied	see *T.* × *lucidrys*
chamaedrys L.	Widely available
- f. ***albiflora***	CCBP ECha ELan EWes WFar WSpi
- 'Nanum'	GMaP XSen
- 'Rose'	EBou SRms
- 'Schneeflocke'	XSen
- 'Spring Gold'	LRHS
- 'Summer Sunshine'	MHoo
aff. ***chamaedrys***	MGil NPol NRya SEdd
flavum	CCCN CSde EBee EPPr XSen
fruticans	Widely available
- 'Agadir'	XSen
- 'Azureum' 🏆H3	CBcs CBod CCBP CCoa CDoC CKel CSde EBee EHyd ELan EPfP EWTr LRHS LSRN MRav SBrt SCob SEND SIvy SMad SNig SPer SPoG SRkn SRms SWvt WKif XSen
I - 'Azureum Compactum'	SCob
- 'Compactum'	CBod CDoC CKel EBee ELan LRHS SEdd SPer SPoG SWvt WAvo WCFE WCot WPGP WSpi
- 'Drysdale'	CCCN CCoa CDoC CKel CSBt EHyd EPfP LRHS SWvt
- 'Ouarzazate' **new**	XSen
'Greystone' **new**	LBar
hircanicum	CAby CCBP CElw EBee EBou ECha EGrl EHyd ELan LRHS LSRN MMuc MNrw NBir SEND SMrm SPhx SRkn XSen
- PAB 13.341	LEdu
- 'Paradise Delight'	CBWd ECtt NLar
- 'Purple Tails'	CChe CSpe CTsd CWCL EBee ELan EMor EPfP GBee MHol MHoo MRav NBir NGrd SRms WFar
§ × ***lucidrys***	Widely available
- 'Lucky Gold'^PBR	SPoG SRms
marum	CTri LRHS MHoo SBrt SRms WJek XSen
massiliense misapplied	see *T.* × *lucidrys*
montanum	ECha XSen
musimonum	EPot
pyrenaicum 🏆H7	EDAr EPot EWes GEdr SGro WAbe
scorodonia	CBod CCBP CHab MHer NLar NMir SRms WHer WJek XSen
- 'Binsted Gold'	LDai NSti
- 'Crispum'	CCBP CKel EHyd EMor LEdu LRHS LWaG MGil MHer NBro NLar NRHS SPer SRms WJek WKif
- 'Crispum Marginatum' (v)	EBee EBou ECha EMor EPPr LEdu LSou MRav WFar
subspinosum	EDAr EPot LRHS WHoo XSen
§ ***viscidum*** 'Lemon and Lime' (v)	ECha NSti

Thalia (*Marantaceae*)

dealbata	CBen ECha EWat LLWG LPfP SArc WMAq XLum

Thalictrum (*Ranunculaceae*)

CC 4576	CExl
from Afghanistan	see *T. isopyroides*
actaeifolium	MBel
- B&SWJ 4664	WCru
- B&SWJ 6310	WCru
- var. ***brevistylum*** B&SWJ 8819	LEdu WCru
- compact B&SWJ 4946	WCru
- 'Perfume Star'	ECtt LEdu SCob SMad WSpi XSte
adiantifolium	see *T. minus* 'Adiantifolium'
alpinum	EDAr EMor EPPr WFar
angustifolium	see *T. lucidum*
'Anne'^PBR	CDor CMil CWCL EBee ECha ECtt EMor ILea LBar LRHS MACG MAvo MBriF MHol MNrw NDov NGBl NLar SEdd SMad SPeP SPoG WCAu WCot WPnP WSpi
aquilegiifolium	Widely available
- 'Album'	CWnw EBee ECha EHyd EMor EPfP GBin GMaP LRHS MACG MBel MCot NBid NBir NRHS SEND SPhx SWvt WCAu WFar WHlf WSpi
- var. ***intermedium*** B&SWJ 10965	WCru
- 'Purpureum'	NBir NLar NQui
- var. ***sibiricum*** B&SWJ 11007	WCru
- 'Thundercloud'	Widely available
- 'White Cloud'	NFav
'Black Stockings' 🏆H7	Widely available
calabricum	NLar
CHANTILLY LACE ('Mactha002') **new**	LBar SHar
chelidonii HWJK 2216	WCru
coreanum	see *T. ichangense*
cultratum	EBee EHyd EPfP LRHS NRHS
dasycarpum	EPPr SMHy SPhx WCot
§ ***delavayi***	Widely available
- BWJ 7800	WCru
- BWJ 7903	WCru
- var. ***acuminatum***	MBel
- - BWJ 7535	WCru
- - BWJ 7971	WCru
- 'Album'	Widely available
- 'Ankum' 🏆H7	CRos EBee EHyd LBar LRHS MMrt MNrw NLar NRHS
- var. ***decorum***	CElw CSpe WCot WCru WPGP
- - BWJ 7770	WCru
- - CD&R 2135	ESwi
- aff. var. ***decorum***	CExl

- 'Gold Laced'	EBee ECtt NLar
- 'Hewitt's Double' (d)	Widely available
- 'Hinkley'	CBWd CMiW ECtt IPot LBar LRHS MBel MNrw NCth NLar WHil WSpi
- var. ***mucronatum***	WCru
- - DJHC 473	WCru
- purple-stemmed BWJ 7748	WCru
aff. ***delavayi***	GElm
diffusiflorum	EBee LRHS WAbe WCru WSHC
dipterocarpum misapplied	see *T. delavayi*
dipterocarpum Franch.	CMac CRos EHyd LRHS NRHS XLum
'Elin' 🏆H7	Widely available
fendleri	GBin
filamentosum	MBel WCot
- B&SWJ 777	WCru
- B&SWJ 4145	WCru
finetii misapplied	ECha LRHS
flavum	CHab CMac EBee EWld GQue NBro NMir SPhx WFar WShi
- 'Chollerton'	see *T. isopyroides*
§ - subsp. ***glaucum***	Widely available
- - 'Ruth Lynden-Bell' 🏆H7	MHol SPoG WCot WHoo
- - 'Silver Sparkler' (v)	WCot
- - 'True Blue'	NDov SGbt
- 'Illuminator'	CDor CElw EHyd EShb LRHS MArl MRav NLar WCot WFar
flexuosum	see *T. minus* subsp. *minus*
honanense BWJ 7962	WCru
§ ***ichangense***	CSpe EBee ECtt EMor EPri GEdr GElm LEdu MBel NWad SPad WCot
- B&SWJ 8203	WCru
- 'Evening Star' (v)	ECtt NCth SMad
- var. ***minus*** 'Chinese Chintz'	WCru
- 'Purple Marble'	CSpe CWGN ESwi LEdu WCot WSpi
§ ***isopyroides***	CRos EBee EHyd EMor ESwi EWTr GKin LEdu LRHS MBel MHid MHol MRav NLar NRHS NWad WCot WHil
javanicum B&SWJ 9506	WCru
- PAB 9431	LEdu WPGP
- var. ***puberulum*** B&SWJ 6770	WCru
johnstonii B&SWJ 9127	WCru
kiusianum	CBor CMiW EBee ECha EHed EMor EPfP EWes GEdr GElm GMaP GMcL LRHS MBel NBPC NBir NGBl NHpl NLar NSla SMad SWvt WAbe WCot WFar WPnP
- Kew form	WSHC
koreanum	see *T. ichangense*
'Little Pinkie' (Censation Series)	CWGN GEdr MMrt SGBe
§ ***lucidum***	CBWd CBod CElw CExl EBee ECtt EShb GBin LBar LEdu MHol MMuc MPie NBPC NGBl NLar NQui NSti SEND SPhx WCot WPnP
minus	GQue LEdu SEND
§ - 'Adiantifolium'	EMor ESwi MRav NGdn SHar SRms WSpi XLum
- var. ***hypoleucum*** B&SWJ 8634	WCru
- subsp. ***kemense***	EBee
§ - subsp. ***minus***	EMor
- var. ***sipellatum*** B&SWJ 5051	WCru
morisonii	CRos EHyd LRHS NRHS
(Nimbus Series) NIMBUS PINK ('Tntnp')	CBod EHed ELan LBar LEdu LRHS MBel SMad SMrm WHil WNPC
- NIMBUS WHITE ('Tntnw')	EHed ELan LBar MBel NSti SMad SMrm SPad WHil WNPC
'Nishiki'	GEdr WFar
omeiense BWJ 8049	WCru
osmundifolium	WCru
petaloideum	EMor LRHS SPhx
- 'Ghent Ebony' **new**	SPeP
platycarpum B&SWJ 2261	WCru
podocarpum B&SWJ 14297	WCru
polygamum	see *T. pubescens* Pursh
przewalskii	WCru
§ ***pubescens*** Pursh	ECha EHyd EMor GJos GMaP LRHS NDov NLar NRHS SPhx
punctatum B&SWJ 1272	ESwi WCru
'Purplelicious'	CBor NCth NLar SMad
ramosum BWJ 8126	WCru
reniforme	LEdu
- B&SWJ 13969	WCru
- GWJ 9311	WCru
- HWJK 2403	WCru
- WJC 13761	WCru
rochebruneanum 🏆H7	Widely available
- 'Lavender Mist'	LSun SPtp
rubescens B&SWJ 10006	WCru
rugosum	CRos EHyd LRHS NRHS
sachalinense RBS 0279	EPPr NLar
shensiense	CExl
simplex	ECha EPPr
- var. ***brevipes*** B&SWJ 4794	WCru
speciosissimum	see *T. flavum* subsp. *glaucum*
sphaerostachyum	see *T. flavum* subsp. *glaucum*
'Splendide'	Widely available
SPLENDIDE WHITE ('Fr21034'PBR) 🏆H7	Widely available
squarrosum	EBee
tenuisubulatum BWJ 7929	WCru
tuberiferum var. ***yakusimense*** B&SWJ 6094	WCru
tuberosum	CBor CElw CMiW CSpe NDov SHar WAbe WCot
- 'Rosy Hardy'	WCot
tubiferum B&SWJ 10999	WCru
'Tukker Princess' 🏆H7	ECtt EWhm ILea LBar NDov NLar SMad WCot
uchiyamae	EBee ESwi EWld WCot WPGP
'Ulrike'	SMHy
urbainii B&SWJ 7085	WCru
'Yubari Mountains'	WFar
'Yulia'	MHol
yunnanense	WCru

Thamnocalamus (Poaceae)

crassinodus 'Gosainkund'	CDTJ MWht
- 'Kew Beauty' 🏆H3	CDTJ EPfP MBrN MWht WCot WPGP
- 'Langtang'	CBdn CDTJ WPGP
- 'Merlyn'	CDTJ EPfP MWht
falconeri	see *Himalayacalamus falconeri*
spathaceus misapplied	see *Fargesia murielae*
spathiflorus subsp. ***nepalensis***	CBdn MWht
tessellatus	see *Bergbambos tessellata*

Thamnochortus (Restionaceae)

cinereus	CPbh XSte
fruticosus	CPbh
insignis 🏆H3	CPbh SPlb
lucens	SPlb

punctatus LRHS
rigidus CCCN CTrC

Thapsia (*Apiaceae*)
decipiens see *Melanoselinum decipiens*
villosa B&SWJ 14014 WCru

Thaspium (*Apiaceae*)
trifoliatum SPhx

Thea see *Camellia*

Thelocactus ✿ (*Cactaceae*)
bicolor subsp. ***heterochromus*** new
- var. ***texensis*** new NMen
- var. ***tricolor*** new NMen
conothelos subsp. NMen
aurantiacus new
hexaedrophorus NMen
subsp. ***lloydii*** new

Thelypteris (*Thelypteridaceae*)
kunthii CLAP EBee ISha LEdu MACG WCot
ovata var. ***lindheimeri*** CBdn EHyd LRHS NRHS
palustris EBee EShb LPfP NBir NBro NLar SRms WFib WPnP XLum
phegopteris see *Phegopteris connectilis*

Theobroma (*Malvaceae*)
cacao CTsd

Thermopsis (*Fabaceae*)
caroliniana see *T. villosa*
chinensis CRos EBee EHyd ELan EPfP GAbr LPla LRHS MHer MMrt MNrw NRHS SBls SPad
fabacea see *T. lupinoides*
lanceolata CAby EBee EHyd EPfP EWld LRHS NQui NRHS SHar WCot WFar WKif
§ ***lupinoides*** CDor CSpe ECha SRms
macrophylla EBee
mollis CExl NBid
montana ECha LBar LRHS MPie WGwG
- var. ***montana*** CWCL EBee EHyd ELan EPfP GBee GMaP LRHS MBel MMuc NBir NGBl NGrd NRHS NSti NWad SEND SGbt SPer
- - NNS 99-480 WCot
rhombifolia new MHer
§ ***villosa*** LPla NGdn NLar

Therorhodion see *Rhododendron*

Thevetia (*Apocynaceae*)
peruviana EAri

Thladiantha (*Cucurbitaceae*)
aff. ***davidii*** BO 16037 new GGro
dubia EBee ESwi SBrt SDix WCot

Thlaspi (*Brassicaceae*)
sp. NGdn
alpinum EPot
bellidifolium GKev
biebersteinii see *Pachyphragma macrophyllum*

Thrinax (*Arecaceae*)
parviflora new NPlm
radiata NPlm

Thryptomene (*Myrtaceae*)
baeckeacea CCCN

Thuja ✿ (*Cupressaceae*)
'Extra Gold' see *T. plicata* 'Irish Gold'
§ ***koraiensis*** IDee NLar
occidentalis GPoy NWea SWeb
- 'Amber Glow' CAco CBrac CKen CSBt GMcL MAsh NHol NLar NWad SCoo SLim SPoG SRms SSha
- 'Anniek'PBR CKen LRHS SCoo SPoG
- Aurea Group CBrac EPot
- 'Bateman Broom' CKen
- 'Beaufort' (v) CKen
- 'Brabant' ♀H7 EDir GDam GMcL LIns LPar NBwr NLar NWea SCoo SGsty SLim WMou
- 'Brobeck's Tower' ♀H7 CKen EPfP NLar SCoo SLim SPoG
- 'Caespitosa' CKen
- 'Cuprea' CKen
- 'Danica' ♀H7 CBrac CMac GKin GMcL LCro LOPS LPar MAsh NWea SCoo SLim SPoG SRms WCFE
- 'Danica Gold' SLim
- 'Degroot's Spire' CKen ELan LRHS NLar SGsty SLim
- 'Douglasii Aurea' (v) CKen
- EMERALD see *T. occidentalis* 'Smaragd'
- 'Ericoides' SRms
- 'Filiformis' SLim
- 'Filips Magic Moment'PBR SPoG
- FIRE CHIEF ('Congabe'PBR) CKen EPfP LPar LRHS NLar SCoo SLim SPoG
- 'Gold Drop' CKen
- 'Golden Anne'PBR LRHS SPoG
- 'Golden Brabant'PBR LRHS
- 'Golden Globe' CKel CWnw LPar LSRN SCoo SLim
- GOLDEN SMARAGD ('Janed Gold'PBR) CWnw EPfP LRHS LSRN NLar SCoo SLim SPoG
- 'Golden Tuffet' ♀H7 CKen CWnw ELan GKin LBee NWad SCoo SLim SPoG
- 'Hetz Midget' ♀H7 GKin NWad SCoo SLim SPlb WFar
- 'Holmstrup' ♀H7 CBod CBrac CMac MAsh SRms SSha
- 'Jantar'PBR LRHS NLar SGsty SLim SPoG
- 'Konfettii' (v) SLim SPoG
- 'Linesville' CKen
- 'Little Gem' SRms
- 'Maria Wn'PBR CKen
- 'Meineke's Zwerg' (v) CKen
- 'Miky' LRHS
- 'Milleri' CKen
- 'Mirjam'PBR (v) CBod CKen SSha
- 'Mr Bowling Ball' LRHS NLar SLim
- 'Ohlendorffii' CKen
I - 'Pygmaea' CKen
- 'Pyramidalis Aurea' GMcL NBwr SCob SGsty
- 'Pyramidalis Compacta' NLar
- 'Recurva Nana' NWad
- 'Rheingold' ♀H7 CAco CBcs CBod CBrac CMac CSBt ELan GKin GMcL LBee LCro LRHS MAsh MGos MMuc NBwr NHol NWea SCoo SEND SLim SPer SPlb SPoG SRms SSha WCFE WFar
§ - 'Smaragd' ♀H7 Widely available
* - 'Smaragd Variegated' (v) CKen
- 'Smokey' CKen
- 'Spiralis' WCFE
- 'Starstruck' SPoG
§ - 'Stolwijk' (v) SLim
- 'Sunkist' ♀H7 CBrac CKen CMac GMcL MAsh NBwr SCoo SRms WFar
- SUNNY SMARAGD ('Hoogi023'PBR) new LCro WHlf
- 'Teddy' EPfP LBee LRHS MAsh NHol NLar NWad SCoo SPoG

	- 'Tiny Tim'	CMac LPar NBwr SGsty SLim SSha SVic
	- TOTEM SMARAGD ('Thucavlo') **new**	LCro
	- 'Trompenburg'	CBod
	- 'Wansdyke Silver' (v)	CMac SLim
	- 'Wareana'	CMac
	- 'Waterfield'	NWad
	- 'White Smaragd' (v)	SCoo SLim
	- 'Yellow Ribbon'	CBod CKen CSBt GMcL SGsty SLim SRms SSha
	orientalis	see *Platycladus orientalis*
	plicata	CBTr CBcs CBrac CCVT CMac CPer CWal ELan IPap LMaj LPar LSto NBwr NWea SCob SPer WTSh
	- 'Atrovirens' ♀H6	CBrac EDir ELan GMcL LBee LBuc LCro LIns LOPS LRHS MAsh MGos MHed NBwr NWea SCob SCoo SEND SEWo SGol SGsty SLim SRms SWvt WAvo WHtc WMat WMou
	- 'Aurea' ♀H6	MAsh SLim SRms
	- 'Can-can' (v)	CBrac NBwr
I	- 'Cole's Variety'	EHeP
	- 'Collyer's Gold'	EBtc LSto SRms
	- 'Copper Kettle'	CBod CKen GKin SLim
	- 'Cuprea'	CKen
	- 'Doone Valley'	CKen NWad
	- 'Excelsa'	LIns LMaj WMou
	- 'Fastigiata'	NBwr
	- 'Gelderland' ♀H6	ELan EPfP MDon SCoo SWeb
	- GOLDY ('4ever'PBR)	CKel CWnw GMcL LRHS NLar SCoo SGsty SLim SPoG
§	- 'Irish Gold' (v)	CMac LRHS
	- 'Little Boy'PBR	CBod MGos
	- 'Martin'	CBrac EHeP GMcL LIns SGsty SRms SSha SWvt
	- 'Rogersii' ♀H6	CBrac CKen CMac MAsh NHol SCoo SPoG SRms SSha
	- 'Semperaurescens' (v)	CMac
	- 'Stolwijk's Gold'	see *T. occidentalis* 'Stolwijk'
	- 'Stoneham Gold' ♀H6	CBrac CMac GKin MAsh MGos NBwr SRms WCFE
	- VERIGOLD ('Courtapli')	MMuc SEND
	- 'Whipcord' ♀H6	CAco CBcs CKel CKen ELan EPfP GMcL LRHS MMuc NHol NLar SCoo SLim SPoG
	- 'Winter Pink' (v)	CKen
	- 'Zebrina' (v) ♀H6	CAco CBcs CBrac CMCN CMac ELan EPfP MAsh MGos MMuc NBwr NLar NWea SCob SCoo SEND SLim SPer SPoG SSha SWvt WAvo WHtc
	standishii	GDam

Thujopsis (*Cupressaceae*)

	dolabrata ♀H6	CAco CBcs CBrac CWal LRHS MMuc NLar SWvt WFar
	- 'Aurea' (v)	CKen LRHS
	- 'Laetevirens'	see *T. dolabrata* 'Nana'
§	- 'Nana'	CAco CKen CMac LCro LRHS NLar SCoo SRms
	- 'Solar Flare'	LRHS NLar
	- 'Variegata' (v)	CMac ELan GKin NLar SRms
	koraiensis (Nakai) hort.	see *Thuja koraiensis*

Thunbergia ✿ (*Acanthaceae*)

	alata	SPoG
	- 'African Sunset'	CCht CSpe EShb LCro
	- (Arizona Series) ARIZONA DARK RED **new**	LCro
	- - ARIZONA ROSE SENSATION ('Volthu7898'PBR) **new**	EBee
	- 'Lemon'	CHll
	- 'Lemon Queen'	SWvt
	- 'Orange Beauty'	CCht SWvt
	- SUNNY SUSY BROWNIE ('Sumthun 04'PBR) (Sunny Susy Series) **new**	LCro
	- (Susie Series) 'Susie Orange Black Eye' **new**	LCro
	- - 'Susie White Black Eye'	CSpe LCro
	- TANGERINE SLICE A-PEEL ('Dl1501')	CSpe WHil
*	***arborea***	CCCN
	battiscombei	CCCN
	coccinea	CCCN
	- B&SWJ 7166	WCru
	erecta	CCCN EShb
	fragrans GWJ 9441	ESwi WCru
	grandiflora ♀H1b	CCCN WFib WSFF
	- 'Alba'	CCCN CHll
	gregorii ♀H1b	CCCN CHll CSpe EShb WFib
	laurifolia B&SWJ 7166	WCru
	'Moonglow'	CCCN
	mysorensis ♀H1b	WFib
	natalensis	CCCN
	'Orange Wonder'	CCCN

Thymbra (*Lamiaceae*)

§	***capitata***	GJos XSen

thyme, caraway see *Thymus herba-barona*

thyme, garden see *Thymus vulgaris*

thyme, lemon see *Thymus citriodorus*

thyme, wild see *Thymus serpyllum*

Thymus ✿ (*Lamiaceae*)

	from Turkey	EWes LEdu SPhx
§	'Alan Bloom'	CRos EHyd LRHS NRHS
	'Albus'	ENfk
	'Anderson's Gold'	see *T. pulegioides* 'Bertram Anderson'
	azoricus	see *T. caespititius*
	'Bressingham'	CBod CTri EBou ECtt EHyd EWhm GAbr GMaP GQue LCro LOPS LRHS MBow MHer MHoo MNHC NGrs NRHS SPlb SRms WIce
	'Caborn Wine and Roses'	CCBP ENfk EPPr SRms WFar WJek
§	***caespititius***	GPoy MHer NRya SPlb SRms WAbe WJek
	caespitosus	see *T. praecox* subsp. *praecox*
	camphoratus	ENfk EWes GArf MBros MHoo NHpl SEdi WAbe WFar WJek
	- 'Derry'	CSpe
	capitatus	see *Thymbra capitata*
§	***carnosus*** Boiss.	XSen
	'Carol Ann' (v)	ENfk EWes MNHC SRms
	CASCATA LEMONADE	ENfk
	ciliatus	XSen
	cilicicus misapplied	see *T. caespititius*
	cilicicus ambig.	MNHC SRms
	cilicicus Boiss. & Bail.	WAbe
	citriodorus misapplied	see *T.* 'Culinary Lemon'
	citriodorus ambig.	CTsd GQue SPhx SRms SVic XLum
	citriodorus (Pers.) Schreb.	CLau LEdu
	citriodorus 'Archer's Gold'	see *T. pulegioides* 'Archer's Gold'
	- 'Aureus'	see *T. pulegioides* 'Aureus'
	- 'Bertram Anderson'	see *T. pulegioides* 'Bertram Anderson'
	- 'Silver Posie'	see *T.* 'Silver Posie'
	'Coccineus'	see *T.* Coccineus Group
§	Coccineus Group ♀H5	Widely available

	- 'Atropurpureus' Schleipfer	see *T.* (Coccineus Group) 'Purple Beauty'
§	- 'Purple Beauty'	ECha ECtt EHyd EPot LRHS MHer NRHS SRms WHoo XSen
§	- 'Red Elf'	NSla
	'Coccineus Major'	EHyd LRHS NRHS SRms
	'Creeping Lemon' misapplied	see *T. pulegioides* 'Kurt'
§	'Culinary Lemon'	CBod CHby CKel CLau ENfk GPoy LCro LOPS MBow MBrN MHer MHoo MNHC MPri SEdi SSut WFar WJek XLum XSen
	'Culinary Lime' **new**	MHoo
	'Dartmoor'	WJek
	'Desboro'	see *T. serpyllum* 'Desborough'
	'Dillington'	ENfk
	doerfleri	XSen
	'Doone Valley' (v)	Widely available
	drucei	see *T. polytrichus* A. Kern. ex Borbás subsp. *britannicus*
	'Duftkissen'PBR	XSen
	'E.B. Anderson'	see *T. pulegioides* 'Bertram Anderson'
	'Elf'	EPot
	erectus	see *T. carnosus* Boiss.
	× ***faustinoi***	CLau
	'Fragrantissimus'	CLau ENfk EWhm GJos GPoy GQue MHer MHoo MNHC SPhx SPlb WJek
	'Golden King' (v)	ECha ELan ENfk LSRN MAsh MHer NGrs SRms
	'Golden Lemon' misapplied	see *T. pulegioides* 'Aureus'
	'Golden Lemon' (v)	WJek
	'Golden Queen' (v)	CBod LRHS SRms WFar
§	'Hartington Silver' (v)	CGBo CRos CTri ECha ECtt EHyd ENfk EPot EWes EWhm GArf LRHS MHer MHoo NBPC NHpl NRHS SLee SPlb SPoG SRms SRot WCav WJek
	herba-barona	CBod CCBP CLau EBou ECha ENfk GPoy GQue MHer MHoo MNHC SRms WFar WJek
	- ***citrata***	see *T. herba-barona* 'Lemon-scented'
§	- 'Lemon-scented'	ECha GPoy LEdu MHer SRms WJek XSen
	'Highland Cream'	see *T.* 'Hartington Silver'
	hirsutus	CKel
§	'Iden'	MHoo WJek
	'Jekka'	CBod CLau EWhm LCro LOPS MHer MNHC SRms WHoo WJek
	'Jekka's Autumn Pink'	WJek
	'Jekka's Bee Haven' **new**	WJek
	'Jekka's Rosy Carpet'	WJek
	'Kurt'	see *T. pulegioides* 'Kurt'
	'Lammefjord'	XSen
	'Lavender Sea'	EWes
	'Lemon Caraway'	see *T. herba-barona* 'Lemon-scented'
	'Lemon Curd'	CLau EMul ENfk MHoo MNHC NHol SPlb SPoG SRms WJek
*	'Lemon Variegated' (v)	ENfk EPfP EWhm LCro LOPS MHoo MNHC SPer SPoG
	'Lilac Time'	ECtt ENfk EWes MHer SPlb SRms WJek
	'Lime'	LEdu WFar
	longicaulis	CBod ECha MHer SAng SRms
	- pine-scented **new**	CBod
	longiflorus	EDAr GJos SPhx
	'Magic Carpet'	WJek
	marschallianus	see *T. pannonicus*
	mastichina	SPhx XSen
	- 'Didi'	MHer
	membranaceus	WAbe
	micans	see *T. caespititius*
	minus	see *Calamintha nepeta*
	neiceffii	CKel ECha
	nitens	XSen
	odoratissimus	SPhx
	'Orange'	CBod LEdu NGrs SEdi SRms WFar
	orange-scented **new**	SEND
§	***pannonicus***	MHer
	- PAB 9021	LEdu
	'Peter Davis'	CBod CLau ENfk LCro MHoo NBPC NBir SPoG SRms WAbe WFar WIce WJek WTor XSen
§	'Pinewood'	MHer WFar WJek XSen
	'Pink Ripple'	CBod CLau ECtt ENfk EWes EWhm LEdu MHer MNHC SRms WHoo WJek
	polytrichus misapplied	see *T. praecox*
	polytrichus A. Kern. ex Borbás	WWild
§	- subsp. ***britannicus***	CBod CKel CTri EBou ECha EWhm GBin GMaP GPoy LCro LEdu LOPS LSto MHer MNHC NBir NBro SPhx SPlb SRms WJek XLum XSen
§	- - 'Thomas's White' ♀H5	CTri
	'Porlock'	CLau CTri EPfP MHer MNHC SRms WHoo WJek
§	***praecox***	EWhm GJos MHer
	- 'Albiflorus'	EWoo MRav XSen
	- subsp. ***arcticus***	see *T. polytrichus* A. Kern. ex Borbás subsp. *britannicus*
	- - 'Albus'	see *T. polytrichus* subsp. *britannicus* 'Thomas's White'
§	- subsp. ***praecox***	CTri GAbr
	prostrate	CBod CKel MHoo
	'Provence'	XSen
	pulegioides	CBod CCBP CHby CTri ENfk GPoy GQue LRHS LSto MBow MHer MHoo NHpl SRms SRot WFar WJek WSFF
§	- 'Archer's Gold'	CBod CRos ECtt EHyd ENfk EPfP EPot GAbr LRHS LSRN MAsh MHer MHoo MNHC MRav NBPC NBir NHol NHpl NRHS SCob SRms WCav WFar
§	- 'Aureus' ♀H5	CBod ENfk GMaP LCro LOPS MAsh SPer SPlb SRms
§	- 'Bertram Anderson' ♀H5	CBod CKel ECha ENfk EPfP GMaP LShi MAsh MHer MHoo NBPC NBir NGrs NRya SPer SPoG SRms WCav WHoo XSen
	- 'Foxley' (v)	CBod CCBP CLau ECul ENfk EPfP EWhm GMaP LRHS MHer MHoo MNHC SPlb SPoG SRms WFar WJek
	- 'Golden Dwarf'	WFar
§	- 'Goldentime'	GQue
§	- 'Kurt'	ENfk LEdu MHer SRms WJek
	- 'Tabor'	CBod CLau EMul ENfk EWhm MHoo MNHC NBPC SRms WGwG
	'Rainbow Falls' (v)	EPfP MHoo NBPC SEdi SRms WFar
	'Rasta' (v)	MHer
	'Redstart'	CBod ECha ECtt ENfk EPot LEdu MHer SRms WJek
	'Ruby Glow'	ECtt ENfk EWes EWhm MHer NBir
	serpyllum ambig.	SPhx SVic WFar XLum
	serpyllum L.	GJos GKev LBuc SPlb SRms
	- var. ***albus***	CBod CRos ECha EHyd GAbr GMaP GPoy GQue LRHS MHoo MNHC NRHS SPer SRms SRot WCav WFar WHoo
	- 'Albus Variegatus'	see *T.* 'Hartington Silver'
	- 'Amadé'	XSen
	- 'Annie Hall'	CRos EHyd EPfP EPot LRHS MAsh MHer MNHC NRHS SRms WCFE WJek

	- 'Atropurpureus'	see *T.* (Coccineus Group) 'Purple Beauty'
	- *coccineus* 'Minor' misapplied	see *T.* Coccineus Group
	- - 'Minor' Bloom	see *T.* 'Alan Bloom'
	- 'Conwy Rose'	WAbe
§	- 'Desborough'	MHer
	- 'East Lodge'	MHer MNHC SRms
	- 'Elfin'	ECtt EWes ITim MHer MRav NSla SPhx SPlb SRms SRot WAbe XSen
	- 'Goldstream' (v)	CRos EBou EHyd ENfk LRHS NRHS SLee SPlb SRms
	- 'Iden'	see *T.* 'Iden'
	- 'Minimalist'	see *T. serpyllum* 'Minor'
	- 'Minimus'	see *T. serpyllum* 'Minor'
§	- 'Minor'	CRos CTri EBou ECha ECtt EDAr EHyd ENfk LCro LOPS LRHS MHer MHoo MNHC NBPC NRHS NSla SLee SPlb SRms SRot WAbe WFar WHoo WSFF
	- 'Minus'	see *T. serpyllum* 'Minor'
	- 'Pink Chintz' ♀H5	Widely available
	- 'Purple Beauty'	see *T.* (Coccineus Group) 'Purple Beauty'
	- 'Red Carpet'	CBod ECtt GAbr SPhx SRms WFar
	- 'Red Elf'	see *T.* (Coccineus Group) 'Red Elf'
	- 'Russetings'	CBod EBou ECtt ENfk EPfP LCro LOPS MHer MHoo MNHC NGrs SDix SPoG SRms WCav WFar
	- 'September'	MHer
	- 'Snowdrift'	CCBP ECtt ECul EDAr EPfP EWoo LCro LOPS MHer MNHC SPlb SRms WFar WIce
	- 'Variegatus'	see *T.* 'Hartington Silver'
	- 'Vey'	CRos EHyd EWes LRHS MHer NRHS SRms
	- 'Wirral White'	XSen
	'Silver King' (v)	ENfk
§	'Silver Posie'	Widely available
	'Silver Queen' (v) ♀H5	CBcs CBod CKel EBou ECha ELan EMor ENfk EPfP EWhm EWoo GMaP LRHS LShi MHoo MNHC NBPC NHol SPer SPhx SPlb SRms SVic WCav WJek
	'Sparkling Bright' (v)	ENfk EWhm
	striatus	LEdu
§	***vulgaris***	Widely available
	- 'Aureus' hort.	see *T. pulegioides* 'Goldentime'
*	- 'Compactus'	CLau ENfk GPoy MHer MHoo MNHC MRav SPhx SRms WFar WJek XSen
	- 'Deutsche Auslese'	see *T. vulgaris*
	- English, winter	SRms
	- French	see *T. vulgaris*
	- 'Lucy'	MHer
	- 'Pinewood'	see *T.* 'Pinewood'
	zygis	XSen

Thysanolaena (*Poaceae*)

latifolia new	WCot

Tiarella ✿ (*Saxifragaceae*)

	ANGEL WINGS ('Gowing'PBR) (Fox Series) ♀H5	CBod MPnt NCth NSti WNPC
	'Appalachian Trail' (American Trails Series)	ECha EMor LBar MPnt NCou NWad SHeu WCav
	'Black Snowflake'	MPnt SHeu
	'Black Velvet'	MPnt SHeu
	'Braveheart'	MPnt SHeu
	'Butter and Sugar'	MPnt
	'Butterfly Wings'	MPnt
	'Candy Striper'	MPnt NLar SHeu
	'Cascade Creeper'PBR	LRHS MPnt NWad SHeu WNPC
	collina	see *T. wherryi*
	cordifolia ♀H5	CBcs CMac CTri EBee ECha EHeP ELan EPfP EWoo GAbr GMaP LPal LPar LRHS LSto MCot MGos MPnt MRav NBir NDov NRHS SCob SPer SRms SWvt WCAu WHoo XLum
	- 'Glossy'	MPnt
	- 'Milk Chocolate'	MPnt
	- 'Oakleaf'	MPnt NBro SHeu WCAu
	- 'Rosalie'	see × *Heucherella alba* 'Rosalie'
	- 'Running Tapestry'	MPnt SHeu
	'Crow Feather'PBR	MPnt SHeu
	'Cygnet'	CDor GMcL MPnt SHeu
	'Dunvegan'	MPnt
	'Elizabeth Oliver'	MPnt
	'Emerald Ellie' (Fox Series)	EMor MPnt SHeu WNPC
	'Fairy's Footsteps'	SHeu
	'Happy Trails' (American Trails Series)	MPnt NWad SHeu WNPC
	'Inkblot'	EMor LRHS MPnt NBro SHeu
	'Iron Butterfly'PBR (v)	CBod CDor CMac CPla EBee ECha EMor EWoo GMaP LRHS LSRN MACG MBel MPnt MRav NLar SCob SEdd SGbt SHeu SPer SPoG SRms WHoo WPnP
	'Iron Cross'	SPlb
	'Jeepers Creepers'PBR	CBod LRHS MPnt SHeu WNPC
	'Martha Oliver'	MPnt
	'Mint Chocolate'	MPnt NBir NGdn NLar SHeu SWvt
	'Moorgrün'	EPPr SHeu
	MORNING STAR ('Tntia042')	GMcL MPnt SHeu SRkn
	'Mystic Mist'PBR (v)	CDor CWGN ECtt LBar MPnt NCou SCoo SHeu SPoG WNPC
	'Neon Lights'PBR	EMor MPnt NBir NCth SHeu SWvt WNPC
§	'Ninja'	GMcL MPnt NBir SCob SWvt
	'Oregon Trail' (American Trails Series)	MNrw MPnt NWad SHeu WNPC
	'Pacific Crest' (American Trails Series)	MPnt SHeu WNPC
	'Pink Bouquet'	CBod CMac CSpe ELan EMor LRHS LSto MACG MPnt NBro NLar SCob SHeu WFar WPnP
	'Pink Brushes'PBR	EMor MPnt SHeu
	'Pink Skyrocket'PBR ♀H6	Widely available
	'Pinwheel'	MPnt
	'Pirate's Patch'PBR	MPnt SHeu
	polyphylla	MACG MPnt SHeu WCru
	- 'Baoxing Pink'	MPnt WCru
	- 'Filigran'	EPfP GQue MPnt NHol SHar SHeu
	'Raspberry Sundae' (Fox Series) ♀H6	CBod EMor LRHS MPnt NLar SHeu WNPC
	'Running Tiger'	LRHS MPnt
	'Sea Foam'	MPnt SHeu
	'Simsalabim'	MPnt
	'Skeleton Key'	MPnt
	'Skid's Variegated' (v)	MPnt SHeu SPoG SWvt
	'Skyrocket'	EMor
	'Spanish Cross'	MPnt SHeu
	'Special Star' (Heucheraholics Series)	SHeu
	'Spring Symphony'PBR ♀H7	Widely available
	STARBURST ('Tntia041'PBR)	MPnt SHeu
	'Sugar and Spice'PBR	CDor CSpe CWGN EHyd EMor EPfP GPSL LRHS LSto MPnt NCth NDov NLar NRHS SHeu WCAu WHlf WNPC
	'Sunset Ridge'PBR (American Trails Series)	LBar MPnt SHeu WNPC
	SYLVAN LACE ('Tntiasl') (Sylvan Series)	LBar MPnt SHeu WNPC
	'Tiger Stripe'	EBee LRHS MPnt NBro SHeu
	'Timbuktu'	MPnt SHeu

trifoliata	MPnt
- var. ***unifoliata***	MPnt
'Viking Ship'	see × *Heucherella* 'Viking Ship'
§ ***wherryi*** ♀H5	CAby CBcs EBee ECha ELan EMor EPfP MACG MBel MPnt NBir NBro SBls SCob SPer SPlb SWvt WCAu WPnP XLum
- 'Bronze Beauty'	MPnt SHeu
- 'Green Velvet'	MPnt SHeu
- 'Heronswood Mist' (v)	SHeu SWvt
- 'Pink Foam'	SHeu

Tibouchina (*Melastomataceae*)

grandifolia	CCCN CHIl CRHN
'Groovy Baby'	CEnd
grossa B&SWJ 10758	WCru
heteromalla	CCCN
organensis	CBcs CBod CCCN CHIl CKel EGrI EHed SEle SHeu SIvy SPoG SWvt
paratropica	CBod CCCN CRHN EAri MGil SIvy WCot
semidecandra misapplied	see *T. urvilleana*
§ ***urvilleana*** ♀H2	CBcs CBct CBod CCCN CEnd CKel CPla CSBt CTsd EAri EGrI EMdy SDix SIvy SRkn SWvt
- 'Compacta'	CCCN
- 'Edwardsii' ♀H2	CRHN SAdn WCot
- variegated (v)	CBcs CCCN CKel SWvt WCot

Tigridia (*Iridaceae*)

immaculata B&SWJ 10393	WCru
§ ***orthantha***	CPla
- 'Red-Hot Tiger'	CSpe EAri EBee WCot WCru WSHC
pavonia	CAby CExl EShb LAma SDeJ WSHC
- 'Alba'	CSpe WSHC
- 'Alba Grandiflora'	GKev LAma SDeJ SDir
- 'Aurea'	GKev LAma SDir
- 'Canariensis'	GKev LAma SDeJ SDir
- 'Lilacea'	CPla GKev LAma SDeJ SDir WSHC
- 'Speciosa'	GKev LAma SDeJ SDir

Tilia ✿ (*Malvaceae*)

americana	CLnd CMCN
- AMERICAN SENTRY ('McKSentry')	IPap
- 'Redmond'	MBlu
amurensis	CMCN
- from Korea	WPGP
argentea	see *T. tomentosa*
begoniifolia	see *T. dasystyla* subsp. *caucasica*
callidonta	WPGP
§ ***caroliniana*** subsp. ***heterophylla***	CMCN EPfP MBlu WPGP
chinensis	CMCN WPGP
- F 30558	WPGP
chingiana	CMCN EBee WPGP
concinna	WPGP
cordata	Widely available
- 'Dainty Leaf'	CAco
- 'Green Globe'	LMaj
- 'Greenspire' ♀H6	CArg CCVT CLnd EBar EHeP EPfP IPap LCro LIns LMaj LPar MRav MTrO NBwr NOrn NWea SCob SEWo SGsty SWeb WMat
- 'Len Parvin'	EBee WPGP
- 'Overture' **new**	WHtc
- 'Rancho'	LPar
- 'Roelvo'	EHeP
- 'Winter Orange' ♀H6	CBcs CBod CEnd EBee ELan EPfP LIns LRHS MBlu MSwo MTrO SCoo SEWo WHtc WMat
dasystyla	CMCN
§ - subsp. ***caucasica***	CMCN EBee WPGP
- - A&L 16	WPGP
- - NJM 13.029	WPGP
endochrysea	WPGP
× ***euchlora***	CArg CCVT CLnd CMCN EBee EHeP EPfP LMaj NBwr NRog NWea SCob SEWo SPer WMat
§ × ***europaea***	CBcs CLnd EWTr LPar MMuc NOrn SEND
- GOLDEN SUNSET ('Wiltil') **new**	LCro WReH
- 'Pallida'	CLnd EHeP LMaj LPar MBlu NRog NWea
- 'Wratislaviensis' ♀H6	EBee EBtc MBlu
- 'Zwarte Linde'	NRog
§ 'Harold Hillier'	CMCN MBlu WPGP
henryana	CBcs CEnd CKel CLnd CMCN CWnw EBee EPfP EWTr IArd MBlu MMuc SCob SEND SMad WHtc WLov WMat WMou WPGP
- 'Arnold Select'	MTrO NWea WPGP
- 'Bluebell'	MBlu
- 'Kerdalo'	WPGP
'Hillieri'	see *T.* 'Harold Hillier'
insularis misapplied	see *T. japonica*, *T. japonica* 'Ernest Wilson'
§ ***japonica***	CMCN EBee EPfP WPGP
- 'Ernest Wilson' ♀H6	CMCN MBlu
- large-leaved, from China	WPGP
kiusiana	CBcs CMCN MBlu WPGP
mandshurica	CMCN WPGP
maximowicziana	CMCN EPfP MBlu WPGP
mexicana	EBee WPGP
- CD&R 1318	WPGP
miqueliana	CMCN EBee MBlu
× ***moltkei***	CMCN EBee IArd WPGP
mongolica	CBcs CMCN EPfP MBlu WMou WPGP
- 'Buda'	WPGP
- 'Harvest Gold'	CBcs MBlu
monticola	see *T. caroliniana* subsp. *heterophylla*
nobilis KR 226	WPGP
oliveri	CBcs CMCN EBee EPfP MBlu WPGP
aff. ***oliveri*** HRS 2808	WPGP
platyphyllos	CAgr CCVT CHab CLnd CMCN CPer CSBt CTri EHeP EPfP IPap LBuc LPar MMuc MTrO NRog NWea SCob SCoo SEND SPer WHtc WMat WTSh
- 'Aurea'	MBlu WMat
- 'Corallina'	see *T. platyphyllos* 'Rubra'
- 'Erecta'	see *T. platyphyllos* 'Fastigiata'
§ - 'Fastigiata'	EHeP
- 'Laciniata'	CMCN MBlu
- 'Pannonia'	CLnd
§ - 'Rubra' ♀H6	CCVT CLnd EBar EHeP MSwo NWea SCob SEWo
- 'Tortuosa'	LMaj MBlu
× ***stellata***	WPGP
§ ***tomentosa***	CAco CLnd CMCN MMuc MSwo NRog NWea SCoo SEND
- 'Brabant' ♀H6	EHeP LMaj LPar SCob
- 'Petiolaris' ♀H6	CArg CBod CCVT CEnd CLnd CMCN EHeP ELan EPfP MBlu MSwo NRog NWea SCob SPer WMou
- 'Silver Globe'	LPar
tuan	WPGP
- var. ***chenmoui***	CMCN EBtc EPfP MBlu WPGP
× ***vulgaris***	see *T.* × *europaea*

Tillaea see *Crassula*

Tillandsia (*Bromeliaceae*)

abdita	LCro NCft
aeranthos	LWei NCft NPic
- var. ***alba***	NCft
- 'Bronze'	NCft
- 'Miniata'	LWei NCft
- 'Minuette'	NCft
- purple-flowered	NCft
- var. ***rosea***	NCft
aeranthos × ***bergeri*** **new**	NCft
aeranthos × ***stricta***	NCft
aizoides	NCft
albertiana	LWei NCft
albertiana × ***argentina***	NCft
albida	LWei NCft NPic SPlb
andicola	NCft
andreana	LWei NCft NPic
araujei	NCft
arequitae	NCft
argentea 🏆H1c	LCro LOPS LWei NCft
argentina	NCft
arhiza	NCft
ariza-juliae	NCft
bagua-grandensis	NCft
baileyi	NCft NPic
- 'Halley's Comet' **new**	NCft
* - var. ***vivipara***	NCft
baileyi × ***ionantha***	LWei NCft
balbisiana	LWei NCft
balsasensis	NCft
bandensis	LWei NCft
bartramii	LWei NCft
bella	NCft
bergeri	LWei NCft NPic SChr SPlb
brachycaulos	NCft
- var. ***multiflora***	LWei NCft NPic
brachycaulos × ***concolor***	NCft
brachycaulos × ***schiedeana***	NCft
brachycaulos × ***streptophylla***	NCft
brachycaulos × ***xerographica***	NCft
bryoides	LWei NCft
bulbosa	LWei NCft NPic SPlb
- 'Gigante'	NCft
butzii	LWei NCft NPic
- var. ***roseiflora***	NCft
cacticola	LWei NCft NPic
cacticola × ***purpurea***	NCft
caerulea	LWei NCft
caerulea × ***straminea***	NCft
'Califano'	NCft
caliginosa	NCft NPic
capillaris	NCft
- f. ***incana***	NCft
- f. ***virescens***	NCft
capitata	NCft NPic
- 'Domingensis'	NCft
- 'Peach'	LCro LWei NCft NPic
- red-leaved	NCft
caput-medusae	LWei NCft NPic
caput-medusae × ***flabellata***	NCft
cardenasii	NCft
caulescens	NCft
caulescens × ***tenuifolia***	NCft
cauligera	NCft
chaetophylla	LWei NCft
chartacea	NCft
chiapensis	NCft
chusgonensis	NCft
circinnatoides	NCft
cocoensis	NCft
compressa	NCft
concolor	LWei NCft
concolor × ***streptophylla***	NCft
confertiflora **new**	NPic
'Cotton Candy'	NCft NPic
crocata	NCft
- 'Brandywine' **new**	NCft
- 'Copper Penny'	NCft
- 'Copper Penny' × ***albertiana***	NCft
- 'Copper Penny' × ***duratii***	NCft
crocata × ***mallemontii***	NCft
crocata × ***usneoides***	NCft
'Curly Slim'	LWei NCft NPic
cyanea	LCro LOPS LWei NCft NPic
delicata	NCft
diaguitensis	LWei NCft
disticha	LWei NCft
duratii	LWei NCft NPic
dyeriana 🏆H1c	NCft NPic
edithae	NCft
ehlersiana	NCft
elongata	NCft
'Eric Knobloch'	NCft
espinosae	NCft
exserta	NCft
exserta × ***juncea***	NCft
extensa	NCft
fasciculata	LWei NCft
'Feather Duster'	NCft
festucoides	LWei NCft
filifolia	NCft
flabellata 🏆H1c	LWei NCft NPic
flavobracteata	NCft
flexuosa	NCft
- viviparous **new**	NCft
floribunda	LWei NCft
× ***floridana***	NCft
fraseri **new**	NPic
fresnilloensis	LWei NCft
fuchsii var. ***fuchsii***	NCft
- f. ***gracilis***	LWei NCft NPic
funckiana	LWei NCft NPic SPlb
- var. ***recurvifolia***	NCft
funebris	NCft NPic
gardneri	LWei NCft
gardneri × ***recurvifolia***	NCft
geminiflora	NCft
geminiflora × ***recurvifolia***	NCft
glabrior	NCft
'Gordon C'	NCft
grao-mogolensis	NCft
hamaleana **new**	NPic
hammeri	NCft
harrisii	NCft NPic
'Heather's Blush'	NCft
heteromorpha	LWei NCft
hondurensis	NCft
'Houston'	LWei NCft
'Houston Enano'	NCft
humilis	NCft
- var. ***simplex***	NCft
incarnata	NCft
intermedia	NCft
ionantha	CDoC LCro LWei NCft NPic
* - 'Fuego'	LWei NCft
- 'Haselnuss'	NCft
- var. ***ionantha***	LCro NCft
- - 'Druid'	NCft

	- var. ***maxima*** 'Huamelula'	see *T. ionantha* var. *stricta*
	- 'Peach'	LWei NCft
	- 'Ron'	NCft
I	- 'Rosea'	LWei NCft
	- 'Rubra'	LWei NCft
	- var. ***scaposa***	see *T. kolbii*
	- 'Silver'	LWei NCft
§	- var. ***stricta***	NCft
	- var. ***vanhyningii***	NCft
	- 'Variegata'	NCft
	ionantha × ***schiedeana***	NCft
	ixioides	NCft
	ixioides × ***reichenbachii***	NCft
	'Jackie Loinaz'	NCft
	jonesii	NCft
	jucunda	NCft
	juncea	LWei NCft NPic
	kammii	LWei NCft NPic
	karwinskyana	NCft
	'Kashkin'	NCft
	kautskyi	NCft
	'Kimberly'	NCft
§	***kolbii***	LWei NCft NPic
	latifolia	LWei NCft
	- var. ***divaricata***	NCft
	- 'Enano Latifolia'	NCft
	- var. ***latifolia***	NCft
	lautneri	LWei NCft
	leiboldiana	LWei NCft
	- 'Mora'[PBR]	NPic
	leonamiana	LWei NCft
	lepidosepela	NCft NPic
	loliacea	LWei NCft
	lorentziana	LWei NCft
	magnusiana	LWei NCft
	mallemontii	LWei NCft NPic
	marconae	LWei NCft
	'Maria Teresa'	NCft
§	***matudae***	NCft
	mauryana	NCft
	mereliana	NCft
	mima var. ***chiletensis***	NCft
	minutiflora	NCft
	mitlaensis	NCft
	montana	NCft
	multiflora new	LCro NPic
	myosura	LWei NCft
	'Mystic Burgundy'	NCft
	'Mystic Flame'	NCft
	'Mystic Haze'	NCft
	'Mystic Rainbow'	NCft
	'Mystic Trumpet'	NCft
	nana	NCft
	neglecta	LWei NCft
I	- 'Rubra'	LWei NCft
	nolleriana	NCft
	oaxacana	LWei NCft NPic
	paleacea	LWei NCft NPic
	- var. ***apurimacensis***	NCft
	- 'Enano Paleacea'	NCft
	paleacea × ***tectorum***	NCft
	pardoi	NCft
	paucifolia	NCft
	pedicellata	NCft
	peiranoi new	NCft
	plagiotropica	LWei NCft
	pohliana	LWei NCft
	× ***polita***	NCft
	polystachia	LWei NCft
	pruinosa	LWei NCft NPic
	- 'Columbia'	NCft
	pseudobaileyi	LWei NCft
	pseudosetacea	LWei NCft

	pueblensis	LWei NCft
	punctulata	LWei NCft
	purpurea	NCft
	- 'Shooting Star'	NCft
	queroensis	NCft
	× ***rectifolia***	LWei NCft
	recurvata	LWei NCft
	recurvifolia	NCft
	'Redy'	NCft
	reichenbachii	LWei NCft
	retorta	LWei NCft
	riohondoensis	NCft
	'Samantha' ♀[H1c]	NPic
	schatzlii	NCft
	schiedeana	LWei NCft
	- 'Major'	LWei NCft
I	- 'Minor'	NCft
	schreiteri	NCft
	schusteri	NCft
	seideliana	LWei NCft
	seleriana	LWei NCft NPic SPlb
	setacea	LWei
	setiformis	LWei NCft
	simulata	NCft
	sphaerocephala	NCft
	spiralipetala	NCft
	sprengeliana	NCft
	stellifera	NCft
	straminea	LWei NCft
	streptocarpa	LWei NCft
	streptophylla	LWei NCft
	stricta	LWei NCft NPic
	- var. ***albifolia***	NCft NPic
I	- 'Amethyst'	NCft
	- green-leaved	NPic
	- 'Grey'	NCft
	- 'Hard Leaf'	NCft NPic
	- var. ***stricta***	NCft
	sucrei	NCft NPic
	tectorum	LWei NCft
	- caulescent	NCft
*	- var. ***filifoliata***	NCft
	- 'Snow'	LWei
	tenuifolia	LWei NCft
	- blue-flowered	NCft
	- bronze-leaved	NCft
I	- 'Minima'	LWei NCft
	- var. ***tenuifolia***	LWei NCft
	- var. ***vaginata***	NCft
	- white-flowered	NCft
	toropiensis	NCft
	tricholepis	LWei NCft
	tricolor	LWei NCft NPic
	- var. ***melanocrater***	LWei NCft
	'Twisted Tim'	NCft
	umbellata new	NPic
	usneoides	CDoC LWaG LWei NCft NPic SHmp SPlb WSFF
	- fine-leaved new	NCft
	- thick-leaved new	NCft
	utriculata subsp. ***pringlei***	NCft
	variabilis	NCft
	velickiana	see *T. matudae*
	velutina	LWei NCft
	'Wonga'	NCft
	xerographica	CDoC LCro LWei NCft NPic
	xiphioides	NCft
	zecheri	NCft
	- var. ***cafayatensis***	LWei NCft

Tinantia (*Commelinaceae*)

	pringlei	GEdr LEdu MPie SBrt SDys WPGP
	- AIM 77	EBee ESwi MNrw WCot

- variegated (v) WCot WFar

Tipuana (*Fabaceae*)

tipu new WJur

Titanopsis (*Aizoaceae*)

calcarea ♀H1c CCCN EAri SSim
fulleri SSim
hugo-schlechteri ♀H1c new EAri
primosii new EAri

Titanotrichum (*Gesneriaceae*)

oldhamii CBcs GEdr SBrt WHlf XSte

Tithonia (*Asteraceae*)

rotundifolia LWaG
- 'Torch' CSpe LWaG SMrm
'Torchlight' SPhx

Todea (*Osmundaceae*)

barbara WPGP

Tofieldia (*Tofieldiaceae*)

coccinea GArf GEdr WCot WCru
furusei GEdr

Tolmiea (*Saxifragaceae*)

menziesii CBod CMac GGro MCot XLum
- 'Cool Gold'PBR GMaP LBar MHtn
- 'Goldsplash' see *T. menziesii* 'Taff's Gold'
- 'Maculata' see *T. menziesii* 'Taff's Gold'
§ - 'Taff's Gold' (v) SPlb XLum
- 'Variegata' see *T. menziesii* 'Taff's Gold'

tomatoes see AGM Vegetables Section

Toona (*Meliaceae*)

§ ***sinensis*** CAgr CBcs CLnd CWal EBee ELan EPfP LEdu MTrO MVil NWea SEND WJur WPGP XVPe
- 'Flamingo' (v) CDow CKel CPer CRos EHyd ELan EPfP LCro LMil LOPS LPar LRHS LSRN MAsh MTrO NLar NRHS NWea SChF SGol SPoG SRHi SWvt WCot WMat XSte XVPe
- 'Lise' CMCN

Torenia (*Linderniaceae*)

Summer Wave Series CCCN

Torilis (*Apiaceae*)

japonica SPhx

Torreya (*Taxaceae*)

californica CAco CMCN
nucifera CAco IDee WJur

Townsendia (*Asteraceae*)

§ ***alpigena*** var. ***alpigena*** GKev
eximia GKev
formosa NHpl
hookeri GArf GKev
incana GEdr
minima GKev
montana see *T. alpigena* var. *alpigena*
parryi GKev
§ ***rothrockii*** GKev
scapigera GEdr
spathulata GKev SPlb
wilcoxiana misapplied see *T. rothrockii*

Toxicodendron ✿ (*Anacardiaceae*)

§ ***orientale*** B&SWJ 3656 WCru
- large-leaved B&SWJ 10884 WCru
§ ***radicans*** GPoy
§ ***succedaneum*** CDTJ
§ ***vernicifluum*** NLar WJur

Trachelium (*Campanulaceae*)

§ ***asperuloides*** SPlb WAbe
caeruleum 'Black Knight' CSpe WCot

Trachelospermum ✿ (*Apocynaceae*)

from Nanjing, China EShb
§ ***asiaticum*** ♀H4 Widely available
- 'Avonbank' WAvo WHtc
- 'Bella' CCCN ETho
- 'Bredon' WAvo WHtc
- CHILI & VANILLA ('Livano') new WCot
- 'Copper Tips' MGil WAvo WHtc
- 'Golden Memories' CBcs CBod CExl CMac CRHN CRos CWCL CWGN EBee EDir EHyd ELan ELon EPfP LRHS LSRN MRav NLar NRHS SCoo SIvy SNig SPoG SRms SWvt WCot
- 'Goshiki' (v) SEle
- 'Kulu Chirimen' WCot
- 'Ōgon-nishiki' (v) CCCN CWGN LRHS SEle SMad SPoG SSha WFar
- 'Pink Showers' CBcs CBod CDoC CKel CMac CWCL CWGN CWnw ELon EPfP ETho LCro LRHS LSRN MAsh MHtn NCth NLar SCoo SNig WCot WHlf WTyc XSte
- 'Summer Sunset' CBcs ELan ELon EShb ESwi MGos MPie SGol SRms WCot
- 'Theta' LRHS WCot WFar WLov WPGP XSte
'Chameleon' ELan SMad
'Christabel Bielenberg' WSpi
jasminoides ♀H4 Widely available
- 'Major' CMac CWCL EBee ELan MAsh MGil SRms
§ - var. ***pubescens*** 'Japonicum' CRHN EHyd LRHS SPoG WBor
- STAR OF TOSCANA ('Selbra'PBR) CBod CCCN CRos CWGN EHyd EPfP ETho ETod EWTr IDee LCro LOPS LPar LRHS LSRN MAsh NLar NRHS SCoo SGsty SPer SPoG
- 'Sunlover' (v) new WHlf
- 'Tricolor' (v) LRHS SEle SGol SGsty SSha SWvt WFar
- 'Variegatum' (v) ♀H4 Widely available
- 'Waterwheel' CBcs CBod CDoC CMac CSde ELan ELon EShb NLar SDix SMad SWvt WLov
- 'White Wings' LRHS SCoo
- 'Wilsonii' CExl CKel CMac CRos ELan ELon EPfP EShb LRHS LSRN MGil MRav NLar SAdn SEND SNig SPer SPoG SWvt WAvo WCot WHtc WTyc
majus misapplied see *T. jasminoides* var. *pubescens* 'Japonicum'
majus Nakai see *T. asiaticum*

Trachycarpus ✿ (*Arecaceae*)

from Manipur CPHo NPlm
§ ***fortunei*** ♀H5 Widely available
fortunei × ***wagnerianus*** EOli LPal SWeb
geminisectus LPal
latisectus CPHo NPlm
martianus LPal
'Naggy' LPal
princeps CBrP CPHo LPal
takil ambig. CPHo

ukhrulensis	LEdu
- NJM 13.085	WPGP
wagnerianus ♀H5	CBrP CCCN CDTJ CExl CPHo CTsd ETod LPal LPar LRHS NPlm SArc SChr WPGP

Trachymene (*Apiaceae*)

coerulea	CSpe EWoo SPhx

Trachystemon (*Boraginaceae*)

orientalis	CCBP CDor CExl CMac CToG EBee ECha EGrI EPfP EWTr LEdu LRHS LShi MAvo MCot MHol MMuc MNrw MRav NBid NLar NWad WBrk WCot WCru WHer WHil WPGP WPnP XLum

Tradescantia (*Commelinaceae*)

albiflora	see *T. fluminensis*
× ***andersoniana*** W. Ludwig & Rohw.	see *T.* Andersoniana Group
§ Andersoniana Group	EGrI ESwi LShi
- 'Angelic Charm' (Charm Series)	ECtt
- 'Baby Doll'	GElm XLum
- 'Baerbel'	XLum
- 'Bilberry Ice'	CDor CKel CMac CWCL ECtt EDAr EHyd EPfP EWTr GElm GMaP LRHS LSun MTin NBPC NBir NBro NGBl NGdn NLar NRHS SBea SCob SGbt SWvt WGwG XLum
- 'Blue and Gold'	CBcs CPla CRos ECtt EHyd EPfP EWhm LRHS MRav NRHS NSti SEdd WCot WHil
- 'Blue Stone'	CDor CKel ECha ECtt EGrI EWld LRHS MAvo MRav SRkn SRms WHoo XLum
- 'Bridal Veil'	WDib
- 'Caerulea Plena'	see *T. virginiana* 'Caerulea Plena'
- CARMINE GLOW	see *T.* (Andersoniana Group) 'Karminglut'
- 'Charlotte'	CDor ECha ECtt EHyd ELan LRHS NBro NGdn NLar NRHS XLum
- 'Concord Grape' ♀H6	CBod CMac ECtt EGrI EHyd ELan EPfP EWoo GBee GElm GMaP LRHS LSun MAvo MGos NBro NChi NGdn NRHS NSti SGbt SPeP SPer WCAu WFar WGwG WHoo WKif WWke XLum
- 'Domaine de Courson'	XLum
- 'Euridice'	EWTr
- 'In the Navy'	LDai NLar
- 'Innocence'	CAby CDor CNor CSBt CTri ECha ECtt EHyd ELan GElm GMaP LBar LRHS MBel NBir NGdn NRHS NSti SCob SGbt SPer SWvt WGwG XLum
- 'Iris Prichard'	EAJP EBee GMaP NLar
- 'Isis'	CAby CSBt EBee ECtt EHyd ELan EWoo GMaP LRHS MRav NBir NGdn NRHS SGbt SPer SWvt WGwG WKif
- 'J.C. Weguelin'	EGrI NBir SRms WCAu XLum
§ - 'Karminglut'	ECtt GLog GMaP LShi NBir NGdn WHoo XLum
- 'Leonora'	EPfP LBar MBel NLar SCob XLum
- 'Little Doll'	CDor ECtt EPfP LRHS NBro NLar NRHS XLum
- 'Little White Doll'	ECtt EWTr NBPC
- 'Mac's Double' (d)	EBee NBPC
- 'Melissa'	XLum
- 'Merlot Clusters'	WWke
- 'Osprey'	CBcs CBod CDor ECha ECtt EGrI EHyd ELan EWoo GElm LRHS LShi MRav NGdn NLar NRHS NSti SPer SRms WCAu WGwG WHoo WKif WWke XLum
- 'Pauline'	MRav NBir NLar XLum
- 'Perinne's Pink'	EBlo EHyd LRHS NRHS NSti WCAu
- 'Pink Chablis'	CBod ECtt EHyd EPfP LBar LRHS MAsh NBro NLar NRHS SPeP WWke XLum
- 'Purewell Giant'	CMac CTri EBlo EHyd LRHS NBro NLar NRHS SWvt WKif
- 'Purple Dome'	CAby ECtt EHyd EPfP GMaP LRHS MAvo MRav NBir NBro NGBl NGdn NRHS SPoG WGwG
- 'Red Grape'	CDor CTtf EHyd LRHS NRHS NSti SCob XLum
- 'Rubra'	EGrI SRms XLum
- 'Sunshine Charm' PBR (Charm Series)	EHyd LRHS NLar NRHS WHil
- 'Sweet Kate'	CBod CMac ECtt LRHS NBro NLar NRHS SGbt SPoG SRms XLum
- 'Sylvana'	EBee
- 'Valour'	CSBt EHyd LRHS NRHS
- 'Zwanenburg Blue'	ECha ECtt EHyd ELan LPal LRHS NLar NRHS SPlb SPoG XLum
'Angel Eyes'	EBee
blossfeldiana 'Variegata'	see *T. cerinthoides* 'Variegata'
bracteata	SBrt
canaliculata	see *T. ohiensis*
§ ***cerinthoides*** 'Variegata' (v) ♀H1c	EShb
crassifolia F&M 258	WPGP
§ ***fluminensis***	SChr WDib
§ - 'Aurea' ♀H1c	EShb
- 'Maiden's Blush' (v)	CSpe EShb MBNS SPlb SVen
- 'Quicksilver' (v) ♀H1c	EShb NGBl
- 'Variegata'	see *T. fluminensis* 'Aurea'
'Green Hill'	LCro LOPS
navicularis	see *Callisia navicularis*
§ ***ohiensis***	SBrt
pallida ♀H1c	EShb
- 'Biltmore Bimbo'	EShb
- 'Kartuz Giant'	EShb MPie WCot
- 'Pale Puma'	EShb
§ - 'Purpurea' ♀H3	CBcs EShb LWaG NGBl SMrm SPlb
pendula	see *T. zebrina*
'Purple Sabre'	see *T. pallida* 'Purpurea'
purpurea	see *T. pallida* 'Purpurea'
sillamontana ♀H3	EShb MPie SChr
I - 'Variegata' (v)	EShb
spathacea	EShb
§ - 'Rainbow' (v) **new**	LCro
- SITARA	see *T. spathacea* 'Rainbow'
- 'Versicolor'	EShb
tricolor	see *T. zebrina*
virginiana	NChi
- 'Alba'	CKel CMac SRms
* - 'Brevicaulis'	ECha NBro
§ - 'Caerulea Plena' (d)	GElm MRav NLar XLum
- 'Rubra'	SPlb
§ ***zebrina*** ♀H1c	CDoC EShb LWaG NHrt
- ***pendula***	see *T. zebrina*
- 'Purpusii' ♀H1c	EShb WDib
- 'Quadricolor' (v) ♀H1c	CDoC EShb

Tragopogon (*Asteraceae*)

crocifolius	CSpe LRHS SPhx
porrifolius	LRHS MCot SBls SDix SPhx SVic WCot WSFF WTre
- 'Mammoth'	EPPr
pratensis	NMir
- subsp. ***orientalis***	LRHS

Trapa (*Lythraceae*)

natans	LPfP

Trautvetteria (*Ranunculaceae*)

carolinensis	ESwi EWes MBel SMad WCot WHil WSHC
- var. ***japonica***	GEdr WCot WCru
- - B&SWJ 10861	WCru
- var. ***occidentalis***	EBee LEdu WCru WFar WPGP

Trichocereus see *Echinopsis*

Trichodiadema (*Aizoaceae*)

densum ♀H1c	SSim
intonsum	SPlb

Trichopetalum (*Asparagaceae*)

§ ***plumosum***	CBro

Trichosanthes (*Cucurbitaceae*)

kirilowii	GGro

Tricuspidaria see *Crinodendron*

Tricyrtis (*Liliaceae*)

B&SWJ 3229 from Taiwan	WCru
'Adbane'	CLAP EWes WGwG
affinis B&SWJ 6182	WCru
- B&SWJ 11169	WCru
- B&SWJ 11442	WCru
- 'Early Bird'	WCru
'Amanagowa'	CLAP
bakeri	see *T. latifolia*
'Blue Wonder'	LBuc LRHS MCot XLum
dilatata	see *T. macropoda*
'Empress'	CAby CBct CDor CLAP ELon EWes GMaP LRHS LSou MAvo NLar NWad SCob SRkn
formosana	CAvo CBod CTri ECha ELan EWoo GKev GLog GMaP ILea LPal LRHS MCot MNrw SCob SDys SRms WAvo WKif WWke
- B&SWJ 306 **new**	LEdu
- B&SWJ 355	WCru
- B&SWJ 3073	WCru
- B&SWJ 3712	WCru
- B&SWJ 6970	WCru
- RWJ 10109	WCru
- 'Dark Beauty'	CBWd CCBP CDor CLAP CMiW ECtt EGrI ELan EMor EWTr LBar LCro MAvo MBel MHol MPnt WCAu WFar WTyc
- 'Emperor' (v)	ESwi
- 'Gilt Edge' (v)	CBct ECtt ELan ELon LSou MNrw NWad SWvt WFar WTre
- aff. f. ***glandosa*** 'Blu-Shing Toad'	ESwi MAvo WCru WFar
- var. ***grandiflora*** 'Long-Jen Violet'	WFar
- - 'W-Ho-ping Toad'	WCru
- 'Ink Spot' **new**	WFar
- 'Kestrel' (v)	CBct ESwi WCot WFar
- 'Samurai' (v)	EBee EWes MCot WSHC
- 'Seiryu'	EBee IPot MBel
- 'Shelley's'	CLAP CSBt
- 'Small Wonder'	LEdu WCru
- 'Spotted Toad'	LEdu WCru
§ - Stolonifera Group	CAvo CBcs CDor CMac EHyd ELan EPfP EShb LRHS MCot NRHS NWad SHar
- - B&SWJ 7046	WCru
- 'Taroko Toad'	WCru
- 'Tiny Toad'	WCru
- 'Variegata' (v)	LEdu NBir SRms
- 'Velvet Toad'	WCru WFar
'Hiki-yuri'	NBPC
§ ***hirta***	CBcs CDor CMac CMiW CTri EBee EGrI EHyd EMor EWTr GKev ILea LCro LRHS LSto MCot MPie NBro NChi NHol NRHS SBls SCob SCoo SDix SGbt SMrm SPlb SWvt WSHC
- B&SWJ 5971	WCru
- B&SWJ 11227	WCru
- 'Alba'	CMac EMor GArf MBel WAvo
- 'Albomarginata' (v)	CKel CMac CToG EBee EHyd EWhm LBar LRHS NRHS NSti SPoG SWvt WFar WGwG WWke
- 'Golden Gleam'	WCot
- 'Matsukaze'	EWes
- 'Miyazaki'	CMac ECtt EMor GElm GKev GPSL IPot LBar LRHS MACG MHer MNrw NRHS NSti SPoG WCAu WSHC XLum
- 'Taiwan Atrianne'	CDor CLAP CToG ECtt EHyd ELan EMor ESwi GElm GPSL LAlb LDai LRHS MBNS MNrw NRHS NWad SGbt SPoG WCAu WGwG
- 'Variegata' (v)	CTri EBee EHyd EWes GKev GMcL LRHS NRHS WCot
Hototogisu	CRos CToG EAJP EBee ECtt EHyd ELan ESwi GElm LBar LRHS MHer MTin NChi NHol NLar NRHS SPoG
ishiiana	EBee WCru WSHC
- var. ***surugensis***	LEdu WCru WFar
japonica	see *T. hirta*
'Kohaku'	GKev
lasiocarpa	ESwi LEdu XLum
- B&SWJ 6861	WCru
- B&SWJ 7103	WCru
- 'Royal Toad'	WCru
§ ***latifolia***	LEdu WCru WFar
- 'Saffron'	WCru
'Lightning Strike' (v)	CDor ESwi WCot WFar
'Lilac Towers'	LRHS
macrantha	WCru WSHC
§ - subsp. ***macranthopsis***	CAby CBct CDor EPot MNrw SBls WCot WCru
- - 'Juro' (d)	WCru
macranthopsis	see *T. macrantha* subsp. *macranthopsis*
* ***macrocarpa***	NChi XLum
§ ***macropoda***	ILea LEdu LRHS
- B&SWJ 1271 from Korea	WCru
- B&SWJ 5013	WCru
- B&SWJ 5847 from Japan	WCru
- B&SWJ 6209	WCru
- B&SWJ 8700	WCru
- B&SWJ 8829	WCru
maculata PAB 3188	LEdu
'Momoyama'	WFar
'Moonlight Treasure'PBR	NHol WCot
nana 'Karasuba'	WFar
ohsumiensis	CMiW ECha
- 'Fukurin-fu' (v)	WCot WFar
perfoliata	LEdu WCru
- 'Spring Shine' (v)	WCru
pilosa	LEdu
PINK FRECKLES ('Innotripf'PBR)	CAvo CBct CChe CDoC CDor CLAP ELon ESwi GDam GMcL LSou NCou SMrm SWvt XSte
'Raspberry Mousse'	ESwi WCAu
ravenii B&SWJ 3229	WCru
- RWJ 10012	WCru
setouchiensis	WCru
'Sinonome'	EBee MNrw

stolonifera	see *T. formosana* Stolonifera Group
suzukii RWJ 10111	WCru
'Taipei Silk'[PBR]	CBod CLAP EHed GKev LBar LOPS SPad
'Tojen'	CLAP CRos EBee ECtt ELon EPfP ESwi EWes GMcL LBar LRHS MACG MNrw NLar NRHS WCAu WFar
'White Towers'	CLAP ECtt EHyd ELan ESwi EWoo LRHS MRav NRHS NSti SGbt SRms WCAu WFar XLum

Trifolium (*Fabaceae*)

arvense	SPhx
badium	SPhx
'Beauty' (Angel Clover Series) **new**	LLWG WHil WWke
'Chocolate' (Angel Clover Series)	LLWG MBNS
dubium	SPhx SPre
fragiferum	NAts
incarnatum	CSpe GJos SPhx
macrocephalum	EBee
'Marriage' (Angel Clover Series) **new**	LLWG
montanum	SPhx
ochroleucon	CDor CTtf EAJP EBee ECtt ELon EWTr GBin GMaP ILea LBar LEdu MACG MBel MCot MHol MPie SBls SBut SEdd SHar SPhx WCAu WFar WPGP
'Onyx' (Angel Clover Series) **new**	WWke
pannonicum	MACG MNrw SPhx
pratense	CHab MHer NMir SCgs SPhx SRms SVic WSFF WWild
- 'Dolly North'	see *T. pratense* 'Susan Smith'
- 'Ice Cool'	see *T. repens* 'Green Ice'
§ - 'Susan Smith' (v)	CCCN EBee EPfP
purpureum	SPhx
repens	LCro LOPS SPhx SVic WSFF
- DARK DEBBIE ('Trifpot001'[PBR])	LEdu
- 'Douglas Dawson'	LDai
- 'Dragon's Blood'	EPPr GMcL LEdu MPie SPer WWke
- 'Estelle'[PBR]	LEdu
- 'Gold Net'	see *T. pratense* 'Susan Smith'
§ - 'Green Ice'	NSti WFar
- 'Harlequin' (v)	WCot
- 'Isabella'[PBR]	LEdu WFar WPGP
- 'Pentaphyllum'	see *T. repens* 'Quinquefolium'
- 'Purpurascens'	EPfP GQue MAsh MBNS MHer NGrd SPoG WFar
§ - 'Purpurascens Quadrifolium'	CAby ECha EPau GAbr GMcL LEdu MCot NFav NMir NPer SPer SPlb WFar WTor WWke
§ - 'Quinquefolium'	XLum
- 'Tetraphyllum Purpureum'	see *T. repens* 'Purpurascens Quadrifolium'
- 'Wheatfen'	LEdu NPer
- 'William'	WCot WFar
rubens	Widely available
- 'Drama'	ELon LEdu MNrw WPGP
- 'Frosty Feathers'	CBWd CBod CDor CFis CSpe EPPr LBar MAvo SBls SHar WNPC
- 'Peach Pink'	CDor ELon EPPr LBar MAvo MMrt SHar SPhx WCot
- 'Red Feathers'	CSpe ELon EPPr EWes GQue LSun MBel MHol SBls SHar SMad
- white-flowered	WCAu
trichocephalum	EBee EPPr MACG MNrw
willdenovii	SPhx

Trigonella (*Fabaceae*)

foenum-graecum	SVic WSFF

Trillidium see *Trillium*

Trillium (*Melanthiaceae*)

albidum [H5]	EHyd EPot EWld GEdr GKev MNrw NRHS
amabile	GEdr
angustipetalum	GEdr GKev
apetalon	GEdr
camschatcense	CExl GEdr LAma
- 'Nemuro'	GEdr
§ ***catesbyi***	CExl EBee GKev ILea ISha LAma MNrw NChi NWad SDir
chloropetalum	CBro CElw EHyd GEdr LRHS NRHS NWad
§ - var. ***giganteum*** [H5]	CExl EGrl GArf GBin GKev LEdu NHar NHpl NSla
- - EBG form	GRum
- var. ***rubrum***	see *T. chloropetalum* var. *giganteum*
- white-flowered	ECha GKev
cuneatum	CBcs CExl CMiW CWCL EBee EHyd GAbr GEdr GKev GMcL ISha LAma MNrw NBir NChi NHol NHpl NRHS NWad SDeJ SDir WFar WPGP WPnP
erectum [H5]	Widely available
- f. ***albiflorum***	ECha EHyd GKev LRHS MNrw NRHS NWad
- red-flowered	GKev
erectum × flexipes	EBee GKev MNrw NBir
flexipes	EPot GEdr GKev ILea ISha LAma MNrw NHol NHpl NWad
- 'Harvington Dusky Pink'	EHyd LRHS NRHS
- 'Harvington Select'	EHyd LRHS NRHS
govanianum	EBee LAma
grandiflorum [H5]	Widely available
- 'Jenny Rhodes'	LEdu
- pale pink-flowered	EHyd NRHS
- f. ***polymerum*** 'Flore Pleno' (d)	CBro EHyd GArf GEdr LRHS NHar NHpl NRHS SDir
- - 'Snowbunting' (d)	EWes GKev LAma LEdu WThu
- f. ***roseum***	GEdr GKev MNrw NRHS
- white-flowered	MCot
kurabayashii	CExl EGrl EHyd EPot EWld GEdr GKev MNrw NRHS WPGP
lancifolium	GKev
luteum [H5]	CBcs CExl CMiW EBee EGrl EHyd EPfP GAbr GArf GEdr GKev GMaP ILea ISha LAma LCro LEdu LOPS MAvo MNrw NChi NHol NHpl NWad SDeJ SDir WHlf WPnP
nivale	GEdr WThu
ovatum f. ***hibbersonii***	GEdr
- 'Roy Elliott'	CExl
parviflorum	GEdr MNrw
pusillum	CExl EGrl GEdr GKev ILea ISha LAma MNrw NHol NHpl
recurvatum	CBcs CWCL EBee EGrl GAbr GEdr GKev ILea ISha LAma LEdu MVil NChi NHol NHpl NWad WPnP
rivale [H4]	CExl GEdr GKev WAbe WSHC
- Purple Heart Group	GEdr
rugelii	EWes GEdr GKev MNrw WSHC
- Askival hybrids	MNrw
rugelii × vaseyi	EWes MNrw
sessile	CExl EGrl GEdr GKev GPSL ISha LAma MNrw NBir NChi NCth NWad SDeJ SDix WKif WPnP
- 'Rubrum'	see *T. chloropetalum* var. *giganteum*
simile	EHyd GKev LEdu MNrw NHpl NRHS

smallii	GEdr LAma
stylosum	see *T. catesbyi*
sulcatum	CExl EHyd GEdr GKev LEdu LRHS MNrw NHpl NRHS WSHC
taiwanense B&SWJ 3411	WCru
tschonoskii	GEdr LAma
undulatum	MNrw
vaseyi	EHyd EWes EWld GEdr GKev ISha MNrw NRHS SDir
viridescens	EBee GEdr LAma

Trinia (*Apiaceae*)

glauca	SPhx

Triosteum (*Caprifoliaceae*)

erythrocarpum	LEdu SMad
himalayanum	GKev NBid WCAu WPnP WSHC
- B&SWJ 7907	ESwi
- BWJ 7907	WCru
pinnatifidum	EBee GGro GKev MMrt

Tripleurospermum (*Asteraceae*)

§ ***maritimum***	WHer
- 'Flaggy Shore' **new**	GElm

Tripogandra (*Commelinaceae*)

serrulata 'Purple Scimitars'	EShb

Tripolium (*Asteraceae*)

§ ***pannonicum***	CEls WHer

Tripsacum (*Poaceae*)

dactyloides	EPPr

Tripterospermum (*Gentianaceae*)

HEHEHE 220 **new**	GEdr
japonicum	GEdr

Tripterygium (*Celastraceae*)

doianum B&SWJ 11467	WCru
aff. ***doianum*** CWJ 12852	WCru
regelii B&SWJ 5453	WCru
- B&SWJ 8666 from Korea	WCru
- B&SWJ 10921	WCru
wilfordii	EBee LEdu
- BWJ 7852 from China	WCru
- NJM 11.029 from China	WPGP
- NMWJ 14466 from Taiwan	WCru
- WWJ 12009	WCru

Tristagma (*Alliaceae*)

nivale	EBee

Triteleia (*Asparagaceae*)

'4U'	NRog
'Aquarius'	CBor EGrI ERCP GKev NRog
bridgesii	NRog
californica	see *Brodiaea californica*
clementina	NRog
§ 'Corrina'	CAvo EBee EPot ERCP GKev LAma NRog
'Crystal Pink'	SDeJ
'Double Touch' (d)	NRog SDeJ WCot
'Foxy'	CAvo CBro CTtf EPot GKev LAma MNrw NRog
grandiflora	WCot
hendersonii	GKev
hyacinthina	GKev NRog WCot
- NNS 06-560	WCot
- blue-flowered	NRog
- white-flowered	NRog
ixioides var. ***scabra***	NRog
- 'Splendens'	CBor GKev NRog
- 'Starlight'	CTri NRog SDeJ
§ ***laxa***	ECha EGrI
- from Butte County, California	NRog
- from Mount Diablo, California	NRog
- 'Allure'	NRog
- dwarf	NRog
§ - 'Koningin Fabiola'	CBod CBro CTtf EGrI GKev LAma MNrw NBir NRog SDeJ SDix WCot WHil
- QUEEN FABIOLA	see *T. laxa* 'Koningin Fabiola'
lilacina	NRog
§ ***peduncularis***	NRog WCot
'Phantasio' (d)	GKev
'Rosy' (d)	CBor GKev
'Rudy'	CAvo CBor CBro CTtf CWCL ERCP GKev LAma MMrt MNrw NRog SDeJ WCot WHil
'Silver Queen'	CAvo EPot ERCP GKev LAma NRog SDeJ WCot
'Twilight'	GKev NRog
uniflora	see *Ipheion uniflorum*
'White Cloud'	CBor GKev

Trithrinax (*Arecaceae*)

brasiliensis	LPal NPlm
campestris	CBrP LPal NPlm

Tritoma see *Kniphofia*

Tritonia (*Iridaceae*)

crocata ♀H3	NRog
- 'Baby Doll'	LEdu NRog
- 'Duchess'	NRog
- 'Serendipity'	EPri
- 'Tangerine'	NRog
deusta	CPbh EPri
- subsp. ***deusta*** **new**	CBor
- subsp. ***miniata***	NRog WPnP
disticha	EGrI SPlb
§ - subsp. ***rubrolucens***	Widely available
dubia	NRog
flabellifolia	NRog
gladiolaris	EAri EPri LEdu NRog
- 'Parvifolia'	GKev
laxifolia	EGrI EPot GKev LAma
parvula	NRog
rosea	see *T. disticha* subsp. *rubrolucens*
securigera	NRog
- subsp. ***watermeyeri***	CBor
squalida	CBor EPri

Trochocarpa (*Ericaceae*)

clarkei	WThu
gunnii	WThu
thymifolia	WThu
- white-flowered	WThu

Trochodendron (*Trochodendraceae*)

aralioides	CBcs CTsd EPfP GArf GKin LPar LRHS LShi MBlu MGos MMuc NLar SDix SSta WPGP XSte
- B&SWJ 1651 from Taiwan	WCru
- B&SWJ 6080 from Japan	WCru
- CWJ 12357 from Taiwan	WCru
- RWJ 9845 from Taiwan	WCru
- from Taiwan	CDTJ WPGP

Trollius (*Ranunculaceae*)

ACE 1187	CExl
acaulis	EWes GAbr

altaicus	EHyd ELan LRHS NRHS
asiaticus	GKev
buddae	LBar MNrw MRav
§ ***chinensis***	GKev
- 'Golden Queen' 🏆H7	Widely available
- 'Morning Sun'	ELan EPfP LRHS WPnP
- orange-flowered	GKev
× ***cultorum*** 'Alabaster'	Widely available
- 'Baudirektor Linne'	MRav NGdn
- 'Byrne's Giant'	GBin LBar
- 'Canary Bird'	NGdn SRms WSpi
- 'Cheddar'	see *T.* × *cultorum* 'Taleggio'
- 'Earliest of All'	CWCL GBin NGdn NLar WSHC WSpi
- 'Etna'	GMcL NLar
§ - 'Feuertroll'	ECha MRav NGdn NLar WSpi
- FIREGLOBE	see *T.* × *cultorum* 'Feuertroll'
- 'Golden Cup'	NBir NGdn
- 'Goldquelle' 🏆H7	EBee GBin
- 'Goliath'	NBPC NLar
- 'Helios'	ECha
- 'Lemon Queen'	CBod CBor CMiW CWat ECtt EHyd EMor EPfP EWTr GKev GMaP LBar LRHS MBel MRav NCth NLar NQui SCob SHar SPer SRms
- 'New Moon'	CBWd CBcs CDor CRos CSpe EBlo EHyd EMor EPfP EShb GBin GKev LBar LLWG LRHS LSto MBNS NChi NCth NQui NRHS SBls SMrm SPoG WHoo WSHC
- 'Orange Crest'	ELon NLar
- 'Orange Globe'	GMaP
- 'Orange Princess' 🏆H7	CDor CWat EHyd GMcL LBar LCro LOPS LRHS MCot NBro NLar NRHS SHar SPer SRms
- 'Orange Queen'	SWvt
- 'Prichard's Giant'	ELon NBro WSpi
§ - 'Superbus' 🏆H7	ELon EPfP GMaP LBar LLWG LPfP MHol NGdn NLar SPer WFar WPnP
- 'T. Smith'	ECtt NBro
§ - 'Taleggio'	CBor CTtf EAJP EHyd ELan EMor EWTr GMaP LBar LRHS MRav NBPC NBro NLar NRHS SHar SPoG SRms SWvt WNPC WPnP WSpi
'Dancing Flame'	CMac EHyd EMor EPfP LCro LOPS LRHS NLar NRHS SHar SPoG SRms WNPC
europaeus	CTtf CWCL EBee ECha EHeP EHyd ELan EMor EPfP EWoo GBin GDam GMcL LEdu LLWG LRHS MACG MHol MRav NGdn NGrd NMir NRHS NSti SCob SRms WShi
- SDR 6306	GKev
- subsp. ***europaeus***	WFar
- 'Lemon Supreme'	CDor ELan EMor EPfP GKev MACG NRHS
- 'Superbus'	see *T.* × *cultorum* 'Superbus'
farreri var. ***farreri***	EBee GKev
- var. ***major*** SDR 2713	GKev
hondoensis	NLar
ircuticus	EMor GKev
laxus 'Albiflorus'	CExl EBee GBin GEdr
ledebourii misapplied	see *T. chinensis*
macropetalus	GKev
papavereus	see *T. yunnanensis* var. *yunnanensis*
pumilus	CBor CRos EBlo ECha EPfP LBar LRHS NLar NRHS SPer WIce
- ACE 1818	CExl MHer
vaginatus	EBee GJos GKev
yunnanensis 🏆H6	CRos EHyd EPfP GBin LRHS NRHS
- orange-flowered	CExl
§ - var. ***yunnanensis***	EBee

Tropaeolum (*Tropaeolaceae*)

azureum	CCCN CExl MVil
brachyceras	CCCN GKev LAma MVil
ciliatum	CBor CCCN EWld GKev MVil NBid WCot WCru WPGP
hookerianum	CExl
- subsp. ***austropurpureum***	CExl
incisum	CCCN
leptophyllum	GKev
majus	ENfk GPoy MHoo SVic
- Alaska Series (v) 🏆H3	ENfk LCro LOPS MHoo MNHC
- - 'Alaska Salmon Orange' **new**	LCro
- 'Banana Split'	CCCN SCob
- 'Black Velvet' (Tom Thumb Series)	LCro LOPS
- 'Blue Pepe'	CLau
§ - 'Darjeeling Double' (d) 🏆H3	EPPr
- 'Darjeeling Gold'	see *T. majus* 'Darjeeling Double'
- 'Empress of India'	CLau LCro MNHC
- 'Hermine Grashoff' (d)	CSpe EPPr
- Jewel Series	ENfk
- 'Ladybird' (Ladybird Series)	SCob
- 'Margaret Long' (d)	CSpe EPPr
- 'Milkmaid'	SCob
- 'Red Wonder'	CCCN WCot
- 'Strawberry Ice'	CLau
- 'Sunset Pink'	CLau
- 'Tip Top Alaska Salmon' (Tip Top Alaska Series) (v)	LOPS
- Whirlybird Series 🏆H3	LCro
minus 'Bloody Mary' **new**	LCro
- 'Ladybird Rose' **new**	LCro
pentaphyllum	CExl CRHN
polyphyllum 🏆H3	CBor CCCN CWCL EAri EBee EPot NBir SMHy
sessilifolium	EBee
smithii	WPGP
speciosum 🏆H5	Widely available
tricolor 🏆H2	CAvo CBor CCCN CRHN GKev SDir WCot
tuberosum	CAgr CAvo CEnd GKev GPoy LAma SDeJ SPoG WKor
- var. ***lineomaculatum*** 'Ken Aslet' 🏆H3	CBor CCCN CSpe ECha EPfP EPot GAbr GKev GMcL LAma LEdu SPer WFar

Trozelia (*Solanaceae*)

§ ***grandiflora***	CCCN SEND

Tsuga ✿ (*Pinaceae*)

canadensis	CAco EPfP LIns LMaj MMuc NWea
- 'Abbott's Dwarf'	CKen NHol
§ - 'Abbott's Pygmy'	CKen
- 'Bacon Cristate'	CKen
- 'Betty Rose' (v)	CKen
- 'Birkett's White'	CKen
- 'Brandley'	CKen LRHS
§ - 'Branklyn'	CKen WCFE
- 'Cappy's Choice'	CKen
- 'Cinnamonea'	CKen
- 'Coffin'	CKen
- 'Cole's Prostrate' 🏆H7	CAco CKen LRHS LSta NLar
- 'Creamey' (v)	CKen
- 'Curley'	CKen
- 'Curtis Ideal'	CKen
- 'Dr Hornbeck'	see *T. canadensis* 'Hornbeck'
- 'Essex'	CKen MGil
* - 'Everitt's Dense Leaf'	CKen
- 'Everitt's Golden'	CKen
- 'Fantana'	GMcL NHol

- 'Gentsch White' (v) LPar
- 'Greenwood Lake' NLar
- 'Hedgehog' NLar
§ - 'Hornbeck' CKen
- 'Horsford' CKen
- 'Horstmann' No 1 CKen
- 'Hussii' CKen NHol
- 'Jacqueline Verkade' CKen MAsh NLar
- 'Jeddeloh' ♀H7 CAco GMcL LPar MAsh NHol NLar SCob
- 'Jervis' CKen NHol NWad
- 'Julianne' CKen
- 'Little Joe' CKen NLar
I - 'Lutea' CKen
- 'Many Cones' CKen
- 'Minima' CKen
- 'Minuta' ♀H7 CKen NHol WAbe
- 'Nana' CKel CWnw
- 'Palomino' CKen
- 'Pendula' ♀H7 CKen LRHS MAsh
- 'Pincushion' CKen
- 'Prostrata' see *T. canadensis* 'Branklyn'
- 'Pygmaea' see *T. canadensis* 'Abbott's Pygmy'
- 'Rugg's Washington Dwarf' CKen
- 'Snowflake' CKen
- 'Stewart's Gem' CKen
- 'Verkade Petite' CKen
- 'Verkade Recurved' CKen
- 'Von Helms' Dwarf' CKen
- 'Warnham' CKen
caroliniana 'La Bar Weeping' CKen
- 'Planting Fields Broom' CKen
chinensis CKen
diversifolia 'Gotelli' CKen
dumosa CKen
heterophylla ♀H6 CAco CBcs CCVT CPer EPfP GJos IPap MMuc NWea SEWo WFar WTSh
- 'Iron Springs' CKen NLar
- 'Laursen's Column' CKen
- 'Thorsens Weeping' CKen NLar
menziesii see *Pseudotsuga menziesii*
mertensiana 'Blue Star' CAco CKen
- 'Elizabeth' CKen
- 'Glauca' CKen
I - 'Glauca Nana' CKen
I - 'Horstmann' CKen
I - 'Nana Pendula' CKen
- 'Quartz Mountain' CKen
sieboldii 'Baldwin' CKen
- 'Green Ball' CKen NLar
- 'Honeywell Estate' CKen
- 'Nana' CKen

Tuberaria (*Cistaceae*)

lignosa WAbe

Tulbaghia ✿ (*Alliaceae*)

acutiloba CAvo GKev LEdu NHoy
alliacea EPri LEdu NHoy WCot
* ***allioides*** CBro
'Cally White' LEdu
capensis LEdu NBir WAvo
capensis* × *violacea NHoy
'Cariad' LEdu
cernua CD&R 199 EBee LEdu
- hybrid EPri
§ ***coddii*** MHer
cominsii CExl EPri LEdu SGro
cominsii* × *violacea CAvo CExl EPri EWTr WHoo
'Cornish Beauty' CTca
'Cornish Candy' new CTca
'Cosmic' CTtf EBee EPPr EPri EWTr LEdu NHoy
'Dark Beauty' NHoy
'Elaine Ann' NHoy
'Fairy Snow' LEdu WCot
'Fairy Star' CCht CTca CWGN ELan EPri EShb LEdu NHoy SMHy WCot WHlf
'Fairy Star Mk II' SMHy
fragrans see *T. simmleri*
- 'Alba' SDeJ
'Hazel' LEdu MHer NHoy
'John May's Special' EShb LEdu NHoy SMHy WCot WHoo
leucantha ♀H2 EPri GKev LEdu NHoy
- H&B 11996 LEdu
ludwigiana MHer
maritima see *T. violacea* var. *maritima*
Marwood seedling LEdu MHer
montana CBor EBee LEdu MPie NHoy SPlb
'Moshoeshoe' LEdu NHoy WPGP
'Moya' GKev
natalensis ♀H2 CBro CTtf GKev
- B&V 421 EPri
- clone 2 pink-flowered B&V 421 LEdu
- pink-flowered LPla
poetica see *T. coddii*
'Purple Eye' ♀H2 CBro CCht CDoC ECha ELan EPPr GBin LBar LCro LEdu LRHS LSou NHoy SCoo SGBe SMHy SMrm SPoG WCot WHlf WNPC WTyc XSte
'Scented Beauty' NHoy
§ ***simmleri*** ♀H3 EPri LEdu SDeJ
- 'Cheryl Renshaw' WCot
'Snow White' LEdu SMHy WCot
verdoorniae LEdu
violacea ♀H3 Widely available
* - 'Alba' CBor EBee EGrI EPri EShb GKev LAma MHer NHoy WCFE WKif WPnP XSen
- 'Dissect White' NHoy SAng
I - 'Fine Form' CKno
- 'Harry Hay' SMHy
- 'John Rider' EPri NHoy SBls
* - var. ***maritima*** CBor EShb LEdu MHer NHoy
- 'Pallida' CAvo CBro CTca EBee LEdu NHoy
- 'Peppermint Garlic' LEdu
- var. ***robustior*** ECha EWes NHoy
- 'Seren' LEdu
§ - 'Silver Lace' (v) ♀H3 Widely available
- 'Variegata' see *T. violacea* 'Silver Lace'
white-flowered NHoy

Tulipa ✿ (*Liliaceae*)

(4) CArg
'Abba' (2) CArg LAma NRog SDeJ
'Abigail' (11) NRog
'Absalon' (9) GKev LAma SDir
'Abu Hassan' (3) ERCP NRog SDeJ WPhe
acuminata (15) ERCP GKev LAma LCro NRog SDeJ SDir WCot WShi
'Ad Rem' (4) ♀H6 NRog SDeJ WPhe
'Ad Rem's Beauty' (4) NRog
'Addis' (14) LAma SDir
'Affaire' (3) LAma LHWs WPhe
'African King' (3) LHWs
aitchisonii see *T. clusiana*
'Akebono' (11) GKev NRog SDeJ SDir
'Akita' (6) NRog
'Aladdin' (6) CArg GKev LCro LOPS NRog SDeJ WPhe
'Aladdin's Record' (6) NRog SDeJ SDir

'Alba Regalis' (1)	GKev LAma SDir
'Albert Heijn' (13)	GKev NRog SDeJ
ALBION STAR ('Mieke Telkamp') (13)	CArg NRog SDeJ
'Aleppo' (7)	SDeJ SDir
'Alfred Cortot' (12) ♀H6	LAma SDeJ
'Algarve' (3)	WPhe
'Ali Baba' (14) ♀H6	NRog WPhe
'Alibi' (3)	ERCP GKev SDeJ
altaica (15) ♀H6	NRog
amabilis	see *T. hoogiana*
'Amazing Grace' (2)	ERCP LHWs WPhe
'Amazing Parrot' (10)	CAby ERCP LCro LHWs
'Amazone' (3)	NRog
'American Dream' (4)	LAma NRog SDir WHlf WPhe
'American Eagle' (7)	SDeJ
anadroma (15)	GKev
'Ancilla' (12) ♀H6	GKev LAma NRog SDeJ WShi
'André Rieu' (5)	LCro LOPS
'Angélique' (11) ♀H6	CAvo EPfP ERCP ETay GKev LAma LCro LOPS LSto NBir NRog SDeJ SPer WHlf WPhe
'Angels Wish' (5) ♀H6	CAvo EPfP ETay LAma NRog SDeJ SDir WPhe
'Annie Schilder' (3)	CAvo ERCP LCro NRog
'Antoinette'PBR (5)	CAvo GKev LCro LOPS NRog SDeJ
'Antraciet' (11)	ERCP LCro LOPS WPhe
'Apeldoorn' (4)	CArg ETay GKev LCro LOPS NBwr NRog SDeJ
'Apeldoorn's Elite' (4) ♀H6	LAma NRog SDeJ
'Apricona' (3)	LAma LHWs
'Apricot Beauty' (1) ♀H6	ERCP GKev LCro LOPS NBir NRog SDeJ SDir WHlf
'Apricot Delight' (4)	ERCP GKev LAma
'Apricot Emperor' (13)	GKev NRog SDeJ SDir
'Apricot Foxx' (3)	CArg GKev LHWs NRog SDeJ
'Apricot Impression'PBR (4)	ERCP LAma LCro LOPS NRog
'Apricot Jewel'	see *T. linifolia* (Batalinii Group) 'Apricot Jewel'
'Apricot Parrot' (10) ♀H6	ERCP GKev LAma NRog SDeJ WHlf
'Aquilla' (11)	LAma SDeJ
'Arabian Beauty' (3)	ETay LCro LOPS
'Arabian Mystery' (3)	GKev NHol SDeJ WHlf
'Aria Card' (7)	SDeJ
'Arie Hoek' (3)	NRog
'Arlette Hanson' (2) **new**	LAma
'Armani' (3)	NRog
armena (15)	GKev NRog
- var. ***armena***	NRog
'Armscote' (7)	NRog
'Artist' (8) ♀H6	CAvo ERCP GKev LAma NRog SDeJ SDir WPhe
'Asahi' (3) **new**	LCro
'Atlantis' (5)	CArg NRog SDeJ WPhe
'Attila' (3)	LAma LCro NRog
aucheriana (15) ♀H5	EPot GKev LAma NRog
australis (15)	GKev NRog
'Authority' (14)	NRog
'Auxerre' (7)	WPhe
'Avant Garde'PBR (2) **new**	WHlf
'Avenue' (3)	WPhe
'Aveyron' (11)	GKev LAma SDir
'Avignon' (5)	ERCP GKev LCro NRog SDeJ
aximensis (15)	EPot GKev
'Baby Blue' (3)	NRog
'Backpacker' (11)	CAvo ERCP
bakeri	see *T. saxatilis* Bakeri Group
'Ballade' (6) ♀H6	ERCP GKev LAma LCro LOPS NRog SDeJ SDir WPhe
BALLADE DREAM	see *T.* 'Sonnet'
'Ballade Gold' (6)	LAma

'Ballade Lady' (6)	NRog
'Ballerina' (6) ♀H6	CAby CArg CAvo EPfP ERCP ETay GKev LAma LCro LOPS NRog SDeJ SPer WHlf WPhe
'Banja Luka' (4)	NRog SDeJ
'Barbados' (7)	LAma SDeJ WPhe
'Barcelona' (3) ♀H6	CAvo ERCP ETay GKev LCro LOPS NRog
'Baronesse' (5)	SDeJ
'Bastia' (7) **new**	LAma
'Bastogne' (3)	NRog
'Bastogne Parrot' (10)	NRog
batalinii	see *T. linifolia* Batalinii Group
'Beau Monde' (3) ♀H6	NRog SDeJ
'Beauty of Apeldoorn' (4)	LAma NRog SPer
'Beauty of Spring' (4)	ETay GKev LAma LHWs
'Beauty Queen' (1)	NRog SDeJ
'Beethoven's Memory' (19)	NRog
'Belicia' (2)	NRog SDir WPhe
'Bell Song' (7)	NRog
'Bellona' (3)	SDeJ
'Berlioz' (12)	ETay SDeJ
'Bestseller' (1)	GKev NRog SDeJ
§ ***biflora*** (15)	EPot ERCP GKev LAma NRog SDeJ
- var. ***major*** (15)	GKev
bifloriformis (15)	GKev NRog
I - 'Maxima' (15)	NRog
- 'Starlight' (15) ♀H6	NRog
'Big Chief' (4) ♀H6	NRog
'Big Smile' (5)	GKev WHlf
binutans (15)	NRog
'Black and White' (9)	LAma
'Black Bean' (5) **new**	LAma
'Black Hero' (11)	CAby ERCP GKev LAma LCro LOPS NRog SDeJ SDir
'Black Jewel' (7)	ERCP GKev NRog SDeJ WPhe
'Black Parrot' (10) ♀H6	CAby CArg CAvo EPfP ERCP ETay GKev LAma LCro LOPS NBwr NRog SDeJ WPhe
'Black Swan' (5)	SDeJ
'Blackjack' (3)	NRog
'Bleu Aimable' (5)	ERCP GKev LAma NRog SDeJ
'Blue Beauty' (3)	GKev LAma LCro LOPS
'Blue Diamond' (11)	CArg ERCP LAma LCro NRog SDeJ SDir WHlf WPhe
'Blue Heron' (7) ♀H6	ERCP GKev LCro LOPS MCot NRog SDeJ
'Blue Parrot' (10)	CArg ERCP GKev LAma LCro LOPS NRog SDeJ
'Blue Ribbon' (3)	LCro LOPS NRog
'Blue Spectacle' (11)	GKev
'Blue Wow' (11)	LCro WHlf
BLUEBERRY RIPPLE	see *T.* 'Zurel'
'Blumex Favourite'PBR (10)	LCro
'Blushing Apeldoorn' (4)	LAma WHlf
'Blushing Beauty' (5)	SDeJ SDir
'Blushing Bride' (5)	SDeJ
'Blushing Girl' (5)	LAma SDeJ
'Blushing Lady' (5)	GKev LAma MCot NBir
'Boa Vista' (11)	ERCP
'Border Legend' (13)	NRog
'Boston' (3)	LAma
'Bourbon Street'PBR (3)	LHWs
'Boutade' (14)	NPer
'Brest' (7)	WPhe
'Brooklyn' (11)	NPer
'Brown Sugar' (3)	CAvo ERCP ETay GKev LAma LCro LHWs LOPS NRog SDir WHlf WPhe
'Brownie' (2)	CAvo ERCP
'Bruine Wimpel' (5)	LCro
'Buddy' (14)	NRog
'Budlight' (6)	LAma LHWs WPhe
'Bulldog' (7)	SDeJ

'Burgundy' (6)	ERCP ETay GKev LAma LCro LOPS NRog SDeJ SDir SPer
'Burgundy Lace' (7)	ETay GKev LAma LCro LOPS NRog SDeJ
'Burning Heart' (4) 🏆H6	CArg NRog SDeJ
butkovii (15)	GKev NRog
'Buttercup' (14)	SDeJ
'Café Noir' (5)	ERCP LAma LCro LHWs LOPS NHol SDir
'Cairo' (3)	ERCP
'Calgary' (3) 🏆H6	CAvo ETay LAma LCro LOPS NRog SDeJ WPhe
'Calgary Flames' (3) 🏆H6	CAvo
'Calypso' (14) 🏆H6	CRos EHyd LRHS NRHS
'Camargue' (5)	LAma NRog SDeJ
'Canasta' (7) 🏆H6	LRHS NRog SDeJ WHlf WPhe
'Candela' (13) 🏆H6	LRHS NRog SDeJ
'Candy Apple Delight' (4)	LAma NRog
'Candy Club' (5)	ERCP ETay LAma LCro NRog SDeJ
'Candy Prince'PBR (1)	CArg CRos EHyd ERCP LAma LCro LRHS NBwr NRHS NRog SDeJ WHlf WPhe
'Canova' (7)	SDeJ
'Cap d'Or' (14)	NRog
'Cape Cod' (14)	ETay LAma NBwr NRog SDeJ
'Cape Town' (1) 🏆H6	LAma SDeJ WPhe
'Caractère' (3)	CArg
'Caravaggio' (2) **new**	LAma
'Caravelle' (5)	ERCP MCot SDeJ
'Cardinal Mindszenty' (2)	ERCP LAma SDeJ
'Caribbean Parrot' (10)	LAma LHWs WPhe
carinata (15)	NRog
'Carnaval de Nice' (11/v) 🏆H6	ERCP ETay GKev LAma LCro LOPS NRog SDeJ SDir WPhe
'Carnaval de Rio' (3)	CAby LCro MBros NRog
'Carola' (3)	LCro
'Carre' (3) **new**	LAma WHlf
'Carrousel' (7)	NRog SDeJ
'Cartouche' (11)	NRog SDeJ WHlf WPhe
'Casa Grande' (14) 🏆H6	LCro
'Casablanca' (11)	NRog
'Cassini' (3)	LAma LSto SDeJ
'Catherina' (5)	GKev LCro LHWs LOPS
§ ***celsiana*** (15)	NRog
'Chansonnette' (3)	ERCP GKev NRog
'Charmeur'PBR (3)	NRog SDeJ
'Charming Beauty' (11)	LCro WHlf
'Charming Lady' (11)	ERCP NRog
'Cheers' (3)	ETay SPer
'Cherry Delight' (4)	LAma
'China Lady' (14)	SDeJ
'China Pink' (6) 🏆H6	ERCP GKev LAma LCro LOPS NRog SDeJ WPhe
'China Town' (8) 🏆H6	ERCP GKev LAma LCro LOPS NRog SDeJ
'Chopin' (12)	LAma NHol
'Christmas Dream' (1)	LAma NRog SDeJ WHlf
'Christmas Marvel' (1)	NRog SDeJ
'Christmas Orange' (1)	WPhe
'Christmas Pearl' (1)	WPhe
'Christmas Sweet' (1)	CArg
chrysantha	see *T. montana*
'Cistula' (6)	ETay GKev NRog SDeJ
'City of Vancouver' (5)	CAvo SDeJ SDir
'Claudia' (6)	CArg ETay NRog SDeJ WHlf WPhe
'Clearwater'PBR (5)	SDeJ WHlf
'Cleveland' (3)	WPhe
'Cloud Nine' (5)	NRog
§ ***clusiana*** (15)	ERCP GKev LAma LHWs NRog WHlf
- f. ***cashmeriana*** (15)	GKev NRog
- var. ***chrysantha*** (15) 🏆H6	CExl EHyd GKev LAma LRHS NRHS NRog WShi
- - 'Tubergen's Gem' (15)	EPot GKev LAma LHWs NRog WHlf WPhe
- 'Cynthia' (15) 🏆H6	CAvo EPot GKev LAma MPie NRog SDeJ SPhx WPhe WShi
- 'Mountains Pride' (15)	NRog
- 'Sheila' (15)	GKev LAma NRog SPhx
§ - var. ***stellata*** (15) 🏆H6	GKev NRog
'Colour Parade' (14)	NRog
'Colour Spectacle'PBR (5)	CAby
'Columbine' (5)	GKev LAma
'Compostella' (14)	NRog
'Concerto' (13)	GKev NPer NRog SDeJ
'Conqueror'PBR (4)	LAma SDir
'Continental' (3)	ERCP GKev LAma
'Cool Crystal' (7)	NRog WPhe
'Coors' (14) 🏆H6	NRog
'Copex' (3) **new**	WHlf
'Copper Image' (11)	ERCP ETay GKev LAma LHWs WPhe
'Coquette' (1)	SDeJ
'Corinna' (5) **new**	LAma
'Corona' (12)	NRog SDeJ WHlf
'Corsage' (14) 🏆H6	SDeJ
'Cortina' (9)	SDeJ
'Cosmopolitan' (4) **new**	LAma
'Couleur Cardinal' (3)	CAvo CRos EHyd ERCP GKev LAma LCro LOPS LRHS NRHS NRog SDeJ
'Cream Cocktail' (4)	MCot
'Cream Flag' (3)	LSto
'Creme Lizard' (10)	NRog
'Crème Upstar' (11)	ERCP GKev LAma LCro LOPS NRog SDeJ WPhe
'Crossfire'PBR (2) **new**	WHlf
'Crystal Star' (7)	CArg
'Cuban Night' (7)	LAma
'Cum Laude' (5)	LAma SDeJ
'Cummins' (7)	ERCP LCro LOPS NRog WHlf WPhe
'Curly Sue' (7)	ERCP ETay MCot NRog WHlf
'Cutie Honey' (6)	WPhe
'Czaar Peter' (14) 🏆H6	NPer NRog SDeJ WPhe
'Dance' (13)	NRog SDeJ
'Danceline' (11)	GKev LAma LCro LHWs
'Darwidesign'PBR (4) **new**	WHlf
'Darwisnow' (3)	GKev
dasystemon (15)	GKev LAma
- from Tajikstan (15)	NRog
dasystemonoides (15)	NRog
'Davenport' (7)	ERCP NRog
'David Teniers' (2)	ERCP NRog SDeJ
'Daydream' (4) 🏆H6	CArg GKev NRog SDeJ SPer
'Daytona' (7)	LCro NRog
'Dazzling Sensation' (11/d/v)	LHWs
'Deirdre' (8)	NRog
'Denmark'PBR (3)	NRog
'Diamond Jubilee' (3) 🏆H6 **new**	ETay
'Diana' (1)	CArg
'Diantha' (14)	NRog
didieri misapplied	see *T. passeriniana*
'Doll's Minuet' (8)	ERCP LAma LCro LOPS NRog SDir SPer WHlf
'Dom Pedro' (5)	LAma
'Don Quichotte' (3) 🏆H6	ERCP LCro LOPS NRog SDeJ
'Donauperle' (14)	SDeJ
'Donna Bella' (14)	SDeJ
'Dordogne' (5) 🏆H6	ERCP LAma LCro NRog SDeJ
'Double Dazzle' (2)	SDir
'Double Flag' (11)	GKev WHlf
'Double Flaming Parrot'PBR (10)	LAma
'Double Focus' (11)	NRog
'Double Red Riding Hood' (14/v)	LAma NRog SDeJ

'Double Touch' (11)	GKev
'Dow Jones'^{PBR} (3)	WPhe
'Dragon King' (3)	SDeJ
'Dream Club' (5) **new**	LAma SDir
'Dream Touch' (11)	ETay LAma LCro LHWs WPhe
'Dreamland' (5) ♀^{H6}	SDeJ
'Drumline' (11) ♀^{H6}	NRog
dubia	GKev
- 'Beldersai' (15)	NRog
'Duc van Tol' (1)	LAma
'Duc van Tol Aurora' (1)	LAma
'Duc van Tol Cochineal' (1) **new**	LAma
'Duc van Tol Double' (2) **new**	LAma
'Duc van Tol Max Cramoisie' (1)	LAma
'Duc van Tol Orange' (1) **new**	LAma
'Duc van Tol Primrose' (1)	LAma
'Duc van Tol Red and White' (1) **new**	LAma
'Duc van Tol Red and Yellow' (1)	GKev LAma SDir
'Duc van Tol Rose' (1)	LAma SDir
'Duc van Tol Salmon' (1)	LAma
'Duc van Tol Scarlet' (1)	LAma
'Duc van Tol Violet' (1)	LAma SDir
'Duc van Tol White' (1)	LAma
'Dynasty' (3)	NRog
'Early Glory' (3)	LCro LOPS
'Early Harvest' (12) ♀^{H6}	GKev LAma NRog SDeJ SDir WHlf
'Easter Surprise' (14) ♀^{H6}	LAma NRog SDeJ SDir
'Ego Parrot' (10)	LCro LOPS
eichleri	see *T. undulatifolia*
'El Niño' (5)	LAma
'Electra' (5)	NHol
'Elegans Alba' (6)	LAma
'Elegant Lady' (6)	GKev LAma LCro MCot NRog SDeJ WHlf
'Elizabeth Arden' (4)	GKev NRog
'Esperanto' (8/v) ♀^{H6}	LAma NPer NRog SDeJ SDir WPhe
'Esprit' (7)	LCro
'Esta Bonita'^{PBR} (3)	WPhe
'Estella Rijnveld' (10)	EPfP ERCP ETay GKev LAma LCro LOPS NRog SDeJ WHlf
'Eternal Flame' (2)	LCro NRog WCot
'Evergreen' (3)	ERCP LCro LHWs LOPS WPhe
'Exotic Emperor' (13)	CAvo ERCP GKev LAma LCro LHWs LOPS MCot NRog SDeJ SDir WHlf WPhe
'Exquisit' (11) **new**	ERCP LAma LCro
'Fabio' (7)	CRos EHyd LRHS NRHS
'Fancy Frills' (7) ♀^{H6}	ERCP GKev LAma NRog SDeJ
'Fancy Parrot' (10)	SDeJ
'Fantasy' (10) ♀^{H6}	LAma NRog
'Fashion' (12)	SDeJ
'Fenna' (15) **new**	SPhx
ferganica (15)	NRog WCot
'Fidelio' (3) ♀^{H6}	SDeJ
'Finola' (11)	GKev LCro LOPS WHlf WPhe
'Fire of Love' (14)	SDir
'Fire Wings' (6)	LAma LHWs
'Firework' (6)	CAvo WPhe
'First Proud' (5) **new**	LAma
'Flair' (1)	CRos EHyd LAma LRHS NBwr NRHS NRog SDeJ
'Flamenco' (7)	NRog SDeJ
'Flaming Baltic' (7) ♀^{H6} **new**	ERCP
'Flaming Club' (5)	LAma
'Flaming Evita'^{PBR} (2)	SDeJ WHlf
'Flaming Flag' (3)	CAvo ETay GKev LAma LCro LOPS
'Flaming Parrot' (10)	CAby ERCP ETay GKev LAma LCro LOPS NRog SDeJ
I 'Flaming Purissima' (13)	GKev LAma NRog SDeJ WPhe
'Flaming Springgreen' (8)	ERCP ETay GKev LAma LCro LOPS NRog SDeJ SPer WHlf WPhe
'Flash Point'^{PBR} (2)	WPhe
'Flashback' (10)	LAma WPhe
'Flig Flag' (3)	ERCP
'Florijn Chic' (6)	LHWs
'Florosa' (8)	LCro LOPS NRog SDeJ
'Flower Power' (10)	LAma NRog
'Fly Away' (6)	CAby CAvo NRog WHlf WPhe
'Flying Dragon' (3) **new**	LAma
'Fontainebleau' (3)	ERCP GKev LCro NRog SDeJ
fosteriana (13)	SVic
'Foxtrot'^{PBR} (2) ♀^{H6}	CAby CAvo ERCP GKev LAma NRog SDeJ SDir WHlf
'Foxy Foxtrot' (2)	GKev LAma NRog SDeJ WPhe
'Françoise' (3)	LCro NRog SDeJ
'Frank Graham' (3)	LHWs
'Franz Léhar' (12)	NRog SDeJ
'Freedom Flame' (3)	LHWs
'Freeman' (11)	SDir
'Fremont'^{PBR} (4) **new**	WHlf
'Fringed Elegance' (7) ♀^{H6}	LCro LOPS
'Fringed Family' (7)	SDeJ
'Fritz Kreisler' (12)	LAma SDeJ
'Für Elise' (14)	NRog SDeJ SDir
'Gabriella' (3)	NRog
'Gaiety' (12)	SDeJ
'Garden Party' (3)	SDeJ
'Gavota' (3) ♀^{H6}	ETay GKev LAma LCro NHol NRog SDeJ WHlf WPhe
'Generaal de Wet' (1)	LCro SDeJ
'Georgette' (5)	LAma
'Gerbrand Kieft' (11) ♀^{H6}	ERCP
gesneriana (15)	GKev SVic WCot
'Gipsy Love' (7)	SDeJ
'Girlfriend' (15)	NRog
'Giuseppe Verdi' (12)	CRos EHyd LAma LRHS NBwr NRHS NRog
'Global Desire' (2)	GKev
'Glück' (12) ♀^{H6}	NRog
'Golden Apeldoorn' (4)	CArg ETay GKev LAma LCro LOPS LSto NBwr NRog SDeJ
'Golden Artist' (8)	GKev LAma LCro LOPS NRog SDeJ SDir
'Golden Dynasty' (3)	CAby
'Golden Emperor' (13)	GKev LAma NRog SDeJ
'Golden Melody' (3)	SDeJ
'Golden Nizza' (11)	LAma NRog
'Golden Oxford' (4)	LAma NRog
'Goldwest' (14)	NRog SDeJ
'Gordon Cooper' (4)	SDeJ
'Gorilla' (7)	LCro
'Goudstuk' (12)	LAma NRog
'Grand Perfection'^{PBR} (3) ♀^{H6}	CAvo GKev LCro LOPS SDeJ
'Granny Award' (11)	LAma
'Green Eyes' (8)	SDeJ
'Green River' (8)	SDeJ
'Green Spirit' (8) **new**	LAma MMrt
'Green Valley' (8)	NRog
'Green Wave' (10)	ERCP LAma LCro LOPS MBros NRog SDeJ WPhe
'Greenstar' (6)	CAby CAvo ERCP GKev LAma LCro LHWs SDir WHlf WPhe
greigii (14)	NRog
grengiolensis (15)	GKev NRog
'Greuze' (5)	LCro
'Groenland' (8)	CAvo GKev LAma LCro LOPS NRog SDeJ SDir WPhe
'Guus Papendrecht' (3)	NRog
'Gwen'^{PBR} (3)	LHWs
hageri (15)	GKev LAma NRog

	- 'Splendens' (15)	NRog SDeJ SPhx
	'Hakuun' (4)	CAby LAma NRog SDir
	'Hamilton' (7)	LAma NRog SDeJ WHlf WPhe
	'Hans Dietrich Genscher' (3)	NRog
	'Happy Generation' (3)	GKev LAma LCro LOPS
	'Happy Hour' (7)	ERCP
	'Happy People' (3) **new**	LCro
	'Harvest Moon' (3)	LHWs
	'Hatsuzakura' (4)	NRog
	'Havran' (3)	CAvo ERCP LAma LCro LOPS NRog SDir WPhe
	'Heart's Delight' (12)	CArg LAma NRog SDeJ
	'Heart's Desire' (3)	WPhe
	'Helmar' (3) ♀H6	CAby LCro NRog SDeJ WPhe
	'Hemisphere' (3)	CArg CAvo GKev LAma LHWs LRHS NRog SDeJ WHlf
	'Hermitage' (3)	ERCP LAma NRog WHlf
	heweri (15)	GKev LAma NRog
	hissarica (15)	NRog
	'Hocus Pocus' (5)	LAma SDeJ
	'Holland Baby' (2)	SDeJ
	'Holland Beauty' PBR (3)	MCot WHlf
	'Holland Chic' (6)	CAby LAma NRog SDeJ
	'Holland Queen' PBR (3)	NRog SDeJ WPhe
	'Hollands Glorie' (4)	SDeJ
	'Hollywood' (8)	LAma
	'Honeymoon' (7)	CAvo ETay LAma LCro LHWs LOPS WHlf WPhe
	'Honky Tonk' (15) ♀H6	CAvo CBor EPfP GKev LAma LCro LOPS NRog SPhx WPhe
§	***hoogiana*** (15)	GKev NRog
	'Horizon' PBR (11)	NRog
	'Hotpants' (3)	CAvo LAma NRog WHlf
§	***humilis*** (15)	CRos EHyd ERCP GKev LRHS NRHS NRog SDeJ WShi
I	- 'Alba' (15)	NRog
	- 'China Carol' (15)	GKev LAma NRog SDeJ
	- 'Eastern Star' (15)	GKev LAma NRog
§	- 'Lilliput' (15)	CAvo CRos EHyd EPot GKev LAma LRHS NRHS NRog SPhx
	- 'Magenta Queen' (15)	NRog
	- 'Odalisque' (15)	EHyd EPot GKev LAma LRHS NRHS NRog
	- 'Persian Pearl' (15)	CAby CAvo EPfP EPot ERCP GKev LAma LCro LOPS LRHS NRog SDeJ SDir SPhx WPhe WTor
*	- 'Pink Charm' (15)	NRog
	- var. ***pulchella*** Albocaerulea Oculata Group (15)	EPot ERCP LAma LCro LOPS NRog
	- 'Rosea' (15)	GKev NRog
I	- 'Rosea Coerulea Oculata' (15)	NRog
	- 'Tête-à-tête' (15)	NRog
§	- Violacea Group (15)	CRos EHyd LRHS NRHS
	- - black base (15)	EPot ERCP GKev LAma LCro NRog
	- - yellow base (15)	EPot GKev LAma NRog
	hungarica	GKev
	'Ice Age' (11)	ETay WPhe
	'Ice Cream' (11)	GKev LAma LCro LOPS NRog SDeJ SDir WHlf WPhe
	'Ice Stick' (12)	NRog SDeJ
	'Ice Wing' (6)	SDir
	'Île de France' (5)	ERCP LAma LCro LOPS NRog SDeJ
	iliensis (15)	EPot GKev NRog
	INDELAND	ERCP
	'Indian Velvet' (5)	LCro LOPS
	'Infinity' (3)	ETay LAma SPer
	ingens (15)	NRog
	'Inner Wheel' (5) **new**	LAma
	'Innuendo' (3)	NRog
	'Insulinde' (9)	GKev LAma
	'Inzell' (3)	LSto
	'Irene Parrot' (10)	LAma SDeJ WHlf
	'Isaak Chic' (6)	LHWs
	'Istanbul' (6)	LHWs
	'Ivory Floradale' (4) ♀H6	GKev LAma NRog SDeJ
	'Jackpot' (3)	SPer WHlf
	'Jacqueline' (6)	LCro
	'Jacuzzi' (3) **new**	LCro
	'James Wild' (5)	GKev
	'Jan Reus' (3)	CAby CAvo ERCP LCro LOPS NRog WPhe
	'Jazz' (6)	ERCP SDir
	'Jeantine' (12)	NRog
	'Jimmy' (3)	LRHS
	'Joanne Woodward' (14)	NRog
	'Johann Strauss' (12)	CArg LAma NRog SPer
	'Juan' (13) ♀H6	NRog
	'Julia Farnese' (9)	GKev
	'Jumbo Beauty' (5)	GKev SDeJ
	'Kansas Proud' (3) **new**	ERCP
§	'Kees Nelis' (3)	NRog WHlf
	'Keizerskroon' (1)	LAma SDeJ
	'Kiev' (14) ♀H6	SDir
	'Kikomachi' (3)	CRos EHyd LRHS NRHS
	'Kingsblood' (5) ♀H6	CAby ERCP LAma LCro NRog SDeJ WHlf
	'Kleurenpracht'	see *T.* 'Princess Margaret Rose'
	'Koh-i-Noor' (1) **new**	LAma
	kolpakowskiana (15) ♀H6	EPot ERCP GKev LAma NRog WShi
	kurdica (15)	LAma NRog
	- purple-flowered (15)	NRog
	'La Belle Époque' (2)	CAvo CKel ERCP GKev LAma LCro LHWs LOPS NRog SDeJ WHlf WPhe
	'La Courtine' (5)	NRog
	'Labrador' (7)	SPer WPhe
	'Lac van Rijn' (1)	GKev LAma
*	'Lady Diana' (14)	NRog
	'Lady Jane' (15) ♀H6	EPfP ERCP ETay GKev LAma NRog SPer WPhe WShi
	'Lady van Eijk' (4) **new**	ERCP
	'Lalibela' (4)	ETay GKev LCro
	'Lambada' (7) ♀H6	CAvo ERCP LCro NRog SDeJ WPhe
	lanata (15)	GKev NRog WCot
	'Laptop' PBR (3) **new**	LCro
	'Lasting Love' (3)	CAby LAma LCro SDir WPhe
	'Latvian Gold' (15)	NRog
	'Le Mogol' (5)	SDir
	'Leen van der Mark' (3)	NRog WPhe
	'Lemon Flight' (7)	WPhe
	'Lemon Giant' (14)	GKev
	'Libretto Parrot' (10)	LCro SDeJ
	'Light and Dreamy' (4)	ERCP GKev LAma LCro LHWs LOPS NRog SDeJ SDir
	'Lilac Crystal' (7)	LCro LOPS
	'Lilac Love' (3) **new**	LAma
	'Lilac Perfection' (11)	GKev NRog SDeJ
	'Lilac Time' (6)	LAma SDir
	'Lilac Wonder'	see *T. saxatilis* (Bakeri Group) 'Lilac Wonder'
	'Lilliput'	see *T. humilis* 'Lilliput'
	'Lilyfire' (6)	NRog SDeJ
	'Lilyrosa' (6)	ETay NRog
	'Limelight' (3)	LAma
	'Lingerie' (7)	SDeJ
	linifolia (15) ♀H5	CAvo EPot ERCP GKev LAma LHWs NRog SDeJ WPhe WShi
§	- Batalinii Group (15) ♀H5	GKev NRog
§	- - 'Apricot Jewel' (15)	EPot ERCP GKev NRog
	- - 'Bright Gem' (15) ♀H5	EPot GKev LAma NPer NRog SDir SPhx WHoo WPhe
	- - 'Bronze Charm' (15)	CAvo EGrI EPot GKev LAma NRog SDeJ WTor

	- - 'Red Gem' (15)	GKev NRog WCot
	- - 'Red Hunter' (15) 𝕐H5	ERCP GKev LAma LRHS NRog SDeJ SDir
	- - 'Salmon Gem' (15)	CAvo ETay LAma
	- - 'Salmon Jewel' (15)	GKev NRog
	- - 'Yellow Jewel' (15)	GKev NRog WShi
§	- Maximowiczii Group (15)	GKev NRog
	'Lion King' (7)	SDeJ
	'Lipgloss' (3)	NHol
	'Little Beauty' (15) 𝕐H6	CAby CAvo CBod CRos EGrl EHyd EPot GKev LAma LCro LOPS LRHS NRHS NRog SDeJ SDir SPer SPhx WCot WHoo WPhe
	'Little Girl' (14)	LAma
	'Little Princess' (15) 𝕐H6	CAvo CRos EHyd EPot GKev LAma LRHS NRHS NRog SDeJ SDir SPhx WHlf WIce
	'Little Star' (15) 𝕐H6	GKev NRog
	'Long Lady' (5)	MCot NRog SDeJ
	'Love Song' (12)	NRog SDeJ
	'Lovely Surprise' (14)	SDeJ
	'Lucky Parrot' (10)	NRog
§	'Lustige Witwe' (3)	SDeJ
	'Mabel' (9)	GKev LAma
	'Macarena' (6)	NRog
	'Madalyn' (6)	CAvo
§	'Madame Lefeber' (13)	GKev LAma LCro LOPS NRog SDeJ
	'Madonna' (10)	EPfP ETay
	'Madras' (5) **new**	LAma
	'Magic Lavender' (3)	LHWs NRog SDir
	'Mango Charm' (3)	GKev LAma LCro LHWs SDeJ SDir
	'March of Time' (14)	NRog
	'Margarita' (2)	GKev LCro LOPS WPhe
	'Marie José' (14)	SDeJ
	'Mariette' (6)	ERCP GKev LAma NRog SDeJ SDir
	'Marilyn' (6)	ERCP NRog SDeJ SDir
	marjolletii (15)	GKev
	'Marquis de la Coquette' (14)	ETay
	'Mary Ann' (14)	LAma NRog
	'Mascotte' (7)	NRog WPhe
	'Master Peace' (7)	LHWs
	'Match' (3)	LCro LOPS
	'Matchmaker' (3)	WPhe
	'Matchpoint' (7/d)	SDeJ
	'Maureen' (5) 𝕐H6	ERCP LAma LCro LOPS NRog SDeJ SDir
	mauritiana 'Cindy' (15)	NRog
	maximowiczii	see *T. linifolia* Maximowiczii Group
	'Maytime' (6)	LAma LCro LOPS NRog SDeJ
	'Maytime Design' (6)	NRog
	'Menton' (5) 𝕐H6	CAby ERCP GKev LAma LCro LOPS NRog SDeJ WPhe
	'Menton Exotic' (11)	ERCP GKev LCro
	'Merlot' (6)	CAby CAvo ERCP ETay GKev LAma LCro LOPS MBros WPhe
	'Merry Christmas' (1)	NRog
	MERRY WIDOW	see *T.* 'Lustige Witwe'
	'Miskodeed' (14)	NRog SDeJ
	'Miss Elegance' (3)	GKev SDir
	'Mistress' (3)	CAvo ERCP ETay LAma LCro LOPS LSto NRog
	'Mistress Mystic' (3)	ERCP
	'Mona Lisa' (6)	SDeJ
	'Mondial'[PBR] (2)	LCro LOPS NRog WPhe
	'Moneymaker' (6) 𝕐H6	ERCP
	'Monsella' (2)	LAma NRog WPhe
§	***montana*** (15)	EPot LAma NRog WCot
	- yellow-flowered (15)	NRog
	'Monte Carlo' (2) 𝕐H6	CArg LAma NRog SDeJ SDir WHlf
	'Monte Orange' (2)	WPhe
	'Montreux' (2)	LAma SDir
	'Moulin Rouge' (3)	NRog
	'Mount Tacoma' (11)	ERCP GKev LAma LCro LOPS NRog SDeJ
	'Mr Van der Hoef' (2)	SDeJ
	'Mrs John T. Scheepers' (5)	SDeJ
	'Muriel' (10)	ERCP NRog
	'Muriel Roze' (10)	LHWs
	'Murillo' (2)	NRog
	'Muscadet' (5) **new**	LCro SDir
	'Mysterious Parrot' (10)	ERCP
	'Mystic van Eijk'[PBR] (4)	ERCP LAma
	'Nachtwacht' (2)	LAma LHWs
	'National Velvet' (3)	EPfP ERCP ETay GKev LAma LCro LOPS SPer
	'Negrita' (3)	CAby CArg CAvo ERCP GKev LAma LCro LOPS MCot NRog SDeJ SDir WHlf WPhe
	'Negrita Double' (11) **new**	LCro
	'Negrita Parrot' (10)	ERCP LAma WHlf
	neustruevae (15)	GKev NRog
	'New Design' (3/v)	LAma LCro LOPS NRog WHlf
	'New Santa' (7)	LHWs WPhe
	'Nicholas Heyek' (3)	LCro
	'Night Club' (5)	CAvo ERCP LAma LCro
	'Nightrider' (8)	ETay LCro LOPS MCot NRog SDeJ WPhe
	'Ollioules' (4) 𝕐H6	NRog SDeJ
	'Olympic Flame' (4) 𝕐H6	LCro LOPS NRog SDeJ
	'Orange Angelique' (11)	LAma WHlf
	'Orange Bouquet' (3) 𝕐H6	NRog SDeJ
	'Orange Brilliant' (13)	GKev LCro LOPS
	'Orange Cassini' (3)	LCro
	'Orange Emperor' (13) 𝕐H6	CAvo ERCP ETay GKev LAma MCot NRog SDeJ SDir
	'Orange Favourite' (10)	ERCP GKev NRog
	'Orange Juice' (3)	WPhe
	'Orange Lion' (4)	WHlf
	'Orange Princess' (11) 𝕐H6	CAvo ERCP GKev LAma LCro LOPS NRog SDeJ SDir WPhe
	'Orange Sun'	see *T.* 'Oranjezon'
	'Orange Toronto' (14)	NRog
	'Orange van Eijk' (4) **new**	LAma
§	'Oranjezon' (4) 𝕐H6	NRog
	'Oratorio' (14) 𝕐H6	NRog SDeJ
	'Orca' (2) **new**	EPfP ETay LAma
	'Oriental Beauty' (14) 𝕐H6	NRog
	orithyioides (15)	NRog
	orphanidea (15)	GKev NRog
	- 'Flava' (15)	ERCP ETay GKev LAma NRog
§	- Whittallii Group (15) 𝕐H6	CAvo ERCP GKev LAma NRog SDeJ WCot WShi
	- - 'Major' (15)	ERCP
	'Oscar' (3)	LAma NHol SDir
	ostrowskiana (15)	GKev NRog
	'Oviedo' (7)	LAma NRog
	'Oxford' (4) 𝕐H6	NRog
	'Pacific Pearl' (7)	CAvo
	'Page Polka' (3)	SDeJ
	'Pallada' (3)	LCro LOPS
	'Parade' (4) 𝕐H6	LAma
	'Parrot King' (10)	NRog SDeJ
	'Parrot Sweet' (10) **new**	LAma
§	***passeriniana*** (15)	GKev NRog
	'Passionale' (3) 𝕐H6	LAma LCro LOPS NBwr NRog SDeJ WPhe
	'Paul Scherer' (3) 𝕐H6	CAby CAvo EPfP ERCP ETay GKev LCro LOPS MMrt NRog SDeJ WPhe
	'Peach Blossom' (2)	CArg EHyd ETay LCro LOPS LRHS NRHS NRog SDeJ
*	'Peaches and Cream'	ETay
	Peacock Group	ETay NBwr SDeJ
	'Peppermintstick' (15) 𝕐H6	CAby CAvo ERCP ETay GKev LAma LCro MPie NRog SDeJ SPhx WHlf

	'Peptalk' (11) **new**	LAma
	'Perestroyka' (5)	LAma SDeJ
	persica	see *T. celsiana*
	'Picture' (5)	ERCP SDeJ
	'Pieter de Leur' (6)	CAby CAvo LCro LOPS
	'Pim Fortuyn' (3) **new**	LCro
	'Pimpernel' (8/v)	LAma SDeJ
	'Pink Diamond' (5)	ERCP LAma LCro MBros NHol SDeJ SDir
	'Pink Dwarf' (12)	GKev NRog SDeJ
*	'Pink Emperor' (13)	GKev
	'Pink Impression' (4) ♀H6	CArg LAma LCro LOPS NRog SDeJ
	'Pink Ribbon' (3)	NRog
	'Pink Sensation' (14)	SDeJ
	'Pink Star' (11)	ERCP GKev LCro
	'Pinocchio' (14)	CArg CRos EHyd GKev LRHS NRHS NRog SDeJ WPhe
	'Pirand' (13) ♀H6	NRog SDeJ
	'Pittsburg' (3)	LAma LCro LOPS
	'Plaisir' (14) ♀H6	LAma NRog
	'Playtime' (6)	NRog
	'Poco Loco' (13)	GKev NRog SDeJ
	polychroma	see *T. biflora*
	praestans (15)	ETay GKev LRHS NRog WShi
	- 'Bloemenlust' (15)	GKev NRog
	- 'Fusilier' (15) ♀H6	CExl GKev LAma NRog SDeJ
	- 'Moondance' (15)	NRog
	- 'Red Sun' (15)	NRog
	- 'Shogun' (15)	CAby CAvo EGrl ERCP GKev LAma NRog SDeJ SDir
	- 'Unicum' (15/v)	LRHS NRog SDeJ SDir
	- 'Van Tubergen's Variety' (15)	GKev LAma NPer NRog
	- 'Yari' (15)	NRog
	- 'Zwanenburg Variety' (15)	GKev NRog
	'Pretty Lady' (6) **new**	LCro
	'Pretty Princess' (3)	CRos ERCP LAma LRHS SDeJ WPhe
	'Pretty Woman' (6)	ETay
	'Prince Albert' (5) **new**	LAma
	'Princeps' (13)	LAma NRog SDeJ
§	'Princess Margaret Rose' (5)	WHlf
	'Princesse Charmante' (14) ♀H6	LCro LOPS NRog
	'Prinses Irene' (3) ♀H6	CAby CArg CAvo CRos EHyd ERCP GKev LAma LCro LOPS LRHS NBir NHol NRHS NRog SDeJ SDir WPhe
	'Prinses Margriet' (3)	ERCP LAma NRog WPhe
	'Professor Röntgen' (10)	ERCP LAma LCro LOPS NRog SDeJ
	pulchella humilis	see *T. humilis*
§	'Purissima' (13) ♀H6	CAvo EPfP GKev LAma LCro LOPS LRHS NRog SDeJ SPer WPhe
	'Purissima Design' (13)	ERCP LAma NRog
	'Purple Bouquet' (3)	LAma SDeJ
	'Purple Doll' (6)	ERCP ETay LAma LCro LOPS
	'Purple Dream' (6)	ERCP LAma LCro LOPS MCot NRog SDeJ WHlf
	'Purple Flag' (3)	LCro LOPS WHlf
	'Purple Lady'[PBR] (3) **new**	LCro
	'Purple Peony' (2)	ERCP
	'Purple Prince' (5)	LRHS
I	'Purple Prince' (1)	CArg LAma LCro LOPS NRHS NRog SDeJ WHlf WPhe
	'Purple Purissima' (13) **new**	LAma
	'Purple Tower' (7)	NRog
	'Quebec' (14)	GKev LAma NRog SDeJ
	'Queen of Marvel' (2)	ERCP NRog SDeJ
	'Queen of Night' (5)	CArg CAvo EPfP ERCP ETay GKev LAma LCro LOPS LSto MBros MCot NBir NBwr NRog SDeJ SDir SPer WHlf WPhe
	'Queensday' (11)	SDeJ
	'Queensland' (7)	LAma NRog WPhe
	'Rai' (10)	SDeJ
	'Rasta Parrot' (10) **new**	LCro
	'Real Time' (7)	WPhe
	'Recreado' (5)	NRog SDeJ
	'Red Baby Doll' (2)	ETay LAma
	'Red Emperor'	see *T.* 'Madame Lefeber'
	'Red Georgette' (5) ♀H6	CAby GKev LAma NBir NRog SDeJ
	'Red Hat' (7) ♀H6	LCro
	'Red Impression'[PBR] (4) ♀H6	ETay LAma LCro LOPS NRog
	'Red Princess' (11) ♀H6	ERCP LAma LRHS NRog WPhe
	'Red Proud' (3) **new**	LCro
	'Red Revival' (1)	GKev
	'Red Riding Hood' (14) ♀H6	CArg CRos EHyd EPfP ETay GKev LAma LCro LOPS LRHS NBir NBwr NRHS NRog SDeJ SPer
	'Red Rover' (3)	LCro LOPS
	'Red Shine' (6) ♀H6	ERCP LCro LOPS NRog SDeJ
	'Red Springgreen' (8)	GKev LAma LCro LOPS NRog SDeJ
	'Red Wing' (7) ♀H6	SDeJ
	'Redwood' (14)	SDeJ
	regelii (15)	NRog
	'Rembrandt' (2) **new**	LAma
	'Rems Favourite' (3)	ERCP LCro LOPS NRog SDeJ WPhe
	'Renown' (5)	NRog SDeJ
	'Request' (3)	ERCP GKev
	'Ridgedale' (11) **new**	LCro
	'Ringo'	see *T.* 'Kees Nelis'
	'Rob Verlinden' (14)	SPer
	'Robassa' (13)	NRog
	'Robinho'[PBR] (11)	GKev
	'Rockery Master' (14)	NRog
	'Rococo' (10)	CAvo ERCP LAma LCro LOPS LRHS NBwr NRog SDeJ SDir WPhe
	'Roi du Midi' (5)	NRog SDeJ
	'Ronaldo' (3)	ERCP GKev LAma LCro LOPS NRog
	'Rosalie' (3)	ERCP LCro NRog SDeJ
	'Rosy Dream' (13)	SDeJ
	'Royal Acres' (2)	LRHS
	'Royal Anthos' (14)	NRog SDeJ
	'Royal Celebration' (6)	ETay SPer
	'Royal Pretender' (6) **new**	LCro
	'Royal Virgin' (3)	LAma
	'Salmon Impression' (4)	ERCP LAma NRog SDeJ WHlf
	'Salmon Jimmy' (3) **new**	ERCP
	'Salmon Parrot' (10)	ETay
	'Salmon Prince' (1) **new**	LCro LSto
	'Salmon van Eijk' (4) **new**	LCro
	'Sanne' (3) ♀H6	CAvo ERCP LCro SDeJ WPhe
	'Santander' (7)	LAma SDeJ
	'Sapporo' (6)	ERCP GKev LCro LOPS
	saracenica (15)	GKev
	saxatilis (15)	GKev LAma LCro LOPS NRog SDeJ
§	- Bakeri Group (15)	SEND
§	- - 'Lilac Wonder' (15) ♀H6	CAby CAvo CExl EPot ERCP GKev LAma LCro LOPS NPer NRog SDeJ SDir WShi
	'Scarlet Baby' (12)	NRog WPhe
	'Scarlet Verona' (2)	LRHS
	schrenkii (15)	EPot ERCP GKev NRog WShi
	'Seadov' (3) ♀H6	LCro LOPS LRHS NRog SDeJ SDir
	'Seattle' (6)	ERCP
	'Secret Perfume' (2)	LHWs
	'Sensual Touch' (7) ♀H6	GKev LAma LHWs NRog SDeJ WPhe
	'Shakespeare' (12)	NRog SDeJ
	'Shirley' (3)	CAvo ERCP GKev LAma LCro LOPS NRog SDeJ SPer
	'Shirley Double' (11)	LAma LHWs
	'Shirley Dream' (3)	SDeJ SDir
	'Showcase' (2) **new**	ERCP LCro
	'Showtime' (14)	SDeJ

'Showwinner' (12) $\mathbb{Y}^{H6}$	GKev LAma MBros NHol NRog SDeJ
'Silk Road' (2)	GKev WHlf
'Silver Parrot' (10)	GKev LAma WPhe
'Silver Standard' (1)	GKev
'Silverstream' (4)	ETay GKev NRog
'Sky High Scarlet' (5) **new**	WHlf
'Slawa'^{PBR} (3)	EPfP ERCP LAma LCro LOPS
'Snow Crystal' (11)	WPhe
'Snow Parrot' (10)	ERCP
'Snow Valley' (7)	ERCP
sogdiana (15)	GKev NRog
'Solar Wind' (15)	NRog
'Solva' (13)	NRog
'Sombrero' (14)	NRog
§ 'Sonnet' (6)	LAma NRog SDeJ
'Sorbet' (5) $\mathbb{Y}^{H6}$	GKev NRog SDeJ
sosnowskyi (15)	GKev
sprengeri (15) $\mathbb{Y}^{H6}$	CAvo CBro CExl CSpe ECha ERCP GKev ITim NRog
- Trotter's form (15)	GKev WCot
'Spring Green' (8) $\mathbb{Y}^{H6}$	CAby CArg CAvo EPfP ERCP ETay GKev LAma LCro LOPS MCot NRog SDeJ WPhe
'Spring Song' (4)	WHlf
'Spryng' (3) $\mathbb{Y}^{H6}$	LHWs SDeJ
'Spryng Break' (3)	LAma LHWs WHlf
'Spryng Tide' (3)	LHWs
'Starfighter' (7)	SDeJ
stellata	see *T. clusiana* var. *stellata*
'Stresa' (12) $\mathbb{Y}^{H6}$	CRos EHyd GKev LRHS NRHS NRog SDeJ
'Striking Match' (6) **new**	LAma
'Striped Bellona' (3)	NRog
'Striped Sail' (3)	LAma
'Strong Gold' (3) $\mathbb{Y}^{H6}$	NRog SDeJ WPhe
'Stunning Apricot' (5)	GKev LCro LOPS
subpraestans (15)	NRog
'Suncatcher' (3)	LAma SDeJ
'Sundowner' (11)	LHWs
'Sunny Prince'^{PBR} (1)	CAvo LCro NRog SDeJ WHlf WPhe
'Sunset Miami' (7)	ERCP LAma
'Sunshine Club' (5) **new**	LAma
'Super Parrot' (10)	WHlf WPhe
'Survivor' (5)	SDeJ
'Swan Wings' (7)	GKev LAma LCro LOPS NRog SDeJ
'Sweet Desire' (2)	SDeJ
'Sweet Impression' (4)	ERCP NRog
'Sweet Lady' (14)	LRHS NRog SDeJ
'Sweet Love' (3)	NRog
'Sweetheart' (13)	GKev LCro LOPS MCot NRog SDeJ WPhe
sylvestris (15)	CAby CAvo CBod EPot ERCP GKev LAma LCro LOPS NBir NRog SDeJ WCot WShi
'Synaeda Amor' (3)	ETay LAma LCro LOPS NRog
'Synaeda Blue' (3) **new**	LCro
'Synaeda King' (6) $\mathbb{Y}^{H6}$	LCro NRog
systola (15)	NRog
'Tabledance' (11)	LRHS
'Taco' (15)	NRog WPhe
'Tarafa' (14)	SDeJ
tarda (15) $\mathbb{Y}^{H6}$	CAvo CBod CExl CRos EHyd EPfP ERCP GKev LAma LCro LOPS LRHS NBwr NRHS NRog SDeJ SPhx WIce WPhe WShi
- 'Kashka-Su' (15)	NRog
'Temple of Beauty' (5) $\mathbb{Y}^{H6}$	ERCP GKev LAma NRog SDeJ
tetraphylla (15)	NRog
'Texas Flame' (10)	GKev LAma NRog SDeJ
'Texas Gold' (10)	LAma NRog SDeJ
'The Edge' (2)	LRHS
'The First' (12)	EPfP GKev LAma NRog
'The Lizard' (9)	GKev SDir
'Thijs Boots' (3) **new**	ERCP
'Tinka' (15) $\mathbb{Y}^{H6}$	GKev LAma NRog
'Tiny Timo' (15)	ERCP LCro NRog
'Tom Pouce' (3)	LCro LOPS NRog WPhe
'Toplips' (11)	LAma SDeJ
'Topparrot' (10)	SDeJ
'Toronto' (14) $\mathbb{Y}^{H6}$	LAma NRog SDeJ
'Toronto Double' (2)	NRog SDeJ
'Toucan' (3)	LAma
'Toyota' (5)	SDeJ
'Très Chic' (6)	CAvo EPfP ETay GKev LAma LCro LOPS NRog SPer
'Tricolored Beauty' (8)	NRog
'Triumphator' (2)	WHlf
'Tropical Dream' (3)	LAma NRog
tschimganica (15)	NRog WCot
- red-flowered	GKev
- yellow-flowered	GKev
tubergeniana 'Keukenhof' (15)	NRog
turkestanica (15) $\mathbb{Y}^{H5}$	CAby CAvo CExl EHyd EPot ERCP GKev LAma LCro LRHS MBros NBwr NPer NRHS NRog SDeJ SPhx WHoo WShi
- 'Dshizak' (15)	NRog
'Turkish Delight' (14)	NPer
'Typhoon' (3)	NRog
'Uncle Tom' (11)	ERCP GKev LAma NRog SDeJ WHlf WPhe
§ ***undulatifolia*** (15)	LAma NRog WCot
- 'Clare Benedict' (15)	NRog
- 'Excelsa' (15)	NRog
'Unique de France'^{PBR} (3)	CAvo NRog
'United States' (14) $\mathbb{Y}^{H6}$	LAma NPer
urumiensis (15) $\mathbb{Y}^{H5}$	EPot ERCP GKev LAma NRog SDeJ SPhx
'Valentine' (3)	SDeJ
'Valery Gergiev' (7)	ERCP NRog SDeJ
'Van der Neer' (1)	NRog SDeJ
'Van Eijk'^{PBR} (4)	LCro WHlf
'Vanilla Cream' (14)	NRog SDeJ
'Vaya con Dios' (7)	LAma LHWs
'Verona' (2)	LRHS NRog SDeJ WPhe
'Véronique Sanson' (3)	ERCP LCro LOPS NRog SDeJ
'Victoria's Secret' (3)	ETay GKev LAma LCro LHWs SDir SPer
'Viking' (2)	LRHS WPhe
'Vincent van Gogh' (7) $\mathbb{Y}^{H6}$	LAma LHWs
violacea	see *T. humilis* Violacea Group
'Violet Beauty' (5)	GKev LCro LOPS SDeJ WPhe
'Violet Bird' (8)	LAma LCro LOPS SDeJ SDir
'Violet Pranaa' (11) **new**	LAma
'Virichic' (8)	ERCP GKev LCro LOPS MCot NRog WPhe
'Viridiflora' (8)	SVic
vvedenskyi (15)	EPot NRog
- 'Tangerine Beauty' (15) $\mathbb{Y}^{H6}$	NRog
'Wallflower' (5)	LAma NRog
'Warbler' (7)	NRog SDeJ
'Washington' (3)	LCro LOPS NRog
'Weber's Parrot' (10)	LCro MCot
'Wedding Gift' (11)	SDeJ
'Weisse Berliner' (3)	LAma LCro NRog
'West Point' (6)	CAby GKev LCro LOPS NRog SDeJ WPhe
'Whispering Dream' (3)	ETay LAma LHWs WPhe
'White Dream' (3)	CArg ETay LCro LOPS NRog SDeJ
'White Emperor'	see *T.* 'Purissima'
'White Liberstar' (3)	ERCP
'White Marvel' (3)	NRog

'White Mountain' (11) new LCro
'White Parrot' (10) CAvo ERCP GKev LAma LCro LOPS MCot NRog SDeJ
'White Prince' (1) GKev LAma LCro WHlf WPhe
'White Triumphator' (6) ♀H6 CArg CAvo ERCP GKev LAma LCro LOPS MCot NBir NRog SDeJ SDir WPhe
whittallii see *T. orphanidea* Whittallii Group
'Wildhof' (3) ♀H6 NRog
§ 'Willem van Oranje' (2) LRHS NRog SDeJ
'Willemsoord' (2) LAma NRog SDeJ
WILLIAM OF ORANGE see *T.* 'Willem van Oranje'
wilsoniana see *T. montana*
'Wisley' (5) ♀H6 GKev LCro LOPS WHlf
'World Expression' (5) ♀H6 NRog SDeJ
'World Friendship' (3) GKev LAma LHWs
'World Peace' PBR (4) LCro LOPS
'World's Favourite' (4) ♀H6 NRog
'Wow' (11) ERCP
'Yellow Flight' (3) LAma NRog SDeJ
'Yellow Pompenette' PBR (11) ♀H6 SDeJ
I 'Yellow Purissima' (13) ♀H6 CAby NRog SDir
'Yellow Spider' (11) WPhe
'Yellow Springgreen' (8) ERCP GKev LAma NRog SDeJ SDir
'Yellow Sun' (10) WPhe
'Yellow Wave' (4) NRog
'Yoko Parrot' (10) SDeJ
'Yokohama' (3) LAma NRog SDeJ
'Yonina' (6) CArg LCro LOPS NRog SDeJ
'Zampa' (14) ♀H6 NRog
'Zombie' (13) NRog
§ 'Zurel' (3) CArg ERCP GKev LAma SDir

tummelberry see *Rubus* 'Tummelberry'

Tunica see *Petrorhagia*

Tunilla (*Cactaceae*)

soehrensii new WJur

Tupistra (*Asparagaceae*)

aurantiaca GEdr GGro LEdu WPGP
- B&SWJ 2267 WCot WCru
- B&SWJ 2401 WCru
chinensis 'Eco China Ruffles' WCot
grandistigma WCot
- B&SWJ 11773 WCru
jinshanensis WCot
urotepala HWJ 562 WCru
wattii B&SWJ 8297 WCru

Turnera (*Passifloraceae*)

diffusa GPoy
var. ***aphrodisiaca***

turnip see AGM Vegetables Section

Turpinia (*Staphyleaceae*)

ternata CWJ 12360 WCru

Tussilago (*Asteraceae*)

farfara GPoy MHer WHer WSFF

Tweedia (*Apocynaceae*)

§ ***coerulea*** ♀H1c CBcs CCCN CDTJ CSpe MGil SChF SIvy SPad SPer SWvt WSFF

Typha (*Typhaceae*)

angustifolia CBen CPud CWat LLWG LPfP NPer SPlb
latifolia CBen CPud CWat LLWG NBir NMir NPer SVic WMAq XLum
- 'Variegata' (v) CWat LLWG LPfP MWts WMAq
§ ***laxmannii*** CBen CPud LLWG LPfP WPnP XLum
lugdunensis MWts
minima CBen CPud CWat EWat GQue LCro LLWG LPfP MWts NPer WHlf WMAq WPnP XLum
shuttleworthii CBen LLWG
stenophylla see *T. laxmannii*

Typhonium (*Araceae*)

giganteum SBrt WCot
horsfieldii MPie
roxburghii EBee WFar

U

ugli see *Citrus × aurantium* (Tangelo Group) 'Ugli'

Ugni ✿ (*Myrtaceae*)

candollei SVen WPGP
§ ***molinae*** Widely available
- PAB 1347 SBrt
- 'Big Burning Pink' LEdu
- 'Butterball' CBcs CBod CDoC CKel CTrC EBee EPfP LEdu LRHS MDon MHoo SPoG SWvt
- 'Flambeau' (v) CAgr CBcs CBod CDoC CEme CExl CKel CMac CSde CTrC EBee EHyd ELan EPfP EShb LEdu LRHS MAsh MGil NLar NRHS SEND SEle SIvy SPoG SRms SWvt WPav
- 'Frampton Feast' new WPGP
- KA'POW ('Yanpow') CBod CCCN CDoC CTrC LCro LRHS MHtn SBmr SEle SPad WPGP WTyc
- 'Miss Green' SBrt
- orange-leaved WJek
- 'Variegata' (v) LEdu WJek
- 'Villarica Strawberry' LEdu WPGP

Ulex (*Fabaceae*)

europaeus CBTr CBcs CCVT CHab CMac CPer CTri EHeP ELan ELon EPfP GMcL LBuc MGil MGos MMuc NBwr NWea SCob SEWo SPer WKor
§ - 'Flore Pleno' (d) ♀H6 CBcs CBod CCoa CDoC CEme CSBt CSde EHeP ELan ELon EPfP GEdr IArd MBlu NBPC NWea SCob SDix WFar WHer
- 'Irish Double' (d) NLar
- 'Plenus' see *U. europaeus* 'Flore Pleno'

Ulmus ✿ (*Ulmaceae*)

americana 'Princeton' SCob
× ***androssowii*** WPGP
bergmanniana WPGP
changii WPGP
chenmoui IArd IDee WPGP
'Clusius' LPar
'Columella' LPar WPGP
davidiana WPGP
- var. ***davidiana*** WPGP
- var. ***japonica*** WPGP
- - 'Prospector' WPGP
'Dodoens' LPar MBlu SCob
'Frontier' SGol WPGP

§ ***glabra***	CAco CPer IPap LPar MGos NRog NWea WTSh
- 'Camperdownii'	CBod CMac ELan SGsty
- 'Lutescens'	NOra WMat
harbinensis	WPGP
× ***hollandica*** 'Belgica' **new**	EHeP
§ - 'Dampieri Aurea' ♀H7	ELon LBuc LPar MAsh MBlu MRav NLar NOrn NRog NWea SPoG
- 'Jacqueline Hillier'	CMac EBee ELan GQue LMaj LPar LRHS MMuc NLar NRya SEND SGBe SGol WFar WLov
- 'Wredei'	see *U.* × *hollandica* 'Dampieri Aurea'
'Homestead'	WPGP
laevis	CLnd CPer WPGP
lamellosa	WPGP
'Lobel'	CCVT EHeP LPar SCob
LUTÈCE ('Nanguen')	CLnd MTrO NOra
× ***mesocarpa***	WPGP
minor	MGos NWea
- 'Dampieri Aurea'	see *U.* × *hollandica* 'Dampieri Aurea'
- var. ***suberosa***	CAco
montana	see *U. glabra*
parvifolia	CAco CMCN CMen EShb WPGP
- 'Geisha' (v)	ELan NLar
- 'Hallelujah'	WPGP
§ - 'Hokkaido'	EPot EWes NLar WAbe
- var. ***lanceolata***	WPGP
- 'Pygmaea'	see *U. parvifolia* 'Hokkaido'
- 'Sagei'	NLar
- 'Yatsubusa'	EPot MRav WPGP
procera	MGos WSFF
- 'Argenteovariegata' (v)	NLar
prunifolia	WPGP
pumila 'Beijing Gold'	ELan NLar
'Regal'	WPGP
'Sapporo Autumn Gold'	CCVT EHeP MRav
szechuanica	WPGP
uyematsui	SMad WPGP
VADA ('Wanoux' PBR)	CKel SGol
villosa	EBee WPGP

Umbellularia (*Lauraceae*)

californica	CMCN NLar

Umbilicus (*Crassulaceae*)

§ ***oppositifolius*** ♀H5	CAby CBod CElw CTri ECha EHyd ELan EPfP GAbr GEdr GKev GLog LRHS MRav NBid NBwr NRHS NSla SPlb SRms SRot WFar WHoo WKif WSHC WTor XLum
- 'Frosted Jade'	see *U. oppositifolius* 'Jim's Pride'
- 'Jane's Reverse' (v)	WCot
§ - 'Jim's Pride' (v)	CBor ECha EMor EWes GKev GPSL MHer MRav NBir NBwr NFav NHpl NPer NRya NWad SPlb SRms WFar WSHC
rupestris	SChr SPhx WHer WShi

Uncinia (*Cyperaceae*)

from Chile	EPPr
* ***cyparissias*** from Chile	NBir
egmontiana	CPla EBee EPfP LShi NWad
rubra	CChe CEnd CKel CRos CSBt EAJP EBee EBlo EHeP EHyd ELan EPfP GElm GMaP GMcL LRHS MDon MGos MRav NRHS NSti NWad SPad SPlb SPoG WChS WFar
§ - 'Belinda's Find' PBR	CBod CKno CPla EBee ELan EMor LLWG LRHS MACG MAsh MBNS MPri MSCN NLar SCoo SMad SPeP SPoG SRms WPnP XSte
- EVERFLAME	see *U. rubra* 'Belinda's Find'
uncinata	CBcs ECha EGrI SDix
* - ***rubra***	CBor CDoC CKno MAsh MBow SCob SRms SWvt

Uniola (*Poaceae*)

latifolia	see *Chasmanthium latifolium*

Urginea (*Asparagaceae*)

maritima	see *Charybdis maritima*

Urospermum (*Asteraceae*)

dalechampii	CCCN

Utricularia (*Lentibulariaceae*)

alpina	SHmp
bisquamata	SHmp
- 'Betty's Bay' ♀H2	CHew NWac
blancheti	NWac
calycifida	SHmp
dichotoma	CHew
geminiloba	CHew
lateriflora	CHew
livida ♀H2	CHew NWac SHmp
longifolia	SHmp
microcalyx	CHew
nephrophylla	CHew
parthenopipes	CHew
paulineae	CHew
praelonga	CHew SHmp
prehensilis	CHew
reniformis	CHew SHmp
sandersonii ♀H2	CHew NWac SHmp
tricolor	CHew SHmp
uniflora	CHew

Uvularia (*Colchicaceae*)

grandiflora ♀H7	Widely available
- gold-leaved	CMiW
- 'Lynda Windsor'	LEdu NHsp WSHC
- var. ***pallida***	CBor CMiW CRos CTtf EBee EBlo ECha EMor EPPr EPfP EPot GBin GEdr GKev ILea LBar LEdu LRHS MRav NCth NHsp NLar NRHS WCru WFar
- 'Susie Lewis'	WCru
grandiflora × ***perfoliata***	CMiW NBir
perfoliata	CExl EBee ECha EDAr EMor EPPr EPfP EPot ESwi GKev LEdu MRav NBir NChi NHpl SPlb WCru WFar
- tall	EPPr
sessilifolia	CBor CExl CMiW EHyd EMor EPfP GKev LEdu LRHS NHsp NLar NRHS WCru
- 'Cobblewood Gold' (v)	EPPr LEdu WCru WFar WSHC

V

Vaccaria see *Gypsophila*

hispanica	see *Gypsophila vaccaria*
segetalis	see *Gypsophila vaccaria*

Vaccinium ✿ (*Ericaceae*)

arctostaphylos	SWvt
'Berkeley' (F)	CAgr CCCN CEnd GKin MBlu SEdi SGsty SPre
BERRYBUX ('Zf08095' PBR) (BrazelBerry Series) (F) **new**	LCro
BLUE DESSERT (F)	LRHS

'Bluejay' (F)	CBod CRos EFPl EHyd ELan EPfP LRHS MAsh NBwr NLar NRHS NRog SCoo SEdi SPoG WLea
'Blueray' (F)	GKin NLar
'Brigitta' (F)	CEnd CTrh EDir EPom NRHS NRog SBdl SCoo SOrN SPoG SPre WLea
chaetothrix	WAbe WThu
'Chandler' (F)	CAgr CArg CDoC CEnd CMac CTrh EPom GKin LCro LRHS MTrO NBwr SEdi SKee SRHi SSFr SSha
consanguineum B&SWJ 10486	WCru
corybosum BLUE SUEDE ('Th682') (F)	CDoC CMac LCro LRHS NLar NRHS XSte
corymbosum (F)	CBcs MNHC SCoo SSta
- 'Ama' (F) **new**	NLar
- 'Aurora'^{PBR} (F)	CTrh
- 'Blauweiss-Goldtraube' (F)	CAgr CBod CSBt EDir ELan EPfP GKin LCro MAsh NLar NRog SCoo SOrN SPoG SVic WLea WTSh
- 'Blue Duke' (F)	LSRN
- 'Blue Pearl' (F)	CMac
- 'Blue Sapphire' (F)	LCro
- 'Bluecrop' (F)	Widely available
- 'Bluegold' (F)	CRos EFPl EHyd EPfP LCro LRHS NBwr NRHS SCoo SPoG
- 'Bluetta' (F)	CAgr CTri ELan SCoo SPoG
- 'Collins' (F)	SBdl
- 'Darrow' (F)	CAgr EDir LCro MTrO NRHS WMat
- 'Dixie' (F)	CBod CSBt NLar
- 'Duke' (F) 🏆^{H6}	CArg CBod CDoC CTrh EFPl ELan EPfP EPom LCro LOPS MCoo MGos NRog NWea SBmr SCoo SPre SRkn SSFr SSha
- 'Elliott' (F)	CDoC CMac LRHS LSRN SRHi XSte
- FLAMINGO ('Hoogi045') (F) **new**	LCro
- 'Grover' (F)	EDir SEdi
- 'Hardyblue' (F)	CAgr
- 'Heerma' (F)	EDir
- 'Hortblue Petite'^{PBR} (F)	CSBt SBdl SVic
- 'Huron'^{PBR} (F)	CTrh
- 'Jersey' (F)	CAgr CEnd CRos CSBt EDir EHyd EPfP LCro LRHS MAsh MGos NLar NRHS NRog SCoo SEdi SPer SPoG SVic
- 'Legacy' (F)	CTrh NRHS WHlf
- 'Liberty'^{PBR} (F)	CTrh EPfP MTrO SBdl
- 'Nelson' (F)	SCoo
- 'Nui' (F)	CEnd EPom LSRN MRav
- 'Patriot' (F)	Widely available
- 'Polaris' (F)	CEnd
- 'Rancocas' (F) **new**	EDir
- 'Reka' (F)	CAgr NPer
- 'Spartan' (F) 🏆^{H6}	CDoC CMac CTrh EPom LCro LRHS LSRN MGos SKee SRHi
- 'Stanley' (F)	CRos EHyd EPfP LRHS NRHS SPoG
- 'Toro' (F)	EDir SPre
- YELLOBERRY BLUE ('Andval1601') (F)	LCro
crassifolium subsp. ***sempervirens*** 'Well's Delight' (F)	EHyd LRHS MAsh
cylindraceum 🏆^{H4}	CBcs CEnd EBee NLar SSta
delavayi	GArf LRHS MAsh NLar SSta WAbe WThu
dunalianum var. ***caudatifolium*** B&SWJ 1716	WCru
- - NMWJ 14558	WCru
- var. ***megaphyllum*** HWJ 515	WCru
'Earliblue' (F)	CAgr CBod CSBt GKin LBuc NRHS NWea SPer SPoG WLea WMat
floribundum	CRos EHyd GArf GMcL LRHS MAsh
glaucoalbum 🏆^{H5}	CMac EBee EGrI EHyd LRHS MAsh MBlu MRav NRHS SPoG
'Goldtraube 71'	LPar MAsh NRog SEdi
griffithianum	SSta
'Herbert' (F)	CAgr CTrh EPom LBuc SEdi
macrocarpon (F)	CRos EHyd LRHS MAsh NRHS SPre SRms WJur WKor
- 'CN' (F)	NLar
- 'Early Black' (F)	EPom GKin IDee NRog SVic WTSh
- 'Hamilton'	EPot GArf WThu
- 'Howes' (F)	NRog
- 'Langlois' (F)	NLar
- 'McFarlin' (F)	NRog
- 'Olson's Honkers' (F)	CAgr
- 'Pilgrim' (F)	CAgr CMac CSBt EDir LCro LEdu LOPS MAsh NRog SBmr SPoG WMat
- 'Red Star' (F)	CTrh
- 'Stevens' (F)	CAgr NRog
moupinense	LRHS MAsh WThu
myrtillus	CAgr EPom GPoy GQue NLar SVic WKor
'Northcountry' (F)	CTrh
'Northland' (F)	CBod CSBt EDir EPfP EPom MAsh MRav MTrO NLar NRHS NRog SCoo SPoG WMat
nummularia	GRum NLar WAbe WThu
'Osorno' (F)	CTrh
ovatum (F)	CMac GKin WThu
- 'Pacific Spear' (F)	SVic
- 'Thundercloud' (F)	EHyd EPfP LRHS MAsh NRHS SSta
§ ***oxycoccos*** (F)	CAgr GPoy MCoo
'Ozarkblue' (F)	EPom LCro NLar NRHS SEdi
palustre	see *V. oxycoccos*
§ 'Pink Lemonade' (F)	CRos CWnw EBee EDir ELan EPfP EPom LAlb LCro LOPS LRHS MHtn MPri NLar NRHS NRog NTrD SBdl SBmr SEdi SPer SPoG SRHi SSFr WHlf
'Pink Sapphire'	see *V.* 'Pink Lemonade'
praestans	GArf
randaiense B&SWJ 14601	WCru
retusum	WThu
'Rubel' (F)	NRHS
sikkimense	GArf
'Spring Surprise'	WAbe WThu
'Sunshine Blue' (F)	CAgr CBod CEnd CTrh EHyd ELan EPom LBuc LRHS MTrO NLar SBmr SPoG SRHi SSFr
'Tophat' (F)	CCCN CSBt LEdu SPad
vitis-idaea	EPfP EWes GPoy MHoo SVic WKor
- 'Compactum'	EWes
- FIREBALLS ('Lirome'^{PBR}) (F)	CDoC LCro NRog
- 'Ida'	LBuc
- Koralle Group 🏆^{H5}	CAgr EPot GArf GKin GMcL NLar NRog NWad
- 'Leucocarpa'	NLar
- subsp. ***minus***	NLar NWad
- MISS CHERRY ('Meliro'^{PBR}) (F)	NLar NRog
- 'Red Candy'^{PBR}	LCro LOPS LRHS
- 'Red Pearl'	EPom MAsh NRog SBmr

Vachellia (*Fabaceae*)

§ ***karroo***	CDTJ SPlb

Valeriana (*Caprifoliaceae*)

'Alba'	see *Centranthus ruber* 'Albus'
alliariifolia	GQue NBro SPhx

- PAB 3001	LEdu WPGP
- var. ***tiliifolia*** **new**	LEdu WPGP
arizonica	EBou
'Coccinea'	see *Centranthus ruber*
dioica	LLWG
fauriei	GGro
hardwickii PAB 8999	LEdu
jatamansi	GGro GPoy SRms
- PAB 6846	LEdu WPGP
montana	CTtf ECha GGro LEdu MMuc NBro NRya SPhx SRms
officinalis	Widely available
- 'Chiri Fu' (v)	WCot
- subsp. ***sambucifolia***	EPPr MNrw MSpe SHar
phu	EGrI
- 'Aurea'	CBod CCBP CDor CHby CMac EBee ECha EGrI EHyd EPfP GKin GQue LBar LRHS MBriF MPie MRav NBid NBir NBro NLar NSti SPer SPoG SRms WCAu
pyrenaica	CKel EBee ECha EPPr GGro LEdu LRHS MBriF MMuc MNrw MPie SDix SEND SHar SPhx SPtp WCot WHrl WPGP
wallrothii	WCot

Valerianella (*Caprifoliaceae*)

§ ***locusta***	CBod GPoy SVic
- 'Medaillon' 🏆H3	LCro LOPS
olitoria	see *V. locusta*

Vallea (*Elaeocarpaceae*)

stipularis	CTsd IArd IDee SBrt

Vallisneria (*Hydrocharitaceae*)

gigantea	LPfP
spiralis	LLWG

Vallota see *Cyrtanthus*

Vancouveria (*Berberidaceae*)

chrysantha	CExl ECha EPPr EPfP GEdr GLog NRya WFar WPGP
hexandra	CExl CMac EBee ECha EGrI EHed EMor EPPr EPfP GEdr GKev GLog ILea LEdu LRHS NBir NSti SPlb WCru WPGP
planipetala	GEdr WCru

Vania see *Thlaspi*

Vasconcellea (*Caricaceae*)

§ ***pubescens***	CDTJ EAri SPlb

Vatricania (*Cactaceae*)

§ ***guentheri*** **new**	NPlm

Vellozia (*Velloziaceae*)

elegans	see *Talbotia elegans*

Veltheimia ✿ (*Asparagaceae*)

§ ***bracteata*** 🏆H2	CPla EPri GKev LAma NRog SDir SGro SRms
- cream-flowered	NRog
- deep pink-flowered	NRog
- 'Lemon Flame'	GKev LAma NRog SDir
- 'Rosalba'	LAma NRog
- yellow-flowered	NRog
§ ***capensis*** 🏆H2	LAma NRog
viridifolia misapplied	see *V. capensis*
viridifolia Jacq.	see *V. bracteata*

× *Venidioarctotis* see *Arctotis*

Venidium see *Arctotis*

Veratrum (*Melanthiaceae*)

album 🏆H7	ECha EMor GEdr GJos GKev GPoy ILea IPot MNrw MRav NBid WCot WPGP WSHC
- PAB 537	LEdu
- 'Auvergne White'	LEdu MNrw
- var. ***flavum***	LPla MNrw WCot WCru
- - 'Primrose Warburg'	GEdr
- subsp. ***lobelianum***	LEdu WCot
- 'Lorna's Green' 🏆H7	MNrw WCot
californicum 🏆H3	CBct EBee ECha EMor LEdu LPla MNrw NBid WCru WPGP WSHC WWFP
formosanum	EBee GEdr MNrw WCot WSHC
- B&SWJ 1575	WCru
- RWJ 9806	WCru
grandiflorum B&SWJ 4416	WCru
maackii	EBee ECha EMor GArf MNrw SMad
- green-flowered	MNrw
- var. ***japonicum***	MNrw
- var. ***maackii***	MNrw
nigrum 🏆H6	CBct CBor CBro EBee ECha EMor EWoo GEdr GKev GMaP ILea LEdu MMrt MNrw MRav NBid NBir NChi SEdd SMad SPlb WCot WCru WMal WSHC
- B&SWJ 4450 from South Korea	WCru
schindleri	GEdr MNrw
- B&SWJ 4068	ESwi WCru
viride	EBee EMor EWes LEdu MNrw NBid WCot WCru

Verbascum (*Scrophulariaceae*)

'Arctic Summer'	see *V. bombyciferum* 'Polarsommer'
arcturus	SVen
'Argentina'	WHer
blattaria	NBir NDov SBut WHer
- f. ***albiflorum***	CSpe LEdu LRHS NDov NGBl SPhx SPlb WHer
- 'White Blush'	LBar LShi WWke
'Blue Lagoon'	CWGN SCob
§ ***bombyciferum***	ECha ELan GMaP LRHS NGBl SCob SPhx SRms
* - 'Arctic Snow'	SPoG
§ - 'Polarsommer'	CSpe LRHS NBir SPer
- 'Silver Lining'	NPer
'Broussa'	see *V. bombyciferum*
'Caribbean Crush'	CRos ECtt EHyd ELan LBar LRHS MBNS SCgs SGBe SPoG WSpi
chaixii	ECha EPPr GAbr MArl MMrt NBir SDix WFar
- 'Album'	Widely available
- 'Sixteen Candles'	NLar WFar
- 'Wedding Candles'	ELan EPfP GElm LSun NGdn SBls SCgs SPtp WFar
'Cherry Helen'PBR	GMcL LCro LOPS LRHS NLar SCob
'Christo's Yellow Lightning' 🏆H6	EBee ECha ECtt GBin LBar LRHS MAvo SDix SPoG WCot
'Clementine'	CBcs EPPr LCro LOPS SCob WFar WHlf WSpi
'Coneyhill Yellow'	EPPr
(Cotswold Group) 'Cotswold Beauty'	CBod ECtt EHyd EPfP EWoo GMaP LRHS LSto MRav NGdn NRHS SCob SHar SPer WCAu WHoo WWke
- 'Cotswold Queen'	CBod ECtt EHyd EPPr EPfP GMaP LCro LOPS LRHS MMrt MRav NRHS SCob SCoo SHar SPer SWvt WCAu WHoo WSpi

	- 'Gainsborough' ♀H6	CBod CDor ECha ECtt EPfP EWTr EWoo GDam GMaP GMcL LCro LOPS LRHS MArl MRav NLar NRHS SCgs SCob SGbt SPer SPoG SWvt WCAu WSpi
	- 'Mont Blanc'	LRHS NRHS
	- 'Pink Domino' ♀H6	CBcs CBod ECtt EHyd EPPr EPfP EWhm GMaP LCro LOPS LRHS LSto MCot MHer MHol MRav NRHS SCgs SCob SPer SWvt WSpi
	- 'Royal Highland'	CBod EBee ECtt EHyd EPfP LRHS MBNS NRHS SWvt
	- 'White Domino'	SPer WSpi
	'Cotswold King'	see *V. creticum*
§	***creticum***	CSpe CTtf SCob WCot
	'Dark Eyes'[PBR]	CWGN ECtt GMcL LRHS NCou NHpl NLar SCoo SGBe WTyc
	dumulosum ♀H4	WAbe
	epixanthinum ♀H5	GJos
	faurei **new**	WCot
	'Firedance'	CBcs ECtt EHyd EPfP GBin LRHS MHol NGBl NRHS SHar SMrm WCAu
	'Golden Wings' ♀H4	EDAr WAbe
	'Helen Johnson'	CBcs CWCL ECtt EHyd GMcL LRHS MGos MRav NLar NRHS SCob SCoo SGbt SWvt WSpi
	'Honey Dijon'	MBros SPad SRHi
	× ***hybridum*** 'Banana Custard'	EHyd EPfP SCgs WSpi
	- 'Copper Rose'	EHyd EPfP
	- 'Snow Maiden'	CTri EPfP LShi SBut SCgs
	- 'Wega'	GJos NLar
	'Jackie'	ECtt EHyd GMcL LRHS SGBe
	'Jackie in Pink'	EPfP LRHS
	'Jackie in Spots'	LRHS
	'Jackie in Yellow'[PBR]	EPfP LRHS WHlf
	'Jester'	ECtt GMcL MBNS SCob SPoG WSpi
	'June Johnson'	ECtt EHyd LRHS NRHS SMrm
	'Kynaston'	CBcs ECtt EHyd EPfP LRHS NRHS SGbt
	'Lavender Lass'	GMcL LBar LRHS NLar WSpi
	'Letitia' ♀H4	EDAr EHyd EPot LRHS NRHS SWvt WAbe
	longifolium var. ***pannosum***	see *V. olympicum*
	lychnitis	GJos NGBl SPhx
	'Megan's Mauve'	WSpi
	'Merlin'[PBR]	CBWd ECtt EHyd EPfP LRHS NRHS SGbt
	nigrum	CHab GJos LShi NGdn NLar NMir SCob SPhx
	- var. ***album***	GJos NGdn NLar WSpi
§	***olympicum***	CBcs CBee EHyd ELan EPfP GJos LRHS MArl NGBl NRHS SCob SDix SRms WCAu WCot XSen
	- f. ***album***	EAJP
	'Petra'	LRHS
	phlomoides	SPhx
	phoeniceum	CBcs CSBt ELan EPPr GJos NBro SCob SPlb SPoG WFar WSpi
*	- 'Album'	CSpe GJos SCob
	- 'Antique Rose'	MACG
	- 'Flush of White'	CDor EAJP EPfP GElm GMcL LBar LRHS MACG NGdn NLar SCob WFar WJam
	- 'Rosetta'	EPfP LBar LSto MCot WFar
	- 'Violetta'	CAby CGBo CSpe CTsd EAJP EPPr EPfP GElm GQue LBar LCro LOPS LRHS LShi LSto MCot MHol NGdn SBls SGbt SPer SPhx WCAu WCFE WCav WFar
	'Pink Kisses'	CRos EHyd LRHS NRHS SGBe
	'Pink Petticoats'	LBar LRHS MBNS NLar
	'Plum Smokey'[PBR]	CBod ECtt LRHS NEoE
	'Primrose Path'	EPfP GMcL LBar NLar SCoo SGBe
	pyramidatum	EBee SPhx
	'Raspberry Ripple'	MRav
	roripifolium	CSpe GJos SPhx
	'Rosie'	ECtt NHpl
	'Southern Charm'	EPfP GJos MACG NQui SCgs SCob WHil
	'Spica'	LBar
	'Sugar Plum'[PBR]	ECtt GMcL LCro LRHS SGBe WCAu WHil
	'Temptress Purple'	SCoo
	thapsus	CBod CCBP CHab EBou ENfk GJos GPoy GQue MArl MBow MHoo MNHC NBir NMir SPhx SRms
	'Tropic Sun' ♀H5	SCgs WHoo
	'Ventnor Giant'	SVen

Verbena (*Verbenaceae*)

	(G)	see *Glandularia*
	Aztec Series	see *Glandularia* Aztec Series
	× ***baileyana*** purple-leaved **new**	WMal
§	***bonariensis*** ♀H4	Widely available
	- 'Little One'	ECha EPPr GBin MAsh SHar
	- 'Lollipop'[PBR]	Widely available
	brasiliensis misapplied	see *V. bonariensis*
	chamaedrifolia	see *Glandularia peruviana*
	hastata	CAby CBod CRos CSpe EBee ECtt EGrl EHyd EPfP EWTr LEdu LRHS LSto LWaG MArl MNrw NLar NRHS NSti SCob SPhx SPlb SRms SWvt WCav WFar WPnP XLum
*	- 'Alba'	CAby CSpe EPfP GElm GKev LDai LRHS MBel NGrs NLar NSti SCob WFar XLum
	- 'Blue Spires'	CBod CTtf EPPr EPfP GKev IPot LRHS MDon NGrs
	- f. ***rosea***	CAby CElw CSpe CTtf EGrl EHyd ELan EPPr EPfP LCro LEdu LOPS MNrw MRav NBir NDov NSti SBls SCob SDix SPer SPhx WCAu WFar WMal WOut WSHC WTyc XLum
	- - 'Pink Spires'	CBWd CBod CKel EPfP IPot LSto MNHC SPeP
	- 'White Spires'	EPfP GQue LSto SBls
	lasiostachys	EBee
	macdougalii	CPla
	- 'Lavender Spires'	ECha EPPr GBin IPot LRHS LSto NDov SHar SHor SPhx SRms WMal WTre
	officinalis	CBod CCBP EBee ENfk GJos GPoy MHer MNHC NAts SRms WHer WSFF
	- var. ***grandiflora*** 'Bampton'	Widely available
	Quartz Series	see *Glandularia* Quartz Series
§	***rigida*** ♀H3	Widely available
	- f. ***lilacina***	LCro
	- - 'Lilac Haze'	CMac
	- - 'Polaris'	EBee ECha EHyd ELan ELon EPfP EShb LRHS LSRN MAsh MSCN NDov NRHS SCob SPer WMal
	- 'Santos'	LBar LCro WHlf WWke
	scabridoglandulosa	see *Junellia succulentifolia*
	serpyllifolia	see *Junellia micrantha*
	stricta	EBee EPPr LBar LRHS NLar SPhx
	- white-flowered **new**	EPPr
	'Triffids Purple Haze' **new**	CTtf
	venosa	see *V. rigida*

Verbesina (*Asteraceae*)

alternifolia	CPla EBee SDix
- 'Goldstrahl'	EPPr WFar

Vernicia (*Euphorbiaceae*)

fordii	SPlb

Vernonia (*Asteraceae*)

angustifolia* × *missurica	SHar WCot
§ ***arkansana***	CBod EBee ECha ECtt EGrI EHyd ESwi EWes LEdu LPla LRHS NLar SDix WFar
- 'Alba'	EBee ECtt ESwi
- 'Betty Blindeman'	MNrw
- 'Mammuth' ♀H7	CAby CKno EBee ECha ECtt ELon EShb EWes EWoo ILea IPot LEdu LRHS MBel MHol MNrw SDix SEdd SHor SMad SPeP SPhx SPoG WCot WHil WTor
baldwinii	EBee ESwi LRHS SPhx
crinita	see *V. arkansana*
fasciculata	EWes LRHS MHol MRav NLar SMHy SMrm SPhx WCot
gigantea	EWes MHer MMuc MNrw NLar SMad
glauca	WCot
lettermannii	CSpe SMHy SPhx
- 'Iron Butterfly'	EBee LEdu SMad WPGP
missurica	ESwi LEdu LRHS SPhx
noveboracensis	EBee EWhm GElm ILea NLar SBls SBut SMad WCAu XLum
- 'Albiflora'	EPPr EWes
- 'White Lightning'	EBee ECha EPPr ILea SDix WHil

Veronica (*Plantaginaceae*)

allionii	GKev
aphylla	GKev
armena	EWes MHer SGro WAbe XSen
(Atomic Ray Series) 'Atomic Hot Pink Ray'	SCob WFar
- 'Atomic Pink-White Ray'	SCob
- 'Atomic Red Ray'	NGBl SCob
- 'Atomic Silvery Pink Ray'	NLar
- 'Atomic Sky Ray'PBR	NLar SCob
austriaca dark blue-flowered	NChi
- var. ***dubia***	see *V. prostrata*
- 'Ionian Skies'	EBou ECtt GBin LEdu MACG NBwr NWad SPer WAbe WIce WKif
§ - subsp. ***teucrium***	CWal EBee MHol SRms
- - 'Crater Lake Blue' ♀H6	CDor CTri EBee ECha ECtt EHyd ELan EPfP EWoo GElm LRHS MArl MAvo MBel MHol MRav NChi NCth SPhx SPlb SRms SWvt WCAu WChS WCot WFar WGwG WKif
- - 'Kapitän'	ECtt EHyd LRHS NGdn NRHS WFar
- - 'Knallblau'	EAJP MNrw NLar WFar
- - 'Royal Blue' ♀H6	CAby CCBP CRos EBee EHyd EPfP GBee GMaP LRHS MAsh MHol NRHS NSti SRms WFar WKif XLum XSen
'Baby Blue'PBR	EPfP
'Baby Doll'PBR	SCob SPoG
beccabunga	CBen CHab CPud CWat EWat GPoy LLWG LPfP MWts NPer SPhx WMAq WSFF WSpi
'Bergen's Blue'	NLar SHar
BLUE BOUQUET	see *V. longifolia* 'Blaubündel'
'Blue Indigo'	MNrw NGdn
'Blue Spire'	WSpi
bombycina	WAbe
- subsp. ***bolkardaghensis***	WAbe
bonarota	see *Paederota bonarota*
caespitosa subsp. ***caespitosa***	WAbe
candida	see *V. spicata* subsp. *incana*
× ***cantiana*** 'Kentish Pink'	EBee WCFE WFar XLum
chamaedrys	NMir XLum
CHRISTY ('Henslerone'PBR)	ECtt EPfP MHol
cinerea ♀H5	SBrt WSHC XSen
dabneyi	SBut
DARK BLUE MOODY BLUES ('Novaverblu')	CBod ELan EPfP MDon WHil
'Dark Martje'	NLar
'Darwin's Blue'	NLar
'Ellen Mae'	ECtt EGrI EPPr EWes MNrw WCAu WCot
'Eveline'PBR	ECtt EPfP NHpl NLar SPer
exaltata (d)	NChi WSpi
'Fairytale'PBR	LRHS LSou NGdn
'Fantasy'	WGoo
filiformis	XLum
formosa	see *Parahebe formosa*
§ ***fruticans***	EDAr GJos
gentianoides	Widely available
- 'Alba'	LEdu
- 'Barbara Sherwood' ♀H7	CRos EBlo EHyd EPfP EWTr LRHS NGdn NRHS WBrk WFar
- 'Blue Bittersweet' **new**	NLar
- 'Blue Streak'	XLum
- 'Little Blues'	EAJP ECha GKev LBar LSun
- 'Maihimmel'	WCAu
- 'Mountain Breeze'	EHyd EPfP LBuc LRHS NRHS SCoo SPoG WFar
- 'Nana'	NBro NLar
- 'Pallida'	EWoo GKev MMuc MRav SCob SPlb XLum
- 'Robusta'	CBod ECha EHyd EPPr GMaP LBar LRHS MAvo NGdn WFar
- 'Tissington White'	CBod CChe CRos CTtf EBee EHyd ELan EPfP GMaP LRHS MCot MHol MPie NBPC NBir NBro NGdn NLar NRHS NWad SCoo SHar SMrm SPoG SRms WBrk WCAu WFar WWke
- 'Variegata' (v)	CBod EBee ECha EHyd ELan EPfP GMaP LBar LRHS MRav NBir NWad SPer WGwG
'Giles van Hees'	SEdd
grandis	EBee LShi MMuc NLar SEND WFar XLum
'Hermannshof' **new**	SAko
incana	see *V. spicata* subsp. *incana*
'Ink'	MAvo
INSPIRE BLUE ('Yabblu'PBR)	CRos LBuc LRHS MPnt NRHS WHil WJam
INSPIRE PINK ('Yabpin'PBR)	CRos EHyd LBuc LRHS MPnt NBir NRHS WHil
kellereri	see *V. spicata*
kiusiana	EBee EBlo ECtt NLar NWad
* - subsp. ***japonica***	LRHS
liwanensis	EPot MNrw XSen
longifolia	CBee CMac CSBt ECha EGrI MBel MSpe NSti WCAu XLum
- 'Alba'	ELan MArl MMuc XLum
- 'Antarctica'	EBee
- 'Blaubart'	XLum
§ - 'Blaubündel'	EHyd ELan NGdn NRHS
- 'Blauer Sommer'	EHyd EPfP LRHS LSou NGdn
§ - 'Blauriesin'	ELan EPfP GMaP MACG MCot NLar SAko SPeP SPer SRms WSpi
- BLUE GIANTESS	see *V. longifolia* 'Blauriesin'
- 'Blue John'	ECtt MPie NDov NLar
- blue-flowered	SBls
- 'Candied Candle'	EBee
- 'Charlotte'PBR (v)	CDor CWGN EBee ECha ECtt EMor EWTr GElm GMaP LBar LCro LOPS

	MBel MHol MSCN NGBl NLar NSti SEdd SHar SPer SPoG WCAu WCot WHlf WTyc
- 'Charming Pink'	CDor LRHS MAvo SAko
- 'Christa'PBR	ECtt LBar
- 'Fascination'	ECtt MSCN NEoE NGdn
- 'Foerster's Blue'	see *V. longifolia* 'Blauriesin'
- 'Lila Karina'	GJos SHor
- 'Lilac Fantasy'	MAvo MRav
- 'Marietta'PBR	CCBP CDor CRos CSpe ECtt EHyd EWTr EWoo GElm LCro LOPS LRHS MAvo MHol NDov NLar NRHS NSti SEdd SPer SPoG SRms WCot WHoo WPnP WTyc
- 'Melanie White'	EWoo MBel WPnP
- 'Pacific Ocean'PBR	NLar
- 'Pink Eveline'PBR	EBee ECtt ELan EPfP LRHS MBros MHol NDov NGdn
- pink-flowered	CMac SBls
- 'Schneeriesin'	EBee ECha EHyd EPfP GBin GMaP LRHS MAvo MRav NBir NLar NRHS SAko WCAu
- (Vernique Series) VERNIQUE BLUE **new**	LBar
- - VERNIQUE WHITE **new**	LBar SIvy
lyallii	see *Parahebe lyallii*
'Martje'	SMrm XLum
MAUVE MOODY BLUES ('Novavermau') (Moody Blues Series)	ELan LRHS WHil
× ***media*** FIRST CHOICE ('Allchoice'PBR)	LBar LSou NLar
- FIRST GLORY ('Alllord'PBR)	CPla ELan LRHS MAsh NRHS WHil
- FIRST KISS ('Allkiss'PBR)	ELan NLar
- FIRST LADY ('Alllady'PBR)	CBod ECtt ELan EPfP LRHS MAsh NFav NLar NRHS WTor
- FIRST LOVE ('Alllove'PBR)	ECtt EHyd ELan EPfP LRHS MPri NFav NGdn NLar NRHS SCob SRms WHil
- FIRST MATCH ('Allvglove'PBR)	EPfP LBar NLar
- FIRST MEMORY ('Allv1461'PBR)	ELan EPfP LBar NLar WTor
montana 'Corinne Tremaine' (v)	SRms
officinalis	GJos XLum
oltensis	EPot SPlb WAbe
orchidea	see *V. spicata* subsp. *orchidea*
orientalis subsp. ***orientalis***	EPot
ornata	SEdd
'Pacific Ocean'	ECtt NLar
pectinata	ECtt
peduncularis 'Oxford Blue'	see *V. umbrosa* 'Georgia Blue'
perfoliata	see *Parahebe perfoliata*
petraea 'Madame Mercier'	EBou SRot XLum
'Pink Damask'	ECtt ELan ELon EPfP GMaP MACG MCot MRav MSpe NDov NGdn NLar SCob SRms WHoo
'Pink Harmony'	EPfP NGBl
PINK MOODY BLUES ('Novaverpin') (Moody Blues Series)	ELan EPfP WHil WHlf
(Plumosa Series) PLUMOSA AMETHYST PLUME	ECtt WFar
- PLUMOSA BLUE PLUME	MHol
- PLUMOSA LAVENDER PLUME	CWGN
§ ***prostrata*** ♀H5	CBod CSpe CTri ECtt EPfP GEdr GJos GKev MAsh NHol SLee SRms WHoo WIce
- 'Aztec Gold'PBR	CMac
§ - 'Blauspiegel'	SRot
- BLUE MIRROR	see *V. prostrata* 'Blauspiegel'
- 'Blue Sheen'	ECtt EHyd LRHS NBir NRHS
- GOLDWELL ('Verbrig') (v)	EBee ECtt LBar MHer WFar
- 'Lavender Mist'	EHyd LRHS NRHS
- 'Lilac Time'	CRos EBou ECtt EHyd EPot GKev LBar LRHS MACG NBir NHol NRHS SLee SRms WAbe WFar WTor
- 'Loddon Blue'	SRms WCot
- 'Minor'	NSla
- 'Mrs Holt'	CRos EBou ECtt EHyd LRHS MHer NBir NLar NRHS NWad SRms WAbe WJam
- 'Nana'	EBou ECtt EPot EWes NBwr NSla
- 'Nestor'	CTri SRms XLum
- 'Rhapsody in Blue'	CRos EHyd LRHS NRHS SRms
- 'Rosea'	SRot
- 'Spode Blue' ♀H5	CMac CRos CTri ECtt EHyd GKev GQue LBar LRHS MHer NRHS SLee SPoG SRms
- 'Trehane'	CPla EBou ECtt EHyd EPfP LBar LRHS LShi MACG MAsh MHer NBwr NRHS NRya NWad SPlb SPoG SRms SRot WFar WIce
'Purpleicious Harmony'PBR	CBod EBee LRHS MACG MBel SCob WHil
repens	NEoE SPlb WWke
'Rosalinde'	NGdn
'Royal Pink'	MRav NLar
rupestris	see *V. prostrata*
saturejoides	SRms
saxatilis	see *V. fruticans*
'Shirley Blue' ♀H6	EGrI ELan EPfP EWTr ILea LCro LOPS LSRN MHer MHol MMuc SHar SPhx SRGP SRms WCAu WCFE WSpi
SKY BLUE MOODY BLUES ('Novaversky') (Moody Blues Series)	WHil WWke
§ ***spicata***	EBee EGrI EHyd ELan GJos LBuc LRHS LSun MBow MRav NRHS SCob SRms WBrk WCAu WFar WHlf WJam WShi XLum
- 'Alba'	CBcs EPfP GJos LRHS MRav NLar SCob WFar XLum
- 'Barcarolle'	SRkn
§ - 'Blaufuchs'	NBwr
- 'Blue Candles'	GElm
- BLUE FOX	see *V. spicata* 'Blaufuchs'
§ - 'Erika'	ECtt NBir NGdn
§ - 'Glory'PBR	CBcs CDor CWGN EHyd ELan GMcL LBar LCro LRHS LSou MMrt NLar NRHS SCob SCoo SMrm SPer SPoG SRHi
- 'Heidekind'	EBee EBou ECha ELan EPot GKev GMaP NBir NGdn SAng SRms SRot WCAu WCav WHlf WHoo WIce XLum
- subsp. ***hybrida***	WHer
I - - 'Elaine's Form'	WCot
§ - 'Icicle'	SCob WCAu
§ - subsp. ***incana*** ♀H4	EBou EPPr EPfP GMcL MMuc SPlb SRkn SRms
- - 'Nana'	NBir SRms
- - 'Silver Carpet'	EHyd LRHS SPer WGwG WSpi
- 'Nana Blauteppich'	EHyd NLar
§ - subsp. ***orchidea***	SRms
- 'Pink Goblin'	EHyd ELan
- 'Pink Marshmallow'	MAsh NLar
- 'Pink Panther'PBR	WCot
- 'Pink Passion'	SCoo
- RED FOX	see *V. spicata* 'Rotfuchs'
- 'Rocket Power Blue'	LRHS

- 'Rocket Power Pink'	LRHS
- 'Romiley Purple'	EBee SPer WSpi
- 'Rosalind'	NLar
- ***rosea***	see *V. spicata* 'Erika'
§ - 'Rotfuchs'	CBcs CGBo CRos ECtt EHyd ELan ELon EPfP GJos GMcL LCro LOPS LRHS MACG MBow MHer MRav NBid NBir NGdn SAng SCob SPer SPoG SRms WCAu WCFE WWke
- 'Royal Candles'	see *V. spicata* 'Glory'
- 'Sightseeing'	GJos NBir SRms
- SNOW CANDLES ('Joca128'PBR)	LBar
- subsp. ***spicata*** 'Nana'	XSen
- 'Total Eclipse'PBR	ELan
- 'Twilight'PBR	ECtt SCob
- 'Ulster Blue Dwarf'	CKel CRos EBee EHyd EPfP EShb GMaP LRHS MACG MTin NGdn NRHS SAng SCob SCoo SMrm SPeP SPoG WCAu XLum
- VERSPI ('Bubblegum Candles'PBR)	SPad SRHi WNPC
- YOUNIQUE BABY RED ('Versbabyred')	EPfP
- YOUNIQUE BABY WHITE ('Versbabywhite')	EPfP MBNS
stelleri	see *V. wormskjoldii*
'Summer Breeze'	NBro
'Sunny Border Blue'	EBee NLar
surculosa	XSen
teucrium	see *V. austriaca* subsp. *teucrium*
'Tidal Pool' **new**	LBar
§ ***umbrosa*** 'Georgia Blue' ♀H5	Widely available
urticifolia	SBrt
virginica	see *Veronicastrum virginicum*
'White Icicle'	see *V. spicata* 'Icicle'
WHITE MOODY BLUES ('Novaverwhi') (Moody Blues Series)	CBod EPfP WHil
whitleyi	MMuc
§ ***wormskjoldii***	EBou GKev MBrN SLee SRms

Veronicastrum ✿ (*Plantaginaceae*)

'Adoration'	CBWd CBod CSpe EBee ECtt ELon EMor EPPr EWhm GElm IPot LBar LCro LOPS LRHS LSun MACG NDov NLar SMHy SMad SPhx SRkn WCot WFar WHlf WSpi WWke
axillare	GGro
brunonianum	WSHC
japonicum var. ***australe*** B&SWJ 11009	WCru
latifolium	WCot
- BWJ 8158	EPPr ESwi WCot WCru
'Red Arrows'	Widely available
sibiricum	CBar CKel CRos EBee ECha EHyd EPfP EShb LRHS LShi MHoo MMuc NRHS SBut SEND SHar SRms WPnP WSpi XLum
- BWJ 6352	WCru WFar
- 'Kobaltkaars'	ECha LPla SMHy
- var. ***yezoense***	ECha WFar
- - RBS 0290	EPPr WFar
villosulum	NBro XLum
§ ***virginicum***	CKno CTri EBee ECtt EPfP GPoy LRHS LSto MHoo NBir NLar SBut SRms WChS WFar WJam WSpi XLum
- 'Album' ♀H7	Widely available
- 'Apollo'	CBWd CBod CWCL EBee ECtt EHyd ELon EPPr EPfP GAbr GMaP GQue LBar LEdu LRHS MHol NBir NBro NGBl NLar NRHS NSti SCob SMHy SPhx SWvt WBor WFar WPGP WSpi
- 'Challenger'PBR	CBor NDov NLar WSpi
- 'Cupid'	CBod CDor CWCL EBee ECtt ELon EMor EPfP EWTr EWes GBin GElm GMaP LEdu LRHS MACG MNrw NDov NGdn NLar SHar STPC WFar WSpi
- 'Diane'	CBWd CDor CKno EAJP EBee ECha ECtt ELon EMor EPPr EPfP EWhm GElm GMaP ILea IPot LBar LEdu LRHS MAvo MCot NDov NLar SCob SHar SPhx SWvt WCAu WHlf WSpi
- 'Du Jardin'	LEdu LPla
- 'Erica'	Widely available
- 'Fascination'	Widely available
- var. ***incarnatum***	see *V. virginicum* f. *roseum*
- 'Klein Erica'	MACG
- 'Lavendelturm' ♀H7	Widely available
- 'Pointed Finger'	GMaP LEdu LRHS NLar SMrm SPhx
§ - f. ***roseum***	CWnw ECha ELan ELon EMor EPPr GMaP GQue LRHS LShi MACG MHoo MRav NBro NDov SGbt SMHy SPhx SWvt WBor WChS WHrl WKif WSpi XLum
- - 'Pink Glow'	Widely available
- 'Spring Dew'	EBee EWoo LRHS MNrw NBid NEoE NGBl NLar SPhx WCAu WHlf WSpi
- 'Temptation'	CBWd EPPr GMaP ILea IPot LBar LEdu LPla LRHS MRav NBro NEoE NLar SHor SPhx WPGP

Vesalea (*Caprifoliaceae*)

§ ***floribunda*** ♀H4	CBcs CBod CExl CKel CMac CSde EBee ECre EGrl EHed EHyd ELan EPfP LCro LRHS MAsh MGil MGos MRav NLar SBrt SGBe SGbt SPer SPoG SRms SSha WCot

Vestia (*Solanaceae*)

§ ***foetida***	CBcs CCCN CExl CMac CPla CTsd EHyd LRHS MGil NSti SBrt SEND WHil WPav
lycioides	see *V. foetida*

Viburnum ✿ (*Adoxaceae*)

NJM 11.008	WPGP
alnifolium	see *V. lantanoides*
atrocyaneum	CExl EBee NWad SBrt WFar
- B&SWJ 7272	EPfP WCru
- HIRD 113	WPGP
betulifolium	CBcs CExl CMCN CSpe EBee EGrl ELan EPfP EWes GKev GKin SAko WPGP
- 'Hohuanshan'	SSta WCru
× ***bodnantense***	CTri EBee WFar
- 'Charles Lamont' ♀H6	Widely available
- 'Dawn' ♀H6	Widely available
- 'Deben' ♀H6	EGrl EPfP NLar SCob SPer
brachyandrum B&SWJ 5784	WCru
bracteatum	NLar
buddlejifolium	CMac EBee EBtc EPfP LRHS MMuc WCru
× ***burkwoodii***	Widely available
- 'Anne Russell'	Widely available
- 'Chenaultii'	MRav
- 'Compact Beauty'	WLov WSpi
- 'Conoy'	ELon WHtc WLov
- 'Fulbrook'	EHyd EPfP LEdu LRHS MAsh MRav SSta

- 'Mohawk' ♀H6	CDoC CEnd CRos EHed EHyd ELon EPfP LRHS MAsh MGos MRav NLar NOrn NRHS SCoo SWvt WCFE WLov WSpi
- 'Park Farm Hybrid' ♀H6	CDoC CExl CKel CMac CRos CTri EBee EGrI ELan ELon EPfP LEdu LRHS MAsh MGos MRav NHol NLar SPer SPoG SRms SSta SWvt WHtc WKif WSpi
calvum	CExl
aff. ***calvum*** WWJ 12012	EBee WCru
× ***carlcephalum*** ♀H6	Widely available
- 'Cayuga' ♀H5	LPar MAsh WLov WSpi
carlesii	CBcs CBod CBrac CCVT CDoC CMac CSpe EGrI ELon EPfP EWTr GKin GMcL GQue LSRN LSou MBlu MDon MGos MRav MSwo SCob SGol SPer SRHi SRms SavN WFar WJur
- B&SWJ 8838	WCru
- 'Aurora' ♀H6	Widely available
- 'Charis'	WKif WPGP
- 'Compactum'	MAsh SSta WLov
- 'Diana' ♀H6	CEnd CKel CMac EBee EHyd ELon EPfP LRHS LSRN MBlu NLar SPer SPoG SSta WLov WPGP WSpi
cassinoides	EBee
'Chesapeake'	EWes MMrt MMuc SEND
chingii	WCru
cinnamomifolium ♀H5	CBcs CExl EHyd ELan EPfP LMaj LRHS NFav NLar SArc SBrt SPer SPoG WCot WSpi
costaricanum B&SWJ 10477	WCru
cotinifolium	CExl
- CC 4541	CExl NLar
cylindricum	EHyd EPfP LEdu SBrt WCru WLov WPav
- B&SWJ 6479 from Thailand	WCru
- B&SWJ 7239	WCru
- B&SWJ 9719 from Vietnam	WCru
- HWJCM 434 from Nepal	WCru
- from Vietnam	IKel
- 'Chino-Crûg'	WCru
davidii ♀H5	Widely available
- (f)	CMac CSBt ELan EPfP MAsh SGbt SPer SPoG SRms
- (m)	CMac CSBt ELan EPfP SGbt SPer SPoG SRms
- 'Angustifolium'	CEnd EBee NLar
dentatum	EBtc
- AUTUMN JAZZ	see *V. dentatum* 'Ralph Senior'
- BLUE MUFFIN ('Christom')	CBcs CDoC EBee EHed ELan SGol
- 'Moonglow'	NLar
- 'Morton'	SSta
- PATHFINDER ('Patzam')	SSta
- var. ***pubescens*** 'Longifolium'	SSta
§ - 'Ralph Senior'	NLar
- 'White and Blue'	NLar
dilatatum	EBtc WJur
- B&SWJ 5844	WCru
- B&SWJ 8734	WCru
- B&SWJ 10830	WCru
- PAB 6831	LEdu
- 'Asian Beauty'	SSta
- CARDINAL CANDY	see *V. dilatatum* 'Henneke'
- 'Erie'	NLar
§ - 'Henneke'	NLar SSta
- 'Iroquois'	SSta
- 'Michael Dodge'	EPfP MBlu NLar
- 'Sealing Wax'	NLar
erosum B&SWJ 8735	WCru

- B&SWJ 8893	WCru
- B&SWJ 11083	WCru
erubescens	EPfP NLar
- HWJK 2163	WCru
- VdL 4122	WPGP
- var. ***gracilipes***	EHed
- 'Milke Danda'	WPGP
- 'Ward van Teylingen'	NLar
'Eskimo' ♀H5	CBcs CCVT CEnd CKel CMac CRos CSBt EBee EHyd ELan EPfP GMcL LRHS MAsh MBNS MBlu MDon MGos NOrn SAko SCoo SGol SPoG SRms SSta SWvt SavN
fansipanense B&SWJ 8302	WCru
- KWJ 12239	WCru
§ ***farreri*** ♀H6	CBcs CBod CMCN CSBt EBee EDir EGrI ELan EPfP GMcL LBuc LEdu LRHS LSRN LSto MACG MGos MRav MSwo NLar NWea SGol SPer SWvt SavN WHtc
- 'Album'	see *V. farreri* 'Candidissimum'
§ - 'Candidissimum'	CExl CKel CMac EBee ELan EPfP LRHS LSRN MMuc MRav NLar SCoo SGol SPer SPoG SRms SWvt WHtc WLov
- 'December Dwarf'	CBod EPfP GMcL SCoo WHlf
- 'Farrer's Pink'	CExl NLar
- 'Nanum'	CMac EGrI EHyd EPfP MAsh MBrN MRav WAvo WCot WHtc WLov
foetidum	LEdu
- var. ***rectangulatum*** B&SWJ 1888	WCru
- - B&SWJ 3451	WCru
fordiae	SPtp
formosanum CWJ 12460	WCru
fragrans Bunge	see *V. farreri*
'Fragrant Cloud'	SWvt
furcatum ♀H6	EPfP GKin NLar WJur WLov
- B&SWJ 5939	WCru
- B&SWJ 10880	WCru
aff. ***furcatum*** new	GKin
× ***globosum*** 'Jermyns Globe'	CMac MRav NLar SEND SGol SPoG WFar
grandiflorum	EPfP NLar
- 'De Oirsprong'	NLar
harryanum	CBod CSBt CTsd EBtc EPfP EWTr GEdr LSto NLar WCru WLov WPGP
henryi	EPfP WCFE
× ***hillieri*** 'Winton' ♀H6	CBcs CBod CKel CMac EBee EHyd EPfP LRHS LSRN MAsh MGos MMrt NBwr NLar NRHS SChF SGol SPoG SRHi WFar WPGP WSpi
hoanglienense	EPfP
- B&SWJ 8281	EBee WCru
- HWJ 934	WCru
- KWJ 12283	WCru
- PAB 7833	LEdu
hupehense MF 93087	SSta
ichangense	NLar
integrifolium CWJ 12424 new	WCru
japonicum	CExl EBee EPfP
- B&SWJ 5968	WCru
× ***juddii***	Widely available
kansuense	CExl
- BWJ 7737	WCru
koreanum B&SWJ 4231	WCru
lantana	CBTr CBod CBrac CCVT CHab CLnd CMac CPer CTri EHeP ELan EPfP EWTr LBuc LIns LPar LSto MNic NWea SCob SEWo SPer SVic WJur WMat WMou WTSh
- 'Aureum'	EPfP MBlu NLar

	- var. ***discolor***	NLar
	- 'Mohican'	NLar
	- 'Variegatum' (v)	ELan
	- 'Xanthocarpum'	SWvt WFar
§	***lantanoides***	SSta
	aff. ***lautum*** B&SWJ 10290	WCru
	'Le Bois Marquis'PBR	CDoC CDow CRos EHed EHyd EPfP LCro LRHS LSRN MAsh MGos MMrt SGol SGsty SPoG
	lentago	CMac EPfP
	luzonicum B&SWJ 3637	WCru
	- var. ***formosanum*** B&SWJ 3585	WCru
	- var. ***oblongum*** B&SWJ 3549	EBee WCru
	- var. ***sinuatum*** B&SWJ 4009	WCru
	macrocephalum	SSta WPGP
	- 'Sterile'	SSta
	mariesii	see *V. plicatum* f. *tomentosum* 'Mariesii'
	mullaha B&SWJ 2251A	WCru
	- GWJ 9227	WCru
	aff. ***mullaha*** GWJ 9388	WCru
	nervosum HWJK 2241	WCru
	- HWJK 2373	WCru
	nudum BRANDYWINE ('Bulk')	EPfP SSta WPGP
	- 'Pink Beauty'	CKel CRos EHed EHyd EPfP LCro LOPS LRHS LSRN MMrt NRHS SAng SChF SGol SGsty SPoG SSta SWvt WFar WGob WPGP WSpi
	- 'Winterthur'	SSta
	obovatum	SBrt
	odoratissimum misapplied	see *V. japonicum*, *V. odoratissimum* var. *arboricola*, *V. odoratissimum* var. *awabuki*
	odoratissimum Ker Gawl.	CKel EBee
	- RWJ 10046	WCru
	- var. ***arboricola***	EBee
	- - B&SWJ 3052	WCru
	- - B&SWJ 3397	WCru
	- - B&SWJ 6913	WCru
§	- var. ***awabuki***	CBod CExl EGrI EPfP LRHS MAsh MBlu MGos SEND SGol WCot
	- - B&SWJ 8404	ESwi WCru
	- - B&SWJ 11374 from Wabuka, Japan	WCru
	- - 'Emerald Lustre'	CBcs WFar
	aff. ***odoratissimum*** B&SWJ 3913 from the Philippines	WCru
	oliganthum 'Kyo Kanzashi'	WPGP
	opulus	Widely available
§	- var. ***americanum***	LRHS NLar WKor
	- - 'Phillips'	CAgr
	- - 'Wentworth'	CAgr
	- 'Amy's Magic Gold'	NLar
	- 'Apricot'	NLar
	- 'Aureum'	CBod CEme CMac ELan LRHS MAsh MGil MGos MMuc MRav NLar SPer SPoG WCFE
	- var. ***calvescens*** B&SWJ 10544	WCru
	- 'Compactum' ♀H6	Widely available
	- 'Fructuluteo'	CMCN SGol
*	- 'Harvest Gold'	SCoo SGol
	- 'Lady Marmalade'	NLar
	- 'Nanum'	EPfP EShb GBin GMcL MRav NFav NLar NWad
	- 'Notcutt's Variety' ♀H6	WLov
	- 'Park Harvest'	CKel EBee EHyd EPfP LRHS NLar SWvt

§	- 'Roseum' ♀H6	Widely available
	- 'Sterile'	see *V. opulus* 'Roseum'
*	- 'Sterile Compactum'	SWvt
	- 'Sylvie'	NLar
	- 'Xanthocarpum' ♀H6	CBcs CBod CExl CKel CMac CRos EBee EHeP EHyd ELan EPfP EShb GBin LRHS MGos MMuc MRav NLar SCob SGol SPer SPoG SRms SWvt WFar WSpi
	parviflorum	GEdr
	parvifolium	NLar
	- B&SWJ 3375	WCru
	- B&SWJ 6768	WCru
	phlebotrichum B&SWJ 11058	WCru
	- B&SWJ 11470	WCru
	pichinchense B&SWJ 10660	WCru
	plicatum	SCob WHlf
	- 'Nanum'	see *V. plicatum* f. *tomentosum* 'Nanum Semperflorens'
	- OPENING DAY ('Piivib-II') **new**	EHed
§	- f. ***plicatum***	SChF
	- - 'Grandiflorum'	CBcs CCCN CKel CMac EPfP LRHS NLar SPer SPoG WCFE WHtc
	- - 'Mary Milton'	ELan IArd MPkF NCth NLar SSta
	- - NEWPORT ('Newzam')	CKel MAsh
	- - 'Pink Sensation'	GBin NLar
	- - 'Popcorn' ♀H6	CDoC CExl CKel CMac CRos EHyd ELan EPfP LPar LRHS LSRN MAsh MMrt NHol NLar SGol SPoG SRHi SSta WLov
	- - 'Rosace'	EHyd EPfP LRHS MAsh MBlu NLar NRHS
	- - 'Rotundifolium'	IArd MGos MRav WFar
	- 'Sterile'	see *V. plicatum* f. *plicatum*
§	- f. ***tomentosum***	MTrO SGol SPoG SSha
	- - 'Cascade' ♀H6	CKel ELan EWTr LRHS SAko WSpi
	- - 'Dart's Red Robin'	ECtt NLar
	- - 'Elizabeth Bullivant'	EHyd LRHS NRHS
	- - KILIMANJARO ('Jww1'PBR)	CBod CDoC CRos CWnw EBee EHyd ELan EPfP GBin GMcL LCro LOPS LRHS LSRN MAsh MBlu MGos MThu MTrO NCth NLar NRHS SCob SGol SPer SPoG WCot WHtc WSpi
	- - KILIMANJARO SUNRISE ('Jww5'PBR)	CBcs CBod CRos EHed EHyd EPfP LCro LOPS LPar LRHS MAsh MGos MPkF MThu NLar NRHS SCoo SEdd SGsty SRHi WHlf WHtc
	- - 'Lanarth'	CBcs CBod CCCN CDoC CExl CMac CRos CSBt CTri EBee EHyd ELan EPfP LRHS LSRN MAsh MBlu MGos NLar SCoo SGbt SGol SGsty SPer SWvt WHtc WSpi
§	- - 'Mariesii' ♀H6	Widely available
	- - 'Molly Schroeder'	MMrt NLar SSta
§	- - 'Nanum Semperflorens'	CBcs CMCN CMac EHed EHyd EPfP ERom EShb LRHS MGos NLar SGol SPoG WFar WLov
	- - 'Pink Beauty' ♀H6	Widely available
	- - 'Saint Keverne'	GKin
	- - 'Shasta'	CKel CMCN EHed EPfP EWTr GMcL LRHS NLar SGol WFar WLov WSpi
	- - 'Shoshoni'	CKel NLar SGol WPGP WSpi
	- - 'Summer Snowflake' ♀H6	CBar CBod CCCN CEnd CKel CRos CWGN EHyd ELan EPfP GMcL LRHS MACG MAsh MSwo NLar NRHS SGol SPer SPoG WFar
	- 'Watanabe'	see *V. plicatum* f. *tomentosum* 'Nanum Semperflorens'

'Pragense' 🏆^{H6}	CBcs CMCN EGrI EPfP LRHS NHol NLar SPer
propinquum	WFar
- CWJ 12395	WCru
- CWJ 12426	WCru
- var. ***propinquum*** Guiz 222	WPGP
prunifolium	EBtc SGol WCru
- 'Mrs Henry's Large'	NLar
× ***rhytidophylloides***	CEnd
- 'Alleghany'	NLar
- 'Willowwood'	CKel EHyd ELan LRHS MAsh MGos NLar SCob SGsty WHtc
rhytidophyllum	CBcs CGBo CKel CMac EHeP EPfP GMcL LIns LMaj LPar LRHS MGos MMuc MSwo NBwr NLar NWea SAdn SArc SCob SEND SGol SPer SRms SWvt WCFE WHtc WJur WSFF
- 'Roseum'	CExl SWvt
- 'Wisley Pink'	MAsh
sambucinum	EBee
- HWJ 838	WCru
- var. ***tomentosum*** HWJ 733	WCru
sargentii B&SWJ 8695	WCru
- 'Onondaga' 🏆^{H6}	Widely available
semperflorens	see *V. plicatum* f. *tomentosum* 'Nanum Semperflorens'
§ ***setigerum***	EPfP NLar SPtp WLov
- BWJ 8409	WCru
SHINY DANCER ('Ncvx1') **new**	LCro
sieboldii	EBtc
- B&SWJ 2837	WCru
- CWJ 12808	WCru
subalpinum	EPfP NLar
taitoense CWJ 12406	WCru
taiwanianum B&SWJ 3009	WCru
- CWJ 12467	WCru
theiferum	see *V. setigerum*
tinoides B&SWJ 10612	WCru
tinus	Widely available
I - 'Compactum'	SWvt
- 'Eve Price' 🏆^{H4}	Widely available
- 'French White' 🏆^{H4}	CBod CBrac CCCN CDoC CKel CMac EBee ELan EPfP EWTr LCro LOPS LRHS MAsh MRav NBwr NLar SCoo SLim SRms SSut SWvt
- 'Gwenllian' 🏆^{H4}	Widely available
- 'Israel'	EShb MBNS
- 'Ladybird'	CDoC CKel CWnw
- 'Lisarose'^{PBR}	CBar CBcs CBod CDoC CEnd EBee EPfP LCro LOPS LPar LSRN LSto MAsh MGos NCth NLar SOrN SPoG SWvt WSpi
- 'Little Bognor'	NLar
- 'Lucidum'	CCoa EPfP LMaj LPar NBwr NLar SGol SGsty
- 'Lucidum Variegatum' (v)	CMac MAsh
* - 'Macrophyllum'	EPfP NLar SWvt
- 'Peter's Purple'	CRos EHyd EPfP LRHS NRHS SPoG
- 'Purpureum'	CBcs CBod CKel CSBt EBee EPfP LPar MAsh MGos MSwo NLar SCoo SPer SSut WFar
- SPIRIT ('Anvi'^{PBR})	CBod CEnd CRos CSBt EHyd ELan EPfP LRHS MAsh NEoE NLar NRHS NWad SCoo SPoG SWeb SWvt WHtc
- 'Spring Bouquet'	MAsh
- subsp. ***subcordatum***	see *V. treleasei*
- 'Variegatum' (v)	CBod CCoa CMac EBee EHyd ELan EPfP LRHS MAsh NBwr NLar NPol NRHS SCob SGol SPoG SRms SWvt SavN WFar WLov
tomentosum	see *V. plicatum* f. *tomentosum*
§ ***treleasei*** B&SWJ 12544	WCru
trilobum	see *V. opulus* var. *americanum*
triphyllum B&SWJ 10757	WCru
- B&SWJ 14298	WCru
utile	LRHS WHtc WThu
aff. ***venustum*** B&SWJ 10477	WCru
wrightii	EPfP IArd MRav
- B&SWJ 5871	WCru
- 'Hessei'	WLov
- var. ***stipellatum*** B&SWJ 5856	WCru
- - B&SWJ 8780A	WCru

Vicia (*Fabaceae*)

americana	EBee
benghalensis	SPhx
cracca	CHab MBow NMir SPhx WSFF
nigricans subsp. ***gigantica***	SBrt
sativa	CHab

Vigna (*Fabaceae*)

caracalla	see *Cochliasanthus caracalla*
radiata	SVic

Villaresia see *Citronella*

Vinca (*Apocynaceae*)

difformis	CBod CCBP CDor CFis CTri ECha IDee LPla SDix SPer SRms WAvo WHer XLum
- Greystone form	CExl EPPr SEND
- 'Jenny Pym'	CBcs CBod CDor CExl CFis CMac EBee ECha EPfP EWes EWld LRHS MBNS MDon NBwr NLar SEND SIvy SPoG SRms WAvo WBor WHoo WOut
- 'Ruby Baker'	CDoC CKel EPPr EPfP EWes LRHS LShi NChi SPoG WAvo WFar WMal
- subsp. ***sardoa***	CBod CKel ECha EHyd EPPr ESwi EWes WCot WFar
- 'Snowmound'	CBod CKel CSBt LRHS MRav NLar SPoG SWvt WAvo
herbacea RCB UA 21	WCot
'Hidcote Purple'	see *V. major* var. *oxyloba*
major	CBcs CBod CBrac CSBt EHeP ELan GMcL GPoy LBuc LCro LPal LPar LRHS LSto MAsh MDon MGos MSwo NBwr NPol NWea SCob SGbt SGol SPer SRms SSha WFar XLum XSen
- 'Alba'	CMac WOut
- subsp. ***balcanica***	XLum
- 'Elegantissima'	see *V. major* 'Variegata'
- var. ***hirsuta*** misapplied	see *V. major* var. *oxyloba*
§ - subsp. ***hirsuta*** (Boiss.) Stearn	CMac WCot XLum
§ - 'Maculata' (v)	CBcs CBod CSBt EHeP EShb GMcL MSwo NBwr SEND SGol SPer SPoG SWvt WAvo
§ - var. ***oxyloba***	CBod CCBP CExl CFis CKel CTri ECha ELan EPPr EPfP EPri EWld LPla LRHS MRav SRms WAvo WBor WHer
- var. ***pubescens***	see *V. major* subsp. *hirsuta* (Boiss.) Stearn
- 'Surrey Marble'	see *V. major* 'Maculata'
§ - 'Variegata' (v) 🏆^{H6}	Widely available
- 'Wojo's Jem' (v)	CMac CRos EHyd ELan EPfP LRHS MGos NRHS SCob SWvt WAvo WCot
minor	CBar CBcs CBod CDoC CSBt EHeP ELan GAbr GBin GKev GKin GMcL

	GPoy GQue LCro LOPS MAsh MDon MGos NWea SCob SVic WBor WFar XLum
- f. ***alba***	CBcs CBod CDoC CMac CRos ECha EPPr EPfP GJos LCro LOPS LRHS LSRN LShi MAsh MDon NLar NRHS NWea SCob SGBe SGol SPer SSha SVic WCot WFar WHlf XLum XSen
§ - - 'Alba Variegata' (v)	CBar CBrac CExl EHeP GMcL LSRN NBwr NEoE NWad SRms WCot WFar WHoo
- - 'Elisa'	NLar
- - 'Gertrude Jekyll'	Widely available
- 'Alba Aureovariegata'	see *V. minor* f. *alba* 'Alba Variegata'
- 'Anna'	NLar
§ - 'Argenteovariegata' (v) ♀H6	CBcs CBod CBrac CDoC CDor CMac CSBt CTri ECha EHyd ELan ELon EPfP GArf GMcL GQue LRHS MGos MMuc MSwo NBwr NChi SCob SGol SPer SRms WFar
§ - 'Atropurpurea' ♀H6	Widely available
§ - 'Aureovariegata' (v)	CBcs CKel CMac EBee EHeP ELan EPPr EPfP GAbr MGos MRav NWea SGol SPer SPlb
§ - 'Azurea Flore Pleno' (d) ♀H6	CDoC CKel CMac CRos CTri ECha EHeP EPPr EPfP EWTr GAbr GQue LRHS LShi LSto MRav NBwr NChi NLar NRHS SPoG SRms SWvt WFar WHoo WMal XLum
- 'Blue and Gold' (v)	EPPr
- 'Blue Drift'	EWes MSwo
- 'Bowles's Blue'	see *V. minor* 'Bowles's Variety'
- 'Bowles's Purple'	GMaP NCou
§ - 'Bowles's Variety' ♀H6	Widely available
- 'Burgundy'	SRms
- 'Caerulea Plena'	see *V. minor* 'Azurea Flore Pleno'
- 'Colada' **new**	EWes
- 'Dartington Star'	see *V. major* var. *oxyloba*
- 'Double Burgundy'	see *V. minor* 'Multiplex'
- 'Evelyne' PBR (v)	WFar
- 'Flower Power'	EPPr NLar
- GREEN CARPET	see *V. minor* 'Grüner Teppich'
§ - 'Grüner Teppich'	EHeP SGol WFar
- 'Halstenbek'	XLum
- 'Illumination' (v)	Widely available
- 'La Grave'	see *V. minor* 'Bowles's Variety'
- 'Marie'	EPPr NLar XSen
- 'Mrs Betty James' (d)	EPPr WCot
§ - 'Multiplex' (d)	EPPr LBuc MSwo SGol SRms
- 'Purpurea'	see *V. minor* 'Atropurpurea'
- 'Ralph Shugert' (v) ♀H6	Widely available
- 'Rubra'	see *V. minor* 'Atropurpurea'
- 'Silver Service' (d/v)	WFar
- 'Snowdrift'	EPPr
- 'Temptation' (d)	CKel WHlf WTyc
- 'Variegata'	see *V. minor* 'Argenteovariegata'
- 'Variegata Aurea'	see *V. minor* 'Aureovariegata'
- 'White Power'	EPPr EWes

Vincetoxicum (*Apocynaceae*)

amplexicaule **new**	GGro
cretaceum PAB 3432	LEdu
forrestii	CExl
fuscatum	EBee
hirundinaria	EBee EPPr GPoy SPhx WCot WHil
- HPA 1358	GGro
nigrum	EBee EPPr NChi WCot
yellow-flowered W&O 7287	GGro

Viola ✿ (*Violaceae*)

'Abigail' (Vtta)	ECtt LEdu LRHS WFar
'Ada Segre' (Vt)	CGro
'Admiral Avellan'	see *V.* 'Amiral Avellan'
'Admiration' (Va)	WGoo
adunca var. ***minor***	see *V. labradorica* ambig.
'Alethia' (Va)	GAbr SDys WGoo
'Alice Kate' (Va)	WGoo
'Alice Witter' (Vt)	CGro SHar
* 'Alison' (Va)	WGoo
altaica	SPlb
'Amelia' (Va)	WGoo
§ 'Amiral Avellan' (Vt)	CDor CGro LShi WFar
'Amy' (Va)	EVic
'Andy Pandy' (Va)	LRHS
'Annalesia' (Vt)	CGro LShi
'Annette Ross' (Va)	WGoo
I 'Annie' (Vt)	CGro
'Ardross Gem' (Va)	GArf LShi MNrw WGoo
'Arkwright's Ruby' (Va)	LShi
arvensis	CHab
'Ashvale Blue' (dPVt)	CGro
'Aspasia' (Va) ♀H5	GAbr MAsh WGoo
'Avril Lawson' (Va)	GKev SHar WGoo
'Baby Blue'	GMcL
'Barbara' (Va)	ECtt WGoo
'Baroness de Rothschild' misapplied	see *V.* 'Baronne Alice de Rothschild'
'Baroness de Rothschild' ambig. (Vt)	CGro LShi WHer
§ 'Baronne Alice de Rothschild' (Vt)	CDor NLar SHar
'Beatrice' (Vtta)	WGoo
'Becky Groves' (Vt)	CGro
'Beetroot' (Vt)	CGro LShi
§ 'Belmont Blue' (C)	CTri EWes GBin GKev GMaP LCro LOPS MHol MRav NBir NSti SCob SHar SPer SRkn WCAu WFar WGoo WSpi
§ ***bertolonii***	WGoo
'Beshlie' (Va) ♀H5	WGoo
* ***betonicifolia albescens***	GGro
biflora	EPPr EWld LShi MNrw
'Blackout' PBR (C)	ECtt
'Blue Butterfly' (C)	MHol
'Blue Ice' (Va)	LRHS WFar
'Blue Moon' (C)	LShi MAsh WGoo
'Blue Moonlight' (C)	MHer MNrw
'Blue Sails' (Va)	EVic
'Blue Tit' (Va)	ECtt
(Bonnie Lassies Series) BONNIE LASSIES EMMA (Va)	CRos LRHS
- BONNIE LASSIES SARAH (Va)	CRos LRHS MHer
'Bonny' (Va)	EVic
'Bo-Peep' (Va)	LRHS
'Boughton Blue'	see *V.* 'Belmont Blue'
'Bournemouth Gem' (Vt)	CDor CGro LShi
§ 'Bowles's Black' (T)	CPla CSpe EPfP MNHC NBro SRms
brevistipulata var. ***hidakana***	GEdr GKev WFar
- var. ***laciniata***	GEdr
'Bridie' (Va) **new**	ECtt EVic
'Bruneau' (dVt)	ECtt WCot WFar
bubanii	GKev
'Budgie' (Va)	LRHS
'Burncoose Yellow' (Va)	WGoo
'Buttercup' (Vtta)	ECtt MHol NLar SDys SPoG WGoo
'Butterpat' (C)	MAsh SHar WFar WGoo
'Candy' (Vt)	CGro EBee WFar
canina	EMor NBro
'Carol' (Vt)	CGro WFar
'Catalina'	CGro
CELESTIAL TWILIGHT ('Smev3') (C)	ECtt LBar

chaerophylloides 'Beni-zuru'	GGro
§ - var. ***sieboldiana***	GGro SBrt
'Charles W. Groves'	see *V.* 'Charles William Groves', *V.* 'Charles Winston Groves'
§ 'Charles William Groves' (Vt)	CGro WFar
§ 'Charles Winston Groves' (Vt)	CGro WFar
'Charlotte' (Va)	WGoo
'Chloe' (Vtta)	CGro
'Christie's Wedding' (Vt)	CGro WFar
'Christmas' (Vt)	CGro LShi WFar
'Citronella' (Va)	LRHS
'Clementina' (Va) 🏆H5	MRav WGoo
'Clive Farrell' (Vt)	MNrw
'Clive Groves' (Vt)	CDor CGro
'Cockatoo' (Va)	LRHS
'Coeur d'Alsace' (Vt)	CGro CLAP EBee ECtt GMaP NLar SHar SRms WFar XLum
'Colette' (Va)	WGoo
'Colombine' (Vt)	CAby CGro LShi MAsh
'Columbine' (Va)	CDor CRos CTtf ECtt EHyd EPfP LBar LRHS LShi MBow MCot MHer MRav NDov NRHS SPoG WCav WFar WGoo WTor
§ 'Conte di Brazza' (dPVt)	LShi NLar WHer
'Cordelia' (Vt)	CDor LShi
cornuta 🏆H5	CDor CElw LRHS MBow MNrw NBir NBro SCob SHar SRms SSut WFar WGoo WHoo
- Alba Group (C) 🏆H5	CDor CElw CSpe CTri ECha EHyd ELan GMaP LCro LOPS LRHS MAsh MBel MCot MHer MHol MNrw NBir NBro NGrd NRHS SBut SCob SPer SRms WGoo WHoo WKif
- 'Alba Minor' (C)	EPfP EWes LRHS LShi NBro NDov WFar
- blue-flowered (C)	MHer
- 'Brimstone' (C)	LShi MHol
- 'Cleopatra' (C)	MHol MNrw
- 'Clouded Yellow' (C)	MHol MNrw WFar
- 'Cream Gem' (C)	MHol WFar
- 'Deltini Honey Bee' (Deltini Series) (C)	MBros
- 'Gypsy Moth' (C)	GAbr LShi MHol
- 'Hobbit Sam' (C) **new**	WFar
- 'Icy But Spicy' (C)	MAsh MHol MRav NDov WFar WGoo
- Lilacina Group (C)	ECha
- 'Maiden's Blush' (C)	MHol WFar
- 'Minor' (C)	EPfP LShi MAsh NBro WGoo
- 'Netta Statham' (C)	MHol WGoo
- 'Pale Apollo' (C)	MHol WFar
- 'Spider' (C)	MAsh MHol MNrw SDys WFar WGoo
- 'Swallowtail' (C)	GAbr MHol
- 'Ulla' (C)	WHer
- 'Victoria's Blush' (C)	CDor CElw EWTr GAbr GBin GMaP MAsh MBel MHol NBir NDov SHar WGoo
- 'Violacea' (C)	MHol
corsica	CSpe SPhx
'Covent Garden' (Vt)	CGro LShi WFar
'Crepuscle' (Vt)	WFar
§ ***cucullata*** 🏆H5	SRms
§ - 'Alba' (Vt)	CGro NBir SRms
* - 'Striata Alba' (Vt)	NBro
'Curlylocks'	ECtt
'Cuty' (Va)	LRHS
'Czar'	see *V.* 'The Czar'
§ 'Czar Bleu' (Vt)	CGro
'Daisy Smith' (Va)	WGoo
'Danielle Molly'	WGoo

'Dawn' (Vtta)	CAby CBod CDor ECtt EPfP EWoo MCot NLar SPoG WFar WGoo WTor
'Delicia' (Vtta)	NDov WGoo
'Des Charentes' (Vt)	CGro LShi
'Desdemona' (Va)	GKev WGoo
'Devon Cream' (Va)	WGoo
'Diana Groves' (Vt)	CGro WFar
'Dick o' the Hills' (Vt)	CDor CGro LShi WFar
dissecta var. ***sieboldiana***	see *V. chaerophylloides* var. *sieboldiana*
'Donau' (Vt)	CGro LShi WCot WFar
'Doreen' (Vt)	WFar
'Double White' (dVt)	CGro WHer
douglasii	SBrt
'Duchesse de Parme' (dPVt)	CGro GMaP NLar SRms WHer
'D'Udine' (dPVt)	CGro ECtt LShi SRms WCot WFar WHer
'E.A. Bowles'	see *V.* 'Bowles's Black'
'Eastgrove Blue Scented' (C)	SDys WFar WGoo WMal
'Eastgrove Ice Blue' (C)	WGoo
eizanensis	GGro
'Elaine Quin' (Va)	ECtt NLar SPoG WGoo WKif
§ ***elatior***	EPPr MNrw
'Eliza May Groves' (Vt)	CGro
'Elizabeth Bailes' (Vt)	CDor LShi
'Elizabeth Lee' (Vt)	WCot
'Elliot Adam' (Va)	WGoo
'Elworthy Velvet'	CElw
'Emperor Magenta Red'	EMor SVic
erecta	see *V. elatior*
'Eris' (Va)	WGoo
'Etain' (Va)	CAby CBod CRos CTsd ECtt EHyd ELan EPfP EShb GAbr LBar LRHS MHol NLar NRHS SCob SMrm SPoG WFar WGoo
'Fabiola' (Vtta)	GAbr
* 'Fantasy'	WGoo
'Fee Jalucine' (dVt)	CGro
'Ferndale' (dPVt)	LShi
'Fiona' (Va)	GAbr MCot SGro WGoo
'Fiona Lawrenson' (Va)	WGoo
'Floella'	LRHS
'Florence' (Va)	WGoo
'Flossy'	LRHS
'Flower Girl' (Va)	LShi
'Foxbrook Cream' (C)	MAsh WGoo
'Francesca' (Va)	WGoo
'Freckles'	see *V. sororia* 'Freckles'
'Fred Morey' (Vt)	CDor CGro WFar
glabella	GGro
'Gladys Findlay' (Va)	WGoo
'Glanmore'	WCot WFar
* 'Glenda'	WGoo
'Glenholme'	LShi WMal
'Gloire de Verdun' (PVt)	CGro
'Governor Herrick' (Vt)	CGro ECtt WCot WFar
gracilis 'Lutea'	CElw
- 'Major'	WGoo
'Green Goddess' PBR (P)	ECtt LBar
§ ***grypoceras*** var. ***exilis***	EPPr SMad
'Gustav Wermig' (C)	MHol WGoo
hancockii	SPtp
'Hannah May'	LRHS
'Heartthrob' (v)	CBod ECtt GEdr MNrw NFav NHpl SMad SPeP SPoG WHil WNPC
§ ***hederacea***	CBod CExl CTsd EMor EWoo GGro GQue LShi SRms WFar WHlf
'Helena' (Va)	WGoo
'Hespera' (Va)	WGoo
heterophylla subsp. ***epirota***	see *V. bertolonii*
'Holdgate'	WGoo
'Hopleys White' (PVt)	CGro

	'Hudsons Blue'	CElw MNrw
	'Huntercombe Purple' (Va) 🏆H5	CRos EHyd LRHS NBir NRHS WFar WGoo
	'Iden Gem' (Va)	ECtt WGoo
	'Inverurie Beauty' (Va) 🏆H5	GAbr GBin GMaP MHer SDys WGoo WKif
	'Irish Elegance'	see *V.* 'Sulfurea'
	'Irish Molly' (Va)	ECtt ELan EPfP GKev LShi MAsh MCot SPoG WFar WGoo WIce WTor
	'Isabel'	SRms WGoo
	'Isabella' (Vt)	CGro LRHS WFar
	'Isobel'	MAsh
	'Ivory Queen' (Va)	GAbr GQue MHer MRav WFar WGoo
	'Jackanapes' (Va) 🏆H5	CBod EBee ECtt ELan LRHS LShi MAsh NLar SPoG WGoo WTor
	'Janet' (Va)	LSRN SDys SPoG
	'Janette' (Va)	WGoo
	'Jean Arnot' (Vt)	LShi
	'Jean Jeannie' (Va)	NDov WFar WGoo
	'Jeannie Bellew' (Va)	ECtt WGoo
	'Jennifer Andrews' (Va)	LShi SGro WGoo
	'Joanna' (Va)	WGoo
	'John Raddenbury' (Vt)	CGro
	'Josephine' (Vt)	CGro
	'Josie' (Va)	SGro WGoo
	'Joyce Mary Paul' (Vt)	CGro
	'Judy Goring' (Va)	WMal
	'Julian' (Va)	GAbr WGoo
	'Juno' (Va)	GAbr
	'Jupiter' (Va)	WCot
	kamtschadalorum	WFar
	'Kerry Girl' (Vt)	CGro WFar
	'Kim' (Vt)	CGro LShi
	'Kitten'	LShi MHol SDys WFar WGoo
	'Kitty White' (Va)	SDys
§	'Königin Charlotte' (Vt)	CGro EHyd EMor EPfP GMaP ISha LRHS LShi LSou MHer SRms SVic WCAu WCot
	koreana	see *V. grypoceras* var. *exilis*
	labradorica misapplied	see *V. riviniana* Purpurea Group
§	***labradorica*** ambig.	CTri EWTr NHpl WCAu WHer
	'Lady Hume Campbell' (dPVt)	CGro WHer
	'Lady Jane' (Vt)	CGro
	'Lavender Lady' (Vt)	CGro
	'Lavender Lights' (Vt)	CDor WFar
	'Lees Blue' (Vt)	CGro WFar
	'Lees Peachy Pink' (Vt)	CGro MNrw
	'Letitia' (Va)	MAsh MNrw
	'Lianne' (Vt)	CGro LShi SRms WCot
	'Lincoln Cathedral'	ECtt LRHS
	'Lindsay'	WGoo
	'Lisa Tanner' (Va)	WGoo
	'Little David' (Vtta) 🏆H5	CTri ECtt LShi MCot NDov WGoo
	'Lord Plunket' (Va)	WGoo
	'Lorna Cawthorne' (C)	SDys WGoo
	'Louisa' (Va)	GAbr WGoo
	'Lucy' (Va)	MAsh
§	***lutea***	LShi SBut SHar WAbe WGoo
	- subsp. ***elegans***	see *V. lutea*
	'Luxonne' (Vt)	CGro
	'Lydia Groves' (Vt)	CDor CGro SRms WCot WFar
	'Lydia's Legacy' (Vt)	CGro
	'Mabel'	LRHS
	'Madame Armandine Pagès' (Vt)	CGro
	'Madeleine Mary Groves' (Vt)	CGro
	'Maggie Mott' (Va) 🏆H5	ECtt GArf MAsh MCot MRav WFar WGoo
	'Magic' (C)	NDov WGoo

	mandshurica	GKev
	- 'Fuji Dawn' (v)	EMor LShi WCot
	'Margaret' (Va)	ECtt WGoo
	'Marie Rose' (Vt)	WFar
	'Marie-Louise' (dPVt)	CGro
I	'Mars'	WSpi
	'Martin' (Va) 🏆H5	CAby CBod ECha ECtt EShb EWoo GMaP LRHS LSRN MAsh MAvo MCot NDov SPoG WFar WGoo WHlf WOld
	'Martini'	LRHS
	'Mary Mouse'	WGoo
	'Marylyn' (Va)	LRHS WFar
	'Mauve Haze' (Va)	WGoo
	'Mauve Radiance' (Va)	WGoo
	'May Mott' (Va)	WGoo
	'Mayfly' (Va)	ECtt
	'Melinda' (Vtta)	WGoo
	'Mercury' (Va)	WGoo
	'Michelle'	LRHS
	'Midnight' (Va)	LRHS
	MINIOLA HEART AQUA	LRHS
	MINIOLA HEART GOLD	LRHS
	MINIOLA HEART ICE BLUE	LRHS
	MINIOLA HEART PURPLE	LRHS
	(Miracle Series) 'Miracle Bride White' (Vt)	WFar
	- 'Miracle Classy Pink' (Vt)	MHol WFar
	- 'Miracle Ice White' (Vt)	NLar
	- 'Miracle Intense Blue' (Vt)	NCth WFar
	'Miss Brookes' (Va)	WGoo
	'Misty Guy' (Vtta)	MAsh
	'Molly Sanderson' (Va) 🏆H5	CAby CRos ECha ECtt EHyd ELan EPfP EShb LBar LRHS LShi MAsh MBow MBros MCot MHer NLar NRHS SCob SMrm SPer SPlb SPoG SRms WCav WFar WGoo WTor
	'Moonlight' (Va) 🏆H5	CRos EHyd ELan LRHS NRHS WGoo
	'Morwenna' (Va)	ECtt MAsh MCot NDov WGoo
	'Mrs Lancaster' (Va)	ECtt ELan EPfP EWoo LSRN LShi MCot NLar NWad SPoG SSut WFar WGoo WTor
	'Mrs Pinehurst' (Vt)	CGro SRms
	'Mrs R. Barton' (Vt)	CDor CGro SRms
	'Myfawnny' (Va)	CRos EHyd LRHS NDov NRHS WFar WGoo
	'Neapolitan'	see *V.* 'Pallida Plena'
	nephrophylla	GGro
	'Neptune' (Va)	WFar
	'Netta Statham'	see *V.* 'Belmont Blue'
	'Nora' (Va)	ECtt NDov WFar WGoo
	'Norah Leigh' (Va)	WGoo
	NORTHERN LIGHTS ('Smev4') (Celestial Series) (Va)	EPfP
	obliqua	see *V. cucullata*
	odorata (Vt)	CBcs CBod CDor CGro CHab CTsd EBee EBou EWTr GPoy GQue LCro LRHS LShi MBow MRav NGrd NMir SRms WBor WCAu WJek
	- 'Alba' (Vt)	CDor CGro CLAP CTsd EBee ELan EMor EPfP GQue LEdu LShi MHer SEND SRms WCAu WFar
	- 'Amelia Violet Groves Stork' (Vt)	CGro
	- 'Amethyst Witch' (Vt)	CGro WFar
	- apricot-flowered	see *V.* 'Sulfurea'
	- 'Bethan Davies' (d/Vt)	WCot
	- 'Carol Lockton' (Vt)	CGro WFar
	- 'Christopher William Groves' (Vt)	CGro
	- 'Copper Pennies' (Vt)	CGro

	- 'Cyclops' (Vt)	CGro
	- 'Dawnie' (Vt)	CGro EBee
	- deep violet-flowered (Vt)	SPtp
	- 'Ellie' (Vt)	WFar
	- 'Empress Augusta' (Vt)	CGro LShi
	- 'Explorateur Dybowski' (Vt)	CGro
	- ***flore-pleno*** (dVt)	EMor
	- 'Frederick Peter Groves Stork' (Vt)	CGro
	- 'Hungarian Beauty' (Vt)	LCro LOPS
	- 'Ivy Thirza Groves' (Vt)	CGro
	- 'Katy' (Vt)	CLAP
	- 'King of Violets' (dVt)	ECtt SHar
	- 'Lees Ivory' (Vt)	CGro
	- 'Little Plum' (Vt)	CGro
	- 'Melanie' (Vt)	CDor CGro CLAP MNrw
	- 'Mrs R.O. Barlow' (Vt)	CLAP WSHC
	- 'Piddle Pink' (Vt)	CGro
	- pink-flowered	see *V. odorata* Rosea Group
	- var. ***praecox*** (Vt) **new**	SEND
	- 'Princess Thirza' (Vt)	CGro
	- ***rosea***	see *V. odorata* Rosea Group
§	- Rosea Group (Vt)	CBod CDor EMor MRav SEND SRms WCot
	- 'Sulphurea'	see *V.* 'Sulfurea'
	- 'Vin d'André Thorp' (Vt)	CGro ECtt
I	- 'Violett Charm' (Vt)	WCot
	'Olive Edwards' (Va)	WGoo
	'Orchid Pink' (Vt)	CGro GMaP MNrw
	orientalis	GEdr
§	'Pallida Plena' (dPVt)	CGro WHer
	palmata	EMor
	palustris	EWat LLWG NLar WShi
	'Pamela Zambra' (Vt)	CGro SHar WSHC
	'Panola Beaconsfield' (Panola Series) (P)	SCob
	papilionacea	see *V. sororia*
	'Parchment' (Vt)	CGro
	'Parme de Toulouse' (dPVt)	CGro EBee NLar WHer XLum
	'Pat Creasy' (Va)	NDov WGoo
	'Pat Kavanagh' (C)	MAsh WGoo
	'Patience'	WGoo
	pedata	LAma MPie WAbe
	- 'Bicolor' (Vt)	WAbe
	pedatifida white-flowered	GEdr
	pensylvanica	see *V. pubescens* var. *eriocarpa*
	'Perle Rose' (Vt)	CGro
	'Petra' (Vtta)	WGoo
	'Pickering Blue' (Va)	WGoo
	pinnata	CTri SBrt
	'Primrose Dame' (Va)	ECtt WGoo
	'Primrose Pixie' (Va)	WGoo
	'Prince Henry' (T)	MNHC
	'Princess of Prussia' (Vt)	CGro
	'Princess of Wales'	see *V.* 'Princesse de Galles'
§	'Princesse de Galles' (Vt)	CGro CTri
	'Prunella' (Va)	LRHS LShi WFar
§	***pubescens*** var. ***eriocarpa***	SRms
	pumila	GEdr
	QUEEN CHARLOTTE	see *V.* 'Königin Charlotte'
	'Raven' (Va)	WGoo
	'Rebecca' (Vtta)	CAby CDor CPla CRos ECtt EHyd ELan EPfP EShb GKev LBar LRHS LSRN MAsh MBel MBow MBros MCot MHol NBir NDov NLar NRHS SPoG WCav WFar WGoo WHer WHlf
	'Rebecca Cawthorne' (C)	MHol
	'Red Charm' (Vt)	CGro WCav
	'Red Giant' (Vt)	CGro MPie
	'Red Lion' (Vt)	CGro
	'Reine des Blanches' (dVt)	ECtt LEdu SRms
	'Reine des Neiges' (Vt)	CBod CDor CGro EMor EWTr LShi WFar
	reniforme	see *V. hederacea*
	riviniana	GJos GQue MBow SCgs WHer WSFF WShi
§	- Purpurea Group	CAby CBcs CBod CDor CMac EBee EBou ECha EMor EPfP EWes EWoo GMaP LRHS LShi MHer MPie MRav NBir NRya SPer SPhx SPlb SRms WFar WJam WJek WWke
	- 'Rosea'	WJek
	- white-flowered	EWes
	'Roscastle Black' (Va)	GBee MAsh NDov WGoo WSpi
	'Rose Marie' (Va)	LRHS WFar
	'Rose Rayne'	LRHS
	'Rosy Rayne' (Va)	LShi WFar
	'Royal Elk' (Vt)	CGro
	'Royal Robe' (Vt)	CGro
	'Royal Wedding' (Vt)	CGro SVic
	'Rubra' (Vt)	EMor SVic XLum
*	***rupestris rosea***	CTri GGro WHer
	sacchalinensis	GGro
	var. ***alpina*** **new**	
	'Saint Helena' (Vt)	CGro
	'Sally' (Vtta)	CGro
	'Sea Horse'	LShi
	selkirkii Pursh ex Goldie	WThu
	- 'Variegata' (v)	GGro
	septentrionalis	see *V. sororia*
	'Sherbet Dip' (Va)	WGoo
	'Showgirl' (Va)	LRHS WFar
	'Silver Lining'	LRHS
	'Silver Samurai' (Vt)	GGro WCot
	'Skylark' (Va)	LRHS WFar
	'Smugglers' Moon' (Va)	ECtt LShi WGoo
	'Sophie' (Vtta)	WGoo
	Sorbet Series (Va)	LCro LOPS MBros MPri
	- SORBET BLACK DELIGHT IMPROVED ('Pas211779') (Va)	MBros
	- SORBET XP T&M Mix (Va)	MBros
	- SORBET YELLOW FROST (Va)	LCro LOPS
§	***sororia***	ECha MNrw NBir NBro SCob
*	- 'Albiflora' (Vt) ♀H6	CTtf EMor EPfP EWTr EWoo GPSL LEdu LRHS LSun MBriF MRav NLar SBea SCob WJek
	- 'Dark Freckles' (Vt)	CGro EBee EMor NLar NRya WFar
§	- 'Freckles' (Vt)	CBro CMac CSBt CTri CTtf EBee EBou ECha EMor EPfP GKev LEdu LSun MAsh MBow MBriF MRav NBir NHpl NLar NRya SCob SMrm SPlb WCAu WCav WFar WHlf WSHC
	- 'Hungarian Beauty' (Vt)	GBin
	- 'Priceana' (Vt)	LEdu MRav NBir SHar SPlb WCot
	- SORORITY SISTERS (mixed) (Vt)	SVic
	- 'Speckles' (Vt/v)	WCot
	- 'Sweet Emma' (Vt)	SPhx
*	'Spencer's Cottage' (Vt)	WGoo
	'Steyning' (Va)	WGoo
	stojanowii	WIce
§	'Sulfurea' (Vt)	CDor CLAP EBou EMor EPfP ISha LShi MBriF MRav NRya WCot WFar
	'Sulfurea' lemon-flowered (Vt)	WFar
	'Sultan' (Vt)	CDor
	'Summer Showers'	LRHS
	'Sundowner' (Va)	ECtt
	'Sunny Jim' (Va)	EVic
	'Sunshine' (Va)	WFar
	'Susan Chilcott' (Vt)	CGro
	'Susanne Lucas' (Vt)	CGro

'Susie' (Va)	ECtt MHol WFar WGoo
'Swanley White'	see *V.* 'Conte di Brazza'
'Sweetheart' (Va)	EVic
'Sybil' (SP)	WGoo
TEARDROPS MIXED (P)	LCro LOPS WHlf
'Teardrops Yesterday, Today, Tomorrow' (P)	LCro LOPS
§ 'The Czar' (Vt)	CTtf SHar SRms
'Tiger Eyes' (Va)	MBow SPoG
'Tom Tit' (Va)	ECtt WGoo
'Tony Venison' (C/v)	ELon NLar WFar
tricolor	CBod CHab ENfk EPfP EWhm GJos GPoy LCro LOPS MHer MHoo MNHC NGrd SPhx SRms WHlf WWild
- 'Sawyer's Black' (T)	ENfk WJek
vaginata	GEdr
verecunda	WOld
- B&SWJ 604a	GGro WCru
§ - var. ***yakusimana***	WThu
'Victoria'	see *V.* 'Czar Bleu'
'Victoria Cawthorne' (C)	LShi MAsh MHol NDov WFar WGoo
'Virginia' (Va)	WGoo
'Vita' (Va)	GAbr SRms WFar WGoo WMal
'Wasp' (Va)	ECtt
'White Ladies'	see *V. cucullata* 'Alba'
'White Pearl' (Va)	LShi WGoo
'White Swan' (Va)	MAsh WFar
'Winifred Jones' (Va)	GKev WGoo
'Winnie' (Va)	LRHS WFar
'Winona Cawthorne' (C)	MHol
'Wisley White'	CRos GBin LRHS MBel MHol NSti
× ***wittrockiana*** COASTAL SUNRISE MIXED (P)	LCro
- Cool Wave Series (P)	LCro
- 'Joker Light Blue' (Joker Series) (P)	LCro LOPS
- Matrix Series (P)	MBros MPri
- - MATRIX CASSIS (P)	MBros
- - MATRIX CLEAR YELLOW (P)	MBros
- - MATRIX MIDNIGHT GLOW ('Pas12374') (P)	SCob
- - MATRIX MORPHEUS (P)	MBros SCob
- - MATRIX RED BLOTCH (P)	MBros
- - MATRIX SUNRISE (P)	MBros
- - MATRIX YELLOW BLOTCH (P)	MBros
'Woodlands Cream' (Va)	WGoo
'Woodlands Lilac' (Va)	WGoo
yakusimana	see *V. verecunda* var. *yakusimana*
'Yellowtail' (Va)	GAbr
yezoensis	GKev
'Zara' (Va)	WGoo
'Zoe' (Vtta)	ECtt EPfP MAsh SPoG WFar WGoo

Viscaria (*Caryophyllaceae*)

vulgaris	see *Lychnis viscaria*

Visnaga (*Apiaceae*)

§ ***daucoides***	CHby CSpe EPfP EWoo LBar LCro LRHS MNHC SPhx SRms
- 'Green Mist'	LCro LOPS MAvo SBut WHlf

Vitaliana (*Primulaceae*)

§ ***primuliflora***	GArf GKev NRya NSla
- subsp. ***assoana***	EPot
- subsp. ***cinerea***	EPot GKev
- subsp. ***praetutiana***	GKev NWad SPlb WAbe

Vitex (*Lamiaceae*)

agnus-castus	CAgr CBWd CBcs CCht CLau CMCN CSde EBee EPri EWTr GPoy LPar LRHS MGil MHoo MMrt MRav NLar SPer WCFE WJek WJur XSen
- f. ***alba***	CRos EHed EHyd LRHS MBlu MMrt NRHS SPoG XSen
- - PAB 9281	LEdu
- - 'Silver Spire'	EBee ELan EPfP SRms WPGP
- BLUE DIDDLEY ('Smvacbd'PBR)	LRHS
- DELTA BLUES ('Piivac-I') **new**	EHed
- f. ***latifolia*** 🏆^{H4}	CCBP CKel CRos ECre EGrl EHyd ELan EPfP LEdu LRHS LSRN MGos MHer MNHC NLar NRHS SEND SEdd SGsty SPoG WHlf WLov WPGP
- 'Santamaria' **new**	XSen
chinensis	see *V. negundo* var. *heterophylla*
FLIP SIDE ('Bailtexone') **new**	EHed
incisa	see *V. negundo* var. *heterophylla*
negundo	LEdu
- var. ***cannabifolia***	XSen
§ - var. ***heterophylla***	CSde EWes XSen

Vitis ✿ (*Vitaceae*)

'Abundante' (F)	WSuV
'Alden' (O/B)	WSuV
'Amandin' (G/W)	WSuV
amurensis	CDoC EPfP WSpi
- B&SWJ 4138	WCru
- B&SWJ 4299	WCru
'Atlantis' (O/W)	WSuV
§ 'Aurore' (W)	CAgr WSuV
'Autumn Royal'	CBod LRHS MTrO NPlm NRog
'Baco Noir' (O/B)	CAgr CEme WSuV
'Bianca' (O/W)	LPar NRog SBmr SSFr WSuV
BLACK HAMBURGH	see *V. vinifera* 'Schiava Grossa'
* 'Black Strawberry' (B)	CAgr MTrO WSuV
§ 'Boskoop Glory' (O/B) 🏆^{H5}	CMac EDir ELan LBuc MBros SBdl SCoo WHtc WSuV
'Brant' (O/B) 🏆^{H5}	Widely available
'Brilliant' (B)	WSuV
'Buffalo' (B)	WSuV
'Cabernet Cortis' (B)	WSuV
californica (F)	NLar
'Canadice' (O/R/S)	WSuV
'Cascade'	see *V.* SEIBEL 13053
'Castel 19637' (B)	WSuV
'Chambourcin' (B)	WSuV
CLARET CLOAK ('Frovit') 🏆^{H5}	CBcs CEme ELan EPfP GBin LRHS LSRN MBlu NLar NRHS SCoo SPer WLov WSpi
coignetiae 🏆^{H5}	Widely available
- B&SWJ 4550 from Korea	WCru
- B&SWJ 4744	WCru
- B&SWJ 8553 from Korea	WCru
- B&SWJ 10882 from Japan	WCru
- B&SWJ 10908 from Japan	WCru
- var. ***glabrescens*** B&SWJ 8537	WCru
- Sunningdale form	NLar
'Dalkauer' (W)	WSuV
'Dutch Black' (O/B)	WSuV
'Edwards No 1' (O/W)	WSuV
'Eger Csillaga' (O/W)	WSuV
'Einset' (B/S)	WSuV
ficifolia	see *V. thunbergii*
flexuosa B&SWJ 5568	WCru
- B&SWJ 6304	WCru
- var. ***choii*** B&SWJ 4101	WCru
- var. ***parvifolia*** B&SWJ 1946	WCru
§ 'Fragola' (O/R)	CAgr CMac CTri ECha EHyd ELan EPfP EPom LCro LOPS LRHS MAsh

MRav NLar NRog SCoo SPoG SPre SRms WMat WSpi WSuV
'Gagarin Blue' (O/B) CAgr EPom SVen WSuV
'Glenora' (F/B/S) CAgr WSuV
'Hecker' (O/W) WSuV
henryana see *Parthenocissus henryana*
'Himrod' (O/W/S) CCCN ELan NRog WSuV
'Horizon' (O/W) WSuV
inconstans see *Parthenocissus tricuspidata*
'Interlaken' (O/W/S) CAgr WSuV
'Isabella' (O/B) new WJur
'Johanniter' (W) SPre WSuV
'Kempsey Black' (O/B) CAgr WSuV
'Kozmapalme Muscatoly' (O/W) WSuV
'Kuibishevski' (O/R) WSuV
'Kyoho' (B) WSuV
labrusca WJur
- 'Concord' (O/B) WJur
LANDOT 244 (O/B) WSuV
LANDOT 3217 (O/B) WSuV
'L'Arcadie Blanche' (W) WSuV
'Léon Millot' (O/G/B) CAgr CSBt LSRN WSuV
'Lucy Kuhlman' (B) WSuV
'Maréchal Foch' (O/B) WSuV
'Maréchal Joffre' (O/R) CAgr WSuV
'Mars' (O/B/S) WSuV
'Merzling' (O/W) WSuV
'Munson R.W.' (O/R) WSuV
'Muscat Bleu' (O/B) CBod CCCN EPom LRHS MTrO NLar NRog SBmr SKee SPoG SSFr WMat WSuV
'Nero'[PBR] (O/O) CAgr
'New York Muscat' (O/B) ♀H5 WSuV
'New York Seedless' (O/W/S) WSuV
'Niagara' (O/W) WSuV
'Niederother Monschrebe' (O/R) WSuV
OBERLIN 595 (O/B) WSuV
'Orion' (O/W) CBod WSuV
'Paletina' (O/W) SEdi WSuV
parsley-leaved see *V. vinifera* 'Apiifolia'
'Perdin' (O/W) WSuV
'Phönix' (O/W) CAgr CCCN EHyd EPom LBuc LCro LOPS LRHS LSRN MAsh MGos MTrO NRHS NRog SBmr SCoo SKee SPer SPoG SPre SSFr SVic WMat WSuV
piasezkii var. ***pagnuccii*** WCru
* 'Pink Strawberry' (O) WSuV
'Pirovano 14' (O/B) WSuV
§ 'Plantet' (O/B) WSuV
'Poloske Muscat' (W) EPom NLar NRog WMat WSuV
pulchra WCru
purpurea 'Spetchley Park' (O/B) CAgr WSuV
quinquefolia see *Parthenocissus quinquefolia*
'Ramdas' (O/W) WSuV
RAVAT 51 (O/W) WSuV
'Rayon d'Or' (O/W) WSuV
'Regent'[PBR] (O/B) CAgr CCCN CTri EPom LCro LOPS LRHS MCoo MGos MTrO NLar NRog SCoo SKee SPer SPoG SPre SVic WMat WSuV
'Reliance' (O/R/S) CAgr WSuV
'Rembrant' (R) CAgr WSuV
riparia NLar
'Romulus' (O/G/W/S) WSuV
'Rondo' (O/B) CAgr NRog SPre SVic WMat WSuV
'Saturn' (O/R/S) CAgr WSuV
'Schuyler' (O/B) CAgr LPar WSuV

SEIBEL (F) EHyd
SEIBEL 5279 see *V.* 'Aurore'
SEIBEL 5409 (W) WSuV
SEIBEL 5455 see *V.* 'Plantet'
SEIBEL 7053 (R) WSuV
SEIBEL 9549 (R) WSuV
§ SEIBEL 13053 (O/B) CEme CMac CRos EHyd LRHS MAsh SRms WSuV
SEIBEL 138315 (R) WSuV
'Seneca' (W) WSuV
'Serena' (O/W) WSuV
§ 'Seyval Blanc' (O/W) CAgr MAsh NRog SVic WSuV
SEYVE VILLARD 12.375 see *V.* 'Villard Blanc'
SEYVE VILLARD 20.473 (F) NPer
SEYVE VILLARD 5276 see *V.* 'Seyval Blanc'
SEYVE VILLARD ambig. EHyd LRHS NPer
'Sirius' (B) WSuV
'Solaris' (O/W) NLar NRog WMat WSuV
'Sovereign Coronation' (B/S) WSuV
'Stauffer' (O/W) WSuV
'Suffolk Seedless' (B/S) WSuV
SUPERIOR SEEDLESS ('Sugraone') NPlm
'Tereshkova' (O/B) CAgr WSuV
'Thornton' (O/S) WSuV
§ ***thunbergii*** B&SWJ 4702 WCru
- 'Lobata' WPGP
'Triomphe d'Alsace' (O/B) CAgr CSBt NPer WSuV
'Trollhaugen' (O/B/S) WSuV
'Trollinger' see *V. vinifera* 'Schiava Grossa'
'Vanessa' (O/R/S) EPom SPer SVic WSuV
'Venus' (O/B/S) LRHS SVic
§ 'Villard Blanc' (O/W) WSuV
vinifera LPal LRHS SGsty SWeb
- 'Abouriou' (O/B) WSuV
- 'Acolon' (O/B) WSuV
- 'Adelheidtraube' (O/W) WSuV
- 'Albalonga' (W) WSuV
§ - 'Alicante' (G/B) CBcs WSuV
§ - 'Apiifolia' new WPGP
- 'Augusta Louise' (O/W) WSuV
- 'Auxerrois' (O/W) WSuV
- 'Bacchus' (O/W) CAgr LBuc LRHS MTrO NLar NRog SCoo SVic WMat WSuV
- 'Baresana' (G/W) SRms
- 'Beauty' (B/S) CAgr
- 'Black Alicante' see *V. vinifera* 'Alicante'
- 'Black Frontignan' (G/O/B) WSuV
- BLACK HAMBURGH see *V. vinifera* 'Schiava Grossa'
- 'Black Monukka' (G/B/S) WSuV
- 'Black Prince' (G/B) CAgr WSuV
- 'Blue Portuguese' see *V. vinifera* 'Portugieser'
§ - 'Bouvier' (W) WSuV
- 'Bouviertraube' see *V. vinifera* 'Bouvier'
- 'Buckland Sweetwater' (G/W) WSuV
- 'Cabernet Sauvignon' (O/B) CRos EBee EDir EHyd EPfP LRHS MAsh MGos NPer NRHS SBmr SVic WSuV
- 'Cardinal' (O/R) EDir WSuV
- 'Carla' (O/R) WSuV
- 'Centennial' (O/N/S) WSuV
- 'Chardonnay' (O/W) CAgr CCCN CDoC CRos EHyd LRHS LSRN MAsh NPer NRog SBmr SPre SVic WSuV
§ - 'Chasselas' (G/O/W) CEme EHyd LRHS NRog WSuV
- 'Chasselas de Fontainebleau' (G/O/W) CWnw SVic
- 'Chasselas d'Or' see *V. vinifera* 'Chasselas'
- 'Chasselas Rosé' (G/R) CAgr MGos NRog SPre WSuV

	- 'Chasselas Rosé Royal' (O/R)	CCCN SVic
	- 'Chasselas Vibert' (G/W)	WSuV
	- 'Chenin Blanc' (O/W)	SVic WSuV
	- 'Ciotat' (F)	EShb MRav WSuV
	- 'Cot Précoce de Tours' (O/B)	WSuV
	- 'Crimson Seedless' (R/S)	CBod NPlm WSuV
	- 'Csabagyöngye' (O/W)	WSuV
	- 'Dattier de Beyrouth' (G/W)	WSuV
	- 'Dattier Saint Vallier' (O/W)	SVic WSuV
	- 'Dolcetto' (O/B)	WSuV
	- 'Dornfelder' (O/R)	CCCN MTrO NLar NRog SCoo SPoG SVic WMat WSuV
	- 'Dunkelfelder' (O/R)	WSuV
	- EARLY RED GLOBE ('Sheegene 5'[PBR]) (R) **new**	NPlm
	- 'Ehrenfelser' (O/W)	WSuV
	- 'Elbling' (O/W)	WSuV
	- 'Exalta' (G/W/S)	WSuV
	- 'Excelsior' (W)	WSuV
	- 'Faber' (O/W)	WSuV
	- 'Fiesta' (W/S)	WSuV
	- 'Findling' (W)	WSuV
	- 'Flame' (R/S)	CAgr EDir MTrO SPer SVic WMat
	- 'Flame Red' (O/D)	CCCN EPom
	- 'Flame Seedless' (G/O/R/S)	CMac EPom NRog SCoo SPoG SPre SSFr WSuV
	- 'Forta' (O/W)	WSuV
	- 'Foster's Seedling' (G/W)	WSuV
	- 'Freisamer' (O/W)	WSuV
	- 'Frühburgunder' (O/B)	WSuV
	- 'Gamay Hâtif des Vosges' (B)	WSuV
	- 'Gamay Noir' (O/B)	SVic WSuV
	- Gamay Teinturier Group (O/B)	WSuV
§	- 'Garnacha Tinta' (B)	SVic
	- 'Gewürztraminer' (O/R)	EHyd LRHS MAsh NRHS SVic WSuV
	- 'Glory of Boskoop'	see *V.* 'Boskoop Glory'
	- 'Golden Chasselas'	see *V. vinifera* 'Chasselas'
	- 'Goldriesling' (O/W)	WSuV
	- 'Grenache'	see *V. vinifera* 'Garnacha Tinta'
	- 'Gros Colmar' (G/B)	WSuV
	- 'Grüner Veltliner' (O/W)	WSuV
	- 'Gutenborner' (O/W)	WSuV
	- 'Helfensteiner' (O/R)	WSuV
	- 'Huxelrebe' (O/W)	SVic WSuV
	- 'Incana' (O/B)	EBee EPfP LRHS MRav SVen WCFE WCot WPGP
	- 'Irsay Olivér' (O/W)	WSuV
	- 'Italia' (O/W)	EDir SWeb
	- 'Juliaumsrebe' (O/W)	WSuV
	- 'Kanzler' (O/W)	WSuV
	- 'Kerner' (O/W)	WSuV
	- 'Kernling' (F)	WSuV
	- 'King's Ruby' (F/S)	WSuV
	- 'Lakemont' (O/W/S)	CAgr CCCN CDoC CMac CRHN CTri EDir EHyd ELan EPfP EPom LEdu LRHS MGos MTrO NLar NRHS NRog NTrD SBmr SCoo SEdi SKee SPoG SPre SSFr SVic WMat WSuV
	- 'Lival' (O/B)	WSuV
	- 'Macabeo'	see *V. vinifera* 'Viura'
	- 'Madeleine Angevine' (O/W)	CAgr CRos EDir EHyd LRHS LSRN MAsh NPer NRHS NRog SPoG SVen SVic WSuV
	- 'Madeleine Céline' (B)	WSuV
	- 'Madeleine Noire' (O/B)	EDir
	- 'Madeleine Royale' (G/W)	WSuV
	- 'Madeleine Silvaner' (O/W)	CRos CSBt EHyd LRHS MAsh NPer NRHS SPoG WSuV
	- 'Madresfield Court' (G/B)	WSuV
	- 'Merlot' (G/B)	EDir EHyd EPfP LRHS NRHS SVic WSuV
§	- 'Meunier' (B)	SVic WSuV
	- 'Mireille' (F)	WSuV
	- 'Morio Muscat' (O/W)	WSuV
§	- 'Müller-Thurgau' (O/W)	LRHS LSRN MAsh NRog SPoG SVic WSuV
	- 'Muscat Blanc à Petits Grains' (O/W)	SWvt
	- 'Muscat de Lierval' (O/B)	WSuV
	- 'Muscat de Saumur' (O/W)	WSuV
	- 'Muscat Hamburg' (G/B)	CKel CRos CWnw LRHS LSRN MAsh SGsty SWvt WSuV
	- 'Muscat of Alexandria' (G/W)	CBcs CBod CCCN CMac CRHN CRos CTri EHyd LRHS MRav NRHS NRog SRms SVic WMat
	- 'Muscat Ottonel' (O/W)	WSuV
	- 'Muscat Saint Laurent' (W)	WSuV
	- 'Nebbiolo' (O/B)	WSuV
	- 'No 69' (W)	WSuV
	- 'Noblessa' (W)	WSuV
	- 'Noir Hâtif de Marseille' (O/B)	WSuV
	- 'Olive Blanche' (O/W)	WSuV
	- 'Optima' (O/W)	WSuV
	- 'Ora' (O/W/S)	LRHS WSuV
	- 'Ortega' (O/W)	NRog WSuV
	- 'Parellada' (W)	SVic
	- 'Perle' (O/W)	WSuV
	- 'Perlette' (O/W/S)	CBod CCCN EDir EPom WSuV
	- 'Petit Rouge' (R)	WSuV
	- 'Picurka' (O/W/S)	SVic
	- 'Pinot Blanc' (O/W)	CCCN EDir EHyd EPfP LCro LOPS LRHS MAsh SVic WSuV
	- 'Pinot Gris' (O/B)	SVic WSuV
	- 'Pinot Noir' (O/B)	CCCN CDoC SVic WSuV
§	- 'Portugieser' (O/B)	WSuV
	- 'Précoce de Bousquet' (O/W)	WSuV
	- 'Précoce de Malingre' (O/W)	CAgr
	- 'Prima' (O/B)	WSuV
	- 'Primavis Frontignan' (G/W)	WSuV
	- 'Purpurea' (O/B) ♀H5	Widely available
	- 'Queen of Esther' (B)	WSuV
	- 'Regner' (O/W)	WSuV
	- 'Reichensteiner' (O/G/W)	CAgr NRog SVic WSuV
	- 'Rhea' (G/O/R)	SVic
	- 'Riesling' (O/W)	CCCN EDir EHyd LRHS MAsh SVic WSuV
	- RIESLING-SILVANER	see *V. vinifera* 'Müller-Thurgau'
	- 'Rotberger' (O/G/B)	WSuV
	- 'Royal Muscadine' (G/O/W)	WMat WSuV
	- 'Saint Laurent' (G/O/W)	SVic WSuV
	- 'Sauvignon Blanc' (O/W)	CCCN EBee EDir EHyd LRHS NRHS SVic WSuV
	- 'Scheurebe' (O/W)	WSuV
§	- 'Schiava Grossa' (G/B/D)	CBcs CBod CDoC CMac CSBt CTri EDir EHeP EHyd EPfP EPom LCro LRHS LSRN MAsh MRav MTrO NBwr NPer NRog SPer SPoG SPre SVic SWvt WMat WSuV
	- 'Schönburger' (O/W)	SVic WSuV
	- 'Schwarzriesling'	see *V. vinifera* 'Meunier'
	- 'Sémillon' (G/O/W)	EHyd LRHS LSRN MAsh SVic
	- 'Senator' (O/W)	WSuV

- 'Septimer' (O/W)	WSuV
- 'Shiraz' (B)	WSuV
- 'Siegerrebe' (O/W/D)	CAgr EHyd LRHS MAsh NPer NRog SPoG SVic WSuV
- 'Silvaner' (O/W)	WSuV
- 'Spetchley Red' (O/B) ♀H5	CBod CRHN MNrw WAvo WCot WCru WLov WPGP WSpi
- strawberry grape	see *V.* 'Fragola'
- 'Suffolk Red' (G/R/S)	EPfP SVic
§ - 'Sultana' (W/S)	CAgr NRog WSuV
- 'Syrah' (G/B)	SVic
- 'Tempranillo'	NPlm SVic
- 'Theresa' (O/W)	WSuV
- 'Thompson Seedless'	see *V. vinifera* 'Sultana'
* - 'Triomphe' (O/B)	SVic
- 'Triomphrebe' (W)	WSuV
- 'Valvin Muscat'	NRog
- 'Verdejo'	SVic
- 'Victoria' (O/W) new	NPlm
§ - 'Viura'	SVic
- 'Vroege van der Laan' (O/W)	NLar SRms WHtc
- 'White Muscat' (W)	WSuV
- 'Wrotham Pinot' (O/B)	WSuV
- 'Würzer' (O/W)	WSuV
- 'Zweigeltrebe' (O/B)	WSuV
* 'White Strawberry' (O/W)	WSuV
'Zalagyöngye' (W)	CAgr WSuV

Volutaria (*Asteraceae*)

muricata	CSpe

Vriesea (*Bromeliaceae*)

'Astrid' ♀H1a	LCro NCft NPic
carinata	NPic
correia-arauji	NCft
delicatula	NCft
'Era' PBR	LCro
fosteriana 'Red Chestnut'	NCft
gigantea 'Nova'	NCft
hieroglyphica	NCft NPic
imperialis	NPic
saundersii	NCft NPic
splendens ♀H1a	NCft NPic SPlb

W

Wachendorfia (*Haemodoraceae*)

multiflora	CPbh
thyrsiflora	CBcs CCht CDoC CExl CTsd EBee IKel LEdu SVen WPGP

Wahlenbergia (*Campanulaceae*)

congesta	NWad
gloriosa	EDAr EPot WAbe
hederacea	GArf
pumilio	see *Edraianthus pumilio*

Waldsteinia (*Rosaceae*)

fragarioides	GKev
geoides	EHed EMor EPPr EWTr GKev LRHS MGil MMuc NEoE NLar XLum
ternata	Widely available
§ - 'Mozaick' (v)	EBee EPPr EShb NBir NFav
- 'Variegata'	see *W. ternata* 'Mozaick'

Wallichia (*Arecaceae*)

disticha	NPlm

walnut, black see *Juglans nigra*

walnut, common see *Juglans regia*

Wasabia (*Brassicaceae*)

wasabi	see *Eutrema japonicum*

Washingtonia (*Arecaceae*)

× ***filibusta***	CCCN SEND
filifera ♀H1c new	NPlm SPlb
robusta	EDir ERom LPal LWaG NHrt NPlm SPlb SWeb

Watsonia (*Iridaceae*)

aletroides	CPbh SDeJ SVen
angusta	CBor CExl CPrp EBee EPri SPlb
ardernei	see *W. borbonica* subsp. ***ardernei*** (Sander) Goldblatt 'Arderne's White'
beatricis	see *W. pillansii*
§ ***borbonica***	CBor CPla CPrp
- subsp. ***ardernei*** misapplied	see *W. borbonica* subsp. ***ardernei*** (Sander) Goldblatt 'Arderne's White'
§ - subsp. ***ardernei*** (Sander) Goldbatt 'Arderne's White'	CExl EPri
- 'Peach Glow'	EBee EGrI EPri ERCP GKev LAma SDeJ SPeP
brevifolia	see *W. laccata*
brick red-flowered	CPrp EPri
coccinea dwarf	CPbh
'Curly Blooms'	CPbh EPri
'Dart Sea Trout'	CPrp EBee EGrI
fourcadei	ECre EGrI
galpinii	WCot
I 'Gigantea'	LRHS XSte
hybrid, burnt orange-flowered	CPbh
- dark pink-flowered	CPbh
- orange-flowered	CPbh
- peach-flowered	CPbh EPri
§ ***laccata***	CPbh EPri
lepida	CPbh SPlb
× ***longifolia***	EBee
marginata	CPbh CPrp
marlothii	WCot
meriana	EBee EGrI GKev LAma MHtn SDeJ
- var. ***bulbillifera***	CPbh CPrp EBee ESwi GAbr WSHC
'Peachy Pink Orphan'	EBee
§ ***pillansii***	CAbb CBcs CCCN CExl CPbh CPrp CTsd ECre EPfP EPri GBin ILea LEdu LRHS NCth SGBe SVen XSte
- apricot-flowered	CAbb CTsd LRHS SGBe
- peach-flowered	CExl
- pink-flowered	CExl CPrp
- red-flowered	CExl NCth
- salmon-flowered	CSpe
- soft pink-flowered	EPri WSHC
pink-flowered	EBee
pyramidata	see *W. borbonica*
'Special Red'	CPbh
'Stanford Scarlet'	CExl CPrp ELon
transvaalensis	CPrp EBee
'Tresco Dwarf Pink'	CExl CPrp EBee EGrI LEdu LRHS WPGP WSHC XSte
Tresco hybrids	CAbb CAby CBcs CExl CPbh EPfP EPri ESwi SRkn
vanderspuyae	CBcs CExl CPrp EGrI EPri
wilmaniae	CExl CPrp EPri WFar

Wattakaka see *Dregea*

Weberbauerocereus (*Cactaceae*)

winterianus new	EAri

Wedelia (*Asteraceae*)

trilobata	see *Sphagneticola trilobata*

Weigela ✿ (*Caprifoliaceae*)

CC 1231	CExl
TCM 12-852	SBrt
'Abel Carrière'	CMac CTri ECtt NWea SRms WCFE WFar WSpi
ALL SUMMER PEACH ('Slingpink')	CKel LCro LOPS MAsh MMrt SRHi
§ ALL SUMMER RED ('Slingco 1'PBR)	CBod CEnd CKel CRos CWGN EHyd EPfP LCro LOPS LRHS MAsh MMrt NLar NRHS SCob SPoG SRHi WHtc WSpi
'Avalanche' misapplied	see *W.* 'Candida'
'Avant Garde'	WLov
BLACK AND WHITE ('Courtacad1'PBR)	CBcs CBod CDoC CKel CRos CWGN CWnw EBee EFPl EHyd ELan EPfP LRHS LSRN MAsh NEoE NLar NRHS SCob SGol SPoG SRHi WHtc
'Boskoop Glory'	SPer
§ BRIANT RUBIDOR ('Olympiade') (v)	CBod CEnd CGBo CMac EDir GMcL MAsh MGos MMrt MMuc MRav NBwr NLar NQui SGol SPer SPlb SPoG WAvo WFar WHtc WSpi
'Bristol Ruby'	Widely available
'Bristol Snowflake'	CMac EHeP EHed EPfP MBlu MHer MSwo NLar SCob SRms
§ 'Candida'	CBrac CTri ELan MRav NLar SGol SGsty SPer WSpi
CAPPUCCINO ('Verweig 2'PBR)	MBlu NLar SGol
CARNAVAL ('Courtalor') ♀H6	CBcs GMcL MRav SCob
'Chameleon'	NEoE SGol
coraeensis ♀H6	CBcs CBod EPfP EWld MBlu MGil MMrt MNrw NLar SBrt WLov
CRIMSON KISSES	see *W.* ALL SUMMER RED
decora B&SWJ 10834	WCru
EBONY AND IVORY ('Velda'PBR)	CKel CRos EFPl EHyd EPfP ILea LCro LOPS LRHS NLar NRHS SGol
'Eva Rathke'	LPar NLar NWea
'Evita'	MBlu
floribunda B&SWJ 10831	WCru
florida	CMac EHeP SavN
- B&SWJ 8439	WCru
* - 'Albovariegata' (v)	CExl
§ - 'Alexandra'PBR ♀H6	CBod CDoC CEme CExl CKel CRos CSBt CWnw EDir EFPl EGrl EHyd ELan EMil GKev LRHS LSRN MAsh MGos MRav NBro SCob SGBe SNig SPer SRkn SSha SWvt WHtc
- ALL SUMMER MONET ('Verweig 8') **new**	LCro
- 'Bicolor'	CMac ELan
- 'Foliis Purpureis'	CBar CBcs CBod CBrac CExl CMac EHeP ELan GMcL LSto MAsh MGos MRav MSwo NBwr NLar NWea SGol SNig SPer SPlb SRms SWvt WAvo WHtc WLov
- 'Gustave Malet'	CMCN
- MAGICAL RAINBOW ('Kolmagira'PBR)	CBod CRos EHyd LBuc LCro LOPS LRHS MAsh MMrt NEoE NRHS SCob SGol SPoG
- 'Milk and Honey'	NBwr SCob
- MINOR BLACK ('Verweig 3'PBR)	CKel EDir EPfP GMcL LRHS MGos NBro NEoE NHol SCob SGol SPoG SRHi
- MONET ('Verweig'PBR) (v)	CDoC CEme CKel CMac CRos CWnw EBee EDir EHyd EPfP GMcL LBuc LCro LRHS LSRN MAsh MDon MGos MMrt NBro NHol NLar NRHS SCob SGBe SGol SPoG SRms
- MOULIN ROUGE ('Brigela'PBR)	EHyd ELan EPfP LRHS MAsh MGos NLar WHtc
- 'Pink Princess'	EHyd LRHS MSwo
- RUBIGOLD	see *W.* BRIANT RUBIDOR
- 'Versicolor'	CExl LShi SMrm SRms
- WINE AND ROSES	see *W. florida* 'Alexandra'
- 'Wings of Fire'PBR	EHyd EPfP LBuc LPar LRHS NLar NRHS SMad SRHi
'Florida Variegata' (v) ♀H6	Widely available
'Gold Rush'	NLar
'Golden Candy'	NEoE SCob
hortensis	CExl
- B&SWJ 10808	WCru
'Hulsdonk'	NLar
japonica 'Dart's Colourdream'	EHed EPfP EWes MMuc SEND SGol
- 'Variegated Dart's Colourdream' (v)	ELon
'Jean's Gold'	MBlu MRav
'Kosteriana Variegata' (v)	CDoC CKel CSBt EBee EDir EHyd EPfP EShb LRHS SRms
'Little Red Robin'	CBod NEoE SCob WFar
'Looymansii Aurea'	CBrac CExl CTri EPfP NBPC NLar SGol SPer SRms WFar
LUCIFER ('Courtared')	CKel WSpi
'Marjorie'	EWTr
maximowiczii	CExl
§ ***middendorffiana***	Widely available
- 'Mango'	CRos EHyd EPfP LCro LOPS LRHS NLar NRHS
'Minuet'	CRos MRav MSwo NEoE SGol
'Mont-Blanc'	MAsh MMrt
NAIN ROUGE ('Courtanin')	CTri NLar
'Nana Variegata' (v)	CKel EDir EHyd ELon EPfP GMcL LCro LRHS LSto NLar NRHS SOrN WFar
NAOMI CAMPBELL ('Bokrashine'PBR)	EGrl SGol
'Newport Red'	see *W.* 'Vanicek'
PICOBELLA ROSA ('Tvp2') **new**	LCro
PINK POPPET ('Plangen'PBR)	CBod CEme CEnd CKel CRos CSBt EHyd ELan EPfP LRHS LSRN MAsh MGos NLar NRHS SCob SCoo SGBe SNig SPoG SRkn SWvt WHlf
praecox	WPGP
- B&SWJ 8705	WCru
'Praecox Variegata' (v) ♀H6	CMac CRos CTri EHyd EPfP LRHS MAsh MRav NBir NRHS SDix SPer SPoG SRms WCFE
'Red Prince' ♀H6	CDoC EBee EFPl EPfP GArf GMcL LPar LRHS MAsh MNrw MSwo NLar SCob SGol SNig
RUBIDOR	see *W.* BRIANT RUBIDOR
RUBIGOLD	see *W.* BRIANT RUBIDOR
'Ruby Anniversary'	CBod SGBe
'Ruby Queen'PBR	CMac
'Rumba'	CMac EBtc
sessilifolia	see *Diervilla sessilifolia*
'Snowflake'	SRms
subsessilis B&SWJ 1056	WCru
- B&SWJ 4206	WCru
'Suzanne' (v)	EPPr
'Tango'	NEoE SSut WAvo WFar
§ 'Vanicek'	CBrac GMcL NWea SCob
'Victoria'	CGBo CMac EDir MGos MSwo NBir SGol SPer
WHITE LIGHTNING ('Wf-2009') (v)	NEoE

Weingartia see *Rebutia*

Weldenia (*Commelinaceae*)

candida	EAri EPot GEdr NHar SChF WCot

Westringia (*Lamiaceae*)

brevifolia	CCCN CSde SVen
eremicola 'Blue'	CAbb CTsd
§ ***fruticosa*** ♀H1c	CBcs CBod CCCN CSde CTsd SRms SVen WLov
- 'Smokie' (v)	CCCN
- 'Variegata' (v)	CCCN CPbh CSde SRms SVen
longifolia	CCCN
rosmariniformis	see *W. fruticosa*
'Wynyabbie Gem'	CAbb CBod CCCN CKel EHyd EPPr SEND SPoG SVen WLov

whitecurrant see *Ribes rubrum* (W); see also AGM Fruit Section

Wigandia (*Boraginaceae*)

caracasana	CTsd

Wikstroemia (*Thymelaeaceae*)

gemmata	see *Daphne gemmata*

wineberry see *Rubus phoenicolasius*

Wisteria (*Fabaceae*)

§ ***brachybotrys***	LRHS MTrO SWeb WSpi
§ - f. ***albiflora*** 'Shiro-kapitan' ♀H6	Widely available
- 'Okayama' ♀H6	CDoC CKel CRos CWnw EHyd EMil EPfP ETho LCro LRHS MGos MTrO NRHS SGsty SLau SWeb WMat
- 'Showa-beni' ♀H6	CAco CEnd CKel CRos CSBt CTri CWGN CWnw EHyd EMil EPfP LMaj LRHS MGil MGos MTrO NLar NRHS SCoo SEND SGsty SLau SNig SPoG SWeb WLov WPGP WSpi
'Burford'	see *W.* × *valderi* 'Burford'
floribunda	CBcs CBrac CRHN EDir MTrO SEWo SGol SWeb
- B&SWJ 12748 from South Korea	WCru
§ - f. ***alba*** 'Shiro-noda' ♀H6	Widely available
- BLACK DRAGON	see *W. floribunda* 'Kokuryū'
- blue-flowered	WLov
§ - 'Domino' ♀H6	CBcs CDoC CKel CMac CRos CWCL CWGN EBee EHyd ELon EPfP LCro LPar LRHS LSRN MAsh MGos MRav MSwo NLar NOrn SCob SCoo SEND SLau SPer SSta SWeb WLov WSpi
- 'Ed's Blue Dragon' (d)	EBee
- 'Eranthema'	see *W.* × *valderi* 'Eranthema'
- f. ***floribunda***	SWeb
- 'Fragrantissima'	see *W. sinensis* var. *sinensis* f. *alba* 'Jako'
- 'Geisha'	CBcs CEnd CKel CRos EHyd ELon EPfP LRHS NLar NRHS SEND SRms WPGP
- 'Golden Dragon'	SWeb
- 'Harlequin'	CBcs CRos CWCL EBee EHyd ELon ETho LCro LRHS SEND WLov
- 'Honey Bee Pink'	see *W. floribunda* f. *rosea* 'Hon-beni'
- 'Issai Perfect'	CRos EHyd LRHS LSRN NLar SCoo
- 'Issai-naga'	NLar
- 'Jakohn-fuji'	see *W. sinensis* var. *sinensis* f. *alba* 'Jako'
- 'Kimono' ♀H5	CBod LRHS NLar SLau
§ - 'Kokuryū' ♀H6	CBcs CDoC CEnd CRos EGrI EMil ETho GBin IPot MAsh MPri MTrO NLar NOrn SCob SGsty SLau SPoG WHtc WLov WSpi
§ - 'Kuchi-beni'	CBcs CBod CEnd CRos CWCL ELan LCro LOPS LRHS LSRN MGos MRav NHol NLar SCob SEND SLau SPer SPoG SRms WHtc
- 'Lawrence' ♀H6	CBcs CMac CRos CWGN EWTr LRHS MGos NLar SCoo SLau SPoG WLov
- 'Lipstick'	see *W. floribunda* 'Kuchi-beni'
- 'Loder's Purple'	SLau
- 'Longissima'	see *W. floribunda* f. *multijuga* 'Kyushaku'
- 'Longissima Alba'	see *W. floribunda* f. *alba* 'Shiro-noda'
- 'Macrobotrys'	see *W. floribunda* f. *multijuga* 'Kyushaku'
- 'Magenta'	EHyd LRHS
- f. ***microphylla*** 'Hime' **new**	WPGP
- 'Mon-nishiki' (v)	WCot
§ - f. ***multijuga***	Widely available
- - 'Cascade'	CBcs LRHS NLar WSpi
§ - - 'Kyushaku'	CKel SLau
- MURASAKI-NAGA	see *W. floribunda* 'Purple Patches'
- 'Nana Richin's Purple'	CEnd
- 'Peaches and Cream'	see *W. floribunda* 'Kuchi-beni'
- 'Pink Ice'	see *W. floribunda* 'Rosea'
§ - 'Purple Patches'	WSpi
- REINDEER	see *W. sinensis* var. *sinensis* f. *alba* 'Jako'
- 'Rolvenden Bronze'	SLau
§ - f. ***rosea*** 'Hon-beni' ♀H6	Widely available
- 'Royal Purple'	see *W. floribunda* 'Kokuryū'
- 'Russelliana'	see *W. floribunda* 'Kokuryū'
- 'Shiro-naga'	see *W. floribunda* f. *alba* 'Shiro-noda'
- 'Snow Showers'	see *W. floribunda* f. *alba* 'Shiro-noda'
- 'Strella'	NLar
- 'Variegata' (v)	CWGN
- 'Violacea Plena'	see *W. floribunda* 'Yae-kokuryū'
§ - 'Yae-kokuryū' (d) ♀H6	Widely available
× ***formosa***	CEnd LCro LOPS SLau
- BLACK DRAGON	see *W. floribunda* 'Kokuryū'
- 'Caroline'	Widely available
- 'Domino'	see *W. floribunda* 'Domino'
- 'Enchantment' **new**	NLar
- 'Issai' Wada *pro parte*	see *W. floribunda* 'Domino'
- 'Ivy Hatch'	WPGP
- 'Kokuryu'	see *W. floribunda* 'Kokuryū'
- 'Yae-kokuryu'	see *W. floribunda* 'Yae-kokuryū'
frutescens	CDoC
- 'Alba'	see *W. frutescens* 'Nivea'
- 'Amethyst Falls' PBR	CBcs CBod CEnd CRos CTsd CWGN ELan EPfP EShb EWTr IArd LBuc LCro LOPS LRHS LSRN MGos SCoo SGsty SPoG WHlf WLov WTyc
- 'Longwood Purple'	CDoC CRos EHyd LCro LRHS NLar NRHS
- var. ***macrostachya*** 'Aunt Dee'	CWGN NLar
- - 'Blue Moon'	GMcL IPot WSpi
- - 'Clara Mack'	CWGN WSpi
§ - 'Nivea'	EHyd EPfP LRHS NRHS
Kapitan-fuji	see *W. brachybotrys*
multijuga 'Alba'	see *W. floribunda* f. *alba* 'Shiro-noda'
sinensis	Widely available
- 'Amethyst' ♀H6	CArg CBcs CDoC CEnd CRos EGrI EHyd EPfP LCro LOPS LRHS LSRN MAsh MGil MGos NRHS SCob SLau SPer SWeb WLov WSpi
- 'Consequa'	see *W. sinensis* 'Prolific'
- 'Cooke's Special'	see *W. sinensis* 'Prolific'
- 'Oosthoek's Variety'	see *W. sinensis* 'Prolific'
I - 'Pink Ice'	EWTr MAsh SRms

	- 'Prematura'	see *W. floribunda* 'Domino'
	- 'Prematura Alba'	see *W. brachybotrys* f. *albiflora* 'Shiro-kapitan'
§	- 'Prolific' 🏆H6	Widely available
	- 'Rosea'	EDir EPfP LMaj LSRN SWvt
	- 'Shiro-capital'	see *W. brachybotrys* f. *albiflora* 'Shiro-kapitan'
	- var. ***sinensis*** f. ***alba***	Widely available
§	- - - 'Jako' 🏆H6	CEnd MGos NHol NLar SLau
	'Tiverton'	LRHS
	× ***valderi***	CDoC CRos LPar NOrn SGsty SWeb WLov
§	- 'Burford' 🏆H6	CEnd CKel CMac CRos CWGN EHyd EMil EPfP LCro LPar LRHS LSRN MAsh MGos MSwo MTrO NOrn SCoo SEND SLau SRms WLov WMat WPGP WSpi
§	- 'Eranthema'	NLar SLau
	- 'Hocker Edge'	SLau
	- 'Lavender Lace'	CBcs EHyd EPfP LRHS LSRN MAsh NLar SCob SLau
§	- 'Murasaki-kapitan'	CEnd CMac CTri CWGN EMil EPfP LRHS MGil SEND SLau WLov
	venusta	see *W. brachybotrys* f. *albiflora* 'Shiro-kapitan'
	- 'Alba'	see *W. brachybotrys* f. *albiflora* 'Shiro-kapitan'
	- var. ***violacea*** misapplied	see *W.* × *valderi* 'Murasaki-kapitan'

Wisteriopsis (*Fabaceae*)

§	***reticulata***	WHlf

Withania (*Solanaceae*)

	sinensis BWJ 8093	WCru
	somnifera	GPoy MHoo

Wittsteinia (*Alseuosmiaceae*)

	vacciniacea	GEdr WCru

Wodyetia (*Arecaceae*)

	bifurcata	NPlm

Wollemia (*Araucariaceae*)

	nobilis	CDTJ ELan EPfP ESwi GBin IKel LPar LRHS MGos NPlm NPoe NTrD NWea SArc SBmr SCoo SPoG WBor WLea

Woodsia (*Woodsiaceae*)

	obtusa	CKel CLAP CWnw EBee EMor EPfP ISha LPal NBro SPoG SRms SRot WCot XLum
	polystichoides	SRms

Woodwardia (*Blechnaceae*)

	from Emei Shan, China	CLAP
	fimbriata 🏆H3	Widely available
	orientalis	CLAP EHed EHyd EMor ESwi LEdu LRHS MAsh NRHS WFib
	- var. ***formosana***	LEdu SPlb
	- - B&SWJ 6865	ESwi WCru
	prolifera 🏆H3	CKel LEdu SPlb WPGP
	radicans 🏆H3	CDTJ EShb EWes LEdu WFib
	unigemmata 🏆H4	CLAP EFer EHed EHyd EMor EPfP EShb EWes LAlb LEdu LRHS NRHS SPlb WAbe WFib WPGP
	virginica	CLAP

Worcesterberry see *Ribes* 'Worcesterberry'

Wulfenia (*Plantaginaceae*)

	amherstiana	GEdr LEdu
	baldaccii	EBee GKev SBrt
	carinthiaca	CBor EBee EMor GArf GEdr GKev GQue LEdu NBir NLar WCot XLum
	- 'Alba'	EMor GEdr GKev
	× ***schwarzii***	CDor CMiW EBee LEdu WSHC

Wurmbea (*Colchicaceae*)

§	***stricta***	WCot

Wyethia (*Asteraceae*)

	amplexicaulis	EAJP GEdr
	angustifolia	SBrt
	helianthoides	CPla
	mollis B&SWJ 14067	WCru

X

Xanthisma (*Asteraceae*)

§	***coloradoense***	NSla

Xanthoceras (*Sapindaceae*)

	sorbifolium 🏆H7	CAgr CBcs CMCN EBee EPfP LRHS MBlu MGil MVil NLar SPoG WPGP WSpi

Xanthocyparis (*Cupressaceae*)

§	***nootkatensis***	CAco MAsh
	- 'Aurea'	CAco
	- 'Boyko's Sundown'	CAco
	- 'Flaming Arrow'	NLar
	- 'Glauca'	CAco
	- 'Gloria Polonica' PBR (v)	CAco NLar
	- 'Golden Waterfall'	CAco NLar
	- 'Gracilis'	CAco
	- 'Green Arrow' 🏆H7	CAco CKen MTrO SLim WMat
	- 'Jubilee'	SLim WCFE WMat
	- 'Kanada'	SLim
	- 'Moon Shot'	CAco SLim
	- 'Nordkroken'	CAco
	- 'Pendula' 🏆H7	CAco CCVT CEme CKen ELan EPfP MAsh MBlu MTrO NBwr NWea
I	- 'Pendula Aurea'	CAco
	- 'Sparkling Arrow'	CAco
	- 'Strict Weeper'	CAco CKen NLar SLim
	- 'Variegata' (v)	CAco
	vietnamensis	CBcs IDee LRHS WPGP

Xanthorhiza (*Ranunculaceae*)

	simplicissima	CBcs EPfP LEdu MGil NLar WCot WPGP

Xanthorrhoea (*Xanthorrhoeaceae*)

	australis	SPlb
	fulva	SPlb
	glauca	CCCN
	johnsonii	NPlm SPlb
	preisii	CTsd NPlm SPlb

Xanthosoma (*Araceae*)

	sagittifolium	EAri LAma
	violaceum	EAri LAma

Xerochrysum (*Asteraceae*)

§	***bracteatum***	SVen
§	- 'Coco'	CSpe
§	- 'Dargan Hill Monarch'	CSpe SRms
	- 'King Fireball'	CSpe
	- 'Nevada Orange'	LRHS
	- 'Nevada Red'	LRHS
	- 'Salmon Rose' **new**	CSpe

Xeronema (*Xeronemataceae*)

callistemon	CBrP CCCN

Xerophyta (*Velloziaceae*)

retinervis	SPlb

Xylorhiza see *Machaeranthera*

Y

Ypsilandra (*Melanthiaceae*)

cavaleriei	CExl GEdr GGro WCot WFar
thibetica	CBct CExl CMil CTtf EBee EPPr EPfP ESwi GEdr GGro GKev LEdu MNrw SMad WCot WCru WSHC

Yucca ✿ (*Asparagaceae*)

aloifolia	CBcs CCCN CDTJ LPal SArc SPlb
§ - f. ***marginata*** (v)	NPlm
- 'Purpurea'	LRHS NPlm
- 'Variegata'	see *Y. aloifolia* f. *marginata*
angustifolia	see *Y. glauca*
arizonica	CDTJ
baccata	CAgr CCCN CDoC SPlb XSen
campestris	CDTJ XSen
carnerosana	CDTJ
cernua	WCot
constricta	CDTJ
decipiens	XSen
§ ***elata***	CCCN NPlm XSen
* ***elegans*** **new**	NPlm
§ ***elephantipes*** ♀H2	CDTJ LCro LOPS NHrt NPlm NTrD SEND
- 'Elmila' (v) **new**	NPlm
- 'Jewel' (v)	EPfP NPlm SEND
- 'Puck' (v)	MPri SEND
- variegated (v)	EBee EOli SEND
faxoniana	CDTJ NPlm SPlb
filamentosa	CBcs CBod CCCN CEme CKel CMac CTri EBee EHeP ELan EPfP LCro LOPS LRHS LSun MGos MSwo SCob SEND SIvy SPer SPlb SRms WHtc XSen
- 'Bright Edge' (v) ♀H4	CBcs CBod CBrac CMac CTri EHeP ELan ELon EPfP LCro LOPS LPal LSRN MRav MSwo SGol SWvt
- 'Color Guard' (v) ♀H5	CBcs CTsd EHyd ELan LRHS MGos NPlm SGBe SIvy SMad SPeP SPoG
- 'Garland's Gold' (v)	CBcs CCCN
- 'Gold Heart' (v)	NPlm
- 'Variegata' (v)	GQue SRms
filifera	EOli LPal NPlm SPlb
- 'Australis' **new**	NPlm
flaccida	XSen
- 'Golden Sword' (v) ♀H4	CBcs CBrac CEme CMac EBee EHeP ELan EPfP GMaP GMcL LRHS LSRN MDon MGos MSwo NLar SCob SRms SWvt WFar WHlf
- 'Ivory' ♀H5	CBcs GBin GMaP LSRN MRav NLar SRms
× ***floribunda***	SArc
§ ***glauca***	SPlb SPtp WCot XSen
gloriosa ♀H5	CBcs CMac CTri ERom LPal LPar SArc SCob SEND SGsty SPer SPlb SWeb SWvt WFar
- 'Aureovariegata'	see *Y. gloriosa* 'Variegata'
- BRIGHT STAR ('Walbristar'PBR) (v) ♀H5	CCht LCro SPeP XSte XVPe
- 'Lone Star' **new**	NPlm
§ - 'Variegata' (v) ♀H5	CBcs CBod CDoC CKel CMac CSBt EGrI EHeP ELan ELon EPfP GMaP LRHS MAsh NPlm NRHS SArc SCob SEND SIvy SPer SPlb SPoG SRms SWeb SWvt WCFE
guatemalensis	see *Y. elephantipes*
harrimaniae	WCot XSen
linearifolia	NPlm
linearis	see *Y. thompsoniana*
mexicana	CDTJ
mixtecana	XSen
queretaroensis	CDTJ
radiosa	see *Y. elata*
recurvifolia ♀H5	SArc
- BANANA SPLIT ('Monca') (v)	WCot
- 'Gold Stream' (v)	WCot
rigida	CDTJ NPlm XSen
rostrata	CCCN CCht CDTJ EAri EOli ETod LPal NPlm SArc SPlb SWeb XSen XSte
- 'Blue Swan' **new**	NPlm
- 'Hidra' **new**	NPlm
- 'Sapphire Skies'	CBcs CMac
rupicola	WCot XSen
§ ***thompsoniana***	CDTJ LPal NPlm XSen
torreyi	CDTJ
whipplei	CBcs CCCN ELan EPfP LRHS SPtp WPGP XSen

Yushania (*Poaceae*)

KR 7698	MWht
§ ***anceps***	CAgr CBcs MMuc MWht SEND
- 'Pitt White'	CAgr CBdn MWht
chungii	CBdn MWht
maculata	CAgr CBdn CExl MWht
Yunnan 5	CExl MWht

Z

Zabelia (*Caprifoliaceae*)

§ ***triflora***	CExl EPfP LAlb MBlu NLar SEND SSha WGob WPGP
§ ***umbellata***	SBrt

Zaluzianskya (*Scrophulariaceae*)

elongata	SPlb
microsiphon	SPlb
ovata	CPbh CTtf CWCL EPot EWld GBin GElm GKev LCro LOPS LRHS LShi MHer NBwr SCoo SPlb SPoG WFar WHlf WIce WOld
- 'Orange Eye'	CPbh ELan GKev NBwr NHpl NSla WIce
- 'Star Balsam'	CAby CBod LRHS SPeP
pulvinata	SPlb
'Semonkong'	SWvt

Zamia (*Zamiaceae*)

floridana	NPlm
furfuracea	LPal NPlm SPlb
pumila	SPlb

Zamioculcas (*Araceae*)

zamiifolia	CCCN CDoC LCro LOPS LWaG NHrt
- RAVEN ('Dowon'PBR)	CDoC LCro LOPS

Zantedeschia (*Araceae*)

§ ***aethiopica***	Widely available
- 'Apple Court Babe'	ELon
- 'Childsiana'	CRos EBee EBlo EHyd EPfP LRHS NRHS
- 'Crowborough' 𝕐^{H4}	Widely available
- 'Flamingo'^{PBR}	CDoC CDor
- 'Flamingo Beauty'	LHWs
- 'Glencoe'	CBct CBod EBee ECtt ESwi GAbr MAvo MHol SMad SPad WCot WFar WPGP WSHC WTyc
- 'Glow'	CExl CMac ECtt WAvo
- 'Green Goddess' 𝕐^{H4}	Widely available
- 'Little Gem'	SMad
- 'Luzon Lovely'	ESwi WCru WFar
- 'Marshmallow'	CBcs CPud CToG ECtt EHyd EPfP LBar LRHS MCot NBPC NRHS WAvo WFar WGwG WTyc
- 'Mr Martin'	CCCN ECtt ELon NCth SWvt WCot WFar
- 'Pershore Fantasia' (v)	CDTJ CExl WAvo WCot WFar
- 'Pink Mist'	GKev LHWs
- 'Spotted Giant'	CDTJ
- 'White Gnome'	WCot WFar
- 'White Sail'	ECtt LRHS NBPC NGdn NRHS
albomaculata	GKev SPlb WPGP
- subsp. ***albomaculata*** **new**	WCot
'Allure'^{PBR}	GKev
'Anneke'	CCCN SDeJ
'Ascari'^{PBR}	CCCN
'Auckland'^{PBR}	SDeJ
'Black Art'	LHWs
'Black Berry'	LHWs
'Black Magic'	CCCN CMac GKev SChr
'Black Star'	see *Z.* 'Edge of Night'
CALLAFORNIA RED ('Gscccare'^{PBR})	WFar
'Cameo'	CCCN SDeJ
'Candy Art'	LHWs
'Cantor'^{PBR}	CRos EHyd LHWs LRHS NRHS
(Captain Series) 'Captain Memphis'^{PBR}	LHWs
- 'Captain Murano'^{PBR}	SPoG
- 'Captain Prado'^{PBR}	CRos EHyd LRHS NRHS SPoG
- 'Captain Romance'^{PBR}	GKev LCro LHWs LOPS
- 'Captain Rosette'^{PBR}	LHWs
- 'Captain Tendens'^{PBR}	SDeJ
- 'Captain Trinity'^{PBR}	LHWs
- 'Captain Ventura'^{PBR}	LHWs
'Chianti'	SDeJ
'Crystal Blush'	SDeJ
'Crystal Clear'	CBod
§ 'Edge of Night'	CBcs CCCN SDeJ
'Festival'^{PBR}	SRms WFar
'Flame'	CBcs CCCN GKev MSCN
'Garnet Glow'	CBod LCro LOPS MHol
'Golden Nugget'	CRos LRHS
'Goliath'	WPGP
'Helen O'Connor'	CExl
'Hercules'	EAri ESwi
'Hot Shot'	WMal
'Kiwi Blush'	CBro CCCN CDoC CDor CExl CKel CPud CSpe CToG EAri ECtt EHyd ELan ELon EPfP EWoo LBar LRHS NBPC NRHS SMrm WCot WFar WGwG
'La Paz'^{PBR} **new**	GKev
'Lime Lady'	ECha
'Mango'	EPri SRms
'Memories'^{PBR}	LRHS
'Mercedes'^{PBR}	CRos EHyd LRHS NRHS
'Morning Queen'	CBod
'Mozart'	CCCN SDeJ
'Nightlife'^{PBR}	SRms
'Odessa'^{PBR}	LCro LOPS MSCN WTyc
odorata	WCot
'Picasso'^{PBR}	CBcs CCCN GKev MSCN SDeJ
'Pink Jewel'^{PBR} **new**	GKev
'Pot of Gold'	GKev
'Red Alert'^{PBR}	CBod GKev MSCN WTyc
'Red Sox'^{PBR}	CCCN SDeJ
rehmannii 𝕐^{H1c}	GKev SDeJ SRms
RUBY SENSATION ('Gsccrute'^{PBR}) **new**	WFar
'Saigon'^{PBR} **new**	GKev
'San Remo'^{PBR}	LRHS
'Siberia'^{PBR}	LRHS
'Summer Sun'^{PBR}	EHyd LRHS
'White Giant'	EPri EWat MAvo WCot
'Yellow Queen'	CBod MSCN

Zanthorhiza see *Xanthorhiza*

Zanthoxylum (*Rutaceae*)

acanthopodium	WJur
- GWJ 9287	WCru
- PAB 8760	LEdu
- WJC 13653	WCru
aff. ***acanthopodium*** WJC 13795	WCru
ailanthoides	CDTJ
- B&SWJ 11115 from Japan	WCru
- B&SWJ 11394 from Japan	WCru
- from Taiwan	WPGP
americanum	ELan ESwi
armatum	CAgr WJur XVPe
- B&SWJ 12753	WCru
- CWJ 12824	WCru
- FMWJ 13091	WCru
- NJM 11.080	WPGP
- PAB 8902	LEdu
bungeanum	NLar WJur
- BWJ 8040	ESwi WCru
coreanum	NLar
dissitum FMWJ 13498	WCru
fauriei B&SWJ 11080	WCru
aff. ***fauriei*** B&SWJ 11371	WCru
- B&SWJ 11523	WCru
* ***giraldii***	EBee WJur
laetum FMWJ 13175	WCru
myriacanthum B&SWJ 11844	WCru
oxyphyllum	CMCN IKel
- GWJ 9428	WCru
- HWJK 2131	WCru
piperitum	CAgr ELan GPoy LEdu SPtp WJek WJur WPGP
- B&SWJ 11377	WCru
- B&SWJ 14677	WCru
- var. ***inerme***	WPGP
- purple-leaved	CBcs CDTJ CExl LEdu WPGP XVPe
scandens	SPlb
schinifolium	CAgr WJur
- B&SWJ 8593	WCru
- B&SWJ 11080	WCru
- B&SWJ 11391	WCru
- B&SWJ 14654	WCru
simulans	CAgr CBcs CExl ESwi LAlb LCro LEdu MBlu MHoo MVil NLar SBrt SPtp WJek WJur WPGP XVPe
stenophyllum	CMCN
tomentellum B&SWJ 13903	WCru
aff. ***yuanjiangense*** FMWJ 13498	WCru

Zauschneria see *Epilobium* (Z)

arizonica	see *Epilobium canum* subsp. *latifolium*
californica	see *Epilobium canum*
- subsp. ***mexicana***	see *Epilobium canum*
villosa	see *Epilobium canum*

Zea (*Poaceae*)

mays 'Variegata' (v)	CSpe

Zebrina see *Tradescantia*

Zelkova ✿ (*Ulmaceae*)

abelicea	CBcs CMCN LRHS MBlu
carpinifolia	CMCN WPGP
- NJM 13.014 from Azerbaijan	WPGP
- NJM 13.016 from Azerbaijan	WPGP
- PAB 13.047	LEdu
'Kiwi Sunset'	MTrO WMat
serrata ♀H6	CAco CBcs CCVT CMCN CMen CTsd EBar EBee EGrI EHeP ELan EShb IPap LMaj LPar MGos MMuc MVil NWea SEND WHtc WJur
- B&SWJ 8491 from Korea	WCru
- 'Burgundy Fall'	MBlu
- 'Goblin'	MBlu NLar
- GREEN VASE ('Flekova')	LMaj MBlu
- 'Kiwi Sunset' PBR	EBee ELan MGos SPoG
- 'Musashino'	SGol
- 'Ogon'	MBlu SGol
- 'Variegata' (v)	CJun MBlu NLar SGol
sicula	WPGP
- 'Ciranna'	EWTr LRHS
× ***verschaffeltii***	CMCN MBlu

Zenobia (*Ericaceae*)

pulverulenta	CBcs CDoC CMac ELan MAsh MBlu MGil MGos
- 'Blue Sky'	CBcs CMCN CRos EHyd EPfP IDee LAlb LPar LRHS MAsh MBlu MGos NLar SPer SPoG WPGP XSte
- 'Misty Blue'	ELan
- f. ***nitida***	CMac
- 'Raspberry Ripple'	CBcs EHyd ELan LRHS MAsh NLar NRHS SPoG

Zephyranthes (*Amaryllidaceae*)

candida	CBor CBro EBee EHyd EPot EWld GKev LAma LPfP LRHS NRHS SDeJ SMrm WAvo WCFE
citrina	CBor CExl GKev LAma SDeJ
drummondii	CBor
'Krakatau'	WCot
La Bufa Rosa Group	CExl WCot
minuta ♀H2	GKev
primulina	CBor
robusta	see *Habranthus robustus*
rosea	CBor GKev LAma SDeJ
traubii from San Carlos	CBor

Zigadenus (*Melanthiaceae*)

elegans	CRos EBee EBlo EDAr EHyd EPfP EPri GAbr LEdu LPla LRHS MHer NRHS SBls SMad WFar WSHC
nuttallii	GKev

Zingiber ✿ (*Zingiberaceae*)

chrysanthum	EAri
clarkei	CTsd
malaysianum	EAri
mioga	CAgr CLau CSpe CTsd EAri ELan GPoy LEdu LRHS SBls SChr SHor SPlb SPtp SRms WPGP XSte XVPe
- 'Crûg's Zing'	EAri LEdu MAvo SBrt WCru WPGP
- 'Dancing Crane' (v)	CMac ESwi LEdu SRms WPGP
- 'White Feather'	EAri LEdu MAvo WPGP
officinale	GPoy SPlb SPre
rubens	EAri

Zinnia (*Asteraceae*)

DAHLIA-FLOWERED MIXED	LCro
elegans	SVic
- (Benary's Giant Series) 'Benary's Giant Lime'	CSpe
- - 'Benary's Giant Salmon Rose' ♀H2 **new**	CSpe
- - 'Benary's Giant Scarlet' ♀H2	CSpe
- - 'Benary's Giant Wine'	CSpe
- 'Envy' (d) ♀H2	LCro
- 'Purple Prince' (d) ♀H2 **new**	LCro
- (Queen Series) 'Queen Lime Orange' (d)	CSpe
- - 'Queen Lime Red' (d) ♀H2	CSpe
- 'Zinderella Lilac' (d) **new**	LCro
marylandica	MBros
Zahara Series	
- - ZAHARA FIRE ('Pas719124')	CSpe
- - ZAHARA RED ('Pas1118265')	SCob
- - ZAHARA STARLIGHT ROSE ('Pas719128')	SCob
- - ZAHARA YELLOW IMPROVED ('Pas951086')	SCob
Oklahoma Series ♀H2	LCro LOPS
PROFUSION MIX (Profusion Series) **new**	MBros
'Red Spider'	CSpe CTtf

Zizia (*Apiaceae*)

aptera	SPhx WSHC
aurea	CBWd CSpe LPla LRHS MBriF MNrw SPhx WSHC XLum

Ziziphus (*Rhamnaceae*)

§ ***jujuba*** (F)	CKel MBlu WJur
- var. ***inermis*** (F) **new**	XVPe
- 'Lang' (F)	CAgr
- 'Li' (F)	CAgr XVPe
sativa	see *Z. jujuba*

Zosima (*Apiaceae*)

absinthifolia	WCot

III
RHS AWARD OF GARDEN MERIT
FRUIT

Award of Garden Merit Fruit

This is a directory of fruit offered by nurseries participating in *RHS Plant Finder 2019* that have been awarded an RHS Award of Garden Merit (AGM). It does not represent a complete list of AGM fruit.

Entries are accompanied by a short description and the relevant **hardiness rating** for the UK (see p.39 for an explanation of these). The figures to the left of the rating indicate the year of the award. Cultivars particularly suitable for culinary use are flagged **(C)**, while **(D)** denotes dessert fruit.

Cultivation

All fruits are best grown in sheltered sites, with protection from spring frosts and cold winds. Brief guidance is given below on suitability for different locations, rootstocks, pollination and storage.

Location

Most of the **apple** cultivars listed here succeed all over the country, including the north of England. Those which have been found to be particularly successful in higher-rainfall and colder areas are **marked with an asterisk**; this is also used to highlight other fruits that have been found to be successful in northern regions. **Pears** crop best in sheltered warm situations; in the more exposed areas and northern counties, some pears will benefit from the protection of walls. **Plums** are susceptible to spring frosts and also need warm summers to ripen fully. Only early ripening plums can be relied upon in the shorter season of northern counties.

Currants, **gooseberries**, **raspberries** and **berry fruits** are generally satisfactory in most parts of the country, but cold winds at flowering time can be a problem. **Strawberries** can be grown all over the country, but will need some protection in exposed sites and from spring frosts. **Blueberries** are hardy plants but require light, well-drained, moisture-retentive, acid soil (pH 4.0–5.5).

Figs can crop satisfactorily in sheltered, warm situations in southern England. In northerly areas they will need protection such as a south-facing wall, or to be grown under glass or in polytunnels.

Pollination

Most tree fruits need to be pollinated by another tree of the same kind growing reasonably close by, which flowers at approximately the same time. Flowering groups are given in descriptions; for good pollination, choose cultivars from the same group, though those from adjacent groups will also serve as pollinators. **Apples** and **pears** listed as triploid are poor pollinators and require a normal (i.e. diploid) pollinator to set fruit. Gardeners should be aware that this diploid pollinator will not itself set fruit unless pollinated by another diploid tree. Many *Malus* species and crab apples, such as 'Golden Hornet' and 'Evereste', are also a good source of pollen for dessert and culinary apples. A number of the **plums** listed are self-fertile or partly self-fertile and will produce crops without a pollinator, but a pollinator is needed for all other plums. **Cherries** listed as self-fertile will crop without a pollinator, but otherwise cherries need a pollinator. Soft fruits are self-fertile, except that **blueberries** may need a pollinator.

Rootstocks

All tree fruits are grafted onto rootstocks of varying vigour. Choice of rootstock will determine the ultimate size of the tree and hence needs to be borne in mind when selecting new trees for the garden. For example, **apple trees** on 'M9' rootstock are suitable for small gardens, while those on 'M25' will produce large, standard trees. The size of the tree will also be determined by the vigour of the cultivar. It is often advisable to obtain a very vigorous cultivar, for example 'Bramley's Seedling', on a more dwarfing stock. **Apples** are available on 'M27' (very dwarfing), 'M9' (dwarfing), 'M26' (semi-dwarfing), 'MM 106' (semi-vigorous), and 'M25' (vigorous) rootstocks. **Pears** are available on 'Quince C' (dwarfing), 'Quince A' (semi-vigorous), 'BA 29' (semi-vigorous) and seedling pear (vigorous) rootstocks. Some pear cultivars are incompatible with a quince rootstock and these are sold with a pear interstock (usually 'Beurré Hardy'). **Plums** are available on 'Pixy' (semi-dwarfing) and 'Saint Julien A' (semi-vigorous) rootstocks; cherries on 'Tabel' (very dwarfing), 'Gisela 5' (dwarfing), and 'Colt' (semi-vigorous).

Storage

Early **apples** and **pears** will not store, but many more of the apple and pear cultivars listed will store to Christmas and some to the spring. This calls for good storage conditions, i.e. a cool, dark, frost-free place that is not subject to fluctuating temperatures. Often this can be achieved in sheds and garages, but in general centrally heated houses are not suitable for long-term storage.

Apple (*Malus domestica*)

98 H6 **'Alkmene'** (D)
Pollination group 2. Aromatic, Cox-like flavour. Good, regular crops; some resistance to scab and mildew. Season: late Sept.–late Oct.
CAgr LPar NOra NRog SBdl SKee

'American Mother' *see* 'Mother'

93 H6 **'Arthur Turner'** (C)
Pollination group 3. Flavoursome cooker. Large, golden exhibition fruit. Good, regular crops; prone to mildew; some resistance to scab. Striking deep pink blossom, for which an Award of Merit was given in 1945. Season: Sept.–Nov.
CArg CBod CCVT CHab CTri EPom LBuc MLod MTrO NOra NRog NWea SBdl SBmr SKee SSFr WJas WMat

93 H6 **'Ashmead's Kernel'** (D)
Pollination group 4. Intense fruit-drop flavour. Cropping erratic; prone to bitter pit. Season: Dec.–Feb.
CAgr CArg CBTr CEnd CHab CLnd CPer CRos CSBt CTri EDir EPfP EPom LBuc LRHS MLod MRav MTrO NOra NRog NWea SBdl SBmr SEdi SKee SLim SSFT SSFr SVic WJas WMat WWct

93 H6 **'Belle de Boskoop'** (C/D)
Triploid. Pollination group 3. Needs little or no extra sugar when cooked; mellows to brisk eating apple. Good, regular crops; very vigorous tree. Season: Oct.–Apr.; keeps well.*
CAgr CEnd CHab NOra NPlm NRog NWea SBdl SKee

93 H6 **'Blenheim Orange'** (C/D)
Triploid. Pollination group 3. Characteristic nutty flavour. Use early for cooking. Some resistance to mildew; very vigorous tree; partial tip-bearer; light crops. Season (C): from late Sept. (D): Oct.–Dec. / Jan.*
CAgr CArg CCVT CHab CLnd CPer CSBt CTri EDir ELan EPfP EPom IArd LBuc LEdu LRHS LSRN MRav MTrO NOra NRHS NRog SBdl SBmr SCob SEND SEWo SEdi SGbt SKee SPer SRHi SSFr SVic WJas WMat WWct

93 H6 **'Bramley's Seedling'** (C)
Triploid. Pollination group 3. Cooks to very sharp, savoury purée; retains acidity to spring. Heavy crops; prone to bitter pit and scab; partial tip-bearer; can bear fruit parthenocarpically; tendency to be biennial if over-cropped; blossom susceptible to frost. Very vigorous tree. Season: Nov.–Mar.; stores well.*
CAgr CArg CBTr CBcs CBod CCVT CEnd CLnd CMac CPer CRos CSBt CTri CWnw EBee EDir EFPl ELan EPfP EPom GDam GKin IPap LBuc LEdu LMaj LPar LRHS LSRN MDon MGos MLod MMuc MPri MRav MTrO NBwr NLar NOra NOrn NRHS NRog NTrD NWea SBdl SBmr SCob SEND SEWo SEdi SKee SLim SOrN SPer SRHi SRms SSFT SSFr SVic SWvt WJas WMat WWct

93 H6 **'Charles Ross'** (C/D)
Pollination group 3. Quite rich flavour; needs no sugar when cooked. Handsome exhibition fruit. Good, regular crops; hardy tree; some resistance to scab. Season: Oct.–Dec.*
CAgr CArg CCVT CEnd CHab CLnd CMac CPer CSBt CTri EDir EPom IArd LBuc LPar LSRN MAsh MLod MRav MTrO NOra NOrn NRog NWea SBdl SBmr SCob SEWo SKee SLim SPer SSFT SSFr WJas WMat WWct

14 H6 **'Christmas Pippin'** (D)
Pollination group 3. Medium vigour; upright spreading habit; good, regular crops. Medium-sized apple of attractive appearance, flushed with colour over yellow background with some russet; crisp, juicy, sweet flesh with rich sweet sharp flavour, developing aromatic quality. Well-flavoured, good quality apple.
CArg CEnd CRos CTri EBee ELan EPfP EPom LBuc LCro LRHS MCoo MLod MPri MTrO NLar NOra NRHS SCoo SGbt SKee SOrN SPoG SSFr WMat

93 H6 **'Discovery'** (D)
Pollination group 3. Bright red, crisp, juicy; keeps longer than most earlies. Ornamental tree. Good, regular crops; partial tip-bearer; good resistance to scab and mildew. Season: mid Aug.–Sept.*
CAgr CArg CBcs CBod CCVT CDoC CLnd CMac CSBt CTri CWnw EBee EDir EFPl EPfP EPom EWTr GBin GKin IPap LBuc LPar LRHS MDon MGos MLod MPri MRav MTrO NBwr NLar NOra NOrn NRog NWea SBdl SBmr SCob SCoo SEdi SGbt SKee SLim SOrN SPer SSFT SSFr SVic WJas WMat WWct

93 H6 **'Dummellor's Seedling'** (C)
Pollination group 4. Also sold as 'Dumelow's Seedling'. Cooks to well-flavoured, juicy purée; retains acidity to spring. Good, regular crops, but fruit can be small for a cooker. Season: Nov.–Apr.*
CHab NOra NRog SBdl SKee

93 H6 **'Edward VII'** (C)
Pollination group 6. Cooks to well-flavoured purée, not as acidic as 'Bramley's Seedling'. Large, regular, exhibition fruit. Deep pink blossom; flowers very late so escapes frosts; needs late-flowering pollinator. Good, regular crops; resistant to scab; some resistance to mildew. Season: Dec.–Apr.*
CHab NOra NRog SBdl SKee WMat WWct

93 H6 **'Egremont Russet'** (D)
Pollination group 2. Characteristic nutty flavour. Good, regular crops; fruit resistant to scab, but prone to leaf scab; very prone to bitter pit and woolly aphids. Season: Oct.–Dec.*
CAgr CArg CBTr CCVT CEnd CHab CLnd CMac CRos CSBt CTri CWnw EBee EDir EFPl ELan EPfP EPom EWTr LBuc LCro LEdu LPar LRHS MAsh MDon MGos MLod MMuc MPri MTrO NBwr NLar NOra NOrn NRog NWea SBdl SBmr SEND SEWo SEdi SKee SLim SPer SRHi SRms SSFT SSFr WJas WMat WWct

93 H6 **'Ellison's Orange'** (D)
Pollination group 4. Rich, aniseed flavour. Good, regular crops; some resistance to scab, but susceptible to canker. Season: late Sept.–late Oct.
CAgr CArg CEnd CHab CLnd CMac CSBt CTri EPfP EPom LBuc LRHS MLod MMuc MPri MTrO NBwr NOra NRog NWea SBdl SBmr SEND SEdi SGbt SKee SPer SRms SSFr SVic SWeb WJas WMat WWct

93 H6 **'Elstar'** (D)
Pollination group 3. Intense flavour, honeyed, crisp. Heavy regular crops. Season: late Oct.–Dec.
CBod CCVT CLnd EDir EPom EWTr LPar MDon NOra SBdl SEdi SKee SSFr

93 H6 **'Emneth Early'** (C)
Pollination group 3. Codlin type, cooking to fluffy purée; needs hardly any sugar. Heavy but biennial crops; needs thinning for size. Some resistance to scab and mildew. Season: Aug.–Sept.*
CAgr CArg CHab NOra NRog SBdl SEdi SKee WMat WWct

'Epicure' *see* 'Laxton's Epicure'

93 H6 **'Fiesta'** (D)
Pollination group 3. Aromatic, Cox-like flavour. Heavy, regular crops; frost-resistant blossom; less prone to disease than Cox, but can be susceptible to scab and develop canker on some sites. Season: Oct.–Dec. / Jan.*
CAgr CArg CBod CCVT CDoC CLnd CMac CTri EBee EPfP EPom EWTr LBuc LPar LRHS MAsh MCoo MDon MGos MLod MMuc MPri MRav MTrO NLar NOra NOrn NRog NWea SBdl SBmr SCoo SEND SEWo SEdi SKee SLim SOrN SPer SPoG SRHi SRms SSFr WJas WMat WWct

'Fortune' *see* 'Laxton's Fortune'

93 H6 **'Golden Noble'** (C)
Pollination group 4. Cooks to a well-flavoured purée, not as acidic as 'Bramley's Seedling'. Attractive blossom. Good, regular crops; partial tip-bearer; some scab and mildew resistance. Season: Oct.–Dec. and longer.
CAgr CTri IArd NOra NRog SBdl SKee

93 H6 **'Greensleeves'** (D)
Pollination group 3. Crisp, brisk, becoming sweeter. Very precocious and heavy, regular crops; needs thinning for good fruit size. Can be susceptible to scab. Season: late Sept.–Oct.; short season once picked.
CAgr CArg CBod CMac CTri ELan EPfP EPom LPar MAsh MGos MMuc MTrO NOra NRog NWea SBdl SBmr SEND SEdi SKee SLim SPer SSFT SSFr WJas WMat WWct

93 H6 **'Grenadier'** (C)
Pollination group 3. Cooks to sharp purée. Heavy, regular crops; good disease resistance. Season: Aug.–Sept.*
CAgr CArg CBod CHab CLnd CTri EDir EPom MDon MGos MMuc MTrO NOra NRog NWea SBdl SEND SEdi SKee SPer SSFT SSFr WMat

14 H6 **'Howgate Wonder'** (C)
Pollination group 3. Very large, late-season, heavy-cropping apple with a very mild flavour. Vigorous; fruit yellow-green flushed with red. Partially self-fertile.
CAgr CArg CBod CCVT CDoC CHab CLnd CSBt CTri EDir EPfP EPom GDam LBuc MDon MLod MMuc MTrO NBwr NOra NRog NWea SBdl SBmr SEdi SKee SPer SSFr SVic WJas WMat WWct

93 H6 **'James Grieve'** (C/D)
Pollination group 3. Savoury, crisp to melting flesh; when cooked keeps shape, with juicy, delicate flavour. Good, regular crops; fruit bruises easily. Prone to scab, canker; resistant to mildew; requires well-drained soil. Season: Sept.–Oct. and longer.*
CAgr CArg CBTr CBcs CBod CCVT CDoC CEnd CHab CLnd CMac CRos CSBt CTri

CWnw EBee EDir EPfP EPom EWTr GDam LBuc LMaj LRHS LSRN MAsh MDon MGos MLod MMuc MPri MRav MTrO NBwr NLar NOra NOrn NRHS NRog NWea SBdl SBmr SCob SCoo SEND SEWo SEdi SGbt SKee SLim SPer SRHi SRms SSFT SSFr SVic SWvt WJas WMat WTSh WWct

93 H6 **'Jonagold'** (D)
Triploid. Pollination group 3. Attractive, crisp, honeyed taste; large fruit. Heavy, regular crops; prone to canker. Fruit can be poorly coloured, but many more colourful sports exist. Vigorous. Season: Nov.–Jan. / Feb.; stores well.
CArg CBod CLnd CTri EDir ELan EPom IArd IPap LMaj LRHS NOra NRog SBdl SEdi SGsty SKee SPer SSFr WWct

93 H6 **'Jupiter'** (D)
Triploid. Pollination group 3. Cox-like flavour, but sharper. Heavy crops, but biennial if allowed to over-crop; fruit can be heavily russetted. Vigorous. Season: late Oct.–Jan.*
CAgr CArg CBod CSBt CTri EDir EPfP LSRN MDon MRav MTrO NLar NOra NRog NWea SBdl SEdi SKee SRHi SSFr WJas WMat

14 H6 **'Kent'** (D)
Pollination group 3. Good flavour; good reliable crops; keeps well.
SKee

93 H6 **'Kidd's Orange Red'** (D)
Pollination group 3. Very attractive; rich aromatic, perfumed taste. Good, regular crops; fruit prone to coarse russet. Season: Nov.–Jan.
CAgr CArg CBod CEnd CMac CRos CTri EBee EPfP EPom LBuc LRHS MLod MTrO NOra NRog NWea SKee SBmr SLon SSFr WMat WWct

93 H6 **'King of the Pippins'** (C/D)
Pollination group 5. Well ripened, good flavour. Cooked, keeps shape, flavoursome; suited to open tarts, etc. Heavy, regular crops; upright habit; good resistance to disease; keeps well. Season: Oct.–Dec.; can store to Feb.*
CArg CHab CLnd EPom MTrO NOra SBdl SKee SVic

93 H6 **'King Russet'** (D)
Pollination group 3. Russetted form of 'King of the Pippins'. Improved eating quality; good distinct russet flavour. Not as heavy cropping. Season: Oct.–Dec.
SBdl

93 H6 **'Lane's Prince Albert'** (C)
Pollination group 3. Cooks to brisk purée, not as acidic as 'Bramley's Seedling'. Large fruit. Good, regular crops; fruit easily bruised. Resistant to scab; very prone to mildew; prone to canker on all but very well-drained soils. Season: Nov.–Mar.; stores well.*
CAgr CArg CHab CLnd CSBt CTri EPfP LRHS MGos MRav MTrO NBwr NOra NRog NWea SBdl SCoo SEdi SSFr SVic SWeb WMat

93 H6 **'Laxton's Epicure'** (D)
Pollination group 3. Delicate, aromatic, Cox-like flavour. Heavy, regular crops; needs thinning for size; prone to bitter pit, canker. Season: late Aug.–Sept. Awarded as 'Epicure'.*
CAgr CEnd CHab CTri NRog SBdl SKee

93 H6 **'Laxton's Fortune'** (D)
Pollination group 3. Sweet, lightly aromatic flavour; needs to colour well for good quality. Good crops, but tendency to be biennial. Fruit bruises easily, can be poorly coloured. Prone to canker, good resistance to scab. Season: Sept.–Oct. Awarded as 'Fortune'.
CArg CHab CMac CSBt CTri IArd MTrO NBwr NOra NRog SBdl SEdi SKee SSFr WMat WWct

14 H6 **'Limelight'** (D)
Pollination group 3. Crisp and refreshing; heavy-cropping.
CArg CDoC EBee MAsh MCoo MLod MTrO NLar NOra NRog NWea SBdl SCoo SKee SSFT SSFr WMat

93 H6 **'Lord Lambourne'** (D)
Pollination group 2. Sweet, juicy, attractive flavour. Skin can become greasy when stored. Good, regular crops. Partial tip-bearer; resistant to mildew. Season: late Sept.–Nov.*
CAgr CArg CEnd CHab CLnd CMac CSBt CTri ELan EPom LSRN MGos MTrO NOra NRog SBdl SBmr SEdi SKee SLon SPer SSFr WJas WMat WWct

93 H6 **'Mother'** (D)
Pollination group 5. Sweet, perfumed, distinctive flavour. Crops can be erratic, light; good resistance to scab and mildew. Also sold as 'American Mother'. Season: Oct.–Dec.*
CAgr CLnd SBdl SKee SSFr

93 H6 **'Peasgood's Nonsuch'** (C/D)
Pollination group 3. Cooks to sweet, delicately flavoured purée; needs no or little extra sugar. Exhibition apple with large, handsome regular shape. Good, regular crops; resistance to mildew and red spider; moderate resistance to scab. Season: late Sept.–Dec.
CAgr CArg CHab EPom IArd LSRN MAsh MTrO NOra NRog SBdl SBmr SKee SLon WMat

93 H6 **'Pixie'** (D)
Pollination group 4. Intensely aromatic, Cox-like flavour, but sharper and firmer-fleshed. Good to heavy crops, but small fruit unless thinned. Very reliable and easy to grow. Season: Dec.–Mar.*

CBod CDoC CSBt EPom LRHS MPri MTrO NOra NRog SBdl SKee SLon WWct

14 H6 **'Red Falstaff'** (D)
Pollination group 3. Late-season, heavy-cropping sport of 'Falstaff' with a fruity flavour and crisp, juicy flesh. Self-fertile and moderately vigorous. Skin flushed with orange-red when ripe. Season: Nov.–Jan.
CAgr CArg CCVT CDoC CEnd CMac CTri EDir EPfP GKin LBuc LCro LRHS LSRN MAsh MLod MPri MTrO NLar NOra NOrn NRHS NRog SBdl SCoo SEND SEWo SGbt SKee SLim SPoG SSFT WMat WWct

19 H6 **'Red Windsor'** (D)
Pollination group 2; partially self-fertile. Perfect for smaller gardens; deep red fruits, ready to eat in September. Happy grown in a large pot; good resistance to many of the common diseases.
CArg CEnd CLnd CMac CRos CTri EBee ELan EPom LBuc LCro LOPS LRHS MAsh MLod MPri MTrO NLar NOra NOrn NRog SCoo SKee SLim SPoG SSFr WMat

93 H6 **'Ribston Pippin'** (D)
Triploid. Pollination group 2. Intense, rich, aromatic flavour; more acidity and more robust than Cox. Good, regular crops; resistant to scab; prone to mildew and canker. Season: Oct.–Jan.
CArg CPer CTri LBuc MRav MTrO NOra NRog NWea SBdl SKee SSFr WJas WMat WWct

93 H6 **'Rosemary Russet'** (D)
Pollination group 3. Sweet-sharp acid drop taste, resembling 'Ashmead's Kernel'. Crops good, regular; vigorous tree with upright habit. Season: Nov. / Dec.–Mar.
CAgr CArg CHab CPer ELan NOra NRog SBdl SBmr SKee SSFr WMat WWct

93 H6 **'Saint Edmund's Pippin'** (D)
Pollination group 2. Very attractive; richly flavoured when fully ripe. Good, regular crops; fruit bruises easily. Prone to mildew. Season: late Sept.–Oct. AGM reconfirmed 2017.*
CHab CPer ELan EPfP MTrO NOra NRog NWea SBmr SKee SSFr

14 H6 **'Santana'** (D)
Pollination group 4. Medium to quite vigorous tree, with upright spreading habit. Good to heavy crop, with low susceptibility to scab. Midseason; picking early Sept. and keeping well. Bright red flushed; sweet, crisp, juicy; good flavour.
LPar NOra SBdl WMat

09 H6 **'Scrumptious'** (D)
Pollination group 3. Regular cropper, good fruit size, attractive ornamental fruit. Good tree habit; easily managed. A good dessert apple: sweet, good flavour, crisp, juicy.
CAgr CArg CBod CCVT CDoC CMac CRos CSBt CTri EBee ELan EPfP EPom LAlb LBuc LCro LOPS LRHS LSRN MAsh MGos MLod MPri MTrO NLar NOra NOrn NRHS NRog NWea SBdl SBmr SCoo SEWo SGbt SKee SLim SOrN SPer SPoG SRHi SSFT SSFr WJas WMat

93 H6 **'Sunset'** (D)
Pollination group 3. Aromatic, like small early Cox, but sharper. Heavy, regular crops, but small fruit. Resistant to scab; prone to mildew and canker. Season: Oct.–Dec.
CAgr CArg CBod CCVT CDoC CEnd CHab CLnd CMac CSBt CTri EBee EPfP EPom GKin LBuc LRHS LSRN MRav MTrO NOra NRog NWea SBdl SBmr SCoo SEND SEdi SKee SLim SPer SSFT SSFr SVic WJas WMat WWct

14 H6 **'Topaz'** (D)
Pollination group 4. Medium vigour, with upright spreading habit. Good crop, with resistance to scab; late season, picking in early / mid October. Medium-sized; red flushed over a yellow background; crisp, juicy flesh, sweet-sharp taste; mellows with keeping.
LPar MTrO NOra SBdl SKee SSFr

93 H6 **'Warner's King'** (C)
Triploid. Pollination group 2. Cooks to well-flavoured purée; not as acidic as 'Bramley's Seedling'. Attractive, deep pink blossom. Heavy, regular crops; fruit can be very large. Prone to bitter pit. Vigorous. Season: late Sept.–Dec.
CTri MTrO NOra NRog SBdl SKee

93 H6 **'Winston'** (D)
Pollination group 4. Aromatic and rich. Good, regular crops; fruit can be rather small; good disease resistance. Season: Dec.–Apr.; keeps well.*
CAgr CBod CCVT CMac CTri EDir LPar NRog SBdl SKee SRms SVic SWeb WWct

93 H6 **'Worcester Pearmain'** (D)
Pollination group 3. Intense strawberry flavour when well-ripened and scarlet. Tip-bearer; heavy, regular crops. Resistant to mildew; some susceptibility to canker. Season: late Sept.–Oct.
CAgr CArg CBcs CBod CCVT CHab CLnd CMac CSBt CTri CWnw EBee EDir EPfP EPom EWTr LBuc LCro LRHS MAsh MLod MMuc MRav MTrO NBwr NOra NRog NWea SBdl SBmr SCoo SEND SEWo SEdi SKee SLim SPer SRHi SSFr WJas WMat WWct

Blackberry (*Rubus fruticosus* agg.)

Season extends from late July to early September.

93 H6 **'Loch Ness'**
Large, well-flavoured berries. Thornless; heavy-cropping; moderate vigour; hardy. Good resistance to purple blotch and botrytis, but prone to downy mildew. Reconfirmed 2015.

CAgr CArg CHab CMac CRos EHyd EPom IArd LCro LOPS LRHS LSRN NRHS NRog NWea SBmr SCoo SKee SSFr SVic

15 H6 **'Loch Tay'**
No spines; has a good blackberry flavour and shiny fruit. Healthy but not too vigorous, producing good replacement canes. Early.
CArg CHab CMac CRos EHyd EPom LRHS NRHS NRog SPoG

Blackcurrant (*Ribes nigrum*)

Season extends from early July to mid August.

95 H6 **'Ben Connan'**
Large fruit; medium long strigs. Heavy crops; compact habit. Good resistance to mildew, leaf-curling midge. Season: early. Reconfirmed after trial 2012.
CAgr CMac CRos CSBt EHyd EPfP EPom GDam LBuc LCro LEdu LOPS LRHS LSRN MAsh MGos MNHC MTrO NLar NRHS NRog NWea SBdl SBmr SCgs SCoo SEND SGbt SKee SPer SPoG SRms SSFr SWvt WMat

12 H6 **'Big Ben'**
Fairly vigorous medium-sized bush, flowering early to midseason. Fruit large and easy to pick. Good yields, showing resistance to mildew and leaf spot. Fresh fruit flavour pleasant to quite sweet; rich when cooked. Good all-round cultivar.
CArg CRos EBee EHyd EPfP EPom LBuc LCro LOPS LRHS LSRN MTrO NRHS SBdl SBmr SGbt SKee SPer SPoG WMat

Blueberry (*Vaccinium corymbosum*)

Blueberries begin to ripen mid July and continue to late August.

03 H6 **'Duke'** (D)
Good flavour, medium to large fruit. Crops well; easy to grow. Flowers late; good for frost-prone sites; partly self-fertile. Season: early.
CArg CBod CDoC CTrh EFPl ELan EPfP EPom LCro LOPS MCoo MGos NRog NWea SBmr SCoo SPre SRkn SSFr SSha

03 H6 **'Spartan'** (D)
Excellent flavour; medium-sized fruit. Quite good crops; not self-fertile. Vigorous; upright habit. Good autumn colour. Season: early–mid.
CDoC CMac CTrh EPom LCro LRHS LSRN MGos SKee SRHi

Cherry (morello) (*Prunus cerasus*)

93 H6 **'Morello'** (C)
Dark red, acid cherry; excellent for preserves, tarts, etc. Regular, good crops; very attractive in blossom; self-fertile. Crops on north-facing site. Season: late July–early Aug.
CAgr CArg CBod CCVT CDoC CLnd CMac CPer CSBt CTri CTsd CWnw EDir ELan EPfP EPom EWTr GDam IPap LBuc LCro LOPS LRHS LSRN MDon MGos MLod MMuc MPri MTrO NBwr NLar NOra NRog SBdl SBmr SEND SEWo SEdi SGbt SKee SLim SPer SSFT SSFr SVic SWvt WJas WMat

Cherry (sweet) (*Prunus avium*)

14 H6 **'Kordia'** (D)
Pollination group 5. Mid to late season; large to very large, true black cherry; bold appearance; excellent rich flavour. Spreading habit; can show some bare wood; medium vigour. Heavy, reliable crops; easy to grow. Not self-fertile; usually pollinated by 'Regina' or 'Sylvia' in commercial orchards; can also be pollinated by 'Summer Sun', 'Stella' (early bloom only). Blossom can be a little frost-sensitive. Good garden cherry.
CArg CBod EDir EPom LPar MTrO NOra SBdl SBmr SKee SSFr WMat WWct

14 H6 **'Lapins'**
Pollination group 4. Mid to late season; large, dark red cherry; very good flavour. Upright habit; medium vigour. Heavy, reliable crops. All-round excellent cherry; self-fertile.
CAgr CArg CBod CLnd EDir EPfP EPom LMaj LPar MRav NLar NOra NWea SEdi SGsty SKee SPoG SSFT SSFr WJas WMat WWct

95 H6 **'Merchant'** (D)
Pollination group 3. Early black cherry; well-flavoured. Regular crops. Pollination: universal donor, but not self-fertile. Season: early July. Reconfirmed 2014.
ELan MTrO NOra NRog SBdl SEdi SKee SSFT SSFr WMat WWct

14 H6 **'Penny'**
Pollination group 4. Mid to late season; dark red, very large, meaty cherry; excellent flavour. Upright spreading habit; medium vigour; prone to some bare wood. Crops well and regularly on Gisela 5; bred for UK conditions. Not self-fertile; pollinated by late to midseason cultivars, e.g. 'Summer Sun', 'Skeena', 'Regina'; needs sufficient pollination to ensure heavy crops.
CAgr CArg CTri EPom MTrO NOra NRog SKee WMat WWct

93 H6 **'Stella'**
Pollination group 4. Black cherry; large, rich, high quality. Heavy, regular crops; self-fertile. Prone to splitting in wet weather. Season: late July. Reconfirmed 2014.

CAgr CArg CBod CDoC CEnd CHab CLnd CMac CPer CSBt CTri CWnw EDir ELan EPfP EPom EWTr IPap LBuc LCro LOPS LPar LRHS MAsh MGos MLod MMuc MRav NBwr NLar NOra NOrn NRHS NRog NTrD NWea SBdl SBmr SCoo SEND SEWo SEdi SGbt SKee SLim SPer SPoG SSFT SSFr SVic SWvt WJas WMat WTSh WWct

04 H6 **'Summer Sun'** (D)
Pollination group 4. Late (July). Produces firm, well-flavoured, red to black fruit. Very good crops. Some resistance to bacterial canker. Attractive, upright, spreading habit; moderate vigour. Not self-fertile. Reconfirmed 2014.
CAgr CArg CBod CLnd CMac CTri EDir EPom LBuc MAsh MGos MLod MTrO NLar NOra NOrn NRog SBdl SCoo SKee SLim SPoG SSFT SSFr WMat WWct

14 H6 **'Sweetheart'**
Pollination group 4. Dark red cherry; latest of the season. Good flavour; very firm fruit. Medium vigour, upright spreading habit. Heavy, regular crops; fruits moderate size. Slightly prone to canker and brown rot. Only late-season self-fertile cultivar available. Prolific blossom, making a tree exceptionally pretty in the spring. Sets dense clusters of fruits, which can be prone to botrytis / brown rot.
CAgr CArg CLnd CTri EPom LCro LMaj LOPS LPar LRHS LSRN MAsh MDon MLod MTrO NOra NRHS NRog NWea SCoo SEWo SKee SLim SPoG SVic WMat

Damson (*Prunus insititia*)

00 H6 **'Farleigh Damson'** (C)
Pollination group 4. Excellent flavour. Regular, heavy crops. Blossom shows some resistance to frost. Season: late Aug.
CAgr CArg CBod CDoC CHab EPfP EPom EWTr LBuc LEdu MDon MTrO NBwr NLar NOra NRog NWea SEdi SKee SPer SVic WMat WWct

98 H6 **'Prune Damson'** (C)
Pollination group 4. Larger fruits than 'Farleigh Damson', but typical damson flavour. Regular, good crops. Season: late Aug.
CAgr CArg CHab CLnd CMac CPer CTri EBee EPfP EPom LBuc LCro LRHS MLod MMuc MPri MTrO NLar NOra NRog NWea SBmr SEND SEWo SGbt SKee SPer SSFr WHtc WJas WMat WWct

Fig (*Ficus carica*)

93 H4 **'Brown Turkey'** (D)
Fruits regularly in the open in southern England and in many parts of the Midlands and East Anglia in a warm position. For good crop, root restriction advisable. Season: mid Aug.–mid Sept., depending on site.
CAgr CBcs CBod CBrac CCCN CCVT CDoC CKel CLnd CMac CPla CRHN CRos CSBt CTri CTsd CWal CWnw EBee EDir EHyd ELan EPfP EPom ETod EWTr IPap LAlb LBuc LCro LEdu LOPS LPal LRHS LSRN MAsh MBlu MDon MGos MHer MHtn MLod MMuc MNHC MPri MRav MTrO NGKo NLar NOra NPer NPlm NRHS NRog NTrD NWea SBls SBmr SCoo SEND SEWo SGBe SGol SGsty SKee SLim SMad SNig SOrN SPer SPlb SPoG SPre SRHi SRms SSFT SSta SVen SVic SWeb SWvt WAvo WFar WJur WLea WLov WMat WMou WPGP WTSh XSen

Gooseberry (*Ribes uva-crispa*)

Season extends from early June to mid August. For culinary use, pick from early June. For ripe fruit pick from early July.

93 H6 **'Careless'** (C/D)
Green fruit. Reliable, good crops. Good for tarts, jam, etc. Prone to mildew. Season: mid.
CSBt CTri EDir EPom LSRN MAsh MGos NBwr NRog SCoo SEdi SPer

94 H6 **'Greenfinch'** (C/D)
Green fruit; compact bush. Some resistance to mildew and leaf spot. Season: mid.
CAgr

93 H6 **'Invicta'** (C/D)
Green fruit; quite good flavour. Heavy crops; very vigorous; spreading habit; large thorns. Some resistance to mildew. Young shoots can be damaged on exposed site. Season: mid; slightly earlier than 'Careless'. Main use culinary.
CAgr CDoC CMac CRos CSBt CTri EDir EHyd EMil EPfP EPom GBin LBuc LCro LOPS LRHS LSRN MAsh MGos MMuc MPri MTrO NBwr NLar NRHS NRog NWea SBdl SBmr SCoo SEND SEdi SKee SPer SPoG SRms SSFr SVic SWvt WMat

93 H6 **'Leveller'** (C/D)
Large, yellow fruit; good dessert quality. Season: mid to late.
MCoo NRog NWea SEdi SPer

93 H6 **'Whinham's Industry'** (C/D)
Red fruit; quite good dessert quality. Heavy, reliable crops. Very susceptible to mildew. Season: mid.
ELan LBuc LSRN MGos MMuc NBwr NRog SCgs SEND SEdi SPer SRms

Grape (*Vitis*)

04 H5 **'Boskoop Glory'** (D)
Black grape. Good outdoor vine for the amateur, both dessert and wine; crops reliably;

disease-resistant. Moderately good flavour, but better than many shop-bought grapes. Awarded as 'Gloire de Boskoop'.
CMac EDir ELan LBuc MBros SBdl SCoo WHtc WSuV

04 H5 **'New York Muscat'** (D)
Black grape. A good dessert Muscat with blackcurrant flavour. Disease-resistant. Best when grown on a warm site or wall.
WSuV

Hazelnut (*Corylus maxima*)

14 H6 **'Gunslebert'**
Good-sized nut; kernel fills the shell; very few blanks. Excellent flavour; very tasty. Midseason. Regular, good crops; nuts held as large clusters of four nuts. Medium vigour tree; moderate amount of suckering. Pollinated by 'Kentish Cob', 'Cosford'. Good tree habit, with a natural goblet shape and exceptionally attractive with prolific catkins making it also an ornamental tree. A mainstay of Kent nut production. Reliable, hardy hazel nut, easy to grow in a garden situation; productive and ornamental; requires a pollinator.
CCVT CMac CTri MTrO NOra SBdl SPoG SRms SSFr WMat

14 H6 **'Kentish Cob'**
Good-sized nut; kernel fills the shell; very few blanks. Excellent flavour; rich and meaty. Early season, cropping before the squirrels become active. Regular, good crops. Medium vigour tree; moderate amount of suckering. Pollinated by 'Gunslebert', 'Cosford', 'Hall's Giant' ('Merveille de Bollwiller'). The main cultivar of commercial nut plantations in Kent. Reliable hazel nut, easy to grow in a garden situation; needs a pollinator.
CAgr CBcs CBTr CPer CSBt CTri EBee ELan EPfP EPom IArd LBuc LRHS MCoo MSwo MTrO NLar NOrn NRog NWea SBdl SEdi SEWo SKee SLim SPer SPoG SRms SSFr SSFT SVic SWvt WMat WMou

Loganberry (*Rubus* × *loganobaccus*)

93 H5 **'Ly 654'** (C)
Large, dark fruit; distinctive flavour; good crops. Thornless. Season: July.
CMac CRos CSBt EHyd EPom LBuc LRHS NRHS NRog SBur SPer SSFr SVic

Medlar (*Mespilus germanica*)

17 H6 **'Iranian'**
Compact bushy tree with small leaves and bunches of fruit. Fruit ripens early, so can be picked before they fall off. Fruit can be eaten off the tree. Has a pleasant taste with a good balance of sweetness and acidity.
CAgr SKee

14 H6 **'Nottingham'**
Mid-sized fruit with good flavour for eating fresh as well as for jelly-making. Good acid–sweetness balance. Very productive, with very open eye. Has potential for splitting and allowing rot to enter. Reconfirmed 2017.
CAgr CArg CBcs CCVT CDoC CEnd CHab CPer CSBt CTri EBee EDir ELan EPfP EPom LBuc LRHS MAsh MGos MMuc MTrO NLar NOra NRog NWea SBmr SCoo SEND SEWo SEdi SKee SLim SPer SPoG SSFT SSFr SVic WMat

Mulberry (*Morus nigra*)

12 H6 **'Chelsea'**
Fruit is especially large and succulent with an intense, rich flavour. It can be eaten fresh, in preserves or made into wine.
CEnd CPer CSBt CTri EBee EPfP EPom LCro LRHS MGos MLod MTrO NLar NOra NWea SCoo SEWo SKee SLim SPer SPoG SSFT WMat

12 H6 **'Jerusalem'**
Large fruit, to 2.5cm long.
MTrO NOra WMat

Pear (*Pyrus communis*)

93 H6 **'Beth'** (D)
Pollination group 4. Attractive; good quality and flavour. Small fruit. Heavy, regular crops. Season: mid / late Aug.–early Sept.; short season once picked.
CAgr CArg CBod CDoC CHab CMac CSBt CTri CTsd EBee EDir EPfP EPom EWTr IArd LBuc LCro MAsh MDon MGos MLod MPri MTrO NLar NOra NRog SBdl SBmr SCoo SEWo SEdi SGbt SKee SLim SPer SSFT SSFr WMat WWct

93 H6 **'Beurré Hardy'** (D)
Pollination group 3. Very melting and fragrant with rose-water perfume. Good, regular crops. Very hardy, vigorous tree; slow to bear; resistant to scab. Season: Nov.–Dec.*
CAgr CArg CCVT CMac CSBt CTri EDir ELan EPfP EPom EWTr IArd IPap LMaj MCoo MDon MLod MTrO NBwr NOra NRog NWea SBdl SBmr SEND SEdi SGsty SKee SPer SSFT SSFr WMat WWct

06 H6 **'Beurré Superfin'** (D)
Pollination group 3. An excellent September-cropping cultivar for the amateur gardener, with a lovely cinnamon-russet colour and an

exquisite flavour. Gives a good, consistent yield and is not over-vigorous. Midseason.
MTrO SBdl SKee SSFr

93 H6 **'Concorde'** (D)
Pollination group 4. Sweet, buttery, fragrant flavour, similar to 'Conference', but superior. Heavy, regular crops; frost-tolerant blossom. Young trees very precocious. Season: late Oct. / Nov.–Dec.
CAgr CArg CBTr CBod CCVT CDoC CMac CPer CRos CSBt CTri EBee EDir EFPl ELan EPfP EPom EWTr IArd LBuc LCro LOPS LRHS LSRN MAsh MDon MGos MLod MPri MRav MTrO NLar NOra NRog NTrD NWea SBdl SBmr SCoo SEWo SEdi SGbt SKee SLim SOrN SPer SPoG SPre SSFT SSFr SVic WJas WMat WWct

93 H6 **'Conference'** (D)
Pollination group 3. Sweet, buttery, quite rich taste. Heavy, regular crops. Can produce fruits without pollinators, but resulting fruits often misshapen. Season: Oct.–Nov. / Dec.*
CAgr CArg CBTr CBcs CBod CCVT CDoC CLnd CMac CPer CRos CSBt CTri CTsd CWnw EBee EDir EFPl ELan EPfP EPom EWTr GBin IPap LBuc LCro LEdu LMaj LOPS LPar LRHS LSRN MAsh MDon MGos MLod MMuc MPri MRav MTrO NBwr NLar NOra NRHS NRog NTrD NWea SBdl SBmr SCoo SEND SEWo SEdi SGbt SGsty SKee SLim SOrN SPer SPoG SSFr SVic SWvt WJas WMat WTSh WWct

93 H6 **'Doyenné du Comice'** (D)
Pollination group 4. Very rich flavour; very juicy, buttery, perfumed. Excellent quality, but moderate crops, although older trees more regular. Vigorous tree; prone to scab. Season: Nov.–Dec. Not compatible with 'Onward'.
CAgr CArg CBcs CBod CCVT CHab CLnd CMac CPer CSBt CTri CWnw EBee EDir ELan EPfP EPom EWTr IArd LBuc LCro LMaj LOPS LRHS MLod MMuc MPri MRav MTrO NBwr NLar NOra NRog NWea SBdl SBmr SCoo SEND SEWo SEdi SKee SLim SOrN SPer SSFr SVic WJas WMat WTSh WWct

06 H6 **'Gorham'** (D)
Pollination group 4. A beautiful green pear with a good covering of russet. Has an excellent flavour; a good reliable cropper and is readily available. Late.
CAgr CPer MTrO NOra SBdl SKee SSFT SSFr WMat

93 H6 **'Joséphine de Malines'** (D)
Pollination group 3. Very rich, buttery and perfumed. Crops good, reliable, but needs warm site. Fruit easily bruised. Tip-bearer; resistant to scab. Season: Nov.–Dec. / Jan.
CAgr IArd MTrO NOra SBdl SKee

Plum (*Prunus domestica*)

00 H5 **'Blue Rock'** (C/D)
Pollination group 1. Quite well-flavoured blue plum. Regular, good crops; not self-fertile. Neat tree. Season: mid Aug.
SKee

95 H5 **'Blue Tit'** (C/D)
Pollination group 5. Pleasant flavour; blue plum. Regular, good crops. Self-fertile. Season: mid Aug.
CAgr CBod EDir EPom MMuc NOra NRog SEND SKee SSFr WMat WWct

98 H5 **'Cambridge Gage'** (D)
Pollination group 4. Honeysweet excellent greengage quality. Reasonably regular crops in favourable situations. Partly self-fertile. Season: mid Aug.
CAgr CArg CBod CCVT CEnd CHab CMac CTri EBee EDir EPfP EPom EWTr LCro LRHS LSRN MAsh MDon MLod MMuc MTrO NOra NRog SBdl SBmr SCoo SEND SEWo SEdi SKee SLim SPer SSFT SSFr WJas WMat WWct

93 H6 **'Czar'** (C/D)
Pollination group 3. Well-flavoured; early blue plum; used for jam but also moderate eating quality. Heavy, regular crops. Self-fertile. Season: mid Aug.
CAgr CArg CBod CCVT CDoC CEnd CHab CLnd CMac CSBt CTri EDir ELan EPfP EPom EWTr IPap LBuc LCro LOPS LPar LRHS MAsh MCoo MDon MGos MLod MMuc MPri MTrO NBwr NOra NRog NWea SBdl SBmr SEND SEWo SEdi SKee SLim SPer SPoG SSFT SSFr SVic SWvt WMat WWct

14 H5 **'Haganta'** (D)
Pollination group 3. Large dark blue plum, late-ripening, with good consistent crop; juicy, sweet; sugary; and stone almost free; good flavour.
CAgr MLod MTrO NOra WMat

93 H5 **'Imperial Gage'** (C/D)
Pollination group 2. Gage quality but not as rich as 'Cambridge Gage'. Regular crops. Partly self-fertile. Season: mid Aug.
CAgr CArg CLnd CMac CPer CSBt CTri EDir EPom EWTr LRHS MDon MMuc MTrO NOra NRog SEND SKee SPer SSFT SSFr WMat

94 H5 **'Jefferson'** (D)
Pollination group 1. Yellow flushed with red; rich, gage quality. Moderate, regular crops. Not self-fertile. Season: mid to late Aug.

CAgr CArg CHab CLnd MTrO NOra NRog SKee SSFr SVic WMat

00 H6 **'Mallard'** (D)
Pollination group 1. Medium-sized red plum; quite good flavour. Good, regular crops. Moderate vigour; not self-fertile. Season: mid–late Aug.
NOra SKee WMat

93 H5 **'Marjorie's Seedling'** (C)
Pollination group 5. Late blue plum. Good for jam. Reliable good crops; vigorous, upright habit. Self-fertile. Season: late Sept.–early Oct.
CAgr CArg CBod CCVT CDoC CEnd CHab CLnd CMac CPer CSBt CTri EDir EPfP EPom LBuc LCro LOPS LRHS LSRN MAsh MGos MLod MMuc MPri MTrO NOra NRog NWea SBdl SBmr SCoo SEND SEdi SKee SLim SPer SSFT SSFr WJas WMat WWct

95 H6 **'Opal'** (D)
Pollination group 3. Small purple plum; good flavour. Reliable, heavy crops; needs thinning. Partly self-fertile. Blossom buds very prone to bird damage. Season: early–mid Aug.
CAgr CArg CCVT CMac CRos CTri CWnw EBee EDir ELan EPfP EPom LBuc LCro LMaj LOPS LPar LRHS LSRN MAsh MDon MGos MLod MMuc MPri MTrO NBwr NLar NOra NOrn NRog NWea SBdl SBmr SCoo SEND SEdi SGbt SKee SLim SSFT SSFr WMat WTSh WWct

93 H5 **'Oullins Gage'** (D)
Pollination group 4. Large, yellow flushed with pink. Not typical gage quality, but quite rich. Heavy, regular crops. Partly self-fertile. Season: mid Aug.
CAgr CArg CCVT CKel CLnd CMac CSBt CTri CWnw EDir ELan EPfP EPom LBuc LCro LRHS MGos MMuc MPri MRav MTrO NBwr NOra NRog SBdl SBmr SCoo SEND SEWo SEdi SKee SPer SPoG SSFT SSFr SVic SWvt WJas WMat WWct

14 H5 **'Purple Pershore'** (C)
Pollination group 3. Good flavour; reliable good crops.
CAgr CHab CTri IArd MLod NOra NRog SKee SSFr WMat WWct

95 H5 **'Valor'** (C/D)
Pollination group 2. Blue, medium-sized plum. Good quality. Moderately good, regular crops. Not self-fertile. Season: late Aug.
LMaj LPar NOra NRog SKee

93 H5 **'Victoria'** (C/D)
Pollination group 3. Red plum; reasonable to good eating quality; excellent for bottling, jam and tarts. Heavy, regular crops. Self-fertile. Season: mid to late Aug.
CAgr CArg CBTr CBod CCVT CDoC CHab CLnd CMac CPer CRos CSBt CTri CTsd CWnw EBee EDir ELan EPfP EPom EWTr GDam GKin IArd IPap LBuc LCro LEdu LMaj LOPS LPar LRHS LSRN MAsh MDon MGos MLod MMuc MPri MRav MTrO NBwr NLar NOra NOrn NRHS NRog NTrD NWea SBdl SBmr SCoo SEND SEWo SEdi SKee SLim SOrN SPer SPoG SSFT SSFr SVic SWvt WJas WMat WTSh WWct

QUINCE (*Cydonia oblonga*)

17 H5 **'Serbian Gold'**
Good resistance to leaf blight, and said to be fireblight-resistant. A compact tree for modern gardens, with a small leaf and pretty flowers. Consistently good cropper, with roundish fruit; quite acidic when eaten raw. Good jelly-making quince.
CMac CPer EBee ELan EPom LRHS MTrO NLar NOra NRog SKee SSFT WMat

RASPBERRY (*Rubus idaeus*)

Raspberries crop from late June to early August. Autumn primocanes from late July to early October.

09 H6 **'All Gold'**
Autumn-cropping. Yellow- / golden-fruited; needs to be left to ripen well before the flavour is fully tasted. Yield generally peaking at the end of August and early September. An upright habit with easy-to-manage cane.
CDoC CMac CPer EPfP EPom NBwr NLar NRog SCoo SPer SRms SVic WMat

93 H6 **'Autumn Bliss'** (D)
Autumn-cropping. Primocane-fruiting (fruiting on current season's canes). Excellent flavour; large fruit. Good crops. Resistant to aphid vectors of virus disease and phytophthora root rot. Season: crops late July to early Oct. Reconfirmed after trial 2009.
CAgr CDoC CMac CPer CRos CSBt CTri EBee EHyd ELan EPfP EPom GDam LBuc LCro LEdu LOPS LRHS LSRN MAsh MGos MNHC MPri NBwr NLar NRHS NRog NWea SBdl SBmr SCgs SCoo SEWo SEdi SGbt SKee SOrN SPer SPoG SRms SSFr SVic WMat

00 H6 **'Glen Ample'** (D)
Summer-cropping. Large fruit, excellent flavour. Recommended for freezing. Heavy crops; spine-free canes. Resistant to main aphid vector of virus disease; some tolerance to phytophthora root rot; some susceptibility to leaf and bud mite. Season: mid. Reconfirmed after trial 2009.
CAgr CArg CMac CPer CRos CSBt CTri EBee EHyd ELan EPfP EPom LBuc LCro

LOPS LRHS LSRN MAsh MCoo NLar NRHS NRog NWea SBdl SBmr SCoo SEWo SEdi SGbt SKee SPer SPoG SRms SSFr SVic WMat

09 H6 **'Glen Magna'** (D)
Summer-cropping. A very vigorous cultivar with long, strong fruiting laterals. It has large fruit with a good flavour. Yields high with a long cropping season.
CAgr CArg CSBt MAsh SCoo SEdi SKee SRms

09 H6 **'Joan J'**
Autumn-cropping. Easy to grow and pick; upright habit; good berry size.
CArg CMac EPom LBuc LSRN NRog SBdl SBmr SPer SRms SSFr

93 H6 **'Malling Admiral'** (D)
Summer-cropping. Good quality; medium to large, attractive fruit. Consistent, moderate to good crops; tall canes; withstands wet conditions, but laterals easily damaged in exposed sites. Good disease resistance. Season: mid to late. Reconfirmed after trial 2009.
CSBt CTri EPfP EPom LSRN MAsh NRog NWea SCoo SKee SPer

93 H6 **'Malling Jewel'** (D)
Summer-cropping. Good flavour and crops. Season: early to mid. Reconfirmed after trial 2009.
CAgr CArg CDoC CSBt CTri EPfP EPom LBuc LSRN MAsh MPri NBwr NRog NWea SEdi SKee SPer SRms

09 H6 **'Polka'**
Autumn-cropping. Early flush of fruit with good berry size and appearance; good upright habit with medium vigorous cane growth.
CArg CDoC CRos EHyd EPfP EPom LBuc LCro LOPS LRHS LSRN MAsh MCoo MRav NRHS NRog SBdl SBmr SCoo SKee SPer SRms SSFr WMat

09 H6 **'Tulameen'**
Summer-cropping. Outstanding cultivar, with strong cane growth and upright habit. Spine-free and easily handled, with exceptional fruit quality and high yield. Less prone to pest and disease than other varieties.
CAgr CArg CDoC CSBt EBee EDir EHyd ELan EPfP EPom LCro LOPS LPar LRHS LSRN MAsh MNHC NBwr NLar NRHS NRog NWea SBdl SCoo SEWo SEdi SKee SPer SPoG SRms SSFr SVic WMat

Redcurrant (*Ribes rubrum*)

Redcurrants crop from mid July to early September.

93 H6 **'Jonkheer van Tets'** (C)
Large, handsome fruit; long strigs. Heavy crops. Season: early.
CAgr CDoC CRos CSBt EDir EHyd EPom GQue IArd LPar LRHS LSRN MAsh MCoo MPri NBwr NLar NRHS NWea SBdl SBmr SCoo SEND SEdi SGbt SKee SPer SRms SSFr WMat

93 H6 **'Red Lake'** (C)
Good quality medium to large fruit; cropping on long trusses. Prone to wind damage in exposed sites; in summer prune early. Season: mid to late.
CAgr CTri EDir ELan EPfP EPom LBuc LEdu MGos MPri NBwr NLar NRog SBmr SEdi SPer SPoG SRms SSFr WMat

19 H6 **'Rovada'** (C)
Heavy-cropping, late summer-ripening cultivar, producing long strings of larger fruit, making it easy to harvest.
CAgr CArg CMac CPer CRos CSBt EHyd EPfP EPom LBuc LEdu LRHS LSRN MAsh NBwr NLar NRHS SBdl SBmr SCoo SEdi SKee SPoG SRms SVic WMat

93 H6 **'Stanza'** (C)
Medium-sized fruit; good quality. Compact habit; heavy crops. Season: mid to late.
CAgr NRog SEND

Strawberry (*Fragaria × ananassa*)

In an early season, strawberries begin to crop mid June; in a late season, mid to late June.

06 H6 **'Alice'** (D)
A good consistent cropper, with a high percentage of mid to large, bright orange-red, sweet, juicy fruit. Scored well in taste tests and performed well at different geographical locations (Stafford, Kent, Dundee) in HDC trials. Has good resistance to verticillium wilt; very useful to home gardener. Mid to late season.
CAgr CMac EPom SCgs

93 H6 **'Cambridge Favourite'** (D)
Good flavour; medium size, but rather soft berries. Moderate crops, with excellent resistance to disease and good runner production. Season: mid.
CAgr CArg CMac CRos CSBt CTri EHyd EMil EPfP EPom GDam GQue LBuc LCro LOPS LRHS MAsh MGos MPri NBwr NRHS NRog SBmr SCgs SEdi SPlb

18 H6 **'Finesse'** (D)
Good yields of bright fruit with good size and good flavour.
CSBt NRHS NRog

18 H6 **'Florence'** (D)
Bright dark red berries of good size; late main season fruit with consistent good flavour.
CAgr CArg CRos CSBt EHyd EPom LRHS NRHS NRog SPer

94 H6 **'Hapil'** (D)
Large glossy berries; good flavour. Heavy crops; vigorous. Susceptible to verticillium wilt. Season: early / mid. Reconfirmed after trial 2004.
EPfP EPom GDam LBuc NRog

93 H6 **'Honeoye'** (D)
Excellent flavour. Heavy crops; susceptible to verticillium wilt. Season: early. Reconfirmed after trial 2004.
CAgr CArg CMac CSBt EPfP EPom GDam LBuc LCro LEdu LOPS LRHS NBwr NRog SPer

18 H6 **'Malling Centenary'** (D)
Large bright red berries with consistently good flavour.
EPom LRHS NRog

94 H6 **'Pegasus'** (D)
Good flavour; quite soft flesh. Good disease resistance; tolerance to verticillium wilt. Season: mid. Reconfirmed after trial 2004 and 2006.
CAgr CRos CSBt EHyd EPfP EPom LRHS NRHS

94 H6 **'Rhapsody'** (D)
Good flavour; medium to large berries. Resistant red core; some resistance to verticillium wilt and mildew. Season: late. Reconfirmed after trial 2006.
CRos EHyd LRHS LSRN NRHS

95 H6 **'Symphony'** (D)
Good flavour; bright, firm berries. Vigorous; good resistance to red core; susceptible to mildew. Good runner production. Season: mid to late. Reconfirmed after trial 2006.
CAgr CRos CSBt EHyd EPfP EPom LBuc LRHS LSRN NRHS SCoo

18 H6 **'Vibrant'** (D)
Early fruit; best June bearer; attractive dark berry with good flavour.
EPom NRog

TAYBERRY (*Rubus*)

93 H5 **'Tayberry'**
Distinctive flavour. Larger fruit; heavier crops than loganberry. Excellent for cooking, freezing, jam, etc. Season: July. Reconfirmed 2015.
CDoC EDir SCoo

WALNUT (*Juglans regia*)

15 H6 **'Franquette'**
Old French variety, known since 19th century; received the designation *appellation d'origine contrôlée* in 1938 as 'Noix de Grenoble' and in 2002 as 'Noix du Perigord'; remains a main market walnut of France; long recommended for planting in UK. Tree upright with rounded crown; moderate vigour; late-leafing; tolerates disease. Good, regular crops; reliable and productive. Nuts easily husked; quite soft shell, and can be cracked with fingers; well-sealed and well-filled nut; medium size, long, oval shape. Flavour excellent. Season: quite late / late. Pollinated by 'Meylanaise', 'Ronde de Montignac', 'Fernette'; reported partially self-fertile.
CAgr MTrO NOra WMat

15 H6 **'Lara'**
French cultivar; seedling of American cultivar 'Payne'. One of the main cultivars of modern walnut plantations. Good habit, making broad spreading tree, but not very vigorous; quite early leafing out; lateral bearing; good disease resistance. Good, regular crops; reliable and productive. Nuts easily husked; medium to quite large, globose; well-sealed, well-filled; well-flavoured as fresh nut and as dried nut. Season: early. Pollinated by 'Franquette', 'Meylanaise' and 'Ronde de Montignac'.
CAgr NOra SBmr WMat

WHITECURRANT (*Ribes rubrum*)

19 H6 **'Blanka'**
Consistent long trusses of pearly white, large, evenly sized berries, with good flavour; easy growing; late cultivar, which extends the season well.
CAgr CArg CMac CPer EHyd LRHS NRog SVic

93 H6 **'White Grape'** (D/C)
Attractive, translucent berries; good flavour. Season: mid July.
CTri LEdu NRog

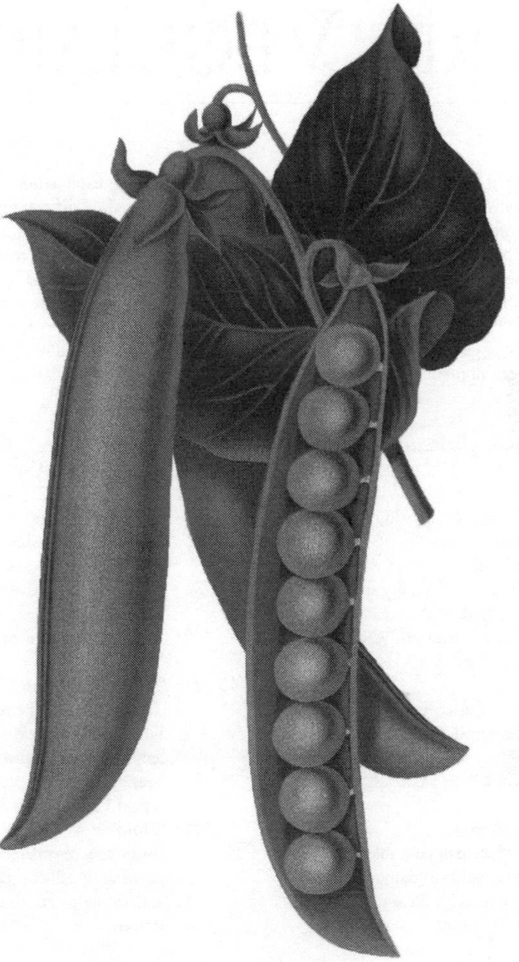

IV

RHS AWARD OF GARDEN MERIT

VEGETABLES

Award of Garden Merit Vegetables

This is a directory of vegetables offered by nurseries participating in *RHS Plant Finder 2019* that have been awarded an RHS Award of Garden Merit (AGM). It does not represent a complete list of AGM vegetables.

Entries are accompanied by a short description and the relevant hardiness rating for the UK. **Hardiness ratings** are explained on p.39. The figures to the left of the rating indicate the year the Award of Garden Merit was given.

Vegetables present some nomenclatural peculiarities that may require explanation. Cultivars that are repeatedly raised by different growers, while retaining their essential characteristics, can become recognisably different. These strains are referred to as maintenances and are often distinguished by the use of **maintenance names** which exist separately from the cultivar name. Here maintenance names appear after the cultivar name separated by a dash following the Vegetable Seed (England) Regulations 2002.

Asparagus (*Asparagus officinalis*)

01 H4 **'Backlim'**
F_1 hybrid; consistently high yield of large spears.
EPom LCro SBmr

93 H4 **'Connover's Colossal'**
Early; heavy yield of good quality spears. Reconfirmed after trial 2001 and 2012.
CSBt CTsd EKin ELan LCro LOPS LSRN MCtn MNHC NRob SVic

01 H4 **'Gijnlim'**
F_1 hybrid; early. Consistently high yield of mid green spears with purple tips. Reconfirmed after trial 2012.
CRos EDel EKin EPom LCro LOPS LRHS NRob SBmr

12 H5 **'Guelph Millennium'**
Bred in Canada. Excellent cold tolerance. Lateness helps to avoid frost damage. Sound yield of slender stems with pleasing flavour.
EPom LCro LOPS SBmr

Aubergine (*Solanum melongena*)

95 H1c **'Bonica'**
F_1 hybrid. Early-cropping, good quality, attractive glossy black fruits are a good size. Plants are tall, but also strong and vigorous. Reconfirmed after trial 2008, 2019.
MCtn

Basil (*Ocimum basilicum*)

12 H1c **'Aroma 2'**
Standard Genovese type. Lovely aroma, good disease resistance, quite tall.
LCro LOPS MCtn

12 H1c **'Lemonade'**
Compact, even plant growing to c.30cm. Aromatic with a sherbet-lemon scent and taste. Fine leaves: keeled as young foliage. Flowers are white, and attractive to bees. Plants hold well and show good disease and weather resistance. Previously listed as basil (× *africanum*).
SRms

12 H1c **'Mrs Burns' Lemon'**
Tall, upright, neat habit, growing to c.60cm. Fine, mid green leaves, aromatic and intensely lemon-scented. Flowers white, and attractive to bees.
CBod EKin MCtn SRms WJek

12 H1c **'Pluto'**
Bush type, of small, even, dome-shaped habit, growing to c.20cm. Leaves are fine, mid green and aromatic. Holds form well and slow to flower.
LCro LOPS

Beans

Broad beans (*Vicia faba*)

95 H5 **'Aguadulce'**
Dark green foliage, showing some variability. Long pods; the highest yielding in the trial. November sown. May also be sold as 'Aquadulce'.
CHby

93 H5 **'Aquadulce Claudia'**
Not too tall; a good compact plant. An early crop when spring sown, but can also be sown in

November. One of the most reliable cultivars for overwintering. Reconfirmed after trial 1999, 2011.
EKin LCro LOPS MBros MCtn NRob

11 H3 **'De Monica'**
Short pods; well filled. Good ratio of seed to pod; excellent cropping.
EKin MCtn SCgs SVic

93 H3 **'Express'**
Quick to mature, with well-filled pods. Spring sown.
EKin MCtn

11 H3 **'Giant Exhibition Longpod'**
Smooth, slender pods of good length; long cropping period.
EKin LRHS MCtn NRob

93 H3 **'Imperial Green Longpod'**
Green-seeded, with long smooth pods; good green colour and flavour; particularly good for freezing. Spring sown. Reconfirmed after trial 1999, 2011.
EKin LCro LOPS MCtn

99 H3 **'Masterpiece Green Longpod'**
Slender, well-filled pods; stands well; good green colour and flavour; suitable for freezing; spring sown; reconfirmed after trial 2011.
EDel EKin LCro LOPS

11 H3 **'Robin Hood'**
Green-seeded; 3–5 seeds per pod. Good yield. Dwarf cultivar, ideal for containers and small gardens.
MCtn

11 H3 **'Suprifin'**
Pale green pods of mid size; pleasant taste. Early-cropping.
LCro LOPS SCgs

93 H3 **'The Sutton'**
Dwarf compact plants, with nice flavour; ideal for smaller gardens or containers and windy situations. Spring sown. Reconfirmed after trial 1999, 2011.
EKin LCro NRob SCgs SVic

99 H4 **'Witkiem' – Manita**
Traditional 'Witkiem' type; sets well. Good early yield, with uniform pods; spring sown; reconfirmed after trial 2011.
CHby EKin

Climbing French beans (*Phaseolus vulgaris*)

00 H2 **'Cobra'**
Very high early yield; long, fleshy, round; very attractive; reconfirmed after trial 2008.
CHby EKin LCro MCtn NRob

93 H2 **'Eva'**
Very early. Long straight fleshy pods, wider-podded than other round varieties. Reconfirmed after trial 2000 and 2008.
CHby

08 H2 **'Golden Gate'**
Good crop of golden, fleshy, flat pods with a sweet, fresh flavour.
CHby LCro

93 H2 **'Hunter'**
Attractive long flat stringless pods. Slow to show seed development. Reconfirmed after trial 2000 and 2008.
EKin MCtn NRob

08 H2 **'Limka'**
Consistently high yields of good quality, flat, light green pods with a good flavour.
CHby

93 H2 **'Musica'**
Quick to mature, with long stringless pods; reconfirmed after trial 2008.
SCgs

Dwarf French beans (*Phaseolus vulgaris*)

93 H2 **'Annabel'**
Dark green colour, compact habit, fine foliage, tender fleshy tasting pods. Reconfirmed after trial 1996, 2010 and 2019.
EKin MCtn

93 H2 **'Sprite'**
Heavy yield, with long, dark green pods on compact bushy plants. Reconfirmed 2019.
EHyd EKin LCro LRHS MCtn NRHS

10 H2 **'Stanley'**
Mid to dark green colour; tender and sweet. Taller plant. Uniform and picks over long period.
MCtn

Runner beans (*Phaseolus coccineus*)

06 H2 **'Benchmaster'**
Long, fairly straight beans, good yield; reconfirmed after trial 2013.
EKin LCro LOPS MBros

06 H2 **'Celebration'**
High yield of attractive, straight, smooth, good quality, fleshy pods with good colour and flavour. Flowers are a decorative pink. Reconfirmed after trial 2013, 2017.
EKin

13 H2 **'Firestorm'**
Hybrid of runner and French bean parentage. Excellent yield, slender, straight, smooth-skinned, fleshy pods. Self-setting. Reconfirmed after trial 2017.
EDel EKin LCro LOPS MCtn

93 H2 **'Liberty'**
Very long pods; a popular show variety.
NRob

13 H2 **'Moonlight'**
Hybrid of runner and French bean parentage; grown commercially. Very high yielding. Easy to pick; leaves pedicel behind on picking. Smooth,

straight, fleshy pods, with good length and nice colour. Self-setting. Reconfirmed after trial 2017.
EHyd EKin LCro LOPS LRHS MCtn NRHS

99 H2 **'Red Rum'**
Good early and late yield; slim, straight, stringless pods of medium length. Reconfirmed after trial 2006, 2013.
EKin

06 H2 **'St George'**
Bicolour variety; prized for ornamental value. Some French bean parentage. Popular commercial variety; easy to pick, leaving pedicel behind. Slender beans, straight, pale green. Reconfirmed after trial 2013, 2017.
CHby

99 H2 **'White Lady'**
Late; very fleshy pods. Reconfirmed after trial 2006, 2013.
CHby EKin LCro LOPS LRHS MBros MCtn NRHS

Beetroot (*Beta vulgaris*)

05 H3 **'Alto'**
F_1 hybrid; early. Cylindrical, uniform, smooth long red roots with very good internal colour and good long shape. Potential to bulk up well. Reconfirmed after trial 2016.
EKin SCgs

93 H3 **'Boltardy'**
Open-pollinated; round red root; good bolting resistance.
EKin LCro LOPS MBros MCtn SVic

16 H3 **'Bona'**
Open-pollinated; round red root; even size with very smooth skin.
MCtn

93 H3 **'Forono'**
Open-pollinated. Cylindrical, with fairly smooth skins and long red roots of moderate uniformity; good internal colour. Slow to bulk up. Reconfirmed after trial 2005.
EKin

93 H3 **'Pablo'**
F_1 hybrid; very early. Uniform round red roots with very smooth skins. Appears to have good bolting resistance. Widely used as a show cultivar. Reconfirmed after trial 2001, 2005 and 2016.
EHyd EKin LRHS MCtn NRHS NRob

01 H3 **'Red Ace'**
F_1 hybrid; uniform round red roots with good flesh colour and no rings. Reconfirmed after trial 2016.
EKin NRob

05 H3 **'Solo'**
F_1 hybrid. Round to slightly flattened shape. Bulks up well; smooth roots of good internal colour. Reconfirmed after trial 2016.
LCro

93 H3 **'Wodan'**
F_1 hybrid with round, slightly flattened shape. Smooth roots; good internal colour. Bulks up well. Reconfirmed after trial 2005, 2016.
EKin

Borecole or curly kale (*Brassica oleracea* Acephala Group)

15 H5 **'Black Magic'**
A new selection of 'Cavolo Nero', with very dark green, strap-leaved type with small blisters. Good yield.
MCtn

99 H5 **'Redbor'**
F_1 hybrid. Tall, uniform plants with open habit; strongly curled purple-green leaves. Good salad leaf, with ornamental value too. Winters well. Reconfirmed after trial 2015.
EDel EKin LCro NRob

93 H5 **'Winterbor'**
F_1 hybrid. Tall plants with finely curled blue-green leaves; winters well. Developed from (but superior to) 'Westland Winter'. Reconfirmed after trial 1999, 2015.
EKin MCtn

Broccoli (*Brassica oleracea* Italica Group)

See under Calabrese for Calabrese broccoli

Purple sprouting

13 H5 **'Cardinal'**
Tidy upright plants, some variability in height, as expected for open-pollinated cultivars. Dense spears of deep purple. Good for late crop.
EKin

95 H5 **'Claret'**
F_1 hybrid. Very tall; heavy yield of dark purple spears from March through April. Reconfirmed after trial 2013.
EDel LCro LOPS NRHS SCgs

13 H5 **'Mendocino'**
Sturdy vigorous plants, with large, attractive deep purple spears of good quality.
EDel

03 H4 **'Red Admiral'**
Early, yielding well with good quality secondaries. Good colour and long stems. Performs better if sown later and grown to produce hardier plants. Reconfirmed after trial 2013.
EDel LCro LOPS SCgs

95 H5 **'Red Arrow'**
Early to midseason; long cropping period.

Good winter hardiness; bushy, vigorous plants. Reconfirmed after trial 2003, 2013.
MCtn

BRUSSELS SPROUTS (*Brassica oleracea* Gemmifera Group)

15 H5 **'Brodie'**
Clean buttons, developing unevenly; mild taste when cooked.
LCro LOPS

99 H5 **'Cascade'**
F_1 hybrid; late. Smooth, clean, well-spaced, fairly round sprouts. Uniform plants which stand and yield well.
EKin LCro LOPS SCgs

15 H4 **'Crispus'**
Early to midseason. Clubroot-resistant; nice colour, with mild, slightly nutty taste when cooked.
EKin

15 H5 **'Doric'**
Tall plants, with sparse large buttons. Slightly bitter, with slight aftertaste when cooked.
EDel

93 H5 **'Igor'**
F_1 hybrid. Mid to late season; attractive, vigorous, uniform plants producing well-spaced, solid, round, mid green sprouts. Reconfirmed after trial 2006.
NRob

15 H4 **'Marte'**
Tall plants with sprouts well spaced. Buttons quite round; good size; nice and dense. Not bitter, even uncooked.
EKin

06 H4 **'Maximus'**
F_1 hybrid; early to mid season. Leading commercial variety; uniform plants, producing a good crop of mid to dark green, smooth, solid sprouts, slightly sweet and crunchy after cooking. Reconfirmed after trial 2015.
EKin LCro

CABBAGE (*Brassica oleracea* Capitata Group)

EARLY RED, NON-STORING – SEPTEMBER TO OCTOBER

96 H3 **'Rookie'**
F_1 hybrid; early. Round to slightly flat heads.
LCro LOPS SCgs

AUTUMN – SEPTEMBER TO NOVEMBER

09 H3 **'Buscaro'**
F_1 hybrid. Attractive dark red, oval-round, well-filled heads. Very short core, with petioles that are not too thick. Stands well.
EDel

09 H3 **'Minicole'**
F_1 hybrid. Good early autumn cultivar with attractive round heads.
EHyd LRHS NRHS NRob

09 H3 **'Red Jewel'**
F_1 hybrid. Attractive, solid, round-headed red cabbage with upright foliage and a short core. Could be grown at a closer spacing.
NRob

SAVOY – SEPTEMBER TO MARCH

01 H5 **'Tundra'**
F_1 hybrid; dark green, slightly blistered leaf; heads solid and attractive. Sweet-tasting; overwinters well. Reconfirmed after trial 2007, 2019.
EKin LCro MCtn SCgs

JANUARY KING – NOVEMBER TO MARCH

08 H5 **'Deadon'**
Uniform, attractive 'January King' type with a flattened round head.
EDel EKin

98 H4 **'Noelle'**
F_1 hybrid; flat, round, heads; dark green leaves with good purple colouring. Winters well. Previously listed as 'Holly'. Reconfirmed after trial 2009 for September–November cropping.
LCro LOPS SCgs

SPRING

11 H5 **'Advantage'**
Good heart. Compact, uniform, with little bolting.
MCtn

93 H5 **'Duncan'**
F_1 hybrid. Mid to dark green uniform heads with well-closed bases. A good early yield; compact neat habit; plants heart slowly to produce small, solid, well-filled heads. Reconfirmed after trial 2001, 2011 as spring greens and hearted cabbage.
EDel LRHS NRHS

11 H5 **'Spring Hero'**
Distinctive round-headed spring cabbage for overwintering. Large, dense ball-shaped heads. Blue-grey, rugose leaves. Showing excellent winter survival.
EKin

SUMMER – JUNE TO AUGUST

16 H2 **'Cabbice'**
Hybrid; Japanese flat cabbage. Sweet, heavy and dense, with good flavour.
EKin

04 H2 **'Candisa'**
F_1 hybrid; early. Uniform, medium green,

well-filled heads, with short core. Reconfirmed after trial 2016.
EKin

16 H2 **'Caraflex'**
Hybrid; early sweetheart type. Quite big for the garden, but capable of making smaller heads.
EDel EKin LCro

98 H2 **'Elisa'**
F_1 hybrid; early. Compact round heads with bright green glossy leaves. Reconfirmed after trial 2016.
EDel

02 H2 **'Hispi'**
F_1 hybrid; early. Smooth, pointed, dark green outer leaves, with good uniformity and well-filled heart.
CHby LCro NRHS NRob

93 H2 **'Stonehead'**
F_1 hybrid; late. Uniform, round, mid green heads. Stands well. Also useful for cropping into the autumn from later planting. Reconfirmed after trial 2016.
EKin LRHS MBros NRHS NRob

CALABRESE BROCCOLI (*Brassica oleracea* Italica Group)

03 H3 **'Belstar'**
F_1 hybrid; May sown. Mid to late season; uniform medium-sized plants, with attractive heads and medium to small buds.
EKin

07 H3 **'Green Magic'**
Autumn-cropping; very good yield of slightly domed, good-sized, mid green heads with small beads. Early to harvest; known to make good side-shoots. Reconfirmed after trial 2013.
EKin MCtn

13 H2 **'Ironman'**
Domed larger heads of tight blue-green buds; healthy foliage.
EDel EKin

03 H3 **'Kabuki'**
F_1 hybrid; May sown; early. Short, compact plants, producing a good crop of medium green, deep, well-rounded heads with uniform buds. Average yield of medium-sized secondaries, produced 3 to 5 weeks after the primary heads. Could be closely spaced to produce baby heads. Reconfirmed after trial 2007, 2013.
EHyd LRHS MCtn NRHS

13 H2 **'Marathon'**
Dome-shaped heads, uniform, mid-size, held high.
EKin LCro LOPS LRHS NRHS

CARROT (*Daucus carota*)

99 H3 **'Adelaide'**
F_1 hybrid; very early. Good weight and colour; sweet-flavoured; quickly forms very smooth, stump-ended roots; almost coreless; fine tops. Ideal for successional sowings and early sowing in frames. Reconfirmed after trial 2006 and 2010 as early, suitable for containers.
EKin LCro SCgs

06 H3 **'Amsterdam Forcing 3'**
Open-pollinated. Relatively smooth with good flesh and core colour; bulks up well. Strong foliage that does not grow too tall.
EKin MCtn

93 H4 **'Bangor'**
F_1 hybrid. Blunt, medium length, smooth roots. Well-filled with good uniform shape and medium orange internal colour. Bulks up well. Can be stored over winter; reconfirmed after trial 2005.
SCgs

14 H3 **'Deep Purple'**
Purple skin and flesh, with tapered roots and pleasant flavour; reasonable uniformity of crop.
MCtn

05 H5 **'Eskimo'**
F_1 hybrid; medium-length, smooth roots with good colour. Useful size, well-filled. Grows with crowns at or below ground level, so very little crown discoloration. Good overwintering cultivar. Reconfirmed after trial 2014.
EKin LCro LOPS MBros MCtn

99 H3 **'Flyaway'**
F_1 hybrid. Maincrop; medium-length, well-filled, stump-ended roots with good flesh and core colour. Good strong tops. Partial resistance (i.e. lack of attraction) to carrot flies. Reconfirmed after trial 2006.
EKin LCro LOPS MCtn

99 H3 **'Maestro'**
F_1 hybrid. Best lifted before Christmas. Blunt, smooth-skinned, medium to slim, fairly well-filled roots, uniform in size and shape. Mid to pale internal colour with some green shoulders. Widely grown by organic carrot growers. Reconfirmed after trial 2005, 2014.
LCro LOPS

10 H3 **'Marion'**
Early to mature; uniform crop of slightly tapered roots with good weight. Smooth skin, deep orange flesh and good core colour. Suitable for containers.
EKin

99 H3 **'Nairobi'**
F_1 hybrid; second early / early maincrop. Strong tops, with uniform, broader-shouldered,

cylindrical, stump-ended roots. Heavy yields. Reconfirmed after trial 2006, 2014.
EKin

93 H3 **'Napoli'**
F_1 hybrid, very early maturing. Slightly tapering; good weight. Smooth skin, core and flesh deep orange. Strong tops for easy pulling; quick to bulk up. Ideal for successional sowings and early sowing in frames. Reconfirmed after trial 2010 as early, suitable for containers.
EKin

06 H3 **'Primo'**
Hybrid; flavoursome crop of good weight. Smooth skin, deep orange colour, with low core–flesh ratio. Reconfirmed after trial 2010 as early, suitable for containers.
LCro LOPS SCgs

14 H3 **'Romance'**
Longer, early-maturing 'Nantes' type, though resembling 'Berlicum'. Smooth skin, no splitting, dense texture, good colour.
MCtn

05 H4 **'Sugarsnax 54'**
F_1 hybrid. Very long, smooth, 'Imperator' type with roots of good internal colour. Suited to deep, light soils. Commercially used, cut into short lengths and sold as pre-packed baton carrots.
EKin MCtn SCgs

05 H3 **'Sweet Candle'**
F_1 hybrid; short, blunt, quite smooth, well-filled, uniform roots. Good internal colour. Reconfirmed after trial 2014.
EKin LCro NRob

14 H3 **'Tozresis'**
A 'Nantes' type. Bred for intermediate carrot fly resistance. Smooth skin, good uniformity, well-stumped root, good colour, nice flavour. Previously listed as 'Resistafly'.
MCtn SVic

CAULIFLOWER (*Brassica oleracea* Botrytis Group)

Coloured and Romanesco

05 H3 **'Graffiti'**
F_1 hybrid. Small to medium, high quality, solid curds of a very attractive amethyst colour. The colour fades a little if boiled, and is retained better if steamed. The raw curds have a good flavour and would be a colourful addition to a salad or dish of crudités. Midseason. Reconfirmed after trial 2006.
EKin LRHS NRHS SVic

05 H3 **'Veronica'**
F_1 hybrid; appetising light green Romanesco type. Uniform good-sized, solid, well-shaped heads.
EDel EKin

Autumn heading – September to November

15 H3 **'Boris'**
Good, deep, round curd.
EKin SCgs

15 H3 **'Clapton'**
Neat, well-covered variety, with lovely curds and good upright habit.
EDel EKin

02 H3 **'Moby Dick'**
F_1 hybrid; early with a short cropping period; uniform, very deep, heavy curds. Good width. Reconfirmed after trial 2015.
LCro LOPS SCgs

Spring heading

05 H5 **'Aalsmeer'**
Open-pollinated cultivar; early midseason. Produces medium to small, cream-coloured, slightly lumpy, well-protected curds that have a good depth. This cultivar produced several multiple heads and side-shoots, many of usable quality.
EKin NRob

97 H5 **'Jerome'**
F_1 hybrid; early midseason. Vigorous plant, producing good quality, well-covered curds. Curds well-rounded, medium to small and cream-coloured. Reconfirmed after trial 2005.
EDel

Summer heading – June to mid July

97 H3 **'Fargo'**
F_1 hybrid; late. Deep, white, well-protected curds. Reconfirmed 2018.
EKin

06 H3 **'Flamenco'**
Hybrid; midseason to late. Very high quality, large to medium-sized, white, solid curds with good depth. Reconfirmed 2018.
NRob

97 H3 **'Nautilus'**
F_1 hybrid; late. Vigorous plants with deep, white, well-protected curds of excellent quality.
LRHS NRHS

Summer or autumn heading

06 H3 **'Aviron'**
Hybrid; late. High quality, well-protected, large to medium-sized solid, white heads. Reconfirmed after trial for autumn heading 2015.
EKin

CELERIAC (*Apium graveolens* var. *rapaceum*)

00 H4 **'Prinz'**
Smooth, deep, white-skinned; small to

medium, flattened and round; compact plant with healthy foliage. Reconfirmed after trial 2011.
CHby EDel EKin LCro MCtn SVic

Celery (*Apium graveolens* var. *dulce*)

93 H2 **'Celebrity'**
Self-blanching, fairly short plants, with ribbed petioles and good flavour. Reconfirmed after trial 2001.
LRHS MCtn NRHS

93 H4 **'Giant Pink' – Mammoth Pink**
Pink-tinged, green variety for blanching or earthing up; solid stems.
NRob

94 H2 **'Victoria'**
F_1 hybrid. Tall, well-filled plants with medium-green, smooth, fleshy petioles. Widely used for commercial crops. Reconfirmed after trial 2005.
EDel EKin MBros

Chard (*Beta vulgaris* subsp. *cicla* var. *flavescens*)

00 H3 BRIGHT LIGHTS
Good colourful mix, including reds, yellows and whites; very ornamental and decorative.
CHby EHyd LRHS NRHS NRob SCgs SVic

00 H3 **'Bright Yellow'**
Bright golden-yellow petioles and mid green puckered leaf; uniform; sweet taste; reconfirmed after trial 2011.
MCtn NRob

11 H3 **'Canary Yellow'**
Green leaves and yellow stem; healthy blister-type attractive glossy leaf. Even stock. Taste is not bitter. No bolting in either sowing during trial.
NRob

00 H3 **'Fordhook Giant'**
Attractive shiny light green, puckered leaf with white stem and long succulent broad white petioles; old blister-leaf chard type.
EKin MCtn NRob

00 H3 **'Rhubarb Chard'**
Dark green leaves and red stem; vigorous but uniform; blister-type leaf; reconfirmed after trial 2011.
EKin LCro LOPS MBros MCtn NRob SVic

Chicory (*Cichorium intybus*)

Radicchio

02 H5 **'Palla Rossa'**
Medium to large heads; well-filled red hearts; fairly uniform. No bolting.
CHby MCtn SRms

Sugar loaf

02 H5 **'Pan di Zucchero'**
Uniform plants with medium to large frames and dark green outer leaves. Hearts blanch well.
CHby

Chilli pepper (*Capsicum annuum*)

06 H1c **'Apache'**
Decorative, growing to 45cm; does well in both large and small pots. Produces large crop of small, juicy, hot peppers that ripen from bright green to red and are held outwards from the stems. Reconfirmed after trial 2013.
CCCN CRos EHyd EKin LRHS MBros MPri NRHS NRob SPre

13 H1c **'Basket of Fire'**
Multi-branched, open habit, height to c.25cm. Numerous upright fruits, maturing through cream, lemon, yellow and orange to red.
CRos EDel EHyd EKin NRHS SPre SVic

13 H1c **'Bolivian Rainbow'**
Compact plant, height c.32 cm, with mid green foliage. Stumpy, broad-based fruit held erect. Fruit ripening cream through orange to red.
SVic

06 H1c **'Caribbean Antillais'**
Quite small, blocky, bright red fruits; aromatic and very hot, of a type widely used in South American and Caribbean cooking. Later-cropping, best sown in January and given a higher temperature to germinate.
SVic

06 H1c **'Demon Red'**
A small, ornamental plant, starred with white flowers, producing an abundant crop of tiny upward-pointing fruits that mature to dark, bright red. Fruits are hot and used in Thai cooking. Reconfirmed after trial 2013.
CRos EHyd EKin LRHS MCtn NRHS SPre SVic

06 H1c **'Etna'**
Attractive bunches of erect, shiny peppers that mature from bright mid green to red, carried on compact plants that are suitable for growing in pots. Large crop of very hot peppers.
CRos EHyd LRHS MCtn NRHS

06 H1c **'Filius Blue'**
Attractive, highly ornamental plants. The young leaves are mid green, becoming very dark green with a purple flush; the plants are covered with purple, orange and bright red fruits that are spicy and hot.
NRob

06 H1c **'Fresno'**
Fairly short, upright-growing plants; very productive. The conical fruits ripen from light green to deep scarlet red, with medium thick flesh that is very hot.
LRHS NRHS

13 H1c **'Hot Thai'**
Bushy yet compact habit, height to 25cm. Dainty dark green foliage. Small, hot fruits (1.5cm in length, and 1cm wide), held erect. Ideal for a windowsill.
CRos EHyd LRHS NRHS

06 H1c **'Hungarian Hot Wax'**
Conical fruits ripening from pale yellow to bright red; medium hot; very good for frying, stuffing and using in salads. One of the easiest to grow. Suitable for growing in pots.
CHby EKin LCro LOPS MCtn NRob SVic

13 H1c **'Krakatoa'**
Compact, bushy plant, with dark green foliage; height c.20cm. Erect clusters of glossy fruit, 3cm long, and 1cm across the base.
CRos EHyd LRHS NRHS

13 H1c **'Loco'**
Bushy plant, height c.25 cm, cascading habit which looks especially attractive in a basket or container. Numerous oblong fruit, c.2cm long, held erect above the foliage. Ripening purple to red.
CRos EHyd LRHS NRHS

14 H1c **'Pot Black'**
Upright plant with branching habit; height c.36cm. Stem, foliage, fruit very dark purple. Fruit blocky in shape, held erect above the foliage. Interesting and unusual variety.
EDel SVic

06 H1c **'Prairie Fire'**
Very attractive, short (20cm high), spreading plants covered in a mass of very small, very hot, upright peppers that ripen from white, through yellow and orange, to red. Compact and multibranched plant; ideal for pots or a windowsill. Reconfirmed after trial 2013.
CCCN CRos EHyd LCro LRHS NRHS NRob SVic

06 H1c **'Super Chili'**
Ornamental plants; well suited to growing in pots. Produces a high yield of very hot, thin-walled fruits that are held upright and ripen from light green to orange-red.
SPre SVic

14 H1c **'Treasure's Red'**
Compact multi-branched plant, with dark green foliage, height c.26 cm. Glossy, conical fruit held in erect clusters. Maturing cream, through orange to red.
LRHS

CHINESE CABBAGE (*Brassica rapa* Pekinensis Group)

03 H3 **'Yuki'**
Barrel-shaped. Medium green, slightly savoyed outer leaves; very short internal stem; medium-sized heavy head; well-blanched. Reconfirmed after trial 2018.
EKin MCtn

CORIANDER (*Coriandrum sativum*)

14 H2 **'Calypso'**
Vigorous, bushy strong growth; holds well; good leaf yield. Ideal size for the home gardener.
EKin MCtn

14 H2 **'Confetti'**
Neat and clean, with distinct fern-like look; uniform. Ideal for smaller gardens.
EKin LCro MCtn MHoo

14 H2 **'Cruiser'**
A compact plant, with big leaves.
EDel

CORNSALAD (*Valerianella locusta*)

94 H3 **'Medaillon'**
Slow-growing, short, thick-leaved under frames.
LCro LOPS

COURGETTE (*Cucurbita pepo*)

93 H2 **'Defender'**
F_1 hybrid. A high yield of medium-sized, slender, very lightly flecked fruits.
EKin LCro MCtn

93 H2 **'Early Gem'**
F_1 hybrid; a high yield of slender, lightly speckled fruits. Easy to see on the plant.
EKin MCtn

13 H2 **'Orelia'**
Upright plant, producing a good yield of yellow fruits. Vigorous, with good mildew resistance.
EKin

13 H2 **'Patio Star'**
Compact plant, ideal for small space or container. No mildew. Glossy, dark green fruits.
EDel

07 H2 **'Romanesco'**
Distinctive, heavily ribbed fruits that hold their flowers. Popular in Italy; the flowers are used for stuffing. Semi-trailing plants; good yield.
EDel LCro

CUCUMBER (*Cucumis sativus*)

02 H1c **'Carmen'**
F_1 hybrid; standard length, dark green, slightly

ribbed fruits. Reconfirmed after trial 2009.
EKin NRob

09 H1c **'Cucino'**
Smooth, small, dark green, uniform fruits with good flavour and texture. Highly productive.
NRHS SVic

09 H1c **'Emilie'**
Useful mid-length fruits with attractive dark green colour and good flavour.
LCro LOPS

95 H2 **'Marketmore'**
Good yield of short, attractive, dark green fruits. Grown in the open garden. Reconfirmed after trial 2001, 2019.
CHby EDel EKin MCtn SCgs

09 H1c **'Mini Munch'**
Highly productive plants producing abundant small, crunchy, shiny-skinned fruits with good flavour.
EKin

ENDIVE (*Cichorium endivia*)

96 H3 **'Pancalieri'**
Very strong cut-leaf type. Does not blanch well.
CHby EKin MCtn

FLORENCE FENNEL (*Foeniculum vulgare* var. *azoricum*)

05 H2 **'Orion'**
F_1 hybrid; vigorous foliage; attractive, medium to large bulbs with a good shape, with few side shoots and clean, with a bright white colour. Reconfirmed after trial 2019.
EKin

GARLIC (*Allium sativum* var. *ophioscorodon*)

04 H4 **'Arno'**
Attractive white with smooth skin for July cropping. Soft neck, stores well, good yield, even size; also performed well at Harlow Carr.
LCro

04 H4 **'Early Wight'**
Very early crop (during May); good fat cloves. Hard neck; best used immediately after harvest.
NRob

04 H4 **'Germidour'**
Late-maturing, virus-free selection. Soft necks; well-packed, purple-skinned cloves.
EDel NRob

04 H4 **'Solent White'**
Late. Soft neck; many purple-skinned, very attractive cloves, with appealing bouquet; high yield; keeps beyond Christmas (up to March). Also performed well at Harlow Carr.
EKin LCro LOPS NRob

LEEK (*Allium porrum*)

AUTUMN & EARLY WINTER

00 H4 **'Jolant' (Swiss Giant Group)**
For December cropping; high yield; medium to dark green flags; long, solid shafts with little bulbing and very few bolters. Low levels of rust infection. Has a long season and peels nicely. Reconfirmed after trial 2002, 2015.
EKin MCtn NRob

00 H4 **'Mammoth Blanch'**
A show variety suitable for December sowing. Early-maturing, with high yields of well-shaped leeks with pale green flags, long, heavy shafts and no bolters.
EKin NRob

00 H4 **'Pancho'**
Good early yield of medium long, mid green, solid shafts with only slight bulbing. Little rust; fast-growing.
LCro LOPS

WINTER HARDY

09 H5 **'Blauwgroene Winter' – Atlanta**
Good open-pollinated cultivar. Dark blue-green, erect flags, with healthy foliage. Medium length of blanch.
EDel EKin MCtn

09 H5 **'Blauwgroene Winter' – Bandit**
Good open-pollinated cultivar. Dark blue-green flags; reasonable length of blanch.
EDel EKin MCtn

15 H5 **'Lancaster'**
Hybrid; lovely leek, dark green and upright; really uniform.
NRob

02 H5 **'Mammoth Pot Leek'**
Uniform, with whole stem blanched and light green flag. High December yield.
EKin NRob

02 H5 **'Oarsman'**
F_1 hybrid; erect plant, with very straight shank, uniform, smooth; flag leaf clean. Good yield. Reconfirmed after trial 2015.
EKin LCro LOPS MCtn

LETTUCE (*Lactuca sativa*)

BUTTERHEAD

97 H2 **'Clarion'**
Open heads, with pale to mid green leaves. Reconfirmed after trial 2002
LCro

COS

12 H2 **'Chartwell'**
Neat, mid-size green Cos; dense, crisp heart.
EKin

07 H2 **'Chatsworth'**
Medium-sized with rugose leaves; dense hearts make a good weight and have a good blanch. Very good flavour.
LCro LOPS

93 H2 **'Little Gem'**
Small solid heads with mid green, medium-blistered leaves. Reconfirmed after trial 1999, 2007, 2012.
CHby CRos EHyd EKin LCro LOPS LRHS MBros MCtn NRHS NRob

99 H2 **'Little Leprechaun'**
Semi-Cos with dark red leaves.
NRob

93 H2 **'Lobjoit's Green Cos'**
Large, rather open heads, with relatively smooth mid green leaves. Reconfirmed after trial 1999.
EKin NRob SVic

12 H2 **'Maureen'**
Uniform crop, with mid green leaves. One of the most popular commercial 'Gem' varieties.
EDel EKin

99 H2 **'Parris Island Cos'**
Vigorous with pale green uniform heads; reconfirmed after trial 2007.
EKin

00 H2 **'Winter Density'**
Semi-Cos with leafy, erect habit; dark green, very uniform. Reconfirmed after trial 2007, 2012.
EDel EKin LCro LOPS MCtn NRob

Crisphead

01 H2 **'Robinson'**
Medium to large frame, good quality solid hearts; reconfirmed after trial 2014.
NRob

03 H2 **'Sioux'**
Smooth leaves, large frame, with a green heart and outer leaves tipped red. Slow to bolt.
LCro LOPS

Leafy

95 H2 **'Black-seeded Simpson Improved'**
Yellow-green leaves with frilled edges. Cos-like in growth.
MCtn

95 H2 **'Catalogna'**
Strong-growing oak-leaved type. Light green slightly blistered leaves.
MCtn SVic

95 H2 **'Cocarde'**
Large oak-leaved type, with bronze green-tinged leaves.
EDel

95 H2 **'New Red Fire'**
Large, with puckered light bronze outer leaves.
EKin MCtn

95 H2 **'Salad Bowl'**
Large open-hearted plants with light green frilled leaves.
CHby EKin LCro LOPS LRHS MCtn NRHS NRob

Mangetout see under Peas

Marrow (*Cucurbita pepo*)

97 H2 **'Tiger Cross'**
F_1 hybrid. High yield of pale-striped fruits.
EKin LCro LOPS LRHS MCtn NRHS SVic

Melon (*Cucumis melo*)

09 H1c **'Alvaro'**
Big crop; attractive pale green skins with dark green stripes and salmon-orange flesh. Good flavour.
EDel SCgs

09 H1c **'Emir'**
Good crop of netted Charentais-type fruits with orange flesh; H2 for outdoor use.
EKin LCro MCtn SCgs

Onion (*Allium* species)

From sets

93 H3 **'Centurion'**
F_1 hybrid. Flattened globe-shaped bulbs with straw-coloured skins of good thickness. Reconfirmed after trial 2002, 2013.
NRob

13 H3 **'Rumba'**
Uniform crop; large bulb size, globe-shaped, with brown skin. Stores well.
EKin NRob

02 H3 **'Sturon'**
Very good yield of globe-shaped, slightly high-shouldered bulbs, with good yellow-brown skins. Reconfirmed after trial 2002, 2013.
CHby EKin LCro LOPS NRob

02 H3 **'Stuttgarter'**
High yield, well shaped, deep bulb, good skin.
EKin LCro LOPS NRob

Maincrop

93 H3 **'Golden Bear'**
F_1 hybrid; early. Thin-skinned, high-shouldered bulbs; do not store well.
MCtn NRob

Red, globe, from seed and sets

05 H3 **'Red Baron'**
High yield of attractive, dark-skinned, globe-shaped bulbs with good internal colour. Plants in the trial grown from seed produced a

higher yield and bolder bulbs than those grown from sets. Reconfirmed after trial 2013.
CHby EKin LCro LOPS LRHS MCtn NRHS NRob

05 H3 **'Redspark'**
Attractive globe-shaped, uniform, medium-sized bulbs with tight, dark skins and good internal colour.
EDel

Salad

04 H4 **'Guardsman'**
F_1 hybrid: cross between *A. fistulosum* and *A. cepa*. Medium to dark green leaves. Very vigorous; well-blanched with some bulbing. Also performed well at Harlow Carr.
MCtn

96 H3 **'Ishikura'**
Strong-growing; long-stemmed; non-bulbing.
MCtn

17 H4 **'Matrix'**
Very even, with very thick roots and good flavour; has a kick.
EDel

04 H3 **'Parade'**
Very straight, strong-growing, uniform plants with good length of blanch; non-builbing; slow to bolt. Also performed well at Harlow Carr.
EDel

93 H4 **'White Lisbon'**
Medium-green leaves with good length of blanch. Good for early and successional sowing. Reconfirmed after trial 2004.
CHby CRos EHyd EKin LCro LOPS LRHS MBros MCtn NRHS NRob SVic

93 H4 **'Winter White Bunching'**
Strong-growing with dark green leaves. Overwinters well.
EKin

Shallot

01 H3 **'Longor'**
Good yield and shape; also suitable for exhibition. Reconfirmed after trial 2018.
LCro LOPS NRob

01 H3 **'Matador'**
F_1 hybrid; thick skins, and good yield.
EDel EKin LRHS MCtn NRHS SVic

PAK CHOI (*Brassica rapa* Chinensis Group)

10 H3 **'Baraku'**
Good germination rate. Little bolting. Compact and uniform, attractive dark green leaf and petiole. Good size for cooking.
MCtn

10 H3 **'Red Choi'**
Good germination rate. Very little bolting. Stands well. Attractive purple leaves and tender green stem. Good hearting, uniform clean, healthy crop. Ideal size for cooking.
EDel EKin

PARSLEY (*Petroselinum crispum*)

97 H6 **'Bravour'**
A reliable cropper; good stalks, well curled.
CBod MHer

97 H4 **'Curlina'**
Compact and uniform; tightly curled.
LCro

93 H6 **'Moss Curled'**
Aromatic, deeply cut, tightly curled leaves and small umbels of yellow-green flowers in summer.
CHby EHyd EKin LRHS MCtn MHoo NRHS NRob SRms

PARSNIP (*Pastinaca sativa*)

01 H5 **'Gladiator'**
F_1 hybrid; very smooth skin, good potential yield, uniform shape, shallow lenticels. Reconfirmed after trial 2009.
EHyd EKin LCro LOPS LRHS MCtn NRHS

PEAS (*Pisum sativum*)

93 H2 **'Hurst Green Shaft'**
Maincrop; heavy yield of dark green, medium-length, pointed pods. Excellent taste, with good number of peas per pod. Nicely progressive yield. Reconfirmed after trial 1998, 2005, 2017.
EKin LCro LOPS MCtn SCgs

05 H2 **'Jaguar'**
Early maincrop; heavy crop of mainly double pods per node. Medium-length pods have an average of seven peas per pod, with good flavour.
MCtn

97 H2 **'Kelvedon Wonder'**
Early maincrop. Long, dark green pods, with an average of 7 to 8 peas per pod. Reconfirmed after trial 2004, 2005.
EDel EKin LCro LOPS MBros MCtn NRob

05 H2 **'Serge'**
Maincrop; semi-leafless plants produce a heavy crop of easy-to-pick pods. Medium-length pods have an average of ten peas per pod, with good flavour.
EKin MBros MCtn

98 H2 **'Show Perfection'**
Maincrop; an exhibition pea, very tall with long dark green pods. A high yield over a long period.
NRob

Mangetout

00 H2 **'Delikata'**
Tall, with similar pods to 'Oregon Sugar Pod'. A shade earlier and carries a heavy crop. Pods soon form strings if not picked regularly. Mildew- and fusarium-resistant.
LCro LOPS

09 H2 **'Oregon Giant'**
Clean, healthy, mid-height plants. Attractive broad, mid-green pods.
EKin

Sugarsnap

00 H2 **'Cascadia'**
Dwarf habit, producing very fleshy, crisp, sweet pods, which remain tender and sweet over a longer period than many snaps. Heavy crops over a long picking season. Reconfirmed after trial 2009.
LCro LOPS SCgs

00 H2 **'Delikett'**
Dwarf habit. Young, dark green pods stringless but soon form strings; become fleshier and sweeter with age. Very well cropped, with a long season of picking. Reconfirmed after trial 2009.
EKin MCtn NRob

00 H2 **'Sugar Ann'**
Medium height. Early to crop and gives a good yield of juicy, sweet pods. Good flavour. Reconfirmed after trial 2009.
CHby EKin

00 H2 SUGAR DWARF SWEET GREEN (**'Norli'**)
Medium height. About the earliest to mature and a heavy cropper, but over a short period and so requires successional sowing. Medium height plants; good for garden use. Reconfirmed after trial 2009.
CHby MCtn

POTATOES (*Solanum tuberosum*)

First early

98 H2 **'Accent'**
A super-tasting new potato, with pale creamy yellow waxy flesh. Eelworm and common scab resistance.
EKin NRob

98 H2 **'Foremost'**
Originally 'Suttons Foremost'. Ever popular new potato with slightly waxy, firm, white, good-flavoured flesh that does not discolour or disintegrate on cooking.
EKin LCro NRob

98 H2 **'Lady Christl'**
Bulks up very quickly. Long oval, shallow-eyed, pale yellow-skinned and creamy flesh which remains firm on cooking. Eelworm-resistant. Reconfirmed after trial 2007; also in 2013 after trial as early for container use.
EKin LCro NRob

07 H2 **'Orla'**
Can also be used as a second early and maincrop. Good yield of round to oval creamy white tubers; flesh slightly waxy with good flavour. Popular with organic gardeners.
EDel NRob

98 H2 **'Red Duke of York'**
Oval red sport of 'Duke of York' with moist pale yellow flesh of superb flavour. Excellent roasted, but a good all-rounder as tubers bulk up quickly if left to mature as a late second early.
EDel EKin LCro LOPS NRob

07 H2 **'Vivaldi'**
Can be left to bulk up as summer baker. Good yield of oval, pale yellow, smooth-skinned tubers with creamy flesh.
EKin LCro LOPS NRob

98 H2 **'Winston'**
Bulks up quickly to produce large, even-shaped tubers. Creamy moist flesh of excellent flavour which does not discolour on cooking.
EKin LCro NRob

Second early

98 H2 **'British Queen'**
Heavy and uniform crop of white-skinned and floury-textured tubers of delicious flavour for all cooking purposes.
EDel NRob

98 H2 **'Charlotte'**
Long oval variety producing yellow-skinned and waxy tubers with creamy yellow flesh of first-class flavour either hot or cold. Reconfirmed after trial 2013 as early for container use.
EDel EKin LCro LOPS NRob

98 H2 **'Kondor'**
Large pale red-skinned oval tubers with tasty, almost waxy, yellow flesh. Very high yields. Excellent for baking.
NRob

98 H2 **'Nadine'**
Exceptionally smooth skin and shallow eyes. Cream flesh with a moist, waxy texture that does not discolour and remains firm on cooking. Heavy uniform yields; scab-free. An exhibitor's favourite. Reconfirmed after trial 2017.
EKin LCro NRob

Early in containers

13 H2 **'Casablanca'**
Clean crop, white flesh, uniform size.
EDel EKin LCro LOPS NRob

98 H2 **'Lady Christl'**
Bulks up very quickly; is also a first early. Long

oval, shallow-eyed, pale yellow-skinned and creamy flesh which remains firm on cooking. Eelworm-resistant. Reconfirmed after trial 2007; also in 2013 after trial as early for container use.
EKin LCro NRob

13 H2 **'Maris Bard'**
White flesh, thin skin, good flavour and texture; fairly uniform crop.
EDel EKin LCro NRob

13 H2 **'Sharpe's Express'**
Heritage variety; white skin, uniform crop size. Slightly waxy, good flavour.
LCro NRob

Early maincrop

13 H2 **'Jazzy'**
Attractive, oval, uniform crop. Yellow skin and flesh, waxy tubers with sweet taste.
EKin NRob

93 H2 **'Maxine'**
Large, smooth, pale red-skinned tubers with white waxy flesh. Uniform tubers so also recommended for exhibitors. Eelworm-resistant. Reconfirmed after trial 1998.
NRob

93 H2 **'Picasso'**
One of the heaviest croppers with creamy skin and striking bright red eyes. Waxy fine-flavoured flesh, particularly when boiled. Eelworm-resistant and good resistance to common scab. Reconfirmed after trial 1998, 2014.
NRob

Maincrop

14 H2 **'Desiree'**
Red skin, light yellow flesh, oval tubers; reliable, and still the world's most popular red.
LCro LOPS

14 H2 **'Maris Piper'**
Cream skin, cream flesh, oval tubers; a massive favourite with gardeners.
LCro LOPS

14 H2 **'Sarpo Mira'**
Red skin, white flesh, oval tubers; still the leading blight benchmark.
EDel LCro LOPS

Salad

98 H2 **'Charlotte'**
Long oval variety producing yellow-skinned and waxy tubers with creamy yellow flesh of first-class flavour either hot or cold. Reconfirmed after trial 2013 as early for container use.
EDel EKin LCro LOPS NRob

03 H2 **'Pink Fir Apple'**
Late main crop. Very vigorous plants; elongated, knobbly tubers; good flavour.
EDel EKin LCro LOPS NRob SVic

03 H2 **'Ratte'**
Early main crop. Oval tubers, waxy, cream flesh; good flavour.
NRob

Radish (*Raphanus sativus*)

13 H2 **'Escala'**
Hybrid. Globe-shaped, bright cherry-red, with thin tap root; not pithy. Very uniform crop.
LCro LOPS

08 H2 **'Lunar'**
Very uniform crop of solid, round, white roots that are crunchy, juicy and have a mild flavour. No pithiness. Tops are short with leaves that are almost entire. Also sold as 'Ping Pong'.
LCro

08 H2 **'Pink Beauty'**
Attractive, shiny pink roots. Crunchy texture and good, sweet flavour. No pithiness.
LCro LOPS MCtn SCgs

96 H2 **'Scarlet Globe'**
Round medium to large red roots.
EKin

96 H2 **'Sparkler'**
Slightly flattened round roots. Unique colour split: red upper with white lower skin. Reconfirmed after trial 2013.
CHby EKin MCtn

Rhubarb (*Rheum* × *hybridum*)

03 H5 **'Fulton's Strawberry Surprise'**
Maincrop. Very attractive bright red colour. Strong plant, but not too vigorous for the garden.
CDoC

03 H5 **'Grandad's Favorite'**
First early. Vigorous plants, high yield, thick, fairly sweet stem, bright colour, good leaf to stem ratio. Suitable for showing.
CRos EBlo EHyd LRHS NRHS

03 H5 **'Hawke's Champagne'**
Second early. Compact plants; high yield potential. Attractive, bright red, medium-length, uniform stems.
WCot

12 H5 **'Raspberry Red'**
First early. High quality rich red stalks. Crops heavily and reliably.
CBod CDoC CMac CRos EPfP EPom LCro LOPS NRHS SPoG

03 H5 **'Timperley Early'**
First early. Thick stems, early, high yield. Bred for forcing; performs very well outside, but even better colour when forced.
CBod CDoC CMac CRos CSBt CTri EBee

EDir EHyd EKin ELan EMil EPfP EPom LCro LEdu LOPS LRHS LSRN MAsh MGos MPri MRav NLar NRHS NRob NRog SBmr SCgs SCoo SEdi SKee SLim SPer SPoG SRHi WMat

SHALLOT SEE UNDER ONIONS

SPINACH (*Spinacia oleracea*)

08 H2 **'Amazon'**
F_1 hybrid; resistant to mildew races 1–10. Vigorous plants that bulk well; leaves are large, round and a good glossy dark green.
MCtn SVic

00 H2 **'Matador'**
F_1 hybrid. Thick, dark green, upright leaf.
EKin

00 H2 **'Medania'**
Open-pollinated; resistant to mildew races 1 and 3. Good yield from slower-growing plants that are slow to bolt. Slightly blistered, large round leaves. Reconfirmed after trial 2008.
EKin MCtn

08 H2 **'Missouri'**
F_1 hybrid; resistant to mildew races 1–10. Heavy yield of bright, medium green leaves with an upright habit.
EKin LCro LOPS

SPINACH BEET (*Beta vulgaris* subsp. *cicla* var. *cicla*)

00 H4 **'Perpetual Spinach'**
Mid to pale green with fairly soft texture, medium vigour; uniform; stable and clean; flat leaf with good green petiole; reconfirmed after trial 2011.
CHby EDel EKin LCro LRHS MBros MCtn NRHS NRob SVic

SQUASHES (*Cucurbita* species)

BUTTERNUT

08 H2 **'Harrier'**
Early crop of small to medium-sized, bell-shaped fruits, with a small seed cavity.
EDel LCro

08 H2 **'Hunter'**
A very high yield of uniformly small to medium, long pear-shaped fruits with a small seed cavity. Early ripening with orange-gold flesh.
EKin MCtn NRob SVic

SUMMER

06 H2 **'Geode'**
Early and heavy crop of uniform, round, mid to pale green, marbled fruits with smallish blossom end scar. Clean, healthy plants.
LRHS NRHS

06 H2 **'Sunburst'**
Hybrid; attractive yellow, scallop-shaped fruits. Used for baby veg; best harvested when small (5–6cm diameter).
EDel NRob

WINTER

11 H2 **'Crown Prince'**
Large fruits, with blue-grey skin and excellent storage quality. Popular, reliable variety. Fruits have high flesh content, of deep orange colour and excellent flavour.
CHby EKin MCtn NRob SVic

11 H2 **'Harlequin'**
High sugar cultivar. Decorative ridged fruits, striped yellow, gold and green; mid-sized with a typical diameter 10–13cm. Good yield per plant and excellent storage quality. Plant has a semi-bush habit. Firm flesh of smooth texture and sweet flavour.
EDel SVic

11 H2 **'Honey Bear'**
High sugar variety. Dark green, mini-acorn-shaped fruits of uniform size, typically 8–10cm in diameter. Sweet flavour; ideal size for baking whole. Compact, bushy habit, giving a reasonable yield of fruits, with excellent storage qualities. Plant demonstrates good resistance to powdery mildew.
MCtn SVic

11 H2 **'Kabocha' large-fruited**
Dark green flattened fruit, typically 15 to 17cm in diameter. Good storage. Flesh is thick, sweet and smooth. Ideal for desserts.
SVic

11 H2 **'Sweet Dumpling'**
Original sweet dumpling type. Uniform crop of small fruit, approximately 9 to 10cm in diameter; ridged, cream-coloured with green stripes and mottling; sweetly flavoured orange flesh. Trailing habit, producing a good yield of fruits with excellent storage quality.
CHby EKin MCtn NRob

SUGARSNAP SEE UNDER PEAS

SWEET CORN (*Zea mays*)

03 H2 **'Earlibird'**
F_1 hybrid; 2nd early supersweet. Uniform cobs; good vigour. Reconfirmed after trial 2009, 2016.
EKin MCtn

03 H2 **'Lark'**
F_1 hybrid; 2nd early extra tender sweet. High yield of well-filled cobs with very sweet, clean

flavour. Reconfirmed after trial 2009, 2016; among the first to be harvested in the trial.
EKin LCro MCtn SVic

03 H2 **'Mainstay'**
F_1 hybrid; maincrop supersweet. Vigorous plants, reliable crop, well-filled cobs.
MBros

09 H2 **'Mirai 003'**
Early; uniform, small, exceptionally sweet cobs.
LCro

03 H2 **'Swift'**
F_1 hybrid; early extra tender sweet. High yield of cobs with excellent eating quality. Good sweet flavour and tender kernels. Very popular variety. Thin pericarp is prone to damage. Reconfirmed after trial 2009, 2016; among the first to be harvested.
EKin LCro MCtn SVic

Sweet pepper (*Capsicum annuum* var. *annuum* Grossum Group)

05 H1c **'Corno di Toro Rosso'**
Open-pollinated; later-cropping. Long, horn-shaped, very fleshy fruits that have a good flavour. Maturing from pale green to bright red. Big fruits, huge yield. Reconfirmed after trial 2016.
CHby LCro MCtn

05 H1c **'Friggitello'**
Open-pollinated; productive plants with small, long, slim, pointed fruits. Ripening from mid green to red; the versatile sweet-flavoured fruits have the appearance of a hot pepper and are also suitable for stirfry and pickling.
MCtn

05 H1c **'Mohawk'**
F_1 hybrid. Medium-sized, blocky, bell-shaped fruits that ripen from dark green to bright yellow / orange; good flavour. Dwarf-growing plants are well suited to growing in pots. Reconfirmed after trial 2016.
CRos EHyd EKin LRHS MBros NRHS

05 H1c **'Redskin'**
F_1 hybrid; small to medium, blocky, bell-shaped fruits that ripen from dark green to a glossy, dark red. Compact plants give a high yield and are well suited to growing in pots. Original windowsill pepper. Reconfirmed after trial 2016.
CRos EHyd EKin LCro LRHS NRHS

05 H1c **'Topepo Rosso'**
Open-pollinated; productive, early-cropping plants. Medium-sized, beef tomato shape that is good for stuffing. Attractive fruits mature from dark green to bright red and have a good flavour.
MCtn

Tomatoes (*Solanum lycopersicum*)

97 H1c **'Alicante'**
Good shape; heavy crop of attractive fruits which ripen well. Very reliable and productive; early to mature; sweet flavour. H2 for outdoor use.
CRos EHyd EKin LCro LOPS LRHS NRHS NRob

13 H1c **'Elegance'**
Strong plants producing high yield of large fruits. Trusses of 8–10 flavoursome fruits.
LRHS

97 H1c **'Golden Sunrise'**
Later-maturing; small yellow fruits.
EKin LCro LOPS LRHS MCtn NRHS NRob SVic

93 H1c **'Outdoor Girl'**
Early. Round red fruits with good flavour.
CRos EHyd LCro LOPS LRHS MCtn NRHS NRob SVic

93 H1c **'Shirley'**
F_1 hybrid; fairly early. Uniform trusses; nice round red fruit of medium size and average flavour. Reconfirmed after trial 1997.
CRos EDel EHyd EKin LRHS MBros NRHS NRob SVic

93 H1c **'Tigerella'**
Interesting attractive striped fruit with quite good flavour; reconfirmed after trial 1997. H2 for outdoor use.
CHby EDel EKin LRHS MCtn NRob SVic

93 H1c **'Yellow Perfection'**
Indeterminate, uniform, round, pale, yellow fruit. H2 for outdoor use.
EKin

Beefsteak

14 H1c **'Beefmaster'**
Multilocular; large fruit; deeply ribbed; light, smooth taste, good yield.
EKin

03 H1c **'Costoluto Fiorentino'**
High yield; medium-sized, attractive bright red, highly ribbed, succulent fruit with good flavour.
LCro LOPS MCtn SCgs

14 H1c **'Gigantomo'**
Irregular-shaped heavy fruit; light but pleasant flavour; good yield.
EKin MBros NRob

03 H1c **'Marmande'**
High yield; large, bright red, attractive fruits, with solid flesh and good flavour.
CHby EKin MCtn

14 H1c **'Orange Wellington'**
Pleasing flavour; orange-golden fruit; smooth skin; cat-faced but not too deep; good yield.
EKin

14 H1c **'Supersteak'**
Multilocular; smooth skin; good-sized fruit; nice taste, good yield.
CRos EHyd LRHS NRHS

14 H1c **'Tomande'**
Multilocular; smooth skin; good-sized fruit; light taste, good yield.
LCro LOPS

Cherry

07 H1c **'Apero'**
Good yield of oval fruits on compact trusses.
MCtn SCgs

07 H1c **'Cherrola'**
High yield, with attractive fruit well spaced on long trusses. Good flavour; not too fleshy inside. Reconfirmed after trial 2017.
LCro LOPS

17 H1c **'Rosella'**
Very high yield, with nice size and good taste.
LCro

07 H1c **'Sakura'**
High yield; very bright fruits carried on long trusses; very sweet flavour.
EDel

98 H1c **'Sun Baby'**
Good trusses of uniform, attractive, yellow fruits. H2 for outdoor use.
MCtn

07 H1c **'Sungold'**
Good yield of attractive round golden-orange fruits. Good flavour.
CHby CRos EDel EHyd EKin LCro LOPS LRHS MCtn NRHS NRob SVic

98 H1c **'Sweet Million'**
F_1 hybrid. Long open trusses of sweet, round, bright red fruits; good yield. Reconfirmed after trial 2017.
CRos EDel EHyd LRHS MBros MCtn NRHS NRob

Plum

04 H1c **'Ildi'**
Vigorous, indeterminate plants; heavy crop of small, attractive, yellow, plum-shaped fruit.
EKin LCro LOPS SCgs

04 H1c **'Sweet Olive'**
F_1 hybrid; very early. Very high yield from vigorous, healthy, determinate plants. Small, red, round to plum-shaped fruits, a little difficult to pick, but of good flavour.
MCtn

Turnip (*Brassica rapa* Rapifera Group)

04 H3 **'Oasis'**
Good early crop of conical white roots.
MCtn

04 H3 **'Primera'**
Uniform crop of flat-shaped roots with purple top and attractive smooth skin. Good internal flesh.
EHyd LRHS NRHS

93 H3 **'Tokyo Cross'**
F_1 hybrid; early. Uniform, medium size, smooth, round, pure white, shiny roots; reconfirmed after trial 1997 and 2004.
LCro LOPS

Save
25%
when you pay
by Direct Debit*
RHS
MEMBER
Join today
RHS
Inspiring everyone to grow
RHS / Joanna Kossak

V
PLANTS FOR POLLINATORS

RHS Plants for Pollinators

Subspecies and cultivars of plants listed here are also **Plants for Pollinators**, except for those that provide significantly reduced floral resources (i.e. pollen and nectar). This includes most doubles.

Key to codes: T tree S shrub C climber B bulb / corm A annual Bi biennial H herbaceous perennial † denotes an archaeophyte (a naturalised plant introduced before 1500)

Wildflowers

Short Grass (up to 15cm)

Ajuga reptans bugle	H
Bellis perennis daisy	H
Campanula rotundifolia common harebell	H
Hippocrepis comosa horseshoe vetch	H
Lotus corniculatus bird's foot trefoil	H
Potentilla anserina silverweed	H
Potentilla erecta tormentil	H
Potentilla reptans creeping cinquefoil	H
Primula veris common cowslip	H
Prunella vulgaris selfheal	H
Ranunculus repens creeping buttercup	H
Sanguisorba minor salad burnet	H
Taraxacum officinale dandelion	H
Thymus polytrichus wild thyme	H
Thymus pulegioides large thyme	H
Trifolium pratense red clover	H
Trifolium repens white clover	H
Veronica chamaedrys germander speedwell	H

Hedges, Shrub Borders and Woodland Edges

Acer campestre field maple	S or T
Alliaria petiolata garlic mustard	Bi
Allium ursinum ramsons	B
Aquilegia vulgaris columbine	H
Ballota nigra black horehound	H
Berberis vulgaris barberry †	S
Bryonia dioica white bryony	H/C
Buxus sempervirens common box	S
Campanula trachelium nettle-leaved bellflower	H
Clematis vitalba old man's beard, traveller's joy	C
Clinopodium vulgare wild basil	H
Cornus sanguinea common dogwood	S
Crataegus monogyna common hawthorn	S or T
Cytisus scoparius common broom	S
Digitalis purpurea common foxglove	Bi
Euonymus europaeus spindle	S
Ficaria verna subsp. *verna* lesser celandine	H
Fragaria vesca wild strawberry	H
Frangula alnus alder buckthorn	S
Galium mollugo hedge bedstraw	H
Galium odoratum sweet woodruff	H
Galium verum lady's bedstraw	H
Geranium robertianum herb robert	A/Bi
Geum urbanum wood avens	H
Hedera helix common ivy	C
Helleborus foetidus stinking hellebore	H
Hyacinthoides non-scripta bluebell	B
Hylotelephium telephium orpine	H
Ilex aquifolium common holly	T
Lamium album white deadnettle	H
Lamium galeobdolon yellow archangel	H
Ligustrum vulgare wild privet	S
Lonicera periclymenum common honeysuckle	C
Malus sylvestris crab apple	T
Malva sylvestris common mallow	H
Myosotis sylvatica wood forget-me-not	H
Primula vulgaris primrose	H
Prunus avium wild cherry, gean	T
Prunus padus bird cherry	T
Prunus spinosa blackthorn, sloe	S
Rhamnus cathartica purging buckthorn	S
Rosa species rose	S
Rubus fruticosus blackberry	S
Salix caprea goat willow (male form only)	S or T
Salix cinerea subsp. *oleifolia* grey willow (male form only)	S
Sanicula europaea sanicle	H
Silene dioica red campion	H
Silene latifolia subsp. *alba* white campion	H
Smyrnium olusatrum alexanders †	Bi
Sorbus aria common whitebeam	T
Sorbus aucuparia rowan, mountain ash	T

Sorbus torminalis wild service tree	T
Stachys officinalis betony	H
Stellaria holostea greater stitchwort	H
Symphytum officinale common comfrey	H
Teucrium scorodonia wood sage	H
Tilia cordata small-leaved lime	T
Viburnum lantana common wayfaring tree	S
Viburnum opulus guelder rose	S
Vicia cracca common tufted vetch	H
Vicia sativa common vetch	H

Disturbed Ground

Agrostemma githago corncockle †	A
Anchusa arvensis bugloss †	A
Anthemis arvensis corn chamomile †	A
Anthemis cotula stinking chamomile †	A
Centaurea cyanus cornflower †	A
Cichorium intybus chicory †	H
Dipsacus fullonum common teasel	Bi
Echium vulgare viper's bugloss	Bi
Glebionis segetum corn marigold †	A
Iberis amara wild candytuft	A
Lamium amplexicaule henbit deadnettle †	A
Matricaria recutita scented mayweed †	A
Mentha arvensis corn mint	H
Myosotis arvensis field forget-me-not †	A/H
Onopordum acanthium cotton thistle †	Bi
Papaver dubium long-headed poppy †	A
Papaver rhoeas common poppy †	A
Sinapis arvensis charlock †	A
Sonchus arvensis perennial sowthistle	H
Tussilago farfara coltsfoot	H
Verbascum thapsus great mullein	Bi

Flower Beds

Calluna vulgaris heather, ling excl. bud-blooming cultivars	S
Erica ciliaris Dorset heath	S
Erica cinerea bell heather	S
Erica tetralix cross-leaved heath	S

Long Grass (above 50cm)

Arctium minus lesser burdock	Bi
Carduus crispus welted thistle	Bi
Carduus nutans musk thistle	Bi
Chamaenerion angustifolium rosebay willowherb	H
Cirsium arvense creeping thistle	H
Cirsium vulgare spear thistle	Bi
Conopodium majus pignut	H
Cynoglossum officinale hound's tongue	H
Daucus carota wild carrot	Bi
Geranium pratense meadow cranesbill	H
Heracleum sphondylium hogweed	Bi
Hypericum perforatum perforate St John's wort	H
Knautia arvensis field scabious	H
Lathyrus pratensis meadow vetchling	H
Pastinaca sativa wild parsnip	Bi
Succisa pratensis devil's bit scabious	H
Tanacetum vulgare tansy †	H
Thalictrum flavum meadow rue	H
Tragopogon pratensis goat's beard	Bi
Verbascum nigrum dark mullein	Bi/H

Medium Height Grass (up to 50cm)

Achillea millefolium common yarrow	H
Achillea ptarmica sneezewort	H
Agrimonia eupatoria agrimony	H
Anthyllis vulneraria kidney vetch	H
Armeria maritima thrift, sea pink	H
Blackstonia perfoliata yellowwort	A
Campanula glomerata clustered bellflower	H
Centaurea nigra common knapweed, hardheads	H
Centaurea scabiosa greater knapweed	H
Centaurium erythraea common centaury	Bi
Echium vulgare viper's bugloss	Bi
Erigeron acris blue fleabane	A/H
Filipendula vulgaris dropwort	H
Helianthemum nummularium common rockrose	H
Hypochaeris radicata cat's ear	H
Inula conyzae ploughman's spikenard	H
Leontodon hispidus rough hawkbit	H
Leucanthemum vulgare ox-eye daisy	H
Linaria vulgaris common toadflax	H
Malva moschata musk mallow	H
Ononis repens common restharrow	H
Origanum vulgare wild marjoram	H
Pilosella officinarum mouse-ear hawkweed	H
Ranunculus acris meadow buttercup	H
Ranunculus bulbosus bulbous buttercup	H
Reseda lutea wild mignonette	Bi/H
Rhinanthus minor yellow rattle	A
Scabiosa spp.	A/H
Scorzoneroides autumnalis autumn hawkbit	H
Silene vulgaris bladder campion	H
Solidago virgaurea goldenrod	H

Ponds, Pond Margins & Wet Soils

Alisma plantago-aquatica water plantain	H
Angelica sylvestris wild angelica	Bi
Butomus umbellatus flowering rush	H
Caltha palustris marsh marigold	H
Cardamine pratensis cuckoo flower, lady's smock	H
Cirsium dissectum meadow thistle	H
Epilobium hirsutum great willowherb	H
Eupatorium cannabinum hemp agrimony	H
Filipendula ulmaria meadowsweet	H
Galium palustre marsh bedstraw	H
Geum rivale water avens	H
Hypericum tetrapterum square-stalked St John's wort	H

Iris pseudacorus yellow iris H
Lotus pedunculatus greater bird's-foot trefoil H
Lychnis flos-cuculi ragged robin H
Lycopus europaeus gypsywort H
Lysimachia nummularia creeping Jenny H
Lysimachia vulgaris yellow loosestrife H
Lythrum salicaria purple loosestrife H
Mentha aquatica water mint H
Menyanthes trifoliata bogbean H
Myosotis scorpioides water forget-me-not H
Nasturtium officinale common watercress H
Nuphar lutea yellow waterlily H
Nymphaea alba white waterlily H
Oenanthe aquatica fine-leaved water dropwort A/Bi
Oenanthe crocata hemlock water dropwort H
Persicaria amphibia amphibious bistort H
Persicaria bistorta common bistort H
Polemonium caeruleum Jacob's ladder H
Pulicaria dysenterica common fleabane H
Ranunculus aquatilis common water crowfoot A/H
Ranunculus flammula lesser spearwort H
Ranunculus fluitans river water crowfoot H
Ranunculus lingua greater spearwort H
Ranunculus sceleratus celery-leaved buttercup A
Sagittaria sagittifolia arrowhead H
Sanguisorba officinalis great burnet H
Scrophularia auriculata water figwort H
Scutellaria galericulata common skullcap H
Stachys palustris marsh woundwort H
Valeriana officinalis common valerian H
Veronica beccabunga brooklime H

Shingle – Gravel Garden

Cakile maritima sea rocket A
Crambe maritima sea kale H
Crithmum maritimum rock samphire H
Eryngium maritimum sea holly H
Glaucium flavum yellow horned poppy Bi/H
Sedum acre biting stonecrop H
Sedum album white stonecrop † H
Silene uniflora sea campion H

Garden Plants

Winter (nov – feb)

Clematis cirrhosa Spanish traveller's joy C
Crocus species crocus (winter-flowering) B
Eranthis hyemalis winter aconite B
× *Fatshedera lizei* tree ivy S
Galanthus nivalis common snowdrop B
Helleborus species and hybrids hellebore (winter-flowering) H
Lonicera × *purpusii* Purpus honeysuckle S
Mahonia species Oregon grape S
Salix aegyptiaca musk willow S
Sarcococca confusa sweet box S
Sarcococca hookeriana sweet box S
Viburnum tinus laurustinus S

Spring (mar – may)

Acer campestre Native plant; field maple S or T
Acer platanoides Norway maple T
Acer pseudoplatanus sycamore T
Acer saccharum sugar maple T
Aesculus hippocastanum horse chestnut T
Ajuga reptans Native plant; bugle H
Arabis alpina subsp. *caucasica* alpine rock cress H
Armeria juniperifolia juniper-leaved thrift H
Aubrieta species aubretia H
Aurinia saxatilis gold dust H
Berberis darwinii Darwin's barberry S
Berberis thunbergii Japanese barberry S
Bergenia species elephant ear H
Buxus sempervirens Native plant; common box S
Caltha palustris Native plant; marsh marigold H
Ceanothus species California lilac S
Cercis siliquastrum Judas tree T
Chaenomeles species Japanese quince S
Cornus mas Cornelian cherry S
Cotoneaster conspicuus Tibetan cotoneaster S
Crataegus monogyna Native plant; common hawthorn S or T
Crocus species crocus (spring-flowering) B
Doronicum × *excelsum* leopard's bane H
Enkianthus campanulatus redvein enkianthus S
Erica carnea alpine heath S
Erica × *darleyensis* Darley Dale heath S
Erysimum species wallflower Bi or H
Euphorbia amygdaloides Native plant; wood spurge H
Euphorbia characias Mediterranean spurge H
Euphorbia cyparissias cypress spurge H
Euphorbia epithymoides cushion spurge H
Euphorbia × *martini* Martin's spurge S
Euphorbia nicaeensis Nice spurge H
Geranium species cranesbill H
Geum rivale Native plant; water avens H
Hebe species hebe S
Helleborus species & hybrids hellebore (spring-flowering) H
Iberis saxatilis alpine candytuft H
Iberis sempervirens perennial candytuft H
Ilex aquifolium Native plant; common holly T
Lamium maculatum spotted dead nettle H
Lunaria annua honesty Bi
Mahonia species Oregon grape (spring-flowering) S
Malus baccata Siberian crab T
Malus domestica edible apple T

Malus floribunda Japanese crab T
Malus hupehensis Hupeh crab T
Malus sargentii Sargent's crab apple T
Mespilus germanica common medlar T
Muscari armeniacum Armenian grape hyacinth B
Nectaroscordum species honey garlic B
Ornithogalum umbellatum common star of Bethlehem B
Pieris formosa lily-of-the-valley bush S
Pieris japonica lily-of-the-valley bush S
Primula veris Native plant; common cowslip H
Primula vulgaris Native plant; primrose H
Prunus avium Native plant; wild & edible cherries T
Prunus domestica wild & edible plums T
Prunus dulcis almond T
Prunus incisa 'Kojo-no-mai' cherry 'Kojo-no-mai' S
Prunus insititia damson T
Prunus laurocerasus cherry laurel S
Prunus mume Japanese apricot T
Prunus padus Native plant; bird cherry T
Prunus pendula f. *ascendens* 'Rosea' flowering cherry T
Prunus persica peach T
Prunus spinosa Native plant; blackthorn, sloe S
Prunus tenella dwarf Russian almond S
Prunus × *yedoensis* flowering cherry T
Pulmonaria species lungwort H
Pyrus communis pear T
Ribes nigrum blackcurrant S
Ribes rubrum Native plant; common redcurrant S
Ribes sanguineum flowering currant S
Salix caprea Native plant; goat willow (male form only) S or T
Salix hastata 'Wehrhahnii' halberd willow 'Wehrhahnii' S
Salix lanata Native plant; woolly willow (male form only) S
Skimmia japonica skimmia S
Smyrnium olusatrum Native plant; alexanders † Bi
Stachyurus chinensis stachyurus S
Stachyurus praecox stachyurus S
Vaccinium corymbosum blueberry S

Summer (June – Aug)

Achillea species yarrow H
Actaea japonica baneberry H
Aesculus indica Indian horse chestnut (resistant to leaf-mining moth) T
Aesculus parviflora bottlebrush buckeye S
Agastache species giant hyssop H
Ageratum houstonianum flossflower A
Alcea rosea hollyhock Bi
Allium species ornamental and edibles (when allowed to flower) B
Alstroemeria species Peruvian lily H
Amberboa moschata sweet sultan A
Amsonia tabernaemontana eastern bluestar H
Anchusa azurea large blue alkanet A
Anchusa capensis Cape alkanet A
Angelica archangelica angelica Bi
Angelica gigas purple angelica Bi
Angelica sylvestris Native plant; wild angelica Bi
Anthemis tinctoria dyer's chamomile H
Antirrhinum majus snapdragon A or H
Aquilegia species columbine H
Arabis allionii Siberian wallflower H
Argemone platyceras crested poppy A or H
Armeria maritima Native plant; thrift H
Aruncus dioicus goat's beard (male form only) H
Asparagus officinalis common asparagus H
Astrantia major greater masterwort H
Borago officinalis borage A
Brachyglottis (Dunedin Group) 'Sunshine' brachyglottis 'Sunshine' S
Brachyglottis monroi Monro's ragwort S
Buddleja davidii butterfly bush S
Buddleja globosa orange ball tree S
Buphthalmum salicifolium yellow ox-eye H
Bupleurum fruticosum shrubby hare's ear S
Calamintha nepeta Native plant; lesser calamint H
Calendula officinalis common marigold A
Callicarpa bodinieri var. *giraldii* beautyberry S
Callistephus chinensis China aster A
Calluna vulgaris Native plant; heather S
Campanula carpatica tussock bellflower H
Campanula glomerata Native plant; clustered bellflower H
Campanula lactiflora milky bellflower H
Campanula latifolia Native plant; giant bellflower H
Campanula medium Canterbury bells Bi
Campanula persicifolia peach-leaved bellflower H
Campsis radicans trumpet honeysuckle C
Caryopteris × *clandonensis* caryopteris S
Catalpa bignonioides Indian bean tree T
Catananche caerulea blue cupidone H
Centaurea atropurpurea purple knapweed H
Centaurea cyanus cornflower † A
Centaurea dealbata mealy centaury H
Centaurea macrocephala giant knapweed H
Centaurea montana perennial cornflower H
Centaurea nigra Native plant; common knapweed H
Centaurea scabiosa Native plant; greater knapweed H
Centranthus ruber red valerian H
Centratherum punctatum Manaos beauty A
Cerinthe major 'Purpurascens' honeywort 'Purpurascens' A
Cirsium rivulare 'Atropurpureum' purple plume thistle H
Clarkia unguiculata butterfly flower A
Clematis vitalba Native plant; old man's beard, traveller's joy C
Cleome hassleriana spider flower A
Consolida ajacis giant larkspur A
Convolvulus tricolor dwarf morning glory C/A
Coreopsis species tickseed H or A

Cornus alba red-barked dogwood S
Cosmos species cosmos A
Crambe cordifolia greater sea kale H
Crataegus monogyna Native plant; common hawthorn S or T
Cucurbita pepo marrow, courgette A
Cuphea ignea cigar flower A
Cynara cardunculus including Scolymus Group globe artichoke and cardoon H
Cynoglossum amabile Chinese forget-me-not H
Dahlia species dahlia H
Delosperma floribundum ice plant H
Delphinium elatum candle larkspur H
Dianthus barbatus sweet william Bi
Dictamnus albus dittany H
Digitalis species foxglove Bi
Dipsacus fullonum Native plant; common teasel Bi
Echinacea purpurea purple coneflower H
Echinops species globe thistle H
Echium vulgare Native plant; viper's bugloss A
Elaeagnus angustifolia oleaster S
Erica cinerea Native plant; bell heather S
Erica erigena Irish heath S
Erica vagans Native plant; Cornish heath S
Erigeron species fleabane H
Eriophyllum lanatum golden yarrow H
Eryngium alpinum alpine eryngo H
Eryngium giganteum Miss Willmott's ghost Bi
Eryngium planum blue eryngo H
Eryngium × *tripartitum* eryngo H
Erysimum species wallflower H or S
Escallonia species escallonia S
Eschscholzia californica California poppy A
Eupatorium cannabinum Native plant; hemp agrimony H
Eupatorium maculatum Joe Pye weed H
Euphorbia cornigera horned spurge H
Euphorbia donii euphorbia H
Euphorbia sarawschanica Zeravshan spurge H
Ferula communis giant fennel H
Foeniculum vulgare common fennel † H
Fragaria × *ananassa* garden strawberry H
Fuchsia species fuchsia – hardy types S
Gaillardia × *grandiflora* blanket flower H
Gaura lindheimeri white gaura H
Geranium species cranesbill (summer-flowering) H
Geranium pratense Native plant; meadow cranesbill H
Geum species avens (summer-flowering) H
Gilia capitata blue thimble flower A
Glebionis segetum corn marigold † A
Gypsophila elegans annual baby's breath A
Hebe species hebe S
Helenium species Helen's flower H
Helianthus annuus common sunflower excl. pollen-free cultivars A
Helianthus debilis cucumberleaf sunflower A
Heliopsis helianthoides smooth ox-eye H
Heliotropium arborescens common heliotrope A
Heracleum sphondylium Native plant; hogweed Bi
Hesperis matronalis dame's violet H
Hydrangea anomala subsp. *petiolaris* climbing hydrangea C
Hydrangea paniculata paniculate hydrangea (only cultivars with many fertile flowers, e.g. 'Kyushu', 'Big Ben', 'Floribunda', 'Brussels Lace') S
Hylotelephium spectabile & hybrids ice plant H
Hylotelephium telephium Native plant; orpine H
Hyssopus officinalis hyssop S
Iberis amara Native plant; wild candytuft A
Ilex aquifolium Native plant; common holly T
Inula species harvest daisy H
Jasminum officinale common jasmine C
Kalmia latifolia mountain laurel S
Knautia arvensis Native plant; field scabious H
Knautia macedonica Macedonian scabious H
Koelreuteria paniculata pride of India T
Lathyrus latifolius broad-leaved everlasting pea H
Laurus nobilis bay tree S
Lavandula angustifolia English lavender S
Lavandula × *intermedia* lavandin S
Lavandula stoechas French lavender S
Lavatera olbia tree lavatera S
Lavatera trimestris annual lavatera A
Leucanthemum × *superbum* Shasta daisy H
Leucanthemum vulgare Native plant; ox-eye daisy H
Liatris spicata button snakewort H
Ligustrum ovalifolium garden privet S
Ligustrum sinense Chinese privet S
Limnanthes douglasii poached egg flower A
Limonium platyphyllum broad-leaved statice H
Linaria maroccana annual toadflax A
Linaria purpurea purple toadflax H
Lobularia maritima sweet alyssum A
Lonicera periclymenum Native plant; common honeysuckle C
Lychnis coronaria rose campion Bi or H
Lychnis flos-cuculi Native plant; ragged robin H
Lysimachia vulgaris Native plant; yellow loosestrife H
Lythrum salicaria Native plant; purple loosestrife H
Lythrum virgatum wand loosestrife H
Malope trifida large-flowered mallow wort A
Malva alcea greater musk mallow H
Malva moschata Native plant; musk mallow H
Matthiola incana hoary stock Bi
Mentha aquatica Native plant; water mint H
Mentha spicata spearmint H
Monarda didyma bergamot H
Myosotis species forget-me-not Bi
Nemophila menziesii baby blue eyes A
Nepeta species catmint H
Nicotiana alata flowering tobacco A
Nicotiana langsdorffii Langsdorff's tobacco A
Nicotiana sylvestris flowering tobacco Bi
Nigella damascena love-in-a-mist A
Nigella hispanica Spanish fennel flower A

Oenothera species evening primrose Bi
Olearia species daisy bush S
Onopordum acanthium cotton thistle Bi
Origanum orites pot marjoram S
Origanum 'Rosenkuppel' marjoram 'Rosenkuppel' H
Origanum vulgare Native plant; oregano, wild marjoram H
Paeonia species peony H
Papaver orientale oriental poppy H
Papaver rhoeas Native plant; common poppy † A
Parthenocissus tricuspidata Boston ivy C
Penstemon species beard-tongue T
Perovskia atriplicifolia Russian sage S
Persicaria amplexicaulis red bistort H
Persicaria bistorta Native plant; common bistort H
Phacelia campanularia Californian bluebell A
Phacelia tanacetifolia fiddleneck A
Phaseolus coccineus scarlet runner bean A
Phlomis species sage S
Phlox paniculata perennial phlox H
Photinia davidiana stranvaesia S
Phuopsis stylosa Caucasian crosswort H
Pileostegia viburnoides climbing hydrangea C
Polemonium caeruleum Native plant; Jacob's ladder H
Potentilla species cinquefoil H or S
Prostanthera cuneata alpine mint bush S
Ptelea trifoliata hop tree S
Pyracantha species firethorn S
Reseda odorata garden mignonette A
Ridolfia segetum false fennel A
Robinia pseudoacacia false acacia T
Rosa species rose S
Rubus fruticosus agg. Native plant; blackberry S
Rubus idaeus Native plant; common raspberry S
Rudbeckia species coneflower H or A
Salvia species sage A or H
Salvia rosmarinus rosemary S
Sanvitalia procumbens creeping zinnia A
Scabiosa spp. A/H
Sidalcea malviflora checkerbloom H
Solidago species goldenrod H
Sorbus aria Native plant; common whitebeam T
Sorbus aucuparia Native plant; mountain ash, rowan T
Spiraea japonica Japanese spiraea S
Stachys byzantina lamb's ear H
Stachys macrantha big sage H
Stokesia laevis Stokes' aster H
Symphoricarpos albus snowberry S
Tagetes patula French marigold A
Tamarix ramosissima tamarisk S
Tanacetum coccineum pyrethrum H
Tanacetum vulgare Native plant; tansy † H
Telekia speciosa yellow ox-eye H
Tetradium daniellii bee-bee tree T
Teucrium chamaedrys Native plant; wall germander H
Thymus species thyme S
Tilia × *europaea* common lime T
Tilia maximowicziana lime T
Tilia oliveri lime T
Tilia platyphyllos Native plant; broad-leaved lime T
Tithonia rotundifolia Mexican sunflower A
Trachymene coerulea blue lace flower A
Trollius species globeflower H
Tropaeolum majus garden nasturtium A
Verbascum species mullein Bi
Verbena bonariensis purple top H
Verbena rigida slender vervain A
Veronica longifolia garden speedwell H
Veronica spicata Native plant; spiked speedwell H
Veronicastrum virginicum Culver's root H
Viburnum lantana Native plant; common wayfaring tree S
Viburnum opulus Native plant; guelder rose S
Vicia faba broad bean A
Weigela florida weigelia S
Zauschneria californica Californian fuchsia S
Zinnia elegans youth and old age A

Autumn (sept – oct)

Aconitum carmichaelii Carmichael's monk's hood H
Actaea simplex simple-stemmed bugbane H
Anemone hupehensis Chinese anemone H
Anemone × *hybrida* Japanese anemone H
Arbutus unedo strawberry tree S or T
Campanula poscharskyana trailing bellflower H
Ceratostigma plumbaginoides hardy blue-flowered leadwort H
Chrysanthemum species & hybrids chrysanthemum H
Clematis heracleifolia tube clematis C
Colchicum species autumn crocus B
Crocus species crocus (autumn-flowering types) B
Dahlia species & hybrids dahlia H
Elaeagnus pungens silverthorn S
Elaeagnus × *submacrophylla* Ebbinge's silverberry S
Fatsia japonica Japanese aralia S
Hedera colchica Persian ivy C
Hedera helix Native plant; common ivy C
Helianthus × *laetiflorus* perennial sunflower H
Leucanthemella serotina autumn ox-eye H
Machaeranthera tanacetifolia tansy-leaf aster A
Salvia species sage (autumn-flowering types) H
Symphyotrichum species and hybrids Michaelmas daisy H
Tilia henryana Henry's lime (one of the last to flower) T

VI
NURSERIES

Nursery Codes and Symbols

The first letter of each nursery code represents the area of the country in which the nursery is situated.

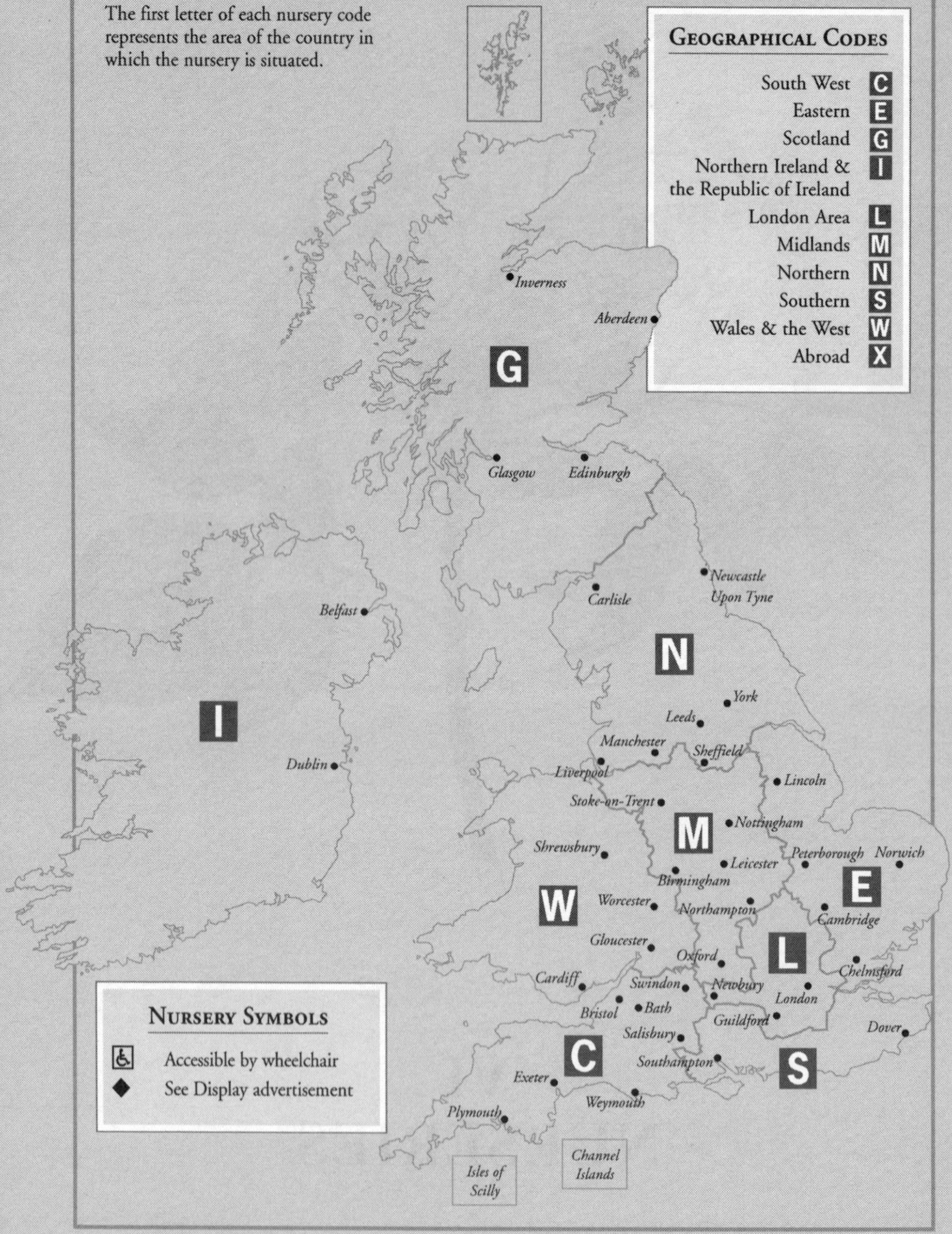

USING THE NURSERY LISTINGS

Your main reference from the Plant Directory is the Nursery Details by Code listing, which includes all relevant information for each nursery in order of nursery code. The Nursery Index by Name is an alphabetical list for those who know a nursery's name but not its code and wish to check its details in the main list.

1 NURSERY DETAILS BY CODE

Once you have found your plant in the Plant Directory, turn to this list to find out the name, address, opening times and other details of the nurseries whose codes accompany the plant.

KEY

♿ Accessible by wheelchair ◆ See Display advertisement

A geographical code is followed by three or four letters reflecting the nursery's name

ESwi **SWINES MEADOW FARM NURSERY** ♿ ◆
47 Towngate East, Market Deeping,
Peterborough, Lincolnshire,
PE6 8LQ
Ⓜ 07432627766
Ⓔ rareplants@me.com
Ⓦ www.swinesmeadowfarmnursery.co.uk
Contact: Colin Ward
Opening Times: 0900-1600 Mon-Sat, 1000-1600 Sun. Closed Jan-Feb except by appt. only.
Min Mail Order UK: £10.00
Min Mail Order EU: £10.00
Credit Cards: All major debit/credit cards except American Express
Specialities: Hardy exotics, tree ferns, bamboos & hostas. Wollemi pine stockist. Many specialities available in small quantities only.
Notes: Delivers to shows. Wheelchair accessible.
OS Grid Ref: TF150113

A brief summary of the plants available

Other information about the nursery

The Ordnance Survey national grid reference for use with OS maps

2 NURSERY INDEX BY NAME

If you are looking for a particular nursery, use this alphabetical index to find it, note its code and then turn to the Nursery Details by Code listing for full information.

Sunnyside Nursery	LSun
Sussex Fruit Trees	SSFT
Swallows Nursery	MSwo
Swines Meadow Farm Nursery	ESwi
T. D. Thursfield	MThu
Taylors Clematis Nursery	NTay
Thorncroft Clematis & Climbers Ltd	ETho
Thuya Alpine Nursery	WThu

How to Use the Nursery Listings

The details given for each nursery have been compiled from information supplied to us in answer to a questionnaire. In some case, because of space constraints, the entries have been abbreviated.

Nurseries are not charged for their entries and inclusion in no way implies a value judgement.

Nursery Details by Code (p.888)

Each nursery is allocated a code, for example GPoy. The first letter of each code indicates the region of the British Isles in which the nursery is situated. In this example G = Scotland. The remaining three or four letters reflect the nursery's name, in this case Poyntzfield Herb Nursery.

In this listing, nurseries are given in alphabetical order of code for quick referral from the Plant Directory. All of the nurseries' details, such as addresses, opening times, etc will be found in this index.

Opening Times

These are published as submitted. It is always advisable, especially if travelling a long distance, to double-check with the nursery before setting out.

Mail Order

Many nurseries offer a mail order service. This is often restricted to certain times of the year or to particular genera. Please check the **Notes** section of the nursery entry for restrictions or special conditions.

In some instances the mail order service extends throughout the European Union. Where this is the case, the minimum charge to the EU will be noted. If this is "Nmc" ("no minimum charge") please note that to send even one plant may involve the nursery in substantial postage and packaging costs. Some nurseries may not be prepared to send tender or bulky plants.

Where a nursery offers a mail order only service, this will be noted under **Opening Times** in the nursery entry. Many nurseries offer a mail order online service with some only operating in this way.

Export

This refers to mail order beyond the EU and indicates nurseries that are prepared to consider this. There is usually a substantial minimum charge and, in addition, all the costs of phytosanitary certificates and Customs have to be met by the purchaser.

Catalogue Cost

Only a small number of nurseries now offer a printed catalogue. Some may not charge or may ask for stamps to bear the cost of postage. If plant lists are available in an electronic format, some nurseries have indicated that they will email them to enquirers.

The majority of nurseries now publish their catalogues only on the internet as this is more cost-effective than producing a printed copy and enables them to reflect stock changes throughout the year.

Specialities

This is where nurseries list the plants or genera in which they specialise and any National Collections that they hold. Please note that some nurseries may charge an entry fee to visit a National Collection. Charges may also be levied to visit any garden to which the nursery is attached.

Nurseries also indicate here if they only have small quantities of individual plants available for sale or if they will propagate to order.

Notes

This section contains: information on restrictions to mail order or export; whether payment in euros is accepted; whether nurseries deliver to shows; details of partial wheelchair access; the nursery site address if this differs from the office address; and any other non-horticultural or general information.

Wheelchair Access ♿

Nurseries are asked to indicate if their premises are suitable for wheelchair users.

We use the wheelchair symbol for those nurseries that tell us their site is fully accessible. Where only partial or restricted access is offered, this is stated in the **Notes** section of the nursery's details and the nursery is not marked with the symbol.

Please note that wheelchair access does not necessarily relate to any gardens to which the nursery may be attached.

The assessment of ease of access is entirely the responsibility of the individual nursery.

Delivers to Shows

Many nurseries will deliver pre-ordered plants to flower shows for collection by customers. Contact the nursery for details of shows that they will be attending.

Payment in Euros

A number of UK nurseries will accept payment in euros. You should check with the nursery concerned before making such a payment, as some will only accept cash and some only cheques, whilst others will expect the purchaser to pay bank charges.

OS Grid Ref

Nurseries are also encouraged to provide their Ordnance Survey national grid reference for use with OS Land Ranger Series maps.

Nursery Index by Name

An alphabetical index of nurseries is included (p.981). Nurseries new to the book and those making a re-entry are shown in embolden type.

Deleted Nurseries

Every year some nurseries ask to be removed from the book. This may be a temporary measure because, for example, they are relocating or because their plant stocks are low due to adverse growing conditions, or it may be permanent following closure, sale, retirement or a change in the way they trade.

Some nurseries miss the deadline for submissions and may ask to re-enter the book in the following edition. Other nurseries do not respond at all and, as we have no current information on their trading status, they are not included in the book.

We recommend that you use the latest edition of the *RHS Plant Finder*

Nursery Details by Code

Please note that all these nurseries are listed in alphabetical order by their code. All nurseries are listed in alphabetical order by their name in the **Nursery Index by Name** on page 981.

South West

CAbb **Abbotsbury Sub-Tropical Gardens** ♿
Abbotsbury, Nr Weymouth, Dorset, DT3 4LA
Ⓣ (01305) 871344
Ⓕ (01305) 871344
Ⓔ info@abbotsburygardens.co.uk
Ⓦ www.abbotsbury-tourism.co.uk/gardens/
Contact: David Sutton
Opening Times: 1000-1800 daily, mid Mar-1st Nov. 1000-1500, Nov-mid Mar.
Credit Cards: Access, Visa, MasterCard, Switch
Specialities: Less common & tender shrubs incl. palms, tree ferns, bamboos & plants from Australia, New Zealand & S. Africa.
Notes: Wheelchair accessible.

CAby **Forde Abbey Nursery** ♿
Forde Abbey, Chard, Somerset, TA20 4LU
Ⓣ (01460) 220231
Ⓔ info@fordeabbey.co.uk
Ⓦ https://www.fordeabbey.co.uk
Contact: Paul Bygrave
Opening Times: 1000-1700 7 days, 1st Mar-31st Oct.
Cat. Cost: None issued.
Credit Cards: All major credit/debit cards
Specialities: Hardy herbaceous perennials.
Notes: Wheelchair accessible.
OS Grid Ref: ST359052

CAco **Acorn Trees and Shrubs**
Hilltown Farm, Rackenford, Tiverton, Devon, EX16 8DX
Ⓣ (01884) 881633
Ⓔ goakey101@gmail.com
Ⓦ www.acorntreesandshrubs.co.uk
Contact: Grahame Oakey
Opening Times: By appt. only, but generally 7 days a week.
Min Mail Order UK: £100.00
Min Mail Order EU: £150.00
Cat. Cost: Full plant listing and photo files available by email only.
Credit Cards: All major credit/debit cards
Specialities: Specialist in conifers, particularly long-needled varieties such as *Pinus montezumae* (several cvs), *holfordiana, schwerinii, psuedostrobus, palustris* & other short-needled varieties. Stock subject to availability.
Notes: Seedling to specimen sizes up to 35yrs old. Enviable collection of short-needled *Pinus parviflora* cvs. Also sells broadleaves and rhododendrons. The conifer collection is probably the most diverse for sale within the UK, with more than 1000 species/cvs. Also sells wholesale. Partial wheelchair access (except toilet).
OS Grid Ref: SS852051

CAgr **Agroforestry Research Trust**
46 Hunters Moon, Dartington, Totnes, Devon, TQ9 6JT
Ⓣ (01803) 840776
Ⓕ (01803) 840776
Ⓔ mail@agroforestry.co.uk
Ⓦ www.agroforestry.co.uk
Contact: Martin Crawford
Opening Times: Not open. Mail order only.
Min Mail Order UK: Nmc
Min Mail Order EU: Nmc
Cat. Cost: 4 × 1st class.
Credit Cards: All major credit/debit cards
Specialities: Top & soft fruit, nut trees including *Castanea, Corylus, Juglans, Pinus.* Also sells seeds. Some plants in small quantities only.
Notes: Euro accepted.

CArg **Ashridge Nurseries**
Grove Cross Barn, Castle Cary, Somerset, BA7 7NJ
Ⓣ (01963) 359444

Ⓕ (01963) 359445
Ⓔ support@ashridgetrees.co.uk
Ⓦ www.ashridgetrees.co.uk
Contact: Rose Hurst
Opening Times: Not open. Mail order only.
Min Mail Order UK: £20.00
Credit Cards: MasterCard, Visa
Specialities: Trees, hedging. Fruit trees & soft fruit incl roses, lavender, climbers & bulbs.

CAvo **Avon Bulbs**
Burnt House Farm, Middle Lambrook, South Petherton, Somerset, TA13 5HE
Ⓣ (01460) 242177/249060
Ⓔ maxine@avonbulbs.co.uk
Ⓦ www.avonbulbs.co.uk
Contact: Chris Ireland-Jones
Opening Times: Mail order only.
Min Mail Order UK: Nmc
Min Mail Order EU: Nmc
Cat. Cost: Free.
Credit Cards: All major credit/debit cards
Specialities: Specialise in named snowdrops, some are only available in small quantities, both 'in the green' in the spring, and as dormant bulbs in the early autumn.
Notes: Can deliver to some shows. A mail-order nursery but pre-booked orders can be collected by prior arrangement.
OS Grid Ref: ST422187

CBar **Barters Plant Centre & Nursery** ♿
Chapmanslade, Westbury, Wiltshire, BA13 4AL
Ⓣ (01373) 832694
Ⓕ (01373) 832677
Ⓔ sales@barters.co.uk
Ⓦ www.barters.co.uk
Contact: Andrew Stone
Opening Times: 0900-1700 Mon-Sat, Mar-Oct 0900-1630 Mon-Sat, Nov-Feb. 1000-1600 Sun (closed Sun Jul-Nov & Jan-Feb).
Cat. Cost: Online only.
Credit Cards: All major debit/credit cards except American Express
Specialities: Wide range of shrubs, herbaceous perennials, container trees, ferns, seasonal bedding plants, ornamental grasses & climbers. Hedging, fruit trees, roses & seasonal bare-root trees and native hedging plants.
Notes: Also sells wholesale. Wheelchair accessible.
OS Grid Ref: ST830480

CBcs **Burncoose Nurseries** ♿
Gwennap, Redruth, Cornwall, TR16 6BJ
Ⓣ (01209) 860316
Ⓔ info@burncoose.co.uk
Ⓦ www.burncoose.co.uk
Contact: C.H. Williams
Opening Times: 0830-1700 Mon-Sat & 1100-1600 Sun.
Min Mail Order UK: Nmc
Min Mail Order EU: Individual quotations for EU sales
Cat. Cost: Free.
Credit Cards: Visa, MasterCard, Maestro, American Express
Specialities: Extensive range of over 3500 ornamental trees & shrubs and herbaceous. Rare & unusual *Magnolia*, *Rhododendron*. Conservatory plants. 30 acre garden.
Notes: 30 acre garden with free entry. Click and collect available. Many care articles and videos to be found on website. Also sells wholesale. Delivers to shows. Wheelchair accessible.
OS Grid Ref: SW742395

CBct **Barracott Plants**
Old Orchard, Calstock Road, Gunnislake, Cornwall, PL18 9AA
Ⓣ (01822) 832234
Ⓜ 07811 207186
Ⓔ gandt@barracottplants.co.uk
Ⓦ www.barracottplants.co.uk
Contact: Geoff & Thelma Turner
Opening Times: By appt. only.
Min Mail Order UK: £20.00
Credit Cards: Paypal
Specialities: Herbaceous plants: shade-loving, foliage & form. *Aspidistra*, *Begonia*, *Bergenia*, *Convallaria*, *Disporum*, *Liriope*, *Maianthemum*, *Plectranthus*, *Polygonatum*, *Schefflera* & ferns.
OS Grid Ref: SX436702

CBdn **Bowden Hostas**
Sales Office: Bowdens Nursery Ltd, Bowden Place, Sticklepath, Devon, EX20 2NL
Ⓣ (01837) 849367
Ⓔ sales@bowdenhostas.com
Ⓦ www.bowdenhostas.com
Contact: Tim Penrose
Opening Times: 1000-1600 Mon-Sat, Apr-Sep. Oct-Mar, please ring before travelling.
Min Mail Order UK: Nmc
Min Mail Order EU: Nmc
Cat. Cost: Online catalogue.
Credit Cards: Visa, Access, EuroCard, Switch
Specialities: *Hosta*, ferns, bamboos, *Agapanthus*. National Plant Collection of *Hosta* (Halcyon and sports) and *Agapanthus* (Pine Cottage hybrids).
Notes: Also sells wholesale. Exports beyond EU.
OS Grid Ref: SX640940

C

CBee **Bee Happy Plants & Seeds**
Lakehayes Nursery, South Chard, Somerset, TA20 2NZ
Ⓣ (01460) 221815
Ⓜ 07976 949893
Ⓔ sarah@beehappyplants.co.uk
Ⓦ www.beehappyplants.co.uk/
Contact: Sarah Holdsworth
Opening Times: By appt. only.
Min Mail Order UK: £8.00
Min Mail Order EU: £10.00
Cat. Cost: Online only.
Credit Cards: All major credit/debit cards
Specialities: *Leptospermum scoparium.*
Notes: Specialist in wild species plants suitable for bees and other pollinators. Also sells wholesale. Delivers to shows.
OS Grid Ref: ST325550

CBen **Bennetts Water Gardens** ♿
Putton Lane, Chickerell, Weymouth, Dorset, DT3 4AF
Ⓣ (01305) 785150
Ⓔ orders@waterlily.co.uk
Ⓦ www.waterlily.co.uk
Contact: James Bennett
Opening Times: 1000-1600 Apr-Sep, Sun-Fri.
Min Mail Order UK: Nmc
Min Mail Order EU: Nmc
Credit Cards: Visa, MasterCard, JCB, Maestro
Specialities: National Plant Collection of *Nymphaea* (hardy water lilies).
Notes: Bare root plants available by mail order. Potted plants available in store. Euro accepted. Wheelchair accessible.
OS Grid Ref: SY650797

CBgR **Beggar's Roost Plants**
Lilstock, Bridgwater, Somerset, TA5 1SU
Ⓣ (01278) 741519
Ⓔ ro@lilstock.eclipse.co.uk
Contact: Lady Rosemary FitzGerald
Opening Times: Not open. Mail order only.
Min Mail Order UK: £10.00
Min Mail Order EU: £15.00
Cat. Cost: 3 × large 2nd class.
Credit Cards: None
Specialities: *Hemerocallis* (incl. heritage) grown in British conditions.
Notes: Mail order for speciality *Hemerocallis*. Ask for list. Euro accepted.
OS Grid Ref: ST168450

CBod **Bodmin Nursery** ♿
Laveddon Mill, Laninval Hill, Bodmin, Cornwall, PL30 5JU
Ⓣ (01208) 72837
Ⓕ (01208) 76491
Ⓔ sales@bodminnursery.co.uk
Ⓦ www.bodminnursery.co.uk
Contact: Mark Lawlor
Opening Times: 0900-1700 Mon-Sat 1000-1600 Sun.
Credit Cards: All major credit/debit cards
Specialities: Herbs, herbaceous & grasses, hardy geraniums & coastal plants. Interesting shrubs, fruit & ornamental trees.
Notes: Wheelchair accessible.
OS Grid Ref: SX053659

CBor **Border Alpines**
Chasty Court, Chasty, Holsworthy, Devon, EX22 6NA
Ⓣ (01409) 253654
Ⓜ 07841 021557
Ⓔ borderalpines@btinternet.com
Ⓦ www.borderalpines.co.uk
Contact: Janette Lowe
Opening Times: By appt. only.
Min Mail Order UK: Nmc
Min Mail Order EU: Nmc
Cat. Cost: Online only.
Credit Cards: None
Specialities: Alpines, dwarf herbaceous & specimen acers. A family-run nursery, selling a range of British-grown alpines, dwarf herbaceous and other hardy perennial plants. Experienced growers and breeders for over 30 years.
Notes: Delivers to shows.

CBrac **Brackendale Nurseries** ♿
Horton Road, Three Legged Cross, Wimborne, Dorset, BH21 6SD
Ⓣ (01202) 822349
Ⓔ sales@brackendalenurseries.co.uk
Ⓦ www.brackendalenurseries.co.uk
Contact: Nicola Stainer
Opening Times: Opening times are subject to seasonal change, please see our website for opening hours.
Credit Cards: All major credit/debit cards
Specialities: Wide range of plants, especially shrubs, conifers and hedging. Established specimen-sized shrubs and native, ornamental and fruit trees available. Acid loving *Azalea*, *Camellia* & *Rhododendron* together with coastal favourites.
Notes: Wheelchair accessible.
OS Grid Ref: SU075059

CBro **Broadleigh Gardens** ♿
Bishops Hull, Taunton, Somerset, TA4 1AE
Ⓣ (01823) 286231
Ⓔ info@broadleighbulbs.co.uk
Ⓦ www.broadleighbulbs.co.uk
Contact: Christine Skelmesdale

Opening Times: 0900-1600 Mon-Fri for viewing only (charity donation). Orders may be collected if notice given.
Min Mail Order UK: Nmc
Min Mail Order EU: Nmc
Cat. Cost: 2 × 1st class.
Credit Cards: All major credit/debit cards
Specialities: Jan catalogue for bulbs in growth & herbaceous woodland plants. Extensive list of *Agapanthus* and other South African bulbs. Jun: dwarf & unusual bulbs. National Plant Collection of Alec Grey hybrid daffodils.
Notes: Display garden and nursery open. Euro accepted as cash payment only. Wheelchair accessible.
OS Grid Ref: ST195251

CBrP **Brooklands Plants**
25 Treves Road, Dorchester, Dorset, DT1 2HE
Ⓣ (01305) 265846
Ⓔ cycads@btinternet.com
Ⓦ brooklandsplants.com
Contact: Ian Watt
Opening Times: By appt. only for collection of plants.
Min Mail Order UK: £50.00 + p&p
Cat. Cost: Online only.
Credit Cards: None
Specialities: *Encephalartos, Dioon, Macrozamia* & *Cycas.*
Notes: Fern and Cycad nursery that also specialises in hardy palms, unusual conifers, plants from New Zealand and plants for the terrarium, including mosses. Generally only small/young specimens available. Some species available in small quantites only. Mail order available on small plants only. Euro accepted.
OS Grid Ref: SY682897

CBTo **Bellamont Topiary**
Long Bredy, Dorset, DT2 9HN
Ⓣ (01308) 482690
Ⓜ 07817 205857
Ⓔ harriet.sykes@btinternet.com
Ⓦ http://www.bellamont-topiary.co.uk/
Contact: Harriet
Opening Times: 0900-1700 Mon-Fri W/ends by appt. only.
Specialities: Topiary.
Notes: British field-grown box topiary shapes and hedging.

CBTr **Bowhayes Trees**
Bowhayes Farm, Venn Ottery, Ottery St Mary, Devon, EX11 1RY
Ⓣ (01404) 812229
Ⓕ (01404) 815800
Ⓔ contact@bowhayestrees.co.uk
Ⓦ https://www.bowhayestrees.co.uk
Contact: Fiona Hughes
Opening Times: 0900-1700 Mon-Fri, 0930-1230 Sat Mar-Oct, By appt. Nov-Feb. Closed Sun.
Min Mail Order UK: £2.95
Credit Cards: All major credit/debit cards
Specialities: Screening, woodland, ornamental and fruit trees. Hedging plants. Bare root and container plants available.
Notes: Bowhayes Trees was established in 1992 as a specialist nursery propagating hybrid willow and poplar trees and providing a wide range of native trees and hedging for delivery across the UK.
OS Grid Ref: SY078913

CBWd **Blooming Wild Nursery** ♿
Cabbage Lane, Horsington, Templecombe, Somerset, BA8 0DA
Ⓣ (01963) 371060
Ⓜ 07977 714314
Ⓔ info@bloomingwild.co.uk
Ⓦ www.bloomingwild.co.uk
Contact: Will & Lauren Holley
Opening Times: 0930-1630 Wed-Fri, 1000-1600 Sat, closed Sun-Tue 1st Mar-31st Oct.
Credit Cards: All major credit/debit cards
Specialities: We have relocated our small family-run nursery from North Dorset to a larger site in South Somerset. We look forward to opening in Mar 2020. We specialise in growing a wide range of herbaceous perennials and ornamental grasses.
Notes: Our nursery is situated about half a mile up Cabbage Lane. We are on the right hand side as the road turns to the left. Wheelchair accessible.
OS Grid Ref: ST838131

CCal **Calamazag Nursery**
St Martins, Looe, Cornwall, PL13 1NX
Ⓜ 07958 167096
Ⓔ calamazagnursery@gmail.com
Ⓦ www.calamazagnursery.co.uk
Contact: Stephen & Benedicte Jenkinson
Opening Times: Not open, mail order only.
Min Mail Order UK: £5.00
Min Mail Order EU: £15.00
Cat. Cost: Online only.
Credit Cards: All major credit/debit cards
Specialities: Wide range of hardy *Dianthus* including Heritage and Species varieties. Wide selection of hardy *Sempervivum.* Plants sold in 10.5cm pots ready to be grown on. (Please note these are NOT plug plants and cannot be planted directly outside).

C

CCBP **CB Plants**
Lower Severalls Nursery, Crewkerne, Somerset, TA18 7NX
Ⓜ 07851 468430
Ⓔ cbplantsinfo@gmail.com
Ⓦ www.cbplants.co.uk
Contact: Catherine Bond
Opening Times: 1000-1700 Wed-Sat early Mar-end Sep.
Min Mail Order UK: £20.00 + p&p
Credit Cards: All major debit/credit cards except American Express
Specialities: Nectar-rich hardy perennials herbs and wild flowers all grown peat-free. Available in small quantities only.
Notes: Small nursery situated just off the A30, half a mile east of Crewkerne.

CCCN **Cross Common Nursery**
The Lizard, Helston, Cornwall, TR12 7PD
Ⓣ (01326) 290722/290668
Ⓔ info@crosscommonnursery.co.uk
Ⓦ www.crosscommonnursery.co.uk
Contact: Kevin Bosustow
Opening Times: 1000-1700 7 days, Apr, May & Jun. Reduced hours Mar, Jul, Aug & Sep, please phone for opening times.
Min Mail Order UK: Nmc
Cat. Cost: Online only.
Credit Cards: All major debit/credit cards except American Express
Specialities: The most southerly nursery in England, offering a wide range of unusual plants & shrubs. Tropical/sub-tropical, coastal plants & conservatory plants. Wide range of citrus trees. Some plants available in small quantities only.
OS Grid Ref: SW704116

CChe **Cherry Tree Nursery** ♿
(Sheltered Work Opportunities Project), off New Road Roundabout, Northbourne, Bournemouth, Dorset, BH10 7DA
Ⓣ (01202) 593537
Ⓔ contactus@cherrytreenursery.org.uk
Ⓦ www.cherrytreenursery.org.uk
Contact: Stephen Jailler
Opening Times: 0800-1600 Mon-Fri, 1000-1600 Wed & B/Hol Mar-Oct 0800-1600 Mon-Fri, 1000-1300 Sat only Nov & Feb. 0800-1600 Mon-Fri, Closed W/ends Dec & Jan. Please telephone for further details, see website or Facebook.
Credit Cards: All major debit/credit cards except American Express
Specialities: Hardy shrubs, trees, perennials, roses, climbers & grasses.
Notes: A registered charity providing work for adults with severe and enduring mental illness. Also sells wholesale. Wheelchair accessible.
OS Grid Ref: SZ083965

CCht **Chestnut Nursery (Sheltered Work Opportunities Project)** ♿
75 Kingland Road, Poole, Dorset, BH15 1TN
Ⓣ (01202) 685999
Ⓔ info@chestnutnursery.org.uk
Ⓦ www.chestnutnursery.org.uk
Contact: Andrew Verreck
Opening Times: 0800-1600 Mon-Fri. 1000-1600 Sat (Mar-Nov) & 1000-1500 Sat (Nov-Xmas). 1000-1500 Sun (Mar-Sep).
Credit Cards: All major credit/debit cards
Specialities: Wide selection of herbaceous perennials, evergreen shrubs, ornamental grasses, annual bedding and southern hemisphere exotics.
Notes: A registered charity providing work for adults with severe and enduring mental illness. Wheelchair accessible.
OS Grid Ref: SZ018909

CCoa **Coastal Hedging**
Marsh Lane Nursery, West Charleton, Kingsbridge, Devon, TQ7 2AQ
Ⓣ (01548) 531734
Ⓜ 07775 201 595
Ⓔ info@coastalhedging.co.uk
Ⓦ www.coastalhedging.co.uk
Contact: William Hornby
Opening Times: By appt. only.
Min Mail Order UK: £6.95
Cat. Cost: Online only.
Credit Cards: All major credit/debit cards
Specialities: *Griselina*, *Elaeagnus*, *Olearia*.
Notes: Euro accepted.
OS Grid Ref: SX752425

CCVT **Chew Valley Trees Ltd** ♿
Chew Road, Winford, Bristol, BS40 8HJ
Ⓣ (01275) 333752
Ⓔ simon@chewvalleytrees.co.uk
Ⓦ www.chewvalleytrees.co.uk
Contact: Wendy Downer
Opening Times: 0800-1700 Mon-Fri all year. 0800-1630 Sat Closed Sun. Closed B/hols & Sat Jul & Aug.
Min Mail Order UK: Nmc
Cat. Cost: Free.
Credit Cards: All major credit/debit cards
Specialities: Native British & ornamental trees, shrubs, fruit trees & hedging.
Notes: Also sells wholesale. Wheelchair accessible.
OS Grid Ref: ST558635

CDoC **Duchy of Cornwall**
Cott Road, Lostwithiel, Cornwall, PL22 0HW
Ⓣ (01208) 872668
Ⓕ (01208) 871809
Ⓔ sales@duchyofcornwallnursery.co.uk
Ⓦ www.duchyofcornwallnursery.co.uk
Contact: Nicky Hill
Opening Times: 0900-1700 Mon-Sat, 1000-1700 Sun.
Cat. Cost: None issued.
Credit Cards: All major credit/debit cards
Specialities: Large range of garden plants including trees, shrubs, roses, perennials, fruit and conservatory plants.
Notes: Partial wheelchair access.
OS Grid Ref: SX112614

CDor **Dorset Perennials**
Berkeley Perennials, Holnest, Sherborne, Dorset, DT9 5PR
Ⓣ (01963) 210643
Ⓕ (01963) 210643
Ⓔ sales@dorsetperennials.co.uk
Ⓦ www.dorsetperennials.co.uk
Contact: Dawn & Martin Preston
Opening Times: Open for collections only. Please check with nursery first.
Min Mail Order UK: Nmc
Cat. Cost: Online only.
Credit Cards: All major credit/debit cards
Specialities: An eclectic mix of hardy perennials, many that have fallen out of the general trade. Plants for herbaceous borders & cottage gardens with a good mix of oddities to tempt the discerning. Particularly good collections of *Ficaria*, *Iris sibirica*, *Epimedium* and *Hosta*.
Notes: All plants available via website. Delivers to shows.
OS Grid Ref: ST662090

CDow **Downside Nurseries** ♿
143 Upper Westwood, Bradford-on-Avon, Wiltshire, BA15 2DE
Ⓣ (01225) 862392
Ⓕ (01225) 862392
Ⓔ info@downsidenurseries.co.uk
Ⓦ www.downsidenurseries.co.uk
Contact: Lorraine Young
Opening Times: 0900-1700, 7 days.
Cat. Cost: Not available.
Credit Cards: All major credit/debit cards
Specialities: Herbaceous perennials, also shrubs, roses, trees & seasonal bedding.
Notes: Traditional family-run retail working nursery set over three acres. Unrivalled choice of quality plants, trees and bedding stock, much of which is grown on site. Wheelchair accessible. Local delivery available on request.
OS Grid Ref: ST805910

CDTJ **Desert to Jungle** ♿
Henlade Garden Nursery, Lower Henlade, Taunton, Somerset, TA3 5NB
Ⓣ (01823) 443701
Ⓜ 07969 652547
Ⓔ plants@deserttojungle.com
Ⓦ www.deserttojungle.com
Contact: Rob Gudge
Opening Times: 1000-1700 Mon, Tue & Thu-Sun (closed Wed), 1st Mar-31st Oct Thu, Fri & Sat only Nov-Feb. Opening times may vary during RHS shows, so please phone to check.
Min Mail Order UK: Nmc
Cat. Cost: Online only.
Credit Cards: All major credit/debit cards
Specialities: Exotic-looking plants giving a desert or jungle effect in the garden incl. *Agave*, *Canna*, aroids, succulents, ferns, tree ferns & bamboos.
Notes: Nursery shares drive with Mount Somerset Hotel. Also sells wholesale. Delivers to shows. Wheelchair accessible.
OS Grid Ref: ST273232

CEls **Elsworth Herbs**
Farthingwood, Broadway, Sidmouth, Devon, EX10 8HS
Ⓣ (01395) 578689
Ⓔ john.twibell@btinternet.com
Contact: Drs J. D. & J. M. Twibell
Opening Times: By appt. only.
Min Mail Order UK: £10.00
Cat. Cost: By email only.
Credit Cards: None
Specialities: National Plant Collection (Scientific & Reference) of *Artemisia*. Stock available in small quantities only. Orders may require propagation from collection material, for which we are the primary reference source. Native coastal plants.
Notes: Mail order only on small scale in exceptional circumstances. Partial wheelchair access.
OS Grid Ref: SY119881

CElw **Elworthy Cottage Plants** ♿
Elworthy Cottage, Elworthy, Nr Lydeard St Lawrence, Taunton, Somerset, TA4 3PX
Ⓣ (01984) 656427
Ⓔ mike@elworthy-cottage.co.uk
Ⓦ www.elworthy-cottage.co.uk
Contact: Mrs J. M. Spiller
Opening Times: By appt. only Apr-Sep & Feb for Galanthus. Open for NGS days.

Credit Cards: All major credit/debit cards
Specialities: Unusual herbaceous plants esp. *Galanthus*, hardy *Geranium*, *Geum*, *Crocosmia*, *Epimedium*, *Monarda*, *Pulmonaria* & *Viola*. Some varieties only available in small quantities. *Galanthus* available by mail order in Feb.
Notes: Nursery on B3188, 5 miles north of Wiveliscombe, in centre of Elworthy village. Mail order for *Galanthus* only. Delivers to shows. Wheelchair accessible.
OS Grid Ref: ST084349

CEme **EMERALD PLANTS**
85 Regal Walk, Bridgwater, Somerset, TA6 4FL
Ⓜ 07909 118470
Ⓔ sales@emeraldplants.co.uk
Ⓦ http://www.emeraldplants.co.uk/
Contact: Olly
Opening Times: Not open, mail order only.
Credit Cards: All major credit/debit cards
Specialities: Shrubs, perennials, bamboos, conifers, ferns, climbers and more.
Notes: Large range of garden plants available to order 24hrs a day from our online garden centre, including over 1000 varieties in stock online at any given time. Also sells wholesale.

CEnd **ENDSLEIGH GARDENS NURSERY**
Milton Abbot, Tavistock, Devon, PL19 0PG
Ⓣ (01822) 870235
Ⓕ (01822) 870513
Ⓔ info@endsleigh-gardens.com
Ⓦ www.endsleighgardens.co.uk
Contact: Adrian Steele
Opening Times: 0800-1700 Mon-Sat 1000-1600 Sun.
Min Mail Order UK: Nmc
Credit Cards: Visa, Access, Switch, MasterCard
Specialities: Choice & unusual trees & shrubs incl. *Acer*, alpines, bamboos, climbers, conifers, *Cornus*, heathers, old apple & cherry varieties, *Rosa*, *Wisteria*. Grafting service. Modern fruit trees, soft fruit and good selection of perennials.
Notes: Wheelchair accessible (but no disabled toilets).
OS Grid Ref: SX398780

CExl **EXCLUSIVE PLANTS NURSERY**
Tretawn, High Cross, Constantine, Falmouth, Cornwall, TR11 5RE
Ⓣ (01326) 341496
Ⓜ 07775 811385
Ⓕ (01326) 341496
Ⓔ info@exclusiveplants.com
Ⓦ www.exclusiveplants.com
Contact: Paul Bonavia
Opening Times: W/ends or by appt. only.
Min Mail Order UK: Nmc
Min Mail Order EU: £25.00
Cat. Cost: 2 × 1st class.
Credit Cards: All major credit/debit cards
Specialities: A plantsperson's nursery, offering rare & unusual plants from around the world. Also new introductions & the best forms of our better known plants.
Notes: Euro accepted.
OS Grid Ref: SW175131

CExo **EXOTIC EARTH PLANTS**
29 The Gardens, Chudleigh, Newton Abbot, Devon, TQ13 0GE
Ⓜ 07392 153875/07825 910801
Ⓔ exoticearthplants@gmail.com
Ⓦ www.exoticearthplants.co.uk
Contact: Lee Betts
Opening Times: Back Garden Nursery – Mail Order sales and Plant Fairs only.
Min Mail Order UK: £14.99
Min Mail Order EU: £14.99
Cat. Cost: £14.99
Credit Cards: All major credit/debit cards
Specialities: *Brugmansia* specialist (Angel Trumpet or formerly *Datura*) including warm group and cold group *Brugmansia*. Working towards applying for a National Collection Status. Species we hold include cultivated and hybrid forms of *aurea, suaveolens, versicolor, insignis arborea, sanguinea* and *vulcanicola*.
Notes: Supplier of Subtropical plants. Collector of *Pleurothallidinae* orchids of S. America, specifically *Masdevallia* and *Dracula*. Member of Brugmansia Growers International, Plant Heritage & Orchid Conservation Alliance.
OS Grid Ref: SX866794

CFis **MARGERY FISH PLANT NURSERY**
East Lambrook Manor Gardens, Silver Street, East Lambrook, South Petherton, Somerset, TA13 5HH
Ⓣ (01460) 240328
Ⓜ 07710 484745
Ⓔ enquiries@eastlambrook.com
Ⓦ www.eastlambrook.com
Contact: Ellie Hanscomb
Opening Times: 1000-1700 Tue-Sat, Feb-Oct, plus B/hol Mons & Sun Feb, May-Jul. Nov-Jan by appt.
Cat. Cost: None issued.
Credit Cards: All major credit/debit cards
Specialities: Cottage garden plants and

C

interesting perennials including hardy *Geranium*, snowdrops and plants propagated from East Lambrook Manor Gardens. Stock available in small quantities only. Major collection of hardy geraniums in garden.
Notes: Partial wheelchair access.
OS Grid Ref: ST431188

CFoP **Foxplants**
2 Old Park Cottages, Woodbury Lane, Devon, Axminster, Devon, EX13 5TL
Ⓜ 07928 805985
Ⓔ jo_fox2@hotmail.com
Ⓦ www.foxplants.com
Contact: Jo Fox
Opening Times: See website.
Min Mail Order UK: £15.00
Cat. Cost: Online only.
Credit Cards: Paypal
Specialities: Independent nursery specialising in *Salvia* and unusual herbaceous perennials.
Notes: All salvias grown by Foxplants are from seed or cuttings collected by reputable plant finders and enthusiasts. Also sells wholesale. Delivers to shows.

CFst **Forest Edge Nurseries (The Heather Garden)**
Verwood Road, Woodlands, Wimborne, Dorset, BH21 8LJ
Ⓣ (01202) 824387
Ⓕ (01202) 829564
Ⓔ info@theheathergarden.co.uk
Ⓦ www.theheathergarden.co.uk
Contact: David Edge
Opening Times: 0900-1630 Mon. Collection available by arrangement on other days.
Min Mail Order UK: £8.95
Cat. Cost: £2.00
Credit Cards: Paypal
Specialities: Heathers incl. *Calluna*, *Erica*, *Daboecia*.
Notes: Also sells wholesale. Euro accepted.

CGBo **Green Box Plants**
Lynash Nurseries, Boozer Pit, Wallditch Lane, Merriott, Somerset, TA16 5PW
Ⓔ info@greenboxplants.co.uk
Ⓦ www.greenboxplants.co.uk
Contact: Miriam Sparrow-Wallis

CGro **C W Groves & Son Ltd** ♿
West Bay Road, Bridport, Dorset, DT6 4BA
Ⓣ (01308) 422654
Ⓔ garden@grovesnurseries.co.uk
Ⓦ www.grovesnurseries.co.uk
Contact: Becky Groves
Opening Times: 0800-1700 Mon-Sat, 10.00-16.00 Sun.
Min Mail Order UK: Nmc
Min Mail Order EU: £15.00 + p&p
Cat. Cost: Free.
Credit Cards: Visa, Switch, MasterCard
Specialities: Established in 1866, a family run garden centre with nursery on site specialising in *Viola odorata*, Parma violets & roses.
Notes: Mainly violets, roses, herbs, soft fruit & grapevines by mail order. Main violet display at nursery in Feb, Mar & Apr. Will export violet seeds only beyond EU. Wheelchair accessible.
OS Grid Ref: SY466918

CHab **Habitat Aid Ltd.**
Hookgate Cottage, South Brewham, Somerset, BA10 0LQ
Ⓣ (01749) 812355
Ⓔ info@habitataid.co.uk
Ⓦ www.habitataid.co.uk
Contact: Nick Mann
Opening Times: Not open. Mail order only.
Min Mail Order UK: £50.00, incl. p&p
Cat. Cost: None issued.
Credit Cards: All major credit/debit cards
Specialities: British trees, wildflowers and seeds. Local provenance seed mixes. Native aquatic plants. Ornamental trees for bees. Heritage fruit trees.
Notes: Also sells wholesale.

CHby **The Herbary**
161 Chapel Street, Horningsham, Warminster, Wiltshire, BA12 7LU
Ⓣ (01985) 844442
Ⓔ info@beansandherbs.co.uk
Ⓦ www.beansandherbs.co.uk
Contact: Pippa Rosen
Opening Times: May-Sep strictly by appt. only.
Min Mail Order UK: Nmc
Min Mail Order EU: Nmc
Cat. Cost: Online only.
Credit Cards: None
Specialities: Culinary, medicinal & aromatic herbs organically grown in small quantities.
Notes: Mail order for seed only. All year for organic vegetable, flower, bean & herb seed. Also sells wholesale.
OS Grid Ref: ST812414

CHew **Hewitt-Cooper Carnivorous Plants**
The Homestead, Glastonbury Road, West Pennard, Somerset, BA6 8NN
Ⓜ 07702 190518

C

Ⓔ sales@hccarnivorousplants.co.uk
Ⓦ www.hccarnivorousplants.co.uk
Contact: Nigel Hewitt-Cooper
Opening Times: Not open.
Min Mail Order UK: Nmc
Min Mail Order EU: Nmc
Cat. Cost: Online only.
Credit Cards: All major credit/debit cards
Specialities: Carnivorous plants.
Notes: Mail order all year. Euro accepted. Delivers to shows.

CHII **HILL HOUSE NURSERY LTD**
Landscove, Nr Ashburton, Newton Abbot, Devon, TQ13 7LY
Ⓣ (01803) 762273
Ⓔ bluebird@hillhousenursery.com
Ⓦ www.hillhousenursery.com
Contact: Mathew Hubbard
Opening Times: 1100-1700 (or dusk, if earlier).
Min Mail Order UK: Nmc
Cat. Cost: None issued.
Credit Cards: All major credit/debit cards
Specialities: 3000+ varieties of plants, most propagated on premises, many rare or unusual. The garden, open to the public with free entry, was laid out by Edward Hyams. Pioneers of glasshouse pest control by beneficial insects.
Notes: Partial wheelchair access to nursery & garden. Seasonal tea room.
OS Grid Ref: SX774664

CHVG **HIDDEN VALLEY GARDENS** ♿
Treesmill, Par, Cornwall, PL24 2TU
Ⓣ (01208) 873225
Ⓜ 07966 230222
Ⓔ hiddenvalleygardens@yahoo.co.uk
Ⓦ www.hiddenvalleygardens.co.uk
Contact: Tricia Howard
Opening Times: 1000-1800 Thu-Mon (closed Tue & Wed), 20th Mar-15th Oct.
Cat. Cost: None issued.
Credit Cards: All major debit/credit cards except American Express
Specialities: Cottage garden plants, *Dahlia* & many perennials which can be seen growing in the garden.
Notes: Some stock available in small quantities only. Display garden (opening times same as nursery). Please phone for directions. Euro accepted. Wheelchair accessible.
OS Grid Ref: SX094567

CJun **JUNKER'S NURSERY**
Higher Cobhay, Milverton, Somerset, TA4 1NJ
Ⓣ (01823) 400075
Ⓔ karan@junker.co.uk
Ⓦ www.junker.co.uk
Contact: Karan Junker
Opening Times: Strictly by appt. only. Email nursery for directions (do not rely on Sat Nav).
Min Mail Order UK: Nmc
Min Mail Order EU: Nmc
Cat. Cost: Free list available by email.
Credit Cards: None
Specialities: Unusual shrubs & trees incl. *Acer palmatum*, *Betula*, *Cornus*, *Daphne*, *Magnolia*, deciduous *Euonymus*, *Ilex*, *Liquidambar*, *Parrotia*, *Stewartia* and *Styrax* cvs. Mature plants available. A wide range of cultivars available in limited numbers of each.
Notes: Extensive display planting to showcase plants growing in natural conditions. We propagate & grow all our own plants on site. An increasing number are grown naturally in open ground, incl. larger sizes plus younger plants in pots. Registered with APHA to issue Plant Passports for mail order.

CKel **KELWAYS PLANTS LTD** ♿
Barrymore Farm, Picts Hill, Langport, Somerset, TA10 9EZ
Ⓣ (01458) 250521
Ⓜ 07515 525230
Ⓔ sales@kelways.co.uk
Ⓦ www.kelways.co.uk
Contact: Andy Martin
Opening Times: 0900-1700 Mon-Sat, 0930-1600 Sun.
Min Mail Order UK: Nmc
Cat. Cost: Online only.
Credit Cards: Paypal
Specialities: *Paeonia*, *Iris*, *Rosa*, *Clematis*, *Dicksonia*, *Cyathea*, tree ferns, herbaceous perennials & shrubs.
Notes: Garden Centre with cafe and mail order service. We also offer contract growing & plant sourcing services for both landscapers and private individuals. Click-and-collect service available. Also sells wholesale. Euro accepted. Wheelchair accessible.
OS Grid Ref: ST434273

CKen **KENWITH CONIFER NURSERY (GORDON HADDOW)** ♿
Blinsham, Off A3124 only, Beaford, Winkleigh, Devon, EX19 8NT
Ⓣ (01805) 603274
Ⓔ info@kenwithconifernursery.co.uk
Ⓦ www.kenwithconifernursery.co.uk
Contact: Gordon Haddow
Opening Times: 1000-1630 Tue-Sat all year.

Closed all B/hols. If travelling a long distance, please phone previous day to ensure nursery will be open.
Min Mail Order UK: £20 + p&p
Cat. Cost: Online only.
Credit Cards: Visa, MasterCard
Specialities: All conifer genera. Grafting a speciality.
Notes: Wheelchair accessible.
OS Grid Ref: SS518160

CKno **Knoll Gardens** ♿
Hampreston, Wimborne, Dorset, BH21 7ND
Ⓣ (01202) 873931
Ⓕ (01202) 870842
Ⓔ enquiries@knollgardens.co.uk
Ⓦ www.knollgardens.co.uk
Contact: N. R. Lucas
Opening Times: 1000-1700 Tue-Sat, Feb-Dec. Open B/hol Mons. See website.
Min Mail Order UK: Nmc
Min Mail Order EU: Nmc
Cat. Cost: None.
Credit Cards: Visa, MasterCard
Specialities: Grasses (main specialism). Flowering perennials. National Plant Collection of *Pennisetum*.
Notes: Also sells wholesale. Wheelchair accessible.

CLAP **Long Acre Plants** ♿
South Marsh, Charlton Musgrove, Wincanton, Somerset, BA9 8EX
Ⓣ (01963) 32802
Ⓕ (01963) 32802
Ⓔ info@longacreplants.co.uk
Ⓦ www.plantsforshade.co.uk
Contact: Nigel Rowland
Opening Times: By appt. only.
Min Mail Order UK: £20.00 + p&p
Cat. Cost: Catalogue available online.
Credit Cards: MasterCard, Visa, Maestro
Specialities: Ferns, woodland bulbs & perennials. Marginal/bog plants. Specialise in plants for shade, carrying a wide range of unusual and tough shade tolerant perennials and ferns.
Notes: Mail order online. Delivers to shows. Wheelchair accessible.

CLau **The Edible Garden Nursery**
Moorland Barn, Whiddon Down, Okehampton, Devon, EX20 2QL
Ⓣ (01647) 400301
Ⓜ 07905 518666
Ⓔ ediblegardennursery@gmail.com
Ⓦ www.theediblegardennursery.co.uk
Contact: Chris Seagon
Opening Times: 1000-1700 Apr-Oct.
Min Mail Order UK: £9.95
Cat. Cost: Online only.
Credit Cards: All major credit/debit cards, Paypal
Specialities: Edible plants. Other varieties available – please phone nursery to enquire. Some varieties are limited in stock.
Notes: Everything grown is edible in some way. All plants are peat, chemical and pesticide free. Delivers to shows (payment in advance).

CLnd **Landford Trees**
Landford Lodge, Landford, Salisbury, Wiltshire, SP5 2EH
Ⓣ (01794) 390808
Ⓔ trees@landfordtrees.co.uk
Ⓦ www.landfordtrees.co.uk
Contact: Ed
Opening Times: 0800-1630 Mon-Thu, 0800-1530 Fri May-Sep, 0800-1700 Mon-Thu 0800-1530 Fri Oct-Apr.
Cat. Cost: Free.
Credit Cards: All major debit/credit cards except American Express
Specialities: Deciduous ornamental trees.
Notes: Also sells wholesale.
OS Grid Ref: SU247201

CLoc **C S Lockyer (Fuchsias)** ◆
Lansbury, 70 Henfield Road, Coalpit Heath, Bristol, BS36 2UZ
Ⓣ (01454) 772219
Ⓔ mary@lockyerfuchsias.co.uk
Ⓦ www.lockyerfuchsias.co.uk
Contact: Mary Lockyer
Opening Times: 1000-1300, 1430-1700 most days, please telephone first.
Min Mail Order UK: 6 plants + p&p
Min Mail Order EU: £12.00 + p&p
Cat. Cost: 4 × 1st class or online.
Credit Cards: All major credit/debit cards
Specialities: *Fuchsia*.
Notes: Many open days & coach parties. Also sells wholesale. Exports beyond EU. Euro accepted. Delivers to shows. Partial wheelchair access.

CMac **Mac Pennys Nurseries**
154 Burley Road, Bransgore, Christchurch, Dorset, BH23 8DB
Ⓣ (01425) 672348
Ⓔ office@macpennys.co.uk
Ⓦ www.macpennys.co.uk
Contact: T. & V. Lowndes & S. Lowndes
Opening Times: 0900-1700 Mon-Sat, 1000-1700 Sun & B/hols. Closed Xmas to New Year.

C

Min Mail Order UK: Nmc
Cat. Cost: A4 sae with 4 × 1st class.
Credit Cards: All major debit/credit cards except American Express
Specialities: Wide range of plants – available in small quantities only.
Notes: Mail order available Oct-Feb incl. UK only. Also sells wholesale. Partial wheelchair access.

CMCN **Mallet Court Nursery** ♿
Marshway, Curry Mallet, Taunton, Somerset, TA3 6SZ
Ⓣ (01823) 481493
Ⓜ 07713 091521
Ⓕ (01823) 481009
Ⓔ malletcourtnursery@btinternet.com
Ⓦ www.malletcourt.co.uk
Contact: J. G. S. & P. M. E. Harris F.L.S.
Opening Times: 0930-1700 Mon-Fri summer, 0930-1600 winter. Sat & Sun by appt.
Min Mail Order UK: Nmc
Min Mail Order EU: Nmc
Cat. Cost: £1.50
Credit Cards: All major credit/debit cards
Specialities: Maples, oaks, *Magnolia*, hollies & other rare and unusual plants including those from China & South Korea.
Notes: Mail order throughout the year. Also sells wholesale. Exports beyond EU. Euro accepted. Wheelchair accessible.

CMen **Mendip Bonsai Studio**
Byways, Back Lane, Downside, Shepton Mallet, Somerset, BA4 4JR
Ⓣ (01749) 344274
Ⓜ 07711 205806
Ⓔ john@mendipbonsai.co.uk
Ⓦ www.mendipbonsai.co.uk
Contact: John Trott
Opening Times: By appt. only. Mail order Oct-Mar.
Min Mail Order UK: £15.00
Cat. Cost: None issued. Workshop lists available.
Credit Cards: All major credit/debit cards
Specialities: *Bonsai, potensai*. Many plants available in small numbers only. Can propagate to order. Young trees for garden or bonsai culture. Many rare & unusual ferns from Japan for 'accent' use and gardens (very limited numbers). PLEASE NOTE that we do not stock large trees/shrubs for the garden, only young plants.
Notes: Talks & lectures on bonsai. Stockist of most bonsai pots, related bonsai sundries & large range of bronze figurines. Mail orders despatched late Mar-early Apr, late Sep-Oct. Delivers to shows by arrangement. We do not stock large trees/shrubs for the garden.

CMHG **Marwood Hill Gardens** ♿
Marwood, Barnstaple, Devon, EX31 4EB
Ⓣ (01271) 342528
Ⓕ (01271) 342528
Ⓔ info@marwoodhillgarden.co.uk
Ⓦ www.marwoodhillgarden.co.uk
Contact: Mrs P. Stout
Opening Times: 1100-1630, 7 days. Closed Nov-Mar.
Min Mail Order UK: £15.00 + p&p
Cat. Cost: Please see website.
Credit Cards: All major credit/debit cards
Specialities: National Plant Collection of *Astilbe*. Large range always in stock.
Notes: Mail order for *Astilbe* only. Wheelchair accessible.
OS Grid Ref: SS545375

CMil **Mill Cottage Plants** ♿
Henley Mill, Henley Lane, Wookey, Somerset, BA5 1AW
Ⓣ (01749) 676966
Ⓜ 07851 698759
Ⓔ millcottageplants@gmail.com
Ⓦ www.millcottageplants.co.uk
Contact: Sally Gregson
Opening Times: By appt. only.
Cat. Cost: Online only.
Credit Cards: All major credit/debit cards
Specialities: Rare *Hydrangea serrata* cvs, *H. aspera* cvs, *Epimedium*, shade & damp-loving plants.
Notes: Please telephone for directions. Euro accepted. Wheelchair accessible.

CMiW **Millwood Plants**
Millwoods, Colleton Mills, Umberleigh, Umberleigh, Devon, EX37 9ET
Ⓜ 07756 515084
Ⓔ millwoodplants@mail.com
Ⓦ www.millwoodplants.com
Contact: Gary Buckingham
Opening Times: 1000-1700 Mon & Tue Mar-Sep.
Specialities: Hardy herbaceous perennials for woodland gardens and shade. Old fashioned roses.
Notes: Hardy, unusual & authentic plants. Traditional propagation methods retain colour, size & hardiness. Exhibits at shows all year. See website for details. Nursery postcode for Sat Nav is EX37 9ES. Delivers to shows.

CNMi **NEWPORT MILLS NURSERY**
Newport Mills Farm, Wrantage, Taunton, Somerset, TA3 6DJ
Ⓣ (01823) 490231
Ⓔ john@newportmillsnursery.net
Ⓦ www.newportmillsnursery.net
Contact: John Barrington
Opening Times: Not open. Mail order only.
Min Mail Order UK: Nmc above £20
Min Mail Order EU: Nmc. EU postal rate per order
Cat. Cost: Free.
Credit Cards: All major credit/debit cards
Specialities: *Dianthus*, including perpetual flowering carnations, with many scented varieties. Exhibition and unusual types. Garden pinks, repeat flowering and exhibition varieties. Small range of *Delphinium elatum* cultivars.
Notes: Plants that are sent out are well-established in 7cm (3inch) pots, not plugs. Plants are sent out all year and are propagated and grown on site at our nursery. No plants are imported. Euro accepted.
OS Grid Ref: ST318234

CNor **NORTHBROOK NURSERY** ♿
47 Northbrook Road, Broadstone, Dorset, BH18 8HD
Ⓣ (01202) 695256
Ⓔ marg@northbrooknursery.co.uk
Ⓦ www.northbrooknursery.co.uk
Contact: Margaret Bailey
Opening Times: 1000-1600 Thu & Fri end Apr-end Sep.
Min Mail Order UK: Nmc
Cat. Cost: None issued.
Credit Cards: Paypal
Specialities: Perennials. Plants available in small quantities only.
Notes: Delivers to shows. Wheelchair accessible.
OS Grid Ref: SZ001947

CPar **PARKS PERENNIALS**
242 Wallisdown Road, Wallisdown, Bournemouth, Dorset, BH10 4HZ
Ⓣ (01202) 524464
Ⓜ 07977 878546
Ⓔ parks.perennials@ntlworld.com
Contact: S. Parks
Opening Times: Apr-Oct most days, please telephone first.
Cat. Cost: None issued.
Credit Cards: All major credit/debit cards
Specialities: Hardy herbaceous perennials.
Notes: Delivers to shows.

CPbh **PENBERTH PLANTS**
St Buryan, Penzance, Cornwall, TR19 6HJ
Ⓜ 07470 909775
Ⓔ info@penberthplants.co.uk
Ⓦ www.penberthplants.co.uk
Contact: Jeff Rowe
Opening Times: Not open. Mail order.
Cat. Cost: Online only.
Credit Cards: All major credit/debit cards
Specialities: *Protea*, *Restio*, succulents and other unusual plants.
Notes: Sells at RHS shows. Open days throughout the year, check website or contact nursery for dates. Card payment accepted at shows. Mail order through website only. Delivers to shows.

CPer **PERRIE HALE NURSERY LTD**
Northcote Hill, Honiton, Devon, EX14 9TH
Ⓣ (01404) 43344
Ⓕ (01404) 47163
Ⓔ faye@perriehale.co.uk
Ⓦ www.perriehale.co.uk
Contact: Faye Davey
Opening Times: 0830-1700 Mon-Fri 0900-1200 Sat Nov-Mar, 0900-1600 Mon-Fri closed Sat Apr-Oct. Aug by appt. only.
Cat. Cost: Free.
Credit Cards: All major debit/credit cards except American Express
Specialities: Broad-leaf trees & conifers; native & evergreen hedging for screening & amenity; soft fruit & shrubs. Family business established 1957, supplying in excess of 700,000 plants per year.
Notes: Sell bare-root stock Oct-Mar, after which pot-grown stock available. Also sells wholesale.
OS Grid Ref: ST176010

CPhi **ALAN PHIPPS CACTI**
62 Samuel White Road, Hanham, Bristol, BS15 3LX
Ⓣ (0117) 9607591
Ⓦ www.cactus-mall.com/alan-phipps/index.html
Contact: A. Phipps
Opening Times: 1000-1700 but prior phone call essential to ensure a greeting.
Cat. Cost: Sae or 2 × IRC (EC only).
Credit Cards: None
Specialities: *Mammillaria*, *Astrophytum* & *Ariocarpus*. Species & varieties will change with times. Ample quantities exist in spring. Limited range of *Agave*.
OS Grid Ref: ST644717

C

CPHo **The Palm House**
8 North Street, Ottery St Mary, Devon,
EX11 1DR
Ⓣ (01404) 815450
Ⓜ 07815 673397
Ⓔ george@thepalmhouse.co.uk
Ⓦ www.thepalmhouse.co.uk
Contact: George Gregory
Opening Times: Open by appt. only.
Cat. Cost: 2 × 1st class.
Specialities: Palms.
Notes: Also sells wholesale.
OS Grid Ref: SY098955

CPla **Plant World Gardens and Nurseries**
St Marychurch Road, Newton Abbot, Devon,
TQ12 4SE
Ⓣ (01803) 872939
Ⓕ (01803) 875018
Ⓔ raybrown@plant-world-seeds.com
Ⓦ www.plant-world-seeds.com
Contact: Doug De Val
Opening Times: 0930-1700 7 days a week, Apr-Oct.
Min Mail Order UK: Nmc
Min Mail Order EU: Nmc
Cat. Cost: Free.
Credit Cards: Visa, Access, EuroCard, MasterCard
Specialities: Alpines, perennials, small shrubs, succulents, herbaceous & patio plants.
Notes: Four acre garden planted as map of the world (entry charge applies). Mail order for seed only (no mail order for plants). Also sells wholesale. Exports beyond EU. Partial wheelchair access (nursery & café only).
OS Grid Ref: SX893693

CPrp **ProperPlants**
Penknight, Edgcumbe Road,
Lostwithiel, Cornwall,
PL22 0JD
Ⓣ (01208) 872291
Ⓜ 07810 434765
Ⓔ sarahwilks52@gmail.com
Ⓦ www.agapanthus-plants.co.uk
Contact: Sarah Wilks
Opening Times: By appt. only Please telephone or email first.
Min Mail Order UK: Nmc
Min Mail Order EU: Nmc
Credit Cards: All major credit/debit cards
Specialities: *Agapanthus*.
Notes: Also sells wholesale. Exports beyond EU. Delivers to shows.
OS Grid Ref: SX093596

CPud **Puddleplants**
The Barn, Cwmceiliog Fawr,
Taliaris, Llandeilo, Carmarthenshire,
SA19 7NL
Ⓣ (01558) 615056
Ⓔ sonia@puddleplants.co.uk
Ⓦ www.puddleplants.co.uk
Contact: David Thomas
Opening Times: Not open, online only.
Min Mail Order UK: Nmc
Cat. Cost: Online only.
Credit Cards: All major credit/debit cards
Specialities: Marginal, bog garden, oxygenating and pond plants. A range of native aquatic plants to the UK available.
Notes: On-line nursery retailing to the public and trade, specialising in British native pond and bog garden plants. Also have a very good selection of ornamentals, including irises (both pond and bog), and water lilies. Deliver anywhere in the UK all year via 24 hour courier. Euro accepted.

CQua **R and A Scamp Quality Daffodils**
49 Mongleath Road, Falmouth, Cornwall,
TR11 4PN
Ⓣ (01326) 317959
Ⓜ 07826 067175
Ⓔ amscamp@qualitydaffodils.com
Ⓦ www.qualitydaffodils.com
Contact: Adrian Scamp
Opening Times: Not open. Mail order only. Viewing by appt. only.
Min Mail Order UK: Nmc
Min Mail Order EU: Nmc
Cat. Cost: 4 × 1st class.
Credit Cards: All major credit/debit cards
Specialities: *Narcissus* hybrids & species. Some stocks have less than 100 bulbs.
Notes: Euro accepted.

CRHN **Roseland House Nursery**
Chacewater, Truro, Cornwall,
TR4 8QB
Ⓣ (01872) 560451
Ⓔ clematis@roselandhouse.co.uk
Ⓦ www.roselandhouse.co.uk
Contact: Charlie Pridham
Opening Times: 1300-1700 Tue & Wed, Apr-Sep. Other times by appt.
Min Mail Order UK: Nmc
Min Mail Order EU: Nmc
Cat. Cost: Online only.
Credit Cards: All major credit/debit cards
Specialities: Climbing & conservatory plants. National Plant Collections of *Clematis viticella* & *Lapageria rosea*. Named *Lapageria* in short supply but occasionally available.

C

Notes: Garden open to the public. Delivers to shows.
OS Grid Ref: SW752445

CRos **Rosemoor Plant Centre (RHS)** ♿ ◆
RHS Garden Rosemoor, Torrington, Devon, EX38 8PH
Ⓣ (01805) 626824
Ⓔ rosemooradmin@rhs.org.uk
Ⓦ www.rhs.org.uk/rosemoor
Contact: Plant Centre Team
Opening Times: 1000-1800 Mon-Sat, 1130-1730 Sun, Apr-Sep (summer). 1000-1700 Mon-Sat, 1030-1630 Sun, Oct-Mar (winter). Closed Easter Sun & Xmas Day.
Cat. Cost: None issued.
Credit Cards: All major credit/debit cards
Specialities: Wide range of shrubs, herbaceous perennials, roses, climbers, alpines & seasonal plants, reflecting the diversity of planting in the garden. Displays themed by colour, position and season, also highlighting plants with the RHS Award of Garden Merit.
Notes: Plant centre attached to RHS Garden Rosemoor. Free entry to Plant Centre, Gift Shop & Restaurant. Accept HTA & RHS vouchers (paper only). Broad range of plants, including many varieties seen growing at RHS Garden Rosemoor. Wheelchair accessible.
OS Grid Ref: SS500176

CSBt **St Bridget Nurseries Ltd** ♿
Old Rydon Lane, Exeter, Devon, EX2 7JY
Ⓣ (01392) 873672
Ⓕ (01392) 876710
Ⓔ sales@stbridgetnurseries.co.uk
Ⓦ www.stbridgetnurseries.co.uk
Contact: Sales Dept
Opening Times: 0900-1700 Mon-Sat, 1030-1630 Sun. Closed Xmas Day, Boxing Day, New Year's Day & Easter Sun.
Min Mail Order UK: Nmc
Cat. Cost: Free.
Credit Cards: All major credit/debit cards
Specialities: General nursery propagating a wide range of top quality plants, with two retail garden centres near Exeter. Founded 1925.
Notes: Mail order available, please contact for prices & carriage charges. Also sells wholesale. Wheelchair accessible.
OS Grid Ref: SX955905

CSde **Seaside Plants**
Marsh Lane Nursery, West Charleton, Kingsbridge, Devon, TQ7 2AQ
Ⓜ 07775 201595
Ⓔ info@seasideplants.co.uk
Ⓦ www.seasideplants.co.uk
Contact: Michael Hornby
Opening Times: Not open. By appt. only.
Min Mail Order UK: Nmc
Min Mail Order EU: Nmc
Cat. Cost: Online only.
Credit Cards: All major credit/debit cards
Specialities: Wide range, esp. coastal plants, *Callistemon*, *Corokia*, *Elaeagnus*, *Euonymus*, *Griselinia*, *Hydrangea*, *Olearia* & *Pittosporum*, grasses & ferns.
Notes: Euro accepted.

CSgt **Strete Gate Camellias**
17 Seymour Drive, Torquay, Devon, TQ2 8PY
Ⓣ (01803) 770710
Ⓜ 07964 824673
Ⓔ plants@stretegatecamellias.co.uk
Ⓦ www.stretegatecamellias.co.uk
Contact: Jeremy Wilson
Opening Times: Nursery not open to public, but collection can be arranged.
Min Mail Order UK: Nmc
Specialities: Growing around 500 varieties of *Camellia*, some in small numbers.
Notes: Nursery is not open to the public and is at a different address, but orders can be collected. Delivers to shows. Also sells wholesale.
OS Grid Ref: SX833455

CSpe **Special Plants**
Hill Farm Barn, Greenways Lane, Cold Ashton, Chippenham, Wiltshire, SN14 8LA
Ⓣ (01225) 891686
Ⓔ derry@specialplants.net
Ⓦ www.specialplants.net
Contact: Derry Watkins
Opening Times: 1000-1700 7 days Mar-Oct. Other times please ring first to check.
Min Mail Order UK: £10.00 + p&p
Cat. Cost: Free.
Credit Cards: All major credit/debit cards
Specialities: Tender perennials, *Pelargonium*, *Salvia*, hardy geraniums, *Anemone*, *Papaver*, umbels & grasses. Many varieties propagated in small numbers only. Also selsl seeds.
Notes: Mail order Sep-Mar only. Delivers to shows.
OS Grid Ref: ST749726

CSta **Staddon Farm Nurseries** ♿
Staddon Road, Holsworthy, Devon, EX22 6NH
Ⓜ 07547 711189
Ⓔ penny@pennysprimulas.co.uk
Ⓦ www.pennysprimulas.co.uk
Contact: Penny Jones
Opening Times: By appt. only.

C

Min Mail Order UK: Nmc
Min Mail Order EU: Nmc
Cat. Cost: Online only.
Credit Cards: All major credit/debit cards
Specialities: *Primula*. National Plant Collection of *Primula sieboldii* Japanese cvs. Modest collection of *Epimedium* & ferns.
Notes: Exports beyond EU. Delivers to shows. Euro accepted. Wheelchair accessible.
OS Grid Ref: SS359031

CSto **STONE LANE GARDENS**
Stone Farm, Chagford, Devon, TQ13 8JU
Ⓣ (01647) 231311
Ⓔ admin@stonelanegardens.com
Ⓦ www.stonelanegardens.com
Contact: Paul Bartlett
Opening Times: By appt. only Mon-Fri. Orders can be made via website, email or phone.
Min Mail Order UK: £9.95
Min Mail Order EU: £40.00
Cat. Cost: Online.
Credit Cards: All major credit/debit cards, Paypal
Specialities: National Collections (scientific status) of *Betula* & *Alnus*,
Notes: Charity devoted to public education through the conservation, research and distribution of Birch and Alder. Arboretum open all year with National Collections of Birch and Alder. See mature specimens of the trees available in our nursery. Admission charge applies.
OS Grid Ref: SX709908

CTca **TRECANNA NURSERY**
The Old Barn, Chilsworthy, Cornwall, PL18 9PB
Ⓣ (01822) 834680
Ⓜ 07785 242148
Ⓔ trecannanursery@gmail.com
Ⓦ www.trecanna.com
Contact: Mark Wash
Opening Times: Not open. Mail order only.
Min Mail Order UK: £22.00
Min Mail Order EU: £40.00
Cat. Cost: Online only.
Credit Cards: All major credit/debit cards
Specialities: Hardier South African plants, specialising in *Crocosmia* & *Eucomis*.
Notes: Talks given to garden societies. Exports within EU.
OS Grid Ref: SX247733

CToG **TOR GARDEN PLANTS**
Tor Gardens, Brentor, Tavistock, Devon, PL19 0NG
Ⓜ 07718 224641
Ⓔ sales@torgardenplants.co.uk
Ⓦ https://www.torgardenplants.co.uk
Contact: Emma Robertson
Credit Cards: All major credit/debit cards
Specialities: Water *Iris*, aquatic, marginal and moisture loving plants.
Notes: We are proud to have supplied water plants for Kampo no Niwa, an RHS Chelsea Flower Show Gold Winning Garden 2019.

CTrC **TREVENA CROSS NURSERIES** ♿
Breage, Helston, Cornwall, TR13 9PY
Ⓣ (01736) 763880
Ⓕ (01736) 762828
Ⓔ sales@trevenacross.co.uk
Ⓦ www.trevenacross.co.uk
Contact: Graham Jeffery
Opening Times: 0900-1700 Mon-Sat, 1030-1630 Sun.
Min Mail Order UK: Nmc
Credit Cards: All major credit/debit cards
Specialities: Southern Hemisphere plants and plants for windy or exposed sites. *Restionaceae*, *Proteaceae*.
Notes: Family owned business operating as a garden centre and growing most stock on site. Garden kitchen café offering daily coffee and lunches. Most of the sales areas under cover. Wheelchair accessible.
OS Grid Ref: SW613284

CTrh **TREHANE NURSERY** ♿
Stapehill Road, Hampreston, Wimborne, Dorset, BH21 7ND
Ⓣ (01202) 873490
Ⓔ office@trehanenursery.co.uk
Contact: Lorraine Keets
Opening Times: 0830-1630 Mon-Fri all year (excl. Xmas & New Year). 1000-1600 Sat in spring & by appt.
Min Mail Order UK: Nmc
Min Mail Order EU: Nmc
Cat. Cost: Free.
Credit Cards: All major credit/debit cards
Specialities: Extensive range of *Camellia* species, cultivars & hybrids. Blueberries. Many new introductions.
Notes: Wheelchair accessible.
OS Grid Ref: SU059000

CTri **TRISCOMBE NURSERIES** ♿ ◆
West Bagborough, Nr Taunton, Somerset, TA4 3HG
Ⓣ (01984) 618267
Ⓔ info@triscombenurseries.co.uk
Ⓦ www.triscombenurseries.co.uk
Contact: S. Parkman
Opening Times: 0900-1730 Mon-Sat.

Min Mail Order UK: Nmc
Cat. Cost: 1 × 1st class.
Credit Cards: None
Specialities: Trees, shrubs, roses, fruit, *Clematis*, herbaceous & rock plants.
Notes: Wheelchair accessible.

CTsd **Treseders Nursery** ♿
Wallcottage Nursery, Lockengate, St. Austell, Cornwall, PL26 8RU
Ⓣ (01208) 832234
Ⓔ Treseders@btconnect.com
Ⓦ www.treseders.co.uk
Contact: James Treseder
Opening Times: 0900-1700 Mon-Sat. Closed Wed. 1000-1600 Sun.
Min Mail Order UK: Nmc
Min Mail Order EU: Nmc
Cat. Cost: Online or by email only.
Credit Cards: All major credit/debit cards
Specialities: A wide range of choice & unusual plants grown in peat-free compost Establishing collection of *Prostanthera*.
Notes: Plants sometimes only available in small quantities. Enquiries welcome. Wheelchair accessible.
OS Grid Ref: SX034618

CTtf **Triffids**
The Nursery, Withy Lane, Oakhill, Radstock, Somerset, BA3 5SE
Ⓣ (01749) 840561
Ⓜ 07779 868133
Ⓔ jackietriffids@hotmail.co.uk
Contact: Jackie Williams
Opening Times: By appt. only. Please phone for details.
Cat. Cost: None issued.
Credit Cards: All major credit/debit cards
Specialities: Traditional & unusual perennials, plants for shade, potted bulbs, *Galanthus*, *Geums*, *Gladiolus* species, *Epimediums* and wildflowers.
Notes: Plants available at plant fairs and shows. Delivers to shows.

CWal **The Walled Gardens of Cannington** ♿
Church Street, Cannington, Somerset, TA5 2HA
Ⓣ (01278) 655042
Ⓜ 07448 450109
Ⓔ bostockp@btc.ac.uk
Ⓦ www.canningtonwalledgardens.co.uk
Contact: Phil Bostock
Credit Cards: All major credit/debit cards
Specialities: Summer flowering herbaceous perennials from our 70m long 'Herbaceous Border'. Blue flowering plants from our blue garden. Mediterranean plants from our dry garden. Sub-tropical plants from our sub-tropical walk and glasshouse. Houseplants, cacti, succulents and tropical plants.
Notes: RHS Partner Garden and part of Bridgewater and Taunton College. The majority of our plants are propagated on-site by staff, students and volunteers from the vast array of plants in our gardens and botanical glasshouse. We also propagate to order. All profits go to the college. Wheelchair accessible.

CWat **The Water Garden** ♿
Hinton Parva, Swindon, Wiltshire, SN4 0DH
Ⓣ (01793) 790558
Ⓔ ben@thewatergarden.co.uk
Ⓦ www.thewatergarden.co.uk
Contact: Ben Newman
Opening Times: 1000-1700 Wed-Sat 1000-1600 Sun.
Min Mail Order UK: £10.00 + p&p
Cat. Cost: 4 × 1st class.
Credit Cards: Visa, Access, Switch
Specialities: Waterlilies, marginal & moisture plants, oxygenators & alpines.
Notes: Also sells wholesale. Wheelchair accessible.

CWCL **Westcountry Nurseries (North Devon) Ltd**
Donkey Meadow, Woolsery, Devon, EX39 5QH
Ⓣ (01237) 431111
Ⓔ info@westcountrylupins.co.uk
Ⓦ www.westcountry-nurseries.co.uk
Contact: Sarah Conibear
Opening Times: Mon-Fri, open for collection of plant orders by appt. only Please ring beforehand 1000-1530 weekdays only, closed w/ends.
Min Mail Order UK: Nmc
Cat. Cost: 2 × 1st class + A5 sae for full colour cat.
Credit Cards: All major credit/debit cards
Specialities: *Lupinus*, *Lewisia*, *Helleborus*, *Clematis*, cyclamen, select perennials, grasses, ferns & climbers. National Plant Collection of *Lupinus*.
Notes: Delivers to shows.
OS Grid Ref: SS351219

CWGN **Walled Garden Nursery** ♿
Brinkworth House, Brinkworth, Nr Malmesbury, Wiltshire, SN15 5DF
Ⓜ 07921 436863
Ⓔ sales@clematis-nursery.co.uk

E

Ⓦ www.clematis-nursery.co.uk
Contact: Fraser Wescott
Opening Times: 1000-1700 Mon-Sat, 1000-1600 Sun Mar-Oct 1030-dusk Mon-Fri, Nov & Feb. Closed Dec & Jan.
Min Mail Order UK: £15.00
Credit Cards: All major credit/debit cards
Specialities: *Clematis* & climbers, with a selection of unusual perennials & shrubs.
Notes: Mail order UK mainland only. Wheelchair accessible.
OS Grid Ref: SU002849

CWGr **National Dahlia Collection**
Varfell Farm, Long Rock, Penzance, Cornwall, TR20 8AQ
Ⓣ (01736) 339276
Ⓜ 07525 867976
Ⓔ info@nationaldahliacollection.co.uk
Ⓦ www.nationaldahliacollection.co.uk
Contact: Emma Lainchbury
Opening Times: Garden open in summer. See website or contact nursery for details.
Min Mail Order UK: 50 tubers or 100 rooted cuttings. Please contact for details
Cat. Cost: Online. Contact nursery for hard copy.
Credit Cards: All major debit/credit cards except American Express
Specialities: National Plant Collection of *Dahlia*. 1600 plus cvs.
Notes: See website for plant availability. Also sells wholesale. Partial wheelchair access.

CWnw **Winrow Nurseries**
Lewis Drove, Panborough, Wells, Somerset, BA5 1PT
Ⓣ (01934) 712571
Ⓔ plants@winrownurseries.com
Ⓦ http://www.winrownurseries.com/
Contact: Lucy Watson
Opening Times: 0800-1600 Mon-Fri.
Credit Cards: All major credit/debit cards
OS Grid Ref: ST467448

Eastern

EACa **Alpine Campanulas (Bellflower Nursery)**
Ⓜ 07879 644958
Ⓔ sue@bellflowernursery.co.uk
Ⓦ www.bellflowernursery.co.uk
Contact: Sue Wooster
Opening Times: Not open to the public.
Min Mail Order UK: £10.00
Cat. Cost: Online only.
Credit Cards: None
Specialities: *Campanula*. National Plant Collection of Alpine *Campanula*. Most stock in small numbers only.
Notes: Hardy plant nursery. Garden design service. A wide selection of plants available at The Leaping Hare Country Store at RHS Partner Garden Wyken Hall, Stanton, Suffolk IP31 2DW.

EAJP **A & J Plants**
Chappel Road, Great Tey, Colchester, Essex, CO6 1JR
Ⓣ (01206) 212124
Ⓕ (01206) 212124
Ⓔ mail@aandjplants.com
Ⓦ www.aandjplants.com
Contact: Jackie Rhodes
Opening Times: Not open. Mail order only. Orders can be collected from nursery by prior arrangement.
Min Mail Order UK: Nmc
Specialities: Wide variety of choice perennials and ornamental grasses propagated on the nursery, some in small quantities.
Notes: Plant centre at Marks Hall Garden (CO6 1TG) stocked with seasonal selection of perennials & grasses. Also sells wholesale. Delivers to shows.

EAri **Arid Plants**
Nayland Road, Colchester, Essex, CM6 3DH
Ⓜ 07973 630359
Ⓔ aridplants@gmail.com
Ⓦ www.arid-plants.co.uk
Contact: Richard Bookham
Opening Times: By appt. only.
Credit Cards: All major credit/debit cards
Notes: Plants sometimes only available in small quantities. Enquiries welcome. Visits by appt. only.

EBak **B & H M Baker** ♿
Bourne Brook Nurseries, Greenstead Green, Halstead, Essex, CO9 1RB
Ⓣ (01787) 476369
Contact: Clive Baker
Opening Times: 0800-1600 Mon-Fri, 0900-1200 & 1400-1600 Sat & Sun, Mar-Jun.
Cat. Cost: 2 × 1st class + 33p.
Credit Cards: All major credit/debit cards
Specialities: *Fuchsia* & conservatory plants.
Notes: Also sells wholesale. Wheelchair accessible.

EBar **Barcham Trees PLC**
Eye Hill Drove, Ely, Cambridgeshire, CB7 5XF
Ⓣ (01353) 720950

Ⓔ info@barchamtrees.co.uk
Ⓦ www.barcham.co.uk
Opening Times: Office hours 0900-1730 Mon-Fri. Nursery visits by appt. only.
Min Mail Order UK: Nmc
Min Mail Order EU: Nmc
Cat. Cost: £20.00
Credit Cards: All major debit/credit cards except American Express
Specialities: Large grower of containerised trees. 478 varieties available, from 10-12cm to 40cm girth.
Notes: As trees range from 3-8 metres, all are despatched on lorries rather than through the mailing service. Also sells wholesale. Delivers to shows. Euro accepted.

EBee **BEECHES NURSERY** ♿
Crown Hill, Ashdon, Saffron Walden, Essex, CB10 2HB
Ⓣ (01799) 584362
Ⓔ sales@beechesnursery.co.uk
Ⓦ www.beechesnursery.co.uk
Contact: Alan Bidwell / Philip Seymour
Opening Times: 0830-1700 Mon-Sat, 0930-1630 Sun & B/hols.
Min Mail Order UK: £15.00
Min Mail Order EU: £20.00
Cat. Cost: Online.
Credit Cards: All major credit/debit cards
Specialities: Herbaceous specialists & extensive range of other garden worthy plants. Rarities available in limited numbers only.
Notes: Orders accepted throughout the year. No trees or very large shrubs by mail order – selected trees can be dispatched direct from our grower. Wheelchair accessible.
OS Grid Ref: TL586420

EBlen **BLENHEIM PLANT AND GARDEN CENTRE**
Bromley Road, Ardleigh, Colchester, Essex, CO7 7SF
Ⓣ (01206) 870605
Ⓔ kirsty@blenheimgardencentre.co.uk
Ⓦ http://www.blenheimgardencentre.co.uk/
Contact: Kirsty Evans
Opening Times: 0900-1700 Mon-Sat, 1000-1600 Sun.
Notes: Blenheim Plant & Garden Centre is a long established independant, family run garden centre in Colchester, with great customer service.

EBlo **BRESSINGHAM GARDENS NURSERY**
Low Road, Bressingham, Diss, Norfolk, IP22 2AB
Ⓣ (01379) 688282
Ⓕ (01379) 687227
Ⓔ info@bressinghamgardens.com
Ⓦ https://www.thebressinghamgardens.com/shop/
Contact: Jason Bloom
Opening Times: (Office) 0830-1630 Mon-Fri. Mail order only.
Min Mail Order UK: £6.95 + p&p
Cat. Cost: Free.
Credit Cards: All major debit/credit cards except American Express
Specialities: Perennials and grasses, many from The Bressingham Gardens' extensive collection raised by Alan Bloom, and more recently Adrian Bloom and garden curator Jaime Blake. All plants grown at Bressingham Gardens Nursery. The 17-acre Bressingham Gardens are open from the end of Mar to end of Oct – visit for inspiration. See our website for details.
Notes: Mail order only. Also sells wholesale.

EBls **PETER BEALES ROSES** ♿ ◆
London Road, Attleborough, Norfolk, NR17 1AY
Ⓣ (01953) 454707
Ⓔ support@peterbealesroses.com
Ⓦ www.classicroses.co.uk
Contact: Tina Limmer
Opening Times: 0900-1700 Mon-Sat, 1000-1600 Sun & B/hols. Closed 25th Dec-2nd Jan.
Min Mail Order UK: Nmc
Min Mail Order EU: Nmc
Cat. Cost: £5.00 outside UK.
Credit Cards: All major debit/credit cards except American Express
Specialities: Large range of perennials, shrubs, *Clematis*, climbers, ornamental trees, fruit, summer & winter bedding. National Plant Collection of species roses.
Notes: Display garden, open all year (free entry). Agent for Classic Garden Element iron work. Also sells wholesale. Exports beyond EU. New wildlife garden. East Anglia's Finest Plant, Craft & Food Fair 2nd May 2020, Rose festival 20-21 Jun 2020. Other workshops, fairs, childrens wildlife day, Halloween and Christmas events will be found on our website. Wheelchair accessible.
OS Grid Ref: TM026929

EBou **BOUNDARY NURSERY**
Colne Road, Bluntisham, Huntington, Cambridgeshire, PE28 3LU
Ⓣ (01487) 842611
Ⓔ herbsandalpines@gmail.com
Ⓦ https://boundarynursery.co.uk/

E

Contact: Peter Reason
Opening Times: By appt. only.
Min Mail Order UK: Nmc
Credit Cards: All major credit/debit cards
Specialities: Range of rockery plants, ground-cover plants, drought-tolerant plants, shade tolerant plants, ones for clay soil, bee and butterfly pollinator friendly plants and ones for coastal regions.
Notes: Offers a range of alpines, perennials, herbs and ornamental grasses for all areas of the garden.
OS Grid Ref: TL369752

EBtc **Botanica**
Chantry Farm, Campsea Ashe, Wickham Market, Suffolk, IP13 0PZ
Ⓣ (01728) 747113
Ⓜ 07535 022803
Ⓔ sales@botanica.org.uk
Ⓦ www.botanicaplantnursery.co.uk
Contact: Jon Rose
Opening Times: 0900-1700 Mon-Fri (0900-1600 in winter), 1030-1600 w/ends. Closed w/ends Jul-Aug.
Min Mail Order UK: £30 + p&p
Cat. Cost: Online only.
Credit Cards: All major debit/credit cards except American Express
Specialities: Range of rare & unusual hardy plants. All stock is English, grown at our nursery and in non-peat based compost.
Notes: Also sells wholesale.
OS Grid Ref: TM328550

ECha **Beth Chatto's Plants and Gardens** ♿
Clacton Road, Elmstead Market, Colchester, Essex, CO7 7DB
Ⓣ (01206) 822007
Ⓕ (01206) 825933
Ⓔ nursery@bethchatto.co.uk
Ⓦ www.bethchatto.co.uk
Contact: David Ward
Opening Times: 1000-1700 Mon-Sun 1st Mar-31st Oct 1000-1600 Mon-Sun, 1st Nov-end Feb.
Min Mail Order UK: See website
Cat. Cost: Online only.
Credit Cards: All major debit/credit cards except American Express
Specialities: Predominantly herbaceous perennials, grasses & ferns. Many unusual for special situations.
Notes: Border design service. Peat-free potting compost used onsite. Delivers to shows. Wheelchair accessible.
OS Grid Ref: TM069238

ECnt **Cants of Colchester Ltd**
Nayland Road, Mile End, Colchester, Essex, CO4 5HA
Ⓣ (01206) 844008
Ⓕ (01206) 855371
Ⓔ enquiries@cantsroses.co.uk
Ⓦ www.cantsroses.co.uk
Contact: Angela Pawsey
Opening Times: 0900-1300, 1400-1630 Mon-Fri. Sat varied, please phone first. Sun closed.
Min Mail Order UK: Nmc
Min Mail Order EU: Nmc
Cat. Cost: Free.
Credit Cards: Visa, MasterCard, Delta, Maestro
Specialities: Roses.
Notes: Celebrated 250 years of being rose specialists in 2015. Bare-root mail order end Oct-end Mar, containers Apr-Oct. Limited bare-root exports beyond EU and worldwide, depending on regulations. Partial wheelchair access.

ECol **Colin Gregory Roses**
Rose Tweed Nursery, 101 Broadgate, Weston, Spalding, Lincolnshire, PE12 6HY
Ⓣ (01406) 371633
Ⓕ (01406) 371633
Ⓔ enquiries@cgregoryroses.com
Ⓦ https://cgregoryroses.com/
Contact: Colin Gregory
Opening Times: 0900-1700 Mon-Fri 1000-1600 Sat, Sun, B/hol Jan-Sep.
Credit Cards: Paypal
Specialities: Roses.
Notes: The nursery is open from mid Jan to Sep, or until stock is sold out. Also sells wholesale.

ECrc **The Crocosmia Gardens**
9 North Street, Caistor, Lincolnshire, LN7 6QU
Ⓜ 07834 725392
Ⓔ thecrocosmiagardens@live.co.uk
Ⓦ www.facebook.com/crocosmiaplants
Contact: Mark Fox
Opening Times: 1000-1700 Mon, Wed-Sun. Closed Tue.
Min Mail Order UK: £5.00
Min Mail Order EU: £5.00
Cat. Cost: None issued.
Credit Cards: None
Specialities: *Crocosmia*. National Collection of *Crocosmia*. Available in small quantities only.
Notes: Sent bareroot only, Oct-Apr. Exports beyond EU. Euro accepted.

ECre **CREAKE PLANT CENTRE** ♿
Leicester Road, South Creake, Fakenham, Norfolk, NR21 9PW
Ⓣ (01328) 823018
Ⓜ 07760 762499
Ⓕ (01328) 823018
Ⓔ trevor-harrison@btconnect.com
Ⓦ www.creakeplantcentre.co.uk
Contact: Mr T. Harrison
Opening Times: 1000-1300 & 1400-1730 Closed Wed and 2 weeks over Xmas and New Year.
Cat. Cost: None issued.
Credit Cards: All major credit/debit cards
Specialities: Unusual shrubs, herbaceous, conservatory plants, old roses, hellebores. Some plants only available in small quantities.
Notes: Delivers to shows. Wheelchair accessible.
OS Grid Ref: TF864353

ECtt **COTTAGE NURSERIES** ♿
Thoresthorpe, Alford, Lincolnshire, LN13 0HX
Ⓣ (01507) 466968
Ⓔ bill@cottagenurseries.net
Ⓦ www.cottagenurseries.net
Contact: W. H. Denbigh
Opening Times: 0900-1700, 7 days 1st Mar-31st Oct 1000-1500, Nov-Feb. Closed 1st Dec-6th Jan.
Min Mail Order UK: £20.00 + p&p
Cat. Cost: Online only.
Credit Cards: Visa, MasterCard, Maestro
Specialities: Hardy perennials. Wide general range.
Notes: Wheelchair accessible.
OS Grid Ref: TF461776

ECul **JOHN CULLEN GARDENS LTD**
Eagle Lodge, Archers Lane, Algarkirk, Lincolnshire, PE20 2AG
Ⓣ (01205) 460567
Ⓜ 07931 634933
Ⓔ design@johncullengardens.com
Ⓦ www.johncullengardens.com
Contact: John Cullen
Opening Times: Not open, online only.
Specialities: Scented plants, plants for pollinators, herbs, shrubs & bulbs.
Notes: A wide selection of plants from shrubs to perennials, bulbs & herbs. Delivers to shows.

EDAr **D'ARCY & EVEREST**
Meadowsweet Nursery, Pidley Sheep Lane (B1040), Pidley, Cambridgeshire, PE28 3FL
Ⓣ (01480) 497672
Ⓔ info@darcyeverest.co.uk
Ⓦ www.darcyeverest.co.uk
Contact: Luke Whiting
Opening Times: Open on selected days, please see website/contact nursery for dates. Also for nursery tour dates (bookable in advance only). Coach parties welcome by appt. Closed Oct-Feb.
Cat. Cost: None available.
Credit Cards: All major credit/debit cards
Specialities: Alpines, perennials & sempervivums.
Notes: Delivers to shows.
OS Grid Ref: TL338762

EDel **DELFLAND NURSERIES LTD** ♿
Benwick Road, Doddington, March, Cambridgeshire, PE15 0TU
Ⓣ (01354) 740553
Ⓕ (01354) 741200
Ⓔ info@delfland.co.uk
Ⓦ www.organicplants.co.uk
Contact: Jill Vaughan
Opening Times: 0900-1600 Mon-Sat 1000-1600 Sun Apr-Oct 0900-1600 Mon-Fri 0900-1300 Sat Nov-Mar.
Min Mail Order UK: £6.95
Cat. Cost: Free.
Credit Cards: All major debit/credit cards except American Express
Specialities: Vegetable, bedding & container plants.
Notes: Mail order and retail organic & peat-free from stock (mainly veg. plants) or to order (for large orders). Retail bedding & container plants not organic or peat-free. Also sells wholesale. Wheelchair accessible.
OS Grid Ref: TL386908

EDir **DIRECT PLANTS LTD**
Mill Hill Nursery, Cliffe-en-howe Road, Pott Row, King's Lynn, Norfolk, PE32 1BY
Ⓣ (01485) 601143/524441
Ⓜ 07771 923886
Ⓔ sales@directplants.co.uk
Ⓦ www.directplants.co.uk
Contact: Karina O'Brien
Specialities: Trees, fruit and hedging.

EFer **THE FERN NURSERY** ♿
Grimsby Road, Binbrook, Lincolnshire, LN8 6DH
Ⓣ (01472) 398092
Ⓔ rtimm@fernnursery.co.uk
Ⓦ www.fernnursery.co.uk
Contact: R. N. Timm
Opening Times: 0900-1600 Sat, Apr-Oct or by appt.
Min Mail Order UK: Nmc

Min Mail Order EU: Nmc
Cat. Cost: Online only.
Credit Cards: All major credit/debit cards
Specialities: Ferns.
Notes: Display garden. Only plants in the mail order part of the catalogue can be sent mail order. Also sells wholesale. Euro accepted. Wheelchair accessible.
OS Grid Ref: TF212942

EFPl **Foundry Plant Centre**
Tasburgh, Norwich, Norfolk, NR15 1NS
Ⓣ (01508) 470357
Ⓔ info@foundryplantcentre.co.uk
Ⓦ www.foundryplantcentre.co.uk
Contact: Martin

EGren **Grenville Nurseries** ♿
Cow Watering Lane, Writtle, Chelmsford, Essex, CM1 3SB
Ⓣ (01245) 420400
Ⓕ (01245) 420400
Ⓔ info@grenvillenurseries.co.uk
Ⓦ www.grenvillenurseries.co.uk
Contact: Charlie Lauman
Opening Times: 0830-1730 Mon-Thu, 0830-1900 Fri, 0900-1700 Sat, 1000-1700 Sun.
Cat. Cost: Online only.
Credit Cards: All major credit/debit cards
Specialities: Trees, shrubs, herbaceous ferns, climbers, grasses and bamboo. Seasonal bareroot and rootball hedging and trees. Bulbs available in large quantities.
Notes: Leading plant nursery open to both the public and trade. Growers of seasonal bedding and herbaceous plants. Also stock seasonal bareroot and rootball hedging and trees and bulbs. Also sells wholesale. Wheelchair accessible.

EGrI **Green Island Gardens**
Park Road, Ardleigh, Colchester, Essex, CO7 7SP
Ⓣ (01206) 230455
Ⓔ info@greenislandgardens.co.uk
Ⓦ www.greenislandgardens.co.uk
Contact: Fiona Edmond
Opening Times: 10th Jan-30th Nov.
Cat. Cost: None issued.
Credit Cards: All major credit/debit cards
Specialities: Acers, camellias and autumn-flowering camellias, cornus, hydrangeas, hamamelis, dwarf rhododendrons.
Notes: Large selection of acers & camellias (incl autumn-flowering camellias). Unusual trees & shrubs, all seen growing in the gardens.
OS Grid Ref: TM056273

EHDe **Harper & Debbage**
33 The Ridgeway, Norwich, Norfolk, NR1 4ND
Ⓣ (01603) 708104
Ⓜ 07889 679444
Ⓔ info@fuchsias.co.uk
Ⓦ www.fuchsias.co.uk
Contact: Kristopher Harper
Opening Times: Not open except for collection of pre-ordered plants by appt. only.
Min Mail Order UK: Nmc
Cat. Cost: Online only.
Credit Cards: All major credit/debit cards
Specialities: *Fuchsia*. National Plant Collection of *Fuchsia* introduced by James Lye.
Notes: Orders may be collected from any of the flower shows or events we attend (listed on our website). Delivers to shows.
OS Grid Ref: TG248096

EHed **Hedgehog Plants and Gardens**
Risby Barns, South Street, Bury St Edmunds, Suffolk, IP28 6QU
Ⓣ (01284) 811055
Ⓔ info@theinterestingplantnursery.co.uk
Ⓦ www.theinterestingplantnursery.co.uk
Contact: Simon or Jay McWilliams
Opening Times: 1000-1700 Mon-Sat 1000-1600 Sun Closed Mon from Oct-end Feb.
Specialities: *Cornus*, *Viburnum*, *Epimedium* and other shrubs and shade-loving plants.
Notes: If you are travelling any distance, please call ahead to check plant availability. Plenty of parking available. Delivers to shows. Please check website for details.
OS Grid Ref: TL796662

EHeP **Hedging Plants Direct** ♿
Long Road West, Dedham, Colchester, Essex, CO7 6ER
Ⓣ (01206) 804732
Ⓜ 07884 186484
Ⓔ info@hedgingplantsdirect.co.uk
Ⓦ www.hedgingplantsdirect.co.uk
Contact: Will Bodsworth
Opening Times: 0730-1630 Mon-Fri, 1000-1400 Sat-Sun.
Min Mail Order UK: No minimum charge
Min Mail Order EU: £75.00
Credit Cards: All major credit/debit cards
Specialities: Based in Essex on a 14 acre nursery we specialise in hedging, large shrubs and semi mature trees.
Notes: Hedging Plants Direct is part of Plants Group and is a family run specialist plant centre open to both general public and

professional landscapes alike. Based at Dedham which is set in the Constable Country in the beautiful Stour valley on the Suffolk-Essex border. Euro accepted. Delivers to shows. Wheelchair accessible.
OS Grid Ref: TM052314

EHyd **HYDE HALL PLANT CENTRE (RHS)** ♿ ◆
RHS Garden Hyde Hall, Rettendon Common, Chelmsford, Essex, CM3 8ET
Ⓣ (01245) 402113
Ⓔ benmansfield@rhs.org.uk
Ⓦ www.rhs.org.uk
Contact: Ben Mansfield
Opening Times: 0930-1600 Mon-Sat, 1000-1600 Sun, Nov-Feb. 0930-1800 Mon-Sat, 1100-1700 Sun, Mar-Oct. Closed Xmas Day & Easter Sun.
Credit Cards: All major credit/debit cards
Notes: Wheelchair accessible.

EIri **IRISESONLINE**
Slade Cottage, Petts Lane, Little Walden, Essex, CB10 1XH
Ⓣ (01799) 526294
Ⓔ enquiries@sladecottageirisesonline.co.uk
Ⓦ www.sladecottageirisesonline.co.uk
Contact: Clare Kneen
Opening Times: By appt. only.
Min Mail Order UK: Nmc
Cat. Cost: Online only.
Credit Cards: None
Specialities: *Iris*. Some varieties available in small quantities only.
Notes: Small family-run nursery. Delivers to shows.
OS Grid Ref: TL546416

EKin **E W KING & CO. LTD. (KINGS SEEDS)**
Monks Farm, Pantling Lane, Coggeshall Road, Kelvedon, Essex, CO5 9PG
Ⓣ (01376) 570000
Ⓕ (01376) 571189
Ⓔ info@kingsseeds.com
Ⓦ www.kingsseeds.com
Contact: Andrew Tokely
Opening Times: 0830-1230 1330-1700 Mon-Fri.
Min Mail Order UK: Nmc
Min Mail Order EU: Nmc
Cat. Cost: Free.
Credit Cards: All major credit/debit cards
Specialities: Vegetable, flower, grass, sweet pea and pea & bean seeds, incl. many hybrid & unusual items.
Notes: Incorporating Suffolk Herbs. Also sells wholesale. Exports beyond the EU.

ELan **LANGTHORNS PLANTERY** ♿
High Cross Lane West, Little Canfield, Dunmow, Essex, CM6 1TD
Ⓣ (01371) 872611
Ⓔ info@langthorns.com
Ⓦ www.langthorns.com
Contact: E. Cannon
Opening Times: 0830-1800 Apr-end Jun. 0830-1730 or dusk (if earlier) 7 days. Closed Xmas fortnight.
Min Mail Order UK: £ 20.00
Cat. Cost: Online only.
Credit Cards: Visa, Access, Switch, MasterCard, Delta
Specialities: Wide general range with many unusual plants.
Notes: Mail order any plant under 4ft tall. Wheelchair accessible.
OS Grid Ref: TL592204

ELon **LONG HOUSE PLANTS** ♿
The Long House, Church Road, Noak Hill, Romford, Essex, RM4 1LD
Ⓣ (01708) 371719
Ⓔ tim@thelonghouse.net
Ⓦ www.longhouse-plants.co.uk
Contact: Tim Carter
Opening Times: 1000-1700 Fri, Sat & B/hols, 1000-1600 Sun, beginning Mar-end Sep, or by appt.
Credit Cards: All major credit/debit cards
Specialities: Choice trees, shrubs, herbaceous perennials & ferns. Many unusual varieties incl. *Agapanthus*, *Aster*, *Camellia*, *Hemerocallis*, *Iris sibirica*, *Kniphofia*, *Phlox* & *Symphyotrichum*. Some only available in small quantities.
Notes: See website for garden open days. Wheelchair accessible. Disabled toilet.
OS Grid Ref: TQ554194

EMac **FIRECREST TREES & SHRUBS NURSERY** ♿
Hall Road, Little Bealings, Woodbridge, Suffolk, IP13 6LG
Ⓣ (01473) 625937
Ⓕ (01473) 625937
Ⓔ firecrest98@tiscali.co.uk
Ⓦ www.firecrest.org.uk
Opening Times: 0900-1500 Tue-Fri, 0900-1200 Sat.
Credit Cards: None
Specialities: Trees & Japanese maples 10-90ltr pots and bare-root hedging Nov-Mar time frame.
Notes: Also sells wholesale. Bareroot mail order only. Euro accepted. Wheelchair accessible.

E

EMal **Marshall's Malmaisons** ♿
Hullwood Barn, Shelley, Ipswich, Suffolk, IP7 5RE
Ⓣ (01473) 822400
Ⓜ 07768 454875
Ⓔ jimmalmaisons@gmail.com
Contact: J. M. Marshall/Sarah Cook
Opening Times: By appt. only.
Min Mail Order UK: £33.00 incl. p&p
Min Mail Order EU: £36.00 incl. p&p
Cat. Cost: 1st class sae.
Credit Cards: None
Specialities: National Plant Collection of Malmaison carnations, perpetual flowering carnations (pre 1970) & Cedric Morris Irises. *Iris* stock only available in small quantities.
Notes: Also sells wholesale. Wheelchair accessible.
OS Grid Ref: TM006394

EMdy **Mandy Plants** ♿
(office) 4 Stevens Road, Little Snoring, Norfolk, NR21 0GZ
Ⓣ (01328) 878144
Ⓜ 07432 112245
Ⓔ enquiries@mandyplants.com
Ⓦ www.mandyplants.com
Contact: Liz Spanton
Opening Times: By appt. only.
Min Mail Order UK: Nmc
Min Mail Order EU: £25.00
Credit Cards: Paypal, all major credit/debit cards
Specialities: *Mandevilla, Dipladenia, Lantana* & other tender perennials.
Notes: Nursery is at Little Snoring, Norfolk. Also sells wholesale. Delivers to shows. Wheelchair accessible.

EMic **Mickfield Hostas** ♿
The Poplars, Wetheringsett Road, Mickfield, Stowmarket, Suffolk, IP14 5LH
Ⓣ (01449) 711576
Ⓕ (01449) 711576
Ⓔ mickfieldhostas@btconnect.com
Ⓦ www.mickfieldhostas.co.uk
Contact: Melanie Collins
Opening Times: 1000-1600, Fri to Mon (Closed Tue-Thu) during May and Jun. All other times by appt. Check website for latest information.
Min Mail Order UK: Nmc
Min Mail Order EU: Nmc
Cat. Cost: Online only.
Credit Cards: All major debit/credit cards except American Express
Specialities: National Plant Collection of *Hosta* containing over 2000 varieties. Waiting list for rarities & some limited quantity plants only available at nursery. Will divide parent plants for collectors if feasible. Expect to pay more for root divisions of mature plants.
Notes: See website for details of cvs held & latest availability. Gardens under development. Delivers to shows. Wheelchair accessible.
OS Grid Ref: TM136619

EMil **Mill Race Garden Centre** ♿
New Road, Aldham, Colchester, Essex, CO6 3QT
Ⓣ (01206) 242521
Ⓔ PlantDesk@swallowaquatics.co.uk
Ⓦ www.millracegardencentre.co.uk
Contact: Plant Area Manager
Opening Times: 0900-1730 Mon-Sat, 1000-1630 Sun.
Min Mail Order UK: £9.00
Credit Cards: All major credit/debit cards
Specialities: Stock available in small quantities only.
Notes: Trees & large shrubs not sent by mail order. Wheelchair accessible.
OS Grid Ref: TL918268

EMor **Moore and Moore Plants** ♿
London Road, Billericay, Essex, CM12 9HR
Ⓜ 07799 865946
Ⓔ contact@mooreandmooreplants.co.uk
Ⓦ www.mooreandmooreplants.co.uk
Contact: Lynne Moore
Opening Times: By appt. only (please email). See website for open weekends new for 2020.
Min Mail Order UK: £15.00
Cat. Cost: Online only.
Credit Cards: All major credit/debit cards
Specialities: Specialists in plants for shady places. Great selection of plants that attract pollinating insects. Most plants available in small quantities only.
Notes: See website or contact nursery for details of open days. Delivers to shows. Wheelchair accessible.

EMul **Lound Plant Centre** ♿
Jay Lane, Lound, Lowestoft, Suffolk, NR32 5LH
Ⓣ (01502) 731431
Ⓔ loundplantcentre@gmail.com
Ⓦ www.loundplantcentre.com
Contact: Paul & Helen Watling
Opening Times: 0900-1700 Mon-Sat summer, 0900-1630 Mon-Sat winter, 1000-1600 Sun all year.
Cat. Cost: N/A

E

Credit Cards: All major credit/debit cards
Notes: A huge range of plants all year. Please contact us with your requirements. Wheelchair accessible.
OS Grid Ref: TM521992

ENfk **Norfolk Herbs** ♿ ◆
Blackberry Farm, Dillington, Dereham, Norfolk, NR19 2QD
Ⓣ (01362) 860812
Ⓕ (01362) 860812
Ⓔ info@norfolkherbs.co.uk
Ⓦ www.norfolkherbs.co.uk
Contact: Rosemary or Oliver Clifton-Sprigg
Opening Times: 0900-1700 Mon-Sat Mar 1st-Sep 30th. 1000-1600 Fri & Sat Oct 1st-Feb 28th. Closed Sun & Dec 24th-Jan 31st. At all other times please contact nursery.
Min Mail Order UK: £8.49
Cat. Cost: 2 × 2nd class.
Credit Cards: All major credit/debit cards
Specialities: Established 1986. Growers & suppliers of naturally raised culinary, medicinal & aromatic herb plants. Salvias, bay trees & scented pelargoniums.
Notes: Sells from nursery, online & at local shows. A founding member of Norfolk Nursery Network. Also sells wholesale. Delivers to shows. Wheelchair accessible.
OS Grid Ref: TF967150

ENor **Norfolk Lavender** ♿
Caley Mill, Heacham, King's Lynn, Norfolk, PE31 7JE
Ⓣ (01485) 570384
Ⓜ 07787 550286
Ⓕ (01485) 571176
Ⓔ info@norfolk-lavender.co.uk
Ⓦ www.norfolk-lavender.co.uk
Contact: Shelley Eagle
Opening Times: 0900-1700 7 days, Apr-Oct 0900-1600 7 days, Nov-Mar.
Min Mail Order UK: Nmc
Cat. Cost: Free.
Credit Cards: All major debit/credit cards except American Express
Specialities: National Plant Collection of *Lavandula*, sect. *L. dentata* & *L. pterostoechas*.
Notes: Wheelchair accessible.
OS Grid Ref: TF685368

EOHP **Old Hall Plants**
1 The Old Hall, Barsham, Beccles, Suffolk, NR34 8HB
Ⓣ (01502) 717475
Ⓔ info@oldhallplants.co.uk
Ⓦ www.oldhallplants.co.uk
Contact: Janet Elliott
Opening Times: By appt. only Please telephone first.
Min Mail Order UK: Nmc
Min Mail Order EU: Nmc
Cat. Cost: 4 × 1st class.
Specialities: House plants. Some plants available in small quantities.
Notes: Partial wheelchair access.
OS Grid Ref: TM396904

EOli **The Norfolk Olive Tree Company** ♿
61-63 Riverside Road, Norwich, Norfolk, NR1 1SR
Ⓜ 07766 730893
Ⓔ thenorfolkolivetreecompany@gmail.com
Ⓦ www.thenorfolkolivetreecompany.co.uk
Contact: Antonia Smith
Opening Times: Wed-Sun winter. Mon-Sun summer.
Min Mail Order UK: £2.95
Min Mail Order EU: £50.00
Credit Cards: All major credit/debit cards
Specialities: We specialise in the *Arbequina*, *Picual* and *Gordal* olive tree. Selection of UK hardy *Agave* grown in Norfolk as well as *Mangave* and *Manfreda*.
Notes: Award-winning suppliers of olive trees, specialising in hardy exotics and mediterranean plants. Delivery UK-wide (extra charges may apply). All of our Olive trees have plant passports and phytosanitary certificates. Wheelchair accessible.

EPau **Paugers Plants Ltd**
Bury Road, Depden, Bury St Edmunds, Suffolk, IP29 4BU
Ⓣ (01284) 850527
Ⓔ enquiries@paugers-plants.co.uk
Ⓦ www.paugers-plants.co.uk
Contact: Geraldine Arnold
Opening Times: 0900-1730 Wed-Sat, 1000-1700 Sun & B/hols, 1st Mar-30th Nov.
Min Mail Order UK: Nmc
Cat. Cost: None issued.
Credit Cards: All major credit/debit cards
Specialities: Hardy shrubs & perennials in large or small quantities.
Notes: Also sells wholesale.
OS Grid Ref: TL783568

EPfP **The Place for Plants** ♿
East Bergholt Place, East Bergholt, Suffolk, CO7 6UP
Ⓣ (01206) 299224
Ⓕ (01206) 299229
Ⓔ sales@placeforplants.co.uk
Ⓦ www.placeforplants.co.uk

E

Contact: Sara Eley
Opening Times: 1000-1700 (or dusk if earlier) 7 days. Closed Easter Sun & Christmas B/hol.
Min Mail Order UK: Nmc
Cat. Cost: Online only.
Credit Cards: All major credit/debit cards
Specialities: Wide range of specialist & popular plants. National Plant Collection of deciduous *Euonymus*. 20 acre mature garden with free access to RHS members Apr-Sep excluding Sun.
Notes: Mail order. Delivers to shows. Euro accepted. Wheelchair accessible.

EPom **Pomona Fruits Ltd**
Pomona House, 12 Third Avenue, Walton-on-the-Naze, Essex, CO14 8JU
Ⓣ (01255) 440410
Ⓕ (01255) 440420
Ⓔ Info@PomonaFruits.co.uk
Ⓦ www.PomonaFruits.co.uk
Contact: Ming Yang/Claire Higgins
Opening Times: Not open. Mail order only.
Min Mail Order UK: Nmc
Cat. Cost: Free.
Credit Cards: All major credit/debit cards
Specialities: Fruit stock.

EPot **Pottertons Nursery** ♿
Moortown Road, Nettleton, Caistor, Lincolnshire, LN7 6HX
Ⓣ (01472) 851714
Ⓔ sales@pottertons.co.uk
Ⓦ www.pottertons.co.uk
Contact: Robert Potterton
Opening Times: 1000-1500 Tue-Fri, Mar-Oct.
Min Mail Order UK: Nmc
Min Mail Order EU: Nmc
Cat. Cost: £2.00 in stamps.
Credit Cards: MasterCard, Visa
Specialities: Alpines, dwarf bulbs & woodland plants.
Notes: Talks given nationally & internationally to garden clubs & societies. Group nursery tours by arrangement. Delivers to shows. Euro accepted. Wheelchair accessible.
OS Grid Ref: TA091001

EPPr **The Plantsman's Preference** ♿
Church Road, South Lopham, Diss, Norfolk, IP22 2LW
Ⓣ (01379) 710810
Ⓜ 07799 855559
Ⓔ tim@plantpref.co.uk
Ⓦ www.plantpref.co.uk
Contact: Tim Fuller
Opening Times: 0930-1700 Fri, Sat & Sun Mar-Oct Other times by appt.
Min Mail Order UK: Nmc
Min Mail Order EU: Nmc
Cat. Cost: Online only.
Credit Cards: All major credit/debit cards
Specialities: Hardy geraniums & ornamental grasses. Unusual & interesting perennials incl. shade/woodland. Some choice shrubs esp. *Caprifoliaceae*. National Plant Collection of *Molinia*.
Notes: Mail order all year except Xmas-New Year. Now-using peat-free compost. Delivers to shows. Wheelchair accessible.
OS Grid Ref: TM041819

EPri **Priory Plants** ♿
1 Covey Cottages, Hintlesham, Nr Ipswich, Suffolk, IP8 3NY
Ⓣ (01473) 652656
Ⓜ 07798 627618
Ⓕ (01473) 652656
Ⓔ sue.mann3@btinternet.com
Contact: Sue Mann
Opening Times: By appt. only Please ring first to avoid disappointment.
Min Mail Order UK: Nmc
Min Mail Order EU: Nmc
Cat. Cost: Online only.
Credit Cards: None
Specialities: Cottage garden perennials, as well as increasing range of South African plants. *Agapanthus*, *Astrantia*, *Dierama*, *Dietes*, *Eucomis*, Siberian *Iris*, *Kniphofia*, *Nerine*, *Tritonia*, *Tulbaghia* & *Watsonia*.
Notes: Sells at plant fairs & agricultural shows. Also sells wholesale. Exports beyond EU. Wheelchair accessible.
OS Grid Ref: TM070448

EPts **Potash Nursery Ltd** ♿
Cow Green, Bacton, Stowmarket, Suffolk, IP14 4HJ
Ⓣ (01449) 781671
Ⓔ enquiries@potashnursery.co.uk
Ⓦ www.potashnursery.co.uk
Contact: M. W. Clare
Opening Times: Not open except for collection of pre-ordered plants by appt. only.
Min Mail Order UK: £24.90
Cat. Cost: 1 × 1st class.
Credit Cards: Visa, Delta, MasterCard
Specialities: *Fuchsia*.
Notes: Peat free. Delivers to shows. Wheelchair accessible.
OS Grid Ref: TM055656

ERCP **ROSE COTTAGE PLANTS**
Bay Tree Farm, Epping Green, Essex, CM16 6PU
Ⓣ (01992) 573775
Ⓔ anne@rosecottageplants.co.uk
Ⓦ www.rosecottageplants.co.uk
Contact: Anne & Jack Barnard
Opening Times: Most Fri Mar-Oct Also by appt. & for special events. See website for details.
Min Mail Order UK: Nmc
Min Mail Order EU: £20.00
Cat. Cost: Online only.
Credit Cards: All major debit/credit cards except American Express
Specialities: Hardy bulbs & dahlias.
Notes: Mail order for *Dahlia* tubers and hardy bulbs. Delivers to shows.
OS Grid Ref: TL435053

ERom **THE ROMANTIC GARDEN** ♿
The Street, Swannington, Norwich, Norfolk, NR9 5NW
Ⓣ (01603) 261488
Ⓜ 07802 722072
Ⓔ enquiries@romantic-garden-nursery.co.uk
Ⓦ www.romantic-garden-nursery.co.uk
Contact: John Powles
Opening Times: 1000-1700 Mon-Sat incl. B/hol Mons.
Min Mail Order UK: £18.00
Credit Cards: All major credit/debit cards
Specialities: Conservatory. *Buxus* topiary, ornamental standards, large specimens. Hedging. Topiary.
Notes: Wheelchair accessible. Also sells wholesale.

ESgI **SEAGATE IRISES** ♿
A17 Long Sutton By-Pass, Long Sutton, Lincolnshire, PE12 9RX
Ⓣ (01406) 364028
Ⓜ 07766 862603
Ⓔ sales@irises.co.uk
Ⓦ www.irises.co.uk
Contact: Chris Davey
Opening Times: 1000-1700 Mon-Sat, 1000-1600 Sun Mar-Oct Other times by appt.
Min Mail Order UK: £20.00 + p&p
Credit Cards: Paypal
Specialities: Different types of *Iris*, bearded, beardless & species hybrids with about 800+ varieties, both historic & modern. Plants available in pots & bareroot in lifting season. Some only available in small quantities. A growing selection of choice perennials.
Notes: Delivers to shows. Wheelchair accessible.
OS Grid Ref: TF437218

EShb **SHRUBLAND NURSERIES**
Maltings Farm, Whatfield Road, Elmsett, Ipswich, Suffolk, IP7 6LZ
Ⓣ (01473) 657012
Ⓜ 07890 527744
Ⓔ gill@shrublandparknurseries.co.uk
Ⓦ www.shrublandparknurseries.co.uk
Contact: Gill & Catherine Stitt
Opening Times: See website or contact nursery.
Min Mail Order UK: Nmc
Min Mail Order EU: Nmc
Credit Cards: All major credit/debit cards, Paypal
Specialities: Conservatory plants, succulents, hardy perennials, climbers, shrubs, ferns & grasses. Some more unusual plants may be in short supply.
Notes: Please check before visiting that nursery is open & that any plants you require are in stock. Delivers to shows.
OS Grid Ref: TM052466

ESMi **STRAIGHT MILE NURSERY GARDENS** ♿
Ongar Road, Pilgrims Hatch, Brentwood, Essex, CM15 9SA
Ⓣ (01277) 374439
Ⓔ info@straightmile.net
Ⓦ www.straightmile.net
Contact: David Sisley
Opening Times: 1000-1600, 7 days (but closed some Weds, phone first).
Min Mail Order UK: Nmc
Cat. Cost: Epimedium catologue only.
Credit Cards: All major debit/credit cards except American Express
Specialities: General nursery stock. Japanese maples, *Epimedium.* Some in small quantities only. Mail order *Epimedium* only.
Notes: Delivers to shows. Wheelchair accessible.
OS Grid Ref: TQ571964

EStr **STRICTLY DAYLILIES**
2 Primes Corner, Histon, Cambridgeshire, CB24 9AG
Ⓣ (01223) 236239
Ⓜ 07765 236880
Ⓔ info@strictlydaylilies.com
Ⓦ www.strictlydaylilies.com
Contact: Paula & Chris Dyason
Opening Times: Mail order only.
Min Mail Order UK: Nmc
Min Mail Order EU: Nmc
Cat. Cost: No charge.
Credit Cards: All major credit/debit cards
Specialities: *Hemerocallis.* Some stock available in small quantities only. National

E

Plant Collection of *Hemerocallis* (post 2014 hybrid registrations).
Notes: Open gardens Fri-Sun in Jul, please phone for confirmation. Also sells wholesale. Exports beyond EU. Delivers to shows. Euro accepted.

ESty **Style Roses** ♿
Cackle Hill Farm, Boston Road North, Holbeach, Lincolnshire, PE12 8AG
Ⓣ (01406) 424089/490006
Ⓜ 07760 626750
Ⓔ mail@styleroses.co.uk
Ⓦ www.styleroses.co.uk
Contact: Margaret Styles
Opening Times: 0900-1700 Mon-Fri at Nursery address only, other times by appt. Rose Field Jun-Oct.
Min Mail Order UK: Nmc
Min Mail Order EU: Nmc
Cat. Cost: Free in UK.
Credit Cards: MasterCard, Visa
Specialities: Standard & Bush garden roses sold bareroot, order from Jul and available for dispatch from Nov-Mar only. Potted roses available all year. Mail order and collection service.
Notes: Nursery at Cackle Hill Farm, Boston Road North, Holbeach, Spalding, Lincolnshire, PE12 8AG. Bush roses av mail order mainland UK all yr, std roses as bare-root Nov-Mar. Potted roses by collection/shows all yr. Export to EU Nov-Mar. Also sells wholesale. Delivers to shows. Wheelchair accessible.

ESwi **Swines Meadow Farm Nursery** ♿ ◆
47 Towngate East, Market Deeping, Peterborough, Lincolnshire, PE6 8LQ
Ⓜ 07432627766
Ⓔ rareplants@me.com
Ⓦ www.swinesmeadowfarmnursery.co.uk
Contact: Colin Ward
Opening Times: 0900-1600 Mon-Sat, 1000-1600 Sun. Closed Jan-Feb except by appt. only.
Min Mail Order UK: £10.00
Min Mail Order EU: £10.00
Credit Cards: All major debit/credit cards except American Express
Specialities: Hardy exotics, tree ferns, bamboos & hostas. Wollemi pine stockist. Many specialities available in small quantities only.
Notes: Delivers to shows. Wheelchair accessible.
OS Grid Ref: TF150113

ETay **Walkers Bulbs @ Taylors**
Washway Road, Holbeach, Lincolnshire, PE12 7PP
Ⓣ (01406) 426216
Ⓔ walkers@taylors-bulbs.com
Ⓦ www.bulbs.co.uk
Contact: Sallyanne Foreman
Opening Times: Mail order only.
Min Mail Order UK: £4.95
Min Mail Order EU: Dependant on parcel weight
Credit Cards: All major credit/debit cards
Specialities: Daffodil.
Notes: We specialise in Daffodils, growing over 400 varieties.

ETho **Thorncroft Clematis & Climbers Ltd**
The Lings, Reymerston, Norwich, Norfolk, NR9 4QG
Ⓣ (01953) 850407
Ⓔ sales@thorncroftclematis.co.uk
Ⓦ www.thorncroftclematis.co.uk
Contact: Peter Skeggs-Gooch
Opening Times: Mail order only. Telephones answered 1000-1600 Mon-Fri.
Min Mail Order EU: £20.00
Cat. Cost: £3.50
Credit Cards: All major credit/debit cards
Specialities: *Clematis*.
Notes: Supply, by mail order, mature garden-ready *Clematis* and other climbing plants 2 years +. Diverse range from all over the world including both unusual & popular varieties. Excellent customer service & advice as well as quality plants. Delivers to shows.

ETod **Todd's Botanics**
Ⓣ (01376) 561212
Ⓔ info@toddsbotanics.co.uk
Ⓦ www.toddsbotanics.co.uk
Contact: Emma Macdonald
Opening Times: Not open, mail order only.
Min Mail Order UK: Nmc
Credit Cards: All major debit/credit cards except American Express
Specialities: Specialists in olives, *Canna*, *Dahlia*, *Cyathea* & *Dicksonia*. Hold a range of tall bearded *Iris* grown in large quantities.
Notes: Website mail order sales but also sells through the larger RHS shows such as Chelsea, Hampton Court and Tatton Park. Also sells wholesale. Euro accepted.

ETWh **Trevor White Old Fashioned Roses**
Bennetts Brier, 59, The Street, Felthorpe, Norwich, Norfolk, NR10 4AB

Ⓣ (01603) 755135
Ⓕ (01603) 755135
Ⓔ sales@trevorwhiteroses.co.uk
Ⓦ www.trevorwhiteroses.co.uk
Contact: Trevor White
Opening Times: 0900-1630 Mon-Fri (office).
Min Mail Order UK: One plant + P&P
Min Mail Order EU: One plant + P&P
Credit Cards: All major credit/debit cards
Specialities: Old, shrub, climbing and rambling roses.
Notes: Specialist grower of roses for over 30 years. All plants grown by us and available via the website. Unique collection of ancient and modern varieties for all types of garden. Bare root plants are top quality and lifted to order (not stored). Some varieties available potted (all in peat-free compost).

EVic **Victorian Violas**
85 Fulmar Road, Lincoln, Lincolnshire, LN6 0RX
Ⓣ (01522) 686343
Ⓔ victorianviolas@gmail.com
Ⓦ www.victorianviolas.co.uk
Contact: Robert Chapman
Opening Times: Not open. Mail order only.
Min Mail Order UK: Nmc
Cat. Cost: Online only.
Credit Cards: None
Specialities: Hardy perennial violas (summer flowering). Named cultivars.
Notes: BACS payments accepted. Also sells wholesale.

EWat **Water Garden Plants**
Beck View, Chequers Road, Gresham, Norwich, Norfolk, NR11 8RQ
Ⓣ (01263) 577627
Ⓔ sales@watergardenplants.co.uk
Ⓦ www.watergardenplants.co.uk
Contact: Anna Robinson
Opening Times: Mail order only.
Min Mail Order UK: Nmc
Min Mail Order EU: Nmc
Cat. Cost: Online.
Credit Cards: All major credit/debit cards
Specialities: Range of water garden plants: water lilies, floating plants, oxygenating plants, marginals, marsh plants. Some stock in small quantities.
OS Grid Ref: TQ585995

EWes **West Acre Gardens** ♿
Tumbleyhill Road, West Acre, King's Lynn, Norfolk, PE32 1UJ
Ⓣ (01760) 755562
Ⓔ info@westacregardens.co.uk
Ⓦ www.westacregardens.co.uk
Contact: J. J. Tuite
Opening Times: 0930-1700 7 days 1st Feb-30th Nov. Other times by appt.
Cat. Cost: None issued.
Credit Cards: Visa, MasterCard, Delta, Switch
Specialities: Very wide selection of herbaceous & other garden plants incl. *Rhodohypoxis*, *Primula auricula* & *Galanthus*. Mail order not available.
Notes: Delivers to shows. Wheelchair accessible.
OS Grid Ref: TF792182

EWhm **Waltham Herbs**
Willow Vale Nursery, North Kelsey Road, Caistor, Lincolnshire, LN7 6SF
Ⓣ (01472) 859481
Ⓜ 07949 883091
Ⓕ (01472) 859481
Ⓔ angelasach2@aol.com
Ⓦ www.walthamherbs.co.uk
Contact: Steve Penney
Opening Times: By appt. only.
Min Mail Order UK: £3.75
Credit Cards: All major credit/debit cards
Specialities: Herbs, lavenders and perennials, also some shrubs. Peat-free and pesticide-free.
Notes: For open days, see website or contact nursery. Delivers to shows.
OS Grid Ref: TA401350

EWld **Woodlands**
Peppin Lane, Fotherby, Louth, Lincolnshire, LN11 0UW
Ⓣ (01507) 603586
Ⓜ 07422 331566
Ⓔ annbobarmstrong@btinternet.com
Ⓦ www.woodlandsplants.co.uk
Contact: Ann Armstrong
Opening Times: Very flexible, year round. Always open Wed afternoons May-Aug. Other times by appt.
Min Mail Order UK: Nmc
Min Mail Order EU: Nmc
Cat. Cost: None issued.
Credit Cards: All major credit/debit cards
Specialities: Small but interesting range of unusual plants, esp. woodland, *Codonopsis* and *Salvia*, all grown on the nursery in limited quantity. National Plant Collection of *Codonopsis*.
Notes: Mature garden, art gallery & refreshments. Credit cards accepted at the nursery only.
OS Grid Ref: TF322918

G

EWoo **Woottens of Wenhaston** ♿
The Iris Field, Hall Road, Wenhaston, Suffolk, IP19 9HF
Ⓣ (01502) 478258
Ⓜ 07802 507693
Ⓕ (01502) 478888
Ⓔ info@woottensplants.co.uk
Ⓦ https://www.woottensplants.com
Contact: Lucinda Skinner
Opening Times: 0900-1700 Mon-Fri for mail order/enquiries. Nursery open 1000-1600 Sat Mar-Oct.
Min Mail Order UK: £7.50
Min Mail Order UK: £25.00
Cat. Cost: Online only.
Credit Cards: All major credit/debit cards
Specialities: *Pelargonium, Hemerocallis, Auricula, Iris* & hardy *Geranium.*
Notes: Suffolk based plant nursery offering the specialties listed above as well as many other herbaceous perennials. Our mail order service runs throughout the year and the nursery is open to the public every Sat from Mar-Oct and select events. Specialist event days throughout the year. Delivers to shows. Wheelchair accessible.
OS Grid Ref: TM429747

EWTr **Walnut Tree Garden Nursery**
Flymoor Lane, Rocklands, Attleborough, Norfolk, NR17 1BP
Ⓣ (01953) 488163
Ⓔ info@wtgn.co.uk
Ⓦ www.wtgn.co.uk
Contact: Jim Paine & Clare Billington
Opening Times: 0900-1700 Wed-Sun 1st Feb-31st Oct or by appt.
Min Mail Order UK: £20.00
Cat. Cost: Online.
Credit Cards: All major credit/debit cards
Specialities: Flowering dogwood: *Cornus florida, C. kousa* & *C. nuttalli* cvs. Crab apple (*Malus*) cvs.
Notes: Delivers to shows.
OS Grid Ref: TL978973

Scotland

GAbr **Abriachan Nurseries**
Loch Ness Side, Inverness, Inverness-shire, IV3 8LA
Ⓣ (01463) 861232
Ⓔ info@lochnessgarden.com
Ⓦ www.lochnessgarden.com
Contact: Mr & Mrs D. Davidson
Opening Times: 0900-1900 daily (dusk if earlier) Feb-Nov.
Min Mail Order UK: Nmc
Cat. Cost: 4 × 1st class.
Credit Cards: All major credit/debit cards
Specialities: Herbaceous perennials, old-fashioned *Primula, Helianthemum,* hardy geraniums, *Sempervivum* & *Primula auricula.*
Notes: Delivers to shows. Partial wheelchair access (to nursery only).
OS Grid Ref: NH571347

GArf **Ardfearn Nursery** ♿
Bunchrew, Inverness, Highland, IV3 8RH
Ⓣ (01463) 243250
Ⓜ 07770 887299
Ⓕ (01463) 711713
Ⓔ ardfearn@gmail.com
Ⓦ www.ardfearn-nursery.co.uk/
Contact: Alasdair Sutherland
Opening Times: 0900-1700 Mon-Fri. W/ends by appt.
Min Mail Order UK: Nmc
Min Mail Order EU: Nmc
Cat. Cost: Online.
Credit Cards: All major credit/debit cards
Specialities: Extensive selection of alpines & woodland plants, including *Ericaceae, Primulaceae,* trilliums & celmisias. Many Asiatic and Southern Hemisphere varieties available.
Notes: Specialist grower of alpines and hardy plants in the Scottish Highlands. Famous for alpines but also grow shrubs, perennials and climbers. Many unusual varieties. Friendly, expert advice. Attend Scottish Rock Garden Club shows. Mail order primarily for alpines only. Wheelchair accessible. Delivers to shows.
OS Grid Ref: NH604461

GAsh **Ashbrook Nursery** ♿
Forfar Road, Arbroath, Angus, DD11 3RB
Ⓣ (01241) 873408
Ⓜ 07746 378024
Ⓔ anne@ashbrooknursery.co.uk
Ⓦ http://www.ashbrooknursery.co.uk
Contact: Anne Webster
Opening Times: 0900-1730 Mon-Sat Mar-Oct, 0900-1630 Mon-Sat Nov-Feb. 1000-1630 Sun.
Credit Cards: All major credit/debit cards
Specialities: Wide range of alpine & herbaceous perennials, bedding & patio plants.
Notes: Nursery located opposite RM Condor Marine Base. Also sells wholesale. Wheelchair accessible.
OS Grid Ref: NO618428

GBee **Beeches Cottage Nursery**
Near Hawksland, Lesmahagow, South Lanarkshire, ML11 9PY
Ⓣ (01555) 893369

Ⓜ 07930 343131
Ⓔ thebeeches.nursery@talktalk.net
Ⓦ www.beechescottage.co.uk
Contact: Margaret & Steven Harrison
Opening Times: 1000-1630 Wed-Sun Mid Mar-end Sep. Open b/hols.
Cat. Cost: None issued.
Credit Cards: All major credit/debit cards
Notes: Fourth generation nurserymen specialising in traditional & unusual, hardy cottage garden perennials. These are grown at 850ft above sea level, and can be seen growing in our display gardens.
OS Grid Ref: NS837403

GBin **BINNY PLANTS** ♿
Binny Estate, Ecclesmachan Road, Near Broxburn, West Lothian, EH52 6NL
Ⓣ (01506) 858931
Ⓜ 07753 626117
Ⓔ contact@binnyplants.com
Ⓦ www.binnyplants.com
Contact: Billy Carruthers
Opening Times: 1000-1700, 7 days. Closed over Christmas & New Year.
Min Mail Order UK: Nmc
Min Mail Order EU: Nmc
Cat. Cost: 4 × 1st class.
Credit Cards: Visa, MasterCard, EuroCard, Maestro
Specialities: Over 250 varieties of *Paeonia*, plus a good range of herbaceous perennials, grasses & ferns incl. *Astilbe*, *Bergenia*, *Geranium*, *Molinia*, *Persicaria* & *Iris*.
Notes: Also sells wholesale. Exports beyond the EU. Delivers to shows. Wheelchair accessible.
OS Grid Ref: NT050732

GCro **CROFT 16 DAFFODILS**
16 Midtown of Inverasdale, Poolewe, Ross-shire, IV22 2LW
Ⓣ (01445) 781717
Ⓔ sales@croft16daffodils.co.uk
Ⓦ www.croft16daffodils.co.uk
Contact: Duncan & Kate Donald
Opening Times: Not open. Mail order only.
Min Mail Order UK: Nmc
Min Mail Order EU: Nmc
Cat. Cost: Online only.
Credit Cards: Paypal
Specialities: National Plant Collection of *Narcissus* bred pre-1930. Some stocks only available in small quantities. A waiting list for *desiderata* is in operation.
Notes: Please order by mid-May for delivery in the same year. Orders unfulfilled in one season will take priority the following year, if then available. Customers outside the EU should contact nursery.
OS Grid Ref: NG822851

GDam **DAMHEAD NURSERY LTD** ♿
Damhead Farm, Lothianburn, Edinburgh, Midlothian, EH10 7DZ
Ⓣ (0131) 445 4698
Ⓜ 07920 520664
Ⓕ (0131) 445 7659
Ⓔ enquiries@damheadnursery.co.uk
Ⓦ www.damheadnursery.co.uk
Contact: Sue Gray
Opening Times: 0800-1630 Mon-Fri.
Credit Cards: All major credit/debit cards
Specialities: Hardy plants for Scottish gardens.
Notes: Also sells wholesale. Wheelchair accessible.

GEdr **EDROM NURSERIES**
Coldingham, Eyemouth, Berwickshire, TD14 5TZ
Ⓣ (01890) 771386
Ⓕ (01890) 771387
Ⓔ mail@edrom-nurseries.co.uk
Ⓦ www.edrom-nurseries.co.uk
Contact: Mr Terry Hunt
Opening Times: Closed to calling public but attend many plant fairs and mail order.
Min Mail Order UK: Nmc
Min Mail Order EU: Nmc
Cat. Cost: Free.
Credit Cards: All major credit/debit cards
Specialities: *Epimedium*, *Gentiana*, *Primula*, *Meconopsis*, *Rhodohypoxis*, *Trillium*, *Hepatica*, Japanese *Saxifraga* & Japanese *Hepatica*.
Notes: Delivers to shows.
OS Grid Ref: NT873663

GElm **ELMLEA PLANTS**
Elmlea, Old Minnigaff, Newton Stewart, Dumfries & Galloway, DG8 6PX
Ⓣ (01671) 402514
Ⓜ 07876 822431
Ⓔ moiradavies@yahoo.co.uk
Ⓦ www.elmleaplants.co.uk
Contact: Giles Davies
Opening Times: 1000-1700 Thu-Mon Mar-Oct Closed Tue & Wed.
Min Mail Order UK: £10.50
Min Mail Order EU: By arrangement
Credit Cards: All major credit/debit cards
Specialities: There is always a good selection of *Geum*, *Achillea* and *Geranium*, a wide choice of late flowers such as *Helenium* and many of the taller perennials which we love.

G

Our range of grasses includes many larger and unusual cultivars as well as choice smaller varieties.
Notes: We are a small, family-run nursery specialising in herbaceous perennials and grasses. We sell here at the nursery, at shows in Scotland, Ireland, Cumbria and by mail order. We grow a wide range of plants, but not in huge quantities so please check for availability. Euro accepted.

GGGa **Glendoick Gardens Ltd**
Glendoick, Perth, Perthshire,
PH2 7NS
Ⓔ orders@glendoick.com
Ⓦ www.glendoick.com
Contact: Kenneth Cox
Opening Times: Nursery not open to the public. Garden centre open 0900-1730 (summer), 0900-1700 (winter) 7 days. Gardens open Apr & May, details on website or contact nursery for details.
Min Mail Order UK: £250.00
Min Mail Order EU: £500.00
Credit Cards: All major debit/credit cards except American Express
Specialities: Rhododendrons, azaleas, ericaceous, & *Meconopsis*. Plants from wild seed. Most but not all plants available at garden centre. Three National Plant Collections.
Notes: Partial wheelchair access (to garden centre).

GGro **Growild Nursery**
Loganhill Farm, Cumnock, East Ayrshire, KA18 3BX
Ⓔ info@growildnursery.co.uk
Ⓦ www.growildnursery.co.uk
Contact: Lisa Wesley & Andrew Blackwood
Opening Times: Not open, mail order only.
Min Mail Order UK: Nmc
Min Mail Order EU: Nmc
Cat. Cost: Online only.
Credit Cards: Paypal
Specialities: Grow rare and unusual species plants, in particular, hardy perennials from Japan, China and the Himalayas. Sell the largest selection of Asian *Impatiens*, *Begonia* & members of the *Urticaceae* family in the UK, as well as woodland plants and rarely grown UK wildflowers that attract pollinating insects.
Notes: No peat-based products are used in the nursery. No chemicals or animal-derived products are used on our plants and only seaweed fertilser is used. We also sell a wide range of seeds collected from our plants all year.

GJos **Jo's Garden Enterprise** ♿
Easter Balmungle Farm, Eathie Road, by Rosemarkie, Ross-shire, IV10 8SL
Ⓣ (01381) 621006
Ⓔ jos_garden_enterprise@hotmail.co.uk
Contact: Joanna Chance
Opening Times: 1000 to dusk, 7 days.
Cat. Cost: None.
Credit Cards: None
Specialities: Alpines & herbaceous perennials. Selection of native wild flowers.
Notes: Wheelchair accessible.
OS Grid Ref: NH600742

GKev **Kevock Garden Plants**
Kevock Road, Lasswade, Midlothian,
EH18 1HX
Ⓣ (0131) 454 0660
Ⓔ info@kevockgarden.co.uk
Ⓦ www.kevockgarden.co.uk
Contact: Elea Strang
Opening Times: Mail order only.
Min Mail Order UK: £30.00
Min Mail Order EU: £30.00
Cat. Cost: 2 × 2nd class.
Credit Cards: All major credit/debit cards
Specialities: Chinese and Himalayan plants. *Trillium*, *Daphne*, *Paeonia*, *Primula*, *Meconopsis*, *Iris*, woodland plants, alpine plants, rock plants, marginal and bog plants, bulbs, Chinese and Himalayan trees and shrubs, *Sorbus*, *Rhododendron*.
Notes: We only sell by mail order as we are a nursery and so we are not open to the public. Please purchase plants by mail order or from plant stalls at the shows we attend. Delivers to shows. Also sells wholesale.

GKin **Kinlochlaich Garden Plant Centre**
c/o Blarchasgaig, Appin, Argyll, PA38 4BB
Ⓜ 07881 525754
Ⓔ fiona@kinlochlaich.plus.com
Ⓦ www.kinlochlaichgardencentre.co.uk
Contact: Fiona Hutchison
Opening Times: 1000-1700 Mar-mid Oct, 1000-1500 or by appt. mid-Oct-Feb.
Cat. Cost: None issued.
Credit Cards: All major credit/debit cards
Specialities: Hardy shrubs, trees, azaleas, perennials. Also Gulf Stream plants such as *Tropaeolum*, *Embothrium*, *Eucryphia*, *Drymis* & more. Good selection of hardy seaside plants.
Notes: Does not offer mail order but will post where possible. Partial wheelchair access (limited due to gravel paths), wheelchair accessible toilet.

GLet **Letham Plants**
11a Letham Mains Holdings, Haddington, East Lothian, EH41 4NW
Ⓣ (01620) 822350
Ⓜ 07842 211712
Ⓔ lethamplants@hotmail.co.uk
Ⓦ www.letham-plants.co.uk
Contact: Caroline Samuel
Opening Times: By appt. only.
Min Mail Order UK: Nmc
Min Mail Order EU: Nmc
Cat. Cost: Online only.
Credit Cards: All major credit/debit cards
Specialities: *Astrantia*, *Dicentra.*
Notes: Also sells wholesale. Delivers to shows. Euro accepted.
OS Grid Ref: NT487730

GLog **Logie Steading Plants** ♿
Logie Steading, Dunphail, Forres, Moray, IV36 2QN
Ⓕ (01309) 611300
Ⓔ panny@logie.co.uk
Ⓦ www.logie.co.uk
Contact: Mrs Panny Laing
Opening Times: 1000-1700 summer, 1000-1600 winter, 7 days, Feb-Xmas.
Credit Cards: All major credit/debit cards
Specialities: Unusual hardy plants, grown in Scotland for Scottish gardens. Large range of hardy geraniums, bold herbaceous plants, grasses & marginal plants, trees and shrubs. Majority of plants propagated from Logie House Garden where they can be seen in their full glory.
Notes: Logie House Garden open every day. Café, farm & garden shop, art gallery, second-hand books, antiques, whisky, wine & river walk. Heritage centre open every day from 1st Feb until Xmas. Check website for seasonal opening hours. Wheelchair accessible (except river walk).
OS Grid Ref: NJ006504

GMaP **Macplants** ♿
Berrybank Nursery, 5 Boggs Holdings, Pencaitland, East Lothian, EH34 5BA
Ⓣ (01875) 341179
Ⓔ sales@macplants.co.uk
Ⓦ www.macplants.co.uk
Contact: Gavin McNaughton
Opening Times: 1030-1700 7 days, Mar-end Sep. 1030-1600 Mon-Fri, Oct Closed Nov-end Feb except by appt.
Min Mail Order UK: Nmc
Cat. Cost: 4 × 2nd class.
Credit Cards: MasterCard, Switch, Visa
Specialities: Herbaceous perennials, alpines, hardy ferns & grasses. *Meconopsis*. National Collection of *Sanguisorba*.
Notes: Also sells wholesale. Delivers to shows. Wheelchair accessible.
OS Grid Ref: NT447703

GMcL **McLaren's Nurseries** ♿
Lochlibo Road, Uplawmoor, Barrhead, East Renfrewshire, G78 4DN
Ⓣ (01505) 850666
Ⓔ matt@mclarensnurseriesltd.co.uk
Ⓦ https://www.mclarensnurseriesltd.co.uk/
Contact: Matt McGowan
Opening Times: 0800-1630 Mon-Fri, 0900-1600 Sat & Sun.
Min Mail Order UK: Nmc
Credit Cards: All major credit/debit cards
Specialities: A family-run business that is one of the largest nurseries in the UK, with over 3200 popular & rarer plants.
Notes: Also sells wholesale. Wheelchair accessible.
OS Grid Ref: NS422542

GPer **Perthshire Heathers**
Starr Farm, Cupar, Fife, KY15 4NP
Ⓜ 07734 175937
Ⓔ irene@perthshireheathers.com
Ⓦ www.perthshireheathers.com
Contact: Irene Lang
Opening Times: By appt. only.
Min Mail Order UK: Nmc
Specialities: Heathers.
Notes: Mail order for large or small orders.

GPoy **Poyntzfield Herb Nursery** ♿
Nr Balblair, Black Isle, Dingwall, Ross-shire, IV7 8LX
Ⓣ (01381) 610352. Phone 1200-1300 or 1800-1900 Mon-Fri 1200-1300 Sat
Ⓔ info@poyntzfieldherbs.co.uk
Ⓦ www.poyntzfieldherbs.co.uk
Contact: Duncan Ross
Opening Times: 1300-1700 Mon-Sat 1st Apr-30th Sep, 1300-1700 Sun May-Aug.
Min Mail Order UK: £10.00 + p&p
Min Mail Order EU: £20.00 + p&p
Cat. Cost: 4 × 1st class.
Credit Cards: All major credit/debit cards
Specialities: Over 400 popular, unusual & rare herbs esp. medicinal. Also seeds.
Notes: Mail order operates in the spring & autumn. Exports beyond the EU. Wheelchair accessible.
OS Grid Ref: NH711642

GPSL **Plants, Shoots and Leaves**
Dovecot Bungalow, Haddington, East Lothian, EH41 4HA

Ⓣ (01620) 823536
Ⓜ 07885 444241
Ⓔ karen.leys@btinternet.com
Ⓦ www.plantsshootsandleaves.co.uk
Contact: Karen Leys
Opening Times: 1000-1700 1st Apr-1st Oct Closed Mon. Please phone first as nursery may be closed when we are attending shows.
Min Mail Order UK: £3.50
Min Mail Order EU: £6.60
Cat. Cost: Online only.
Credit Cards: All major credit/debit cards
Specialities: *Epimedium,* hardy geraniums. perennials and some shrubs. Some available in small quantities only.
Notes: Delivers to shows. Euro accepted. Partial wheelchair access.
OS Grid Ref: NT500730

GQue **Quercus Garden Plants Ltd**
Whitmuir Farm, Lamancha, West Linton, Scottish Borders, EH46 7BB
Ⓣ (01968) 660708
Ⓔ quercusgardenplants@gmail.com
Ⓦ www.quercusgardenplants.co.uk
Contact: Rona Dodds
Opening Times: 1000-1700 Wed-Sun.
Cat. Cost: Online only.
Credit Cards: All major credit/debit cards
Specialities: Tough plants for Scottish gardens. Wide range of plants, including old favourites and many unusual varieties of herbaceous perennials, grasses, trees, shrubs & plants for shade, wet ground and other challenging garden area suited to growing in exposed gardens.
Notes: Our plants are grown at 850ft above sea level, making them tough and well acclimatised to Scottish growing conditions. Virtually all plants propagated on site. Display gardens show customers what can be grown in these challenging conditions.
OS Grid Ref: NT192512

GRum **Rumbling Bridge Nursery**
Briglands Estate, Rumbling Bridge, Kinross, Perth and Kinross, KY13 0PS
Ⓣ (01577) 840160
Ⓔ hello@rumblingbridgenursery.co.uk
Ⓦ www.rumblingbridgenursery.co.uk
Contact: Graeme Butler
Opening Times: By appt. only, all year. Phone before visiting.
Min Mail Order UK: Nmc
Cat. Cost: Online only.
Credit Cards: None
Specialities: Alpines, woodland plants, dwarf shrubs, dwarf ericaceous, *Cyclamen, Primula auricula* cultivars.
Notes: All plants grown in peat-free compost, except ericaceous shrubs. UK (only) Mail order all year. Delivers to shows. Partial wheelchair access to sales area.
OS Grid Ref: NT025479

N. Ireland & Republic

IArd **Ardcarne Garden Centre** ♿
Ardcarne, Boyle, Co. Roscommon, F52 RY61 Ireland
Ⓣ +353 (7196) 67091
Ⓕ +353 (7196) 67341
Ⓔ info@ardcarne.ie
Ⓦ www.ardcarne.ie
Contact: James Wickham, Mary Frances Dwyer, Kirsty Ainge
Opening Times: 0900-1800 Mon-Sat, 1200-1800 Sun & B/hols.
Credit Cards: Access, Visa, American Express
Specialities: Native & unusual trees, choice perennials, roses, plants for coastal areas, fruit trees, incl. heritage Irish apple trees, vegetable plants, specimen plants & semi-mature trees. Wide general range.
Notes: Café. Groups & tours welcome. Ample free parking. Garden design & landscape service available. Euro accepted. Wheelchair accessible.

IBal **Bali-Hai Mail Order Nursery**
42 Largy Road, Carnlough, Ballymena, Co. Antrim, N. Ireland, BT44 0EZ
Ⓣ (028) 2888 5289
Ⓜ 07708 257164
Ⓔ balihainursery@btinternet.com
Ⓦ www.mailorderplants4me.com
Contact: Mrs M. E. Scroggy
Opening Times: Mon-Sat by appt. only.
Min Mail Order UK: Nmc
Min Mail Order EU: Nmc
Cat. Cost: Online only.
Credit Cards: All major credit/debit cards
Specialities: National Plant Collection of *Hosta* and *Agapanthus,* part planted in 1.5 acres, open to the public by appt. *Crocosmia, Rhodohypoxis,* tree ferns & other perennials. Hostas grown to order.
Notes: Also sells wholesale. Export beyond EU restricted to bare-root perennials, no grasses. Euro accepted.

IDee **Deelish Garden Centre**
Deelish, Skibbereen, Co. Cork, P81FD34 Ireland
Ⓣ +353 (28) 21374
Ⓕ +353 (28) 21374

Ⓔ sales@deelish.ie
Ⓦ www.deelish.ie
Contact: Bill & Rain & Noah Chase
Opening Times: 1000-1800 Mon-Sat, 1400-1800 Sun.
Min Mail Order UK: Nmc
Min Mail Order EU: Nmc
Credit Cards: Visa, MasterCard, Access, Paypal
Specialities: Unusual plants for the mild coastal climate of Ireland. Conservatory plants. Sole Irish agents for Chase Organic Seeds.
Notes: No mail order outside Ireland & UK. Euro accepted.

IDic **COLIN DICKSON T/A DICKSON NURSERIES**
50 Milecross Road, Newtownards, Co. Down, N. Ireland, BT23 4SR
Ⓜ 07821 922204
Ⓔ mail@dickson-roses.co.uk
Ⓦ www.dickson-roses.co.uk
Contact: Colin Dickson
Opening Times: 0800-1430 Mon-Thu. 0800-1230 Fri. Closed w/ends.
Min Mail Order UK: Nmc
Min Mail Order EU: £25.00 + p&p
Cat. Cost: Free.
Credit Cards: None
Specialities: Roses esp. modern Dickson varieties. Limited selection, check website or contact nursery. Most varieties available in small quantities only.
Notes: Also sells wholesale.

IKel **KELLS BAY HOUSE AND GARDENS**
Kells, Cahersiveen, Kerry, V23 EP48 Ireland
Ⓣ +353 (66) 947 7975
Ⓜ +353 (87) 7776666
Ⓔ billy@kellsbay.ie
Ⓦ www.kellsbay.ie
Contact: Billy Alexander
Opening Times: Gardens are open all year from 0900 to dusk. Nursery is open daily, but we advise you to contact us in advance of a visit as we are not always there.
Cat. Cost: By email free of charge.
Credit Cards: All major credit/debit cards
Specialities: We specialise in Southern Hemisphere ferns, especially the genera *Blechnum*, *Cyathea*, *Dicksonia*, *Doodia* and *Lophosoria*.
Notes: The Kells Bay Gardens Plant Centre is an enthusiast-owned nursery that specialises in the import of Tree Ferns and other rare and unusual exotics from around the world. Delivers to shows.

ILea **LEAMORE NURSERY**
Cronroe, Ashford, Co. Wicklow, A67 Y681 Ireland
Ⓣ +353 (87) 227 8850
Ⓔ info@leamorenursery.com
Ⓦ www.leamorenursery.com
Contact: Phil Havercroft
Opening Times: Not open.
Min Mail Order UK: €25
Min Mail Order EU: €25
Cat. Cost: Online only.
Credit Cards: All major credit/debit cards
Specialities: *Paeonia* & other perennials. Most items in large quantities. Itoh peonies & some more unusual items only available in small quantities.
Notes: Bare-root peonies supplied in autumn, available to order from Jul (on website). Founding members of the Irish Specialist Nursery Association (ISNA). Also sells wholesale. Delivers to shows. Sterling & Euro accepted.
OS Grid Ref: SG235945

IPap **PAPERVALE TREES**
48 Old Newry Road, Rathfriland, Newry, County Down, BT34 5BQ
Ⓣ (02830) 850059
Ⓜ 07753 117837
Ⓔ info@papervaletrees.com
Ⓦ www.papervaletrees.com
Contact: Jonathan Jackson
Opening Times: Mon-Fri by appt. only, 0800-1800 Sat.
Min Mail Order UK: Nmc
Min Mail Order EU: Nmc
Cat. Cost: Available online.
Credit Cards: All major credit/debit cards
Specialities: Almost 300 varieties of home-grown containerised trees grown in peat-free compost.
Notes: Based at the foothills of the Mourne mountains, Papervale Trees produces almost 300 species and cultivars of 'Home Grown' trees. Our range includes many hard to find varieties as well as traditional garden favourites, all grown in peat-free compost. Also sells wholesale. Delivers to shows.
OS Grid Ref: SB231884

IPot **THE POTTING SHED**
Bolinaspick, Camolin, Enniscorthy, Co. Wexford, Y21 TD93 Ireland
Ⓣ +353 86 6045715
Ⓔ susan@camolinpottingshed.com
Ⓦ www.camolinpottingshed.com
Contact: Susan Carrick
Opening Times: 1300-1700 Thu-Fri 29th Mar-

6th Sep, other times by prior arrangement.
Min Mail Order UK: Nmc
Min Mail Order EU: Nmc
Cat. Cost: 3 × 1st class.
Credit Cards: MasterCard, Visa, American Express
Specialities: Grow a wide range of unusual, hard to find & new introductions of herbaceous perennials, ornamental grasses *Clematis* and *Wisteria*.
Notes: Member of the Irish Specialist Nursery Assoc. (ISNA). Orders outside Ireland can only be delivered by courier, charges at cost. Delivers to shows. Euro accepted.

L

IRos **Ros Ban Wildlife Garden** ♿
Common, Raphoe, Co. Donegal, F93 HH0X Ireland
Ⓣ +353 (74) 91 45336
Ⓜ +353 (8608) 05214
Ⓔ Rosbangarden@gmail.com
Contact: Ann Kavanagh
Opening Times: Garden open, morning to evening, Easter to Sep.
Credit Cards: None
Notes: Plants available in season from the garden. Please check plant availability with nursery before travelling. Euro accepted. Wheelchair accessible.

ISha **Shady Plants** ♿
Coolbooa, Clashmore, Waterford, P36EY19 Ireland
Ⓣ +353 (24) 86998
Ⓜ +353 8605 42171
Ⓔ mike@shadyplants.ie
Ⓦ www.shadyplants.net
Contact: Mike Keep
Opening Times: Not open, mail order only.
Min Mail Order UK: Nmc
Min Mail Order EU: Nmc
Cat. Cost: Online only.
Credit Cards: MasterCard, Paypal, Visa
Specialities: Ferns, *Arisaema*, trilliums & erythroniums.
Notes: We specialise in hardy ground ferns and also have a wide range of other shade-loving plants such as aroids, trilliums, erythroniums and others. We do not use chemical pesticides or herbicides in our production, preferring organic methods such as nematodes & predator attraction. Delivers to shows. Euro accepted. Wheelchair accessible.

ITim **Timpany Nurseries & Gardens** ♿
77 Magheratimpany Road, Ballynahinch, Co. Down, N. Ireland, BT24 8PA
Ⓣ (028) 9756 2812
Ⓜ 07711 428477
Ⓔ s.tindall@btconnect.com
Ⓦ www.timpanynurseries.com
Contact: Susan Tindall
Opening Times: 1000-1730 Tue-Sat, Sun by appt.
Min Mail Order UK: £40.00 + p&p
Min Mail Order EU: £40.00 + p&p
Cat. Cost: £3.50
Credit Cards: All major debit/credit cards except American Express
Specialities: *Androsace, Cassiope, Celmisia, Cyclamen, Dianthus, Galanthus, Meconopsis, Hosta, Primula, Primula auricula, Rhodohypoxis* & *Saxifraga*.
Notes: Delivers to shows. Wheelchair accessible.

London Area

LAlb **Alban Hill Nurseries** ♿
High Street, Sherington, Buckinghamshire, MK16 9QP
Ⓣ (01234) 711513
Ⓔ steve@albanhillnurseries.co.uk
Ⓦ https://albanhillnurseries.co.uk
Contact: Steve Illsley
Opening Times: 0900-1700 Mon-Sat, 1030-1630 Sun.
Credit Cards: All major credit/debit cards
Notes: Wheelchair accessible.
OS Grid Ref: SP888394

LAma **Jacques Amand International Ltd** ♿
The Nurseries, 145 Clamp Hill, Stanmore, Middlesex, HA7 3JS
Ⓣ (0208) 4207110
Ⓕ (0208) 9546784
Ⓔ bulbs@jacquesamand.co.uk
Ⓦ www.jacquesamandintl.com
Contact: Stuart Chapman
Opening Times: 0900-1700 Mon-Fri, 1000-1600 Sat.
Min Mail Order UK: Nmc
Min Mail Order EU: Nmc
Cat. Cost: 1 × 1st class.
Credit Cards: All major credit/debit cards
Specialities: Rare and unusual species bulbs esp. *Arisaema, Trillium, Fritillaria*, tulips.
Notes: Also sells wholesale. Exports beyond EU. Delivers to shows. Euro accepted. Wheelchair accessible.
OS Grid Ref: TQ154919

LAyl **Aylett Nurseries Ltd** ♿
North Orbital Road, St Albans, Hertfordshire, AL2 1DH
Ⓣ (01727) 822255

Ⓕ (01727) 823024
Ⓔ info@aylettnurseries.co.uk
Ⓦ www.aylettnurseries.co.uk
Contact: Julie Aylett
Opening Times: 0830-1730 Mon-Fri, 0830-1700 Sat, 1030-1630 Sun.
Cat. Cost: Free.
Credit Cards: All major credit/debit cards
Specialities: *Dahlia*. 2-acre trial ground and garden adjacent to garden centre.
Notes: Wheelchair accessible.
OS Grid Ref: TL169049

LBar **Barnes Nurseries**
46 Woodmansterne Lane, Wallington, Surrey, SM6 0SW
Ⓣ (0208) 6478213
Ⓔ barnes_nurseries@hotmail.com
Ⓦ www.barnesnurseries.co.uk
Contact: Jan Phillips
Credit Cards: All major credit/debit cards
Specialities: Perennials.
Notes: Perennial garden nursery.

LBee **Beechcroft Nursery** ♿
127 Reigate Road, Ewell, Surrey, KT17 3DE
Ⓣ (0208) 3934265
Ⓕ (0208) 3934265
Contact: C. Kimber
Opening Times: 1000-1600 Mon-Sat, 1000-1400 Sun & B/hols. Closed Xmas-New Year week.
Cat. Cost: None issued.
Credit Cards: All major credit/debit cards
Specialities: Conifers.
Notes: Wheelchair accessible.

LBom **Boma Garden Centre** ♿
Corner of Islip and Peckwater Streets, Kentish Town, London, NW5 2DL
Ⓣ (0207) 2844999
Ⓔ boma@bomagardencentre.co.uk
Ⓦ https://www.bomagardencentre.co.uk
Contact: Kim Glanvill
Opening Times: 0900-1800 Mon-Sat 1100-1700 Sun Mar-Oct 0900-1700 Mon-Sat 1000-1600 Sun Nov-Feb.
Credit Cards: All major debit/credit cards except American Express
Notes: Wide range of indoor and outdoor plants suitable for London homes, gardens and terraces. Wheelchair accessible.

LBuc **Buckingham Nurseries** ♿
14 Tingewick Road, Buckingham, Buckinghamshire, MK18 4AE
Ⓣ (01280) 822133
Ⓕ (01280) 815491
Ⓔ web-enquiries@hedging.co.uk
Ⓦ www.buckingham-nurseries.co.uk
Contact: R. J. & P. L. Brown
Opening Times: 0830-1730 (1800 in summer) Mon-Sat, 1000-1600 Sun.
Min Mail Order UK: Nmc
Min Mail Order EU: Nmc
Cat. Cost: Free.
Credit Cards: Visa, MasterCard, Maestro
Specialities: Bare-rooted and container grown hedging. Fruit trees, soft fruit, trees, shrubs, herbaceous perennials, alpines, grasses & ferns.
Notes: Garden centre with a large range of container grown plants, many unusual. Well stocked shop and restaurant. Wheelchair accessible.
OS Grid Ref: SP676333

LCro **Crocus.co.uk**
Nursery Court, London Road, Windlesham, Surrey, GU20 6LQ
Ⓣ (01344) 578000
Ⓔ customerservices@crocus.co.uk
Ⓦ www.crocus.co.uk
Contact: Customer Care Team
Opening Times: Online & Mail order only. Order lines open 24hrs, 7 days.
Min Mail Order UK: Nmc + delivery charges
Cat. Cost: Free.
Credit Cards: All major debit/credit cards except American Express
Specialities: Large nursery selling perennials, shrubs, climbers, roses, bulbs, ferns, grasses, herbs & house plants.
Notes: Online and mail order nursery. Two open days a year (see website for details). Also sells wholesale.

LDai **Daisy Roots**
(Office) 8 Gosselin Road, Bengeo, Hertford, Hertfordshire, SG14 3LG
Ⓜ 07958 563355
Ⓔ anne@daisyroots.com
Ⓦ www.daisyroots.com
Contact: Annie Godfrey
Opening Times: 1000-1600 Fri & Sat Mar-Oct, or by appt.
Min Mail Order UK: £15.00
Cat. Cost: Online only.
Credit Cards: All major credit/debit cards
Specialities: Ever-increasing range of choice & unusual perennials, particularly *Agastache, Anthemis, Centaurea, Digitalis, Erysimum, Salvia* & *Sedum.* Some plants available in small quantities only.

Notes: Nursery is at Jenningsbury, London Road, Hertford Heath, SG13 7NS. Delivers to shows.

LEdu **Edulis** ♿
(office) 1 Flowers Piece, Ashampstead, Reading, Berkshire, RG8 8SG
Ⓣ (01635) 578113
Ⓜ 07802 812781
Ⓔ edulisnursery@gmail.com
Ⓦ www.edulis.co.uk
Contact: Paul Barney
Opening Times: 1000-1600 Tue & Wed, & by appt. Apr-Oct Nov-Mar by appt. only. See website or contact nursery for open days.
Min Mail Order UK: £20.00 + p&p
Min Mail Order EU: £30.00 + p&p
Cat. Cost: Online only.
Credit Cards: All major debit/credit cards except American Express
Specialities: Unusual edibles, ferns, shade lovers, permaculture plants & many of our own collections.
Notes: Nursery is at The Walled Garden, Tidmarsh Lane, Pangbourne, RG8 8HT. Also sells wholesale. Delivers to shows. Euro accepted. Wheelchair accessible.
OS Grid Ref: SU615747

LFlit **Flittons Nursery** ♿
51 Woodmansterne Lane, Wallington, Surrey, SM6 0SW
Ⓣ (0208) 6693053
Ⓔ flittonsnursery@btinternet.com
Ⓦ http://www.flittonsnursery.co.uk/
Contact: Diana Flower
Opening Times: 0900-1700 Mon-Sat, 0900-1630 Sun (summer). 0900-1600 Mon-Sat, closed Mon (winter).
Credit Cards: All major credit/debit cards
Specialities: Bedding plants – particularly for baskets and pots, shrubs.
Notes: Growers of herbaceous perennials, bedding plants, vegetable plants and hanging baskets. Wheelchair accessible.

LHGe **The Hardy Geranium Nursery**
Ⓔ info@hardygeraniumnursery.co.uk
Ⓦ https://hardygeraniumnursery.co.uk/
Contact: Suzie Dewey
Opening Times: Not open, mail order only via website 24/7.
Credit Cards: All major credit/debit cards
Specialities: Specialise in hardy geraniums, holding over 100 different cultivars in stock at the height of the growing season.
Notes: This nursery is not open to the public. Sales are strictly via the website, online only. Website open 24/7. The nursery is closed throughout the winter months.

LHkn **R Harkness & Co. Ltd.**
The Rose Gardens, Cambridge Road, Hitchin, Herts, SG4 0JT
Ⓣ (01462) 420402
Ⓔ harkness@roses.co.uk
Ⓦ www.roses.co.uk
Contact: Philip Harkness
Opening Times: 0900-1700 Mon-Fri (Office).1000-1600 daily during spring/summer Mon-Fri only during winter (Rose Shop).
Min Mail Order UK: £2.95
Min Mail Order EU: Nmc
Cat. Cost: Free.
Credit Cards: American Express, Visa, Access, Switch, Delta
Specialities: Roses.
Notes: Also sells wholesale. Delivers to shows.

LHom **Home Farm Plants**
Home Farm, Shantock Lane, Bovingdon, Hertfordshire, HP3 0NG
Ⓜ 07773 798068
Ⓔ homefarmplants@gmail.com
Ⓦ www.homefarmplants.co.uk
Contact: Graham Austin
Opening Times: 0900-1730 Fri & Sat, 1000-1600 Sun, viewing by appt. only Mon-Thu, 1st Apr-end Oct (subject to weather conditions).
Cat. Cost: 1st class sae for list.
Credit Cards: All major debit/credit cards except American Express
Specialities: Delphinium elatum (over 60 varieties). Hardy perennials. Show area of 200+ delphiniums (contact nursery for flowering times). Some varieties only available in small quantities.
Notes: If travelling, please contact nursery to confirm plant availability. Delivers to shows. Partial wheelchair access.

LHWs **H W Hyde and Son**
Hilltop Farm, Rusper Road, Rusper, West Sussex, RH12 4QS
Ⓣ (0118) 9340011
Ⓜ 07557 530845
Ⓔ info@hwhyde.co.uk
Ⓦ www.hwhyde.co.uk
Contact: Richard
Opening Times: Open by appt.
Min Mail Order UK: £3.75
Min Mail Order EU: £15.00
Credit Cards: All major credit/debit cards
Specialities: Bulbous plants including lilies,

Narcissus, Tulipa, Zantedeschia, Dahlia, Alstroemeria, Camassia.
Notes: Family run business started in 1926 by Herbert William Hyde, currently run by his 3 Grandchildren, Sarah, Richard and Elizabeth. Exports to EU. Also sells wholesale. Delivers to shows.

LIns **INSTANT LANDSCAPES T/A INSTANT HEDGES** ♿
Red Oak Farm, Hulcott Lane, Hulcott, Aylesbury, Buckinghamshire, HP22 5AX
Ⓣ (01296) 399585
Ⓔ sales@instanthedges.co.uk
Ⓦ https://www.instanthedges.co.uk/
Contact: Nick Angel
Opening Times: 0830-1730 Mon-Fri, 0830-1500 Sat by appt. only.
Min Mail Order UK: Nmc
Min Mail Order EU: Nmc
Cat. Cost: Free.
Credit Cards: All major credit/debit cards
Specialities: Instant Landscapes Ltd is a British nursery specialising in the growth and supply of semi-mature and mature trees, shrubs and instant hedging.
Notes: From our Buckinghamshire nursery we are conveniently located to service the whole of the UK, with over 15 miles of instant hedging troughs ready to go and more than 3000 pleached and shaped trees from box heads to multi-stem umbrellas and topiary. We welcome visitors to our nursery on an appt. only basis. Please call on (01296) 399585. Euro accepted. Delivers to shows. Wheelchair accessible.
OS Grid Ref: SP847411

LLWG **LILIES WATER GARDENS** ♿
Broad Lane, Newdigate, Surrey, RH5 5AT
Ⓣ (01306) 631064
Ⓜ 07801 166244
Ⓔ mail@lilieswatergardens.co.uk
Ⓦ www.lilieswatergardens.co.uk
Contact: Simon Harman
Opening Times: 0900-1700 Tue-Sat, Mar-Aug. By appt. only Sep-Feb.
Min Mail Order UK: Nmc
Min Mail Order EU: Nmc
Cat. Cost: Online only.
Credit Cards: All major credit/debit cards
Specialities: A range of water lilies, moist perennials, bog-garden, pond, marginal & oxygenating plants for all types of water features. Alpine plants, rushes and grasses.
Notes: UK and EU postage and packing prices calculated on weight, starts at £5.00. Wheelchair accessible.

LMaj **MAJESTIC TREES**
Chequers Meadow, Chequers Hill (Junc 9, M1), Flamstead, St Albans, Hertfordshire, AL3 8ET
Ⓣ (01582) 843881
Ⓔ info@majestictrees.co.uk
Ⓦ www.majestictrees.co.uk
Contact: Andy Miles
Opening Times: 0830-1700 Mon-Fri. 1000-1600 Sat, Nov-Feb, 1000-1700 Sat, Mar-Oct Closed Sun, B/hols, Xmas through New Year.
Credit Cards: MasterCard, Visa, Switch, Maestro
Specialities: Semi-mature & mature containerised trees primarily grown in AirPots from 50ltr to 5000ltr.
Notes: Also sells wholesale. Supplies for private & public planting needs, inlcuding flower shows. Comprehensive delivery & planting services available. All stock using the planting service carries a one year estabishment warranty (subject to conditions). Delivers to shows. Euro accepted. Disabled access by golf buggy can be arranged by appt. Partial wheelchair access to building.
OS Grid Ref: TL081408

LMil **MILLAIS NURSERIES** ♿
Crosswater Farm, Crosswater Lane, Churt, Farnham, Surrey, GU10 2JN
Ⓣ (01252) 792698
Ⓔ sales@rhododendrons.co.uk
Ⓦ www.rhododendrons.co.uk
Contact: David Millais
Opening Times: 1000-1700 Mon-Fri all year. Please phone or see website for additional weekend opening in spring.
Min Mail Order UK: Nmc
Min Mail Order EU: Nmc
Cat. Cost: Free list on request. Full cat online.
Credit Cards: All major credit/debit cards
Specialities: Rhododendrons, azaleas, magnolias, camellias & acers. Garden open in spring.
Notes: Mail order all year. Also sells wholesale. Wheelchair accessible.
OS Grid Ref: SU856397

LOPS **RHS PLANT SHOP: RHSPLANTS.CO.UK** ◆
Nursery Court, London Road, Windlesham, Surrey, GU20 6LQ
Ⓣ (01344) 578822
Ⓔ customerservices@rhsplants.co.uk
Ⓦ www.rhsplants.co.uk
Contact: Customer Care Team
Opening Times: Not open. Mail order online only.
Min Mail Order UK: Nmc

Credit Cards: All major debit/credit cards except American Express
Notes: Large range of plants, including a substantial range of RHS AGM plants.

LPal **The Palm Centre** ♿
Ham Central Nursery, Ham, Richmond, Surrey, TW10 7HA
Ⓣ (0208) 2556191
Ⓕ (0208) 2556192
Ⓔ sales@palmcentre.co.uk
Ⓦ www.palmcentre.co.uk
Contact: Robert Tudor
Opening Times: 0900-1700 (or dusk in winter) Mon-Sat, 1000-1600 Sun.
Min Mail Order EU: £300.00 + p&p
Cat. Cost: No printed catalogue available.
Credit Cards: All major debit/credit cards except American Express
Specialities: Palms, ferns, bamboos, indoor plants. National Collection of *Trachycarpus*.
Notes: Retail and trade nursery specialised in palm trees, mediterranean and exotic hardy plants. Also sells wholesale. Delivers to shows. Euro accepted. Wheelchair accessible.

LPar **Paramount Plants & Gardens Ltd**
131 Theobalds Park Road, Crews Hill, Enfield, London, EN2 9BH
Ⓣ (0208) 3678809
Ⓜ 07802 952517
Ⓔ info@paramountplants.co.uk
Ⓦ https://www.paramountplants.co.uk/
Contact: Paula Sheehan
Opening Times: On-line store open 24/7.
Min Mail Order UK: Nmc
Min Mail Order EU: Nmc
Credit Cards: All major credit/debit cards
Specialities: Whilst we stock a good cross section of all plants in a wide range of sizes, our specialist areas are mature hedging, mature trees including Japanese acers and conifers, topiary including unique cloud trees, mediteranean plants such as olive trees and hardy tropical plants such as Chusan palms.
Notes: Established over 25 years ago, Paramount Plants & Gardens is a family-run online retailer of mature trees, plants and hedging, with well over 1,000 plants in our ever-growing collection. Based in Crews Hill, North London, we deliver our plants, no matter the size, throughout the entire UK. Delivers to shows.

LPfP **Plants for Ponds Ltd**
Ⓣ (01992) 661165
Ⓜ 07465 222676
Ⓔ info@plantsforponds.co.uk
Ⓦ www.plantsforponds.co.uk
Contact: Lucy Bostock
Opening Times: 0900-1700 Mon-Fri for telephone enquiries.
Credit Cards: Visa, MasterCard, Paypal, American Express
Specialities: Waterlilies, marginal plants, oxygenating plants, floating plants, deep water plants, moisture lovers, bog plants and aquatic plants.
Notes: Plants for Ponds provides cold water grown aquatic plants straight to your door. We specialise solely in plants perfect for UK ponds and lakes. Always happy to help and offer advice on the phone or via email.

LPla **The Plant Specialist** ♿
7 Whitefield Lane, Great Missenden, Buckinghamshire, HP16 0BH
Ⓣ (01494) 866650
Ⓔ enquire@theplantspecialist.co.uk
Ⓦ www.theplantspecialist.co.uk
Contact: Sean Walter
Opening Times: 1000-1700 Wed-Sat, 1000-1600 Sun, Apr-Oct 1000-1600 B/hol Mon.
Cat. Cost: None issued.
Credit Cards: All major credit/debit cards
Specialities: Herbaceous perennials, grasses, half-hardy perennials, bulbs.
Notes: Delivers to shows. Wheelchair accessible.

LPmr **Primrose Hall Peonies**
Toddington Road, Westoning, Bedford, Bedfordshire, MK45 5AH
Ⓣ (01525) 878924
Ⓕ (01525) 878924
Ⓔ customerservice@primrosehall.co.uk
Ⓦ www.primrosehallpeonies.co.uk
Contact: Tracy Gibbon
Opening Times: 0930-1600 Mon-Fri. Please note we are often in the nursery and cannot answer the phone, an email will usually be more reliable.
Min Mail Order UK: Nmc
Min Mail Order EU: Nmc
Credit Cards: All major credit/debit cards
Specialities: National Plant Collection Holder *Itoh* hybrids.
Notes: Also sells wholesale. Delivers to shows. Euro accepted.

LRHS **Wisley Plant Centre (RHS)** ♿ ◆
RHS Garden, Wisley, Woking, Surrey, GU23 6QB
Ⓣ (01483) 211113
Ⓔ wisleyplantcentre@RHS.org.uk
Ⓦ www.rhs.org.uk/wisleyplantcentre

Contact: Wisley Plant Centre
Opening Times: 0900-1700 Mon-Sat, Oct-Feb. 0900-1800 Mon-Sat, Mar-Sep. 1100-1700 Sun all year, browsing from 1030.
Credit Cards: All major credit/debit cards
Specialities: Over 10,000 plants, many rare or unusual available in our stunning new Plant Centre, reflecting the plantings in the RHS flagship garden at Wisley. Also houseplants, bedding plants, bulbs & seed potatoes, plus a range of garden sundries and gifts.
Notes: Plants subject to seasonal availability. A further range of plants is available online via www.rhsplants.co.uk. Wheelchair accessible.

LSem **SEMPERVIRENS** ♿
Bridge farm Nursery, Hospital Bridge Road, Whitton, Middlesex, TW2 6LH
Ⓣ (0208) 8987131
Ⓔ office@sempervirens.co.uk
Ⓦ www.sempervirens.co.uk
Contact: Denise Westmarland
Opening Times: 0730-1700 Mon-Fri, 0900-1600 Sat, Mar to end of Nov. 1000-1600 Sun, Mar to end of Sep.
Min Mail Order UK: £100.00
Credit Cards: Visa, MasterCard
Specialities: Wide range of shrubs, trees, climbers, perennials, hedgeing & specimen plants.
Notes: Also sells wholesale. Wheelchair accessible.

LShi **SHIRE PLANTS**
The Paddock, Buckingham Road, Gawcott, Buckinghamshire, MK18 1TN
Ⓣ (01280) 817800
Ⓔ enquiries@shireplants.co.uk
Ⓦ https://shireplants.co.uk
Contact: Matt Killick
Opening Times: Please see website for opening times. Collection of orders welcome by arrangement.
Cat. Cost: Online only.
Credit Cards: All major credit/debit cards
Specialities: Unusual, heritage and rare plants. Specialities include old fashioned Pinks (*Dianthus*), perennial tufted violas, sweet violets, perennial wallflowers (*Erysimum*) and hardy *Chrysanthemum*.
Notes: Traditional plant nursery offering an expanding range of plants, many of which are not widely available. A mix of heritage varieties, new discoveries and familiar favourites. Everything sold is grown on site and we are happy to offer advice about the plants we grow and sell.
OS Grid Ref: SP685322

LSou **SOUTHON PLANTS** ♿
Mutton Hill, Dormansland, Lingfield, Surrey, RH7 6NP
Ⓣ (01342) 870150
Ⓔ lyn@southon-plants.co.uk
Ⓦ www.southon-plants.co.uk
Contact: Lyn Southon
Opening Times: See website or telephone for up-to-date opening hours.
Cat. Cost: Online only.
Credit Cards: All major credit/debit cards
Specialities: New & unusual hardy & tender perennials, specialising in *Agapanthus* (over 30 varieties), & *Heuchera* (over 30 varieties). Many new varieties for tender perennials/patio plants.
Notes: Wheelchair accessible.

LSRN **SPRING REACH NURSERY** ♿
Long Reach, Ockham, Guildford, Surrey, GU23 6PG
Ⓣ (01483) 284769
Ⓜ 07884 432666
Ⓕ (01483) 284769
Ⓔ info@springreachnursery.co.uk
Ⓦ www.springreachnursery.co.uk
Contact: Nick Hourhan
Opening Times: Open 7 days 1000-1700 Mon-Sat, 1030-1630 Sun. Open B/hols. Closed 23rd Dec-2nd Jan.
Min Mail Order UK: Nmc
Min Mail Order EU: Nmc
Credit Cards: All major credit/debit cards
Specialities: Shrubs, evergreen climbers, *Clematis*, perennials, roses, grasses, ferns, bamboos, trees, hedging, soft fruit & top fruit. Plants for chalk & clay. Deer & rabbit proof plants. Specimen & acid-loving plants.
Notes: Please ring for mail order details. Also sells wholesale. Delivers to shows. Wheelchair accessible.

LSta **STAFFORD LAKE NURSERY**
Knaphill, Woking, Surrey, GU21 2SJ
Ⓣ (01483) 289066
Ⓜ 07738 241871
Ⓔ enquiries@staffordlake.co.uk
Ⓦ www.staffordlake.co.uk
Contact: Mark Roberts
Opening Times: Open by appt. only.
Min Mail Order UK: Nmc
Specialities: Growers of hostas, dwarf conifers & hedging. Propagates as many own plants as possible. Currently selling only English hostas either out of divisions or from an English tissue culture programme.
Notes: Also sells wholesale. Attends various shows (check with nursery for details).

L

LSto **STOTTS NURSERY** ♿
Ibstone Road, Stokenchurch, High Wycombe, Buckinghamshire, HP14 3XS
Ⓜ 07542 718307
Ⓔ billystott@stottsnursery.co.uk
Ⓦ www.stottsnursery.co.uk
Contact: Billy Stott
Opening Times: 1000-1700 Tue-Sat British summertime. 1000-1600 Tue-Sat winter – Greenwich Mean Time. Check website.
Credit Cards: All major credit/debit cards
Specialities: Hardy plants.
Notes: Hardy plant specialists. Peat free and UK grown. We offer a wide range of common and unusual hardy annuals, perennials, shrubs, climbers and a wide range of hedging plants, pot grown and bare rooted. Wheelchair accessible.
OS Grid Ref: SU752379

LSun **SUNNYSIDE NURSERY**
Upper Allotments, New Road, Northchurch, Hertfordshire, HP4 1NJ
Ⓜ 07743 552154
Ⓔ philsmith2004@yahoo.co.uk
Contact: Philip Smith
Opening Times: 0900-1700 Mon-Fri summer. Closed Sat, Sun & B/hols. 1000-1600 Tue-Fri winter. 10 or more shows during the season. Please contact the nursery for details.
Cat. Cost: Availability list on request.
Credit Cards: All major credit/debit cards
Specialities: Hardy perennials, alpines & ornamental grasses. Some plants available in small quantities only.
Notes: Please phone for stock availability & updates. Trade discounts available with orders of £100 & free local deliveries.

LSvl **SAVILL GARDENS VISITOR CENTRE** ♿
Wick Lane, Englefield Green, Egham, Surrey, TW20 0UU
Ⓣ (01784) 485401
Ⓔ chloe.wragg@thecrownestate.co.uk
Ⓦ www.windsorgreatpark.co.uk
Contact: Chloe Wragg
Opening Times: 0930-1800 (summer), 0930-1630 (winter).
Credit Cards: All major debit/credit cards except American Express
Specialities: Plants available in small numbers only.
Notes: Wheelchair accessible.

LTop **TOPIARY ARTS**
(office) Vine Cottage, Newbury Road, Hermitage, Thatcham, Berkshire, RG18 9TB
Ⓣ (01635) 202878
Ⓜ 07775 602704
Ⓔ jcb@topiaryarts.com
Ⓦ www.topiaryarts.com
Contact: James Crebbin-Bailey
Opening Times: By appt. only.
Min Mail Order UK: £30
Cat. Cost: Free.
Credit Cards: Paypal
Specialities: Topiary. Many individual sculptural pieces.
Notes: Nursery is at Walled Garden, Copped Hall, Upshire, Epping, Essex CM16 5HS. Field stock area. English grown plants. Also sells wholesale. Delivers to shows. Additional nursery in Hermitage, Berkshire. Please contact office for appointment to view.

LWaG **WALWORTH GARDEN** ♿
206 Manor Place, London, SE17 3BN
Ⓣ (0207) 5822652
Ⓔ info@walworthgarden.org.uk
Ⓦ walworthgarden.org.uk
Contact: George Hudson
Opening Times: 0900-1700 Mon-Sun Mar-Oct, 0900-1600 Mon-Sun Nov-Feb.
Credit Cards: All major credit/debit cards
Notes: Located on the fringes of central London, we specialise in plants for the city garden, growing plants that thrive in dry and shady conditions, promote biodiversity, pollinators and give a luscious jungle feel. We also propagate houseplants for plant lovers without the outdoor space. Wheelchair accessible.

LWdG **WOODHAM NURSERY**
Eastbourne Road, South Godstone, Surrey, RH9 8JB
Ⓣ (01342) 892331
Ⓔ woodhamnursery@gmail.com
Ⓦ www.woodhamnursery.co.uk
Contact: Henry Powers
Opening Times: 0900-1700 Mon-Sun all year.
Specialities: All types of herbs, bedding plants, peonies, tree peonies and Christmas trees. Growers of scented roses.
Notes: Seasonal availability.

LWei **WEIRD PLANTS BY GILL**
59 Wintringham Way, Purley On Thames, Reading, Berkshire, RG8 8BH
Ⓜ 07478 930030
Ⓔ weirdplantsbygill@gmail.com
Ⓦ gillsweirdplants.co.uk/
Contact: Gill Passman
Specialities: *Tillandsia*.
Notes: Over 10 years experience growing and

selling airplants (*Tillandsia*). Also sells wholesale. Delivers to shows.

Midlands

MACG **Ashdale Cottage Garden Plants**
204 Lambley Lane, Gedling, Nottingham, Nottinghamshire, NG4 4PB
Ⓣ (0115) 8457864
Ⓔ info@ashdale-nursery.co.uk
Ⓦ www.ashdale-nursery.co.uk
Contact: Mick and Dani
Opening Times: 0900-1700 Mon-Sat, 1000-1600 Sun, Mar-Oct.
Cat. Cost: None issued.
Credit Cards: All major credit/debit cards
Specialities: Wide range of rare and unusual herbaceous perennials.
Notes: Hardy perennials & classic cottage garden plants. Delivers to shows.
OS Grid Ref: SK622443

MArl **Arley Hall Nursery** ♿
Estate Office, Arley Hall & Gardens, Northwich, Cheshire, CW9 6NA
Ⓣ (01565) 777479
Ⓔ arleyhallplantnursery@gmail.com
Ⓦ www.arleyhallandgardens.com
Contact: Rob Groom
Opening Times: 1000-1730 Mon-Sun 1st Mar-31st Oct.
Cat. Cost: 4 × 1st class.
Credit Cards: All major credit/debit cards
Specialities: Wide range of herbaceous incl. many unusual varieties, some in small quantities. Wide range of unusual pelargoniums.
Notes: Nursery is beside car park at Arley Hall Gardens. Wheelchair accessible.
OS Grid Ref: SJ673808

MAsh **Ashwood Nurseries Ltd** ♿
Ashwood Lower Lane, Ashwood, Kingswinford, West Midlands, DY6 0AE
Ⓣ (01384) 401996
Ⓕ (01384) 401108
Ⓔ info@ashwoodnurseries.com
Ⓦ www.ashwoodnurseries.com
Contact: Rachel Maiden & Steve Lampit
Opening Times: Winter 0830-1700 Mon-Sat, 0900-1700 Sun. Summer 0830-1730 Mon-Sat, 0900-1730 Sun.
Min Mail Order UK: Nmc
Min Mail Order EU: Nmc
Cat. Cost: 4 × 1st class.
Credit Cards: All major credit/debit cards
Specialities: Large range of hardy plants, shrubs & dwarf conifers. Roses, alpines & herbaceous plants. Also specialises in auriculas, *Cyclamen*, *Galanthus*, hellebores, *Hepatica*, *Hydrangea* & *Salvia*. National Plant Collection of *Lewisia*.
Notes: Tea room overlooking display garden. Ample parking. Regular events. Groups by appt. to visit private garden. Wheelchair accessible.
OS Grid Ref: SO865879

MAvo **Avondale Nursery** ♿
(office) 57, Pine Tree Close, Redditch, Worcestershire, B97 6NW
Ⓜ 07367 590620
Ⓔ enquiries@avondalenursery.co.uk
Ⓦ www.avondalenursery.co.uk
Contact: Gary Leaver
Opening Times: 1000-1600, 1400-1700 Mon-Fri, 1030-1630 Sat & Sun, Mar-Sep. Other times by appt.
Cat. Cost: 4 × 1st class.
Credit Cards: All major credit/debit cards
Specialities: Rare & unusual perennials esp. asters, *Eryngium*, *Geranium*, *Geum*, *Crocosmia*, *Sanguisorba* & grasses. National Plant Collections of *Symphyotrichum novae-angliae*, *Anemone nemorosa* & *Sanguisorba*.
Notes: Nursery is at Russell's Nursery, Mill Hill, Baginton, near Coventry CV8 3AG. Display garden open. Groups welcome. Wheelchair accessible.
OS Grid Ref: SP339751

MBel **Bluebell Cottage Nursery** ♿
Lodge Lane, Dutton, Cheshire, WA4 4HP
Ⓣ (01928) 713718
Ⓔ info@bluebellcottage.co.uk
Ⓦ www.bluebellcottage.co.uk
Contact: Sue Beesley
Opening Times: 1000-1700 Wed-Sun & B/hols, 1st Apr-end Sep. By appt. only outside these dates.
Min Mail Order UK: £4.95 (based on weight)
Cat. Cost: Online only.
Credit Cards: All major credit/debit cards
Specialities: *Achillea*, *Anthemis*, *Brunnera*, *Centaurea*, *Echinacea*, *Geranium*, *Geum*, *Lychnis*, *Persicaria*, *Potentilla*, *Sanguisorba*, *Thalictrum* & ornamental grasses. Some items stocked in small quantities.
Notes: Mail order available all year. Peat-free. No neonicotinoid pesticides used. Plants are fully established, ready to plant out in 9cm (3 pots). RHS Partner Garden open Apr-Sep. Refreshments available. Delivers to shows. Wheelchair accessible.
OS Grid Ref: SJ586779

M

MBlu **Bluebell Arboretum & Nursery** ♿
Annwell Lane, Smisby, Nr Ashby de la Zouch, Derbyshire, LE65 2TA
Ⓣ (01530) 413700
Ⓔ sales@bluebellnursery.com
Ⓦ www.bluebellnursery.com
Contact: Robert & Suzette Vernon
Opening Times: 0900-1700 Mon-Sat & 1030-1630 Sun, Mar-Oct 0900-1600 Mon-Sat (not Sun) Nov-Feb. Closed 24th Dec-1st Jan incl. & Easter Sun.
Min Mail Order UK: £8.95
Min Mail Order EU: Nmc
Cat. Cost: £1.50 + 3 × 1st class.
Credit Cards: Visa, Access, Switch, MasterCard
Specialities: Specialists in rare & unusual plants. Uncommon trees & shrubs. Rare *Acer, Betula, Cornus, Fagus, Magnolia, Liquidambar, Quercus* & *Tilia*. Woody climbers.
Notes: 9-acre woodland garden & arboretum surrounds nursery. RHS partner garden. Guide dogs only. We are a working nursery, so please wear appropriate clothing & sturdy footwear if visiting. Delivers to shows. Wheelchair accessible but please call first if weather wet.
OS Grid Ref: SK344187

MBNS **Barnsdale Gardens** ♿
Exton Avenue, Exton, Oakham, Rutland, LE15 8AH
Ⓣ (01572) 813200
Ⓔ info@barnsdalegardens.co.uk
Ⓦ www.barnsdalegardens.co.uk
Contact: Charlotte Darch
Opening Times: 0900-1700 Mar-May & Sep-Oct, 0900-1900 Jun-Aug, 1000-1600 Nov-Feb, 7 days. Closed 24th & 25th Dec.
Min Mail Order UK: Nmc
Min Mail Order EU: Nmc
Cat. Cost: Online only.
Credit Cards: All major credit/debit cards
Specialities: Wide range of choice & unusual garden plants but specialising in perennials.
Notes: Mail order from website or by telephone ordering only. Delivers to Gardeners' World Live flower show. Wheelchair accessible.
OS Grid Ref: SK912108

MBow **Fawside Farm Nursery**
Fawside Farm, Longnor, Buxton, Derbyshire, SK17 0RA
Ⓜ 07919 556425
Ⓔ julie.norfolk@acorncapital.co.uk
Ⓦ www.Fawsidefarmnursery.com
Contact: Julie Norfolk
Opening Times: By appt. only.
Min Mail Order UK: £25.00
Cat. Cost: Online.
Credit Cards: Paypal
Specialities: Bee-friendly hardy perennials, British wildflowers and herbs. It is a small nursery so does not have large numbers of all the varieties. Large orders can be grown by arrangement.
Notes: The nursery is situated 1,000ft above sea level in the Pennines and we aim to grow hardy species of plants to survive in these conditions as well as being wildlife friendly. We use peat-free compost, use organic growing methods & recycle our pots. Visitors very welcome – please call to arrange a visit. Also sells wholesale.

MBriF **Bridge Farm Plants**
Bridge Farm, Main Road, Lower Hartshay, Derbyshire, DE5 3RP
Ⓣ (01773) 742848
Ⓜ 07812 350132
Ⓔ alisonfarnsworth@btinternet.com
Contact: Alison Farnsworth
Opening Times: By appt. only.
Specialities: Herbaceous perennials and bulbs.
Notes: Interesting range, including half-hardy and tender. Most in small quantities only. Delivers to shows.

MBrN **Bridge Nursery** ♿
Nursery Barn, Tomlow Road, Napton, Warwickshire, CV47 8HX
Ⓣ (01926) 812737
Ⓔ chris.dakin25@yahoo.com
Ⓦ www.Bridge-Nursery.co.uk
Contact: Christine Dakin & Philip Martino
Opening Times: 1000-1600 Sat, Sun & B/hol Mons Mar-Oct Other times by appt.
Min Mail Order UK: £10.00
Cat. Cost: Online only.
Credit Cards: All major credit/debit cards
Specialities: Ornamental grasses, sedges & bamboos. Also range of shrubs & perennials. Display garden.
Notes: Limited range available by mail order, please check with nursery. Also sells wholesale. Euro accepted. Wheelchair accessible.
OS Grid Ref: SP463625

MBros **Brookside Nursery** ♿
School Lane, Hints, Tamworth, Staffordshire, B78 3DW
Ⓣ (0333) 335 6789
Ⓔ info@brooksidenursery.co.uk
Ⓦ www.brooksidenursery.co.uk
Contact: James Thomas

Opening Times: 0900-1700 Mon-Sat, 1000-1600 Sun 1st Mar-31st Oct Closed 1st Nov-28th Feb. Office & Customer Services Mon-Fri 0900-1700 all year.
Cat. Cost: Free – Postal and Online.
Credit Cards: All major credit/debit cards
Specialities: *Begonia, Lobelia, Petunia, Geranium.*
Notes: Producer of bedding and hanging basket plants. Veg & perennials sold as young plug plants and bare root plants for mail order and as finished plants for collection from the nursery. Also sells wholesale. Wheelchair accessible.

MCls Coles Plant Centre ♿
624 Uppingham Road, Thurnby, Leicestershire, LE7 9QB
Ⓣ (0116) 241 8394
Ⓕ (0116) 243 2311
Ⓔ info@colesplantcentre.co.uk
Ⓦ www.colesplantcentre.co.uk
Contact: Mark Goddard
Opening Times: 0800-1700 Mon-Fri, 0900-1700 Sat & Sun.
Credit Cards: MasterCard, Switch
Specialities: Fruit, ornamental trees & shrubs.
Notes: Wheelchair accessible.

MCms Chrysanthemums Direct
Holmes Chapel Road, Over Peover, Knutsford, Cheshire, WA16 9RA
Ⓣ (0800) 0467443
Ⓜ 07977 312593
Ⓔ sales@chrysanthemumsdirect.co.uk
Ⓦ www.chrysanthemumsdirect.co.uk
Contact: Martyn Flint
Opening Times: Not open. Mail order only.
Min Mail Order UK: Nmc
Min Mail Order EU: Nmc
Cat. Cost: 4 × 1st class.
Credit Cards: All major credit/debit cards
Specialities: *Chrysanthemum.* Young plants grown to order. Delivery within 28 days.
Notes: Delivers to shows.

MCoo Cool Temperate
(office) 45 Stamford Street, Awsworth, Nottinghamshire, NG16 2QL
Ⓜ 07952 019376
Ⓔ phil.corbett@cooltemperate.co.uk
Ⓦ www.cooltemperate.co.uk
Contact: Phil Corbett
Opening Times: 0900-1700, 7 days. Please ring/write first.
Min Mail Order UK: Nmc
Cat. Cost: Online or via email.
Credit Cards: None
Specialities: Tree fruit, soft fruit, nitrogen-fixers, hedging, own-root fruit trees. Many species available in small quantities only.
Notes: Nursery at Newton's Lane, Cossall, Notts NG16 2YH.
OS Grid Ref: SK473433

MCor Morlas Plants
Woodlands, Nant Lane, Selattyn, Oswestry, Shropshire, SY10 7HA
Ⓣ (01691) 655824
Ⓜ 07930 221062
Ⓔ jane@morlasplants.co.uk
Ⓦ www.morlasplants.co.uk
Contact: Jane Rowlinson
Opening Times: Not open. Mail order only.
Min Mail Order UK: Nmc
Min Mail Order EU: Nmc
Cat. Cost: Online only.
Credit Cards: Paypal
Specialities: We grow and breed *Galanthus* species and cultivars, *Erythronium, Narcissus* and other bulbs. Some of our rare named plants are available in limited numbers only. All our plants are grown in peat-free compost.
Notes: Formerly Cornovium Snowdrops, we offer in the green snowdrops from the 1st Jan every year on our website to our UK and EU customers. We also offer dormant bulbs during the summer months, and supply dormant bulbs to the US every summer. Please see our website for more details. Exports beyond EU.

MCot Coton Manor Garden
Guilsborough, Northampton, Northamptonshire, NN6 8RQ
Ⓣ (01604) 740219
Ⓔ pasleytyler@cotonmanor.co.uk
Ⓦ www.cotonmanor.co.uk
Contact: Kelly Goldsmith
Opening Times: 1200-1730 Tue-Sat, 1st Apr-27th Sep. Also Sun Apr, May & B/hol w/ends. Other times in working hours by appt.
Cat. Cost: Online only.
Credit Cards: All major credit/debit cards
Specialities: Wide-range of herbaceous perennials (1200+ varieties), some available in small quantities only. Also many tender perennials & selected shrubs.
Notes: Garden open. Tea rooms. Garden school. Partial wheelchair access.
OS Grid Ref: SP675715

MCtn Chiltern Seeds Ltd
Crowmarsh Battle Barns,114 Preston Crowmarsh, Wallingford, Oxfordshire, OX10 6SL

Ⓣ (01491) 824675
Ⓔ info@chilternseeds.co.uk
Ⓦ www.chilternseeds.co.uk
Contact: Any member of staff
Opening Times: Mail order only. Normal office hours, Mon-Fri.
Min Mail Order UK: Nmc
Min Mail Order EU: Nmc
Cat. Cost: Free.
Credit Cards: All major debit/credit cards except American Express
Specialities: Large selection of wild flowers, trees, shrubs, cacti, annuals, houseplants, vegetables & herbs.
Notes: Exports beyond EU. Customer's responsibility to ensure no restrictions & special import requirements apply.

M

MDon **DONINGTON NURSERIES** ♿
Kings Mills, Park Lane, Castle Donington, Derbyshire, DE74 2RS
Ⓣ (01332) 853004
Ⓕ (01332) 853793
Ⓔ sales@doningtonnurseries.co.uk
Ⓦ https://www.gardencentrederby.com
Contact: Rebecca
Opening Times: 0900-1700 Mon-Sat, 1000-1600 Sun Mar-Jun. Jul-Feb reduced, varied hours – check website for details.
Cat. Cost: None.
Credit Cards: All major credit/debit cards
Specialities: Home grown laurel (*Prunus*) hedging. Large range of ornamental plants – subject to seasonal availability – please phone ahead of your visit to check stocks.
Notes: A traditional plant based nursery with a large number of trees, shrubs and other plants. Home grown perennials and seasonal bedding. Delivery available locally around Derby, Notts. Leics charges apply. Wheelchair accessible.
OS Grid Ref: SK421273

MEch **ECHIUM WORLD**
The Walled Garden, Thoresby Park, Nr Ollerton, Nottinghamshire, NG22 9EP
Ⓜ 07957602073
Ⓔ echiumworld@gmail.com
Ⓦ www.echiumworld.co.uk
Contact: Linda Heywood
Opening Times: 1000-1600 Thu & Sun from 5th Apr 2020, £3 entry. Other times by appt. Group visits welcome. Check website.
Min Mail Order UK: £9.95
Credit Cards: Paypal
Specialities: The Echium Garden & Plant nursery occupies a corner of the old Victorian walled garden at Thoresby Park, Nottinghamshire, currently under renovation. Showcasing over 35 varieties of *Echium* including the giant tree *Echium*, *Echium pinanana* that grows to over 5 metres tall. Plant & Seed sales. Please call or email to arrange order collection. See website for further information.
Notes: *Echium* including rare & endangered species. Varieties on display in planting schemes throughout the Echium Garden. Suppliers of Echium plants and seeds for wildlife gardens. Plants grown onsite. National Collection of *Echium* species & cvs from the Macaronesian Islands.

MFry **FRYER'S ROSES AND GARDEN CENTRE** ♿
Manchester Road, Knutsford, Cheshire, WA16 0SX
Ⓣ (01565) 755455
Ⓔ webenquiries@bluediamond.gg
Ⓦ www.fryersroses.co.uk
Contact: Diana Woodman
Opening Times: 0900-1800 Mon-Sat & 1030-1630 Sun.
Min Mail Order UK: £6.50 (bare root)
Min Mail Order EU: Contact nursery
Cat. Cost: Free.
Credit Cards: All major debit/credit cards except American Express
Specialities: Stocks over 250 varieties of roses. New roses usually launched at RHS Hampton Court Palace Flower Show. Bare root roses available for sale from Nov-Mar, potted roses available all year.
Notes: Talks held throughout the year, contact nursery for information. Group bookings available. Export depending on country, please contact the nursery to discuss. Wheelchair accessible.
OS Grid Ref: SJ738803

MGil **JOHN GILLIES** ♿
at Russell's Garden Centre, Mill Hill, Baginton, Warwickshire, CV8 3AG
Ⓜ 07546 064961
Ⓔ enquiries@gilliesrareplants.com
Ⓦ www.gilliesrareplants.com
Contact: John Gillies
Opening Times: 1000-1700 Wed, Thu, Fri & Sat, 1030-1630 Sun 1st Mar-30th Sep. Closed Mon & Tue. Closed Easter Sun. Open B/hol Mon. 1000-1600 Sat, 1030-1600 Sun 1st Oct-30th Nov Oct-Nov. Other times by appt.
Cat. Cost: Online only.
Credit Cards: All major credit/debit cards
Specialities: Offer a range of choice & rare plants of all types.

Notes: Please contact nursery before visiting to ensure plant you require is currently in stock. Wheelchair accessible.
OS Grid Ref: SP337750

MGos **Goscote Nurseries Ltd** ♿
Syston Road, Cossington, Leicestershire, LE7 4UZ
Ⓣ (01509) 812121
Ⓔ sales@goscote.co.uk
Ⓦ www.goscote.co.uk
Contact: James Toone
Opening Times: 7 days, all yr round (Not Xmas to New Year).
Cat. Cost: Online only.
Credit Cards: Visa, Access, MasterCard, Delta, Switch
Specialities: Japanese maples, rhododendrons & azaleas, *Magnolia*, *Camellia*, *Pieris* & other *Ericaceae*. Ornamental trees & shrubs, conifers, fruit, heathers, alpines, roses, *Clematis* & unusual climbers.
Notes: Design & landscaping service available. Café & show garden. Also sells wholesale. Wheelchair accessible.
OS Grid Ref: SK602130

MHCG **Hill Close Gardens** ♿
Bread and Meat Close, Warwick, Warwickshire, CV34 6HF
Ⓣ (01926) 493339
Ⓜ 07533 401934
Ⓔ headgardener@hcgt.org.uk
Ⓦ www.hillclosegardens.com
Contact: Neil Munro
Opening Times: 1100-1700, 7 days, Apr-Oct 1100-1600 Mon-Fri only, Nov-Mar.
Cat. Cost: 2 × 1st class or online.
Credit Cards: All major credit/debit cards
Specialities: Hold dispersed National Plant Collection of hardy *Chrysanthemum*. Also specialise in *Symphyotrichum* (asters) & *Galanthus*.
Notes: Small retail nursery attached to heritage garden which is open to the public. Wheelchair accessible.
OS Grid Ref: SP277647

MHed **HedgeXpress** ♿
Buckland Road, Bampton, Oxfordshire, OX18 2AA
Ⓣ (01993) 850979
Ⓔ sales@hedgexpress.co.uk
Ⓦ www.hedgexpress.co.uk
Contact: Gavin Stevens
Opening Times: 0900-1600, Mon-Fri.
Min Mail Order UK: £120
Cat. Cost: Online only.
Credit Cards: All major credit/debit cards, Paypal
Specialities: Hedging, lavenders & lawn edging.
Notes: Also sells wholesale. Wheelchair accessible.
OS Grid Ref: SP322024

MHer **The Herb Nursery** ♿
Thistleton, Oakham, Rutland, LE15 7RE
Ⓣ (01572) 767658
Ⓔ info@herbnursery.co.uk
Ⓦ www.herbnursery.co.uk
Contact: Peter & Christine Bench
Opening Times: 0900-1700 Mon-Sat, incl. B/hols 1000-1600 Sun. Closed Xmas until 1st Feb.
Cat. Cost: Free with A5 sae.
Credit Cards: All major credit/debit cards
Specialities: Herbs, wild flowers, cottage garden plants and a range of alpines. Large collections of *Pelargonium, Thymus, Mentha, Lavandula* & *Salvia*.
Notes: Open garden weekend 13th and 14th June (see website for details). Five acres of nursery, gardens and woodland not normally open to the public. Refreshments available. Proceeds to village church repairs and maintenance. Delivers to shows. Wheelchair accessible.

MHid **Hidden Paradise Plants** ♿
7 Lumber Lane, Burtonwood, Newton-le-Willows, Warrington, Cheshire, WA5 4AS
Ⓣ (01925) 229100
Ⓔ timothyatkinson@msn.com
Ⓦ www.sound-garden-designs.co.uk
Contact: Tim Atkinson
Opening Times: By appt. only.
Min Mail Order UK: Nmc
Cat. Cost: 2 × 1st class.
Credit Cards: None
Specialities: Species *Rhododendron, Hedychium, Cautleya*.
Notes: Delivers to shows. Wheelchair accessible.
OS Grid Ref: SJ948901

MHiT **Hilltop Nurseries (Nottingham) Ltd** ♿
164-166 Lambley Lane, Gedling, Nottingham, Nottinghamshire, NG4 4PB
Ⓣ (0115) 961 2054
Ⓔ lesley@hilltopnurseries.co.uk
Ⓦ www.hilltopnurseries.co.uk
Contact: Lesley Heyhoe
Notes: Wheelchair accessible.

M

MHol **Hollies Farm Plant Centre**
Uppertown, Bonsall, Nr Matlock, Derbyshire, DE4 2AW
Ⓣ (01629) 822734
Ⓔ rbrt.wells@gmail.com
Ⓦ www.holliesfarmplantcentre.co.uk
Contact: Robert or Linda Wells
Opening Times: 0900-1700 every day except Wed.
Credit Cards: All major credit/debit cards
Specialities: Range of rare & unusual herbaceous perennials.
Notes: Garden designers welcome.

MHoo **Hooksgreen Herbs Ltd**
Hooksgreen Farm, Oulton Heath, Stone, Staffordshire, ST15 8TN
Ⓜ 07775563857
Ⓔ sales@hooksgreenherbs.com
Ⓦ www.hooksgreenherbs.com
Contact: Louise Roycroft
Opening Times: By appt. only.
Min Mail Order UK: £10.00
Min Mail Order EU: £10.00
Credit Cards: All major credit/debit cards
Specialities: Culinary, medicinal & scented herbs.
Notes: Delivers to shows.

MHost **North Staffordshire Hostas**
6 Spinney Close, Endon, Stoke-on-Trent, Staffordshire, ST9 9BP
Ⓣ (01782) 502345
Ⓜ 07837 581109
Ⓔ robert.e.barlow@btopenworld.com
Ⓦ www.northstaffordshirehostas.co.uk
Contact: Robert Barlow
Opening Times: By appt. only.
Min Mail Order UK: £20.00
Cat. Cost: Online only.
Specialities: *Hosta.*
Notes: Mail order only. Open days 2020: 17 May, 13 June & 18 July 1000-1700. Plants sold at shows and fairs during the year. We are aiming to increase our Hosta collection to 450 plus cultivars. Delivers to shows.

MHtn **Hintons Nursery** ♿
Coventry Road, Guy's Cliffe, Warwick, Warwickshire, CV34 5FJ
Ⓣ (01926) 492273
Ⓔ info@hintonsnursery.co.uk
Ⓦ www.hintonsnursery.co.uk
Contact: Sarah Ridgeway
Opening Times: 0900-1600 Mon-Sat, 1000-1630 Sun Apr-Jun. 0900-1600 Mon-Sat, 1000-1600 Sun Jul-Mar.
Min Mail Order UK: Nmc
Credit Cards: All major debit/credit cards except American Express
Specialities: Specialise in fruit (soft fruit & trees) and veg. Nearly 200 varieties of veg plants ready to plant out. Also offer more unusual fruit such as Chilean guava, honeyberries, worcesterberries, *Aronia* and pluots.
Notes: Grow & sell all types of plant from alpines, herbs, aquatics, herbaceous, shrubs and climbers to trees, ferns, bamboos & roses in a range of sizes. Plug plants for summer bedding available in spring. Also sells wholesale. Wheelchair accessible.
OS Grid Ref: SP289636

MIdl **Middleton Nurseries**
Coppice Lane, Middleton, Tamworth, Staffordshire, B78 2BT
Ⓣ (0121) 3084077
Ⓔ sales@middletonnurseries.co.uk
Ⓦ www.middletonnurseries.co.uk
Contact: John Zako
Opening Times: By appt. only. Online store.
Min Mail Order UK: £5.00
Cat. Cost: Online.
Credit Cards: All major credit/debit cards
Specialities: We specialise in growing *Salvia* which are all available to purchase at our Online store. Our collections can also be purchased at all the RHS shows.
Notes: Middleton Nurseries are located in the village of Middleton in Staffordshire and have been growing plants since 1975. We are dedicated to growing new & unusual perennials, specialising in the *Salvia* species. We attend the RHS shows up and down the country. We also have our own online store. Delivers to shows. Also sells wholesale.

MJac **Jackson's Nurseries**
72 Main Street, Clifton Campville, Nr Tamworth, Staffordshire, B79 0AP
Ⓣ (01827) 373307
Ⓔ jacksonsnurseries.fuchsias@gmail.com
Contact: N. Jackson
Opening Times: 0900-1800 Mon & Wed-Sat, 1000-1700 Sun.
Cat. Cost: 2 × 1st class.
Credit Cards: None
Specialities: *Fuchsia.*
Notes: Also sells wholesale.

MJon **C & K Jones** ♿
Golden Fields Nurseries, Barrow Lane, Tarvin, Cheshire, CH3 8JF
Ⓣ (01829) 740663

Ⓕ (01829) 741877
Ⓔ ck.jones@jonestherose.co.uk
Ⓦ www.jonestherose.co.uk
Contact: Keith & Rachael Jones
Opening Times: By appt. only. Mail order.
Min Mail Order UK: 1 plant + p&p
Min Mail Order EU: Nmc
Cat. Cost: £1.00
Credit Cards: MasterCard, Visa, Maestro, Electron, Solo
Specialities: Roses.
Notes: Also sells wholesale. Wheelchair accessible.

MLod **LODGE FARM PLANTS & WILDFLOWERS** ♿
Lodge Farm, Case Lane, Fiveways, Hatton, Warwick, Warwickshire, CV35 7JD
Ⓜ 07962 222276
Ⓔ lodgefarmplants@btinternet.com
Ⓦ www.lodgefarm-plants.com
Contact: Nik Cook
Opening Times: 1000-1630 winter. 1000-1730 summer.
Min Mail Order UK: Nmc
Cat. Cost: No catalogue. See website.
Credit Cards: All major credit/debit cards
Specialities: Fruit trees, trained fruit trees, ornamental trees, native trees, hedging, wildflowers, herbs and soft fruit.
Notes: Trees sell out very quickly, please contact us with your requirements. We will be happy to reserve them for you. Euro accepted. Wheelchair accessible.
OS Grid Ref: SP223700

MMen **MINTOPIA**
Fullersmoor Cottage, Smithy Lane, Brown Knowl, Cheshire, CH3 9JY
Ⓜ 07782 378697
Ⓔ intmintmint@gmail.com
Ⓦ https://mintopia.bigcartel.com/
Contact: Simon Poole
Opening Times: Online only.
Min Mail Order UK: £1.50
Credit Cards: Paypal
Specialities: *Mentha* collection of just less than 100 varieties. As our stock grows, we intend to seek National Collection Holder status. Very rare sub-species, hybrid and varieties available. Option to buy small collections for those with specific interests.
Notes: Mintopia is a plastic-free, organic cottage industry that collects and specialises in *Mentha* (Mint). We offer bare-root, plug, pot and specimen-sized plants, often propagated to order. Please note that we are not open to the public, but offer an online mail order service. Please contact us if you wish to order plants larger than bare-root to arrange correct payment. Larger plants may take longer to be delivered.

MMrt **MORTON NURSERIES LTD** ♿
Mansfield Road, Morton, Retford, Nottinghamshire, DN22 8HE
Ⓣ (01777) 702530
Ⓜ 07940 434398
Ⓔ enquiries@morton-nurseries.com
Ⓦ www.morton-nurseries.co.uk
Contact: Gill McMaster
Opening Times: 1000-1600 Tue-Sat, incl B/hols. Closed Sun/Mon.
Min Mail Order UK: £5.00 + p&p
Cat. Cost: None issued.
Credit Cards: All major credit/debit cards
Specialities: Shrubs & perennials.
Notes: Delivers to shows. Wheelchair accessible.
OS Grid Ref: SK671187

MMuc **MUCKLESTONE NURSERIES**
Rock Lane, Mucklestone, Nr Market Drayton, Shropshire, TF9 4FA
Ⓣ (01630) 674284
Ⓜ 07714 241667/07714 241668
Ⓔ info@botanyplants.co.uk
Ⓦ www.botanyplants.co.uk
Contact: William & Louise Friend
Opening Times: 0930-1700 (or dusk) Wed, Fri, Sat. Please check website for details.
Min Mail Order UK: Nmc
Cat. Cost: Online.
Credit Cards: All major credit/debit cards
Specialities: A range of trees and plants for acid & damp soils. Also grow complementary range for dry, chalk & coast at our Kent nursery. Extensive grounds showing plants in situ. Small numbers only of each variety available.
Notes: Please send plant requests by email or contact Louise Friend on 07714 241667 to discuss orders & availability. Plants listed under nursery code SEND (in Kent) can be ordered for collection from Mucklestone or sent/delivered direct. Talks by arrangement in Shropshire/Staffs/Cheshire area.
OS Grid Ref: SJ728373

MNHC **THE NATIONAL HERB CENTRE** ♿
Banbury Road, Warmington, Nr Banbury, Oxfordshire, OX17 1DF
Ⓣ (01295) 690999
Ⓕ (01295) 690034
Ⓔ info@herbcentre.co.uk

M

Ⓦ www.herbcentre.co.uk
Contact: Plant Centre Staff
Opening Times: 0900-1730 Mon-Sat, 1030-1700 Sun.
Min Mail Order UK: Nmc
Credit Cards: All major credit/debit cards
Specialities: Herbs, culinary & medicinal. Extensive selection of rosemary, thyme & lavender in particular.
Notes: Next day delivery UK mainland only, signature required. Carriage charge of £10.00 for orders valued up to £50, more for larger orders. Wheelchair accessible.
OS Grid Ref: SP413471

M

MNic **Nicholson Nurseries Limited** ♿
The Park, North Aston, Bicester, Oxfordshire, OX25 6HL
Ⓣ (01869) 340342
Ⓔ plantsales@nicholsonsgb.com
Ⓦ www.nicholsonsgb.com
Contact: Merlin Brooke-Little
Opening Times: 0730-1630 Mon-Fri, 0830-1630 Sat & B/hols. Closed Sun.
Cat. Cost: Free.
Credit Cards: All major credit/debit cards
Specialities: We specialise in container-grown native hedging species such as hawthorn, spindle, hazel & privet, and grow our own *Quercus* ilex hedging, stilted and feathered.
Notes: A family-run plant centre and nursery, established in 1979. We grow native hedging plants and curate a stunning selection of plants in our plant centre. Many either grown ourselves or UK sourced. Specialising in ornamental, specimen trees, shrubs and native hedging. Also sells wholesale. Wheelchair accessible.
OS Grid Ref: SP475287

MNrw **Norwell Nurseries & Gardens** ♿
Woodhouse Road, Norwell, Near Newark, Nottinghamshire, NG23 6JX
Ⓣ (01636) 636337
Ⓔ wardha@aol.com
Ⓦ www.norwellnurseries.co.uk
Contact: Dr Andrew Ward
Opening Times: 1000-1700 Mon, Wed-Fri & Sun (Wed-Mon May & Jun). By appt. Aug & 18th Oct-1st Mar.
Min Mail Order UK: £25.00 + p&p
Min Mail Order EU: £40.00
Cat. Cost: 3 × 1st class or online.
Credit Cards: None
Specialities: Large collection of 2500+ unusual herbaceous perennials esp. hardy geraniums, Geum, pond & bog plants, cottage garden plants, *Hemerocallis*, grasses, *Trillium* & woodland plants. National Plant Collection of hardy *Chrysanthemum* & *Astrantia*.
Notes: One acre garden & tea room. Talks given and garden tours. Hardy Plant Society names as within top perennial gardens. Also sells wholesale. Delivers to shows. Wheelchair accessible.
OS Grid Ref: SK767616

MPhe **Phedar Nursery**
42 Bunkers Hill, Romiley, Stockport, Cheshire, SK6 3DS
Ⓣ (0161) 430 3772
Ⓔ mclewin@phedar.com
Ⓦ www.phedar.com
Contact: Will McLewin
Opening Times: Frequent but irregular. Please phone to arrange appt.
Min Mail Order UK: Nmc
Min Mail Order EU: Nmc
Cat. Cost: Online or write for printed version.
Credit Cards: None
Specialities: Species *Helleborus, Paeonia*. Limited stock of some rare items.
Notes: Also sells wholesale. Exports beyond EU subject to destination & on an ad-hoc basis only. Please contact nursery for details. Euro accepted.
OS Grid Ref: SJ936897

MPie **Piecemeal Plants** ♿
Whatton House Gardens, Nr Kegworth, Loughborough, Leicestershire, LE12 5BG
Ⓣ (01509) 672056
Ⓜ 07950 757444
Ⓔ nursery@piecemealplants.co.uk
Ⓦ www.piecemealplants.co.uk
Contact: Mary Thomas
Opening Times: 1300-1630 (longer hours in summer) Thu & Fri, early Apr-mid Sep. 1300-1700 Suns May. For further details, telephone, see website or follow on Facebook. Also open by appt. all year.
Cat. Cost: Online only.
Credit Cards: All major credit/debit cards
Specialities: Wide range of quality, hardy herbaceous perennials. Unusual varieties & cottage garden favourites. Most in small quantities. Limited selection of shrubs, flowering bulbs, half hardy & tender plants.
Notes: Nursery located at entrance to Whatton House Gardens, behind House. Access via main gate on A6 between Kegworth and Hathern. Gardens also open (see website). Parking in front of house. Delivers to shows (mainly Midlands specialist Plant Fairs). Wheelchair accessible.
OS Grid Ref: SK494242

MPkF **PACKHORSE FARM NURSERY** ♿
Sandyford House, Lant Lane, Tansley, Matlock, Derbyshire, DE4 5FW
Ⓣ (01629) 57206
Ⓜ 07974 095752
Ⓕ (01629) 57206
Contact: Hilton W. Haynes
Opening Times: 1000-1500 Tue & Wed, 1st Apr-30th Sep. Other times by appt. only.
Cat. Cost: 2 × 1st class for plant list.
Credit Cards: None
Specialities: Acer, rare stock is limited in supply. Other more unusual hardy shrubs, trees & conifers.
Notes: Delivers to shows. Wheelchair accessible.
OS Grid Ref: SK322617

MPnt **PLANTAGOGO.COM**
Jubilee Cottage Nursery, Snape Lane, Englesea Brook, Crewe, Cheshire, CW2 5QN
Ⓣ (01270) 820335
Ⓜ 07713 518271
Ⓔ info@plantagogo.com
Ⓦ www.plantagogo.com
Contact: Vicky & Richard Fox
Opening Times: By appt. only See description for open days.
Min Mail Order UK: £9.95
Min Mail Order EU: Price on application
Cat. Cost: Online only.
Credit Cards: All major credit/debit cards
Specialities: Specialist nursery of *Heuchera, Heucherella* & *Tiarella*. Large selection of perennials. Plants listed in the book available in good quantities, others not listed available on request. National Plant Collections of *Heuchera, Heucherella* & *Tiarella*.
Notes: Open days with homemade cake & coffee/tea daily 1000-1600 3rd-5th Apr, 27th & 28th Jun, 2nd-4th Oct 2020. Nursery open half days (no appt. required) 9.30-1300 23rd-28th May, 29th-31st May 2020. Plants sold for garden designers. Delivers to shows. Partial wheelchair access.
OS Grid Ref: SJ750516

MPri **PRIMROSE COTTAGE NURSERY** ♿
Altrincham Road, Styal, Wilmslow, Cheshire, SK9 4JE
Ⓜ 07798 754457
Ⓔ info@primrosecottagenursery.co.uk
Ⓦ www.primrosecottagenursery.co.uk
Contact: Caroline Dumville
Opening Times: 0930-1630 Mon-Sat, 1000-1630 Sun (summer). 0930-1600 Mon-Sat, 1000-1600 Sun (winter).
Credit Cards: All major credit/debit cards
Specialities: Perennials, herbs, patio & hanging basket plants, always lots of new & unusual varieties. Shrubs, roses, ornamental trees, fruit trees, soft fruit bushes, bedding & vegetable plants.
Notes: In Styal Village, close to National Trust Quarry Bank Mill and estate. Village café next door to nursery. Wheelchair accessible.

MPtr **PETRICHOR BULB SPECIALISTS**
Great Warford, Cheshire, SK9 7TT
Ⓣ (01925) 730992
Ⓜ 07500 937363
Ⓔ info@bulbspecialists.co.uk
Ⓦ www.bulbspecialists.co.uk
Contact: Bert Blankers
Opening Times: By appt. only.
Specialities: Our main crops are *Allium, Agapanthus, Camassia, Fritilaria, Scilla* peruviana, *Ornithogalum saundersiae* & *Eucomis*.
Notes: We sell bulbs and bulbous plants in season. Delivers to shows. Also sells wholesale.

M

MRav **RAVENSTHORPE NURSERY** ♿
6 East Haddon Road, Ravensthorpe, Northamptonshire, NN6 8ES
Ⓣ (01604) 770548
Ⓔ ravensthorpenursery@hotmail.com
Contact: Jean & Richard Wiseman
Opening Times: 1000-1800 (or dusk if earlier) Wed-Sat, B/hol Mons in May.
Cat. Cost: None issued.
Credit Cards: Visa, MasterCard
Specialities: Huge range of perennials, shrubs & trees with numerous unusual varieties, many of which can be seen growing in the display garden. Some plants only available as dug from garden during the lifting season.
Notes: Wheelchair accessible.
OS Grid Ref: SP665699

MSCN **STONYFORD COTTAGE NURSERY** ♿
Stonyford Lane, Cuddington, Northwich, Cheshire, CW8 2TF
Ⓣ (01606) 888970/888128 (answerphone)
Ⓔ stonyfordcottage@yahoo.co.uk
Ⓦ www.stonyfordcottagenursery.co.uk
Contact: Andrew Overland
Opening Times: 1000-1700 Tue-Sat & B/hol Mons. Mar-Oct.
Min Mail Order UK: Nmc
Min Mail Order EU: Nmc
Cat. Cost: None.
Credit Cards: All major credit/debit cards
Specialities: Wide range of herbaceous perennials, *Iris*, hardy *Geranium*, moisture-loving & bog plants. *Sempervivum, Paeonia*, candelabra *Primula*.

Notes: Wheelchair accessible.
OS Grid Ref: SJ580710

MSpe **SpecialPerennials.com**
Ⓜ 07716 990695
Ⓔ plants@specialperennials.com
Ⓦ www.specialperennials.com
Contact: Janet & Martin Blow
Opening Times: Not open. Strictly no visitors.
Cat. Cost: Online only.
Credit Cards: Paypal
Specialities: *Helenium*, *Phlox*, *Salvia* and other herbaceous plants for summer colour. All plants available in fairly small numbers.
Notes: Small nursery growing garden worthy plants. Featured on Gardener's World in 2014. See our website for a list of plant fairs attended where we can bring orders. Delivers to shows (orders delivered to plant fairs free of p&p charge). Plants for sale at Plant Hunters' Fairs only – advance orders for collection at a fair welcome.

MSwo **Swallows Nursery** ♿
Mixbury, Brackley, Northamptonshire, NN13 5RR
Ⓣ (01280) 847721
Ⓜ 07913 973180
Ⓔ enq@swallowsnursery.co.uk
Ⓦ www.swallowsnursery.co.uk
Contact: Chris Swallow
Opening Times: 0900-1300 & 1400-1700 (earlier in winter) Mon-Fri, 0900-1300 Sat.
Min Mail Order UK: £15.00
Cat. Cost: 3 × 1st class (plus phone number).
Credit Cards: All major credit/debit cards
Specialities: Growing a wide range, particularly shrubs, climbers, trees & roses.
Notes: Trees not for mail order unless part of larger order. Nursery transport used where possible, esp. for trees. Also sells wholesale. Wheelchair accessible.
OS Grid Ref: SP607336

MThu **T. D. Thursfield**
Kerry Hill Nurseries, Eaves Lane, Bucknall, Stoke-on-Trent, Staffordshire, ST2 8NA
Ⓣ (01782) 302498
Ⓜ 07977 464363
Ⓔ tdthursfield@aol.com
Ⓦ www.tdthursfield.co.uk
Contact: Susan Thursfield
Opening Times: 0900-1730 Mon-Fri, 0930-1630 Sat, 1000-1600 Sun.
Cat. Cost: None issued.
Credit Cards: All major debit/credit cards except American Express
Specialities: Broad selection of hardy nursery stock.
Notes: Traditional family nursery founded in the 1930s. Also sells wholesale. Delivers to shows. Partial wheelchair access (to main sales areas).

MTin **The Tiny Plant Company**
25 Owley Wood Road, Weaverham, Cheshire, CW8 3LF
Ⓣ (01606) 851146
Ⓔ thetinyplantco@hotmail.com
Ⓦ www.tinyplantcompany.co.uk
Contact: Matt Wood
Opening Times: Not open. Mail order only.
Min Mail Order UK: £3.00
Cat. Cost: Online only.
Credit Cards: All major credit/debit cards
Specialities: Newly-opened small nursery. All plants available in very small quantities only.
Notes: Delivers to shows.

MTrO **Trees Online**
ICAM Ltd, c/o Emerald Accountancy Services, 3rd Floor, Staveley Hall, Staveley Hall Drive, Chesterfield, Derbyshire, S43 3TN
Ⓣ (0800) 0431057
Ⓜ 07904 179772
Ⓔ info@trees-online.co.uk
Ⓦ https://www.trees-online.co.uk
Contact: Alan Russell
Opening Times: Online business only.
Credit Cards: All major credit/debit cards
Specialities: Wide range of ornamental and fruit trees.
Notes: An online tree supplier covering ornamental, bare root, artificial, hedging, fruit and memorial urns with trees. Free UK mainland delivery and 3 year limited tree warranty. Delivers to shows. Also sells wholesale.

MVil **Village Plants Nursery Ltd** ♿
7 Bosden Fold Road, Hazel Grove, Stockport, Manchester, Cheshire, SK7 4LQ
Ⓣ (0161) 4569009
Ⓔ info@kevinpratt.co.uk
Ⓦ www.kevinpratt.co.uk
Contact: Kevin Pratt
Opening Times: 0900-1600 Mon, Thu, Fri, Sat 1000-1600 Sun Closed Tue & Wed.
Min Mail Order UK: £10.00
Cat. Cost: Online only.
Credit Cards: All major credit/debit cards
Specialities: Propagation of rare shrubs.
Notes: Small nursery run from home. Many trees and shrubs not widely available and

many rare plants only available in small quantities. Plantman's collection of rare, woody plants. Seasonal bedding and hanging baskets. Always phone first before travelling from a distance. Wheelchair accessible.
OS Grid Ref: SJ923718

MWht **Whitelea Nursery** ♿
Whitelea Lane, Tansley, Matlock, Derbyshire, DE4 5FL
Ⓣ (01629) 55010
Ⓕ (01629) 55010
Ⓔ sales@uk-bamboos.co.uk
Ⓦ www.uk-bamboos.co.uk
Contact: David Wilson
Opening Times: By appt.
Min Mail Order UK: Nmc
Cat. Cost: Online only. Price list available 2 × 1st class.
Credit Cards: None
Specialities: Bamboos. Substantial quantities of 45 species/cvs of bamboo, remainder stocked in small numbers only. Limited stocks of grasses, trees & shrubs.
Notes: Mail order limited by carrier restrictions, please contact nursery or see website for details. Also sells wholesale. Wheelchair accessible.
OS Grid Ref: SK325603

MWts **Waterside Nursery**
Sharnford, Leicestershire
Ⓣ (01455) 273730
Ⓜ 07931 557082
Ⓔ info@watersidenursery.co.uk
Ⓦ www.watersidenursery.co.uk
Contact: Linda Smith
Opening Times: Mail order only.
Min Mail Order UK: Nmc
Cat. Cost: Online only.
Credit Cards: All major credit/debit cards
Specialities: Aquatic pond plants, marginal shelf pond plants, miniature waterlilies, water lilies, submerged oxygenating plants, bog garden & moisture-loving plants.

Northern

NAbi **Abi and Tom's Garden Plants**
Halecat Nursery, Witherslack, Grange Over Sands, Cumbria, LA11 6RT
Ⓣ (015395) 52946
Ⓔ info@halecatplants.co.uk
Ⓦ www.abiandtom.co.uk
Contact: Abi Attwood
Opening Times: 7 days Mar-Sep. Oct opening varies. See website for winter opening times.
Cat. Cost: Online.
Credit Cards: All major credit/debit cards
Specialities: Hardy herbaceous perennials, including grasses and ferns.
Notes: We are a family-run working nursery, specialising in hardy herbaceous perennials. Our range of cottage garden plants is adventurous and inspiring, all set amongst beautiful display gardens and borders. We also stock a range of trees, shrubs and bedding plants.
OS Grid Ref: SD433838

NAts **Natural Surroundings**
Bayfield, Nr Glandford, Holt, Norfolk, NR25 7JN
Ⓣ (01263) 711091
Ⓔ wildlife@naturalsurroundings.info
Ⓦ www.naturalsurroundings.info
Contact: Anne Harrap
Opening Times: 1000-1700, 7 days May-Sep. 1000-1600 Tue-Sun Oct-Mar. Open B/hol Mons.
Credit Cards: All major debit/credit cards except American Express
Specialities: British wild flowers, native trees, shrubs and cottage garden plants, plus a selection of unusual hardy perennials. Also seed.
Notes: Propagate & grow in peat-free compost. Plants available in limited quantities. Wildlife-friendly demonstration gardens and semi-natural meadows open to the public (small charge). Group visits by arrangement. Talks to clubs and societies in Norfolk.
OS Grid Ref: TG047840

NBid **Bide-A-Wee Cottage Gardens** ♿
Stanton, Netherwitton, Morpeth, Northumberland, NE65 8PR
Ⓣ (01670) 772004
Ⓜ 07484 637216
Ⓕ (01670) 772004
Ⓔ mark.bideawee@gmail.com
Ⓦ www.bideawee.co.uk
Contact: Mark Robson
Opening Times: 1300-1700 Wed-Sat 11th Apr-12th Sep 2020. Group visits at other times, except Sun.
Min Mail Order UK: £28.00
Cat. Cost: Online only.
Credit Cards: All major credit/debit cards
Specialities: Unusual herbaceous perennials, *Agapanthus*, *Primula*, ferns, grasses. National Plant Collection of *Centaurea*.
Notes: Wheelchair accessible.
OS Grid Ref: NZ132900

NBir **BIRKHEADS SECRET GARDENS & NURSERY**
Birkheads Lane, Sunniside, Gateshead, Newcastle, Tyne & Wear
Ⓣ (01207) 232262
Ⓜ 07778 447920
Ⓔ birkheadsnursery@gmail.com
Ⓦ www.birkheadssecretgardens.co.uk
Contact: Christine Liddle
Opening Times: 1100-1700 Sat and Sun & 1000-1700 Wed-Fri in summer. Closed Mon & Tue. (Pre-booked coach groups Tue only). Open B/hol Mons. Please check website for spring & winter opening hrs.
Cat. Cost: None issued.
Credit Cards: All major credit/debit cards
Specialities: Hardy herbaceous perennials, grasses, hardy bulbs & herbs. *Allium, Euphorbia, Galanthus, Geranium, Iris Primula, Sedum* & *Rodgersia.*
Notes: RHS Partner Garden. Gardens are on a sloping site so wheelchair access is limited to the nursery & coffee shop, please ring for special access directions. Coffee shop closes 30 mins before the gardens. Winter months opening times much reduced. Please check our website before setting out.
OS Grid Ref: NZ220569

NBPC **THE BARN PLANT CENTRE & GIFT SHOP** ♿
The Square, Scorton, Near Garstang, Preston, Lancashire, PR3 1AU
Ⓣ (01524) 793533
Ⓔ kshorrock@hotmail.co.uk
Ⓦ http://www.plantsandgifts.co.uk/
Contact: Karl Shorrock
Opening Times: 0900-1700 Mon-Fri, 1000-1800 Sat-Sun.
Credit Cards: All major credit/debit cards
Specialities: 800 varieties of perennials.
Notes: Large gift shop & coffee bar. Wheelchair accessible.
OS Grid Ref: GR501487

NBro **BROWNTHWAITE HARDY PLANTS** ♿
Fell Yeat, Casterton, Kirkby Lonsdale, Lancashire, LA6 2JW
Ⓣ (015242) 71340 (after 1800 hours).
Ⓦ www.hardyplantsofcumbria.co.uk
Contact: Chris Benson
Opening Times: 1000-1700, 1st Apr-20th Sep.
Min Mail Order UK: Nmc
Cat. Cost: 3 × 1st for fern list.
Credit Cards: None
Specialities: Herbaceous perennials and hardy ferns incl. *Athyrium, Dryopteris, Polystichum, Hosta, Primula, Hydrangea paniculata* & *Hydrangea serrata* varieties.
Notes: Follow brown signs from A65 between Kirkby Lonsdale & Cowan Bridge. Mail order for ferns. Delivers to shows. Wheelchair accessible.
OS Grid Ref: SD632794

NBwr **BEARDSWORTHS NURSERIES & GARDEN CENTRE** ♿
Whitehall Road, Cleckheaton, West Yorkshire, BD19 6PL
Ⓣ (01274) 871869
Ⓜ 07966 479085
Ⓔ sales@beardsworths.co.uk
Ⓦ beardsworths.co.uk
Contact: Rob Kellett
Opening Times: 0730-1700 Mon-Fri, 0800-1700 Sat, 1000-1600 Sun.
Min Mail Order UK: £4.99
Credit Cards: All major credit/debit cards
Specialities: Hardy trees, shrubs, perennial, hedging.
Notes: Beardsworths are growers of hardy trees, shrubs, hedging, perennials and alpines. Supplying the trade and public since 1982. Wheelchair accessible.
OS Grid Ref: SE173263

NCft **CRAFTYPLANTS**
(office) 64 Dunkirk Lane, Leyland, Lancashire, PR25 1TX
Ⓣ (0161) 820 8606
Ⓔ sales@craftyplants.co.uk
Ⓦ www.craftyplants.co.uk
Contact: Graham Sigsworth/Alex Donaldson
Opening Times: Mail order only. Not open except for nursery open days (see website or phone for details).
Min Mail Order UK: Nmc
Min Mail Order EU: Nmc
Cat. Cost: Online. Printed list available on request.
Credit Cards: All major credit/debit cards
Specialities: *Tillandsia.* Interesting cacti, succulents, bromeliads and other unusual plants.
Notes: Nursery at Eezitill, Startley Nook, Preston PR4 4XW. Attends some flower shows & plant fairs (see events page on website or call for dates). Also sells wholesale. Delivers to shows.

NChi **CHIPCHASE CASTLE NURSERY** ♿
Chipchase Castle, Wark, Hexham, Northumberland, NE48 3NT
Ⓜ 07575 714002
Ⓔ chipchaseplants@aim.com

Ⓦ www.chipchasenursery.com
Contact: Mark Cummings
Opening Times: 1000-1600 Thu-Sun & B/hol Mons, 1st Apr (or Easter if earlier) to end Aug.
Min Mail Order UK: £10.00
Credit Cards: All major credit/debit cards
Specialities: Rare & unusual herbaceous esp. *Pulmonaria, Geum, Geranium* (100+), *Potentilla, Vinca, Trillium* & *Primula*. Some plants only available in small quantities.
Notes: Delivers to shows. Wheelchair accessible for accompanied wheelchair users.
OS Grid Ref: NY880758

NCou **Courtyard Planters** ♿
9 Westgate, Otley, West Yorkshire, LS21 3AT
Ⓣ (01943) 462390
Ⓔ katie@courtyardplanters.co.uk
Ⓦ www.courtyardplanters.co.uk
Contact: Katie Burnett
Opening Times: 0930-1700 Tue-Sat. Closed Jan.
Cat. Cost: Online only.
Credit Cards: All major debit/credit cards except American Express
Specialities: Perennials. Plants for heavy clay soils. Peat free.
Notes: Gardening classes & workshops. Also sells wholesale. Wheelchair accessible.
OS Grid Ref: SE201455

NCth **Caths Garden Plants** ♿
The Walled Garden, Heaves Hotel, Heaves, Levens, Cumbria, LA8 8EF
Ⓣ (01539) 561126
Ⓔ cathsgardenplants61126@gmail.com
Ⓦ www.cathsgardenplants.co.uk
Contact: Rachel James
Opening Times: Please check website for up-to-date information.
Min Mail Order UK: £15.00
Credit Cards: All major credit/debit cards
Specialities: Perennials.
Notes: We have a wide range of traditional and unusual herbaceous perennials, and a large selection of herbaceous *Paeonia*, all grown outside, naturally. Delivers to shows. Wheelchair accessible.
OS Grid Ref: SD497867

NDal **Daleside Nurseries Ltd** ♿
Ripon Road, Killinghall, Harrogate, North Yorkshire, HG3 2AY
Ⓣ (01423) 506450
Ⓕ (01423) 527872
Ⓔ contact@dalesidenurseries.co.uk
Ⓦ www.dalesidenurseries.co.uk
Contact: Any member of staff
Opening Times: 0830-1700 Mon-Sat, 1030-1630 Sun. Winter hours: 0830-1600 Mon-Sat (closed Sun) Jan 0830-1630 Mon-Sat, 1030-1630 Sun, Feb.
Cat. Cost: Online only.
Credit Cards: All major debit/credit cards except American Express
Specialities: Many plants & trees not generally available. Container-grown fruit trees: apples, pears & soft fruit. Container-grown trees. Conifers, *Clematis* & hardy perennials.
Notes: Wheelchair accessible.
OS Grid Ref: SE287590

NDav **Dave Parkinson Plants**
4 West Bank, Carlton, Goole, East Yorkshire, DN14 9PZ
Ⓣ (01405) 860693
Ⓦ www.daveparkinsonplants.co.uk
Contact: Mary Parkinson
Opening Times: Not open. Mail order only.
Min Mail Order UK: £12 + p&p
Min Mail Order EU: Nmc
Cat. Cost: 1st class stamp.
Credit Cards: None
Specialities: Hardy orchids. Terrestrial South African *Dis*a orchids, species & hybrids.
Notes: Sells at RHS & Orchid Shows and by mail order. Exports beyond EU. Delivers to shows.

NDov **Dove Cottage Nursery & Garden** ♿
Shibden Hall Road, Halifax, West Yorkshire, HX3 9XA
Ⓣ (01422) 203553
Ⓔ info@dovecottagenursery.co.uk
Ⓦ www.dovecottagenursery.co.uk
Contact: Stephen & Kim Rogers
Opening Times: 1000-1700 Thu-Sat, 2nd Apr-19th Sep & 13th Apr, 5th Jul, 9th Aug. Please check website or phone before travelling.
Cat. Cost: £3.00.
Credit Cards: All major credit/debit cards
Specialities: Herbaceous perennials & selected grasses, many displayed in adjoining naturalistic garden.
Notes: Wheelchair accessible.
OS Grid Ref: SE115256

NDro **Drointon Nurseries** ♿
Plaster Pitts, Norton Conyers, Ripon, North Yorkshire, HG4 5EF
Ⓣ (01765) 641849
Ⓜ 07909 971529
Ⓔ info@auricula-plants.co.uk
Ⓦ www.auricula-plants.co.uk

Contact: Robin & Annabel Graham
Opening Times: Open days in spring, otherwise by appt. only.
Min Mail Order UK: Nmc
Min Mail Order EU: Nmc
Cat. Cost: 4 × 1st class.
Credit Cards: All major credit/debit cards
Specialities: *Primula auricula*. More than 1150 cvs of show, alpine, double & border auriculas. Limited stock of any one cultivar. National Plant Collection of *Primula auricula* (borders).
Notes: Also sells wholesale. Exports beyond EU. Wheelchair accessible.
OS Grid Ref: SE315753

N

NDry **Dryad Nursery**
130 Prince Rupert Drive, Tockwith, York, North Yorkshire, YO26 7PU
Ⓣ (01423) 358791
Ⓔ dryadnursery@gmail.com
Ⓦ www.dryad-home.co.uk
Contact: Anne Wright
Opening Times: Not open, mail order only.
Min Mail Order UK: £5.50
Min Mail Order EU: £8.70
Cat. Cost: Online only.
Credit Cards: Paypal
Specialities: Miniature and species *Narcissus*, *Galanthus*, wood anemones, *Hepatica* and other small bulbs.
Notes: Grower and breeder of miniature daffodils, snowdrops and hepaticas. Holder of large collection of wood anemones. All plants available in limited numbers and from seasonal lists only. Exports beyond EU. All our plants are propagated at the nursery, or by Brian Duncan in Ireland.

NEoE **East of Eden Nursery** ♿
Ainstable, Carlisle, Cumbria, CA4 9QN
Ⓣ (01768) 896604
Ⓜ 07788 142969
Ⓔ roger@east-of-eden-nursery.co.uk
Ⓦ www.east-of-eden-nursery.co.uk
Contact: Roger Proud
Opening Times: Mar-Nov. Days & times variable, so please phone or email before calling.
Min Mail Order UK: £10.00
Cat. Cost: None issued.
Credit Cards: All major credit/debit cards
Specialities: Interesting & unusual shrubs, perennials & alpines, esp. astilbes & geums, with over 60 new *Geum* cvs, bred & raised on nursery.
Notes: Delivers to shows. Wheelchair accessible.
OS Grid Ref: NY467504

NFav **Perennial Favourites Ltd** ♿
East Park View, Blyth, Northumberland, NE24 3AY
Ⓣ (01670) 540653
Ⓜ 07805 607128
Ⓔ gardener@perennialfavourites.co.uk
Ⓦ www.perennialfavourites.co.uk
Contact: Adam Greenwold
Opening Times: 0730-1700, 7 days, Apr-Oct 0900-1600, Wed-Sat Nov-Mar.
Credit Cards: All major credit/debit cards
Specialities: Specialising in hardy herbaceous perennials, but also supplying alpines and shrubs tolerant of the North Sea coastal climate.
Notes: Perennial and alpine nursery, seaside plants. Also sells wholesale to trade. Wheelchair accessible.
OS Grid Ref: NZ320812

NGBl **Garden Blooms**
Fieldgate, Mill Field Road, Fishlake, Doncaster, Yorkshire, DN7 5GH
Ⓣ (01302) 288145
Ⓔ info@gardenblooms.co.uk
Ⓦ www.gardenblooms.co.uk
Contact: Liz Webster
Opening Times: Open by appt. or on open days. Contact nursery for details.
Min Mail Order UK: Nmc
Cat. Cost: Online only.
Credit Cards: All major credit/debit cards
Specialities: Hardy & tender perennials, especially *Rudbeckia*, & small range of conservatory/house plants. Some plants available in small quantities only.
Notes: Delivers to shows. Credit card payments not accepted over the phone.
OS Grid Ref: SE659148

NGdn **Garden House Nursery** ♿
The Square, Dalston, Carlisle, Cumbria, CA5 7LL
Ⓣ (01228) 710297
Ⓜ 07595 219082
Ⓔ stephickso@hotmail.co.uk
Ⓦ www.gardenhousenursery.co.uk
Contact: Stephen Hickson
Opening Times: 0930-1700 Mon-Fri, 1000-1630 Sat-Sun, mid-Mar-Oct. Please ring if visiting at w/ends.
Cat. Cost: Plant list online only.
Credit Cards: All major credit/debit cards
Specialities: *Geranium*, *Hosta*, *Hemerocallis*, *Iris*, grasses, *Brunnera*, *Pulmonaria* & *Aconitum*.
Notes: Also sells wholesale. Wheelchair accessible.
OS Grid Ref: NY369503

NGKc **G&K CARNATIONS**
52 Abbotside Close, Urpeth Grange, Ouston, Chester Le Street, County Durham, DH2 1TQ
Ⓣ (01914) 106725
Ⓜ 07544 394241
Ⓔ gandkcarnations@gmail.com
Ⓦ https://www.gandkcarnations.com/
Contact: Keith
Opening Times: Not open.
Min Mail Order UK: £10.00
Cat. Cost: Free.
Specialities: Perpetual and border *Dianthus.*
Notes: We grow and supply border, perpetual and spray carnations as well as some garden pinks. Mail order available and plants available at shows around the UK.

NGKo **GREENKOOS**
16 Elm Grove, Droylsdon, Greater Manchester, M43 6LP
Ⓣ (0161) 612 5705
Ⓜ 07806 893816
Ⓔ keeflong@hotmail.com
Ⓦ http://www.greenkoos.co.uk
Contact: Keith Long
Opening Times: By appt. only.
Min Mail Order UK: £20.00
Cat. Cost: Online only.
Credit Cards: All major credit/debit cards
Specialities: Exotic and architectural plants including *Brugmansia, Lochroma, Canna,* Aroids and *Eucomis*. Also grow and sell a wide range of trees, shrubs, perennials, ferns, *Bonsai* and medicinal plants.
Notes: Plant nursery based in Manchester, best known for their *Brugmansia*. No online shop available yet. Please phone or email nursery for orders or details of plant fairs attended. Delivers to shows.
OS Grid Ref: SJ 890119

NGrd **GARDENER'S COTTAGE PLANTS**
Gardener's Cottage, Bingfield, Newcastle-upon-Tyne, Tyne and Wear, NE19 2LE
Ⓣ (01434) 672594
Ⓜ 07500 895052
Ⓔ andrew@gcplants.co.uk
Ⓦ www.gcplants.co.uk
Contact: Andrew Davenport
Opening Times: 1000-1600 Fri-Sat, Apr-Sep incl.
Min Mail Order UK: £20.00
Min Mail Order EU: £20.00
Credit Cards: None
Specialities: Perennials, herbs and wildflowers. The nursery runs on sustainable and organic principles whereby all plants sold are propagated on site, without chemicals, in peat-free composts and reycled pots.
Notes: Also sells at plant fairs. Contact nursery for details.

NGrs **GRASMERE GARDEN CENTRE** ♿
Church Stile, Grasmere, Cumbria, LA22 9SW
Ⓣ (015394) 35255
Ⓔ more@grasmeregardens.com
Contact: Ant Waugh
Opening Times: 0930-1800 Apr-Oct, 0930-1730 Nov-Mar.
Credit Cards: All major credit/debit cards
Notes: Wheelchair accessible.

NHal **HALLS OF HEDDON**
West Heddon Nurseries, Heddon-on-the-Wall, Northumberland, NE15 0JS
Ⓣ (01661) 852445
Ⓔ enquiry@hallsofheddon.co.uk
Ⓦ www.hallsofheddon.co.uk
Contact: David Hall
Opening Times: 0900-1700 Mon-Sat 1000-1700 Sun.
Min Mail Order UK: £10.00
Min Mail Order EU: £35.00
Cat. Cost: 3 × 2nd class.
Credit Cards: MasterCard, Visa, Switch, Delta
Specialities: *Chrysanthemum* & *Dahlia.*
Notes: Also sells wholesale.
OS Grid Ref: NZ122679

NHar **HARTSIDE NURSERY GARDEN**
Penrith Road, Alston, Cumbria, CA9 3BL
Ⓣ (01434) 381372
Ⓕ (01434) 381372
Ⓔ enquiries@plantswithaltitude.co.uk
Ⓦ www.plantswithaltitude.co.uk
Contact: Mr Neil Huntley
Opening Times: 1130-1630 Tue-Fri & 1230-1600 Sat, Sun & B/hols, Mar-Jun. 1130-1630 Tue-Fri, Jul-Oct. Other times by appt. only.
Min Mail Order UK: Nmc
Cat. Cost: 4 × 1st class.
Credit Cards: All major credit/debit cards
Specialities: *Primula,* including asiatic, petiolaris, european species and forms of P. *allionii*, saxifrages, autumn flowering gentians, erythoniums, roscoeas, trilliums.
Notes: If visiting our nursery we strongly advise checking our opening hours, especially during busy periods and in adverse weather conditions. Please check website for latest news. Delivers to shows.
OS Grid Ref: NY708447

NHaw **THE HAWTHORNES NURSERY** ♿
Marsh Road, Hesketh Bank, Nr Preston, Lancashire, PR4 6XT

Ⓣ (01772) 812379
Ⓔ richardhaw@talktalk.net
Ⓦ www.hawthornes-nursery.co.uk
Contact: Irene & Richard Hodson
Opening Times: 0900-1800 7 days, Mar-Jun & Thu-Sun, Jul-Oct. Gardens open for Plant Heritage.
Min Mail Order UK: £10.00
Min Mail Order EU: Nmc
Cat. Cost: None issued.
Credit Cards: None
Specialities: *Clematis*. National Plant Collection of *Clematis viticella, viorna* & *texensis* groups.
Notes: Exports beyond EU. Euro accepted. Wheelchair accessible.

N

NHol **HOLDEN CLOUGH NURSERY** ♿
Holden, Bolton-by-Bowland, Nr Clitheroe, Lancashire, BB7 4PF
Ⓣ (01200) 447447
Ⓔ info@holdencloughnursery.com
Ⓦ www.holdencloughnursery.com
Contact: Kate Lawson
Opening Times: 0900-1700 Mon-Sat, 1030-1630 Sun, incl. B/hols. Closed Xmas Day & Boxing Day.
Min Mail Order UK: Nmc
Min Mail Order EU: Nmc
Cat. Cost: 2 × 1st class.
Credit Cards: All major credit/debit cards
Specialities: Large general list incl. perennials, esp. *Crocosmia*, shrubs, dwarf conifers, alpines, heathers, grasses & ferns.
Notes: Seasonal mail order on some items. Also sells wholesale on some items. Exports beyond EU. Delivers to shows. Wheelchair accessible.
OS Grid Ref: SD773496

NHoy **HOYLAND PLANT CENTRE**
Market Street, Hoyland, Barnsley, South Yorkshire, S74 0ET
Ⓣ (01226) 744466
Ⓜ 07717 182169
Ⓕ (01226) 744466
Ⓔ hoylandplantcentre@btconnect.com
Ⓦ www.somethingforthegarden.co.uk
Contact: Steven Hickman
Opening Times: Open by appt. only.
Min Mail Order UK: Nmc
Min Mail Order EU: Nmc
Cat. Cost: Free online.
Credit Cards: All major credit/debit cards
Specialities: National Plant Collections of *Agapanthus* & *Tulbaghia*. Also holds a large collection of *Clivia* & *Nerine*.
Notes: Sells mail order or at major flower shows. Also sells wholesale. Exports beyond EU. Delivers to shows. Euro accepted. Partial wheelchair access. Top of the nursery and glasshouse accessible for most wheelchairs.
OS Grid Ref: SE372010

NHpl **HARPERLEY HALL FARM NURSERIES** ♿
Harperley, Stanley, Co. Durham, DH9 9UB
Ⓣ (01207) 233318
Ⓜ 07944 644126
Ⓔ enquiries@harperleyhallfarmnurseries.co.uk
Ⓦ www.harperleyhallfarmnurseries.co.uk
Contact: Gary McDermott
Opening Times: 0930-1630 7 days.
Min Mail Order UK: Nmc
Min Mail Order EU: Nmc
Cat. Cost: None issued.
Credit Cards: All major credit/debit cards
Specialities: Growers of a wide range of alpine & woodland plants, incl. *Meconopsis* & *Primula*, many of which are rare or unusual.
Notes: Also sells wholesale. Delivers to shows. Euro accepted. Wheelchair accessible.

NHrt **HORTOLOGY LTD**
Unit 1D, Marconi Road, Burgh Road Industrial Estate, Carlisle, Cumbria, CA2 7NA
Ⓜ 07824 330819
Ⓔ info@hortology.co.uk
Ⓦ https://hortology.co.uk
Contact: Mark McCance
Opening Times: Online only.
Credit Cards: All major credit/debit cards
Specialities: *Alocasia, Aloe, Agave, Aglaeonema, Aspidistra, Asplenium, Beaucarnea, Calathea, Chamaedorea, Chlorophytum, Chrysalidocapus, Crassula, Dracaena, Epipremnum, Euphorbia, Ficus, Howea, Monstera, Maranta, Maranta, Nephrolepsis, Pachira, Peperomia, Philodendron, Sansevieria, Spathiphyllum, Strelitzia, Yucca.*
Notes: Inspirational, quality assured houseplants, indoor plant pots & planters for lush living. Wellbeing style, delivered directly to your home or office. Create your urban jungle, mix & match sleek designer plants or retro rustic pots with exotic rainforest foliage, woodland ferns or desert cacti.

NHsp **HARE SPRING COTTAGE PLANTS**
Church Orchard, Church Wind, Alne, York, North Yorkshire, YO61 1RX
Ⓜ 07792 376805
Ⓔ stella@harespringcottageplants.co.uk
Ⓦ www.harespringcottageplants.co.uk
Contact: Stella Exley
Opening Times: By appt. only.
Min Mail Order UK: Nmc

Min Mail Order EU: Nmc
Cat. Cost: Online only.
Credit Cards: All major debit/credit cards except American Express
Specialities: *Camassia, Uvularia* & *Sidalcea*. National Plant Collection of *Camassia*. Some specialist plants available in small quantities only.
Notes: Sells at and delivers to specialist plant fairs. Talks to specialist groups & societies by arrangement. See website for open days Also sells wholesale. Delivers to shows. Euro accepted. Please call nursery to discuss accessibility requirements.

NJRG **JRG Dahlias**
22 Summerville Road, Milnthorpe, Cumbria, LA7 7DF
Ⓣ (01539) 562691
Ⓔ jack@jrg-dahlias.co.uk
Ⓦ www.jrg-dahlias.co.uk
Contact: Jack Gott
Opening Times: By appt. only.
Min Mail Order UK: £10.00 + p&p
Min Mail Order EU: Price with order
Cat. Cost: Sae: 110mm × 220mm, 2nd class.
Credit Cards: Paypal
Specialities: *Dahlia*. Some available in small quantities only.
Notes: Delivers to shows.

NLAp **Laneside Hardy Orchid Nursery** ♿
74 Croston Road, Garstang, Lancashire, PR3 1HR
Ⓣ (01995) 605537
Ⓜ 07946 659661
Ⓔ jcrhutch@aol.com
Ⓦ www.lanesidehardyorchids.co.uk
Contact: Jeff Hutchings
Opening Times: Not open, mail order only.
Min Mail Order UK: Nmc
Min Mail Order EU: Nmc
Cat. Cost: None issued.
Credit Cards: All major credit/debit cards
Specialities: Wide range of hardy, terrestrial orchids for the garden, meadow and alpine house.
Notes: Sales via shows and online shop. Delivers to shows. Exports beyond EU. Wheelchair accessible.

NLar **Larch Cottage Nurseries** ♿
Melkinthorpe, Penrith, Cumbria, CA10 2DR
Ⓣ (01931) 712404
Ⓔ plants@larchcottage.co.uk
Ⓦ www.larchcottage.co.uk
Contact: Peter & Joanne Stott
Opening Times: Daily from 0900-1700 (or dusk in winter), all year excl. Xmas, Boxing Day & New Year's Day.
Min Mail Order UK: £20.00 + p&p
Credit Cards: All major credit/debit cards
Specialities: Comprehensive plant collection in unique garden setting. Rare & unusual plants, particularly shrubs, trees, perennials, dwarf conifers & Japanese maples. *Acer, Hamamelis, Magnolia* & *Cornus* kousa cvs. Old-fashioned roses, bamboo & alpines.
Notes: Terraced restaurant, art gallery and shop open everyday. RHS partner gardens open Wed-Sun throughout the summer. Please check website for details. Wheelchair accessible.
OS Grid Ref: NY315602

NMen **Mendle Nursery** ♿
Holme, Scunthorpe, North Lincolnshire, DN16 3RF
Ⓣ (01724) 850864
Ⓔ ann.earnshaw@tiscali.co.uk
Ⓦ www.mendlenursery.co.uk
Contact: Mrs A. Earnshaw
Opening Times: 1000-1600 Tue-Sun.
Min Mail Order UK: Nmc
Min Mail Order EU: Nmc
Credit Cards: Paypal
Specialities: *Jovibarba, Sempervivum*, cacti & succulents.
Notes: Wheelchair accessible.
OS Grid Ref: SE925070

NMir **Mires Beck Nursery** ♿
Low Mill Lane, North Cave, Brough, East Riding, Yorkshire, HU15 2NR
Ⓣ (01430) 421543
Ⓕ (01430) 421543
Ⓔ sales@miresbeck.co.uk
Ⓦ www.miresbeck.co.uk
Contact: Sue Hewitt
Opening Times: 1000-1600 7 days, 1st Mar-30th Sep. 1000-1600 Mon-Fri, 1st Oct-30th Apr.
Min Mail Order UK: Nmc
Credit Cards: All major debit/credit cards except American Express
Specialities: Wildflower plants of Yorkshire provenance.
Notes: Mail order for wildflower plants & plugs only. Also sells wholesale. Wheelchair accessible.
OS Grid Ref: SE889316

NNor **Norcroft Nurseries** ♿
19 Carlton Gardens, Stanwix, Carlisle, Cumbria, CA3 9NR
Ⓣ (01228) 597681

Ⓜ 07887 781555
Ⓔ info@norcroftnurseries.co.uk
Ⓦ www.norcroftnurseries.co.uk
Contact: Keith Bell
Opening Times: By appt. only.
Min Mail Order UK: Nmc
Cat. Cost: 2 × 2nd class.
Credit Cards: None
Specialities: *Hosta.*
Notes: Visits by appt. only – please ring nursery to arrange. Also sells wholesale. Euro accepted. Wheelchair accessible.
OS Grid Ref: NY397572

NONu **Orchard Nurseries**
48 Hopgrove Lane South, York, Yorkshire, YO32 9TG
Ⓣ (01904) 421153
Ⓔ orchardnurseries@aol.com
Ⓦ orchardnurseries-york.co.uk
Contact: Chris Small
Opening Times: 0900-1700 Mon-Sat, 1000-1700 Sun. Other times by appt.
Credit Cards: Visa, MasterCard
Notes: We are a small retail nursery selling trees, shrubs & perennials. We also grow seasonal bedding & vegetable plants, with a few more unusual varieties. We pride ourselves on quality plants, service & advice. Whether you are new to gardening or a more accomplished gardener, we've got something for all.

NOra **Orange Pippin Ltd**
(office) 33 Algarth Rise, Pocklington, York, Yorkshire, YO42 2HX
Ⓣ (01759) 392007
Ⓔ trees@orangepippin.com
Ⓦ www.orangepippintrees.co.uk
Contact: Maureen Borrie
Opening Times: Not open. Mail order online only.
Min Mail Order UK: Nmc
Min Mail Order EU: Nmc
Cat. Cost: Online only.
Credit Cards: MasterCard, Visa
Specialities: Specialist online retailer of fruit and ornamental trees.
Notes: We list over 280 fruit varieties, traditional and modern. Wide choice of rootstocks & tree forms. We also offer over 300 ornamental tree varieties, including a wide range of flowering cherries, crab apples, rowan trees and many more. Fruit tree expert available most days. See website for ornamental trees www.pippintrees.co.uk. Order online all year. Deliveries from Aug-Apr. Exports beyond EU (to USA).

NOrn **Ornamental Trees Ltd**
The Nursery Office, Farnley Hall Estate, Farnley, West Yorkshire, LS21 2QF
Ⓣ (01943) 660870
Ⓔ sales@ornamental-trees.co.uk
Ⓦ www.ornamental-trees.co.uk
Contact: Nigel Coultas
Opening Times: Mail order only. 0800-1800, Mon-Fri, 0900-1200, Sat.
Min Mail Order UK: Nmc
Cat. Cost: Online only.
Credit Cards: MasterCard, Visa
Specialities: Specialise in ornamental and fruit trees, including mature trees.
Notes: Delivers to shows.

NPer **Perry's Plants** ♿
The River Garden, Sleights, Whitby, North Yorkshire, YO21 1RR
Ⓜ 07879 498623
Ⓔ richardperry008@hotmail.co.uk
Ⓦ www.perrysplants.co.uk
Contact: Sharon & Richard Perry
Opening Times: 1000-1700 mid-Mar to Oct.
Cat. Cost: N/A
Credit Cards: None
Specialities: *Lavatera, Malva, Erysimum, Euphorbia, Anthemis, Osteospermum* & *Hebe.* Uncommon hardy & container plants & aquatic plants.
Notes: Euro accepted. Wheelchair accessible.
OS Grid Ref: NZ869082

NPic **Every Picture Tells a Story**
Ormskirk Old Road, Bickerstaffe, Merseyside, L39 0HD
Ⓣ (0151) 286 2033
Ⓜ 07847 939867
Ⓔ don@every-picture.com
Ⓦ www.everypicture-shop.com
Contact: Don Billington
Opening Times: 1000-1700.
Min Mail Order UK: £1.00
Credit Cards: All major credit/debit cards
Specialities: *Aechmea, Guzmania* & *Tillandsia.* Other plants available in small quantities. National Collections of Bromeliads (*Aechmea, Billbergia* & *Neoregelia*).
Notes: Delivers to shows.

NPlm **The Palm Tree Company**
Mead Croft, Clitheroe Road, Whalley, Lancashire, BB7 9AD
Ⓣ (01254) 447964
Ⓜ 07970 772743
Ⓔ sales@thepalmtreecompany.com
Ⓦ www.thepalmtreecompany.com
Contact: Christopher Day

Opening Times: Online only 24hrs 7 days.
Credit Cards: All major credit/debit cards
Specialities: Palm trees, olive trees, tree ferns, yuccas, large cacti, grapevines, large agaves, bamboo, topiary trees, citrus trees, cycads, dasylirions, unusual collector palms.
OS Grid Ref: SD735374

NPnk **PRIMROSE BANK** ♿
Redroofs, Dauby Lane, Kexby, York, Yorkshire, YO41 5LH
Ⓣ (01759) 380220
Ⓜ 07774 944447
Ⓔ suegoodwill@yahoo.co.uk
Ⓦ www.primrosebank.co.uk
Contact: Sue Goodwill
Opening Times: 1000-1700 Thu-Sat Please telephone for opening times Jul-Oct.
Cat. Cost: None issued.
Credit Cards: All major credit/debit cards
Specialities: *Hydrangea, Galanthus, Primula* & *Echinacea.*
Notes: Delivers to shows. Wheelchair accessible.
OS Grid Ref: SE696508

NPoe **POETS COTTAGE SHRUB NURSERY** ♿
Lealholm, Whitby, North Yorkshire, YO21 2AQ
Ⓣ (01947) 897424
Ⓜ 07813 252303
Ⓔ enquiries@poetscottage.co.uk
Ⓦ www.poetscottage.co.uk
Contact: Ilona J. McGivern
Opening Times: 1300-1530 Feb, 0900-1700 Mar-Christmas, 7 days. Closed Jan.
Cat. Cost: None issued.
Credit Cards: All major debit/credit cards except American Express
Specialities: Conifers, pines, trees, shrubs, herbaceous, alpines, herbs & *Acer.*
Notes: Wheelchair accessible.

NPol **POLEMONIUM PLANTERY** ♿
28 Sunnyside, Trimdon Grange, Co. Durham, TS29 6HF
Ⓣ (01429) 881529
Ⓔ dandd@polemonium.co.uk
Ⓦ www.polemonium.co.uk
Contact: Dianne Nichol-Brown
Opening Times: By appt. only or see website.
Min Mail Order UK: £10.00
Cat. Cost: 3 × 1st class.
Credit Cards: All major credit/debit cards, Paypal
Specialities: National Plant Collections of *Polemonium, Collomia, Gilia, Fragaria vesca, Leptodactylon* (*Polemoniaceae*) & *Hakonechloa.*
Notes: Also sells wholesale. Delivers to shows. Wheelchair accessible.
OS Grid Ref: NZ369353

NQui **QUIET CORNER PLANTS**
(office) 20 Grove Road, Brandon, Co. Durham, DH7 8AW
Ⓜ 07932 159204
Ⓔ hal@uwclub.net
Ⓦ www.quietcornerplants.co.uk
Contact: Howard Leslie
Opening Times: By appt. only.
Min Mail Order UK: Nmc
Cat. Cost: Online only.
Credit Cards: All major credit/debit cards
Specialities: Hardy herbaceous & shrubby perennials, incl. small quantities of lesser known and harder to find plants.
Notes: Nursery is at Misty Blue Farm, Rock Road, Kirk Merrington, Co. Durham, DL16 7HJ. Also sells wholesale. Delivers to shows.

NRHS **HARLOW CARR PLANT CENTRE (RHS)** ◆
RHS Garden Harlow Carr, Crag Lane, Harlow Carr, Harrogate, North Yorkshire, HG3 1QB
Ⓣ (01423) 724666
Ⓕ (01423) 569521
Ⓔ nigeleaton@rhs.org.uk
Ⓦ www.rhs.org.uk
Contact: Nigel Eaton
Opening Times: 0930-1700 Mon-Sun.
Specialities: Wide general range, particularly alpines.
Notes: Programme of free plant events throughout the year. Please ring or check website for details. Customer ordering system for plants which need to be collected from the plant centre (no mail order).

NRob **W ROBINSON & SON (SEEDS & PLANTS) LTD** ♿
Sunny Bank, Forton, Nr Preston, Lancashire, PR3 0BN
Ⓣ (01524) 791210
Ⓕ (01524) 791933
Ⓔ info@mammothonion.co.uk
Ⓦ www.mammothonion.co.uk
Contact: Miss Robinson
Opening Times: 1000-1600 7 days Mar-Jun, 0800-1700 Mon-Fri Jul-Feb.
Min Mail Order UK: £2.75
Min Mail Order EU: £5.25
Cat. Cost: Free.
Credit Cards: All major credit/debit cards
Specialities: Mammoth vegetable seed. Onions, leeks, tomatoes & beans. Range of

unusual and heritage vegetable seeds. Range of vegetable plants in the spring.
Notes: Also sells wholesale. Exports beyond EU. Delivers to shows. Wheelchair accessible.

NRog **R V ROGER LTD** ♿
The Nurseries, Malton Road, Pickering, North Yorkshire, YO18 7JW
Ⓣ (01751) 472226
Ⓔ sales@rvroger.co.uk
Ⓦ www.rvroger.co.uk
Contact: Ian Roger
Opening Times: 0800-1700 Mon-Sat 1000-1600 Sun.
Min Mail Order UK: Nmc
Min Mail Order EU: Nmc
Cat. Cost: £1.00
Credit Cards: All major credit/debit cards
Specialities: Holders of National Collection of *Erythronium*.
Notes: Third generation family-owned business, established in 1913 growing hardy stock at the foot of the North York Moors. Also sells wholesale. Exports beyond EU. Wheelchair accessible.
OS Grid Ref: SE801827

NRya **RYAL NURSERY** ♿
East Farm Cottage, Ryal, Northumberland, NE20 0SA
Ⓣ (01661) 886562
Ⓔ ruthhadden@btinternet.com
Contact: R. Hadden
Opening Times: Mar-Jul by appt. please telephone in advance.
Cat. Cost: Sae.
Credit Cards: None
Specialities: Alpine & woodland plants, mainly available in small quantities only. National Collection of *Primula marginata*.
Notes: Also sells wholesale. Delivers to shows. Wheelchair accessible.
OS Grid Ref: NZ015744

NSla **SLACK TOP ALPINE NURSERY**
Alpine House, 22A Slack Top, Hebden Bridge, West Yorkshire, HX7 7HA
Ⓣ (01422) 845348
Ⓜ 07392 856395
Ⓔ enquiries@slacktopnurseries.co.uk
Ⓦ www.slacktopnurseries.co.uk
Contact: Michael & Allison Mitchell
Opening Times: 1000-1700 Fri-Sun only, Mar-Aug & B/hols. Other times by appt.
Min Mail Order UK: £20.00
Min Mail Order EU: £50.00
Cat. Cost: 2 × 1st class A5 sae or online.
Credit Cards: All major credit/debit cards
Specialities: Alpine, rockery & woodland plants. *Saxifraga, Hepatica.*
Notes: Talks given to gardening clubs & other groups by appt. Delivers to shows. Euro accepted. Partial wheelchair access. (Some areas of garden inaccessible.)
OS Grid Ref: SD977286

NSti **STILLINGFLEET LODGE NURSERIES** ♿
Stewart Lane, Stillingfleet, York, YO19 6HP
Ⓣ (01904) 728506
Ⓔ info@stillingfleetlodgenurseries.co.uk
Ⓦ www.stillingfleetlodgenurseries.co.uk
Contact: Vanessa Cook
Opening Times: 1300-1700 Wed & Fri, 1st Apr-30th Sep. 1300-1700, 1st & 3rd Sat & Sun in each month.
Cat. Cost: Online only.
Credit Cards: All major credit/debit cards
Specialities: Foliage & unusual perennials. Hardy geraniums, *Pulmonaria*, variegated plants & grasses.
Notes: Wheelchair accessible.

NSue **SUE PROCTOR PLANTS** ♿
69 Ings Mill Avenue, Clayton West, Huddersfield, West Yorkshire, HD8 9QG
Ⓣ (01484) 866189
Ⓜ 07917 006636
Ⓔ hostas@sueproctorplants.co.uk
Ⓦ www.sueproctorplants.com
Contact: Sue Proctor
Opening Times: By appt. only Please telephone first.
Cat. Cost: 1st class sae.
Credit Cards: All major credit/debit cards
Specialities: *Hosta*, incl. miniature *Hosta*.
Notes: Wheelchair accessible.
OS Grid Ref: SE256110

NSum **SUMMERDALE GARDEN NURSERY**
Summerdale House, Cow Brow, Lupton, Carnforth, Cumbria, LA6 1PE
Ⓣ (01539) 567210
Ⓔ summerdale@btinternet.com
Ⓦ www.summerdalegardenplants.co.uk
Contact: Gail Sheals
Opening Times: 1100-1630 Mar to end of Aug.
Min Mail Order UK: £20.00
Cat. Cost: Online only.
Credit Cards: Paypal
Specialities: Shade-loving perennials. *Primula*, including P. *auricula* cultivars.
Notes: Mail order for primulas only.
OS Grid Ref: SD545819

NTay **TAYLORS CLEMATIS NURSERY** ♿
Sutton Road, Sutton, Nr Askern,
Doncaster, South Yorkshire,
DN6 9JZ
Ⓣ (01302) 700716
Ⓜ 07793 201808
Ⓔ info@taylorsclematis.co.uk
Ⓦ www.taylorsclematis.co.uk
Contact: Chris Cocks
Opening Times: Open by appt. only.
Min Mail Order UK: Nmc
Min Mail Order EU: Nmc
Cat. Cost: £1.00
Credit Cards: All major credit/debit cards
Specialities: *Clematis* (over 400 varieties).
Notes: Largest selection of *Clematis* in the UK. Nursery is open by appt. only Delivers to shows. Wheelchair accessible.
OS Grid Ref: SE552122

NTPC **TREE PEONY COMPANY**
Willow Cottage, Rillington, Malton,
North Yorkshire, YO17 8JU
Ⓣ (01944) 758280
Ⓔ info@treepeony.co.uk
Ⓦ www.treepeony.co.uk
Contact: Thelma Scruton, Roger Scruton
Min Mail Order UK: £15.00
Min Mail Order EU: Nmc
Cat. Cost: None.
Credit Cards: None
Specialities: Tree peonies. *Paeonia suffruticosa, P. Gansu Group, P. rockii.*
Notes: Also sells wholesale. Euro accepted. Delivers to shows.

NTrD **TREE2MYDOOR LTD**
Ⓣ (161) 870 6590
Ⓔ hello@tree2mydoor.com
Ⓦ https://tree2mydoor.com/
Contact: David Sharp
Opening Times: 0900-1600 Mon-Fri. Closed Sat-Sun.
Min Mail Order UK: £4.90
Min Mail Order EU: £15.00
Credit Cards: All major credit/debit cards
Specialities: Trees.
Notes: Tree2mydoor specialise in sending a wide variety of trees, plants and shrubs as gifts around the UK & Ireland. Browse 100s of varieties perfect for any occasion such as anniversaries, birthdays & memorials. We offer both consumer and large bulk corporate ordering.

NWac **WACK'S WICKED PLANTS**
Nr Scampston Walled Garden, Scampston,
North Yorkshire, YO17 8NG
Ⓜ 07530 176624
Ⓔ info@wackswickedplants.co.uk
Ⓦ www.wackswickedplants.co.uk
Contact: Peter Walker
Opening Times: By appt. only.
Min Mail Order UK: Nmc
Min Mail Order EU: Nmc
Credit Cards: All major credit/debit cards
Specialities: *Sarracenia, Dionaea, Drosera, Darlingtonia, Cephalotus* all year. *Pinguicula, Nepenthes, Utricularia* during growing season.
Notes: We specialise in hardy carnivorous plants. Euro accepted. Delivers to shows.

NWad **WADDOW LODGE GARDEN** ♿
Clitheroe Road, Waddington,
Clitheroe, Lancashire,
BB7 3HQ
Ⓣ (01200) 429145
Ⓔ peterfoleyhcn@hotmail.co.uk
Ⓦ www.gardentalks.co.uk
Contact: Peter Foley
Opening Times: By appt. only all year. Also open under NGS (May and Jul) once again in 2020.
Min Mail Order UK: Nmc
Min Mail Order EU: Nmc
Cat. Cost: Online only.
Credit Cards: None
Specialities: An ever-developing plantsman's garden with an interesting plant collection. Some plants may only be available in small numbers.
Notes: Open for group visits by appt. (incl. evenings). Wheelchair accessible.
OS Grid Ref: SD732434

NWea **WEASDALE NURSERIES LTD.**
Newbiggin on Lune, Kirkby Stephen,
Cumbria, CA17 4LX
Ⓣ (015396) 23246
Ⓕ (015396) 23277
Ⓔ sales@weasdale.com
Ⓦ www.weasdale.com
Contact: Andrew Forsyth
Opening Times: 0830-1730 Mon-Fri (closed for lunch 13.00-14.00). Closed w/ends & B/hols.
Min Mail Order UK: Nmc
Min Mail Order EU: Nmc
Cat. Cost: Free.
Credit Cards: All major credit/debit cards
Specialities: Hardy forest trees, hedging, broadleaved & conifers. Specimen trees & shrubs grown at 850ft (260m) elevation. Some rarer plants grown in small batches, so availability can't be guaranteed. Peat-free.

Notes: Mail order a speciality. Mail order Nov-Apr only. Also sells wholesale to VAT registered customers.
OS Grid Ref: NY689800

NWsh **Westshores Nurseries**
82 West Street, Winterton,
Scunthorpe, Lincolnshire,
DN15 9QF
Ⓣ (01724) 733940
Ⓜ 07875 732535
Ⓔ westshnur@aol.com
Ⓦ www.westshores.co.uk
Contact: Gail & John Summerfield
Opening Times: By appt. only.
Min Mail Order UK: £15.00
Min Mail Order EU: £15.00
Cat. Cost: Online only.
Credit Cards: All major credit/debit cards
Specialities: Ornamental grasses, autumn flowering perennials & scented pelargoniums.
Notes: Wide selection of talks for gardening clubs and Hardy Plant Society groups located up to 100 miles (or 3 hours) away in one direction.
OS Grid Ref: SE927187

S

Southern

SAdn **Ashdown Forest Garden Centre & Nursery** ♿
Duddleswell, Ashdown Forest, East Sussex, TN22 3JP
Ⓣ (01825) 712300
Ⓔ info@ashdownforestgardencentre.co.uk
Ⓦ www.ashdownforestgardencentre.co.uk
Contact: Victoria Falletti
Opening Times: 0900-1700 winter, 0900-1700 summer. Greenfingers Café open 0930-1700.
Min Mail Order UK: Nmc
Credit Cards: All major credit/debit cards
Specialities: *Lapageria, Fuchsia*, conservatory climbers & unusual shrubs. Available in small quantities only.
Notes: Wheelchair accessible.
OS Grid Ref: TQ468283

SAko **Akorn and Oake**
18 Twyford Avenue, Southampton,
Hampshire, SO15 5NP
Ⓣ (023) 8034 4040
Ⓜ 07973 149404
Ⓔ stefan.rau@hotmail.co.uk
Contact: Stefan Rau
Opening Times: Open by appt. only.
Specialities: *Saxifraga.*
Notes: Delivers to shows.

SAll **Allwoods (Hassocks) Ltd** ♿
London Road, Hassocks, West Sussex,
BN6 9NA
Ⓣ (01273) 844229
Ⓔ plants@allwoods.net
Ⓦ www.allwoods.net
Contact: David & Emma James
Opening Times: Office 0900-1630 Mon-Fri. Answer machine all other times. Office is closed B/hols and Xmas-New Year. Visits by prior appt. only.
Min Mail Order UK: Nmc
Min Mail Order EU: Nmc
Credit Cards: All major debit/credit cards except American Express, Paypal
Specialities: Large collection of Garden Pinks & Carnations. Unusual & rare pelargoniums and an interesting succulent range – many not found elsewhere. A selection of *Fuchsia* & other garden plants. All British grown direct from our Sussex nursery.
Notes: All listed varieties available as plugs but choice varies depending on time of year. Please phone before travelling to avoid disappointment &/or to ensure order is ready for collection. Plant nursery is NOT open to visitors without prior appointment. Also sells wholesale. Wheelchair accessible.

SAlS **Alstroemeria Select**
Dingley Dell, Toddington Road,
Westoning, Bedfordshire,
MK45 5AH
Ⓣ (01525) 878924
Ⓔ customerservice@alstroemeriaselect.co.uk
Ⓦ www.alstroemeriaselect.co.uk
Contact: Angela Oliver
Opening Times: 0900-1600 Mon-Fri. We are often in the nursery so do email with queries if no answer on telephone.
Min Mail Order UK: Nmc
Min Mail Order EU: Nmc
Credit Cards: All major credit/debit cards
Specialities: Around 200 varieties of *Alstroemeria.*
Notes: Small, family run nursery growing and supplying stock. Not open to the public but plants can be collected by prior arrangement. Also sells wholesale. Delivers to shows.

SAng **Angharad Pike Gardener and Plants** ♿
Old Workshop, St Peters Road, Hayling Island, Hampshire, PO11 0RX
Ⓣ (02392) 468036
Ⓜ 07753 225670
Ⓔ angharad.pike@gmail.com
Ⓦ www.angharadpike.com

Contact: Angharad Pike
Opening Times: Please see website for opening times.
Credit Cards: All major credit/debit cards, American Express
Notes: All plants listed are available to view in the gardens at The Old Workshop. Plants can be pre-ordered for collection at any of the Open Gardens we are attending. Plants are sold in 1litre pots, grown in peat-free compost. All our plants are British grown. Wheelchair accessible.
OS Grid Ref: SU731037

SApu **Apuldram Roses**
Crouchers Farm, 163 Birdham Road, Apuldram, Chichester, West Sussex, PO20 7EQ
Ⓣ (01243) 785769
Ⓔ enquiries@apuldramroses.co.uk
Ⓦ www.apuldramroses.co.uk
Contact: Elizabeth Sawday
Opening Times: Winter 1000-1600 Mon to Fri & 1000-1300 Sat. Summer 1000-1700 Mon-Fri & 1000-1600 Sat.
Min Mail Order UK: £10.00
Credit Cards: All major credit/debit cards,
Specialities: Roses.
Notes: Specialist rose grower. Lots of friendly, helpful advice given if wanted.

SArc **Architectural Plants Ltd** ♿
Stane Street, North Heath, Pulborough, West Sussex, RH20 1DJ
Ⓣ (01798) 879213
Ⓔ enquiries@architecturalplants.com
Ⓦ www.architecturalplants.com
Contact: Sophie Pett-Gallacher
Opening Times: Nursery 0900-1700 Mon-Sat & B/hols. Closed Sun. Café 1000-1600 Mon-Sat.
Cat. Cost: Free.
Credit Cards: All major debit/credit cards except American Express
Specialities: Architectural plants & hardy exotics esp. rare evergreen & seaside exotics, spikey plants, yuccas/agaves, climbers, evergreen trees and shrubs, topiary & bamboos.
Notes: Café & shop. Also sells wholesale. Delivers to shows. Wheelchair accessible (& wheelchairs available on site).
OS Grid Ref: TQ192262

SavN **Savin Nurseries**
Hillside Road, Stondon, Bedfordshire, SG16 6LP
Ⓣ (01462) 850680
Ⓔ savinbase@hotmail.co.uk
Ⓦ www.savinnurseries.co.uk
Contact: Darryl Savin
Opening Times: 0830-1745 Mon-Fri, 0830-1700 Sat, 1000-1600 Sun (winter).
Credit Cards: All major debit/credit cards except American Express
Specialities: *Bonsai*, bedding, house plants, acers, perennials, olives.
Notes: Family run nursery growing their own bedding plants, shrubs, perennials and small trees.

SBdl **Grow at Brogdale** ♿
Brogdale Farm, Brogdale Road, Faversham, Kent, ME13 8XZ
Ⓣ (01795) 531888
Ⓕ (01795) 531710
Ⓔ fruit@brogdaleonline.co.uk
Ⓦ https://www.brogdaleonline.co.uk
Contact: Donna Cooper
Opening Times: 1000-1600 Mon-Sun.
Min Mail Order UK: Nmc
Min Mail Order EU: Nmc
Cat. Cost: £4.95
Credit Cards: All major credit/debit cards
Specialities: Rare and heritage varieties of apple, pear, cherry, plum and nuts.
Notes: Fruit trees grafted by hand from the trees in the National Fruit Collection, with rare and heritage varieties being our specialism. Exports beyond EU. Euro accepted. Also sells wholesale. Wheelchair accessible.
OS Grid Ref: TR006505

SBea **Bean Place Nursery**
Watersfield, Bletchenden Road, Headcorn, Kent, TN27 9JB
Ⓜ 07841 484822
Ⓔ info@beanplace.co.uk
Ⓦ www.beanplace.co.uk
Contact: Timothy Waters
Opening Times: By appt. only.
Min Mail Order UK: £5.95
Cat. Cost: Online.
Credit Cards: None
Specialities: Ornamental grasses, herbaceous perennials & cottage garden plants.
Notes: Growers of hardy herbaceous perennials, bearded iris, ornamental grasses and hardy garden ferns. Delivers to shows.

SBGi **Bamboo Giant** ♿
Athelas Plants, Hooe Road, Ninfield, Sussex, TN33 9EL
Ⓣ (01424) 563045
Ⓜ 07703 325321

Ⓔ matt@bamboogiant.co.uk
Ⓦ www.bamboogiant.co.uk
Contact: Matt
Opening Times: 0900-1700 Mon-Sat, 1000-1600 Sun. 1000-1600 B/hols.
Min Mail Order UK: Nmc
Credit Cards: All major credit/debit cards
Specialities: *Phyllostachys.*
Notes: We are a family run specialist bamboo nursery selling online and retail. We stock a range of clumping and non-clumping bamboo perfect for any environment for screening and adding privacy to your garden. Also sells wholesale. Wheelchair accessible.
OS Grid Ref: TQ698109

SBls **BLACKSTEM PLANTS**
Shepherds Lodge, Clay Hill Road, Lamberhurst, Kent, TN3 8LT
Ⓜ 07973 129102
Ⓔ info@blackstemplants.co.uk
Ⓦ www.blackstemplants.co.uk
Contact: Carole Lamond
Opening Times: By appt. only spring until autumn.
Credit Cards: All major credit/debit cards, Paypal
Specialities: Interesting and unusual perennials and grasses.
Notes: All plants grown at the nursery from seed, cuttings or division. Plants sold at specialist plant fairs in Kent & Sussex. Pre-orders welcome for collection at events. Nursery open by appontment only from spring until autumn. Delivers to shows.
OS Grid Ref: TQ652368

SBmr **BLACKMOOR NURSERIES**
Blackmoor Estate, Blackmoor, Nr Liss, Hampshire, GU33 6BS
Ⓣ (01420) 477978
Ⓔ jon@blackmoor.co.uk
Ⓦ www.blackmoor.co.uk
Contact: Jon Munday
Opening Times: 0730-1600.
Min Mail Order UK: Nmc
Min Mail Order EU: Nmc
Cat. Cost: None issued.
Credit Cards: All major credit/debit cards
Specialities: Fruit trees, soft fruit & ornamental trees.
Notes: Blackmoor is one of the very few nurseries in the UK offering gardeners the opportunity to buy fruit plants directly from our nursery. It is part of the Blackmoor Estate in Hampshire, which has been maintained by the Selborne family for several generations.
OS Grid Ref: SU779336

SBrt **BRIGHTON PLANTS** ♿
New Hall Lane, Small Dole, Sussex, BN5 9YJ
Ⓜ 07955 744802
Ⓔ brighton.plants@gmail.com
Ⓦ www.brightonplants.blogspot.com
Contact: Steve Law
Opening Times: Open by appt. only Please email/phone before visiting.
Min Mail Order UK: Nmc
Min Mail Order EU: Nmc
Cat. Cost: 4 × 1st class.
Credit Cards: None
Specialities: Hardy herbaceous and woody plants. Drought-tolerant plants.
Notes: Delivers to shows. Euro accepted. Wheelchair accessible.
OS Grid Ref: TQ208132

SBut **BUTTERFLY COTTAGE GARDEN PLANTS** ♿
(Office), 55 Middle Brook Street, Winchester, Hampshire, SO23 8DQ
Ⓣ (01962) 621882
Ⓜ 0796 2869105
Ⓔ andrew.ward203@ntlworld.com
Ⓦ www.butterflycottageplants.co.uk
Contact: Andy Ward
Opening Times: Open Mar-Sep 1000-1600 Thu, Fri and most Sats. (Please telephone for Sat opening times).
Min Mail Order UK: Nmc
Cat. Cost: Online only.
Credit Cards: All major credit/debit cards
Specialities: Growing perennials to attract a variety of pollinators, including many garden-worthy natives. Also old-fashioned Pinks. Limited numbers of each variety as all grown at nursery. Order early to avoid disappointment.
Notes: Nursery is at Cheriton Village, Alresford, Hants SO24 0PW. See website for directions. Please check plant availability before travelling from a distance. Wheelchair accessible. Delivers to shows.
OS Grid Ref: SU583972

SCam **CAMELLIA GROVE NURSERY** ♿
Market Garden, Lower Beeding, Horsham, West Sussex, RH13 6PP
Ⓣ (01403) 891412
Ⓔ lp@hortic.com
Ⓦ www.camellia-grove.com
Contact: Chris Loder
Opening Times: 1000-1600 Mon-Sat, please phone first so we can give you our undivided attention.
Min Mail Order UK: Nmc
Min Mail Order EU: Nmc

Cat. Cost: Please enquire.
Credit Cards: All major debit/credit cards except American Express
Specialities: *Camellia japonica, C. williamsii, C. sasanqua* & *C. reticulata*, from the purest white to richest red flowers.
Notes: Also sells wholesale. Exports beyond EU. Delivers to shows. Euro accepted. Wheelchair accessible.
OS Grid Ref: TQ221255

SCgs **Cottage Garden Plants and Seeds**
Little Orchard, Single Street, Berrys Green, Westerham, Kent, TN16 3AA
Ⓣ (01732) 866439
Ⓜ 07910 874483
Ⓔ info@cottagegardenseeds.co.uk
Ⓦ www.cottagegardenseeds.co.uk
Contact: Shirley Tullett
Opening Times: Open spring & summer by appt. only.
Min Mail Order UK: £3.75
Cat. Cost: Free.
Credit Cards: All major credit/debit cards
Specialities: We specialise in plants with The Award of Garden Merit and plants that are easy to grow and perform well over a long period.
Notes: Euro payment via Paypal only.

SChF **Charleshurst Farm Nursery**
Loxwood Road, Plaistow, Billingshurst, West Sussex, RH14 0NY
Ⓣ (01403) 752273
Ⓜ 07736 522788
Ⓔ info@charleshurstplants.co.uk
Ⓦ www.charleshurstplants.co.uk
Contact: Clive Mellor
Opening Times: Normally 0900-1730 Fri, Sat, Sun, Feb-Oct, but please ring before travelling.
Min Mail Order UK: Nmc
Min Mail Order EU: Nmc
Cat. Cost: Online only.
Credit Cards: All major credit/debit cards
Specialities: Shrubs including some more unusual species. Good range of Daphnes & Japanese maples.
Notes: Delivers to shows. Euro accepted.
OS Grid Ref: TQ015308

SChr **John Churcher**
47 Grove Avenue, Portchester, Fareham, Hampshire, PO16 9EZ
Ⓣ (023) 9232 6740
Ⓜ 07717 495861
Ⓔ johnchurcher47@btinternet.com
Contact: John Churcher
Opening Times: By appt. only Please phone or email.
Min Mail Order UK: Nmc
Min Mail Order EU: Nmc
Cat. Cost: None issued.
Credit Cards: None
Specialities: Hardy exotics for the mediterranean-style garden, incl. palms, tree ferns, *Musa*, hedychiums, cycads, *Agave*, *Aloe, Opuntia* & echiums. Stock available in small quantities only.
OS Grid Ref: SU614047

SCit **The Citrus Centre** ♿
West Mare Lane, Pulborough, West Sussex, RH20 2EA
Ⓣ (01798) 872786
Ⓔ enquiries@citruscentre.co.uk
Ⓦ www.citruscentre.co.uk
Contact: Amanda & Chris Dennis
Opening Times: 0930-1600 Tue-Sat. Phone or check website for Xmas & B/hol opening times.
Min Mail Order UK: Nmc
Min Mail Order EU: Nmc
Cat. Cost: Online.
Credit Cards: Visa, MasterCard
Specialities: Citrus & citrus relatives.
Notes: Wheelchair accessible.

SCob **Coblands Garden Centre**
Dryhill Lane, Sundridge, Kent, TN14 6AA
Ⓣ (01959) 561274
Ⓔ sevenoaks@coblands.co.uk
Ⓦ https://www.coblands.co.uk/
Contact: Coblands Sales Team
Opening Times: 0800-1700 Mon-Sat 1000-1600 Sun.
Min Mail Order UK: Nmc
Min Mail Order EU: Nmc
Credit Cards: All major debit/credit cards except American Express
Notes: Wide range of shrubs & established specimen plants. Herbaceous perennials including many new varieties.
OS Grid Ref: TQ586487

SCoo **Cooling's Nurseries Ltd** ♿
Rushmore Hill, Knockholt, Sevenoaks, Kent, TN14 7NN
Ⓣ (01959) 532269
Ⓕ (01959) 534092
Ⓔ Plantfinder@coolings.co.uk
Ⓦ www.coolings.co.uk
Contact: Mark Reeve or Garry Norris
Opening Times: 0900-1700 Mon-Sat & 0900-1630 Sun. Extended opening hours Apr-Jul 0900-1730 Mon-Sat.

Min Mail Order UK: Nmc
Cat. Cost: None issued.
Credit Cards: All major debit/credit cards except American Express
Specialities: Large range of perennials, conifers & bedding plants. Many unusual shrubs & trees. Third generation family business.
Notes: Display garden. Coffee shop. Wheelchair accessible.
OS Grid Ref: TK477610

SDay **A La Carte Daylilies**
Little Hermitage, St Catherine's Down, Ventnor, Isle of Wight, PO38 2PD
Ⓣ (01983) 730512
Ⓔ andy.hyjack@googlemail.com
Ⓦ www.alacartedaylilies.co.uk
Contact: Jan & Andy Wyers
Opening Times: Mail order only. Open by appt. only. Nursery is located on an unmade private road which may be difficult to find. Please phone/email for directions.
Min Mail Order UK: Nmc
Min Mail Order EU: Nmc
Cat. Cost: 3 × 1st class.
Credit Cards: None
Specialities: *Hemerocallis*. National Plant Collection of miniature & small flowered *Hemerocallis* & large flowered *Hemerocallis* (post-1960 award-winning cvs).
Notes: Euro accepted.
OS Grid Ref: SZ499787

SDeJ **P. de Jager & Sons Ltd** ♿ ◆
Church Farm, Ulcombe, Maidstone, Kent, ME17 1DN
Ⓣ (01622) 840229
Ⓕ (01622) 844073
Ⓔ flowerbulbs@dejager.co.uk
Ⓦ www.dejager.co.uk
Contact: George Clowes
Opening Times: Mail order only. Orders taken from 0900-1700 Mon-Fri.
Min Mail Order UK: Nmc
Min Mail Order EU: Nmc
Cat. Cost: Free.
Credit Cards: All major credit/debit cards
Specialities: Wide range of all flower bulbs.
Notes: Also sells wholesale. Exports beyond EU. Euro accepted. Wheelchair accessible.

SDir **Direct Bulbs**
Mault-Ley, 6, Hillside Close, Teg Down, Winchester, Hampshire, SO22 5LW
Ⓣ (01962) 840038
Ⓜ 07766 517703
Ⓔ tim.woodland@btconnect.com
Ⓦ www.directbulbs.co.uk
Contact: Jo Woodland
Opening Times: Mail order only.
Min Mail Order UK: £5.95
Min Mail Order EU: £20.00
Credit Cards: All major credit/debit cards
Specialities: All types of flower bulbs.
Notes: Also sells wholesale. Suppliers of spring and summer flowering bulbs.

SDix **Great Dixter Nurseries** ♿
Dixter Road, Northiam, Rye, East Sussex, TN31 6PH
Ⓣ (01797) 254044
Ⓔ nursery@greatdixter.co.uk
Ⓦ www.greatdixter.co.uk
Contact: Michael Morphy
Opening Times: 0900-1700 Mon-Sat, 1000-1700 Sun Apr-end Oct 0900-1230 & 1330-1630 Mon-Fri, 0900-1230 Sat, Sun closed Nov-end Mar.
Min Mail Order UK: Nmc
Cat. Cost: £1.00
Credit Cards: All major credit/debit cards
Specialities: *Clematis*, shrubs and plants. Gardens open.
Notes: Usual and unusual shrubs and perennials. Mail order Oct to end of Mar. Wheelchair accessible.
OS Grid Ref: TQ821251

SDow **Downderry Nursery** ♿
Pillar Box Lane, Hadlow, Nr Tonbridge, Kent, TN11 9SW
Ⓣ (01732) 810081
Ⓔ info@downderry-nursery.co.uk
Ⓦ www.downderry-nursery.co.uk
Contact: Dr Simon Charlesworth
Opening Times: 1000-1700 Thu-Sun, 1st May-27th Sep & B/hols. Other times by appt.
Min Mail Order UK: Nmc
Min Mail Order EU: Nmc
Cat. Cost: Free.
Credit Cards: Delta, MasterCard, Maestro, Visa
Specialities: National Plant Collections of *Lavandula* and *Rosmarinus*.
Notes: Wheelchair accessible.
OS Grid Ref: TQ625521

SDys **Dysons Nurseries** ♿
Great Comp Garden, Platt, Sevenoaks, Kent, TN15 8QS
Ⓣ (01732) 885094
Ⓜ 07887 997663
Ⓔ dysonsorders@greatcompgarden.co.uk
Ⓦ www.dysonsalvias.com

Contact: William T. Dyson
Opening Times: 1000-1700 7 days 1st Mar-31st Oct. Other times by appt.
Cat. Cost: Online only.
Credit Cards: All major credit/debit cards
Specialities: *Salvia* & an eclectic range of choice and uncommon plants.
Notes: Delivers to shows. Wheelchair accessible.

SEdd **Eddington House Nursery**
Eddington Road, Nettlestone/Seaview, Isle of Wight, Hampshire, PO34 5EF
Ⓜ 07837 589478
Ⓔ info@eddingtonhousenursery.co.uk
Ⓦ www.eddingtonhousenursery.co.uk
Contact: Ian Chadwick
Opening Times: 1000-1700 Mon-Sat (Closed Sun). Closed Dec-Jan except by appt.
Min Mail Order UK: Nmc
Cat. Cost: Online only.
Credit Cards: All major credit/debit cards
Specialities: Succulents, perennials & dry garden plants planted in display gardens which are being developed. A large selection of our succulents are grown to order or in small batch numbers, as the collection grows we will aim to make more varieties available on demand.
Notes: Home to the Isle of Wight Rare Plant Fair featuring many specialist nurseries, plant groups and related organisations, speakers, café, live band and open gardens. See website for plant availability. Some plants are grown as stock plants and can be grown to order.
OS Grid Ref: SZ626900

SEdi **Edibleculture** ♿
The Horticultural Unit, The Abbey School, London Road, Faversham, Kent, ME13 8RZ
Ⓣ (01795) 537662
Ⓜ 07926 961056
Ⓔ info@edibleculture.co.uk
Ⓦ www.edibleculture.co.uk
Contact: Chris or David
Opening Times: 0900-1700 Mon-Sat 1000-1600 Sun, Mar-Jan. Jan-Feb by appt. only but telephone/email orders taken.
Cat. Cost: online only.
Credit Cards: All major credit/debit cards
Specialities: Herbs, vegetables, fruit trees and soft fruit, herbaceous perennials, hedgerow plants.
Notes: UK's first plastic free nursery and garden centre. Focus on interesting plants grown sustainably. Specialists in establishing and maintaining orchards. Wheelchair accessible.

SEle **Eleplants Nursery**
32 Framfield Road, Uckfield, East Sussex, TN22 5AH
Ⓜ 07810 660109
Ⓔ eleplantsnursery@talk21.com
Ⓦ www.eleplantsnursery.co.uk
Contact: Martin Batchelor
Opening Times: Not open. By appt. only.
Min Mail Order UK: Nmc
Min Mail Order EU: Nmc
Credit Cards: All major credit/debit cards, Paypal
Specialities: Shrubs.
Notes: Exports beyond EU. Delivers to shows.

SEND **East Northdown Nursery** ♿
George Hill Road (B2052), Margate, Kent, CT10 3BN
Ⓣ (01843) 862060
Ⓜ 07714 241667/07714 241668
Ⓔ info@botanyplants.co.uk
Ⓦ www.botanyplants.co.uk
Contact: Louise & William Friend
Opening Times: 0900-1700/dusk 7 days, all year except Sun & Mon in winter. Closed Xmas week. See website for details.
Min Mail Order UK: Nmc
Min Mail Order EU: Nmc
Cat. Cost: Online only.
Credit Cards: All major credit/debit cards
Specialities: Chalk & coast-loving plants. Specimen shrubs & bamboos available. Complementary range of plants for damp/acid conditions available to order from our Mucklestone Nursery (MMuc). Collection of rare Mediterranean plants.
Notes: Tea room, gardens, grounds and business centre. Close to Botany Bay. Lectures given to gardening groups in Kent. Garden tours by appt. See website for full list & details. Please include your address when emailing us. Wheelchair accessible.
OS Grid Ref: TR383702

SEsH **Essentially Hops**
Chalkpit Farm, Adisham Road, Bekesbourne, Canterbury, Kent, CT4 5EU
Ⓣ (01227) 830666
Ⓔ shop@essentiallyhops.co.uk
Ⓦ http://www.essentiallyhops.co.uk
Contact: Ashley
Opening Times: 0900-1700 Mon-Sat.
Credit Cards: Visa, MasterCard
Specialities: Over 40 varieties of hops including English, foreign, dwarf and ornamental varieties.
Notes: Hop plants for sale. Also specialise in

growing hop garlands (bines/vines) for traditional home decoration. Some hops grown on the farm are supplied to brewers. Hop plants and growing equipment available from the shop and online. Also sells wholesale.

SEWo **English Woodlands** ♿
Burrow Nursery, Herrings Lane, Cross-in-Hand, Heathfield, East Sussex, TN21 0UG
Ⓣ (01435) 862992
Ⓔ sales@englishwoodlands.com
Ⓦ www.englishwoodlands.com
Contact: Joanne Carter
Opening Times: 0800-1700 Mon-Fri. 0800-1600 Sat. Closed Sun & B/hols.
Min Mail Order UK: £25.00
Cat. Cost: Free.
Credit Cards: All major debit/credit cards except American Express
Specialities: Trees, shrubs, hedging. Please telephone to check plant availability before visiting.
Notes: Also sells wholesale. Wheelchair accessible.
OS Grid Ref: TQ567222

SFai **Fairweather's Garden Centre** ♿
High Street, Beaulieu, Hampshire, SO42 7YB
Ⓣ (01590) 612307
Ⓔ info@fairweathers.co.uk
Ⓦ www.fairweathers.co.uk
Contact: Sue Greaves
Opening Times: 0900-1700 7 days.
Min Mail Order UK: Nmc
Cat. Cost: None issued.
Credit Cards: Visa, MasterCard
Specialities: *Agapanthus* & *Lavandula*.
Notes: Wheelchair accessible.

SFra **National Collection of Francoa**
30 Compton Way, Winchester, Hampshire, SO22 4HS
Ⓜ 07889 453810
Ⓔ francoa@summersgd.co.uk
Ⓦ www.summersgd.co.uk
Contact: Susan Summers
Opening Times: See website for details.
Specialities: Plant Heritage 'Horticultural' Collection of *Francoa*, awarded 2017. Plants available in small quantities only, please contact by email.
Notes: All available plants are grown from seed collected from plants held in the National Collection. Plants may not be true to type. Plants will be posted (Royal Mail) once BACS payment received for order and postage. Cash payments accepted if plants are collected.
OS Grid Ref: SU459275

SGBe **Garden Beauty**
Hook Lane, Southampton, Hampshire, SO31 9HH
Ⓣ (01489) 550830
Ⓕ (01489) 660630
Ⓔ sales@gardenbeauty.co.uk
Ⓦ https://www.gardenbeauty.co.uk/
Contact: Stephanie Hansen
Opening Times: Not open, mail order only.
Min Mail Order UK: £4.99
Cat. Cost: Online only.
Credit Cards: All major credit/debit cards
Specialities: Hebes, shrubs, perennials, grasses. British grown in peat free compost. Specimen plants also available.
Notes: Offer a range of new, rare and unusual plants grown at their nurseries in Southampton, as well as old favourites. Varieties are chosen to perform well in gardens with many having the RHS AGM. Continually testing and introducing new varieties. Standard delivery charge of £4.99 per order. See website for further details.

SGbt **Gilbert's Nursery** ♿
Dandy's Ford Lane, Sherfield English, Romsey, Hampshire, SO51 6DT
Ⓣ (01794) 322566
Ⓔ gilbertsnursery@aol.com
Ⓦ www.gilbertsnursery.co.uk
Contact: Nick Gilbert
Opening Times: 0900-1700 Tue-Sat, 1000-1630 Sun, all year. Dahlia field open from 2nd week Aug to 2nd week Oct.
Min Mail Order UK: Nmc
Min Mail Order EU: Nmc
Cat. Cost: 2 × 1st class.
Credit Cards: All major debit/credit cards except American Express
Specialities: *Dahlia*. Proper plant nursery with many unusual plants & staff happy to share their knowledge & help with plant selection.
Notes: Dahlia field with over 400 cvs on view (grass pathways). See above for opening times or go to www.gilbertsdahlias.co.uk. Tea room. Delivers to shows. Wheelchair accessible.

SGol **Golden Hill Nurseries** ♿
Lordsfield, Goudhurst Road, Marden, Kent, TN12 9LT
Ⓣ (01622) 833218
Ⓜ 07826 523655
Ⓔ enquiries@goldenhillplants.com
Ⓦ www.goldenhillplants.com
Contact: Roger Butler
Opening Times: 0900-1700 Mon-Sat, 1st Mar-31st Oct 0900-1600 Mon-Sat, 1st Nov-28th Feb. 1100-1600 Sun from 3rd Sun in Feb-end Nov.

Min Mail Order UK: Nmc
Cat. Cost: Online only.
Credit Cards: All major credit/debit cards
Specialities: *Hydrangea, Chaenomeles, Camellia* & *Viburnum.* Specimen trees & shrubs, ground cover and hedging.
Notes: Also sells wholesale. Euro accepted. Delivers to shows. Wheelchair accessible.

SGro **Growing Delights**
1 Appledore Cottages, Near Bow, Crediton, Devon, EX17 6JR
Ⓜ 07874 678175
Ⓔ growingdelights@gmail.com
Ⓦ www.growingdelights.co.uk
Contact: Lesley Baker
Opening Times: Not open.
Min Mail Order UK: £15 + p&p
Cat. Cost: Online only.
Credit Cards: Paypal
Specialities: Unusual plants, alpines & drought-tolerant plants. Plants to attract bees & butterflies. Please note, a very small nursery so only able to supply small quantities.
Notes: Almost entirely growing peat-free. A small nursery only able to supply plants in small quantities. No plants mailed Dec-Jan. Plants can be collected by arrangement and from sales & shows. Delivers to shows if attending. Have previously sent plants to EU but not sure yet if that will still be possible.

SGsty **Garden Style Plant Centre** ♿
Farnham Road, Holt Pound, Farnham, Surrey, GU10 4LD
Ⓣ (01420) 521092
Ⓔ sales@gardenstyle.co.uk
Ⓦ www.gardenstyle.co.uk
Opening Times: 0900-1730 Mon-Sat, 1030-1630 Sun.
Credit Cards: All major credit/debit cards
Specialities: Bamboo, climbers, conifers, hedging, evergreen & deciduous shrubs, fruit & ornamental trees, topiary.
Notes: Suppliers of larger plants to enhance your garden since 1991. Also sells wholesale. Delivers to shows. Wheelchair accessible.
OS Grid Ref: SU810354

SHaC **Hart Canna** ♿
Lincluden Nursery, Shaftesbury Road, Bisley, Woking, Surrey, GU24 9EN
Ⓣ (01252) 514421
Ⓜ 07762 950000
Ⓔ sales@hartcanna.com
Ⓦ www.hartcanna.co.uk
Contact: Keith Hayward
Opening Times: By appt. only.
Min Mail Order UK: Nmc
Min Mail Order EU: Nmc
Cat. Cost: Online only.
Credit Cards: All major credit/debit cards
Specialities: *Canna.* National Plant Collection of *Canna.*
Notes: Also sells wholesale. Euro accepted. Delivers to shows. Wheelchair accessible.

SHar **Hardy's Cottage Garden Plants**
Priory Lane Nursery, Freefolk Priors, Whitchurch, Hampshire, RG28 7FA
Ⓣ (01256) 896533
Ⓔ info@hardysplants.co.uk
Ⓦ www.hardysplants.co.uk
Contact: Rosemary Hardy
Opening Times: 1000-1700 Mon-Sat, 1000-1600 Sun 1st Mar-30th Sep. 1000-1600 Mon-Fri, Oct 1000-1500 Mon-Fri, 1st Nov-28th Feb. Closed 23rd Dec-4th Jan.
Min Mail Order UK: Nmc
Cat. Cost: Online only.
Credit Cards: Visa, Access, Electron, Switch, Solo
Specialities: Wide range of herbaceous perennials incl. *Achillea, Gaura, Geum, Geranium, Hemerocallis, Heuchera, Lathryus vernus, Paeonia, Penstemon* & *Salvia.*
Notes: Accepts HTA Gift Tokens. Offers trade discount. Delivers to shows.

SHeu **Heucheraholics** ♿
Boldre Nurseries, Southampton Road, Lymington, Hampshire, SO41 8ND
Ⓣ (01590) 670581
Ⓜ 07973 291062
Ⓔ jooles.heucheraholics@gmail.com
Ⓦ www.heucheraholics.co.uk
Contact: Julie Burton/Sean Atkinson
Opening Times: By appt. only (except open days) Please phone or see website for details.
Min Mail Order UK: Nmc
Min Mail Order EU: Please contact nursery to discuss
Cat. Cost: Online only.
Credit Cards: All major credit/debit cards, Paypal
Specialities: *Heuchera, Heucherella, Pulmonaria, Tiarella.*
Notes: Working nursery in the New Forest. Toilet facilities. Well-behaved dogs welcome. See website or contact nursery for details of open days. Visits by groups can be arranged, please contact nursery for details. See website for open days. Delivers to shows. Wheelchair accessible.
OS Grid Ref: SZ310934

SHmp **HAMPSHIRE CARNIVOROUS PLANTS**
Stroudwood Nursery, Stroudwood Lane, Lower Upham, Southampton, Hampshire, SO32 1HG
Ⓣ (023) 8047 3314
Ⓜ 07703 258296
Ⓕ (023) 8047 3314
Ⓔ sales@hantsflytrap.com
Ⓦ www.hantsflytrap.com
Contact: Matthew Soper
Opening Times: By appt. only.
Min Mail Order UK: Nmc
Min Mail Order EU: £50.00 + p&p
Credit Cards: All major credit/debit cards
Specialities: Carnivorous plants esp. *Cephalotus, Darlingtonia, Dionaea, Drosera, Heliamphora, Nepenthes, Pinguicula, Sarracenia* & *Utricularia.*
Notes: Also sells wholesale. Exports beyond EU. Delivers to shows. Euro accepted. Partial wheelchair access.
OS Grid Ref: SU514091

SHor **THE PLANT CENTRE AT HORTUS LOCI**
Hound Green, Hook, Hampshire, RG27 8LQ
Ⓣ (01189) 326487
Ⓔ enquiries@hlpantcentre.co.uk
Ⓦ http://hortusloci.co.uk
Contact: Robin Wallis/John Winterson
Opening Times: 0900-1630 Mon-Sat 0930-1630 Sun winter. 0900-1730 Mon-Sat 0930-1730 summer.
Specialities: Wide range of own-grown perennials, including many large pot sizes. Specialists in supplying & planting very large and mature plants.
Notes: While most good garden centres in the UK can boast a few hundred different varieties, here at The Plant Centre we have access to well over 4000. This means that our customers not only have much more choice, but will be able to get hold of the latest plant introductions much sooner than elsewhere. Also sells wholesale.

SHyH **HYDRANGEA HAVEN** ♿
Market Garden, Lower Beeding, West Sussex, RH13 6PP
Ⓣ (01403) 891412
Ⓔ lp@hortic.com
Ⓦ www.hydrangea-haven.com
Contact: Chris Loder
Opening Times: 1000-1600 Mon-Sat, please phone first.
Min Mail Order UK: Nmc
Min Mail Order EU: Nmc
Cat. Cost: Please enquire.
Credit Cards: All major debit/credit cards except American Express
Specialities: *Hydrangea*: mophead, lacecap & panicle. *Agapanthus.*
Notes: Also sells wholesale. Exports beyond EU. Delivers to shows. Euro accepted. Wheelchair accessible.
OS Grid Ref: TQ221255

SIri **IRIS OF SISSINGHURST**
Roughlands Farm, Goudhurst Road, Marden, Kent, TN12 9NH
Ⓣ (01622) 831511
Ⓔ orders@irisofsissinghurst.com
Ⓦ www.irisofsissinghurst.com
Contact: Sue Marshall
Opening Times: Contact nursery or see website for opening times.
Min Mail Order UK: Nmc
Min Mail Order EU: Nmc
Cat. Cost: Online only.
Credit Cards: None
Specialities: *Iris*, short, intermediate & tall bearded, *ensata, sibirica* & many species.
Notes: Euro accepted. Delivers to shows (pre-ordered plants).
OS Grid Ref: TQ735437

SIvy **IVY HATCH PLANT SUPPLIES**
Coach Road, Ivy Hatch, Kent, TN15 0PE
Ⓜ 07769 604468
Ⓔ debs@ivyhatchplantsupplies.co.uk
Ⓦ www.ivyhatchplantsupplies.co.uk
Contact: Debs Ednie
Opening Times: By appt. only.
Min Mail Order UK: £5.00
Min Mail Order EU: £10.00
Cat. Cost: None.
Credit Cards: Paypal
Specialities: Hardy salvias and succulents including *Echeveria.* Good variety of *Aeonium* and a range of tropical plants.
Notes: Sole supplier for The World Garden Nursery, Lullingstone Castle. Unusual varieties. Limited stock, can source/grow to order. Also sells wholesale. Full range avail. by mail order or at The World Garden Nursery, Lullingstone, Kent. Exports beyond EU (restrictions apply).

SJap **THE JAPANESE GARDEN CENTRE** ♿
Addlestead Road, East Peckham, Kent, TN12 5DP
Ⓣ (01622) 872403
Ⓔ info@buildajapanesegarden.com
Ⓦ www.buildajapanesegarden.com
Contact: Mark

Opening Times: 1000-1600 7 days.
Credit Cards: MasterCard, Visa
Specialities: Japanese plants.
Notes: Established in 1993 to cater solely for the provision of plants and materials suitable for Japanese gardens in the UK. Plants stocked range from small plants to specimen trees. Also sells wholesale. Wheelchair accessible.
OS Grid Ref: TQ662485

SKee **KEEPERS NURSERY**
Gallants Court, Gallants Lane, East Farleigh, Maidstone, Kent, ME15 0LE
Ⓣ (01622) 326465
Ⓔ nurserymanager@keepers-nursery.co.uk
Ⓦ www.keepers-nursery.co.uk
Contact: Karim Habibi
Opening Times: By appt. only.
Min Mail Order UK: £14.50
Cat. Cost: Online only.
Credit Cards: Visa, MasterCard, Switch, Maestro
Specialities: A very large range of old & rare as well as modern fruit tree varieties on a variety of rootstock & in different trained forms. Custom grafting, plants to order from National Collection. Soft fruit plants & nut trees.
Notes: A family-run fruit tree nursery producing and selling the widest range of bare root fruit trees in the country. Orders taken from May onwards for distribution throughout the following winter period. Limited number of open days. Open for collection of orders by arrangement through winter months only.

SKin **KINGS BARN TREES**
Wheler Stables, Welford Road, Husbands Bosworth, Leicestershire, LE17 6JL
Ⓜ 07815 189350
Ⓔ sales@kingsbarntrees.co.uk
Ⓦ www.kingsbarntrees.co.uk
Contact: Annetta Toolan
Opening Times: Not open. Mail order via website only.
Min Mail Order UK: £3.00
Min Mail Order EU: £9.95
Cat. Cost: Online only.
Credit Cards: All major credit/debit cards
Specialities: Grow containerised trees, specialising in *Eucalyptus*. *Eucalyptus* available in small quantities only.

SLau **THE LAURELS NURSERY**
Benenden, Cranbrook, Kent, TN17 4JU
Ⓣ (01580) 240463
Ⓦ www.thelaurelsnursery.co.uk
Contact: Peter or Sylvia Kellett
Opening Times: 0900-1200 Sat. Other times by appt.
Min Mail Order UK: £30
Cat. Cost: Free.
Credit Cards: All major debit/credit cards except American Express
Specialities: Container ornamental trees, shrubs & climbers especially birch, beech *Wisteria* & *Acer* palmatum varieties.
Notes: Mail order of small *Wisteria* only. Also sells wholesale. Delivers to shows. Partial wheelchair access.
OS Grid Ref: TQ815313

SLBF **LITTLE BROOK FUCHSIAS** ♿
Ash Green Lane West, Ash Green, Nr Aldershot, Hampshire, GU12 6HL
Ⓣ (01252) 329731
Ⓜ 07817 272361
Ⓔ carol@littlebrookfuchsias.co.uk
Ⓦ www.littlebrookfuchsias.co.uk
Contact: Carol Gubler
Opening Times: 1000-1700 Wed-Sun, 1st Jan-28th Jun.
Cat. Cost: 70p + sae.
Credit Cards: All major credit/debit cards
Specialities: *Fuchsias*, old & new.
Notes: Nursery located off White Lane in Ash Green. Wheelchair accessible.
OS Grid Ref: SU901496

SLdr **LODER PLANTS** ♿
Market Garden, Long Hill, Lower Beeding, West Sussex, RH13 6PP
Ⓣ (01403) 891412
Ⓔ sales@rhododendrons.com
Ⓦ www.rhododendrons.com
Contact: Chris Loder
Opening Times: 1000-1600 Mon-Sat, please telephone first.
Min Mail Order UK: Nmc
Min Mail Order EU: Nmc
Cat. Cost: Please enquire.
Credit Cards: All major debit/credit cards except American Express
Specialities: Rhododendrons & azaleas in all sizes. Some in very limited quantities only. *Agapanthus*.
Notes: Also sells wholesale. Exports beyond EU. Delivers to shows. Euro accepted. Wheelchair accessible.
OS Grid Ref: TQ221255

SLee **LEESA'S NOT JUST ALPINES**
Ⓜ 07900 815636
Ⓔ leesasnotjustalpines@gmail.com

Ⓦ www.leesasalpines.co.uk
Contact: Leesa Barrett
Opening Times: Please call or email for any enquiries.
Specialities: Alpines and perennials.
Notes: Small nursery growing a good selection of garden worthy alpine and rock garden plants. A range of cottage garden perennials also available. Also sells wholesale. Delivers to shows.

SLim **LIME CROSS NURSERY** ♿
Herstmonceux, Hailsham, East Sussex, BN27 4RS
Ⓣ (01323) 833229
Ⓔ info@limecross.co.uk
Ⓦ www.limecross.co.uk
Contact: Vicky Tate, Anita Green
Opening Times: 0830-1700 Mon-Sat & 1000-1700 Sun.
Min Mail Order UK: £12.00
Cat. Cost: Online only.
Credit Cards: All major credit/debit cards
Specialities: Conifers, trees, shrubs & climbers.
Notes: Wheelchair accessible.
OS Grid Ref: TQ642125

SMad **MADRONA NURSERY** ♿
Pluckley Road, Bethersden, Kent, TN26 3EG
Ⓔ madrona@hotmail.co.uk
Ⓦ www.madrona.co.uk
Contact: Liam Mackenzie
Opening Times: 1000-1700 Sat, Mon & Tue, 1300-1700 Sun. 14th Mar-1st Nov. Other times by appt.
Cat. Cost: Free.
Credit Cards: All major credit/debit cards
Specialities: Unusual shrubs, conifers & perennials. *Eryngium.*
Notes: Delivers to shows. Euro accepted. Wheelchair accessible.
OS Grid Ref: TQ918419

SMDa **MARCUS DANCER PLANTS**
Kilcreggan, Alderholt Road, Sandleheath, Fordingbridge, Hampshire, SP6 1PT
Ⓣ (01425) 652747
Ⓜ 07709 922730
Ⓔ marcus.dancer@btopenworld.com
Ⓦ www.clematisplants.co.uk
Contact: Marcus Dancer
Opening Times: By appt. only.
Credit Cards: All major credit/debit cards
Notes: Collection of plants by prior arrangement only. Please email or ring to enquire about availability. Delivers to shows.

SMHy **MARCHANTS HARDY PLANTS** ♿
2 Marchants Cottages, Mill Lane, Laughton, Lewes, East Sussex, BN8 6AJ
Ⓜ 07377 145970
Ⓔ marchantsnursery@gmail.com
Ⓦ www.marchantshardyplants.co.uk
Contact: Paul Seaborne
Opening Times: Nursery open 1000-1700 Wed-Sat, mid-Mar to mid-Oct. Garden opens later in spring 1000-1700 Wed-Sat, mid-May to mid-Oct. Please check website before travelling.
Cat. Cost: Website download or collect from nursery.
Credit Cards: Visa, MasterCard
Specialities: Uncommon hardy perennials and choice range of grasses. Many varieties of *Agapanthus, Aster, Epimedium, Galanthus, Molinia, Polypodium, Salvia,* & *Sangiusorba.* Please refer to website for catalogue. Email or call before travelling as many unusual plants may be limited in number.
Notes: Unique specialist nursery with display garden repute. Stock mostly propagated by skilled and knowledgeable staff on site. Please check opening hours before you travel. Orders confirmed in advance may be collected from plant fairs. Check website for events. Pre-booked groups and tours welcome. Euro accepted. Delivers to shows. Wheelchair accessible.
OS Grid Ref: TQ506119

SMil **MILES JAPANESE MAPLES**
Cherries, Fox Court, Storrington, West Sussex, RH20 4JL
Ⓣ (01903) 745572
Ⓜ 07927 550769
Ⓔ miles@milesjapanesemaples.co.uk
Ⓦ milesjapanesemaples.co.uk
Contact: Miles Hayward
Opening Times: By appt. only.
Min Mail Order UK: Nmc
Cat. Cost: Online only.
Credit Cards: All major credit/debit cards
Specialities: *Acer palmatum.*
Notes: Delivers to shows.

SMor **MOREHAVENS**
Stocks Lane, Meonstoke, Hampshire, SO32 3NQ
Ⓣ (01489) 878501
Ⓔ morehavens@camomilelawns.co.uk
Ⓦ www.camomilelawns.co.uk
Contact: E. Clements
Opening Times: Mail order direct to you only. Open for pre-arranged collection.

S

Min Mail Order UK: £21.00
Min Mail Order EU: £21.00 + p&p
Cat. Cost: Free.
Credit Cards: All major credit/debit cards, Paypal
Specialities: *Chamaemelum nobile* 'Treneague' & *Chamaemelum nobile* dwarf.
Notes: Also sells wholesale.

SMrm **Merriments Gardens** ♿
Hawkhurst Road, Hurst Green, East Sussex, TN19 7RA
Ⓣ (01580) 860666
Ⓕ (01580) 860324
Ⓔ stephen@merriments.co.uk
Ⓦ www.merriments.co.uk
Contact: Imogen Stephens
Opening Times: 0900-1700 Mon-Sat, 1000-1630 Sun.
Cat. Cost: Online only.
Credit Cards: Visa, Access, American Express
Specialities: Specialist in perennials. Extensive range of unusual perennials, tender perennials, grasses & annuals. Also large selection of roses & seasonal shrubs. 4-acre show garden.
Notes: Wheelchair accessible.

SNig **Nightingale Nursery Ltd** ♿
Gardeners Lane, East Wellow, Romsey, Hampshire, SO51 6AD
Ⓣ (023) 80814350
Ⓔ gfnightingale4@gmail.com
Ⓦ www.nightingalenursery.co.uk
Contact: Graham Farmiloe
Opening Times: 0800-1700 Mon-Fri & open 7 days from mid-Mar to mid-Jun. 0800-1630 winter.
Cat. Cost: Free via email for wholesale only.
Credit Cards: All major debit/credit cards except American Express
Specialities: Specialists in *Clematis.* We also grow climbers & wall shrubs, herbaceous (for retail only), seasonal Bedding & hanging baskets.
Notes: Also sells wholesale. Wheelchair accessible.

SOrN **Orchard Nursery Plant Centre Ltd**
Holtye Road, East Grinstead, West Sussex, RH19 3PP
Ⓣ (01342) 311657
Ⓔ enquiries@orchardnursery.co.uk
Ⓦ www.orchardnursery.co.uk
Contact: Clare Bradford
Opening Times: 0900-1730 Mon-Sat, Apr-Nov (0900-1700 during winter) 1000-1600 Sun all year.
Specialities: Perennials are our passion. We also grow the majority of our own seasonal bedding stock.
Notes: As a retail nursery, we pride ourselves on the quality of the plants that we grow and source from our trusted suppliers. Set within an old walled garden, the aspect of the nursery is perfect for growing, and the atmosphere we try to create is much more relaxed and natural, rather than clinical.

SPad **Paddock Plants**
The Paddock, Upper Toothill Road, Rownhams, Southampton, Hampshire, SO16 8AL
Ⓣ (023) 8073 9912
Ⓜ 07763 386717
Ⓔ rob@paddockplants.co.uk
Ⓦ https://paddockplants.co.uk
Contact: Rob & Joanna Courtney
Opening Times: See website for details.
Min Mail Order UK: £4.95
Cat. Cost: Online only.
Credit Cards: All major credit/debit cards
Specialities: *Abutilon* hybrids. Some varieties are currently only available in limited quantities.
Notes: A family-run nursery offering an interesting range of perennials, grasses, ferns & shrubs, incl. some more unusual varieties or plants new to the UK market. All plants are grown in a peat-free medium. Courier delivery throughout the UK. Delivers to shows.
OS Grid Ref: SU383177

SPeP **Peake Perennials** ♿
Shaftesbury Road, Child Okeford, Dorset, DT11 8EQ
Ⓣ (01202) 244510
Ⓜ 07708 872918
Ⓔ helen@peakeperennials.co.uk
Ⓦ www.peakeperennials.co.uk
Contact: Helen Hunt
Opening Times: 0900-1700 Mon-Fri, Closed Tue. 1000-1600 Sat, Sun & B/hols. 1000-1600 Nov & Dec. Closed Jan.
Credit Cards: All major credit/debit cards
Specialities: Specialising in tall & unusual herbaceous perennials & grasses. Also increasing stock range of popular perennials with a twist. Reservation service for out of stock plants. Local delivery. Range of landscaping perennials.
Notes: For details of special events we attend please telephone or check website for details. Register on the website for regular news on events and plants. Wheelchair accessible. Delivers to shows.

SPer **Perryhill Nurseries Ltd** ♿
Edenbridge Road, Hartfield, East Sussex, TN7 4JP
Ⓣ (01892) 770377
Ⓔ sales@perryhillnurseries.co.uk
Ⓦ www.perryhillnurseries.co.uk
Contact: P. J. Chapman
Opening Times: 0900-1700 7 days, 1st Mar-31st Oct 0900-1630, 1st Nov-28th Feb.
Min Mail Order UK: Nmc
Cat. Cost: Online only.
Credit Cards: Maestro, Visa, Access, MasterCard
Specialities: Wide range of trees, shrubs, perennials, roses, fruit trees & soft fruit. Unusual & rare plants may be available in small quantities.
Notes: Mail order despatch depends on size & weight of plants. Wheelchair accessible.
OS Grid Ref: TQ480375

S

SPet **Pettet's Nursery** ♿
Drainless Road, Eastry, Sandwich, Kent, CT13 0EA
Ⓣ (01304) 613869
Ⓜ 07940 337520
Ⓕ (01304) 613869
Ⓔ pettets.nursery@btconnect.com
Ⓦ www.pettetsnursery.co.uk
Contact: Terry Pettet
Opening Times: 1000-1600 Tue-Sun, Mar-Oct Closed Mon (except B/hol). Closed Nov-Feb.
Min Mail Order UK: £12.00
Cat. Cost: Online only.
Credit Cards: None
Specialities: *Pelargonium*: scented-leaf, decorative regal, angel, species.
Notes: Delivers to shows. Wheelchair accessible.

SPhx **Phoenix Perennial Plants**
Paice Lane, Medstead, Alton, Hampshire, GU34 5PR
Ⓣ (01420) 560695
Ⓜ 07909 528191
Ⓔ marina@phoenixperennialplants.co.uk
Ⓦ www.phoenixperennialplants.co.uk
Contact: Marina Christopher
Opening Times: By appt. only.
Credit Cards: All major credit/debit cards
Specialities: Perennials, many uncommon & hardy, selected for beneficial insects particularly pollinators. *Agastache, Centaurea, Salvia, Sanguisorba, Sedum, Thalictrum, Verbascum*, bulbs, prairie plants, umbellifers & late-flowering perennials.
Notes: Also sells wholesale. Delivers to shows.
OS Grid Ref: SU657362

SPlb **Plantbase** ♿
Sleepers Stile Road, Cousley Wood, Wadhurst, East Sussex, TN5 6QX
Ⓣ (01892) 785599
Ⓜ 07967 601064
Ⓔ plantbaseuk@gmail.com
Ⓦ www.plantbase.co.uk
Contact: Graham Blunt
Opening Times: 1000-1700, 7 days all year (appt. advisable).
Min Mail Order UK: Nmc
Min Mail Order EU: Nmc
Cat. Cost: Online only.
Credit Cards: All major credit/debit cards
Specialities: Wide range of alpines, perennials, shrubs, climbers, waterside plants, herbs, Australasian, South African & South American plants in particular. Some available in small quantities only.
Notes: Delivers to shows. Euro accepted. Wheelchair accessible.

SPoG **The Potted Garden Nursery** ♿
Ashford Road, Bearsted, Maidstone, Kent, ME14 4NH
Ⓣ (01622) 737801
Ⓔ markreeve@coolings.co.uk
Ⓦ www.thepottedgarden.co.uk
Contact: Mark Reeve
Opening Times: 0900-1700 Mon-Sat & 0900-1630 Sun. Extended opening hours Apr-Jul 0900-1730 Mon-Sat. Xmas/New Year period opening times on website or answerphone.
Credit Cards: All major credit/debit cards
Notes: Mail order not available. Wheelchair accessible.
OS Grid Ref: TQ810550

SPre **Plants4Presents** ◆
The Glasshouses, Fletching Common, Newick, Lewes, East Sussex, BN8 4JJ
Ⓣ (01825) 721162
Ⓔ plants@4presents.co.uk
Ⓦ www.plants4presents.co.uk
Contact: Emily Rae
Opening Times: Not open. Mail order only.
Min Mail Order UK: Nmc
Cat. Cost: Online only.
Credit Cards: All major credit/debit cards
Specialities: Well-established nursery offering a range of unusual flowering and fruiting plants, incl. citrus trees.
Notes: Delivers to shows.

SPtp **PlantsToPlant.com**
Paragon Plants, Fromefield, Ratley Lane, Awbridge, Romsey, Hampshire, SO51 0HN

Ⓣ (01794) 341123
Ⓔ info@plantstoplant.com
Ⓦ www.plantstoplant.com
Contact: David West
Opening Times: Not open. Mail order only.
Min Mail Order UK: Nmc
Cat. Cost: Online only.
Credit Cards: All major credit/debit cards, Paypal
Specialities: Rare & hard to find special garden plants of all types. *Cotoneaster* a speciality.
Notes: Mail order only through website or ebay. Orders can be collected by appt. only.

SPVi **Pineview Plants**
Pineview, 19 Windmill Hill, Wrotham Heath, Sevenoaks, Kent, TN15 7SU
Ⓣ (01732) 882945
Ⓜ 07736 420016
Ⓔ colin@pineviewplants.co.uk
Ⓦ www.pineviewplants.co.uk
Contact: Colin Moat
Opening Times: By appt. only.
Min Mail Order UK: £15.00 + p&p
Cat. Cost: Online only.
Credit Cards: All major credit/debit cards, Paypal
Specialities: Shade loving plants including *Epimedium, Actaea, Roscoea, Sanguisorba* & *Thalictrum.* Wide range of ferns, some orchids & herbaceous perennials.
Notes: The majority of plants are propagated on site and many are only available in small quantities. Delivers to shows – see list on website.

SRGP **Rosie's Garden Plants**
Fieldview Cottage, Pratling Street, Aylesford, Kent, ME20 7DG
Ⓣ (01622) 715777
Ⓜ 07740 696277
Ⓕ (01622) 715777
Ⓔ jcaviolet@aol.com
Ⓦ www.rosiesgardenplants.biz
Contact: Jacqueline Aviolet
Opening Times: Not open. Mail order only.
Min Mail Order UK: Nmc
Min Mail Order EU: Nmc
Cat. Cost: Online only.
Credit Cards: None
Specialities: Hardy *Geranium, Symphyotrichum, Aster,* herbs & roses.
Notes: Some species & varieties available in small quantities. Exports beyond EU.

SRHi **Rotherhill Nurseries** ♿
School Lane, Stedham, Midhurst, West Sussex, GU29 0PD
Ⓣ (01730) 813687
Ⓔ enquiries@rotherhill.co.uk
Ⓦ www.rotherhill.co.uk
Contact: Hannah von der Heyde
Opening Times: 0900-1700 Mon-Fri, 1030-1630 Sun. 1000-1600 Cafe.
Credit Cards: All major credit/debit cards
Specialities: We specialise in a wide range of hedging along with a good shrub selection. We have a large interestingly stocked fern tunnel, Acer tunnel and a large seasonal perennial and bedding selection. Large parts of our stock are potted in either bio-degradable or recyclable pots.
Notes: Here at Rotherhill we supply bedding, perennials, shrubs, hedging and trees to the general public and trade. We particularly focus on our extensive hedging selection, acers and ferns. We are staffed with knowledgeable individuals, each bringing a different aspect of horticulture to the team. Wheelchair accessible.

SRiv **River Garden Nurseries**
Troutbeck, Otford, Sevenoaks, Kent, TN14 5PH
Ⓜ 07717 277175
Ⓔ box@river-garden.co.uk
Ⓦ www.river-garden.co.uk
Contact: Jenny Alban Davies
Opening Times: By appt. only.
Min Mail Order UK: £10.00 + p&p
Min Mail Order EU: £50.00 + p&p
Cat. Cost: Online only.
Credit Cards: None
Specialities: *Buxus* species & cultivars. *Buxus* topiary.
Notes: Also sells wholesale. Delivers to shows.
OS Grid Ref: TQ523593

SRkn **Rapkyns Nursery**
Street End Lane, Broad Oak, Heathfield, East Sussex, TN21 8UB
Ⓣ (01825) 830065
Ⓜ 07771 916933
Ⓔ rapkynsnursery@hotmail.com
Ⓦ www.rapkynsnursery.co.uk
Contact: Steven Moore
Opening Times: 1000-1700 Tue, Thu & Fri, Mar-Oct incl. or by appt.
Min Mail Order UK: Nmc
Min Mail Order EU: Nmc
Cat. Cost: Online only.
Credit Cards: All major credit/debit cards
Specialities: Unusual shrubs, perennials & climbers including asters, geraniums,

penstemons & grasses. New collections of *Crocosmia, Anemone, Heuchera, Heucherella, Phlox, Coreopsis* & *Helleborus*. Extensive range of *Salvia* & *Monarda*.
Notes: Nursery next door to Scotsford Farm, TN21 8UB. Mail order Sep-Apr incl. Also sells wholesale. Partial wheelchair access. Delivers to shows.
OS Grid Ref: TQ604248

SRms **Rumsey Gardens** ♿
117 Drift Road, Clanfield, Waterlooville, Hampshire, PO8 0PD
Ⓣ (023) 9259 3367
Ⓔ info@rumsey-gardens.co.uk
Ⓦ www.rumsey-gardens.co.uk
Contact: Mrs M. A. Giles
Opening Times: 0900-1700 Mon-Sat & 1000-1600 Sun & B/hols. Closed Xmas to New Year B/Hol.
Min Mail Order UK: £15.00
Cat. Cost: Online only.
Credit Cards: Visa, MasterCard
Specialities: Wide general range. Herbaceous, alpines, heathers & ferns. National & International Plant Collection of *Cotoneaster*.
Notes: Wheelchair accessible.

SRot **Rotherview Nursery** ♿
Ivyhouse Lane, Three Oaks, Hastings, East Sussex, TN35 4NP
Ⓣ (01424) 756228
Ⓔ rotherview@btinternet.com
Ⓦ www.rotherview.com
Contact: Wendy Bates
Opening Times: 1000-1600.
Min Mail Order UK: £10.00
Min Mail Order EU: Nmc
Cat. Cost: 6 × 1st class.
Credit Cards: All major credit/debit cards
Specialities: *Camellia*, alpines and ferns.
Notes: Rotherview Nursery and Coghurst Camellias are on the same site. Delivers to shows. Euro accepted. Wheelchair accessible.

SSea **Seale Rose Garden**
Seale Nurseries, Seale Lane, Seale, Farnham, Surrey, GU10 1LD
Ⓣ (01252) 782410
Ⓔ catherine@sealenurseries.demon.co.uk
Ⓦ www.sealenurseries.co.uk
Contact: David & Catherine May
Opening Times: Please phone for details.
Cat. Cost: None issued.
Credit Cards: Visa, Access, Delta, MasterCard
Specialities: Roses & *Pelargonium*. Some varieties in short supply, please phone first.
Notes: Opening times vary according to season. Please telephone for details.
OS Grid Ref: SU887477

SSem **Sempervivums By Post**
Ⓔ sempervivumsbypost@gmail.com
Ⓦ www.sempervivumsbypost.co.uk
Contact: Becky Scott
Opening Times: Not open.
Min Mail Order UK: £15.00 + postage
Credit Cards: All major credit/debit cards
Specialities: Sempervivums. A selection of cacti and other succulents.
Notes: Our nursery was established in 1981. In early 2018, we started a specialised internet shop to sell Sempervivums by post to anywhere in the UK. The response has been fantastic since then. We offer the best varieties, the best quality plants, at the best prices – plus a genuine first-class service.

SSFr **Southern Fruit Trees** ♿
The Old Grain Dryer Corner, Blackmoor, Hampshire, GU33 6BP
Ⓣ (01420) 488822
Ⓜ 07760 245524
Ⓔ neil@southernfruittrees.co.uk
Ⓦ www.southernfruittrees.co.uk
Contact: Neil Smith
Opening Times: 0900-1600 7 days, Nov-Apr. Webshop open all year.
Min Mail Order UK: Nmc
Cat. Cost: Free.
Credit Cards: All major credit/debit cards
Specialities: Over 200 varieties of fruit trees all grown in our Hampshire nursery, specialising in trained fruit including espalier, cordon and fan-trained stone fruit.
Notes: Wheelchair accessible.
OS Grid Ref: SU778335

SSFT **Sussex Fruit Trees**
Hook Farm, Nettlesworth Lane, Heathfield, East Sussex, TN21 9EN
Ⓜ 07745 379526
Ⓔ mark@sussexfruittrees.co.uk
Ⓦ www.sussexfruittrees.co.uk
Contact: Mark Piper
Opening Times: 0800-1700, 7 days.
Specialities: Grows & sells a wide range of fruit trees on various rootstocks. Some Sussex apple tree cultivars.
Notes: Also provides delivery, planting, pruning, grafting, orchard maintenance & tree sundries. Delivers to shows (pre-ordered plants).

S

SSha **SHALLOWMEAD NURSERIES LTD** ♿
Boldre Lane, Lymington, Hampshire,
SO41 8PA
Ⓣ (01590) 672550
Ⓔ mail@shallowmead.co.uk
Ⓦ www.shallowmead.co.uk
Contact: Kate Brady
Opening Times: 0900-1700 summer, 0900-1600 winter.
Credit Cards: All major credit/debit cards
Specialities: Hardy exotic shrubs from mediterranean climate zones from around the world, especially southern hemisphere. Also offer a good range of conifers, grasses and more unusual plants.
Notes: Shallowmead Nurseries is a family-run business, established in 1947. We propagate the majority of our plants on site from cuttings, seeds and division, and are proud to offer a good range of quality plants in sizes ranging from 9cm liner pots to 45ltr specimen varieties. Wheelchair accessible.
OS Grid Ref: SZ319975

SSien **SIENNA HOSTA**
Knap Hill Nursery, Barrs Lane, Knaphill,
Surrey, GU21 2JW
Ⓣ (01483) 663160
Ⓔ nursery@siennahosta.co.uk
Ⓦ www.siennahosta.co.uk
Contact: Ollie
Opening Times: Not open. Mail order only.
Min Mail Order UK: £5.00
Credit Cards: All major credit/debit cards
Specialities: *Hosta* growers with over 30 years' experience. Over 800 varieties held within the collection with many available to order via our website. Availability may vary throughout the season.
Notes: Orders sent 1st class Royal Mail all year. We aim to send out orders placed before 12pm Mon-Thu on the same day. Orders placed Fri-Sun will be sent on Mon.

SSim **SIMPLY SUCCULENTS**
(office) 5 Galliard Street, Sandwich, Kent,
CT13 9BG
Ⓜ 07548 947357
Ⓔ simplysucculents@gmx.co.uk
Ⓦ www.simplysucculents.co.uk
Contact: John Chandler
Opening Times: Not open. Mail order online only.
Min Mail Order UK: Nmc
Cat. Cost: Online only.
Specialities: Succulents for home, garden & containers.
Notes: Online sales only.

SSta **STARBOROUGH NURSERY** ♿
Starborough Road, Marsh Green, Edenbridge,
Kent, TN8 5RB
Ⓣ (01732) 865614
Ⓔ starborough@hotmail.co.uk
Contact: Sales
Opening Times: 0900-1600 Thu, Fri & Sat. Closed Jan, Jul & Aug or open by appt. only. Please phone first if travelling.
Credit Cards: Visa, Access
Specialities: Rare & unusual shrubs esp. *Daphne*, *Acer*, rhododendrons & azaleas, *Magnolia* & *Nyssa*.
Notes: Some plants only available in larger sizes or in small numbers and are not listed. Please request a supplementary list from the nursery. Arrangements can be made for collections from Cornwall. Deliveries can be made at cost. Planting & landscaping services available. Wheelchair accessible.

SSut **DAN SUTTON**
(office) 142 Hawks Road, Hailsham,
East Sussex, BN27 1NA
Ⓣ (01323) 845270
Ⓜ 07772 869645
Ⓔ suttonnursery@gmail.com
Ⓦ www.suttonnursery.co.uk
Contact: Dan Sutton
Opening Times: By appt. only.
Min Mail Order UK: £7.50
Cat. Cost: Online only.
Credit Cards: Paypal
Specialities: Herbaceous perennials, bulbs/corms, incl. *Crocosima*, grasses, specimen bamboos, *Fargesia robusta*, *F. scabrida* & *Borinda boliana*. Coastal and drought-tolerant plants.
Notes: Nursery at Park Wood Farmhouse, Upper Dicker, Hailsham, BN27 3QL. Landscape design. Also sells wholesale. Delivers to shows (pre-ordered plants).

STPC **THE PLANT COMPANY** ♿
Rose Barn, Coolham Road,
West Chiltington, Pulborough,
West Sussex, RH20 2LH
Ⓣ (01403) 740100
Ⓔ sales@theplantco.co.uk
Ⓦ www.theplantco.co.uk
Contact: Tim Ricketts
Opening Times: 0900-1730 Mon-Fri.
Min Mail Order UK: £8.95
Cat. Cost: Online only.
Credit Cards: All major debit/credit cards except American Express
Specialities: A range of herbaceous, shrubs and grasses.

S

Notes: Also sells wholesale. Delivers to shows. Wheelchair accessible.
OS Grid Ref: TQ111196

SVen **Ventnor Botanic Garden** ♿
Undercliff Drive, Ventnor, Isle of Wight, PO38 1UL
Ⓣ (01983) 855397
Ⓔ sales@botanic.co.uk
Ⓦ www.botanic.co.uk
Contact: Chris Kidd
Opening Times: 1000-1700 7 days summer, 1000-1600 7 days winter.
Min Mail Order UK: Nmc
Min Mail Order EU: Nmc
Cat. Cost: None issued.
Credit Cards: All major debit/credit cards except American Express
Specialities: Coastal, drought-tolerant, mediterranean & southern hemisphere plants. Rare & esoteric half-hardy trees, shrubs & perennials. National Plant Collection of hardy & half-hardy *Puya*.
Notes: Also sells wholesale. Wheelchair accessible.
OS Grid Ref: SZ548768

SVic **Victoriana Nursery Gardens** ♿
Challock, Ashford, Kent, TN25 4DG
Ⓣ (01233) 740529
Ⓔ help@victoriananursery.co.uk
Ⓦ www.victoriananursery.co.uk
Contact: Serena Shirley
Opening Times: 0930-1615 (or dusk if sooner) Mon-Fri, 1030-1500 (or dusk if sooner) Sat.
Cat. Cost: Free by post or online.
Credit Cards: All major credit/debit cards
Specialities: Heritage & unusual vegetable plants, seeds, fruit trees & bushes. Specialist grower of chillies & tomatoes, with annual tasting days. Also 600+ varieties of *Fuchsia*.
Notes: Also sells wholesale. Wheelchair accessible.
OS Grid Ref: TR018501

SWCr **Coolings Wych Cross Garden Centre** ♿
Colemans Hatch Road, Forest Row, East Sussex, RH18 5JW
Ⓣ (01342) 822705
Ⓕ (01342) 828246
Ⓔ wychcross@coolings.co.uk
Ⓦ www.coolings.co.uk
Contact: Louise Kemp
Opening Times: 0900-1700 Mon-Sat Aug-Feb, 0900-1730 Mon-Sat Apr-Jul, 1000-1630 Sun.
Min Mail Order UK: Nmc
Cat. Cost: Free.
Credit Cards: All major debit/credit cards except American Express
Specialities: Specialises in roses. A wide selection of climbers and herbaceous plants.
Notes: Coffee shop on site. Outstanding views over the Ashdown Forest. Wheelchair accessible.
OS Grid Ref: TQ420320

SWeb **Web Garden Centre**
Meadow Farm, Sway Road, Tiptoe, Lymington, Hampshire, SO41 6FR
Ⓣ (01590) 637443
Ⓔ info@webgardencentre.com
Ⓦ www.webgardencentre.com
Contact: Alan
Opening Times: By appt. only. Please telephone to arrange.
Min Mail Order UK: Nmc
Min Mail Order EU: Nmc
Cat. Cost: Online only.
Credit Cards: All major credit/debit cards
Specialities: Web Garden Centre specialise in specimen, ornamental and architectural plants, all forms of topiary and evergreen screening plants.
Notes: Web Garden Centre are an online nursery supplying plants daily at great prices throughout the UK. Next day delivery available. Euro accepted. Also sells wholesale.
OS Grid Ref: SZ263971

SWvt **Wolverton Plants Ltd** ♿
Wolverton Common, Tadley, Hampshire, RG26 5RU
Ⓣ (01635) 298453
Ⓜ 07880 971397
Ⓔ plantranch2000@hotmail.com
Contact: Julian Jones
Opening Times: 0900-1700 (or dusk Nov-Feb), 6 days. Closed Wed & Xmas/New Year.
Credit Cards: All major credit/debit cards
Specialities: Wide range of herbaceous perennials & shrubs grown on a commercial scale for the public.
Notes: Horticultural club visits welcome by prior arrangement. Able to source plants for the public and Garden Designers. Also sells wholesale. Euro accepted. Wheelchair accessible.
OS Grid Ref: SU555589

Wales and the West

WAbe **Aberconwy Nursery**
Graig, Glan Conwy, Conwy, LL28 5TL
Ⓣ (01492) 580875
Ⓔ enquiries@aberconwynursery.co.uk

Ⓦ www.aberconwynursery.co.uk
Contact: Tim Lever
Opening Times: 1000-1600 Tue-Fri (and occasional Sat) Mar-Sep inc.
Cat. Cost: 2 × 2nd class.
Credit Cards: Visa, MasterCard
Specialities: Alpines, including specialist varieties, esp. gentians, dionysias, dwarf *Dianthus, Primula, Saxifraga* & dwarf ericaceous plants. Some choice shrubs & woodland plants incl. smaller ferns.
Notes: Delivers to shows.
OS Grid Ref: SH799744

WAln **L. A. ALLEN**
Windy Ridge, Llandrindod Wells, Powys, LD1 5NY
Ⓔ elandem80@gmail.com
Contact: Les Allen
Opening Times: Mail order only. Open by prior appt.
Min Mail Order UK: Nmc
Min Mail Order EU: Nmc
Cat. Cost: 6 × 1st class.
Credit Cards: None
Specialities: All sections of *Primula auricula*, alpine auricula, show-edged, show-self, doubles, show-stripe. Surplus plants from private collection so available in small quantities. Occasionally only 1 or 2 available of some cvs.
Notes: Also sells wholesale.

WAvo **PERSHORE COLLEGE GARDEN CENTRE & NURSERY** ♿
Avonbank, Pershore, Worcestershire, WR10 3JP
Ⓣ (0330) 1357277
Ⓔ pershorenurseries@wcg.ac.uk
Ⓦ www.wcg.ac.uk/plantcentre
Contact: Josh Egan-Wyer
Opening Times: 0900-1700 Mon-Sat 1000-1630 Sun (0900-1630 Mon-Sat 1030-1600 Sun in winter).
Credit Cards: All major debit/credit cards except American Express
Specialities: Extensive range of shrubs, perennials and good garden plants incl. National Plant Collections of *Penstemon* (pre-1995 cvs) & *Philadelphus* cvs. Several college raised.
Notes: Also sells wholesale. Wheelchair accessible.
OS Grid Ref: SO957447

WBor **BORDERVALE PLANTS** ♿
Nantyderi, Sandy Lane, Ystradowen, Cowbridge, Vale of Glamorgan, CF71 7SX
Ⓣ (01446) 774036
Ⓔ bordervaleplants@gmail.com
Ⓦ www.bordervale.co.uk
Contact: Claire E. Jenkins
Opening Times: 1000-1700 Fri-Sun & B/hols mid Mar-mid Sep. Often open Mon-Thu. Please check or make an appt. any day if travelling some distance.
Cat. Cost: 3 × 1st class.
Specialities: Unusual herbaceous perennials, trees, shrubs & roses, as well as cottage garden plants, many displayed in the 2-acre garden.
Notes: Garden open mid-May to mid-Sep when nursery open. Also open for NGS. Contact nursery for details. Delivers to shows. Wheelchair accessible.
OS Grid Ref: ST022776

WBrk **BROCKAMIN PLANTS** ♿
Brockamin, Old Hills, Callow End, Worcestershire, WR2 4TQ
Ⓣ (01905) 830370
Ⓔ stone.brockamin@btinternet.com
Contact: Margaret Stone
Opening Times: By appt. only.
Credit Cards: None
Specialities: National Plant Collections of *Symphyotrichum novae-angliae, Geranium sanguineum, G. macrorrhizum* & *G. × cantabrigiense*. Plants available in small quantities only.
Notes: Wheelchair accessible.
OS Grid Ref: SO830488

WCAu **CLAIRE AUSTIN HARDY PLANTS**
White Hopton Farm, Wern Lane, Sarn, Newtown, Powys, SY16 4EN
Ⓣ (01686) 670342
Ⓔ enquiries@claireaustin-hardyplants.co.uk
Ⓦ www.claireaustin-hardyplants.co.uk
Contact: Claire Austin
Opening Times: Mail order only. Open by appt. for the NGS.
Min Mail Order UK: Nmc
Min Mail Order EU: Nmc
Cat. Cost: Free, UK only.
Credit Cards: MasterCard, Visa, Switch
Specialities: *Paeonia, Iris, Hemerocallis* & hardy plants. National Plant Collections of bearded *Iris*.

WCav **CAVES FOLLY NURSERIES** ♿
Evendine Lane, Colwall, Malvern, Worcestershire, WR13 6DX
Ⓣ (01684) 540631
Ⓜ 07918 649276
Ⓔ bridget@cavesfolly.com

Ⓦ www.cavesfolly.com
Contact: Bridget Evans
Opening Times: 1000-1700 Thu-Sat Mar-Nov. Other times By appt.
Min Mail Order UK: £6.00
Cat. Cost: Free.
Credit Cards: All major credit/debit cards
Specialities: Organically grown perennials and alpines.
Notes: Nursery has grown plants in peat free organic compost for 35 yrs+. Certified by the Soil Association. Majority of plants grown from our own seed, division or cuttings. Also sells wholesale. Delivers to shows. Wheelchair accessible.
OS Grid Ref: SO751114

WCFE CHARLES F ELLIS
Oak Piece Nurseries, Stanway Road, Stanton, Nr Broadway, Worcestershire, WR12 7NQ
Ⓣ (01386) 584077
Ⓔ ellisplants@cooptel.net
Ⓦ www.ellisplants.co.uk
Contact: Charles Ellis
Opening Times: By appt. only.
Min Mail Order UK: £15.00
Cat. Cost: None issued.
Credit Cards: None
Specialities: Wide range of shrubs, conifers, climbers & perennials, some unusual. All available in small quantities only. A few specimen sizes (but not for mail order).

WChS CHICKENSTREET
1-3 The Stanyards, Gobowen, Oswestry, Shropshire, SY11 4NG
Ⓣ (01691) 657178
Ⓔ enquiry@chickenstreet.co.uk
Ⓦ www.chickenstreet.co.uk
Contact: Jill Cawthray
Opening Times: Mail order only.
Min Mail Order UK: £5.50
Cat. Cost: On-line catalogue only.
Specialities: A good selection of grasses and easy care perennials that associate well in naturalistic plantings. Combinations for sunny, shady or boggy areas with emphasis on plants for pollinators and wildlife.
Notes: Plants are propagated by ourselves and therefore stock may vary throughout the year. Generally plants are only sent out during the growing season between early Mar and Nov. Delivers to shows.

WCot COTSWOLD GARDEN FLOWERS
Sands Lane, Badsey, Evesham, Worcestershire, WR11 7EZ
Ⓣ nursery: (01386) 833849 or mail order: (01386) 422829
Ⓕ nursery: (01386) 49844
Ⓔ info@cgf.net
Ⓦ www.cgf.net
Contact: Bob Brown
Opening Times: 0900-1730 Mon-Fri &1000-1730 Sat & Sun, Mar-Sep. W/ends Oct-Feb by appt. only.
Min Mail Order UK: Nmc
Min Mail Order EU: Nmc
Cat. Cost: Free.
Credit Cards: All major debit/credit cards except American Express
Specialities: A very wide range of easy to grow & unusual perennials & succulents.
Notes: Delivers to shows. Euro accepted. Partial wheelchair access.
OS Grid Ref: SP077426

WCra CRANESBILL NURSERY
1 Waverley Road, Mossley Estate, Bloxwich, Walsall, West Midlands, WS3 2SW
Ⓣ (01684) 770733
Ⓜ 07500 600205
Ⓔ gary@cranesbillnursery.com
Ⓦ www.cranesbillnursery.com
Contact: Gary Carroll
Opening Times: Mail order only. Not open to the public. Collections by appt. only.
Min Mail Order UK: Nmc
Min Mail Order EU: £25.00
Cat. Cost: Free.
Credit Cards: All major credit/debit cards
Specialities: Hardy geraniums, Approx 200 varieties in stock. Can supply large quantities with 6-8 weeks notice. Please contact nursery for further details.
Notes: Cranesbill Nursery is the longest established UK specialist in Hardy Geraniums. Most of our stock is listed on the website when available, however we do also have limited stock of some unusual geraniums, so always ask.
OS Grid Ref: SO940378

WCru CRûG FARM PLANTS ♿
Griffith's Crossing, Caernarfon, Gwynedd, LL55 1TU
Ⓣ (01248) 670232
Ⓜ 07774 980842
Ⓔ mailorder@crug-farm.co.uk
Ⓦ www.mailorder.crug-farm.co.uk
Contact: B. and S. Wynn-Jones
Opening Times: 0930-1630 Thu-Sat, 1st Sat in Apr to 4th Sat in Sep. Or Mon-Fri by appt. all year.
Min Mail Order UK: Nmc
Min Mail Order EU: Nmc
Cat. Cost: Online only.

Credit Cards: All major credit/debit cards
Specialities: Mostly self, wild collected new introductions from Asia, Americas & southern Europe. Especially *Araliaceae*, *Asparagaceae*, shade tolerant perennials & shrubs. Unusual or rare trees, shrubs, herbaceous & bulbous. Many supplied bare-rooted when dormant.
Notes: Delivery by overnight carrier for UK & Ireland. Courier for rest of EU or dedicated vehicle for large orders. Delivers to shows. Wheelchair accessible.
OS Grid Ref: SH509652

WDib **Dibleys Nurseries** ♿ ◆
Llanelidan, Ruthin, Denbighshire, LL15 2LG
Ⓣ (01978) 790677
Ⓕ (01978) 790668
Ⓔ info@dibleys.com
Ⓦ www.dibleys.com
Contact: R. Dibley
Opening Times: 1000-1700 Mon-Sat (closed Sun), Apr-Aug. 1000-1700 Mon-Fri, Mar, Sep & Oct.
Min Mail Order UK: Nmc
Min Mail Order EU: Nmc
Cat. Cost: Free.
Credit Cards: Visa, Access, Switch, Electron, Solo
Specialities: *Streptocarpus, Columnea, Solenostemon, Saintpaulia* & other gesneriads & *Begonia*. National Collections of *Streptocarpus, Saintpaulia* & *Petrocosmea.*
Notes: Also sells wholesale. Euro accepted. Delivers to shows. Wheelchair accessible.

WeWi **West Wales Willows**
The Mill, Gwernogle, Carmarthen, Carmarthenshire, SA32 7SA
Ⓣ (01267) 202309
Ⓔ info@westwaleswillows.co.uk
Ⓦ www.westwaleswillows.co.uk
Contact: Justine Burgess
Opening Times: Open by appt. only.
Credit Cards: All major credit/debit cards
Specialities: National Collection Holder for *Salix* (Willow). Specialist grower of over 250 varieties of *Salix*. Sells living willow cuttings from Dec-Mar via mail order.
Notes: For details of open days and cultivation courses please see website.

WFar **Farmyard Nurseries**
Dol Llan Road, Llandysul, Carmarthenshire, SA44 4RL
Ⓣ (01559) 363389
Ⓜ 01267 220259
Ⓔ sales@farmyardnurseries.co.uk
Ⓦ www.farmyardnurseries.co.uk
Contact: Richard Bramley
Opening Times: 0900-1700 7 days, excl. Xmas Day, Boxing Day & New Year's Day.
Min Mail Order UK: 3 plants
Min Mail Order EU: 3 plants
Cat. Cost: None issued.
Credit Cards: Visa, Switch, MasterCard
Specialities: Huge range of home grown shrubs & herbaceous perennials, trees, climbers, alpines, conifers & bedding plants. National Collection of *Primula sieboldii* & *Sarracenia*. Specialise in *Hosta, Monarda*, hardy *Begonia*, hardy *Chrysanthemum, Impatiens, Sempervivum* & *Roscoea.*
Notes: Additionally sells from shop/yard in Carmarthen. Also sells wholesale. Partial wheelchair access (not garden or some areas of the nursery).
OS Grid Ref: SN421406

WFib **Fibrex Nurseries Ltd** ♿
Honeybourne Road, Pebworth, Stratford-on-Avon, Warwickshire, CV37 8XP
Ⓣ (01789) 720788
Ⓔ sales@fibrex.co.uk
Ⓦ www.fibrex.co.uk
Contact: Heather Godard-Key
Opening Times: 0900-1700 Mon-Fri, 2nd Mar-31st Aug. 0900-1600 Mon-Fri, 1st Sep-28th Feb. 1030-1600 Sat & Sun, 4th Apr-28th Jun. Closed last week Dec & 1st week Jan. Closed Easter Sun & Aug B/hol Mon.
Min Mail Order UK: £10.00 + p&p
Min Mail Order EU: £20.00 + p&p
Cat. Cost: 3 × 1st class.
Credit Cards: MasterCard, Visa, Maestro
Specialities: *Hedera*, ferns, *Pelargonium*, named tuberous begonias, *Hibiscus rosa-sinensis* cvs, hardy geraniums. National Plant Collections of *Pelargonium* & *Hedera*. Plant collections subject to time of year, please check by phone.
Notes: Also sells wholesale. Delivers to shows. Wheelchair accessible.
OS Grid Ref: SP133458

WGob **The Gobbett Nursery**
Farlow, Kidderminster, Worcestershire, DY14 8TD
Ⓣ (01746) 718647
Ⓔ chris.link59@gmail.com
Ⓦ www.thegobbettnursery.co.uk
Contact: C. H. Link
Opening Times: By appt. only.
Cat. Cost: None issued.
Credit Cards: None
Specialities: *Syringa* & *Cornus, Iris sibirica, Iris ensata.*
Notes: Delivers to shows.
OS Grid Ref: SO648811

W

WGoo **Wildegoose Nursery** ♿
The Walled Garden, Lower Millichope, Munslow, Craven Arms, Shropshire, SY7 9HE
Ⓣ (01584) 841890
Ⓜ 07798 628762
Ⓔ office@wildegoosenursery.co.uk
Ⓦ www.wildegoosenursery.co.uk
Contact: Laura Willgoss
Opening Times: 1000-1630 Fri-Sun, 27th Mar-4th Oct 2020.
Min Mail Order UK: Nmc
Min Mail Order EU: Nmc
Cat. Cost: 1st class sae.
Credit Cards: All major credit/debit cards
Specialities: *Viola*, incl. stock from Bouts Cottage Nursery. Herbaceous perennials & grasses. Some varieties propagated in small quantities.
Notes: Delivers to shows. Wheelchair accessible. Site is on a slope with gravel paths.

W

WGrf **Hardy Eucalyptus**
Grafton Nursery, Worcester Road, Grafton Flyford, Worcester, Worcestershire, WR7 4PW
Ⓣ (01905) 888 098
Ⓜ 07515 261511
Ⓔ office@hardy-eucalyptus.com
Ⓦ www.hardy-eucalyptus.com
Contact: Hilary Collins
Opening Times: Not open. Please order online or phone to arrange a suitable time.
Min Mail Order UK: £10.00
Min Mail Order EU: £35.00
Credit Cards: All major credit/debit cards
Specialities: *Eucalyptus*.
Notes: Specialise in a range of *Eucalyptus* suitable for growing in UK gardens, incl. a selection of smaller growing varieties ideal for modern town gardens. Also stocks more vigorous varieties for flower arranging, foliage and firewood production. Also sells wholesale. Delivers to shows.

WGwG **Gwynfor Growers**
Gwynfor, Pontgarreg, Llangrannog, Llandysul, Sir Ceredigion, SA44 6AU
Ⓣ (01239) 654151
Ⓔ info@gwynfor.co.uk
Ⓦ www.gwynfor.co.uk
Contact: S. & A. Hipkin
Opening Times: 1000-1800 Wed-Thu or sunset if earlier. Other times by appt.
Min Mail Order UK: Nmc
Cat. Cost: Online only.
Credit Cards: All major credit/debit cards, Paypal
Specialities: National Plant Collection of *Rosmarinus* cvs. Specialist supplier of Welsh fruit trees. Classic & contemporary plants grown organically & peat-free. Some plants available in small quantities only. Rarities propagated to order.
Notes: Plants also available at local farmers' markets, plant fairs & some NGS Open Gardens. Delivers to shows.
OS Grid Ref: SN331536

WHCr **Hergest Croft Gardens**
Hergest Estate Office, Ridgebourne Road, Kington, Herefordshire, HR5 3EG
Ⓣ (01544) 230160
Ⓜ 07968 435627
Ⓔ gardens@hergest.co.uk
Ⓦ www.hergest.co.uk
Contact: Stephen Lloyd
Opening Times: 1200-1730, 7 days, Apr-Oct.
Cat. Cost: None issued.
Credit Cards: All major credit/debit cards
Specialities: *Acer*, *Betula* & unusual woody plants.
Notes: Partial wheelchair access.
OS Grid Ref: SO286567

WHer **The Herb Garden & Historical Plant Nursery**
Frondeg, Gilfachreda, New Quay, Ceredigion, SA45 9SP
Ⓣ (01545) 580893
Ⓜ 07840 106956
Ⓔ corinnetremaine@gmail.com
Ⓦ www.historicalplants.co.uk
Contact: Corinne Tremaine
Opening Times: By appt. only.
Cat. Cost: Online only.
Credit Cards: None
Specialities: Rare herbs, rare natives & wild flowers, rare, unusual & historical perennials, old roses, heritage Pinks & Parma Violets.

WHil **Hillview Hardy Plants** ♿
(off B4176), Worfield, Nr Bridgnorth, Shropshire, WV15 5NT
Ⓣ (01746) 716454
Ⓜ 07974 391608
Ⓔ hillview@onetel.net
Ⓦ www.hillviewhardyplants.com
Contact: Ingrid, John & Sarah Millington
Opening Times: 1000-1700 Mon-Sat, Mar-mid Oct. At other times, please phone first.
Min Mail Order UK: Nmc
Min Mail Order EU: £20.00 + p&p
Cat. Cost: Online only.
Credit Cards: All major credit/debit cards
Specialities: Choice herbaceous perennials incl. *Acanthus*, *Albuca*, *Aquilegia*, *Primula auricula*, *Eucomis*, *Ixia*, South African bulbs.

National Collections of *Acanthus, Albuca* & *Primula auricula*.
Notes: Also sells wholesale. Exports beyond EU. Delivers to shows. Euro accepted. Wheelchair accessible.
OS Grid Ref: SO772969

WHlf **HAYLOFT PLANTS**
Manor Farm, Pensham, Pershore, Worcestershire, WR10 3HB
Ⓣ (01386) 562999
Ⓕ (01386) 553833
Ⓔ customercare@hayloftplants.co.uk
Ⓦ https://hayloft.co.uk/
Contact: Evie Gormley
Opening Times: Not open. Mail order only.
Min Mail Order UK: Nmc
Min Mail Order EU: Nmc
Cat. Cost: Free.
Credit Cards: All major debit/credit cards except American Express
Notes: Mail order only.

WHoo **HOO HOUSE NURSERY**
Hoo House, Gloucester Road, Tewkesbury, Gloucestershire, GL20 7DA
Ⓣ (01684) 293389
Ⓕ (01684) 293389
Ⓔ nursery@hoohouse.co.uk
Ⓦ www.hoohouse.co.uk
Contact: Julie & Robin Ritchie
Opening Times: 1000-1700 Mon-Sat, 1100-1700 Sun. Please ring to check Nov-Jan.
Cat. Cost: 3 × 1st class.
Credit Cards: All major credit/debit cards
Specialities: Wide range of herbaceous & alpines grown peat-free. *Aster, Cyclamen, Geranium, Penstemon, Saxifraga* & many later-flowering varieties.
Notes: Also sells wholesale. Partial wheelchair access.
OS Grid Ref: SO893293

WHrl **HARRELLS HARDY PLANTS**
(office) 15 Coxlea Close, Evesham, Worcestershire, WR11 4JS
Ⓣ (01386) 443077
Ⓜ 07799 577120 or 07733 446606
Ⓔ mail@harrellshardyplants.co.uk
Ⓦ www.harrellshardyplants.co.uk
Contact: Liz Nicklin & Kate Phillips
Opening Times: By appt. only Please telephone.
Min Mail Order UK: Nmc
Min Mail Order EU: Nmc
Cat. Cost: Online plant list.
Credit Cards: None
Specialities: Display gardens showcase wide range of hardy perennials, esp. *Hemerocallis* & grasses.
Notes: Nursery located off Rudge Rd, Evesham. Please phone for directions or see website. Exports beyond EU. Partial wheelchair access.
OS Grid Ref: SP033443

WHtc **HUTCHINGS AND SON**
Badsey Lane, Knowle Hill, Evesham, Worcestershire, WR11 7EN
Ⓣ (01386) 834441
Ⓜ 07957 530964
Ⓔ enquiries@hutchingsandson.co.uk
Ⓦ www.hutchingsandson.co.uk
Contact: Matthew & Helen Hutchings
Opening Times: 0930-1600 Tue-Fri 1200-1600 Sat.
Cat. Cost: On-line only.
Specialities: We specialise in trees and shrubs including fruit trees and conifers. We stock a large variety of plants in small numbers. We have a large number of *Trachycarpus fortunei*.
Notes: We are a small business, our sales display area is grassed and muddy when wet. We only deliver up to 20 miles from site.
OS Grid Ref: SP066444

WIce **ICE ALPINES** ♿
Lye Head Road, Bewdley, Worcestershire, DY12 2UW
Ⓣ (01299) 269219
Ⓕ (01562) 510003
Ⓔ icealpines@googlemail.com
Ⓦ www.icealpines.co.uk
Contact: Mark Lagomarsino
Opening Times: Mail order. Open by appt. only.
Min Mail Order UK: Nmc
Min Mail Order EU: £18
Credit Cards: All major credit/debit cards
Specialities: British grown alpine & rockery plants.
Notes: Delivers to shows. Wheelchair accessible.

WJam **GREENJJAM NURSERIES**
Ginger Farm, Upper Hook Road, Upton Upon Severn, Worcestershire, WR8 0SA
Ⓜ 07980 277709
Ⓔ info@greenjjam.co.uk
Ⓦ www.greenjjam.co.uk
Contact: Julia Mitchell
Opening Times: Open by appt. only and when the gate is.
Min Mail Order UK: £18.00
Credit Cards: All major credit/debit cards
Specialities: Family run nursery propagating and growing almost all of the plants we sell. *Penstemon*, hardy perennials, white-flowering

and white variegated plants. *Penstemon* available May to Sep. Other plants all year.
Notes: Our nursery is now located at our new address at Ginger Farm. Mail order will commence summer 2020. Please see website for updates and availability. Delivers to shows.

WJas **Paul Jasper Trees**
The Lighthouse (office only), Bridge Street, Leominster, Herefordshire, HR6 8DX
Ⓔ jaspertreescouk@aol.com
Ⓦ www.jaspertrees.co.uk
Contact: Paul Jasper
Opening Times: Not open. Mail order only.
Min Mail Order UK: £25.00 + p&p
Cat. Cost: Online only.
Credit Cards: All major credit/debit cards
Specialities: Many unusual varieties of *Malus domestica* & *Prunus*.
Notes: Good range of fruit & ornamental trees. Modern & traditional fruit tree varieties. 100 ornamental tree varieties, direct from the grower. Less popular varieties available in small quantities only. See website for details.

W

WJek **Jekka's Herb Farm** ♿
Rose Cottage, Shellards Lane, Alveston, Bristol, South Gloucestershire, BS35 3SY
Ⓣ (01454) 418878
Ⓔ sales@jekkas.com
Ⓦ www.jekkas.com
Contact: Jekka McVicar
Opening Times: Open on specific days only. Please check website or contact nursery for dates.
Min Mail Order UK: £10.00
Min Mail Order EU: £18.00
Cat. Cost: Online only.
Credit Cards: Visa, MasterCard, Delta, Maestro
Specialities: Specialist herb farm with a herbetum containing over 300 culinary herbs. The collection contains herbs from all around the world.
Notes: Wheelchair accessible.

WJur **Jurassicplants Nurseries**
Waen Road, Waen, St Asaph, Denbighshire, LL17 0DY
Ⓣ (01745) 812028
Ⓜ 07909 100255
Ⓔ office@jurassicplants.co.uk
Ⓦ www.jurassicplants.co.uk
Contact: Dr Zoltan Hamori & Magdolna Hamori-Kovacs
Opening Times: Mail order only, but orders can be collected. Phone line open 0800-1800 Mon-Sat. Also contact by email, facebook or through our website.
Min Mail Order UK: Nmc
Min Mail Order EU: Nmc
Cat. Cost: Free.
Credit Cards: All major credit/debit cards
Specialities: All of our plants are propagated and grown on our nursery in North Wales, from fresh stock of seeds collected by the Jurassic Team. Mail order to the UK and EU in unique, secure packaging. Please visit our website for full range, with secure payment. Cheques also accepted.
Notes: We offer many unusual woody fruits/edibles, tropical fruits, rare Fig (*Ficus carica*) and Pomegranate (*Punica granatum*) varieties, along with rare and unusual ornamental trees and shrubs, dwarf species, *Bonsai* starters, plants with autumn and winter colours, acid- and chalk loving species. Euro accepted.
OS Grid Ref: SJ062997

WKif **Kiftsgate Court Gardens** ♿
Kiftsgate Court, Chipping Camden, Gloucestershire, GL55 6LN
Ⓣ (01386) 438777
Ⓔ anne@kiftsgate.co.uk
Ⓦ www.kiftsgate.co.uk
Contact: Mrs J. Chambers
Opening Times: 1200-1800 Sat-Wed, May, Jun & Jul. 1400-1800 Sat-Wed, Aug. 1400-1800 Sun, Mon & Wed, Apr & Sep.
Cat. Cost: None issued.
Credit Cards: All major debit/credit cards except American Express
Specialities: Small range of unusual plants.
Notes: Wheelchair accessible.
OS Grid Ref: SP170430

WKor **Kore Wild Fruit Nursery**
Bridport House, Cilcennin, Lampeter, Ceredigion, SA48 8RL
Ⓣ (01570) 470439
Ⓔ info@korewildfruitnursery.co.uk
Ⓦ www.korewildfruitnursery.co.uk
Contact: Coral Guppy
Opening Times: Mail order only.
Min Mail Order UK: Nmc
Min Mail Order EU: Nmc
Cat. Cost: Free.
Credit Cards: All major credit/debit cards
Specialities: Range of mainly hardy trees, shrubs and perennials that produce edible fruit and some perennial veg. Unusual plants for indoors. Exotic and native species available.
Notes: Ideal for a range of uses, aspects and soil types. All plants propagated on site in 7cm pots and sold when 1 to 3 years old. Plants available all year. Customers can arrange to collect.

WLav **The Lavender Garden**
Ashcroft Nurseries, Nr Ozleworth,
Kingscote, Tetbury, Gloucestershire,
GL8 8YF
Ⓣ (01453) 860356
Ⓜ 07837 582943
Ⓔ andrew007bullock@aol.com
Ⓦ www.thelavenderg.co.uk
Contact: Andrew Bullock
Opening Times: 1100-1700 Sat & Sun. Weekdays variable, please phone. 1st Nov-1st Mar by appt. only.
Min Mail Order UK: £10.00 + p&p
Min Mail Order EU: £20.00 + p&p
Cat. Cost: Online only.
Credit Cards: All major credit/debit cards
Specialities: *Lavandula*, *Buddleja*, plants to attract butterflies, herbs & wildflowers. National Plant Collection of *Buddleja*.
Notes: Also sells wholesale. Delivers to shows. Partial wheelchair access.
OS Grid Ref: ST798948

WLea **Leaf Creative Design Ltd** ♿
Leaf Creative Plant Centre, Ross Road,
Huntley, Gloucestershire,
GL19 3EX
Ⓣ (01452) 830837
Ⓔ enquiries@leafcreative.co.uk
Ⓦ www.leafcreative.co.uk
Contact: Neil Evans
Opening Times: 0900-1700 Mon-Sat, 1000-1600 Sun.
Min Mail Order EU: £50.00
Credit Cards: All major credit/debit cards
Notes: Wheelchair accessible. Delivers to shows. Also sells wholesale.
OS Grid Ref: SO713194

WLov **Lovegroves**
The Old Chapel, Pendock, Gloucestershire,
GL19 3PG
Ⓣ (01531) 650918
Ⓜ 07973 331142
Ⓔ clare@plants-paradise.co.uk
Ⓦ www.plants-paradise.co.uk
Contact: Clare Lovegrove
Opening Times: Mail order or by appt. only.
Min Mail Order UK: Nmc
Cat. Cost: Available by email or download from website only.
Credit Cards: All major credit/debit cards
Specialities: Interesting selection of trees, shrubs, ferns and climbers; many of which are rare or unusual. All grown in peat-free compost.
Notes: Traditional plant nursery, producing an inspiring collection of desirable trees and shrubs grown in the UK. Collection of plants by prior arrangement. Delivers to shows.
OS Grid Ref: SO786326

WMad **Madley Plants** ♿
Birch House, Madley, Herefordshire, HR2 9NT
Ⓣ (01981) 784011
Ⓜ 07774 424443
Ⓔ contact@madleyplants.co.uk
Ⓦ www.madleyplants.co.uk
Contact: Michele Blackmore
Opening Times: 1000-1600 Feb-Mar, 0900-1700 Apr-Jul, 1000-1600 Aug-Dec, Closed Jan.
Credit Cards: All major debit/credit cards except American Express
Notes: Wheelchair accessible.

WMal **Malcolm Allison Nurseries**
79 Byron Road, St Mark's, Cheltenham,
Gloucestershire, GL51 7EY
Ⓣ (01242) 256349
Ⓜ 07817 730509
Ⓔ majallison2000@yahoo.com
Ⓦ http://www.malcolmallisonplants.com
Contact: Malcolm Allison
Opening Times: Visitors welcome by appt.
Credit Cards: Paypal
Specialities: Drought tolerant perennials, cultivars of *Nerine*, *Sarniensis*, *Cistus* & *Halimium species* & *cultivars.*
Notes: Wide range of hardy and half-hardy herbaceous plants, many available only in small quantities.
OS Grid Ref: SO914286

WMAq **Merebrook Water Plants**
Kingfisher Barn, Merebrook Farm, Hanley
Swan, Worcester, Worcestershire,
WR8 0DX
Ⓜ 07989 528647
Ⓔ roger@pondplants.co.uk
Ⓦ www.pondplants.co.uk
Contact: Roger Kings
Opening Times: Not open. Mail order only.
Min Mail Order UK: Nmc
Min Mail Order EU: £25.00
Cat. Cost: Online only.
Credit Cards: All major credit/debit cards
Specialities: Hardy *Nymphaea*, Louisiana irises & other aquatic plants. International Waterlily & Water Gardening Society accredited collection.
Notes: Full range of pond plants including water lilies, marginal and deeper marginal plants, oxygenating plants, wetland and bog plants and moisture-loving plants.
OS Grid Ref: SO802425

WMat **The Tree Shop at Frank P. Matthews Ltd.** ♿
Berrington Court, Tenbury Wells, Worcestershire, WR15 8TH
Ⓣ (01584) 812800
Ⓕ (01584) 811830
Ⓔ treeshop@fpmatthews.co.uk
Ⓦ www.frankpmatthews.com
Contact: Steve Grosvenor
Opening Times: 0730-1700 Mon-Fri 0900-1600 Sat.
Cat. Cost: 4 × 1st class.
Credit Cards: All major credit/debit cards
Specialities: Fruit & deciduous ornamental trees.
Notes: Also sells wholesale. Wheelchair accessible.
OS Grid Ref: SO571676

WMil **Anne Milner**
Meadow House, Baunton, Cirencester, Gloucestershire, GL7 7BB
Ⓣ (01285) 643731
Ⓔ anne.milner@btinternet.com
Ⓦ www.blissiris.co.uk
Contact: Anne Milner
Opening Times: By appt. only.
Min Mail Order UK: Nmc
Min Mail Order EU: Nmc
Cat. Cost: 50p (UK) £1.00 (EU) to cover postage.
Credit Cards: None
Specialities: National Plant Collection of *Iris* (A.J. Bliss introductions). Available in small quantities only.
Notes: Euro accepted. Delivers to some shows, check with nursery.

WMon **National Plant Collection of Monarda** ♿
Glyn Bach, Near Pont Hywel, Efailwen, Pembrokeshire, SA66 7JP
Ⓣ (01994) 419104
Ⓜ 07828 199303
Ⓔ carole_whittaker@hotmail.com
Ⓦ www.glynbachgardens.co.uk
Contact: Carole Whittaker
Opening Times: Open by appt. & May-Oct for collection of orders only.
Cat. Cost: Online only for our customers.
Credit Cards: None
Specialities: National Plant Collection of *Monarda*. Limited stock available.
Notes: Gardens open under Plant Heritage and by appt. Talks given. If travelling some distance please contact nursery to check plant availability. Wheelchair accessible.
OS Grid Ref: SN132275

WMou **Mount Pleasant Trees Ltd** ♿
Rockhampton, Berkeley, Gloucestershire, GL13 9DU
Ⓣ (01454) 260348
Ⓔ info@mountpleasanttrees.com
Ⓦ www.mountpleasanttrees.com
Contact: Tom Locke & Elizabeth Murphy
Opening Times: 0830-1630 Mon-Fri, 0830-1230 Sat, Oct-Apr.
Cat. Cost: Free.
Credit Cards: All major credit/debit cards
Specialities: Wide range of trees for forestry, hedging, woodlands & gardens esp. *Populus, Salix, Tilia* & *Quercus*.
Notes: Mail order available for plants under 1m in height, quotes on request, p&p quoted on individual basis. Also sells wholesale. Wheelchair accessible.
OS Grid Ref: ST654929

WNHG **New Hope Gardens** ♿
(office) The Old Chapel, Cefn Einion, Nr Bishops Castle, Shropshire, SY9 5LF
Ⓣ Office (01588) 630750
Ⓔ markwzenick@aol.com
Ⓦ www.newhopegardens.com
Contact: Mark Zenick
Opening Times: Please call or email for open days or to schedule an appt. to visit the nursery.
Min Mail Order UK: Nmc
Min Mail Order EU: Nmc
Cat. Cost: Online only. Plant list on request.
Credit Cards: All major credit/debit cards
Specialities: American bred, British grown, *Hemerocallis*. Ships bare-rooted plants. Daylily plants are growing and for sale at New Hope Gardens, Colebatch Farm, Shropshire on open w/ends.
Notes: Wheelchair accessible.
OS Grid Ref: SO872317

WNPC **Newent Plant Centre** ♿
Little Verzons Farm, Hereford Road, Ledbury, Herefordshire, HR8 2PZ
Ⓣ (01531) 670121
Ⓔ markmoir999@btinternet.com
Ⓦ www.newentplantcentre.co.uk
Contact: Mark Moir
Opening Times: 0900-1700 Mon-Sat, 1000-1600 Sun.
Credit Cards: All major credit/debit cards
Specialities: Extensive range of *Heuchera* & *Euphorbia*. Herbaceous perennials, climbers, shrubs, trees, alpines, herbs, roses & fruit.
Notes: Coffee shop & deli on site. Delivers to shows. Wheelchair accessible.
OS Grid Ref: SO665395

WOld **Old Court Nurseries** ♿
Colwall, Nr Malvern, Worcestershire, WR13 6QE
Ⓣ (01684) 540416
Ⓜ 07971 522891
Ⓔ oldcourtnurseries@btinternet.com
Ⓦ www.autumnasters.co.uk
Contact: Paul, Meriel or Helen Picton
Opening Times: 1400-1700 Wed-Sat, Apr-Aug. 1100-1700 Wed-Sun, Aug. 1100-1700 7 days, 1st Sep-20th Oct. Also by appt. Apr to Oct.
Min Mail Order UK: Nmc
Min Mail Order EU: Nmc
Cat. Cost: Free.
Credit Cards: All major debit/credit cards except American Express
Specialities: National Collection of Michaelmas Daisies. Herbaceous perennials and tender succulents.
Notes: Mail order sent in spring only. Display garden open Apr-Oct, plus some early season open days. See website or contact nursery for further information. Wheelchair accessible.
OS Grid Ref: SO759430

WOut **Out of the Common Way**
Penhyddgan, Boduan, Pwllheli, Gwynedd, LL53 8YH
Ⓣ (01758) 721577
Contact: Margaret Mason
Opening Times: By appt. only.
Min Mail Order UK: Nmc
Min Mail Order EU: Nmc
Cat. Cost: A5 sae or electronic.
Credit Cards: None
Specialities: *Labiates*, esp. *Salvia*. Also *Geranium* & *Crocosmia*. Native plants. Some plants propagated in small quantities only. Will propagate Salvias to order.
Notes: Delivers to shows. Euro accepted.

WPav **Paviour and Davies Plants** ♿
(office) Dame School, Castle Street, Wigmore, Herefordshire, HR6 9UA
Ⓣ (01568) 770005
Ⓜ 07966 580812
Ⓔ markpaviour@gmail.com
Ⓦ www.paviouranddaviesplants.co.uk
Contact: Mark Paviour
Opening Times: By appt. only.
Min Mail Order UK: Nmc
Cat. Cost: Online.
Credit Cards: None
Specialities: Plants of Chilean and Argentinian origin together with a selection of unusual plants from Australasia. All plants propagated and grown on site. National Plant Collection of *Azara*. Some plants only available in small numbers.
Notes: Groups welcome by appt. Talks given by arrangement. Delivers to shows. Wheelchair accessible.
OS Grid Ref: SO429556

WPGP **Pan-Global Plants** ♿
The Walled Garden, Frampton Court, Frampton-on-Severn, Gloucestershire, GL2 7EX
Ⓣ (01452) 741641
Ⓜ 07801 275138
Ⓔ info@panglobalplants.com
Ⓦ www.panglobalplants.com
Contact: Nick Macer
Opening Times: 1100-1700 Wed-Sun 1st Feb-31st Oct. Also B/hols. Closed 2nd Sun in Sep. Winter months by appt. please telephone first.
Min Mail Order UK: £25.00
Min Mail Order EU: £35.00
Cat. Cost: 4 × 1st class.
Credit Cards: Maestro, MasterCard, Visa, Solo, Delta
Specialities: Serious plantsman's nursery offering a wide selection of rare & desirable trees, shrubs, herbaceous, bamboos, exotics, climbers, ferns etc. Specialities incl. *Magnolia, Hydrangea, Tilia, Betula, Sorbus*, Bamboo & *Agavaceae*.
Notes: Wheelchair accessible.
OS Grid Ref: SO750080

WPhe **Pheasant Acre Plants** ◆
3 Pheasant Walk, Pen-y-Fai, Bridgend, Mid Glamorgan, CF31 4DU
Ⓣ (01656) 664086
Ⓜ 07816 236462
Ⓔ sales@pheasantacreplants.co.uk
Ⓦ www.pheasantacreplants.co.uk
Contact: Rob Evans
Opening Times: By appt. only.
Min Mail Order UK: Nmc
Min Mail Order EU: Nmc
Cat. Cost: £1.00
Credit Cards: All major credit/debit cards
Specialities: Bulbous. Ornamental. *Gladiolus*.
Notes: Open days throughout the year. Delivers to shows. Euro accepted.

WPnP **Penlan Perennials**
Landre, Drefach, Llanybydder, Ceredigion, SA40 9YD
Ⓣ (01570) 480097
Ⓜ 07984 880241
Ⓔ info@penlanperennials.co.uk
Ⓦ www.penlanperennials.co.uk
Contact: Graham & Julie Moore
Opening Times: 1000-1700 Tue-Sun from 1st Mar.

Min Mail Order UK: Nmc
Min Mail Order EU: Nmc
Cat. Cost: Online only.
Credit Cards: All major credit/debit cards
Specialities: Aquatic, marginal & bog plants. Shade-loving & woodland perennials, ferns, hardy geraniums & shrubs, all grown organically in peat-free compost.
Notes: Mail order all year, next day delivery. Secure online web ordering. Also sells wholesale. Euro accepted. Delivers to shows.
OS Grid Ref: SN500464

WReH **ReadyHedge Ltd & Hedgegrow Ltd**
Court Gate Nursery, Eckington, Pershore, Worcestershire, WR10 3BB
Ⓣ (01386) 750585
Ⓕ (01386) 750197
Ⓔ sales@readyhedgeltd.com
Ⓦ www.readyhedgeltd.com
Contact: Richard Gosling
Opening Times: 0800-1630 Mon-Thu, 0800-1530 Fri. Closed Sat & Sun.
Credit Cards: All major debit/credit cards except American Express
Notes: Readyhedge are growers & suppliers of quality instant hedging and screening. Readyhedge Ltd is a wholesale nursery growing high quality instant hedging and screening plants for all landscaping projects. The Readyhedge trough range is grown in 1m troughs and is ready spaced for ease of planting.
OS Grid Ref: SO921174

W

WRou **Roualeyn Nurseries**
Trefriw, Conwy, LL27 0SX
Ⓣ (01492) 640548
Ⓔ roualeynnursery@btinternet.com
Ⓦ www.roualeynfuchsias.co.uk
Contact: Colin Jones
Opening Times: 1000-1600 Sat & Sun only 2nd Mar-30th Jun.
Min Mail Order UK: £15.00
Cat. Cost: 2 × 1st class sae.
Credit Cards: All major credit/debit cards
Specialities: *Fuchsia*.
Notes: Orders may be collected from any of the flower shows listed in current catalogue. Delivers to shows.
OS Grid Ref: SH632778

WSFF **Saith Ffynnon Wildlife Plants** ♿
Downing Road, Whitford, Holywell, Flintshire, CH8 9EN
Ⓣ (01352) 711198
Ⓜ 07979 603846
Ⓕ (01352) 716777
Ⓔ Jan@7wells.org
Ⓦ www.7wells.co.uk
Contact: Jan Miller
Opening Times: NGS Open day 6th Sep, other times by appt.
Min Mail Order UK: Nmc
Min Mail Order EU: Nmc
Cat. Cost: 2 × 1st class (list only) or full catalogue online.
Credit Cards: All major credit/debit cards
Specialities: Plants and seeds to attract bees, butterflies & other wildlife. Natural dye plants. Miniature garden plants, National Collection of *Eupatorium*. Stock available in small quantities unless ordered well in advance.
Notes: Percentage of profits go to conservation. Credit cards accepted via website only. Also sells wholesale. Euro accepted. Wheelchair accessible.
OS Grid Ref: SJ154775

WSHC **Stone House Cottage Nurseries**
Church Lane, Stone, Nr Kidderminster, Worcestershire, DY10 4BG
Ⓜ 07817 921146
Ⓔ louisa@shcn.co.uk
Ⓦ www.shcn.co.uk
Contact: L. N. Arbuthnott
Opening Times: 1000-1700 Wed-Sat, early Apr-late Aug.
Credit Cards: All major credit/debit cards
Specialities: Small general range esp. wall shrubs, climbers & unusual plants.
Notes: Partial wheelchair access.
OS Grid Ref: SO863750

WShi **Shipton Bulbs**
Y Felin, Henllan Amgoed, Whitland, Carmarthenshire, SA34 0SL
Ⓣ (01994) 240637
Ⓕ (01994) 240637
Ⓔ john@shiptonbulbs.co.uk
Ⓦ www.shiptonbulbs.co.uk
Contact: John Shipton
Opening Times: By appt. only.
Min Mail Order UK: Nmc
Min Mail Order EU: Nmc
Cat. Cost: Sae.
Credit Cards: All major credit/debit cards
Specialities: Native British bulbs. Bulbs & plants for naturalising.
Notes: Also sells wholesale. Euro accepted.
OS Grid Ref: SN188207

WSpi **Spinneywell Nursery**
Spinneywell Farm, Waterlane, Oakridge, Stroud, Gloucestershire, GL6 7PH

Ⓜ 07879 133046
Ⓔ wendy@spinneywell.co.uk
Ⓦ www.plantproviders.co.uk
Contact: Wendy Asher
Opening Times: 0900-1700 Wed-Sat Mar-Oct, otherwise by prior appt. only. Please telephone before travelling. Also advertised open days & weekend events. Check website or contact nursery for details.
Min Mail Order UK: £10.00 + p&p
Min Mail Order EU: £30.00 + p&p
Cat. Cost: Online only.
Credit Cards: All major credit/debit cards
Specialities: *Buxus, Daphne, Euphorbia*, ferns, grasses, hellebores, hardy geraniums, unusual shrubs *Taxus* (yew) and topiary.
Notes: Plant sourcing service available. Mail order and organised collections/deliveries only. Also sells wholesale.
OS Grid Ref: SO921044

WSSs **Shropshire Sarracenias** ♿
Beaufort, Coppice Drive, Wrockwardine Wood, Telford, Shropshire, TF2 7BP
Ⓣ (01952) 612452
Ⓔ mike@carnivorousplants.uk.com
Ⓦ www.carnivorousplants.uk.com
Contact: Mike King
Opening Times: By appt. only.
Min Mail Order UK: Nmc
Min Mail Order EU: Nmc
Cat. Cost: 2 × 1st class.
Credit Cards: Paypal
Specialities: *Sarracenia. Dionaea* muscipula & forms. Some stock available in small quantities only. National Plant Collections of *Sarracenia* & *Dionaea*.
Notes: Exports beyond EU. Delivers to shows. Euro accepted. Wheelchair accessible.
OS Grid Ref: SJ689085

WSuV **Sunnybank Vine Nursery (National Vine Collection)**
Cwm Barn, King Street, Ewyas Harold, Rowlestone, Herefordshire, HR2 0EE
Ⓣ (01981) 240256
Ⓔ Sarah@sunnybankvines.co.uk
Ⓦ www.sunnybankvines.co.uk
Contact: Sarah Bell
Opening Times: Not open. Open day annually – see website for details.
Min Mail Order UK: £15.00 incl. p&p
Min Mail Order EU: £23.00 incl. p&p
Cat. Cost: Online only.
Credit Cards: None
Specialities: Vines. National Plant Collection of *Vitis* vinifera (hardy, incl. dessert & wine). Small quantities of 60-70 varieties available as rooted plants, the entire collection usually available as bare wood cuttings for own propagation depending upon wood ripening this season.
Notes: Open day once a year advertised on both nursery & Plant Heritage websites. Exports beyond EU by arrangement.

WThu **Thuya Alpine Nursery**
Glebelands, Hartpury, Gloucestershire, GL19 3BW
Ⓣ (01452) 700548 (ring between 1900-2100 hours)
Ⓜ 07435 419667
Contact: S. W. Bond
Opening Times: 1000-dusk Sat & B/hols. 1100-dusk Sun, Weekdays appt. advised.
Min Mail Order UK: £7.00 + p&p
Min Mail Order EU: £14.00 + p&p
Cat. Cost: 4 × 2nd class.
Credit Cards: None
Specialities: Wide and changing range including rarities, available in small quantities only.
Notes: Will deliver plants to AGS shows only. Partial wheelchair access.

WTor **Tortworth Plants Ltd**
Old Lodge Farm, Tortworth, Wotton-under-Edge, Gloucestershire, GL12 8HF
Ⓣ (01454) 260020
Ⓕ (01454) 260020
Ⓔ info@tortworthplants.co.uk
Ⓦ www.tortworthplants.co.uk
Contact: Rebecca Flint or Tim Hancock
Opening Times: By appt. only.
Min Mail Order UK: Nmc
Cat. Cost: Online or 2 × 1st for plant list.
Credit Cards: All major credit/debit cards
Specialities: Herbaceous perennials & alpines, incl. the more unusual.
Notes: Also sells wholesale. Partial wheelchair access. Delivers to shows.

WTre **Walled Garden Treberfydd**
Llangasty, Brecon, Powys, LD3 7PX
Ⓣ (01874) 730169
Ⓜ 07711 222700
Ⓔ alison@walledgardentreberfydd.com
Ⓦ www.walledgardentreberfydd.com
Contact: Alison Sparshatt
Opening Times: 1000-1700 daily, Apr-Oct. For Nov-Mar opening times see website or contact nursery.
Cat. Cost: Online only.
Credit Cards: All major credit/debit cards
Specialities: Old-fashioned plant nursery in a walled Victorian kitchen garden. Hardy plants

W

grown in Wales which are structural, unusual, herbal or fragrant. Special emphasis on herbs & perennial vegetables. Many varieties propagated in small quantities only.
Notes: Events & workshops throughout the year. Contact nursery for details.
OS Grid Ref: SO128255

WTSh **Tree Shop Ltd**
Unit 16, Harts Barn, Monmouth Road, Longhope, Gloucestershire, GL17 0QD
Ⓣ (01452) 832100
Ⓕ (01452) 831273
Ⓔ office@tree-shop.co.uk
Ⓦ www.tree-shop.co.uk
Contact: Helen Conneely & Lorraine Organ
Opening Times: By appt. only 0830-1600 Mon-Fri. Please phone first.
Min Mail Order UK: Nmc
Cat. Cost: Free.
Credit Cards: All major debit/credit cards except American Express
Specialities: Trees, hedging, shrubs.
OS Grid Ref: SO679185

W

WTyc **Ty Cwm Nursery**
Penfordd, Llanybydder, Ceredigon, SA40 9XE
Ⓣ (01570) 480655
Ⓔ helenwarrington@hotmail.co.uk
Ⓦ www.tycwmnursery.co.uk
Contact: Helen Warrington
Opening Times: 1000-1800, 1st Mar-30th Sep, Tue-Sun. Closed Mon.1st Oct-31st Feb by appt. only, we are here most of the time.
Min Mail Order UK: Nmc
Min Mail Order EU: Nmc
Cat. Cost: Online only.
Credit Cards: All major credit/debit cards
Specialities: Carnivorous plants & unusual perennials including a good selection for shade. Also sell shrubs, climbers, bedding, fruit and veg plants. Many rare items not listed available in small quantities.
Notes: Partial wheelchair access to nursery area. Cafe with wheelchair access open 1000-1700. Toilet with wheelchair access. Delivers to shows.

WViv **Viv Marsh Postal Plants**
Hunkington Nurseries, Walford Heath, Shrewsbury, Shropshire, SY4 2HT
Ⓣ (01939) 291475
Ⓔ mail@postalplants.co.uk
Ⓦ www.postalplants.co.uk
Contact: Mr Viv Marsh
Opening Times: Open 2 w/ends a year. Please phone or see website for details.
Min Mail Order UK: £30.00
Min Mail Order EU: £30.00
Cat. Cost: Free.
Credit Cards: All major credit/debit cards
Specialities: Specialists in *Alstroemeria* and tall bearded *Iris*. National Plant Collection of *Alstroemeria*, viewing by appt.
Notes: Partial wheelchair access (to tunnels, no disabled toilet).
OS Grid Ref: SJ445197

WWbk **The Willow Bank**
Ragmans Lane Farm, Cats Hill, Bishopswood, Lower Lydbrook, Gloucestershire, GL17 9PA
Ⓣ (01594) 861782
Ⓜ 07947 728186
Ⓔ info@thewillowbank.com
Ⓦ www.thewillowbank.com
Contact: Steve Pickup
Opening Times: Office manned Nov-Mar. We can be contacted via email all year.
Min Mail Order UK: £10 courier charge for orders under £50
Min Mail Order EU: Contact us for shipping costs
Credit Cards: All major credit/debit cards
Specialities: Specialise in *Salix* ssp, including *S. viminalis* 'Super Willow', *S.* × *rubra* 'Eugenei', *S. purpurea* 'Dark Dicks', *S. dasyclados*, *S. miyabeana*, S. *triandra*, S. *x rubra* 'Harrisons Seedling', *S. alba* 'Vitellina, *S.* × *fraglis* 'Flanders Red'.
Notes: Professional Willow growers with over 30 years experience of growing Willow for living structures (domes, tunnels etc.). Kits for windbreak, garden and boundary hedging, grow your own firewood plantations, willow cuttings for basketry and crafts. Willow for spiling and environmental purposes.
OS Grid Ref: SO605117

WWct **Walcot Organic Nursery**
Walcot Lane, Drakes Broughton, Pershore, Worcestershire, WR10 2AL
Ⓣ (01905) 841587
Ⓜ 07780 547983
Ⓔ enquiries@walcotnursery.co.uk
Ⓦ www.walcotnursery.co.uk
Contact: Kevin O'Neill
Opening Times: 0800-1700 Mon-Fri. 1000-1300 Sat. Sat only Nov-Mar.
Min Mail Order UK: £16.00
Cat. Cost: Free.
Credit Cards: All major credit/debit cards
Specialities: Growers of Organic fruit trees – apples, plums, damsons, pears, cherries, quinces & crab apples on different rootstocks. Supplied bare-rooted while dormant from late Nov until end of Mar.

Notes: Also sells wholesale. Nursery buildings accessible for wheelchairs.
OS Grid Ref: SO944461

WWFP **Whitehall Farmhouse Plants**
Sevenhampton, Cheltenham, Gloucestershire, GL54 5TL
Ⓣ (01242) 820772
Ⓜ 07711 021034
Ⓔ victoria@wfplants.co.uk
Ⓦ www.wfplants.co.uk
Contact: Victoria Logue
Opening Times: By appt. only.
Min Mail Order UK: Nmc
Credit Cards: None
Notes: A very small nursery producing a few interesting & easy, mostly hardy perennials for the garden. All plants held in very small quantities only.
OS Grid Ref: SP018229

WWild **The Wildflower Nursery**
Hackett Farm, Reynalton, Kilgetty, Pembrokeshire, SA68 0XN
Ⓜ 07854 845014
Ⓔ info@thewildflowernursery.co.uk
Ⓦ www.thewildflowernursery.co.uk
Contact: Lindsey Jones
Opening Times: Open by appt. only.
Min Mail Order UK: £4.99
Cat. Cost: Online only.
Credit Cards: All major credit/debit cards
Specialities: British wild flower plants.
Notes: Sells online only.

WWke **Wykeham Gardens** ♿
The Yard at Crowcroft, Leigh Sinton, Malvern, Worcestershire, WR13 6ED
Ⓣ (01684) 578381
Ⓜ 07976 444618
Ⓔ wykehamgardens@btinternet.com
Ⓦ www.wykehamgardens.com
Contact: Rachael Nitz-Mahy
Opening Times: 1000-1700 Thu-Sat, 1100-1500 Sun & B/hols.
Credit Cards: All major credit/debit cards
Notes: We are a small family run nursery growing garden favourites alongside more unusual varieties and plants for shade. We also stock a selection of pots & containers, seeds, tools, quality wild bird food and wildlife items as well as local handmade garden art. Delivers to shows. Wheelchair accessible.

WWtn **Westonbury Mill Water Garden** ♿
Pembridge, Herefordshire, HR6 9HZ
Ⓣ (01544) 388650
Ⓕ (01544) 388650
Ⓔ westonburymillnursery@gmail.com
Ⓦ www.westonburymillwatergardens.com
Contact: Richard Pim
Opening Times: 1100-1700 daily, 1st Apr-30th Sep. By appt. only at other times & to arrange collection. Please contact nursery for orders outside open season.
Specialities: Range of herbaceous plants with special emphasis on plants for the water garden & bog areas. Plants available in small quantities. Seasonal availability varies as stock sells out. Contact nursery to confirm availability before travelling.
Notes: Café. Wheelchair accessible.

Abroad

XBar **Barnhaven Primroses**
Keranguiner, Plestin-les-grèves, Brittany, 22310 France
Ⓣ +33 (2) 9635 6841
Ⓜ +33 (6) 06623687
Ⓔ info@barnhaven.com
Ⓦ www.barnhaven.com
Contact: Rob and Jodie Mitchell
Opening Times: 1400-1700 Feb-May. For visits outside this period, please phone first.
Min Mail Order UK: Nmc
Min Mail Order EU: Nmc
Credit Cards: Visa, MasterCard, Paypal
Specialities: *Primula*. French National Plant Collection of Barnhaven *Primula* hybrids. Certified collection of *Primula auricula* cvs. Old-fashioned and double primroses. Large collection of Asiatic and Alpine *Primula*. Seeds & plants available worldwide.
Notes: Exports beyond EU. Euro & sterling accepted. Delivers to shows.

XFro **Frosch Exclusive Perennials**
Ziegelstadelweg 5a, Dietramszell, 83623 Germany
Ⓣ +49 (8027) 9049975
Ⓜ +49 172 8422050
Ⓕ +49 (8027) 904 9975
Ⓔ info@cypripedium.de
Ⓦ www.cypripedium.de
Contact: Michael Weinert
Opening Times: Not open. Mail order only. Orders taken between 0700-2200 hours.
Min Mail Order UK: £350.00 + p&p
Min Mail Order EU: £350.00 + p&p
Cat. Cost: Online only.
Credit Cards: None
Specialities: *Cypripedium* hybrids. Hardy orchids.
Notes: Also sells wholesale. Exports beyond EU. Euro accepted.

XLum **ATELIER DU VÉGÉTAL**
Ferme Miane, 25 route du libraire, 24100 Bergerac, France
Ⓣ +33 (5) 5357 6215
Ⓔ contact@atelierduvegetal.com
Ⓦ www.atelierduvegetal.com
Contact: Jordi & Amélie Tura
Opening Times: 0800-1730 Mon-Sat. Closed Sun.
Min Mail Order UK: Nmc
Min Mail Order EU: Nmc
Cat. Cost: Online only.
Credit Cards: Visa, MasterCard, Paypal
Specialities: Hardy perennials. Grasses. Plants for dry gardens. Large collection of *Geranium, Aster, Acanthus, Miscanthus.*
Notes: Also sells wholesale. Exports beyond EU. Delivers to shows. Euro accepted.

XSen **GAEC SENTEURS DU QUERCY** ♿
Mas de Fraysse, Escamps, Lot, 46230 France
Ⓣ +33 (0) 5652 10162
Ⓔ contact@senteursduquercy.com
Ⓦ www.senteursduquercy.com
Contact: Frédéric Prévot
Opening Times: 1400-1800 spring & summer (excl. Aug). Other times, incl. Aug by appt.
Min Mail Order UK: Nmc
Min Mail Order EU: Nmc
Cat. Cost: £5.00
Specialities: *Salvia, Iris, Phlomis, Teucrium, Lavandula* and drought tolerant plants. French National Collection of *Salvia* species.
Notes: Euro accepted. Delivers to shows. Wheelchair accessible.

XSte **PÉPINIÈRES STERVINOU**
1 Lieu-Dit Kerguelen, Guipronvel, 29290 Milizac-Guipronvel, France
Ⓣ 00 33 (0) 298 07 28 00
Ⓕ 00 33 (0) 298 07 20 99
Ⓔ contact@stervinou.fr
Ⓦ www.stervinou.fr
Contact: Yves Stervinou
Min Mail Order UK: €45.00
Min Mail Order EU: €45.00
Cat. Cost: Online only.
Credit Cards: MasterCard, Visa
Specialities: We specialise in ericaceous plants such as *Camelia* (200 varieties), *Rhododendron* (100 varieties), *Magnolia, Michelias,* Japanese and Chinese *Azalea.* Other specialities include our large collection of unusual shrubs (*Restio, Protea* etc.) and perennials (*Watsonia, Agapanthus* etc.).
Notes: Our family-run nursery has been operating in Brittany, France since 1944. We produce a wide variety of high-quality plants for sale to garden centres and nurseries, but also to numerous individual collectors. Also sells wholesale.

XVPe **VÉGÉTAL 85** ♿
la fouiniere, la chaize le vicomte, 85310 France
Ⓣ +0033 251 05 78 41
Ⓜ +0033 608 02 59 24
Ⓔ mhdoyon@vegetal85.fr
Ⓦ www.pepiniere-vegetal85.fr
Contact: Marc-Henri Doyon
Opening Times: 0800-1800 Mon-Sat. Closed Sat Jul-Aug.
Credit Cards: All major credit/debit cards
Specialities: Rare and unusual plants. *Asiminatriloba, Accasellowana, Gardenia jasminoides,* hardy citrus and hardy exotics.
Notes: Employee-owned nursery producing rare, new and uncommon shrubs. We also produce uncommon fruit trees and hardy exotics. Delivers to shows. Wheelchair accessible.

Nursery Index by Name

Nurseries that are included in the *RHS Plant Finder* for the first time this year (or have been reintroduced after a significant absence) are marked in **bold type**.

Full details of the nurseries will be found in **Nursery Details by Code** on page 888. For a key to the geographical codes, see the start of **Nurseries**.

Butterfly Cottage Garden Plants	SBut
C & K Jones	**MJon**
C S Lockyer (Fuchsias)	CLoc
C W Groves & Son Ltd	CGro
Calamazag Nursery	CCal
Camellia Grove Nursery	SCam
Cants of Colchester Ltd	ECnt
Caths Garden Plants	**NCth**
Caves Folly Nurseries	WCav
CB Plants	CCBP
Charles F Ellis	WCFE
Charleshurst Farm Nursery	SChF
Cherry Tree Nursery	CChe
Chestnut Nursery (Sheltered Work Project) Opportunities	CCht
Chew Valley Trees Ltd	CCVT
ChickenStreet	WChS
Chiltern Seeds Ltd	MCtn
Chipchase Castle Nursery	NChi
Chrysanthemums Direct	MCms
Citrus Centre, The	SCit
Claire Austin Hardy Plants	WCAu
Coastal Hedging	CCoa
Coblands Garden Centre	SCob
Coles Plant Centre	**MCls**
Colin Dickson t/a Dickson Nurseries	IDic
Colin Gregory Roses	**ECol**
Cool Temperate	MCoo
Cooling's Nurseries Ltd	SCoo
Coolings Wych Cross Garden Centre	**SWCr**
Coton Manor Garden	MCot
Cotswold Garden Flowers	WCot
Cottage Garden Plants and Seeds	**SCgs**
Cottage Nurseries	ECtt
Courtyard Planters	NCou
Craftyplants	NCft
Cranesbill Nursery	WCra
Creake Plant Centre	ECre
Crocosmia Gardens, The	**ECrc**
Crocus.co.uk	LCro
Croft 16 Daffodils	GCro
Cross Common Nursery	CCCN
Crûg Farm Plants	WCru
Daisy Roots	**LDai**
Daleside Nurseries Ltd	NDal
Damhead Nursery Ltd	GDam
Dan Sutton	SSut
D'Arcy & Everest	EDAr
Dave Parkinson Plants	NDav
Deelish Garden Centre	IDee
Delfland Nurseries Ltd	EDel
Desert to Jungle	CDTJ
Dibleys Nurseries	WDib
Direct Bulbs	SDir
Direct Plants Ltd	**EDir**
Donington Nurseries	MDon
Dorset Perennials	CDor
Dove Cottage Nursery & Garden	NDov
Downderry Nursery	SDow
Downside Nurseries	CDow
Drointon Nurseries	NDro
Dryad Nursery	NDry
Duchy of Cornwall	CDoC
Dysons Nurseries	SDys
E W King & Co. Ltd. (Kings Seeds)	EKin
East Northdown Nursery	SEND
East of Eden Nursery	NEoE
Echium World	MEch
Eddington House Nursery	SEdd
Edible Garden Nursery, The	CLau
Edibleculture	SEdi
Edrom Nurseries	GEdr
Edulis	LEdu
Eleplants Nursery	SEle
Elmlea Plants	**GElm**
Elsworth Herbs	CEls
Elworthy Cottage Plants	CElw
Emerald Plants	CEme
Endsleigh Gardens Nursery	CEnd
English Woodlands	SEWo
Essentially Hops	SEsH
Every Picture Tells a Story	**NPic**
Exclusive Plants Nursery	CExl
Exotic Earth Plants	**CExo**
Fairweather's Garden Centre	SFai
Farmyard Nurseries	WFar
Fawside Farm Nursery	MBow
Fern Nursery, The	EFer
Fibrex Nurseries Ltd	WFib
Firecrest Trees & Shrubs Nursery	EMac
Flittons Nursery	**LFlit**
Forde Abbey Nursery	**CAby**
Forest Edge Nurseries (The Heather Garden)	CFst
Foundry Plant Centre	**EFPl**
Foxplants	CFoP
Frosch Exclusive Perennials	XFro
Fryer's Roses and Garden Centre	MFry
G&K Carnations	**NGKc**
GAEC Senteurs Du Quercy	XSen
Garden Beauty	SGBe
Garden Blooms	NGBl
Garden House Nursery	NGdn
Garden Style Plant Centre	SGsty
Gardener's Cottage Plants	NGrd
Gilbert's Nursery	SGbt
Glendoick Gardens Ltd	GGGa
Gobbett Nursery, The	WGob
Golden Hill Nurseries	SGol
Goscote Nurseries Ltd	MGos
Grasmere Garden Centre	NGrs
Great Dixter Nurseries	SDix
Green Box Plants	**CGBo**
Green Island Gardens	EGrI
Greenjjam Nurseries	**WJam**

Greenkoos	NGKo
Grenville Nurseries	EGren
Grow at Brogdale	SBdl
Growild Nursery	GGro
Growing Delights	SGro
Gwynfor Growers	WGwG
H W Hyde and Son	LHWs
Habitat Aid Ltd.	CHab
Halls of Heddon	NHal
Hampshire Carnivorous Plants	SHmp
Hardy Eucalyptus	WGrf
Hardy Geranium Nursery, The	LHGe
Hardy's Cottage Garden Plants	SHar
Hare Spring Cottage Plants	NHsp
Harlow Carr Plant Centre (RHS)	NRHS
Harper & Debbage	EHDe
Harperley Hall Farm Nurseries	NHpl
Harrells Hardy Plants	WHrl
Hart Canna	SHaC
Hartside Nursery Garden	NHar
Hawthornes Nursery, The	NHaw
Hayloft Plants	**WHlf**
Hedgehog Plants and Gardens	EHed
HedgeXpress	MHed
Hedging Plants Direct	**EHeP**
Herb Garden & Historical Plant Nursery, The	WHer
Herb Nursery, The	MHer
Herbary, The	CHby
Hergest Croft Gardens	WHCr
Heucheraholics	SHeu
Hewitt-Cooper Carnivorous Plants	CHew
Hidden Paradise Plants	MHid
Hidden Valley Gardens	CHVG
Hill Close Gardens	MHCG
Hill House Nursery Ltd	**CHll**
Hilltop Nurseries (Nottingham) Ltd	**MHiT**
Hillview Hardy Plants	WHil
Hintons Nursery	MHtn
Holden Clough Nursery	NHol
Hollies Farm Plant Centre	MHol
Home Farm Plants	LHom
Hoo House Nursery	WHoo
Hooksgreen Herbs Ltd	**MHoo**
Hortology Ltd	**NHrt**
Hoyland Plant Centre	NHoy
Hutchings and Son	**WHtc**
Hyde Hall Plant Centre (RHS)	EHyd
Hydrangea Haven	SHyH
Ice Alpines	WIce
Instant Landscapes T/A Instant Hedges	**LIns**
Iris of Sissinghurst	SIri
Irisesonline	EIri
Ivy Hatch Plant Supplies	SIvy
Jackson's Nurseries	MJac
Jacques Amand International Ltd	LAma
Japanese Garden Centre, The	SJap

Jekka's Herb Farm	WJek
John Churcher	SChr
John Cullen Gardens Ltd	ECul
John Gillies	MGil
Jo's Garden Enterprise	GJos
JRG Dahlias	NJRG
Junker's Nursery	CJun
Jurassicplants Nurseries	**WJur**
Keepers Nursery	SKee
Kells Bay House and Gardens	IKel
Kelways Plants Ltd	CKel
Kenwith Conifer Nursery (Gordon Haddow)	CKen
Kevock Garden Plants	GKev
Kiftsgate Court Gardens	WKif
Kings Barn Trees	SKin
Kinlochlaich Garden Plant Centre	GKin
Knoll Gardens	CKno
Kore Wild Fruit Nursery	WKor
L . A. Allen	WAln
Landford Trees	CLnd
Laneside Hardy Orchid Nursery	NLAp
Langthorns Plantery	ELan
Larch Cottage Nurseries	NLar
Laurels Nursery, The	SLau
Lavender Garden, The	WLav
Leaf Creative Design Ltd	WLea
Leamore Nursery	ILea
Leesa's not just Alpines	SLee
Letham Plants	GLet
Lilies Water Gardens	LLWG
Lime Cross Nursery	SLim
Little Brook Fuchsias	SLBF
Loder Plants	SLdr
Lodge Farm Plants & Wildflowers	MLod
Logie Steading Plants	GLog
Long Acre Plants	CLAP
Long House Plants	ELon
Lound Plant Centre	**EMul**
Lovegroves	WLov
Mac Pennys Nurseries	CMac
Macplants	GMaP
Madley Plants	**WMad**
Madrona Nursery	SMad
Majestic Trees	LMaj
Malcolm Allison Nurseries	WMal
Mallet Court Nursery	CMCN
Mandy Plants	EMdy
Marchants Hardy Plants	SMHy
Marcus Dancer Plants	**SMDa**
Margery Fish Plant Nursery	CFis
Marshall's Malmaisons	EMal
Marwood Hill Gardens	CMHG
McLaren's Nurseries	**GMcL**
Mendip Bonsai Studio	CMen
Mendle Nursery	NMen
Merebrook Water Plants	WMAq

Merriments Gardens	SMrm
Mickfield Hostas	EMic
Middleton Nurseries	Midl
Miles Japanese Maples	**SMil**
Mill Cottage Plants	CMil
Mill Race Garden Centre	EMil
Millais Nurseries	LMil
Millwood Plants	CMiW
Mintopia	**MMen**
Mires Beck Nursery	NMir
Moore and Moore Plants	EMor
Morehavens	SMor
Morlas Plants	MCor
Morton Nurseries Ltd	MMrt
Mount Pleasant Trees Ltd	WMou
Mucklestone Nurseries	MMuc
National Collection of Francoa	**SFra**
National Dahlia Collection	CWGr
National Herb Centre, The	MNHC
National Plant Collection of Monarda	WMon
Natural Surroundings	NAts
New Hope Gardens	WNHG
Newent Plant Centre	WNPC
Newport Mills Nursery	CNMi
Nicholson Nurseries Limited	MNic
Nightingale Nursery Ltd	SNig
Norcroft Nurseries	NNor
Norfolk Herbs	ENfk
Norfolk Lavender	ENor
Norfolk Olive Tree Company, The	EOli
North Staffordshire Hostas	MHost
Northbrook Nursery	CNor
Norwell Nurseries & Gardens	MNrw
Old Court Nurseries	WOld
Old Hall Plants	EOHP
Orange Pippin Ltd	NOra
Orchard Nurseries	**NONu**
Orchard Nursery Plant Centre Ltd	**SOrN**
Ornamental Trees Ltd	NOrn
Out of the Common Way	**WOut**
P. de Jager & Sons Ltd	SDeJ
Packhorse Farm Nursery	MPkF
Paddock Plants	SPad
Palm Centre, The	**LPal**
Palm House, The	CPHo
Palm Tree Company, The	**NPlm**
Pan-Global Plants	WPGP
Papervale Trees	IPap
Paramount Plants & Gardens Ltd	LPar
Parks Perennials	CPar
Paugers Plants Ltd	EPau
Paul Jasper Trees	WJas
Paviour and Davies Plants	WPav
Peake Perennials	SPeP
Penberth Plants	CPbh
Penlan Perennials	WPnP
Pépinières Stervinou	XSte
Perennial Favourites Ltd	NFav
Perrie Hale Nursery Ltd	**CPer**
Perryhill Nurseries Ltd	SPer
Perry's Plants	NPer
Pershore College Garden Centre & Nursery	WAvo
Perthshire Heathers	GPer
Peter Beales Roses	EBls
Petrichor Bulb Specialists	MPtr
Pettet's Nursery	SPet
Pheasant Acre Plants	WPhe
Phedar Nursery	MPhe
Phoenix Perennial Plants	SPhx
Piecemeal Plants	MPie
Pineview Plants	SPVi
Place for Plants, The	EPfP
Plant Centre at Hortus Loci, The	SHor
Plant Company, The	STPC
Plant for Ponds Ltd	**LPfP**
Plant Specialist, The	LPla
Plant World Gardens and Nurseries	CPla
Plantagogo.com	MPnt
Plantbase	SPlb
Plants, Shoots and Leaves	GPSL
Plants4Presents	SPre
Plantsman's Preference, The	EPPr
PlantsToPlant.com	SPtp
Poets Cottage Shrub Nursery	NPoe
Polemonium Plantery	NPol
Pomona Fruits Ltd	EPom
Potash Nursery Ltd	EPts
Potted Garden Nursery, The	SPoG
Pottertons Nursery	EPot
Potting Shed, The	IPot
Poyntzfield Herb Nursery	GPoy
Primrose Bank	NPnk
Primrose Cottage Nursery	MPri
Primrose Hall Peonies	LPmr
Priory Plants	EPri
ProperPlants	CPrp
Puddleplants	CPud
Quercus Garden Plants Ltd	GQue
Quiet Corner Plants	NQui
R and A Scamp Quality Daffodils	CQua
R Harkness & Co. Ltd.	LHkn
R V Roger Ltd	NRog
Rapkyns Nursery	SRkn
Ravensthorpe Nursery	MRav
ReadyHedge Ltd & Hedgegrow Ltd	**WReH**
RHS Plant Shop: RHSplants.co.uk	LOPS
River Garden Nurseries	SRiv
Romantic Garden, The	ERom
Ros Ban Wildlife Garden	IRos
Rose Cottage Plants	ERCP
Roseland House Nursery	CRHN
Rosemoor Plant Centre (RHS)	CRos
Rosie's Garden Plants	SRGP
Rotherhill Nurseries	**SRHi**

Rotherview Nursery	SRot
Roualeyn Nurseries	WRou
Rumbling Bridge Nursery	GRum
Rumsey Gardens	SRms
Ryal Nursery	NRya
Saith Ffynnon Wildlife Plants	WSFF
Savill Gardens Visitor Centre	LSvl
Savin Nurseries	SavN
Seagate Irises	ESgI
Seale Rose Garden	SSea
Seaside Plants	CSde
Sempervirens	**LSem**
Sempervivums By Post	SSem
Shady Plants	**ISha**
Shallowmead Nurseries Ltd	**SSha**
Shipton Bulbs	WShi
Shire Plants	LShi
Shropshire Sarracenias	WSSs
Shrubland Nurseries	EShb
Sienna Hosta	SSien
Simply Succulents	SSim
Slack Top Alpine Nursery	NSla
Southern Fruit Trees	SSFr
Southon Plants	LSou
Special Plants	CSpe
SpecialPerennials.com	MSpe
Spinneywell Nursery	WSpi
Spring Reach Nursery	LSRN
St Bridget Nurseries Ltd	CSBt
Staddon Farm Nurseries	CSta
Stafford Lake Nursery	**LSta**
Starborough Nursery	SSta
Stillingfleet Lodge Nurseries	NSti
Stone House Cottage Nurseries	WSHC
Stone Lane Gardens	CSto
Stonyford Cottage Nursery	MSCN
Stotts Nursery	**LSto**
Straight Mile Nursery Gardens	ESMi
Strete Gate Camellias	CSgt
Strictly Daylilies	EStr
Style Roses	ESty
Sue Proctor Plants	NSue
Summerdale Garden Nursery	NSum
Sunnybank Vine Nursery (National Vine Collection)	WSuV
Sunnyside Nursery	LSun
Sussex Fruit Trees	SSFT
Swallows Nursery	MSwo
Swines Meadow Farm Nursery	ESwi
T. D. Thursfield	MThu
Taylors Clematis Nursery	NTay
Thorncroft Clematis & Climbers Ltd	ETho
Thuya Alpine Nursery	WThu
Timpany Nurseries & Gardens	ITim
Tiny Plant Company, The	MTin
Todd's Botanics	ETod
Topiary Arts	LTop
Tor Garden Plants	**CToG**
Tortworth Plants Ltd	WTor
Trecanna Nursery	**CTca**
Tree Peony Company	NTPC
Tree Shop at Frank P. Matthews Ltd, The	WMat
Tree Shop Ltd	WTSh
Tree2mydoor Ltd	**NTrD**
Trees Online	MTrO
Trehane Nursery	CTrh
Treseders Nursery	CTsd
Trevena Cross Nurseries	CTrC
Trevor White Old Fashioned Roses	ETWh
Triffids	CTtf
Triscombe Nurseries	CTri
Ty Cwm Nursery	WTyc
Végétal 85	XVPe
Ventnor Botanic Garden	SVen
Victorian Violas	EVic
Victoriana Nursery Gardens	SVic
Village Plants Nursery Ltd	MVil
Viv Marsh Postal Plants	WViv
W Robinson & Son (Seeds & Plants) Ltd	NRob
Wack's Wicked Plants	**NWac**
Waddow Lodge Garden	NWad
Walcot Organic Nursery	WWct
Walkers Bulbs @ Taylors	**ETay**
Walled Garden Nursery	CWGN
Walled Garden Treberfydd	WTre
Walled Gardens of Cannington, The	**CWal**
Walnut Tree Garden Nursery	EWTr
Waltham Herbs	EWhm
Walworth Garden	**LWaG**
Water Garden Plants	EWat
Water Garden, Water	CWat
Waterside Nursery	MWts
Weasdale Nurseries Ltd.	NWea
Web Garden Centre	SWeb
Weird Plants by Gill	LWei
West Acre Gardens	EWes
West Wales Willows	**WeWi**
Westcountry Nurseries (North Devon) Ltd	CWCL
Westonbury Mill Water Garden	WWtn
Westshores Nurseries	NWsh
Whitehall Farmhouse Plants	WWFP
Whitelea Nursery	MWht
Wildegoose Nursery	WGoo
Wildflower Nursery, The	WWild
Willow Bank, The	**WWbk**
Winrow Nurseries	**CWnw**
Wisley Plant Centre (RHS)	LRHS
Wolverton Plants Ltd	SWvt
Woodham Nursery	**LWdG**
Woodlands	EWld
Woottens of Wenhaston	EWoo
Wykeham Gardens	**WWke**

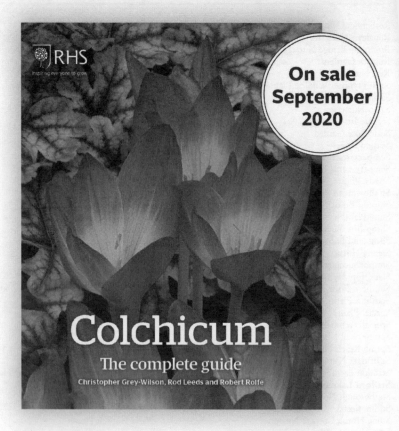

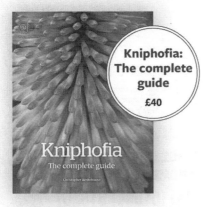

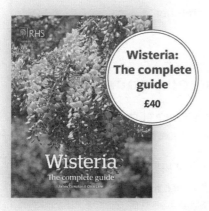

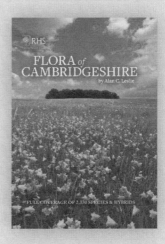

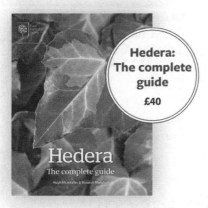

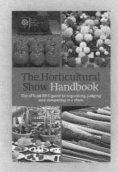

INDEX OF ADVERTISERS